W9-CKI-198

Hoover's Handbook of

American Business

2020

HOOVERS™

A D&B COMPANY

Austin, Texas

A D&B COMPANY

10 9 8 7 6 5 4 3 2 1

Publishers Cataloging-in-Publication Data

Hoover's Handbook of American Business 2020

    Includes indexes.

    ISBN: 978-1-64141-560-6

    ISSN 1055-7202

    1. Business enterprises — Directories. 2. Corporations — Directories.

HF3010 338.7

U.S. AND WORLD BOOK SALES

Mergent Inc.

580 Kingsley Park Drive
Fort Mill, SC
29715
Phone: 704-559-6961
e-mail: skardon@ftserussell.com
Web: www.mergentbusinesspress.com

Mergent Inc.

Executive Managing Director: John Pedernales

Publisher and Managing Director of Print Products : Thomas Wecera

Director of Print Products: Charlot Volny

Quality Assurance Editor: Wayne Arnold

Production Research Assistant: Davie Christna

Data Manager: Jason Horvat

MERGENT CUSTOMER SUPPORT FOR PRINT
Support and Fulfillment Manager: Thomas Wecera 212-413-7726

ABOUT MERGENT INC.

For over 100 years, Mergent, Inc. has been a leading provider of business and financial information on public and private companies globally. Mergent is known to be a trusted partner to corporate and financial institutions, as well as to academic and public libraries. Today we continue to build on a century of experience by transforming data into knowledge and combining our expertise with the latest technology to create new global data and analytical solutions for our clients. With advanced data collection services, cloud-based applications, desktop analytics and print products, Mergent and its subsidiaries provide solutions from top down economic and demographic information, to detailed equity and debt fundamental analysis. We incorporate value added tools such as quantitative Smart Beta equity research and tools for portfolio building and measurement. Based in the U.S., Mergent maintains a strong global presence, with offices in New York, Charlotte, San Diego, London, Tokyo, Kuching and Melbourne. Mergent, Inc. is a member of the London Stock Exchange plc group of companies. The Mergent business forms part of LSEG's Information Services Division, which includes FTSE Russell, a global leader in indexes.

Abbreviations

AFL-CIO – American Federation of Labor and Congress of Industrial Organizations
AMA – American Medical Association
AMEX – American Stock Exchange
ARM – adjustable-rate mortgage
ASP – application services provider
ATM – asynchronous transfer mode
ATM – automated teller machine
CAD/CAM – computer-aided design/computer-aided manufacturing
CD-ROM – compact disc – read-only memory
CD-R – CD-recordable
CEO – chief executive officer
CFO – chief financial officer
CMOS – complementary metal oxide silicon
COO – chief operating officer
DAT – digital audiotape
DOD – Department of Defense
DOE – Department of Energy
DOS – disk operating system
DOT – Department of Transportation
DRAM – dynamic random-access memory
DSL – digital subscriber line
DVD – digital versatile disc/digital video disc
DVD-R – DVD-recordable
EPA – Environmental Protection Agency
EPROM – erasable programmable read-only memory
EPS – earnings per share
ESOP – employee stock ownership plan
EU – European Union
EVP – executive vice president
FCC – Federal Communications Commission
FDA – Food and Drug Administration
FDIC – Federal Deposit Insurance Corporation

FTC – Federal Trade Commission
FTP – file transfer protocol
GATT – General Agreement on Tariffs and Trade
GDP – gross domestic product
HMO – health maintenance organization
HR – human resources
HTML – hypertext markup language
ICC – Interstate Commerce Commission
IPO – initial public offering
IRS – Internal Revenue Service
ISP – Internet service provider
kWh – kilowatt-hour
LAN – local-area network
LBO – leveraged buyout
LCD – liquid crystal display
LNG – liquefied natural gas
LP – limited partnership
Ltd. – limited
mips – millions of instructions per second
MW – megawatt
NAFTA – North American Free Trade Agreement
NASA – National Aeronautics and Space Administration
NASDAQ – National Association of Securities Dealers Automated Quotations
NATO – North Atlantic Treaty Organization
NYSE – New York Stock Exchange
OCR – optical character recognition
OECD – Organization for Economic Cooperation and Development
OEM – original equipment manufacturer
OPEC – Organization of Petroleum Exporting Countries
OS – operating system
OSHA – Occupational Safety and Health Administration

OTC – over-the-counter
PBX – private branch exchange
PCMCIA – Personal Computer Memory Card International Association
P/E – price to earnings ratio
RAID – redundant array of independent disks
RAM – random-access memory
R&D – research and development
RBOC – regional Bell operating company
RISC – reduced instruction set computer
REIT – real estate investment trust
ROA – return on assets
ROE – return on equity
ROI – return on investment
ROM – read-only memory
S&L – savings and loan
SCSI – Small Computer System Interface
SEC – Securities and Exchange Commission
SEVP – senior executive vice president
SIC – Standard Industrial Classification
SOC – system on a chip
SVP – senior vice president
USB – universal serial bus
VAR – value-added reseller
VAT – value-added tax
VC – venture capitalist
VoIP – Voice over Internet Protocol
VP – vice president
WAN – wide-area network
WWW – World Wide Web

Contents

List of Lists

HOOVER'S RANKINGS

Companies Profiled

vi

Companies Profiled (continued)

Companies Profiled (continued)

Companies Profiled (continued)

Companies Profiled (continued)

About Hoover's Handbook of American Business 2020

In these tough economic times, it pays to have all the facts, whether you're making business, financial, or employment decisions. When you need information about companies, *Hoover's Handbook of American Business* is the place to turn for answers. Throughout its history, it has stood as one of America's respected sources of business information, packed with the information you need.

We at Hoover's Business Press pledge we will continue our work to add more value to this already valuable resource. So search away for the business information you need to make the important decisions facing you. Leave the fact-finding and digging and the sorting and sifting to the editors at Hoover's.

Hoover's Handbook of American Business is the first of our four-title series of handbooks that covers, literally, the world of business. The series is available as an indexed set, and also includes *Hoover's Handbook of World Business, Hoover's Handbook of Private Companies,* and *Hoover's Handbook of Emerging Companies.* This series brings you information on the biggest, fastest-growing, and most influential enterprises in the world.

HOOVER'S ARCHIVES FOR BUSINESS NEEDS

In addition to the 2,550 companies featured in our handbooks, comprehensive coverage of more than 6 years of Hoovers Books are published in the Hoovers Archives.. Our goal is to provide one site that offers authoritative, updated intelligence on US and global companies, industries, and the people who shape them. Stay with the Hoovers famaily of products and History and package the books with the archives products.

We welcome the recognition we have received as a provider of high-quality company information — online, electronically, and in print — and continue to look for ways to make our products more available and more useful to you.

We believe that anyone who buys from, sells to, invests in, lends to, competes with, interviews with, or works for a company should know all there is to know about that enterprise. Taken together, this book and the other Hoover's products and resources represent the most complete source of basic corporate information readily available to the general public.

This latest version of *Hoover's Handbook of American Business* contains, as always, profiles of the largest and most influential companies in the United States. Each of the companies profiled here was chosen because of its important role in American business. For more details on how these companies were selected, see the section titled "Using Hoover's Handbooks."

HOW TO USE THIS BOOK

This book has four sections:

1. "Using Hoover's Handbooks" describes the contents of our profiles and explains the ways in which we gather and compile our data.

2. "A List-Lover's Compendium" contains lists of the largest, smallest, best, most, and other superlatives related to companies involved in American business.

3. The company profiles section makes up the largest and most important part of the book — 750 profiles of major US enterprises.

4. Three indexes complete the book. The first sorts companies by industry groups, the second by headquarters location. The third index is a list of all the executives found in the Executives section of each company profile.

Using Hoover's Handbooks

SELECTION OF THE COMPANIES PROFILED

The 750 enterprises profiled in this book include the largest and most influential companies in America. Among them are:

- more than 710 publicly held companies, from 3M to Zions Bancorporation
- more than 30 large private enterprises (such as Cargill and Mars)
- several mutual and cooperative organizations (such as State Farm and Ace Hardware)
- a selection of other enterprises (such as Kaiser Foundation Health Plan, the US Postal Service, and the Tennessee Valley Authority) that we believe are sufficiently large and influential enough to warrant inclusion.

In selecting these companies, our foremost question was "What companies will our readers be most interested in?" Our goal was to answer as many questions as we could in one book — in effect, trying to anticipate your curiosity. This approach resulted in four general selection criteria for including companies in the book:

1. Size. The 500 or so largest American companies, measured by sales and by number of employees, are included in the book. In general, these companies have sales in excess of $2 billion, and they are the ones you will have heard of and the ones you will want to know about. These are the companies at the top of the *FORTUNE*, *Forbes*, and *Business Week* lists. We have made sure to include the top private companies in this number.

2. Growth. We believe that relatively few readers will be going to work for, or investing in, the railroad industry. Therefore, only a few railroads are in the book. On the other hand, we have included a number of technology firms, as well as companies that provide medical products and services — pharmaceutical and biotech companies, health care insurers, and medical device makers.

3. Visibility. Most readers will have heard of the Hilton Worldwide and Harley-Davidson companies. Their service or consumer natures make them household names, even though they are not among the corporate giants in terms of sales and employment.

4. Breadth of coverage. To show the diversity of economic activity, we've included, among others, a professional sports team, one ranch, the Big Four accounting firms, and one of the largest law firms in the US. We feel that these businesses are important enough to enjoy at least "token" representation. While we might not emphasize certain industries, the industry leaders are present.

ORGANIZATION

The profiles are presented in alphabetical order. This alphabetization is generally word by word, which means that Legg Mason precedes Leggett & Platt. You will find the commonly used name of the enterprise at the beginning of the profile; the full, legal name is found in the Locations section. If a company name is also a person's name, like Walt Disney, it will be alphabetized under the first name; if the company name starts with initials, like J. C. Penney or H.J. Heinz, look for it under the combined initials (in the above examples, JC and HJ, respectively). Basic financial data is listed under the heading Historical Financials; also included is the exchange on which the company's stock is traded if it is public, the ticker symbol used by the stock exchange, and the company's fiscal year-end.

The annual financial information contained in the profiles is current through fiscal year-ends occurring as late as May 2014. We have included certain nonfinancial developments, such as officer changes, through September 2014.

OVERVIEW

In the first section of the profile, we have tried to give a thumbnail description of the company and what it does. The description will usually include information on the company's strategy, reputation, and ownership. We recommend that you read this section first.

HISTORY

This extended section, included for almost all companies in the book, reflects our belief that every enterprise is the sum of its history and that you have to know where you came from in order to know where you are going. While some companies have limited historical awareness, we think the vast majority of the enterprises in this book have colorful backgrounds. We have tried to focus on the people who made the enterprises what they are today. We have found these histories to be full of twists and ironies; they make fascinating reading.

EXECUTIVES

Here we list the names of the people who run the company, insofar as space allows. In the case of public companies, we have shown the ages and total compensation of key officers. In some cases the published data is for the previous year although the company has announced promotions or retirements since year-end. Total compensation is the sum of salary, bonus, and the value of any other benefits, such as stock options or deferred compensation.

Although companies are free to structure their management titles any way they please, most modern corporations follow standard practices. The ultimate power in any corporation lies with the shareholders, who elect a board of directors, usually including officers or "insiders" as well as individuals from outside the company. The chief officer, the person on whose desk the buck stops, is usually called the chief executive officer (CEO). Often, he or she is also the chairman of the board.

As corporate management has become more complex, it is common for the CEO to have a "right-hand person" who oversees the day-to-day operations of the company, allowing the CEO plenty of time to focus on strategy and long-term issues. This right-hand person is usually designated the chief operating officer (COO) and is often the president of the company. In other cases one person is both chairman and president.

A multitude of other titles exists, including chief financial officer (CFO), chief administrative officer, and vice chairman. We have always tried to include the CFO, the chief legal officer, and the chief human resources or personnel officer. Our best advice is that officers' pay levels are clear indicators of who the board of directors thinks are the most important members of the management team.

The people named in the Executives section are indexed at the back of the book.

The Executives section also includes the name of the company's auditing (accounting) firm, where available.

LOCATIONS

Here we include the company's full legal name and its headquarters, street address, telephone and fax numbers, and Web site, as available. The back of the book includes an index of companies by headquarters locations.

In some cases we have also included information on the geographic distribution of the company's business, including sales and profit data. Note that these profit numbers, like those in the Products/Operations section below, are usually operating or pretax profits rather than net profits. Operating profits are generally those before financing costs (interest income and payments) and before taxes, which are considered costs attributable to the whole company rather than to one division or part of the world. For this reason the net income figures (in the Historical Financials section) are usually much lower, since they are after interest and taxes. Pretax profits are after interest but before taxes.

Headquarters for companies that are incorporated in Bermuda, but whose operational headquarters are in the US, are listed under their US address.

PRODUCTS/OPERATIONS

This section lists as many of the company's products, services, brand names, divisions, subsidiaries, and joint ventures as we could fit. We have tried to include all its major lines and all familiar brand names. The nature of this section varies by company and the amount of information available. If the company publishes sales and profit information by type of business, we have included it.

COMPETITORS

In this section we have listed companies that compete with the profiled company. This feature is included as a quick way to locate similar companies and compare them. The universe of competitors includes all public companies and all private companies with sales in excess of $500 million. In a few instances we have identified smaller private companies as key competitors.

HISTORICAL FINANCIALS

Here we have tried to present as much data about each enterprise's financial performance as we could compile in the allocated space. The information varies somewhat from industry to industry and is less complete in the case of private companies that do not release data (although we have always tried to provide annual sales and employment). There are a few industries, venture capital and investment banking, for example, for which revenue numbers are unavailable as a rule.

The following information is generally present.

A 5-year table, with relevant annualized compound growth rates, covers:
- Sales — fiscal year sales (year-end assets for most financial companies)
- Net income — fiscal year net income (before accounting changes)
- Net profit margin — fiscal year net income as a percent of sales (as a percent of assets for most financial firms)
- Employees — fiscal year-end or average number of employees
- Stock price — the fiscal year close
- P/E — high and low price/earnings ratio
- Earnings per share — fiscal year earnings per share (EPS)
- Dividends per share — fiscal year dividends per share
- Book value per share — fiscal year-end book value (common shareholders' equity per share)

The information on the number of employees is intended to aid the reader interested in knowing whether a company has a long-term trend of increasing or decreasing employment. As far as we know, we are the only company that publishes this information in print format.

The numbers on the left in each row of the Historical Financials section give the month and the year in which the company's fiscal year actually ends. Thus, a company with a March 31, 2018, year-end is shown as 3/18.

In addition, we have provided in graph form a stock price history for most public companies. The graphs, covering up to five years, show the range of trading between the high and the low price, as well as the closing price for each fiscal year. Generally, for private companies, we have graphed net income, or, if that is unavailable, sales.

Key year-end statistics in this section generally show the financial strength of the enterprise, including:

- Debt ratio (long-term debt as a percent of share-holders' equity)
- Return on equity (net income divided by the average of beginning and ending common share-holders' equity)
- Cash and cash equivalents
- Current ratio (ratio of current assets to current liabilities)
- Total long-term debt (including capital lease obligations
- Number of shares of common stock outstanding
- Dividend yield (fiscal year dividends per share divided by the fiscal year-end closing stock price)
- Dividend payout (fiscal year dividends divided by fiscal year EPS)
- Market value at fiscal year-end (fiscal year-end closing stock price multiplied by fiscal year-end number of shares outstanding)

Per share data has been adjusted for stock splits. The data for public companies has been provided to us by Mergent Inc. Other public company information was compiled by Hoover's, which takes full responsibility for the content of this section.

In the case of private companies that do not publicly disclose financial information, we usually did not have access to such standardized data. We have gathered estimates of sales and other statistics from numerous sources.

Hoover's Handbook of

American Business

A List-Lover's Compendium

The 300 Largest U.S. Public Companies by Sales in
Hoover's Handbook of American Business 2020

Rank	Company	Sales ($ mil.)	Rank	Company	Sales ($ mil.)	Rank	Company	Sales ($ mil.)
1	Walmart Inc	$514,405	60	Energy Transfer Operating LP	$54,087	119	Eli Lilly & Co	$24,556
2	Exxon Mobil Corp	$290,212	61	Energy Transfer LP	$54,087	120	Duke Energy Corp	$24,521
3	mazon.com Inc	$280,522	62	Pfizer Inc	$53,647	121	Thermo Fisher Scientific Inc	$24,358
4	Apple Inc	$260,174	63	Goldman Sachs Group Inc	$52,528	122	Qualcomm Inc	$24,273
5	Berkshire Hathaway Inc	$247,837	64	Cisco Systems Inc	$51,904	123	US Foods Holding Corp	$24,175
6	UnitedHealth Group Inc	$226,247	65	Morgan Stanley	$50,193	124	NGL Energy Partners LP	$24,017
7	McKesson Corp	$214,319	66	Cigna Corp (New)	$48,650	125	Halliburton Company	$23,995
8	CVS Health Corp	$194,579	67	American International Group	$47,389	126	Cummins, Inc.	$23,771
9	AmerisourceBergen Corp.	$179,589	68	HCA Healthcare Inc	$46,677	127	Synnex Corp	$23,757
10	AT&T Inc	$170,756	69	Charter Communications Inc (	$45,764	128	Amgen Inc	$23,747
11	Chevron Corporation	$166,339	70	T-Mobile US Inc	$44,998	129	Paccar Inc.	$23,496
12	Alphabet Inc	$161,857	71	American Airlines Group Inc	$44,541	130	Southern Co.	$23,495
13	Ford Motor Co. (DE)	$155,900	72	Delta Air Lines Inc (DE)	$44,438	131	CenturyLink Inc	$23,443
14	Costco Wholesale Corp	$152,703	73	American Express Co.	$43,281	132	Micron Technology Inc.	$23,406
15	Cardinal Health, Inc.	$145,534	74	Dow Inc	$42,951	133	International Paper Co	$23,306
16	General Motors Co	$137,237	75	Best Buy Inc	$42,879	134	Visa Inc	$22,977
17	Walgreens Boots Alliance Inc	$136,866	76	Tyson Foods Inc	$42,405	135	Baker Hughes Company	$22,877
18	JPMorgan Chase & Co	$131,412	77	Merck & Co Inc	$42,294	136	Dollar Tree Inc	$22,823
19	Verizon Communications Inc	$130,863	78	Honeywell International Inc	$41,802	137	Penske Automotive Group Inc	$22,785
20	Microsoft Corporation	$125,843	79	United Airlines Holdings Inc	$41,303	138	Bristol-Myers Squibb Co.	$22,561
21	General Electric Co	$121,615	80	Allstate Corp	$39,815	139	Southwest Airlines Co	$22,428
22	Kroger Co (The)	$121,162	81	World Fuel Services Corp.	$39,750	140	Lennar Corp	$22,260
23	Fannie Mae	$120,101	82	Oracle Corp	$39,506	141	Gilead Sciences Inc	$22,127
24	Valero Energy Corp	$117,033	83	General Dynamics Corp	$39,350	142	ManpowerGroup	$21,991
25	Federal Reserve System	$116,764	84	Deere & Co.	$39,258	143	AFLAC Inc.	$21,758
26	Phillips 66	$114,217	85	NIKE Inc	$39,117	144	Union Pacific Corp	$21,708
27	Bank of America Corp	$110,584	86	TJX Companies, Inc.	$38,973	145	Rite Aid Corp.	$21,640
28	Comcast Corp	$108,942	87	ConocoPhillips	$38,727	146	Tesla Inc	$21,461
29	Home Depot Inc	$108,203	88	Tech Data Corp.	$37,239	147	AutoNation, Inc.	$21,413
30	Wells Fargo & Co (New)	$101,060	89	Enterprise Products Partners	$36,534	148	United Natural Foods Inc.	$21,387
31	Citigroup Inc	$97,120	90	Publix Super Markets, Inc.	$36,396	149	CBRE Group Inc	$21,340
32	Marathon Petroleum Corp.	$97,102	91	Exelon Corp	$35,985	150	Whirlpool Corp	$21,037
33	Anthem Inc	$92,105	92	Plains All American Pipeline	$34,055	151	McDonald's Corp	$21,025
34	Dell Technologies Inc	$90,621	93	Plains GP Holdings LP	$34,055	152	Marriott International, Inc.	$20,758
35	Johnson & Johnson	$81,581	94	Northrop Grumman Corp	$33,841	153	DXC Technology Co	$20,753
36	International Business Machi	$79,591	95	Sprint Corp (New)	$33,600	154	Burlington Northern & Santa F	$20,747
37	United Technologies Corp	$77,046	96	AbbVie Inc	$32,753	155	Exelon Generation Co LLC	$20,437
38	Boeing Co.	$76,559	97	INTL FCStone Inc.	$32,742	156	Kohl's Corp.	$20,229
39	Target Corp	$75,356	98	Capital One Financial Corp	$32,377	157	AECOM	$20,173
40	Freddie Mac	$73,598	99	3M Co	$32,136	158	Netflix Inc	$20,156
41	Intel Corp	$71,965	100	Progressive Corp. (OH)	$31,979	159	PNC Financial Services Group	$19,993
42	United Parcel Service Inc	$71,861	101	CHS Inc	$31,900	160	Danaher Corp	$19,893
43	Lowe's Companies Inc	$71,309	102	Coca-Cola Co (The)	$31,856	161	Lear Corp.	$19,810
44	Facebook Inc	$70,697	103	Abbott Laboratories	$30,578	162	Performance Food Group Co	$19,744
45	FedEx Corp	$69,693	104	Travelers Companies Inc (The	$30,282	163	Avnet Inc	$19,519
46	Disney (Walt) Co. (The)	$69,570	105	Philip Morris International	$29,805	164	Bank of New York Mellon Corp	$19,213
47	MetLife Inc	$67,941	106	Arrow Electronics, Inc.	$29,677	165	Fluor Corp.	$19,167
48	Procter & Gamble Co (The)	$67,684	107	Hewlett Packard Enterprise C	$29,135	166	Hartford Financial Services	$18,955
49	Federal Reserve Bank Of New Y	$65,090	108	PBF Energy Inc	$27,186	167	Occidental Petroleum Corp	$18,934
50	PepsiCo Inc	$64,661	109	Raytheon Co.	$27,058	168	Molina Healthcare Inc	$18,890
51	Archer Daniels Midland Co.	$64,341	110	Starbucks Corp.	$26,509	169	Genuine Parts Co.	$18,735
52	Prudential Financial Inc	$62,992	111	Kraft Heinz Co (The)	$26,268	170	Freeport-McMoRan Inc	$18,628
53	Albertsons Companies Inc	$60,535	112	Mondelez International Inc	$25,868	171	Kimberly-Clark Corp.	$18,486
54	Centene Corp	$60,116	113	U.S. Bancorp (DE)	$25,775	172	Emerson Electric Co.	$18,372
55	Sysco Corp	$60,114	114	Macy's Inc	$25,739	173	Tenet Healthcare Corp.	$18,313
56	Lockheed Martin Corp	$59,812	115	Dollar General Corp	$25,625	174	WestRock Co	$18,289
57	HP Inc	$58,756	116	Altria Group Inc	$25,364	175	Synchrony Financial	$18,253
58	Humana, Inc.	$56,912	117	Jabil Inc	$25,282	176	Carmax Inc.	$18,173
59	Caterpillar Inc.	$54,722	118	Nucor Corp.	$25,067	177	PayPal Holdings Inc	$17,772
						178	HollyFrontier Corp	$17,715

SOURCE: MERGENT INC., DATABASE, FEBRUARY 2020

The 300 Largest U.S. Public Companies by Sales in
Hoover's Handbook of American Business 2020 (continued)

Rank	Company	Sales ($ mil.)	Rank	Company	Sales ($ mil.)	Rank	Company	Sales ($ mil.)
179	DR Horton Inc	$17,593	220	Principal Financial Group In	$14,237	261	Steel Dynamics Inc.	$11,822
180	Sherwin-Williams Co (The)	$17,534	221	BlackRock Inc	$14,198	262	Lithia Motors Inc	$11,821
181	Becton Dickinson And Co	$17,290	222	United States Steel Corp.	$14,178	263	Icahn Enterprises LP	$11,777
182	XPO Logistics, Inc.	$17,279	223	Automatic Data Processing In	$14,175	264	MGM Resorts International	$11,763
183	EOG Resources, Inc.	$17,275	224	Community Health Systems, In	$14,155	265	Tenneco Inc	$11,763
184	Sunoco LP	$16,994	225	Kinder Morgan Inc.	$14,144	266	NVIDIA Corp	$11,716
185	General Mills Inc	$16,865	226	Qurate Retail Inc	$14,070	267	Sempra Energy	$11,687
186	PG&E Corp (Holding Co)	$16,759	227	Loews Corp.	$14,066	268	Ball Corp	$11,635
187	NextEra Energy Inc	$16,727	228	Arconic Inc	$14,014	269	Group 1 Automotive, Inc.	$11,601
188	Sears Holdings Corp	$16,702	229	Stanley Black & Decker Inc	$13,982	270	Unum Group	$11,599
189	Robinson (C.H.) Worldwide, I	$16,631	230	Textron Inc	$13,972	271	Xcel Energy Inc	$11,537
190	Gap Inc	$16,580	231	VF Corp.	$13,849	272	Reliance Steel & Aluminum Co	$11,535
191	Western Digital Corp	$16,569	232	Las Vegas Sands Corp	$13,739	273	DaVita Inc	$11,405
192	Lincoln National Corp.	$16,424	233	DISH Network Corp	$13,621	274	Fox Corp	$11,389
193	Core Mark Holding Co Inc	$16,395	234	Kellogg Co	$13,547	275	LabCorp	$11,333
194	Jones Lang LaSalle Inc	$16,318	235	Alcoa Corporation	$13,403	276	Tennessee Valley Authority	$11,318
195	CDW Corp	$16,241	236	Dominion Energy Inc (New)	$13,366	277	Santander Holdings USA Inc.	$11,313
196	Aramark	$16,227	237	Salesforce.Com Inc	$13,282	278	Norfolk Southern Corp	$11,296
197	American Electric Power Co I	$16,196	238	L Brands, Inc	$13,237	279	Corning Inc	$11,290
198	Cognizant Technology Solutio	$16,125	239	Henry Schein Inc	$13,202	280	Uber Technologies Inc	$11,270
199	Nordstrom, Inc.	$15,860	240	BJs Wholesale Club Holdings	$13,007	281	Navistar International Corp.	$11,251
200	Texas Instruments, Inc.	$15,784	241	Truist Financial Corp	$12,996	282	Expedia Group Inc	$11,223
201	Colgate-Palmolive Co.	$15,544	242	State Street Corp.	$12,973	283	Grainger (W.W.), Inc.	$11,221
202	Goodyear Tire & Rubber Co.	$15,475	243	Reinsurance Group of America	$12,876	284	Quanta Services, Inc.	$11,171
203	PPG Industries Inc	$15,374	244	Discover Financial Services	$12,848	285	Adobe Inc	$11,171
204	Omnicom Group, Inc.	$15,290	245	Toyota Motor Credit Corp.	$12,836	286	Crown Holdings Inc	$11,151
205	Ross Stores Inc	$14,984	246	Ameriprise Financial Inc	$12,835	287	Baxter International Inc	$11,127
206	Marsh & McLennan Companies I	$14,950	247	Jacobs Engineering Group, In	$12,738	288	FirstEnergy Corp	$11,035
207	Mastercard Inc	$14,950	248	Global Partners LP	$12,673	289	Office Depot, Inc.	$11,015
208	Waste Management, Inc. (DE)	$14,914	249	DTE Energy Co	$12,669	290	Entergy Corp. (New)	$11,009
209	Stryker Corp	$14,884	250	Edison International	$12,657	291	Charles Schwab Corp	$10,989
210	Lauder (Estee) Cos., Inc. (T	$14,863	251	Southern California Edison C	$12,611	292	Pilgrims Pride Corp.	$10,938
211	Illinois Tool Works, Inc.	$14,768	252	ONEOK Inc	$12,593	293	eBay Inc.	$10,800
212	Ecolab Inc	$14,668	253	Consolidated Edison Inc	$12,337	294	Live Nation Entertainment In	$10,788
213	Federal Reserve Bank of San F	$14,660	254	CSX Corp	$12,250	295	Universal Health Services, I	$10,772
214	Applied Materials, Inc.	$14,608	255	Equitable Holdings Inc	$12,078	296	Molson Coors Beverage Co	$10,770
215	Booking Holdings Inc	$14,527	256	Bed, Bath & Beyond, Inc.	$12,029	297	AES Corp.	$10,736
216	ViacomCBS Inc	$14,514	257	Penney (J.C.) Co.,Inc. (Hold	$12,019	298	Devon Energy Corp.	$10,734
217	Biogen Inc	$14,378	258	LKQ Corp	$11,877	299	Consolidated Edison Co. of N	$10,680
218	Murphy USA Inc	$14,363	259	AutoZone, Inc.	$11,864	300	CenterPoint Energy, Inc	$10,589
219	Parker-Hannifin Corp	$14,320	260	Florida Power & Light Co.	$11,862			

The 300 Most Profitable Public U.S. Companies
Hoover's Handbook of American Business 2020

Rank	Company	Net Income ($ mil.)	Rank	Company	Net Income ($ mil.)	Rank	Company	Net Income ($ mil.)
1	Apple Inc	$55,256	60	3M Co	$4,570	119	Alexion Pharmaceuticals Inc.	$2,404
2	Microsoft Corporation	$39,240	61	Qualcomm Inc	$4,386	120	Colgate-Palmolive Co.	$2,400
3	Alphabet Inc	$34,343	62	BlackRock Inc	$4,305	121	Publix Super Markets, Inc.	$2,381
4	JPMorgan Chase & Co	$32,474	63	Bank of New York Mellon Corp	$4,266	122	Abbott Laboratories	$2,368
5	Bank of America Corp	$28,147	64	Enterprise Products Partners	$4,172	123	Nucor Corp.	$2,361
6	Wells Fargo & Co (New)	$22,393	65	NVIDIA Corp	$4,141	124	Lowe's Companies Inc	$2,314
7	Intel Corp	$21,048	66	Occidental Petroleum Corp	$4,131	125	Emerson Electric Co.	$2,306
8	Exxon Mobil Corp	$20,840	67	Brookfield Property REIT Inc	$4,091	126	Southwest Airlines Co	$2,300
9	AT&T Inc	$19,370	68	Prudential Financial Inc	$4,074	127	Automatic Data Processing In	$2,293
10	Facebook Inc	$18,485	69	NIKE Inc	$4,029	128	Concho Resources Inc	$2,286
11	Citigroup Inc	$18,045	70	Berkshire Hathaway Inc	$4,021	129	Allstate Corp	$2,252
12	Fannie Mae	$15,959	71	Booking Holdings Inc	$3,998	130	Northrop Grumman Corp	$2,248
13	Verizon Communications Inc	$15,528	72	Walgreens Boots Alliance Inc	$3,982	131	Southern Co.	$2,242
14	Johnson & Johnson	$15,297	73	Delta Air Lines Inc (DE)	$3,935	132	Ford Motor Credit Company LL	$2,228
15	Chevron Corporation	$14,824	74	Procter & Gamble Co (The)	$3,897	133	Plains All American Pipeline	$2,216
16	Comcast Corp	$13,057	75	Mondelez International Inc	$3,870	134	TD Ameritrade Holding Corp	$2,208
17	PepsiCo Inc	$12,515	76	HCA Healthcare Inc	$3,787	135	Paccar Inc.	$2,195
18	Burlington Northern & Santa F	$12,119	77	Anthem Inc	$3,750	136	Fifth Third Bancorp (Cincinn	$2,193
19	Visa Inc	$12,080	78	Costco Wholesale Corp	$3,659	137	Lam Research Corp	$2,191
20	UnitedHealth Group Inc	$11,986	79	Starbucks Corp.	$3,599	138	Florida Power & Light Co.	$2,171
21	Cisco Systems Inc	$11,621	80	Charles Schwab Corp	$3,507	139	Cummins, Inc.	$2,141
22	Amazon.com Inc	$11,588	81	General Dynamics Corp	$3,484	140	United Airlines Holdings Inc	$2,129
23	Pfizer Inc	$11,153	82	T-Mobile US Inc	$3,468	141	S&P Global Inc	$2,123
24	Home Depot Inc	$11,121	83	Constellation Brands Inc	$3,436	142	Regeneron Pharmaceuticals, I	$2,116
25	Oracle Corp	$11,083	84	EOG Resources, Inc.	$3,419	143	Cognizant Technology Solutio	$2,101
26	Disney (Walt) Co. (The)	$11,054	85	CSX Corp	$3,309	144	Ameriprise Financial Inc	$2,098
27	Goldman Sachs Group Inc	$10,459	86	Deere & Co.	$3,253	145	Vertex Pharmaceuticals, Inc.	$2,097
28	Freddie Mac	$9,235	87	Truist Financial Corp	$3,237	146	Stryker Corp	$2,083
29	Morgan Stanley	$8,748	88	Eli Lilly & Co	$3,232	147	Tyson Foods Inc	$2,022
30	International Business Machi	$8,728	89	HP Inc	$3,152	148	International Paper Co	$2,012
31	Amgen Inc	$8,394	90	Valero Energy Corp	$3,122	149	Exelon Corp	$2,010
32	Philip Morris International	$7,185	91	Kroger Co (The)	$3,110	150	CME Group Inc	$1,962
33	U.S. Bancorp (DE)	$7,096	92	Devon Energy Corp.	$3,064	151	ViacomCBS Inc	$1,960
34	Altria Group Inc	$6,963	93	TJX Companies, Inc.	$3,060	152	Intercontinental Exchange In	$1,933
35	American Express Co.	$6,921	94	Energy Transfer Operating LP	$3,020	153	Waste Management, Inc. (DE)	$1,925
36	Honeywell International Inc	$6,765	95	Adobe Inc	$2,951	154	American Electric Power Co I	$1,924
37	General Motors Co	$6,732	96	Thermo Fisher Scientific Inc	$2,938	155	M & T Bank Corp	$1,918
38	Walmart Inc	$6,670	97	Target Corp	$2,937	156	Marriott International, Inc.	$1,907
39	NextEra Energy Inc	$6,638	98	AFLAC Inc.	$2,920	157	Netflix Inc	$1,867
40	Coca-Cola Co (The)	$6,434	99	Fortive Corp	$2,914	158	KeyCorp	$1,866
41	Micron Technology Inc.	$6,313	100	Raytheon Co.	$2,909	159	Lennar Corp	$1,849
42	ConocoPhillips	$6,257	101	Synchrony Financial	$2,790	160	T Rowe Price Group, Inc.	$1,838
43	Lockheed Martin Corp	$6,230	102	Marathon Petroleum Corp.	$2,780	161	PPL Corp	$1,827
44	Merck & Co Inc	$6,220	103	Discover Financial Services	$2,742	162	Equitable Holdings Inc	$1,820
45	Caterpillar Inc.	$6,147	104	Norfolk Southern Corp	$2,722	163	MPLX LP	$1,818
46	Capital One Financial Corp	$6,015	105	Applied Materials, Inc.	$2,706	164	Activision Blizzard, Inc.	$1,813
47	McDonald's Corp	$5,924	106	Las Vegas Sands Corp	$2,698	165	Archer Daniels Midland Co.	$1,810
48	Union Pacific Corp	$5,919	107	Duke Energy Corp	$2,666	166	Hartford Financial Services	$1,807
49	Biogen Inc	$5,889	108	Danaher Corp	$2,651	167	eBay Inc.	$1,786
50	Mastercard Inc	$5,859	109	Cigna Corp (New)	$2,637	168	Lauder (Estee) Cos., Inc. (T	$1,785
51	AbbVie Inc	$5,687	110	Progressive Corp. (OH)	$2,615	169	Air Products & Chemicals Inc	$1,760
52	Phillips 66	$5,595	111	Freeport-McMoRan Inc	$2,602	170	Regions Financial Corp	$1,759
53	Texas Instruments, Inc.	$5,580	112	State Street Corp.	$2,599	171	General Mills Inc	$1,753
54	United Technologies Corp	$5,537	113	Illinois Tool Works, Inc.	$2,563	172	Citizens Financial Group Inc	$1,721
55	Gilead Sciences Inc	$5,455	114	Travelers Companies Inc (The	$2,523	173	Public Storage	$1,711
56	PNC Financial Services Group	$5,301	115	PayPal Holdings Inc	$2,459	174	Prologis LP	$1,698
57	MetLife Inc	$5,123	116	Dominion Energy Inc (New)	$2,447	175	Energy Transfer LP	$1,694
58	Bristol-Myers Squibb Co.	$4,920	117	Simon Property Group, Inc.	$2,440	176	Humana, Inc.	$1,683
59	United Parcel Service Inc	$4,791	118	VMware Inc	$2,422	177	Prudential Annuities Life As	$1,683

SOURCE: MERGENT INC., DATABASE, FEBRUARY 2020

Rank	Company	Net Income ($ mil.)	Rank	Company	Net Income ($ mil.)	Rank	Company	Net Income ($ mil.)
178	Sysco Corp	$1,674	219	Virginia Electric & Power Co	$1,282	260	Corning Inc	$1,066
179	Boston Scientific Corp.	$1,671	220	Cheniere Energy Partners L P	$1,274	261	CBRE Group Inc	$1,063
180	Charter Communications Inc (	$1,668	221	Ally Financial Inc	$1,263	262	Healthpeak Properties Inc	$1,061
181	Qwest Corp	$1,665	222	Xcel Energy Inc	$1,261	263	WEC Energy Group Inc	$1,061
182	Halliburton Company	$1,656	223	VF Corp.	$1,260	264	E*TRADE Financial Corp	$1,052
183	Marsh & McLennan Companies I	$1,650	224	Steel Dynamics Inc.	$1,258	265	Sempra Energy	$1,050
184	Prologis Inc	$1,649	225	DXC Technology Co	$1,257	266	Hewlett Packard Enterprise C	$1,049
185	Lincoln National Corp.	$1,641	226	Wells Fargo Real Estate Inve	$1,238	267	Republic Services Inc	$1,037
186	Baxter International Inc	$1,624	227	American Tower Corp (New)	$1,236	268	Paychex Inc	$1,034
187	DR Horton Inc	$1,619	228	Comerica, Inc.	$1,235	269	Raymond James Financial, Inc	$1,034
188	AutoZone, Inc.	$1,617	229	Becton Dickinson And Co	$1,233	270	Eversource Energy	$1,033
189	Kinder Morgan Inc.	$1,609	230	Textron Inc	$1,222	271	LiveRamp Holdings Inc	$1,029
190	Fox Corp	$1,595	231	Qurate Retail Inc – Com Ser	$1,208	272	Electronic Arts	$1,019
191	Dollar General Corp	$1,589	232	Twitter Inc	$1,206	273	PulteGroup Inc	$1,017
192	Ross Stores Inc	$1,587	233	Amphenol Corp.	$1,205	274	Medical Properties Trust Inc	$1,017
193	DISH Network Corp	$1,575	234	AES Corp.	$1,203	275	Gap Inc	$1,003
194	Intuit Inc	$1,557	235	Consolidated Edison Co. of N	$1,196	276	Uber Technologies Inc	$997
195	Northern Trust Corp	$1,556	236	Franklin Resources Inc	$1,196	277	Westlake Chemical Corp	$996
196	Principal Financial Group In	$1,547	237	CoBank, ACB	$1,191	278	Chemours Co (The)	$995
197	Southern Copper Corp	$1,543	238	Fiserv Inc	$1,187	279	Monster Beverage Corp (New)	$993
198	Yum! Brands Inc	$1,542	239	Garrett Motion Inc	$1,180	280	Jones Financial Companies LL	$990
199	Blackstone Group Inc (The)	$1,542	240	Hershey Company (The)	$1,178	281	Continental Resources Inc.	$988
200	Parker–Hannifin Corp	$1,512	241	KLA Corp	$1,176	282	Hormel Foods Corp.	$979
201	Icahn Enterprises LP	$1,507	242	United Rentals Inc	$1,174	283	Pioneer Natural Resources Co	$978
202	Best Buy Inc	$1,464	243	DTE Energy Co	$1,169	284	AvalonBay Communities, Inc.	$975
203	Public Service Enterprise Gr	$1,438	244	Netapp Inc	$1,169	285	SVB Financial Group	$974
204	Ecolab Inc	$1,429	245	ONEOK Inc	$1,152	286	Brighthouse Life Insurance C	$967
205	Zoetis Inc	$1,428	246	KKR & Co Inc	$1,131	287	Motorola Solutions Inc	$966
206	Tennessee Valley Authority	$1,417	247	Cleveland–Cliffs Inc (New)	$1,128	288	Jefferies Financial Group In	$965
207	American Airlines Group Inc	$1,412	248	Intuitive Surgical Inc	$1,128	289	New Residential Investment C	$964
208	Kimberly–Clark Corp.	$1,410	249	Molson Coors Beverage Co	$1,117	290	Alliance Data Systems Corp.	$963
209	Huntington Bancshares Inc	$1,393	250	United States Steel Corp.	$1,115	291	L3Harris Technologies Inc	$949
210	Consolidated Edison Inc	$1,382	251	Salesforce.Com Inc	$1,110	292	Alabama Power Co	$945
211	Analog Devices Inc	$1,363	252	Sherwin–Williams Co (The)	$1,109	293	Roper Technologies Inc	$944
212	Cardinal Health, Inc.	$1,363	253	Macy's Inc	$1,108	294	BorgWarner Inc	$931
213	PPG Industries Inc	$1,341	254	HollyFrontier Corp	$1,098	295	Qurate Retail Inc	$916
214	Kellogg Co	$1,336	255	Marathon Oil Corp.	$1,096	296	Santander Consumer USA Holdi	$916
215	Magellan Midstream Partners	$1,334	256	Host Hotels & Resorts Inc	$1,087	297	Sirius XM Holdings Inc	$914
216	Omnicom Group, Inc.	$1,326	257	Eastman Chemical Co	$1,080	298	FirstEnergy Corp	$912
217	O'Reilly Automotive, Inc.	$1,324	258	Duke Energy Carolinas LLC	$1,071	299	RiverSource Life Insurance C	$905
218	Moody's Corp.	$1,310	259	Agilent Technologies, Inc.	$1,071	300	Centene Corp	$900

The 300 Largest U.S. Public Employers in
Hoover's Handbook of American Business 2020

Rank	Company	Employees	Rank	Company	Employees	Rank	Company	Employees
1	Walmart Inc	2,200,000	60	Best Buy Inc	125,000	119	Autoliv Inc	67,000
2	Amazon.com Inc	798,000	61	Barrett Business Services, I	122,958	120	ASGN Inc	66,200
3	Kelly Services, Inc.	506,800	62	Alphabet Inc	118,899	121	Baker Hughes Company	66,000
4	United Parcel Service Inc	481,000	63	Tenet Healthcare Corp.	115,500	122	Caesars Entertainment Corp	66,000
5	Kroger Co (The)	453,000	64	Honeywell International Inc	114,000	123	Brookdale Senior Living Inc	65,400
6	Yum China Holdings Inc	450,000	65	Intel Corp	110,800	124	Marsh & McLennan Companies I	65,000
7	Home Depot Inc	413,000	66	Lockheed Martin Corp	110,000	125	Texas Roadhouse Inc	64,900
8	Berkshire Hathaway Inc	389,000	67	Caterpillar Inc.	104,000	126	Goodyear Tire & Rubber Co.	64,000
9	Target Corp	360,000	68	Abbott Laboratories	103,000	127	Anthem Inc	63,900
10	International Business Machi	350,600	69	General Dynamics Corp	102,900	128	Cummins, Inc.	62,610
11	Starbucks Corp.	346,000	70	XPO Logistics, Inc.	100,000	129	Coca-Cola Co (The)	62,600
12	Walgreens Boots Alliance Inc	342,000	71	Procter & Gamble Co (The)	97,000	130	Brinks Co (The)	62,400
13	UnitedHealth Group Inc	300,000	72	3M Co	96,163	131	Bed, Bath & Beyond, Inc.	62,000
14	Lowe's Companies Inc	300,000	73	AutoZone, Inc.	96,000	132	Western Digital Corp	61,800
15	CVS Health Corp	295,000	74	Charter Communications Inc (	95,100	133	Hewlett Packard Enterprise C	61,600
16	Aramark	283,500	75	Penney (J.C.) Co.,Inc. (Hold	95,000	134	Genesis Healthcare Inc	61,300
17	General Electric Co	283,000	76	Bloomin' Brands Inc	93,000	135	LabCorp	61,000
18	Cognizant Technology Solutio	281,600	77	Pfizer Inc	92,400	136	GameStop Corp	61,000
19	TJX Companies, Inc.	270,000	78	United Airlines Holdings Inc	92,000	137	Southwest Airlines Co	60,800
20	AT&T Inc	268,000	79	Whirlpool Corp	92,000	138	Stanley Black & Decker Inc	60,767
21	PepsiCo Inc	267,000	80	Northrop Grumman Corp	90,000	139	Marathon Petroleum Corp.	60,350
22	Albertsons Companies Inc	267,000	81	CBRE Group Inc	90,000	140	Morgan Stanley	60,348
23	HCA Healthcare Inc	262,000	82	Jones Lang LaSalle Inc	90,000	141	Halliburton Company	60,000
24	Wells Fargo & Co (New)	259,000	83	Delta Air Lines Inc (DE)	89,000	142	Laureate Education Inc	60,000
25	JPMorgan Chase & Co	256,105	84	Sears Holdings Corp	89,000	143	American Express Co.	59,000
26	Costco Wholesale Corp	254,000	85	L Brands, Inc	88,900	144	Automatic Data Processing In	58,000
27	United Technologies Corp	243,200	86	Ross Stores Inc	88,100	145	IQVIA Holdings Inc	58,000
28	Synnex Corp	240,900	87	Emerson Electric Co.	88,000	146	Brinker International, Inc.	56,147
29	FedEx Corp	239,000	88	Universal Health Services, I	87,100	147	HP Inc	56,000
30	Half Robert International In	231,600	89	Community Health Systems, In	87,000	148	Parker-Hannifin Corp	55,610
31	Disney (Walt) Co. (The)	223,000	90	AECOM	86,000	149	Healthcare Services Group In	55,000
32	McDonald's Corp	210,000	91	Chipotle Mexican Grill Inc	83,000	150	Six Flags Entertainment Corp	54,400
33	Bank of America Corp	204,000	92	Conduent Inc	82,000	151	Interpublic Group of Compani	54,000
34	Citigroup Inc	204,000	93	Tenneco Inc	81,000	152	Hyatt Hotels Corp	54,000
35	Publix Super Markets, Inc.	202,000	94	McKesson Corp	80,000	153	Sherwin-Williams Co (The)	53,368
36	Jabil Inc	200,000	95	Mondelez International Inc	80,000	154	Fluor Corp.	53,349
37	Ford Motor Co. (DE)	190,000	96	O'Reilly Automotive, Inc.	79,174	155	Rite Aid Corp.	53,100
38	Comcast Corp	190,000	97	DaVita Inc	77,700	156	PNC Financial Services Group	53,063
39	Darden Restaurants, Inc. (Un	184,514	98	NIKE Inc	76,700	157	T-Mobile US Inc	53,000
40	Dollar Tree Inc	182,100	99	Cisco Systems Inc	75,900	158	International Paper Co	53,000
41	Marriott International, Inc.	176,000	100	VF Corp.	75,000	159	Ascena Retail Group Inc	53,000
42	Hilton Worldwide Holdings In	169,000	101	Cigna Corp (New)	73,800	160	TTEC Holdings Inc	52,400
43	Lear Corp.	164,100	102	Amphenol Corp.	73,600	161	Pilgrims Pride Corp.	52,100
44	General Motors Co	164,000	103	Philip Morris International	73,500	162	Jacobs Engineering Group, In	52,000
45	Boeing Co	161,100	104	Deere & Co.	73,489	163	Sykes Enterprises, Inc.	51,600
46	Dell Technologies Inc	157,000	105	U.S. Bancorp (DE)	73,333	164	Corning Inc	51,500
47	Verizon Communications Inc	144,500	106	Cracker Barrel Old Country S	73,000	165	Bank of New York Mellon Corp	51,300
48	Microsoft Corporation	144,000	107	MGM Resorts International	72,000	166	WestRock Co	51,100
49	Tyson Foods Inc	141,000	108	Exxon Mobil Corp	71,000	167	LKQ Corp	51,000
50	ABM Industries, Inc.	140,000	109	Danaher Corp	71,000	168	RMR Group Inc (The)	50,600
51	Apple Inc	137,000	110	Nordstrom, Inc.	71,000	169	Prudential Financial Inc	50,492
52	Oracle Corp	136,000	111	Advance Auto Parts Inc	71,000	170	Freeport-McMoRan Inc	50,200
53	Johnson & Johnson	135,100	112	Omnicom Group, Inc.	70,400	171	Genuine Parts Co.	50,000
54	Dollar General Corp	135,000	113	Becton Dickinson And Co	70,093	172	Las Vegas Sands Corp	50,000
55	Gap Inc	135,000	114	Thermo Fisher Scientific Inc	70,000	173	Baxter International Inc	50,000
56	Macy's Inc	130,000	115	Sysco Corp	69,000	174	Facebook Inc	49,942
57	DXC Technology Co	130,000	116	Merck & Co Inc	69,000	175	American International Group	49,600
58	Kohl's Corp.	129,000	117	HanesBrands Inc	68,000	176	Cardinal Health, Inc.	49,500
59	American Airlines Group Inc	128,900	118	Raytheon Co.	67,000	177	Foot Locker, Inc.	49,331

SOURCE: MERGENT INC., DATABASE, FEBRUARY 2020

The 300 Largest U.S. Public Employers in
Hoover's Handbook of American Business 2020 (continued)

Rank	Company	Employees	Rank	Company	Employees	Rank	Company	Employees
178	Ecolab Inc	49,000	219	Dillard's Inc.	39,000	260	Travelers Companies Inc (The	30,400
179	Tesla Inc	48,817	220	Cheesecake Factory Inc. (The	38,700	261	BG Staffing Inc	30,349
180	Chevron Corporation	48,600	221	Eli Lilly & Co	38,680	262	Epam Systems, Inc.	30,156
181	MetLife Inc	48,000	222	Vail Resorts Inc	38,500	263	Duke Energy Corp	30,083
182	Lauder (Estee) Cos., Inc. (T	48,000	223	Kraft Heinz Co (The)	38,000	264	Encompass Health Corp	30,060
183	Illinois Tool Works, Inc.	48,000	224	PVH Corp	38,000	265	AbbVie Inc	30,000
184	Berry Global Group Inc	48,000	225	Hertz Global Holdings Inc (N	38,000	266	ManpowerGroup	30,000
185	Capital One Financial Corp	47,600	226	Union Pacific Corp	37,483	267	BorgWarner Inc	30,000
186	StarTek, Inc.	47,500	227	Progressive Corp. (OH)	37,346	268	Avis Budget Group Inc	30,000
187	Centene Corp	47,300	228	Micron Technology Inc.	37,000	269	Avery Dennison Corp	30,000
188	Cedar Fair LP	47,300	229	Qualcomm Inc	37,000	270	Sprouts Farmers Market Inc	30,000
189	Select Medical Holdings Corp	47,100	230	Newell Brands Inc	37,000	271	AMERCO	30,000
190	Jones Financial Companies LL	47,000	231	Casey's General Stores, Inc.	36,841	272	Texas Instruments, Inc.	29,888
191	Fidelity National Informatio	47,000	232	Goldman Sachs Group Inc	36,600	273	MAXIMUS Inc.	29,600
192	Michaels Companies Inc	47,000	233	Dow Inc	36,500	274	Southern Co.	29,192
193	Quest Diagnostics, Inc.	46,000	234	Republic Services Inc	36,000	275	ExlService Holdings Inc	29,100
194	Allstate Corp	45,700	235	Truist Financial Corp	35,852	276	Icahn Enterprises LP	29,034
195	CenturyLink Inc	45,000	236	ON Semiconductor Corp	35,700	277	United States Steel Corp.	29,000
196	Cintas Corp	45,000	237	Big Lots, Inc.	35,600	278	Tractor Supply Co.	29,000
197	American Eagle Outfitters, I	45,000	238	National Oilwell Varco Inc	35,063	279	Sprint Corp (New)	28,500
198	Office Depot, Inc.	44,000	239	Textron Inc	35,000	280	Qurate Retail Inc – Com Ser	28,255
199	Ulta Beauty Inc	44,000	240	Salesforce.Com Inc	35,000	281	Williams Sonoma Inc	28,200
200	Burlington Stores Inc	44,000	241	Colgate-Palmolive Co.	34,500	282	Paccar Inc.	28,000
201	Waste Management, Inc. (DE)	43,700	242	Kellogg Co	34,000	283	News Corp (New)	28,000
202	Humana, Inc.	43,600	243	NCR Corp.	34,000	284	Universal Corp	28,000
203	Arconic Inc	43,000	244	Yum! Brands Inc	34,000	285	PPG Industries Inc	27,800
204	Sanmina Corp	43,000	245	Exelon Corp	33,383	286	Hunt (J.B.) Transport Servic	27,621
205	Mohawk Industries, Inc.	42,100	246	Bright Horizons Family Solut	33,350	287	Cerner Corp.	27,400
206	Acadia Healthcare Company In	42,100	247	Gallagher (Arthur J.) & Co.	33,300	288	Red Robin Gourmet Burgers In	27,283
207	Abercrombie & Fitch Co	42,000	248	Addus HomeCare Corp	33,153	289	Qurate Retail Inc	27,226
208	Burlington Northern & Santa F	41,000	249	Crown Holdings Inc	33,000	290	Penske Automotive Group Inc	27,000
209	Kimberly-Clark Corp.	41,000	250	EMCOR Group, Inc.	33,000	291	Mattel Inc	27,000
210	Dick's Sporting Goods, Inc	40,700	251	Xerox Holdings Corp	32,400	292	Ingles Markets Inc	27,000
211	State Street Corp.	40,142	252	HireQuest Inc	32,230	293	TTM Technologies Inc	27,000
212	General Mills Inc	40,000	253	Leidos Holdings Inc	32,000	294	O-I Glass Inc	26,500
213	Stryker Corp	40,000	254	Boston Scientific Corp.	32,000	295	Cannae Holdings Inc	26,413
214	Huntington Ingalls Industrie	40,000	255	Cooper-Standard Holdings Inc	32,000	296	BJs Wholesale Club Holdings	26,383
215	AMC Entertainment Holdings I	39,802	256	Archer Daniels Midland Co.	31,600	297	Nucor Corp.	26,300
216	Ryder System, Inc.	39,600	257	LHC Group Inc	30,985	298	Booz Allen Hamilton Holding	26,100
217	RR Donnelley & Sons Company	39,500	258	Amkor Technology Inc.	30,850	299	AutoNation, Inc.	26,000
218	Quanta Services, Inc.	39,200	259	Sally Beauty Holdings Inc	30,500	300	Masco Corp.	26,000

The Mergent 500 Largest Global Corporations (By Revenues)

Rank	Company	Sales ($ mil.)	Rank	Company	Sales ($ mil.)	Rank	Company	Sales ($ mil.)
1	Walmart Inc	$514,405	68	Siemens AG (Germany)	$94,741	135	Prudential Financial Inc	$62,992
2	China Petroleum & Chemical C	$420,334	69	Bosch (Robert) GmbH (Germany	$93,582	136	Mitsui & Co., Ltd.	$62,825
3	Royal Dutch Shell Plc	$396,556	70	Nestle SA	$93,269	137	Seven & i Holdings Co. Ltd.	$61,297
4	PetroChina Co Ltd	$342,176	71	Anthem Inc	$92,105	138	Toyota Tsusho Corp	$61,066
5	BP PLC	$303,282	72	Aedas Homes SAU	$91,413	139	Albertsons Companies Inc	$60,535
6	Exxon Mobil Corp	$290,212	73	SK C&C Co Ltd	$91,042	140	Dai-ichi Life Holdings Inc	$60,237
7	Amazon.com Inc	$280,522	74	Dell Technologies Inc	$90,621	141	Centene Corp	$60,116
8	Toyota Motor Corp	$272,933	75	Uniper SE	$89,608	142	Sysco Corp	$60,114
9	Volkswagen AG	$270,093	76	Carrefour S.A.	$89,230	143	Lockheed Martin Corp	$59,812
10	Cementos Bio-Bio S.A. (Chile)	$262,569	77	HSBC Holdings Plc	$88,667	144	Rewe-Zentral AG (Germany, Fed	$59,300
11	Apple Inc	$260,174	78	CITIC Ltd	$88,459	145	Alimentation Couche-Tard Inc	$59,118
12	Berkshire Hathaway Inc	$247,837	79	ENI S.p.A.	$88,109	146	HP Inc	$58,756
13	UnitedHealth Group Inc	$226,247	80	Banco Santander SA	$87,740	147	Unilever Plc (United Kingdom	$58,384
14	Glencore PLC	$219,754	81	Hyundai Motor Co., Ltd.	$86,836	148	Unilever N.V.	$58,384
15	Samsung Electronics Co Ltd	$218,651	82	SoftBank Group Corp	$86,707	149	POSCO (South Korea)	$58,282
16	McKesson Corp	$214,319	83	Enel SpA	$86,659	150	Repsol S.A.	$57,263
17	CVS Health Corp	$194,579	84	Credit Agricole SA	$86,655	151	Tokyo Electric Power Company	$57,236
18	Daimler AG	$191,662	85	Deutsche Telekom AG	$86,641	152	Humana, Inc.	$56,912
19	Total SA	$184,106	86	Hitachi, Ltd.	$85,608	153	Brookfield Asset Management	$56,771
20	AmerisourceBergen Corp.	$179,589	87	Mexican Petroleum	$85,492	154	Societe Generale	$56,486
21	Hon Hai Precision Industry C	$173,087	88	Reliance Industries Ltd	$85,217	155	Alibaba Group Holding Ltd	$56,136
22	AT&T Inc	$170,756	89	Peugeot SA	$84,775	156	Nippon Steel Corp (New)	$55,786
23	Industrial and Commercial Ba	$167,571	90	EDF Trading Ltd	$83,472	157	Telefonica SA	$55,763
24	Chevron Corporation	$166,339	91	Electricite de France	$83,472	158	Country Garden Holdings Co L	$55,112
25	Alphabet Inc	$161,857	92	Tesco PLC	$83,156	159	LG Electronics Inc	$55,020
26	Ford Motor Co. (DE)	$155,900	93	Assicurazioni Generali S.p.A	$83,137	160	Caterpillar Inc.	$54,722
27	Costco Wholesale Corp	$152,703	94	BNP Paribas (France)	$82,614	161	Deutsche Bahn AG	$54,655
28	Ping An Insurance (Group) Co	$150,600	95	Johnson & Johnson	$81,581	162	Anheuser Busch InBev SA/NV	$54,619
29	China Construction Bank Corp	$145,666	96	Equinor ASA	$79,593	163	Korea Electric Power Corp KE	$54,380
30	Cardinal Health, Inc.	$145,534	97	International Business Machi	$79,591	164	Energy Transfer Operating LP	$54,087
31	Mitsubishi Corp	$145,414	98	Sony Corp	$78,250	165	Energy Transfer LP	$54,087
32	Honda Motor Co., Ltd.	$143,472	99	United Technologies Corp	$77,046	166	CNP Assurances S.A.	$53,966
33	General Motors Co	$137,237	100	Aeon Co. Ltd. (Japan)	$76,885	167	LVMH Moet Hennessy Louis Vui	$53,651
34	Walgreens Boots Alliance Inc	$136,866	101	Boeing Co.	$76,559	168	Pfizer Inc	$53,647
35	JPMorgan Chase & Co	$131,412	102	ArcelorMittal SA	$76,033	169	Novartis AG Basel	$53,166
36	SAIC Motor Corp Ltd	$131,165	103	Target Corp	$75,356	170	America Movil SAB de CV	$52,797
37	Verizon Communications Inc	$130,863	104	Deutscher Sparkassen-und Giro	$74,762	171	Goldman Sachs Group Inc	$52,528
38	Agricultural Bank of China L	$127,091	105	Nippon Life Insurance Co.	$74,447	172	Christian Dior SE	$52,345
39	Fiat Chrysler Automobiles NV	$126,443	106	Freddie Mac	$73,598	173	Cisco Systems Inc	$51,904
40	Microsoft Corporation	$125,843	107	Airbus SE	$72,957	174	China Pacific Insurance (Gro	$51,519
41	General Electric Co	$121,615	108	Panasonic Corp	$72,263	175	Royal Bank of Canada (Montre	$51,310
42	Kroger Co (The)	$121,162	109	PTT Public Co Ltd	$72,216	176	Lenovo Group Ltd	$51,038
43	Fannie Mae	$120,101	110	Intel Corp	$71,965	177	Vinci SA	$50,895
44	PJSC Gazprom	$118,260	111	United Parcel Service Inc	$71,861	178	Continental AG (Germany, Fed	$50,852
45	Rosneft Oil Co OJSC (Moscow)	$118,200	112	BASF SE	$71,775	179	Shanghai Jinfeng Investment C	$50,700
46	Valero Energy Corp	$117,033	113	Koninklijke Ahold Delhaize N	$71,600	180	Itau Unibanco Holding S.A.	$50,422
47	Federal Reserve System	$116,764	114	China Communications Constru	$71,365	181	Kia Motors Corp. (South Kore	$50,216
48	AXA SA	$115,360	115	Lowe's Companies Inc	$71,309	182	Morgan Stanley	$50,193
49	Japan Post Holdings Co Ltd	$115,356	116	Facebook Inc	$70,697	183	Banco Bilbao Vizcaya Argenta	$49,391
50	PJSC Lukoil	$115,300	117	Indian Oil Corp., Ltd. (Indi	$70,561	184	Vodafone Group Plc	$49,039
51	Allianz SE	$114,506	118	Deutsche Post AG	$70,487	185	Tianjin Tianhai Investment C	$48,918
52	Phillips 66	$114,217	119	Japan Post Insurance Co Ltd	$70,168	186	SK Innovation Co Ltd	$48,894
53	Bayerische Motoren Werke AG	$111,634	120	FedEx Corp	$69,693	187	MS&AD Insurance Group Holdin	$48,722
54	Bank of America Corp	$110,584	121	Disney (Walt) Co. (The)	$69,570	188	Tokio Marine Holdings Inc	$48,654
55	Comcast Corp	$108,942	122	Engie SA	$69,394	189	Cigna Corp (New)	$48,650
56	Home Depot Inc	$108,203	123	MetLife Inc	$67,941	190	Denso Corp. (Japan)	$48,425
57	China Railway Group Ltd	$107,648	124	AUDI AG	$67,851	191	Mitsubishi UFJ Financial Gro	$48,360
58	Nippon Telegraph & Telephone	$107,273	125	China Evergrande Group	$67,778	192	Sumitomo Corp.	$48,212
59	China Mobile Limited	$107,122	126	Procter & Gamble Co (The)	$67,684	193	Compagnie de Saint-Gobain	$47,874
60	China Railway Construction C	$106,149	127	JD.com, Inc.	$67,171	194	State Bank Of India	$47,832
61	ITOCHU Corp (Japan)	$104,751	128	Marubeni Corp.	$66,832	195	Orange	$47,393
62	Nissan Motor Co., Ltd.	$104,514	129	Roche Holding AG	$65,947	196	American International Group	$47,389
63	Wells Fargo & Co (New)	$101,060	130	Renault S.A. (France)	$65,756	197	Zurich Insurance Group AG	$47,180
64	JXTG Holdings Inc	$100,499	131	Munich Re Group	$65,285	198	JBS S.A.	$46,811
65	Citigroup Inc	$97,120	132	Federal Reserve Bank Of New Y	$65,090	199	HCA Healthcare Inc	$46,677
66	Marathon Petroleum Corp.	$97,102	133	PepsiCo Inc	$64,661	200	Manufacturers Life Insurance	$46,621
67	Petroleo Brasileiro SA	$95,584	134	Archer Daniels Midland Co.	$64,341			

The **Mergent** 500 Largest Global Corporations (By Revenues)

Rank	Company	Sales ($ mil.)	Rank	Company	Sales ($ mil.)	Rank	Company	Sales ($ mil.)
201	Rallye S.A. Neuilly-Sur-Sein	$46,313	268	Fresenius SE & Co KGaA	$38,398	335	Jiangxi Copper Co., Ltd.	$31,300
202	KDDI Corp	$45,875	269	China Shenhua Energy Co., Lt	$38,396	336	British American Tobacco Plc	$31,270
203	Toronto Dominion Bank	$45,798	270	Talanx AG	$38,387	337	L'Oreal S.A.	$30,849
204	Charter Communications Inc (	$45,764	271	J.Sainsbury PLC	$37,921	338	BT Group Plc	$30,690
205	Bunge Ltd.	$45,743	272	Centrica Plc	$37,902	339	CRH Plc	$30,680
206	Tencent Holdings Ltd.	$45,461	273	Banco Bradesco SA	$37,545	340	Compass Group PLC (United Ki	$30,628
207	Bayer AG	$45,334	274	Daiwa House Industry Co Ltd	$37,415	341	Abbott Laboratories	$30,578
208	Saudi Basic Industries Corp -	$45,101	275	Tech Data Corp.	$37,239	342	Medtronic PLC	$30,557
209	T-Mobile US Inc	$44,998	276	Brookfield Business Partners	$37,168	343	Air France-KLM	$30,365
210	American Airlines Group Inc	$44,541	277	Swiss Re AG	$37,047	344	Travelers Companies Inc (The	$30,282
211	Wilmar International Ltd	$44,498	278	Mitsubishi Heavy Industries	$36,827	345	Sumitomo Life Insurance Co.	$30,217
212	Delta Air Lines Inc (DE)	$44,438	279	Barclays PLC	$36,730	346	Industria De Diseno Textil I	$30,036
213	Baoshan Iron & Steel Co Ltd	$44,372	280	Vale SA	$36,575	347	Kansai Electric Power Co., I	$29,868
214	Tata Motors Ltd	$44,312	281	Enterprise Products Partners	$36,534	348	Philip Morris International	$29,805
215	BHP Group Plc	$44,288	282	Aisin Seiki Co Ltd	$36,509	349	CNH Industrial NV	$29,706
216	BHP Group Ltd	$44,288	283	Publix Super Markets, Inc.	$36,396	350	Arrow Electronics, Inc.	$29,677
217	Pegatron Corp	$43,813	284	AIA Group Ltd.	$36,297	351	Veolia Environnement	$29,673
218	UBS Group AG	$43,790	285	SK Hynix Inc	$36,277	352	European Investment Bank	$29,499
219	Hanwha Corp	$43,717	286	Exelon Corp	$35,985	353	Unicredit SpA	$29,489
220	Zhejiang Material Industrial	$43,694	287	Canon Inc	$35,937	354	Schneider Electric SE	$29,454
221	ZF Friedrichshafen AG (Germa	$43,687	288	Meiji Yasuda Life Insurance	$35,810	355	Bank of Montreal (Quebec)	$29,416
222	Volvo AB	$43,662	289	Gazprom Neft PJSC	$35,717	356	Samsung Life Insurance Co Lt	$29,245
223	American Express Co.	$43,281	290	Fujitsu Ltd	$35,690	357	PKN Orlen SA	$29,228
224	China Vanke Co Ltd	$43,278	291	George Weston Ltd	$35,665	358	Hewlett Packard Enterprise C	$29,135
225	Accenture plc	$43,215	292	Suning.com Co Ltd	$35,613	359	Wistron Corp	$29,084
226	Dow Inc	$42,951	293	Power Corp. of Canada	$35,440	360	Gree Electric Appliances Inc	$29,080
227	Best Buy Inc	$42,879	294	Mitsubishi Chemical Holdings	$35,428	361	Medipal Holdings Corp	$28,732
228	Casino Guichard Perrachon S.	$42,528	295	Bank Nova Scotia Halifax	$35,409	362	Sumitomo Electric Industries	$28,697
229	Jardine Matheson Holdings Lt	$42,527	296	CK Hutchison Holdings Ltd	$35,384	363	Suncor Energy Inc	$28,629
230	Tyson Foods Inc	$42,405	297	JFE Holdings Inc	$34,979	364	Manulife Financial Corp	$28,618
231	Woolworths Group Ltd	$42,307	298	Suzuki Motor Corp.	$34,959	365	Commonwealth Bank of Austral	$28,589
232	Merck & Co Inc	$42,294	299	Loblaw Companies Ltd	$34,718	366	Subaru Corp	$28,539
233	China Unicom (Hong Kong) Ltd	$42,289	300	Power Financial Corp	$34,601	367	SAP SE	$28,295
234	China United Network Communi	$42,289	301	Quanta Computer Inc	$34,439	368	Poly Real Estate Group Co.,	$28,285
235	Deutsche Bank AG	$42,277	302	E.ON SE	$34,327	369	Danone	$28,230
236	ACS Actividades de Construcc	$42,244	303	Metro AG (New)	$34,141	370	International Consolidated A	$27,950
237	Metallurgical Corp China Ltd	$42,094	304	Jardine Strategic Holdings L	$34,094	371	Samsung C&T Corp (New)	$27,945
238	Honeywell International Inc	$41,802	305	Enbridge Inc	$34,057	372	LafargeHolcim	$27,921
239	Lufthansa AG (Germany, Fed.	$41,656	306	Plains All American Pipeline	$34,055	373	Naturgy Energy Group SA	$27,873
240	United Airlines Holdings Inc	$41,303	307	Plains GP Holdings LP	$34,055	374	ABB Ltd	$27,662
241	Sanofi	$40,857	308	Xiamen Xiangyu Co Ltd	$34,021	375	Lloyds Bank plc	$27,660
242	Sumitomo Mitsui Financial Gr	$40,840	309	Toshiba Corp	$33,972	376	Anglo American Plc (United K	$27,610
243	Magna International Inc	$40,827	310	Northrop Grumman Corp	$33,841	377	Chubu Electric Power Co Inc	$27,406
244	Mitsubishi Electric Corp	$40,814	311	SoftBank Corp (New)	$33,829	378	Adecco Group AG	$27,332
245	Xiamen C & D Inc	$40,763	312	Lloyds Banking Group Plc	$33,745	379	Hochtief AG	$27,328
246	Rio Tinto Ltd	$40,522	313	Taiwan Semiconductor Manufac	$33,722	380	China Taiping Insurance Hold	$27,324
247	Rio Tinto Plc (United Kingdo	$40,522	314	Sprint Corp (New)	$33,600	381	Randstad NV	$27,269
248	ThyssenKrupp AG	$40,281	315	ING Groep NV	$33,500	382	PBF Energy Inc	$27,186
249	Iberdrola SA	$40,169	316	Schlumberger Ltd	$33,250	383	East Japan Railway Co.	$27,108
250	innogy SE	$40,154	317	Bridgestone Corp. (Japan)	$33,192	384	Koc Holdings AS	$27,074
251	Idemitsu Kosan Co Ltd	$39,958	318	Cnooc Ltd.	$32,997	385	Raytheon Co.	$27,058
252	Hongkong And Shanghai Bankin	$39,831	319	AbbVie Inc	$32,753	386	Coles Group Ltd (New)	$26,949
253	Sberbank Russia	$39,817	320	INTL FCStone Inc.	$32,742	387	Ferguson PLC (New)	$26,798
254	Allstate Corp	$39,815	321	Chubb Ltd	$32,717	388	KB Financial Group, Inc.	$26,732
255	World Fuel Services Corp.	$39,750	322	Sompo Holdings Inc	$32,567	389	HSBC Bank Plc (United Kingdo	$26,718
256	Bouygues S.A.	$39,624	323	Capital One Financial Corp	$32,377	390	Qingdao Haier Co Ltd	$26,651
257	Oracle Corp	$39,506	324	Great-West Lifeco Inc	$32,334	391	Starbucks Corp.	$26,509
258	GlaxoSmithKline Plc	$39,351	325	Prudential Plc	$32,202	392	CJ Corp (Korea)	$26,481
259	General Dynamics Corp	$39,350	326	Mazda Motor Corp. (Japan)	$32,189	393	Bollore SA	$26,393
260	Deere & Co.	$39,258	327	3M Co	$32,136	394	NEC Corp	$26,308
261	NIKE Inc	$39,117	328	Progressive Corp. (OH)	$31,979	395	Kraft Heinz Co (The)	$26,268
262	A.P. Moller - Maersk A/S	$39,019	329	CHS Inc	$31,900	396	OMV AG (Austria)	$26,259
263	LyondellBasell Industries NV	$39,004	330	Coca-Cola Co (The)	$31,856	397	Heineken Holding NV (Netherl	$26,238
264	TJX Companies, Inc.	$38,973	331	CRRC Corp Ltd	$31,851	398	Flex Ltd	$26,211
265	Imperial Brands PLC	$38,896	332	Compal Electronics Inc	$31,640	399	Aluminum Corp of China Ltd.	$26,204
266	ConocoPhillips	$38,727	333	Hyundai Mobis Co Ltd (South	$31,527	400	Mondelez International Inc	$25,868
267	Intesa Sanpaolo S.P.A.	$38,614	334	Wal-Mart de Mexico S.A.B. de	$31,372			

Rank	Company	Sales ($ mil.)	Rank	Company	Sales ($ mil.)	Rank	Company	Sales ($ mil.)
401	Nokia Corp	$25,839	435	Standard Chartered Plc	$24,038	469	Visa Inc	$22,977
402	U.S. Bancorp (DE)	$25,775	436	NGL Energy Partners LP	$24,017	470	Baker Hughes Company	$22,877
403	Imperial Oil Ltd	$25,774	437	Australia & New Zealand Bank	$24,001	471	Huayu Automotive Systems Com	$22,850
404	Macy's Inc	$25,739	438	Halliburton Company	$23,995	472	S-Oil Corp	$22,839
405	Heineken NV (Netherlands)	$25,734	439	Empresas COPEC SA	$23,970	473	Dollar Tree Inc	$22,823
406	Volvo Car Corp. (Sweden)	$25,707	440	AntarChile S.A. (Chile)	$23,970	474	Henkel AG & Co KGAA	$22,788
407	Dollar General Corp	$25,625	441	Johnson Controls Internation	$23,968	475	Tata Steel Ltd	$22,786
408	Xiaomi Corp	$25,430	442	Great-West Life Assurance Co	$23,955	476	Penske Automotive Group Inc	$22,785
409	Altria Group Inc	$25,364	443	Fomento Economico Mexicano,	$23,888	477	Telecom Italia SpA	$22,733
410	Xiamen International Trade Gr	$25,302	444	Alfresa Holdings Corp Tokyo	$23,844	478	Aviva Plc (United Kingdom)	$22,725
411	Jabil Inc	$25,282	445	ONEX Corp (Canada)	$23,785	479	Mitsubishi Motors Corp. (Jap	$22,706
412	Barclays Bank Plc	$25,257	446	McKesson Europe AG	$23,782	480	National Australia Bank Ltd.	$22,686
413	Cie Generale des Etablisseme	$25,226	447	Cummins, Inc.	$23,771	481	WH Group Ltd	$22,605
414	Safran	$25,177	448	Synnex Corp	$23,757	482	Broadcom Inc (DE)	$22,597
415	Adidas AG	$25,097	449	Amgen Inc	$23,747	483	POSCO Daewoo Corp	$22,580
416	Formosa Petrochemical Corp	$25,096	450	ENBW Energie Baden-Wuertt	$23,744	484	Bristol-Myers Squibb Co.	$22,561
417	Nucor Corp.	$25,067	451	Yanzhou Coal Mining Co Ltd	$23,699	485	Olam International Ltd.	$22,447
418	Cosmo Energy Holdings Co Ltd	$25,016	452	Mitsubishi Shokuhin Co., Ltd	$23,661	486	Southwest Airlines Co	$22,428
419	Westpac Banking Corp	$24,975	453	Ericsson	$23,554	487	New China Life Insurance Co	$22,414
420	Ceconomy AG	$24,808	454	Paccar Inc.	$23,496	488	Daikin Industries Ltd	$22,404
421	Shanghai Construction Group	$24,795	455	Southern Co.	$23,495	489	Surgutneftegas PJSC	$22,325
422	Mapfre SA	$24,724	456	Korea Gas Corp. (South Korea	$23,487	490	Lennar Corp	$22,260
423	Huaneng Power International	$24,695	457	Holding CMA-CGM (France)	$23,476	491	Financiere De L Odet SA (Fra	$22,148
424	Komatsu Ltd	$24,609	458	CenturyLink Inc	$23,443	492	Gilead Sciences Inc	$22,127
425	Eli Lilly & Co	$24,556	459	Micron Technology Inc.	$23,406	493	AstraZeneca Plc	$22,090
426	Telefonaktiebolaget LM Erics	$24,536	460	Ultrapar Participacoes SA	$23,369	494	ManpowerGroup	$21,991
427	Duke Energy Corp	$24,521	461	NN Group NV (Netherlands)	$23,337	495	X5 Retail Group NV	$21,989
428	Thermo Fisher Scientific Inc	$24,358	462	International Paper Co	$23,306	496	Orix Corp	$21,975
429	L'Air Liquide S.A.	$24,278	463	Morrison (Wm.) Supermarkets	$23,173	497	FUJIFILM Holdings Corp	$21,956
430	Qualcomm Inc	$24,273	464	Hennes & Mauritz AB	$23,166	498	China Overseas Land & Invest	$21,892
431	Sodexo	$24,235	465	Weichai Power Co Ltd	$23,153	499	Canadian Imperial Bank Of Co	$21,832
432	China Resources Pharmaceutic	$24,219	466	Shanghai Pharmaceuticals Hol	$23,128	500	LG Display Co Ltd	$21,829
433	US Foods Holding Corp	$24,175	467	Endesa S.A.	$23,127			
434	China Grand Automotive Servi	$24,159	468	Nippon Steel Trading Corp	$23,032			

Hoover's Handbook of

American Business

The Companies

1st Source Corp

Need a bank? Don't give it a 2nd thought. Contact 1st Source Corporation parent of 1st Source Bank which provides commercial and consumer banking services through some 80 branches in northern Indiana and southwestern Michigan. The bank offers deposit accounts; business agricultural and consumer loans; residential and commercial mortgages; credit cards; and trust services. Its specialty finance group provides financing for aircraft automobile fleets trucks and construction and environmental equipment through about two-dozen offices nationwide; such loans account for nearly half of 1st Source's portfolio.

Operations

1st Source Bank subsidiary Specialty Finance Group offers specialized financing for new and used private and cargo aircraft automobiles and light trucks for leasing and rental agencies medium and heavy duty trucks and construction and environmental equipment. Another subsidiary 1st Source Insurance provides commercial and retail property/casualty coverage and life and health coverage. 1st Source Corporation Investment Advisors serves trust and investment clients of 1st Source Bank as well as the investment advisor of Wasatch Mutual Funds.

Geographic Reach

Indiana-based 1st Source serves customers across around 20 counties in Michigan and its home state.

Sales and Marketing

1st Source offers commercial and agricultural loans and leases to the transportation construction and real estate sectors. It offers retail loans to individuals.

Financial Performance

1st Source Corporation's revenues have been climbing for the past five years. Similarly net income has been on an upward trajectory.

In 2017 revenue increased 10% to a record $284.3 million as both interest and non-interest income rose. Net interest income grew 9% while non-interest income (including equipment rentals trust and wealth advisory fees and gains on investment securities) grew 11%.

Thanks to the higher revenue net income rose 18% to $68.1 million in 2017.

The company ended 2017 with $78 million in cash and cash equivalents a 28% decline from what it had at the end of 2016. Operating activities provided some $113 million and financing activities provided another $315 million but investment activities used $462 million that year.

Strategy

1st Source has been investing in its technology to better serve its customers. It invested $1.3 million on a new customer relationship management system during 2017 and it expects to continue development and implementation of that project. It also spent $2.2 million on cyber security initiatives that year. Additionally the company is increasing the bandwidth at its branches.

When it believes it can serve a new customer base the bank adds new branches to its network. In 2018 it opened a location on the campus of Indiana University South Bend. However like all banking companies 1st Source has seen a decline in transactions at its branches as customers embrace mobile banking. During 2017 the company consolidated three locations.

To improve its mobile experience 1st Source offers live customer support via Facebook Messenger.

EXECUTIVES

Chairman And Ceo, Christopher J. (Chris) Murphy, age 72, $726,923 total compensation
Evp Administration Secretary And General Counsel, John B. Griffith, age 61, $328,429 total compensation
Evp Cfo And Treasurer, Andrea G. Short, age 56, $275,769 total compensation
President 1st Source Bank, James R. Seitz, age 66, $325,010 total compensation
Svp And Chief Credit Officer 1st Source Bank, Jeffrey L. Buhr, $226,565 total compensation
President 1st Source Insurance, John Ball
Vice President, Sean Brady
Vice President Of Sales Officer, Scott Carter
Assistant Vice President Construction Equipment Financing Sales, Robert Mater
Assistant Vice President, Amy Wagoner
Vice President, Rick Michalski
Vice President, John Lutz
Vice President, Luke Squires
Assistant Vice President, Adam Hamilton
Vice President, Dave Smedley
Senior Vice President Online Home Banking Division, Jim Seitz
Asstant Vice President Small Business Banking, Julie Herring
Assistant Vice President, Michele Miller
Assistant Vice President Manager Of Tale, Janet Hughes
Vice President Andamp; Controller Loan Accounting, Dave Crim
Vice President And Trust Officer, Alberta Barker
Vice President, David Silvers
Vice President, Denise Myers
Vice President Trust Tax Manager, Pam Stearns
Assistant Vice President, Bryan Byers
Vice President And Retirement Services Manager, Steven Perlewitz
Assistant Vice President Infrastructure And Networks, Steven Moore
Vice President And Trust Officer, Michael Evans
Vice President, Richard Curran
Assistant Vice President, Mark Taylor
Vice President, Robert Jamieson
Auditors: BKD LLP

LOCATIONS

HQ: 1st Source Corp
100 North Michigan Street, South Bend, IN 46601
Phone: 574 235-2000
Web: www.1stsource.com

PRODUCTS/OPERATIONS

2017 Sales

	$ mil.	% of total
Interest		
Loans & leases	194	62
Taxable investment securities	13	4
Tax-exempt investment securities	2	1
Other	1	-
Interest expenses		
Non-interest		
Equipment rentals	30	10
Trust fees	21	7
Debit card income	11	4
Service charges on deposit accounts	9	3
Insurance commissions	5	2
Mortgage banking	4	2
Gains on investment securities available-for-sale	4	1
Other	10	4
Total	**284**	**100**

Selected Subsidiaries

1st Source Bank
  1st Source Capitol Corporation
  1st Source Corporation Investment Advisors Inc.
  1st Source Insurance Inc.
  1st Source Solar 1 LLC
  1st Source Specialty Finance Inc.

Michigan Transportation Finance Corporation
SFG Aircraft Inc.
SFG Commercial Aircraft Leasing
SFG Equipment Leasing Corporation I
Washington and Michigan Insurance Inc.
1st Source Funding LLC
1st Source Intermediate Holding LLC
1st Source Master Trust
Trustcorp Mortgage Company

COMPETITORS

Bank of America	Old National Bancorp
Fifth Third	PNC Financial
Huntington Bancshares	U.S. Bancorp
JPMorgan Chase	Wells Fargo
KeyCorp	

HISTORICAL FINANCIALS

Company Type: Public

Income Statement   FYE: December 31

	ASSETS ($ mil.)	NET INCOME ($ mil.)	INCOME AS % OF ASSETS	EMPLOYEES
12/18	6,293	82	1.3%	1,150
12/17	5,887	68	1.2%	1,125
12/16	5,486	57	1.1%	1,150
12/15	5,187	57	1.1%	1,150
12/14	4,829	58	1.2%	1,100
Annual Growth	6.8%	9.1%	—	1.1%

2018 Year-End Financials

Debt ratio: 1.33%
Return on equity: 11.13%
Cash ($ mil.): 99
Current ratio: —
Long-term debt ($ mil.): —

No. of shares (mil.): 25
Dividends
  Yield: 2.3%
  Payout: 31.8%
Market value ($ mil.): 1,040

	STOCK PRICE ($) FY Close	P/E High/Low	Earnings	Dividends	Book Value
12/18	40.34	19 12	3.16	0.96	29.56
12/17	49.45	20 16	2.60	0.76	27.70
12/16	44.66	20 12	2.22	0.72	26.00
12/15	30.87	16 13	2.17	0.67	24.75
12/14	34.31	16 13	2.17	0.65	23.41
Annual Growth	4.1%		9.8%	10.4%	6.0%

3M Co

Loath to be stuck in one industry 3M makes everything from tape to high-tech security gear. The diversified company's products fall under four segment categories: Safety & Industrial Transportation & Electronics Health Care and Consumer. 3M boasts some of the world's most recognizable consumer brands including Post-it notes Scotch tapes Scotchgard fabric protectors Scotch-Brite scouring pads Filtrete home air filters and ACE bandages. 3M sells products directly to users and through numerous wholesalers retailers distributors and dealers worldwide. The company generates about 60% of its sales outside the US. 3M was founded in 1902 as a small mining venture in Northern Minnesota called Minnesota Mining and Manufacturing Company.

HISTORY

Five businessmen in Two Harbors Minnesota founded Minnesota Mining and Manufacturing (3M) in 1902 to sell corundum to grinding-wheel manufacturers. The company soon needed to raise working capital. Co-founder John Dwan offered his friend Edgar Ober 60% of 3M's stock. Ober persuaded Lucius Ordway VP of a plumbing business to help underwrite 3M. In 1905 the two took over the company and moved it to Duluth.

In 1907 future CEO William McKnight joined 3M as a bookkeeper. Three years later the plant moved to St. Paul. The board of directors declared a dividend to shareholders in the last quarter of 1916 and 3M hasn't missed a dividend since. The next two products 3M developed — Scotch-brand masking tape (1925) and Scotch-brand cellophane tape (1930) — assured its future

McKnight introduced one of the first employee pension plans in 1931 and in the late 1940s he implemented a vertical management structure. 3M introduced the first commercially viable magnetic recording tape in 1947.

In 1950 after a decade of work and $1 million in development costs 3M employee Carl Miller completed the Thermo-Fax copying machine which was the foundation of 3M's duplicating division.

Products in the 1960s included 3M's dry-silver microfilm photographic products carbonless papers overhead projection systems and medical and dental products. The company moved into pharmaceuticals radiology energy control and office markets in the 1970s and 1980s.

A 3M scientist developed Post-it Notes (1980) because he wanted to attach page markers to his church hymnal. Recalling that a colleague had developed an adhesive that wasn't very sticky he brushed some on paper and began a product line that now generates hundreds of millions of dollars each year.

In 1990 the company bought sponge maker O-Cel-O. But not all of its inventions have brought 3M good news. In 1995 along with fellow silicone breast-implant makers Baxter International and Bristol-Myers Squibb it agreed to settle thousands of personal-injury claims related to implants. The companies paid an average of $26000 per claim.

3M spun off its low-profit imaging and data-storage businesses in 1996 as Imation Corp. and closed its audiotape and videotape businesses. The next year 3M sold its National Advertising billboard business to Infinity Outdoor for $1 billion and its Media Network unit (a printer of advertising inserts) to Time Warner.

The company created the 3M Nexcare brand for its line of first-aid and home health products in 1998. To regain earnings growth 3M closed about 10% of its plants in the US and abroad; it also discontinued unprofitable product lines. The next year 3M sold its heart-surgery-equipment health care unit to Japan's Terumo and its Eastern Heights Bank subsidiary to Norwest Bank of Minnesota. It also bought out Hoechst AG's 46% stake in Dyneon LLC a fluorine elastomer joint venture between the two companies.

3M bought Polaroid's Technical Polarizer and Display Films business and a controlling stake in Germany-based Quante AG (telecom systems) in 2000. In addition the company decided to halt the manufacture of many of its Scotchgard-brand repellent products due to research revealing that one of the compounds (perfluorooctane sulfonate) used in the manufacturing process is "persistent and pervasive" in the environment and in people's bloodstreams. As 2000 drew to a close 3M named GE executive James McNerney to succeed L. D. DeSimone as its chairman and CEO. With the sale of Eastern Heights and several health care businesses (including its cardiovascular systems unit) 3M was rewarded with its second-best financial performance in 14 years.

3M then bought Robinson Nugent (electronic connectors) and MicroTouch Systems (touch screens) in 2001. It also announced plans to cut 6000 jobs and authorized a stock buy-back program of up to $2.5 billion.

The company changed its legal name from Minnesota Mining and Manufacturing Company to 3M Company that year. Also in 2002 3M restructured its business segments around end uses rather than products or raw materials. So the Health Care segment encompassed everything from transdermal skin patches to software for hospital coding and classification. Similarly the Consumer and Office Business unit became responsible for Post-its O-Cel-O sponges wood-finishing materials and air conditioner filters. By the end of that year the company had cut more than 8500 jobs 11% of its total workforce.

Nevertheless a strong year in 2003 emboldened the company to look to expand. 3M closed a deal to buy fellow Minnesota resident HighJump Software a maker of supply chain software for businesses in February 2004. CEO McNerney left 3M in 2005 to join Boeing in the same capacity and was replaced by George Buckley formerly of the Brunswick Corporation.

That year the company made a billion-dollar acquisition of liquid filtration producer CUNO. 3M's own filtration products business — primarily air filters — amounted to more than $1 billion in annual sales before the deal and the deal added nearly half that. (3M eventually changed CUNO's name to 3M Purification.)

The company signaled a new strategic direction in 2006 when it broke up its pharmaceutical unit along geographic lines and sold it in pieces. In total 3M got $2.1 billion for the sale of its pharmaceutical operations. The next year it sold HighJump Software. High-tech venture capital firm Battery Ventures bought HighJump to set it up as a standalone company.

The company then ran through another string of acquisitions in 2007 buying companies such as Unifam Lingualcare Innovative Paper Technologies and Diamond Productions.

Its 2008 acquisition of protection products maker Aearo Technologies helped 3M's sales growth in the area of safety security and protection services. It added to the unit with the purchase (through its 3M Canada subsidiary) of Toronto-based MTI PolyFab which makes thermal and acoustic insulation for aerospace products. 3M also capitalized on its purchase of Beiersdorf subsidiary Futuro which makes medical products such as wraps elastic bandages and compression hosiery.

3M made two moves into the high-tech security field in 2010. The company acquired Cogent Inc. for $943 million. Known as Cogent Systems the firm provides finger palm face and iris biometric systems for governments law enforcement agencies and commercial enterprises. 3M also acquired Attenti Ltd. an Israeli manufacturer of people-tracking technology for $230 million. Attenti makes remote monitoring devices to track people awaiting trial or on probation as well as for eldercare facilities to monitor patient safety.

The company expanded its consumer and office business line in 2010 by acquiring a majority stake in Japanese company A-One the top office label brand in Asia and the second-largest label business worldwide. It also acquired Alpha Beta Enterprise a manufacturer of box sealing tape and masking tape headquartered in Taiwan. Both acquisitions will expand 3M's presence in the global packaging market.

Also in 2010 3M acquired J.R. Phoenix Ltd. a manufacturer of hand hygiene and skin care products for health care and professional use. The majority of J.R. Phoenix products are sold under the Laura Line brand in Canada. The deal expanded 3M's line of hand hygiene skin care products to the healthcare market in Canada. The company also acquired UK-based Dailys Ltd. a global supplier of non-woven disposable chemical protective coveralls for industrial use.

The company made several acquisitions in 2010 including Minnesota-based Arizant which manufactures forced-air warming garments designed to prevent hypothermia in surgical settings a growing international market estimated at some $1 billion per year.

3M completed nine acquisitions in 2011 that totaled $649 million including the do-it-yourself unit and professional division of France's GPI Group a manufacturer and marketer of home improvement products such as tapes hooks insulation and floor protection products. The deal boosts 3M's presence in Western Europe. It also added to its growing Industrial and Transportation segment by acquiring a majority stake in Switzerland-based Winterthur Technology Group an international supplier of precision grinding technologies that makes grinding tools used in the aircraft automotive industrial and steel industries.

Back in the US it acquired Florida-based Nida-Core a manufacturer of structural honeycomb core and fiber-reinforced foam core materials and Nida-Core's French affiliate Structiso SARL. The acquisition allows 3M's Engineered Products and Solutions department to build on its composite and engineered materials product portfolio.

In a related deal in 2012 3M acquired Maryland-based CodeRyte which provides clinical natural language processing (NLP) technology and computer-assisted coding for healthcare outpatient providers. Terms of the sale were not disclosed. 3M will apply CodeRyte's NLP technology to its new 3M 360 Encompass system used by its 3M Health Information Systems division for clinical documentation and coding workflows. More than 5000 hospitals worldwide use 3M's coding for patient data for measurement and reimbursement purposes. The 3M system also addresses data problems resulting from health care reform requirements.

In an effort to broaden its global presence in office education and consumer products in 2012 3M acquired the Office and Consumer Products business of Avery Dennison Corp. for $550 million.

Continuing a quest for technology buys on 2012 3M acquired the Federal Signal Technologies Group (FSTech) from Federal Signal Corp. for $110 million in cash. FSTech focuses on hardware and software services for the $3 billion electronic tolling industry. The business also complements offerings from 3M's Traffic Safety Systems Division.

Growing its ceramics portfolio in 2012 it also bought advanced technical ceramics producer Ceradyne for $860 million. The deal adds Ceradyne's advanced ceramics technologies portfolio to its own diversified product line.

In 2014 3M formed partnership with US-China Clean Energy Research Center Building Energy Efficiency Consortium under which 3M participates in research on building efficiency strategies tools and practices in areas such as building envelope technologies and integration of new construction materials for increasing energy efficiency.

In a move aimed at bringing greater economic efficiencies to Premier's more than 100000 health care provider members in 2014 the company reached a group purchasing agreement with health care alliance company Premier Inc. for multiple catheter securement and stability products. The new agreement allows them to take advantage of special pricing and terms pre-negotiated by Premier.

In 2013 the company and China-based Hunan Reshine New Material Company signed a patent license agreement to expand the use of nickel manganese and cobalt in lithium ion batteries (in growing demand in consumer electronics automotive and other markets).

That year in order to expand its manufacturing assets in Asia 3M Company invested in plants in China and Singapore to support the growing window film business.

It also signed a patent license agreement with Korea-based ECOPRO to further expand the use of nickel-manganese-cobalt (NMC) cathode materials in lithium ion batteries.

EXECUTIVES

Evp Safety And Graphics, Frank R. Little, age 58
Chairman President And Ceo, Inge G. Thulin, age 66, $1,483,929 total compensation
Research And Development Corporate Technology (industrial Markets), Joaquin Delgado, age 59, $629,074 total compensation
Vice Chair And Evp, Hak Cheol (H.C.) Shin, age 62, $765,496 total compensation
Evp International Operations, Julie L. Bushman, age 57, $599,029 total compensation
Evp Industrial Business Group, James L. (Jim) Bauman, age 59
Evp And Coo, Michael F. Roman, age 59, $747,022 total compensation
Svp And Cfo, Nicholas C. Gangestad, age 54, $681,551 total compensation
Evp Health Care, Michael G. Vale, age 53, $633,302 total compensation
Evp Electronics And Energy Business Group, Ashish K. Khandpur, age 51
Svp Business Development And Marketing And Sales, Jon T. Lindekugel, age 55
Svp Business Transformation And Information Technology, Eric Hammes
Vp And Cio It, John Turner
National Sales Manager, Jim Stevens
Vice President Finance International And Staff Information Technology, Ippocratis Vrohidis
Vice President And Chief Design Officer, Eric Quint
National Sales Manager, Daryl Charton
Vice President Research And Development 3m Infection Prevention Division, Ann Meitz
Information Technology Sales Vice President, Dave Herington
Vice President Finance And Treasurer, Sarah Grauze
National Sales Manager, Gina Kuehn
National Sales Manager, Jay Reese
Vice President, Jerome Hamilton
National Account Manager, Rick Bennett
Vice President Global Supply Chain, Val Young
Vice President And Associate General Counsel, Ann M Hanrahan
Vp Of Marketing, Douglas Michael
National Account Manager, Pat Kinate
Vice President Business And Marketing, Ingrid Blair
Vice President Engineering, Hector Dalton
Vice President Mobile Interactive Solutions Division, Mark Colin
Vice President International, Jim Walsh
National Sales Manager, Timothy Mogck
Vice President Of Marketing, Sharon Cohen
Vice President Internal Audit, Dave Werpy
National Sales Manager, Corey Willson
Vice President And General Manager Corrosion Protection Products, Paiul Acito
Vice President, Janice Angell
Vice President Society Communications, Peter Fritz
Market Vice President For Automotive, Steve Deb Schreiner
Vice President And Chief Sustainability Officer 3m Research And Development, Gayle Schueller
National Sales Manager, Monica Marston
National Account Manager, Bart Rasmussen

Vp And Gm Traffic Safety And Security Division 3m Safety And Graphics Business, John Riccardi
National Sales Manager, Michael Kidd
Vice President, Brian Spiewak
National Sales Manager, Steve Shogren
National Sales Manager, Chris Decolli
Vice President Environmental Health And Safety Operations, Jean Sweeney
National Sales Manager, Scott McConnell
Vice President Global Marketing 3m Unitek Orthodontic Products, Marcello Napol
Executive Vice President Of Customer Relations, Moe Nozari
National Sales Manager, David Zelgart
Vice President Of Sales And Marketing, Harlan Brown
National Accounts Manager, Randy Morgan
Senior Vice President Human Resources, Marlene M Mcgrath
Vice President Engineering And Manufacturing, Billy Roberts
National Sales Manager, Casey Nolden
National Account Manager, David Radliff
Vice President Cio, Ernie Park
Senior Vice President Legal Affairs General Counsel, Ivan Fong
Vice President, Corrado Dugo
Vice President, John Huberty
Vice President, Janette Shimanski
National Accounts Manager, Jim Buchanan
Vice President, Bill Myers
Vice President And General Manager Automotive Afte, Laino Richard
Global Vice President Of Research And Development, David Segal
Global Medical Director, Oyebode Taiwo
National Account Manager, MIKE ZIELINSKI
Vice President Biometrics Solutions, Ramsey Billups
Vice President And General Manager, Erik Aunan
Vice President Global Human Resources Business Operations, Jonathan Ruppel
National Sales Manager, Andrew Petrone
Vice President And Head Of The Automotive Division, Tony Stokes
National Sales Manager, Ed Weksner
Vp Of Sales, Bob Roberts
Corporate Treasurer And Vice President Investor Relations, Matt Ginter
Treasurer, Jan Angell
Treasurer, William Schmoll
Assistant Secretary, Michael Dai
Auditors: PricewaterhouseCoopers LLP

LOCATIONS

HQ: 3M Co
3M Center, St. Paul, MN 55144-1000
Phone: 651 733-1110   **Fax:** 651 733-9973
Web: www.3M.com

2018 Sales

	$ mil.	% of total
United States	12,840	39
Asia Pacific	10,254	31
Europe Middle East and Africa	6,654	21
Latin America and Canada	3,024	9
Other Unallocated	(7)	-
Total	**32,765**	**100**

PRODUCTS/OPERATIONS

2018 Sales

	$ mil.	% of total
Industrial	12,267	35
Safety and Graphics	6,827	19
Health Care	6,021	17
Electronics and Energy	5,472	15
Consumer	4,796	14
Corporate and unallocated	50	-
Eliminations	(2668)	-
Total	**32,765**	**100**

Selected Segments and Products

Industrial and Transportation
  Automotive aftermarket products
  Automotive products
  Closures for disposable diapers
  Coated and nonwoven abrasives
  Films
  Filtration products
  Specialty adhesives
  Tapes
Health Care
  Dental products
  Drug delivery systems
  Health information systems
  Infection prevention
  Medical and surgical supplies
  Microbiology products
  Skin health products
Safety Security and Protection
  Commercial cleaning products
  Consumer safety products
  Corrosion protection products
  Floor matting
  Occupational health and safety products
  Safety and security products
  Track and trace products
Consumer and Office
  Carpet and fabric protectors
  Commercial cleaning products
  Fabric protectors (Scotchgard)
  High-performance cloth (Scotch-Brite)
  Home-improvement products
  Repositionable notes (Post-it)
  Scour pads (Scotch-Brite)
  Sponges (O-Cel-O)
  Tape (Scotch)
Display and Graphics
  Commercial graphics systems
  Optical films for electronic display
  Specialty film and media products
  Traffic control materials
Electro and Communications
  Insulating and splicing products for electronics telecommunications and electrical industries
  Packaging and interconnection devices

Selected Mergers and Acquisitions

COMPETITORS

ACCO Brands	Henkel
BASF SE	Honeywell
Bayer AG	International
Beiersdorf	Illinois Tool Works
Bostik	Johnson & Johnson
Bridgestone	Kimberly-Clark
Carlisle Companies	RPM International
Corning	Ricoh Company
Danaher	S.C. Johnson
GE	Sealed Air Corp.
H.B. Fuller	Sika

HISTORICAL FINANCIALS

Company Type: Public

Income Statement				FYE: December 31
	REVENUE ($ mil.)	**NET INCOME ($ mil.)**	**NET PROFIT MARGIN**	**EMPLOYEES**
12/19	32,136	4,570	14.2%	96,163
12/18	32,765	5,349	16.3%	93,516
12/17	31,657	4,858	15.3%	91,536
12/16	30,109	5,050	16.8%	91,584
12/15	30,274	4,833	16.0%	89,446
Annual Growth	**1.5%**	**(1.4%)**	**—**	**1.8%**

2019 Year-End Financials

Debt ratio: 45.73%
Return on equity: 46.02%
Cash ($ mil.): 2,353
Current ratio: 1.41
Long-term debt ($ mil.): 17,629

No. of shares (mil.): 575
Dividends
  Yield: 3.2%
  Payout: 68.3%
Market value ($ mil.): 101,474

STOCK PRICE ($)		P/E		PER SHARE ($)		
	FY Close	High/Low		Earnings	Dividends	Book Value
12/19	176.42	28	19	7.81	5.76	17.50
12/18	190.54	28	20	8.89	5.44	16.99
12/17	235.37	30	21	7.93	4.70	19.44
12/16	178.57	22	16	8.16	4.44	17.26
12/15	150.64	22	18	7.58	4.10	19.21
Annual Growth	4.0%	—	—	0.8%	8.9%	(2.3%)

Abbott Laboratories

With activities ranging from filling baby bottles to making generic medications and cardiovascular devices Abbott Laboratories is a diverse health care products manufacturer. Its cardiovascular and neuromodulation segment makes products for cardiac rhythm management electrophysiology and other areas of cardiovascular care. Abbott's diagnostics division makes laboratory testing systems and point-of-care tests. The nutritional products division makes such well-known brands as Similac infant formula and Ensure supplements. Abbott also sells branded generic medicines (including gastroenterology and women's health products) in emerging markets and makes the FreeStyle diabetes care line.

Operations

Abbott operates in four reportable segments: Cardiovascular and Neuromodulation Nutritional Products Diagnostic Products and Established Pharmaceutical Products.

A global leader in cardiovascular product sales the Cardiovascular and Neuromodulation segment is Abbott's largest bringing in about 30% of total sales. It researches and manufactures devices in the areas of cardiac rhythm management heart failure electrophysiology vascular disease and structural repair as well as neuromodulation devices to treat movement and chronic pain disorders. Products include Assurity and Endurity pacemakers MitraClip valve repair systems XIENCE drug-eluting stents and TactiCath and FlexAbility ablation catheters.

The Diagnostics segment (about 25% of total sales) makes laboratory systems that screen and diagnose for cancer cardiovascular disease fertility and infectious diseases among others. It also makes rapid diagnostics systems for infectious diseases and other conditions; point-of-care testing systems; molecular diagnostics for genetic (DNA and RNA) and genomic testing; and laboratory informatics and automation tools.

The Nutritional Products segment (25% of revenue) sells pediatric and adult formulations around the world. Brands include Similac Ensure Isomil Glucerna PediaSure and Zone Perfect. The segment also provides nutritional products used for enteral feeding in health care facilities.

Abbott's Established Pharmaceutical Products (some 15% of sales) are branded generics marketed in emerging markets. These include gastroenterology drugs (such as Creon Duspatel and Heptral) women's health products (Duphaston and Femoston) cardiovascular and metabolic offerings (Lipanthyl Teveten and Synthroid among others) pain and central nervous system medications (Serc Brufen and Sevedol) and respiratory drugs and vaccines (Influvac Biaxin Klacid and Klacirid).

The group's Other segment which brings in around 5% of revenue includes Abbott's Diabetes Care operations.

Geographic Reach

Abbott Park Illinois-based Abbott has about 95 manufacturing plants as well as R&D facilities in countries around the globe including Brazil Canada China Colombia Germany India Ireland the Netherlands Pakistan Russia Spain Singapore the UK and the US.

The company's products are sold in more than 160 countries allowing the company to reduce dependence on any specific market. Abbott earns about 35% of its revenues in the US. Other major markets include China Germany India Japan Switzerland and the Netherlands each accounting for around 5% of sales.

Sales and Marketing

Abbott conducts distribution operations both from its own distribution centers and through third-party partners. Established pharmaceutical and nutritional customers include health care organizations wholesalers pharmacies retailers government agencies consumers and third-party distribution entities. Diagnostic and cardiovascular and neuromodulation products are sold to blood banks hospitals surgery centers physicians medical labs plasma protein therapeutic companies government agencies alternative testing sites and commercial laboratories.

Financial Performance

Acquisitions drove a 50% spike in Abbott's annual revenue over the past five years. Expansion centered on the Cardiovascular and Neuromodulation segment and the Diagnostics segment most notably through the 2017 purchases of St. Jude Medical and Alere. Net income remained positive but has fluctuated significantly from year to year as the company restructured to focus on core growth areas.

Revenue rose 12% to $30.6 billion in 2018 up from $27.4 billion the prior year. Diagnostics sales increased 34% as the unit reported full-year results from the October 2017 Alere acquisition (boosting rapid diagnostics sales) as well as higher core laboratory and molecular product sales. The Cardiovascular and Neuromodulation segment grew 6% on higher sales of electrophysiology structural heart and neuromodulation products. Established Pharmaceutical Product sales rose 7% driven by double-digit growth in India and China while the Nutritionals division reported 4% growth on strong sales in the US and several Asian markets.

Net income rose 400% to some $2.4 billion in 2018 following a sharp drop the previous year as the company posted strong revenue growth and regained balance between earnings and expenses. Income had declined 66% to $477 million in 2017 due to higher operating expenses related to the St. Jude acquisition and higher taxes on foreign subsidiary earnings (a result of the US Tax Cuts and Jobs Act).

Abbott ended 2018 with $3.8 billion in cash down $5.6 billion from 2017. Operating activities contributed $6.3 billion while investing activities used $1.4 billion (mostly on acquisitions of property and equipment) and financing activities used $10.4 billion on debt repayments.

Strategy

Abbott has shuffled its business portfolio over the past decade to keep pace with modern medical needs striving to achieve #1 or #2 positions in core markets. More than half of 2018 sales came from businesses and products added over the past six years.

In addition to completing large acquisitions Abbott has stayed ahead of the competition by developing and launching a steady stream of new products across its business segments. Recent product launches in the Cardiovascular and Neuromodulation segment include the Advisor HD Grid Mapping Catheter (Sensor Enabled) a next-generation MitraClip valve repair device and the XIENCE Sierra coronary stent.

Recent R&D efforts in the Diagnostics segment include the roll-out of its suite of next-generation Alinity diagnostic systems which the company sees as laboratory game-changers in efficiency and productivity. Abbott expanded manufacturing capacity for the Alinity line in 2018 along with capacity for its Freestyle Libre glucose monitoring system (part of the Diabetes Care business). The company is also focused on expanding sales of Nutritional and Established Pharmaceutical products in emerging markets including China and India as well as Nutritionals in the US.

The company is working to pay down debt which rose to some $27.9 billion after the 2017 acquisitions of St. Jude Medical and Alere. Debt was reduced by about $8.3 billion in 2018 as the company executed a successful cash-flow improvement initiative but a high level of indebtedness leaves the group somewhat strapped for cash which could create problems if market or business conditions arise that require capital investment.

Mergers and Acquisitions

The company's operations were changed significantly through two key acquisitions made in 2017. Abbott became one of the world's largest makers of cardiovascular devices when it bought St. Jude Medical in a deal valued at $23.6 billion. St. Jude Medical was combined with Abbott's Vascular Products segment to create the new Cardiovascular and Neuromodulation segment. The company also significantly boosted its Diagnostics division through the acquisition of Alere for $4.5 billion.

Company Background

Dr. Wallace Abbott started making his dosimetric granule (a pill that supplied uniform quantities of drugs) at his home outside Chicago in 1888. The company was incorporated as Abbott Alkaloidal Company in 1894 and changed its name to Abbott Laboratories in 1915.

During WWI Abbott scientists synthesized anesthetics previously available only from Germany. Abbott expanded its research capacity products and sales force and went public in 1929. International operations began in the mid-1930s with branches in Argentina Brazil Cuba Mexico and the UK. Abbott contributed to the WWII effort by ratcheting up US production of penicillin. It later developed antibiotic erythromycin. Consumer infant and nutritional products joined the roster in the 1960s diagnostic equipment followed in the 1970s.

The company spun off its proprietary pharmaceutical products division including top-selling autoimmune drug Humira (the first fully-human monoclonal antibody drug approved by the FDA in 2002) into AbbVie in 2013.

To focus on cardiovascular and diagnostic operations Abbott sold its Abbott Medical Optics subsidiary to Johnson & Johnson for $4.3 billion in early 2017.

HISTORY

Dr. Wallace Abbott started making his dosimetric granule (a pill that supplied uniform quantities of drugs) at his home outside Chicago in 1888. Aggressive marketing earned Abbott the American Medical Association's criticism though much of the medical profession supported him.

During WWI Abbott scientists synthesized anesthetics previously available only from Germany. Abbott improved its research capacity in 1922 by buying Dermatological Research Laboratories; in 1928 it bought John T. Milliken and its well-trained sales force. Abbott went public in 1929.

International operations began in the mid-1930s with branches in Argentina Brazil Cuba Mexico and the UK.

Abbott was integral to the WWII effort; the US made only 28 pounds of penicillin in 1943 before the company began to ratchet up production. Consumer infant and nutritional products (such as Selsun Blue shampoo Murine eye drops and Similac formula) joined the roster in the 1960s. The FDA banned Abbott's artificial sweetener Sucaryl in 1970 saying it might be carcinogenic and in 1971 millions of intravenous solutions were recalled following contamination deaths.

EXECUTIVES

Svp And Chief Marketing And External Affairs Officer, Elaine R. Leavenworth, age 61
Vice President Diagnostic Commercial Operations Europe Africa And Middle East, Jaime Contreras
Vp Licensing And Acquisitions, William Chase
Chairman And Ceo, Miles D. White, age 63, $1,900,000 total compensation
Evp Human Resources, Stephen R. (Steve) Fussell, age 62, $454,689 total compensation
Evp Ventures, John M. Capek, age 57, $675,000 total compensation
Business Unit Director Managed Healthcare Pharmaceutical Products Division, Heather L. Mason, age 59
Svp And Group President Cardiovascular And Neuromodulation, Eric S. Fain, age 58
Evp Medical Devices, Robert B. Ford, age 45
Evp Diagnostic Products, Brian J. Blaser, age 54, $692,057 total compensation
Evp General Counsel And Secretary, Hubert L. Allen, age 53, $650,000 total compensation
Svp Finance And Cfo, Brian B. Yoor, age 49, $584,231 total compensation
Svp U.s. Nutrition, Roger M. Bird, age 62
Svp Abbott Vascular, Deepak Nath, age 46
Svp Established Pharmaceuticals Latin America, Daniel Salvadori, age 40
Svp Diabetes Care, Jared L. Watkin, age 51
Evp Established Pharmaceuticals Emerging Markets, Andrew H. Lane, age 48
President Cardiovascular And Neuromodulation, Michael T. (Mike) Rousseau, age 63
Svp International Nutrition, Joseph (Joe) Manning, age 50
Senior Non It Management Chief Executive Officer Chief Financial Officer Vice President Directo, Randi Pickens
Senior Vice President, Ann Long
Vp Of Internal Audit, David Mark
Vp Of Compensation And Benefits, Mary Moreland
Vp Of Intellectual Property Strategy, Andy Brookes
Medical Director, Thomas Podsadecki
Senior Vice President Central Region, Pamela Switalski
Evp Corporate Development, Richard W Ashley, age 77
Divisional Vice President, Brian Wentworth
Senior Vice President, Maureen Snider
Vice President Sales Training And Development, Randee Stelman
Group Vice President, Tiffany Cincotta
Division Vice President Pediatric Commercial Operations, Rich Schaefer
Vice President Marketing And Human Resources, Jennifer Pestikas
Medical Director, Roger Trinh
Medical Director, Gwendolyn Janssen
Vice President, Thomas Brown
Divisonal Vp Of Infrastructure Services, Paul Hennenfent
Svp Of Developed Markets Of Established Pharma, Jean-yves Pavee
Svp Of Global Commercial Integration, Denis Gestin
Sr. Vp Core Laboratory Diagnostics Global Commercial Operations., Jaime Conteras

Regional Vice President Public Relations, Natalie Christensen
Svp Abbott Vascular, Chuck Brynelsen
Svp Established Pharmaceuticals Emerging Markets, Sean Shrimpton
Svp Established Pharmaceuticals Latin America, Alejandro Wellisch
Divisional Vp Operations, Brad Roberts
Area Treasurer, Quintin Noble
Board Member, Phebe Novakovic
Board Member, Sally Blount
Board Member, Samuel Scott
Board Member, Roxanne Austin
Board Member, William Osborn
Auditors: Ernst & Young LLP

LOCATIONS

HQ: Abbott Laboratories
100 Abbott Park Road, Abbott Park, IL 60064-6400
Phone: 224 667-6100
Web: www.abbott.com

2017 Sales

	$ mil.	% of total
US	9,673	35
China	2,146	8
Germany	1,366	5
Japan	1,255	5
India	1,237	4
Netherlands	929	3
Switzerland	841	3
Russia	664	2
France	628	2
Brazil	541	2
Italy	507	2
UK	498	2
Colombia	494	2
Canada	443	2
Vietnam	427	2
Other countries	5,741	21
Total	**27,390**	**100**

PRODUCTS/OPERATIONS

2017 Sales by Segment

	$ mil.	% of total
Cardiovascular and Neuromodulation	8,911	33
Nutritionals	6,925	25
Diagnostics	5,616	20
Established Pharmaceuticals	4,287	16
Other	1,651	6
Total	**27,390**	**100**

Selected Products

Nutritional
  Alimentum (infant formula)
  EAS nutritional brands
  AdvantEdge (nutritional supplements)
  Myoplex (nutritional supplements)
  Ensure (adult nutrition)
  Freego (enteral pump)
  Glucerna (nutritional beverage for diabetics)
  Isomil (soy-based infant formula)
  Jevity (liquid food for enteral feeding)
  NeoSure (infant formula)
  Osmolite
  Pedialyte (pediatric electrolyte solution)
  PediaSure (children's nutrition)
  Similac (infant formula)
  Zone Perfect (nutritional bars)
Established Pharmaceuticals (branded generics)
  Creon (pancreatic enzyme replacement therapy)
  Duphaston (progesterone deficiency)
  Klacid (macrolide antibiotic)
Diagnostic
  Abbott PRISM (high-volume blood-screening system)
  ARCHITECT (clinical chemistry system)
  Cell-Dyn (hematology systems and reagents)
  Diagnostic and screening assays
  Informatics and automation solutions for lab use
  i-STAT (blood analyzer)
  m2000 (instrument that detects and measures infectious agents)
  Vysis (genomic-based tests)
Medical Devices
  Acculink/Accunet (carotid stent)

Hi-Torque Balance Middleweight (coronary guidewire licensed from Asahi Intecc)
MitraClip (valve repair)
Multi-Link 8 Multi-Link Mini Vision and Multi-Link Vision (coronary metallic stents)
Perclose (vessel closure)
StarClose (vessel closure)
Trek (balloon dilation)
Xience V Xience nano and Xience Prime (drug-eluting stents)

COMPETITORS

Allergan plc	Mannatech
Bard	Mead Johnson
Baxter International	Mylan
Becton Dickinson	Nestlé
Boston Scientific	Perrigo
Cordis	Roche Holding
Danone	Sandoz International
Dr. Reddy's	GmbH
GNC	Schiff Nutrition
Heinz	International
Herbalife Ltd.	Sun Pharmaceutical
Johnson & Johnson	Teva
LifeScan	

HISTORICAL FINANCIALS

Company Type: Public

Income Statement

FYE: December 31

	REVENUE ($ mil.)	NET INCOME ($ mil.)	NET PROFIT MARGIN	EMPLOYEES
12/18	30,578	2,368	7.7%	103,000
12/17	27,390	477	1.7%	99,000
12/16	20,853	1,400	6.7%	75,000
12/15	20,405	4,423	21.7%	74,000
12/14	20,247	2,284	11.3%	77,000
Annual Growth	10.9%	0.9%		7.5%

2018 Year-End Financials

Debt ratio: 29.13%
Return on equity: 7.71%
Cash ($ mil.): 3,844
Current ratio: 1.62
Long-term debt ($ mil.): 19,359

No. of shares (mil.): 1,755
Dividends
  Yield: 1.5%
  Payout: 84.2%
Market value ($ mil.): 126,984

	STOCK PRICE ($) FY Close	P/E High/Low		PER SHARE ($) Earnings	Dividends	Book Value
12/18	72.33	55	42	1.33	1.12	17.39
12/17	57.07	213	145	0.27	1.06	17.72
12/16	38.41	48	39	0.94	1.04	13.94
12/15	44.91	17	13	2.92	0.96	14.40
12/14	45.02	31	24	1.49	0.88	14.27
Annual Growth	12.6%	—	—	(2.8%)	6.2%	5.1%

AbbVie Inc

AbbVie is vying for dominance in the world of medications. The firm develops and commercializes biopharmaceutical and small molecule drugs with a focus on immunology oncology virology and neuroscience. Its primary product is Humira best known as a rheumatoid arthritis drug; it accounts for some 60% of sales and is the world's top-selling prescription drug. Other key products include cancer treatment Imbruvica and hepatitis C drug Mavyret. Products are sold globally but the US is AbbVie's largest market. With the pending expiration of Humira's patent protection AbbVie is looking for the next big thing. It might have found it with its agreement to buy Allergan for $63 billion in 2019.

Operations

AbbVie focuses on treating conditions such as chronic autoimmune diseases (including rheumatoid arthritis psoriasis and Crohn's disease) cancers and viral conditions (including hepatitis C and HIV). It also has products that address metabolic or hormonal conditions endocrinology ailments and neurological disorders (including Parkinson's disease).

Top product Humira is a biologic therapy that treats several autoimmune conditions and generates nearly $20 billion in sales or about 60% of total revenue. Humira sales continue to grow despite patent protection loss in Europe in 2018; US protection will last until 2023. Leukemia and lymphoma drug Imbruvica and hepatitis C medication Mayvret each account for 10% of sales. Other major offerings include Creon (enzyme insufficiency) Lupron (endometriosis) Synthroid (hyperthyroidism) and Synagis (respiratory syncytial virus).

The company has a pipeline of medications in clinical development that covers such areas as oncology neurology immunology cystic fibrosis and women's health. It has a number of partnerships with other pharma firms to develop new treatments including Alector (Alzheimer's disease) and Calico Life Sciences (age-related diseases).

Geographic Reach

AbbVie collects about two-thirds of sales from the US. Key foreign markets include Brazil Canada France Germany Italy Japan the Netherlands Spain and the UK.

The Chicago-based company has six primary manufacturing facilities in the US (in Illinois Puerto Rico Massachusetts and Michigan) and five key international plants (in Italy Ireland Germany Singapore). It operates seven US R&D facilities in Illinois California and Massachusetts as well as one R&D center in Germany.

Sales and Marketing

AbbVie uses a combination of direct and third-party resources to market and sell its products worldwide. In the US AbbVie markets directly to physicians consumers managed care providers insurers pharmacy benefit managers (PBMs) hospitals and government agencies (including the US Department of Veterans Affairs and the Department of Defense). Products are primarily distributed through independent wholesalers; some sales are made directly to pharmacies and patients. Internationally AbbVie principally markets to payers physicians and regulatory bodies and sells products directly and through distributors.

Three wholesale distributors — McKesson Cardinal Health and AmerisourceBergen — account for nearly all of US sales. Reliance on these firms could leave AbbVie vulnerable to distribution issues should any of them face financial difficulties or switch to alternative products.

AbbVie spent $1.1 billion on advertising in 2018 versus $846 million in 2017 and $764 million in 2016.

Financial Performance

AbbVie has seen steady revenue growth since its 2013 spin-off from former parent Abbott Labs. Overall sales increased about 65% between 2014 and 2018 as the company added indications for Humira and expanded its product portfolio through acquisitions and new drug launches. The firm is confident that its expansion efforts will make up for sales losses from the impending Humira patent loss which has already taken effect in European markets. Net income has fluctuated but has remained in the $5 billion range for the past four years.

In 2018 revenue grew 16% to $32.8 billion as sales of Humira continued to grow primarily in the US (thanks largely to its approval for new indications and favorable pricing); international Humira sales increased slightly despite loss of patent protection in the European Union. Increased sales of Imbruvica Mayvret and Venclexta also contributed to growth. US sales rose 18% and international revenue rose 13%. Revenue growth was marginally offset by declining sales of drugs including Viekira AndroGel and Kaletra.

Net income rose 7% in 2018 to some $5.7 billion primarily due to income tax benefits related to the 2017 Tax Act. The increase occurred despite higher operating costs from R&D programs production expenses and sales and administrative expenses.

AbbVie ended 2018 with $7.3 billion in cash down $2 billion from 2017. Operating activities contributed $13.4 billion while investing activities used $1 billion (mostly on property and equipment acquisitions and other acquisitions and investments) and financing activities used $14.4 billion via treasury stock purchases and paid dividends.

Strategy

Facing the patent expiration of top-selling drug Humira AbbVie is focused on maintaining a strong R&D pipeline. The company has more than 60 compounds or indications in the pipeline including treatments in immunology oncology neuroscience cystic fibrosis and women's health. If candidates successfully reach the market the expensive and often risky pharmaceutical development process pays off for the company. Recent product approvals include hepatitis C treatment Mayvret (2017) myeloid leukemia drug Venclexta (2018) and endometriosis medication Orilissa (2018). AbbVie plans to keep adding to its research programs through strategic licensing deals and partnerships.

The company also pursues strategic acquisitions to boost its drug development stockpile and lighten its dependence on Humira and other key treatments. In 2019 AbbVie agreed to buy Allergan for $63 billion. The purchase would bring a raft of treatments such as Botox to AbbVie. The deal is expected to close in early 2020.

Humira — the world's top-selling prescription medicine — now faces competition in Europe where its basic patent expired in October 2018. At the time of the patent expiration five biosimilars from companies including Amgen and Mylan had gained approval in Europe. The company expects that Humira will face biosimilar competition in the US in 2023. To maintain sales of Humira as long as possible the company is working to expand indications for the blockbuster drug maintain market leadership in existing categories and increase its presence in international markets where patent protection remains.

Thanks to years of revenue growth the company in 2018 announced a five-year plan to invest some $2.5 billion in capital projects in the US; it is also exploring the expansion of certain domestic facilities.

Mergers and Acquisitions

In 2019 AbbVie agreed to buy fellow drugmaker Allergan for $63 billion. The purchase will boost the company's revenue as it looks for a Humira replacement. Allergan will add new product lines including beauty medications (such as Botox) and eye care treatments (such as Restasis) as well as offerings that compliment AbbVie's offerings in neurology digestive diseases women's health and other fields. The deal is expected to close in early 2020.

Company Background

Biopharmaceutical research company AbbVie was formed in 2012 by former parent Abbott Labs which spun off AbbVie into a separate publicly-traded company in 2013. As the company faced the patent expirations of many of its top sellers in the following years (including Aluvia TriCor Nias-

pan and Humira) it focused on expanding its R&D operations.

After a failed attempt to purchase Irish rare-disease medication manufacturer Shire for $54 billion in 2014 AbbVie instead pumped up its oncology pipeline by acquiring Pharmacyclics for $20.8 billion in 2015 and Stemcentrx for $5.8 billion in 2016.

EXECUTIVES

Chairman And Ceo, Richard A. (Rick) Gonzalez, age 65, $1,600,000 total compensation

Evp External Affairs General Counsel And Corporate Secretary, Laura J. Schumacher, age 56, $979,369 total compensation

Evp Commercial Operations, Carlos Alban, age 56, $888,461 total compensation

Evp And Cfo, William J. Chase, age 51, $979,369 total compensation

President Pharmacyclics, Wulff-Erik von Borcke

Svp Operations, Azita Saleki-Gerhardt, age 56

Evp Research And Development And Chief Scientific Officer, Michael E. Severino, age 53, $960,969 total compensation

Evp And Chief Strategy Officer, Henry O. Gosebruch, $894,523 total compensation

Vp And Chief Ethics And Compliance Officer, Karen Hale

Group Medical Director, Aileen Pangan

Vice President Human Resources And Operations, Leanna Walther

Divisional Vice President Global Pharmaceutical Sciences, Juergen Zeidler

Vice President, Sharon Greenlees

Senior Vice President, Jeffrey R Stewart

Associate Medical Director Physician Professional Development Program, Christopher Ocampo

Associate Medical Director Infectious Diseases Develop, Susan Rhee

Vice President Pharmacy Immunology And Neurology Supply Chain, Chris Mlynek

Vice President, Tiffany Cincotta

Divisional Vice President, Katie Rielly-gauvin

Medical Director, Melissa Wigderson

Dvp Immunology Research, Lisa Olson

Vice President Immunology Global Commercial Development, Nisha Burns

Vice President Quality Assurance, Marilyn Frontz

Vice President And General Manager Abbvie Germany, Patrick Horber

Senior Medical Director, Earle Bain

Medical Director, David Carter

National Sales Manager, Cheryl Lawrence-tarr

Divisional Vice President, Tracie Haas

Vice President Business Human Resources Global Commercial Operations, Heather Lowe

Group Medical Director, Margaret Burroughs

Vice President Regional Manufacturing Operations Europe, Thomas Scheidmeir

Vice President Tax, Scott Reents

Vice President Licensing And Aqcuisitions Immunology, Suzanne Lebold

Medical Director, Kevin Douglas

Vice President Corporate Strategy Office, Scott Brun

Medical Director, Daniel Cohen

Medical Director, Gwen Levy

Vice President Assistant Treasurer, Tabetha Skarbek

Vp Business Human Resources, Jen Smith

Vice President And Assistant Corporate Controller, Ross Berman

Vice President And Treasurer, Amarendra Duvvur

Medical Director, David Geller

Associate Medical Director, Just Genius

Vice President Oncology Discovery And Early Development, Thomas Hudson

Medical Director, Anjla Sood

Senior Medical Director, Johannes Wolff

Vice President Therapeutic Area, Dawn Carlson
Senior Vice President Biologic Prod
  Superintendent, Juan Gonzalez Martinez
Associate Medical Director, Apinya Lertratanakul
Medical Director Neuroscience Development,
  Maurizio Facheris
Vice President Corporate Strategy Group, Leah
  Bloom
Vice President, Davidsen Steve
Vice President Heor Virology Endocrinology
  Renal, Vipan Sood
Medical Director Oncology Early Development,
  Greg Vosganian
Vice President Device Solutions Combination
  Product Development, Ramakrishna Venugopalan
Auditors: Ernst & Young LLP

LOCATIONS

HQ: AbbVie Inc
  1 North Waukegan Road, North Chicago, IL 60064-
  6400
Phone: 847 932-7900
Web: www.abbvie.com

2017 Sales

	$ mil.	% of total
US	18,251	65
Germany	1,157	4
UK	807	3
Japan	764	3
France	730	3
Canada	659	2
Spain	521	2
Italy	475	2
Brazil	410	1
The Netherlands	362	1
Other	4,080	14
Total	**28,216**	**100**

PRODUCTS/OPERATIONS

2017 Sales

	$ mil.	% of total
Humira	18,427	65
Imbruvica	2,573	9
Hepatitis C products	1,274	5
Creon	831	3
Lupron	829	3
Synthroid	781	3
Synagis	738	3
AndroGel	577	2
Kaletra	423	1
Sevoflurane	410	1
Duodopa	355	1
Other	998	4
Total	**28,216**	**100**

COMPETITORS

Amgen	Merck
AstraZeneca	Novartis
Bayer AG	Pfizer
Bristol-Myers Squibb	Roche Holding
Eli Lilly	Sanofi
GlaxoSmithKline	Teva
Johnson & Johnson	

HISTORICAL FINANCIALS

Company Type: Public

Income Statement   FYE: December 31

	REVENUE ($ mil.)	NET INCOME ($ mil.)	NET PROFIT MARGIN	EMPLOYEES
12/18	32,753	5,687	17.4%	30,000
12/17	28,216	5,309	18.8%	29,000
12/16	25,638	5,953	23.2%	30,000
12/15	22,859	5,144	22.5%	28,000
12/14	19,960	1,774	8.9%	26,000
Annual Growth	**13.2%**	**33.8%**	**—**	**3.6%**

HOOVER'S HANDBOOK OF AMERICAN BUSINESS 2020

2018 Year-End Financials

Debt ratio: 67.92%	No. of shares (mil.): 1,478
Return on equity: ***,***.**%	Dividends
Cash ($ mil.): 7,289	Yield: 3.8%
Current ratio: 0.98	Payout: 98.0%
Long-term debt ($ mil.): 35,002	Market value ($ mil.): 136,333

	STOCK PRICE ($) FY Close	P/E High/Low		PER SHARE ($) Earnings	Dividends	Book Value
12/18	92.19	34	21	3.66	3.59	(5.71)
12/17	96.71	30	18	3.30	2.56	3.20
12/16	62.62	18	14	3.63	2.28	2.91
12/15	59.24	23	15	3.13	2.02	2.45
12/14	65.44	63	42	1.10	1.66	1.09
Annual Growth	**8.9%**	**—**	**—**	**35.1%**	**21.3%**	**—**

ABM Industries, Inc.

Many businesses hope to clean up but diversified facilities services contractor ABM counts on it. The company primarily offers janitorial services to owners and operators of office buildings hospitals manufacturing plants schools shopping centers and transportation facilities throughout the US UK Canada and Puerto Rico. ABM also provides maintenance of mechanical electrical and plumbing systems and it operates more than 2000 parking lots and garages mainly at airports across some 40 states. ABM makes most of its revenue in the US.

Operations

ABM operates through six reportable segments: Business & Industry ("B&I") Aviation Technology & Manufacturing (T&M) Education Technical Solutions and Healthcare.

The B&I segment brings in about 45% of ABM's total revenue. It handles the group's janitorial facilities engineering and parking services for commercial properties and sports and entertainment venues. In addition it provides vehicle maintenance to rental car companies.

The Aviation segment provides airlines and airports with specialized offerings including janitorial services passenger assistance catering logistics and air cabin maintenance. It brings in some 15% of revenue.

The T&M segment provides janitorial facilities engineering and parking services to the high-tech manufacturing and industrial sectors. It also brings in around 15% of revenue.

The Education segment serves public school districts private schools and colleges and universities with janitorial custodial landscaping and facilities engineering services. It brings in another 15% of revenue.

The Technical Solutions segment specializes in mechanical and electrical services. It accounts for more than 5% of revenue.

The Healthcare segment which brings in the rest of ABM's revenue offers clinical engineering food and nutrition laundry and linen parking and patient transportation services to hospitals and other care facilities.

Geographic Reach

ABM has more than 350 locations throughout the US UK Puerto Rico and Canada. The US accounts for about 95% of revenue.

Sales and Marketing

ABM's sales and marketing efforts are conducted by corporate subsidiary regional branch and district offices. The company serves some 20000 clients.

ABM spent $2.3 million on advertising expenses in fiscal 2018 up from $2.2 million in fiscal 2017 and $2.1 million in fiscal 2016.

Financial Performance

ABM's revenue has been trending up across the past several years. Acquisitions have largely driven the growth while increased demand for the company's services has also led to organic growth. Net income slipped in 2016 and 2017 but rebounded to a record high in 2018.

Revenue increased 18% to $6.4 billion in fiscal 2018 (ended October). That increase was partly due to the addition of GCA which ABM acquired in 2017; organic growth in the B&I T&M Aviation and Technical Solutions segments also contributed to the rise.

With the higher revenue net income totaled $97.8 million in fiscal 2018 versus just $3.8 million in 2017 when the company had $74.3 million in discontinued operations charges.

The company ended fiscal 2018 with $39.1 million in net cash about $24 million less than it had at the end of fiscal 2017. Operating activities provided $320.9 million while investing activities used $48.1 million and financing activities used $295.8 million.

Strategy

Like other conglomerates in the business services sector ABM has grown mainly by acquiring local and regional operating companies and their client rosters. Its 2017 acquisition of GCA brought an additional $1 billion in revenue during fiscal 2018. As a provider of essential janitorial facility engineering electrical and lighting and HVAC services among others the company remains highly profitable — even during economic downturns.

The company's 2020 Vision strategic transformation initiative is intended to differentiate ABM in the marketplace. The initiative includes plans to accelerate revenue growth for certain industry groups and beneficial cost savings through the realignment of ABM's business operations to better support specific industries. ABM has experienced savings from the realignment which included divesting non-core operations such as the government services business. The company is now investing in its information technology infrastructure by upgrading its human resources enterprise resource planning labor management and other platforms. ABM also generates cost savings by centralizing many business functions such as marketing sales and accounting.

Mergers and Acquisitions

In a sweeping move to expand ABM acquired rival GCA Services Group (GCA) for $1.25 billion in cash and stock in mid-2017. The purchase fortified ABM's core facility services offerings and enhanced its presence in the education and commercial sectors.

Company Background

Morris Rosenberg invested $4.50 in a bucket and cleaning tools and began cleaning San Francisco storefront windows in 1909. Later that year he purchased Chicago Window Cleaning for $300 and armed with new supplies and a Ford Model T began offering annual cleaning contracts. He changed the company's name to American Building Maintenance in 1913 to emphasize its broadening services. By 1920 the company had established three west coast offices and it became the first contractor to clean a major college campus when it signed an agreement with Stanford University in 1921.

The company added cleaning supplies to its offerings in 1927 with the acquisition of Easterday Janitorial Supply Company and continued to grow even during the Great Depression by providing cleaning services cheaper than its clients could provide for themselves. ABM expanded to the East Coast in 1932. Morris Rosenberg died in 1935 leaving the company to his oldest son Theodore who bought electrical services company Alta Electric the following year. During WWII ABM cleaned Navy ships and wired amphibious vehicles called Water Buffaloes. By the end of the war it operated 17 offices in the US and Canada.

Now called American Building Maintenance Industries the company went public in 1962 with Theodore serving as chairman and younger brother Sydney as CEO. To diversify its services ABM Industries stepped up its acquisition pace in the late 1960s buying Ampco Auto Parks (1967 parking facilities) Commercial Air Conditioning (1968 equipment maintenance) and General Elevator Corporation (1969 elevator maintenance and repair).

HISTORY

Morris Rosenberg invested $4.50 in a bucket and cleaning tools and began cleaning San Francisco storefront windows in 1909. Later that year he purchased Chicago Window Cleaning for $300 and armed with new supplies and a Ford Model T began offering annual cleaning contracts. He changed the company's name to American Building Maintenance in 1913 to emphasize its broadening services. By 1920 the company had established three west coast offices and it became the first contractor to clean a major college campus when it signed an agreement with Stanford University in 1921.

The company added cleaning supplies to its offerings in 1927 with the acquisition of Easterday Janitorial Supply Company and continued to grow even during the Great Depression by providing cleaning services cheaper than its clients could provide for themselves. ABM expanded to the East Coast in 1932. Morris Rosenberg died in 1935 leaving the company to his oldest son Theodore who bought electrical services company Alta Electric the following year. During WWII ABM cleaned Navy ships and wired amphibious vehicles called Water Buffaloes. By the end of the war it operated 17 offices in the US and Canada.

Now called American Building Maintenance Industries the company went public in 1962 with Theodore serving as chairman and younger brother Sydney as CEO. To diversify its services ABM Industries stepped up its acquisition pace in the late 1960s buying Ampco Auto Parks (1967 parking facilities) Commercial Air Conditioning (1968 equipment maintenance) and General Elevator Corporation (1969 elevator maintenance and repair).

ABM Industries continued to expand its business into diverse services and regions through a three-decade buying spree. In 1981 the company combined its air-conditioning elevator lighting and energy services into American Technical Services Company (Amtech) to better focus on the high-growth tech and energy businesses. A management-led buyout of the company failed in 1990 on opposition from the Rosenberg brothers. Although ABM Industries' president stepped down and several lawsuits were filed following the aborted LBO the company continued to post impressive sales and profit numbers.

The company shortened its name to ABM Industries in 1994 the same year William Steele was named CEO. Sydney Rosenberg retired as chairman in 1997 marking the end of family control. The following year the company formed a Facility Services division to provide one-stop shopping for all of its services. It moved into landscaping services in 1999 with the purchase of Commercial Landscape Systems. The following year Steele stepped down as CEO and Henrik Slipsager a former executive of Dutch services giant ISS was tapped as the company's new chief.

In 2001 ABM sold off its Easterday Janitorial Supply subsidiary to AmSan West. ABM acquired six companies in 2001 and 2002 including Lakeside Building Maintenance a large Midwestern janitorial contractor. In 2003 the company sold its Amtech Elevator Services to Otis Elevator Company for $112 million. Two years later the company sold its CommAir Mechanical Services unit to Carrier Corp.

In 2005 ABM sold the last of its mechanical operations divesting its water treatment business to San Joaquin Chemicals. ABM made one of the biggest deals in its history in 2007 when it obtained rival facility services company OneSource Services paying about $390 million. The operations of OneSource including more than 10000 commercial accounts in the US Canada and Puerto Rico were integrated into those of ABM Janitorial throughout 2008.

In order to focus on its core operations in late 2008 the company sold the operating assets of its Amtech Lighting Services business to a unit of OSRAM SYLVANIA for about $34 million. ABM acquired several companies in 2009 and 2010 including Diversco and The Linc Group. It also snatched up several cleaning and engineering businesses — Control Building Services Control Engineering Services and TTF Assets — located primarily in New Jersey and New York. Collectively these businesses generate annual revenues of about $50 million and cater to the commercial institutional and pharmaceutical industries.

EXECUTIVES

Evp Abm Onsite Services Northeast, Scott Salmirs, age 57, $793,333 total compensation
Evp And Cfo, D. Anthony Scaglione, age 46, $466,666 total compensation
Evp And President Business And Industry, Rene Jacobsen
Evp And Coo, Scott Giacobbe, age 56
Vice President Deputy General Counsel And Assistant Secretary, Barbara Smithers
Ea To Evp And General Counsel Board Of Director's Liaison And Notary Public, Mimi Benderman
Svp And President Abm Technical Solutions, Mark Newsome
Vice President Safety, Duong HO
Vice President Payroll, Marlene Scott
Senior Vice President And Chro, David Goodes
Executive Vice President And President Aviation Group, Tom Marano
Vice President Business Development Abm Technical Solutions, Paul Robinson
Svp Strategy And Transformation, Tom Gallo
Svp Of National Parking And Transportation, Arnold Klauber
Svp Of Operations Of Abm Education, Tom Martin
Svp Of Operations Of Abm Education, Myron Luckenbach
Vice President Sales, Tom Haller
Vice President Central Region, Jim Spencer
Vice President Global Development, Erik Lorensen
Chairman, Sudhakar Kesavan, age 65
Board Member, Arturo Garcia
Auditors: KPMG LLP

LOCATIONS

HQ: ABM Industries, Inc.
One Liberty Plaza, 7th Floor, New York, NY 10006
Phone: 212 297-0200
Web: www.abm.com

2018 Sales

	$ mil.	% of total
US	5,997	93
Other	444	7
Total	**6,442**	**100**

PRODUCTS/OPERATIONS

2018 Sales by Segment

	$ mil.	% of total
Business & Industry	2,917	45
Aviation	1,023	16
Technology & Manufacturing	924	14
Education	837	13
Technical Solutions	465	7
Healthcare	273	4
Total	**6,442**	**100**

Selected Services

Electrical
Energy solutions
Facilities engineering
HVAC & mechanical
Janitorial
Landscape & turf
Parking & transportation

COMPETITORS

ARAMARK	Mercury Air Group
Comfort Systems USA	PrimeFlight
EMCOR	ServiceMaster
Healthcare Services	Siemens AG
IAP Worldwide Services	Sodexo USA
ICTS International	Temco Service
ISS A/S	Industries

HISTORICAL FINANCIALS

Company Type: Public

Income Statement
FYE: October 31

	REVENUE ($ mil.)	NET INCOME ($ mil.)	NET PROFIT MARGIN	EMPLOYEES
10/19	6,498	127	2.0%	140,000
10/18	6,442	97	1.5%	140,000
10/17	5,453	3	0.1%	140,000
10/16	5,144	57	1.1%	110,000
10/15	4,897	76	1.6%	120,000
Annual Growth	**7.3%**	**13.7%**	**—**	**3.9%**

2019 Year-End Financials

Debt ratio: 21.70%	No. of shares (mil.): 66
Return on equity: 8.50%	Dividends
Cash ($ mil.): 58	Yield: 1.9%
Current ratio: 1.41	Payout: 54.1%
Long-term debt ($ mil.): 744	Market value ($ mil.): 2,427

	STOCK PRICE ($) FY Close	P/E High/Low	Earnings	Dividends	Book Value
10/19	36.46	22 14	1.90	0.72	23.16
10/18	30.75	30 19	1.47	0.70	22.04
10/17	41.97	640546	0.07	0.68	21.00
10/16	39.08	40 26	1.01	0.66	17.52
10/15	28.40	25 20	1.33	0.64	17.96
Annual Growth	**6.4%**	**— —**	**9.3%**	**3.0%**	**6.6%**

ACE HARDWARE CORPORATION

In an age of big-box home improvement centers (Home Depot Lowes) wholesaler Ace makes the case for the local hardware store. By sales it is the leading hardware cooperative in the US. Ace dealer-owners operate more than 95% of the 5200 Ace Hardware-branded stores home centers and lumber and building materials locations selling more than 115000 products across the US and about 70 other countries. Ace also provides value-added services such as advertising market research merchandising assistance site location store format design retail training insurance and technology assistance. From about 25 warehouses Ace distributes such products as electrical and plumbing supplies garden equipment hand tools housewares and power tools. Ace was founded in 1924 by a group of Chicago hardware store owners.

HISTORY

A group of Chicago-area hardware dealers — William Stauber Richard Hesse Gern Lindquist and Oscar Fisher — decided in 1924 to pool their hardware buying and promotional costs. In 1928 the group incorporated as Ace Stores named in honor of the superior WWI fliers dubbed aces. Hesse became president the following year retaining that position for the next 44 years. The company also opened its first warehouse in 1929 and by 1933 it had 38 dealers.

The organization had 133 dealers in seven states by 1949. In 1953 Ace began to allow dealers to buy stock in the company through the Ace Perpetuation Plan. During the 1960s Ace expanded into the South and West and by 1969 it had opened distribution centers in Georgia and California — its first such facilities outside Chicago. In 1968 it opened its first international store in Guam.

By the early 1970s the do-it-yourself market began to surge as inflation pushed up plumber and electrician fees. As the market grew large home center chains gobbled up market share from independent dealers such as those franchised through Ace. In response Ace and its dealers became a part of a growing trend in the hardware industry — cooperatives.

Hesse sold the company to its dealers in 1973 for $6 million (less than half its book value) and the following year Ace began operating as a cooperative. Hesse stepped down in 1973. In 1976 the dealers took full control when the company's first Board of Dealer-Directors was elected.

After signing up a number of dealers in the eastern US Ace had dealers in all 50 states by 1979. The co-op opened a plant to make paint in Matteson Illinois in 1984. By 1985 Ace had reached $1 billion in sales and had initiated its Store of the Future Program allowing dealers to borrow up to $200000 to upgrade their stores and conduct market analyses. Former head coach John Madden of the National Football League's Oakland Raiders signed on as Ace's mouthpiece in 1988.

A year later the co-op began to test ACENET a computer network that allowed Ace dealers to check inventory send and receive e-mail make special purchase requests and keep up with prices on commodity items such as lumber. In 1990 Ace established an International Division to handle its overseas stores. (It had been exporting products since 1975.) EVP and COO David Hodnik became president in 1995. That year the co-op added a net of 67 stores including a three-store chain in Russia. Expanding further internationally Ace signed a five-year joint-supply agreement in 1996 with Canadian lumber and hardware retailer Beaver Lumber. Hodnik added CEO to his title in 1996.

Ace fell further behind its old rival True Value in 1997 when ServiStar Coast to Coast and True Value merged to form TruServ (renamed True Value in 2005) a hardware giant that operated more than 10000 outlets at the completion of the merger.

Late in 1997 Ace launched an expansion program in Canada. (The co-op already operated distribution centers in Ontario and Calgary.) In 1999 Ace merged its lumber and building materials division with Builder Marts of America to form a dealer-owned buying group to supply about 2700 retailers. Ace gained 208 member outlet stores in 2000 but saw 279 member outlets terminated. The next year it gained 220 but lost 255.

Sodisco-Howden bought all the shares of Ace Hardware Canada in February 2003. To better serve international members Ace opened its first international buying office in Hong Kong in April 2004.

In all the company added 131 new stores in 2005. That year after 33 years with the company David F. Hodnik retired as president and CEO of Ace Hardware. He was succeeded by COO Ray A. Griffith.

In 2007 Griffith sent a letter to Ace's retailers saying the company was considering changing from a cooperative to a traditional corporation to become more competitive and to better fuel growth. Shortly after the company announced an accounting shortfall of about $150 million or nearly half of its equity which was uncovered while Ace prepared to convert formats. The error turned out to be an accident by a mid-level employee.

In 2009 Ace launched Aisle411 a free product-location service that can be accessed via phone similar to dialing for information. The company launched the service after learning that shoppers who were unable to find a product either left (about 20% of the time) or asked store associates for assistance (about 60%) which created a high demand for staff attention. Dedicated to pleasing its shoppers Ace was ranked "Highest in Customer Satisfaction among Home Improvement Stores" by J.D. Power and Associates in 2007 2008 and 2009.

In mid-2010 the hardware store chain became the first retailer — outside of Sears and Kmart stores — to sell Craftsman brand tools.

In January 2011 the company reorganized its international division into a stand-alone entity: Ace Hardware International Holdings. Ace Hardware owns about 78% of the newly-created entity.

In December 2012 Ace exited the paint manufacturing business with the sale of its paint manufacturing division including two paint manufacturing plants near Chicago to Valspar Corp. for about $45 million. Under the terms of the sale Valspar will continue to make and supply Ace-branded paint under a long-term supply agreement. Also it will supply a comprehensive line of Valspar-branded paints to Ace retail stores.

EXECUTIVES

President And Ceo, John S. Venhuizen, age 49
Vp Information Technology And Cio, Karen Fedyszyn
Evp Cfo And Chief Risk Officer, Bill Guzik
Vice President Merchandising, Frank Carroll
Associate Vice President, James Mallaney
Svp Of Marketing, Brian Wyborg
Vice President Of Marketing, Brian Wiborg
Vice President Of Merchandising And Vice President Of Finance, Lori Bossmann
Vice President Of Information Technology, Alan Sommer
Vice President, Dale Ganz
Vp Retail Operations And New Business, John Tovar
Svp And Chief Marketing Officer, Kim Lefko
Vice President Of Merchandising, John Sommers
Vice President Secretary, Tim Novac
Vice President, Ken Nicholas
Chairman, Jim Ackroyd
Auditors: ERNST & YOUNG LLP CHICAGO IL

LOCATIONS

HQ: ACE HARDWARE CORPORATION
2200 KENSINGTON CT, OAK BROOK, IL 605232100
Phone: 630 368-3393

PRODUCTS/OPERATIONS

2014 Sales

	$ mil.	% of total
Wholesale Revenues	4,466	95
Retail Revenues	233	5
Total	**4,700**	**100**

Selected Services

Assembly
Automotive chip key cutting
Blade sharpening
Glass & Acrylic sheet cutting
Glass Repair
Hunting/Fishing licenseIn-store lock servicing

Selected Brands

ACCO BRANDS
ACME
ADANAC
BIG BEN
BILCO
EUREKA
EVEREADY

COMPETITORS

84 Lumber	McCoy Corp.
Akzo Nobel	Menard
BMC Stock	Northern Tool
Costco Wholesale	Orgill
Do it Best	Sears
Fastenal	Sutherland Lumber
Grossman's	True Value
Home Depot	United Hardware
Kmart	Distributing
Lowe's	Wal-Mart

HISTORICAL FINANCIALS

Company Type: Private

Income Statement

FYE: December 30

	REVENUE ($ mil.)	NET INCOME ($ mil.)	NET PROFIT MARGIN	EMPLOYEES
12/17	5,388	147	2.7%	4,500
12/16*	5,125	161	3.1%	—
01/16	5,045	156	3.1%	—
01/15	4,700	141	3.0%	—
Annual Growth	4.7%	1.4%	—	—

*Fiscal year change

Activision Blizzard, Inc.

Activision Blizzard answers the Call of Duty to make video games that millions of users play for billions of hours. The company is the biggest producer of video games including some of the most durable franchises: World of Warcraft Guitar Hero Candy Crush and Call of Duty. Newer blockbuster titles are Overwatch and Skylanders. Users play Activision Blizzard's games on PCs game consoles and mobile devices. The company also creates games based on licensed properties from Marvel and DreamWorks Animation. Activision Blizzard is expanding its theater of operations to games products and service for TV movies toys and a professional esports league.

Operations

Activision Blizzard operates in three segments: Activision Blizzard and King.

Activision which accounts for about 35% of revenue produces the company's signature Call of Duty franchise a first-person shooter game for console and PCs; and Skylanders a children-oriented game primarily for consoles. Activision agreed to transfer its publishing rights for the Destiny franchise to Bungie as part of the termination of their publishing relationship in 2018. The segment has about 55 million monthly active users (MAU).

Blizzard about a third of revenue produces another high-profile game World of Warcraft a subscription-based massive multi-player online role-playing game (MMORPG) for the PC as well as StarCraft a real-time strategy game for the PC and Overwatch a team-based first-person shooter game PC and console platforms. The segment also includes the activities of Overwatch League and Major League Gaming business as well as its online gaming service Blizzard Battle.net. Blizzard has about 35 million MAUs.

King about 30% of revenue develops PC and mobile games that include Candy Crush Farm Heroes Pet Rescue Bubble Witch and more than 200 other titles. King counts some 268 million MAUs.

Activision Blizzard is showing decreasing dependence on its top franchise games. The top three games Call of Duty Candy Crush and World of Warcraft account for 60% of revenue down from about three-quarters of revenue several years ago.

Geographic Reach

Activision Blizzard depends on the Americas for more than half its revenue. It gets about a third from Europe and about 15% from the Asia/Pacific region. The company has about 100 facilities in some 20 countries around the world. Overall the company has players in about every country and it notes that Candy Crush is played on all continents including Antarctica.

Sales and Marketing

Activision Blizzard markets its games on multiple platforms including social media such as Facebook Twitter and YouTube online advertising print and broadcast advertising direct response and product sampling. The company delivers content through retail channels or digital downloads including subscriptions full-game sales and in-game purchases as well as licenses of software to third-party or related-party companies that distribute Blizzard products.

The company's major customers are Apple more than 15% if revenue Sony about 15% and Google about 10%.

Financial Performance

Activision Blizzard's revenue has risen for the past four years with help from the King Digital Media acquisition. Sales jumped more than 40% in 2016 immediately following the deal and increased another 7% in each of the next two years.

In 2018 revenue hit a company high of $7.5 billion compared to $7 billion in 2017. The increase came from higher sales of Activision games ? Destiny 2 Call of Duty: World War II and Call of Duty: Black Ops 4 and Spyro Reignited Trilogy — released in 2018 and 2017. King games sales rose with help from Candy Crush Friends Saga while Blizzard sales dipped from lower Overwatch revenue.

Activision Blizzard's profit reached $1.8 billion in 2018 (another company high) compared to a $273 million profit in 2017. Besides higher revenue the company reduced costs to 73% of revenue in 2018 from 81% of revenue in 2017.

The company's coffers held $4.2 billion in cash and equivalents in 2018 compared to $4.7 billion the year before. In 2018 cash flow from operations was $1.8 billion while investing and financing ac-

tivities used $230 million and $2 billion respectively.

Activision Blizzard has significant long-term debt about $2.7 billion which could limit its flexibility in dealing with changes in the market.

Strategy

From big games come big bucks and that's why Activision Blizzard is shifting resources to further develop its blockbuster franchises and create new ones. In 2019 the company said it would add development talent to its biggest games to make sure customers get content they want to return to. It plans to increase the number of developers working on Call of Duty Candy Crush Overwatch Warcraft Hearthstone and Diablo 20% in 2019.

For Call of Duty the company expects more resources to provide more frequent content updates and events and accelerate its expansion across platforms and geographies. Another plan is to start a professional city-based Call of Duty esports league.

Activision Blizzard is also upping investment in Overwatch esports as well as live services the Battlenet platform and advertising.

To pay for the investment Activision Blizzard is streamlining its back office operations consolidating some commercial operations and revamping consumer marketing capabilities to reflect the continuing move to a largely digital network.

Geographically the company has seen solid results from Blizzard's business in China and it extended the partnership with NetEase through January 2023.

Mergers and Acquisitions

Activision Blizzard's King mobile game division has acquired analytics and engagement firm Omniata. The deal is consistent with King's practice of using internal analytics and marketing as much as possible to promote its games such as Candy Crush Saga. Those games have been played by billions of people but King needs a constant flow of data to figure out how to best acquire new users.

EXECUTIVES

Ceo, Robert A. (Bobby) Kotick, age 56, $2,375,858 total compensation

Cfo, Spencer Neumann, age 49

Ceo Activision, Eric Hirshberg, age 51, $961,677 total compensation

President And Ceo Blizzard Entertainment, Michael (Mike) Morhaime, age 51, $957,378 total compensation

President And Ceo Consumer Products Division, Timothy J. (Tim) Kilpin, age 59

Chief Customer Officer, Brian Hodous, age 55, $533,365 total compensation

Chief Corporate Officer, Dennis Durkin, age 48, $787,185 total compensation

Ceo King Digital Entertainment, Riccardo Zacconi, age 50, $415,928 total compensation

President And Ceo Major League Gaming (mlg), Pete Vlastelica

President And Coo, Collister (Coddy) Johnson, age 42

Senior Vice President Investor Relations And Treasurer, Kristin Southey

Vice President Audit, Chuck Shapiro

Vp Global Benefits, Milt Ezzard

Vice President, Linda Howard

Vp Infrastructure And Operations, Todd Szalla

Senior Vice President European Publishing, Joerg Trouvain

Vice President Marketing, Mark Meadows

Vice President Infrastructure And Operations, Pmp Archer

Vice President Of Marketing, Jonathan Anastas

Vice President Finance North America, Diego Abba

Vice President Of Marketing, Lori Davis

Vice President Of Operations, Marcus Sanford

Senior Vice President Cio And Head Global Strategic Sourcing, Bertrand Leroux

Vice President Production, Alex Peters

Vice President Sales Strategy, Jennifer Mirabelli

Vice President Of International Consumer Products, Philippe Bost

Senior Vice President, Allen Adham

Vice President Infrastructure And Operations, Keith Archer

Chairman, Brian G. Kelly, age 56

Cfo Activision Publishing, Thomas Tippl, age 53

Board Member, Peter Nolan

Treasurer, John Coyne

Auditors: PricewaterhouseCoopers LLP

LOCATIONS

HQ: Activision Blizzard, Inc.
3100 Ocean Park Boulevard, Santa Monica, CA 90405
Phone: 310 255-2000
Web: www.activisionblizzard.com

2018 Sales

	$ mil.	% of total
Americas	3,880	52
Europe Middle East and Africa	2,618	35
Asia Pacific	1,002	13
Total	**7,500**	**100**

PRODUCTS/OPERATIONS

2018 Sales

	$ mil.	% of total
Blizzard	2,738	36
Activision	2,266	30
King	2,090	28
Other segments	459	6
Elimination	(53)	-
Total	**7,500**	**100**

2018 Sales

	$ mil.	% of total
Console	2,538	34
Mobile and ancillary	2,175	29
PC	2,180	29
Other	607	8
Total	**7,500**	**100**

2018 Sales

	$ mil.	% of total
Subscription licensing and other revenues	5,245	70
Product sales	2,255	30
Total	**7,500**	**100**

COMPETITORS

Capcom	SEGA
Disney Interactive	Sony
Studios	Square Enix
Electronic Arts	Take-Two
Konami	Tencent Holdings
Lucasfilm	Turbine Inc.
Entertainment	Ubisoft
Microsoft	ZeniMax Media
Nintendo	Zynga
Rovio Entertainment	

HISTORICAL FINANCIALS

Company Type: Public

Income Statement — FYE: December 31

	REVENUE ($ mil.)	NET INCOME ($ mil.)	NET PROFIT MARGIN	EMPLOYEES
12/18	7,500	1,813	24.2%	9,900
12/17	7,017	273	3.9%	9,800
12/16	6,608	966	14.6%	9,600
12/15	4,664	892	19.1%	7,300
12/14	4,408	835	18.9%	6,800
Annual Growth	14.2%	21.4%	—	9.8%

2018 Year-End Financials

Debt ratio: 14.98%	No. of shares (mil.): 763
Return on equity: 17.42%	Dividends
Cash ($ mil.): 4,225	Yield: 0.7%
Current ratio: 2.31	Payout: 14.4%
Long-term debt ($ mil.): 2,671	Market value ($ mil.): 35,552

	STOCK PRICE ($)	P/E		PER SHARE ($)		
	FY Close	High/Low	Earnings	Dividends	Book Value
12/18	46.57	35 18	2.35	0.34	14.88
12/17	63.32	185102	0.36	0.30	12.49
12/16	36.11	35 22	1.28	0.26	12.23
12/15	38.71	33 15	1.19	0.23	10.98
12/14	20.15	21 15	1.13	0.20	10.02
Annual Growth	23.3%	— —	20.1%	14.2%	10.4%

Adobe Inc

Adobe Systems makes software that helps customers create distribute and manage digital content from the cloud. One of the top publishing software providers it has been known for brands such as Acrobat Photoshop and Dreamweaver. Adobe serves customers such as content creators and web application developers with its digital media products and marketers advertisers publishers and others with its digital marketing business. A long-time publisher of traditional software packages Adobe is moving its products to cloud-based versions. Subscriptions account for more than 80% of revenue. In 2018 Adobe bought Marketo a marketing-automation company for $4.75 billion.

Operations

Adobe's Digital Media segment about 70% of revenue includes products such as Photoshop and Illustrator under the umbrella of the Adobe Creative Cloud a subscription service.

Its Digital Experience segment more than 25% of revenue includes tools for creating managing and measuring digital advertising and marketing initiatives. Elements within the segment are Adobe Advertising Cloud Adobe Analytics Cloud Adobe Marketing Cloud and Magento Commerce Cloud.

The Print and Publishing unit less than 5% of revenue includes authoring and publishing software and tools that are licensed to manufacturers of workflow software printers and other output equipment.

Geographic Reach

The US is Adobe's largest market representing more than 50% of revenue; other North American countries contribute about 5%. The EMEA (Europe Middle East and Africa) region generates nearly 30% of revenue and the Asia-Pacific region led by Japan contributes about 15%.

Headquartered in San Jose California Adobe has field offices in about 30 countries across the Americas Asia and Europe.

Sales and Marketing

Adobe sells directly and through distributors resellers systems integrators and retailers. In addition it licenses its technology to hardware manufacturers for integration into their products.

Financial Performance

Adobe Systems' revenue more than doubled from 2014-2018 propelled by its digital offerings and higher sales through subscriptions.

Revenue rose 23% to $9 billion in 2018 (ended September) an increase of $1.7 billion from than 2017. Sales from Adobe Experience Cloud grew 20% while subscription revenue jumped 26% year-to-year. Other factors boosting revenue were sales from Magento's commerce platform and Marketo's marketing cloud.

Net income was no slouch for Adobe in 2018 increasing more than 50% to about $2.6 billion in 2018 from 2017 due to the higher subscription revenue as well as a decrease in the provision for income taxes. (The company's effective tax rate was 7% in 2018 compared to 21% in 2017 due the US Tax Cuts and Jobs Act).

Cash and cash equivalents stood at $1.6 billion at the end of 2018 compared to $2.3 billion at the close of 2017. Operations generated about $4 billion in cash in 2018 while investing activities used $4.7 billion and investing activities used $5.7 billion.

Adobe's indebtedness rose to $4.1 billion in 2018 from $1.9 billion in 2017 doubling its debt-to-equity ratio. A higher level of debt could affect it how the responds to changing economic conditions and reduce cash flow for other expenses.

Strategy

Adobe Systems' charge into the cloud and a subscription-based business model has paid off for the company. It has reported rising revenue and net income for the past five years and driven its profit margin to about 28% in 2018 from about 7% in 2014.

Just about every product in Adobe's portfolio has the word cloud in it. The company has added digital marketing applications and services to its digital media offerings which has raised subscriptions to account for about 88% of revenue from about 75% of revenue in 2016. Its applications also are made to use and view on mobile devices.

The Adobe Experience Manager (AEM) product which helps customers organize create and manage the delivery of creative assets and other content across digital marketing channels has been a hit with customers according to the company.

As it has moved into more areas Adobe faces bigger competitors with longer histories of cloud operations such as Oracle and Salesforce.com as well as enterprise software providers such as SAS and SAP.

Adobe has spent more than $7.7 billion in the past two years on acquisitions to bolster its marketing cloud and analytics offerings.

Mergers and Acquisitions

In 2019 Adobe Systems bought Allegorithmic the maker of Substance a tool for creating 3D textures and materials in game and video post-production. Adobe intends to combine Allegorithmic's Substance 3D design tools with Creative Cloud's imaging video and motion graphics tools for video game creators visual effects artists in film and television designers and marketers.

Adobe Systems acquired Marketo for $4.75 billion in 2018 in Adobe's biggest acquisition. The deal bolstered Adobe's marketing offerings with Marketo's business-to-business marketing platform combining Adobe's Experience Cloud analytics content personalization advertising and commerce capabilities with Marketo's lead management and account-based marketing technology. Marketo had been bought out by Vista Equity Partners in 2016 for $1.8 billion after about three years as a public company.

Earlier in 2018 Adobe Systems agreed to buy Magento Commerce for $1.7 billion in an attempt to move into ecommerce. Magento's customers use its technology to operate their online stores. Adobe intends to cross-sell its digital marketing products to Magento customers. The companies have some customers in common such as Coca-Cola Warner Music Group Nestlé and Cathay Pacific. Customers that Magento brings to the table include Canon Helly Hansen Paul Smith and Rosetta Stone. The deal is expected to close in the 2018 third quarter.

In 2017 Adobe Systems bought the SkyBox technology assets from Mettle a developer 360-degree and virtual reality software. The Skybox tools are designed for post-production in Adobe Premiere Pro CC and Adobe After Effects CC and complement Adobe Creative Cloud's 360/VR cinematic production technology. Adobe integrated SkyBox plugin functionality into subsequent releases of Premiere Pro and After Effects.

Company Background

When Charles Geschke hired John Warnock as chief scientist for Xerox's new graphics and imaging lab he set the stage for one of the world's largest software makers. While at the Xerox lab the pair developed the PostScript computer language which tells printers how to reproduce digitized images on paper. When Xerox refused to market it the duo left that company and started Adobe (named after a creek near their homes in San Jose California) in 1982.

HISTORY

When Charles Geschke hired John Warnock as chief scientist for Xerox's new graphics and imaging lab he set the stage for one of the world's largest software makers. While at the Xerox lab the pair developed the PostScript computer language which tells printers how to reproduce digitized images on paper. When Xerox refused to market it the duo left that company and started Adobe (named after a creek near their homes in San Jose California) in 1982.

EXECUTIVES

Evp And General Manager Digital Media, Bryan Lamkin, age 58, $568,590 total compensation

Evp And Chief Marketing Officer, Ann Lewnes, age 57

Evp General Counsel And Corporate Secretary, Michael A. (Mike) Dillon, age 60

Evp And Cfo, Mark S. Garrett, age 61, $698,977 total compensation

Chairman President And Ceo, Shantanu Narayen, age 55, $1,010,260 total compensation

Evp Customer And Employee Experience, Donna Morris, age 51

Evp Worldwide Field Operations, Matthew A. (Matt) Thompson, age 61, $673,720 total compensation

Evp And General Manager Digital Marketing, Bradley (Brad) Rencher, age 45, $573,514 total compensation

Evp And Cto, Abhay Parasnis, age 44, $183,583 total compensation

Vice President Licensing And Associate General Counsel, Joe Ramirez

Vice President Tax, Barry Slivinsky

Senior Vice President Worldwide Sales And Field Operations, Matt Thompson

Vice President Customer Care, Lambert Walsh

Vice President Product Development, Govind Balakrishnan

Vice President Manager Director, Angelica Pina

Vp Global Government Relations And Public Policy, Jace Johnson

Vice President Product Management, Bill Ingram

Area Vice President, Laura Riesterer-Randa

Assistant Vice President Sales Adobe Mar, Allen Jeffries

Vice President Licensing And Associate General Counsel, Joseph Ramirez

Vp Strategy And Operations Cloud Technology, Kira Dales

Vice President Chief Accounting Officer And Corporate Controller, Mark Garfield

Auditors: KPMG LLP

LOCATIONS

HQ: Adobe Inc
345 Park Avenue, San Jose, CA 95110-2704
Phone: 408 536-6000
Web: www.adobe.com

2018 Sales

Americas:	$ mil.	% of total
United States	4,632	53
Other	484	5
Europe Middle East & Africa	2,550	28
APAC:		
Japan	609	8
Other	753	6
Total	**9,030**	**100**

PRODUCTS/OPERATIONS

2018 Sales

By Segment	$ mil.	% of total
Digital Media	6,325	70
Digital Experience	2,443	27
Publishing	261	3
Total	**9,030**	**100**

2018 Sales

	$ mil.	% of total
Subscription	7,992	88
Products	622	7
Services and support	485	5
Total	**9,030**	**100**

Products

Creativity and Design
Creative Cloud
Photoshop
Lightroom
Dreamweaver
InDesign
Illustrator (graphic artwork creation)
Adobe XD
Adobe Premiere Pro
After Effects
Dimension
Acrobat Pro
Animate
Adobe Audition1
Bridge
Media Encoder
InCopy
Prelude
Fuse
Marketing and Analytics
Analytics
Advertising Cloud
Audience Manager
Campaign
Experience Cloud
Experience Manager
Media Optimizer
Primetime
Target
PDF and E-Signature
Acrobat Pro DC
Acrobat Pro 2017
Acrobat Standard DC
Adobe DC for teams
Adobe DC for enterprise
Document Cloud
Export PDF
Fill & Sign for Mobile

COMPETITORS

Apple Inc.	Getty Images
Autodesk	Google
Avid Technology	IBM
Box Inc.	Microsoft
Canon	Quark
Citrix Systems	SAS Institute
Dropbox	Shutterstock

HISTORICAL FINANCIALS

Company Type: Public

Income Statement   FYE: November 29

	REVENUE ($ mil.)	NET INCOME ($ mil.)	NET PROFIT MARGIN	EMPLOYEES
11/19	11,171	2,951	26.4%	22,634
11/18*	9,030	2,590	28.7%	21,357
12/17	7,301	1,693	23.2%	17,973
12/16	5,854	1,168	20.0%	15,706
11/15	4,795	629	13.1%	13,893
Annual Growth	**23.5%**	**47.1%**	**—**	**13.0%**

*Fiscal year change

2019 Year-End Financials

Debt ratio: 19.93%	No. of shares (mil.): 482
Return on equity: 29.76%	Dividends
Cash ($ mil.): 2,650	Yield: —
Current ratio: 0.79	Payout: —
Long-term debt ($ mil.): 988	Market value ($ mil.): 149,298

	STOCK PRICE ($) FY Close	P/E High/Low	PER SHARE ($) Earnings	Dividends	Book Value
11/19	309.53	51 34	6.00	0.00	21.83
11/18*	250.89	52 32	5.20	0.00	19.20
12/17	179.52	54 30	3.38	0.00	17.22
12/16	99.73	47 31	2.32	0.00	15.02
11/15	92.17	73 55	1.24	0.00	14.06
Annual Growth	**35.4%**	**—**	**48.3%**	**—**	**11.6%**

*Fiscal year change

Advance Auto Parts Inc

Advance Auto Parts (AAP) has taken the lead in the race to become the #1 provider of automotive aftermarket parts in North America. Serving both the do-it-yourself (DIY) and professional installer markets AAP operates nearly 5000 stores under the Advance Auto Parts Autopart International (AI) Carquest and Worldpac banners in the US and Canada. Its stores carry brand-name and private-label replacement parts batteries maintenance items and automotive chemicals for individual car and truck owners. AAP's Carquest AI and Worldpac stores cater to commercial customers including garages service stations and auto dealers.

Operations

Parts and batteries account for about 65% of Advance Auto Parts' total product sales; the rest comes from accessories and chemicals (about 20%) engine maintenance (nearly 15%) and other products. It carries a wide range of national and private label brands including Bosch Castrol Moog and Prestone as well as Autocraft Tough One Wearever and Carquest.

The company's namesake banner is the largest and includes nearly 4400 stores that serve both the professional and DIY markets with some 21000 aftermarket auto parts. Carquest which has about 400 locations focuses more heavily on the professional market and also serves about 1200 independently owned stores that operate under the Carquest name. The Autopart International and Worldpac banners (with some 185 stores and about 145 stores respectively) target the professional market offering imported aftermarket and OEM products and private-label parts.

Geographic Reach

Roanoke Virginia-based Advance Auto Parts has stores across the US as well as Puerto Rico the US Virgin Islands and Canada. Florida is the company's largest market with North Carolina New York Ohio Texas Pennsylvania and Georgia other major markets for the retailer.

The company has store support centers in Newark California; Raleigh North Carolina; Norton Massachusetts; and Roanoke Virginia. It has distribution centers in some 35 US states and about 5 Canadian provinces.

Sales and Marketing

Advance Auto Parts serves professional customers (garages service stations auto dealers) as well as DIY consumers. The professional market accounts for about 60% of total sales.

The company builds its marketing and advertising campaigns around radio television direct marketing mobile and social media and local in-store marketing. It is focused on creating an omnichannel experience where customers can buy online and pick up in stores. In addition its "Speed Perks" customer loyalty campaign targets core DIY customers and emphasizes service.

Advance Auto Parts spent $120 million on advertising in 2018 compared to about $100 million in 2017 and 2016.

Financial Performance

Since hitting nearly $10 billion in 2014 following the purchase of General Parts International Advance Auto Parts' revenue had been on a steady decline; it did jump slightly in 2018 however. Net income has been a little more sporadic see-sawing between $425 million and $500 million over the past five years.

In 2018 the company reported revenue of $9.6 billion up 2% from the prior year. It saw an overall improvement in its business across all regions resulting in comparable store sales growth of 2.3% (the highest in eight years).

Net income however declined to $423.8 million that year down 11% from 2017. The drop is primarily due to a tripling of provision for income taxes year-over-year because of a one-time benefit in 2017 related to the Tax Act.

Cash at the end of 2018 was $896.5 million an increase of $349.6 million from the prior year (and up more than $750 million in the past three years). Cash from operations contributed $811 million to the coffers while investing activities used $191.8 million mainly for capital expenditures. Financing activities used another $263.9 million for dividends to stockholders and a stock repurchase program.

Strategy

In 2017 Advance Auto Parts announced a five-year plan to improve the customer experience and drive consistent results in both the professional and DIY spaces. A significant part of this initiative involves investing in technology.

The company is focused on creating a common product catalog visible to customers and team members across all its brands and using data from that catalog (lookups purchase history) to evolve from a supply-driven to a demand-driven inventory. A related project is the optimization and streamlining of Advance Auto Parts' end-to-end supply chain. It invested nearly $200 million in 2018 in IT and supply chain initiatives.

With Amazon encroaching on many industries including auto parts retail enhancing its omnichannel capabilities is also a major need for Advance Auto Parts. It launched a faster website in mid-2017 that also offers an expanded product portfolio for online shoppers. In addition in 2018 Advance Auto Parts introduced MyAdvance.com a platform for professional customers that brings together multiple online tools and capabilities and partnered with Amazon rival Walmart.com to help drive DIY growth.

Plans for 2019 include the full rollout of the Walmart.com partnership new dynamic assortment capabilities and a mobile app.

Company Background

Founded as Advance Stores Company in 1929 AAP was a general merchandise retailer until the 1980s. From there the company shifted its focus to automotive parts retailing targeting DIY customers. It initiated a professionald delivery program in 1996.

In 2014 AAP acquired General Parts International (GPI) for about $2.1 billion — creating the largest automotive aftermarket parts provider in North America with $9 billion-plus in annual sales. GPI a privately-held distributor and supplier of original equipment and aftermarket replacement parts to commercial markets owned the CAR-QUEST and WORLDPAC brands. The deal added 1233 Carquest stores 103 Worldpac branches in 45 states and Canada and the business of nearly 1400 independently-owned Carquest stores to AAP's network.

EXECUTIVES

President And Ceo, Thomas R. (Tom) Greco, age 60, $803,852 total compensation

Svp E-commerce, Scott Bauhofer

President Â– Northern Division, Maria Ayres

President Southern Division, David McCartney

President Western Division, Mike Pack

President Autopart International, Michael Creedon

President Worldpac, Robert B. (Bob) Cushing, age 65, $453,910 total compensation

President Carquest Canada, Steve Gushie

Evp General Counsel And Secretary, Tammy M. Finley, age 52, $400,005 total compensation

Svp And Cio, James A. (Andy) Paisley

Svp And Chief Marketing Officer, Walter Scott

Evp And Cfo, Thomas B. (Tom) Okray, age 56, $86,540 total compensation

Svp Supply Chain, Todd Greener

Evp Supply Chain Strategy And Transformation, Leslie Keating

Svp Professional Business, Al Wheeler

Assistant Vice President Strategic Store Systems, Craig Anderman

National Sales Manager, Chad Schnitz

Vice President, Warren Shatzer

Vice President Of Human Resources, Kathy Gillis

Vice President Store Development, Jim Germann

Senior Vice President General Counsel And Corporate Secretary, Sarah Powell

Senior Vice President Finance, James Doran

Vice President Commercial Marketing, John Hanighen

Vp Infrastructure And Operations, Ken Moore

Evp Supply Chain, Reuben E Slone

Vp Of It Applications Development, Ben Jorgensen

Svp Marketing Insights And Analytics, Yogi Jashnani

Vp Of Investor Relations, Elisabeth Eisleben

Senior Vice President Chief Accounting Officer Controller, Andrew Page

Chairman, Jeffrey C. Smith

Auditors: DELOITTE & TOUCHE LLP

LOCATIONS

HQ: Advance Auto Parts Inc
2635 East Millbrook Road, Raleigh, NC 27604
Phone: 540 362-4911
Web: www.AdvanceAutoParts.com

PRODUCTS/OPERATIONS

2018 Sales

	% of total
Parts & Batteries	66
Accessories & Chemicals	20
Engine Maintenance	13
Other	1
Total	**100**

Selected Products

Parts & Batteries
Batteries and battery accessories
Belts and hoses
Brakes and brake pads
Chassis parts
Climate control parts
Clutches and drive shafts
Engines and engine parts
Exhaust systems and parts
Hub assemblies
Ignition components and wire
Radiators and cooling parts
Starters and alternators
Steering and alignment parts
Acsessories & Chemicals
AC chemicals and accessories
Air fresheners
Antifreeze and washer fluid
Electrical wire and fuses
Electronics
Floor mats seat covers and interior accessories
Hand and specialty tools
Lighting
Performance parts
Sealants adhesives and compounds
Tire repair accessories
Vent shades mirrors and exterior accessories
Washes waxes and cleaning supplies
Wiper blades
Engine Maintenance
Air filters
Fuel and oil additives
Fuel filters
Grease and lubricants
Motor Oil
Oil filters
Part cleaners and treatments
Transmission fluid

Selected Brands

Bosch
Castrol
Dayco
Denso
Gates
Monroe
Moog
Prestone
Purolator
Trico
Wagner

COMPETITORS

Amazon.com	Replacement Parts
AutoZone	Sears
Fisher Auto Parts	Somerset Tire Service
Genuine Parts	TBC Retail
Keystone Automotive Operations	U.S. Auto Parts
	Uni-Select
O'Reilly Automotive	VIP
Pep Boys	Wal-Mart

HISTORICAL FINANCIALS

Company Type: Public

Income Statement

FYE: December 29

	REVENUE ($ mil.)	NET INCOME ($ mil.)	NET PROFIT MARGIN	EMPLOYEES
12/18	9,580	423	4.4%	71,000
12/17	9,373	475	5.1%	71,000
12/16*	9,567	459	4.8%	74,000
01/16	9,737	473	4.9%	73,000
01/15	9,843	493	5.0%	73,000
Annual Growth	(0.7%)	(3.7%)	—	(0.7%)

*Fiscal year change

2018 Year-End Financials

Debt ratio: 11.57%
Return on equity: 12.20%
Cash ($ mil.): 896
Current ratio: 1.57
Long-term debt ($ mil.): 1,045

No. of shares (mil.): 72
Dividends
　Yield: 0.0%
　Payout: 4.1%
Market value ($ mil.): 11,265

	STOCK PRICE ($) FY Close	P/E High/Low	PER SHARE ($) Earnings	Dividends	Book Value
12/18	155.46	32 18	5.73	0.24	49.00
12/17	99.69	27 12	6.42	0.24	46.19
12/16*	169.12	28 22	6.20	0.24	39.54
01/16	150.51	31 22	6.40	0.24	33.56
01/15	158.56	24 16	6.71	0.24	27.41
Annual Growth	(0.5%)	— —	(3.9%)	(0.0%)	15.6%

*Fiscal year change

Advanced Micro Devices Inc

Advanced Micro Devices (AMD) makes a range of microprocessors that power a wide range of devices from PCs to industrial machinery. The company produces microprocessors that power PCs servers and game consoles and embedded processors that control functions in machines used in industrial control and automation as well as medical imaging telecommunications and avionic equipment. Besides processors AMD makes graphics cards and systems-on-a-chip. In recent years the company has armed itself with new product families: Radeon for graphics and Ryzen for computing to strengthen its position against longtime rival and market leader Intel. About 80% of AMD's sales are from international customers.

Operations

AMD operates through two segments: Computing and Graphics and Enterprise Embedded and Semi-custom. Computing and Graphics products accounting for about two-thirds of sales include AMD's Ryzen chips for PCs and Radeon graphic processors for game systems and other devices. The products from the Enterprise Embedded and Semi-custom segment about a third of sales are used in data centers kiosks machine-to-machine applications and security and storage systems.

AMD outsources manufacturing of its products to third-party foundries including GLOBAL-FOUNDRIES and Taiwan Semiconductor Manufacturing Company. AMD performs assembly test and packaging of its microprocessors and embedded processors.

Geographic Reach

Accounting for about 40% of sales China (including Taiwan) is the AMD's largest geographic market. The US and Japan each generate about 20% of AMD's sales while Singapore accounts for about 10%.

AMD's corporate headquarters is in Santa Clara California but most of its US operations are conducted at its Austin Texas facilities. Overall the company has about 40 locations in about 25 countries with about 20 in the Asia/Pacific region (where it has assembly test and packaging facilities). In addition AMD has research and development facilities in the US and design and development engineering teams in Australia China Canada India Singapore and Taiwan.

Sales and Marketing

AMD markets its products through a direct sales force as well as through a network of independent distributors and sales representatives.

The company counts on three companies Microsoft Sony and HP Inc. for about a third of sales. Other customers include Amazon Acer Asus Dell Huawei Lenovo and Samsung.

Financial Performance

AMD's revenue has increased by a leap and a bound in the past two years rising at a higher than 20% rate as manufacturers have increasingly adopted its newer chips.

In 2018 AMD's sales rose 23% to $6.5 billion an increase of about $1.3 billion from 2017 with its newer products accounting more about two-thirds of sales. The Computing and Graphics segment's revenue jumped nearly 40% in 2018 from 2017 from higher prices and great shipment volumes driven by demand for Ryzen processors. The segment also got a boost from increased sales in China and Taiwan in 2018. The Enterprise Embedded and Semi-Custom segment's sales inched up about 3% year-to-year on higher sales of the EPYC server products.

While AMD spent more on research and development and sales and marketing in 2018 the company posted a $337 million profit for the year compared to a $33 million loss in 2017. The higher sales and lower tax payments sent more money to the bottom line for the year.

AMD had about $1.1 billion in cash and equivalents in 2018 about $2 million less than 2017. In 2018 operations generated $34 million investing activities used $170 million and financing activities provided $28 million.

Strategy

AMD has plotted a comeback over the past several years after it lost ground to Intel in microprocessors and to Nvidia in graphics processors. High adoption rates of the Ryzen and EPYC chips have added to AMD's market share.

PC makers and other electronics firms snapped up the new versions of the members of the Ryzen family of processors which includes the Threadripper a high-end chip for desktop computers and Mobile a fast processor for ultrathin notebooks. The Ryzen processor was adopted by major PC manufacturers. The EPYC chip has spread AMD's footprint in the server market while Radeon graphics chips found datacenter customers in Baidu and Amazon Web Services.

AMD has shown off its gaming expertise in becoming the sole supplier of semi-custom graphics cards for Microsoft's Xbox and Sony's Playstation consoles. (Those companies which account for more 20% of AMD's sales have shipped some120 million AMD-powered consoles.) Google made a major gaming score in 2019 when Google chose the chipmaker's graphics cards to power the graphics rendering of its Stadia cloud-based game system.

Although AMD has released hot chips and grown significantly in recent years it still labors in the shadow cast by Intel one of the biggest chipmakers in the world. Intel maintains a dominant market position and greater financial resources than AMD.

Beyond the PC AMD looks to provide processors for virtual reality devices and other technologies that have the potential to become big markets. The company's acquisition of Nitero was made to further its ambitions in virtual reality and augmented reality.

Mergers and Acquisitions

In 2017 AMD acquired Nitero a developer of technologies for making wireless headsets for virtual reality and augmented reality applications. User would get a more immersive virtual reality experience without being tethered to a device by wired headsets. The acquisition provides AMD with a broader portfolio of intellectual property capable for Wi-Fi headsets.

Company Background

Founded in 1969 AMD has survived and sometimes thrived during the ups and downs of the age of the microprocessor. The company has con-stantly battled Intel the business's big kahuna trying to find an edge in price and performance.

EXECUTIVES

Svp And Cfo, Devinder Kumar, age 64, $530,005 total compensation
President And Ceo, Lisa Su, age 50, $886,340 total compensation
Svp Global Operations, Chekib Akrout, age 61
Svp And Cto, Mark D. Papermaster, age 58, $549,994 total compensation
Svp And General Manager Enterprise Embedded And Semi-custom Business Group, Forrest E. Norrod, age 53, $530,005 total compensation
Svp And General Manager Computing And Graphics Business Group, James R. (Jim) Anderson, age 47, $499,990 total compensation
Vice President Information Technology And Chief Information Officer, Frederick Mapp
Corporate Vice President Of Investor Relations, Ruth Cotter
Corporate Vice President Finance, Gary Lloyd
Vice President Finance And Sales Operations, Denise Gourlay
Vp Operations, Keivan Keshvari
Corporate Vice President Finance, Pearly Teh
Chairman, John E. Caldwell, age 69
Auditors: Ernst & Young LLP

LOCATIONS

HQ: Advanced Micro Devices Inc
2485 Augustine Drive, Santa Clara, CA 95054
Phone: 408 749-4000
Web: www.amd.com

2018 Sales

	$ mil.	% of total
China	2,516	39
US	1,327	21
Japan	1,225	19
Singapore	728	11
Europe	470	7
Other regions	209	3
Total	**6,475**	**100**

PRODUCTS/OPERATIONS

2018 Sales

	$ mil.	% of total
Computing and Graphics	4,125	64
Enterprise Embedded and Semi-Custom	2,350	36
Total	**6,475**	**100**

Selected Products

Computing
  Accelerated processing units (APUs; Fusion combines central processing and graphics processing units on a single chip)
  Microprocessors (Ryzen Athlon Opteron Phenom Sempron and Turion lines)
  Motherboard reference design kits and chipsets
Graphics
  Embedded graphics processing units
  Macintosh notebook and desktop PC graphics processors (Radeon)
  Motherboard chipsets (for AMD and Intel processors)
  Server and workstation graphics processing units
Personal connectivity
  Embedded processors
  Networking chips

COMPETITORS

ARM Holdings	NVIDIA
Analog Devices	NXP Semiconductors
Atmel	STMicroelectronics
Hitachi	Samsung Electronics
Infineon Technologies	Silicon Integrated
Intel	Systems
Marvell Technology	Texas Instruments
Matrox Electronic	VIA Technologies
Systems	

HISTORICAL FINANCIALS

Company Type: Public

Income Statement

FYE: December 28

	REVENUE ($ mil.)	NET INCOME ($ mil.)	NET PROFIT MARGIN	EMPLOYEES
12/19	6,731	341	5.1%	11,400
12/18	6,475	337	5.2%	10,100
12/17	5,329	43	0.8%	8,900
12/16	4,272	(497)	—	8,200
12/15	3,991	(660)	—	9,100
Annual Growth	**14.0%**	**—**	**—**	**5.8%**

2019 Year-End Financials

Debt ratio: 8.06%
Return on equity: 16.71%
Cash ($ mil.): 1,503
Current ratio: 1.95
Long-term debt ($ mil.): 486

No. of shares (mil.): 1,170
Dividends
  Yield: —
  Payout: —
Market value ($ mil.): 54,031

	STOCK PRICE ($) FY Close	P/E High/Low		PER SHARE ($) Earnings	Dividends	Book Value
12/19	46.18	150	55	0.30	0.00	2.42
12/18	17.82	96	28	0.32	0.00	1.26
12/17	10.28	380	244	0.04	0.00	0.63
12/16	11.34	—	—	(0.60)	0.00	0.44
12/15	2.92	—	—	(0.84)	0.00	(0.52)
Annual Growth	**99.4%**	**—**	**—**	**—**	**—**	**—**

ADVENTIST HEALTH SYSTEM SUNBELT HEALTHCARE CORPORATION

EXECUTIVES

Pres, Donald Jernigan
V Pres, Robert Henderschedt
Coordinator, Pennie Moore
Administration Assisant, Almeda Tyren
Regional Laboratory Administra, Dhobie Wong
Information Security, Teresa Majors
Physician, Wasim Ahmar
Physician, Wynn Sullivan
Vice President, Barbara Flynn
Admin Director Strategic Plann, Belinda Grant
Prin, Daniel Nassar

LOCATIONS

HQ: ADVENTIST HEALTH SYSTEM SUNBELT HEALTHCARE CORPORATION
900 HOPE WAY, ALTAMONTE SPRINGS, FL 327141502
Phone: 407 357-1000
Web: WWW.ADVENTHEALTH.COM

HISTORICAL FINANCIALS

Company Type: Private

Income Statement

FYE: December 31

	REVENUE ($ mil.)	NET INCOME ($ mil.)	NET PROFIT MARGIN	EMPLOYEES
12/18	10,974	635	5.8%	78,000
12/17	10,083	1,167	11.6%	—
12/16	9,651	806	8.4%	—
12/14	519	26	5.1%	—
Annual Growth	**114.4%**	**121.7%**	**—**	**—**

ADVOCATE HEALTH AND HOSPITALS CORPORATION

EXECUTIVES

Pres, James H Skogsbergh
Vp, Patricia Smith-Calascibetta
Manager Clinical Engineering T, Steven Vanderzee
Director of Professional Devel, Linda Plewniak
Site Compliance Officer, Shelly Carling
Social Worker, Alberto Godinez
Data Design, Aleksandar Aleksic
Manager Tax Accounting, Amanda Kabat
Manager, Amy Cerny
Supervisor, Damir Radisic
Rn, Elizabeth Wilson
Auditors: ERNST & YOUNG US LLP CHICAGO

LOCATIONS

HQ: ADVOCATE HEALTH AND HOSPITALS CORPORATION
3075 HIGHLAND PKWY, DOWNERS GROVE, IL 605151288
Phone: 630 572-9393
Web: WWW.ADVOCATEGIVING.ORG

HISTORICAL FINANCIALS

Company Type: Private

Income Statement				FYE: December 31
	REVENUE ($ mil.)	NET INCOME ($ mil.)	NET PROFIT MARGIN	EMPLOYEES
12/17	5,310	243	4.6%	4,110
12/13	4,072	392	9.6%	—
12/12	3,645	419	11.5%	—
12/01	2,014	114	5.7%	—
Annual Growth	6.2%	4.8%	—	—

ADVOCATE HEALTH CARE NETWORK

EXECUTIVES

Ceo-Pres, James H Skogsbergh
Director of Practice Acquisiti, Brian Rust
Administrative Assistant, Gail Michalski
Human Resources Consultant, Irma Martinez
Finance Manager Payroll and, Lynn Bicknase
Analyst 1 AMG Information Syst, Merilee Nielsen
Director of Claims Risk Manage, Sue Bujold-Lee
Physician, Alma Buckner
Director Hospitalist, Ana Nowell
Director of Practice Managemen, Angela Luridas
Business Office Associate II C, Brandi Archer
Auditors: ERNST & YOUNG LLP CHICAGO IL

LOCATIONS

HQ: ADVOCATE HEALTH CARE NETWORK
3075 HIGHLAND PKWY FL 6, DOWNERS GROVE, IL 605155563
Phone: 630 572-9393
Web: WWW.ADVOCATEHEALTH.COM

HISTORICAL FINANCIALS

Company Type: Private

Income Statement				FYE: December 31
	REVENUE ($ mil.)	NET INCOME ($ mil.)	NET PROFIT MARGIN	EMPLOYEES
12/15	5,392	60	1.1%	25,000
12/06	3,268	286	8.8%	—
12/05	2,973	140	4.7%	—
12/04	2,779	143	5.2%	—
Annual Growth	6.2%	(7.6%)	—	—

AECOM

AECOM is one of the world's top engineering and design groups. The company provides planning consulting architectural and engineering design services for civil and infrastructure construction to public and private clients in more than 150 countries. The company also offers other services including logistics and consulting in a range of end markets that include energy and environmental construction. Some of AECOM's major projects include the USTA Billie Jean King National Tennis Center Taizhou Bridge in China Crossrail London (the largest construction in Europe) and New York City's Second Avenue Subway. AECOM generates more than a quarter of its sales outside the US.

Operations

AECOM operates through four business segments: Design and Consulting Services (DCS) Construction Services (CS) Management Services (MS) and AECOM Capital.DCS generates about 40% of the company's total revenue and consists of planning consulting architectural and engineering design services. CS includes construction for buildings energy infrastructure and industrial facilities and accounts for around 40% of sales. MS at about 20% of revenue includes AECOM's facilities management and maintenance training logistics consulting technical assistance and systems integration and IT services.The company invests in real estate infrastructure projects and public/private partnerships through AECOM Capital.

Geographic Reach

Based in Los Angeles AECOM serves clients in more than 150 countries. The company generates more than 70% of its revenue from the US about 10% from Europe and less than 20% from the Asia-Pacific region Canada and other areas.

It has primary office locations in the US as well as in Australia Hong Kong Russia the United Arab Emirates and the UK.

Sales and Marketing

AECOM serves several sectors such as transportation facilities environmental energy water and government.

AECOM's revenue is split about evenly between private sector clients and government entities. Roughly 45% of its revenue derived from governments is from direct contracts with US federal government agencies (Departments of Defense Energy Justice and Homeland Security); the remainder comes from state and local governments as well as foreign governments.

Financial Performance

After a breakout year in fiscal 2015 which saw revenue more than double due to its acquisition of URS AECOM reported a small drop in revenue in 2016 but rebounded in 2017 and 2018 on strong performance from its three main segments particularly Construction Services. The company's net income fell 40% between 2014 and 2018 due to massive losses in 2014 and 2015 partially offset by gains of more than 250% in 2017 when its acquisition and integration expenses dropped significantly.

AECOM added 11% to its revenue in 2018 compared with 2017. The company saw sales in its Design and Consulting Services (DCS) Construction Services (CS) and Management Services (MS) segments increase by 8.7% 12.9% and 10.6% respectively. Residential housing storm disaster relief in the Americas and increases in the Asia-Pacific and Europe Middle East and Africa (EMEA) regions drove up DCS income. Gains in its CS segment owed to construction of residential high-rise buildings in New York City and the inclusion of revenue from acquisitions in 2018 and 4Q17. US government projects — including US Army projects in the Middle East and US Air Force contracts — bolstered MS revenue.

The company's net income fell 60% to $136.5 million in 2018 due mostly to an impairment of assets held for sale including goodwill related to the anticipated selloff of the company's non-core oil and gas businesses (which AECOM announced in Q2 of 2018).

AECOM added $84.4 million to its cash stores in 2018. Operations provided $774.6 million; Investments used $59 million and financings used $624.9 million. Investment spend decreased compared to the previous year thanks to the company abstaining from acquisitions and greater return on investment from unconsolidated joint ventures. Financing activity increased due to common stock repurchases net distributions to noncontrolling interests and net debt repayments.

Strategy

AECOM believes that its diversification is key to growth. It has cultivated diversified end markets funding (50:50 private:public) and capabilities during its transition from solely engineering design to construction and then ultimately operations and maintenance.

Infrastructure is a major target for the company which is boosting its expertise in that area through internal investment (including the creation of a federal contracting division) and acquisitions (including the 2017 purchase of Shimmick). In January 2019 the company released its second annual report on the future of infrastructure which surveyed more than 10000 residents of 10 major global cities on their infrastructure concerns. In addition in mid-2017 the company announced plans to hire some 3000 workers to support its infrastructure operations in the US and the rest of the North America.

The company is already a leader in "mega projects" worth more than $1 billion; current projects that fit that description include West Gate Tunnel in Melbourne Australia and the San Roque Multipurpose Dam in Luzon Philippines.

Although AECOM's acquisition spending in its last three fiscal years has been miniscule compared to the billions it paid for USR in late 2014 growth by acquisition remains a large part of the company's strategy as it works to cement its leadership position in existing markets and enter new ones.

Mergers and Acquisitions

In 2017 AECOM agreed to pay $175 million to acquire heavy civil construction company Shimmick which operates primarily in California and the western US. The purchase complements AECOM's North American offerings and better positions it to take advantage of upcoming infrastructure projects particularly in the western US.

Company Background

AECOM formed in 1990 through the merger of five subsidiaries of Ashland Inc. Since then more than 50 companies have joined AECOM. The company completed its initial public offering in 2007.

EXECUTIVES

Associate Vice President Network Architect, Michael Bradvica
Vice President Communications, Frank Pollare
Vice President Leasing, David B Kilpatrick
Chief Executive Aecom Capital, John T. Livingston
President Major Pursuits, Frederick W. (Fred) Werner, age 66, $661,540 total compensation
Svp And Chief Marketing And Communications Officer, Heather Rim
Chairman And Ceo, Michael S. (Mike) Burke, age 55, $1,276,928 total compensation
Group President Construction Services, Daniel P. McQuade, age 59
Evp And General Counsel, Carla J. Christofferson, age 51
Chief Executive Europe The Middle East India And Africa (emia), Steve Morriss
President Technical And Operational Services, Randall A. (Randy) Wotring, age 62, $705,389 total compensation
Evp And Cfo, W. Troy Rudd, age 55, $528,851 total compensation
Evp And Chief Human Resources Officer, Mary E. Finch, age 49
Chief Executive Europe The Middle East India And Africa (emia), Lara Poloni
Senior Vice President, Stephen Polechronis
Vice President, Herbert Higginbotham
Associate Vice President, Atma Sookram
Vice President, Mark Kelley
Vice President, John S Prizner
Associate Vice President, Samuel Pickard
Vice President Energy, Shawn Kelly
Vice President, Rod Mccrary
Associate Vice President, Robert Humbert
Assistant Vice President Casu, Andy Shepard
Svp Mergers And Acquisitions, Matt Clark
Associate Vice President, George Sholy
Vice President Global Tax, Donna Cote
Vice President, Will Wright
Vice President Marketing, Fran Hegeler
Group Associate Vice President Contracts Compliance And Internal Audit, Edward Condoleo
Vice President, Ron Osborne
Assistant Vice President Techn, Richard Silos
Associate Vice President, Dean Simpson
Assoc. Vice President, James Fillis
First Vice President, Ryan Mahoney
Vice President Legal, Bob Foran
Associate Vice President, Chris Mcguire
Associate Vice President, David Plotkin
Executive Vice President Design And Consulting Services Americas, Matthew Cummings
Executive Vice President, Bill Endres
Vice President Aviation, Frank Wengler
Associate Vp, Dennis Struecker
Associate Vp, Wendy Thu
Senior Vice President Corporate Finance, Roger Willard
Vice President Technical Services, Jeff Brier
Executive Vice President Mid Atlantic Region Tishman Construction, John Barron
Senior Vice President Assistant General Counsel Head Of Litigation, Laura Abrahamson
Associate Vice President Project Management, Jeff Endersby
Senior Vice President Operations Finance, Charles Thuss
Vice President Of Operations Support, Richard Blagg
Vice President Corporate Development And Mergers And Acquisitions, Stan Lin
Evp And General Manager Federal Construction Services, Vern Kuehn

Evp And General Manager Nuclear And Environment, Todd Wright
Evp, Vahid Ownjazayeri
Senior Vice President Strategic Planning And Technical Services, Mark Morris
Vice President Operations And, Brad White
Associate Vice President, John Holmes
Vice President, Dan Shumaker
Executive Vice President, Rebecca Nolan
Senior Vice President Pacific Region Business Line Lead, Sujan Punyamurthula
First Vice President, Amy Chase
Vice President Of Business Development, Rick Randall
Vice President Marketing And Business Development, Carol Papillo
Vice President Strategic Captures Managementservices Group, Matt Einseln
Vice President Purchasing, Marty Adelman
Senior Vice President Operations, Steve Richards
Vice President Senior Project Manager, Karen Maestas
Senior Vice President Talent Management, Susan Dumond
Vice President, Richard Romig
Associate Vice President, Alastair Macgregor
Senior Vice President Chicago Metro Area Executive, Denise Casalino
Vice President, James Karl
Associate Vice President, Brent Miyazaki
Vice President Director Of Healthcare Facilities Business Line Infrastructure Environment, Joe Greenan
Corporate Vice President Strategy, Jennifer Whiting
Associate Vice President, Raymond O'donnell
Vice President Of Learning Solutions, Redmond Chris
Vice President And Treasurer Corporate Officer, Judy Rodgers
Vice President, Garry Lay
Vice President Transportation, Daniel Faust
Vice President, Carlos Garcia
Associate Vice President, Jerry Farhat
Vice President Project Executive, Robert Sullivan
Vice President Principal Geologist, Robert Macwilliams
Senior Vice President, Russel Rudden
District Vice President, Lee Grant
Vice President, Michael Gasparro
Senior Vice President Engineering And Om Oil Gas, Ken Martinez
Vice President, Thomas Elsroth
Associate Vice President, James Sullivan
Vice President Water Resources, Richard Millet
Vice President, Melad Hanna
Vice President Regional Managing Principal Buildings Places, Bob Lavey
Vice President, Bill Rohrer
Vice President Manager Environmental Planning, Jeff Rice
Vice President Of Government Relations, Tom Tilas
Vice President, Steve Wilcox
Vice President Pbr Program Manager, John Heinicke
Vice President And Chief Engineer, Feury John
Vice President Emerging Technology, Seth Finkel
Vice Chairman, Daniel R. (Dan) Tishman, age 64
Advisory Board Member, Antonio Santoro
Secretary, Evelyn Serrano
Secretary, Annis Catherine
Auditors: Ernst & Young LLP

LOCATIONS

HQ: AECOM
1999 Avenue of the Stars, Suite 2600, Los Angeles, CA 90067
Phone: 213 593-8000
Web: www.aecom.com

2018 Sales

	$ mil.	% of total
US	14,753	73
Europe	1,984	10
Asia/Pacific	1,440	7
Canada	1,212	6
Other foreign countries	765	4
Total	**20,155**	**100**

PRODUCTS/OPERATIONS

Selected Services
Architecture & Design
Construction
Decommissioning & Closure
Engineering
Environmental Services
International Development
IT & Cybersecurity
Operations & Maintenance
Planning & Consulting
Program Management/Construction Management
Risk Management & Resilience
Specialized Services
  Cities Solutions
  Equity Investment
  Fabrication
  Process Technologies
  Public/Private Partnerships
Technical Services

2018 Sales

	$ mil.	% of total
Design and Consulting Services	8,223	41
Construction Services	8,238	41
Management Services	3,693	18
Total	**20,155**	**100**

COMPETITORS

Amec Foster Wheeler	MWH Global
Bechtel	Parsons Brinckerhoff
Black & Veatch	Parsons Corporation
EMCOR	STV
Fluor	Skidmore Owings
Henkels & McCoy	Stantec
Jacobs Engineering	Terracon
KBR	Tetra Tech
Louis Berger	Tutor Perini

HISTORICAL FINANCIALS

Company Type: Public

Income Statement FYE: September 30

	REVENUE ($ mil.)	NET INCOME ($ mil.)	NET PROFIT MARGIN	EMPLOYEES
09/19	20,173	(261)	—	86,000
09/18	20,155	136	0.7%	87,000
09/17	18,203	339	1.9%	87,000
09/16	17,410	96	0.6%	87,000
09/15	17,989	(154)	—	92,000
Annual Growth	**2.9%**	**—**	**—**	**(1.7%)**

2019 Year-End Financials

Debt ratio: 23.53%	No. of shares (mil.): 157
Return on equity: (-6.71%)	Dividends
Cash ($ mil.): 1,080	Yield: —
Current ratio: 1.17	Payout: —
Long-term debt ($ mil.): 3,285	Market value ($ mil.): 5,915

	STOCK PRICE ($) FY Close	P/E High/Low		PER SHARE ($) Earnings	Dividends	Book Value
09/19	37.56	—	—	(1.66)	0.00	23.43
09/18	32.66	46	37	0.84	0.00	26.07
09/17	36.81	18	12	2.13	0.00	25.37
09/16	29.73	58	37	0.62	0.00	21.88
09/15	27.51	—	—	(1.04)	0.00	22.53
Annual Growth	**8.1%**	**—**	**—**	**—**	**—**	**1.0%**

AEROTEK, INC.

Aerotek a unit of staffing powerhouse Allegis Group offers commercial and technical staffing services throughout North America Europe and Asia Pacific. Through several divisions Aerotek staffs workers such as engineers mechanics scientists and technical professionals as well as administrative staff members general laborers and tradespeople. The company also provides training and support services. Along with aerospace auto and engineering companies Aerotek's clients include companies from the construction energy manufacturing health care and finance industries.

Operations

Aerotek solutions include staffing services workforce management engineering support and government services. Its staffing services provide short-term seasonal high-volume and niche contract support. It also offers contract-to-hire talent for project-based positions with the option to hire contractors as permanent employees.

Workforce management services comprise customized support for complex projects and business lines with specific timelines. Sciences support includes clinical and lab services across a range of industries through various delivery models. Aerotek also provides support and services to the government and government subcontractors with capabilities focused on contracts security compliance business development program management and finance.

Geographic Reach

Aerotek is headquartered in Hanover MD. The company has office locations in Asia Pacific (Australia Hong Kong China and Japan) Europe (Belgium France Germany Netherlands Sweden and UK) and North America (Canada and the US). Aerotek also operates a network of more than 250 non-franchised offices.

Sales and Marketing

Aerotek serves a wide variety of industries more than 18000 clients and 300000 contract employees every year.

Strategy

Aerotek has expanded its operations over the years through organic growth and acquisitions especially in niche markets such as the biotechnology health care clinical research chemical and plastics sectors. Despite economic ups and downs demand within these industries has been consistent along with engineering. Aerotek has also widened its client focus to include minority and woman-owned companies.

Company Background

Aerotek was founded in 1983 in Baltimore MD by entrepreneurs Steve Bisciotti and Jim Davis. It got its start by providing engineering staffing for the aerospace and defense industries and later for automotive manufacturers and suppliers. In 1990 the company formed Telecommunications Services now known as TEKsystems which has been recognized as the top information technology staffing firm in the US by the IT Services Business Report.

In 1993 Aerotek acquired Onsite Engineering & Management focused on environmental and energy services staffing. It later branched out to include staffing for other industries including biotechnology pharmaceuticals healthcare light industrial and light technical. It opened its first European office in 1993 and two years later expanded into Canada with an office in Mississauga Ontario.

In 1998 Allegis Group was formed as the parent entity of several operating companies including Aerotek TEKsystems and Onsite. In 2001 Aerotek and Onsite merged to become Onsite Companies and in 2004 Onsite Companies changed its name to Aerotek Inc. to leverage the reputation of the Aerotek name.

EXECUTIVES

Vp Technical And Professional Services, Mark Cooper
President, Todd M. Mohr
Cfo, Thomas B. (Tom) Kelly
Svp Operations, John Flanigan
Regional Vp Northeast, John Rudy
Regional Vp Midwest, Marty Schager
Regional Vp Central, Mike Hansen
Regional Vp West, Tony Bartolucci
Regional Vp Northwest, Brooks Wells
Vp Canada, Bryan Toffey
Regional Vp Southwest, Brad Kennedy
Regional Vp Mid-atlantic, Jeff Colvin
Regional Vp Southeast, Greg Jones
Vice President Client Delivery, Vinayak Nayak
Vice President Of Finance, James Mann
Regional Vice President, Anthony Bartolucci
Auditors: PRICEWATERHOUSECOOPERS LLP B

LOCATIONS

HQ: AEROTEK, INC.
7301 PARKWAY DR, HANOVER, MD 210761159
Phone: 410 694-5100
Web: WWW.AEROTEK.COM

PRODUCTS/OPERATIONS

INDUSTRIES SERVED

Accounting
Administrative & Support Services
Aerospace Aviation & Defense
Architecture & Design
Automotive
Construction
Customer Service
Energy & Utilities
Engineering
Environmental
Financial Services
Government & Public Administration
Healthcare
Manufacturing
Pharmaceutical
Sciences
Warehouse & Distribution

COMPETITORS

AMN Healthcare	Kforce
Adecco	MSX International
Bryant Bureau	ManpowerGroup
CDI	On Assignment
COMFORCE	Pinnacle Staffing
Insight Global	Randstad Holding
Integrity Staffing	Robert Half
Kelly Services	Roth Staffing

HISTORICAL FINANCIALS

Company Type: Private

Income Statement				FYE: December 31
	REVENUE ($ mil.)	NET INCOME ($ mil.)	NET PROFIT MARGIN	EMPLOYEES
12/17	6,070	0	—	4,200
12/16	5,565	0	—	—
12/15	5,492	0	—	—
12/14	5,353	0	—	—
Annual Growth	4.3%	—	—	—

AES Corp.

The AES Corp. is a world power producer. The US-based company has interests in about 70 generation facilities in more than 15 countries throughout the Americas Asia Africa Europe and the Middle East. AES sells electricity to utilities industrial users and intermediaries. The company also sells power directly to end-users such as homes and businesses mainly in Latin America and the US. Natural gas generates the biggest share of electricity while renewables generate about 30%. The US supplies about 40% of AES' revenue. Overall AES provides power to some 2.4 million customers.

HISTORY

Applied Energy Services (AES) was founded in 1981 three years after passage of the Public Utilities Regulation Policies Act which enabled small power firms to enter electric generation markets formerly dominated by utility monopolies. Co-founders Roger Sant and Dennis Bakke who had served in President Nixon's Federal Energy Administration saw that an independent power producer (IPP) could make money by generating cheap power in large volumes to sell to large power consumers and utilities.

AES set about building massive cogeneration plants (producing both steam and electricity) in 1983. The first plant Deepwater went into operation near Houston in 1986. By 1989 AES had three plants on line and it then opened plants in Connecticut and Oklahoma. In 1991 the company formally renamed AES went public but one plant's falsified emissions reports caused AES's stock to plummet in 1992.

Facing environmental groups' opposition to new power plant construction and an overall glut in the US power market AES bought interests in two Northern Ireland plants in 1992 and began expanding into Latin America in 1993. Also in 1993 AES set up a separately traded subsidiary AES China Generating Co. to focus on Chinese development projects. AES won a plant development contract with the Puerto Rico Electric Power Authority (1994) and a bid to privatize an Argentine hydrothermal company (1995).

In 1996 AES began adding stakes in electric utility and distribution companies to its portfolio including interests in formerly state-owned Brazilian electric utilities Light-Servi §os de Eletricidade (1996) and CEMIG (1997); one Brazilian and two Argentine distribution companies (1997); and a distribution company in El Salvador (1998).

AES almost doubled its revenues after buying Destec Energy's international operations from NGC (now Dynegy) in 1997. By the next year prospects in international markets were dimming so AES turned to the US market again. It bought three California plants from Edison International and arranged for The Williams Companies to supply natural gas to the facilities and market the electricity generated. AES also won a bid to buy six plants from New York State Electric & Gas (now Energy East) affiliate NGE.

Also in 1998 despite black days in many world markets AES bought 90% of Argentine electric distribution company Edelap and a 45% stake in state-owned Orissa Power Generation in India. Its moves paid off: AES posted a 70% gain in sales that year.

It bought CILCORP an Illinois utility holding company in an $886 million deal in 1999. Boosting its presence in the UK AES bought the Drax power station a 3960-MW coal-fired plant from National

Power. It also bought a majority stake in Brazilian data transmission company Eletronet from Brazil's government-owned utility ELETROBR S. In 2000 AES increased its interests in Brazilian power distributors. It also gained a 73% stake (later expanded to 87%) in Venezuelan electric utility Grupo EDC in a $1.5 billion hostile takeover.

The next year AES bought IPALCO the parent of Indianapolis Power & Light in a $3 billion deal. Also in 2001 AES acquired the outstanding shares of Chilean generation company Gener in which it previously held a 60% stake.

That year AES moved to take control of CANTV Venezuela's #1 telecom company. Through Grupo EDC which already owned 6.9% of CANTV AES offered to buy 43.2% of the company. But AES withdrew the offer after the CANTV board rejected it. (AES sold Grupo EDC's stake in CANTV the following year.) AES also sold some generation assets in Argentina to TOTAL FINA ELF (now TOTAL) for about $370 million.

In 2002 AES sold its 24% interest in Light Servi os de Eletricidade (Light) to Electricit de France (EDF) in exchange for a 20% stake in Brazilian utility Eletropaulo (increasing its stake in Eletropaulo to 70%). In that same year the company sold its retail energy marketing unit (AES NewEnergy) to Constellation Energy Group for $240 million and its CILCORP subsidiary which holds utility Central Illinois Light to Ameren.

In 2007 the company acquired two 230 MW petroleum coke-fired power generation facilities in Tamuin Mexico for $611 million. It also bought a 51% stake in Turkish power generator IC ICTAS Energy Group.

AES has faced controversy in Brazil where an unstable power market has caused the company to default on debts incurred from its purchases of stakes in local utilities (as well as bankrupt telecom firm Eletronet) in recent years. To restructure its debt with Banco Nacional de Desenvolvimento Economico e Social (BNDES) AES completed a deal in 2007 in which the firm's interests in AES Eletropaulo AES Uruguaiana AES Tiete and AES Sul was placed into a new holding company (Brasiliana Energia). AES owns 50.1% of that company while BNDES holds 49.9%.

To raise cash in 2008 and 2009 AES sold the AES Ekibastuz power plant and Maikuben coal mine in Kazakhstan to Kazakhmys (renamed KAZ Minerals) for $1.1 billion.

In 2008 the company boosted it assets in the Philippines acquiring the 660 MW Masinloc coal-fired power plant in Barangay Bula for $930 million.

EXECUTIVES

Evp And Cfo, Thomas M. (Tom) O'Flynn, $683,000 total compensation

Ceo, Andrés R. Gluski, $1,165,000 total compensation

Evp General Counsel And Corporate Secretary, Brian A. Miller, $585,000 total compensation

Vp Integrated Utilities Dominican Republic, Julian Nebreda

Svp Technology And Services And Cio, Elizabeth Hackenson, $433,000 total compensation

Svp And Coo, Bernerd Da Santos, $456,000 total compensation

President Asia Strategic Business Unit (sbu), Marty Crotty

President Europe Strategic Business Unit (sbu), Mark Green

President Mexico Central America And The Caribbean (mcac) Strategic Business Unit (sbu), Manuel Pérez Dubuc

President Us Strategic Business Unit (sbu), Ken Zagzebski

President And Coo, Patrick Moran

Vp Global Network And Ciso, Scott Goodhart

Vice President Of Human Resources, James Valdez

Vp Storage Europe, Paul Mccusker

Vice President Of Information Systems, Ramon Eulacio

Vice President (human Resources), Paritosh Mishra

Vice President Finanzas, Rosa Alvarado

Vp Portfolio Management, Rick Sturges

Svp Global Engineering And Construction, Mike Chilton

Chairman, Charles O. Rossotti

Board Member, Tarun Khanna

Board Member, Kristina Johnson

Board Member, John Morse

Auditors: Ernst & Young LLP

LOCATIONS

HQ: AES Corp.
4300 Wilson Boulevard, Arlington, VA 22203
Phone: 703 522-1315   **Fax:** 703 528-4510
Web: www.aes.com

2018 Sales

	$ mil.	% of total
United States	3,462	36
Chile	2,087	19
Dominican Republic	884	8
El Salvador	768	7
Brazil	527	5
Argentina	487	4
Panama	438	4
Colombia	428	4
Bulgaria	426	4
Mexico	399	3
United Kingdom	390	3
Vietnam	245	2
Jordan	95	1
Philippines	93	-
Kazakhstan	- -	
Other non-US	76	-
Total	**10,736**	**100**

PRODUCTS/OPERATIONS

2018 Sales

	$ mil.	% of total
Regulated	2,939	27
Non-Regulated	7,797	73
Total	**10,736**	**100**

Selected Electric Utilities and Distribution Companies

AES CLESA (electric utility El Salvador)
AES Edelap (electric utility Argentina)
AES Eden (electric utility Argentina)
AES Edes (electric utility Argentina)
AES Gener (electric generation Chile)
AES India Private Ltd.
AES SeaWest Inc.
Brasiliana Energia
 AES Sul Distribuidora Gaucha de Energia SA (AES Sul electric utility Brazil)
 AES Tiete (power generation Brazil)
 AES Uruguaiana (power generation Brazil)
 Eletropaulo Metropolitana Eletricidade de São Paulo S.A. (AES Electropaulo electric distribution Brazil)
CAESS (electric utility El Salvador)
Companhia Energética de Minas Gerais (CEMIG Brazil)
DPL (electric utility US)
EEO (electric utility El Salvador)
IC ICTAS Energy Group (power generation Turkey)
IPALCO Enterprises Inc. (holding company)

COMPETITORS

CPFL Energia	Exelon
Calpine	IBERDROLA
CenterPoint Energy	International Power
Duke Energy	NextEra Energy
E.ON UK	PG&E Corporation
Edison International	Public Service
Endesa S.A.	Enterprise Group
Enersis	Sempra Energy

HISTORICAL FINANCIALS

Company Type: Public

Income Statement

FYE: December 31

	REVENUE ($ mil.)	NET INCOME ($ mil.)	NET PROFIT MARGIN	EMPLOYEES
12/18	10,736	1,203	11.2%	9,000
12/17	10,530	(1,161)	—	10,500
12/16	13,586	(1,130)	—	19,000
12/15	14,963	306	2.0%	21,000
12/14	17,146	769	4.5%	18,500
Annual Growth	(11.0%)	11.8%	—	(16.5%)

2018 Year-End Financials

Debt ratio: 59.33%
Return on equity: 32.56%
Cash ($ mil.): 1,166
Current ratio: 1.14
Long-term debt ($ mil.): 17,636

No. of shares (mil.): 662
Dividends
 Yield: 3.6%
 Payout: 28.7%
Market value ($ mil.): 9,577

	STOCK PRICE ($) FY Close	P/E High/Low	Earnings	PER SHARE ($) Dividends	Book Value
12/18	14.46	9 6	1.81	0.52	6.17
12/17	10.83	— —	(1.76)	0.48	5.00
12/16	11.62	— —	(1.71)	0.44	5.42
12/15	9.57	31 20	0.44	0.40	5.53
12/14	13.77	15 12	1.06	0.20	6.18
Annual Growth	1.2%	— —	14.3%	27.0%	(0.0%)

AFLAC Inc

To soften the financial stresses during periods of disability or illness Aflac sells supplemental health and life insurance policies including coverage for accidents intensive care dental vision and disability as well as for specific conditions (primarily cancer) and general life policies. It is a leading supplier of supplemental insurance in the US and is an industry leader in Japan's life and cancer insurance markets. Aflac which is marketed through — and is an acronym for — American Family Life Assurance Company sells policies that pay cash benefits to more than 50 million people worldwide for hospitalization emergency treatment and medical appliances.

Operations

Aflac operates through two reportable segments — Aflac Japan and Aflac U.S. The Japan segment accounts for about 70% of total revenue while the US accounts for the remainder. Aflac Japan became a subsidiary of its parent to better fit the importance of that market.

The firm acts as a management company overseeing the operations of its subsidiaries by providing funding and management services. Its primary line of business is voluntary supplemental and life insurance. Aflac U.S. markets and administers group products through Continental American Insurance Company (dba Aflac Group Insurance).

In addition to accident term and whole life and cancer coverage Aflac offers short-term disability critical care hospital indemnity dental and vision products. Aflac individual and group insurance help provide protection to more than 50 million people.

Geographic Reach

Despite its US roots Aflac relies heavily on Japan where it makes about 70% of its insurance sales and where its policies fill in gaps not covered by the national health insurance system. Aflac has a presence in all 50 US states Puerto Rico and the Virgin Islands.

Sales and Marketing

In Japan Aflac primarily sells through independent corporate agencies in which corporations form subsidiaries to sell to their employees suppliers and customers. More than 100000 associates are employed via this model.

Japanese banks and postal offices sell insurance. Aflac has agreements with 90% of Japan's banks and offers cancer insurance in more than 20000 postal outlets providing a key outlet.

In the US Aflac is focusing on group insurance with larger customers. Here the company provides supplemental coverage to major medical plans. Building on strong brand recognition — due largely to the company's TV ads — Aflac has included independent brokers. The Aflac US sales force includes about 8500 agents and brokers.

Financial Performance

Aflac generated $21.7 billion in revenue in 2018 as it saw some growth in net premiums from 2017. However net premiums have not returned to levels from five years ago when revenue was 4% higher. This is due in part to Aflac's shift in Japan away from low-performing savings products toward more profitable cancer life and medical insurance.

However in that same time period the company has seen a decline in the amount of benefits and expenses it pays. As a result net income outside benefits from the US Tax Act has been steady. In 2018 net income totaled $2.9 billion hardly unchanged from 2014.

Operating cash also has been steady totaling $6 billion — to be expected as cash is used primarily to purchase investments to meet future policy obligations

Strategy

Aflac is focusing on improving and expanding its distribution network product development and customer service. Key to that is the development of IT centers in both the US and Japan. Also Aflac has an investment fund to support startups developing digital technologies that may end up supporting Aflac core functions. To date the company has invested more than $50 million.

In Japan where Aflac already covers about 25% of all households the company has created new health and life insurance products to attract even more customers. And to boost distribution Aflac Japan and Japan Post Holdings have an alliance which has boosted the number of postal outlets offering Aflac's cancer products from 1000 to more than 20000

HISTORY

American Family Life Assurance Company (AFLAC) was founded in Columbus Georgia in 1955 by brothers John Paul and William Amos to sell life health and accident insurance. Competition was fierce and the little company did poorly. With AFLAC nearing bankruptcy the brothers looked for a niche.

The polio scares of the 1940s and 1950s had spawned insurance coverage written especially against that disease; the Amos brothers (whose father was a cancer victim) took a cue from that concept and decided to sell cancer insurance. In 1958 they introduced the world's first cancer-expense policy. It was a hit and by 1959 the company had written nearly a million dollars in premiums and expanded across state lines.

The enterprise grew quickly during the 1960s especially after developing its cluster-selling approach in the workplace where employers were usually willing to make payroll deductions for premiums. By 1971 the company was operating in 42 states.

While visiting the World's Fair in Osaka in 1970 John Amos decided to market supplemental cancer coverage to the Japanese whose national health care plan left them exposed to considerable expense from cancer treatment. After four years the company finally won approval to sell in Japan since the policies did not threaten existing markets and because the Amoses found notable backers in the insurance and medical industries. AFLAC became one of the first US insurance companies to enter the Japanese market and it enjoyed an eight-year monopoly on the cancer market. Back in the US in 1973 AFLAC organized a holding company and began buying television stations in the South and Midwest.

The 1980s were marked by US and state government inquiries into dread disease insurance. Critics said such policies were a poor value because they were relatively expensive and covered only one disease. However the inquiries led nowhere and demand for such insurance increased bringing new competition. In the 1980s AFLAC's scales tilted: US growth slowed while business grew in Japan which soon accounted for most of the company's sales.

EXECUTIVES

Evp Treasurer And Head Of Corporate Finance And Development, Kenneth S. (Ken) Janke, age 61
President, Kriss Cloninger, age 71, $975,000 total compensation
Chairman And Ceo, Daniel P. (Dan) Amos, age 67, $1,441,100 total compensation
Evp And Cfo, Frederick J. (Fred) Crawford, age 55, $700,000 total compensation
President Aflac International; Chairman Aflac Japan, Charles D. Lake, age 58, $333,333 total compensation
Evp And General Counsel, Audrey Boone Tillman, age 54
President Aflac, Paul S. Amos, age 44, $700,000 total compensation
President Aflac U.s., Teresa L. White, age 53
Svp And Chief Marketing Officer, Gail A. Galuppo, age 55
Svp Business Services; President And Ceo Communicorp, Eric B. Seldon
Evp And Global Chief Investment Officer, Eric M. Kirsch, age 58, $593,800 total compensation
Managing Director And Global Head Of Credit Global Investments, Bradley E. Dyslin
Svp And Cio, Julia K. Davis
Managing Director And Head Of Global Investments And Corporate It, J. Pete Kelso
Evp Global Chief Risk Officer And Chief Actuary, J. Todd Daniels, age 48
Senior Managing Director And Global Head Macro Investment Strategy Quantitative Research And Trading Global Investments, Timothy (Chip) Stevens
Managing Director And Chief Investment Officer Global Investments, Teresa Q. McTague
President Aflac Corporate Ventures, Nadeem G. Khan
Vice President, Darlene Porter
Vice President Controller Financial Reporting And Regulatory Compliance, Michael Bruder
Executive Vice President And Chief Financial Officer, Rob Moran
Senior Vice President Chief Service Officer, Jamie Lee
Vice President Trade Operations, Evan Philippopoulos
Assistant Vice President Marketing, James Wardrup
Second Vice President, Kevin Dunlap
Second Vice President Travel Meetingsand Incentives, Heidi Carlisle
Second Vice President, Marty Pearson

Vice President U.s. Internal Audit, Lamar Barnett
Second Vice President, Gary Allen
Vice President, Michael Fisher
Senior Vice President Chief Compliance Officer U.s., Thomas L McDaniel
Second Vice President Customer Service, Tammy Briggs
Second Vice President Investor Relations, Robin Mullins
Avp Senior Risk Analyst, Alexander Lin
Vice President Product Innovation And Marketing, Stephanie Shields
Vice President Agents Commissions, Debra Beckley
Vice President, Jamie Rizzo
Regional Vice President Aflac Broker Channel, Jay Hutchins
Svp Corporate Planning Corporate Secretariat Crisis Management Aflac Life Insurance Japan, Tomoya Utsude
Vice President Product Development, Jason Van Pelt
Senior Vice President Chief Esg And Communications Officer, Catherine Hernandez-blades
Senior Vice President Head Of Financial Planning And Analysis, Steven Beaver
Senior Vice President Global Risk And Corporate Reinsurance Officer, Michel G Perreault
Senior Vice President Of Internal Operations, Virgil R Miller
Second Vice President Shareholder Services, Patricia A Bell
Seconv Vice President Event Productions, Oz R Roberts
Executive Vice President, Kenneth S Janke
Vice President Innovation Technology, Joe Parsons
Vice President Human Resources And Chief People Officer, Brenda Mullins
Assistant Vice President Trade Operations, Rama Kolluri
Vice President And Counsel Federal Affairs, Bradley Knox
Second Vice President Product Development And Implementation, Wendy L Herndon
Senior Vice President Global Security Chief Information Security Officer, Timothy Callahan
Senior Vp, Ron Sanders
Vice President Privacy Compliance, Brian Mckeen
Avp Compliance Manager, Victor Charles
Market Vice President Broker Sales, Michael Naumann
Board Member, Jeromy Song
Board Member, Jim Aiken
Board Member, Barbara Rimer
Board Member, Melvin Stith
Board Member, Douglas Johnson
Board Member, David Bowers
Board Member, Toshihiko Fukuzawa
Vice Chairman Of Aflac Life Insurance Japan, Hiroshi Yamaguchi
Board Member, Aaron Kenny
Auditors: KPMG LLP

LOCATIONS

HQ: AFLAC Inc
1932 Wynnton Road, Columbus, GA 31999
Phone: 706 323-3431   **Fax:** 706 596-3488
Web: www.aflac.com

PRODUCTS/OPERATIONS

2017 Sales

	$ mil.	% of total
Aflac Japan	15,028	69
Aflac U.S.	6,289	29
Corporate	210	1
Other	140	1
Total	**21,667**	**100**

2017 Sales

	$ mil.	% of total
Net premiums	18,531	85
Net investment income	3,220	15
Other	67	-
Adjustments	(151)	-
Total	**21,667**	**100**

COMPETITORS

American Fidelity Assurance Company	Meiji Yasuda Life
American National Insurance	MetLife
	Nippon Life Insurance
Asahi Mutual Life	Taiyo Life
CNO Financial	Torchmark
Colonial Life & Accident	Unum Group

HISTORICAL FINANCIALS
Company Type: Public

Income Statement
FYE: December 31

	ASSETS ($ mil.)	NET INCOME ($ mil.)	INCOME AS % OF ASSETS	EMPLOYEES
12/18	140,406	2,920	2.1%	11,390
12/17	137,217	4,604	3.4%	11,318
12/16	129,819	2,659	2.0%	10,212
12/15	118,296	2,533	2.1%	9,915
12/14	119,767	2,951	2.5%	9,525
Annual Growth	4.1%	(0.3%)	—	4.6%

2018 Year-End Financials

Debt ratio: 4.12%	No. of shares (mil.): 755
Return on equity: 12.15%	Dividends
Cash ($ mil.): 4,337	Yield: 2.2%
Current ratio: —	Payout: 27.5%
Long-term debt ($ mil.): —	Market value ($ mil.): 34,411

	STOCK PRICE ($) FY Close	P/E High/Low		PER SHARE ($) Earnings	Dividends	Book Value
12/18	45.56	24	11	3.77	1.04	31.06
12/17	87.78	15	12	5.77	0.87	31.50
12/16	69.60	23	17	3.21	0.83	25.24
12/15	59.90	22	19	2.93	0.79	20.86
12/14	61.09	20	17	3.25	0.75	20.73
Annual Growth	(7.1%)	—	—	3.8%	8.5%	10.6%

AG Mortgage Investment Trust Inc

AG Mortgage Investment Trust invests in acquires and manages a diverse portfolio of residential mortgage assets as well as other real estate-related securities and financial assets. Residential mortgage-backed securities backed by US government agencies including Fannie Mae Freddie Mac and Ginnie Mae known as "Agency RMBS" make up about 70% of the mortgage real estate investment trust's (REIT) portfolio. Credit assets including RMBS not issued or backed by the government account for most of the rest. Formed in 2011 by executives of investment adviser Angelo Gorden looking to profit from a recovery in the US mortgage bond market the mortgage REIT is managed by a subsidiary of Angelo Gordon.

IPO

The REIT went public in June 2011 with an offering worth $110 million far less than the $300 million it initially planned on raising.

Financial Performance

AG Mortgage reported net interest income of $125.4 million in 2013 up from $81.4 million and $17.1 million in 2012 and 2011 respectively. However substantial losses on other income sources and rising expenses led to a loss of $31.6 million in 2013 versus a profit of $135 million in 2012. Cash flow from operations has risen steeply since the REIT's inception from $15.4 million in 2011 to $130.8 million in 2013.

The REIT's portfolio was valued at $3.4 billion at the end of 2013.

Strategy

In the months after its IPO the REIT primarily focused on investing in Agency RMBS. However as market conditions and US monetary policy evolved the firm has focused more on credit assets of late. Indeed the REIT has gradually shifted its deployment of capital to its credit portfolio increasing its allocation as a percentage of assets from 9% to 22% to nearly 35% as of December 31 2011 2012 and 2013 respectively.

In January 2014 the mortgage REIT closed on a $10 million commercial real estate investment secured by a hotel property.

EXECUTIVES

Cfo Principal Accounting Officer And Treasurer, Brian C. Sigman, age 41, $150,000 total compensation

Chairman And Ceo, David N. Roberts, age 57

President And Chief Investment Officer, Jonathan Lieberman, age 56

General Counsel And Secretary, Raul E. Moreno, age 38, $28,493 total compensation

Auditors: PricewaterhouseCoopers LLP

LOCATIONS

HQ: AG Mortgage Investment Trust Inc
245 Park Avenue, 26th Floor, New York, NY 10167
Phone: 212 692-2000
Web: www.agmit.com

COMPETITORS

ARMOUR Residential REIT	Hatteras Financial
	MFA Financial
Annaly Capital Management	MFResidential
Bimini Capital Management	PIMCO REIT
	PennyMac Mortgage
Capstead Mortgage	Provident Mortgage Capital
Galiot Capital	

HISTORICAL FINANCIALS
Company Type: Public

Income Statement
FYE: December 31

	ASSETS ($ mil.)	NET INCOME ($ mil.)	INCOME AS % OF ASSETS	EMPLOYEES
12/18	3,548	1	0.0%	—
12/17	3,789	118	3.1%	—
12/16	2,628	63	2.4%	—
12/15	3,164	13	0.4%	—
12/14	3,458	109	3.2%	—
Annual Growth	0.6%	(65.4%)	—	—

2018 Year-End Financials

Debt ratio: 0.31%	No. of shares (mil.): 28
Return on equity: 0.23%	Dividends
Cash ($ mil.): 31	Yield: 12.4%
Current ratio: —	Payout: —
Long-term debt ($ mil.): —	Market value ($ mil.): 458

	STOCK PRICE ($) FY Close	P/E High/Low		PER SHARE ($) Earnings	Dividends	Book Value
12/18	15.93	—	—	(0.42)	1.98	22.82
12/17	19.01	5	5	3.77	2.00	25.34
12/16	17.11	10	6	1.80	1.90	23.68
12/15	12.84	1952	1258	0.01	2.28	23.58
12/14	18.57	6	5	3.37	2.40	25.81
Annual Growth	(3.8%)	—	—	—	(4.8%)	(3.0%)

AGCO Corp.

This company has been plowing the furrow of premium agricultural equipment since 1990. AGCO makes tractors combines hay and forage tools sprayers grain storage and protein production systems seeding and tillage implements and replacement parts for agricultural end uses. It sells through a global network of more than 4000 dealers and distributors spanning about 140 countries. It also builds diesel engines gears and generators through its power engines unit. Core brands include Massey Ferguson GSI Challenger Valtra (Finland-based) and Fendt (Germany). AGCO Finance offers financing services to retail customers and dealers via a venture with Rabobank a Dutch bank specializing in agricultural loans. Europe accounts for nearly half of AGCO's sales.

Operations

Tractors account for more than 55% of AGCO's sales and replacement parts nearly 15%. Combines and application equipment each make up less than 5% of revenue; grain storage and protein production systems and other machinery products account for about 20%

Geographic Reach

AGCO has manufacturing locations in the US France Italy Finland Germany Austria Hungary Denmark Brazil and China. It manufactures and assembles its products in about 50 locations worldwide including six locations where the company operates joint ventures. Europe is its largest market representing about 53% of net sales followed by North America at around a quarter of sales.

Sales and MarketingAGCO distributes its products primarily through a network of more than 4000 independent dealers and distributors who are responsible for retail sales to the equipment's end user in addition to after-sales service and support of the equipment. Distributors also sell its products through a network of dealers supported by the distributor. Sales are not dependent on any specific dealer distributor or group of dealers. AGCO also sources machinery and parts from third parties to control costs inventory and supply partly in response to the high seasonality of agricultural machinery demand.

Financial Performance

AGCO's revenue is closely linked to shifts in the agricultural industry. In recent years strong global crop production has kept agricultural commodities prices low reducing farm incomes. As a result AGCO's revenue has been choppy the last five years dipping about 4% between 2014 and 2018. However AGCO's sales have been on the upswing since 2016 as farmers began replacing older equipment after years of pent-up demand.

Sales in 2018 increased nearly 13% to $9.4 billion compared to $8.3 billion in 2017. Growth in 2018 was fueled in North America by the positive effects of AGCO's 2017 acquisition of Precision Planting as well as higher tractor sprayer hay tool and grain storage equipment sales. AGCO also saw increased demand in France Germany the UK Australia and China.

Net income increased 53% to $285.5 million in 2018 compared to 2017 primarily due to higher net sales and operating margin.

Cash at the end of 2018 was $326.1 million a decrease of $41.6 million from the prior year. Cash from operations contributed $595.5 million to the coffers while investing activities used $205.5 million mainly for capital expenditures. Financing activities used $413.3 million primarily for debt repayment.

Strategy

AGCO continued to invest through the market downturn. The squeeze forced the company into seeking solutions to product development that marry innovation with cost reduction. AGCO developed its global platform and module strategy which leverages common product architectures and standardizes components across AGCO's manufacturing sites and brands lowering costs and improving its products.

The company has made significant investments in smart farming technology that leverages data collected from machinery to increase productivity. AGCO now offers a full line of smart farming equipment that serve the needs of a farm's entire operations from soil preparation and planting spraying and harvesting to grain storage and protein production. The company's IDEAL combine launched in 2019 has more than 80 onboard computers and sensors that provide data visualization of the machinery's operation.

AGCO further boosted its smart ag offerings in 2019 with the announcement of a strategic partnership with Solinftec a provider of digital agriculture solutions. The deal allows AGCO customers access to Solinftec's digital offerings including onboard computers soil sensors and algorithms that enable real-time insights that improve agricultural efficiency. Solinftec's solutions launched in Brazil in early 2019 for producers of sugarcane soybeans cotton and corn and will be available to US soybean and corn producers in 2020.

The market downturn had the additional effect of prompting AGCO to improve its operational efficiency in search of margin growth amid low revenue. The company targeted purchasing factory productivity and product development. AGCO also balanced reductions in sales and administrative and fixed manufacturing costs with focused spending.

Mergers and Acquisitions

Strategic acquisitions have supported AGCO's international growth.

In 2017 AGCO completed the $940 million of GSI Holdings Corp from Centerbridge Partners. GSI's primary business lines are grain-storage equipment and equipment used in raising hogs and poultry such as ventilation fans for barns and watering systems. The company markets its equipment under half a dozen brand names.

Also in 2017 the company also acquired Precision Planting LLC for $198.1 million. Precision Planting headquartered in Tremont Illinois manufactures high-tech planting equipment. The acquisition provides AGCO with an opportunity to expand its precision farming technology offerings globally.

HISTORY

In 1861 American Edward Allis purchased the bankrupt Reliance Works a leading Milwaukee-based manufacturer of sawmills and flour-milling equipment. Under shrewd management The Reliance Works of Edward P. Allis & Co. weathered financial troubles - bankruptcy in the Panic of 1873 — but managed to renegotiate its debt and recover.

By the time Allis died in 1889 Reliance Works employed some 1500 workers.

The company branched into different areas of manufacturing in the late 19th century and by the 20th century the Edward P. Allis Co. (as it was then known) was the world leader in steam engines. In 1901 the company merged with another manufacturing giant Fraser & Chalmers to form the Allis-Chalmers Company. In the 1920s and 1930s Allis-Chalmers entered the farm equipment market.

Although overshadowed by John Deere and International Harvester (IH) Allis-Chalmers made key contributions to the industry — the first rubber-tired tractor (1932) and the All-Crop harvester. Allis-Chalmers spun off its farm equipment business in the 1950s and phased out several unrelated products. The company with its orange-colored tractors expanded and prospered from the 1940s through the early 1970s. Then the chafing farm economy of the late 1970s and early 1980s hurt Allis-Chalmers' sales.

After layoffs and a plant shutdown in 1984 the company was purchased in 1985 by German machinery maker Klockner-Humbolt-Deutz (KHD) who moved the company (renamed Deutz-Allis) to Georgia. In the mid-1980s low food prices hurt farmers and low demand hurt the equipment market. KHD was never able to bring profits up to a satisfactory level and in 1990 the German firm sold the unit to the US management in a buyout led by Robert Ratliff. Ratliff believed the company could succeed by acquiring belly-up equipment makers turning them around and competing on price. It was renamed AGCO in 1991.

EXECUTIVES

Svp And Cfo, Andrew H. (Andy) Beck, age 55, $530,000 total compensation
Svp; General Manager Asia/pacific And Africa, Gary L. Collar, age 62, $480,000 total compensation
Chairman President And Ceo, Martin H. Richenhagen, age 66, $1,345,575 total compensation
Svp; General Manager Americas, Robert B. Crain, age 59, $306,667 total compensation
Svp And Chief Supply Chain Officer, Hans-Bernd Veltmaat, age 64, $575,000 total compensation
Svp; General Manager Europe And Middle East, Rob Smith, age 53, $566,512 total compensation
Vice President General Counsel, Debra Kuper
National Sales Manager, Martin Mills
Vice President Of Financial, Julio Escossi
Vice President Director Manager, Joey Goodson
Vice President, Reiner Pagel
Vice President Engineering, Sam Freesmeyer
Vice President Product Line, Matt Rushing
Vice President Finance, Brian Zydel
Vice President, Kent Butler
Vice President Human Resources, Lauri Lipka
Vp Strategy And Integration, Karsten Pedersen
Senior Vice President Human Resources, Lucinda Smith
Vice President, Steve White
Vice President Finance, Frederic Devienne
Vice President Director Manager, John Benefield
Vice President Distribution Development, Alistair Mclelland
Senior Vice President Engineering, Helmut Endres
Vice President Engineering, Malcolm Shute
Vice President Global Purchasing Materials Logistics And 3rd Party, Mike Clem
Vice President, Chelsea Honnette
Assistant Secretary, Lynnette Schoenfeld
Assistant Treasurer, Chris Smither
Auditors: KPMG LLP

LOCATIONS

HQ: AGCO Corp.
4205 River Green Parkway, Duluth, GA 30096
Phone: 770 813-9200
Web: www.agcocorp.com

2017 Sales

	$ mil.	% of total
Europe/Africa/Middle East	4,614	57
North America	1,876	24
South America	1,063	12
Asia/Pacific	752	7
Total	**8,306**	**100**

2016 Sales

	% of total
United States	19
Other Europe	15
Germany	12
South America	12
France	10
Finland and Scandinavia	9
United Kingdom and Ireland	6
Canada	4
Middle East and Algeria	4
Asia	4
Australia and New Zealand	3
Mexico Central America and Caribbean	2
Africa	2
Total	**100**

PRODUCTS/OPERATIONS

2017 Sales

	$ mil.	% of total
Tractors	4,785	57
Replacement parts	1,305	16
Grain storage and protein production systems	1,049	13
Other machinery	582	7
Combines	349	4
Application equipment	235	3
Total	**8,306**	**100**

Selected Products

Application equipment
Combine Harvesters
Grounds care
Hay and forage
Implements attachments and material handling
Power generation
Seeding and tillage
Tractors

COMPETITORS

Buhler Industries	Komatsu
CNH Industrial	Kubota
Caterpillar	Mahindra
Deere	Toro Company

HISTORICAL FINANCIALS

Company Type: Public

Income Statement				FYE: December 31
	REVENUE ($ mil.)	NET INCOME ($ mil.)	NET PROFIT MARGIN	EMPLOYEES
12/18	9,352	285	3.1%	21,200
12/17	8,306	186	2.2%	20,500
12/16	7,410	160	2.2%	19,800
12/15	7,467	266	3.6%	19,600
12/14	9,723	410	4.2%	20,800
Annual Growth	(1.0%)	(8.7%)	—	0.5%

2018 Year-End Financials

Debt ratio: 19.14%	No. of shares (mil.): 76
Return on equity: 9.58%	Dividends
Cash ($ mil.): 326	Yield: 1.0%
Current ratio: 1.28	Payout: 16.7%
Long-term debt ($ mil.): 1,275	Market value ($ mil.): 4,261

STOCK PRICE ($) FY Close	P/E High/Low	PER SHARE ($) Earnings	Dividends	Book Value
12/18	55.67	20 14	3.58	0.60	38.32
12/17	71.43	32 25	2.32	0.56	38.08
12/16	57.86	31 22	1.96	0.52	34.93
12/15	45.39	19 14	3.06	0.48	33.86
12/14	45.20	13 10	4.36	0.44	38.68
Annual Growth	5.3%	— —	(4.8%)	8.1%	(0.2%)

AGFIRST FARM CREDIT BANK

The expenses involved in equipping and operating a farm add up quickly which is where AgFirst Farm Credit Bank comes in. AgFirst is one of a half-dozen members of the Farm Credit System a federally chartered network of agricultural and rural lending cooperatives. Boasting $30 billion in assets the bank provides financing to 19 farmer-owned agricultural credit associations. The associations in turn offer mortgages and loans to some 80000 farmers agribusinesses and rural home-owners through 280 branches in 15 eastern states and Puerto Rico. They also offer crop insurance credit-related life insurance and financial planning services. Instead of accepting deposits AgFirst raises money by selling bonds and notes on the capital markets.

Operations

AgFirst's capital markets arm arranges participates in and sells loan syndications for agribusinesses. Its correspondent lending unit buys sells and services agricultural and rural home loans throughout the US. About 68% of the bank's loan portfolio consisted of direct notes in 2014 while purchased participations/syndications made up another 19% of loan assets. The rest of the portfolio consisted of correspondent lending (12%) and loans to OFIs (less than 1%).

The bank makes almost all of its money from interest income. About 79% of its total revenue came from loan interest in 2014 with another 18% of revenue coming from interest on investment securities and other assets. The remainder of its revenue mostly came from loan fees.

Geographic Reach

Columbia South Carolina-based AgFirst serves 15 eastern US states and Puerto Rico. Its largest markets are in Florida North Carolina Georgia Virginia and Pennsylvania. The bank is also active in Alabama Delaware the District of Columbia Kentucky Louisiana Maryland Mississippi Ohio South Carolina Tennessee West Virginia and Puerto Rico.

Financial Performance

AgFirst Farm Credit Bank has struggled to grow its annual revenues and profits over the past several years as its loan assets have not increased and as interest margins continue to be squeezed in the low-interest environment.

The bank's revenue fell 7% to $703.8 million during 2014 as its loan assets barely grew to $20.9 billion or about the same levels as they've been since 2010.

Revenue declines in 2014 coupled with a rise in insurance fund premiums and salaries caused Ag-First's net income to shrink 17% to $380.3 million for the year. The bank's operating cash levels fell sharply to $370.9 million on lower cash earnings and unfavorable working capital changes mostly related to changes in accounts receivables balances.

Strategy

AgFirst has focused on maintaining strong personal relationships with its local customer base. It's also been investing more in security-based IT investments to protect its customers from security breaches. In 2015 it built a modern Data Center to accommodate the bank's growth with 1 Petabyte of data.

Company Background

The Farm Credit System was established by Congress in 1916 to provide a reliable source of credit for US farmers and ranchers.

EXECUTIVES

Ceo, Leon T. (Timmy) Amerson
Svp And Cfo, Charl L. Butler
Svp And Cio, Benjamin F. Blakewood
Senior Vice President, David Bridges
Vice President Executive Account Manager, Michael Mancini
Vice President Capital Markets, Neda Beal
Vice President Technology Information Technology, Tony Stone
Vice President Chief Audit Officer, William Beckham
Executive Vice President, Larry Doyle
Vice President Corporate Services, Maribeth Corbett
Vice President Operations, James Camp
Vice President, Steven Oshea
Vice President Of Investments And Funding, Richard Wilkins
Vice Chairman, Dale R. Hershey
Chairman, Robert H. Spiers
Board Member, Robert Holden
Auditors: PRICEWATERHOUSECOOPERS LLP MI

LOCATIONS

HQ: AGFIRST FARM CREDIT BANK
  1901 MAIN ST, COLUMBIA, SC 292012443
Phone: 803 799-5000
Web: WWW.AGFIRST.COM

PRODUCTS/OPERATIONS

2014 Sales

	$ mil.	% of total
Interest		
Loans	566	79
Investment securities & other	127	18
Non-interest		
Loan fees	8	2
Building lease income	3	—
Net other-than-temporary impairment losses	(1.4)	—
Gains (losses) on called debt	(7.7)	—
Gains (losses) on investments net	0	—
Gains (losses) on other transactions	0	—
Other	7	1
Total	703	100

COMPETITORS

AgriBank	Farm Family Holdings
Bank of America	First National of
COUNTRY Financial	Nebraska
Cat Financial	Rabo AgriFinance

HISTORICAL FINANCIALS

Company Type: Private

Income Statement

FYE: December 31

	ASSETS ($ mil.)	NET INCOME ($ mil.)	INCOME AS % OF ASSETS	EMPLOYEES
12/17	32,487	344	1.1%	530
12/15	30,620	336	1.1%	—
Annual Growth	3.0%	1.2%	—	—

Agilent Technologies, Inc.

EXECUTIVES

Ceo-Pres, Michael R McMullen
Sr V Pres-Cfo, Robert W McMahon
Sr V Pres Hr, Dominique P Grau
Sr V Pres-General Counsel-Sec, Michael Tang
V Pres-Cao-Corp Contrl, Rodney Gonsalves
Technical Marketing Manager, Tonya Baran
Svp-Pres Order Fulfillment, Henrik Ancher-Jensen
Svp, Mark Doak
Svp, Samraat S Raha
Svp, Jacob Thaysen
Program Manager, Bill Flickinger
Auditors: PricewaterhouseCoopers LLP

LOCATIONS

HQ: Agilent Technologies, Inc.
  5301 Stevens Creek Blvd., Santa Clara, CA 95051
Phone: 800 227-9770   **Fax:** 408 345-8474
Web: www.agilent.com

COMPETITORS

AMETEK	Life Technologies
AWR	Corporation
Abbott Labs	National Instruments
Advantest	PerkinElmer
Aeroflex	Rohde & Schwarz
Affymetrix	Shimadzu
Anritsu	Spirent
Ansoft	Tektronix
Applied Materials	Teledyne LeCroy
Beckman Coulter	Teradyne
Bio-Rad Labs	Thermo Fisher
Bruker	Scientific
Danaher	Ventana Medical
Fluke Corporation	W. R. Grace
GE Healthcare	Waters Corp.
HEIDENHAIN Corp.	Yokogawa Electric
IBM Software	Zygo
Illumina	telent

HISTORICAL FINANCIALS

Company Type: Public

Income Statement

FYE: October 31

	REVENUE ($ mil.)	NET INCOME ($ mil.)	NET PROFIT MARGIN	EMPLOYEES
10/19	5,163	1,071	20.7%	5,400
10/18	4,914	316	6.4%	5,100
10/17	4,472	684	15.3%	13,500
10/16	4,202	462	11.0%	12,500
10/15	4,038	401	9.9%	11,800
Annual Growth	6.3%	27.8%	—	(17.8%)

2019 Year-End Financials

Debt ratio: 25.47%	No. of shares (mil.): 309
Return on equity: 23.00%	Dividends
Cash ($ mil.): 1,382	Yield: 0.8%
Current ratio: 1.53	Payout: 19.6%
Long-term debt ($ mil.): 1,791	Market value ($ mil.): 23,412

STOCK PRICE ($) FY Close	P/E High/Low	PER SHARE ($) Earnings	Dividends	Book Value
10/19	75.75	24 18	3.37	0.66	15.36
10/18	64.79	76 62	0.97	0.60	14.37
10/17	68.03	32 20	2.10	0.53	15.00
10/16	43.57	34 25	1.40	0.46	13.12
10/15	37.76	46 28	1.20	0.40	12.57
Annual Growth	19.0%	— —	29.5%	13.2%	5.1%

AGNC Investment Corp

AGNC Investment (formerly American Capital Agency) is taking on the rocky real estate market. The real estate investment trust (REIT) was created in 2008 to invest in securities backed by single-family residential mortgages and collateralized mortgage obligations guaranteed by government agencies Fannie Mae Freddie Mac and Ginnie Mae. The Maryland-based REIT is externally managed and advised by American Capital AGNC Management a subsidiary of US publicly traded alternative asset manager American Capital which spun off American Capital Agency in 2008 but retained about a 33% stake in the REIT.

Operations

American Capital Agency generates income from investing in leveraged agency mortgage-backed securities (agency MBS) which consist of residential mortgage pass-through securities and collateralized mortgage obligations (CMOs) backed by federal agencies. About 97% of its total revenue came from interest income in 2014 while the remainder came from gains on agency securities sales. It may also collect gains on derivative instruments and other securities.

Its leverage was 5.3 times its stockholders' equity in 2014 (down from 7.3 times in 2013).

Financial Performance

American Capital Agency's revenue and profits had been trending higher over the past few years as the security valuations rose with the strengthening housing market leading to higher interest income.

The REIT's revenues and profits fell steeply in 2014 mostly as it lost $1.24 billion on derivative instruments and other securities (compared to a gain of $1.2 billion in 2013). Additionally its investment portfolio value declined by 29% after shifting its investments from MBS repo funded assets to TBA dollar roll funded assets which led to 33% less interest income.

American Capital Agency's operating cash levels fell by 35% to $1.62 billion in 2014 due to lower cash earnings.

Strategy

Set up as an investment vehicle American Capital Agency's chief goal is to preserve its net asset value (NAV) and generate risk-adjusted returns for shareholders through regular monthly dividends and net realized gains from its investments and hedging activities.

The REIT's investment strategy as it reiterated in 2015 is designed to: manage a portfolio of agency securities and similar assets with attractive risk-adjusted returns; take advantage of undervalued agency securities in the market; manage financing interest rate prepayment and extension risks; preserve its net book value; and continue providing regular monthly distributions to its shareholders as a REIT.

Company Background

American Capital Agency raised some $300 million from its 2008 IPO. The REIT used the proceeds from the offering to build and develop its investment portfolio.

EXECUTIVES

Pres-Cio-Ceo, Gary D Kain
Chb, Prue B Larocca
Exec V Pres-Cfo, Peter J Federico
Sr V Pres-Gen Counsel-Cco-Sec, Kenneth L Pollack
Sr V Pres-Cao, Bernice E Bell
Sr V Pres Agency Portfolio Inv, Christopher J Kuehl
Payroll Staff, Opal Newton
Information Specialist, Ryan Webb
Auditors: Ernst & Young LLP

LOCATIONS

HQ: AGNC Investment Corp
2 Bethesda Metro Center, 12th Floor, Bethesda, MD 20814
Phone: 301 968-9315   **Fax:** 301 968-9301
Web: www.agnc.com

COMPETITORS

ARMOUR Residential REIT	CIFC
Annaly Capital Management	Capstead Mortgage
Anworth Mortgage Asset	Chimera
Bimini Capital Management	Hatteras Financial
	JAVELIN Mortgage
	MFA Financial
	Redwood Trust

HISTORICAL FINANCIALS

Company Type: Public

Income Statement   FYE: December 31

	ASSETS ($ mil.)	NET INCOME ($ mil.)	INCOME AS % OF ASSETS	EMPLOYEES
12/18	109,241	129	0.1%	56
12/17	70,376	771	1.1%	56
12/16	56,880	623	1.1%	54
12/15	57,021	215	0.4%	3
12/14	67,766	(233)	—	—
Annual Growth	12.7%	—	—	—

2018 Year-End Financials

Debt ratio: 0.25%	No. of shares (mil.): 536
Return on equity: 1.38%	Dividends
Cash ($ mil.): 921	Yield: 12.3%
Current ratio: —	Payout: 1,028.5%
Long-term debt ($ mil.): —	Market value ($ mil.): 9,407

	STOCK PRICE ($) FY Close	P/E High/Low		PER SHARE ($) Earnings	Dividends	Book Value
12/18	17.54	95	82	0.21	2.16	18.47
12/17	20.19	11	9	2.04	2.16	22.37
12/16	18.13	11	9	1.79	2.30	22.22
12/15	17.34	41	31	0.54	2.48	23.62
12/14	21.83	—	—	(0.72)	2.61	26.72
Annual Growth	(5.3%)	—	—	—	(4.6%)	(8.8%)

Air Products & Chemicals Inc

Air Products and Chemicals has built a solid business out of gasses and liquids. The company produces and distributes atmospheric process and specialty gases in the US and across the world. It is a leading hydrogen supplier and also provides helium nitrogen argon and carbon dioxide among other gases. Air Products and Chemicals which generates more than half its revenue outside the Americas also provides related equipment and services (air separation hydrocarbon recovery natural gas liquefaction etc.) to customers in the energy electronics chemicals metals and manufacturing industries.

HISTORY

In the early 1900s Leonard Pool the son of a boilermaker began selling oxygen to industrial users. By the time he was 30 he was district manager for Compressed Industrial Gases. In the late 1930s Pool hired engineer Frank Pavlis to help him design a cheaper more efficient oxygen generator. In 1940 they had the design and Pool established Air Products in Detroit (initially sharing space with the cadavers collected by his brother who was starting a mortuary science college). The company was based on a simple breakthrough concept: the provision of on-site gases. Instead of delivering oxygen in cylinders Pool proposed to build oxygen-generating facilities near large-volume gas users and then lease them reducing distribution costs.

Although industrialists encouraged Pool to pursue his ideas few orders were forthcoming and the company faced financial crisis. The outbreak of WWII got the company out of difficulty as the US military became a major customer. During the war the company moved to Chattanooga Tennessee for the available labor.

The end of the war brought with it another downturn as demand dried up. By waiting at the Weirton Steel plant until a contract was signed Pool won a contract for three on-site generators. Weirton was nearly the company's only customer. Pool relocated the company to Allentown Pennsylvania to be closer to the Northeast's industrial market where he could secure more contracts with steel companies.

The Cold War and the launching of the Sputnik satellite in 1957 propelled the company's growth. Convinced that Soviet rockets were powered by liquid hydrogen the US government asked Air Products to supply it with the volatile fuel. The company entered the overseas market that year through a joint venture with Butterley (UK) to which it licensed its cryogenic processes and equipment. The company went public in 1961 and formed a subsidiary in Belgium in 1964.

Air Products diversified into chemicals when it bought Houdry Process (chemicals and chemical-plant maintenance 1962) and Airco's chemicals and plastics operations in the 1970s. The company continued to diversify in the mid-1980s as it built large-scale plants for its environmental- and energy-systems business and added Anchor Chemical and the industrial chemicals unit of Abbott Labs.

In 1995 and 1996 Air Products expanded into China and other countries by winning 20 contracts with semiconductor makers. It bought Carburos Metálicos Spain's #1 industrial gas supplier in 1996. To focus on its core gas and chemical lines the company shed most of its environmental- and energy-systems business.

Expanding further in Europe Air Products bought the methylamines and derivatives unit of UK-based Imperial Chemical Industries (ICI) in 1997. The company sold its remaining interest in American Ref-Fuel (a waste-to-energy US operation).

In 1998 Air Products bought Solkatronic Chemicals and opened a methylamines plant in Florida to complement its ICI purchase. To further target semiconductor makers it formed Air Products Electronic Chemicals and allied with AlliedSignal Chemical (now part of Honeywell International).

The next year Air Products and France's L'Air Liquide agreed to buy and break up BOC Group. European Union regulators initially approved the deal but in 2000 the companies shelved the plan when other regulatory issues arose. Also in 2000 Air Products sold its polyvinyl alcohol business to Celanese for about $326 million. The company boosted its European presence in 2001 with the acquisition of Messer Griesheim's (Germany) respiratory home-care business and 50% of AGA's Netherlands industrial gases operations.

Air Products was hurt by the slowdown in manufacturing primarily in the electronics and steel industries which are major customers for gases. Its chemical revenues also were hurt by pressure on pricing. To improve profits the company initiated cost cuts including job cuts (about 10% of its employees) and divestitures such as its US packaged gas business.

The company broadened its health care operations in late 2002 by acquiring American Homecare Supply. It appeared briefly that Air Products wanted to devote a great deal of attention to the health care business. The company had created its Air Products Healthcare unit in 1999 and expanded it greatly three years later with the acquisition of American Homecare Supply. Air Products proceeded to add to the division through subsequent acquisitions; however the US portion of the business never performed to the company's expectations and Air Products sold the domestic operations of the health care unit in 2008 and 2009.

It also decided to divest its chemicals operations in the latter half of the decade. Those operations included the production of catalysts surfactants and intermediates derived from vinyl acetate monomer (VAM) all of which it sold in 2008. Air Products had sold its amines business to chemical company Taminco in 2006. The company's polymers operations which were run through a joint venture with Wacker-Chemie called Air Products Polymers were divested in 2008. The company sold most of its holdings in the JV to Wacker for $265 million though two facilities that had belonged to the joint venture were sold to Ashland Performance Materials.

In 2007 Air Products made a small but strategic move into Eastern Europe. The company took advantage of Linde's selloff of some BOC assets after the German company bought BOC in 2006. Air Products acquired the Polish Gazy SP for just under $500 million with the hopes of moving into the Central and Eastern European markets to take advantage of the migration of manufacturing to the region.

In 2010 the company made a major bid to buy rival Airgas but it was rejected. The Airgas board considered the $5.1 billion offer too low. Air Products extended its tender offer to Airgas stockholders several times making its "best and final offer" of $70 a share in December 2010. Airgas also rejected that offer.

In late 2012 Air Products opened an advanced gas applications laboratory in Shanghai to support the increasing needs in high-growth markets in China across Asia.

In addition to growing organically the company has been divesting operations to focus on its higher growth operations and to pursue strategic acquisitions. By early 2012 the company began divesting units to focus on more profitable operations. It sold its homecare business in continental Europe (which supplied oxygen and infusion treatments in Belgium France Germany Portugal and Spain) to Germany's Linde for $750 million. The company also began evaluating its homecare assets in Argentina Brazil Ireland and the UK.

With more money in its coffers from divestments in 2012 the company acquired Germany-based ROVI Cosmetics International which develops delivery systems for the personal care industry in Europe. The unit is now part of the company's Performance Materials division. To extend its Latin American footprint Air Products in 2012 acquired a 67% stake in Indura S.A. an industrial gas company in Chile for $884 million.

Expanding its portfolio of industrial gases offerings in North America to include liquid carbon dioxide in 2013 Air Products acquired EPCO Carbon Dioxide Products Inc. a privately-held Louisiana-based producer and marketer of liquid carbon dioxide.

EXECUTIVES

Chairman President And Ceo, Seifi Ghasemi, age 73, $1,200,000 total compensation
Evp Industrial Gases, Corning F. Painter, age 58, $573,077 total compensation
President Industrial Gases Europe And Africa, Ivo Bols
President Industrial Gases Asia, Wilbur W. Mok, age 59
President Industrial Gases Middle East India Egypt And Turkey, Richard Boocock
Svp And Cfo, M. Scott Crocco, age 56, $581,923 total compensation
President Industrial Gases Americas, Marie Ffolkes
Evp Materials Technologies, Guillermo Novo, age 58, $465,000 total compensation
President China Industrial Gases, Choon Seong Saw
Vp And Cio, Alyssa A. Budraitis
President Air Products Korea, Kyo Yung (K Y) Kim
President Air Products San Fu, Eugene Y. C. Lu
President Southeast Asia Industrial Gases, Alex Tan
Vp Corporate Development, Kearney Klein
Svp And Chro, Jennifer Grant
Vice President Chief Audit Executive, Melissa Schaeffer
Auditors: KPMG LLP

LOCATIONS

HQ: Air Products & Chemicals Inc
7201 Hamilton Boulevard, Allentown, PA 18195-1501
Phone: 610 481-4911   **Fax:** 610 481-5900
Web: www.airproducts.com

2018 Sales

	$ mil.	% of total
US	3,149	35
Europe/Middle East	2,292	26
Asia (Excluding China & India)	904	10
China	1,585	18
Other (Canada Latin America India)	998	11
Total	**8,930**	**100**

PRODUCTS/OPERATIONS

2018 Sales

	$ mil.	% of total
Industrial Gases- Americas	3,758	42
Industrial Gases- EMEA	2,193	24
Industrial Gases- Asia	2,458	28
Industrial Gases- Global	436	5
Corporate and other	84	1
Total	**8,930**	**100**

Selected Products and Services

Industrial Gases
  Argon
  Carbon dioxide
  Carbon monoxide
  Helium
  Hydrogen
  Nitrogen
  Oxygen
  Synthesis gas
Equipment and Services
  Air-pollution control systems
  Air-separation equipment
  Hydrogen-purification equipment
  Natural gas-liquefaction equipment

COMPETITORS

Airgas	Messer Group
Iwatani International	Praxair
L'Air Liquide	Taiyo Nippon Sanso
Matheson Tri-Gas	The Linde Group

HISTORICAL FINANCIALS

Company Type: Public

Income Statement

FYE: September 30

	REVENUE ($ mil.)	NET INCOME ($ mil.)	NET PROFIT MARGIN	EMPLOYEES
09/19	8,918	1,760	19.7%	17,700
09/18	8,930	1,497	16.8%	16,300
09/17	8,187	3,000	36.6%	15,300
09/16	9,524	631	6.6%	18,600
09/15	9,894	1,277	12.9%	19,700
Annual Growth	(2.6%)	8.3%	—	(2.6%)

2019 Year-End Financials

Debt ratio: 17.56%
Return on equity: 16.06%
Cash ($ mil.): 2,248
Current ratio: 2.54
Long-term debt ($ mil.): 3,227
No. of shares (mil.): 220
Dividends
  Yield: 2.0%
  Payout: 57.6%
Market value ($ mil.): 48,901

	STOCK PRICE ($) FY Close	P/E High/Low	PER SHARE ($) Earnings	Dividends	Book Value
09/19	221.86	29 19	7.94	4.58	50.15
09/18	167.05	25 22	6.78	5.20	49.46
09/17	151.22	11 10	13.65	3.62	46.19
09/16	150.34	54 40	2.89	3.34	32.57
09/15	127.58	27 20	5.88	3.20	33.66
Annual Growth	14.8%	— —	7.8%	9.4%	10.5%

AIRGAS, INC.

Airgas hopes its industrial customers walk on its air. The US industrial gas distributor's North American network of more than 1100 locations includes retail stores gas fill plants specialty gas labs production facilities (17 air separation plants) and distribution centers. Airgas distributes argon carbon dioxide hydrogen nitrogen oxygen and a variety of medical and specialty gases as well as dry ice and protective equipment (hard hats goggles). Its gases production unit operates air-separation plants that produce oxygen nitrogen and argon. The company also sells welding machines. The company is owned by Air Liquide SA.

Operations

The industrial manufacturing and repair and maintenance industries account for about a quarter each of the Airgas' sales; customers primarily make fabricated metal products industrial transportation and equipment chemical products and primary metal products. Other industries served include medical and health services agriculture mining repair and maintenance and wholesale trade.

Airgas' distribution business accounts for 88% of the company's 2016 sales. Almost all of its sales come from distributing bulk gases (nitrogen oxygen argon helium) gas cylinders and welding equipment. Airgas also produces gases to supply its regional distribution companies. Its other operations consist of six business units that manufacture and/or distribute carbon dioxide dry ice nitrous oxide ammonia and refrigerant gases. Gas and rent represented 61% of the distribution business segment's sales in fiscal 2016; hard goods 39%.

The distribution business operates a network of multiple use facilities consisting of 900 branches 300 cylinder fill plants 70 regional specialty gas laboratories 11 national specialty gas laboratories one research and development center two specialty gas equipment centers 11 acetylene plants and 16 air separation units as well as six national hard-goods distribution centers and various customer call centers buying centers and administrative offices.

Airgas' All Other Operations business segment consists of six operating segments all of which primarily manufacture and/or distribute single gas product lines (carbon dioxide dry ice nitrous oxide ammonia and refrigerant gases along with a nitrogen services business). It has 90 branch/distribution locations eight liquid carbon dioxide and 14 dry ice production facilities and three nitrous oxide production facilities.

Geographic Reach

Operating in all 50 states Airgas is the largest distributor of packaged gases in the US with a 25% market share. Outside the US it conducts operations mostly in Canada but also operates in the UAE Mexico Russia and in parts of Europe. It got less than 2% of its fiscal 2016 (ending in March) revenues from outside the US.

Sales and Marketing

The company serves customers in a range of industries including Manufacturing and Metal Fabrication Non-Residential (Energy and Infrastructure) Construction Life Sciences and Healthcare Food Beverage and Retail Energy and Chemical Production and Distribution Basic Materials and Services. It also has government clients.

Airgas markets its products and services through multiple sales channels including branch-based representatives retail stores telesales strategic customer account programs catalogs e-Business and other distributors.

Manufacturing & Metal Fabrication customers account for 30% of sales while Non-Residential (Energy & Infrastructure) Construction accounts for 15% and Food Beverage & Retail for 13%. Each bringing in more than 10% of sales are its Energy & Chemical Production & Distribution and Basic Materials & Services customers. Government & Other Life and Sciences & Healthcare customers account for the rest.

Strategy

Prior to its 2016 acquisition by global rival Air Liquide Airgas had grown its operations through acquisitions in its core businesses. It has bought more than 500 companies since its founding in 1986 and focuses on high-growth products with strong cross-selling opportunities. In fiscal 2016 it purchased 18 businesses (22 in fiscal 2015) with historical annual sales of $85 million. Airgas also grew through organic expansion.

HISTORY

In the early 1980s Peter McCausland was a corporate attorney involved in mergers and acquisitions for Messer Griesheim a large German industrial gas producer. When the German firm declined McCausland's recommendation in 1982 to buy Connecticut Oxygen he raised money from private sources and bought it himself. He acquired other distributors and then left Messer Griesheim in 1987 to run Airgas full-time.

Airgas began buying mostly small local and regional gas distributors in the US. By 1994 strategy shifted to purchasing larger "superregional" distributors such as Jimmie Jones Co. and Post Welding Supply of Alabama which added about $70 million combined to the company's revenues.

Airgas then began "rolling up" additional similar businesses. In 1995 it bought more than 25 companies and two years later it added more than 20 gas distributors. Also in 1997 Airgas expanded its manufacturing capabilities by building five plants that could fast-fill whole pallets of gas cylinders (the old manual system rolls cylinders two at a time). By 2000 the company had about 100 cylinder fill plants.

Struggling to integrate acquisitions while dealing with softening markets Airgas began a companywide realignment in 1998. To that end it sold its calcium carbide and carbon products operations to former partner Elkem ASA later that year; the company also consolidated 34 hubs into 16 regional companies and sold its operations in Poland and Thailand to Germany-based Linde in 1999.

In 2000 Airgas acquired distributor Mallinckrodt's Puritan-Bennett division (gas products for medical uses) with 36 locations in the US and Canada. The company also acquired the majority of Air Products' US packaged gas business excluding its electronic gases and magnetic resonance imaging-related helium operations in 2002.

In 2004 and 2005 it bought units from giants like Air Products and Chemicals BOC and LaRoche Industries. In 2006 Airgas continued to build with the purchase of 10 businesses including Union Industrial Gas which supplies Texas and much of the Southwest and then Linde's US bulk gas business for $495 million the next year. Linde in the process of integrating its 2006 acquisition of BOC then sold to Airgas a portion of its US packaged gas business for $310 million.

Rival Air Products had made a major bid to buy Airgas in 2010 but was rebuffed. Air Products extended its tender offer to Airgas stockholders several times and made a "best and final offer" of $70 a share (almost $6 billion) in December 2010. Airgas said it was holding out for $78 a share and rejected that offer too. In early 2011 a Delaware judge ruled for Airgas in a suit brought by Air Products to set aside a "poison pill" defense used by the Airgas board to fend off the takeover try. Following the verdict Air Products dropped its bid.

Airgas acquired six businesses in 2010 including Tri-Tech an independent distributor with 16 locations throughout Florida Georgia and South Carolina and annual sales of $31 million.

In 2011 Airgas reorganized its 12 regional segments into four new business support divisions — North South Central and West — to leverage a new SAP information systems platform in 2011. Each of the units is headed by a division president. The new company structure is designed to accelerate sales growth and pricing management and create operating efficiencies.

In fiscal 2012 the company added eight businesses with total annual sales of about $106 million. The largest of the businesses acquired were ABCO Gases Welding and Industrial Supply Company (ABCO); Pain Enterprises; and Industrial Welding Supplies of Hattiesburg (doing business as Nordan Smith). Connecticut-based ABCO has 12 industrial and gas welding supply locations throughout New England. Indiana-based Pain operates 20 dry ice and liquid carbon dioxide production and distribution sites. Mississippi-based Nordan Smith has 17 locations that distribute industrial medical and specialty gases and supplies thoughout Alabama Arkansas and Mississippi.

In 2013 Airgas retained Chicago-based Acquity Group as a key partner in helping the company continue to provide new online digital customer platforms. As one of the leading digital marketing companies the Acquity Group will provide its e-channel expertise in leading the design and implementation of Airgas' new content-rich website.

In 2013 Airgas acquired two US-based industrial gas and welding supply distributors that complement the Airgas portfolio of products and services. Combined annual revenues for the two acquired businesses are more than $30 million.

In fiscal 2013 the company also acquired Illinois-based The Encompass Gas Group (one of the largest privately-owned suppliers of industrial medical and specialty gases and related hardgoods in the US) with about $55 million in annual revenues in 2012.

EXECUTIVES

Coo, Andrew R. (Andy) Cichocki, $296,936 total compensation
President Airgas North Division, Pamela J. (Pam) Claypool
Vice President Construction, John Appolonia
Svp Sales And Marketing, Ronald J. (Ron) Stark
Svp And Cio, Robert A. Dougherty, $263,779 total compensation
President Airgas South, John F. Sheehan
Svp And Cfo, Robert M. (Bob) McLaughlin, $470,453 total compensation
Division President Gases Production, Thomas S. Thoman
Division President West, Douglas L. (Doug) Jones
Svp And General Counsel, Robert H. Young, $397,272 total compensation
Division President Central, Terry L. Lodge
President East Region, Jack Appolonia
Ceo, Pascal Vinet
Vice President Area Sales, Ross Jones
Vice President Of Information Technology Airgas Mid South, George Turner
Vice President Central Division, Don Berndsen
Vice President Safety And Compliance, Jim McCarthy
Vice President Business Development, Bruce Woerner
Regional Vice President Healthcare, Linda Wissink
Vice President, James Cook
Regional Vice President Of Finance, Jana Bittinger
National Sales Manager, Jerry Anderskow
Vice President Finance, Monica Garza
Vice President Of Plant Operations, Roger Weber
Vice President Of Bulk Operations, Steve Scheuring
Vice President Construction Markets, Jason Vetterick
Vice President Of Finance, Jennifer Mihaljcic
Vice President Of Finance, Michael Maley
Vice President Strategic Accounts, Otto Gaus
Area Vice President, Jeff Mann
Assistant Vice President, Brian Blackwood
Vice President Operations, Tom Mulqueen
Assistant Vice President Corporate Development, Brian Shammo
Vice President Hardgoods, David Levin
Regional Vice President Usa East, Adam Needles
Vice President, Chris Brazell
Division Vice President Of Sales, Mark Johnston
Vice President, Wayne Wilson
National Account Manager, Don Wallenfelsz
Area Vice President, Gene Klein
Area Vice President, Ron Weber
Vice President Internal Audit, E Coyne
National Account Manager, Earl Dyck
Vice President Of Sales, Marcelo Feistauer
Vice President Gulf Coast Region, Scott Koonce
Vice President Area, Luke Aass
Vice President Bulk Sales And Operations, Thomas Archie
Vice President Credit And Collections, Ed Burke
National Account Manager, Thomas White
Area Vice President, Beth Medford
National Account Manager, Daniel Christenson
Vice President Total Access, Kerrie Sodano
Vice President Bulk Sales And Operations, Richard Cassano
Vp Manufacturing, Jill Barth
Area Vice President, Brad Kahn
Vice President Of Food And Beverage, Bill Baker
Vice President Of Safety And Compliance, Chris Herbert
Division Vice President Human Resources, Stamy Paul
Vp Safety And Compliance, Curtis Henson
Chairman, Pierre Dufour
Vice Chairman, Michael J. (Mike) Graff
Auditors: KPMG LLP PHILADELPHIA PENNSY

HQ: AIRGAS, INC.
259 N RADNOR CHESTER RD # 100, RADNOR, PA
190875240
Phone: 610 687-5253
Web: WWW.AIRGAS.COM

PRODUCTS/OPERATIONS

2016 sales

	% of total
Manufacturing & Metal Fabrication	29
Non Residential (Energy & Infrastructure) construction	15
Life Science & Healthcare	14
Food Beverage & Retail	13
Energy & Chemical Production & Distribution	12
Basic Material & Services	11
Government & Others	6
Total	**100**

2016 sales

	$ mil.	% of total
Distribution	4,716	88
Other Operations	635	12
Adjustments	(38.2)	-
Total	**5,313**	**100**

Selected Products and Services

Products
 Carbon dioxide
 Dry ice
 Industrial gases
 Argon
 Helium
 Hydrogen
 Liquid oxygen
 Nitrogen
 Nitrous oxide
 Oxygen
 Safety equipment
 Specialty gases

Services

 Container rental
 Welding equipment rental

Selected Subsidiaries

Airgas Canada
Airgas Carbonic
Airgas East
Airgas Great Lakes
Airgas Intermountain
Airgas Medical Services
Airgas Mid America
Airgas Mid South
Airgas Nitrous Oxide
Airgas Nor Pac
Airgas North Central
Airgas Northern California & Nevada
Airgas Refrigerant
Airgas Safety
Airgas South
Airgas Southwest
Airgas Specialty Gases
Airgas Specialty Products
Airgas West
National Welders Supply Company dba Airgas National
 Welders
Nitrous Oxide Corp.
Red-D-Arc
WorldWide Welding LLC

COMPETITORS

Air Products	Praxair Distribution
Lincoln Electric	Valley National Gases
Matheson Tri-Gas	W.W. Grainger

HISTORICAL FINANCIALS

Company Type: Private

Income Statement   FYE: March 31

	REVENUE ($ mil.)	NET INCOME ($ mil.)	NET PROFIT MARGIN	EMPLOYEES
03/15	5,304	368	6.9%	17,070
03/13	4,957	340	6.9%	—
Annual Growth	3.4%	3.9%	—	—

AK Steel Holding Corp.

Automobile sales help AK Steel's business keep rolling though it also has operations in the infrastructure and manufacturing industries. The company manufactures carbon stainless and electrical steel. It sells hot- and cold-rolled carbon steel to construction companies steel distributors and service centers and automotive and industrial machinery producers. AK Steel also sells cold-rolled and aluminum-coated stainless steel to automakers. The company produces electrical steels (iron-silicon alloys with unique magnetic properties) for makers of power transmission and distribution equipment.

Operations

AK Steel operates on a consolidated integrated basis in order to use the most appropriate equipment and facilities for the production of each product. The company's carbon products account for about two-thirds of revenue followed by stainless and electrical products about 30% and tubular the remainder.

Its major subsidiaries include AK Tube LLC AK Coal Resources Inc and Magnetation LLC. AK Tube produces carbon and stainless electric resistance welded tubular steel products for truck automotive and other markets.

It produces flat-rolled value-added carbon steels including premium-quality coated cold-rolled and hot-rolled carbon steel products and specialty stainless and electrical steels that are sold in sheet and strip form as well as carbon and stainless steel that is finished into welded steel tubing.

It also works through joint ventures to share costs. Its Magnetation LLC joint venture with Magnetation Inc. uses advanced magnetic separation technology to recover iron ore from existing stockpiles of previously-mined material.

In addition AK Steel indirectly owns 50% of Vicksmetal/Armco Associates a joint venture with Sumitomo unit Vicksmetal Company. The joint venture slits electrical steel primarily for AK Steel and for third parties.

Geographic Reach

AK Steel is based in West Chester Ohio and operates eight steel plants two coke plants three tube manufacturing plants and eight tooling and stamping operations across the US Canada and Mexico. The company also operates subsidiaries in the UK the Netherlands Italy France Germany and other countries. US is the largest market accounting for about 90% of revenue.

Sales and Marketing

AK Steel sells a major portion of its flat-rolled carbon steel products and stainless steel products to US automotive manufacturers and to distributors service centers and converters. It sells electrical steel products (in the US and globally) to manufacturers of power transmission and distribution

transformers and electrical motors and generators to the infrastructure and manufacturing customers.

The automotive industry accounted for about two-thirds of the company's sales with Ford and Fiat Chrysler among its biggest customers. Other major markets are distributors and converters about 20% and infrastructure and manufacturing about 15%.

AK Steel ships about 70% of its flat-rolled steel products to contract customers with the balance to customers in the spot market at prevailing prices at the time of sale.

Financial Performance

In the last decade AK Steel's revenue reduced from a peak of $7.6 billion in 2008 to $5.6 billion in 2013 before climbing back up unstably to hover around the $6 billion mark. Despite stable revenue however the company is hardly profitable posting more than $2 billion in losses in the last eight years.

Net sales increased 3% to $6 billion primarily due to a 7% hike in average selling price per flat-rolled steel ton stemming from higher automotive and carbon spot market sales as well as surcharge revenue.

Net income was positive for the first time in eight years posting just $6 million in profits compared to $8 million in losses from the year prior primarily due to a $80 million positive change year-over-year in credit for termination of pellet agreements followed by a $20 million income tax benefit compared to prior year.

Cash holdings reduced from $173 million in the beginning of the year to $38 million. Operations generated close to $200 million and financing activities around $175 million mostly in issuance of long-term debt. But it was more than offset by investment activities which took away close to $510 million mostly in new acquisitions.

Strategy

The steel industry has been consolidating for years as market leaders snap up troubled companies. AK Steel has maintained its independence in part because of it's a leading supplier of high-grade niche products such as components of stainless steel exhaust systems for carmakers.

The company's 2017 purchase of Precision Partners Holding Co. for about $360 million gets it deeper into automotive market. Based in Canada Precision supplies auto parts that meet the industry's requirements for lighter vehicles. It has eight plants in Ontario Kentucky and Alabama. Precision specializes in the design and engineering of tooling and die making and the stamping of complex hard-to-manufacture automotive components.

In 2016 AK Steel took several actions financially that strengthened its balance sheet and provided room to maneuver financially in investing in research and development as well as acquisitions. The company moved in to its new Research and Innovation Center in Middletown Ohio in 2016. The facility includes pilot lines and operational simulators for developing new products and services.

The company also pulled away from selling steel on the spot market where prices are volatile and have low margins.

Mergers and Acquisitions

AK Steel bought Precision Partners Holding Co. for about $360 million in 2017 to move deeper into supplying steel to the automotive industry.

HISTORY

George Verity who was in the roofing business in Cincinnati around the turn of the century often had trouble getting sheet metal so in 1900 he founded his own steel company American Rolling Mill. His first plant in Middletown Ohio was followed by a second production facility 11 years later in Ashland Kentucky. Plant superintendent

John Tytus whose family was in paper milling applied those rolling techniques to make American Rolling Mill's steel more uniform in thickness. In 1926 Columbia Steel developed a process to overcome several production problems inherent in the Tytus method and in 1930 American Rolling Mill bought Columbia Steel. The company changed its name to Armco Steel in 1948.

Armco began diversifying in the 1950s and continued diversifying until the early 1980s. Subsidiaries were involved in coal oil and gas-drilling equipment and insurance and financial services among other things. In 1978 the company changed its name to Armco Inc.

Armco began shedding subsidiaries in the early 1980s. Sales and market share increased as the company approached the billion-dollar mark at the end of the decade. In 1989 Armco formed Armco Steel Company with Japan's Kawasaki Steel Corporation.

The company's sales reached $1.3 billion in 1991 though the high operating expenses in the steel industry of the 1990s kept profits low. Armco began looking outside the company for help and in 1992 it persuaded retired steel executive Tom Graham to head the company. Graham brought with him another industry veteran Richard Wardrop who would succeed Graham as CEO in 1995. After evaluating the company's holdings the two divested more than 10 subsidiaries and divisions. Armco also worked on improving quality and customer service with special emphasis placed on timely delivery.

In 1994 Armco's limited partnership with Kawasaki was altered and AK Steel Holding Corporation was formed with AK Steel Corporation as its main subsidiary and the Middletown and Ashland plants as its production base. The holding company went public the same year raising more than $650 million enabling the company to pay off its debt.

AK Steel Holding moved its headquarters to Middletown Ohio in 1995. Despite many naysayers Graham then pushed a plan to build a state-of-the-art $1.1 billion steel production facility. Many doubted the wisdom of going into long-term debt so soon after coming out of the hole — especially when a similar facility had produced lackluster results for Inland Steel. Graham stuck by his plant and in 1997 ground was broken on the facility in Spencer County near Rockport Indiana (Rockport Works). Graham retired that year and Wardrop took over as chairman.

In 1998 the company opened its Rockport Works cold-rolling mill and began operating a hot-dip galvanizing and galvannealing line. The next year AK Steel bought former parent Armco for $842 million. AK Steel acquired welded steel tubing maker Alpha Tube Corporation (renamed AK Tube LLC) in 2001. In late 2001 the company took a charge of $194 million for losses in its pension fund which had been battered by a weak stock market and lowered interest rates.

AK Steel sold its Sawhill Tubular Division to John Maneely Company (Collingswood NJ) for roughly $50 million in 2002.

AK Steel offered to purchase National Steel which was operating under Chapter 11 bankruptcy protection. However AK Steel's bid was trumped in 2003 by one from U.S. Steel that included a ratified labor agreement with the United Steelworkers of America. AK Steel also lost out in an effort to acquire Rouge Industries (later Severstal North America).

Chairman and CEO Wardrop and president John Hritz left their posts in September 2003. CFO James Wainscott was named president and CEO and Robert Jenkins became chairman. (Wainscott succeeded Jenkins as chairman in January 2006.)

In an effort to reduce its debt AK Steel in 2004 sold its Douglas Dynamics unit a maker of snow and ice removal equipment for $260 million and its Greens Port Industrial Park a 600-acre development in Houston for $75 million.

In 2007 the company moved its corporate headquarters to West Chester Ohio.

EXECUTIVES

Vp Finance And Cfo, Jaime Vasquez, age 58
Ceo, Roger K. Newport, age 54, $579,551 total compensation
President And Coo, Kirk W. Reich, age 51, $479,551 total compensation
Vp Engineering Raw Materials And Energy, Maurice A. Reed, age 56
Executive Vice President Of Information Technology, Steve Boston
Vp Hr, Stephanie Bisselberg
Director, James A. Thomson, age 75
Auditors: Ernst & Young LLP

LOCATIONS

HQ: AK Steel Holding Corp.
9227 Centre Pointe Drive, West Chester, OH 45069
Phone: 513 425-5000   **Fax:** 513 425-5220
Web: www.aksteel.com

2016 Sales

	$ mil.	% of total
United States	5,226	89
Foreign countries	655	11
Total	**5,882**	**100**

PRODUCTS/OPERATIONS

2016 Sales (by Market)

	% of total
Automotive	66
Distributors & converters	18
Infrastructure & manufacturing	16
Total	**100**

2016 Sales (by product)

	$ mil.	% of total
Carbon steel	4,014	68
Stainless & electrical steel	1,654	29
Tubular steel	193	3
Other	20	0
Total	**5,882**	**100**

Carbon Steels

Carbon Steels
Alumized
Coil coated products
Cold rolled
Electrogalvanized
Enameling products
Hot dip galvanized
Hot dip galvannealed
Hot rolled
Ultalume®;
Stainless Steels
Austentic
Duplex Alloy
Ferritic
Martensitic
Precipitation hardening
Electrical Steels
Nonoriented
Oriented
TRAN-COR®; H
Antimicrobial Coated Steels

COMPETITORS

ArcelorMittal USA	Steel Dynamics
Dofasco	Union Electric Steel
Feralloy	United States Steel
Kobe Steel USA	Worthington Industries
Nucor	

HISTORICAL FINANCIALS

Company Type: Public

Income Statement				FYE: December 31
	REVENUE ($ mil.)	NET INCOME ($ mil.)	NET PROFIT MARGIN	EMPLOYEES
12/18	6,818	186	2.7%	9,500
12/17	6,080	6	0.1%	9,200
12/16	5,882	(7)	—	8,500
12/15	6,692	(509)	—	8,500
12/14	6,505	(96)	—	8,000
Annual Growth	**1.2%**	**—**		**4.4%**

2018 Year-End Financials

Debt ratio: 44.15%
Return on equity: ***,***,**%
Cash ($ mil.): 48
Current ratio: 1.95
Long-term debt ($ mil.): 1,993

No. of shares (mil.): 315
Dividends
　Yield: —
　Payout: —
Market value ($ mil.): 710

	STOCK PRICE ($) FY Close	P/E High/Low		PER SHARE ($) Earnings	Dividends	Book Value
12/18	2.25	11	4	0.59	0.00	0.32
12/17	5.66	556	207	0.02	0.00	(0.69)
12/16	10.21	—	—	(0.03)	0.00	(0.87)
12/15	2.24	—	—	(2.86)	0.00	(5.50)
12/14	5.94	—	—	(0.65)	0.00	(2.78)
Annual Growth	**(21.5%)**			**—**	**—**	**—**

Alabama Power Co

Alabama Power sure powers much of Alabama. In continuous existence since 1906 this wholly-owned subsidiary of the Southern Company is a vertically integrated utility that provides electric service to retail and wholesale customers in Alabama and to wholesale customers in the Southeast region. Owning coal reserves near Plant Gorgas it boasts an annual production capacity of 6.2 million KWs of fossil steam from six generation stations as well as 1.7 million KWs each of nuclear steam and hydroelectric generation capacity. The company also markets and sells electric appliances and outdoor lighting services.

Geographic Reach

Alabama Power sells electricity and services to approximately 400 cities and towns including Anniston Birmingham Gadsden Mobile Montgomery and Tuscaloosa as well as in rural areas. It also sells electricity wholesale to 14 municipally-owned electric distribution systems.

Financial Performance

Revenue of Alabama Power went up by $150 million in 2017 to just over $6 billion. Most of that gain from rates and pricing hikes in retail and affiliate wholesale revenue increases of 40% due to higher natural gas prices. However the company has limited growth potential in the near term due to the lack of scope for customer growth and fluctuating revenue due to weaker demand stemming from warmer winters.

Profits went up just over 3% to $848 million due to an increase in higher rates charged to customers in 2017 in addition to refunds gained from 2016 partially offset by a decrease in retail revenues due to milder weather and slightly lower customer usage.

Cash holdings went up to $544 million. Operations provided $1.8 billion which was more than offset by investments of $1.9 billion mostly in property additions. However financing contributed $163 million keeping cash holdings in the positive.

Company Background
In 2011 Alabama Power completed a six-year $1.7 billion clean air project that called for the installation of scrubbers (air pollution control devices) at all seven of its largest coal fired plants in Alabama. By 2010 six scrubbers were in operation at four power plants in Jefferson Shelby Walker and Mobile counties.

In 2009 Alabama Power began exploring the possibility of generating power by burning wood and other renewable fuels at one of its coal-fired plants in response to government regulations calling for lower carbon emissions. In 2010 the company teamed up with The Westervelt Company agreeing to buy biomass-fuel (waste wood material) from the timber company.

EXECUTIVES

Vice President Corporate Secretary And Assistant Treasurer, William Zales
Evp Customer Services, Greg Barker
Chairman President And Ceo, Mark Crosswhite
Vice President, Richard Hutto
Vice President, Michael Saxon
Vice President, William Bowers
Vp Production, Jim Heilbron
Vice President Marketing, Tony Smoke
Vice President Birmingham Division, Bobbie Knight
Executive Vice President, Steve Spencer
Vice President Employee Relations And Associate General Counsel, Chris Miller
Vice President, Patrick Murphy
Vice President Of Governmental Relations, Quentin Riggins
Vice President, Ronald Smith
Vice President, Mark Crews
Vice President, Vickie Thrasher
Vice President Governmental Affairs, Alexia Borden
Auditors: DELOITTE & TOUCHE LLP

LOCATIONS

HQ: Alabama Power Co
600 North, 18th Street, Birmingham, AL 35203
Phone: 205 257-1000
Web: www.alapower.com

PRODUCTS/OPERATIONS

2016 Sales

	$ mil.	% of total
Retail		
Residential	2,322	39
Commercial	1,627	27
Industrial	1,416	24
Other retail	(43)	.
Wholesale	352	6
Other	215	4
Total	**5,889**	**100**

COMPETITORS

AEP	Entergy
AES	Ferrellgas Partners
Alagasco	NextEra Energy
Duke Energy	Sempra Energy

Company Type: Public

Income Statement   FYE: December 31

	REVENUE ($ mil.)	NET INCOME ($ mil.)	NET PROFIT MARGIN	EMPLOYEES
12/18	6,032	945	15.7%	6,650
12/17	6,039	866	14.3%	6,613
12/16	5,889	839	14.2%	6,805
12/15	5,768	811	14.1%	6,986
12/14	5,942	800	13.5%	6,935
Annual Growth	0.4%	4.3%	—	(1.0%)

2018 Year-End Financials

Debt ratio: 30.39%	No. of shares (mil.): 30
Return on equity: 12.69%	Dividends
Cash ($ mil.): 313	Yield: 5.2%
Current ratio: 0.97	Payout: 86.1%
Long-term debt ($ mil.): 7,923	Market value ($ mil.): 725

	STOCK PRICE ($) FY Close	P/E High/Low		Earnings	PER SHARE ($) Dividends	Book Value
12/18	23.74	—	—	(0.00)	1.25	254.38
12/17	26.58	—	—	(0.00)	0.39	233.16
Annual Growth	(2.8%)	—	—	—	33.6%	2.2%

Alaska Air Group, Inc.

The fifth-largest airline in the US Alaska Air Group ferries more than 46 million passengers each year to nearly 120 destinations through its two carrier brands Alaska Airlines and Horizon Air. It completes an average of 1200 flights per day from the US Canada and Mexico. The group's primary hub is Seattle (accounting for around three-quarters of passengers) but it also flies out of key markets such as Portland Oregon; Los Angeles; and Anchorage Alaska. Alaska Airlines' fleet comprises about 160 Boeing 737 and about 40 Bombardier Q400 turboprops. Alaska Air Group expanded in 2016 with the acquisition of Virgin America and wasted no time integrating the company and eliminating the Virgin America brand.

Operations
Alaska Air comprises three reportable segments Mainline Regional and Horizon.

The Mainline segment accounts for some 80% of Alaska Air's sales and offers long-haul flights from the western US particularly Seattle Portland and the Bay Area throughout the US Canada Mexico and Costa Rica on its 162 Boeing 737s and 71 Airbus A320s. It also includes cargo services mainly to and within Alaska.

Alaska Air's Regional business consists of shorter-haul flights operated by Horizon SkyWest and PenAir (collectively Air Group) which together carry around 10 million passengers annually in Washington Oregon Idaho and California. Horizon's fleet which carries some 70% of Air Group's regional passengers comprises 26 E175 jets and 39 Bombardier Q400 turboprops. The Regional segment generates 15% of Alaska Air's sales.

The Horizon segment brings in the remaining 5% or so of sales. It consists of capacity sold to Alaska under capacity purchase agreements.

Geographic Reach
Alaska Air Group serves nearly 120 destinations through an expansive network in Alaska the contiguous 48 states Hawaii Canada Costa Rica and Mexico. The company leases operations training

and aircraft maintenance facilities in Portland and Spokane as well as line maintenance stations in Boise Bellingham Eugene San Jose Medford Redmond Seattle and Spokane. It also leases call center facilities in Phoenix and Boise.

Sales and Marketing
Alaska Air's airline tickets are distributed through the airline's website and through traditional and online travel agencies. The travel agencies use global distribution systems to obtain fare and inventory data from airlines and reservation call centers located in Phoenix; Kent Washington; and Boise Idaho.

As its name implies Alaska Air Group transports more passengers between Alaska and the US mainland than any other airline. Besides its own flights the passenger segment provides passenger service through contracts with SkyWest Airlines and Peninsula Airways.

Financial Performance
Alaska Air's revenue has achieved lift-off in recent years as the Virgin America acquisition took sales to new heights.

In 2018 the company's sales grew 5% to $8.3 billion as network expansion and aircraft additions expanded Mainline capacity by 5% helping Alaska Air grow passenger numbers by 1.8 million. The Regional business took delivery of 25 new E175s growing capacity by 20%.

Net income fell sharply in 2018 down 54% to $437 million as increases in oil prices had a knock-on effect on Alaska Air's fuel costs to the tune of roughly $500 million. Wages and benefits also grew substantially due to a 7% increase in full-time employees a result of general business growth and certain ground-handling positions being taken in-house.

Alaska Air's cash on hand fell $83 million during 2018 ending the year at $114 million. The company's operations generated $1.2 billion while its investing activities used $631 million and its financing activities used $647 million. Alaska Air's main cash uses were aircraft and other flight equipment purchases capital expenditures net payments of long-term debt and dividends.

Strategy
After the milestone acquisition of Virgin America in 2016 Alaska Air wasted no time integrating the company its operations and discontinuing the Virgin America name. Airline mergers typically take years to complete due to the messy nature of integrating booking maintenance and dispatch systems combining labor unions training cabin crew and repainting and retrofitting jets. But Alaska had Virgin America more or less fully integrated by the start of 2019.

To bring the acquired Virgin America jets (all Airbuses compared to Alaska's previously all-Boeing fleet) in line with its flight strategy Alaska added more first class seats fitted seats with tablet holders and power outlets enabled satellite WiFi and introduced an extra-legroom section.

HISTORY

Pilot Mac McGee started McGee Airways in 1932 to fly cargo between Anchorage and Bristol Bay Alaska. He joined other local operators in 1937 to form Star Air Lines which began airmail service between Fairbanks and Bethel in 1938. In 1944 a year after buying three small airlines Star adopted the name Alaska Airlines.

The company expanded to include freight service to Africa and Australia in 1950. This expansion coupled with the seasonal nature of the airline's business caused losses in the early 1970s. Developer Bruce Kennedy gained control of the board turning the firm around by the end of 1973. But the Civil Aeronautics Board forced the carrier to drop service to northwestern Alaska in 1975 and by 1978 it served only 10 Alaskan cities and Seattle.

Kennedy became CEO the next year. The 1978 Airline Deregulation Act allowed Alaska Air to move into new areas as well as regain the routes it had lost. By 1982 it was the largest airline flying between Alaska and the lower 48 states.

In 1985 the airline reorganized forming Alaska Air Group as its holding company. The next year Alaska Air Group bought Jet America Airlines (expanding its routes eastward to Chicago St. Louis and Dallas) and Seattle-based Horizon Air Industries (which served 30 Northwest cities). When competition in the East and Midwest cut profits in 1987 Kennedy shut down Jet America to focus on West Coast operations.

To counterbalance summer traffic to Alaska the airline began service to two Mexican resorts in 1988. Fuel prices and sluggish traffic hurt 1990 earnings but Alaska Air Group stayed in the black unlike many other carriers. Kennedy retired as chairman and CEO in 1991.

That year the airline began service to Canada and seasonal flights to two Russian cities. Neil Bergt's MarkAir airline declared war cutting fares and horning in on Alaska Air Group's territory. Alaska Air Group's profits were slashed and MarkAir went into bankruptcy.

Alaska Air extended Russian flights to year-round in 1994. The airline began service to Vancouver in 1996. That year it became the first major US carrier to use the GPS satellite navigation system. In 1997 it added service to more than a dozen new cities but halted service to Russia because of that country's economic woes in 1998.

Alaska Air Group and Dutch airline KLM agreed to a marketing alliance in 1998 that included reciprocal frequent-flier programs and code-sharing and in 1999 it added code-sharing agreements with several major airlines including American and Continental. Alaska Airlines developed an online check-in system a first among US carriers.

In 2000 an Alaska Airlines MD-83 crashed into the Pacific Ocean near Los Angeles killing all 88 people on board. A federal investigation of Alaska Airlines' maintenance practices found deficiencies but the FAA eventually accepted the airline's plan to tighten safety standards.

Like most carriers in the latter part of 2001 Alaska Airlines cut back its flights as a result of reduced demand after the September 11 terrorist attacks. As demand slowly returned in 2002 Alaska Airlines began to add new destinations and increase the number of flights on some established routes.

In its biggest deal ever Alaska Air Group in late 2016 acquired Virgin America for $2.6 billion.

EXECUTIVES

Vice President Information And Technology Alaska Airlines, Kris Kutchera
Chairman President And Ceo Alaska Air Group Inc. Chairman And Ceo Alaska Airlines Inc. And Chairman Virgin America And Horizon Air Industries Inc., Bradley D. (Brad) Tilden, age 58, $487,600 total compensation
President And Ceo Horizon Air Industries Inc., Gary L. Beck
Svp Communications And External Affairs, Joseph A. (Joe) Sprague, $303,846 total compensation
Staff Vp Finance And Controller; Staff Vp Finance And Controller Alaska Airlines, Brandon S. Pedersen, age 52, $390,769 total compensation
Evp And Chief Commercial Officer Alaska Airlines, Andrew R. Harrison, age 48, $383,077 total compensation
President And Coo Alaska Airlines, Benito (Ben) Minicucci, age 52, $426,923 total compensation

Coo Horizon Air Industries Inc., Constance Von Muehlen
Vp, Diana Shaw
Vice President Of Operation, Bill Mackay
Vice President Maintenance And Engineering Alaska Airlines, Kurt Kinder
Vice President Airport Operations And Customer Service Alaska Airlines, Wayne Newton
Vice President Strategic Sourcing And Supply Chain Management, Ann Ardizzone
Regional Vice President Alas Ka, Marilyn Romano
Vice President Marketing Alaska Airlines, Sangita Woerner
Vice President Marketing, Gwen Bacon
Vice President Revenue Management, Kevin Ger
Vice President Bay Area Alaska Airlines, Annabel Chang
Vice President Of Customer Service, Renee Spicer
Vice President External Relations, Diana Birkett Rakow
Senior Vice President Purchasing Officer, Erik Null Davies
Senior Vice President Maintenance And Engineering, Constance Vonmuehlen
Vp Sales, David Oppenheim
Vice President Finance And Treasurer Alaska Airlines, Mark Eliasen
Board Member, Bridget Thompson
Board Member, Helvi Sandvik
Board Member, Susan Li
Auditors: KPMG LLP

LOCATIONS

HQ: Alaska Air Group, Inc.
19300 International Boulevard, Seattle, WA 98188
Phone: 206 392-5040
Web: www.alaskaair.com

PRODUCTS/OPERATIONS

2018 Sales

	$ mil.	% of total
Passenger Revenue	7,632	92
Mileage Plan other revenue	434	5
Cargo and other	198	3
Total	**8,264**	**100**

2018 Sales

	$ mil.	% of total
Alaska		
Mainline	7,063	80
Regional	1,197	14
Horizon	512	6
Consolidating	(508)	-
Total	**8,264**	**100**

Selected Products and Services

Accessible services
Baggage
Book a Shipment
Children traveling alone
Customer of size
Delayed baggage
Emergency exit row
General Air Freight
GoldStreak®; Package Express
Infants and children
Price a Shipment
Priority Air Freight
Rate charts and surcharges
Ticket receipt
Track a Shipment
Traveling with pets

COMPETITORS

Aeromexico	JetBlue
Air Canada	Mesa Air
Allegiant Travel	SkyWest
American Airlines Group	Southwest Airlines
Delta Air Lines	United Continental
Hawaiian Holdings	WestJet

HISTORICAL FINANCIALS

Company Type: Public

Income Statement

FYE: December 31

	REVENUE ($ mil.)	NET INCOME ($ mil.)	NET PROFIT MARGIN	EMPLOYEES
12/18	8,264	437	5.3%	23,376
12/17	7,933	1,034	13.0%	23,156
12/16	5,931	814	13.7%	19,112
12/15	5,598	848	15.1%	15,143
12/14	5,368	605	11.3%	13,952
Annual Growth	**11.4%**	**(7.8%)**	**—**	**13.8%**

2018 Year-End Financials

Debt ratio: 19.27%
Return on equity: 11.70%
Cash ($ mil.): 105
Current ratio: 0.61
Long-term debt ($ mil.): 1,617

No. of shares (mil.): 123
Dividends
  Yield: 2.1%
  Payout: 36.3%
Market value ($ mil.): 7,496

	STOCK PRICE ($) FY Close	P/E High/Low		PER SHARE ($) Earnings	Dividends	Book Value
12/18	60.85	21	16	3.52	1.28	30.45
12/17	73.51	12	7	8.35	1.20	30.24
12/16	88.73	14	8	6.54	1.10	23.77
12/15	80.51	13	9	6.56	0.80	19.26
12/14	59.76	22	9	4.42	0.50	16.18
Annual Growth	**0.5%**	—	—	**(5.5%)**	**26.5%**	**17.1%**

ALASKA PERMANENT FUND CORPORATION

EXECUTIVES

Ceo, Angela Rodell
Coo*, Marcus Frampton
Chief Financial Officer*, Valerie Mertz
Information Specialist, Andrew Loney
Principal, Chris Poag
Communications Manager, Paulyn Swanson
Portfolio Manager, Timothy Andreyka
Controller, John Seagren
Human Resources Director, Chad Brown
Investment Officer Real Estate, Christi Grussendorf
Senior Associate Private Marke, Jared Brimberry
Auditors: KPMG LLP ANCHORAGE AK

LOCATIONS

HQ: ALASKA PERMANENT FUND CORPORATION
801 W 10TH ST STE 302, JUNEAU, AK 998011878
Phone: 907 796-1500
Web: WWW.APFC.ORG

HISTORICAL FINANCIALS

Company Type: Private

Income Statement

FYE: June 30

	ASSETS ($ mil.)	NET INCOME ($ mil.)	INCOME AS % OF ASSETS	EMPLOYEES
06/18	67,671	5,109	7.6%	50
06/17	61,824	6,675	10.8%	—
06/16	55,346	(30)	—	—
06/15	55,900	1,586	2.8%	—
Annual Growth	**6.6%**	**47.7%**	**—**	**—**

Albertsons Companies Inc

Auditors: DELOITTE & TOUCHE LLP

LOCATIONS

HQ: Albertsons Companies Inc
250 Parkcenter Blvd., Boise, ID 83706
Phone: 208 395-6200
Web: www.AlbertsonsCompanies.com

HISTORICAL FINANCIALS
Company Type: Public

Income Statement
FYE: February 23

	REVENUE ($ mil.)	NET INCOME ($ mil.)	NET PROFIT MARGIN	EMPLOYEES
02/19	60,534	131	0.2%	267,000
02/18	59,924	46	0.1%	275,000
02/17	59,678	(373)	—	—
02/16	58,734	(502)	—	—
Annual Growth	1.0%	—	—	—

2019 Year-End Financials

Debt ratio: 52.43%	No. of shares (mil.): 277
Return on equity: 9.23%	Dividends
Cash ($ mil.): 926	Yield: —
Current ratio: 1.21	Payout: —
Long-term debt ($ mil.): 10,437	Market value ($ mil.): —

	STOCK PRICE ($) FY Close	P/E High/Low		PER SHARE ($) Earnings	Dividends	Book Value
02/19	0.00	—	—	(0.00)	0.00	5.22
Annual Growth						

ALBERTSONS COMPANIES, INC.

Albertsons Companies is one of the biggest supermarket retailers in the US with nearly 2300 stores in some 35 states and the District of Columbia. In addition to traditional grocery items many of the stores offer pharmacies and coffee shops and nearly 400 include adjacent gas stations. The company operates under some 20 banners including Albertsons Vons Jewel-Osco Shaw's/Star Market Safeway Acme and United. It also owns meal kit company Plated. Albertsons Companies which traces its roots to 1939 is owned by Cerberus Capital Management which has been looking to take the company public for quite some time. In 2018 the retailer called off its pending acquisition of the Rite Aid pharmacy chain amid investor pushback.

HISTORY

J. A. "Joe" Albertson Leonard Skaggs (whose family ran Safeway) and Tom Cuthbert founded Albertson's Food Center in Boise Idaho in 1939. Albertson who left his position as district manager for Safeway to run the store thought big from the start. The 10000-sq.-ft. store was not only eight times the size of the average competitor it also offered an in-store butcher shop and bakery one of the country's first magazine racks and homemade "Big Joe" ice-cream cones. The men ended their partnership in 1945 the year Albertson's was incorporated and by 1947 it operated six stores in Idaho.

The company opened its first combination food store and drugstore a 60000-sq.-ft. superstore in 1951 and began locating stores in growing suburban areas. Albertson's went public to raise expansion capital in 1959 and by 1960 had 62 stores in Idaho Oregon Utah and Washington. The food retailer acquired Greater All American Markets (1964) a grocery chain based in Downey California and Semrau & Sons (1965) of Oakland which aided the company's thrust into the California market.

Albertson's and the Skaggs chain (by this time run by L. S. Skaggs Jr.) reunited temporarily in 1969 financing six Skaggs-Albertson's food-and-drug-combination stores. (The partnership dissolved in 1977 with each side taking half of the units.) By 1986 the company had reached $5 billion in sales a fivefold increase over 1975.

The company purchased 74 Jewel Osco combination food stores and drugstores (mostly in Arkansas Florida Oklahoma and Texas) from American Stores in 1992. Co-founder Albertson died in 1993 at age 86.

In 1997 the United Food and Commercial Workers union which represents supermarket employees sued Albertson's alleging the company forced employees to work overtime without pay. (It was settled in 1999 resulting in a $22 million charge.) Also in 1997 Albertson's began selling gasoline at a few stores. Acquisitions the next year (including Buttrey Food and Drug Stores) added stores and states. That year the company began serving online customers in the Dallas-Fort Worth area.

In 1999 the grocer revisited its roots when it acquired American Stores (Skaggs' successor) which operated more than 1550 stores in 26 states. To obtain regulatory approval for the $12 billion deal Albertson's sold 145 stores in overlapping markets in three states (most were in California).

In 2001 Larry Johnston former CEO of GE Appliances took over as chairman and CEO of Albertson's. Facing increasing competition (especially from Wal-Mart) Johnston announced in March 2002 aggressive restructuring plans that included job cuts and closing 95 stores in under-performing markets specifically Memphis and Nashville Tennessee and Houston and San Antonio Texas.

Already allowing customers to order drugs online (from its online drugstore Savon.com) and groceries in Seattle Albertson's expanded its online operations to San Diego in 2001 and in early 2002 to Los Angeles San Francisco and parts of Oregon and Washington. Albertson's exited the New England drugstore market in 2002 when it sold 80 New England Osco stores to Brooks Pharmacy.

In February 2004 Albertson's launched its "Blue Ribbon" brand of beef a private-label line of roasts and steaks. Also in February the company consolidated its Southwest Intermountain Northwest and Rocky Mountain divisions to form a new Intermountain West division and combined the Acme and Florida divisions into a new Eastern Division.

A four-and-a-half month strike by grocery workers in Southern California ended in March 2004. The dispute pitted workers' demands for continued generous health care coverage vs. management's call for cost cuts to remain profitable in the face of Wal-Mart's entry into the Southern California grocery market. In April Albertson's completed the acquisition of JS USA Holdings which runs Shaw's and Star Markets stores in New England from UK grocer J Sainsbury. The deal to buy Shaw's was worth about $2.4 billion (cash and leases). In September Albertson's gained a toehold in the gourmet-food market with the purchase of Bristol Farms the operator of about a dozen upscale food markets in Southern California. In October Albertson's combined its Northern and Southern California food divisions into a single business unit the newly formed California Food Division. In an effort to improve efficiency Albertson's reorganized its supply chain food operations and Six Sigma Quality functions in May 2005.

In June 2006 Albertson's was sold to a consortium that included SUPERVALU CVS Cerberus Capital Management and Kimco for about $9.7 billion. Following the acquisition and the divvying up of Albertson's assets the surviving company went private and changed its name to Albertsons LLC. Concurrently Johnston left Albertsons and was succeeded by Robert Miller chairman of drugstore chain Rite Aid and the former head of Fred Meyer for eight years in the 1990s. Of the company's 27 price-impact Super Saver stores 25 closed their doors in mid-2006. Also in June the company put about 45 stores on the auction block. (It was announced in late 2006 that discount apparel retailer Ross Stores would acquire these stores.) In July the company shut down its online shopping service Albertsons.com.

In February 2007 Albertsons sold 132 grocery stores and two distribution centers in Northern California and Nevada to Save Mart Supermarkets for an undisclosed amount. Other recent closings include stores in Texas in the Dallas-Fort Worth Austin and Longview markets; Colorado; and Oklahoma.

Albertsons also sold eight of its stores in Wyoming to SUPERVALU in January 2008. The divestments continued in September with the sale of 49 supermarkets in Florida to Publix Super Markets for about $500 million. Also in 2008 Albertsons sold about 100 of its Express fuel centers in Arizona Colorado Florida Louisiana and Texas to Valero Energy and Reb Oil.

EXECUTIVES

Evp And General Counsel, Robert A. (Bob) Gordon
Evp Operations, Wayne A. Denningham
Chief Marketing & Merchandising Officer, Shane Sampson
President Jewel Osco, Mike Withers
President Seattle Division, Karl Schroeder
President Houston Division, Sidney Hopper
Chairman And Ceo, Robert G. (Bob) Miller
Chief Administrative Officer, Justin Dye
President Southwest Division, Shane Dorcheus
President United, Robert Taylor
Evp And Cio, Anuj Dhanda
President Portland Division, Greg McNiff
President Southern Division, Dennis Bassler
Evp East Operations, Susan Morris
President Shaws, Paul Gossett
President Southern California Division, Lori Raya
President Acme Markets Division, Dan Croce
Evp And Cfo, Bob Dimond
Evp West Region Operations, Jim Perkins
Evp Human Resources Labor Relations Public Affairs And Government Relations, Andrew (Andy) Scoggin
Evp Corporate Development And Real Estate, Justin Ewing
President Eastern Division, Dan Valenzuela
President Northern California Division, Tom Schwilke
President Denver Division, Todd Broderick
President Intermountain Division, Brad Street
Svp Merchandising, Dennis Clark
Vp Food Safety And Quality Assurance, Jerry Norland

Evp And Chief Data And Analytics Officer, Gautam Kotwal
Vice President Merchandising Strategy, Merritt Mccoy
Auditors: DELOITTE & TOUCHE LLP BOISE

LOCATIONS

HQ: ALBERTSONS COMPANIES, INC.
250 E PARKCENTER BLVD, BOISE, ID 837063999
Phone: 208 395-6200
Web: WWW.ALBERTSONS.COM

PRODUCTS/OPERATIONS

2018 Sales

	$ mil.	% of total
Non-perishables	26,372	44
Perishables	24,921	41
Pharmacy	4,987	8
Fuel	3,456	6
Other	799	1
Total	**60,535**	**100**

COMPETITORS

ALDI	Quality Food
Amazon.com	Roundy's
Costco Wholesale	Stater Bros.
Fry's Food	Target Corporation
H-E-B	Wal-Mart
Kroger	Wegmans
Lidl	Winn-Dixie
Publix	

HISTORICAL FINANCIALS

Company Type: Private

Income Statement				FYE: February 23
	REVENUE ($ mil.)	NET INCOME ($ mil.)	NET PROFIT MARGIN	EMPLOYEES
02/19	60,534	131	0.2%	275,000
02/18	59,924	46	0.1%	
Annual Growth	1.0%	183.2%	—	—

Alcoa Corporation

Auditors: PricewaterhouseCoopers LLP

LOCATIONS

HQ: Alcoa Corporation
201 Isabella Street, Suite 500, Pittsburgh, PA 15212-5858
Phone: 412 315-2900
Web: www.alcoa.com

HISTORICAL FINANCIALS

Company Type: Public

Income Statement				FYE: December 31
	REVENUE ($ mil.)	NET INCOME ($ mil.)	NET PROFIT MARGIN	EMPLOYEES
12/18	13,403	227	1.7%	14,000
12/17	11,652	217	1.9%	14,600
12/16	9,318	(400)	—	14,000
12/15	11,199	(863)	—	16,000
12/14	13,147	(256)	—	
Annual Growth	0.5%	—	—	—

2018 Year-End Financials

Debt ratio: 11.31%	No. of shares (mil.): 184
Return on equity: 4.58%	Dividends
Cash ($ mil.): 1,113	Yield: —
Current ratio: 1.42	Payout: —
Long-term debt ($ mil.): 1,801	Market value ($ mil.): 4,911

	STOCK PRICE ($) FY Close	P/E High/Low	PER SHARE ($) Earnings	Dividends	Book Value
12/18	26.58	49 21	1.20	0.00	29.17
12/17	53.87	46 24	1.16	0.00	24.42
12/16	28.08	— —	(2.19)	0.00	30.91
Annual Growth	(1.4%)	— —	—	—	(1.4%)

Alerus Financial Corp

EXECUTIVES

President; Chief Executive Officer Chairman Director, Randy Newman
Regional President Twin Cities, Sara Ausman
Vice President Commercial Relationship Manager, Robert Hartzell
Auditors: CliftonLarsonAllen LLP

LOCATIONS

HQ: Alerus Financial Corp
401 Demers Avenue, Grand Forks, ND 58021
Phone: 701 795-3200   **Fax:** 701 795-3378
Web: www.alerusfinancial.com

HISTORICAL FINANCIALS

Company Type: Public

Income Statement				FYE: December 31
	ASSETS ($ mil.)	NET INCOME ($ mil.)	INCOME AS % OF ASSETS	EMPLOYEES
12/18	2,179	25	1.2%	—
12/17	2,137	15	0.7%	—
12/16	2,050	14	0.7%	—
12/15	1,744	16	0.9%	—
12/14	1,488	20	1.4%	—
Annual Growth	10.0%	6.3%		

2018 Year-End Financials

Debt ratio: 2.70%	No. of shares (mil.): 13
Return on equity: 13.70%	Dividends
Cash ($ mil.): 40	Yield: 2.7%
Current ratio: —	Payout: 28.8%
Long-term debt ($ mil.): —	Market value ($ mil.): 265

	STOCK PRICE ($) FY Close	P/E High/Low	PER SHARE ($) Earnings	Dividends	Book Value
12/18	19.25	14 10	1.84	0.53	14.30
12/17	20.45	18 15	1.10	0.48	13.18
12/16	17.00	19 16	1.00	0.44	12.47
12/15	18.90	17 15	1.17	0.42	13.61
12/14	19.75	42 14	1.44	0.38	(0.00)
Annual Growth	(0.6%)	— —	6.3%	8.4%	

Alleghany Corp.

Alleghany is a holding company with a focus on property/casualty reinsurance and insurance. Its subsidiaries include Transatlantic Holdings (TransRe) which offers property/casualty reinsurance (risk coverage for insurers) globally through Transatlantic Reinsurance Fair American and Trans Re Zurich. The group also issues specialty property/casualty insurance policies through RSUI Group and CapSpecialty. Targeting small and mid-sized US firms CapSpecialty underwrites specialty lines including commercial property fidelity surety and professional lines. Alleghany's offerings are marketed in the US and abroad.

HISTORY

Alleghany was formed in 1929 by Clevelanders Mantis and Oris Van Sweringen as a pyramid railroad holding company. It collapsed in 1934 and after passing through several hands it was bought in 1937 by speculator Robert Young with backing from Woolworth heir Allan Kirby.

Young resurrected the company's Chesapeake and Ohio railroad but another holding Missouri Pacific Railroad (Mo-Pac) failed to thrive and Young embarked on a 40-year struggle to maximize Mo-Pac's value. Young focused on railroads even as the industry declined but he also made other investments including a chunk of IDS (which became the US's largest mutual fund company) and real estate. He also trimmed company holdings from nearly 70 to about 10. By the time Young committed suicide in 1958 Alleghany was in trouble and Kirby who had always kept to the shadows took over.

In his first three years at the helm Kirby fought a takeover attempt by Abraham Sonnabend and a proxy fight with investors John and Clint Murchison. After being ousted briefly in 1961 Kirby re-emerged in control of the company. Allan suffered a stroke in 1965 and his son Fred Morgan "F. M." Kirby II took over.

In 1966 the company sold its interest in the New York Central railroad (bought in 1945) and eight years later finally emerged from the Mo-Pac mess with about $42 million in cash and some stock. Alleghany used the cash to buy metal fabricating company MSL Industries and the rest of IDS.

Fred Kirby's mantra was flexibility and in 1984 he sold IDS to American Express for a then-flabbergasting $800 million including a pile of stock. Kirby used these proceeds to buy Chicago Title & Trust the same year. Two years later he liquidated the old Alleghany and reincorporated Alleghany Financial CT&T's parent as Alleghany Corporation.

Kirby used the cash from the American Express deal to buy and then spin off a construction company. Other purchases followed in the 1990s including more title operations a California thrift and in 1991 Celite which produced filtration materials. This line was expanded the next year with the purchase of Harborlite. After several purchases in direct insurance (quickly flipped for a profit) in 1993 Alleghany bought Underwriters Re.

In 1994 and 1995 the company bought up shares of Burlington Northern Railroad which merged with Santa Fe in 1995.

In the 1990s CT&T lost market share through industry consolidation so in 1998 Alleghany spun off CT&T's title operations (later acquired by Fidelity National Financial). The next year hit by a down market in reinsurance Alleghany agreed to sell Underwriters Re to Swiss Reinsurance keeping its hand in the market via Alleghany Underwriting Holdings Ltd. (AUL).

In 1999 the company bulked up its asset management operations through acquisitions and in 2000 its industrial fastener business Heads & Threads International bought Acktion's Reynold's Fasteners unit. In 2001 Alleghany sold Lloyd's reinsurer Alleghany Underwriting to Bermuda-based Talbot Holdings and Dutch bank ABN Amro bought the company's asset management business.

The company built up its insurance operations with the purchase of Resurgens Specialty Underwriting (RSUI Group) a subsidiary of British insurance powerhouse Royal & Sun Alliance. It also expanded insurance operations with the 2004 acquisitions of Capitol Transamerica and Darwin National Assurance Company (formerly known as U.S. AEGIS Energy Insurance Company) later renamed as Darwin Professional Underwriters. In early 2006 it took Darwin through an initial public offering and used the funds to reduce its equity interest while retaining majority ownership. (Alleghany's 55% stake in Darwin was sold to Allied World Assurance in 2008.)

While Alleghany collected insurance firms it shed other operations. The company sold Heads & Threads to a management-led investors group in 2004. In 2005 it sold its World Minerals subsidiary (diatomite production) to the US branch of Imerys in a deal valued at about $217 million.

Hurricane Katrina took a serious bite out of profits in 2005. In response Alleghany Insurance Holdings created AIHL Re a reinsurance subsidiary to provide reinsurance directly to RSUI while RSUI worked to reduce its exposure and increased its prices on property insurance. Once the reinsurance market settled down AIHL Re was allowed to go dormant in 2008.

During the quieter 2006 and 2007 hurricane seasons Alleghany found it still had an appetite for insurance providers. The company plunked down $120 million in cash to purchase 33% of monoline homeowners insurance provider Homesite Group in 2006 and spent $198 million to acquire Employers Direct in 2007.

Alleghany held 55% of Darwin Professional Underwriters a specialty property/casualty insurance writer but in 2008 sold it to Allied World Assurance for approximately $300 million.

F. M. Kirby retired as chairman at the end of 2006. His brother Allan Kirby retired from the board in 2010 leaving Jefferson Kirby F. M.'s son as the last family member on the board as directors. F. M. died at the age of 91 in early 2011.

Transatlantic Holdings caught Alleghany's eye and in early 2012 the company paid some $3.4 billion for the long-tail reinsurer. The deal's announcement in late 2011 ended a months-long buyout battle for Transatlantic.

EXECUTIVES

Vice President Of Finance And Accounting, Jerry Borrelli

Chairman And Ceo Capspecialty Inc. (f/k/a Capitol Transamerica Corporation), Stephen J. Sills, age 70

Chairman Alleghany Capital Corporation, Udi Toledano, age 69

President And Ceo, Weston M. Hicks, age 63, $1,000,000 total compensation

President And Ceo Alleghany Properties, David J. Bugatto, age 54

President And Ceo Transatlantic Holdings Inc., Michael C. (Mike) Sapnar, age 52

Chairman President And Ceo Pacific Compensation Corporation, Janet D. (Jan) Frank, age 68

Svp Head Of Fixed Income And Treasurer, Roger B. Gorham, age 56, $600,000 total compensation

Svp General Counsel And Secretary, Christopher K. Dalrymple, age 51, $650,000 total compensation

Chairman And Ceo Rsui Group Inc., David E. (Dave) Leonard

Svp And Cfo, John L. (Jack) Sennott, age 53, $650,000 total compensation

Evp, Joseph P. Brandon, age 60, $825,000 total compensation

President And Ceo Alleghany Capital Corporation, David Van Geyzel

Vp Finance And Chief Risk Officer, Kerry J. Jacobs

Vice President And Tax Director, John Carr

Executive Vice President, Ken Apfel

Chairman, Jefferson W. Kirby, age 57

Auditors: Ernst & Young LLP

LOCATIONS

HQ: Alleghany Corp.
1411 Broadway, 34th Floor, New York, NY 10018
Phone: 212 752-1356
Web: www.alleghany.com

PRODUCTS/OPERATIONS

2017 Sales

	$ mil.	% of total
Reinsurance		
Casualty & other	2,626	41
Property	1,181	18
Insurance		
RSUI Group	721	11
Cap Specialty	260	4
PacificComp	163	3
Net investment income	451	7
Net realized capital gains	107	2
Other	928	14
Adjustments	(16.9)	-
Total	**6,424**	**100**

2017 Sales

	$ mil.	% of total
Net premiums earned	4,955	77
Net investment income	451	7
Net realized capital gains	107	2
Other	928	14
Adjustments	(16.9)	-
Total	**6,424**	**100**

Selected Subsidiaries

Alleghany Capital Corporation
Alleghany Properties LLC
CapSpecialty Inc.
Roundwood Asset Management LLC
RSUI Group Inc.
Transatlantic Holdings Inc.

COMPETITORS

AIG	OdysseyRe
CNA Surety	PartnerRe
California Casualty	Reinsurance Group of
Everest Re	America
General Re	RenaissanceRe
Hannover Re	State Farm
Liberty Mutual Agency	Swiss Re
Munich Re Group	Travelers Companies
Nationwide	

HISTORICAL FINANCIALS

Company Type: Public

Income Statement				FYE: December 31
	ASSETS ($ mil.)	NET INCOME ($ mil.)	INCOME AS % OF ASSETS	EMPLOYEES
12/18	25,344	39	0.2%	9,300
12/17	25,384	90	0.4%	4,402
12/16	23,756	456	1.9%	3,420
12/15	22,846	560	2.5%	3,135
12/14	23,489	679	2.9%	2,067
Annual Growth	**1.9%**	**(50.9%)**	**—**	**45.6%**

2018 Year-End Financials

Debt ratio: 6.59%	No. of shares (mil.): 14
Return on equity: 0.49%	Dividends
Cash ($ mil.): 1,038	Yield: 1.6%
Current ratio: —	Payout: 381.6%
Long-term debt ($ mil.): —	Market value ($ mil.): 9,086

	STOCK PRICE ($) FY Close	P/E High/Low	PER SHARE ($) Earnings	Dividends	Book Value
12/18	623.32	250 215	2.62	10.00	527.75
12/17	596.09	112 89	5.85	0.00	553.20
12/16	608.12	21 15	29.59	0.00	515.24
12/15	477.93	15 13	35.13	0.00	486.02
12/14	463.50	12 9	41.40	0.00	465.51
Annual Growth	**7.7%**	**—**	**(49.8%)**	**—**	**3.2%**

Allegiance Bancshares Inc

Auditors: Crowe LLP

LOCATIONS

HQ: Allegiance Bancshares Inc
8847 West Sam Houston Parkway N., Suite 200, Houston, TX 77040
Phone: 281 894-3200
Web: www.allegiancebank.com

HISTORICAL FINANCIALS

Company Type: Public

Income Statement				FYE: December 31
	ASSETS ($ mil.)	NET INCOME ($ mil.)	INCOME AS % OF ASSETS	EMPLOYEES
12/18	4,655	37	0.8%	569
12/17	2,860	17	0.6%	375
12/16	2,450	22	0.9%	327
12/15	2,084	15	0.8%	310
12/14	1,280	9	0.7%	304
Annual Growth	**38.1%**	**42.7%**	**—**	**17.0%**

2018 Year-End Financials

Debt ratio: 5.89%	No. of shares (mil.): 21
Return on equity: 7.39%	Dividends
Cash ($ mil.): 268	Yield: —
Current ratio: —	Payout: —
Long-term debt ($ mil.): —	Market value ($ mil.): 710

	STOCK PRICE ($) FY Close	P/E High/Low	PER SHARE ($) Earnings	Dividends	Book Value
12/18	32.37	19 12	2.37	0.00	32.04
12/17	37.65	30 23	1.31	0.00	23.20
12/16	36.15	21 9	1.75	0.00	21.59
12/15	23.65	18 15	1.43	0.00	20.17
Annual Growth	**8.2%**	**—**	**13.5%**	**—**	**12.3%**

ALLEGIS GROUP, INC.

Allegis Group is one of the world's largest staffing and recruitment firms. Among its group of staffing companies are Aerotek (engineering automotive and scientific professionals) Aston Carter (recruitment for accounting finance and professional skills) and TEKsystems (information technology staffing and consulting). Other Allegis Group units include sales support outsourcer MarketSource. Allegis Group operates through more than 500 locations worldwide. Chairman Jim Davis helped found the company (originally known as Aerotek) in 1983 to provide contract engineering personnel to two clients in the aerospace industry.

Operations

Operating through a group of 10 companies Allegis Group serves businesses and organizations from the engineering automotive finance IT life sciences and other industries. The company also serves government agencies and subcontractors. Aerotek and TEKsystems are among the group's largest and most established companies; other Allegis companies provide niche services including disability recruitment through its Getting Hired unit and legal recruitment though Major Lindsey & Africa.

Allegis Group's core services include staffing and recruitment (screening onboarding and retention) executive search (CEO and board member services) sales force outsourcing and workforce management.

Geographic Reach

Hanover Maryland-based Allegis Group operates more than 500 locations around the globe including offices throughout the US Canada the UK and Europe as well as in the Middle East Asia and Asia Pacific region.

Financial Performance

Privately held Allegis Group doesn't publish consolidated financials; however the firm reports bringing in more than $12 billion in revenue each year.

Company Background

In 1983 Stephen Bisciotti and Jim Davis founded the company (originally known as Aerotek) in Maryland. At the time their firm matched job seekers with aeronautics engineering and light industrial positions. In the late 1980s the company expanded into the IT application markets.

Aerotek extended its reach into commercial environmental and energy industries through its 2001 acquisition of Onsite Companies. The company later changed its name to Allegis Group while the other divisions remained separate companies until eventually consolidating under the Allegis Group banner.

EXECUTIVES

It Vice President Of Finance, Celeste Slifer
Cfo, Paul J. Bowie
President, Andy Hilger
Senior Vice President, Mary Pat Smith
Vice President Organizational Development, Andrew Hilger
Vice President Human Resources, Tanya Axenson
Chairman, James C. (Jim) Davis
Auditors: PRICEWATERHOUSECOOPERS LLP BA

LOCATIONS

HQ: ALLEGIS GROUP, INC.
7301 PARKWAY DR, HANOVER, MD 210761159
Phone: 410 579-3000
Web: WWW.ALLEGISGROUP.COM

PRODUCTS/OPERATIONS

Selected Subsidiaries

Aerotek
Aerotek Aviation LLC
Aerotek Canada
Aerotek Scientific LLC
Allegis Group Canada
Allegis Group India
Major Lindsey & Africa
MarketSource Inc

Stephen James Associates
TEKsystems
  TEKsystems Canada
  TEKsystems Netherlands
  TEKsystems United Kingdom

COMPETITORS

ASG Renaissance	Kelly Services
Adecco	Korn/Ferry
CDI	ManpowerGroup
Curran Partners	RDL Corporation
ExecuNet	Randstad Holding
Heidrick & Struggles	Robert Half
Horton International	Snelling Staffing
Innovative Management Solutions Group	Volt Information

HISTORICAL FINANCIALS

Company Type: Private

Income Statement				FYE: December 31
	REVENUE ($ mil.)	NET INCOME ($ mil.)	NET PROFIT MARGIN	EMPLOYEES
12/17	12,296	0	—	85,000
12/16	11,502	0	—	—
12/15	11,222	0	—	—
12/14	10,827	0	—	—
Annual Growth	4.3%	—	—	—

Alliance Data Systems Corp.

Alliance Data Systems provides private-label credit card financing and processing and database and direct marketing services to more than 2000 companies. In a given year it holds the credit for more than $15 billion in card balances. Its client base includes retailers like J. Crew Pottery Barn and Victoria's Secret as well as banks (Bank of America) grocery and drugstore chains gas stations and hospitality media and pharmaceutical companies. The company also develops and operates customer loyalty programs such as its Canadian-focused AIR MILES program. Additionally it performs database marketing predictive modeling and strategic consulting. In 2019 the company agreed to sell its Epsilon data-driven personalized marketing services business to Publicis Groupe.

Operations

Alliance Data Systems operates three main business segments: Card Services Epsilon and LoyaltyOne.

Card Services generates about 55% of the company's revenue by operating private label and co-branded credit card accounts for retailers. The retailers achieve a degree of brand loyalty and Alliance gathers customer information and buying habits with which it helps the retailer more precisely target customers for future sales. Card Services manages more than 160 credit card programs whose consumer membership exceeds 40 million accounts. Alliance provides the credit behind the cards processes sales transactions and helps its clients leverage card branding to drive consumer loyalty.

The Epsilon segment serves roughly 1600 clients in industries such as financial services insurance media and entertainment automotive retail and hospitality. It gathers consumer data largely

through its loyalty programs and credit card transactions then analyzes it to design client-customized digital and direct mail marketing programs. The segment generates about 30% of revenue. In 2019 the company agreeed to sell Epsilon to Publicis Groupe for a net price of about $4 billion.

LoyaltyOne accounts for about 20% of revenue. The segment gathers customer information through its loyalty programs to help Alliance clients design and implement marketing programs. It operates one of Canada's largest loyalty programs AIR MILES through which consumers earn miles as they shop at more than 150 brand name retailers. The BrandLoyalty program offers similar objectives for grocers primarily in Europe and Asia with a growing presence in North America.

Geographic Reach

The US accounts for more than 80% of Alliance Data Systems' revenue a share that has increased in recent years as Canada's share has decreased. The company is growing in EMEA and Asia Pacific.

Alliance has about a dozen facilities in the US including its corporate headquarters in Plano Texas a large facility in Columbus Ohio and offices in Texas Illinois and Idaho among others. Its LoyaltyOne segment operates in Canada and The Netherlands. The company's only other international facility is an Epsilon office in Bengaluru India.

Sales and Marketing

Although significant revenue is generated by card-carrying consumers Alliance's key customers are name brand retailers. It is through the likes of L Brands (owner of Victoria's Secret and Bath & Body Works) and Ascena Retail Group (Lane Bryant and dressbarn) that Alliance issues new cards increases the number of consumer customers and mines data essential to the Epsilon segment. The company typically enters into multi-year contracts with such retail partners. To manage loan loss risk from its credit card account holders Alliance targets retail brands that appeal to middle and upper-class consumers and intentionally avoids issuing cards to sub-prime borrowers.

Its 10 largest clients account for about 35% of total revenue. The LoyaltyOne business counts Bank of Montreal and Canada-based grocer Sobeys as its largest clients together representing 35% of segment revenue.

The company operates in a highly competitive market contending with marketing services companies credit card issuers and data processing companies as well as with the in-house staffs of current and potential clients.

Financial Performance

Alliance's revenue and profits have more than doubled since 2011 as consumers' use of reward programs and credit and debit cards has ballooned.

Revenue increased 8% to $7.7 billion in 2017 from $7.1 billion in 2016. Services revenue rose 4% driven by double-digit growth in its automotive agency and digital CRM offerings. Finance charges revenue increased 15% from higher average credit card and loan receivables. Redemption revenue slumped 6% from a slowdown in short-term loyalty programs because of fewer campaigns and their timing. Revenue dipped in the second half of 2017 because Alliance suspended payments for customers affected by hurricanes.

Net income jumped 52% to $789 million in 2017 from 2016 with help from higher revenue and a tax benefit from the US Tax Cuts and Jobs Act.

Alliance had $4.2 billion in cash in 2017 compared to $1.8 billion in 2016. In 2017 operations generated $2.6 billion and financing activities provided $4 billion while investing activities used $4.3 billion.

Strategy

Alliance's strategy includes building its Card Services customer base shifting Epsilon's product mix towards targeted direct marketing and shoring up LoyaltyOne following the impact of an Ontario Canada law change.

With credit and debit card use driving Alliance's financial performance the company continues to seek co-branded partnerships with a variety of retailers to increase its borrower base. The company signed a long-term agreement to provide branded credit card programs to Boscov's Department Store (the largest family-owned department chain in the US) clothing retailer Forever 21 and luxury home furnishings shop Restoration Hardware.

Following industry shifts Alliance is trending away from mass marketing (such as direct mailings) and moving towards direct personalized efforts made possible by mining data from its huge consumer base and applying data analytics to design targeted ads. In recent years it experienced time-to-market slowness and cost competition that impeded sales. It is addressing these problems with renewed focus on its less-customized (and less expensive) technology offerings and redirecting some of its focus into the mid-market space and into digital marketing.

The LoyaltyOne business was hit hard in 2016 with a law change in the province of Ontario Canada that rescinded the company's 5-year expiration of loyalty points. Assuming other provinces would follow Alliance took the step to change its valuation model and accepted a more than $200 million hit to revenue. The business stabilized in 2018 fortified by major sponsors and most collectors that stuck with the program. The largest sponsor Bank of Montreal renewed in 2017.

Following a strategic review Alliance announced plans to sell its Epsilon business to Publicis Groupe for a net price of about $4 billion in 2019. The company said the strategies that would improve Epsilon were different than those for its Card Services business. The company expects proceeds from the sale to go to pay down debt buy back shares and pay dividends.

Company Background

Alliance Data Systems was formed by the 1996 acquisition by Welsh Carson Anderson & Stowe of J.C. Penney's transaction services business and L Brands' credit card bank operation Comenity Bank (formerly World Financial Network Bank which is now a subsidiary of the company.

EXECUTIVES

Evp And Cfo, Charles L. Horn, age 58, $627,000 total compensation

President And Ceo, Edward J. (Ed) Heffernan, age 56, $1,114,000 total compensation

Evp; President Loyaltyone, Bryan A. Pearson, age 56, $459,895 total compensation

Evp; President Epsilon, Bryan J. Kennedy, age 50, $602,500 total compensation

Evp; President Retail Credit Services, Melisa A. Miller, age 60, $602,500 total compensation

Svp And Chief Accounting Officer, Laura Santillan

Vice President, Shelley Whiddon

Vice President Corporate Human Resources, Calvin Hilton

Regional Vp Care Center Operations, Lance Beck

Vp Internal Audit, Shane Hogan

Vice President Business Solutions Delivery, Paula Stranges

Senior Vice President And Treasurer, Jeff Chesnut

Vice President Strategic Development, Patrick Leonhart

Vice President Business Solutions Development, Jen Williamson

Vp Operations Contact Centers, Christopher Judge

Vice President Internal Marketing And Communications, Karen Smith

Vp Corporate Affairs And Head Strategic Insights, Rodney Davenport

Vice President Retail Marketing, Mary O'donnell

Vp Sales Card Services, Darian Culbertson

Vice President Risk Management, Tom Giancola

Chairman, Robert A. Minicucci, age 66

Svp General Counsel And Secretary, Joseph Motes

Board Member, Bruce Anderson

Auditors: DELOITTE & TOUCHE LLP

LOCATIONS

HQ: Alliance Data Systems Corp.
3075 Loyalty Circle, Columbus, OH 43219
Phone: 614 729-4000
Web: www.alliancedata.com

PRODUCTS/OPERATIONS

2017 Sales by Segment

	$ mil.	% of total
Card Services	4,170	55
Epsilon	2,272	29
LoyaltyOne	1,303	16
Corporate & other	0	-
Eliminations	(27.4)	-
Total	**7,719**	**100**

2017 Sales

	$ mil.	% of total
U.S.	6,336	82
Canada	742	10
Europe Middle East & Africa	485	6
Asia Pacific	140	2
Other	15	0
Total	**7,719**	**100**

2017 Sales

	$ mil.	% of total
Finance charges net	4,171	54
Services	2,612	34
Redemption	935	12
Total	**7,719**	**100**

Selected Products and Services

Epsilon
  Marketing Services
  Agency services
  Database design & management
  Data services
  Analytical services
  Traditional & digital communications
LoyaltyOne
  AIR MILES Reward program
  Loyalty services
  Customer analytics
  Creative services
Private Label Services & Credit
  Receivables Financing
  Underwriting & risk management
  Receivables funding
  Processing Services
  New account processing
  Bill processing
  Remittance processing
  Customer care
  Marketing Services

COMPETITORS

ATCO I-Tek	Discover
Affinion Group	Maritz
American Express	PGi
Capital One	Payment Processing
Chockstone	Total System Services

HISTORICAL FINANCIALS

Company Type: Public

Income Statement

FYE: December 31

	REVENUE ($ mil.)	NET INCOME ($ mil.)	NET PROFIT MARGIN	EMPLOYEES
12/18	7,791	963	12.4%	20,000
12/17	7,719	788	10.2%	20,000
12/16	7,138	515	7.2%	17,000
12/15	6,439	596	9.3%	16,000
12/14	5,302	506	9.5%	15,000
Annual Growth	**10.1%**	**17.4%**	**—**	**7.5%**

2018 Year-End Financials

Debt ratio: 44.06%
Return on equity: 46.00%
Cash ($ mil.): 3,863
Current ratio: 2.15
Long-term debt ($ mil.): 10,527

No. of shares (mil.): 53
Dividends
  Yield: 1.5%
  Payout: 13.0%
Market value ($ mil.): 8,014

	STOCK PRICE ($) FY Close	P/E High/Low		PER SHARE ($) Earnings	Dividends	Book Value
12/18	150.08	16	8	17.49	2.28	43.67
12/17	253.48	19	15	14.10	2.08	33.49
12/16	228.50	38	24	7.34	0.52	28.89
12/15	276.57	35	28	8.85	0.00	33.02
12/14	286.05	34	27	7.87	0.00	37.55
Annual Growth	**(14.9%)**	**—**	**—**	**22.1%**	**—**	**3.8%**

Allstate Corp

Ya gotta hand it to Allstate: The "good hands" company has managed to work its way towards the top of the property/casualty insurance pile. Serving more than 16 million households the company is the second-largest personal lines insurer in the US just behind rival State Farm. Its Allstate Protection segment sells auto homeowners and other property/casualty insurance products in Canada and the US. Allstate Life provides life insurance through subsidiaries including Allstate Life and American Heritage Life. The group also provides voluntary benefits such as short-term disability and critical illness policies. Other units include Allstate Roadside Services and consumer protection plan provider SquareTrade.

Operations

Allstate operates through seven segments: Allstate Protection Service Businesses Allstate Life Allstate Benefits Allstate Annuities Discontinued Lines and Coverages and Corporate and Other.

The Allstate Protection segment's property and liability businesses — which cover about 16 million households — account for more than 90% of Allstate's total premiums. Most of the segment's sales come from traditional auto and homeowners policies. In addition to traditional policies Allstate sells specialty products including coverage for motorcycle and boat owners renters and landlords and mobile home dwellers. The segment includes subsidiaries Esurance (auto insurance) Encompass (package policies) and Answer Financial (agency sales) operate online. Commercial products are geared towards small business owners.

The Service Businesses segment includes consumer protection plan provider SquareTrade telematics unit Arity Allstate Roadside Services and Allstate Dealer Services.

In late 2017 the company restructured its former Allstate Financial segment into three separate segments. Allstate Life offers traditional interest-sensitive and variable life insurance products. Allstate Benefits provides voluntary benefits policies such as life accident short-term disability and critical illness policies. Allstate Annuities comprises the run-off annuity business which the company exited in 2014. While these segments account for approximately 10% of the company's total revenue Allstate primarily considers them to be useful for deepening relationships with Allstate Protection customers.

The Discontinued Lines and Coverages segment includes results from coverage Allstate no longer writes and run-off businesses.

Geographic Reach

Allstate's largest property/casualty markets are California Florida New York and Texas. The company operates throughout the US and in Puerto Rico the US Virgin Islands Guam and Canada. It has some 500 administrative claims handling data processing and other facilities in North America. It also leases properties in Northern Ireland (three) India (two) and London (two).

Sales and Marketing

Allstate maintains a network of about 10400 exclusive agencies which sell its Allstate-branded insurance products through approximately 24000 licensed sales professionals. It also offers these products and Encompass-branded products through some 2500 independent agencies that are primarily located in rural areas of the US.

Allstate Financial products are sold through exclusive agencies (and approximately 100 exclusive specialists) and 6000 workplace enrolling independent agents. Other products are sold through financial representatives online and over the phone.

In 2017 Allstate spend $8.3 million on advertising versus $11.2 million in 2016.

Financial Performance

Allstate's revenue has grown steadily over the past five years; it rose 5% to $38.5 billion in 2017. This gain was largely driven by a 3% or $1 billion increase in property and liability insurance premiums. The acquisition of consumer protection plan firm SquareTrade further helped overall revenue. Additionally the company saw net realized capital gains in 2017 versus net realized capital losses the prior year. These gains were partially offset by higher catastrophe losses related to hurricanes wildfires and wind and hail storms.

The higher revenue boosted net income (which had fallen in 2015 and 2016) by 70% to $3.2 billion. A benefit related to 2017 tax legislation also lifted its bottom line. However net income was negatively impacted by a $59 million net loss in the Service Businesses segment as the company invested in its various units.

Operating cash flow also rose increasing 8% to $4.3 billion.

Strategy

Allstate is focused on growing its number of insurance policies in force increasing premiums maintaining profitability in the auto segment and increasing returns in the homeowners and annuity segments. It is also focused on proactively managing its investments modernizing its operating model and building long-term growth platforms. To grow policy sales the company is enhancing its independent agency network (especially in targeted geographic areas) sales support organization and online sales platforms. It is also working to increase cross-sales of voluntary benefit products through its exclusive agents as well as to form new strategic alliances and develop new product offerings. For example the company has recently launched protection for home-sharing hosts and for Uber rideshare drivers. Allstate Canada introduced products to protect homeowners from sewer backups and water damage in 2018. Subsidiary Esurance

is expanding both by adding new complementary products and by launching its products in new geographical locations. At the same time Allstate is working to reduce its operational costs.

The company is continuing to invest in automotive telematics or wireless device technologies that track drivers' habits through which it can provide more accurate policy pricing.

Catastrophe management is also a key part of the company's stability. To limit its exposure to catastrophic claims in the face of increasing severe weather events in recent years Allstate has quit writing new homeowners policies in some coastal areas including California and Florida that are vulnerable to hurricane wind storms and earthquakes. In 2016 the company began writing a limited number of homeowner policies in certain areas of California. And while it still renews existing homeowners policies in California the company tweaked its underwriting to reduce exposure to claims for fires following earthquakes. Unfortunately 2017 had several major events including hurricanes severe storms and wildfires which caused the company more than $3 billion in catastrophe losses.

Mergers and Acquisitions

In 2018 Allstate bought Arizona-based InfoArmor which provides employee identity protection for $525 million. The acquisition added to Allstate Benefits' voluntary identity protection offerings.

In early 2017 Allstate acquired rapidly growing consumer protection plan provider SquareTrade which specializes in extended warranties for electronics devices. The $1.4 billion deal expanded Allstate's consumer-focused offerings adding some 25 million protection plans.

HISTORY

Allstate traces its origins to a friendly game of bridge played in 1930 on a Chicago-area commuter train by Sears president Robert Wood and a friend insurance broker Carl Odell. The insurance man suggested Sears sell auto insurance through the mail. Wood liked the idea financed the company and in 1931 put Odell in charge (that hand of bridge must have shown Wood that Odell was no dummy). The company was named Allstate after one of Sears' tire brands. Allstate was born just as Sears was beginning its push into retailing and Allstate went with it selling insurance out of all the new Sears stores.

Growth was slow during the Depression and WWII but the postwar boom was a gold mine for both Sears and Allstate. Suburban development made cars a necessity; 1950s prudence necessitated car insurance; and Sears made it easy to buy the insurance at their stores and increasingly at freestanding agencies.

In the late 1950s Allstate added home and other property/casualty insurance lines. It also went into life insurance — in-force policies zoomed from zero to $1 billion in six years the industry's fastest growth ever.

Sears formed Allstate Enterprises in 1960 as an umbrella for all its noninsurance operations. In 1970 that firm bought its first savings and loan (S&L). The insurer continued to acquire other S&Ls and to add subsidiaries throughout the 1970s and 1980s.

This strategy dovetailed with Sears' strategy which was to become a diversified financial services company. In 1985 Sears introduced the Discover Card through Allstate's Greenwood Trust Company. However by the late 1980s it was obvious Sears would never be a financial services giant. Moreover it was losing so much in retailing that by 1987 Allstate was the major contributor to corporate net income. Sears began to dismantle its financial empire in the 1990s.

Allstate also suffered from a backlash against high insurance rates. When Massachusetts instituted no-fault insurance in 1989 Allstate stopped writing new auto insurance there. Later the company had to refund $110 million to customers to settle a suit with California over rate rollbacks required by 1988's Proposition 103.

Allstate went public in 1993 when Sears sold about 20% of its stake. That year it began reducing its operations in Florida to protect itself against high losses from hurricanes. Two years later the retailer sold its remaining interest to its shareholders. Also in 1995 Allstate sold 70% of PMI its mortgage insurance unit to the public.

EXECUTIVES

Vice President, Sari Macrie
Svp Corporate Relations, Victoria Dinges
Chairman President And Ceo The Allstate Corporation And Allstate Insurance Company, Thomas J. Wilson, age 61, $1,200,000 total compensation
Vice President Finance, Norma Gorman
Senior Vice President, Bryan Anderson
Evp Marketing Innovation And Corporate Relations Allstate Insurance, Sanjay Gupta, age 51
President Allstate Financial, Mary Jane B. Fortin, $632,752 total compensation
President Service Businesses, Don Civgin, age 58, $776,885 total compensation
Evp Product Integration And Management, W. Guy Hill
Evp Product Operations Allstate Insurance, Steven P. Sorenson, age 55
Evp Brand Operations Allstate Insurance, Thomas M. Troy
Evp Technology And Strategic Ventures, Suren Gupta, age 57, $537,404 total compensation
President West Territory Allstate Personal Lines, Thomas F. Clarkson
President East Territory, David Prendergast
President Allstate Personal Lines, Glenn T. Shapiro
Evp Allstate Brand Distribution Allstate Insurance Company (aic), Katherine (Kathy) Mabe
Vice Chairman The Allstate Corporation And Allstate Insurance Company, Steven E. (Steve) Shebik, age 62, $770,673 total compensation
Evp General Counsel And Secretary Allstate Corp And Allstate Insurance Company (aic), Susan L. Lees, age 61
Evp Allstate Personal Lines Business Transformation, Brian R. Bohaty
Evp Human Resources, Harriet K. Harty, age 52
Evp And Chief Investment Officer; President Allstate Investments, John Dugenske
Evp And Cfo The Allstate Corporation And Allstate Insurance Company, Mario Rizzo
Field Vice President Midwest Region, Alice Byrne
Vice President Of Technology, Patricia Coffey
Assistant Vice President, Mark Mcgillivray
Assistant Vice President, Steve King
Assistant Vice President, Terrance Ray
Assistant Vice President, Kathy Winn
Assistant Vice President And Chief Actuary, Errol Cramer
Vice President And Assistant General Counsel, William Vainisi
Senior Vice President Corporate Relations, Stacy Sharpe
Vice President And Assistant General Counsel, Mary Jo quinn
Vice President Integrated Marketing Communications, Pam Hollander
Vice President National Accounts, Brian Frank
Senior Vice President And Chief Ethics Compliance And Privacy Officer, Kelly Noll
Project Management Office Vice President, Shawn Broadfield
Vice President Human Resources, Joseph Testor

Senior Vice President Marketing, Lisa Cochrane
Assistant Vice President, Jeffrey Deigl
Vice President Human Resources, Amy Mills
West Central Region Field Senior Vice President, Jeff Thompson
Vice President Investor Relations, Robert Block
Assistant Vice President Claims, James Murray
Field Senior Vice President, Troy Hawkes
Vice President Marketing And Business, Patrick Rogers
Assistant Vice President Claims, Christine Sullivan
Vice President Director Manager, Carl Majeski
Vice President Product Technology, Daniel Butch Necastro
Assistant Vice President Claims, Pam Overton
Assistant Vice President, James Haidu
Vice President Insurance Reserves, Shantelle Thomas
Senior Vice President Call Center, Dan Murray
Vice President Customer Experience, Christina Metzger
Vice President Of National Account Management, Kerry Flack
Senior Vice President Digital Transformation, Robert Wasserman
Field Vice President, Roger Odle
Vice President, Heather Vangrevenhof
Vice President And Senior Key Account Manager, Stephen Lipker
National Account Manager, Kimberly Purdy
Assistant Vice President P Ccso, Marcie Molek
Assistant Vice President Allstate Marketing Customer Communication Division, Richard Heneberry
Vice President Director Manager, Beth Drinan
Vice President Talent Acquisition, Cathy Winn
Senior Vice President Vehicle Product Management, Julie Parsons
Senior Vice President And Group Chief Information Officer, Peter Logothetis
Assistant Vice President, Ron Stouffer
Vice President Business Development, Jerry Lamparski
Vice President Business Development, Glenn Solfest
Senior Vice President, Kellie Rakes
Vice President, Elizabeth Smith
Assistant Vice President Finance, Kevin Corbett
Vice President Risk Assesment, Bob Roberts
Vice President Sales And Marketing, Alita Collier
Vice President, Angela Booles
Vice President, Steve Miller
Assistant Vice President And Assistant General Counsel, Steve Ihm
Vice President Manager Director, Bob Halter
Vice President Director Manager, Howard Gurvitz
Senior Vice President Human Resources, Joan Crockett
Assistant Vice President Talent Acquisition, Tom Hall
Vice President Business Development, Victoria Blake
Vice President, Tony Smid
Assistant Vice President Claims, Sharon Broome
Vice President, Shane O'Brien
Floridian Executive Vice President, George Grawe
Vice President Product Operations Allstate, Guy W Hill
Executive Vice President Human Resources, Liz Oppenhuis
Vice President Policy Administ, Lori Rutten
Executive Vice President, Christina Migielicz
Vice President Of Coiled Tubing And Cementing, Katie R Jones
Vice President Finance, Michael Kasper
Afvp, Brian Walsh
Vice President Finance, Joy Ann Sweet
Vice President Tax, Karen Gardner
Vice President, Ralph Eureste

Vice President Of Sales Emerging Businesses Affinity Solutions, Rob Gamble Rob Gamble
Vice President Field, Armond Bechard
Senior Vice President, Robert Apatoff
Assistant Vice President Compliance, Diane Ierna
Vice President Human Resources, Joan Naughton-Gerdes
Vice President Sales And Marketing Encompass At Allstate, Dan Maloney
Vice President Investor Relations, Cindy Guenther
Vice President Information Technology Group, James Baum
Vice President Marketing, Christian Lopez
Assistant Vice President Financial Resource Admin., Mike Scardina
Vice President, Jessica Rivera
Vice President Marketing, Lisad Cochrane
Vice President Risk Management, Jeffrey Thompson
Senior Vice President Human Resources, Solmirin Becky
Sr. Vice President, Robert Becker
Vice President, Bonnie Lee
Vice President Of Private Client Services, Luke Doebele
Senior Vice President And Treasurer, Jess Merten
Vice President, Brandon Richter
Senior Vice President, Donna Morgan
Vp And Assistant Treasurer, Stephanie Neely
Vice President Strategic Alliances, Pamela Reed
Vice President Agency Services, Christopher Gilbert
Senior Vice President Sales And Strategic Alliances, Neiciee Durrence
Vice President Agency Services, Debbie Shytle
Vice President, Pat Macellaro
Senior Vice President Global Business Development, Paul Lubbers
Vice President Agency Services, Shelley Conine
Vice President Business Development, David Burgis
Vice President Regional Sales Manager, Andrea Bolger
Vice President Allstate Sales Channel, Dennis Adams
Vice President Business Development, Erin Elliot
Assistant Vice President Information Technology Wo, Mike Escobar
Vice President Of Field, Thom Depagnier
Vice President National Field Sales, Joseph Mccormick
Second Vice President, Jamie Coyle
Executive Vice President, Tom Troy
Assistant Vice President Of Operations, Wesley Sadler
Vice President Of Sales And Marketing, Joe Jamerson
Vp Hr, Anthony Ciambrone
Executive Vice President, Koch Richard
Vice President, Reisinger Mark
Field Vice President, Mark Testa
Vice President, Christine Richards
Executive Vice President And Chief Operating Officer, Hooks Charlotte
Executive Vice President And Chief Distribution Officer, Aldrich Jason
Vice President, Bowers Mandy
Vice President, Cisneros Carlos
Treasurer, James Jonske
Treasurer, Michelle Ackerman
Board Member, Perry Traquina
Board Member, Jacques Perold
Board Member, Michael Eskew
Secretary, Larry Smith
Auditors: Deloitte & Touche LLP

LOCATIONS

HQ: Allstate Corp
2775 Sanders Road, Northbrook, IL 60062
Phone: 847 402-5000
Web: www.allstate.com

PRODUCTS/OPERATIONS

2017 Sales

	$ mil.	% of total
Property/liability		
Auto	21,878	57
Homeowners	7,310	19
Other personal lines	1,750	5
Commercial lines	495	1
Other business lines	883	2
Others	1,879	5
Allstate Financial	4,294	11
Corporate & other	35	-
Total	**38,524**	**100**

Selected Subsidiaries

Allstate Insurance Company of Canada
Allstate Life Insurance Company
Allstate Motor Club
American Heritage Life Insurance Company
Encompass Insurance Company
Esurance Insurance Company
Kennett Capital Inc.
Northbrook Indemnity Company
Pafco Insurance Company (Canada)

COMPETITORS

Farmers Group	Prudential
GEICO	State Farm
Hanover Insurance	The Hartford
Liberty Mutual	Torchmark
MetLife	Travelers Companies
Nationwide	USAA
Progressive Corporation	

HISTORICAL FINANCIALS

Company Type: Public

Income Statement

FYE: December 31

	ASSETS ($ mil.)	NET INCOME ($ mil.)	INCOME AS % OF ASSETS	EMPLOYEES
12/18	112,249	2,252	2.0%	45,700
12/17	112,422	3,189	2.8%	42,900
12/16	108,610	1,877	1.7%	43,500
12/15	104,656	2,171	2.1%	41,600
12/14	108,533	2,850	2.6%	40,200
Annual Growth	0.8%	(5.7%)	—	3.3%

2018 Year-End Financials

Debt ratio: 5.75%
Return on equity: 10.27%
Cash ($ mil.): 499
Current ratio: —
Long-term debt ($ mil.): —

No. of shares (mil.): 332
Dividends
  Yield: 2.2%
  Payout: 30.8%
Market value ($ mil.): 27,433

	STOCK PRICE ($) FY Close	P/E High/Low	PER SHARE ($) Earnings	Dividends	Book Value
12/18	82.63	17 13	5.96	1.84	64.19
12/17	104.71	12 9	8.36	1.48	63.52
12/16	74.12	16 12	4.67	1.32	56.21
12/15	62.09	14 11	5.05	1.20	52.56
12/14	70.25	11 8	6.27	1.12	53.36
Annual Growth	4.1%	— —	(1.3%)	13.2%	4.7%

ALLY BANK

Ally Bank is on your side when it comes to banking. Formerly known as GMAC Bank Ally Bank (which is a subsidiary of government-backed Ally Financial)Â offers savings and money market accounts as well as traditionalÂ and no-penalty CDs.

The online bank also offers interest checking accounts. The bankÂ offers its services online and over the phone; it operates no physical branch locations. Clients also can use any ATM in the US and Ally will reimburse any fees charged by other banks. Ally Bank was revamped and renamed in 2009 in the midst of GM's (very public) financial difficulties. Predecessor GMAC Bank had been in operation since 2001.

EXECUTIVES

Chb-Pres-Ceo, Diane E Morais
Exec V Pres, Jeffrey J Brown
Cfo, James N Young
Secretary, Cathy L Quenneville
Director of Remarketing Sales, Mark Juday
Operations Manager, Michael Snel
Area Sales Manager, Anthony Stoothoff
CRA Officer, Jan Bergeson
Senior Credit Manager, Anthony Zimmer

LOCATIONS

HQ: ALLY BANK
6985 S UNION PARK CTR # 435, MIDVALE, UT
840474177
Phone: 801 790-5005
Web: WWW.ALLY.COM

COMPETITORS

Bank of America	Citibank
BofI	E*TRADE Bank
Charles Schwab	State Farm

HISTORICAL FINANCIALS

Company Type: Private

Income Statement   FYE: December 31

	ASSETS ($ mil.)	NET INCOME ($ mil.)	INCOME AS % OF ASSETS	EMPLOYEES
12/16	123,547	1,273	1.0%	42
12/07*	28,472	291	1.0%	—
06/06	3,586	0	0.0%	—
Annual Growth	38.0%	114.3%	—	—

*Fiscal year change

Ally Financial Inc

Ally Financial wants to be your friend in the financing business. Ally operates branchless online-only retail bank Ally Bank which offers deposit mortgage (through Ally Home) and credit card products. Ally also provides auto financing for 18000 auto dealerships (mostly GM and Chrysler) and their customers. Ally Financial offers financing services for large- and mid-market companies through Ally Corporate Finance. Then known as GMAC the company was bailed out by the US government following the global financial crisis after which it took its current name. After several years of majority state ownership it went public in 2014.

Operations

Ally Financial carries more than $167 billion in assets. The company operates four business segments: Automotive Finance Insurance Mortgage and Corporate Finance.

Automotive Finance is Ally's biggest earner at some 70% of sales. The segment provides auto financing to consumers auto dealers companies and

municipalities. Insurance the next biggest at roughly 20% of sales offers consumer finance protection and insurance products through its automotive dealer channel. It also sells commercial insurance directly to dealers.

The Mortgage segment accounting for a few percent of sales manages a held-for-investment consumer mortgage portfolio and bulk purchases high-quality jumbo loans. The segment also offers direct-to-consumer mortgages under Ally Home consisting of a variety of jumbo and conforming fixed- and adjustable-rate mortgage products with the assistance of third-party fulfillment partner LenderLive.

Corporate Finance offers senior secured leveraged cash flow and asset-based loans to US-based middle market companies; it accounts for a few percent of Ally's total revenue.

Geographic Reach

Ally Financial focuses almost entirely on the US. It has corporate offices in Detroit; New York City; and Charlotte North Carolina. As an online-only bank Ally has no physical branch network. Its services are available in most US states with California and Texas having the highest concentrations of loans (at around 25% combined).

Sales and Marketing

Ally Financial and its subsidiaries serve 5.7 million consumers and 18500 auto dealers. Some of its top clients include General Motors and Chrysler.

Ally sells its consumer financial and insurance products primarily through the automotive dealer channel. It sells commercial insurance products directly to dealers. As a direct bank Ally Bank raises deposit funds via its internet telephone mobile and mail channels.

Financial Performance

Ally Financial's interest income from its primary businesses has increased by the low double-digits for a few years while revenue from its shrinking legacy GM operating lease portfolio has gone the opposite way to a more-or-less net neutral effect. Total revenue in fiscal 2017 increased an immaterial $31 million to $9.9 billion for that reason.

Net income fell 13% to $929 million as higher operating income was offset by an increase in provision for loan losses an increase in noninterest expense to support the launch of consumer and commercial product offerings and a $111 million increase in income tax paid during the year (relating to US tax reform at the tail end of 2017).

Cash and cash equivalents decreased $1.7 billion to $4.3 billion as cash from operations fell around $500 million; cash used in investing activities decreased $343 million due to lower purchases of available-for-sale securities; and cash from financing activities fell $1.6 billion due to changes in short-term borrowings.

Strategy

Ally is always looking for ways to develop and innovate on its products and services. To enhance its automotive finance offerings relationships and digital capabilities in 2017 Ally Financial expanded on the Blue Yield platform acquired in 2016 by introducing Clearlane an online automotive lender exchange. The product adds to Ally's direct-to-consumer capabilities and provides an end-to-end digital platform for consumers seeking financing and dealers looking to drive online sales. Clearlane generates revenue by charging fees for successful lead referrals to auto lenders and insurance providers and enhances the bank's ability to partner with other direct lenders and online auto distributors. The bank also grew its relationship with Carvana an online used car platform by providing $2 billion in purchases of retail installment sales contracts and warehouse financing.

Additionally Ally launched Ally Home a direct-to-consumer mortgage offering in December 2016. The product further fleshed out its online banking

service. Unlike Ally Bank's other products Ally Home's customers have access to a team of experts in the shape of the Ally Home Team.

Mergers and Acquisitions

In June 2016 Ally expanded into online brokerage after buying digital wealth management and broker-dealer TradeKing Group for $275 million. TradeKing had some $4.5 billion in client assets at the time. It also acquired assets from Blue Yield that Ally rebranded as Clearlane to expand its automotive financing offering.

Company Background

In February 2013 Ally sold its Canadian auto finance business to Royal Bank of Canada. A few months later it sold its Mexican insurance business ABA Seguros to ACE for $865 million. In October it sold its business in Europe and Latin America as well as a joint venture in China to GM Financial for $611 million. Also in 2013 it sold its business lending operations to Walter Investment Management Corp. completed the sales of agency mortgage servicing rights (MSRs) to Ocwen Financial Corp. and Quicken Loans Inc. and exited the correspondent lending channel.

Ally Financial was founded as a subsidiary of General Motors in 1919. It was owned by GM until 2006 when the automaker sold a 51% stake in the company to the Cerberus Capital Management investment group for some $7 billion.

EXECUTIVES

President Auto Finance, Timothy M. (Tim) Russi, age 56, $541,800 total compensation
Cio, Michael Baresich
Ceo And Director, Jeffrey J. (JB) Brown, age 45, $1,000,000 total compensation
President And Ceo Ally Commercial Finance Llc, William (Bill) Hall
President Consumer And Commercial Banking Products, Diane Morais, age 53, $550,000 total compensation
Cfo, Christopher A. Halmy, age 50, $600,000 total compensation
President Ally Insurance, Douglas Timmerman
Chief Risk Officer, David Shevsky, age 57, $500,000 total compensation
Executive Vice President Organizational Effectiveness, Renee Otjen
Chairman, Franklin W. (Fritz) Hobbs, age 71
Treasurer, Bradley Brown
Auditors: DELOITTE & TOUCHE LLP

LOCATIONS

HQ: Ally Financial Inc
Ally Detroit Center, 500 Woodward Avenue, Floor 10, Detroit, MI 48226
Phone: 866 710-4623
Web: www.ally.com

PRODUCTS/OPERATIONS

2017 sales

	$ mil.	% of total
Financing revenue and other interest income	8,322	84
Insurance premiums and service revenue earned	973	10
Gain on mortgage and automotive loans net	68	1
Other gain on investments net	102	1
Other income	408	4
Loss on extinguishment of debt	(7)	-
Total	**9,866**	**100**

2017 Sales

	% of total
Automotive Finance	71
Insurance	19
Corporate Finance	2
Mortgage Finance	4
Corporate and Other	4
Total	**100**

Selected Products and Services

Bank
Online Savings
Interest Checking
Money Market
Credit Card
Ally CashBack Credit Card
Auto
Personal
Business
RVs
Home Loans
Buy a Home
Refinance
Invest
Self-Directed Trading
Managed Portfolios
Forex & Futures
Research & Tools
Ally Invest API

COMPETITORS

Bank of America
Citigroup
Ford Motor Credit
Mercedes-Benz Credit
Mercedes-Benz Financial Services USA
Mitsubishi Motors Credit of America
Toyota Motor Credit
Volkswagen Financial Services

HISTORICAL FINANCIALS
Company Type: Public

Income Statement
FYE: December 31

	ASSETS ($ mil.)	NET INCOME ($ mil.)	INCOME AS % OF ASSETS	EMPLOYEES
12/18	178,869	1,263	0.7%	8,200
12/17	167,148	929	0.6%	7,900
12/16	163,728	1,067	0.7%	7,600
12/15	158,581	1,289	0.8%	7,100
12/14	151,828	1,150	0.8%	6,900
Annual Growth	4.2%	2.4%	—	4.4%

2018 Year-End Financials

Debt ratio: 26.09%	No. of shares (mil.): 404
Return on equity: 9.44%	Dividends
Cash ($ mil.): 4,537	Yield: 2.4%
Current ratio: —	Payout: 18.9%
Long-term debt ($ mil.): —	Market value ($ mil.): 9,175

	STOCK PRICE ($) FY Close	P/E High/Low	PER SHARE ($) Earnings	Dividends	Book Value
12/18	22.66	10 7	2.95	0.56	32.77
12/17	29.16	14 9	2.04	0.40	30.87
12/16	19.02	9 7	2.15	0.16	28.52
12/15	18.64	— —	(2.66)	0.00	27.88
12/14	23.62	4727 11	1.83	0.00	32.07
Annual Growth	(1.0%)	— —	12.7%	—	0.5%

Alphabet Inc

If you don't know what the term Google means there's a leading search engine you can use to find out. Core to the Google's business is its ubiquitous Search product; other key products and platforms include Android Chrome Gmail Google Drive Google Maps Google Play and YouTube which each have over one billion monthly active users worldwide. The firm generates revenue through ad sales in two categories: Performance Advertising creates and delivers relevant ads that users click on and Brand Advertising lets businesses run ad campaigns to promote brand awareness. Google is owned by Alphabet Inc. a holding company that also includes emerging businesses such as self-driving cars and drone delivery.

Operations

Because the technology industry demands constant innovation Google has been nothing short of relentless in its efforts to develop or acquire new services and products. Since its founding as search engine the company has branched out to provide a wide range of popular services such as Webmail (Gmail) interactive maps (Google Maps) Web browsing (Google Chrome) voice search (Google Assistant) and video (YouTube).

In addition its Android operating system is a platform for mobile products. Google hardware includes Pixel 3 phones Chromebook laptops Google Nest and the Google Home Hub smart display. The company sells digital content such as apps music and movies through Google Play Store. It also offers a suite of cloud computing services through Google Cloud.

Beyond its advertising business which accounts for the majority of revenue (85%) the firm generates a smaller share of revenue (about 15%) from apps movies music and other digital content purchased through Google Play; the sale of Google hardware devices; and Google Cloud offerings. Parent company Alphabet's non-Google offerings which fall under the "Other Bets" business unit account for less than half a percent of the holding company's revenue.

Despite this plethora of diverse offerings Google's original mission still remains: to organize the world?s information and make it universally accessible and useful.

Geographic Reach

The Mountain View California-based Google operates from more than 80 offices in some 50 countries. International domains include Google.ba Google.dm Google.nr Google.co.jp and Google.ca and the Google interface is available in more than 100 languages.

The US accounts for about 45% of Alphabet's revenue and Google is responsible for nearly all of Alphabet's revenue. Europe Middle East and Africa accounts for the next largest share of business (about 33%) followed by the Asia/Pacific region (some 15%) and Other Americas (about 5%).

Sales and Marketing

Google's parent company Alphabet reported sales and marketing expenses of $15.3 billion $12.9 billion and $10.5 billion in 2018 2017 and 2016 respectively. In 2018 the firm reported an increase in promotion related expenses for its Google Cloud offerings and the Google Assistant product as well as a 12% increase in headcount for employees in sales and marketing and related support functions.

Financial Performance

While Alphabet replaced Google as the company's publicly-traded entity in 2015 Alphabet's non-Google offerings which fall under the "Other Bets" business unit accounted for less than half a percent of the holding company's revenue in 2018. Operating as Google or Alphabet during the last five fiscal years the company has reported year-over-year revenue growth fueled by the increasing penetration of the internet across demographics and geographies. Sales have doubled since 2014.

In 2018 sales grew 23% to $136.8 billion led by an increase in mobile search and higher advertiser activity. Google experienced growth in video advertising on YouTube as well as growth in desktop search due to improvements in ad formats and delivery. The company also reported strength in programmatic buying and higher revenue from Google Cloud offerings hardware sales and in-app purchases.

Net income more than doubled in 2018 rising from $12.7 billion to $30.7 billion. The company benefited from a lower effective corporate tax rate thanks to the U.S. Tax Cuts and Jobs Act enacted in 2017. It also reported higher other income related to the adoption of new accounting standards.

Cash at the end of 2018 was $16.7 billion an increase of $6 billion from the prior year. Cash from operations contributed $48 billion to the coffers while investing activities used $28.5 billion mainly for capital expenditures. Financing activities used another $13.2 billion.

Strategy

A key part of Google's strategy is to deepen enhance and further the integration of its Google Cloud Platform. It also focused on continually improving the quality and applicability of its voice and translation services strengthening security rolling out machine-learning and natural language processing and enhancing its G Suite of communication tools (Gmail Docs Drive Calendar and Hangouts). Its Chrome Enterprise is an integrated back-end solution that provides the tools needed to run a business.

Meanwhile as consumers increasingly use smart phones to access the internet more people are looking at Google's ads more often. However the company's growth ? while still positive ? may be showing signs of a slowdown. Mobile ad views have increased substantially but these ads cost less than ads viewed on desktop computers so the price Google can command for mobile ads is less.

Despite massive and rapid growth (or perhaps because of it) Google faces its fair share of challenges. Critics of the company have alleged it engages in anti-competitive practices privacy violations and data leaks among other transgressions. Another concern for the company is rising costs. Google is spending more to acquire content for YouTube market new hardware products and build new data centers.

Mergers and Acquisitions

In 2019 Google agreed to buy Looker a developer of software for analyzing big data for $2.6 billion in cash. Looker would become part of the Google Cloud unit providing the unit's customers with business intelligence. The companies have done business together and share about 350 customers. The deal is Google's biggest since the $3.4 billion acquisition of Nest in 2014. The transaction was expected to close in 2019.

Earlier in 2019 Google agreed to acquire Alooma a company that helps companies move data from multiple locations to one data warehouse to accelerate growth of its cloud operations. In Google's case that single data warehouse would be its Google Cloud service. Google wants to make it as easy as possible to move customers to it cloud services as it tries to catch up with Amazon Web Services and Microsoft's Azure cloud services.

Company Background

Google is the product of two computer science grad students Sergey Brin and Larry Page who met in 1995 at Stanford University where they studied methods of searching and organizing large datasets. They discovered a formula to rank the order of random search results by relevancy and in 1997 they adopted the name Google to their findings. In 1998 the two presented their discovery at the World Wide Web Conference and by 1999 they had raised almost $30 million in funding from private investors venture capital firms and Stanford University. Later that year the Google site was launched.

In 2014 the once highly secretive company went public in one of the most anticipated IPOs ever raising $1.6 billion. Alphabet was launched the following as the holding company for Google and other subsidiaries. The corporate restructure was designed to provide some separation between

Google's core search business and its increasingly diverse side projects. Alphabet replaced Google as the publicly-traded entity.

HISTORY

Google is the product of two computer science grad students Sergey Brin and Larry Page who met in 1995 at Stanford University where they studied methods of searching and organizing large datasets. They discovered a formula to rank the order of random search results by relevancy and in 1997 they adopted the name Google to their findings. In 1998 the two presented their discovery at the World Wide Web Conference and by 1999 they had raised almost $30 million in funding from private investors venture capital firms and Stanford University. Later that year the Google site was launched.

Brin and Page hired tech industry veteran Eric Schmidt (former CTO at Sun Microsystems and former CEO of Novell) in 2001 as Google's CEO. Brin previously the company's chairman adopted the role of president of technology and Page previously CEO of Google became president of product. Also in 2001 Google launched AdWords its search-based advertising service. The following year the company launched another advertising service the context-based AdSense.

In 2004 the company entered the social networking sphere with the launch of its Orkut product which allows users (by invitation only) to search and connect with one another through online networks of friends. Later that year the once highly secretive company went public in one of the most anticipated IPOs ever raising $1.6 billion.

In October 2015 Google became a subsidiary of Alphabet Inc.

EXECUTIVES

Vice President Engineering Google, Vic Gundotra
Ceo, Sundar Pichai, age 47
Svp And Cfo Alphabet Inc. And Google Inc., Ruth M. Porat, age 62
President Enterprise Sales, Tariq M. Shaukat, age 46
Vp And Ceo Google Israel, Meir Brand
Vice President Google Creative Lab, Robert Wong
Vice President Finance, Tom Hutchinson
Vice President Of Marketing, Sherene Thompson
Board Member, Marc Ellenbogen
Auditors: Ernst & Young LLP

LOCATIONS

HQ: Alphabet Inc
1600 Amphitheatre Parkway, Mountain View, CA 94043
Phone: 650 253-0000
Web: www.abc.xyz

PRODUCTS/OPERATIONS

Selected Products & Advertising Platforms

AdWords
DoubleClick Digital Marketing
Google Analytics
Google Consumer Surveys
Google Display Network
Google for Retail
Google+ for Brands
YouTube

COMPETITORS

AOL	MSN
Apple Inc.	Myspace
Ask.com	NetEase
Baidu	SINA
Blucora	Shopping.com

CityGrid Media	Shopzilla
Conversant	Sohu.com
Daum Communications	Spotify
Facebook	Twitter
LiveJournal	Yahoo!
LookSmart	craigslist

HISTORICAL FINANCIALS

Company Type: Public

Income Statement — FYE: December 31

	REVENUE ($ mil.)	NET INCOME ($ mil.)	NET PROFIT MARGIN	EMPLOYEES
12/19	161,857	34,343	21.2%	118,899
12/18	136,819	30,736	22.5%	98,771
12/17	110,855	12,662	11.4%	80,110
12/16	90,272	19,478	21.6%	72,053
12/15	74,989	16,348	21.8%	61,814
Annual Growth	21.2%	20.4%	—	17.8%

2019 Year-End Financials

Debt ratio: 1.65%
Return on equity: 18.12%
Cash ($ mil.): 18,498
Current ratio: 3.37
Long-term debt ($ mil.): 4,554
No. of shares (mil.): 688
Dividends
Yield: —
Payout: —
Market value ($ mil.): 921,949

	STOCK PRICE ($) FY Close	P/E High/Low		Earnings	Dividends	Book Value
12/19	1,339.39	27	21	49.16	0.00	292.65
12/18	1,044.96	29	22	43.70	0.00	255.38
12/17	1,053.40	59	44	18.00	0.00	219.50
12/16	792.45	30	24	27.85	0.00	201.12
12/15	778.01	33	21	23.59	0.00	175.07
Annual Growth	14.5%	—	—	20.1%	—	13.7%

Altice USA Inc

Auditors: KPMG LLP

LOCATIONS

HQ: Altice USA Inc
1 Court Square West, Long Island City, NY 11101
Phone: 516 803-2300
Web: www.alticeusa.com

HISTORICAL FINANCIALS

Company Type: Public

Income Statement — FYE: December 31

	REVENUE ($ mil.)	NET INCOME ($ mil.)	NET PROFIT MARGIN	EMPLOYEES
12/18	9,566	18	0.2%	12,185
12/17	9,326	1,520	16.3%	9,414
12/16	6,017	(832)	—	15,300
Annual Growth	26.1%	—	—	(10.8%)

2018 Year-End Financials

Debt ratio: 67.87%
Return on equity: 0.40%
Cash ($ mil.): 298
Current ratio: 0.45
Long-term debt ($ mil.): 22,653
No. of shares (mil.): 709
Dividends
Yield: 12.3%
Payout: 6,783.3%
Market value ($ mil.): 11,713

	STOCK PRICE ($) FY Close	P/E High/Low		Earnings	Dividends	Book Value
12/18	16.52	77	6487	0.03	2.04	5.36
12/17	21.23	16	8	2.18	1.29	7.77
12/16	0.00	—		—(8,320.00)	0.00	20,977.02
/0.00	—			—(0.00)	0.00	(0.00)
Annual Growth	—	—	—	—	—	—

ALTICOR INC.

Where there's a will (and an army of independent sales representatives) there's Amway. Operated through holding company Alticor Amway is the world's top direct-selling company with millions of individual ABOs (Amway Business Owners) pitching everything from air filters to vitamins. The company makes some 450 unique products across the categories of nutrition (which generates about half of sales) beauty and personal care and home. It is active in more than 100 countries across the globe with Asia (led by China) its largest market. Alticor is controlled by the families of Rich DeVos and Jay Van Andel who founded Amway in 1959.

Operations
Nutrition products (supplements skin care products weight management programs) account for about 50% of total Amway sales. Beauty and personal care items (makeup shampoo toothpaste) generate about a quarter of sales and home products (water and air filters cookware cleaners) contribute about 20%. The company's top products include Nutrilite supplements Artistry color cosmetics eSpring water treatment systems and XS energy drinks.

Geographic Reach
Based in Ada Michigan Amway operates in more than 100 countries. Its top markets by sales are China the US and South Korea; other leading markets include India Japan Malaysia Russia Taiwan and Thailand.

The company has manufacturing facilities farms and warehouses in Brazil China Hungary India Japan Mexico the Netherlands Poland Russia South Korea Taiwan Thailand Vietnam and the US.

Sales and Marketing
Amway's 450-plus products are marketing worldwide by more than 3 million independent distributors who purchase the products and resell them. The company provides a host of support services including personal mentors brand centers online learning tools and call centers.

Financial Performance
While privately-owned Alticor doesn't report full results Amway reported global sales of $8.6 billion in 2017 down from $8.8 billion in 2016.The company points to a challenging Chinese market for its revenue decline over the past few years

Strategy
Amway's strategy is pretty straight-forward: continue to enhance and expand its line of products to serve more markets and appeal to more customers and create tools that make selling those products easier for the 3+ million ABOs (Amway Business Owners).

In 2017 Amway introduced a new formula for its Nutrilife Double X product one of the best-selling supplements in the world that includes a phytonutrient blend designed to help the body fight free radicals. Other additions to the company's product portfolio that year include a reformulated Essentials by Artistry skincare line and its first in-car air filtration system Atmosphere Drive. Amway also pushed its XS brand of energy drinks into new countries in 2017 including China and India with more launches planned for 2018. The company has more than 800 patents worldwide and another 250 pending applications.

Direct selling of course looks a lot different in the age of Amazon than it did some 60 years ago when Amway was founded. The company has been making significant investment in tools and technologies in recent years to enable its ABOs to better compete. It has spent some $70 million in mobile apps for ABOs including the flagship Amway MyBiz app which provides back office data and analytics. In addition Amway has boosted its own customer service capabilities with instant messaging bots and other technologies to help it handle the more than 12 million annual customer requests. Other recent initiatives include a content sharing app for ABOs in the Philippines a beauty app for customers in South Korea and a one-stop product education and purchase portal in for ABOs in China.

EXECUTIVES

President And Director; President Amway; And President Quixtar, Doug DeVos
Executive Vice President Of Sales Amway Regions, Jim Payne
General Vice President Attorney, Scott Balfour
Vice President Regulatory Affairs And Quality Assurance, John Coyle
Vice President Internal Audit, Nick Thole
Vp Human Resources, Kelly Savage
Chairman, Steve Van Andel
Tres, Jeffery C Tuori

LOCATIONS

HQ: ALTICOR INC.
 7575 FULTON ST E, ADA, MI 493550001
Phone: 616 787-1000
Web: WWW.AMWAY.COM

PRODUCTS/OPERATIONS

2017 Sales

	% of total
Nutrition	50
Beauty & personal care	26
Home	21
Other	3
Total	**100**

Selected Brands

Nutrition
 Nutrilite
Beauty & personal care
 Artistry
 G&H
 Glister
 Satinique
Home
 Amway Home
 Atmosphere Sky
 eSpring
 iCook
Other
 XS

COMPETITORS

Avon	Melaleuca
Bath & Body Works	New Avon
Bluestem Brands	Newell Brands
Colgate-Palmolive	Nikken
Estée Lauder	Nu Skin
Forever Living	Procter & Gamble
GNC	Revlon

Herbalife Ltd.	Shaklee
Johnson & Johnson	Tupperware Brands
L'Oréal	Unilever PLC
Mary Kay	

HISTORICAL FINANCIALS

Company Type: Private

Income Statement   FYE: December 31

	REVENUE ($ mil.)	NET INCOME ($ mil.)	NET PROFIT MARGIN	EMPLOYEES
12/16	8,783	0	—	14,000
12/15	9,459	0	—	—
12/14	10,804	0	—	—
12/13	11,754	0	—	—
Annual Growth	(9.3%)	—	—	—

Altria Group Inc

The house the Marlboro Man built Altria Group owns the largest cigarette company in the US. Altria operates through subsidiary Philip Morris USA which sells Marlboro — the world's #1-selling cigarette brand. Controlling about half of the US tobacco market Altria manufactures cigarettes under the Parliament Virginia Slims and Basic brands among many others. Altria however has diversified from solely a cigarette maker to a purveyor of cigars and pipe tobacco through John Middleton Co. and Nat Sherman; smokeless tobacco products through UST; and wine through Ste. Michelle Wine Estates. The company also owns a 10% stake in brewing giant AB InBev.

HISTORY

Philip Morris opened his London tobacco store in 1847 and by 1854 was making his own cigarettes. Morris died in 1873 and his heirs sold the firm to William Thomson just before the turn of the century. Thomson introduced his company's cigarettes to the US in 1902. American investors bought the rights to leading Philip Morris brands in 1919 and in 1925 the new company Philip Morris & Co. introduced Marlboro which targeted women smokers and produced modest sales.

When the firm's larger competitors raised their prices in 1930 Philip Morris Companies countered by introducing inexpensive cigarettes that caught on with Depression-weary consumers. By 1936 it was the fourth-biggest cigarette maker.

The firm acquired Benson & Hedges in 1954. It signed ad agency Leo Burnett which promptly initiated the Marlboro Man campaign. Under Joseph Cullman (who became president in 1957) Philip Morris experienced tremendous growth overseas. After dipping to sixth place among US tobacco companies in 1960 it rebounded at home thanks to Marlboro's growing popularity among men (Marlboro became the #1 cigarette brand in the world in 1972).

In 1970 Philip Morris bought the nation's seventh-largest brewer Miller Brewing and with aggressive marketing it vaulted to #2 among US beer makers by 1980. To protect itself against a shrinking US tobacco market in 1985 Philip Morris paid $5.6 billion for General Foods (Kool-Aid Post Stove Top). In 1988 it bought Kraft (Miracle Whip Velveeta). The next year Philip Morris joined Kraft with General Foods.

In 1994 Australian Geoffrey Bible became CEO. By late 1998 the company and its rivals had settled tobacco litigation with most states agreeing to pay about $250 billion over 25 years to receive protection from further state suits.

In 1999 Philip Morris bought three cigarette brands (L&M Chesterfield and Lark) from the Brooke Group. The US government filed a massive lawsuit against Big Tobacco and Philip Morris admitted — no kidding — that smoking increases the risk of getting cancer and other illnesses.

In 2000 Philip Morris vowed to appeal after a state court awarded $74 billion in punitive damages to Florida smokers. The court later ruled that Philip Morris Lorillard and the Liggett Group would pay at least $709 million in the case regardless of the outcome but would not have to pay damages until after the appeals are resolved. A Los Angeles jury awarded Richard Boeken $3 billion in punitive damages. The company appealed even after Boeken later agreed to reduced damages of $100 million. (Boeken died in 2002.)

In December 2000 Philip Morris completed its purchase of Nabisco Holdings for $18.9 billion. In June 2001 Philip Morris spun off Kraft Foods in what was the second-largest IPO in US history; it retained an 84% stake in the company and 97% of the voting rights.

In April 2002 CFO Louis Camilleri succeeded Bible as CEO; in September Camilleri became chairman upon Bible's retirement. In July 2002 Philip Morris sold Miller Brewing to South African Breweries for $5.6 billion ($3.6 billion in SAB stock and the assumption of $2 billion in Miller debt) in July 2002.

In the ongoing saga of tobacco-related litigation Philip Morris said it would appeal an October 2002 verdict by a California jury that ordered the company to pay $28 billion in punitive damages the most ever in an individual tobacco liability lawsuit (later reduced to $28 million). In January 2003 Philip Morris changed its name to Altria Group in an effort to distance itself from its tobacco litigation. In April a Florida appeals court threw out the state's multibillion-dollar judgment (made in 2000) against Philip Morris USA and four other US tobacco companies stating that thousands of Florida smokers could not lump their complaints together in a single case.

In March 2003 Philip Morris USA lost an Illinois lawsuit which claimed the company's use of the word "light" was misleading and violated Illinois consumer fraud laws. The judge ordered Philip Morris USA to pay damages of $10 billion and post a $12 billion bond. The Illinois Supreme Court has lowered the bond to $7 billion and agreed to hear Philip Morris USA's appeal of the original verdict.

In 2005 Altria purchased a $4.8 billion stake in Indonesia's third-largest tobacco firm PT Hanjaya Mandala Sampoerna which makes kreteks or clove cigarettes. Also in 2005 the company formed a long-term alliance with China National Tobacco Corp.

In mid-2006 Altria unseated Roger Deromedi from Kraft's top spot and appointed Irene Rosenfeld to head the company. The executive realignment was part of Altria's plan to spin off Kraft. Deromedi a 28-year Kraft veteran had been under fire for the unit's stale sales since taking over as sole CEO in 2003. Rosenfeld spent more than 20 years at Kraft and exited the firm in mid-2003 as president of Kraft Foods North America. The former chairman and CEO of Frito-Lay Rosenfeld is known for her integration expertise as well as restructuring and turning around companies.

In March 2007 Altria completed the spinoff of Kraft Foods to Altria shareholders. Also in 2007 Altria bought US cigar maker John Middleton from privately held Bradford Holdings. Based in Pennsylvania John Middleton specializes in machine-made cigars — most notably the Black & Mild brand. The deal was valued at $2.2 billion. A year later in March 2008 Altria spun off its Philip Morris International arm also to shareholders and moved its headquarters from New York City's Park Avenue to Richmond Virginia to be closer to its bread and butter operations. (As part of the move Altria in late 2007 agreed to sell the headquarters that has housed the firm since 1982 to a unit of privately held Global Holdings for some $525 million. Altria relocated about 100 of its about 500 employees in the move from New York City to Richmond.)

In January 2009 the company purchased smokeless tobacco maker UST as well as its wine business. The $11 billion deal gave Altria a significant foothold in the US smokeless tobacco market garnering popular brands Copenhagen and Skoal into Altria's fold. Following the acquisition Altria consolidated the sales forces of UST's U.S. Smokeless Tobacco brands and Philip Morris USA and relocated U.S. Smokeless Tobacco Company to Richmond Virginia. Altria has since launched a new versions of certain brands designed to compete with value-priced brands such as Reynolds American's Grizzly and Swedish Match AB's Timber Wolf.

In June 2009 the passage of the Family Smoking and Tobacco Control Act by the US Congress gave the U.S. Food and Drug Administration unprecedented authority to regulate tobacco products including the authority to regulate marketing ban candy flavorings and reduce nicotine in tobacco products.

EXECUTIVES

Chairman President And Ceo, Martin J. (Marty) Barrington, $1,408,333 total compensation

President And Ceo Ste. Michelle Wine Estates, Theodor P. (Ted) Baseler

Svp Research Development And Regulatory Affairs And Chief Innovation Officer, James E. (Jim) Dillard, $530,833 total compensation

President And Ceo Altria Group Distribution, Craig A. Johnson, $901,667 total compensation

Coo, Howard A. Willard, $833,333 total compensation

President And Ceo U.s. Smokeless Tobacco, Brian W. Quigley

Cfo, William F. (Billy) Gifford, $640,833 total compensation

Evp And General Counsel, Denise F. Keane, $938,500 total compensation

Vp Investor Relations Altria Client Services, Clifford B. (Cliff) Fleet

President Nu Mark, Jody L. Begley

Vp And Cio, Daniel C. Cornell

Svp Corporate Citizenship Altria Client Services, Jennifer Hunter

Vice President State Government Affairs, Henry Turner

Vice President Human Resources, Rodger Rolland

Svp Communications And Corporate Affairs Ste. Michelle Wine Estates, Kari Leitch

Senior Vice President Compliance Officer, Elizabeth Escalera

Svp Research Development And Sciences; Chief Innovation Officer, James Dillard Iii

Vice President, Nicole Bielawski

Auditors: PricewaterhouseCoopers LLP

LOCATIONS

HQ: Altria Group Inc
6601 West Broad Street, Richmond, VA 23230
Phone: 804 274-2200
Web: www.altria.com

PRODUCTS/OPERATIONS

2018 Sales

	$ mil.	% of total
Smokeable products	22,297	88
Smokeless products	2,262	9
Wine	691	3
All Other	114	-
Total	**25,364**	**100**

COMPETITORS

Altadis U.S.A.	Loews
British American Tobacco	North Atlantic Trading
	Ravenswood Winery
Constellation Brands	Reynolds American
E. & J. Gallo	Sebastiani Vineyards
Imperial Brands	Swedish Match
Japan Tobacco	Treasury Wine Estates

HISTORICAL FINANCIALS

Company Type: Public

Income Statement				FYE: December 31
	REVENUE ($ mil.)	NET INCOME ($ mil.)	NET PROFIT MARGIN	EMPLOYEES
12/18	25,364	6,963	27.5%	8,300
12/17	25,576	10,222	40.0%	8,300
12/16	25,744	14,239	55.3%	8,300
12/15	25,434	5,241	20.6%	8,800
12/14	24,522	5,070	20.7%	9,000
Annual Growth	0.8%	8.3%	—	(2.0%)

2018 Year-End Financials

Debt ratio: 46.27%
Return on equity: 46.17%
Cash ($ mil.): 1,333
Current ratio: 0.20
Long-term debt ($ mil.): 11,898

No. of shares (mil.): 1,874
Dividends
Yield: 6.0%
Payout: 81.5%
Market value ($ mil.): 92,560

	STOCK PRICE ($) FY Close	P/E High/Low	PER SHARE ($) Earnings	Dividends	Book Value
12/18	49.39	19 13	3.68	3.00	7.89
12/17	71.41	15 12	5.31	2.54	8.09
12/16	67.62	10 8	7.28	2.35	6.57
12/15	58.21	23 18	2.67	2.17	1.47
12/14	49.27	20 13	2.56	2.00	1.53
Annual Growth	0.1%	— —	9.5%	10.7%	50.7%

Amazon.com Inc

Amazon.com began as Earth's biggest bookstore but has become Earth's biggest everything store. Its website still offers millions of books as well as other media home furnishings clothing pet supplies office products and hundreds of other product categories (with items often ordered and delivered the same day). The company is also the dominant cloud services provider (through Amazon Web Services or AWS) an influential entertainment company through its video streaming operations a force to be reckoned with in grocery with its ownership of natural foods chain Whole Foods and a leader in digital personal assistant devices with Alexa and its Echo product line.

HISTORY

Jeff Bezos was researching the Internet in the early 1990s for hedge fund D.E. Shaw. He realized that book sales would be a perfect fit with e-commerce because book distributors already kept meticulous electronic lists. Bezos who as a teen had dreamed of entrepreneurship in outer space took the idea to Shaw. The company passed on the idea but Bezos ran with it trekking cross country to Seattle (close to a facility owned by major book distributor Ingram) and typing up a business plan along the way.

Bezos founded Amazon.com in 1994. After months of preparation he launched a website in July 1995 (Douglas Hofstadter's Fluid Concepts and Creative Analogies was its first sale); it had sales of $20000 a week by September. Bezos and his team kept working with the site pioneering features that now seem mundane such as one-click shopping customer reviews and e-mail order verification.

Amazon went public in 1997. Moves to cement the Amazon.com brand included becoming the sole book retailer on AOL's website and Netscape's commercial channel.

In 1998 the company launched its online music and video stores and it began to sell toys and electronics. Amazon also expanded its European reach with the purchases of online booksellers in the UK and Germany and it acquired the Internet Movie Database. Bezos also expanded the company's base of online services buying Junglee (comparison shopping) and PlanetAll (address book calendar reminders).

By midyear Amazon.com had attracted so much attention that its market capitalization equaled the combined values of profitable bricks-and-mortar rivals Barnes & Noble and Borders Group even though their combined sales were far greater than the upstart's. Late that year Amazon formed a promotional link with Hoover's publisher of this profile.

After raising $1.25 billion in a bond offering early in 1999 Amazon.com began a spending spree with deals to buy all or part of several dotcoms. However some have since been sold (HomeGrocer.com) and others have gone out of business or bankrupt — Pets.com living.com (furniture). It also bought the catalog businesses of Back to Basics and Tool Crib of the North.

Amazon.com began conducting online auctions in early 1999 and partnered with venerable auction house Sotheby's. Also that year Amazon added distribution facilities including one each in England and Germany.

In 2000 the company inked a 10-year deal with Toysrus.com to set up a co-branded toy and video game store. (The partnership came to a bitter end in 2006 after Toys "R" Us sued Amazon.com when it began selling toys from other companies.) Also that year Amazon.com added foreign-language sites for France and Japan.

In 2001 Amazon cut 15% of its workforce as part of a restructuring plan that also forced a $150 million charge. That year the company also made a deal with Borders to provide inventory fulfillment content and customer service for borders.com. As part of a deal to expand their marketing partnership AOL invested $100 million in Amazon.com in 2001. Later that year Amazon purchased some assets from Egghead.com (which filed for Chapter 11 in August) and relaunched the site.

In 2002 the firm introduced clothing sales featuring hundreds of retailers including names such as The Gap Nordstrom and Lands' End. Amazon.com received accreditation from ICANN (the Internet Corporation for Assigned Names and Numbers) as an Internet domain name registrar becoming one of about 160 entities permitted to register Internet addresses.

The company launched its Search Inside the Book feature in 2003. The tool allows customers to search the text inside books for more relevant search returns. At launch the search feature covered more than 120000 books from over 190 publishers. Amazon expanded into China in 2004 with the purchase of Joyo.com. (It renamed the unit Joyo Amazon in 2007.)

In 2005 Amazon launched Amazon Prime a two-day shipping service for an annual fee of $79.

Amazon.com began testing the online dry grocery waters in 2006. It launched the Amazon Fresh delivery service for the Seattle area a year later to include perishables.

The company acquired shopping site Shopbop.com in 2006 boosting its apparel offerings. Also that year IBM filed a pair of patent infringement lawsuits alleging that Amazon.com has been violating at least five of its patents — including technologies that govern how the online retailer handles product recommendations and displays advertising — for about four years. In 2007 the two companies settled the litigation and signed a long-term patent cross-license agreement.

The Internet bookseller in November 2007 introduced the Kindle an electronic portable book reader. The launch Amazon's first foray into the tech hardware market is aimed at kindling demand for electronic books.

Also in 2007 Amazon launched Endless.com which sells shoes and accessories; Askville.com where users can solicit answers from others on the site; and the Amazon MP3 site which offers digital music free of copyright restrictions. In addition Amazon acquired audiobook publisher Brilliance Audio.

Amazon stayed focused on entertainment in 2008. The company launched Amazon Video On Demand a service that gives customers the option to stream or download ad-free digital movies and TV shows on Macs or PCs. It also purchased AbeBooks an online retailer of more than 110 million primarily used rare and out-of-print books as well as Shelfari a social-networking site for booklovers. Additionally Amazon.com sold its UK and German online DVD rental services to Internet movie-rental company LOVEFiLM International in exchange for stock. The deal gave Amazon about a 40% stake in LOVEFiLM.

Shopping was also at the top of Amazon's list in 2008. In May the company invested in The Talk Market a user-generated TV Shopping Channel. In June Amazon launched an online office supplies store and sewed up the acquisition of the online fabrics retailer Fabrics.com.

In June 2009 Amazon agreed to pay Toys "R" Us $51 million to settle a dispute dating back to 2004. The settlement was related to a partnership that gave the toy seller exclusive rights to supply some of the toys on Amazon's site. In November Amazon completed its $888 million acquisition of shoe e-tailer Zappos.com — the #1 online shoe and apparel retailer. (Besides footwear and clothing Zappos also sells handbags housewares and beauty products.) The purchase allowed Amazon to boost its sales and expand its products portfolio by leveraging Zappos' widely recognized customer service expertise.

In mid-2010 Amazon acquired Woot Inc. a pioneer in the deal-of-the-day genre of online retailing. While neither Amazon or Woot would disclose the selling price reports valued the deal at about $110 million in cash.

In January 2011 Amazon completed its move to a new corporate headquarters in Seattle's South Lake Union neighborhood. Amazon also made several acquisitions that year. The company acquired the remaining shares it didn't already own in LOVEFiLM International. It purchased a pair of UK companies: online book seller The Book Depository and digital agency Pushbutton (later folding the operation into its Amazon Development Centre in London). The behemoth also picked up

voice-to-text startup Yap based in Charlotte North Carolina that year.

Kiva Systems which Amazon bought in 2012 was purchased to provide the firm with a boost in automation capabilities. Amazon picked up some former talent including Amazon ex Dave Schappell when it bought online education marketplace Teachstreet and shuttered the site in 2012. Acquiring England's Evi and its namesake cloud-based Artificial Intelligence expertise in 2012 offered Amazon a leg up in answer engine technology.

To extend the reach of its Kindle range Amazon in 2013 acquired Poland's IVONA Software. Months after being bought by Amazon in 2013 social cataloging company Goodreads announced it had amassed some 20 million members. In 2013 Amazon also purchased electrowetting display panel expert Liquavista from Samsung Electronics which had held the company for fewer than three years.

Investments in 2014 include acquiring the .buy domain for nearly $4.6 million. Besides the domain purchase Amazon has been focused on games. It acquired Silent Hill: Homecoming video game developer Double Helix Games based in Irvine California. Its newest release Strider is available on five platforms. Amazon also bought cloud-based digital comics platform ComiXology in 2014. In late 2014 Amazon purchased game-streaming site Twitch which boasted 55 million monthly active users after talks with Google turned to anti-trust concerns.

EXECUTIVES

Ceo Worldwide Consumer Business, Jeffrey A. (Jeff) Wilke, age 53, $175,000 total compensation
Chairman President And Ceo, Jeffrey P. (Jeff) Bezos, age 56, $81,840 total compensation
Ceo Amazon Web Services, Andrew R. (Andy) Jassy, age 52, $175,000 total compensation
Svp And Cfo, Brian T. Olsavsky, $160,000 total compensation
Vice President, Sharon Chiarella
Vice President Home Improvements, John Witham
Vice President, Seth Dallaire
Vice President, David Criscione
Vice President Worldwide Discovery, Kim Rachmeler
Vice President E Commerce Platform Services, Gene Pope
Vice President Information Technology, Kathryn Giorgianni
Vice President Corporate Sales Development, Robert Saltzman
Vice President Logistics, Michael Indresano
Vice President Global Inventory Platform, Jason Murray
Vice President Finance Softlines, Rebecca Hollingsworth
Vice President, Adrian Cockcroft
Senior Vice President, Steve Kessel
Auditors: Ernst & Young LLP

LOCATIONS

HQ: Amazon.com Inc
   410 Terry Avenue North, Seattle, WA 98109-5210
Phone: 206 266-1000   **Fax:** 206 266-1821
Web: www.amazon.com

2018 Sales

	$ mil.	% of total
North America	141,366	61
International	65,866	28
AWS	25,655	11
Total	**232,887**	**100**

2018 Sales

	$ mil.	% of total
US	160,146	69
Germany	19,881	9
UK	14,524	6
Japan	13,829	6
Other countries	24,507	10
Total	**232,887**	**100**

PRODUCTS/OPERATIONS

2018 Sales

	$ mil.	% of total
Online stores	122,987	53
Third-party seller services	42,745	18
AWS	25,655	11
Physical stores	17,224	8
Subscription services	14,168	6
Other	10,108	4
Total	**232,887**	**100**

Selected Departments

Apparel shoes and jewelry
Books
   Books
   Kindle e-books
   Textbooks
   Magazines
Computers and office
   Computers and accessories
   Computer components
   Office products and supplies
   PC games
   Software
Digital downloads
   Amazon shorts
   Game downloads
   Kindle Store
   MP3 downloads
Electronics
   Audio TV and home theater
   Camera photo and video
   Car electronics and GPS
   Cell phones and service
   Home appliances
   MP3 and media players
   Musical instruments
   Video games
Grocery health and beauty
   Beauty
   Diapers
   Gourmet food
   Grocery
   Health and personal care
   Natural and organic
Home and garden
   Bedding and bath
   Furniture and decor
   Home appliances
   Home improvement
   Kitchen and dining
   Patio lawn and garden
   Pet supplies
   Sewing craft and hobby
   Vacuums and storage
Kindle
   Books
   Blogs
   Magazines
   Newspapers
Movies music and games
   Blu-ray
   Movies and TV
   Music
   Musical instruments
   Video games
   Video On Demand
Sports and outdoors
   Action sports
   Camping and hiking
   Cycling
   Exercise and fitness
   Fan gear
   Golf
   Team sports
Tools auto and industrial
   Automotive
   Home improvement
   Industrial and scientific

Lighting and electrical
Motorcycle and ATV
Outdoor power equipment
Plumbing fixtures
Power and hand tools
Toys kids and baby
 Apparel (kids and baby)
 Baby
 Books
 Movies
 Music
 Software
 Toys and games
 Video games

Selected Operations

A9.com (search technology development)
Amazon.ca (Canada)
Amazon.cn (China)
Amazon.de (Germany)
Amazon.fr (France)
Amazon.co.jp (Japan)
Amazon.co.uk (UK)
Audible (audiobooks and other recorded content)
Endless (shoes and handbags)
Internet Movie Database (IMDb)
IVONA Software
Joyo (China)
LOVEFiLM International Ltd.
Whole Foods Market (grocery stores)
Woot.com (US)
Zappos.com (US)

COMPETITORS

Alibaba Group	Netflix
Costco Wholesale	Overstock.com
Google	Sprouts
HSN	Target Corporation
Home Depot	Wal-Mart
Kroger	Wayfair
Lowe's	eBay
Microsoft	

HISTORICAL FINANCIALS

Company Type: Public

Income Statement   FYE: December 31

	REVENUE ($ mil.)	NET INCOME ($ mil.)	NET PROFIT MARGIN	EMPLOYEES
12/19	280,522	11,588	4.1%	798,000
12/18	232,887	10,073	4.3%	647,500
12/17	177,866	3,033	1.7%	566,000
12/16	135,987	2,371	1.7%	341,400
12/15	107,006	596	0.6%	230,800
Annual Growth	27.2%	110.0%	—	36.4%

2019 Year-End Financials

Debt ratio: 10.39%	No. of shares (mil.): 498
Return on equity: 21.95%	Dividends
Cash ($ mil.): 55,021	Yield: —
Current ratio: 1.10	Payout: —
Long-term debt ($ mil.): 23,414	Market value ($ mil.): 920,224

	STOCK PRICE ($) FY Close	P/E High/Low	PER SHARE ($) Earnings	Dividends	Book Value
12/19	1,847.84	86 64	23.01	0.00	124.62
12/18	1,501.97	99 57	20.14	0.00	88.69
12/17	1,169.47	189 119	6.15	0.00	57.25
12/16	749.87	169 96	4.90	0.00	40.43
12/15	675.89	542 224	1.25	0.00	28.42
Annual Growth	28.6%	—	—107.1%	—	44.7%

Ambac Financial Group, Inc.

Ambac has scaled back in a major way. Holding company Ambac Financial operates through subsidiaries including its flagship unit Ambac Assurance Everspan Financial Guarantee and Ambac Assurance UK. The businesses offered financial guarantees and related services to customers around the world. Ambac Assurance guaranteed public finance and structured finance obligations but it has stopped offering new business and placed its existing business in run-off (meaning it still accepts premium payments due on existing policies and pays out claims as it can).

Operations

In addition to its core financial guarantee offerings in better days Ambac also insured infrastructure and utility finance deals internationally. Its Ambac Financial Services unit offered interest rate swaps credit swaps and investment management primarily to states and municipal authorities tied to their bond financing. These operations are also in run-off through means including transaction terminations settlements and scheduled contract amortizations.

How did a once-solid municipal bond insurer fall so hard? Along with other US bond insurers including FGIC and MBIA the US subprime mortgage meltdown knocked the wind out of Ambac. Its financial guarantee business fizzled and the company began to post heavy losses. Meanwhile Ambac's portfolio bulged with collateralized debt obligations (CDOs) of asset-backed securities — the financial equivalent of a sack of rotten potatoes once the credit markets turned sour.

Geographic Reach

Ambac's run-off operations primarily bring in revenues from the US market which accounts for three-fourths of revenues. The company also has international operations (also in runoff) in markets including the UK (some 20% of revenues) Australia Austria Germany and Italy.

Financial Performance

Ambac's run-off (existing account) insurance operations brought in some $644 million in revenues in 2015 nearly doubling that of 2014. Those improved earnings marked a turnaround after a couple of years of declining revenues; they were a result of increased premiums earned lower losses on derivatives and a gain on extinguishment of debt.

Net income has remained relatively flat for the past few years and in 2015 rose a modest 2% to $492 million. That was thanks to the higher revenue but partially offset by goodwill impairment charges incurred in 2014.

After reporting an operating cash outflow of $971 million in 2014 Ambac had an inflow of operating cash totaling $87.5 million in 2015 as it has lower losses and loss expenses.

Strategy

Ambac is hoping to diversify its business and has its sights set on either buying or developing new business. It is interested in such activities as advisory services asset management and even insurance. In late 2015 the group launched a residential property investment program.

HISTORY

Mortgage Guaranty Insurance Corporation (MGIC) in 1971 founded American Municipal Bond Assurance Corporation (Ambac Indemnity) in Milwaukee. That year Ambac wrote the very first municipal bond insurance policy — for a bond to fund a medical building and a sewage treatment facility in Juneau Alaska. New York City's 1975 moratorium on debt payments helped make the new product more attractive. The company wrote the first insurance policies for mutual funds (1977) and secondary market municipal bonds (1983). In 1981 Ambac moved to New York; four years later it became a Citibank subsidiary. It went public in 1991.

In 1995 Ambac and rival MBIA allied to offer bond insurance overseas. Two years later the company formed a UK subsidiary to serve Europe. In recognition of the growing market the joint venture was amended in 2000 to provide for individual operations by the two partners in Europe though they continued to reinsure each other there and to work jointly in Japan. Ambac went on a buying spree in 1996 and 1997 buying the investment advisory and broker dealer operations of Cadre and Construction Loan Insurance (renamed Connie Lee Holdings) a guarantor of college bonds and hospital infrastructure bonds.

In 1998 as Ambac lost share in the US municipal bond market because it declined to cut premiums the company began concentrating on asset-backed securities and international bonds. Two years later Ambac entered the Japanese market through a joint venture with Yasuda Fire & Marine.

In late 2010 after missing a scheduled interest payment and failing to reach an agreement for a prepackaged bankruptcy proceeding with its creditors the company voluntarily filed for Chapter 11 bankruptcy protection. Through the filing Ambac hoped to restructure more than $1.6 billion in outstanding debt. The company also haggled with the IRS over $700 million in allegedly improper tax refunds received between 2003 and 2008.

The bankruptcy court approved a plan of reorganization for Ambac in 2012 and the plan went into effect the following year.

EXECUTIVES

Senior Managing Director Chief Accounting Officer And Controller, Robert B. Eisman, age 51, $500,000 total compensation

President And Ceo Ambac Financial Group And Ambac Assurance Corporation, Claude L. LeBlanc, age 54

Senior Managing Director Cfo And Treasurer, David Trick, age 48, $770,000 total compensation

President Ceo And Director, Nader Tavakoli, age 60, $1,800,000 total compensation

Senior Managing Director And General Counsel, Stephen M. Ksenak, age 53, $525,000 total compensation

Senior Managing Director Restructuring And Corporate Development, David Barranco, age 48

Senior Managing Director Cio And Chief Administrative Office, Michael Reilly, age 62

Assistant Vice President Business Applications And Support, Sarbah Arthur

Vice President Automation Support, Alexandre Duarte

Assistant Vice President And Closing Coordinator, Yolanda Ortiz

Vice President, Valerie Anderson

First Vice President Structured Real Estate, Gregory Mayer

Vice President, Gary Stein

First Vice President, Sunil Rao

Vice President Technology, Scott Brown

Senior Vice President Internal Auditing, Dean Rogers

Assistant Vice President Risk Operations, Pranay Nadkarni

Assistant Vice President Finance, Chris Dudonis

Vice President Of Technology, Charu Kanbur

Avp In Technology, Venka Korsapati

Assistant Vice President Payroll, Yanira Vergara
First Vice President Housing Group, Kelly Wimmer
First Vice President Credit Risk Management,
  Robert Bose
Vice President Of Finance, David Harris
Vice President, Linda Ebrahim
First Vice President, Sulexan Chery
Vice President, Alice Wong
First Vice President, Roza Dimitrova
Vice President, Veronica Prasad
Chairman, Jeffrey S. Stein
Board Member, Ian Haft
Member Board Of Directors, Alexander Greene
Auditors: KPMG LLP

LOCATIONS

HQ: Ambac Financial Group, Inc.
  One State Street Plaza, New York, NY 10004
Phone: 212 658-7470   **Fax:** 212 208 3414
Web: www.ambac.com

2015 Permiums by Geographic

	$ mil.	% of total
United States	229	73
United Kingdom	68	22
Other international	14	5
Total	**312**	**100**

PRODUCTS/OPERATIONS

2015 Net Premiums

	$ mil.	% of total
Accelerated earnings	137	44
Public Finance	97	31
International Finance	43	14
Structured Finance	34	11
Total	**312**	**100**

2015 Sales

	$ mil.	% of total
Net premiums earned	312	44
Total net investment income	266	37
Net realized investment gains	53	8
Net change in fair value of credit derivatives	41	6
Income (loss) on variable interest entities	31	4
Other income	7	1
Net other-than-temporary impairment losses recognized in earnings	(25.6)	-
Derivative products	(42.5)	-
Total	**644**	**100**

Selected Services

Adversely Classified Credit
Amendment Waiver and Consen
Credit Risk Management (CRM)
International Finance Insured Portfolio
U.S. Public Finance Insured Portfolio
U.S. Structured Finance

COMPETITORS

Assured Guaranty   MBIA
FGIC

HISTORICAL FINANCIALS

Company Type: Public

Income Statement				FYE: December 31
	ASSETS ($ mil.)	NET INCOME ($ mil.)	INCOME AS % OF ASSETS	EMPLOYEES
12/18	14,588	267	1.8%	113
12/17	23,192	(328)	—	124
12/16	22,635	74	0.3%	154
12/15	23,728	493	2.1%	171
12/14	25,159	484	1.9%	188
Annual Growth	(12.7%)	(13.8%)	—	(11.9%)

2018 Year-End Financials

Debt ratio: 56.19%	No. of shares (mil.): 45
Return on equity: 17.99%	Dividends
Cash ($ mil.): 63	Yield: —
Current ratio: —	Payout: —
Long-term debt ($ mil.): —	Market value ($ mil.): 782

	STOCK PRICE ($) FY Close	P/E High/Low		PER SHARE ($) Earnings	Dividends	Book Value
12/18	17.24	5	3	3.99	0.00	35.12
12/17	15.98	—	—	(7.25)	0.00	30.52
12/16	22.50	16	7	1.64	0.00	37.94
12/15	14.09	3	1	10.72	0.00	37.41
12/14	24.50	3	2	10.31	0.00	31.09
Annual Growth	(8.4%)	—	—	(21.1%)	—	3.1%

AMC Entertainment Holdings Inc.

AMC Entertainment shines when the lights go down. The company whose initials once stood for American Multi-Cinema is the #1 movie theater chain in the US and the world. It owns partially owns or operates about 660 theaters with 8200 screens most of which are in megaplexes (units with more than 12 screens and stadium seating). It also has a significant presence in Europe through London-based subsidiary Odeon & UCI Cinemas Group. AMC also owns about 25% of MovieTickets.com. Chinese investment firm Wanda Group bought AMC in 2012 and took the company public again in 2013. AMC acquired Odeon and Carmike in 2016 and has agreed to acquire Nordic Cinema Group which will swell its total theater pool to over 1000.

Operations

AMC owns 152 IMAX screens and has a 44% IMAX market share and 2643 3D screens in the US. It has been rolling out plush reclining seats that provide greater comfort and better viewing angles and operates 19 dine-in theaters with seat-side service.

Geographic Reach

AMC Entertainment has 660 theaters with 8200 screens in the US its largest market. It also has 243 theaters with 2236 screens via subsidiary Odeon in the UK Ireland Germany Austria Italy Spain and Portugal. Once the acquisition of Nordic Cinema Group is closed it will have a further 68 theaters across Sweden Norway Finland Lithuania Latvia and Estonia.

Financial Performance

AMC is in good shape. In fiscal 2015 (ended December) AMC recorded revenue growth of 9% to $2.9 billion. Admissions and food and beverage revenue were both up by over $100 million reflecting the success of the company's introduction of dining options. Net income climbed 63% to $103 million. AMC's cash position strengthened with cash from operations climbing 57% to $467 million due to higher earnings and decreases in payments for film.

Strategy

Chinese parent company Dalian Wanda's desire to be global cultural titan has driven AMC into an acquisition frenzy. In the space of four months it made three industry-shaking acquisitions. In November 2016 it acquired Odeon & UCI Cinemas Group a UK-based chain with a presence in Europe for $1.2 billion. At the end of the year it acquired

US rival Carmike for $1.1 billion overtaking Regal Entertainment as the US's (and the world's) #1 cinema chain. And in early 2017 it announced an agreement to acquire Nordic Cinema Group which has multiplexes across Scandinavia and the Baltics for $929 million. After the acquisitions are sewn up AMC will own over 1000 multiplexes across the US and Europe.

Higher cinema prices and improved home cinema options have pushed AMC towards ramping up the quality of its multiplexes in order to stay ahead. It has been renovating its theaters including improved sight and sound but efforts have been led by the introduction of plush electric reclining seats that provide greater comfort and improved viewing angles. The reclining seats take up 60% more space than regular seats and thus each theater loses some two-thirds of its seating capacity. However AMC has found counter-intuitively that attendance is up 75% due to the greater appeal of a luxury experience. Mid-week crowds up in particular. AMC freezes prices for the year after renovation in order to drive interest in the new format increasing them thereafter. The company will be rolling out refitted theaters into its acquired Carmike mutiplexes.

AMC is also using enhanced food and beverage options to entice movie lovers. Its dine-in theaters combine the dinner and movie experience with full kitchen facilities seat-side servers and a separate bar and lounge area. The company has converted about a nearly 20 smaller theaters with the new dine-in theatre option. A secondary purpose behind the re-fit is to rejuvenate theaters approaching the end of their useful lives.

Mergers and Acquisitions

AMC acquired UK cinema company Odeon & UCI Cinemas Group for $1.21 billion from private equity firm Terra Firma in November 2016. Odeon & UCI is the UK's largest cinema chain and brings with it 242 theaters with 2236 screens.

In the same year it acquire one of its US rivals Carmike for $1.1 billion. Carmike has 271 locations.

And in January 2017 AMC reached an agreement to acquire Nordic Cinema Group which brings with it 68 screens across Scandinavia and the Baltics. Nordic will be absorbed into Odeon & UCI.

HISTORY

After performing in tent shows around the Midwest Edward Dubinsky settled in Kansas City Missouri and opened his first movie theater in 1920. Dubinsky who later changed his name to Durwood had opened about a dozen theaters and drive-ins by the 1950s. After he died in 1960 his son Stanley took control of the business. Three years later Stanley Durwood ushered in a new age of movie-viewing by opening the first mall-based theater with multiple screens. The company which became American Multi-Cinema in 1968 expanded the multiplex concept throughout the 1970s. In 1983 American Multi-Cinema shortened its name to AMC and went public.

The company opened theaters at a furious rate growing at about 100 screens a year for five years. This left it with a massive debt however and AMC posted little or no profit between 1988 and 1992. The company later restructured laying off employees and reducing its total number of screens to 1600 in 1994. AMC opened a 24-screen theater in Dallas in 1995. A year later a new AMC theater in Ontario California became the first to have 30 screens. In 1997 AMC teamed with Planet Hollywood to develop Planet Movies a restaurant theater and retail concept.

To reduce debt the next year AMC transferred 13 theaters to a real estate investment trust it had created; it then leased the theaters back to AMC. In 1999 the US Justice Department filed a lawsuit against AMC claiming the company's theaters denied handicapped individuals access to better stadium-style seats. The first Planet Movie opened that summer in Columbus Ohio but financial problems at Planet Hollywood put further projects on hold. Stanley Durwood died later that year after a long battle with cancer. He was replaced by co-chairman Peter Brown.

In 2000 AMC partnered with several entertainment companies to form MovieTickets.com a joint venture created to sell movie tickets over the Web. The company also began experimenting with the digital distribution of movies via satellite. In 2002 AMC acquired Gulf States Theatres (which included five theatres in the New Orleans area) and the bankrupt rival exhibitor GC Companies (which included 66 theatres throughout the US).

The following year a federal court ruled AMC violated regulations regarding accommodations for people in wheelchairs. As a result the company announced plans to spend $21 million over five years to modify 113 stadium-style theaters.

At the end of 2004 AMC ceased to be publicly traded after it was purchased by Marquee Holding an affiliate of J.P. Morgan Partners and Apollo Advisors. Early the next year AMC combined its National Cinema Network movie theater advertising sales business with Regal Entertainment's Regal CineMedia to form the jointly owned National CineMedia. (Cinemark later bought 21% of AMC's interest in National CineMedia.)

The company bought rival Loews Cineplex in 2006 significantly boosting its holdings adding some 2000 screens to AMC's network and expanding its international presence to about 12 countries. The combined company retained the AMC Entertainment name and AMC CEO Peter Brown continued in his position.

AMC filed an IPO in late 2006 hoping to raise $750 million. Investors shunned the $17-a-share asking price. Citing unfavorable market conditions the company withdrew the IPO the following year.

In 2007 AMC Entertainment sold its 9% share in online ticket Fandango to Comcast for some $20 million. Later in 2007 the company announced another IPO. AMC withdrew an IPO in 2008 while the economy was crashing; it had attempted to raise $500 million through the offering after a string of hits at the summer 2007 box office.

Brown retired in 2009 and was replaced by Gerardo Lopez. Also in 2008 AMC exited the Mexican market when it sold its interests in Grupo Cinemex. That chain operated about 45 theaters with nearly 500 screens primarily in the Mexico City metropolitan area.

Hoping the third time's a charm AMC filed another IPO in 2010. However it shelved those plans two years later due to unfavorable market conditions.

The company purchased more than 90 movie houses from Kerasotes ShowPlace Theatres in 2011. In 2012 it announced plans to be acquired by Chinese investment firm Wanda Group.

EXECUTIVES

Evp Global Development, Mark A. McDonald, age 60, $361,490 total compensation
Evp And Cfo, Craig R. Ramsey, age 67, $483,923 total compensation
Evp Us Operations, John D. McDonald, age 61, $467,112 total compensation
President Ceo And Director, Adam M. Aron, age 65
Evp And Chief Marketing Officer, Stephen A. Colanero, age 52

Evp Chief Content And Programming Officer, Elizabeth Frank, age 49, $474,327 total compensation
Vice President Enterprise Is, Derrick Leggett
Vp Food And Beverage Marketing, Tonya Mangels
Vp Theatre Systems, Scott Winters
Vice President Finance, Debbi Webber
Vice President Communications And Events, Francisco Ybarra
Chairman, Lin Zhang, age 47
Board Member, Lloyd Hill
Auditors: Ernst & Young LLP

LOCATIONS

HQ: AMC Entertainment Holdings Inc.
One AMC Way, 11500 Ash Street, Leawood, KS 66211
Phone: 913 213-2000
Web: www.amctheatres.com

2014 Sales

	$ mil.	% of total
US	2,688	100
Other	7	-
Total	**2,695**	**100**

PRODUCTS/OPERATIONS

2015 Sales

	$ mil.	% of total
Admissions	1,892	64
Food and beverage	910	31
Other	144	5
Total	**2,946**	**100**

2015 Theaters

	No.
California	49
Illinois	43
New York	24
Florida	22
Indiana	20
New Jersey	26
Texas	33
Colorado	12
Georgia	12
Washington	12
Pennsylvania	10
Maryland	10
Missouri	11
Arizona	10
Michigan	9
Ohio	9
Massachusetts	9
Virginia	8
Louisiana	7
Other	51
Total	**387**

COMPETITORS

Brenden Theatre	Laemmle Theatres
Carmike Cinemas	Landmark Theatres
Cinemark	Marcus Corporation
Cineplex	National Amusements
Clearview Cinemas	Pacific Theatres
Hoyts Cinemas	Regal Entertainment
IMAX	

HISTORICAL FINANCIALS

Company Type: Public

Income Statement
FYE: December 31

	REVENUE ($ mil.)	NET INCOME ($ mil.)	NET PROFIT MARGIN	EMPLOYEES
12/18	5,460	110	2.0%	39,802
12/17	5,079	(487)	—	39,843
12/16	3,235	111	3.5%	41,373
12/15	2,946	103	3.5%	21,300
12/14	2,695	64	2.4%	19,700
Annual Growth	**19.3%**	**14.5%**		**19.2%**

2018 Year-End Financials

Debt ratio: 57.50%	No. of shares (mil.): 103
Return on equity: 6.27%	Dividends
Cash ($ mil.): 313	Yield: 19.1%
Current ratio: 0.59	Payout: 573.1%
Long-term debt ($ mil.): 5,377	Market value ($ mil.): 1,271

	STOCK PRICE ($) FY Close	P/E High/Low	Earnings	Dividends	Book Value
12/18	12.28	23 13	0.41	2.35	13.51
12/17	15.10	— —	(3.80)	0.80	16.55
12/16	33.65	31 18	1.13	0.80	18.25
12/15	24.00	34 22	1.06	0.80	15.81
12/14	26.18	41 30	0.66	0.60	15.55
Annual Growth	**(17.2%)**	**—**	**(11.2%)**	**40.7%**	**(3.5%)**

AMCAP FUND INC

EXECUTIVES

President, Marry Clemeson
Treas, Mary C Hall
Sr V Pres, Gordon Crawford
Sr V Pres, Paul G Haaga Jr
SEC, Julie Williams
Principal, Walter Stern

LOCATIONS

HQ: AMCAP FUND INC
333 S HOPE ST STE LEVB, LOS ANGELES, CA 900713003
Phone: 213 486-9200

HISTORICAL FINANCIALS

Company Type: Private

Income Statement
FYE: February 28

	ASSETS ($ mil.)	NET INCOME ($ mil.)	INCOME AS % OF ASSETS	EMPLOYEES
02/18	64,019	9,994	15.6%	300
02/16	44,148	(2)	—	—
Annual Growth	**20.4%**	**—**	**—**	**—**

Amerant Bancorp Inc

Auditors: PricewaterhouseCoopers LLP

LOCATIONS

HQ: Amerant Bancorp Inc
220 Alhambra Circle, Coral Gables, FL 33134
Phone: 305 460-4038
Web: www.mercantilbank.com

HISTORICAL FINANCIALS

Company Type: Public

Income Statement
FYE: December 31

	ASSETS ($ mil.)	NET INCOME ($ mil.)	INCOME AS % OF ASSETS	EMPLOYEES
12/18	8,124	45	0.6%	911
12/17	8,436	43	0.5%	939
12/16	8,434	23	0.3%	—
12/15	0	15		—
Annual Growth	**—**	**45.0%**	**—**	**—**

2018 Year-End Financials

Debt ratio: 15.81%
Return on equity: 6.11%
Cash ($ mil.): 85
Current ratio: —
Long-term debt ($ mil.): —

No. of shares (mil.): 44
Dividends
Yield: 0.0%
Payout: 87.0%
Market value ($ mil.): 580

	STOCK PRICE ($) FY Close	P/E High/Low		PER SHARE ($) Earnings	Dividends	Book Value
12/18	13.01	54	6	1.08	0.94	16.76
12/17	0.00	—	—	1.02	0.00	17.73
Annual Growth	—	—	—	1.9%	—	(1.9%)

Ameren Corp

Ameren provides the power that lights much of Illinois and Missouri. As the sole distributor in its service region the holding company distributes electricity to 2.4 million customers and natural gas to 900000 customers through regulated utility subsidiaries Union Electric (which does business as Ameren Missouri) and Ameren Illinois. Ameren has generating capacity of about 10200 megawatt of primarily coal-fired power most of which is owned by Ameren Missouri. Ameren supplements its customers' electricity needs by purchasing additional electricity from third parties.

HISTORY

More than 30 St. Louis companies had built a chaotic grid of generators and power lines throughout the city by 1900. Two years later many of them merged into the Union Company which attracted national notice when it lit the St. Louis World's Fair in the first broad demonstration of electricity's power. In 1913 the company by then named Union Electric (UE) began buying electricity from an Iowa dam 150 miles away — the greatest distance power had ever been transmitted in such quantity.

UE pushed into rural Missouri and began buying and building fossil-fuel plants. Despite a slowdown during the Depression UE built Bagnell Dam on Missouri's Osage River in the early 1930s to gather power for a hydroelectric plant. At the onset of WWII construction began on new plants with larger generators and lower production costs; however demand for electricity lagged. In the late 1940s UE compensated by joining a "power pool" a system of utilities with interconnected transmission lines that shared electricity.

Growth in the 1950s came from acquisitions including Missouri Power & Light (1950) and Missouri Edison (1954). During the 1960s and 1970s UE built five new plants including the Labadie plant (2300 MW) one of the largest coal-fired plants in the US.

UE began producing nuclear energy in 1984 at its Callaway nuke. High costs and the expenses of a scrapped second plant caused UE to battle the Missouri Public Service Commission throughout the 1980s for rate increases.

Charles Mueller became president in 1993 and CEO one year later. He oversaw continued staff reductions and cost cutting through the 1990s in an increasingly competitive market. In 1997 UE expanded into Illinois through its purchase of CIPSCO which owned utility Central Illinois Public Service Company (CIPS).

CIPS began as a Mattoon Illinois streetcar company in the early 1900s. The firm bought Mattoon's electric power plant in 1904 and began growing its power business buying small electric companies in the 1920s and 1930s. CIPS built five generating units in the 1940s and 1950s and became part-owner (along with UE) of Electric Energy Inc. which built a power plant on the Ohio River. The company bought Illinois Electric and Gas Company in the 1960s and the state's Gas Utilities in the 1980s. To prepare for competition under deregulation CIPS created holding company CIPSCO in the 1990s to diversify.

UE's purchase of CIPSCO expanded its geographic scope and the new company was named Ameren in 1997 to reflect its American energy focus. The next year the company committed to adding generating capacity through several natural gas-fired combustion turbines. It joined nine other utilities to form the Midwest Independent System Operator to manage their transmission needs.

In 1999 Ameren bought a 245-mile railroad line between St. Louis and Kansas City to help the area's economic development. Looking for new opportunities in deregulated energy markets the company purchased Data & Metering Specialties.

In 2000 Ameren created subsidiary AmerenEnergy Generating to operate its nonregulated power plants and affiliate AmerenEnergy Marketing to sell the generating facilities' power. When deregulation took effect in Illinois in 2002 the company transferred AmerenCIPS' power plants to AmerenEnergy Generating. In 2003 Ameren acquired CILCORP the holding company for electric and gas utility Central Illinois Light (now operating as AmerenCILCO) from independent power producer AES in a $1.4 billion deal. To further expand its utility operations Ameren acquired power and gas utility Illinois Power from Dynegy in a $2.3 billion deal in 2004.

In 2007 Ameren subsidiary AmerenUE moved into wind power operations by contracting to buy 100 MW of wind power from Horizon Wind Energy's Rail Splitter Wind Farm located near Delavan Illinois.

In 2010 the company combined AmerenIP AmerenCIPS and AmerenCILCO into one entity Ameren Illinois in order to streamline operations and reduce confusion among customers. The three Illinois utilities have operated as a single business since 2004 and deliver energy to more than 1100 communities. Ameren Illinois also operates some 21400 miles of natural gas distribution and transmission lines.

Ameren's overall revenues decreased by 9% in 2012 due to a 24% drop Merchant Generation sales caused by lower market prices and a sales contract in 2011 that was not supplied in 2012. Ameren Illinois' revenues dropped by 10% due to lower wholesale distribution revenues primarily due to lower demand and the recognition of a reserve for revenues subject to a refund which dropped revenues by $6 million. Ameren Missouri's revenues declined by only 3% due to reduced purchased power expenses as a result of a FERC-ordered refund which helped to improve margins.

The company reported a net loss of $974 million in 2012 (a whopping 288% drop compared to 2011) due to lower sales and higher operating expenses as well as an increase in impairment and other charges.

Ameren opened a waste-to-energy plant in 2012.

In 2012 Ameren Missouri entered into an agreement with Westinghouse Electric to exclusively support Westinghouse's application for the Department of Energy's Small Modular Reactors investment funds of up to $452 million.

In order to focus on its regulated operations and offload a number of older an expensive-to-maintain coal-fired plants in 2013 Ameren sold its merchant generation business Ameren Energy Resources to an affiliate of Dynegy. Dynegy's subsidiary Illinois Power Holdings bought Ameren Energy Resources (and its subsidiaries Ameren Energy Generating Company AmerenEnergy Resources Generating Company and Ameren Energy Marketing Company). The deal is expected to generate about $900 million in cash and savings for Ameren.

It also agreed to sell three merchant gas-fired energy centers which were not part of the Dynegy transaction to a special purpose entity affiliated with and formed by Rockland Capital.

To leverage abundant natural gas supplies and low wholesale costs in 2013 Ameren Illinois outlined details of a legislative proposal to accelerate the modernization of Illinois' aging natural gas delivery infrastructure.

The company also opened its first hydroelectric center in the state in 2013.

In 2013 Ameren Illinois opened a $3.3 million testing facility to facilitate research and development of smart grid technologies and support the state's economic development and job creation goals.

EXECUTIVES

Chairman President And Ceo, Warner L. Baxter, age 58, $1,040,000 total compensation
Evp And Cfo, Martin J. Lyons, age 52, $640,000 total compensation
Chairman And President Ameren Illinois, Richard J. Mark, age 64, $490,000 total compensation
Chairman And President Ameren Missouri, Michael L. Moehn, age 50, $512,000 total compensation
Chairman And President Ameren Transmission Company, Shawn E. Schukar, age 55
Svp And Cio Ameren Services, Mary P. Heger
Vice President Of Corporate Communications, David Hunt
Vice President, Joseph Power
Vice President Human Resources, Steve Honor
Vice President And Controller, Mark Brawley
Senior Vice President General Counsel And Secretary, Steven R Sullivan
Vice President External Affairs, Scott Wiseman
Vice President Nuclear Operations, Kevin Diya
Vice President Energy Delivery, David N Wakeman
Vp Corporate Development, Stephen Kidwell
Vice President External Affairs And Communications Ameren Missouri, Warren Wood
Svp Corporate Strategy And Innovation, Mark Fronmuller
Assistant Treasurer, Stephen Lux
Board Member, Steven Lipstein
Board Member, Ellen Fitzsimmons
Board Member, Ed Coleman
Board Member, Jennifer Wolfrom
Board Member, Walter Galvin
Auditors: PricewaterhouseCoopers LLP

LOCATIONS

HQ: Ameren Corp
1901 Chouteau Avenue, St. Louis, MO 63103
Phone: 314 621-3222
Web: www.ameren.com

PRODUCTS/OPERATIONS

2018 Sales

	$ mil.	% of total
Electric	5,339	85
Gas	952	15
Total	**6,291**	**100**

2018 Sales

	$ mil.	% of total
Ameren Missouri	3,589	56
Ameren Illinois Electric Distribution	1,547	24
Ameren Illinois Natural Gas	815	13
Ameren Transmission	433	7
Adjustments	(93)	-
Total	**6,291**	**100**

COMPETITORS

AES
Alliant Energy
Commonwealth Edison
Empire District
  Electric
Great Plains Energy
Southern Union

HISTORICAL FINANCIALS

Company Type: Public

Income Statement				FYE: December 31
	REVENUE ($ mil.)	NET INCOME ($ mil.)	NET PROFIT MARGIN	EMPLOYEES
12/18	6,291	815	13.0%	8,838
12/17	6,177	523	8.5%	8,615
12/16	6,076	653	10.7%	8,629
12/15	6,098	630	10.3%	8,527
12/14	6,053	586	9.7%	8,527
Annual Growth	**1.0%**	**8.6%**	**—**	**0.9%**

2018 Year-End Financials

Debt ratio: 33.20%
Return on equity: 11.00%
Cash ($ mil.): 16
Current ratio: 0.57
Long-term debt ($ mil.): 7,859

No. of shares (mil.): 244
Dividends
  Yield: 2.8%
  Payout: 55.6%
Market value ($ mil.): 15,949

	STOCK PRICE ($) FY Close	P/E High/Low	PER SHARE ($) Earnings	Dividends	Book Value
12/18	65.23	21 16	3.32	1.85	31.21
12/17	58.99	30 24	2.14	1.78	29.61
12/16	52.46	20 16	2.68	1.72	29.28
12/15	43.23	18 14	2.59	1.66	28.63
12/14	46.13	20 15	2.40	1.61	27.67
Annual Growth	**9.0%**	**—**	**8.5%**	**3.5%**	**3.1%**

American Airlines Group Inc

American Airlines Group (AAG) is the largest airline in the US and one of the largest in the world. The company's mainline carriers provide scheduled air transportation along with its group of regional subsidiaries and third-party regional carriers operating as American Eagle. It also offers freight and mail services through its cargo division. In all American operates nearly 6700 flights daily to 350 destinations in more than 50 countries. It operates about 950 mainline aircraft and almost 600 regional aircraft. AAG is also part of the oneworld alliance where member carriers share airport lounge facilities and offer interconnected loyalty programs.

Operations

AAG provides scheduled air transportation through its mainline carrier network as well as through regional carriers. Its mainline segment accounts for more than two thirds of total sales and operates close to 950 aircraft. Regional operations (about 15% of total sales) provide services under the "American Eagle" brand. American Eagle carriers include wholly-owned subsidiaries Envoy PSA and Piedmont. Third-party regional carriers including Republic Mesa Compass ExpressJet SkyWest and Trans States.

The company's Cargo segment (accounts for less than 5% of total sales) also provides a wide range of freight and mail services with facilities and interline connections available across the globe.

Geographic Reach

Headquartered in Fort Worth TX AAG flies to 350-plus destinations in more than 50 countries. Its hubs are located in Charlotte Chicago Dallas/Fort Worth Los Angeles Miami New York Philadelphia Phoenix and Washington DC with international services to Canada Central and South America Asia Europe Australia and New Zealand.

Sales and Marketing

AAG sells its tickets through several distribution channels including its website (www.aa.com) reservations centers and third-party distribution channels. Its loyalty program offers rewards to travelers for their continued patronage. Advertising costs in 2017 were $135 million up $20 million from 2016.

Financial Performance

American Airlines recovered in 2017 after posting two straight years of revenue declines. Net sales increased 5% to $42.2 billion compared with $40.2 billion in 2016. Mainline and regional passenger revenues added up to $36.1 billion a $1.6 billion hike from the previous year.

AAG's net income decreased by 65% from $2.7 billion in 2016 to $1.9 billion in 2017. The drop was mainly due to nearly $1 billion in net interest expense and higher operating costs (primarily increasing fuel prices and employee wages). Since its merger with US Air in 2015 American has been investing more than $5 billion annually in capital expenditures for its fleet products and team members. The company reports that by 2021 it will reduce capex to $2 billion.

Cash at the end of fiscal 2017 was $295 million a decrease of $27 million from the prior year. Cash from operations contributed $4.7 billion to the coffers while investing activities used $3.6 billion mainly for capital expenditures. Financing activities used another $1.1 billion for dividends to stockholders and the company's stock repurchase program.

Strategy

AAG is planning significant investments to expand capacity focusing on its hubs in Dallas/Fort Worth (DFW) and Charlotte and adding new routes to medium- and smaller-sized cities such as South Bend IN Panama City FL and Missoula MT. In 2019 American plans to add 15 gates and 100 departures per day at DFW and in 2020 seven new gates at Charlotte with another 75 daily departures.

The company is targeting increased revenues from continued investments in product and customers. These include a refresh of its Admiral's Club facilities in Boston Charlotte and Pittsburgh TV capabilities for domestic flights and high-speed WiFi. Corporate clients can now book travel through aa.com as a result of the company's integration with SAP Concur TripLink and through a new partnership with Alibaba customers in Asia can make payments using Alipay on aa.com/China. American also cites operational reliability as one of its top corporate priorities and is reviewing its planning processes to ensure better service during summer and year-end holiday peak periods.

With a new product segmentation strategy AAG aims to increase passenger sales by close to 10% in 2018. The company introduced Premium Economy an upgrade to its Basic Economy class with plans to further leverage this higher-value product with increased merchandising efforts. It has also removed the carry-on bag restriction in Basic Economy allowing AAG to offer basic economy to more markets.

Mergers and Acquisitions

AAG in mid-2017 made a significant move to expand internationally with the announcement of a $200 million equity investment in China Southern Airlines and a 2018 codesharing agreement with China Southern is giving customers access to additional destinations in China as well as North and South America. AAG customers are able to access nearly 40 destinations beyond Beijing and more than 30 destinations beyond Shanghai.

Company Background

In 2011 American Airlines' parent company AMR Corporation filed for bankruptcy. It emerged from Chapter 11 in late 2013 and at the same time merged with rival US Airways in a mega deal worth $11 billion. The milestone transaction created the world's largest airline. The combined entity formed the American Airlines Group and is led by former US Airways CEO Doug Parker.

HISTORY

In 1929 Sherman Fairchild created a New York City holding company called the Aviation Corporation (AVCO) combining some 85 small airlines in 1930 to create American Airways. In 1934 the company had its first dose of financial trouble after the government suspended private airmail for months. Corporate raider E. L. Cord took over and named the company American Airlines.

EXECUTIVES

Evp Corporate Affairs, Stephen L. (Steve) Johnson, age 62, $600,936 total compensation
Chairman And Ceo, W. Douglas (Doug) Parker, age 57, $1 total compensation
Evp People And Communications, Elise R. Eberwein, age 53
Evp And Cfo, Derek J. Kerr, age 54, $600,936 total compensation
President, Robert D. Isom, age 55, $641,306 total compensation
Evp And Cio, Maya Leibman, age 54, $600,936 total compensation
Vp Corporate Development And Treasurer American Airlines, Beverly K. Goulet, age 64
Vice President People Services, Jocelyn Moore
Vp Global Marketing, Janelle Anderson
Auditors: KPMG LLP

LOCATIONS

HQ: American Airlines Group Inc
4333 Amon Carter Blvd., Fort Worth, TX 76155
Phone: 817 963-1234   **Fax:** 817 967-9641
Web: www.aa.com

2017 Sales

	$ mil.	% of total
DOT Domestic	29,612	70
DOT Latin America	5,422	13
DOT Atlantic	5,059	12
DOT Pacific	2,114	5
Total	**42,207**	**100**

Selected Hub Locations

Charlotte
Chicago
Dallas/Fort Worth (DFW)
Los Angeles
Miami
New York City
Philadelphia
Phoenix
Washington DC

PRODUCTS/OPERATIONS

2017 Sales

	$ mil.	% of total
Mainline passenger	29,238	69
Regional passenger	6,895	16
Cargo	800	2
Other	5,274	13
Total	**42,207**	**100**

Selected Carriers

Regional Subsidiaries
Envoy
PSA
Piedmont
Regional Third-Party Carriers
Republic
Mesa
Compass
ExpressJet
SkyWest
Trans States

COMPETITORS

Air France-KLM	Hawaiian Holdings
Alaska Air	JetBlue
Delta Air Lines	Lufthansa
Echo Global	Southwest Airlines
FedEx	Spirit Airlines
Frontier Airlines	UPS
Greyhound	

HISTORICAL FINANCIALS

Company Type: Public

Income Statement				FYE: December 31
	REVENUE ($ mil.)	NET INCOME ($ mil.)	NET PROFIT MARGIN	EMPLOYEES
12/18	44,541	1,412	3.2%	128,900
12/17	42,207	1,919	4.5%	126,600
12/16	40,180	2,676	6.7%	122,300
12/15	40,990	7,610	18.6%	118,500
12/14	42,650	2,882	6.8%	113,300
Annual Growth	**1.1%**	**(16.3%)**	**—**	**3.3%**

2018 Year-End Financials

Debt ratio: 40.40%
Return on equity: 75.17%
Cash ($ mil.): 429
Current ratio: 0.48
Long-term debt ($ mil.): 21,179

No. of shares (mil.): 460
Dividends
Yield: 1.2%
Payout: 13.2%
Market value ($ mil.): 14,790

	STOCK PRICE ($) FY Close	P/E High/Low		PER SHARE ($) Earnings	Dividends	Book Value
12/18	32.11	19	10	3.03	0.40	(0.37)
12/17	52.03	14	10	3.90	0.40	8.26
12/16	46.69	10	5	4.81	0.40	7.46
12/15	42.35	5	3	11.07	0.40	9.02
12/14	53.63	13	6	3.93	0.20	2.90
Annual Growth	**(12.0%)**	—	—	**(6.3%)**	**18.9%**	**—**

AMERICAN ASSETS TRUST, INC.

American Assets Trust is a self-administered real estate investment trust (REIT) that owns develops and operates upscale retail office and residential property mostly in Northern and Southern California but also in Oregon Washington Texas and Hawaii. Its 6 million square foot portfolio includes around 10 shopping centers more than handful of office buildings a 369-room hotel and retail complex and five multi-family residential properties. Its tenants include SalesForce Autodesk the Veterans Benefits Administration and well-known retailers such as Kmart Lowe's Sports Authority Old Navy and Vons. Formed in 1967 as American Assets the firm went public in 2011.

Operations

The REIT leases retail office and multifamily properties as well as hotels. Its retail portfolio which made up 35% of its revenue during 2015 spans 3 million rentable square feet while its office holdings (34% of revenue) measure 2.7 million square feet.

In addition American Assets Trust mixed-use property (19% of revenue) the Embassy Suites at Waikiki Beach Walk in Honolulu is a 369-room all-suite hotel with approximately 97000 square feet of accompanying retail space. The REIT generates the rest of its revenue from its more than 1500 multifamily units in San Diego and Imperial Beach California.

Geographic Reach

San Diego-based American Assets Trust's primary markets include San Diego; the San Francisco Bay area; Portland Oregon; Bellevue Washington; and Oahu Hawaii. More than 50% of its property by square footage was located in Southern and Northern California at the end of 2015 while over 15% of its property space was in Oregon. The rest of its properties were in Hawaii (11% of square footage) Texas (10%) and Washington state (9%).

Sales and Marketing

The REIT's largest five tenants by revenue in 2015 included: Salesforce (8% of annualized base rent) Autodesk (3%) Kmart (3%) Lowe's (3%) the Veterans Benefits Administration (2%) and the Insurance Company of the West (2%). Its properties that year were 98.6% leased.

The company has been increasing its marketing spend in recent years. It spent $2.1 million on marketing during 2015 up from $1.62 million and $1.55 million in 2014 and 2013 respectively.

Financial Performance

America Assets Trusts' annual revenues have risen more than 35% since 2011 as its property valuations have appreciated and have commanded higher rental rates. While more volatile its annual profits have more than doubled over the period on declining interest expenses as the REIT has paid down its long-term debt.

The REIT's revenue climbed 6% to $275.6 million during 2015 thanks to rental income growth mostly from its office properties which benefited from higher occupancy and rental rates. Rental income also grew from its mixed-use property as its hotel occupancy rate jumped by almost 10 percentage points to 89.6% and as its revenue per available room (revPAR) grew 13%. Retail rental revenue grew with higher rental rates while its multifamily rental revenue also rose with the completion of its Hassalo on Eighth property late in the year.

Revenue growth in 2015 combined with a $7.1 million gain from the sale of its Rancho Carmel Plaza property drove the American Asset Trust's net income up 73% to almost $54 million. The REIT's operating cash levels rose 5% to $110.7 million as cash-based rental income increased.

Strategy

American Assets Trust's properties are in located in developed areas where new construction is difficult which helps to keep competition out and rental and occupancy rates stable. The REIT prefers to develop or acquire properties in such high-barrier-to-entry areas in its core markets which include San Diego; the San Francisco Bay area; Portland Oregon; Bellevue Washington; and Oahu Hawaii.

American Asset Trust's other key strategy is redeveloping and improving existing properties to command higher rental rates. It also makes its properties more attractive to potential tenants by signing well-known brands such as Apple Store Banana Republic Pottery Barn and Starbucks as retail tenants.

Company Background

American Assets Trust went public in January 2011 with an offering valued at about $564 million. (About $4 million of that figure went to chairman Ernest Rady who controlled the company prior to its IPO.) The IPO proceeds were used to repay debt and to purchase and renovate property.

EXECUTIVES

Chairman President And Ceo, Ernest S. Rady, $259,616 total compensation
Ceo And President, John W. Chamberlain
Evp And Cfo, Robert F. Barton, $373,846 total compensation
Vp Construction And Development, Jerry Gammieri, $186,923 total compensation
Vp Retail Properties, Chris Sullivan
Vp Office Properties, Jim Durfey
Vp And Regional Manager Portland, Wade Lange
Auditors: ERNST & YOUNG LLP SAN DIEGO

LOCATIONS

HQ: AMERICAN ASSETS TRUST, INC.
11455 EL CAMINO REAL # 200, SAN DIEGO, CA 921302047
Phone: 858 350-2600

2015 Properties

	No.
Southern California	7
Northern California	4
Hawaii	3
Oregon	2
Texas	1
Washington	1
Total	**18**

PRODUCTS/OPERATIONS

2015 Sales

	$ mil.	% of total
Rental Income		
Retail	97	35
Office	92	34
Mixed-Use	53	19
Multifamily	18	7
Other Property Income	13	5
Total	**275**	**100**

Selected Tenants

Alliant International University
Autodesk Inc.
California Bank & Trust
Caradigm USA LLC
Drug Enforcement Administration
Foodland Super Market
HDR Engineering
Inome Inc.
Insurance Company of the West
Integra Telecom Holdings
Kmart
Lowe's
Marshalls
McDermott Will & Emery
Nordstrom Rack
Officemax
Old Navy
Portland Energy Conservation
Quiksilver
salesforce.com inc.
Sports Authority
Sprouts Farmers Market
Treasury Call Center
Veterans Benefits Administration
Vons

Selected Properties

Retail
Alamo Quarry
Carmel County Plaza
Carmel Mountain Plaza
Del Monte Shopping Center
Lomas Sante Fe Plaza
Rancho Carmel Plaza
Solana Beach Towne Centre
South Bay Market Place
The Shops at Kalakaua
Waikele Center

Mixed-use
Waikiki Beach Walk - Hotel
Waikiki Beach Walk - Retail

Multi-family
Imperial Beach Gardens
Loma Palisades
Mariner's Point
Santa Fe Park RV Resort

Office
Fireman's Fund Headquarters
Solana Beach Corporate Centre
The Landmark at One Market
Torrey Reserve Campus
Valencia Corporate Center

COMPETITORS

CBL & Associates	Macerich
Properties	Simon Property Group
GGP	Taubman Centers
Hersha Hospitality	

HISTORICAL FINANCIALS

Company Type: Private

Income Statement				FYE: December 31
	ASSETS ($ mil.)	NET INCOME ($ mil.)	INCOME AS % OF ASSETS	EMPLOYEES
12/17	2,259	40	1.8%	113
12/16	1,986	45	2.3%	—
12/15	1,978	53	2.7%	—
12/14	1,941	31	1.6%	—
Annual Growth	5.2%	8.8%	—	—

American Axle & Manufacturing Holdings Inc

American Axle & Manufacturing (AAM) is GM's right-hand man for driveline systems forged products and metal cast parts. AAM manufactures engineers and designs axles driveshafts and chassis components mainly for light trucks and SUVs but also for cars and crossover vehicles. The Tier 1 supplier gets more than 40% of its business from GM. Other customers include Fiat-Chrysler Ford and Jaguar Land Rover. AAM operates about 90 manufacturing facilities around the world and generates 80% of its revenue from North America.

Operations

American Axle & Manufacturing operates four business segments: Driveline Metal Forming Powertrain and Casting.

Driveline generates about 60% of sales and designs and manufactures driveshafts power transfer units rear drive modules transfer cases and electric and hybrid driveline products and systems. Its

products end up in light trucks SUVs crossover vehicles passenger cars and commercial vehicles.

Metal Forming accounts for about 15% of sales and produces axle and transmission shafts ring and pinion gears differentials transmissions and shafts and suspension components. It serves OEMs (original equipment manufacturers) and Tier 1 automotive suppliers.

Powertrain brings in about 15% of sales. It produces transmission modules and differential assemblies transmission valve bodies connecting rod forging and assemblies torsional vibration dampers and variable valve timing products.

Lastly Casting produces differential cases steering knuckles control arms brackets and turbo charger housings. It serves the global light vehicle commercial and industrial markets and generates around 10% of sales.

Geographic Reach

American Axle & Manufacturing's nearly 90 manufacturing sites are found in the US Midwest (Michigan Indiana Illinois Ohio) as well as 16 other countries including Brazil the UK France Germany India Mexico South Korea and Thailand.

After the US which accounts for more than 45% of company sales American Axel's second largest market is Mexico at about 35%. Other principle geographies include Europe (nearly 10% of sales) China (5%) and Other Asia (nearly 5%).

Sales and Marketing

GM and Fiat-Chrysler together account for nearly 55% of American Axle & Manufacturing's (AAM) sales. AAM is the principal supplier of light truck and SUV rear-wheel-drive components to GM. It supplies Fiat-Chrysler with driveline systems for heavy-duty Ram full-size pickup trucks the AWD Jeep Cherokee and a passenger car driveshaft program.

Financial Performance

Except for a slight dip in 2015 American Axle & Manufacturing's (AAM) revenue has seen steady growth the last five years nearly doubling between 2014 and 2018. As US consumer preference has shifted away from sedans AMM has benefitted from its stable of components for trucks SUVs and crossovers.

Sales in 2018 increased 16% to $7.3 billion compared to $6.3 billion in 2017. Growth in 2018 was partly due to nearly $740 million in additional revenue from the 2017 acquisition of Metaldyne Performance Group. Sales also got a boost from higher production volumes of products for crossover vehicles as well as from new business for vehicles including the Mercedes-AMG.

AMM posted a net income loss of $57.5 million in 2018 compared to net income of $337.1 million in 2017 primarily due to higher costs associated with product launches and costs stemming from the Metaldyne acquisition.

Cash at the end of 2018 was $478.9 million an increase of $102.1 million from the prior year. Cash from operations contributed $771.5 million to the coffers while investing activities used $478.2 million mainly for capital expenditures. Financing activities used $184.5 million primarily for payments on long-term debt and capital lease obligations.

Strategy

The acquisition of Metaldyne Performance Group (MPG) in 2017 was a landmark for American Axle & Manufacturing (AAM). In addition to a revenue boost and its ascension to global Tier 1 automotive supplier status the acquisition also represented a major step in AAM's goal to diversify its client base and reduce its dependence on GM. Accounting for more than 65% of AAM's sales in 2016 sales to GM fell to about 40% of AAM's total sales in 2018.

AAM's product strategy is based on anticipating demand for technologies that reduce emissions in-

crease fuel economy and minimize the environmental impact of vehicles. Recent product developments on those lines have included its EcoTrac Disconnecting AWD system e-AAM hybrid and electric driveline systems Quantum lightweight axle technology high-efficiency axles PowerLite axles and PowerDense gears. The MPG acquisition also brought in new products and technologies.

To streamline its operations and further reduce debt AMM announced in 2019 that it would sell its US iron castings division (Grede) to funds managed by Gamut Capital Management for $245 million. AMM will retain its Mexico-based iron castings operations.

The company executed on its strategy of expanding its geographic footprint in 2018 with the formation of a joint venture with China-based Liuzhou Wuling Automobile Industry Co. a subsidiary of Guanxi Automobile Group. The venture Liuzhou AMM Automotive Driveline System Co. will manufacture independent rear axles and driveheads for SAIC-GM-Wuling a joint venture between GM and SAIC that is the largest maker of rear-wheel drive light vehicles in China. The deal enhances AMM's position in the Chinese automotive market.

Also in 2018 AMM sold the aftermarket operations of its Powertrain business to Hidden Harbor Capital Partners for about $50 million. The deal will allow AMM to continue its focus on driveline systems for OEM customers.

Mergers and Acquisitions

In one of its largest deals to date AAM in 2017 acquired Metaldyne Performance Group for $3.3 billion. The combination created a global supplier with broad capabilities across the powertrain drivetrain and driveline product lines. More importantly it will also diversify its customer base so it won't be as reliant on GM as a primary customer. The deal also helped in AMM's efforts to vertically integrate its supply chain by securing a steady supply of parts to its largest manufacturing facility.

Company Background

What eventually became American Axle & Manufacturing (AAM) got its start in 1917 when GM built a plant in Detroit to make aircraft parts on a site where AMM's headquarters now stands. Auto parts were added to the product mix and by 1920 two additional factories had been built as the automotive industry grew.

In 1992 GM announced it was putting 18 manufacturing sites up for sale including five plants that made up GM's Final Drive and Forge Business unit. Former Chrysler executive Richard E. Dauch formed an investment team and purchased the five driveline and forging plants from GM. American Axle & Manufacturing became an independent company in 1994. AMM went public in 1999.

EXECUTIVES

Chairman And Ceo, David C. Dauch, age 55, $1,150,000 total compensation
President, Michael K. Simonte, age 55, $640,000 total compensation
President Powertrain, Gregory S. (Greg) Deveson
President Driveline, Alberto L. Satine, age 62, $510,000 total compensation
President Metal Formed Products, Norman Willemse, age 62, $450,000 total compensation
President Casting, Timothy E. (Tim) Bowes
Treasurer, Christopher J. (Chris) May, age 49, $391,667 total compensation
Vp And Cio, Donald Wright
Svp Global Procurement And Supplier Quality Engineering, Tolga Oal
Vice President Human Resources, Terri M Kemp
Vice President Quality Warr And Customer Satisf American Axle And Manufacturing Holdings Inc, Allan R Monich

Vice President, Tom Szymanski
Vice President Human Resources, Carla Wesley
Vice President Operations, Inacio Moniguchi
Vice President Of Finance, Chaitanya Apte
Vice President, Matthew Hett
Auditors: DELOITTE & TOUCHE LLP

LOCATIONS

HQ: American Axle & Manufacturing Holdings Inc
  One Dauch Drive, Detroit, MI 48211-1198
Phone: 313 758-2000
Web: www.aam.com

2017 Sales

	$ mil.	% of total
US	3,319	53
Mexico	1,393	22
Canada	310	5
China	297	5
All Other Asia	291	5
Europe and other	492	8
South America	161	2
Total	**6,266**	**100**

PRODUCTS/OPERATIONS

2017 Sales

	$ mil.	% of total
Driveline	4,039	65
Metal Forming	830	13
Powertrain	806	13
Casting	589	9
Total	**6,266**	**100**

Selected Products

Axles
Brackets
Control arms
Connecting rod forging and assemblies
Driveshafts
Differential assemblies and cases
Rear drive modules
Ring and pinion gears
Suspension components
Thin wall castings
high-strength ductile iron castings
Steering knuckles
Torsional vibration dampers
Transfer cases
Transmission modules
Transmission valve bodies
Turbo charger housings
Variable valve timing products

COMPETITORS

AxleTech International	Linamar Corp.
Carraro	Magna International
Dana	Meritor
FCA US	Tower International
Ford Motor	Visteon
GKN	ZF Friedrichshafen

HISTORICAL FINANCIALS
Company Type: Public

Income Statement
FYE: December 31

	REVENUE ($ mil.)	NET INCOME ($ mil.)	NET PROFIT MARGIN	EMPLOYEES
12/18	7,270	(57)	—	25,000
12/17	6,266	337	5.4%	25,000
12/16	3,948	240	6.1%	13,100
12/15	3,903	235	6.0%	13,050
12/14	3,696	143	3.9%	12,820
Annual Growth	**18.4%**	**—**	**—**	**18.2%**

2018 Year-End Financials

Debt ratio: 50.71%
Return on equity: (-3.81%)
Cash ($ mil.): 476
Current ratio: 1.50
Long-term debt ($ mil.): 3,686
No. of shares (mil.): 111
Dividends
  Yield: —
  Payout: —
Market value ($ mil.): 1,240

	STOCK PRICE ($) FY Close	P/E High/Low		PER SHARE ($) Earnings	Dividends	Book Value
12/18	11.10	—	—	(0.51)	0.00	13.28
12/17	17.03	7	4	3.21	0.00	13.80
12/16	19.30	6	4	3.06	0.00	6.93
12/15	18.94	9	6	3.02	0.00	3.96
12/14	22.59	12	9	1.85	0.00	1.50
Annual Growth	**(16.3%)**	**—**	**—**	**—**	**—**	**72.6%**

AMERICAN BALANCED FUND, INC.

EXECUTIVES

Chb-Ceo, Robert G O'Donnell
Pres, Paul G Haaga Jr
V Pres, Hilda L Applbaum
Sr V Pres, Abner Goldstine
Sr V Pres, John H Smet
V Pres, J Dale Harvey
V Pres, Jeffrey T Lager
Asst Treas, R Marcia Gould
SEC, Patrick F Quan
Auditors: DELOITTE & TOUCHE LLP COSTA M

LOCATIONS

HQ: AMERICAN BALANCED FUND, INC.
  1 MARKET, SAN FRANCISCO, CA 941051596
Phone: 707 864-3945
Web: WWW.CAPITALGROUP.COM

HISTORICAL FINANCIALS
Company Type: Private

Income Statement
FYE: December 31

	ASSETS ($ mil.)	NET INCOME ($ mil.)	INCOME AS % OF ASSETS	EMPLOYEES
12/17	128,462	23,932	18.6%	9
12/15	87,394	4,903	5.6%	—
12/00	6,203	832	13.4%	—
12/99	5,996	218	3.6%	—
Annual Growth	**18.6%**	**29.8%**	**—**	**—**

American Business Bank (Los Angeles, CA)

Auditors: Grant Thorton LLP

LOCATIONS

HQ: American Business Bank (Los Angeles, CA)
  523 W. 6th Street, Suite 900, Los Angeles, CA 90014
Phone: 213 430-4000
Web: www.americanbusinessbank.com

HISTORICAL FINANCIALS
Company Type: Public

Income Statement
FYE: December 31

	ASSETS ($ mil.)	NET INCOME ($ mil.)	INCOME AS % OF ASSETS	EMPLOYEES
12/18	2,157	16	0.8%	—
12/17	1,873	8	0.4%	—
12/16	1,843	12	0.7%	—
12/15	1,671	12	0.7%	—
12/14	1,535	11	0.7%	27
Annual Growth	**8.9%**	**9.4%**	**—**	**—**

2018 Year-End Financials

Debt ratio: —
Return on equity: —
Cash ($ mil.): 103
Current ratio: —
Long-term debt ($ mil.): —
No. of shares (mil.): 7
Dividends
  Yield: —
  Payout: —
Market value ($ mil.): 243

	STOCK PRICE ($) FY Close	P/E High/Low		PER SHARE ($) Earnings	Dividends	Book Value
12/18	31.55	20	15	2.09	0.00	21.42
12/17	39.40	39	32	1.07	0.00	20.27
12/16	34.95	20	16	1.72	0.00	18.26
12/15	32.25	19	16	1.67	0.00	18.06
12/14	27.76	20	18	1.54	0.00	(0.00)
Annual Growth	**3.3%**	**—**	**—**	**8.0%**	**—**	**—**

American Electric Power Co Inc

Serving markets in Ohio Michigan Indiana and other midwestern states American Electric Power (AEP) is one of the largest power generators and distributors in the US. The holding company owns the nation's largest electricity transmission system a network of more than 40000 miles. It also nearly 227000 miles of distribution lines. AEP's electric utilities boasts 5.4 million customers in 10 states and has about 23000 megawatts of largely coal-fired generating capacity although it is adding renewable sources to its generation portfolio. AEP is also a top wholesale energy company.

HISTORY

In 1906 Richard Breed Sidney Mitchell and Henry Doherty set up American Gas & Electric (AG&E) in New York to buy 23 utilities from Philadelphia's Electric Company of America. With properties in seven northeastern US states AG&E began acquiring and merging small electric properties creating the predecessors of Ohio Power (1911) Kentucky Power (1919) and Appalachian Power (1926). AG&E also bought the predecessor of Indiana Michigan Power (1925).

By 1926 the company was operating in Indiana Kentucky Michigan Ohio Virginia and West Virginia. In 1935 AG&E engineer Philip Sporn later known as the Henry Ford of power introduced his high-voltage high-velocity circuit breaker. AG&E picked up Kingsport Power in 1938.

Becoming president in 1947 Sporn began an ambitious building program that continued through the 1960s. Plants designed by AG&E (renamed American Electric Power in 1958) were among the world's most efficient and electric rates stayed 25%-38% below the national average.

AEP bought Michigan Power in 1967 six years after Donald Cook succeeded Sporn as president. Cook who refused to attach scrubbers to the smokestacks of coal-fired plants was criticized in the early 1970s by environmental protesters. AEP's first nuclear plant named in Cook's honor went on line in Michigan in 1975. He retired in 1976.

The firm moved from New York to Columbus Ohio in 1980 after buying what is now Columbus Southern Power (formed in 1883). It set up AEP Generating in 1982 to provide power to its electric utilities.

AEP began converting its second nuke Zimmer to coal in 1984. In 1992 AEP finally began installing scrubbers at its coal-fired Gavin plant in Ohio after being ordered to comply with the Clean Air Act. It also cleaned up its image by planting millions of trees in 1996.

The company formed AEP Communications after Congress passed the Telecommunications Act of 1996. The next year AEP jumped into the UK's deregulated electric market; AEP and New Century Energies (now Xcel Energy) bought Yorkshire Electricity (later Yorkshire Power Group) for $2.8 billion. However a $109 million UK windfall tax on the transaction — and increased wholesale competition — hurt AEP's bottom line.

As the normally staid electric industry succumbed to merger mania AEP agreed in 1997 to buy Central and South West (CSW) of Texas in a $6.6 billion deal. AEP's sales would nearly double and CSW was to bring its own UK utility SEEBOARD and other overseas holdings.

In 1998 AEP bought a 20% stake in Pacific Hydro an Australian power producer and CitiPower an Australian electric distribution company. AEP also bought Equitable Resources' Louisiana natural gas midstream operations including an intrastate pipeline. In 1999 China's Pushan Power Plant (70%-owned by AEP) began operations. Environmental concerns resurfaced that year when the EPA sued the utility alleging its old coal-powered plants which had been grandfathered from the Clean Air Act had been quietly upgraded to extend their lives.

Regulators approved the company's acquisition of CSW in 2000 but AEP had to agree to relinquish control of its 22000 miles of transmission lines to an independent operator. The CSW deal closed later that year. (However the SEC's approval of the deal was challenged by a federal appeals court in 2002.)

AEP sold its 50% stake in Yorkshire Power Group to Innogy (now RWE npower) in 2001; it also purchased Houston Pipe Line Co. (which it later sold in early 2005) from Enron for $727 million. AEP became one of the largest US barge operators that year when it bought MEMCO Barge Line from Progress Energy. It also purchased two UK coal-fired power plants (4000 MW) from Edison Mission Energy a subsidiary of Edison International in a $960 million deal.

In 2002 AEP sold its UK utility SEEBOARD to Electricité de France in a $2.2 billion deal; it also sold its Australian utility CitiPower to a consortium led by Cheung Kong Infrastructure and Hongkong Electric for $855 million. The following year the company sold two of its competitive Texas retail electric providers (WTU Retail Energy and CPL Retail Energy) to UK utility Centrica. It also divested its power plant development subsidiary AEP Pro Serv and its stakes in telecom firms C3 Communications and AFN.

The company sold two UK power plants to Scottish and Southern Energy for $456 million in 2004 and it sold a 50% stake in a third UK plant to Scottish Power in a $210 million deal. AEP also

sold four independent power plants in Florida and Colorado to Bear Stearns for $156 million that year.

In 2006 the company sold its Plaquemine cogeneration plant to Dow Chemical for $64 million. Also that year it formed a joint venture company with MidAmerican Energy Holdings to build and own new electric transmission assets within the Electric Reliability Council of Texas.

AEP settled an eight-year lawsuit with the US government in 2007 and agreed to pay more than $4.6 billion to reduce hazardous air pollution from 16 coal-burning power plants.

In 2011 the company reached a $425 million settlement covering all claims with BOA and Enron related to their purchase of Houston Pipeline Company from Enron in 2001.

Growing its retail business in the US in 2012 AEP acquired Chicago-based Blue Star Energy and its independent retail electric supplier BlueStar Energy Solutions. The company has about 23000 customer accounts. The deal also gives AEP the opportunity to hedge the output of its soon-to-be unregulated Ohio power generation.

By the end of 2012 AEP was operating 310 MW of wind power facilities and had about 180 MW of long-term purchase power agreements for wind power.

In 2013 AEP received the regulatory go-ahead to separate its AEP Ohio-owned generation assets from its Ohio distribution and transmission operations and complete transfer of that generation to AEP's competitive generation company (AEP Generation Resources) and regulated affiliates Appalachian Power and Kentucky Power.

To create a more customer friendly service in 2013 AEP launched a new enhanced version of its website at aepenergy.com. optimized for mobile devices.

EXECUTIVES

Svp And Chief Administrative Officer, Lana L. Hillebrand, age 59, $490,680 total compensation
Executive Vice President Sales And Marketing, John Powers
Vice Chairman, Robert P. (Bob) Powers, age 65, $723,773 total compensation
President And Coo Southwestern Electric Power, Venita McCellon-Allen, age 60, $410,919 total compensation
Vice President Transmission Engineering And Project Services, Scott Moore
Vp Corporate Communications; President American Electric Power Foundation, Dale E. Heydlauff, age 59
Evp External Affairs, Charles R. Patton, age 60
Evp Energy Supply, Charles E. (Chuck) Zebula, age 59, $446,310 total compensation
President And Coo Aep Ohio, Julie Sloat, age 46
Svp Energy Marketing Administration Aep Service, Brian X. Tierney, age 52, $730,800 total compensation
President And Coo Public Service Company Of Oklahoma, J. Stuart Solomon, age 57
Chairman President And Ceo, Nicholas K. (Nick) Akins, age 59, $1,325,077 total compensation
Evp General Counsel And Secretary, David M. Feinberg, age 50, $615,354 total compensation
Evp Generation, Mark C. McCullough, age 59
Evp Utilities, Paul Chodak, age 55
Evp Aep Transmission And President And Coo Aep Transmission Holding Company (aepthco), Lisa M. Barton, age 53, $532,039 total compensation
President And Coo Kentucky Power, Matthew J. Satterwhite, age 46
President And Coo Indiana Michigan Power, Toby L. Thomas
Vp Projects Controls And Construction Generation, Chris T. Beam

President And Coo Aep Texas, Judith Talavera
Vice President, Thomas Householder
Senior Vice President Engineering Projects And Filed Services, William L Sigmon
Vice President Of Human Resources, Vicki Zeiger
Vice President And Deputy General Counsel Commercial And Transactional Services, Gary Prescott
Senior Vice President Strategic Policy Analysis American Electric Power Service Corporation, Bruce H Braine
Senior Vice President Operations And Performance Transformation, Barbara Radous
Vice President And Director, John Keane
Senior Vice President Chief Accounting Officer And Controller, Joe Buonaiuto
Vice President, Lance Sogan
Vice President Energy Marketing Asset Investments And Renewables, Kevin Brady
Senior Vice President Commercial Operations, Todd Busby
Vice President, Andy Reis
Vice President Governmental Affairs American Elec, Anthony Kavanagh
Vice President And Chief Security Officer, Stan Partlow
Senior Vice President, Jeffrey Cross
Senior Vice President Governmental Affairs, Tony Kavanagh
Vice President Construction, Frederick Burns
Senior Vice President Of Marketing, Brian Neville
Vice President Customer Operations, Helen Murray
Vice President Information Technology, Brian Bueter
Vice President Marketing Operations, Bob Bradish
Senior Vice President Grid Development, A Wade Smith
Svp Fossil And Hydro Generation, Daniel Lee
National Account Manager, James B Clark
Vice President Trading, John Sniffen
National Account Manager, James Clark
Vice President Fuel Procurement, Mark Leskowitz
Vp And Chief Digital Officer, Derek Kramer
Vice President Of Government Affairs, Greg Clark
Secretary, Timothy King
Secretary, Robert Mckinney
Auditors: PricewaterhouseCoopers LLP

LOCATIONS

HQ: American Electric Power Co Inc
1 Riverside Plaza, Columbus, OH 43215-2373
Phone: 614 716-1000 **Fax:** 614 223-1823
Web: www.aep.com

PRODUCTS/OPERATIONS

2018 Sales

	$ mil.	% of total
Vertically Integrated Utilities	9,645	60
Transmission and Distribution Utilities	4,653	29
Generation and Marketing	1,940	11
Other Revenue and adjustments	(43.2)	-
Total	**16,195**	**100**

Selected Subsidiaries

AEP Energy Services Inc. (energy marketing and trading)
AEP Generating Co. (electricity generator marketer)
AEP Retail Energy (retail energy marketing in deregulated territories)
AEP Texas Central Company (formerly Central Power and Light electric utility)
AEP Texas North Company (formerly West Texas Utilities electric utility)
AEP Towers (wireless communications towers)
Appalachian Power Company (electric utility)
Columbus Southern Power Company (electric utility)
Indiana Michigan Power Company (electric utility)
Kentucky Power Company (electric utility)
Kingsport Power Company (electric utility)
Ohio Power Company (electric utility)
Public Service Company of Oklahoma (electric utility)

Southwestern Electric Power Company (electric utility)
Wheeling Power Company (electric utility)
Utility Distribution/Customer Service Divisions
AEP Ohio (handles distribution customer service and external affairs functions for Columbus Southern Power Company Ohio Power Company and Wheeling Power Company)
AEP Texas (handles distribution customer service and external affairs functions for AEP Texas Central Company and AEP Texas North Company)
Appalachian Power (handles distribution customer service and external affairs functions for Appalachian Power Company and Kingsport Power Company)
Indiana Michigan Power (handles distribution customer service and external affairs functions for Indiana Michigan Power Company)
Kentucky Power (handles distribution customer service and external affairs functions for Kentucky Power Company)
Public Service Company of Oklahoma (handles distribution customer service and external affairs functions for Public Service Company of Oklahoma)
Southwestern Electric Power Company (handles distribution customer service and external affairs functions for Southwestern Electric Power Company)

COMPETITORS

BP	Entergy
CMS Energy	Exelon
CenterPoint Energy	FirstEnergy
Constellation Energy Group	PG&E Corporation
DTE	Sempra Energy
Dominion Energy	Southern Company
Duke Energy	TVA
	Xcel Energy

HISTORICAL FINANCIALS

Company Type: Public

Income Statement				FYE: December 31
	REVENUE ($ mil.)	NET INCOME ($ mil.)	NET PROFIT MARGIN	EMPLOYEES
12/18	16,195	1,923	11.9%	17,582
12/17	15,424	1,912	12.4%	17,666
12/16	16,380	610	3.7%	17,634
12/15	16,453	2,047	12.4%	17,405
12/14	17,020	1,634	9.6%	18,529
Annual Growth	(1.2%)	4.2%	—	(1.3%)

2018 Year-End Financials

Debt ratio: 36.71%	No. of shares (mil.): 493
Return on equity: 10.30%	Dividends
Cash ($ mil.): 534	Yield: 3.3%
Current ratio: 0.48	Payout: 64.8%
Long-term debt ($ mil.): 21,648	Market value ($ mil.): 36,865

	STOCK PRICE ($) FY Close	P/E High/Low		PER SHARE ($) Earnings	Dividends	Book Value
12/18	74.74	21	16	3.90	2.53	38.66
12/17	73.57	20	16	3.88	2.39	37.19
12/16	62.96	57	46	1.24	2.27	35.38
12/15	58.27	15	13	4.17	2.15	36.44
12/14	60.72	19	14	3.34	2.03	34.37
Annual Growth	5.3%	—	—	4.0%	5.7%	3.0%

American Equity Investment Life Holding Co

American Equity Investment Life Holding (American Equity Life) helps middle-income investors plan for a cushier retirement. The company issues and administers fixed-rate and indexed an-nuities through subsidiaries American Equity Investment Life Insurance Eagle Life Insurance Company and American Equity Investment Life Insurance Company of New York. Licensed in 50 states and the District of Columbia the company sells its products through various channels including about 24000 independent agents and about 30 national marketing associations. American Equity Life also offers a variety of whole term and universal life insurance products. The company targets individuals between the ages of 45 and 75.

Geographic Reach

American Equity Life is licensed in all fifty US states but five states bring in a large portion of its business. Florida Texas California Pennsylvania and North Carolina together account for about one-third of American Equity Life's direct premiums.

Sales and Marketing

American Equity Life distributes its products through independent agents brokers/agents banks registered investment advisors and other channels.

Financial Performance

American Equity Life's revenue has been turbulent over the past few years: It declined in 2014 2015 and 2016 rebounded (and then some) in 2017 and slipped a bit in 2018. Except for 2016 though net income has been rising rapidly; these gains have been driven by higher annuity business volume and investment spread earned.

In 2018 revenue fell 2% to $2.9 billion largely due to losses related to changes in fair values of derivatives. The company also had net realized losses on investments and premiums and other considerations declined.

Net income more than doubled in 2018 rising from $174.6 million in 2017 to $458 million. That year the average amount of annuity account balances outstanding increased 6% while the company's investment spread stayed steady at $1.2 billion. Tax reforms that cut the statutory federal income tax also helped the bottom line.

The company ended 2018 with $344.4 million $1.1 billion less than it had at the end of 2017. Financing activities provided $1.3 billion in net cash and operating activities provided another $43.2 million while investing activities used $2.4 billion.

Strategy

As the company's target demographic — US individuals between the ages of 45 and 75 — continues to expand American Equity Life hopes to take advantage of the resulting demand for fixed index annuity products. It has several strategies in place to encourage growth including expanding and enhancing its distribution network: It intends to boost its offerings to its channel partners to ultimately grow its business.

American Equity Life is also working to increase sales by introducing innovative and competitive new products. With its focus on fixed index and fixed rate annuities the company has launched a number of first-of-its-kind policy riders. It uses its expertise as well as technological advances to both improve its investment management activities and operate more efficiently. The company's 2018 sales were boosted by new products in the guaranteed lifetime income benefit market and the strength of its accumulation products.

Exceptional customer experience is another area of focus.

Ongoing low interest rates have challenged the company's efforts to hit its target rate for investment spread. Additionally certain index strategies have had higher options costs which has raised the firm's aggregate cost of money. And although American Equity remains a leader in the fixed index annuity space new competition has decreased the company's overall market share.

Company Background

David Noble founded American Equity Life in 1995. The company went public in 2003.

EXECUTIVES

Chairman President And Ceo, John M. Matovina, age 64, $727,500 total compensation

Svp And National Marketing Director American Equity Life, Ronald J. (Ron) Grensteiner, age 56, $510,000 total compensation

Evp And Chief Investment Officer, Jeffrey D. (Jeff) Lorenzen, age 53, $445,000 total compensation

Cfo And Treasurer, Ted M. Johnson, age 49, $500,000 total compensation

Evp And Coo, Bruce D. Cheek

Evp General Counsel And Corporate Secretary, Renee D. Montz, age 47, $356,250 total compensation

Vice President: Information Management, Ted Hughes

Assistant Vice President Andndash; Technical Services, Kevin Seuferer

Avp Qa, Dennis Young

Assistant Vice President, Janelle Leatherman

Vice President Financial Reporting And Tax, Aaron Boushek

Assistant Vice President, Young Dennis

Assistant Vice President Product Development, Samuel Richeson

Vice President Investor Relations, Steven Schwartz

Vice President Information Technology, Ann Cannavo

Auditors: KPMG LLP

LOCATIONS

HQ: American Equity Investment Life Holding Co
6000 Westown Parkway, West Des Moines, IA 50266
Phone: 515 221-0002
Web: www.american-equity.com

PRODUCTS/OPERATIONS

2018 Sales

	$ mil.	% of total
Net investment income	2,722	92
Fees & commissions	224	7
Total premiums earned	26	1
Adjustments	(37.2)	-
Total	**2,936**	**100**

COMPETITORS

Allianz Life	National Western
Aviva	Northwestern Mutual
Great American Life	Prudential
Integrity Life	Sammons Financial

HISTORICAL FINANCIALS

Company Type: Public

Income Statement				FYE: December 31
	ASSETS ($ mil.)	NET INCOME ($ mil.)	INCOME AS % OF ASSETS	EMPLOYEES
12/18	61,625	458	0.7%	554
12/17	62,030	174	0.3%	515
12/16	56,053	83	0.1%	530
12/15	49,041	219	0.4%	490
12/14	43,989	126	0.3%	418
Annual Growth	8.8%	38.1%	—	7.3%

2018 Year-End Financials

Debt ratio: 1.20%	No. of shares (mil.): 90
Return on equity: 17.45%	Dividends
Cash ($ mil.): 344	Yield: 1.0%
Current ratio: —	Payout: 5.5%
Long-term debt ($ mil.): —	Market value ($ mil.): 2,525

	STOCK PRICE ($) FY Close	P/E High/Low		PER SHARE ($) Earnings	Dividends	Book Value
12/18	27.94	7	5	5.01	0.28	26.55
12/17	30.73	16	11	1.93	0.26	31.91
12/16	22.54	25	13	0.97	0.24	26.04
12/15	24.03	11	8	2.72	0.22	23.90
12/14	29.19	17	12	1.58	0.20	28.13
Annual Growth	(1.1%)	—	—	33.4%	8.8%	(1.4%)

American Express Co.

American Express makes money even if you do leave home without it. Best known for its charge cards and revolving credit cards the company is also one of the world's largest providers of travel services. And yes the company still issues traveler's checks. Its travel agency operations have thousands of locations worldwide and its Travelers Cheque Group is the world's largest issuer of traveler's checks. Still the company's charge and credit cards are its bread and butter; American Express boasts $190 billion in assets and $1.2 trillion in annual billed business and has about 114 million cards in circulation in 140-plus countries. About three-quarters of company?s total sales comes from US.

HISTORY

In 1850 Henry Wells and his two main competitors combined their delivery services to form American Express. When directors refused to expand to California in 1852 Wells and executive William Fargo formed Wells Fargo while remaining at American Express.

American Express merged with Merchants Union Express in 1868 and developed a money order to compete with the government's postal money order. Fargo's difficulty in cashing letters of credit in Europe led to the offering of Travelers Cheques in 1891.

In WWI the US government nationalized and consolidated all express delivery services compensating the owners. After the war American Express incorporated as an overseas freight and financial services and exchange provider (the freight operation was sold in 1970). In 1958 the company introduced the American Express charge card. It bought Fireman's Fund American Insurance (sold gradually between 1985 and 1989) and Equitable Securities in 1968.

James Robinson CEO from 1977 to 1993 hoped to turn American Express into a financial services supermarket. The company bought brokerage Shearson Loeb Rhoades in 1981 and investment banker Lehman Brothers in 1984 among others. In 1987 it introduced Optima a revolving credit card to compete with MasterCard and Visa. It had no experience in underwriting credit cards though and was badly burned by losses.

Most of the financial units were combined as Shearson Lehman Brothers. But the financial services supermarket never came to fruition and losses in this area brought a steep drop in earnings in the early 1990s. Harvey Golub was brought in as CEO in 1993 to restore stability.

The company sold its brokerage operations as Shearson (to Travelers now Citigroup) and spun off investment banking as Lehman Brothers in 1994. In late 1996 it teamed with Advanta Corp. to allow Advanta Visa and MasterCard holders to earn points in the American Express Membership Rewards program. The move sparked a lawsuit from Visa and MasterCard which prohibit their member banks from doing business with American Express. That set off a spate of lawsuits culminating in the US Justice Department filing an antitrust suit against Visa and MasterCard. A federal judge sided with the Justice Department in 2001 but Visa and MasterCard appealed.

In 1997 Kenneth Chenault became president and COO putting him in line to succeed Golub.

Online banking service Membership B@nking was launched in 1999. That year American Express invested in Ticketmaster (the ticketing giant that merged with Live Nation Entertainment in 2010). In 2000 the company established a headquarters in Beijing to develop business in China. Also that year American Express bought more than 4500 ATMs from Electronic Data Systems (now HP Enterprise Services) making it a leading US operator of ATMs.

In 2001 Chenault replaced Golub as chairman and CEO. American Express was hit hard that year by bad investments in below-investment grade bonds by its money-management unit which shaved about $1 billion from earnings. Adding to its woes the company's employees at its New York City headquarters across the street from the World Trade Center were displaced by the 2001 terrorist attacks; its headquarters reopened in May 2002.

To grow its corporate travel management business Amex acquired Rosenbluth International a leading global travel management company with corporate travel operations in 15 countries in 2003. When Rosenbluth became fully integrated into the organization in mid-2004 American Express announced a relaunch of its corporate travel organization renamed American Express Business Travel.

American Express underwent a mild shakeup in late 2004 when it cut 2.5% of its workforce in a restructuring that included the company's business travel operations. The restructuring also included the sale of the company's banking operations in Bangladesh Egypt Luxembourg and Pakistan and the relocation of some finance operations. On a brighter note the company that year announced a milestone agreement with Industrial and Commercial Bank of China (ICBC) one of the biggest banks in China to issue the first American Express-branded credit cards in that country.

To focus on its travel and credit card operations the company in 2005 spun off Ameriprise Financial (formerly American Express Financial Advisors) a provider of insurance mutual funds investment advice and brokerage and asset management services. Toward that same end American Express sold its Tax and Business Services division to H&R Block and its UK-based American Express Financial Services Europe to TD Waterhouse (now part of TD AMERITRADE). Also in 2005 the company sold its equipment leasing business to Key Equipment Finance.

In 2007 the company's business travel division bought the rest of Farrington American Express Travel Services Limited it didn't already own. The travel management company had been a joint venture with Farrington Travel. The move was part of American Express's global expansion push especially in the Asia-Pacific region.

The company discontinued its Travelers Cheque card that year after determining that customers preferred paper travelers checks over a stored-value card. However sales of the travelers checks continued to decline in 2007 affected by the rising use of ATMs among other factors.

Also in 2007 American Express reached a $2.5 billion settlement with Visa and other defendants including JPMorgan Chase Capital One U.S. Bancorp and Wells Fargo dropping them from the lawsuit that alleged the companies conspired to block American Express from the bank-issued card business in the US. The following year it reached a $1.8 billion settlement with Mastercard the final remaining defendant in the suit.

American Express sold the international operations of American Express Bank to Stanchart in 2008.

American Express became a banking holding company in 2009. As a result it received some $3.4 billion from the Troubled Asset Relief Fund (TARP) early that year; it repaid the debt within months.

EXECUTIVES

Evp And Cio, Marc D. Gordon, age 58
Evp And Cfo, Jeffrey C. (Jeff) Campbell, age 58, $1,000,000 total compensation
Chairman And Ceo, Stephen J. (Steve) Squeri, age 60, $1,350,000 total compensation
Evp And General Counsel, Laureen E. Seeger, age 57, $800,000 total compensation
Group President Global Consumer Services, Douglas E. Buckminster, age 59, $700,000 total compensation
President Global Risk Banking & Compliance And Chief Risk Officer, Denise Pickett
Group President Global Merchant & Network Services, Anré Williams, age 53
President Global Services Group, Paul D. Fabara, age 53
Chief Corporate Affairs Officer, Michael J. OÁ'Neill, age 65
Chief Strategy Officer, Mohammed Badi
President Global Commercial Services, Anna Marrs
Chief Marketing Officer, Elizabeth Rutledge
Vp Marketing Aeis, Matt Harris
Vice President And General Manager Of Sm, Howard Grosfield
Vice President Human Resources, Christine Anderson
Vp Treasury Controller And Head Accounting Policy, Kimberly Scardino
Vice President Information Insights, Ayesha Almeida
Vice President Of Sales And Marketing, David Bonalle
Vice President Of Marketing, Kathleen King
Vice President Information Technology Operations And Infosec, Bo Gorham
Evp Global Infrastructure And Digital Workplace, Brian Saluzzo
Vice President, Liwen Liang
Vp Brand Management, Susan Stashower
Vice President Architecture And Strategy, Howard Johnson
Vice President Operations, Nicole Samuels
Vice President, Leslie Morris
Vice President Capabilities Planning And Enablement, Jaime Hullinger
Vice President Marketing And Analytics Direct Deposits, Jamee Lubkemann
Vice President Corporate Integrated Marketing Sales, Stacey Staaterman
Vice President Technologies, Jennifer Weber
Vice President Technologies, Amy Heydon
Senior Vice President Human Resources Relationship Leader And Head Of Talent, Gaby Giglio
Vice President Online Commerce Marketing, Carl Barkey
Vice President And General Manager Client Solutions, Howard Fulton
Vice President Human Resources Business Partner, Connie Schan
Svp Risk Management, Shen Chang
Vice President, Shreya Patel
Senior Vice President And Marketing Us Middle Market Global Corporate Payments, Pablo Ribas

Svp Global Security Group Global Corporate Services, Mic Chandrani
Vice President Client Management, Larry Restiano
Vice President, David Carroll
Vice President Marketing Development, Trang Dinh
Vice President International Analytics Data Analytics And Capabilities, Kathleen Haggerty
Vice President, Sanjay Khanna
Executive Vice President Human Resources, Manu Narang
Vice President Of Marketing, Greg Keeley
Vice President Global Marketing And Product Management Japa Global Commercial Card, Stephen Pendergast
Vice President Operational Excellence Entreprise Functions, Betty Xu
Vice President Social Marketing Innovation, Phil Wilson
Senior Vice President, John Stack
Vice President Global Business And Market Development, David Wolf
Vice President, Ravi Varma
Vice President Direct Marketing Acquisitions And N, Tina Eide
Vice President Customer Service, Laurie Farquhar
Vice President Finance Manda Controller, Dylan Haverty-Stacke
Vice President, Lananh Hoang
Vice President Consumer Card Marketing, Molly Brady
Vice President Authentication Account Takeover And Enterprise Fraud Capabilities, Chad Gonzales
Vice President International Network Marketing And Business Insights, Sujata Bhatia
Vice President Risk Management, Sanjay Gwalani
Vice President And Senior Counsel, Emily Goodman Binick
Vice President, Roxanna Wall
Vice President Operational Excellence Finance And Global Business Services, Rita Magann
Vice President Web Engineering Platform Security And Advanced Frameworks, Deepak Arora
Vice President Compliance And Ethics, Glenn Jarvis
Vice President Global Loyalty Solutions, Sarah Sugarman
Vice President Demand Management, Colleen Doyle
Vp Quality Controllership, Robert Frost
Vice President, Jen Humpal
Vice President And Senior Counsel, Jeremy Dyme
Vice President Learning And Development Global Servicing Network, Emma Hanman
Evp Enterprise Risk Management, Alex Weldon
Vice President, Victor Gold
Vice President, Katie Naylor
Vice President, Ulrik Philipson
Vice President Operations, John Koslow
Vice President And Chief Advertising Counsel, Ellie Boragine
Senior Vice President Of Intl Risk Management, David Nigro
Vice President, Brady Fife
Vice President And Controller, Lawrence Belmonte
Senior Vice President Of Global Human Resources, Gabriella Giglio
Vice President Digital Acquisition, John Dotto
Senior Vice President Finance, Christina Wong
Vice President Fraud, Nancy Yee
Vice President Government Relations, Sean Peterson
Vice President Global Operations And Financial Management, Paul Garvey
General Auditor Senior Vice President, Julie Scammahorn
Vice President Us Benefits, Tammy Yee
Senior Vice President Global Head Of Tax Chief Tax Officer, Joe Gagliano
Vice President Of Human Resources, Kim Seymour

Vice President Risk Management, Lei Chen
Vice President Human Resources World Service, Madelyn Marino
Vice President Business Development, Franki Schmidt
Vice President Technologies Communications, Gerilyn Cammaroto
Vice President Global Credit And Fraud Risk Management Capabilities, Lynn Almoro
Senior Vice President, Joseph Quagliata
Vice President Of Credit Operations, Todd Schemm
Vice President Of Consumer And Small Business Services Technologies, Miles Farrel
Foreign Exchange Vice President, Helen Grace
Vice President Small Merchant Marketing, Sangeeta Naik
Vice President Tax Audits, Donald Worrell
Vice President Engineering, Anchal Gupta
Executive Vice President, Steve Squeri
Vice President End User Computing, Gary Kensey
Vice President Global Risk Oversight, Wenbiao Zhao
Vice President Strategic Communications, Frank Vaccaro
Vice President Of Finance, Julie Bush
Vice President Corporate Development Mergers And Acquisitionsmp;a And Strategic Investments, Hans Fleming
Vice President, Linda Marshall
Vice President David Jones Strategic Alliance, Kylea Boward
Vice President National Client Group, Greg Hybl
Vice President Lfo Finance, Jessica Lieberman
Senior Vice President And General Manager Head Of Service Delivery Emea American Express Business T, Suzan Kereere
Vice President International Finance, Jason Brown
Vice President Digital Product Engineering And Data Analytics, Vivek Tripathi
Vice President Technologies Finance, Phil Konort
Vice President Technical Architecture, Jamie Kenas
Vice President Of International, Tom Young
Vice President Finance And Human Resources, Alicia Marrone
Vice President, Tom Taris
Vice President Business Development, Lisa L Rankin
Vp Finance, Phyllis Mccormick
Senior Vice President Employee And Shareholder Communications, Pat Locke
Vice President, Eduardo Gomez Garcia
Svp Enterprise Digital Group, Luke Gebb
Senior Vice President Global Brand Integration And Insights, Mary Reilly
Vice President Enterprise Data Governance, Jennifer Curtiss
Vice President Finance, Kirstie Myers
Assoicate Vice President, Carol Varner
Vice President Global Account Dev, Chris Yule
Vice President Lfo Open Finance, Rob Pereless
Vice President Global Commercial Card Ri, Ray Didonato
Vice President Lfo Technologies, Michael Ullrich
Vice President, Cheryl Daniels
Vice President Custoemr Experience, Holly Hamilton
Vice President Global Reengineering, Cathy D Reber
Vice President Service Delivery, Jacinthe Ladouceur
Vice President, Linda Presti
Vice President Uk Small Merchants, John Lemonius
Vice President, Jeffrey Irvine
Vice President Consumer Card Customer Strategy, Kelly Stevens
Vice President Executive Compensation, Anil Agarwal
Vice President Mandamp;a Controllership, Cory Vieira

Vice President Open Digital Strategy And Services Development, Scott Belous
Vice President Human Resources East Asia, Sonia Cargan
Senior Vice President, Pam Codispoti
Vice President Customer Marketing Analytics, Mahasweta Dhawan
Vice President Global Media American Express, Joseph Bihlmier
Vice President Global Business Development, Steve Murphy
Vice President Retail Travel Network, Ellen Bettridge
Executive Vice President Principal Accounting Officer Corporate Controller, Richard Petrino
Auditors: PricewaterhouseCoopers LLP

LOCATIONS

HQ: American Express Co.
200 Vesey Street, New York, NY 10285
Phone: 212 640-2000   **Fax:** 212 640-0404
Web: www.americanexpress.com

2016 Sales

	% of total
United States	74
Europe the Middle East and Africa (EMEA)	10
Japan Asia/Pacific and Australia (JAPA)	9
Latin America Canada and the Caribbean (LACC)	7
Total	**100**

PRODUCTS/OPERATIONS

2016 Sales

	$ mil.	% of total
Non-interest		
Discount revenue	18,680	56
Net card fees	2,886	9
Other commissions & fees	2,753	8
Other	2,029	6
Interest		
Loans including fees	7,205	21
Interest & dividends on investment securities	131	-
Deposits with banks & other	139	-
Total	**33,823**	**100**

2016 Sales by Segment

	% of total
U.S. Consumer Services (USCS)	39
Global Commercial Services (GCS)	30
International Consumer and Network Services (ICNS)	17
Global Merchant Services (GMS)	14
Total	**100**

COMPETITORS

BCD Travel	JPMorgan Chase
Bank of America	JTB Corp.
Barclays	MasterCard
Capital One	Ovation Travel Group
Citibank	PayPal
Discover	Visa Inc
Expedia	Western Union
HSBC	

HISTORICAL FINANCIALS

Company Type: Public

Income Statement				FYE: December 31
	ASSETS ($ mil.)	NET INCOME ($ mil.)	INCOME AS % OF ASSETS	EMPLOYEES
12/18	188,602	6,921	3.7%	59,000
12/17	181,159	2,736	1.5%	55,000
12/16	158,893	5,408	3.4%	56,400
12/15	161,184	5,163	3.2%	54,800
12/14	159,103	5,885	3.7%	54,000
Annual Growth	4.3%	4.1%	—	2.2%

2018 Year-End Financials

Debt ratio: 30.98%
Return on equity: 34.16%
Cash ($ mil.): 27,445
Current ratio: —
Long-term debt ($ mil.): —

No. of shares (mil.): 847
Dividends
 Yield: 1.5%
 Payout: 18.2%
Market value ($ mil.): 80,736

	STOCK PRICE ($) FY Close	P/E High/Low	PER SHARE ($) Earnings	Dividends	Book Value
12/18	95.32	14 11	7.91	1.44	26.32
12/17	99.31	33 25	2.97	1.31	21.22
12/16	74.08	13 9	5.65	1.19	22.68
12/15	69.55	18 13	5.05	1.10	21.33
12/14	93.04	17 14	5.56	0.98	20.21
Annual Growth	0.6%	— —	9.2%	10.1%	6.8%

American Financial Group Inc

American Financial Group (AFG) insures American businessmen in pursuit of the Great American Dream. Through the Great American Insurance Group of companies and its flagship Great American Insurance Company AFG offers commercial property/casualty insurance with a focus on specialties such as workers' compensation professional liability ocean and inland marine and multiperil crop insurance. The company also provides surety coverage for contractors and risk management services. For individuals and employers AFG provides a wide range of annuity policies through its Great American Financial Resources Inc. (GAFRI) subsidiary.

Operations

AFG operates through two primary segments — Property and Casualty Insurance and Annuity— and two smaller segments — Run-Off Long-Term Care and Life and Other (which includes holding company activities).

The Property and Casualty Insurance segment is the largest accounting for more than 70% of AFG's annual revenues. Its operations are divided into more than 30 businesses including property and transportation (marine crops and commercial auto) specialty casualty (professional excess and surplus workers' compensation and general liabilities) and specialty financial (fidelity and surety lend/lease risk management).

In the Annuities segment (which accounts for about a quarter of total revenue) GAFRI offers fixed rate and indexed annuity products through underwriting companies Great American Life Insurance and Annuity Investors Life Insurance.

Geographic Reach

AFG's largest markets include California Illinois Texas New York and Florida. The company has more than 120 locations throughout North America and Europe.

Sales and Marketing

AFG primarily markets its insurance policies through a nationwide network of independent agents and brokers although a small number are written through employee agents. Annuity products are marketed through a retail network of approximately 65 national marketing organizations managing general agents financial advisors and independent brokers.

The company's customers include Wells Fargo BB&T PNC Financial Services LPL Financial and Regions Financial.

Financial Performance

AFG's revenue which has grown over the past five years increased 6% to $6.9 billion in 2017.Net earned property/causualty premiums rose 6% (largely due to an increase in property and transportation business) and net investment income rose 8% but those gains were partially offset by a very slight decline in net earned life accident and health premiums.

Net income which had been on the decline jumped 84% to a record $649 million in 2016. Leading factors in that jump were decreases in life accident and health benefits paid out and in provisions for income taxes. In 2017 net income normalized somewhat falling to $475 million as property/casualty annuity and other expenses increased. Additionally the company had higher earnings in annuities life and the run-off long-term care segments.

Cash flow from operations increased 57% to $1.8 billion that year due to positive changes in insurance claims and reserves and in managed investment entities' assets and liabilities.

Strategy

Like all property/casualty insurers AFG seeks to balance out calm and catastrophe by operating on long-term income cycles where years of profits balance out years of increased claims. The company sees opportunity in such areas as workers' compensation and commercial auto coverage and it has worked to build its operations both organically and through acquisitions.

In terms of annuities AFG is focused on fixed and indexed products and has steered away from offering variable annuities and other types of offerings where it doesn't have a competitive advantage. The company has invested in these operations and introduced product enhancements recently to take advantage of volatility in the equity markets.

To focus on core operations the company has sold off supplemental benefits and other units. In 2016 it sold its struggling Neon (formerly Marketform) medical malpractice operations which provided coverage in 30 countries (primarily in Australia Italy and the UK).

Mergers and Acquisitions

AFG expands its property/casualty operations through acquisitions in existing and new markets such as medical malpractice and workers' compensation. In 2018 it agreed to buy ABA Insurance Services (ABAIS) from American Bankers Mutual Insurance for $28 million. ABAIS provides directors and officers liability and other insurance products for banks small businesses and not-for-profit organizations. That deal will boost AFG's specialty casualty operations.

In mid-2016 the company acquired the rest of transportation-focused National Interstate Corporation it didn't already own for $320 million.

HISTORY

When his father became ill in the mid-1930s Carl Lindner Jr. dropped out of high school to take over his family's dairy business. He built it into a large ice-cream store chain called United Dairy Farmers. Lindner branched out in 1955 with Henthy Realty and in 1959 he bought three savings and loans. The next year Lindner changed the company's name to American Financial Corp. (AFC). He took it public in 1961 using the proceeds to buy United Liberty Life Insurance (1963) and Provident Bank (1966).

Lindner also formed the American Financial Leasing & Services Company in 1968 to lease airplanes computers and other equipment. In 1969 the company acquired Phoenix developer Rubenstein Construction and renamed it American Continental. AFC bought several life casualty and mortgage insurance firms in the 1970s including National General parent of Great American Insurance Group later the core of AFC's insurance segment. The company also moved into publishing by buying 95% of the Cincinnati Enquirer paperback publisher Bantam Books and hardback publisher Grosset & Dunlap.

But the publishing interests soon went back on the block as Lindner concentrated on insurance which was then suffering from an industry-wide slowdown. In addition to selling the Enquirer AFC spun off American Continental in 1976. American Continental's president was Charles Keating who had joined AFC in 1972 and whose brother published the Enquirer. Keating (who was later jailed released then eventually pleaded guilty in connection with the failure of Lincoln Savings) underwent an SEC investigation during part of his time at AFC for alleged improprieties at Provident Bank. The bank was spun off in 1980.

Lindner took AFC private in 1981. That year following a strategy of bottom-feeding the firm began building its interest in the non-railroad assets of Penn Central the former railroad that had emerged from bankruptcy as an industrial manufacturer. Later that decade AFC increased its ownership in United Brands (later renamed Chiquita Brands International) from 29% to 45%. Lindner installed himself as CEO and reversed that company's losses. In 1987 AFC acquired a TV company Taft Communications (renamed Great American Communications) entailing a heavy debt load. To reduce its debt AFC trimmed its holdings including Circle K Hunter S&L and an interest in Scripps Howard Broadcasting.

Great American Communications went bankrupt in 1992 and emerged the next year as Citicasters Inc. (sold 1996). In 1995 Lindner created American Financial Group to effect the merger of AFC and Premier Underwriters of which he owned 42%. The result was American Financial Group (AFG).

AFG's results in the 1990s were uneven and it typically did not make an underwriting profit. In 2003 the insurer kept operating expenses down (partly by merging two of its holding company subsidiaries into AFG) and swung to a profit even though premium revenue was down.

The company shed some commercial lines to concentrate on its property/casualty and life and annuities businesses. To refine its mix AFG transferred Atlanta Casualty Company Infinity Insurance Company Leader Insurance Company and Windsor Insurance Company into 40%-owned Infinity Property and Casualty which went public in 2003. In 2004 the business exchanged its stake in Provident Financial Group for a holding in National City Corporation.

Founder and chairman Carl Lindner retired as CEO in 2005 and died in 2011. No one was named to replace him as chairman but two of his sons Carl Lindner III and Craig Lindner carried on as co-CEOs.

EXECUTIVES

Co-president Co-ceo And Director, S. Craig Lindner, age 64, $1,150,000 total compensation
Co-president Co-ceo And Director, Carl H. Lindner, age 66, $1,150,000 total compensation
Evp And Cfo, Joseph E. (Jeff) Consolino, age 52, $868,269 total compensation
Svp And Chief Administrative Officer, Michelle A. (Shelly) Gillis, age 50, $332,315 total compensation
Svp And General Counsel, Vito C. Peraino, age 63, $565,962 total compensation
Divisional Senior Vice President Product Management Property And Inland Marine Division Gaic, Julie Kadnar

Divisional Senior Vice President Great American Professional Risk Insurance Services, Robert Nagaishi
Associate Vice President Infrastructure And Operations, James Niehaus
Assistant Vice President, John Fronduti
Vp And Assistant General Counsel, Mark Weiss
Divisional Vice President Development And Reinsurance Crop Insurance Division Gaic, Dean Clarke
Senior Vice President, Chester Eng
Vice President Human Resources, Scott Beeken
Vice President, Howard Baird
Senior Vice President Underwriting Republic Indemnity, David Harkins
Vice President Underwriting Executive Liability Division, Bob Rubin
Assistant Vice President Marketing And Sales, Douglas Grebe
Senior Vice President Financial Mid Continent Group Gaic, Gregg Jones
Divisional Senior Vice President Bonds North California Office Gaic, Francis Plante
Divisional Vp Marketing Executive Liability Division Great American Insurance Group, Jonathan Starck
Divisional Vice President Claims Specialty Human Services Division Gaic, Doug Svenkerud
Divisional Vice President Loss Prevention Ocean Marine Division Gaic, Edward Wilmot
Divisional Senior Vice President Specialty Excess And Surplus Division Great American Insurance Group, Brian Sloan
Divisional Vice President Dallas Excess Liability Division Gaic, Kathleen Zale
Vp Excess Liability Division Great American Insurance Group, Christopher Bright
Divisional Vice President Marketing Trucking Division Gaic, Tim Clinton
Divisional Senior Vice President Ocean Marine East Regional Office Gaic, Forrest Downing
Divisional Svp Occupational Accident Trucking Division Great American Insurance Group, Mary Ford
Divisional Vice President Underwriting Environmental Division Great American Insurance Group, Sara Brothers
Divisional Vice President San Francisco Excess Liability Division Great American Insurance Group, Marcus Lampley
Divisional Vp Claims And Cincinnati Operations Financial Insitution Services Great American Insurance Group, Pat Sinnard
Avp And Actuary Gafri, Richard Sutton
Vp Taxes, H Kim Baird
Divisional Vice President Fidelity And Crime Division New York Great American Insurance Group, George Pierce Jr
Vice President, Rhonda Royals
Divisional Vice President And Actuary, Rebecca Schriml
Divisional Vice President Annuity Group, Donna Carrelli
Vice President Claims, Brad Fisher
Senior Counsel And Vice President, Ruth Stark
Assistant Vice President And Senior Corporate Counsel, Freeman Durham
Vice President Of Claims, Steve Winborn
Board Member, Gregory Joseph
Board Member, Kenneth Ambrecht
Auditors: Ernst & Young LLP

LOCATIONS

HQ: American Financial Group Inc
  301 East Fourth Street, Cincinnati, OH 45202
Phone: 513 579-2121
Web: www.afginc.com

PRODUCTS/OPERATIONS

2017 Sales

	$ mil.	% of total
Net earned insurance premiums	4,601	67
Net investment income	1,831	27
Income of managed investment entities	222	3
Realized gains on securities	5	-
Other	206	3
Total	**6,865**	**100**

COMPETITORS

AIG	MetLife
Allianz	Pacific Life
Arch Capital	RLI
CNA Financial	The Hartford
Chubb Limited	Tokio Marine
Cincinnati Financial	Travelers Companies
HCC Insurance	W. R. Berkley
Jackson National Life	XL Group plc
Liberty Mutual	Zurich Insurance Group
Markel	

HISTORICAL FINANCIALS
Company Type: Public

Income Statement
FYE: December 31

	ASSETS ($ mil.)	NET INCOME ($ mil.)	INCOME AS % OF ASSETS	EMPLOYEES
12/18	63,456	530	0.8%	7,600
12/17	60,658	475	0.8%	600
12/16	55,072	649	1.2%	400
12/15	49,859	352	0.7%	400
12/14	47,535	452	1.0%	7,200
Annual Growth	**7.5%**	**4.1%**	**—**	**1.4%**

2018 Year-End Financials

Debt ratio: 2.05%	No. of shares (mil.): 89
Return on equity: 10.29%	Dividends
Cash ($ mil.): 1,515	Yield: 4.9%
Current ratio: —	Payout: 76.0%
Long-term debt ($ mil.): —	Market value ($ mil.): 8,084

	STOCK PRICE ($) FY Close	P/E High/Low		PER SHARE ($) Earnings	Dividends	Book Value
12/18	90.53	20	14	5.85	4.45	55.66
12/17	108.54	20	16	5.28	4.79	60.38
12/16	88.12	12	9	7.33	2.15	56.55
12/15	72.08	19	14	3.94	2.03	52.50
12/14	60.72	12	10	4.97	1.91	55.63
Annual Growth	**10.5%**	**—**	**—**	**4.2%**	**23.5%**	**0.0%**

AMERICAN HIGH INCOME TRUST

EXECUTIVES

President, Larry Clemmenson
V Pres-Treas, Mary C Cremin
V Pres, Michael J Downer
SEC, Julie F Williams
Auditors: DELOITTE & TOUCHE LLP COSTA M

LOCATIONS

HQ: AMERICAN HIGH INCOME TRUST
  333 S HOPE ST STE 5200, LOS ANGELES, CA 900713061
Phone: 949 766-6305

HISTORICAL FINANCIALS
Company Type: Private

Income Statement
FYE: September 30

	ASSETS ($ mil.)	NET INCOME ($ mil.)	INCOME AS % OF ASSETS	EMPLOYEES
09/18	16,817	577	3.4%	1
09/16	17,336	1,555	9.0%	—
Annual Growth	**(1.5%)**	**(39.1%)**	**—**	**—**

AMERICAN HONDA FINANCE CORPORATION

If you're fonda the idea of driving a Honda you might want to call on American Honda Finance. Operating as Honda Financial Services the company provides retail financing in the US for Honda and Acura automobiles motorcycles all-terrain vehicles power equipment and outboard motors. Its American Honda Service division administers service contracts while Honda Lease Trust offers leases on new and used vehicles. Honda Financial Services also offers dealer financing and related dealer services. Ancillary services include servicing loans and securitizing and selling loans into the secondary market. A subsidiary of American Honda Motor the company began as a wholesale motorcycle finance provider in 1980.

Operations

American Honda Finance (AHF) acquires retail installment contracts and closed-end vehicle lease contracts from purchasers and lessees and authorized Honda and Acura dealers. It also provides these authorized dealers with wholesale flooring and commercial loans.

AHF also acquires used auto loans of non-Honda and non-Acura vehicles and provides these third-party dealers iwth wholesale loans. Additionally the company offers vehicle service contracts services underwriting and pricing of consumer financing services and incentive financing programs for Honda and Acura products.

Geographic Reach

The company is headquartered in Torrance California and operates nine regional offices that support all authorized Honda and Acura dealers across North America.

Financial Performance

While full financials of the subsidiary were not available American Honda Finance's (AHF) revenue has been on the uptrend as auto sales continue to strengthen along with the US economy. Revenue in fiscal 2014 (ended March 31 2014) grew by 22% to Â 5.97 trillion ($58.1 billion) thanks to larger revenues from its parent company's auto business and positive foreign currency exchange rates.

Despite higher selling general and administrative expenses and R&D expenses AHF's operating income also increased 39% to Â 290.9 billion ($2.83 billion) in 2014 after the company continued its cost reduction measures.

Strategy

American Honda Finance Corp. (AHFC) exists to provide stability to support sales of new and used Honda and Acura vehicles throughout North America Honda Motor's largest market. To that end AHFC seeks to preserve funding diversity balanced liquidity and maintain a prudent maturity profile. To spur growth of its US business in 2012 the company opened its ninth regional office a 25000-square-foot facility in Charlotte North Carolina to serve Honda buyers in the Carolinas Maryland Tennessee Virginia and West Virginia.

EXECUTIVES

Ceo, Hideo Tamaka
Sr V Pres*, Stephan Smith
V Pres-Cfo*, John Weisickle
Information Specialist, Hung Le
Information Technology Directo, David Newallis
Information Technology Directo, John Thompson
Corporate Recruiter, Breanna Robinson
Assistant Manager ABS Accounti, Jean Yamatsuka
Admin Asst, Debbie Lemire
Marine OEM Sales Manager, Dennis Ashley
Dealer Relations Manager, Jessica Havalotti
Auditors: KPMG LLP LOS ANGELES CALIFOR

LOCATIONS

HQ: AMERICAN HONDA FINANCE CORPORATION
20800 MADRONA AVE, TORRANCE, CA 905034915
Phone: 310 972-2239
Web: WWW.HONDAFINANCIALSERVICES.COM

Selected Offices
Alpharetta GA
Charlotte NC
Cypress CA
Elgin IL
Holyoke MA
Irving TX
San Ramon CA
Torrance CA
Wilmington DE

COMPETITORS

Ally Financial
Automotive Finance Corporation
Bank of America
Credit Acceptance
Ford Motor Credit
Mercedes-Benz Financial Services USA
Mitsubishi Motors Credit of America
Toyota Motor Credit

HISTORICAL FINANCIALS

Company Type: Private

Income Statement				FYE: March 31
	ASSETS ($ mil.)	NET INCOME ($ mil.)	INCOME AS % OF ASSETS	EMPLOYEES
03/17	69,854	753	1.1%	1,000
03/16	66,653	910	1.4%	—
03/08	50,526	(45)	—	—
03/07	41,431	394	1.0%	—
Annual Growth	5.4%	6.7%	—	—

American International Group Inc

EXECUTIVES

Pres, Salvatore De Fini
V Pres*, David Walsh
Chief of Infrastructure Transf, Al Stuart
Accounting Staff, Ian Galloway
Auditors: PricewaterhouseCoopers LLP

LOCATIONS

HQ: American International Group Inc
175 Water Street, New York, NY 10038
Phone: 212 770-7000
Web: www.aig.com

HISTORICAL FINANCIALS

Company Type: Public

Income Statement				FYE: December 31
	ASSETS ($ mil.)	NET INCOME ($ mil.)	INCOME AS % OF ASSETS	EMPLOYEES
12/18	491,984	(6)	—	49,600
12/17	498,301	(6,084)	—	49,800
12/16	498,264	(849)	—	56,400
12/15	496,943	2,196	0.4%	66,400
12/14	515,581	7,529	1.5%	65,000
Annual Growth	(1.2%)	—	—	(6.5%)

2018 Year-End Financials

Debt ratio: 7.02%	No. of shares (mil.): 866
Return on equity: (-0.01%)	Dividends
Cash ($ mil.): 2,873	Yield: 3.2%
Current ratio: —	Payout: —
Long-term debt ($ mil.): —	Market value ($ mil.): 34,153

	STOCK PRICE ($) FY Close	P/E High/Low		PER SHARE ($) Earnings	Dividends	Book Value
12/18	39.41	—	—	(0.01)	1.28	65.04
12/17	59.58	—	—	(6.54)	1.28	72.49
12/16	65.31	—	—	(0.78)	1.28	76.66
12/15	61.97	38	29	1.65	0.81	75.10
12/14	56.01	11	9	5.20	0.50	77.69
Annual Growth	(8.4%)	—	—	—	26.5%	(4.3%)

American National Insurance Co. (Galveston, TX)

True to its name American National Insurance Company offers agricultural commercial and personal property/casualty insurance as well as life insurance annuities supplemental health credit and other types of insurance throughout the US Puerto Rico and other territories. Its subsidiaries include Garden State Life Insurance Standard Life and Accident Insurance and Farm Family Holdings. American National markets its products through independent and career agents broker-dealers employee benefit advisors financial representatives and managing general underwriters.

Operations
American National operates in five segments: Life (including whole term universal indexed and variable life insurance) Annuity (fixed indexed and variable annuity products) Health (Medicare Supplement stop-loss credit disability insurance) Property/Casualty (personal and commercial coverage) and Corporate and Other (income from investments not related to the insurance segments as well as non-insurance operations).

While the company considers its Life and Annuity segments its main areas of focus it earns more of its premiums from property/casualty insurance. In fact the Property/Casualty segment brings in some 40% of the company's total revenues. Altogether premiums account for more than 60% of revenues. Investment income accounts for another 30%.

American National has more than $100 billion in life insurance in-force.

Geographic Reach
American National is licensed to conduct business in all 50 states the District of Columbia and Puerto Rico. Business is conducted in New York by American National Life Insurance Company of New York.

The company serves about 6 million customers.

Sales and Marketing
American National markets life insurance and annuities through Independent Marketing Group (IMG) which targets middle-income and wealthy clients. IMG markets policies through financial institutions employee benefits organizations broker-dealers marketing organizations and independent agents and brokers. It also sells life insurance using direct mail internet and telemarketing campaigns. The company's Career Sales and Service Division primarily serves the middle-income market (life annuities and health coverage) though exclusive employee agents.

The group's Health segment serves middle-income seniors self-insured employers and individuals and performs marketing through independent agents and managing general underwriters.

Financial Performance
American National's revenues have hovered around $3 billion for the past five years. In 2017 revenue rose 6% to $3.4 billion. This increase was driven by gains in property/casualty and life premiums (but partially offset by declines in annuity and accident and health premiums). Net investment income also trended upward that year but other policy revenues (including mortality charges and earned policy service fees) fell 19%. Overall the company had a strong performance despite an increase in catastrophe losses — largely as a result of flooding damage to automobiles.

Net income— which had declined for three straight years — rose 173% to $493.7 million in 2017. That was primarily due to higher realized investment earnings and lower policyholder benefits. These gains led to an increase in operating cash flow which rose 23% to $495.9 million.

Strategy
In its quest to be a leading financial products and services company American National aims to maintain the conservative business practices it has upheld for more than a century including controlling risk factors in its growth and investment strategies. The company looks to maintain strong finances through profitable growth primarily by investing in its distribution channels expanding into new geographic markets attracting and training employees and enhancing marketing programs. It also introduces new products it deems promising: For example in 2018 American National began offering flood insurance in California.

As Baby Boomers reach retirement age the company expects that two of its core segments Life and Annuity will continue to see growth. Its size and financial strength provide it with the ability to introduce new products to this demographic to remain competitive.

In the health insurance sector American National is working to expand in the work site market; however it remains cautious as the future of the Affordable Care Act remains in question.

Another key strategy is improving its use of technology to improve its operating efficiencies and the services it offers its customers. The company is committed to providing exemplary customer service and to offering innovative diversified and competitively priced products to meet the needs of its policyholders and agents.

American National occasionally grows by acquiring like-minded businesses. It also divests or shutters businesses after reassessing their value.

Moody National Bank is a trustee agent of various American National shareholders; it has some 49% voting power of American National's common stock which could potentially limit the company's level of flexibility.

Company Background

American National was founded by Galveston businessman W. L. Moody in 1905. The Moody Foundation a charitable trust controlled by W L. Moody descendant Robert Moody and his family and the Moody National Bank together own about 70% of the company.

Based in hurricane-prone Galveston Texas American National knows first-hand the importance of property/casualty insurance and how to evaluate risk. The company withdrew from writing some policies along the Atlantic and Gulf coasts in 2005 and in 2008 it moved its claims processing facilities further inland to San Antonio.

American National launched the American National Life Insurance Company of New York in 2010.

EXECUTIVES

Evp Independent Marketing Group, David A. Behrens, age 56, $532,569 total compensation

Chairman President And Ceo, James E. Pozzi, age 68, $918,847 total compensation

Evp Cfo Treasurer And Multiple Line (ml) And Property And Casualty (p&c) Operations, Timothy A. Walsh, age 57, $400,400 total compensation

Evp Career Sales And Service Division, Hoyt J. Strickland, age 62, $375,353 total compensation

Vice President Health Administration, Tracy Milina

Vice President Application Development, Toya Harper

Vice President, Wayne Smith

Evp Health Insurance Operations, James Stelling

Vice President Broker Dealer Marketing, Steven Dobbe

National Sales Manager, Mike Sawdey

Assistant Vice President Life Insurance, Sharon Garner

Vice President Special Markets, Mark Walker

National Sales Manager, Kendra Kelly

Vice President, Kara Phillips

National Sales Manager, Michael Kresl

Vice President Life Policy Administration, Bruce Pavelka

Assistant Vice President, Wayne Cucco

Assistant Vice President And Assistant Actuary, Michael Shumate

Associate Medical Director, Kim Mlcak

National Sales Manager, J Taylor

Svp Application Development And Support, Meredith Mitchell

Senior Vice President Securities Investments, Gordon Dixon

Vice President Human Resources, Olivia Smith

Vice President Marketing, Debie Knowles

Assistant Vice President Data Communications Messaging (its), Jimmy Watson

National Sales Manager, Jason Weaver

Assistant Vice President And Director Telecommunications, James McEniry

Senior Vice President Actuary, Frank Broll

Vice President Fixed Income, Anne Lemire

Vice President, Bob Schefft

Assistant Vice President And Associate Medical Director, John White

Assistant Vice President Director Life Marketing Sales Director, Clu Jon O'Neal

Svp Independent Marketing Group Operations, Lee Ferrell

National Sales Manager, Thomas Granata

Assistant Vice President Of Claims, Brittany Newsom

Assistant Vice President Of Claims, Grisselda Esquivel

National Sales Manager, Alice Pitts

Assistant Vice President Sales Executive, Ryan Bauer

Svp And Chief Marketing Officer Multiple Line, Scott Campbell

Vice President, Trish Boudreaux

Assistant Vice President Financial Planning And Analysis, Erika Lozano

National Sales Manager, Ronnie Russell

National Sales Manager, Brooke ChFC

Vice President Sales, Dan Safriet

Vice President Commercial Services, Iris Gillies

Vice President Information Technology, Jeff Mills

Vice President Chief Life, Byrd Matthew

Vice President Life New Business, Chairez Philip

Avp Financial Marketing Credit Insurance Division, Eddie Waters

National Sales Manager, David Mcelroy

Assistant Vice President Of Claims, Thomas Legrand

National Sales Manager, James Tadeo

Vice President Sales, Gretta Bassett

Vice President Direct Marketing And Sales, Richard Katz

Vice President And Health Actuary, Bill Watson

Assistant Vice President, William Josep Hogan

Vice President, Ryan Novak

Secretary, Mark Flippin

Auditors: KPMG LLP

LOCATIONS

HQ: American National Insurance Co. (Galveston, TX)
One Moody Plaza, Galveston, TX 77550-7999
Phone: 409 763-4661   **Fax:** 409 766-6502
Web: www.anico.com

PRODUCTS/OPERATIONS

2017 Sales

	$ mil.	% of total
Premiums		
Property/Casualty	1,360	40
Life	328	10
Annuity	222	6
Accident & Health	156	5
Net investment income	966	28
Other policy revenue	248	7
Realized investment gains	104	3
Other	37	1
Adjustments	(13.3)	-
Total	**3,411**	**100**

Selected Subsidiaries

American National Life Insurance Company of Texas (ANTEX)
American National Life Insurance Company of New York
American National Property and Casualty Company (ANPAC)
ANICO Financial Services Inc.
Garden State Life Insurance Company
Pacific Property and Casualty Company
Standard Life and Accident Insurance Company
United Farm Family Insurance Company

COMPETITORS

Allstate	Nationwide
American Financial Group	New York Life
CNO Financial	Penn Mutual
Farmers Group	Prudential
HCI Group	State Farm
Mutual of Omaha	Torchmark
National Western	USAA

HISTORICAL FINANCIALS

Company Type: Public

Income Statement   FYE: December 31

	ASSETS ($ mil.)	NET INCOME ($ mil.)	INCOME AS % OF ASSETS	EMPLOYEES
12/18	26,912	159	0.6%	4,640
12/17	26,386	493	1.9%	4,621
12/16	24,533	181	0.7%	4,597
12/15	23,746	242	1.0%	4,736
12/14	23,552	247	1.0%	3,138
Annual Growth	3.4%	(10.4%)	—	10.3%

2018 Year-End Financials

Debt ratio: 0.51%
Return on equity: 3.03%
Cash ($ mil.): 268
Current ratio: —
Long-term debt ($ mil.): —

No. of shares (mil.): 26
Dividends
 Yield: 2.5%
 Payout: 14.2%
Market value ($ mil.): 3,421

	STOCK PRICE ($) FY Close	P/E High/Low		PER SHARE ($) Earnings	Dividends	Book Value
12/18	127.24	22	19	5.91	3.28	195.54
12/17	128.25	7	6	18.31	3.28	194.82
12/16	124.61	19	14	6.71	3.26	172.85
12/15	102.27	13	10	9.02	3.14	165.55
12/14	114.26	13	11	9.18	3.08	164.94
Annual Growth	2.7%	—	—	(10.4%)	1.6%	4.3%

American Tower Corp (New)

Growth in wireless communications is taking American Tower to new heights. The company rents space on towers and rooftop antenna systems to wireless carriers and radio and TV broadcasters who use the infrastructure to enable their services. It operates about 40000 wireless towers in the US some 58000 in India and more than 50000 throughout the rest of the world. Its portfolio additionally includes approximately 950 Distributed Antenna System networks used mainly for indoor communications (malls casinos and arenas). American Tower also offers tower-related services such as site acquisition structural analysis to determine support for additional equipment and zoning and permitting management services.

Operations

American Tower's primary business is the leasing of antenna space on multi-tenant communications sites. It provides the service to wireless providers radio and television broadcast companies wireless data providers government agencies and municipalities and tenants from several other industries.

The company operates five business segments mostly based in regions where it leases its properties. The US Property segment is its largest and accounts for nearly 55% of revenue. The three other geographic segments are Latin America Property 20% of revenue EMEA Property10% of revenue and Asia Property 10% of revenue. The Services segment which generates 1% of revenue acquires sites and offers zoning and permitting services and structural analysis to support its site leasing businesses.

Geographic ReachBoston MA-headquartered American Tower operates its corporate functions in the US and runs distributed operations in its non-US markets. The company produces most of its revenue in the US. However the company is pursuing geographic expansion and the percentage of non-US activity is rising. More than 15% of revenue comes from India about 10% originates in Brazil and more than 5% comes from Mexico. The communications firm also operates in a variety of countries in EMEA (Germany Ghana Nigeria South Africa and Uganda) and in Latin America (Argentina Chile Colombia Costa Rica and Peru).

Sales and MarketingAmerican Tower's top four tenants generate most of its total revenue: about 20% from AT&T Mobility about 15% from Verizon Wireless about 10% from Sprint and about 10% from T-Mobile. Other top tenants include Tata Airtel Idea Cellular Telefonica Nextel International Telecom Italia MTN Group Limited and Vodafone.

Financial Performance

American Tower experienced explosive growth in both revenue and net income over the past several years. Between 2010 and 2016 revenue and net income averaged a near-20% increase each year as consumer demand for wireless products rose around the world.

In 2016 revenue rose 14% year-over-year to $6.6 billion. Across all geographies American Tower saw growth in new sites and growth in additional leases on existing sites. More than half of the year's revenue increase originated in Asia which saw about $337 million generated by new sites primarily as the result of the company's 2016 Viom acquisition. Revenue from newly acquired or constructed sites contributed about $100 million of growth in 2017.

Net income jumped 25% to $1.2 billion in 2017 compared to 2016's $956 million due to increased revenue and a multi-point drop in operating expense margin.

Cash grew by about $15 million in 2017 to end the year with $802 million in the coffers. Uses of cash included $2.8 billion and $113 million for investing and financing activities respectively. They were more than offset by contributions from operating activities which included net income.

Strategy

Wireless communication is growing rapidly throughout the world due to increased demand for new customers wanting to connect (such as in emerging markets) and for existing customers wanting more bandwidth at higher speeds. American Tower wants to capitalize on this trend by expanding its property footprint and making the most out of the property and towers it already owns and operates. It intends to achieve this with geographic expansion opportunistic acquisition of additional towers and maximizing occupancy of its existing towers.

As evidenced by the increasing revenue share coming from non-US sources American Tower is expanding more rapidly overseas than at home. Its recent acquisition of Viom Networks more than tripled its number of towers in India. A follow-on purchase in late 2017 added 20000 more communication sites to its India portfolio bringing its total to more than 70000 sites. Its ATC Europe segment plunged into the French market in 2017 with the acquisition of 2400 wireless towers. Additionally the company purchased in 2016 about 900 towers across a variety of countries.

The costs of increasing tenant occupancy on existing sites is less than acquiring a new site and erecting new towers. The company has a global average of approximately 1.9 tenants per tower and hopes to increase that rate through targeted sales and marketing activities. It believes that towers that are at or near capacity can be upgraded or augmented to meet future tenant demand with relatively modest capital investment.

Mergers and Acquisitions

In late 2017 ATC India agreed to purchase some 20000 communication sites in India from two firms Vodafone and Idea Cellular for $1.2 billion.

In early 2017 ATC Europe a 51%-49% joint venture between ATC and Netherlands-based PGGM spent approximately $750 million to acquire FPS Towers an owner and operator of 2400 wireless tower sites in France.

In 2016 American Tower purchased a 51% controlling interest for $1.1 billion in Viom Networks Ltd a telecommunications infrastructure company that owns and operates about 42000 wireless towers and 200 indoor distributed antenna system (DAS) networks in India. Viom was renamed to ATC Telecom Infrastructure Private Ltd and is part of ATC's Asia geographic region.

EXECUTIVES

Evp And Cfo, Thomas A. (Tom) Bartlett, age 60, $750,000 total compensation
Chairman President And Ceo, James D. (Jim) Taiclet, age 58, $1,100,000 total compensation
Evp International Operations; President Latin America And Emea, William H. (Hal) Hess, age 56, $650,000 total compensation
Evp And President Us Tower, Steven C. Marshall, age 58, $650,000 total compensation
Evp; President Asia, Amit Sharma, age 59
Evp Chief Administrative Officer General Counsel And Secretary, Edmund (Ed) DiSanto, age 67, $600,000 total compensation
Svp Treasurer And Investor Relations, Leah C. Stearns
Ceo Europe Middle East And Africa, Stephen Harris
Senior Vice President Corporate Legal, Ruth Dowling
Senior Vice President Finance Latam, Alejandro Messmacher
Senior Vice President Information Technology And Pe Ust, James Blestowe
Chief Sales Officer, Vivek Garg
Auditors: DELOITTE & TOUCHE LLP

LOCATIONS

HQ: American Tower Corp (New)
116 Huntington Avenue, Boston, MA 02116
Phone: 617 375-7500
Web: www.americantower.com

2017 Sales

	$ mil.	% of total
U.S.	3,703	56
India	1,164	17
France	59	1
Germany	63	1
Ghana	122	2
Nigeria	213	3
South Africa	106	2
Uganda	60	1
Argentina	15	-
Brazil	620	10
Chile	40	1
Colombia	89	1
Costa Rica	19	-
Mexico	364	5
Paraguay	2	-
Peru	17	-
Total	**6,663**	**100**

PRODUCTS/OPERATIONS

2017 Sales

	$ mil.	% of total
Property	6,566	99
Services	98	1
Total	**6,664**	**100**

COMPETITORS

Crown Castle International	SBA Communications
LCC International	VelociTel
Microwave Transmission Systems	

HISTORICAL FINANCIALS

Company Type: Public

Income Statement

	REVENUE ($ mil.)	NET INCOME ($ mil.)	NET PROFIT MARGIN	EMPLOYEES
				FYE: December 31
12/18	7,440	1,236	16.6%	5,026
12/17	6,663	1,238	18.6%	4,752
12/16	5,785	956	16.5%	4,507
12/15	4,771	685	14.4%	3,371
12/14	4,100	824	20.1%	2,974
Annual Growth	16.1%	10.6%	—	14.0%

2018 Year-End Financials

Debt ratio: 64.10%	No. of shares (mil.): 441
Return on equity: 21.36%	Dividends
Cash ($ mil.): 1,208	Yield: 1.9%
Current ratio: 0.51	Payout: 113.7%
Long-term debt ($ mil.): 18,405	Market value ($ mil.): 69,771

	STOCK PRICE ($) FY Close	P/E High/Low	PER SHARE ($) Earnings	Dividends	Book Value
12/18	158.19	60 48	2.77	3.15	12.10
12/17	142.67	57 38	2.67	2.62	14.56
12/16	105.68	59 42	1.98	2.17	15.84
12/15	96.95	73 61	1.41	1.81	15.69
12/14	98.85	52 39	2.00	1.40	9.97
Annual Growth	12.5%	— —	8.5%	22.5%	5.0%

Ameriprise Financial Inc

Ameriprise Financial provides a variety of financial products including mutual funds savings plans annuities personal trust services and insurance products. It does so through its various brands and affiliates — which include Ameriprise Financial Services Columbia Management and RiverSource. Ameriprise manages some $900 billion in assets for more than 2 million individual institutional and small business clients primarily in the US with a growing international presence. It markets and administers its products primarily through a network of some 10000 financial advisors. Founded in 1894 Ameriprise Financial was spun off from American Express in 2005.

Operations

Ameriprise operates four main segments: Advice & Wealth Management Asset Management Annuities and Protection.

Its Advice & Wealth Management segment includes 2200 employee advisors and 7700 independent franchises. Together they provide financial planning advice and brokerage services primarily to the firm's US retail clients. The segment generates about 40% of revenue.

Asset Management (25% of revenue) offers investment management and products to retail high-net-worth and institutional clients globally. It does so through Columbia Management in the US and Threadneedle internationally. Columbia manages about 160 140 funds (mutual funds ETFs etc.) and about 70 variable insurance trust funds (VIT Funds) in the US while Threadneedle manages more than 180 funds outside the US.

The Annuities segment provides variable and fixed annuity products to individual clients via Ameriprise's RiverSource subsidiary. The fourth segment Protection offers Ameriprise clients insurance products including life disability income and property casualty. RiverSource accounts for about 20% of net revenue while Protection brings in more than 15%.

Geographic Reach

Ameriprise Financial and its affiliates are headquartered in Minneapolis Minnesota. Other primary offices are in New York City Boston and London. The US is by far its largest market generating more than 95% of the firm's revenue and possessing approximately 90% of its long-lived assets. Ameriprise's non-US presence is mostly through its Columbia Threadneedle brand which has activities in the UK and Europe in addition to an early-stage presence in the other major continents.

Sales and Marketing

Ameriprise's customers are varied ranging from individuals to universities to corporations. It employs a variety of methods to market and sell to this diverse group. The company's primary retail clients come from the 'mass affluent consumer' segment which controls almost half of all investable assets in the US. The firm markets to them through its financial advisor network and its website. Ameriprise tends to the non-retail segment (institutional & high-net-worth individuals) by nurturing direct relationships with entities such as university endowments pension plans sovereign wealth funds and foundations.

Financial Performance

Thanks to appreciating financial markets and a growing investor base Ameriprise Financial's asset-based fees have led it to consistent revenue and profit growth over the past several years. Since the Great Recession of 2008-2009 revenues have steadily climbed from a low of $7 billion to more recent amounts more than $12 billion. Net income followed a similar albeit more varied trend with a loss of $36 million in 2008 followed by years of $1 billion earnings appreciating to $2 billion in 2014 before settling lower in recent years.

In 2017 Ameriprise grew its revenue 3% to just above $12.0 billion reversing two years of revenue decline. The improvement came mostly from the Advice & Wealth management segment which grew due to higher wrap account assets higher earnings on brokerage cash and increased transactional activity. On the downside the Protection segment's revenue fell 9% due to the impact of unlocking and lower premiums.

Net income grew 12% to $1.5 billion roughly par for the course over the last five years. Net income expanded as the company achieved higher net revenue and lower total expenses particularly benefits claims losses and settlement expenses.

Cash on hand declined 5% to $5.1 billion as operating cash was impacted by changes in receivables and and brokerage deposits partially offset by lower purchases of available-for-sale securities.

Strategy

Ameriprise's long-term strategy involves a portfolio shift to pursue high growth areas in Advice & Wealth Management and Asset Management. It also has a near-term tactical strategy to target two key segments: individuals with $100000 or more in investable assets and high-net-worth people and institutional investors.

In furtherance of that strategy the company in 2019 agreed to sell its Ameriprise Auto & Home business unit to American Family Insurance Mutual Holding for about $1.1 billion.

Between 2010 and 2016 the financial firm orchestrated a shift in assets under management which altered the mix of its pretax operating earnings from one heavily weighted towards Protection & Annuities (55% in 2010) to one weighted towards Advice & Wealth Management (AWM). AWM saw wrap account assets increase $47.1 billion or 23% in 2017

Its advisor network is crucial to growing and maintaining its base of individuals with $100000 or more in assets. The network model is one of a relationship-based direct sales organization in which the company makes considerable investment in technology training and support in addition to a plethora of financial products (mutual funds annuities life insurance). Occasionally Ameriprise adds to its network through acquisition which it did in 2016 with the purchase of Emerging Global Advisors and in 2017 with the purchase of Investment Professionals Inc.

The high-net-worth and institutional client segment is global in scale and therefore requires an approach that is not reliant on the advisor network. Instead Ameriprise offers a broad spectrum of investment advice and products through third parties and its Columbia Threadneedle subsidiary. Global geographic expansion innovations to investment solutions and delivering competitive investment performance are key to growing the fees and commissions received for this segment's fundamental metric assets under management (AUM).

EXECUTIVES

Chairman And Ceo, James M. (Jim) Cracchiolo, age 60, $1,025,000 total compensation

Ceo Global Asset Management, William F. (Ted) Truscott, age 58, $675,000 total compensation

Evp And Cfo, Walter S. Berman, age 77, $675,000 total compensation

Evp Human Resources, Kelli A. Hunter, age 58

President Advice And Wealth Management Products And Service Delivery, Joseph E. (Joe) Sweeney, age 58, $550,000 total compensation

Chief Strategy Officer; President Insurance And Annuities, John R. Woerner, age 50

Evp Marketing Corporate Communications And Community Relations, Deirdre D. McGraw, age 49

Coo; President Advice & Wealth Management Business Development, Neal Maglaque

Evp And Cio, Randy Kupper

Evp And Global Chief Investment Officer, Colin Moore, $475,000 total compensation

Evp Ameriprise Franchise Group, Bill Williams

Evp Ameriprise Advisor Group, Pat O'Connell

Evp And General Counsel, Karen Wilson Thissen

Vice President, Michael Jastrow

Vp Application Development, Scott Wilgenbusch

Vice President Operations, George Tsafaridis

Vice President Of Marketing, Heather Melloh

Vice President Human Resources, Karen Dekker

Vice President Technology Operations, Heather Null Hanscom

Vice President Underwriting And Chief Underwriter, Thor Holmgren

Vice President Corporate Communications And Community Relations, Sharon Hughes

Vice President Head Of Fixed Income Capital Markets Trading, Pete Sirbu

Vp Compensation, John Cronin

Vice President Financial Applications Support Controllership, John Mead

Vice President Appointed Actuary, Stephen Blaske

Vice President External Products Group, Tracy Anderson

Regional Vice President, Tara Eisenbeis

Vice President Wholesaling Operations, Mike Kirchner

Vp Controller, Michael Mattox

Senior Vice President Investor Relations, Alicia Charity

Vice President Managed Accounts, Eric Paluck

Vice President Marketing, Linda Moriarty

Vice President P1 Business Development, Craig Wallenta

Financial Advisor And Vp Brehm And Murray, Jay Murray

Vp Technologies, Nabil N Boudani

Vice President, Dan Dziekciowski

Associate Vice President, Jeffrey Hess

Vice President Human Resources Business Partner, Melanie Demont

Vice President Compliance, Stephanie Rustad

Field Vice President, Todd Orton

Vice President Business Development And National, Lynn Abbott

Vice President Human Resources Services, Jay Rasula

Vice President Risk Management Owned Assets, David Berger

Vice President, Paul Major

Svp Corporate Tax, Richard Bush

Vice President=clr Project Management Office, Mike Greene

Vice President Underwriting, Tom Botsford

Vice President, Chip Pierron

Vice President General Manager Managed Products, Greg Nordmeyer

Vice President Clearing Operations, Dan McAskin

Vice President Architecture, Tom Esselman

Financial Advisor Vice President, Barry Craine

Senior Vice President Treasurer, Jim Hamalainen

Senior Franchise Field Vice President, Dean Mcgill

Franchise Field Vice President, Matthew Roesser

Vice President Information Technology, Clarissa C Ramos

Vice President Product Management, Sarah Arnold

Vice President Portfolio Manager, Nic Pifer

Senior Vice President Corp Comm And Community Relations Ameriprise Financial Inc., Deirdre Davey

Vice President, Erika Perrault

Vp Sox Compliance Re Engineering And Technology Audit, Margo Esson

Vice President And Group Counsel, Kurt Johansen

Associate Vice President, Michael King

Region Vice President, Matthew Miller

Regional Vice President, John Leahy

Vice President Finance, Jennifer Seifriz

Vice President Finance, Rob Bardot

Vp Head Of Advice Wealth Management Ops, Manish Ganatra

Vice President Training And Development, Lamont Boykins

Vice President Of Technical Department, Jacqueline Glockner

Vice President Field Strategy And Implement, Mark Traut

Vice President Human Capital Projects, Carol Hondlik

Vp Technology, Ernie Smith

Vice President, Nancy Anderson

Vice President, Jason Miller

Executive Vice President Ameriprise Advisor Group, Patrick O'connell

Vice President Treasury, Shweta Jhanji

Senior Regional Vice President Insurance West, Bj Seastone

Vice President Human Resources Organization Development, Kristin Kooda-chizek

Vice President And India Head Of Technology, Rajeev Sethi

Vice President And Financial Advisor, Edward Moran

Vice President, Kurtis Larson

Vice President Strategic Transformation, Michael Jordan

Associate Vice President Financial Advisor, Jeffrey Lynn

Vice President Investment Management Annuity Products, Kevin St John

Vice President Derivative And Product Risk, Manuel Balsera

Vice President Complex Product Management Wmps, Steven Williamson

Vice President, Gary Farthing

Vice President Financial Advisor, Alan Holt

Vice President, Paul Seals

Vice President Investment Advisor, Christine Pall

Vice President Cfp Mba, Stan Roberts

Regional Vice President Retirement Wealth Strateg, Joseph Peppe

Financial Advisor And Associate Vice President, Peter Christenson

Division Vice President Riversource Annuities, Doug Brewers

Vp Diversity And Inclusion, Rudy Rodriguez

Vice President Financial Advisor, Nathan Foret

V.p. Sales, Andrew Wright

Vice President Marketing Strategy Retail Retirement, Abu Arif

Vice President Planning And Administration, Matt Haglund

Vice President Risk Management, Jennifer Zwach

Divisional Vice President, Michael DeLorenzo

Associate Vice President Of Finance, Brian Mccabe

Associate Vice President, Bob Dennis

Vice President, Pradeep Gokhale

Associate Vice President Investments, John Stella

Associate Vice President, Karen Hartley

Vice President, Christopher Grella

Regional Vice President, Rob Elstad

Vice President Diversity And Inclusion Ameriprise Financial, Rodolfo Rodriguez

Financial Advisor: Vice President, Amy Boyle

Vice President Treasury, Mike Pollei

Vice President And Investment Officer, Josh Waterman

Vice President Finance, Dawn Brockman

Vice President Treasury, Christy Powers

Vice President Finance, Dave Melander

Vice President Finance (columbia Threadneedle Investments), Brian Engelking

Vice President Annuity Product Development, Steve Wolfrath

Vice President Editorial Planning And Governance, Tracey Domke

Franchise Region Vice President, Barry Stockdale

Vice President, James J Obrien

Vice President Flight Operations And Chief Pilot, Steve Kozlow

Associate Vice President, Daniel Shontere

Regional Vice President, Tim McClurg

Vice President Federal Government Affairs, Elizabeth Varley

Regional Vice President, John Berg

Vice President Financial Advisor, Mark Masson

Associate Vice President, Mark Silbert

Regional Vice President Retirement Wealth Strategies, William Considine

Franchise Field Vice President Pacific Northwest, George Varones

Vice President I And A Pmo, Abir Roy

Vice President And Group Counsel, Edward Walton

Vp Big Data Analytics And Corporate Systems Technology, Sachin Mehta

Vice President, Amanda Payne

Franchise Field Vice President Assistant, Deborah Gable

Associate Vice President Financial Advisor, Clare Hiatt

Vice President Financial Advisor, James Motteler

Vice President, James Obrien

Vice President, Jason Reiling

Vice President, Luke Malloy

Vice President Finance, Margulis Michael

Associate Vice President, Gardner Quin

Vice President Financial Advisor, Rath Colin

Vice President, Hagenbach Scott

Vice President, Lomsdalen Stephen

Vice President Wealth Management Solutions National Sales Manager, David Lieberman

Regional Vice President Annuities New England, Doug Lawrence

Vice President Wealth Management Solutions, Allen Rodrigues

Associate Vice President, Michael Handzo

Vice President Financial Advisor, Alan Ronald

Associate Vice President Financial Advisor, Jeff Lynn

Auditors: PricewaterhouseCoopers LLP

LOCATIONS

HQ: Ameriprise Financial Inc
1099 Ameriprise Financial Center, Minneapolis, MN 55474
Phone: 612 671-3131
Web: www.ameriprise.com

PRODUCTS/OPERATIONS

2017 Sales

	$ mil.	% of total
Annuities	98,276	67
Protection	18,039	12
Advice & Wealth Management	13,270	9
Corporate & other	9,492	6
Asset Management	8,393	6
Total	**147,470**	**100**

2017 Sales

	$ mil.	% of total
Management & financial advice fees	6,392	53
Distribution fees	1,770	15
Net investment income	1,509	13
Premiums	1,394	12
Other revenues	1,010	7
Banking & deposit interest expense	(48)	-
Total	**12,027**	**100**

PRODUCTS & SERVICES

Cash Cards & Lending
Financial Planning
Insurance & Annuities
Investments
Personal Trust Services

Selected Subsidiaries and Affiliates

American Enterprise Investment Services Inc.
Ameriprise Financial Services Inc.
Ameriprise Certificate Company
Ameriprise Trust Company
Columbia Management Investment Advisers LLC
Columbia Management Investment Distributors Inc.
IDS Property Casualty Insurance Company
J. & W. Seligman & Co. Incorporated
RiverSource Distributors Inc.
RiverSource Life Insurance Co. of New York
Threadneedle Asset Management Holdings

Selected Brands

Ameriprise Financial®;
Columbia Management®;
RiverSource®;

COMPETITORS

AXA Financial	MassMutual
Allstate	Merrill Lynch
Bank of America	MetLife
Bank of New York Mellon	Nationwide Financial
Calamos Asset Management	New York Life
Capital Group	Northwestern Mutual
Charles Schwab	PNC Financial
Citigroup	Primerica
FMR	Principal Financial
First Eagle Investment Mangement	Prudential
John Hancock Financial Services	Regions Financial
Lincoln Financial Group	State Street
	TIAA
	U.S. Bancorp

HISTORICAL FINANCIALS

Company Type: Public

Income Statement   FYE: December 31

	REVENUE ($ mil.)	NET INCOME ($ mil.)	NET PROFIT MARGIN	EMPLOYEES
12/18	12,835	2,098	16.3%	14,000
12/17	12,027	1,480	12.3%	13,000
12/16	11,696	1,314	11.2%	13,000
12/15	12,170	1,562	12.8%	13,000
12/14	12,268	1,619	13.2%	12,209
Annual Growth	1.1%	6.7%	—	3.5%

2018 Year-End Financials

Debt ratio: 3.51%
Return on equity: 36.22%
Cash ($ mil.): 3,097
Current ratio: 0.68
Long-term debt ($ mil.): 4,610

No. of shares (mil.): 136
Dividends
  Yield: 3.3%
  Payout: 24.8%
Market value ($ mil.): 14,229

	STOCK PRICE ($) FY Close	P/E High/Low		PER SHARE ($) Earnings	Dividends	Book Value
12/18	104.37	13	7	14.20	3.53	40.99
12/17	169.47	18	12	9.44	3.24	40.90
12/16	110.94	15	10	7.81	2.92	40.66
12/15	106.42	16	12	8.48	2.59	42.20
12/14	132.25	16	12	8.30	2.26	44.37
Annual Growth	(5.7%)	—	—	14.4%	11.8%	(2.0%)

Ameris Bancorp

Ameris Bancorp enjoys the financial climate of the Deep South. It is the holding company of Ameris Bank which holds roughly $3.6 billion in assets and serves retail and consumer customers through more than 75 full-service and mortgage branches in Alabama Georgia South Carolina and northern Florida. In addition to its standard banking products and services the bank also provides treasury services mortgage and refinancing solutions and investment services through an agreement with Raymond James Financial. Loans secured by commercial real estate accounted for approximately 45% of the company's loan portfolio while 1-4 family residential and construction & land development mortgages accounted for nearly a quarter and about 10% respectively.

Operations

Like most banks Ameris earns the vast majority of its recurring revenue (71.5%) from interest income from loans. Nearly 80% of these loans are made up of commercial real estate 1-4 family residential and construction & land development loans. The remaining 20% are from a mix of commercial multi-family residential and consumer loans (home improvement home equity personal lines of credit auto loans and student loans).

Traditional banking products (deposit accounts) and services along with investment products and services (which primarily earn income from fees and commissions) made up about 28% of the bank's annual sales in fiscal 2013.

Sales and Marketing

Through an acquisition-oriented growth strategy Ameris seeks to grow its brand and presence in the markets it currently serves in Georgia Alabama Florida and South Carolina as well as in neighboring communities. In addition the bank expects its community-oriented philosophy will help strengthen existing customer relations and attract new customers.

The company spent $1.62 million on advertising and public relations in Fiscal Year 2013 just under the $1.622 million it spent in 2012 and more than double the $722000 it spent in 2011. The company increased its advertising spending by $900000 during 2012 to support its revenue and growth- strategies during the year.

Financial Performance

Ameris carried $3.67 billion in total assets as of December 31 2013. Loans made up $2.5 billion (approximately 68.9% of total assets). The bank also reported carrying $3 billion in deposits.

Ameris' net revenue dipped in fiscal 2013 declining 5% to $163 million from its high of $172 million in 2012 mostly from an $11.3 million dip in non-interest revenue. But this dip in non-interest revenue is primarily because the bank recorded a large gain of $20 million from acquisitions in 2012. When excluding this acquisition gain from 2012's revenues and thanks to $6.1 million revenue increase in mortgage banking activity management reports that total non-interest income actually increased $8.7 million in 2013 compared to 2012. A decline in interest-earning loan assets from $2.47 billion in 2013 compared to $2.5 billion in 2012 also played a role in the dip in net revenues.

Thanks to aggressive acquisitions and despite revenue decreasing net income jumped a whopping 43% to $20 million in 2013 from $14 million in 2012. This is only slightly below the bank's net income high of $21 million in 2011. It's most notable acquisition of Prosperity Bank increased Ameris' total assets by $744.9 million and added $449.7 million in loans to its interest-earning loan portfolio. Adding to the extra income from new loans Ameris collected higher net interest margins on all of its loans which increased to 4.74% in 2013 from 4.60% in 2012.

Strategy

Ameris plans to continue using its community banking philosophy to lessen its risk and identify prime local lending markets. Management reports that by encouraging a personalized service experience and building deeper customer relationships the bank has already grown a "substantial" base of low-cost core deposits (which pad the bank's reserves and lessen financial risk). And between its bench of experienced decision makers and lenders operating in a "decentralized" structure (which differentiates Ameris from mega banks) and its deep familiarity with local markets management believes the bank can better identify prime growth markets (for lending and bank services) with managed risk in the years ahead.

Mergers and Acquisitions

Integral to the bank's growth strategy Ameris has aggressively acquired banks to broaden its reach into its primary southern markets.

In 2019 the company's shareholders voted to acquire Fidelity Southern the holding company for Fidelity Bank. The combined company will have $16.2 billion in assets. Following the transaction Ameris will have more than 70 branches and some $4.7 billion in deposits in the Atlanta metropolitan area and about 25 branches and roughly $1.8 billion in deposits in the Jacksonville metropolitan area.

Ameris Bancorp purchased Jacksonville Bancorp and its eight branches more than doubling its branch network in Jacksonville Illinois to 14 branches.

Company Background

In addition to acquiring several troubled and failing banks with help from the FDIC Ameris merged with Prosperity Bank in 2013 which broadened its reach into Florida through Prosperity's branches in St. Augustine Jacksonville Panama City Lynn Haven Palatka and Ormand Beach.

Georgia's economy was one of the hardest hit in the US during the recession and Ameris has taken advantage of the plethora of banks seized by regulators in the state. Since 2009 the company has acquired about 10 failed banks in Georgia though FDIC-assisted transactions adding some 20 branches to its network. Ameris also snagged the failed First Bank of Jacksonville in Florida which had two locations.

EXECUTIVES

Chief Banking Executive Ameris Bancorp And Ameris Bank, Andrew B. (Andy) Cheney, age 69, $400,000 total compensation

Evp And Chief Credit Officer, Jon S. Edwards, age 57, $260,000 total compensation

Evp Chief Administrative Officer And Corporate Secretary, Cindi H. Lewis, age 65, $90,333 total compensation

President And Ceo, Edwin W. (Ed) Hortman, age 65, $625,000 total compensation

Evp And Banking Group President Ameris Bancorp And President Ameris Bank, Lawton E. Bassett

Evp Cfo And Coo, Dennis J. Zember, age 49, $320,000 total compensation

Evp And Chief Risk Officer, Stephen A. Melton, $275,000 total compensation

Evp And Chief Banking Officer, James A. LaHaise

Exec V Pres-cio, Thomas Limerick

Assistant Vice President, Ann Dunn

Vice President Branch Manager, Colleen Cline

Vice President, Thomas Luther

Senior Vice President, Rob Kowkabany

Vice President Special Assets Division, Leo Story

Vice President Residential Mortgage, Greg Seabaugh

Senior Vice President Division President Construction, Chap Bennett

Vice President Commercial Lender, Greg Marini

Senior Vice President, Karen Cross

Assistant Vice President Commercial Banker, Jason Glas

Senior Vice President, Jw Dukes

Vice President Senior Treasury Services Advisor, Lori Putnam

Vice President, Connie Romay

Vice President Mortgage Sales Manager, Marlene Buhler

Senior Vice President, Jayson Griffin

Vice President Treasury Services Product And Risk Management, Debbie Dennis

Vice President Business Banker, Robbie Nichols

Senior Vice President Commercial Banking, Gerald Lockhart

Senior Vice President, Frank Cox

Senior Vice President Commercial Lending, Jennifer Ccim

Chairman, Daniel B. Jeter, age 67

Board Member, William Bowen

Auditors: Crowe LLP

LOCATIONS

HQ: Ameris Bancorp
3490 Piedmont Rd NE, Suite 1550., Atlanta, GA 30305
Phone: 404 639-6500
Web: www.amerisbank.com

PRODUCTS/OPERATIONS

2016 sales chart

	$ mil.	% of total
Interest income:		
Interest and fees on loans	218	64
Interest on taxable securities	17	5
Interest on nontaxable securities	1	-
Interest on deposits in other banks	0	-
Interest on federal funds sold	- -	
Non Interest income:		
Service charges on deposit accounts	42	13
Mortgage banking activity	48	14
Other service charges commissions and fees	3	1
Net gains on sales of securities	- -	
Gain on sale of SBA loans	3	1
Other noninterest income	7	2
Total	344	100

2016 sales chart

	% of total
Banking Division	91
Retail Mortgage Division	5
Warehouse Lending Division	3
SBA Division	1
Total	100

Selected Acquisitions

American United Bank
Central Bank of Georgia
Darby Bank & Trust
First Bank of Jacksonville
High Trust Bank
Montgomery Bank & Trust
One Georgia Bank
Satilla Community Bank
Tifton Banking Company
United Security Bank

COMPETITORS

BBVA Compass Bancshares	First South Bancorp (NC)
Bank of America	Regions Financial
Capital City Bank	Southwest Georgia
Colony Bankcorp	Financial
Community Capital Bancshares	SunTrust
	Thomasville Bancshares

HISTORICAL FINANCIALS

Company Type: Public

Income Statement				FYE: December 31
	ASSETS ($ mil.)	NET INCOME ($ mil.)	INCOME AS % OF ASSETS	EMPLOYEES
12/18	11,443	121	1.1%	1,804
12/17	7,856	73	0.9%	1,460
12/16	6,892	72	1.0%	1,298
12/15	5,588	40	0.7%	1,304
12/14	4,037	38	1.0%	1,027
Annual Growth	29.8%	33.0%	—	15.1%

2018 Year-End Financials

Debt ratio: 2.05%	No. of shares (mil.): 47
Return on equity: 10.71%	Dividends
Cash ($ mil.): 644	Yield: 0.0%
Current ratio: —	Payout: 14.2%
Long-term debt ($ mil.): —	Market value ($ mil.): 1,504

	STOCK PRICE ($) FY Close	P/E High/Low		PER SHARE ($)		
			Earnings	Dividends	Book Value
12/18	31.67	21 11	2.80	0.40	30.66
12/17	48.20	26 21	1.98	0.40	21.59
12/16	43.60	23 12	2.08	0.30	18.51
12/15	33.99	27 18	1.27	0.20	15.98
12/14	25.64	18 13	1.46	0.15	13.67
Annual Growth	5.4%	— —	17.7%	27.8%	22.4%

AmerisourceBergen Corp.

AmerisourceBergen is the source for many of North America's pharmacies and health care providers. The distribution company serves as a go-between for drug makers and the pharmacies doctors' offices hospitals and other health care providers that dispense drugs. Operating primarily in the US it distributes generic branded and over-the-counter pharmaceuticals as well as some medical supplies and other products using its network of more than two dozen facilities. Its specialty distribution unit focuses on sensitive and complex biopharmaceuticals. Other operations include pharmaceutical packaging commercialization and consulting services and animal health product distribution.

HISTORY

In 1977 Cleveland millionaire and horse racing enthusiast Tinkham Veale went into the drug wholesaling business. His company Alco Standard (now IKON Office Solutions) already owned chemical electrical metallurgical and mining companies but by the late 1970s the company was pursuing a strategy of zeroing in on various types of distribution businesses.

Alco's first drug wholesaler purchase was The Drug House (Delaware and Pennsylvania); the next was Duff Brothers (Tennessee). The company then bought further wholesalers in the South East and Midwest. Its modus operandi was to buy small well-run companies for cash and Alco stock and leave the incumbent management in charge.

By the early 1980s Alco was the US's third-largest wholesale drug distributor and growing quickly (28% between 1983 and 1988) at a time of mass consolidation in the industry (the number of wholesalers dropped by half between 1980 and 1992). In 1985 Alco Standard spun off its drug distribution operations as Alco Health Services retaining 60% ownership.

Alco Health boosted its sales above $1 billion mostly via acquisitions and expanded product lines. The company offered marketing and promotional help to its independent pharmacy customers (which were beleaguered by the growth of national discounters) and also targeted hospitals nursing homes and clinics.

The US was in the midst of its LBO frenzy in 1988 but an Alco management group failed in its attempt. Rival McKesson then tried to acquire Alco Health but that deal fell through for antitrust reasons. Later in 1988 management turned for backing to Citicorp Venture Capital in another buyout attempt. This time the move succeeded and a new holding company Alco Health Distribution was formed.

In 1993 Alco Health was named as a defendant in suits by independent pharmacies charging discriminatory pricing policies; a ruling the next year limited its liability. To move away from a reliance on independent drugstores Alco Health began targeting government entities and others.

Alco Health went public as AmeriSource Health in 1995. Throughout the next year AmeriSource made a series of acquisitions to move into related areas including inventory management technology drugstore pharmaceutical supplies and disease-management services for pharmacies.

In 1997 AmeriSource acquired Alabama-based Walker Drug for $140 million adding 1500 independent and chain drugstores in the Southeast to its customer list. That year McKesson once again made an offer to buy AmeriSource this time for $2.4 billion while two other major wholesale distributors Cardinal Health and Bergen Brunswig reached a similar pact. The deals were scrapped in 1998 when the Federal Trade Commission voted against both pacts and a federal judge supported that decision.

Later that year AmeriSource signed a five-year deal to become the exclusive pharmaceutical supplier to not-for-profit Sutter Health; in 1999 it renewed similar contracts with the US Department of Veterans Affairs and Pharmacy Provider Services Corporation. That year AmeriSource bought Midwest distributor C.D. Smith Healthcare.

In 2001 AmeriSource bought Bergen Brunswig and the combined company renamed itself AmerisourceBergen.

Its AmerisourceBergen Packaging Group (ABPG) was taken apart in 2012 and its American Health Packaging and AndersonBrecon businesses were moved into other divisions. In 2013 the company sold its AndersonBrecon division which provided contract packaging services to an investor group led by Frazier Healthcare for some $308 million. It also sold its AmerisourceBergen Canada Corporation (ABCC) pharma distribution business that year while retaining its Canadian specialty distribution operations.

In 2012 its biggest customer Medco Health Solutions (17% of revenues) merged with Express Scripts which contracted with one of Amerisource-Bergen's competitors; however following the merger Express Scripts alleviated concerns when it signed a new supply agreement with AmerisourceBergen.

In 2013 AmerisourceBergen signed a 10-year agreement to supply Walgreen Boots Alliance.

EXECUTIVES

Vice President, Stan Byrum
Chairman President And Ceo, Steven H. Collis, age 58, $1,234,231 total compensation
Evp And Cfo, Tim G. Guttman, age 60, $706,539 total compensation
Evp And Chief Communications & Administration Officer, Gina K. Clark, age 62
Vp Deputy General Counsel And Secretary, John G. Chou, age 63, $621,231 total compensation
Group President Pharmaceutical Distribution And Strategic Global Sourcing, James F. (Jim) Cleary, age 56
Evp And President Health Systems Physician Practices And Strategic Health Solutions, Peyton R. Howell, age 52
Evp And Cio, Dale Danilewitz, age 57
Group President Global Commercialization Services And Animal Health, Robert P. Mauch, age 52, $593,077 total compensation
Evp And Chief Human Resources Officer, Kathy H. Gaddes, age 56
Evp Strategy And Development, Sun Park, age 43
Vice President Strategic Accounts, Kent Rischar
Vp Integration, Frank Napoli
Vice President Gerneric Rx Product Development, Brian Jones
Vice President Information Systems, Dennis Hone
Vice President Operations, Joe Williamson
Vice President Professional Services, Kathryn Uchida
Vice President Strategic Accounts, Melissa Passo
Vice President And Manager Distribution Center, Frank Delac
Vice President, Derek Idalski
Vice President Strategic Accounts, Susan Bertot
Human Resource Vice President Director Manager, Matijasich Richard
Vice President Sales, Lianne Chung

Vice President Information Technology, Michael Wondrasch
Vice President Of Strategic Accounts, Matt Johnson
Vice President Professional Services, Ben Shaffer
Vice President Of Professional Services, Thomas Renshaw
Gvp Business Development, Bruce Bennett
Vice President Financial Planning And Analysis, Jeannine Altrogge
Vice President Sales, David Tingue
Vice President Community Pharmacy Buying Groups, Rich Hazinski
Segment Vice President, Jeff Sharkey
Senior Vice President Sales Csp, Lisa Mash
Vice President Of Human Resources, Jay Webster
Vice President Contracts Chargebacks, Linda Ewald
Vice President Finance, Nik Kristic
Vice President Global Sourcing Operations, Barbara Miller
Vice President National Accounts Ltc Gpo's, Rick Miller
Vice President, Andrew Schultz
Vice President Of Information Technology, Sandy Piscitello
Pharmacy Manager, Troy Rebert
Vice President Health Sys Solutions, Rick Lang
Vice President Health Systems Sales, Michael Haddad
Vice President Integration Management Business Architect, Emily D Lightfoot
Vice President Financial Processes, Brian Mangiaracina
Vice President Customer Solutions, Jeff Wilkinson
Vice President Generics Sales, Russell Procopio
Lead Vice President Sales, Scott Snyder
Senior Vice President, Joe Short
Vice President Supply Chain Solutions, Wesley Jones
Executive Assistant To Senior Vice President Chief Human Resources Officer And Chief Information Officer, Kelly Jakeman
Vice President Tax, Daniel Hirst
Vice President Risk Management, Walter Hope
Senior Vice President Strategic Accounts, Steve Iampietro
Vice President Infrastructure And Technology, John Demartino
Senior Vice President Of Marketing, Thomas Connolly
Vice President Marketing, Michael Davenport
Vice President Marketing, Michael Clarke
Vice President Market Development, Vicki Cooney
Sales Vice President, Catherine Carminati
Senior Vice President Finance Amerisourcebergen Drug, David Senior
Vice President Nephrology, William Venus
Senior Vice President Strategic Accounts Community And Specialty Pharmacy, Tom Mullin
Vice President Communications, Gabriel Weissman
Vp Applications Development, Jadine Yamashita
Vice President Human Resources, Rosalyn Wesley
Vice President Procurement, Lindell Denny
Vice President, Blake Jarrell
Vice President Financial Processes, Brian Managiaracina
Vice President Policy, Stacie Heller
Vice President Accounts Payable, Judi Schmidt
Vp Chief Information Security Officer, Alden Sutherland
Senior Vice President Corporate Controller, Lazarus Krikorian
Vice President Supply Chain Solutions, Michael Kody
Vice President Strategy For Provider Solutions, Vicki Albrecht
Vice President Specialty Client Strategies, Erin K Rausch

Vice President Inside Sales And Operations,
Joseph Perrault
Vice President Business Information Solutions,
Eric Besse
Vice President Engineering, John Shook
Senior Vice President Of Government Affairs And Public Policy, Rita Norton
Vice President Of Pricing Global Sourcing And Manufacturer Relations, Alexander Kugler
Vice President Consumer Products Strategic Global Sourcing, Doug Trueman
Vice President Relationship Manager, Matthew Winter
Vice President Health Systems Solutions, Steve Miller
Vice President Of Marketing, Rick Oyler
Vice President Of Infrastructure Services, Ty Mallard
Vice President Strategic Accounts, Joseph Cappello
Vp Marketing, Carolina Lobo
Vice President And Controller Western Financial Center, Mark Krikorian
Board Member, Douglas Conant
Board Member, Lon R Greenberg
Auditors: Ernst & Young LLP

LOCATIONS

HQ: AmerisourceBergen Corp.
1300 Morris Drive, Chesterbrook, PA 19087-5594
Phone: 610 727-7000   **Fax:** 610 647-0141
Web: www.amerisourcebergen.com

PRODUCTS/OPERATIONS

2018 Sales by Segment

	$ mil.	% of total
Pharmaceutical Distribution Services	161,699	96
Other	6,332	4
Adjustments	(92.4)	-
Total	**167,939**	**100**

COMPETITORS

Cardinal Health	Medline Industries
Express Scripts	Owens & Minor
FFF Enterprises	Quality King
Henry Schein	UPS
McKesson	

HISTORICAL FINANCIALS

Company Type: Public

Income Statement

				FYE: September 30
	REVENUE ($ mil.)	NET INCOME ($ mil.)	NET PROFIT MARGIN	EMPLOYEES
09/19	179,589	855	0.5%	22,000
09/18	167,939	1,658	1.0%	21,000
09/17	153,143	364	0.2%	20,000
09/16	146,849	1,427	1.0%	19,000
09/15	135,961	(134)	—	17,500
Annual Growth	**7.2%**	**—**	**—**	**5.9%**

2019 Year-End Financials

Debt ratio: 11.47%	No. of shares (mil.): 206
Return on equity: 29.44%	Dividends
Cash ($ mil.): 3,374	Yield: 1.9%
Current ratio: 0.95	Payout: 35.6%
Long-term debt ($ mil.): 4,354	Market value ($ mil.): 17,023

	STOCK PRICE ($) FY Close	P/E High/Low	PER SHARE ($) Earnings	Dividends	Book Value
09/19	82.33	23 17	4.04	1.60	13.92
09/18	92.22	14 10	7.53	1.52	13.76
09/17	82.75	58 41	1.64	1.46	9.47
09/16	80.78	16 11	6.32	1.36	9.68
09/15	94.99	— —	(0.62)	1.16	3.06
Annual Growth	**(3.5%)**	**— —**	**—**	**8.4%**	**46.0%**

Amgen Inc

Amgen is among the biggest of the biotechs. The company uses cellular biology and medicinal chemistry to target cancers kidney ailments inflammatory disorders and metabolic diseases. Its top protein-based therapeutic products include Neulasta and Neupogen (both used as anti-infectives in cancer patients) Aranesp and Epogen (used to fight anemia in chronic kidney disease and cancer patients) and Enbrel for rheumatoid arthritis. In addition Amgen has extensive drug research and development programs. Its products are marketed in approximately 100 countries to doctors hospitals pharmacies and other health care providers.

HISTORY

Amgen was formed as Applied Molecular Genetics in 1980 by a group of scientists and venture capitalists to develop health care products based on molecular biology. George Rathmann a VP at Abbott Laboratories and researcher at UCLA became the company's CEO and first employee. Rathmann decided to develop a few potentially profitable products rather than conduct research. The company initially raised $19 million.

Amgen operated close to bankruptcy until 1983 when company scientist Fu-Kuen Lin cloned the human protein erythropoietin (EPO) which stimulates the body's red blood cell production. Amgen went public that year. It formed a joint venture with Kirin Brewery in 1984 to develop and market EPO. The two firms also collaborated on recombinant human granulocyte colony stimulating factor (G-CSF later called Neupogen) a protein that stimulates the immune system.

Amgen joined Johnson & Johnson subsidiary Ortho Pharmaceutical (later Ortho-McNeil Pharmaceutical) in a marketing alliance in 1985 and created a tie with Roche in 1988. Fortunes soared in 1989 when the FDA approved Epogen (the brand name of EPO) for anemia. (It is most commonly used to counter side effects of kidney dialysis.)

In 1991 Amgen received approval to market Neupogen to chemotherapy patients. A federal court ruling also gave it a US monopoly for EPO. The following year Amgen won another dispute forcing a competitor to renounce its US patents for G-CSF.

As the company grew it needed to transform itself from startup to going concern; to do so Amgen hired MCI veteran Kevin Sharer as president in 1992. Neupogen's usage was expanded in 1993 to include treatment of severe chronic neutropenia (low white-blood-cell count).

In 1993 Amgen became the first American biotech to gain a foothold in China through an agreement with Kirin Pharmaceuticals to sell Neupogen (under the name Gran) and Epogen there. The purchase of Synergen in 1994 added another research facility accelerating the pace of and increasing the number of products in research and clinical trials.

Although Amgen had two proven sellers in Epogen and Neupogen its growth lay in its pipeline. In 1997 Amgen and partner Regeneron Pharmaceuticals reported the failure of human trials for a drug to treat Lou Gehrig's disease. Still its new drug Stemgen for breast cancer patients undergoing chemotherapy was recommended for approval by an FDA advisory committee in 1998.

Amgen had to swallow a couple of tough legal pills in 1998. First a dispute with J&J over Amgen's 1985 licensing agreement with Ortho Pharmaceu-

tical ended when an arbiter ordered Amgen to pay about $200 million. Later that year however Amgen won a legal battle with J&J over the rights to a promising anemia drug.

Work on its product pipeline continued in 1999: Amgen ended development of obesity and Parkinson's disease drugs after clinical trials produced discouraging results while it began human tests with partner Guilford Pharmaceuticals on a drug designed to regenerate damaged nerve cells in the brains of Parkinson's disease patients. (Guildford and Amgen ended the collaboration in 2001.)

In 2000 the firm resumed its battle to keep its stranglehold on the Epogen market: It sued Transkaryotic Therapies and Aventis (later Sanofi-Aventis) for alleged patent violations over its Epogen product in both the US and the UK. Although it initially won its case in the UK that verdict was overturned in 2002 making Amgen vulnerable to competition before Epogen's patents expire in 2004. That year it won EU and US approval for Aranesp an updated version of Epogen; Amgen in 2002 teamed with former J&J marketing partner Fresenius to sell Aranesp in Germany and take some market share away from J&J. Meanwhile an arbitration committee found J&J had breached its contract with Amgen when it sold Procrit to the dialysis market which Amgen had reserved for itself in their 1985 licensing deal.

In 2003 the company bought leukemia and rheumatoid arthritis drugs maker Immunex. As part of the FTC's blessing of the $10.3 billion union Amgen and Immunex licensed some technologies to encourage competition. Merck Serono gained access to Enbrel data and Regeneron Pharmaceuticals licensed some interleukin inhibitor rights.

The next year Amgen spent $1.3 billion to purchase the remaining 79% of cancer treatment technology maker Tularik that it did not already own.

In the 2010s Amgen worked to extend its reach in international markets. In addition to extending its product offerings into high-growth regions such as Japan China Russia and Africa the firm made select international acquisitions.

EXECUTIVES

Senior Vice President Global Value Access And Policy, Joshua Ofman
Svp Us Commercial Operations, Laura Hamill
Evp Full Potential Initiatives, Brian M. McNamee, age 63
Svp Global Marketing And Commercial Development, Suzanne Blaug
Evp Global Commercial Operations, Anthony C. (Tony) Hooper, age 64, $1,031,788 total compensation
Svp General Counsel And Secretary, Jonathan P. Graham, age 58, $916,789 total compensation
Evp And Cfo, David W. Meline, age 61, $946,733 total compensation
Svp Global Business Services, Michael A. Kelly, age 62, $511,757 total compensation
Evp Research And Development, Sean E. Harper, age 56, $946,246 total compensation
Chairman And Ceo, Robert A. (Bob) Bradway, age 57, $1,531,731 total compensation
Svp Global Medical And Chief Medical Officer, Paul R. Eisenberg
Svp And Head European Region, Corinne Le Goff
Evp Operations, Esteban Santos
Vice President, Brian Kotzin
Executive Vice President, Madhavan Balachandran
Medical Director, Lucy Yan
Vp Human Resources, John Oakes
Medical Director Medical Sciences, Jane Parnes
Medical Director International Development Amgen International, Georg Kreuzbauer

Vice President Market Access And Payer Strategy,
Tom Rice
Vice President Us Government Affairs, Greg
Portner
Vice President Of Global Archi, Kyle Cribbs
Vp Operations, Jesse Daignault
Vice President Business Development, David
Piacquad
Medical Director, Vladimir Hanes
Vice President Finance And Treasurer, Mary
Lehmann
Vice President General Manager Germany, Roland
Wandeler
National Sales Manager, Mike Ellis
Vice President Corporate Accounts, Aston William
Vice President Of Pre Clinical Research, David
Balaban
Vice President General Manager Us Bone Health
Bu, Ken Keller
Administrative Coordinate Government Relations,
Janice Vasquez
Vice President, Rob Lenz
Vice President Sales, Jeff Ludwig
Vice President Investor Relations, Arvind Sood
Vice President Operations, Martin Vantrieste
Vice President Global Development, Richard
Markus
Executive Medical Director, Primal Kaur
Senior Executive Assistant To Kurt Gustafson
Vice President Operations Finance Commercial
Manufacturing, Heidi Katz
Senior Vice President, Kristen Anderson
National Sales Manager, Garvan Byrne
Vp Of Marketing, Dave Marek
Vice President, Karen Laureano
Vice President Singapore Site Operations, Arleen
Paulino
Senior Vice President Global Business Services
And Finance, Judy Gawlik Brown
Executive Vice President Global Commercial
Operations, Tony Hooper
Medical Director, David Chien
Medical Director, Laurence Cheng
Vice President Global Product General Manager,
Simon Clowes
Vice President Amgen Global Safety And
Labeling, Isma Benattia
Medical Director Medical Affairs Cardiovascular,
Kiran Philip
Vp Us Medical Affairs, Robert Cuddihy
Senior Vice President Global Medical And Chief
Medical Officer, Darryl Sleep
Senior Vice President Finance, Joe Peter
Treasurer, Loretta Joseph
Auditors: Ernst & Young LLP

LOCATIONS

HQ: Amgen Inc
One Amgen Center Drive, Thousand Oaks, CA 91320-
1799
Phone: 805 447-1000   **Fax:** 805 447-1010
Web: www.amgen.com

2017 Sales

	$ mil.	% of total
U.S.	18,029	79
Rest of the world	4,820	21
Total	**22,849**	**100**

Selected Locations

Algeria
Australia
Austria
Belgium
Brazil
Bulgaria
Canada
China
Colombia
Croatia
Czech Republic
Denmark

Egypt
Estonia Japan
Finland
France
Germany
Greece
Hong Kong
Hungary
Iceland
India
Ireland
Italy
Latvia
Lithuania
Luxembourg
Mexico
Netherlands
Norway
Poland
Portugal
Romania
Russia
Saudi Arabia
Slovakia
Slovenia
South Africa
Spain
Sweden
Switzerland
Turkey
United Arab Emirates
United Kingdom
United States

PRODUCTS/OPERATIONS

2017 Sales

	$ mil.	% of total
Product sales	21,795	95
Other revenues	1,054	5
Total	**22,849**	**100**

2017 Sales

	$ mil.	% of total
ENBREL	5,433	24
Neulasta	4,534	20
Aranesp	2,053	9
Prolia	1,968	9
Sensipar/Mimpara	1,718	8
XGEVA	1,575	7
EPOGEN	1,096	5
NEUPOGEN	835	4
KYPROLIS	642	3
Vectibix	642	3
Nplate	549	2
Repatha	319	1
BLINCYTO	175	0
Other	256	1
Other revenues	1,054	4
Total	**22,849**	**100**

Top Selling Products
Neupogen/Neulasta (chemotherapy-induced neutropenia
   - low white blood cells and cancer-related infections)
Enbrel (rheumatoid arthritis psoriasis)
Aranesp (chemotherapy-induced anemia and chronic
   renal failure anemia sustained duration Epogen)
Epogen (anemia in chronic renal failure)
Sensipar/Mimpara (also known as Mimpara chronic
   kidney disease)
Xgeva (to prevent bone fractures)
Vectibix (monoclonal antibody for colorectal cancer)
Nplate (romiplostim for autoimmune bleeding disorder
   ITP or immune thrombocytopenic purpura)
Prolia (postmenopausal osteoporosis)

COMPETITORS

AbbVie	Merck
AstraZeneca	Merck KGaA
Bayer HealthCare	Millennium: The Takeda
Pharmaceuticals Inc.	Oncology Company
Celgene	Nektar Therapeutics
Chugai	Regeneron
Eli Lilly	Pharmaceuticals
Genentech	Sanofi
GlaxoSmithKline	Teva
Hospira	UCB
Janssen Biotech	

HISTORICAL FINANCIALS

Company Type: Public

Income Statement

FYE: December 31

	REVENUE ($ mil.)	NET INCOME ($ mil.)	NET PROFIT MARGIN	EMPLOYEES
12/18	23,747	8,394	35.3%	21,500
12/17	22,849	1,979	8.7%	20,800
12/16	22,991	7,722	33.6%	19,200
12/15	21,662	6,939	32.0%	17,900
12/14	20,063	5,158	25.7%	17,900
Annual Growth	4.3%	12.9%	—	4.7%

2018 Year-End Financials

Debt ratio: 51.09%
Return on equity: 44.48%
Cash ($ mil.): 6,945
Current ratio: 2.79
Long-term debt ($ mil.): 29,510

No. of shares (mil.): 629
Dividends
   Yield: 2.7%
   Payout: 138.2%
Market value ($ mil.): 122,564

	STOCK PRICE ($) FY Close	P/E High/Low	PER SHARE ($) Earnings	Dividends	Book Value
12/18	194.67	16 13	12.62	5.28	19.85
12/17	173.90	70 56	2.69	4.60	34.95
12/16	146.21	17 13	10.24	4.00	40.47
12/15	162.33	19 14	9.06	3.16	37.25
12/14	159.29	25 16	6.70	2.44	33.90
Annual Growth	5.1%	— —	17.2%	21.3%	(12.5%)

Amphenol Corp.

A connected world needs connections at the basic level: from component to component and from device to device. That's where Amphenol Corp. comes in. The company is a leading manufacturer of connector and interconnect products for the communications industrial automotive aerospace and military markets. Amphenol's interconnect products are used to conduct electrical and optical signals in computers wired and wireless communications networking equipment vehicles aircraft and spacecraft and energy applications. Amphenol also makes high-speed and specialized coaxial cable. Nearly three-fourths of its sales come from outside the US.

Operations

Amphenol's Interconnect Products and Assemblies segment accounts for about 95% of sales through the design and manufacture of connectors and connector systems as well as antennas and sensors. The Cable Products and Solutions segment accounts for 5% of revenue from sales of cables and components for the broadband communications and information technology markets.

In terms of markets information technology and data communications industrial and automotive each account for about 20% of revenue. Mobile devices account for about 15% of revenue; military and mobile networks each supply about 10% each; and broadband communications and commercial aerospace about 5% each.

Geographic Reach

Amphenol based in Wallingford Connecticut has broad geographic coverage with about 430 locations — manufacturing facilities warehouses and offices — in more than 30 countries around the world. The company handles its own manufacturing with facilities in low-cost manufacturing areas and near customers. China accounts for about a third of Amphenol's sales and the US provides about a quarter of sales with other countries supplying the rest.

Sales and Marketing

Amphenol's products have wide distribution winding up in more than 10000 customer locations worldwide (one customer can have components sent to multiple manufacturing locations). Its products are sold directly to original equipment manufacturers (OEMs) electronic manufacturing services (EMS) firms original design manufacturers (ODMs) cable system operators and IT companies. Such end customers account for about 85% of sales while sales through manufacturers' representatives and distributors account for the remaining sales.

The company's sales are heavily weighted in the communications industry. The combination of sales to information technology and data communication mobile device mobile network and broadband communications companies adds up to about half of its revenue.

Financial Performance

Amphenol has been on a nine-year run of annual revenue increases averaging about 10%. Net income has followed a similar pattern interrupted by the impact of the US Tax Cuts and Jobs Act in 2017 before resuming in 2018.

In 2018 sales rose 17% to $8.2 billion from 2017 driven by growth in the mobile devices industrial automotive information technology and data communications military mobile networks and commercial aerospace markets. Sales to the broadband communications market declined. Sales to China rose 25% in 2018 from 2017 while sales to the US and other countries grew 13%.

Amphenol posted a $1.2 billion profit in 2018 nearly doubling the 2017 profit. The 2018 net income figure included an income tax benefit of $14.5 million and about $20 million in tax benefits from stock option exercises as well as higher sales.

In 2018 Amphenol had $1.3 billion in cash in its coffers about $400 million less than in 2017. Operations generated $1.1 billion in 2018 while investing and financing activities used $442 million and $1 billion respectively.

Strategy

Amphenol has been willing to buy what is doesn't have in-house making more than 20 acquisitions in the past five years.

The company also has embraced geographic diversity. China and the US are its biggest single country markets and international revenue not counting China provides about 40% of the total. Amphenol places manufacturing facilities globally especially in low-cost areas.

With much of its sales and operations overseas Amphenol could be affected by trade tensions between the US and China. Tariffs set on goods by the US and China the company's two biggest markets could have an impact of its pricing and its sales. In the Americas changes to the North American Free Trade Agreement (NAFTA) which were being negotiated in early 2018 also could affect Amphenol.

Amphenol has maintained a handle on expenses even as sales have increased. The company has cut the cost of sales as a percentage of revenue for the past four years.

Mergers and Acquisitions

In 2018 Amphenol acquired SSI the sensor manufacturing division of SSI Technologies Inc. for about $400 million. SSI designs and makes sensors the automotive and industrial markets.

Also in 2018 Amphenol acquired CTI Industries based in Canada. Applications for CTI's cable assemblies include automotive embedded computing and industrial.

In 2017 Amphenol bought Phitek Systems Limited a New Zealand-based provider of interconnects for in-flight entertainment systems in commercial aircraft for about $60 million. The acquisition adds to Amphenol's line of products used throughout airplanes a product line that accounts for less than 5% of revenue.

Other acquisitions strengthened Amphenol's automotive business. In late 2017 the company closed on its acquisition of Sunpool a China-based company that makes antennas for the Chinese automotive market. The company made several other acquisitions in 2017 for a total of about $200 million.

Company Background

Amphenol was founded in 1932 to make sockets to plug vacuum tubes into radios. Its first customer was RCA.

EXECUTIVES

Svp And Group General Manager It And Communications Products Division, Richard E. (Rick) Schneider, age 61, $490,000 total compensation

Vp And Group General Manager Worldwide Rf And Microwave Products, Richard A. (Adam) Norwitt, age 50, $1,061,000 total compensation

Svp And Group General Manager Military And Aerospace Operations Group, Luc Walter, age 60, $560,000 total compensation

Svp And Cfo, Craig A. Lampo, age 49, $450,000 total compensation

Svp And Group General Manager Worldwide Rf And Microwave Products, Zachary W. Raley, age 50, $500,000 total compensation

Vp And Group General Manager Global Interconnect Systems Group, Jean-Luc Gavelle, age 59

Vp And Group General Manager Automotive And Sensor Products Division, John Treanor, age 61

Vp And Group General Manager Industrial Products Group, Martin W. Booker, age 60

Vp And Group General Manager It Communications Products Group, William J. Doherty, age 60

Vp And General Manager Mobile Consumer Products Group, Yaobin (Richard) Gu

Chairman, Martin H. Loeffler, age 75

Auditors: DELOITTE & TOUCHE LLP

LOCATIONS

HQ: Amphenol Corp.
358 Hall Avenue, Wallingford, CT 06492
Phone: 203 265-8900   **Fax:** 203 265-8746
Web: www.amphenol.com

2018 Sales

	$ mil.	% of total
China	2,594	32
US	2,241	27
Other countries	3,366	41
Total	**8,202**	**100**

PRODUCTS/OPERATIONS

2018 Sales

	$ mil.	% of total
Interconnect products & assemblies	7,781	95
Cable products	420	5
Total	**8,202**	**100**

Selected Products

Interconnect products
  Fiber Optic
  Harsh Environment
  High-speed
  Power Busbars and Distribution Systems
  Radio Frequency
  Antennas
Cable Products   Coaxial
  Power
  Specialty
Others Antennas
  Flexible and Rigid Printed Circuit Boards
  Switches

COMPETITORS

3M	Huber + Suhner Inc.
Belden	Japan Aviation
Carlisle Companies	Electronics Industry
CommScope	Molex
Delphi Automotive	Panduit
Systems	Radiall
Esterline	Sensata
Hirose Electric	TE Connectivity
Hon Hai	Yazaki

HISTORICAL FINANCIALS
Company Type: Public

Income Statement   FYE: December 31

	REVENUE ($ mil.)	NET INCOME ($ mil.)	NET PROFIT MARGIN	EMPLOYEES
12/18	8,202	1,205	14.7%	73,600
12/17	7,011	650	9.3%	70,000
12/16	6,286	822	13.1%	62,000
12/15	5,568	763	13.7%	50,700
12/14	5,345	709	13.3%	50,700
Annual Growth	**11.3%**	**14.2%**	**—**	**9.8%**

2018 Year-End Financials

Debt ratio: 35.55%	No. of shares (mil.): 298
Return on equity: 30.10%	Dividends
Cash ($ mil.): 1,279	Yield: 1.0%
Current ratio: 1.86	Payout: 22.8%
Long-term debt ($ mil.): 2,806	Market value ($ mil.): 24,184

	STOCK PRICE ($) FY Close	P/E High/Low	Earnings	Dividends	Book Value
12/18	81.02	24 19	3.85	0.88	13.46
12/17	87.80	43 31	2.06	0.70	13.05
12/16	67.20	26 17	2.61	0.58	11.92
12/15	52.23	24 20	2.41	0.53	10.51
12/14	53.81	47 20	2.21	0.45	9.38
Annual Growth	**10.8%**	**— —**	**14.9%**	**18.3%**	**9.4%**

Analog Devices Inc

Analog Devices Inc. (ADI) is a leading maker of mixed-signal analog and digital integrated circuits (ICs) that convert real-world phenomena such as pressure temperature and sound into digital signals. It linear chips translate. Its 45000 devices include converters amplifiers power management products and digital signal processors (DSPs). The company's chips are used in industrial process controls medical and scientific instruments communications gear computers automobiles and consumer electronics. ADI claims more than 125000 customers around the world with most revenue from customers outside the US. The company makes half of its devices while contractors make the rest.

Operations

ADI operates in four market areas: industrial communications automotive and consumer.

The industrial market segment about 50% of revenue makes devices for process control systems oscilloscopes connected motion and robotics laboratory chemical and environmental analyzers environmental control systems and scales.

The communications market segment 20% of revenue provides devices for processing signals that are converted back and forth from analog to digital while transmitting and receiving data.

The automotive market segment about 15% of revenue develops products used in applications in hybrid electric car audio voice and video processing and connectivity.

The consumer market segment about 15% of revenue provides devices for user interfaces music movies photographs as well as analog digital and mixed-signal devices for the consumer electronics market.

ADI's main third-party manufacturer is Taiwan Semiconductor Manufacturing Co.

Geographic Reach

The US is ADI's biggest single-company market accounting for about a third of sales followed by China with about 20% and Japan about 10%. On a regional basis customers in Europe account for about a quarter of ADI's revenue.

Headquartered in Norwood Massachusetts the company has facilities in the US the Philippines Ireland India and China. ADI has wafer fab facilities in Massachusetts California Washington and Limerick Ireland. The company operates assembly and wafer sort facilities in Penang Malaysia and test facilities in the Philippines and Singapore.

Sales and Marketing

Although more than 55% of ADI's sales are made through distributors the company also sells through direct sales offices and sales representatives worldwide and via its website. While Apple has been a strong customer for ADI the phone and computer maker has been moving more of its technology needs in-house. Including Apple the company's 20 largest customers account for about 35% of revenue.

The company has no dominant product with its 10 highest revenue-producing offerings delivering about 15% of revenue.

Financial Performance

ADI's revenue had increased three years in a row boosted by acquisitions. Its net income level was steady until it doubled in 2018 (ended November) from 2017.

The company posted a 21% revenue increase taking it to $6.2 billion in 2018 from 2017 fueled by contributions to all segments from the Linear acquisition. The biggest segment jump was the 32% rise in industrial sales while automotive revenue increased 23% and communication's sales were 20% higher in 2018. The consumer segment's sales dropped 23% due to decreased demand for products used in portable consumer applications while Linear contributions offset an even bigger drop.

Revenue shot up to $1.5 billion in 2018 from $727.3 billion on the strength of the revenue increase and similar level of costs year-to-year.

ADI's coffers held $816.6 million in cash and equivalents in 2018 about $44 million more than in 2017. In 2018 operations generated $714 million while investing and financing activities used $89 million and $580.7 million respectively.

Strategy

ADI's nearly $15 billion Linear Technology acquisition which closed in 2017 was a major step in the company's expansion of its products and markets. With Linear ADI grabs high-ranking market share across data convertors power management amplifiers interface and high-performance radio frequency and microwave devices. ADI expects the business combination to achieve about $150 million in manufacturing and operating savings. Some of those savings are to come from the closure of a wafer fabrication facility in the US and a test facility in Singapore.

ADI has products that fit growing markets in communications for extending 4G networks and building out 5G networks; automotive for autonomous vehicles safety control and entertainment; and in a range of industrial applications.

The company continues to save money by closing and consolidating facilities. It plans to close a manufacturing facility in California and a test facility in Singapore and move those operations to other company-owned plants and to contractors.

Besides reeling in the big Linear Technology fish ADI has made smaller acquisitions to provide more capabilities that provide additional value to its customers. Transactions have brought aboard technologies for internet of things applications cloud security and LIDAR.

Mergers and Acquisitions

In 2018 ADI acquired Symeo a privately held company based in Munich Germany that specializes in RADAR hardware and software for autonomous automotive and industrial applications. Symeo's signal processing algorithms bolster Analog's offerings.

ADI bought OneTree Microdevices for an undisclosed amount in March 2017. One Tree is a fabless semiconductor company with a GaAs and GaN amplifier portfolio for cable TV and fiber-to-the-home applications. The acquisition extends Analog's product lineup to those uses.

ADI in 2017 acquired Linear Technology also a maker of analog ICs for about $15 billion. While both companies produce ADI their product mixes are complementary executives said.

ADI also made acquisitions concentrated in autonomous vehicles. ADI acquired Innovasic a developer of Ethernet technology that allows for deterministic real-time communication; the cyber security products of Sypris which can provide customers with sensor-to-cloud security products; and technology from Vescent Photonics that should help ADI develop a solid state scanning LIDAR system that complements its RADAR-based ADAS products.

EXECUTIVES

President And Ceo, Vincent T. Roche, age 59, $827,692 total compensation
Svp Global Operations And Technology, Joseph (John) Hassett, age 61
Svp And Cto, Peter Real, age 59, $376,008 total compensation
Svp Communications And Automotive Business Group, Rick D. Hess, age 65, $519,231 total compensation
Svp Worldwide Sales And Digital Marketing, Martin Cotter, age 54
Svp Finance And Cfo, Prashanth Mahendra-Rajah, age 49
Vp Foundry Operations, Mark Smrtic
Vp Automotive, Mark Gill
Vice President, Chris Jacobs
Vice President Finance And Supply Chain, Jim Mollica
Vice President Supply Chain Planning And Logistics, Mike Errera
Svp Hr, Jean Philibert
Vice President Assembly And Test Operations, Steve Lattari
Senior Vice President Automotive Communications And Aerospace And Defense, Greg Henderson
Vp General Counsel And Secretary, Larry Weiss
Vice President Chief Information Security Officer, Mark Hyslip
Chairman, Ray Stata, age 85
Board Member, Neil Novich
Board Member, Bruce Evans
Board Member, Edward Frank
Board Member, Mark Little
Board Member, Lisa Su
Auditors: Ernst & Young LLP

LOCATIONS

HQ: Analog Devices Inc
One Technology Way, Norwood, MA 02062-9106
Phone: 781 329-4700
Web: www.analog.com

2018 Sales

	$ mil.	% of total
United States	2,105	34
Rest of North and South America	103	2
Europe	1,471	24
Japan	716	11
China	1,210	19
Rest of Asia	593	10
Total	**6,200**	**100**

PRODUCTS/OPERATIONS

2018 Sales

	$ mil.	% of total
Industrial	3,102	50
Automotive	988	16
Consumer	856	14
Communications	1,252	20
Total	**6200.9**	**100**

COMPETITORS

Analogic	Microchip Technology
Broadcom	NXP Semiconductors
Cirrus Logic	ON Semiconductor
DENSO	Qualcomm CDMA
Infineon Technologies	ROHM
Integrated Device Technology	STMicroelectronics
	Semtech
Intersil	Silicon Labs
Marvell Technology	Texas Instruments
Maxim Integrated Products	

HISTORICAL FINANCIALS

Company Type: Public

Income Statement				FYE: November 2
	REVENUE ($ mil.)	NET INCOME ($ mil.)	NET PROFIT MARGIN	EMPLOYEES
11/19	5,991	1,363	22.8%	16,400
11/18*	6,200	1,495	24.1%	15,800
10/17	5,107	727	14.2%	15,300
10/16	3,421	861	25.2%	10,000
10/15	3,435	696	20.3%	9,700
Annual Growth	14.9%	18.3%	—	14.0%

*Fiscal year change

2019 Year-End Financials

Debt ratio: 25.67%
Return on equity: 12.04%
Cash ($ mil.): 648
Current ratio: 1.32
Long-term debt ($ mil.): 5,192
No. of shares (mil.): 368
Dividends
  Yield: 0.0%
  Payout: 57.5%
Market value ($ mil.): 40,281

	STOCK PRICE ($) FY Close	P/E High/Low	PER SHARE ($) Earnings	Dividends	Book Value
11/19	109.37	34 22	3.65	2.10	31.79
11/18*	87.18	25 19	3.97	1.89	29.69
10/17	91.21	44 30	2.07	1.77	27.57
10/16	63.53	23 18	2.76	1.66	16.76
10/15	60.12	31 22	2.20	1.57	16.26
Annual Growth	16.1%	— —	13.5%	7.5%	18.3%

*Fiscal year change

Anixter International Inc

EXECUTIVES

Pres-Ceo, William A Galvin
Chb*, Samuel Zell
Exec V Pres Fin-Cfo, Theodore A Dosch
Exec V Pres-General Counsel-Co, Justin C Choi
Exec V Pres-CIO, Scott Ramsbottom
Exec V Pres Oprs, Orlando McGee
Evp Network & Security Sol, William C Geary II
Evp Human Resources, Rodney A Smith
Board Member, Linda Bynoe
Board Member, Lord Blyth
Director, Scott Gulson
Auditors: Ernst & Young LLP

LOCATIONS

HQ: Anixter International Inc
2301 Patriot Blvd., Glenview, IL 60026
Phone: 224 521-8000
Web: www.anixter.com

COMPETITORS

Acuity Brands	Kirby Risk
Agilysys	Lawson Products
Air Products	MSC Industrial Direct
Airgas	Park-Ohio Holdings
Arrow Electronics	Patterson Companies
Avnet	Precision Industries
Border States Electric	Premier Farnell
Consolidated	Rexel
Electrical	Richardson Electronics
Crescent Electric	Sonepar
Supply	TESSCO
Fastenal	Tech Data
Genuine Parts	United Stationers
Gexpro	W.W. Grainger
Graybar Electric	WESCO International
Henry Schein	Watsco
Ingram Micro	

HISTORICAL FINANCIALS

Company Type: Public

Income Statement   FYE: December 28

	REVENUE ($ mil.)	NET INCOME ($ mil.)	NET PROFIT MARGIN	EMPLOYEES
12/18	8,400	156	1.9%	9,300
12/17	7,927	109	1.4%	8,900
12/16*	7,622	120	1.6%	8,900
01/16	6,190	127	2.1%	8,700
01/15	6,445	194	3.0%	9,100
Annual Growth	6.8%	(5.4%)	—	0.5%

*Fiscal year change

2018 Year-End Financials

Debt ratio: 26.90%
Return on equity: 10.35%
Cash ($ mil.): 81
Current ratio: 1.95
Long-term debt ($ mil.): 1,251

No. of shares (mil.): 33
Dividends
  Yield: —
  Payout: —
Market value ($ mil.): 1,825

	STOCK PRICE ($) FY Close	P/E High/Low	Earnings	Dividends	Book Value
12/18	53.88	18 11	4.58	0.00	46.38
12/17	76.00	27 19	3.21	0.00	43.35
12/16*	81.05	23 11	3.59	0.00	38.64
01/16	60.39	23 15	3.81	0.00	35.44
01/15	88.18	18 13	5.84	0.00	34.19
Annual Growth	(11.6%)	— —	(5.9%)	—	7.9%

*Fiscal year change

Annaly Capital Management Inc

A real estate investment trust (REIT) Annaly Capital Management invests in and finances residential and commercial assets. It primarily manages a portfolio of mortgage-backed securities including mortgage pass-through certificates collateralized mortgage obligations and agency callable debentures. Commencing operations in 1997 the firm typically invests in high-quality securities issued or guaranteed by the likes of Freddie Mac Fannie Mae and Ginnie Mae and backed by single-family residential mortgages. More than 90% of Annaly's assets are agency mortgage-backed securities which carry an implied AAA rating. The firm is externally managed by Annaly Management Company LLC.

Operations

Annaly invests through four primary groups: Agency Residential Credit Commercial Real Estate and Middle Market Lending. The Agency group primarily invests in agency mortgage-backed securities and related derivatives. The Residential Credit group invests in non-agency mortgage-backed assets within securitized products and residential mortgage loan markets. Commercial Real Estate writes and invests in commercial mortgage loans securities and related assets and Middle Market Lending provides customized debt financing to middle-market businesses.

Financial Performance

Annaly's net interest income which comprises the bulk of its annual revenue has been in a slow decline over the last few years. In fiscal 2017 net interest income fell 4% to $1.5 billion as growth in interest earning assets was offset by a higher increase in interest bearing liabilities. Total assets reached a record $99.9 billion a 17% increase.

Net income in 2017 was up 10% to $1.6 billion as lower net interest income was offset by higher realized and unrealized gains higher other income and lower general and administrative expenses.

The company recorded an $833.2 million decrease in cash on hand in 2017 with its coffers standing at $706.6 million at the end of the period.

Strategy

Annaly makes its money based on the interest rate spread: When interest rates go down Annaly's returns tend to go up. It does this by borrowing short-term loans which typically carry lower interest rates and using that money to invest in mortgage-backed securities which typically carry higher rates. As such the troubled economy actually benefited the REIT as lowered short-term interest rates translated into higher interest income.

However in an environment where the Federal Reserve has carried out interest rate hikes Annaly's strategy of earning income from the spread could be threatened. With rate hikes expected to continue the REIT is increasingly focusing on gains from its credit assets investment portfolio which are tied to long-term rates.

In addition to funding purchases of mortgage-backed securities through short-term repurchase agreements Annaly raises investment funds through equity and debt offerings. It seeks to minimize prepayment risk by structuring a diversified portfolio with a variety of prepayment characteristics and through other means; it also increases the size of its balance sheet when opportunities are likely to allow growth in earnings per share.

In mid-2017 Annaly sold Pingora Holdings (acquired the previous year with the purchase of Hat-

teras Financial) to Bayview Asset Management. Pingora is a specialized asset manager focused on investing in mortgage servicing rights and servicing residential mortgages.

Mergers and Acquisitions

In September 2018 Annaly acquired MTGE Investment Corp. for $900 million. MTGE is an investment trust that invests in and manages a leveraged portfolio of agency mortgage investments non-agency mortgage investments and other real estate-related investments. The acquisition enhances the scale liquidity and access to capital of Annaly's platform.

EXECUTIVES

Cfo, Glenn A. Votek, age 60, $91,346 total compensation
Chairman President And Ceo, Kevin G. Keyes, age 51, $375,000 total compensation
Chief Legal Officer, Anthony C. Green
Chief Investment Officer, David L. Finkelstein, age 46
Chief Credit Officer, Timothy P. Coffey, age 45
Vp It, Christopher Sullivan
Vice President, George Varghese
Vp Business Development, David Burgess
Auditors: Ernst & Young LLP

LOCATIONS

HQ: Annaly Capital Management Inc
1211 Avenue of the Americas, New York, NY 10036
Phone: 212 696-0100   **Fax:** 212 696-9809
Web: www.annaly.com

COMPETITORS

AG Mortgage Investment Trust	Institutional Financial Markets
Capstead Mortgage	JAVELIN Mortgage
Drive Shack	MFA Financial
Impac Mortgage Holdings	Redwood Trust
	iStar Financial Inc

HISTORICAL FINANCIALS

Company Type: Public

Income Statement   FYE: December 31

	ASSETS ($ mil.)	NET INCOME ($ mil.)	INCOME AS % OF ASSETS	EMPLOYEES
12/18	105,787	54	0.1%	170
12/17	101,760	1,569	1.5%	152
12/16	87,905	1,433	1.6%	189
12/15	75,190	466	0.6%	149
12/14	88,355	(842)	—	25
Annual Growth	4.6%	—	—	61.5%

2018 Year-End Financials

Debt ratio: 7.60%
Return on equity: 0.38%
Cash ($ mil.): 1,735
Current ratio: —
Long-term debt ($ mil.): —

No. of shares (mil.): 1,313
Dividends
  Yield: 12.2%
  Payout: 47.0%
Market value ($ mil.): 12,901

	STOCK PRICE ($) FY Close	P/E High/Low	Earnings	Dividends	Book Value
12/18	9.82	— —	(0.06)	1.20	10.74
12/17	11.89	9 7	1.37	2.49	12.82
12/16	9.97	8 6	1.39	3.17	12.33
12/15	9.38	26 22	0.42	1.20	12.71
12/14	10.81	— —	(0.96)	1.20	14.06
Annual Growth	(2.4%)	— —	—	(0.0%)	(6.5%)

Anthem Inc

Health benefits provider Anthem through a number of subsidiaries provides health coverage to more than 40 million members in the US. One of the nation's largest health insurers Anthem is a Blue Cross and Blue Shield Association licensee in more than a dozen states (where it operates as Anthem Empire and BCBS) and provides non-BCBS plans under the Unicare Amerigroup CareMore Simply Healthcare HealthSun HealthLink and other brands in more than 25 states. Plans include PPO HMO POS indemnity and hybrid plans offered to employers individuals and Medicare and Medicaid recipients. Anthem also provides administrative services to self-insured groups as well as specialty insurance.

HISTORY

Anthem's earliest predecessor prepaid hospital plan Blue Cross of Indiana was founded in 1944. Unlike other Blues Blue Cross of Indiana never received tax advantages or mandated discounts so it competed as a private insurer. Within two years it had 100000 members; by 1970 there were nearly 2 million.

Blue Shield of Indiana another Anthem precursor also grew rapidly after its 1946 formation as a mutual insurance company to cover doctors' services. The two organizations shared expenses and jointly managed the state's Medicare and Medicaid programs.

The 1970s and early 1980s were difficult as Indiana's economy stagnated and health insurance competition increased. In 1982 the joint operation restructured adding new management and service policies to improve its performance.

Following the 1982 merger of the national Blue Cross and Blue Shield organizations the Indiana Blues merged in 1985 as Associated Insurance Companies. The next year the company moved outside Indiana began diversifying to help insulate itself from such industry changes as the shift to managed care and renamed itself Associated Group to reflect a broader focus.

By 1990 Associated Group had more than 25 operating units with nationwide offerings including health insurance HMO services life insurance insurance brokerage financial services and software and services for the insurance industry.

The group grew throughout the mid-1990s buying health insurer Southeastern Mutual Insurance (including Kentucky Blue Cross and Blue Shield) in 1992 diversified insurer Federal Kemper (a Kemper Corporation subsidiary) in 1993 and Seattle-based property/casualty brokerage Pettit-Morry in 1994. That year it entered the health care delivery market with the creation of American Health Network.

In 1995 the company merged with Ohio Blues licensee Community Mutual and took the Anthem name. Merger-related charges caused a loss that year.

Anthem bounced back the next year thanks to cost-cutting and customers switching to its more profitable managed care plans. Anthem divested its individual life insurance and annuity business and its Anthem Financial subsidiaries. Its 1996 deal to buy Blue Cross and Blue Shield of New Jersey fell apart in 1997 because of New Jersey Blue's charitable status. Anthem did manage to buy Blue Cross and Blue Shield of Connecticut that year.

Anthem in 1997 sold four property/casualty insurance subsidiaries to Vesta Insurance Group. It bought the remainder of its Acordia property/casualty unit (workers' compensation) then sold Acordia's brokerage operations. That year Anthem was involved in court battles regarding the Blue mergers in Kentucky as well as in Connecticut where litigants feared a rise in their premiums. Expenses related to merging Blues organizations contributed to a loss that year.

Anthem shed the rest of its noncore operations in 1998 selling subsidiary Anthem Health and Life Insurance Company to Canadian insurer Great-West Life Assurance. Its proposed purchase of Blue Cross and Blue Shield of Maine (which it acquired in 2000) and merger with the Blues in Rhode Island were met with outcries similar to those that dogged earlier pairings.

Larry Glasscock was appointed president and CEO of the company in 1999. Under Glasscock's leadership Anthem aggressively expanded through mergers and acquisitions. It bought Blues plans in Colorado Nevada and New Hampshire in 1999 and finalized the acquisition of Maine's Blue plan in 2000.

In 2001 it became a publicly traded company and sold its military insurance business to Humana. In the next couple of years it snapped up Virginia-based Trigon Healthcare and a Wisconsin Blue plan.

And in 2004 Anthem made its biggest leap yet merging with WellPoint Health Networks in a deal that made it the nation's largest health insurer. After the merger — which added Blue plans in California Georgia Missouri and Wisconsin — Anthem changed its name to WellPoint. The company changed its name back to Anthem in 2014.

EXECUTIVES

Evp And Chief Administrative Officer, Gloria M. McCarthy, age 66, $699,999 total compensation
President Ceo And Director, Gail K. Boudreaux
Evp And Cfo, John E. Gallina, age 59, $623,918 total compensation
Evp And President Government Business, Peter D. Haytaian, age 49, $740,371 total compensation
Evp And General Counsel, Thomas C. Zielinski, age 68
Evp And President Commercial And Specialty Business, Brian T. Griffin, age 60, $740,368 total compensation
Evp And Chief Clinical Officer, Craig E. Samitt, age 54
President Medicare East Region, Tomas Orozco
President Life And Disability, Greg Poulakos
President Specialty, Nicholas L. Brecker
Senior Vice President; President And Chief Executive Officer Anthem National Accounts, John Langenus
Vice President Information Technology, Sean Keneally
Vice President And Chief Information Security Officer, Roy Mellinger
Assistant Vice President Information Technology Project Management Office, Sheri Coyner
Regional Vice President And Medical Director, Tony Linares
Regional Vice President, Julie Theodore
Regional Vice President Central Ohio Health Service Area, Scott Gerhart
Vice President Physician Services, Carol Swecker
Vice President Pharmacy Sales And Account Management, Kelly McNulty
Vice President Strategic Marketing, Danielle Robinson
Staff Vice President Enterprise Services, Cornelius Healy
Vice President, Renee Hunter
Vice President Corporate Accounting And Reporting, Ryan Judy
Executive Vice President And President And Chief Executive Officer Commercial And Specialty Busines, Ken Goulet
Senior Vice President Provider Alignment Solutions, Colin Drozdowski
Medical Director And State, Kimberly L Roop
Vice President Marketing, James Jackson
Vp Analtics Strategy And Integrations, Tanya Rylee
Senior Vice President Public Affairs, Julie Goon
Vice President Information Technology, James Marshall
Svp Corporate Communications, Bonnie Jacobs
Vice President Comm Operations Insightsandanalytics, Katy Berry
Vice President Strategy Planningandexecution, Manan Shah
Medical Director, Ronald Koenig
Vice President Finance, Colleen Parsons
Staff Vice President Business Continuation, Steve Labrique
Staff Vice President Systems Migration, Tracy Tutson
Vice President And Counsel, Ronald Odom
Senior Vice President And Chief Compliance Officer, Edward Stubbers
Vice President Care Management Operational Solutions, Lisa Ledford-Crissey
Vice President Provider Alignment Solutions, Hongmai Pham
Director Of Government Relations, Nick DeJong
Vice President Tax, Christopher LaFollette
Vice President Marketing, Erin Miller
Senior Business Intelligence Developer, Darpan Desai
Vice President And Chief Security Officer, Greg Wurm
Regional Vice President Finance And Medicare, Kevin Wirges
Vice President Medical And Clinical Pharmacy Policy, John Whitney
Regional Vice President Of Federal Government Relations, Samuel Marchio
Vice President And Counsel, Jason Wagner
Assistant Vice President Enterprise Pmo, Vanslyke Carol
Staff Vice President Contracting Admin, Jim Taske
Vice President Compliance Csbd, Sherry Call
Staff Vice President Strategic Initiatives Accountable Care Solutions, Ryan Schoettle
Regional Vice President Senior Clinical Officer, Maureen Dempsey
Medical Director, Lynn Cooman
Medical Director, Jo Nishimoto
Senior Vice President Anthem National Accounts, Kenneth Goulet
Vice President And General Manager Key Accounts And Small Group, Joe Greenberg
Board Member, Robert L Dixon
Chairman, Joseph R. Swedish, age 67
Board Member, Bessie Clark
Secretary, Neelam Kothari
Auditors: Ernst & Young LLP

LOCATIONS

HQ: Anthem Inc
220 Virginia Avenue, Indianapolis, IN 46204
Phone: 800 331-1476
Web: www.antheminc.com

PRODUCTS/OPERATIONS

2017 Sales

	$ mil.	% of total
Premiums	83,647	93
Administrative fees	5,380	6
Net investment income	866	1
Net realized gains on financial instruments	144	-
Other	33	-
Adjustments	(33.1)	
Total	**90,039**	**100**

2017 Premiums

	% of total
Government Business	54
Commercial and Specialty Business	46
Other	-
Total	**100**

Selected Operations

Blue-licensed subsidiaries
  Anthem Blue Cross (California)
  Anthem Blue Cross and Blue Shield (Colorado
  Connecticut Kentucky Indiana Maine Missouri Nevada
  New Hampshire Ohio Virginia Wisconsin)
  Blue Cross Blue Shield of Georgia
  Empire Blue Cross Blue Shield (New York)
Non-Blue Cross Subsidiaries and Affiliates
  AIM Specialty Health (benefits management)
  American Imaging Management (Diagnostic imaging)
  Anthem Life Insurance (life and accident)
  Anthem Workers' Compensation
  CareMore (Medicare Advantage and special needs plans)
  DeCare Dental (Dental benefit management)
  HealthLink (Administrative services)
  Golden West Dental & Vision (Dental/vision California)
  Meridian Resource Company (Cost containment)
  National Government Services (Administration of government contracts)
  Resolution Health (Cost containment)
  TrustSolutions (Fraud prevention)
  UniCare (Health care plans)

COMPETITORS

Aetna	Kaiser Foundation
CIGNA	Health Plan
Centene	Medical Mutual
Delta Dental Plans	Molina Healthcare
EmblemHealth	UnitedHealth Group
Humana	WellCare Health Plans

HISTORICAL FINANCIALS

Company Type: Public

Income Statement

FYE: December 31

	REVENUE ($ mil.)	NET INCOME ($ mil.)	NET PROFIT MARGIN	EMPLOYEES
12/18	92,105	3,750	4.1%	63,900
12/17	90,039	3,842	4.3%	56,000
12/16	84,863	2,469	2.9%	53,000
12/15	79,156	2,560	3.2%	53,000
12/14	73,874	2,569	3.5%	51,500
Annual Growth	5.7%	9.9%	—	5.5%

2018 Year-End Financials

Debt ratio: 26.84%
Return on equity: 13.63%
Cash ($ mil.): 3,934
Current ratio: 1.56
Long-term debt ($ mil.): 17,217

No. of shares (mil.): 257
Dividends
  Yield: 1.1%
  Payout: 21.1%
Market value ($ mil.): 67,600

	STOCK PRICE ($) FY Close	P/E High/Low		PER SHARE ($) Earnings	Dividends	Book Value
12/18	262.63	20	15	14.19	3.00	110.88
12/17	225.01	16	10	14.35	2.70	103.49
12/16	143.77	16	12	9.21	2.60	95.17
12/15	139.44	18	13	9.38	2.50	88.21
12/14	125.67	14	9	8.99	1.75	90.45
Annual Growth	20.2%	—	—	12.1%	14.4%	5.2%

Anworth Mortgage Asset Corp.

What's an Anworth? Depends on the mortgage market. An externally managed real estate investment trust (REIT) Anworth Mortgage invests in finances and manages residential mortgage-related assets primarily mortgage-backed securities (MBS) guaranteed by the US government or federally sponsored entities Fannie Mae Freddie Mac and Ginnie Mae. As a REIT the trust is exempt from paying federal income tax so long as it distributes dividends back to shareholders. Anworth Mortgage funds its investment activities mainly through short-term loans.

EXECUTIVES

President And Chief Investment Officer, Joseph E. McAdams, age 50, $700,000 total compensation
Evp, Heather U. Baines, age 77, $50,495 total compensation
Chairman And Ceo, Joseph Lloyd McAdams, age 73
Svp And Portfolio Manager, Bistra Pashamova, age 48, $275,000 total compensation
Cfo Treasurer And Secretary, Charles J. Siegel, age 69, $250,000 total compensation
Auditors: RSM US LLP

LOCATIONS

HQ: Anworth Mortgage Asset Corp.
  1299 Ocean Avenue, 2nd Floor, Santa Monica, CA 90401
Phone: 310 255-4493   **Fax:** 310 434-0070
Web: www.anworth.com

COMPETITORS

AG Mortgage Investment Trust	Hatteras Financial
ARMOUR Residential REIT	Huntington Preferred Capital
American Capital Agency Corp.	MFA Financial
Annaly Capital Management	Redwood Trust
Capstead Mortgage	Two Harbors
	Webster Preferred Capital

HISTORICAL FINANCIALS

Company Type: Public

Income Statement

FYE: December 31

	ASSETS ($ mil.)	NET INCOME ($ mil.)	INCOME AS % OF ASSETS	EMPLOYEES
12/18	5,037	(6)	—	—
12/17	5,765	54	0.9%	—
12/16	5,395	22	0.4%	—
12/15	6,636	14	0.2%	—
12/14	7,298	28	0.4%	—
Annual Growth	(8.9%)			

2018 Year-End Financials

Debt ratio: 0.74%
Return on equity: (-1.01%)
Cash ($ mil.): 3
Current ratio: —
Long-term debt ($ mil.): —

No. of shares (mil.): 98
Dividends
  Yield: 13.8%
  Payout: —
Market value ($ mil.): 398

	STOCK PRICE ($) FY Close	P/E High/Low		PER SHARE ($) Earnings	Dividends	Book Value
12/18	4.04	—	—	(0.16)	0.56	5.90
12/17	5.44	13	11	0.47	0.60	7.11
12/16	5.17	32	23	0.17	0.60	6.84
12/15	4.35	67	54	0.08	0.60	7.10
12/14	5.25	31	23	0.18	0.56	7.15
Annual Growth	(6.3%)	—	—	—	(0.0%)	(4.7%)

Apache Corp

Apache Corporation an oil and gas exploration and production company has onshore and offshore operations in major oil patches around the world including in the US Egypt and the UK's North Sea oil fields. In the US it is active in the Gulf of Mexico the Gulf Coast of Texas and Louisiana the Permian Basin in West Texas the Anadarko Basin in Oklahoma. The company boasts worldwide estimated proved reserves of 1.2 billion barrels of oil equivalent.

Operations

Apache explores for develops and produces natural gas crude oil and natural gas liquids (NGLs) in the US Egypt and the UK.

Apache's North America Onshore segment owns significant liquid hydrocarbon deposits across 6.7 million gross acres onshore in the US of which around 70% is undeveloped. About 55% of Apache's worldwide production and 70% of its proved reserves are onshore in the US. Apache's major North American holdings are in the Permian basin in West Texas and New Mexico and the Mid-continent/Gulf region. It also works offshore in the Gulf of Mexico.

In Egypt Apache holds 5.6 million acres across 25 concessions in the Western Desert. Leases range from four to 20 years. Around 70% of its acreage is undeveloped.

Apache's North Sea operations contribute nearly 15% of total production and consists of around 10% of total proved reserves.

Geographic Reach

Apache has exploration and production assets in the US Egypt and the UK. The US and Egypt accounts for about 40% each of total company revenue. The UK bring in some 20% revenue and the rest mostly comes from Canada.

Sales and Marketing

Apache sells its natural gas to local distribution companies utilities end-users and major oil companies.

The company's NGL production is sold under contracts.

Apache's major customers include China Petroleum & Chemical Corporation (20% of sales) Egyptian General Petrol Corporation and BP and Royal Dutch Shell.

Financial Performance

Revenue at Apache has fallen by almost half in the 2008-17 period reducing from a high of $12.4 billion to just over $6 billion. Profits in that decade fluctuated wildly with the worst hit coming from the oil price plunge of 2014-16 when the company lost some $20 billion over three years.

Apache revenue increased 20% from $5.4 billion in 2016 to $6.4 billion in 2017 thanks to a 25% spike in crude oil prices leading to a $426 million increase in revenue over 2016 as well as a $102 million increase in NGL revenue.

Net income fared even better. From losing $1.4 billion in 2016 the company posted profits of $1.3 billion in 2017 breaking a three-year losing streak. The improvement came mostly due to the reduction of impairment charges in 2017 compared to the year before (by almost $1 billion) as well as a $324 million decrease in depreciation and amortization charges.

Cash holdings increased from $1.4 billion to $1.7 billion in 2017. Operating activities provided $2.4 billion in 2017. In contrast investment activities used some $1.4 billion in cash (mostly in plant property and equipment purchase) and a further $720 million in financing activities.

Strategy

The oil price downturn of 2014-16 cost Apache a massive $20 billion and forced the company to realign its costs with the new lower commodity price environment.

The company is pursuing radical portfolio curtailment measures? in 2017 2016 and 2015 Apache divested assets totaling $1.4 billion $134 million and $1.5 billion respectively. In 2017 alone the company sold off Canadian assets Midale and House Mountain leases to the Permian and Midcontinent/Gulf Coast regions and the North Sea gathering (SAGE) facility.

Some good news came late 2017 as commodity prices started recovering and benefits from tax reforms kicked in. This will especially be helpful to Apache's capital-intensive project to build up the Alpine High field and infrastructure.

For 2018-20 period Apache plans to invest around $7.5 billion in its upstream segment and a further $1.0 billion in the midstream development of Alpine High. The investments are expected to increase Apache's growth rate by more than 10%.

However with global trade war risks rising in 2018 pitting the US against the EU and China Apache's dependency on foreign customers including China Petroleum & Chemical Corporation the Egyptian General Petroleum Company and the Royal Dutch Shell may become a significant issue.

HISTORY

Originally Raymond Plank wanted to start a magazine. Then it was an accounting and tax-assistance service. Plank and his co-founding partner Truman Anderson had no experience in any of these occupations but their accounting business succeeded. In the early 1950s Plank and Anderson branched out again founding APA a partnership to invest in new ventures including oil and gas exploration. The partnership founded Apache Oil in Minnesota in 1954. Investors put up the money and Apache managed the drilling spreading the risk over several projects.

As problems with government regulations in the oil industry mounted during the 1960s Apache diversified into real estate. The real estate operations were pivotal in driving a wedge between Plank and Anderson. In 1963 Anderson called a board meeting to ask the directors to fire Plank. Instead Anderson resigned and Plank took over.

EXECUTIVES

Vice President, Lisa Stewart
Evp And General Counsel, P. Anthony Lannie, age 64, $675,000 total compensation
Senior Region Vice President Egypt Midcontinent Gulf Coast Gulf Of Mexico And International New Ventures, James L. (Jim) House, age 57, $600,000 total compensation
President And Ceo, John J. Christmann, age 52, $1,100,000 total compensation
Evp Corporate Reservoir Engineering, W. Kregg Olson, age 65, $625,000 total compensation

Region Vp North Sea Region And Managing Director Apache North Sea, Jon Graham, age 65
Senior Region Vp Permian Region, Faron J. Thibodeaux, age 59
Senior Region Vp North Sea And Canada, Grady L. Ables, age 58
Senior Region Vice President Delaware Basin Region, Steven J. Keenan, age 63
Svp North America Land Government Affairs And Real Estate, Timothy R. Custer, age 58
Evp And Cfo, Stephen J. Riney, age 59, $675,000 total compensation
Evp Operations Support, Timothy J. Sullivan, age 63, $625,000 total compensation
Region Vice President Egypt Region And General Manager Apache Egypt, David Chi, age 45
Svp Midstream And Marketing, Brian W. Freed
Senior Vice President, Dominic J Ricotta
Vp Corporate Communications And Public Affairs, Castlen Kennedy
Vice President Information Technology, Phillip Vo
Vice President Executive Office, Rob Johnston
Rvp Australia, Tim Wall
Senior Vice President And Gene, Panthony Lannie
Vp Engineering Technical Services, Lucian Wray
Executive Vice President Exploration And Production Technology, Michaels Bahorich
Vice President Operations, Mark Trento
Executive Vice President, Jon A Jeppesen
Vice President Business Development Midstream And Marketing, Robert W Bourne
Vp Operations Delaware Basin And North America Un, Navneet Behl
Vice President And Treasurer, Ben C Rodgers
Vp Information Technology, Phil West
Evp And General Counsel, P Anthony Lannie
Chairman, John E. Lowe, age 61
Board Member, William Montgomery
Board Member, Amy Nelson
Board Member, Annell Bay
Assistant Treasurer, Genie Panaccione
Auditors: Ernst & Young LLP

LOCATIONS

HQ: Apache Corp
One Post Oak Central, 2000 Post Oak Boulevard, Suite 100, Houston, TX 77056-4400
Phone: 713 296-6000
Web: www.apachecorp.com

2016 sales

	% of total
US	37
Egypt	38
UK (North Sea)	19
Canada	6
Total	**100**

PRODUCTS/OPERATIONS

2016 sales

	$ mil.	% of total
Oil	4,172	78
Gas	967	18
Natural gas liquids	228	4
Other	(13)	-
Total	**5,354**	**100**

COMPETITORS

Abraxas Petroleum	Hess Corporation
Adams Resources	Jones Energy
Anadarko Petroleum	Pioneer Natural
BP	Resources
Chesapeake Energy	Qatargas
Chevron	Range Resources
Devon Energy	Royal Dutch Shell
EOG	Santos Ltd
Exxon Mobil	XTO Energy
Helmerich & Payne	

HISTORICAL FINANCIALS
Company Type: Public

Income Statement

FYE: December 31

	REVENUE ($ mil.)	NET INCOME ($ mil.)	NET PROFIT MARGIN	EMPLOYEES
12/18	7,424	40	0.5%	3,420
12/17	6,423	1,304	20.3%	3,356
12/16	5,354	(1,405)	—	3,727
12/15	6,366	(23,119)	—	3,860
12/14	13,851	(5,403)	—	4,950
Annual Growth	**(14.4%)**	**—**	**—**	**(8.8%)**

2018 Year-End Financials

Debt ratio: 38.01%	No. of shares (mil.): 374
Return on equity: 0.55%	Dividends
Cash ($ mil.): 714	Yield: 3.8%
Current ratio: 1.22	Payout: 909.0%
Long-term debt ($ mil.): 8,054	Market value ($ mil.): 9,836

	STOCK PRICE ($) FY Close	P/E High/Low	PER SHARE ($) Earnings	Dividends	Book Value
12/18	26.25	448231	0.11	1.00	19.03
12/17	42.22	19 11	3.41	1.00	19.47
12/16	63.47	— —	(3.71)	1.00	16.44
12/15	44.47	— —	(61.20)	1.00	6.79
12/14	62.67	— —	(14.06)	0.95	68.89
Annual Growth	**(19.6%)**	**—**	**—**	**1.3%**	**(27.5%)**

APPLE HOSPITALITY REIT, INC.

EXECUTIVES

Pres-Ceo, Justin G Knight
Exec Chb*, Glade M Knight
Exec V Pres-Coo, Kristian M Gathright
Evp-Cfo, Bryan Peery
Exec V Pres-Clo, David P Buckley
Exec V Pres-CIO, Nelson G Knight
Chief Operating Officer, Kristian Gathright
Board Member, Bruce Matson
Board Member, Daryl Nickel
Board Member, Glenn Bunting
Manager Director, Debra Quin
Auditors: ERNST & YOUNG LLP RICHMOND V

LOCATIONS

HQ: APPLE HOSPITALITY REIT, INC.
814 E MAIN ST, RICHMOND, VA 232193306
Phone: 804 344-8121
Web: WWW.APPLEHOSPITALITYREIT.COM

HISTORICAL FINANCIALS
Company Type: Private

Income Statement

FYE: December 31

	ASSETS ($ mil.)	NET INCOME ($ mil.)	INCOME AS % OF ASSETS	EMPLOYEES
12/14	3,779	6	0.2%	62
12/13	1,491	115	7.7%	—
12/12	1,526	75	4.9%	—
12/11	1,700	69	4.1%	—
Annual Growth	**30.5%**	**(54.0%)**	**—**	**—**

Apple Inc

Ask Siri to name the most successful company in the world and it might respond: Apple. And it's not just out of familial pride. Apple consistently ranks highly in profit revenue market capitalization and consumer cachet. In 2018 the company became the first reach a trillion dollar market capitalization however briefly. The iPhone in its 11th year has been the company's golden goose generating tens of billions in revenue and profit. Other familiar Apple products and services include Mac computers and iPad tablets as well as iTunes the App store and Apple Music. Primarily a consumer-oriented company Apple has inked alliances with Accenture General Electric and IBM to deepen its penetration of the enterprise market. About 60% of revenue comes from outside the Americas.

HISTORY

College dropouts Steve Jobs (1955-2011) and Steve Wozniak founded Apple in 1976 in California's Santa Clara Valley. After Jobs' first sales call brought an order for 50 units the duo built the Apple I in his garage and sold it without a monitor keyboard or casing. Demand convinced Jobs there was a distinct market for small computers and the company's name (a reference to Jobs' stint on an Oregon farm) and the computer's user-friendly look and feel set it apart from others.

By 1977 Wozniak added a keyboard color monitor and eight peripheral device slots (which gave the machine considerable versatility and inspired numerous third-party add-on devices and software). Sales jumped from $7.8 million in 1978 to $117 million in 1980 the year Apple went public. In 1983 Wozniak left the firm and Jobs hired PepsiCo's John Sculley as president. Apple rebounded from failed product introductions that year by unveiling the Macintosh in 1984. After tumultuous struggles with Sculley Jobs left in 1985 and founded NeXT a designer of applications for developing software. That year Sculley ignored Microsoft founder Bill Gates' appeal for Apple to license its products and make the Microsoft platform an industry standard.

Apple blazed the desktop publishing trail in 1986 with its Mac Plus and LaserWriter printers. The following year it formed the software firm that later became Claris (and ultimately FileMaker). The late 1980s brought new competition from Microsoft whose Windows operating system (OS) featured a graphical interface akin to Apple's. Apple sued but lost its claim to copyright protection in 1992.

In 1993 Apple unveiled the Newton handheld computer but sales were slow. Earnings fell drastically so the company trimmed its workforce. (Sculley was among the departed.) In 1994 Apple cried "uncle" and began licensing clones of its OS hoping a flurry of cheaper Mac-alikes would encourage software developers. By 1996 struggling Apple realized Mac clones were stealing sales. That year it hired Gilbert Amelio formerly of National Semiconductor as CEO.

The company bought NeXT in 1997 but sales kept dropping and it subsequently cut about 30% of its workforce canceled projects and trimmed research costs. Meanwhile Apple's board ousted Amelio and Jobs took the position back on an interim basis. The CEO forged a surprising alliance with Microsoft which included releasing a Mac version of Microsoft's popular office software. To protect market share Jobs also stripped the cloning license from chief imitator Power Computing and put it out of business.

In 1998 Apple jumped back into the race with its colorful cocktail of iMacs and its first server software the Mac OS X. That year the company also revamped its profitable Claris unit (by cutting 300 employees shifting most operations to Apple and renaming it FileMaker) and stopped making its Newton handheld device and printer products.

Apple in 1999 opened a new chapter in portable computing with the introduction of its iBook laptop and (taking a cue from Dell) began selling built-to-order systems online. In 2000 after two and a half years as the semipermanent executive in charge Jobs took the "interim" out of his title and revamped the company's Web site around a suite of consumer Internet services. Jobs unveiled overhauled desktop lines later that year including an eight-inch cube-shaped G4. The company ended 2000 on a sour note as an industrywide slowdown and poor response to the G4 cube resulted in Apple's first unprofitable quarter in years.

Apple opened 2001 with another round of product upgrades including faster processors components such as CD and DVD burners and an ultra-slim version of its PowerBook called Titanium. The company also made a move to reclaim some of its slipping share in the education market purchasing software maker PowerSchool. Soon Apple confirmed a long-rumored plan to open a chain of retail stores in the US. The company then acquired DVD authoring software maker Spruce Technologies. In line with its strategy to market Macs as "digital hubs" for devices such as cameras and other peripherals Apple closed the year with the introduction of a digital music player called the iPod.

In 2002 Apple introduced a new look for its iMac line; featuring a half-dome base and a flat-panel display supported by a pivoting arm the redesign was the first departure from the original (and at the time radical) all-in-one design since iMac's debut in 1998. Looking to reclaim market share in the education sector Apple then introduced the eMac — a computer similar to the iMac to be sold only to students and educators (Apple later introduced a retail version). It continued its product push that year with the announcement that it would begin offering a rack-mount server called Xserve. In 2004 Apple debuted a streamlined iMac design powered by its G5 processor.

Apple announced it would begin incorporating Intel processors into its PC lines in 2005 ending more than a decade of using PowerPC microprocessors; the transition was completed the following year. Also that year Apple Motorola and Cingular Wireless (now AT&T Mobility) announced the debut of a mobile phone with iTunes functionality. Apple also unveiled the iPod nano an updated (and even smaller) version of its miniature iPod model as well as an iPod capable of playing video. In 2006 Apple reached a settlement in a dispute with Creative Technology over technology used in digital music players; Apple agreed to pay the company $100 million in exchange for a license to use Creative's patent related to navigation and organization.

The company also launched an online movie service in 2006 and previewed a device called iTV for watching downloaded content on televisions. (Apple announced availability of its television device redubbed Apple TV early the following year.)

Apple unveiled a mobile phone offering called the iPhone in 2007. To reflect the growing breadth of its product portfolio the company announced it would change its name from Apple Computer to simply Apple. The company kicked off 2008 with the release of an updated Apple TV device in conjunction with an iTunes movie rental service.

Looking toward the continued development of its mobile devices Apple purchased P.A. Semi a developer of low-power processors in 2008. In another move intended to bring more of its chip design in-house Apple bought Intrinsity a provider of chip design software in 2010.

After beginning 2011 with a leave of absence and then stepping down as CEO Steve Jobs died on October 5 2011. COO Tim Cook had been named CEO after Jobs' resignation though Jobs retained the chairman title until his death.

EXECUTIVES

Svp Worldwide Marketing, Philip W. Schiller, age 59, $494,942 total compensation
Svp Software Engineering, Craig Federighi, age 50
Svp General Counsel And Secretary, D. Bruce Sewell, age 61, $1,000,000 total compensation
Svp Retail And Online Stores, Angela Ahrendts, age 58, $1,000,000 total compensation
Svp Internet Software And Services, Eduardo H. (Eddy) Cue, age 55, $1,000,000 total compensation
Chief Design Officer, Jonathan Ive
Svp And Cfo, Luca Maestri, age 56, $1,000,000 total compensation
Coo, Jeffrey E. (Jeff) Williams, age 55, $947,596 total compensation
Svp Hardware Engineering, Daniel (Dan) Riccio, age 57, $1,000,000 total compensation
Svp Hardware Technologies, Johny Srouji
Vp Technology, Kevin Lynch
Vice President Corporate Development, Adrian Perica
Vp Hr, Danielle Lambert
Vice President, Celia Vigil
Vp Advertising Platforms, Todd Teresi
Vice President Corporate Law, Kyle Andeer
National Account Manager, Jed Bludworth
V P, Antonia Fuentes
Senior Vice President Of Design Apple, Jony Ive
First Vice President Of Human Resources, Ann Bowers
Vice President Of Product Design, Doug Field
Vp Communications, Steve Dowling
Senior Vice President, Jan Larson
Vice President Of Corporate Information Security, George Stathakopoulos
Vice President Negotiation Apple Content, Pete Distad
Vice President Product Integrity, Steve Kenner
Vp Finance, Mark Donnelly
Svp Retail And People, Deirdre O'brien
Vp Apple Care, Tara Bunch
Vp Procurement, Tony Blevins
Vice President Hardware Engineering, Kate Bergeron
Vice President, Jennifer Bailey
Vp Americas And Northeast Asia, Douglas Beck
Vp Siri, Bill Stasior
Vice President User Interface Design, Alan Dye
Vice President Of Marketing, Bob Jones
Vice President Of Marketing, Nancy Macintosh
Vice President Cloud Services, Peter Stern
Vice President Platform Architecture, Tim Millet
National Account Manager, Luke Hagekyriakou
Managing Director Latin America Csac, Jorge Velez
Vice President Finance, Donal Conroy
Vice President Enterprise And Government, John Solomon
Vice President Visi. Hardware Engineering, Bob Mansfield
National Sales Manager, Eric Dubois
Vice President Operations, Priya Balasubramaniam
Vice President, Siobhan Murphy
Vice President Of Marketing, Peggy Ann
Senior Vice President Worldwide Marketing, David Schiller
Chairman, Arthur D. (Art) Levinson, age 69
Vice President And Treasurer, Gary Wipfler
Auditors: Ernst & Young LLP

LOCATIONS

HQ: Apple Inc
One Apple Park Way, Cupertino, CA 95014
Phone: 408 996-1010   **Fax:** 408 974-2483
Web: www.apple.com

2018 Sales

	$ mil.	% of total
Americas	112,093	42
Europe	62,420	24
Asia/Pacific		
China	51,942	20
Japan	21,733	8
Rest of Asia Pacific	17,404	6
Total	**265,595**	**100**

PRODUCTS/OPERATIONS

2018 Sales

	$ mil.	% of total
iPhone	166,699	63
Services	37,190	14
Mac	25,484	10
iPad	18,805	7
Other products	17,417	6
Total	**265,417**	**100**

Selected Products

Hardware
  Desktop computers (iMac Mac mini Mac Pro)
  Displays (Cinema Thunderbolt)
  External hard drives (Airport Time Capsule)
  Keyboards
  Media devices (Apple TV)
  Mice (Magic Mouse)
  Mobile phones (iPhone)
  Portable computers (MacBook MacBook Air MacBook Pro)
  Portable digital music player (iPod touch)
  Tablet computers (iPad)
  Wearable technology (Apple Watch)
  Webcams (iSight)
  Wireless networking systems (AirPort)
Software
  MultimediaDVD Studio Pro FinalCut GarageBand iDVD iLife suite iMovie Photo iTunes Quicktime Soundtrack)
  Networking (Apple Remote Desktop AppleShare IP)
  Operating systems (macOS iOS watchOS tvOS)
  Personal productivity (AppleWorks FileMaker iWork Keynote Pages)
  Server (Mac OS X Server)
  Web browser (Safari)
Online Services
  Applications for iPad iPhone iPod touch (App Store)
  Applications for Mac (Mac App Store)
  Music Streaming (Apple Music)
  Cloud service (iCloud)
  E-books (iBooks)
  Electronic greeting cards (iCard)
  E-mail (Webmail)
  Online multimedia store (iTunes)
  Personal Web page creation (HomePage)
  Remote network storage (iDisk)
  Software (antivirus backup)
  Technical support (AppleCare)

COMPETITORS

AT&T	Google
Acer	HP
Adobe Systems	HTC Corporation
Alphabet Inc.	IBM
Amazon.com	LG Electronics
Best Buy	Lenovo
BlackBerry	Microsoft
Bose	Netflix
CASIO COMPUTER	Nokia
Cisco Systems	PayPal
Comcast	Philips Electronics
Ericsson	Samsung Electronics
Facebook	Sony
Fitbit	Spotify
Garmin	Wal-Mart

HISTORICAL FINANCIALS

Company Type: Public

Income Statement

FYE: September 28

	REVENUE ($ mil.)	NET INCOME ($ mil.)	NET PROFIT MARGIN	EMPLOYEES
09/19	260,174	55,256	21.2%	137,000
09/18	265,595	59,531	22.4%	132,000
09/17	229,234	48,351	21.1%	123,000
09/16	215,639	45,687	21.2%	116,000
09/15	233,715	53,394	22.8%	110,000
Annual Growth	**2.7%**	**0.9%**	**—**	**5.6%**

2019 Year-End Financials

Debt ratio: 31.92%—
Return on equity: 56.07%
Cash ($ mil.): 48,844
Current ratio: 1.54
Long-term debt ($ mil.): 91,807

Dividends
Yield: 0.0%
Payout: 25.2%
Market value ($ mil.): —

	STOCK PRICE ($) FY Close	P/E High/Low	PER SHARE ($) Earnings	Dividends	Book Value
09/19	218.82	19 12	11.89	3.00	20.37
09/18	225.74	19 13	11.91	2.72	22.53
09/17	154.12	18 11	9.21	2.40	26.15
09/16	112.71	15 11	8.31	2.18	24.03
09/15	114.71	14 10	9.22	1.98	21.39
Annual Growth	**17.5%**	—	**6.6%**	**10.9%**	**(1.2%)**

Applied Materials, Inc.

Applied Materials is the leading producer of the machines that make computer chips flat panel TVs and solar energy devices. The company's equipment handles the complex processes of making chips from laying down patterns on silicon at the beginning to packaging them for shipment at the end. Its display business produces equipment for manufacturing organic light-emitting diodes (OLEDs) and other display technologies for TVs personal computers and smart phones. The services business offers manufacturing consulting and automation software. Based in California Applied has factories around the world. Asian customers account for about 75% of revenue.

Operations

Applied operates in three segments: Semiconductor Systems Applied Global Services and Display.

Semiconductor Systems 65% of revenue makes a wide range of manufacturing equipment used to fabricate integrated circuits including patterning systems transistor and interconnect products metrology inspection and review systems and packaging technologies. Key products are the Vantage the Radiance and Centura Systems VIISta Systems the Raider and Nokota Platforms and the Centura RP Epi.

Applied Global Services about 20% of revenue provides products that improve equipment and fab performance and productivity including spares upgrades services and factory automation software for semiconductor display and other products.

The Display and Adjacent Markets segment about 15% of revenue engineers products for making liquid crystal displays (LCDs) organic light-emitting diodes (OLEDs) and other display technologies for TVs personal computers tablets smart phones and other consumer-oriented devices as well as equipment for flexible substrates.

Geographic Reach

Applied has operations in the US Asia/Pacific and Europe. Customers in China account for about 30% of revenue which puts Applied at risk of being affected by trade tensions between the US and China. Customers in South Korea account for about 20% of revenue and those in the US and Japan each supply about 10% of Applied's revenue.

Products in Semiconductor Systems are manufactured in Santa Clara California; Austin Texas; Gloucester Massachusetts; Kalispell Montana; Rehovot Israel; and Singapore. Products in the Display and Adjacent Markets segment are manufactured in Alzenau Germany and Tainan Taiwan. Other products are manufactured in Treviso Italy.

Sales and Marketing

Due to the highly technical nature of its products Applied's direct sales force does most of the company's marketing and selling worldwide. Applied's biggest customers for chip-making equipment are three of the biggest chipmakers: Samsung Electronics Taiwan Semiconductor Manufacturing Company and Intel each accounting for more than 10% of revenue.

Financial Performance

Applied Materials has manufactured strong revenue gains in the past five years doubling its top line driven by rising demand for semiconductors.

Applied's 2018 (ended October) revenue rose 18% to $17.2 billion from 2017 on stronger sales across its businesses. Semiconductor sales were up 15% as customers added production capacity and moved to new technologies while Display and Adjacent Markets revenue jumped 31% on increased demand for equipment used in making TVs and mobile devices.

Net income slipped to $3.3 billion in 2018 from $3.4 billion the year before because of a hit from the US Tax Cuts and Jobs Act. Income before taxes was about $4.7 billion in 2018.

Applied's coffers held $3.4 billion in cash and equivalents in 2018 compared to $5 billion in 2017. Cash from operations was about $3.8 billion in 2018 while investing activities provided $571 million and financing activities used $5.9 billion.

Strategy

Applied Materials sees growth in semiconductors driven by the expansion of the internet of things big data and artificial intelligence and technologies such as augmented and virtual reality. In displays the company forecasts continuing demand for big and small screens. It is investing in research development and engineering to help its customers make more chips and with fewer defects.

Applied Materials revved up its R&D spending in 2018 to more than $2 billion about $245 million higher than 2017. R&D in the Semiconductor Systems and Display and Adjacent Markets segments address etch e-beam inspection and materials engineering. In etch R&D Applied focuses on supporting the adoption of precision etch technology for the growing use of 3D logic and memory chips.

Applied has teamed with the State of New York to create a center to research the materials processes and technologies to make computer chips in the future. Applied has agreed to spend $600 million in the first seven years of the partnership while New York is to spend $250 million on tools and equipment.

Besides R&D the company pumped more capital into improving plants and property for new ones. Capital spending rose to $622 million in 2018 an 80% increase from 2017.

Applied has moved into other areas of technology to reduce its exposure to the volatility of the semiconductor business. While it's grown quickly the Display and Adjacent Market depends on three customers for almost 60% of sales with one customer account for about a third of the segment's sales.

Mergers and Acquisitions

Applied agreed to acquire Kokusai Electronics which provides high-productivity batch processing systems and services for memory foundry and logic customers for $2.2 billion in 2019. The seller was investment firm KKR. Kokusai's systems complement Applied's portfolio in single-wafer processing systems and could enhance Applied's position with customers in Japan and Asia. With completion of the deal Kokusai would become part of Applied's Semiconductor Products Group and continue to be based in Tokyo. The transaction was expected to close in 2020.

Company Background

The leading maker of computer chip-making equipment Applied Materials has helped drive the technology revolution of the past 50 years. The company was founded in 1967 in Mountain View California as a maker of chemical vapor deposition systems for fabricating semiconductors. After years of rapid growth the company went public in 1972. It has added the manufacturing of equipment for solar technology and displays to its portfolio to help temper the ups and downs of the cyclical semiconductor industry.

HISTORY

Applied Materials was founded in 1967 in Mountain View California as a maker of chemical vapor deposition systems for fabricating semiconductors. After years of rapid growth the company went public in 1972. Two years later it purchased wafer maker Galamar Industries.

In 1975 Applied Materials suffered a 45% drop in sales as the semiconductor industry (and the US economy) contracted. Financial and managerial problems plagued the company following the recession so in 1976 James Morgan a former division manager for conglomerate Textron was chosen to replace founder Michael McNeilly as CEO. Two years later Morgan also became chairman.

After selling Galamar (1977) and other non-core units and extending the company's line of credit Morgan announced a plan to move into Japan. The company's first joint venture Applied Materials Japan was set up in 1979.

Applied got into the ion implanter market in 1980 through its acquisition of the UK's Lintott Engineering.

EXECUTIVES

Vice President, Erix Yu
Vp Business Management Thin Films Products Busines, William Mcclintock
Vice President And General Manager Etch And Cleans Business, Ellie Yieh
Svp Engineering, Gino Addiego, age 59, $457,692 total compensation
Group Vp; General Manager Transistor And Interconnect Group, Steve Ghanayem
Svp General Counsel And Secretary, Thomas F. Larkins, $489,231 total compensation
Group Vp; General Manager Imaging And Process Control Group, Robert J. Perlmutter, age 62
Svp And Cto; President Applied Ventures, Omkaram (Om) Nalamasu, age 60, $468,846 total compensation
Group Vp And Cio, Jay Kerley
Svp And Cfo, Daniel (Dan) Durn, age 52
President And Ceo, Gary E. Dickerson, age 61, $1,019,231 total compensation
Svp; General Manager New Markets And Service Group, Ali Salehpour, age 57, $560,577 total compensation
Group Vp; General Manager Patterning And Packaging Group, Prabu G. Raja
Regional President, Russell Tham

Vice President Controller And Chief Accounting Officer, Charles Read
Vice President Human Resources, Blake Wolfe
Corporate Vp Applied Materials Fellow Engineering And Product Technology Development Display And Flexible Technology Business Group, John White
Corporate Vp Applied Materials Fellow And Gm Dielectric Cvd Products Dielectric Deposition Products Semiconductor Products Group, Hari Ponnekanti
Vice President And Treasurer, Robert Friess
Corporate Vice President And General Manager Of Display Business Group, Brian Shieh
Vice President Global Internal Audit, Jean Chun
Vice President, Aninda Moitra
Vice President Marketing, Shayne Bennett
Vice President, Karin Basilio
Vice President, Ramesh Viswanathan
Vice President And General Manager Of Front End Products Division, Sundar Ramamurthy
Vice President, Mike Parcella
Vice President And General Manager Service And Spares Applied Global Services, Seehack Foo
Vice President, Brent Bloom
Vice President Intellectual Property, James Wilson
Vp It Enterprise Process Solutions, Simon Dunning
Corporate Vice President, Mehdi Vaez-iravani
Vice President And General Manager, Mukund Srinivasan
Corporate Vice President, Hussein Fawaz
Vice President Marketing And Business Development, Lior Engel
Vice President Non Semi Operations, Robert Davis
Vice President General Management, Ta Won Kim
Vice President Marketing And Business Development, Lee Fang Chew
Vice President Engineering, Sanjay Natarajan
Chairman, Thomas J. (Tom) Iannotti, age 63
Board Member, Alexander Karsner
Assistant Treasurer, Randy Webb
Assistant Treasurer Customer, Brad Mccurrie
Assistant Treasurer, Avi Cohen-Hillel
Auditors: KPMG LLP

LOCATIONS

HQ: Applied Materials, Inc.
3050 Bowers Avenue, P.O. Box 58039, Santa Clara, CA 95052-8039
Phone: 408 727-5555
Web: www.appliedmaterials.com

2018 Sales

	$ mil.	% of total
Asia/Pacific		
China	5,113	29
Korea	3,603	21
Taiwan	2,732	16
Japan	2,405	14
Southeast Asia	802	5
US	1,532	9
Europe	1,066	6
Total	**17,253**	**100**

PRODUCTS/OPERATIONS

2018 Sales

	$ mil.	% of total
Semiconductor Systems	10,903	63
Applied Global Services	3,754	22
Display and Adjacent Markets	2,498	14
Corporate & Other	98	1
Total	**17,253**	**100**

Products and Technologies
Semiconductor
Display
Solar
Roll to Roll WEB Coating
Emerging Technologies and Products
Automation Software
Product Library

Selected Products

Chemical mechanical polishing/planarization systems (wafer polishing)
Deposition systems (deposit layers of conducting and insulating material on wafers)
Dielectric deposition (chemical vapor deposition or CVD)
Metal (CVD electroplating or physical vapor deposition)
Silicon and thermal deposition
Sputtering (physical vapor deposition) for solar cells
Thin-film silicon solar cells
Web coating for flexible solar cells
Etch systems (remove portions of a wafer surface for circuit construction)
Inspection systems (defect review for reticles — patterned plates which hold precise images of chip circuit patterns — and wafers)
Ion implant systems (implant ions into wafer surface to change conductive properties)
Manufacturing process optimization software
Metrology systems
CD-SEM (scanning electron microscope system)
Optical monitoring systems (for glass or web coating systems)
Rapid thermal processing systems (heat wafers to change electrical characteristics)

COMPETITORS

AIXTRON	Micronic Laser Systems
ASM International	Nikon
Ebara	Sumitomo Heavy
Hitachi	Industries
Hitachi Kokusai	Tokyo Electron
Electric	ULVAC
KLA-Tencor	Veeco Instruments
Lam Research	

HISTORICAL FINANCIALS

Company Type: Public

Income Statement

FYE: October 27

	REVENUE ($ mil.)	NET INCOME ($ mil.)	NET PROFIT MARGIN	EMPLOYEES
10/19	14,608	2,706	18.5%	22,000
10/18	17,253	3,313	19.2%	21,000
10/17	14,537	3,434	23.6%	18,400
10/16	10,825	1,721	15.9%	16,700
10/15	9,659	1,377	14.3%	15,500
Annual Growth	**10.9%**	**18.4%**	**—**	**9.1%**

2019 Year-End Financials

Debt ratio: 27.93%
Return on equity: 36.05%
Cash ($ mil.): 3,129
Current ratio: 2.30
Long-term debt ($ mil.): 4,713

No. of shares (mil.): 916
Dividends
Yield: 0.0%
Payout: 28.6%
Market value ($ mil.): 51,040

	STOCK PRICE ($) FY Close	P/E High/Low	PER SHARE ($) Earnings	Dividends	Book Value
10/19	55.72	19 10	2.86	0.82	8.97
10/18	32.36	19 10	3.23	0.60	7.07
10/17	56.69	18 9	3.17	0.40	8.82
10/16	28.66	20 10	1.54	0.40	6.69
10/15	16.44	23 13	1.12	0.40	6.56
Annual Growth	**35.7%**	**— —**	**26.4%**	**19.7%**	**8.1%**

Aramark

Keeping employees fed and clothed is a mark of this company. ARAMARK is one of the leading contract foodservice providers in the world and a high-ranking uniform supplier in the US. The company offers corporate dining services and operates concessions at sports arenas and other entertainment venues while its ARAMARK Refreshment Services unit is a leading provider of vending and beverage services. The firm also provides facilities management services. Through ARAMARK Uniform and Career Apparel the company supplies uniforms for healthcare public safety and technology workers. US customers generate about three-quarters of the company's revenue.

HISTORY

Davre Davidson began his career in foodservice by selling peanuts from the backseat of his car in the 1930s. He landed his first vending contract with Douglas Aircraft (later McDonnell Douglas now part of Boeing) in 1935. Through that relationship Davidson met William Fishman of Chicago who had vending operations in the Midwest. Davidson and Fishman merged their companies in 1959 to form Automatic Retailers of America (ARA). Davidson became chairman and CEO of the new company; Fishman served as president.

Focusing on candy beverage and cigarette machines ARA became the leading vending machine company in the US by 1961 with operations in 38 states. Despite slimmer profit margins ARA moved into food vending in the early 1960s. It acquired 150 foodservice businesses between 1959 and 1963 quickly becoming a leader in the operation of cafeterias at colleges hospitals and work sites. The company (which changed its name to ARA Services in 1966) grew so rapidly that the FTC stepped in; ARA agreed to restrict future food vending acquisitions.

ARA provided foodservices at the 1968 Summer Olympics in Mexico City beginning a long-term relationship with the amateur sports event. The company also diversified into publication distribution that year and in 1970 it expanded into janitorial and maintenance services. A foray into residential care for the elderly began in 1973 (and ended in 1993 with the sale of the subsidiary). ARA also entered into emergency room staffing services (sold 1997). The company expanded into child care (National Child Care Centers) in 1980.

CFO Joseph Neubauer became CEO in 1983 and was named chairman in 1984. To avoid a hostile takeover shortly thereafter he led a $1.2 billion leveraged buyout. After the buyout ARA began refining its core operations. It acquired Szabo (correctional foodservices) in 1986 Children's World Learning Centers in 1987 and Coordinated Health Services (medical billing services) in 1993.

ARA changed its name to ARAMARK in 1994 as part of an effort to raise its profile with its ultimate customers the public. The company's concession operations suffered from long work stoppages in baseball (1994) and hockey (1995). ARAMARK acquired Galls (North America's #1 supplier of public safety equipment) in 1996 and in 1997 announced plans to become 100% employee-owned.

The following year ARAMARK entered into a joint venture with privately held Anderson News Company exchanging its magazine distribution operations for a minority stake in the new business. In 2000 the company was on hand to supply foodservices to the Olympic Games in Sydney.

With the new millennium the company was focused on expansion buying the food and beverage concessions business of conglomerate Ogden Corp. for $236 million. The company penned a 10-year deal with Boeing in 2000 to supply foodservices to about 100 locations one of the biggest foodservice contracts ever. It also bought the Correctional Foodservice Management division of G4S Secure Solutions (USA) then named The Wackenhut Corporation.

ARAMARK continued its expansion with the purchase of ServiceMaster's management services division in 2001 for about $800 million — opening doors in nonfood management groundskeeping and custodial services. However the company lost a bid to cater the 2002 Olympic Games in Salt Lake City to rival Compass Group. In late 2001 ARAMARK went public.

The company bought Hilton's 14 Harrison Conference Centers and university lodgings for about $49 million in 2002. Also it paid $100 million for Premier Inc.'s Clinical Technology Services which maintains and repairs clinical equipment in about 170 hospitals and healthcare facilities in the US. ARAMARK also completed its acquisition of Fine Host Corporation which added approximately 900 client locations for about $100 million.

In 2003 ARAMARK exited the child care business when it sold its Educational Resources unit (operator of Children's World Learning Centers) to Michael Milken's Knowledge Learning Corporation for $225 million. ARAMARK later bought Restauraci 'n Colectiva and Rescot a foodservice company based in Zaragoza Spain. Longtime executive Bill Leonard was named president and CEO that year with Neubauer taking on the title of executive chairman.

Expanding its Canadian presence in cleanroom services in 2004 ARAMARK acquired Toronto-based Cleanroom Garments a supplier of apparel and accessories for Canadian manufacturers in pharmaceutical aerospace and automotive industries. The company's Healthcare Management Services group meanwhile signed a 10-year agreement with Evanston Northwestern Healthcare to provide managed services to three Chicago-area hospitals. That year ARAMARK made its first foray into China by acquiring a 90% stake in Bright China Service Industries a facilities services firm. After a brief reign Leonard resigned that year and Neubauer returned to being CEO of the company.

In 2007 Neubauer with the backing of such investment firms as CCMP Capital Thomas H. Lee Partners and Warburg Pincus took ARAMARK private for $8.3 billion including the assumption of $2 billion in debt.

The company provided catering and other foodservices for the 2008 Olympic Games in Beijing. That year ARAMARK also acquired The Patman Group expanding its reach into India.

In 2011 ARAMARK sold its ownership stake in SeamlessWeb to Spectrum Equity Investors for $50 million. SeamlessWeb provides online and mobile food ordering.

EXECUTIVES

Chairman President And Ceo, Eric J. Foss, age 61, $1,622,625 total compensation
Evp Human Resources, Lynn B. McKee, age 63, $666,475 total compensation
Svp Controller And Chief Accounting Officer, Joseph M. (Joe) Munnelly, age 55, $384,503 total compensation
Coo Uniform And Refreshment Services, Brad C. Drummond
Coo International, Brent J. Franks
Evp And Cfo, Stephen P. (Steve) Bramlage, age 48, $300,000 total compensation
Coo Europe, Harrald F. Kroeker, age 61
Coo Healthcare Education And Facilities, Victor L. Crawford, age 58
Coo Sports Leisure Corrections And Business Dining, Marc Bruno
Evp General Counsel And Secretary, Stephen R. (Steve) Reynolds, age 61, $517,650 total compensation
Coo Emerging Markets, Marty Welch
Senior Vice President Finance, Christina Morrison
Vice President Strategic Partnerships, Brian Drew

Associate Vice President Of Marketing, Karen Parker
Vice President Of Operations, Chuck Reynolds
Vice President Strategic Partnerships, Ed Snowden
Vice President Of Human Resources, Lynn Farrell
Regional Vice President, Patrick Liebler
Vice President Global Operational Excellence, Autumn Bayles
Assistant Vice President, Ray Verlinghieri
Regional Vice President, Peter J Evola
Vice President Finance, Eric Brown
Vice President Of Sales, Betsy Kline
Vp And Chief Diversity Officer, Ash Hanson
Vice President Of Global Business Servic, Brian Gabbard
Vice President Of Operations, Mark Peden
Vice President Of Tax, Robert Deitz
Assistant Vice President Decision Support, Brannon Transue
Regional Vice President, Alicia Kent
Vice President Global Account Development, Hans G Lindh
Vice President Of Business Development, Timothy Grant
Associate Vice President Investments, Philip Desilva
Regional Vice President Aramark Business Dining, Prentiss Hall
Vice President Compensation And Benefits, Scott Haverlock
Vice President Global Security, Edward Hanko
National Account Manager, Sarah Crandell
Regional Vice President, Winston Wright
Vice President Sales South Region, Karen Mitchal
Associate Vice President, Laurie Garrett
Senior Vice President, John Hanner
Vice President Pricing Strategy, Yogesh Bhardwaj
Associate Vice President Consumer Insights, Jill Marchick
Vice President Strategic Development Aramark Healthcare, Mike Morgioni
Regional Vice President, Anthony Barber
Regional Vice President, Stephen Cantrell
National Account Manager, Steve Kennedy
Vp Of It, Brendan O'malley
Area Vice President, Lockerman Chris
Vice President Of Sales, Gregory David
Board Member, David Barr
Auditors: KPMG LLP

LOCATIONS

HQ: Aramark
2400 Market Street, Philadelphia, PA 19103
Phone: 215 238-3000
Web: www.aramark.com

2018 Sales

	$ mil.	% of total
United States	11,795	75
International	3,994	25
Total	**15,789**	**100**

PRODUCTS/OPERATIONS

2018 Sales

	$ mil.	% of total
FSS United States	10,137	64
FSS International	3,655	23
Uniform	1,996	13
Total	**15,789**	**100**

Brands
Brands
WearGuard
Crest
Aramark

Services
Food hospitality and facilities
Rental sale and maintenance of uniform apparel and other items

Selected Operations

Food and support services
 ARAMARK Colleges and Universities
 ARAMARK Conference Centers
 ARAMARK Convention Centers
 ARAMARK Correctional Services
 ARAMARK Cultural Attractions
 ARAMARK Facility Services
 ARAMARK Food Services
 ARAMARK Healthcare
 ARAMARK Higher Education
 ARAMARK Innovative Dining Solutions
 ARAMARK Parks and Resorts
 ARAMARK Refreshment Services (vending services)
 ARAMARK Senior Living
 ARAMARK Sports and Entertainment
Uniform and career apparel
 ARAMARK Cleanroom Services
 ARAMARK Uniform & Career Apparel
 Galls (tactical equipment and apparel)

COMPETITORS

ABM Industries	G&K Services
Autogrill	Healthcare Services
Centerplate	ISS A/S
Cintas	SSP
Compass Group	Serco
Delaware North	Sodexo
Elior	UniFirst

HISTORICAL FINANCIALS

Company Type: Public

Income Statement

FYE: September 27

	REVENUE ($ mil.)	NET INCOME ($ mil.)	NET PROFIT MARGIN	EMPLOYEES
09/19	16,227	448	2.8%	283,500
09/18	15,789	567	3.6%	274,400
09/17	14,604	373	2.6%	260,500
09/16*	14,415	287	2.0%	266,500
10/15	14,329	235	1.6%	265,500
Annual Growth	3.2%	17.4%	—	1.7%

*Fiscal year change

2019 Year-End Financials

Debt ratio: 48.65%	No. of shares (mil.): 247
Return on equity: 14.17%	Dividends
Cash ($ mil.): 246	Yield: 1.0%
Current ratio: 0.98	Payout: 20.7%
Long-term debt ($ mil.): 6,612	Market value ($ mil.): 10,658

	STOCK PRICE ($) FY Close	P/E High/Low	PER SHARE ($) Earnings	Dividends	Book Value
09/19	43.02	24 15	1.78	0.44	13.40
09/18	43.02	20 16	2.24	0.42	12.28
09/17	40.61	27 22	1.49	0.41	10.01
09/16*	38.03	32 25	1.16	0.38	8.83
10/15	30.83	34 26	0.96	0.35	7.85
Annual Growth	8.7%	— —	16.7%	6.3%	14.3%

*Fiscal year change

Archer Daniels Midland Co.

Archer-Daniels-Midland (ADM) forges every link in the food chain from field to processing to store. One of the world's largest processors of agricultural commodities the company converts corn oilseeds and wheat into products for food animal feed industrial and energy uses at 280 processing plants worldwide. The company is also a leading manufacturer of protein meal vegetable oil corn sweeteners flour biodiesel ethanol and other value-added food and feed ingredients. ADM operates an extensive US grain elevator and global transportation network that buys stores transports and resells feed commodities for the agricultural processing industry connecting crops with markets on six continents.

Operations

Archer-Daniels-Midland (ADM) conducts its business through four operating segments: Agricultural Services Corn Processing Oilseeds Processing and Wild Flavors and Specialty Ingredients.

Agricultural Services accounts for nearly half of ADM's revenue and buys stores cleans and transports agricultural commodities such as oilseeds corn wheat milo oats rice and barley. It resells them as food and feed ingredients and as raw materials for the agriculture processing industry.

The Oilseeds segment generates nearly 45% of sales and processes soybeans and soft seeds (such as cottonseeds sunflower seeds canola rapeseed and flaxseed) into vegetable oils and protein meals. Vegetable oils are either sold as raw oils or further refined into salad oils or hydrogenated into margarine and shortening. Partly refined oils are also turned into biodiesel or sold to other manufacturers for use in industrial applications such as paint and chemicals. The protein meals are typically used as a food for livestock particularly poultry. In Europe and South America the segment operates "grain elevators" (storage facilities) port facilities and transport assets.

The Corn Processing segment accounts for 15% of sales and carries out corn wet and dry milling to convert corn into sweeteners starches syrups glucose dextrose and bioproducts. The bulk of its operations are in the mid-US but it also has operations in China Bulgaria Morocco and Turkey. It also ferments dextrose to produce alcohol and amino acids.

Wild Flavors and Specialty Ingredients brings in most of the remaining revenue and produces natural flavor ingredients flavor systems natural colors proteins emulsifiers and soluble fiber among other specialty products. Additionally it buys processes and sells edible beans and soy proteins; it also sells gluten-free and high-protein pastas.

In total ADM has 271 owned or leased US or non-US processing plants and 514 owned or leased US or non-US procurement facilities.

A big part of ADM's business is getting products from one place to another. It has developed a comprehensive transportation network that moves commodities and processed products around the world. It owns or leases thousands of trucks trailers railroad tank and hopper cars river barges towboats and ocean-going vessels.

Geographic Reach

The US is Archer-Daniels-Midlands's largest market accounting for more than 45% of total sales. Switzerland accounts for more than 20% and Germany around 5%. More than 160 other countries contribute the rest. ADM currently owns or leases 270 processing plants and more than 510 procurement facilities 25% of which are located outside of the US.

The company also has 230 warehouses and terminals primarily used as bulk storage facilities and around 40 innovation centers.

ADM has Agricultural Services processing plants in North America and Europe; Agricultural Services procurement facilities in North America South America and Europe; Corn Processing plants in North America South America Europe and Asia. Oilseeds processing plants in North America South America Europe Asia and Africa; Oilseeds Processing procurement facilities in North America South America and Europe; and Wild Flavors and Specialty Ingredients operations in North America South America Europe and Asia.

Sales and Marketing

Archer-Daniels-Midland's products are distributed mainly in bulk from processing plants or storage facilities directly to customers' facilities. ADM has developed transportation capability to move both commodities and processed products virtually anywhere in the world.

Financial Performance

Archer-Daniels-Midland's revenue has declined steadily since 2013. In fiscal 2016 revenue fell a further 8% to $62.3 billion mostly because of lower average sales prices and the disposal of the sugar ethanol and cocoa businesses partially offset by contributions from acquisitions.

Net income fell 30% to $1.3 billion due to gains recorded in the previous year on the sale of the cocoa and chocolate business and lower earnings in fiscal 2016 due to their sale. The company also recorded lower global crushing and origination margins and lower international merchandising results.

Cash from operations fell by $1 billion to $1.5 billion due to changes in working capital.

Strategy

To stay abreast of changes in consumer tastes Archer-Daniels-Midland made a number of acquisitions in the gluten-free and high-protein space. Acquisitions include Harvest Innovations (minimally processed soy proteins and gluten-free ingredients) and Caterina Foods (gluten-free and high-protein pastas) integrated into the Wild Flavors segment.

The company's strategy involves expanding the volume and diversity of crops that it merchandises and processes expanding the global reach of its core model and expanding its value-added product portfolio. One of ADM's strategies is to expand the global reach of its core model may include expanding or developing its business in emerging market areas such as Asia Eastern Europe the Middle East and Africa. As the company adds new products to its portfolio it is keeps an eye on operations that fail to meet expectations. To that end in 2016 ADM sold its sugarcane ethanol operations in Limeira do Oeste in the Brazilian state of Minas Gerais and the year before that it sold its cocoa and chocolate business as well.

Mergers and Acquisitions

In early 2017 Archer-Daniels-Midland acquired Crosswind Industries a manufacturer of private label pet treats and foods as well as specialty ingredients.

The company made a number of acquisitions in 2016. In February it acquired Harvest Innovations an industry leader in minimally processed expeller-pressed soy proteins oils and gluten-free ingredients) for $84 million. In April it bought a 50% interest in Egyptian firm Medsofts Group that manages merchandising and supply chain operations; in September Caterina Foods a maker of gluten-free and high-protein pastas; and in May the remaining 60% interest in Amazon Flavors a Brazilian manufacturer of natural extracts emulsions and compounds. It also agreed to acquire from Tate & Lyle a Casablanca Morocco-based corn wet mill that produces glucose and native starch.

HISTORY

John Daniels began crushing flaxseed to make linseed oil in 1878 and in 1902 he formed Daniels Linseed Company in Minneapolis. George Archer another flaxseed crusher joined the company the following year. In 1923 the company bought Midland Linseed Products and became Archer Daniels Midland (ADM). ADM kept buying oil processing companies in the Midwest during the 1920s. It also started to research the chemical composition of linseed oil.

ADM entered the flour milling business in 1930 when it bought Commander-Larabee (then the #3 flour miller in the US). In the 1930s the company discovered a method for extracting lecithin (an emulsifier food additive used in candy and other products) from soybean oil significantly lowering its price.

The enterprise grew rapidly following WWII. By 1949 it was the leading processor of linseed oil and soybeans in the US and was fourth in flour milling. During the early 1950s ADM began foreign expansion in earnest.

In 1966 the company's leadership passed to Dwayne Andreas a former Cargill executive who had purchased a block of Archer family stock. Andreas focused ADM on soybeans including the production of textured vegetable protein a cheap soybean by-product used in foodstuffs.

EXECUTIVES

Svp Chief Risk Officer And President North America, Mark A. Bemis, age 58

Svp Agricultural Services Business Unit; President Europe, Joseph D. (Joe) Taets, age 53, $700,008 total compensation

Evp And Cfo, Ray G. Young, age 58, $825,048 total compensation

Svp General Counsel And Secretary, D. Cameron Findlay, age 60, $700,000 total compensation

Svp Chief Strategy Officer And Chief Sustainability Officer, Ismael Roig, age 52

Svp And President Corn Processing, Christopher M. (Chris) Cuddy, age 45

Chairman And Ceo, Juan R. Luciano, age 57, $1,283,340 total compensation

President Adm Europe Middle East And Africa (emea), Pierre-Christophe Duprat, age 51

Svp And Cto, Todd A. Werpy, age 56

Svp And President Oilseeds Processing Business Unit, Gregory A. (Greg) Morris, age 47, $650,004 total compensation

Svp And President Wild Flavors And Specialty Ingredients, Vince F. Macciocchi, age 53

President North Asia, Donald Chen, age 56

President Southeast Asia Australia And New Zealand And Global Destination Marketing, Ian Pinner, age 46

President Global Trade, Gary McGuigan

Vice President, Brent Flickinger

Vice President Of Research And Development, Leif Solheim

President Health And Wellness Senior Vice President, Vikram Luthar

Executive Vice President And Chief Risk Officer, Roger Hoffman

Vice President Bio Products, John Hansen

Vice President Human Resources Canada And Cost Management, Crocifissa Mandraccia

Senior Vice President Human Resources, Michael D'ambrose

Vice President Environmental, Mark E Calmes

Vice President Global Food Marketing, Mark Rainey

Vice President Of Insurance And Risk Management, Brendan Gardiner

National Account Manager, Thomas Frangione

Board Member, Patrick Moore

Board Member, Debra Sandler

Board Member, Donald Felsinger

Board Member, Terrell Crews

Board Member, Pierre Dufour

Board Member, Francisco Sanchez

Auditors: Ernst & Young LLP

LOCATIONS

HQ: Archer Daniels Midland Co.
77 West Wacker Drive, Suite 4600, Chicago, IL 60601
Phone: 312 634-8100
Web: www.adm.com

2015 Sales

	$ mil.	% of total
US	31,828	47
Switzerland	11,681	17
Germany	3,436	5
Other countries	20,757	31
Total	**67,702**	**100**

PRODUCTS/OPERATIONS

2015 Sales

	$ mil.	% of total
Agricultural services	33,658	44
Oilseeds processing	29,393	39
Corn processing	10,051	13
Wild Flavors and Specialty Ingredients	2,423	3
Other	634	1
Intersegment Elimination	(8457)	-
Total	**67,702**	**100**

Selected Commodities

Barley
Corn
Milo (sorghum)
Oats
Oilseeds
Rice
Rye
Wheat

Selected Brands

Consumer food
  Casa (canned refried beans)
  Commander (wheat flour)
  Five Roses (wheat flour)
  Gigantic (wheat flour)
  Midland Harvest (rice)
  Novasoy (soy supplement)
  Top King (wheat flour)
  VegeFull (cooked ground beans)
Industrial food
  Ambrosia (chocolate)
  CardioAid (plant sterol)
  EnviroStrip (dry-stripping)
  Evolution Chemicals (sustainable alternative chemical)
  NovaLipid (fats and oils)
  NovaSoy (isoflavones)
  VegeFull (dried bean-based food ingredient)

Selected Products

Agricultural
  Fertilizer
Feed ingredients
  Animal nutrition
  Corn co-products
  Milling products
  Oils/energy products
  Premixes
  Specialty feed ingredients
Food
  Acidulants
  Beverage alcohol
  Edible beans and bean ingredients
  Fiber
  Flour and whole grains
  Lecithin
  Natural-source vitamin E
  Oils
  Plant sterols
  Polyols and gums
  Proteins
  Rice
  Soy isoflavones
  Starches
  Sweeteners
Fuel
  Biodiesel
  Ethanol
Industrials
  Acidulants
  De-icers

Dispersants
Dust control products
Emulsifiers and thickeners
Fermentation nutrients
Fertilizers
Industrial oils
Polyols
Propylene glycol
Solvents
Starches
Superabsorbents

Selected Services

Agriculture
  Grain merchandising
  Grain milling
  Grain processing
Information
  Billing and invoicing
  Inventory
  Logistics
  Payment
  Product search
Transportation
  Land
  Rail
  Truck
  Water
  Ocean
  River

Selected Subsidiaries Joint Ventures and Other Holdings

Almidones Mexicanos S.A. (50% wet corn milling plant Mexico)
Alfred C. Toepfer International (80% agricultural commodities trading and processed products Germany)
Compagnie Industrielle et Financiere des Produits Amylaces SA (Luxembourg) (42% joint venture investments in food feed ingredients and bioenergy)
Eaststarch C.V. (50% wet corn milling plants Netherlands)
Edible Oils Limited (50% procure package sell edible oils UK)
Golden Peanut LLC (100% peanut hulls oil meal and seed)
Gruma S.A.B. de C.V (23% corn flour and corn tortilla manufacturer Mexico)
Kalama Export Company (45% grain export elevator)
Red Star Yeast LLC (40% joint venture fresh and dry yeast manufacturer US and Canada)
Stratas Foods LLC (50% procure package sell edible oils North America)
Telles LLC (50% market sell corn-based bioplastic)

COMPETITORS

AGRI Industries	Ingredion
Abengoa Bioenergy	Liberty Vegetable Oil
Ag Processing Inc.	LifeLine
Ajinomoto	Little Sioux Corn
Andersons	Processors
Barry Callebaut	Louis Dreyfus Group
Bartlett and Company	MGP Ingredients
Bayer CropScience	Malt Products
Brenntag North America	Corporation
Bunge Limited	Nestlé
CHS	Nisshin Oillio
CP Kelco	Northern Growers
Cargill	Omega Protein
Cosun	Pacific Ethanol
Danisco A/S	Pioneer Hi-Bred
Dow AgroSciences	Renewable Energy Group
DuPont Agriculture	Riceland Foods
General Mills	Scoular
Green Brick Partners	Syngenta
Green Plains	Südzucker
Hain Celestial	Tate & Lyle
Hershey	

HISTORICAL FINANCIALS

Company Type: Public

Income Statement				FYE: December 31
	REVENUE ($ mil.)	NET INCOME ($ mil.)	NET PROFIT MARGIN	EMPLOYEES
12/18	64,341	1,810	2.8%	31,600
12/17	60,828	1,595	2.6%	31,300
12/16	62,346	1,279	2.1%	31,800
12/15	67,702	1,849	2.7%	32,300
12/14	81,201	2,248	2.8%	33,900
Annual Growth	(5.7%)	(5.3%)	—	(1.7%)

2018 Year-End Financials

Debt ratio: 20.54%	No. of shares (mil.): 559
Return on equity: 9.71%	Dividends
Cash ($ mil.): 1,997	Yield: 3.2%
Current ratio: 1.75	Payout: 42.0%
Long-term debt ($ mil.): 7,698	Market value ($ mil.): 22,902

	STOCK PRICE ($) FY Close	P/E High/Low	PER SHARE ($) Earnings	Dividends	Book Value
12/18	40.97	16 12	3.19	1.34	33.96
12/17	40.08	17 14	2.79	1.28	32.88
12/16	45.65	22 14	2.16	1.20	29.97
12/15	36.68	18 11	2.98	1.12	30.08
12/14	52.00	16 11	3.43	0.96	30.73
Annual Growth	(5.8%)	—	(1.8%)	8.7%	2.5%

Arconic Inc

Arconic makes engineered products?primarily made from aluminum steel nickel and titanium? can help you fly drive build and generate power. Created in 2016 when it was spun off from the aluminum giant Alcoa Arconic has retained the parts businesses of its predecessor?engineered products like fastening systems or castings; rolled products like aluminum sheets and plates; and transportation and construction products. With operations in some 20 countries Arconic is a top provider of specialty materials to the aerospace commercial transportation automotive defense building and construction oil & gas and packaging industries. It generates about two-third of it revenue in the US.

Operations

Arconic's operations consist of three segments: Engineered Products and Solutions Global Rolled Products and Transportation and Construction Solutions.

Engineered Products & Solutions about 45% of revenue is what Arconic is known for in the aerospace and commercial transportation circles. Making up close to half of the company?s annual revenue this segment?s products include superalloy fastening systems seamless rolled rings investment castings used in jet engines as well as various extruded machined and formed aircraft parts.

Arconic?s Global Rolled Products segment about 40% of sales manages the production and sale of aluminum sheets and plates that are mainly used in the manufacturing of machinery and equipment and consumer durables. While major customers belong to the aerospace transportation and construction industries Arconic also manufactures aseptic foil for the packaging end market.

About 15% of sales come from the company?s Transport & Construction business that sells integrated aluminum structural systems architectural

extrusions and forged aluminum commercial vehicle wheels.

Geographic Reach

Arconic headquartered in New York has operations in around 20 countries worldwide though the majority of its activity and sales are in the US (65% of revenue) and Europe (25% of revenue). Arconic also has had operations in Brazil Canada China Hungary Japan and Russia.

Sales and Marketing

Arconic's aluminum titanium and nickel superalloy products are sold directly to customers and distributors. The company relies on the aerospace industry for more than 75% of its sales. Other markets are the automotive commercial transportation construction and industrial equipment defense and packaging industries.

Financial Performance

Arconic has posted higher revenue each year since it spun off from Alcoa in 2016.

In 2018 Arconic's revenue rose 8% to $14 billion up $1.1 billion from the previous year driven by higher volumes in all of its segments. There was strong growth in the aerospace engines and defense automotive commercial transportation industrial and building and construction end markets. Adding to the sales increase were higher aluminum pricing and favorable product mix. Sales of products for the industrial gas turbine market were lower year-over-year.

Arconic posted a $642 million profit in 2018 compared to a loss of $74 million in 2017 on higher sales and gains from the sale of a rolling mill.

Arconic held $2.3 billion in cash in 2018 compared to $2.1 billion in the previous year. In 2018 operating activities produced $217 million and investing activities provided $565 million while financing activities used $649 million.

Strategy

In 2016 Alcoós thriving parts business was strategically spun off from its legacy aluminum assets in pursuit of higher profits. Since then the spinoff company Arconic has struggled to find sure footing despite rising revenue and high demand. The company flirted with selling itself to a private equity firm Apollo Global Management in early 2019 but decided against the deal.

Instead Arconic plans to split into two parts: a rolling sheet-metal producer and a parts maker. The separation could be accomplished in 2020.

In the meantime the company plans to cut costs by a total of $260 million in 2019 and 2020. Part of the cost-cutting has come through divestments including the sale of its forgings business in the UK and an aluminum rolling mill in Brazil for a total of about $112 million.

Arconic also has conducted a massive stock buyback program spending $900 million through mid-2019. The board has authority to spend another $600 million on buybacks.

In early 2019 Arconic moved to address its problems in meeting demand investing $100 million to expand its hot mill capability and add downstream equipment capabilities to make industrial and automotive aluminum products. The company had trouble keeping pace with increasing demand in 2018.

Company Background

Arconic was born when aluminum giant Alcoa Corporation broke itself into two companies in 2016 one to own the company's aluminum assets (Alcoa Corp) and the other to own a growing specialty parts business (Arconic). The overarching motif behind the split was simple— to let Arconic's parts business—with its higher margins and greater growth prospects—thrive unhindered from its unattractive legacy assets.

HISTORY

In 1886 two chemists one in France and one in the US simultaneously discovered an inexpensive process for aluminum production. The American Charles Hall pursued commercial applications. Two years later with an investor group led by Captain Alfred Hunt Hall formed the Pittsburgh Reduction Company. Its first salesman Arthur Davis secured an initial order for 2000 cooking pots.

In 1889 the Mellon Bank loaned the company $4000. In 1891 the firm recapitalized with the Mellon family holding 12% of the stock.

Davis led the business after Hunt died in 1899 and stayed on until 1957 (he died in 1962 at age 95). The company introduced aluminum foil (1910) and found applications for aluminum in new products such as airplanes and cars. It became the Aluminum Company of America in 1907.

By the end of WWI Alcoa had integrated backward into bauxite mining and forward into end-use production. By the 1920s the Mellons had raised their stake to 33%.

The government and Alcoa had debated antitrust issues in court for years since the smelting patent expired in 1912. Finally a 1946 federal ruling forced the company to sell many operations built during WWII as well as its Canadian subsidiary (Alcan).

In the competitive aluminum industry of the 1960s Alcoa's lower-cost production helped it seize market share especially in beverage cans. In the 1970s Alcoa began offering engineered products such as aerospace components and in the 1980s it invested in research acquisitions and plant modernization.

Paul O'Neill (former president of International Paper) arrived as CEO in 1987 and shifted the company's focus back to aluminum. Sales and earnings set records the next two years but plunged afterward reflecting a weak global economy and record-low aluminum prices. Then the fall of the Soviet Union in the early 1990s led to a worldwide glut as Russian exports soared.

In 1994 Alcoa cut its production as part of a two-year accord with Western and Russian producers. That year the company agreed to pool its alumina and chemical operations with Australia's Western Mining Corp.

Alcoa formed a joint venture with Shanghai Aluminum Fabrication Plant in China. The company expanded in Europe in 1996 acquiring Italy's state-run aluminum business followed by the purchase of Inespal Spain's state-run aluminum operations in 1998. Alcoa also bought #3 US aluminum producer Alumax for $3.8 billion in 1998 but only after divesting its cast-plate operations.

Known by the nickname "Alcoa" since the late 1920s the company adopted that as its official name in 1999. O'Neill retired as CEO in 1999; COO Alain Belda succeeded him. Later that year Alcoa bought the 50% of aluminum auto parts maker A-CMI that it did not already own from Hayes Lemmerz International.

In 2000 Alcoa bought aluminum extrusion maker Excel Extrusions from Noranda (now called Falconbridge) and paid $4.5 billion for Reynolds Metals after agreeing to divest some assets — including all of Reynolds' alumina refineries — to satisfy regulators. The same month Alcoa acquired Cordant Technologies. Alcoa also assumed Cordant's 85% ownership of Howmet International (castings) as a result of the transaction — and later acquired the remainder of Howmet. Late in 2000 President-elect George W. Bush named Alcoa's chairman Paul O'Neill to be treasury secretary. (O'Neill subsequently resigned the post in December 2002.)

Alcoa sold its majority stake in the Worsley alumina refinery (Australia) to BHP Billiton in 2001 for about $1.5 billion as part of its refinery divestments. Treasury Secretary O'Neill completed the sale of his more than $90 million worth of Alcoa stock and options in June. In late November Alcoa and BHP Billiton combined their North American metals distribution businesses to create Integris Metals — a joint venture with revenues of about $1.5 billion. (The two subsequently sold the JV to Ryerson in 2005.)

In 2013 Alcoa and Russia's VSMPO-AVISMA the world?s largest manufacturer of titanium ingots and forged products agreed to join forces to meet growing demand for high-end titanium and aluminum products for aircraft manufacturers worldwide. The joint venture combines Alcoa's expertise in manufacturing value-add products with VSMPO-AVISMA's leadership in titanium production to manufacture high-end aerospace goods such as landing gear and forged wing components at Alcoa's plant in Samara.

In 2013 Alcoa completed the expansion of aluminum lithium capacity at its Kitts Green facility in the UK to serve the growing demand for the company's 3rd-generation aluminum lithium alloys. Alcoa projects its aluminum lithium revenues will quadruple by 2020 to nearly $200 million.

In 2013 the company also announced a second major North American expansion to meet the growing demand for light durable and recyclable aluminum sheet for automotive production.

EXECUTIVES

Evp Corporate Development Strategy And New Ventures, Christoph Kollatz, age 58, $531,250 total compensation

Ceo And Director, Charles P. (Chip) Blankenship, age 53

President International Project Development And Asset Management, Kenneth (Ken) Wisnoski, age 64

Evp; Group President Alcoa Engineered Products And Solutions, Karl Tragl, age 57, $453,125 total compensation

Evp And Group President Alcoa Transportation And Construction Solutions, Tim D. Myers, age 53

President Arconic Global Rolled Products And Arconic Defense, Eric V. Roegner, age 50

Evp And Cto, Raymond J. (Ray) Kilmer

Evp And Cfo, Ken Giacobbe, $386,250 total compensation

Evp Human Resources And Environment Health Safety And Sustainability, Vas Nair, age 53

Evp Legal, Kate Ramundo

Vice President Finance, Jim Herring

Vice President Controller, Paul Myron

Vice President Technology Alcoa Fastening Systems, Martin Ryan

Vice President Compensation And Benefits, Brian Redmond

Vice President Strategy And Marketing, Raj Reddy

Executive Vice President Human Resources, Neil Marchuk

Vp Operations, Torben Kaese

Chair, John C. Plant, age 66

Vice President Treasurer, Peter Hong

Board Member, Dave Miller

Chief Securities And Governance Counsel And Assistant Secretary, Margaret Lam

Vice Chair And Website, Tom Fletcher

Auditors: PricewaterhouseCoopers LLP

LOCATIONS

HQ: Arconic Inc
201 Isabelle Street, Suite 200, Pittsburgh, PA 15212-5872
Phone: 412 553-1940
Web: www.arconic.com

2018 Sales

Country	$ mil.	% of total
United States	9,137	65
France	936	7
Hungary	823	6
United Kingdom	737	5
China	632	4
Russia	553	4
Germany	302	2
Brazil	214	2
Canada	285	2
Japan	170	1
Other	225	2
Total	**12,960**	**100**

PRODUCTS/OPERATIONS

2018 Sales by Segment

	$ mil.	% of total
Engineered Products and Solutions	6,316	44
Global Rolled Products	5,764	41
Transportation and construction Solutions	2,126	15
Eliminations of intersegment sales	(160)	-
Corporate	(32)	15
Total	**14,014**	**100**

2018 Sales by product

	$ mil.	% of total
Innovative products	5,588	40
Engines	2,940	21
Engineered structures	1,839	13
Fastening systems	1,531	11
Architectural aluminum systems	1,140	8
Aluminum wheels	969	7
Other	7	-
Total	**14**	**100**

Selected Products

Engineered Products and Solutions
  Arconic Engines
  Arconic Engineered Structures
  Arconic Fastening Systems
Global Rolled Products
  Aerospace and Automotive Products
  Brazing Commercial Transportation and Industrial Solutions
Transportation and Construction Solutions
  Building and Construction Systems
  Arconic Wheel and Transportation Products
Certified Reference Material
  Spectrochemical Reference Materials

COMPETITORS

Accuride
Aleris Corp.
Apogee Enterprises
Berkshire Hathaway
Constellium
Doncasters
Eramet
Kaiser Aluminum
Kobe Steel
Nippon Steel & Sumitomo Metal Corporation
Novelis

HISTORICAL FINANCIALS

Company Type: Public

Income Statement				FYE: December 31
	REVENUE ($ mil.)	NET INCOME ($ mil.)	NET PROFIT MARGIN	EMPLOYEES
12/18	14,014	642	4.6%	43,000
12/17	12,960	(74)	—	41,500
12/16	12,394	(941)	—	41,500
12/15	22,534	(322)	—	60,000
12/14	23,906	268	1.1%	59,000
Annual Growth	**(12.5%)**	**24.4%**	**—**	**(7.6%)**

2018 Year-End Financials

Debt ratio: 33.86%   No. of shares (mil.): 483
Return on equity: 12.25%   Dividends
Cash ($ mil.): 2,277   Yield: 1.4%
Current ratio: 1.87   Payout: 18.4%
Long-term debt ($ mil.): 5,896 Market value ($ mil.): 8,148

	STOCK PRICE ($) FY Close	P/E High/Low		Earnings	PER SHARE ($) Dividends	Book Value
12/18	16.86	23	12	1.30	0.24	11.53
12/17	27.25	—	—	(0.28)	0.24	10.20
12/16	18.54	—	—	(2.31)	0.09	11.66
12/15	9.87	—	—	(0.93)	0.00	27.58
12/14	15.79	28	16	0.63	0.00	30.34
Annual Growth	**1.7%**	**—**	**—**	**19.9%**	**—**	**(21.5%)**

ARMOUR Residential REIT Inc.

ARMOUR Residential hopes to protect its investments with the strength of the US government. A real estate investment trust or REIT ARMOUR Residential invests in single-family residential mortgage-backed securities issued or guaranteed by Fannie Mae Freddie Mac and Ginnie Mae. The company's investments include fixed-rate adjustable-rate and hybrid adjustable-rate mortgages (hybrid mortgages start off with fixed rates that may eventually increase as the loan matures). To a lesser extent the company also invests in government-issued bonds unsecured notes and other debt. Formed in 2008 ARMOUR Residential is externally managed by ARMOUR Residential Management LLC.

Operations

ARMOUR Residential's revenue is mostly made up of interest income from its Agency Securities holdings most of which are available for sale. Movement in its non-recurring less predictable gains/losses from its investments however make a greater impact on its annual profits.

Geographic Reach

The REIT is based in Vero Beach Florida.

Sales and Marketing

ARMOUR trades its securities and derivatives with banks brokers dealers or principal counter parties (originators GSEs and other investors).

Financial Performance

Note: This analysis uses financials from the company's annual report.

Despite earning steady interest income over the past few years ARMOUR Residential has been suffering annual losses mostly due to significant realized and unrealized derivative investment losses.

The REIT's interest income fell 19% to $365.3 million during 2015 mostly as its securities portfolio balance shrank 13% to $13.76 billion and as its net interest margins dwindled 10 basis points to 1.39%.

ARMOUR's losses receded to $31.2 million in 2015 (compared to a $179 million loss in 2014) mostly as its derivative losses fell by half as the REIT decreased its total interest rate swap contracts aggregate notional balance to $8.8 billion (compared to $13 billion in 2014). The REIT's operating cash levels fell 24% to $238.26 million for the year mostly due to the decline in cash-based interest income resulting from a smaller portfolio.

Strategy

Funded by equity capital and borrowed funds ARMOUR Residential invests in Agency Securities that are backed by mortgage loans with somewhat higher interest rates. Because its portfolio is guaranteed by Fannie Freddie or Ginnie ARMOUR Residential believes that its investments — despite being backed by higher interest rate/higher-risk mortgages — are subject to less risk when compared to other types of real estate securities not supported by government agencies. The REIT also follows targeted leverage ratios and risk management protocols to minimize risk.

Mergers and Acquisitions

In April 2016 ARMOUR Residential purchased JAVELIN Mortgage Investment Corp. for $85.2 million. Lazard Freres and Co. LLC served as the REIT's financial advisor.

EXECUTIVES

Vice Chairman Co-ceo And President, Jeffrey J. Zimmer, age 62, $871,904 total compensation
Co-vice Chairman Co-ceo Cio And Head Risk Management, Scott J. Ulm, age 60, $871,904 total compensation
Cfo, James R. Mountain, $80,425 total compensation
Coo, Mark Gruber, $104,699 total compensation
Chairman, Daniel C. Staton
Auditors: DELOITTE & TOUCHE LLP

LOCATIONS

HQ: ARMOUR Residential REIT Inc.
3001 Ocean Drive, Suite 201, Vero Beach, FL 32963
Phone: 772 617-4340
Web: www.armourreit.com

COMPETITORS

AG Mortgage Investment Trust	Capstead Mortgage
American Capital Agency Corp.	Hatteras Financial
	MFA Financial
Annaly Capital Management	Orchid Island Capital
	Provident Mortgage Capital
Anworth Mortgage Asset	TMAC Mortgage
Apollo Residential Mortgage	

HISTORICAL FINANCIALS

Company Type: Public

Income Statement

FYE: December 31

	ASSETS ($ mil.)	NET INCOME ($ mil.)	INCOME AS % OF ASSETS	EMPLOYEES
12/18	8,464	(105)	—	—
12/17	8,928	181	2.0%	—
12/16	7,978	(45)	—	—
12/15	13,055	(31)	—	19
12/14	16,285	(179)	—	19
Annual Growth (15.1%)		—	—	—

2018 Year-End Financials

Debt ratio: —	No. of shares (mil.): 43
Return on equity: (-8.65%)	Dividends
Cash ($ mil.): 221	Yield: 11.1%
Current ratio: —	Payout: —
Long-term debt ($ mil.): —	Market value ($ mil.): 896

	STOCK PRICE ($) FY Close	P/E High/Low		PER SHARE ($) Earnings	Dividends	Book Value
12/18	20.50	—	—	(2.92)	2.28	25.75
12/17	25.72	7	5	4.17	2.28	31.67
12/16	21.69	—	—	(1.67)	3.02	29.74
12/15	21.76	—	—	(1.09)	1.65	33.40
12/14	3.68	—	—	(4.32)	4.80	39.63
Annual Growth 53.6% (10.2%)		—	—		—(17.0%)	

ARMY & AIR FORCE EXCHANGE SERVICE

Paraphrasing the Army's longtime recruiting slogan buy all that you can buy at the PX (Post Exchange). The Army and Air Force Exchange Service (AAFES) runs about 3100 facilities including PXs and BXs (Base Exchanges) at US Army and Air Force bases in 30-plus countries all 50 US states and five US territories. Its presence includes some 180 retail stores and more than 1000 fast-food outlets (brands like Burger King and Taco Bell) as well as convenience stores/gas stations movie theaters and beauty shops. AAFES — which serves active-duty military personnel reservists retirees and their families — also sells goods online. Although it's a government agency under the DOD it receives less than 5% of its funding from the department.

Operations

While the AAFES receives little federal money it pays neither taxes nor rent to occupy US government property. Its retail prices average about 25% less than the competition.

AAFES is also a major employer of veterans and military families. About 85 percent of its associates are connected to the military.

Geographic Reach

AAFES operates facilities in 30-plus countries all 50 US states and Washington DC and five US territories (Guam Puerto Rico US Virgin Islands Northern Mariana Islands and American Samoa). It also has contingency locations in Afghanistan Kuwait Iraq Saudi Arabia Jordan Qatar United Arab Emirates Romania Poland Bulgaria Bosnia and Kosovo.

Sales and Marketing

Besides its primary brick-and-mortar business AAFES boasts an online presence at shopmyexchange.com.

About 55% of its 13 million customers are military family members with retirees accounting for about 20% and active duty military and guardsmen/reservists each making up about 10%.

Financial Performance

In 2016 AAFES reported revenue of $8.3 billion and earnings of $384 million. Revenue is down about 20% since 2011 amid a shrinking customer base (fewer military personnel) and increased competition from online and other retailers.

Some two-thirds of its earnings go into Army Installation Management Command and Air Force Services programs for amenities such as libraries and youth centers. During the past decade AAFES has contributed more than $2.4 billion to these programs.

Strategy

As with most retailers AAFES shops are facing increased competition from discounters such as Walmart and online sites such as Amazon. In addition the organization is grappling with a smaller armed forces.

To combat these issues in recent years AAFES has enhanced the stores' product portfolio with top brands such as Disney and Michael Kors. It has also invested in the online customer experience and added shipping centers within stores that will allow for quicker and cheaper shipping for online purchases.

In late 2017 AAFES significantly expanded its customer base with a new online benefit rolled out to honorably discharged veterans that allows them to shop at AAFES' online stores. As a result the organization saw online sales more than double during Veterans Day weekend that year.

EXECUTIVES

Director And Ceo, Thomas C. (Tom) Shull
Evp And Chief Logistics Officer, Karen Stack
President And Chief Merchandising Officer, Ana Middleton
Deputy Director, Mike Immler
Coo, David Nelson
Cfo, James Jordan
Evp And Cio, Philip Stevens
Vice President Planning Allocation Replenishment, Sean Shaw
Auditors: ERNST & YOUNG LLP DALLAS TX

LOCATIONS

HQ: ARMY & AIR FORCE EXCHANGE SERVICE
3911 S WALTON WALKER BLVD, DALLAS, TX 752361598
Phone: 214 312-2011

PRODUCTS/OPERATIONS

Selected Merchandise & Services

Barber & beauty shops
Books newspapers & magazines
Catalog services
Concessions
Food facilities
Gas stations & auto repair
Military clothing stores
Movie theaters
Retail stores
Vending centers

COMPETITORS

7-Eleven	Fred's
99 Cents Only	Kroger
Amazon.com	METRO AG
Best Buy	Sears Holdings
Big Lots	Sport Clips
Costco Wholesale	Supercuts
Dollar General	Target Corporation
Dollar Tree	Wal-Mart
Family Dollar Stores	

HISTORICAL FINANCIALS

Company Type: Private

Income Statement

FYE: February 3

	REVENUE ($ mil.)	NET INCOME ($ mil.)	NET PROFIT MARGIN	EMPLOYEES
02/18*	7,210	299	4.2%	35,000
01/17	6,952	292	4.2%	—
Annual Growth	3.7%	2.5%	—	—

*Fiscal year change

Arrow Electronics, Inc.

Arrow Electronics hits its target markets with a quiver of thousands of electronic products. The company is a leading global distributor of electronic components and computer products alongside rival Avnet. It sells semiconductors passive components interconnect products and computer peripherals to more than 150000 equipment manufacturers and commercial customers. Arrow also provides value-added services such as materials planning design and engineering inventory management and contract manufacturing. It distributes products from manufacturers that include Hitachi Foxconn Microsoft Dell Technologies and Intel. The company operates from more than 600 locations across the globe.

Operations

Arrow Electronics operates in two segments — global components and Enterprise Computing Solutions (ECS). Global components accounts for more than two-thirds of sales. Its product offerings consist of semiconductors passive electro-mechanical interconnect products (capacitors resistors potentiometers power supplies relays switches and connectors) and computing and memory products. More than two-thirds of the unit's sales are from semiconductor products and related services.

Arrow's ECS business sells hardware software storage and security products to value-added resellers. ECS has expanded its offerings adding professional consulting cloud computing managed services and technical training. Software is the unit's biggest seller accounting for more than 40% of revenue.

Geographic Reach

Arrow Electronics based in Englewood Colorado generates more than 45% of sales from the Americas (mostly the US) with Europe the Middle East and Africa (EMEA) accounting for nearly 30% and the Asia-Pacific region contributing 25%.

The company has 300 sales offices and 45 distribution centers in more than 80 countries.

Sales and Marketing

Arrow Electronics serves more than 125000 OEMs and contract manufacturers through its components business segment and value-added resellers through its ECS business segment. Most of its sales are made on an order-by-order basis rather than through long-term sales contracts.

The company's customers are in aerospace and defense alternative energy automotive computers gaming industrial equipment instrumentation medical and scientific devices networking optoelectronics and telecommunications equipment.

Financial Performance

After several years of low-single digit revenue growth Arrow Electronics' 2017 sales jumped 13% to $26.8 billion a company record from 2016. Its global components business supplied all but a small fraction of the $3 billion overall increase with higher sales in the Americas EMEA and Asia/Pacific on growth in the industrial transportation aerospace and defense consumer and communications markets. The ECS segment's revenue was flat year-to-year.

Net income fell to $402 million in 2017 from about $523 million in 2016 because of spending about $60 million to pay off some debt restructuring charges that were about $20 million higher than 2016 and a federal income tax increase of about $97 million due to the US Tax Cuts and Jobs Act of 2017.

Arrow had about $730 million in cash in 2017 an increase from $534 million the year before.

Strategy

Arrow Electronics has implemented what it calls a "sensor to sunset" strategy which means supplying the hardware and software that companies need to use the full range of cloud computing and the Internet of Things. The strategy encompasses the components that gather data the computing power and software that analyze data and offerings that put it to use.

The company maintains its competitive edge by offering more value-added services to diversify its revenue stream. It also keeps a large supplier base so that customers can procure from a one-stop shop rather than purchase from several different vendors.

Along with rival Avnet Arrow has made acquisitions to corral competition increase its footprint and multiply product offerings. The acquisition of eInfochips (and its 1500 engineers) was made to strengthen Arrow's capability to staff large engineering jobs. The eInfochips engineers have expertise in chip design hardware and software and cloud-based tools.

More than 45% if Arrow's revenue comes from semiconductor products and related services. Such dependence makes Arrow susceptible to the semiconductor industry's boom-and-bust cycles as well as occasional shortages and surplus of products that can wreak havoc on pricing.

Mergers and Acquisitions

Arrow Electronics continues to expand its service capabilities and global presence primarily through acquisitions. Most of the activity has been in the global components segment which made more than 15 deals in the past several years expanding products and services offerings extending its geographic reach in the Asia/Pacific region and to boost its digital capabilities.

In 2018 Arrow Electronics acquired eInfochips a design and managed services company. Headquartered in San Jose California eInfochips also has locations in India and Europe. They company has customers in retail consumer goods industrial automation health care and aerospace.

In 2016 acquired the global internet media portfolio focused on technology and electronic design from UBM including EE Times EDN ESM Embedded EBN TechONline and Datasheets.com.

EXECUTIVES

Chairman President And Ceo, Michael J. (Mike) Long, age 61, $1,150,000 total compensation
Svp And Chro, Gretchen Zech
Vp And Cio, Vincent P. (Vin) Melvin, age 55
President Global Components, Andrew D. (Andy) King, age 55, $500,000 total compensation
Svp And Chief Strategy Officer, M. Catherine (Cathy) Morris, age 60, $475,000 total compensation
President Global Enterprise Computing Solutions, Sean J. Kerins, age 56, $550,000 total compensation
Svp And Cfo, Christopher D. (Chris) Stansbury, age 53, $452,308 total compensation
Vp Global Communications, John Hourigan
Vice President Semiconductor Marketing, Murdoch Fitzgerald
Vice President And Treasurer, Michael Taunton
Senior Vice President Human Resources, John McMahon
Vp Legal Affairs, Martin Hillery
Vice President Global Supply Chain, Timothy Kolbus
Vp Corporate Marketing And Communications, Richard Kylberg
Vice President Digital Marketing And General Manager Verical, Darryl Shaper
Svp And Chief Strategy Officer, M Catherine Morris
Vice President Business Transformation A, Cedric Doignie
Auditors: Ernst & Young LLP

LOCATIONS

HQ: Arrow Electronics, Inc.
9201 East Dry Creek Road, Centennial, CO 80112
Phone: 303 824-4000
Web: www.arrow.com

2016 Sales

	$ mil.	% of total
Americas	11,442	48
Europe Middle East & Africa	6,772	28
Asia/Pacific	5,609	24
Total	**23,825**	**100**

Selected Acquisitions

FY2015
immixGroup Inc.
FY2014
Data Mogul AG
FY 2013
ComputerLinks
FY 2012
ALTIMATE Group
Asset Recovery Corporation
Global Link Technology
Redemtech
Seed International
TechTurn

PRODUCTS/OPERATIONS

2016 Sales

	$ mil.	% of total
Global Components	15,408	65
Global Enterprise computing solutions (ECS)	8,416	35
Total	**23,825**	**100**

Selected Products and Services

Computer Products
 Communication control equipment
 Controllers
 Design systems
 Desktop computers
 Flat-panel displays
 Microcomputer boards and systems
 Monitors
 Printers
 Servers
 Software
 Storage products
 System chassis and enclosures
 Workstations
Electronic Components
 Capacitors
 Connectors
 Potentiometers
 Power supplies
 Relays
 Resistors
 Switches

Services

Analysis implementation and support
Component design
Contract manufacturing
Forecast and order management
Inventory management

COMPETITORS

Avnet	Richardson Electronics
Digi-Key	SYNNEX
Future Electronics	TTI Inc.
Heilind Electronics	Tech Data
Ingram Micro	WPG Holdings
N.F. Smith	Yosun
Newark Corporation	ePlus

HISTORICAL FINANCIALS
Company Type: Public

Income Statement | | | | FYE: December 31

	REVENUE ($ mil.)	NET INCOME ($ mil.)	NET PROFIT MARGIN	EMPLOYEES
12/18	29,676	716	2.4%	20,100
12/17	26,812	401	1.5%	18,800
12/16	23,825	522	2.2%	18,700
12/15	23,282	497	2.1%	18,500
12/14	22,768	498	2.2%	17,000
Annual Growth	6.8%	9.5%	—	4.3%

2018 Year-End Financials
Debt ratio: 19.60%
Return on equity: 13.94%
Cash ($ mil.): 509
Current ratio: 1.55
Long-term debt ($ mil.): 3,239

No. of shares (mil.): 85
Dividends
Yield: —
Payout: —
Market value ($ mil.): 5,874

	STOCK PRICE ($) FY Close	P/E High/Low		PER SHARE ($) Earnings	Dividends	Book Value
12/18	68.95	11	8	8.10	0.00	62.51
12/17	80.41	19	15	4.48	0.00	56.47
12/16	71.30	13	8	5.68	0.00	49.64
12/15	54.18	12	10	5.20	0.00	45.56
12/14	57.89	12	9	4.98	0.00	43.32
Annual Growth	4.5%	—		12.9%	—	9.6%

Arrow Financial Corp.

Arrow Financial has more than one shaft in its quiver. It's the holding company for two banks: $2 billion-asset Glens Falls National Bank operates 30 branches in eastern upstate New York while $400 million-asset Saratoga National Bank and Trust Company has around 10 branches in Saratoga County. Serving local individuals and businesses the banks offer standard deposit and loan products as well as retirement trust and estate planning services and employee benefit plan administration. Its subsidiaries include: McPhillips Insurance Agency and Upstate Agency which offer property and casualty insurance; Capital Financial Group which sells group health plans; and North Country Investment Advisors which provides financial planning services.

Operations
Arrow Financial's loan portfolio consisted of residential real estate mortgages and home equity loans (40% of loan assets) commercial and commercial real estate loans (31%) and indirect auto loans (29%) at the end of 2015.

The banking group makes more than 70% of its revenue from interest income. About 58% of Arrow Financial's total revenue came from loan interest (including fees) during 2015 while another 14% came from interest on taxable and tax-exempt investment securities. The rest of its revenue came from insurance commissions (9% of revenue) customer service fees (9%) fiduciary activity income (8%) and other miscellaneous income sources.

Geographic Reach
Glens Falls National Bank has 30 branches in eastern upstate New York (in Warren Washington Saratoga Essex and Clinton Counties). Saratoga Springs-based Saratoga National Bank operates nine branches in Saratoga Albany and Rensselaer Counties.

Financial Performance
Arrow Financial Corporation's revenues and profits have been slowly rising since 2013 mostly as steady — and more creditworthy — loan growth has spurred more interest income.

The group's revenue climbed 4% to $98.86 million during 2015 mostly as 7%-plus growth in loan and other interest-earning assets continued to spur additional interest income.

Revenue growth in 2015 pushed Arrow Financial's net income up 6% to $24.66 million. The banking group's operating cash levels dipped 6% to $28.93 million despite earnings growth mostly due to unfavorable working capital changes.

Strategy
Arrow Financial has been working its loan portfolio quality by implementing smarter lending strategies with stronger underwriting and collateral control procedures and credit review systems.

It's also slowly expanding its business and branch network in the Capital District of New York which has been a key market for the bnak's growth. In September 2015 its Saratoga National Bank subsidiary opened its ninth branch in Troy. In June 2014 it opened a new branch in Colonie after opening two new branches in Queensbury and Clifton Park in 2013.

EXECUTIVES

Svp Arrow Financial Corporation And President And Ceo Saratoga National Bank And Trust Company, David S. (Dave) DeMarco, $178,500 total compensation
Director Arrow Financial Corporation And Chairman Saratoga National Bank And Trust, Raymond F. (Ray) O'Conor, $178,500 total compensation
President And Ceo, Thomas J. (Tom) Murphy, age 61, $300,000 total compensation
Svp And Cfo Arrow Financial Corporation And Evp And Cfo Glens Falls National Bank And Trust Company, Edward J. Campanella, age 51
Assistant Vice President, Suzanna Bernd
Vice President, Jim Brown
Vice President Trust Officer, Laura Vamvalis
Vice President Strategy And Operations, Ryan Mascarenhas
Vice President, Peter Capozzola
Executive Vice President Marketing, Dennis Martinez
Chairman, Thomas L. Hoy, age 70
Board Member, David Kruczlnicki
Board Member, Michael B Clarke
Board Member, Colin Read
Board Member, Tenee Casaccio
Board Member, Mark Behan
Board Member, Elizabeth Miller
Auditors: KPMG LLP

LOCATIONS
HQ: Arrow Financial Corp.
250 Glen Street, Glens Falls, NY 12801
Phone: 518 745-1000
Web: www.arrowfinancial.com

PRODUCTS/OPERATIONS

2015 Sales

	$ mil.	% of total
Interest and dividend income		
Interest and Fees on Loans	56	58
Fully Taxable	8	8
Exempt from Federal Taxes	5	6
Non-interest income		
Fees for Other Services to Customers	9	9
Insurance Commissions	9	9
Income From Fiduciary Activities	7	8
Other	2	2
Total	98	100

Selected Subsidiaries
Glens Falls National Bank and Trust Company
Arrow Properties Inc. (real estate investment trust)
Capital Financial Group Inc.
Glens Falls National Community Development Corporation
Glens Falls National Insurance Agencies LLC (dba McPhillips Agency)
Loomis & LaPann Inc.
NC Financial Services Inc.
North Country Investment Advisers Inc.
Upstate Agency LLC
Saratoga National Bank and Trust Company

COMPETITORS

Ballston Spa Bancorp	Community Bank System
Bank of America	KeyCorp
Citizens Financial Group	NBT Bancorp
	TrustCo Bank Corp NY

HISTORICAL FINANCIALS
Company Type: Public

Income Statement | | | | FYE: December 31

	ASSETS ($ mil.)	NET INCOME ($ mil.)	INCOME AS % OF ASSETS	EMPLOYEES
12/18	2,988	36	1.2%	516
12/17	2,760	29	1.1%	533
12/16	2,605	26	1.0%	524
12/15	2,446	24	1.0%	511
12/14	2,217	23	1.1%	513
Annual Growth	7.7%	11.6%	—	0.1%

2018 Year-End Financials
Debt ratio: 0.67%
Return on equity: 13.98%
Cash ($ mil.): 84
Current ratio: —
Long-term debt ($ mil.): —

No. of shares (mil.): 14
Dividends
Yield: 3.2%
Payout: 41.1%
Market value ($ mil.) 477

	STOCK PRICE ($) FY Close	P/E High/Low		PER SHARE ($) Earnings	Dividends	Book Value
12/18	32.02	16	13	2.43	1.00	18.08
12/17	33.95	20	16	1.98	0.92	16.88
12/16	40.50	23	14	1.80	0.90	15.78
12/15	27.17	17	15	1.70	0.90	14.63
12/14	27.49	17	15	1.61	0.88	13.79
Annual Growth	3.9%	—		10.8%	3.1%	7.0%

Asbury Automotive Group Inc

Car dealership giant Asbury Automotive Group oversees around 93 new vehicle franchises representing around 80 dealership locations in about a dozen states including the Carolinas Florida Texas and Virginia. The dealerships sell some 30 different brands of US and non-US new and used vehicles. Asbury also offer parts servicing and collision repair from about 25 repair centers and two stand-alone used vehicle stores as well as financing insurance and warranty and service contracts. The auto dealer has grown by acquiring large locally branded dealership groups as well as smaller groups and individually owned dealerships throughout the US. Customers include individual buyers and fleet operators.

Operations

Asbury sells in the region of 100000 new vehicles each year representing around 55% of its total revenues. Used car sales bring in 30%. The company also operates a parts and services division (10% of revenue) and a finance and insurance division (5%).

Some 80% of Asbury's sales come from import brands. Honda represents around 15% of new vehicle revenue while Nissan and Toyota each account for slightly more than 10%.

Geographic Reach

Duluth Georgia-based Asbury Automotive operates dealerships in more than 15 metropolitan markets throughout the US. Aside from the Carolinas Florida Texas and Virginia Asbury has dealerships in Indiana Georgia Mississippi and Missouri.

Sales and Marketing

Asbury advertises on TV radio and newspaper as well as through internet-based campaigns including search engine marketing website optimization and through third-party websites.

Financial Performance

Six consecutive years of revenue growthstalled in fiscal 2016 flattening out at $6.5 billion.

A slight fall in new and used vehicle sales was mostly offset by an increase in parts and service revenue to a net negative effect of $60.6 million or less than 1% of total sales.

Net income was also virtually unchanged falling $2.2 million to $167.2 million.

Cash from operations fell 8% to $142.3 million.

Strategy

With revenue growth flagging and net income not much better Asbury's management bought back shares to boost its share price. It spent around $162 million on share repurchases in the first four months of 2017.

Asbury has been selling off underperforming dealerships. It exited Arkansas entirely and sold four stores representing five franchises. On the other hand it acquired a Chevrolet franchise and an Isuzu truck franchise in Indianapolis Indiana in 2017.

To help drive sales in a more cost effective manner Asbury is decreasing its advertising spend per vehicle while increasing its focus on digital. It has improved its e-commerce offering and now sells vehicles online.

Mergers and Acquisitions

In 2017 Asbury bought Hare Chevrolet a Chevrolet dealership that also runs a collision center and Isuzu dealership and a truck center.

EXECUTIVES

Vp Corporate Development And Real Estate, George C. Karolis, age 44, $397,728 total compensation

President And Ceo, David W. Hult, age 53, $745,182 total compensation

Vp And Cio, Barry Cohen

Svp And Cfo, Sean D. Goodman, age 54

Vice President Manufacturer Relations, Matthew Mees

Vice President Finance Vice President Finance, Thomas Mccollum

Senior Vice President Chro, Jed Milstein

Sr V Pres Oprs, John S Hartman

Chairman, Thomas C. DeLoach, age 72

Vice Chairman, Craig T. Monaghan, age 62

Board Member, Tom Reddin

Auditors: Ernst & Young LLP

LOCATIONS

HQ: Asbury Automotive Group Inc
2905 Premiere Parkway N.W., Suite 300, Duluth, GA 30097
Phone: 770 418-8200
Web: www.asburyauto.com

PRODUCTS/OPERATIONS

2017 Sales

	$ mil.	% of total
New vehicles	3,561	55
Used vehicles	1,834	28
Parts & services	786	12
Finance & insurance	275	5
Total	**6,456**	**100**

2017 Sales

	% of total
Imports	46
Luxury	34
Domestic	20
Total	**100**

Selected Brands

Coggin Automotive Group
Courtesy Autogroup
David McDavid Auto Group
Gray-Daniels Auto Family
Nalley Automotive Group
Plaza Motor Company

COMPETITORS

AutoNation	Penske Automotive
Buchanan Automotive	Group
CarMax	Ron Tonkin Family of
Ferman Automotive	Dealerships
Group 1 Automotive	Scott-McRae
Hendrick Automotive	Sonic Automotive
Island Lincoln-Mercury	

HISTORICAL FINANCIALS

Company Type: Public

Income Statement				FYE: December 31
	REVENUE ($ mil.)	NET INCOME ($ mil.)	NET PROFIT MARGIN	EMPLOYEES
12/18	6,874	168	2.4%	8,200
12/17	6,456	139	2.2%	8,000
12/16	6,527	167	2.6%	7,900
12/15	6,588	169	2.6%	8,600
12/14	5,867	111	1.9%	8,300
Annual Growth	4.0%	10.8%	—	(0.3%)

2018 Year-End Financials

Debt ratio: 69.43%	No. of shares (mil.): 19
Return on equity: 38.74%	Dividends
Cash ($ mil.): 8	Yield: —
Current ratio: 1.19	Payout: —
Long-term debt ($ mil.): 866	Market value ($ mil.): 1,290

	STOCK PRICE ($) FY Close	P/E High/Low		PER SHARE ($) Earnings	Dividends	Book Value
12/18	66.66	9	7	8.28	0.00	24.46
12/17	64.00	10	7	6.62	0.00	18.94
12/16	61.70	9	6	7.40	0.00	13.16
12/15	67.44	15	10	6.41	0.00	12.68
12/14	75.92	21	12	3.71	0.00	15.60
Annual Growth	(3.2%)	—	—	22.2%	—	11.9%

Ascena Retail Group Inc

Ascena Retail Group operates more than 3500 specialty stores throughout the US Puerto Rico and Canada. Its largest chain Justice courts "tweens" at nearly 850 stores and online. The company offers premium women's clothing through about 300 Ann Taylor stores and about 670 LOFT stores. It also offers plus-size wear through some 750 Lane Bryant stores and about 350 Catherines stores. Ascena also operates about a dozen Lou & Grey clothing stores which target younger women. The company sold its women's clothing chain Maurices Inc. to an affiliate of OpCapita LLP in 2019. Ascena has announced it is closing its 730 dressbarn stores which courted working women.

Operations

Ascena Retail Group operates four business segments: Premium Fashion Value Fashion Plus Fashion and Kids Fashion. The Premium Fashion segment accounted for about 35% of total sales while Value Fashion accounted for more than 25% Plus Fashion for about 20% and Kids Fashion for nearly 20%.The Premium segment sells upscale women's apparel shoes and accessories through the Ann Taylor and LOFT brands. The company's Value Fashion segment is undergoing a major change. The segment consisted of the Maurice's and dressbarn chains which the company has sold and is closing respectively. Maurice's stores offered core and plus-size women's casual clothing career wear dressy apparel active wear and accessories. dressbarn offers moderate-to-better quality career special occasion and casual fashion for working women.

Plus Fashion consists of Lane Bryant and Catherines. Lane Bryant offers plus-size fashion (plus-sizes 14-28); Catherines offers a full range of plus-sizes (16-34 and 0x-5x) and extended sizes (28-34 and 4x-5x). Lane Bryant's and Catherine's stores are concentrated in suburban and small towns. Kids Fashion (nearly 20% of sales) which consists of the Justice brand offers fashionable apparel to girls who are ages 6 to 12.

Geographic Reach

New Jersey-based Ascena Retail Group's 4600 specialty stores are located across the US states as well as in Puerto Rico and Canada. The Justice operate more than 40 stores in Canada. LOFT and Ann Taylor also has about 15 stores combined in Canada. Additionally Justice has about 85 and LOFT has five international franchise stores. International revenue from company-operated stores and franchised stores accounts for approximately 2% of consolidated annual net sales. The company is seeking additional international opportunities for its brands.

Sales and Marketing

Ascena Retail employs a variety of advertising and marketing strategies across its retail brands. The company engages in customer research promotional events window and in-store marketing materials as well as direct mail online social media and magazine advertising. In 2018 the company spent $265.1 million on advertising and marketing compared with $269.1 million the previous year.

Financial Performance

Ascena Retail Group has seen uneven revenue growth in recent years battling for customers in a competitive retail environment. Revenue dropped slightly to $6.5 billion in 2018 a 1% decrease from the year prior. The decrease was driven by lower sales in nearly all of its segments excluding kids. Net loss was $39.7 million in fiscal year 2018 compared to a net loss of $1 billion in fiscal year 2017. Selling general and administrative expenses fell by 1% in fiscal 2018 to $2 billion. Cash provided by operating activities was $273.9 million in fiscal 2018 while investing activities used $134.4 million. Financing activities used another $226.2 million.

Strategy

Ascena Retail Group is overhauling its business as it attempts to change its trajectory after some challenging years.Moving to focus on its segments with the most growth potential the company has made major changes involving some of its largest store chains in 2019. Ascena sold a majority interest in its women's clothing chain Maurices Inc. which has 1000 store locations to an affiliate of OpCapita LLP in 2019; the company will keep a minority interest in Maurices and provide business services to the chain.

Ascena plans to close all 650 dressbarn stores a chain which courted working women by the end of 2019. The company said the move will strengthen its overall financial performance.

The company has been reducing costs for several years with a goal to produce a cost savings of $300 million. Ascena also plans to locate an additional $150 million in savings which will drive operating margin rate expansion.

Ascena continues to invest in its omnichannel strategy to provide customers a seamless shopping experience. The company has been transitioning its store brands onto a single omnichannel operating platform. In fiscal 2018 the company expanded its Riverside California distribution center to support both brick-and-mortar and omnichannel operations.

HISTORY

Roslyn Jaffe started The Dress Barn in 1962. Focusing on career women in need of reasonably priced wardrobes the store offered a 20%-50% discount from department store prices. By the mid-1970s Dress Barn had 18 stores and was expanding through acquisitions. It went public in 1983. The Dress Barn Woman division was introduced three years later. The company discontinued its casual apparel stores (SBX) in fiscal 1995.

The discount appeal of Dress Barn stores has been undermined in recent years by the increased use of moderately priced private-label brands by major department stores. Manufacturers such as Jones Apparel Group have also entered the retail market via factory outlets. In its rapid expansion during the 1990s Dress Barn countered this trend by focusing on combination stores offering both regular and larger-size merchandise. These larger stores (8000-9000 sq. ft.) provide the company a greater presence in shopping center locations and have lower operating costs.

Dress Barn added shoe departments and petite sizes in 1996 and 1997 and stepped up closures of poorly performing stores. It continued doing so in fiscal 1998 and 1999 while opening new combo stores and converting existing stores to the combo format. Dress Barn introduced a mail-order catalog in the fall of 1999 and launched a website the following year. The Jaffes' son David was named CEO in early 2002; Roslyn's husband Elliot remains chairman.

Dress Barn's longtime search for acquisition opportunities was consummated in January 2005 with the purchase of specialty chain Maurices which targets younger women (ages 17 to 34) in small to metro fringe markets with more fashion-forward merchandise.

In 2009 Dress Barn tapped into the teen market again with its purchase of Tween Brands and the retailer's Justice stores.

The company changed its name in January 2011 to Ascena Retail Group and adopted a holding company structure. In June 2012 the firm acquired plus-size retailer Charming Shoppes for about $900 million.

EXECUTIVES

Vice President Real Estate Dressbarn, Richard Sosnovy
Chairman And Ceo, David R. Jaffe, age 60, $1,019,231 total compensation
President And Ceo Ascena Brands, Gary P. Muto, age 59
Evp And Chief Human Resources Officer, John Pershing, age 48, $557,812 total compensation
President And Coo, Brian E. Lynch, age 62
Evp And Cfo, Robb Giammatteo, age 47, $509,615 total compensation
Evp And General Counsel, Duane D. Holloway, $215,385 total compensation
Svp Real Estate And Store Planning Justice, Alan Hochman
Vice President Of Global Sourcing, Carolyn Eberly
Assistant Vice President Operational Transformation, Amy Bednarek
Vice President Infrastructure Security And Operations, Andre Gold
Assistant Vice President Application Integration, Greg Duncan
Vice President Corporate Compensation, Donna Vancourt
Vp Corporate Benefits Ascena Retail Group, Isabella Spiegel
Vice President Corporate Tax, Tom Calderwood
Svp Stores And Store Operations Justice, Chris Kaighn
Vice President Operational Transformation, Vic Bhargava
Vice President Information Technology Maurices, Gerard Darby
Auditors: DELOITTE & TOUCHE LLP

LOCATIONS

HQ: Ascena Retail Group Inc
933 MacArthur Boulevard, Mahwah, NJ 07430
Phone: 551 777-6700   **Fax:** 845 369-8001
Web: www.ascenaretail.com

PRODUCTS/OPERATIONS

Selected Brands
Ann Taylor
Ann Taylor Loft
Cacique
Catherines
Dressbarn
Justice
Lane Bryant
Lane Bryant Outlet
Loft
Lou & Grey
Maurices
Right Fit

2016 Stores

	No.
ANN	1,022
Maurices	993
Justice	937
DressBarn	809
Lane Bryant	772
Catherines	373
Total	**4,906**

2016 Sales

	$ mil.	% of total
ANN	2,330	33
Justice	1,106	16
Lane Bryant	1,130	16
Maurices	1,101	16
Dress Barn	993	14
Catherines	333	5
Total	**6,995**	**100**

COMPETITORS

American Eagle Outfitters	L Brands
Avenue Stores	Macy's
Aéropostale	Old Navy
Burlington Coat Factory	Ross Stores
Christopher & Banks	Saks
Deb Shops	Sears
Dillard's	Stage Stores
Kohl's	Target Corporation
	Wal-Mart

HISTORICAL FINANCIALS

Company Type: Public

Income Statement   FYE: August 3

	REVENUE ($ mil.)	NET INCOME ($ mil.)	NET PROFIT MARGIN	EMPLOYEES
08/19	5,493	(661)	—	53,000
08/18*	6,578	(39)	—	63,000
07/17	6,649	(1,067)	—	64,000
07/16	6,995	(11)	—	66,000
07/15	4,802	(236)	—	48,000
Annual Growth	**3.4%**	—	—	**2.5%**

*Fiscal year change

2019 Year-End Financials

Debt ratio: 49.58%	No. of shares (mil.): 9
Return on equity: (-139.70%)	Dividends
Cash ($ mil.): 329	Yield: —
Current ratio: 1.45	Payout: —
Long-term debt ($ mil.): 1,338	Market value ($ mil.): 3

	STOCK PRICE ($) FY Close	P/E High/Low	PER SHARE ($) Earnings	Dividends	Book Value
08/19	0.33	— —	(67.00)	0.00	15.21
08/18*	4.02	— —	(4.00)	0.00	81.36
07/17	2.32	— —	(109.60)	0.00	84.16
07/16	8.13	— —	(1.20)	0.00	191.89
07/15	12.56	— —	(29.20)	0.00	186.04
Annual Growth	**(59.8%)**	—	—	—	**(46.5%)**

*Fiscal year change

ASCENSION HEALTH ALLIANCE

EXECUTIVES

Ceo, Joseph Impicciche
Int Pres-Ceo, Joseph R Impicciche
Sr Exec Advsr, Sister Bernice Coreil DC
Evp, John D Doyle
Evp, Robert J Henkel
Evp, Susan Nestor Levy
Evp, Sister Maureen McGuire DC
Evp, David B Pryor
Executive Administrative Assis, Teresa Hatton
Regional Director, Andrew Gwin
Cco Clinical & Network Svs, Richard Fogel
Auditors: ERNST & YOUNG LLP ST LOUIS M

LOCATIONS

HQ: ASCENSION HEALTH ALLIANCE
101 S HANLEY RD STE 450, SAINT LOUIS, MO 631053463
Phone: 314 733-8000

Income Statement				FYE: June 30
	ASSETS ($ mil.)	NET INCOME ($ mil.)	INCOME AS % OF ASSETS	EMPLOYEES
06/17	34,320	1,638	4.8%	111,719
06/16	32,469	(339)	—	—
06/15	30,963	(42)	—	—
Annual Growth	5.3%	—	—	—

Associated Banc-Corp

A lot of Midwesterners are associated with Associated Banc-Corp the holding company for Associated Bank. One of the largest banks based in Wisconsin the bank operates about 200 branches in that state as well as in Illinois and Minnesota. Catering to consumers and local businesses it offers deposit accounts loans mortgage banking credit and debit cards and leasing. The bank's wealth management division offers investments trust services brokerage insurance and employee group benefits plans. Commercial loans including agricultural construction and real estate loans make up more than 60% of bank's loan portfolio. The bank also writes residential mortgages consumer loans and home equity loans.

Operations

Associated Banc-Corp boasts total assets of more than $27 billion making it one of the 50 largest publicly traded US bank holding companies. More than 70% of revenue comes from interest income mostly from loans. Roughly 60% of Associated Banc-Corp's $18 billion loan portfolio consists of commercial and industrial real estate construction commercial real estate loans and lease financing.

Nearly 30% of the company's income is from non-interest sources including: trust service fees service charges insurance commissions brokerage and annuity commissions and mortgage banking income among others. It also offers benefits consulting services through its Associated Financial Group subsidiary.

Geographic Reach

The company offers a full range of financial products and services in more than 200 banking locations serving more than 100 communities throughout Wisconsin Illinois and Minnesota and commercial financial services in Indiana Michigan Missouri Ohio and Texas.

Sales and Marketing

Associated Banc-Corp spent $26.1 million on business development and advertising in 2014 compared to $23.3 million in 2013 and $21.3 million in 2012.

Financial Performance

Associated Banc-Corp's revenue has remained flat for the past several years at just above $1 billion. Revenue in 2014 inched up by less than 1% to $1.03 billion mostly thanks to higher interest income as loan assets grew by 11% and as interest and dividends on investment securities also grew by double digits. Offsetting much of this growth the company's net mortgage banking income shrunk by $28 million (56%) driven by lower gains on sales and related income as secondary mortgage production declined.

Profit levels have been steadily rising over the past several years since losses in 2009 and 2010

with net income in 2014 rising by 1% to $190.51 million. Higher revenue combined with lower interest expenses on deposits and lower personnel costs all helped to boost the company's bottom line.

Despite higher earnings cash from operations fell 56% to $212.74 million primarily as the company made fewer net proceeds from the sale of its mortgage loans held for sale. The company's total loans grew by 11% to $17.6 billion in 2014 while total deposits rose by 9% to $18.77 billion.

Strategy

The company intends to continue pursuing a profitable growth strategy by carefully screening its prospective customers in light of the risks expenses and difficulties frequently encountered by companies in significant growth stages of development. Associated Banc-Corp hopes to keep its momentum going via organic growth including increasing its fee income and commercial deposits among other measures. It is also remodeling or relocating many of its branches.

Associated Banc-Corp also plans to continue strong loan business growth. For 2015 the company expects high single-digit annual average loan growth after posting loan double-digit loan growth across most categories in 2014.

Mergers and Acquisitions

Associated purchased BankMutual a Wisconsin-based bank in 2018.

In early 2015 subsidiary Associated Financial Group agreed to buy Minnesota-based Ahmann & Martin Co a risk and benefits consulting firm to gain new clients and expand its financial risk and insurance product and service lines.

Company Background

Hampered by one of the worst economic environments in recent history the bank saw an increase in nonperforming loans (particularly business- and housing-related loans) and more than tripled its provision for loan losses from 2008 to 2009. The company cut its losses in 2010 and nearly turned a profit as it concentrated on improving its credit quality. It moved away from construction lending and its nonperforming loans and its provisions for loan losses decreased. Even though 2011 revenues were down Associated Banc-Corp returned to profitability as credit quality continued to improve.

EXECUTIVES

Evp And Chief Risk Officer, Arthur G. (Art) Heise, age 61

President And Ceo, Philip B. (Phil) Flynn, age 61, $1,250,000 total compensation

Evp General Counsel And Corporate Secretary, Randall J. Erickson, age 60, $406,667 total compensation

Evp And Head Retail Banking, David L. Stein, age 55, $545,849 total compensation

Evp And Chief Human Resources Officer, Judith M. Docter, age 58

Evp And Chief Credit Officer, Scott S. Hickey, age 63, $644,531 total compensation

Evp And Chief Strategy Officer, Oliver Buechse, age 50

Evp And Head Commercial Real Estate, Breck F. Hanson

Evp And Head Corporate Banking, Donna N. Smith

Evp And Head Specialized Industries And Commercial Financial Services, John A. Utz, $348,417 total compensation

Evp And Head Community Markets, Timothy J. Lau

Evp And Cfo, Christopher J. Del Moral-Niles, $477,500 total compensation

Evp And Chief Audit Executive, Patrick J. Derpinghaus

Evp Cio And Coo, James Yee, $458,333 total compensation

Evp And Head Private Client And Institutional Services, William M. Bohn

President Southern Illinois, Phillip Hickman

Senior Vice President Investme, Sara Walker

Vice President Information Security Engineer, Patrick Pirwitz

Assistant Vice President Insured Risk Manager, Jean Ehren

Assistant Vice President Residential Mortgage Lender, Brandon Strayer

Vice President Customer Care Program And Operations Manager, Wendy Kumm

Senior Vice President Specialized Financial Services Insurance Industry, Peter Bulandr

Vice President Commercial Lending, Jon Hein

Vice President Of Call Centre, Michael Fumelle

Vice President, Ed Parada

Vice President Atm Channel Manager, Deanna Helminiak

Senior Vice President Commer, Julian LaMue

Vice President Treasury Management Officer, Shelly Lapoint

Vice President Foreign Exchange, Jessie Bushmaker

Assistant Vice President Senior Bank Manager, Kim Klinkner

Executive Vice President, Diana Paltz

Vice President, Brett Stone

Assistant Vice President Residential Loan Officer, Kim Anders

Senior Vice President, Diane Gantner

Executive Vice President And Director Human Resources, Judy Docter

Assistant Vice President Senior Branch Manager, Ernesto Guillen

Sr. Branch Manager Avp, Jake Nyen

Avp Digital Solutions Sr Analyst, John Krueger

Vp Business Analyst Manager, Brad Abts

Vice President Field Exams, Jeff Kohr

Vice President International Banking, Paul Eversman

Senior Vice President Regional Manager, Gregory T Warsek

Vice President Public Relations Senior Manager, Jennifer Kaminski

Svp Standardized Services Manager Commercial Support Services, Jason Wilson

Vice President Of Operation Management, Caryn Levey

Svp And Business Solutions Director It Shared Services, Bob Kapla

Vice President Senior Client Advisor, Chad Heath

Vice President Commercial Banking Relationship Manager, Scott Hoerth

Vice President Investments, Brad Hanna

Porfolio Manager Vice President, Mark Buechler

Vice President Senior Contract Management, Jeremy Allen

Assistant Vice President Administrative Analyst Project Administrator, Nata Nash

Vice President And Portfolio Manager, Liliana Huerta

Vice President, Ryun Van Cuyk

Senior Vice President, Jessica Brandom

Senior Vice President Group Manager, Michael Sedivy

Vice President, John Adams

Vice President, Mickey Moran

Vice President Design And Construction Services, Anthony Ferro

Senior Vice President Senior Manager Interactive Consumer Marketing, Jennifer Ott

Vice President Senior Systems Analyst, Steven Weber

Executive Vice President Chief Credit Officer, John Hankerd

Vice President Market Manager, Chris Davis

Senior Vice President, Farhan Iqbal

Vice President, Adam Demont
Vice President Senior Project Manager, Melissa
Birling
Svp Texas Market Manager, Dean Rosencrans
Vice President, Dave Bolwerk
Vice President Relationship Manager Government
Banking, Joseph Hockers
Vice President Relationship Manager, Gary Krenke
Vice President, David Brookfield
Vice President Portfolio Manager, John Lotzer
Avp Talent Acquisition Consultant, Ashley Koepke
Vice President Experiential Marketing Manager,
Jenny Strachota
Vice President And Multicultural And Affordable
Sales Integration Manager, LaDonna Reed
Vice President Process Architect, Mary Thornton
Assistant Vice President, Michael Corbett
Senior Vice President Special Loan Group Team
Lead, Mike Waltz
Vice President Senior Program Manager, Marck
Simson
Vice President Human Resource Business
Partner, Lynn Smits
Assistant Vice President, Kimberly Mccann
Senior Vice President Market Manager
Commercial Real Estate, Jim Vitt
Vice President Of Private Banking, Welter Douglas
Svp Private Banking Credit Manager, Daniel Bishop
Vice President Private Banker, Gene Williams
Vp Sr Project Manager Commercial Banking, Kristi
Hatcher
Vice President Telecommunications Services
Lead, Don Cross
Avp And Senior Records Management Analyst,
Adam Mcvey
Vice President Private Banking Manager, Tracy
Stansbury
Vice President Operations Senior Unit Manager,
Teriann Van Sistine
Senior Vice President, Kathy Bozek
Vice President Business Intelligence, Amit
Padgilwar
Senior Vice President, Daniel Holzhauer
Vp Risk And Controls Manager Operations And
Technology, Kevin Ress
Vice President Information Technology, Kathleen
Wenzel
Vice President Portfolio Management, John Shaw
Vice President Senior Benefits Consultant, Dustin
Rossow
Vice President Leadership Development Program
Manager, Heidi Smith
Vp And Sr Relationship Manager Retirement Plan
Services, Scott Hoene
Vice President Special Loans Group, Michael
Stevens
Assistant Vice President Business Banking
Officer, Chelsea Horton
Vice President, Barb Pahnke
Vice President Portfolio Manager, Steven Berglund
Vice President, Judith Wood
Senior Vice President, Anthony Pecora
Assistant Vice President, Jim Larchrid
Vice President Foreign Exchange, Angie Kappel
Avp International Trade Capital Markets, Sonia Ott
Vice President, Lisa Sawczuk
Vp Mortgage Warehouse Group, Joseph Souza
Vice President, Jon Gluckman
Vice President Portfolio Manager, Laurie Johnson
Svp Commercial Banking Team Leader, Andrew
Shallow
Assistant Vice President, Jeffrey Schaefer
Assistant Vice President Residential Loan Officer,
Tammy Niemann
Bank Manager Assistant Vice President, Lynn
Lusch
Assistant Vice President Bank Manager, Boyd
Schenck
Vice President And Senior Relationship Manager
Trust Officer, Chad Borns

Senior Vice President, Karen Dunevant
Vice President, Sonia Schneider
Chairman, William R. Hutchinson, age 76
Treasurer, Tim Watson
Auditors: KPMG LLP

LOCATIONS

HQ: Associated Banc-Corp
433 Main Street, Green Bay, WI 54301
Phone: 920 491-7500
Web: www.associatedbank.com

PRODUCTS/OPERATIONS

2016 Sales

	$ mil.	% of total
Interest		
Loans including fees	659	58
Investment securities including dividends and Interest	127	11
Other	4	0
Noninterest		
Insurance Commissions	80	7
Service charges on deposit accounts	66	6
Card-based & other nondeposit fees	50	4
Trust Service fees	46	4
Other	108	10
Total	**1,144**	**100**

2016 Sales

	% of total
Community Consumer and Business	59
Corporate and Commercial Specialty	36
Risk Management and Shared Services	5
Total	**100**

COMPETITORS

Bank Mutual	Northern Trust
Harris	TCF Financial
KeyCorp	U.S. Bancorp

HISTORICAL FINANCIALS

Company Type: Public

Income Statement   FYE: December 31

	ASSETS ($ mil.)	NET INCOME ($ mil.)	INCOME AS % OF ASSETS	EMPLOYEES
12/18	33,647	333	1.0%	4,655
12/17	30,483	229	0.8%	4,388
12/16	29,139	200	0.7%	4,441
12/15	27,715	188	0.7%	4,383
12/14	26,821	190	0.7%	4,300
Annual Growth	**5.8%**	**15.0%**	—	**2.0%**

2018 Year-End Financials

Debt ratio: 2.36%
Return on equity: 9.51%
Cash ($ mil.): 728
Current ratio: —
Long-term debt ($ mil.): —

No. of shares (mil.): 164
Dividends
 Yield: 3.1%
 Payout: 32.8%
Market value ($ mil.): 3,254

	STOCK PRICE ($) FY Close	P/E High/Low		PER SHARE ($) Earnings	Dividends	Book Value
12/18	19.79	15	10	1.89	0.62	22.99
12/17	25.40	18	15	1.42	0.50	21.18
12/16	24.70	20	12	1.26	0.45	20.32
12/15	18.75	17	14	1.19	0.41	19.42
12/14	18.63	17	13	1.16	0.37	18.48
Annual Growth	**1.5%**	—	—	**13.0%**	**13.8%**	**5.6%**

ASSOCIATED WHOLESALE GROCERS, INC.

Associated Wholesale Grocers (AWG) knows its
customers can't live on bread and milk alone. The
second-largest retailer-owned distribution cooperative in the US (behind Wakefern Food Corporation) AWG supplies more than 3800 grocery retail
outlets in more than half of the US states from 10
distribution centers which collectively have some
7 million square feet of space. In addition to its
wholesale grocery operation AWG offers a variety
of business services to its members including marketing and merchandising programs retail accounting supermarket development and access to low-
cost merchandise through its Value Merchandisers
subsidiary. AWG was founded by a group of independent grocers in 1924.

Geographic Reach

Kansas City-headquartered Associated Wholesale Grocers began in Missouri and its operations
are generally centered on that state. It operates
ten wholesale divisions in Missouri Nebraska
Kansas Oklahoma Louisiana Alabama Tennessee
and Wisconsin. Its distribution activities extend
into another 25 states.

AWG's Valu Merchandisers subsidiary is gaining
a foothold in non-US regions such as the
Caribbean Central & South America and the Middle East.

Sales and Marketing

As a cooperative AWG serves the needs of its
members who collectively determine how best to
utilize the co-ops operations. Its board of directors
is made up of nearly 20 people each a key executive at a grocer retail chain which receives products
from AWG.

AWG serves up several private label brands to
stores. They include Superior Selections Clearly
Organic Best Choice Always Save and IGA.

Financial Performance

Associated Wholesale Grocers (AWG) has
grown net sales in recent years from $7.8 billion
in 2016 to more recent results exceeding $9.0 bil-
lion. Net income has trended positively over the
same period from $175 million in 2012 to a spiked
of more than $225 million in 2014 to a current re-
sult near $190 million.

For the year 2016 net sales grew 3% to $9.2
billion. Product price deflation pushed sales lower
as did the loss of Albertsons' membership in the
distribution co-op. AWG gained 800 new member
stores in conjunction with its unification with Affiliated Foods Midwest which increased sales sufficiently to overcome the negative influencers.

Net income for the year was $190 million 4%
lower than the prior year due to a corresponding
increase in the co-op's general and administrative
expenses.

Strategy

As a supplier to primarily independent and non-
national grocers the co-op must retain size in order
to compete with larger corporate firms. Years 2016
and 2017 saw its size shrink in Texas particularly
in the hotly contested Dallas-Fort Worth market.
Associated Wholesale Grocers lost two key members Albertsons (owner of Tom Thumb's and Safeway) and WinCo. It countered this by uniting with
Affiliated Foods Midwest a distribution co-op with
some 800 retail stores but the loss of such notable
members is expected influence AWG's posturing
within the North Texas area.

AWG continues to build sales of its billion-dollar private-label products line which includes the Best Choice IGA and Always Save brands. In addition to marketing the products as lower-cost alternatives to brand-name products the co-op has been investing in efforts to make sure the quality of its private-label items matches competing national brands. The company also owns and operates the Value Merchandisers Company (VMC) which offers some 22000 nonfood items to its members including health and beauty care general merchandise and seasonal and promotional products.

Operating in a fragmented business AWG competes with a large number of local and regional suppliers as well as distributors of specialty items. The food wholesale business also has its share of national giants including C & S Wholesale Nash-Finch and wholesale grocery and retail company SUPERVALU.

EXECUTIVES

Svp And Division Manager Nashville, Mike Danes
Evp And Chief Marketing Officer, Steve Arnold
Svp And Division Manager Memphis, Gary Jennings
Svp Finance, David Carl
Svp Distribution, Richard Kearns
Svp And Cio, Jon Payne
Svp And Division Manager Fort Worth, Linda Lawson
Svp Springfield, Tim Bellanti
President And Ceo, David Smith
Svp And Division Manager Oklahoma City, Danny Lane
Svp Grocery Products, Dan Funk
Svp Perishables, Jerry Edney
Svp And Division Manager Gulf Coast, Bob Durand
President Valu Merchandisers Company (vmc), Dave Sutton
President Always Fresh, Michael Schumacher
Vp Sales And Merchandising Memphis Division, David Gates
Senior Vice President, Maurice Henry
Vice President Of Sales Great Lakes, Sonny Leon
Vice President Of Fresh Merchandising Bakery Deli And Food Service, Daniel Koch
Director, Bob Hufford
Vice Chairman, Don Woods

LOCATIONS

HQ: ASSOCIATED WHOLESALE GROCERS, INC.
5000 KANSAS AVE, KANSAS CITY, KS 661061135
Phone: 913 288-1000
Web: WWW.AWGINC.COM

COMPETITORS

Affiliated Foods	GSC Enterprises
Affiliated Foods Midwest	H. T. Hackney
Albertsons	McLane
Alex Lee	SUPERVALU
C&S Wholesale	SpartanNash
Central Grocers	Wakefern Food
Dearborn Wholesale Grocers	Wal-Mart
	WinCo Foods

HISTORICAL FINANCIALS

Company Type: Private

Income Statement				FYE: December 31
	REVENUE ($ mil.)	NET INCOME ($ mil.)	NET PROFIT MARGIN	EMPLOYEES
12/17	9,703	199	2.1%	5,500
12/15	8,935	198	2.2%	—
12/14	8,934	226	2.5%	—
12/13	8,380	192	2.3%	—
Annual Growth	3.7%	0.8%	—	—

Assurant Inc

From appliance protection to trailer park coverage Assurant aims to give its customers peace of mind. The company provides a diverse range of specialty insurance products such as manufactured home coverage creditor-placed homeowners insurance pre-need funeral policies and extended service contracts for electronics appliances and vehicles. Assurant's products are distributed through sales offices and independent agents across North America and in Latin America Europe and the Asia/Pacific region.

Operations

Assurant operates through three primary segments: Global Lifestyle Global Housing and Global Preneed. The largest segment Global Lifestyle provides mobile device protection and extended service contracts for consumer electronics and appliances vehicle protection and credit and related insurance. That segment accounts for more than half of the company's total revenues.

The Global Housing segment offers lender-placed insurance multi-family housing products (renters insurance and related offerings). Other products include homeowners flood and manufactured housing insurance. Assurant sold its mortgage solutions (such as property inspection valuation and title services) business for $35 million in mid-2018. Global Housing brings in about 35% of Assurant's revenues.

The Global Preneed segment offers pre-funded funeral insurance and annuities in the US and Canada. It accounts for more than 5% of total revenue.

Geographic Reach

More than 75% of Assurant's sales are in the US but the company also operates in Canada Latin America Europe and the Asia/Pacific region. It has locations in Argentina Brazil Canada Chile China Colombia France Germany Italy Ireland Mexico Peru Puerto Rico South Korea Spain and the UK. In all the company has 45 offices worldwide including 34 offices in North America.

Sales and Marketing

Assurant sells its products through independent brokers agents financial institution representatives and third-party marketing organizations as well as through retail outlets including mortgage loan offices funeral homes and retailers. It markets multi-family housing products through property management companies and affinity marketing partners.

Financial Performance

After years of modest growth Assurant's revenue declined 27% in 2016 and another 12% to $6.4 billion in 2017. This was partially driven by a 12% decline in net earned premiums in the housing and lifestyle businesses. Improving economic conditions have lessened demand for lender-placed insurance for example. The Global Lifestyle segment had an 8% revenue decline (to $3.8 billion) while Global Housing's revenue fell 5% to $2.3 billion. Net investment income also dropped that year. These declines were partially offset by an increase in Global Preneed's revenue which rose 3% to $443 million.

In 2016 net income nearly tripled largely due to a decline in losses and expenses related to the winding down of Assurant Health. The following year net income fell 8% to $519.6 million in 2017. This was largely due a reduction in net gains from the prior sale of the employee benefits arm as well as an increase in catastrophe-related losses from Hurricanes Harvey Irma and Maria. However net income for the Global Lifestyle segment rose 15%

in 2017 as the company saw growth in its mobile and vehicle protection businesses.

Despite the drop in profits cash flow from operations rose a whopping 388% to $530.4 million that year. This increase was chiefly due to positive changes in insurance policy reserves and expenses which were again related to the divestiture of Assurant Health.

Strategy

Assurant works to develop innovative niche products within the lifestyle and housing markets. Its target areas for growth are connected living (primarily extended service contracts for mobile devices and consumer electronics and appliances) multi-family housing and vehicle protection services. To focus on these key markets Assurant exited the health insurance and employee benefits businesses in 2016. With a wary eye on US health care reform it divested the underperforming Assurant Health (which as an insurer focused on serving small employers and individuals struggled under the Affordable Care Act) that year. It sold certain Assurant Health assets to National General Holdings and shuttered the rest of the business.

Also that year the company sold Assurant Employee Benefits (another underperforming unit) to Sun Life Financial in a deal valued at some $975 million. That sale further allowed Assurant to focus on such products as property credit renters funeral and flood policies. In 2018 the company sold its mortgage solutions operations to Dallas-based Xome Holdings for $35 million.

In 2016 the company launched Assurant Product Protection which allows e-commerce businesses to offer extended protection plans to their customers. Other new products include small business protection against losses from data breaches (offered in partnerships with cybersecurity firms My DigitalShield and SnoopWall) and protection from cyberattacks to small business website owners (offered in partnership with another cybersecurity firm GamaSec).

Assurant typically expands by pursuing a conservative acquisition strategy investing in purchases that neatly complement its existing offerings. For example it is buying The Warranty Group to boost its vehicle and lifestyle product portfolio. The company has also grown through organic measures; its rental insurance customer base rose 20% during 2017.

In addition Assurant partners with other companies to expand its reach. In 2017 the company established partnerships with AppleCare Services Darty and KDDI further growing its lifestyle operations. Late that year it joined forces with Fair a property/casualty firm that allows customers to use an app to get a car on a temporary basis.

Mergers and Acquisitions

Assurant acquired Canadian mobile device repair outfit All Tech-Neek Electronics (ATNE) in March 2019. The addition of ATNE which operates in Ontario broadened Assurant's presence in Canada.

In 2018 Assurant bought a controlling stake in The Warranty Group. The $2.5 billion deal greatly expanded the number of automobiles Assurant covers as well as boosting its financial service contract and extended service contract numbers and growing its international operations.

In 2017 Assurant bought Green Tree Insurance Agency from Walter Investment Management for $125 million plus additional performance-based payouts. Green Tree sells housing protection products such as homeowners' and manufacturing housing insurance.

Company Background

Assurant traces its roots to the LaCrosse Mutual Aid Association which was founded in 1892 to provide disability insurance in Wisconsin. The company formerly known as Fortis Inc. was spun off by the Fortis group (now known as Ageas) in 2004 and became publicly traded.

EXECUTIVES

Evp Chief Legal Officer And Secretary, Bart R. Schwartz, age 66, $595,000 total compensation

President Global Home, Michael P. Campbell

Evp And Chief Communication And Marketing Officer, Francesca Luthi

President And Ceo, Alan B. Colberg, age 57, $955,000 total compensation

Evp And Treasurer; President And Chief Investment Officer Assurant Asset Management, Christopher J. Pagano, age 55, $639,583 total compensation

Evp Cfo And Treasurer, Richard S. Dziadzio, age 56, $283,205 total compensation

Evp And Coo, Gene E. Mergelmeyer, age 60, $657,500 total compensation

Evp And Cto, Ajay Waghray, age 57, $338,335 total compensation

Evp And Chief Human Resources Officer, Robyn Price Stonehill, age 47

President Global Lifestyle, Keith W. Demmings

Evp And Chief Strategy Officer, Robert A. Lonergan

Senior Vice President Human Resources, Cynthia Lowden

Vice President Information Technology Transformation And Innovation, Norbert Monfort

Senior Vice President, Lynn Gelsomin

Senior Vice President Global Sales And Business Development, Allen Tuthill

Senior Vice President And Chief Compliance Officer, Doris Vigo

Senior Vice President Head Investments, Paul Koenig

Senior Vice President Chief Accounting Officer And Controller, Daniel Pacicco

Executive Vice President Valuations, Jennifer Sells

Senior Vice President Portfolio Manager, Matthew Sosland

Vice President, John Sheehan

Vp Brand And Marketing Strategy, Krystl Black

Vp Business Unit And International Marketing, Margaret Nagle

Svp Corporate Development, Joe Pehota

Senior Vice President Global Head Of Risk, R David Conner

Vice President Us Business Development, Dave Ronis

Chair, Elaine D. Rosen, age 66

Board Member, Debra Perry

Auditors: PricewaterhouseCoopers LLP

LOCATIONS

HQ: Assurant Inc
28 Liberty Street, 41st Floor, New York, NY 10005
Phone: 212 859-7000
Web: www.assurant.com

2017 Sales

	$ mil.	% of total
US	4,980	78
Other countries	1,434	22
Total	**6,415**	**100**

PRODUCTS/OPERATIONS

2017 Sales by Segment

	$ mil.	% of total
Lifestyle	3,510	55
Housing	2,250	35
Preneed	443	7
Corporate & other	210	3
Total	**6,415**	**100**

COMPETITORS

Allstate	Home Buyers Warranty
AmTrust Financial	Homesteaders Life
American Home Shield	Maiden Holdings
Americo	Monumental Life
Asurion	NGL Insurance
Bankers Financial	Nationwide
First American	State Farm
Great American Insurance Company	Warrantech

HISTORICAL FINANCIALS

Company Type: Public

Income Statement

FYE: December 31

	ASSETS ($ mil.)	NET INCOME ($ mil.)	INCOME AS % OF ASSETS	EMPLOYEES
12/18	41,089	251	0.6%	14,750
12/17	31,843	519	1.6%	14,750
12/16	29,709	565	1.9%	14,700
12/15	30,043	141	0.5%	16,700
12/14	31,562	470	1.5%	17,600
Annual Growth	**6.8%**	**(14.6%)**	**—**	**(4.3%)**

2018 Year-End Financials

Debt ratio: 4.88%	No. of shares (mil.): 61
Return on equity: 5.35%	Dividends
Cash ($ mil.): 1,254	Yield: 2.5%
Current ratio: —	Payout: 57.2%
Long-term debt ($ mil.): —	Market value ($ mil.): 5,537

	STOCK PRICE ($) FY Close	P/E High/Low	PER SHARE ($) Earnings	Dividends	Book Value
12/18	89.44	28 21	3.98	2.28	82.57
12/17	100.84	11 9	9.39	2.15	81.47
12/16	92.86	10 7	9.13	2.03	73.26
12/15	80.54	42 29	2.05	1.37	68.70
12/14	68.43	11 9	6.44	1.06	74.77
Annual Growth	**6.9%**	**— —**	**(11.3%)**	**21.1%**	**2.5%**

AT&T Inc

If there's a way to communicate there's a good chance AT&T Inc. provides it. The company offers wireless wireline satellite WiFi IP network Virtual Private Network and fiber optic cable services. It is one of the biggest wireline and wireless providers in the US with more than 174 million subscribers. It offers digital TV voice and internet service through its U-verse brand and satellite Pay-TV through DIRECTV. AT&T acquired Time Warner Inc. in 2018 after winning a court challenge by the US government. The deal added Time Warner's content such as HBO and CNN to AT&T's distribution capabilities. The US supplies more than 90% of revenue.

Operations

AT&T's Communications segment is its biggest segment generating about 85% of revenue. The unit provides wireless and wireline telecom video and broadband services to consumers in the US and businesses in the US and around the world. Parts of the Communications segment are: the Entertainment Group which provides video internet interactive and targeted advertising and voice services to residential customers in the US as well as the DIRECTV and U-verse services; Consumer Mobility which serves business governmental wholesale customers and individual subscribers who purchase wireless services through employers; and

the Business Wireline segment which provides advanced IP-based services as well as traditional voice and data services to business customers.

The WarnerMedia segment more than 10% of revenue develops produces and distributes feature films television gaming and other content globally. Media properties include Turner; Home Box Office; and Warner Bros.

The WarnerMedia Segment (more than 10% of revenue) develops produces and distributes feature films television gaming and other content in various physical and digital formats globally. This segment includes Turner HBO and Warner Bros.

The company's Latin America segment about 5% of revenue provides entertainment and wireless services outside the US. This segment contains the Vrio and Mexico businesses.

AT&T operates an advertising service called Xandr that develops targeted advertising based on data analysis from the company's 170 million customer relationships.

Geographic Reach

Dallas Texas-based AT&T has tried to increase its international telecommunications operations but still gets more than 90% of revenue from the US. Mexico and Brazil are two its biggest international markets.

Sales and Marketing

AT&T is nothing if not ubiquitous. The company is a big advertiser to businesses and consumers with presence on TV print and online. The company operates its own retail stores where it offers smartphones from major manufacturers such as Apple and Samsung. The company spends more than $5 billion a year on advertising.

Financial Performance

AT&T's revenue has risen at a 7% annual rate for the past five years which includes a year of lower revenue (2017).

The company added about $10.2 billion to its top line in 2018 with sales hitting $170.7 billion. The 2018 increase was mostly due to the Time Warner acquisition and growth in the Xandr segment. The Communication segment's sales fell under pressure from developing technology and shifts in customer behavior (although equipment sales were higher).

Net income dropped about $10 billion from 2017 to $19.4 billion in 2018. The difference was a tax benefit received from the US Tax Cuts and Jobs Act in 2017 as opposed to a tax payment in 2018.

AT&T's cash holdings dropped to $5.5 billion in 2018 from $50.9 billion in 2017 as the company spent about $44 billion on acquisitions including Time Warner in 2018. Operations generated $43.6 billion in 2018 while investing activities used $63.1 billion and financing activities used $25.9 billion.

Strategy

As the US wireless phone market becomes saturated (AT&T and Verizon count more than 280 million subscribers between them) carriers are looking for ways to generate more traffic on their networks to generate revenue. AT&T Inc. bought a content carrier DIRECTV in 2015. AT&T added to it content capabilities with the 2018 acquisition of Time Warner and its properties such as HBO and CNN. With those assets in hand AT&T sold its stake in the Hulu streaming service to Hulu for $1.4 billion. AT&T said it would use the proceeds to reduce debt. The sale makes way for AT&T to provide its own streaming video service in 2019.

One concern is whether HBO can maintain its cultural cache built on series such as The Sopranos and Game of Thrones that were developed under Hollywood-oriented leadership under the telecommunications-focused AT&T.

In 2019 AT&T intends to build on its early mobile 5G network milestones reached in 2018 when it launched a version of the service in parts of a dozen cities.

In 2018 AT&T began work on FirstNet a government funded nationwide network for first-responders and public agencies. A possible bonus AT&T would be excess wireless capacity that it could use for its paying customers.

Mergers and Acquisitions

AT&T acquired AppNexus a digital advertising firm in 2018 for a reported price of $1.6 billion. With AppNexus AT&T seeks to speed the growth of its advertising platform. The purchase brings to AT&T some 400 software engineers and product managers with experience in machine learning and predictive analytics advertising technology and video. AT&T intends to integrate AppNexus's technologies with AT&T's first-party data premium video content and distribution.

In 2018 AT&T acquired AlienVault a cybersecurity firm adding to its communications security offerings.

AT&T's acquisition of Time Warner for $85 billion a process that began in 2016 concluded in 2018. Time Warner's holdings include HBO CNN TNT TBS and the Warner Bros. Studio which produces movies such as the Harry Potter franchise and TV shows (such as the Big Bang Theory).

EXECUTIVES

Ceo Business Solutions And International, F. Thaddeus Arroyo, age 55

President And Ceo Sbc Southwest, William A. (Bill) Blase, age 64

Sevp And Cfo, John J. Stephens, age 60, $870,833 total compensation

Chairman And Ceo, Randall L. Stephenson, age 59, $1,791,667 total compensation

Ceo At&t Entertainment And Internet Services At&t Services Inc., John T. Stankey, age 57, $965,833 total compensation

Executive Vice President - Home Solutions, Lori M. Lee, age 53

President Public Sector And Wholesale Solutions, Xavier Williams

Ceo At&t Communications, John M. Donovan, age 58, $858,833 total compensation

Sevp External And Legislative Affairs At&t Services Inc., Robert W. (Bob) Quinn, age 58

Sevp And General Counsel, David R. McAtee, age 50

Sevp And Chief Compliance Officer, David S. Huntley, age 60

Ceo New Advertising & Analytics Company, Brian Lesser

President Business Operations At&t Business, Sorabh Saxena

Senior Vice President Business Marketing Sbc Operations Inc, Mark Keiffer

Assistant Vice President Growth Platforms, Marcus Owenby

Vice President, Judy Phillips

Vice President Shared Services, Kevin Jeffries

Senior Vice President Of Emerging Devices, Chris Penrose

Assistant Vice President, Guy Bevente

National Account Manager, Jon Quayle

Sales Vice President Premier Client Group, Sean Murphy

Area Vice President Government Solutions Group, Tim Walsh

Senior Vice President Finance, David Muro

Assistant Vice President C And E Osp, James Keown

Vice President Of Workforce Development And Diversity, Belinda Grant-anderson

Regional Vice President, Craig Warbinton

Vice President, Jeffrey Yoakum

Assistant Vice President Wi Fi Services, Josh Goodell

Vice President Wholesale Wireline Sales, Joan Jambor

Assistant Vice President Life Cycle Management, Armond Suraci

Assistant Vice President Sales Operations, Sandra Galst

Assistant Vice President Ran Engineering, Rajive Beri

Regional Vice President Business Integrated Solutions At At And T Mobility, Maurice Styles

Assistant Vice President Sales, Erin Miller

Vice President Financial Planning, George Goeke

Senior Vice President Corporate Strategy, Steve McGaw

Senior Vice President, Charlie Mensching

Vice President Of Acquisitions, James Bielar

Rvp, Meredith Caram

Associate Vice President, Tara Colon

Assistant Vice President Network Services, Raymond Perkins

Vice President Fleet Operations, Jerome Webber

Vice President, Karen Bennett

Assistant Vice President Firstnet, Doug Clark

Senior Vice President Global Solutions And Sales Operations, Alex Parker

Vice President Human Resources, Gary Oliver

Vice President Information Technology Operations, Robert Gamiel

Assistant Vice President Business Advertising, Kelly Thengvall

Vice President And General Manager, Gary Lackhouse

Sales Vice President, Steve Williams

Regional Vice President, Angela Rutherford

Vice President Operations Royal Dutch Shell, John Walton

Assistant Vice President Communications, Sarah Donohue

Regional Vice President Global Access Management, Bob Flappan

Vice President, Michele Smith

Svp Corporate Real Estate Atandt Operations, J Schleyer

Assistant Vice President Information Technology, Kristi Dryden

Vice President Project Managment, Maria Dillard

Director Of Government Relations, Jane Sosebee

Regional Vice President Public Affairs, Sage Rhodes

Vice President Of Chemical Development, Damon Holzer

Vice President U Verse Product Managemetn, G W Shaw

Att Ravpn Contact, Sam Tuffaha

Vice President Head Product And Business Development At&t Adworks, Matthew Van Houten

Director Evpn, Gregory Feenstra

Sales Center Vice President, Caitlin Brown

Rvp Business Integrated Solutions, Martha K Wells

Vice President, Michael Flanagan

Vice President Small Business Product Management, Tom Hughes

Regional Vice President, Stephen Vergine

Sales Center Vice President, Vicky Santangelo

Executive Vice President Wholesale And Gem Solutio, Sherry Morse

Assistant Vice President Project Program Management, William Schutts

Assistant Vice President (assistant Vice President) Accounting, Lonnie Shirey

Vice President Of Project Development, Jeff Lewis

Vice President Of Engineering, Polly Bessel

National Account Manager, Kevin Moore

Sales Vice President, Michael Dechiara

National Account Manager, Dean Ramsey

Sales Center Vice President, Steve D'Lugos

At And T Home Solutions Assistant Vice President, Valerie Scheder

Sales Center Vice President, Margaret Rooney-Mcmillen

Vice President, Dan Lafond

Vice President, Kuruvilla Cherian

Assistant Vice President Accounting, James Lacy

Avp Customer Experience, Nicole Rafferty

Avp Project Program Management, Lorena Narvaez

Assistant Vice President Information Technology, Jeff Seymour

Area Vice President Growth Markets, Jennifer Jones

Vice President, Steve Mitchell

Customer Network Operations Vice President, Marvonia Walker

Client Executive Vice President, Knute A Olson

Sales Vice President, Fred Monacelli

Vice President Audit Services, Gerry Chicoine

Vice President Broadband And Narrowband Operations, Diane Young

Vice President And Senior Counsel, Diana Fellure

Vice President Business Development At And T Government Solutions, Robert Caffrey

Assistant Vice President Life Cycle Management Global Customer Service, Judy Miller

Senior Vice President Labor Relations Sbc Services, Michael Rodriguez

Assistant To Assistant Vice President Product Advertising, Pam Krueger

Vice President Antenna Solutions, Chad Townes

Executive Vice President Historian, Olga De La Vega

National Sales Manager Small Business Solutions, Jeff Ketler

Senior Vice President Signature Global Client Groups, John Finnegan

Assistant Vice President Technical Project Management Antenna Solutions Group, Stephen McNamara

Vice President Supply Chain Operations, Jim McGuire

Vice President Corporate Strategy, Christopher Sambar

Vice President Platforms And Enablers, Brad Mohs

Senior Vice President Advanced Solutions, Abhi Ingle

Architecture And Vendor Vice President, Ron Fowinkle

Assistant Vice President Billing Operations, Wesley Carpenter

Vice President Market Insights, Helen McGrath

Vice President Service Platforms, Pari Bajpay

Vice President Premier Client Group, Trish Renz

Vice President General Manager, Bob Holliday

Assistant Vice President Information Technology Operations, David Brickhaus

Vice President Glbl Managed Services And Outsourcing, Constance Diehl-boyle

Vice President, Jack Duffy

Assistant Vice President Digital Care Strategy, Kim Keating

Solution Implementation Manager At And T Vpn Tunneling Services, Brian Congleton

Senior Vice President Managed Services, Robin Young

Assistant Vice President National Security Network Regulatory, Brooks Fitzsimmons

Vice President At&t University, Nate Edwards

First Vice President Membership, Barry Winkler

Senior Vice President Employee Communications And Corporate Sponsorships, Gail Torreano

Rvp Sales, Jim Medenis

Vice President Sales, Kevin McKeand

Vice President Of U Verse Media Sales, Chris Monteferrante

Assistant Vice President External And Legislative Affairs, Gloria Corey

Vice President, Randy Cook

Senior Vice President Of Customer Experience, Carmen P Nava

Assistant Vice President Information Technology, Joseph Green

Intellectual Property Vice President, Ronald Sherman

Assistant Vice President Regulatory And External Affairs, Pat Wingo
Area Vice President Silicon Valley Growth Markets, Thomas McDonough
Vice President Platform Strategy And Solutions, Richard Batelaan
Sale Vice President, Jeffrey Hefflinger
Vice Presdient, Trudy Vankirk
Regional Vice President Public Relations, Robert Schauer
Assistant Vice President Network Services, Robert Spieler
Regional Vice President Southeast, Ivan Somavilla-castro
Vice President Civil, Mike Leff
Area Vice President, Karime Bavrica
Vice President Benefits, Susan Colburn
Assistant To Assistant Vice President Information Technology, Kathleen Wiegand
National Sales Manager, David Plante
National Account Manager, Dom Cimmino
Vpn Product Manager, Andrew Sullivan
Executive Vice President Client Services, Casey Coleman
Rvp Business Integrated Solutions, Brian A Quinn
Senior Vice President Business Product Management, Joe Lueckenhoff
Auditors: Ernst & Young LLP

LOCATIONS

HQ: AT&T Inc
    208 S. Akard St., Dallas, TX 75202
Phone: 210 821-4105
Web: www.att.com

2018 Sales

	$ mil.	% of total
United States	154,795	91
Europe	4,073	2
Mexico	3,100	2
Brazil	2,420	2
Asia/Pacific Rim	2,215	1
Latin America Other	3,055	2
Total	**170,756**	**100**

PRODUCTS/OPERATIONS

2018 Sales

	$ mil.	% of total
Service	152,345	89
Equipment	18,411	11
Total	**170,756**	**100**

2018 Sales

	$ mil.	% of total
Communications	144,631	83
WarnerMedia	18,941	11
Latin America	7,652	4
Xandr	1,740	1
Corporate and Other	1,191	1
Certain Significant Items	(3.399)	-
Total	**170,756**	**100**

Selected Services
Voice
    Local
    Long-distance
    Wholesale
Data
    Application management
    Data equipment sales
    Data storage
    Database management
    Dedicated Internet service
    Digital television
    Directory and operator assistance
    Disaster recovery
    Enterprise networking
    Hardware and operating system management
    Internet access and network integration
    Managed Web hosting
    Network design
    Network implementation

Network installation
Network integration
Network management
Outsourcing
Packet services
Private lines
Satellite video
Switched and dedicated transport
Voice-over-IP networks
Wholesale networking
WiFi

COMPETITORS

Altice USA	Equinix
América M vil	Frontier
CenturyLink	Communications
Charter Communications	Sprint Communications
Comcast	T-Mobile USA
Consolidated	Telef nica
Communications	U.S. Cellular
Cox Communications	Verizon
DISH Network	

HISTORICAL FINANCIALS
Company Type: Public

Income Statement   FYE: December 31

	REVENUE ($ mil.)	NET INCOME ($ mil.)	NET PROFIT MARGIN	EMPLOYEES
12/18	170,756	19,370	11.3%	268,000
12/17	160,546	29,450	18.3%	252,000
12/16	163,786	12,976	7.9%	268,000
12/15	146,801	13,345	9.1%	281,450
12/14	132,447	6,224	4.7%	253,000
Annual Growth	**6.6%**	**32.8%**	**—**	**1.5%**

2018 Year-End Financials
Debt ratio: 33.19%—
Return on equity: 11.92%
Cash ($ mil.): 5,204
Current ratio: 0.80
Long-term debt ($ mil.): 166,250

Dividends
    Yield: 7.0%
    Payout: 70.1%
Market value ($ mil.): —

	STOCK PRICE ($) FY Close	P/E High/Low	Earnings	PER SHARE ($) Dividends	Book Value
12/18	28.54	14 10	2.85	2.00	25.28
12/17	38.88	9 7	4.76	1.96	22.94
12/16	42.53	21 16	2.10	1.92	20.06
12/15	34.41	15 13	2.37	1.88	19.96
12/14	33.59	31 27	1.19	1.84	16.65
Annual Growth	**(4.0%)**	**— —**	**24.4%**	**2.1%**	**11.0%**

ATHENE ANNUITY & LIFE ASSURANCE COMPANY

EXECUTIVES

Ceo, James R Belardi
Pres, Chip Smith
V Pres Fin, Cfo, David Attaway
Evp, Matthew Easley
Pres, Guy H Smith
Exec V Pres, Christopher Grady
Sr V Pres, Rod Mims
Delivery Project Executive, Judy Burington
Finance Manager, Kristian Pflieger

LOCATIONS

HQ: ATHENE ANNUITY & LIFE ASSURANCE COMPANY
    2000 WADE HAMPTON BLVD, GREENVILLE, SC
    296151037
Phone: 864 609-1000
Web: WWW.ATHENE.COM

HISTORICAL FINANCIALS
Company Type: Private

Income Statement   FYE: December 31

	ASSETS ($ mil.)	NET INCOME ($ mil.)	INCOME AS % OF ASSETS	EMPLOYEES
12/13	11,775	49	0.4%	120
12/12	10,481	11	0.1%	—
Annual Growth	**12.3%**	**330.4%**		

Atlantic Capital Bancshares Inc

Auditors: Ernst & Young LLP

LOCATIONS

HQ: Atlantic Capital Bancshares Inc
    945 East Paces Ferry Road N.E., Suite 1600, Atlanta,
    GA 30326
Phone: 404 995-6050
Web: www.atlanticcapitalbank.com

HISTORICAL FINANCIALS
Company Type: Public

Income Statement   FYE: December 31

	ASSETS ($ mil.)	NET INCOME ($ mil.)	INCOME AS % OF ASSETS	EMPLOYEES
12/18	2,955	28	1.0%	340
12/17	2,891	(3)	—	353
12/16	2,727	13	0.5%	347
12/15	2,638	(1)	—	361
12/14	1,314	7	0.6%	106
Annual Growth	**22.4%**	**39.6%**	**—**	**33.8%**

2018 Year-End Financials
Debt ratio: 1.68%
Return on equity: 9.03%
Cash ($ mil.): 268
Current ratio: —
Long-term debt ($ mil.): —

No. of shares (mil.): 25
Dividends
    Yield: —
    Payout: —
Market value ($ mil.): 414

	STOCK PRICE ($) FY Close	P/E High/Low	Earnings	PER SHARE ($) Dividends	Book Value
12/18	16.37	19 13	1.09	0.00	12.80
12/17	17.60	— —	(0.15)	0.00	11.99
12/16	19.00	35 22	0.53	0.00	12.10
12/15	14.98	— —	(0.09)	0.00	11.79
Annual Growth	**2.2%**	**— —**		**—**	**2.1%**

Atlantic Union Bankshares Corp

Union Bankshares (formerly Union First Market Bankshares) is the holding company for Union Bank & Trust which operates approximately 100 branches in central northern and coastal portions of Virginia. The bank offers standard services such as checking and savings accounts credit cards and certificates of deposit. Union Bank & Trust maintains a loan portfolio heavily weighted towards real estate: Commercial real estate loans make up more than 30% while one- to four-family residential mortgages and construction loans account for approximately 15% and 20% respectively. The bank also originates personal and business loans.

EXECUTIVES

Evp And Director Of Mortgage And Wealth Management, Jeffrey W. Farrar, age 58
Evp Union Bankshares And Chief Retail Officer Union Bank & Trust, Elizabeth M. Bentley, age 58, $268,491 total compensation
Evp And Chief Risk Officer, David G. (Dave) Bilko, age 59
President And Ceo Union Bankshares Corporation And Ceo Union Bank & Trust, John C. Asbury, age 54
Evp And Cfo, Robert M. (Rob) Gorman, age 60, $351,167 total compensation
Evp Union Bankshares And Chief Banking Officer Union Bank & Trust, D. Anthony (Tony) Peay, age 59, $348,997 total compensation
Evp And Cio, M. Dean Brown, age 54, $259,625 total compensation
Svp And Chief Marketing Officer, L. Duane Smith, age 52
Evp And Chief Human Resource Officer, Loreen A. LaGatta, age 50
Evp And President Union Bank & Trust, John G. Stallings, age 52
Vice President Commercial Lender, Greg Gruner
Vice President Business Banking Relationship Manager, Ann Hillsman
Senior Vice President And Trust Advisor Union Wealth Management, Jack Catlett
Senior Vice President, Michael Horan
Vice President And Trust Advisor Union Wealth Management, Sharon Barcalow
Assistant Vice President Commercial Real Estate, Diana Allen
Vice President And Senior Branch Manager, Sherry Cillo
Vice President And Senior Branch Manager, Terri Hirst
Assistant Vice President Branch Manager, Jody Hardy
Senior Vice President Private Banking Services And Client Advisor Rjfs, Norfleet Stallings
Senior Vice President, Mike Walsh
Vice President Uis Financial Advisor, Chris Rinehart
Vice President And Senior Market Manager, Cheryl Kirby
Evp And President Union Bank And Trust, Maria P Tedesco
Senior Vice President Union Bank And Trust Company, Jay Baldwin
Vice President And Trust Advisor, Barbara Dickinson
Vice President Private Banking Services And Client Advisor Rjfs, Brian Adams
Vice President Uis And Financial Advisor Rjfs, John Faith
Vice President Uis And Financial Advisor Rjfs, Mason Garner
Vice President Uis And Financial Advisor Rjfs, Michael Johnson
Vice President Uis And Financial Advisor Rjfs, Preston Wall
Vice President Uis And Financial Advisor Rjfs, John Tekavec
Vice President And Portfolio Manager Union Wealth Management, Michael Snow
Senior Vice President Private Banking Services And Client Advisor Rjfs, Ben Mason
Svp, Michael D'aiutolo
Vp Director Digital Marketing, Valerie Wiederhorn
Vp Director Community Engagement, Kat Costello
Vp Svp Portfolio Manager, Chris O'brien
Vice Chairman Union Bankshares Corporation And Union Bank & Trust, G. William (Billy) Beale, age 69
Chairman, Raymond D. (Ray) Smoot, age 72
Auditors: Ernst & Young LLP

LOCATIONS

HQ: Atlantic Union Bankshares Corp
1051 East Cary Street, Suite 1200, Richmond, VA 23219
Phone: 804 633-5031
Web: www.bankatunion.com

PRODUCTS/OPERATIONS

2015 Sales

	$ mil.	% of total
Interest		
Loans including fees	247	72
Other	29	9
Noninterest		
Other service charges commission and fees	15	5
Service charges on deposit accounts	18	5
others	30	9
Adjustments	(0.3)	-
Total	**341**	**100**

Selected Subsidiaries
Union First Market Bank
Union Insurance Group LLC
Union Investment Services Inc.
Union Mortgage Group Inc.

COMPETITORS

BB&T	PNC Financial
Bank of America	Regions Financial
C&F Financial	SunTrust
Eastern Virginia Bankshares	TowneBank
JPMorgan Chase	Wells Fargo

HISTORICAL FINANCIALS
Company Type: Public

Income Statement · FYE: December 31

	ASSETS ($ mil.)	NET INCOME ($ mil.)	INCOME AS % OF ASSETS	EMPLOYEES
12/18	13,765	146	1.1%	1,609
12/17	9,315	72	0.8%	1,149
12/16	8,426	77	0.9%	1,416
12/15	7,693	67	0.9%	1,422
12/14	7,359	52	0.7%	1,471
Annual Growth	**16.9%**	**29.1%**	**—**	**2.3%**

2018 Year-End Financials

Debt ratio: 4.86%	No. of shares (mil.): 65
Return on equity: 9.85%	Dividends
Cash ($ mil.): 260	Yield: 3.1%
Current ratio: —	Payout: 39.6%
Long-term debt ($ mil.): —	Market value ($ mil.): 1,863

	STOCK PRICE ($) FY Close	P/E High/Low	PER SHARE ($) Earnings	Dividends	Book Value
12/18	28.23	19 12	2.22	0.88	29.17
12/17	36.17	23 18	1.67	0.81	23.92
12/16	35.74	21 12	1.77	0.77	22.95
12/15	25.24	18 13	1.49	0.68	22.23
12/14	24.08	23 19	1.14	0.58	21.66
Annual Growth	**4.1%**	**— —**	**18.1%**	**11.0%**	**7.7%**

AURORA HEALTH CARE, INC.

EXECUTIVES

Innovation Manager, Moiz Dawoodbhai
Executive Assistant Chief of S, Zoemy Soto
Staff, Andy Monfre
Internal Medicine, Charles Brummitt
Supervisor, David Krum
Purchasing Account Manager Sou, Dennis Monahan
Research Associate, Lynn Erickson
Strategic Project Manager, Marian Tate
Human Resources Generalist, Mary Miller
Internist, Amy M Wachowiak
Treasurer, Thomas Komula
Auditors: DELOITTE & TOUCHE LLP MILWAUK

LOCATIONS

HQ: AURORA HEALTH CARE, INC.
750 W VIRGINIA ST, MILWAUKEE, WI 532041539
Phone: 800 326-2250
Web: WWW.AURORAHEALTHCARE.ORG

HISTORICAL FINANCIALS
Company Type: Private

Income Statement · FYE: December 31

	REVENUE ($ mil.)	NET INCOME ($ mil.)	NET PROFIT MARGIN	EMPLOYEES
12/17	5,334	437	8.2%	30,000
12/16	5,124	385	7.5%	—
12/15	4,930	428	8.7%	—
Annual Growth	**4.0%**	**1.1%**		

Autoliv Inc

The world's #1 manufacturer of car safety equipment Autoliv aims to save lives by increasing the survivability statistics of traffic accidents. It makes components such as seat belts airbags anti-whiplash systems and safety electronics. Other products include rollover protection systems steering wheels (with airbags) night vision systems radar systems and child seats. The company caters to about every car maker in the industry and has more than 100 locations around the globe. Car making giant GM Renault/Nissan is one of its largest customers. Autoliv was established in 1956.

Operations

Autoliv operates through two business segments: passive safety (75% of net sales; airbags and seatbelts) and electronics (25%; electronics and active safety). By product airbags account for around half of Autoliv's total revenue seatbelts 25% passive safety electronics 10% active safety products 5% and brake control systems 5%.

Geographic Reach

Autoliv has about 20 crash test tracks more than 20 technical centers and about 80 production facilities in more than 25 countries. Its US operations are overseen by Autoliv ASP Inc. Its revenue is well diversified geographically taking in broadly comparable amounts from its three regions. The Asia/Pacific region is the largest at more than 35% of sales while and the Americas and Europe regions both generate more than 30%.

Sales and Marketing

Autoliv is dependent on a small number of global automakers. Autoliv's top five customers account for more than half of total company sales and the ten largest 80%. Its largest customers are Renault/Nissan Honda Ford and Hyundai/Kia. Other customers include BWM Mercedes Volvo Volkswagen Toyota FCA PSA Group and Great Wall Motors.

Autoliv has a market share in the passive safety sector of around 40%

Financial Performance

Aside from a small dip in 2015 Autoliv has posted consistent revenue growth in recent years fueled by expanding global light-vehicle production (particularly in China) as well as acquisitions. On the flip side Autoliv has struggled to attain meaningful profit growth.

In fiscal 2017 sales grew 3% to $10.4 billion as higher global light vehicle production drove passive safety equipment growth. Seatbelt sales grew 5% and airbags 2%. In the Electronics segment brake control systems grew strongly thanks to demand for automotive radars cameras with driver assist systems and ADAS-ECU (driver assistance software) while restraint control systems faltered amid lower demand from North America Japan and South Korea. By geography Autolive grew everywhere except the Americas which shrank by 4% as GM (General Motors) shifted to a new vehicle platform.

Net income fell 26% to $427 million as goodwill impairments worth $234 million capacity optimization initiatives (costing $26 million) antitrust matters ($18 million) and business segment separation ($9 million) weighed on operating margins.

Cash inflow from operations increased 8% to $936 reflecting higher growth in the underlying business.

Strategy

Autoliv's growth strategy is based on geographical and technological developments. European Union road-fatality reduction targets are encouraging automakers to find new ways to improve car safety. With physical systems (airbags chassis design seatbelts) reaching a high level of sophistication automakers are looking to new technologies such as on-board sensors to reduce the frequency and impact of accidents further. In response to this demand-driver Autoliv increased its R&D spend in electronics and passive safety from $524 million in 2015 to $741 million in 2017 or in relative terms from 5.7% of total sales to 7.1%. As a result order intake for Active Safety products grew by 300% to $1.6 billion in 2017 while lifetime electronics order intake increased from $1.1 billion in 2015 to $4.0 billion in 2017.

Autoliv is developing its presence in autonomous driving and driver assistance via a joint venture named Zenuity with Volvo. It has also form partnerships with Seeing Machines for driver mon-itoring systems Velodyne for LiDAR solutions and NVIDA (with Zenuity) for AI computing systems.

Given the different skills and pace of technology advancement Autoliv plans to spin off its Electronics business in 2018.

The company also seeks to maintain balance between its three primary geographies although rapid growth in China made the Asia/Pacific region Autoliv's largest geography. It achieved balance by making timely investments and strengthening its technical and support capabilities. It has made substantial investments in its manufacturing capabilities in China and Japan.

Mergers and Acquisitions

Autoliv is focused on acquisitions in two key areas: active safety systems and growth markets.

In November 2017 Autoliv completed the $16.9 million acquisition of Fotonic i Norden (Fotonic) headquartered in Stockholm and Skellefte in Sweden.

In 2016 the company acquired a 51% interest in the entities that formed Autoliv-Nissin Brake Systems (ANBS) for approximately $263 million in cash. ANBS designs manufactures and sells products in the brake control and actuation systems business. Nissin Kogyo retained a 49% interest in ANBS.

HISTORY

Autoliv traces its origins back to 1956 when Autoliv AB a Swedish corporation pioneered automotive seat belt technology. By 1967 the company had invented the retractor belt. Granges Weda AB another maker of seat belt retractors acquired the company in 1975. Electrolux bought the Granges Group (later renamed SAPA) in 1989 and changed its name to Electrolux Autoliv. Throughout the 1980s and 1990s the company continued to grow through acquisitions buying seat belt manufacturing operations primarily in Europe but also in Australia and New Zealand. In 1994 the company changed its name to Autoliv AB and went public with Electrolux selling all its shares during the offering.

EXECUTIVES

Chairman President And Ceo, Jan Carlson, age 59, $1,376,766 total compensation
Cto, Steven (Steve) Fredin, age 57, $578,240 total compensation
President Passive Safety, Mikael Bratt, age 52
Group Vp Research And Development And Cto, Johan L ¶fvenholm, age 50
Group Vp Finance And Cfo, Mats Backman, age 51, $381,074 total compensation
China Vice President Quality, Jesse Crookston
Vice President Global Business Unit, Walter Guertler
Vice President Manufacturing, Shigetoh Masashi
Vp Passive Safety, Stephanie Jett
Treasurer, Thomas Williams
Auditors: Ernst & Young AB

LOCATIONS

HQ: Autoliv Inc
  Klarabergsviadukten 70, Section B7, Stockholm SE-111 64
Phone: (46) 8 587 20 600
Web: www.autoliv.com

2016 Sales

	$ mil.	% of total
Asia		
China	1,766	18
Japan	949	9
Rest of Asia	901	9
Americas	3,380	34
Europe	3,075	30
Total	**10,073**	**100**

PRODUCTS/OPERATIONS

2017 Sales

	$ mil.	% of total
Passive Safety	8,134	78
Electronics	2,322	22
Corporate and other	5	-
Inter-segment sales	(66.6)	-
Total	**10,382**	**100**

2017 Sales

	$ mil.	% of total
Asia		
China	1,839	18
Japan	1,040	10
Rest of Asia	965	9
Americas	3,247	31
Europe	3,290	32
Total	**10,382**	**100**

Selected Products

Anti-whiplash seats
Child restraints
Electronics
Frontal airbags
Inflators
Leg airbags
Seat belts
Side-impact airbags
Steering wheels

Selected Subsidiaries and Affiliates

Airbags International Ltd (UK)
Autoflator AB
Autoliv AB
Autoliv Argentina SA
Autoliv ASP BV (The Netherlands)
Autoliv ASP Inc. (US)
Autoliv Australia Proprietary Ltd
Autoliv Autosicherheitstechnik GmbH (Germany)
Autoliv BKI SA (Spain)
Autoliv BV (The Netherlands)
Autoliv Canada Inc
Autoliv Cankor Otomotiv Emniyet Sistemleri Sanayi Ve (Turkey)
Autoliv China Electronics Co. Ltd
Autoliv do Brasil Ltda.
Autoliv East Europe AB
Autoliv Electronics AB
Autoliv Electronics SAS (France)
Autoliv France SNC
Autoliv Holding BV (The Netherlands)
Autoliv Holding Inc. (US)
Autoliv Holding Ltd. (UK)
Autoliv Italia S.P.A.
Autoliv Japan Ltd
Autoliv KFT (Hungary)
Autoliv KLE SAU (Spain)
Autoliv Ltd (UK)
Autoliv Nichiyo Co. (Japan)
Autoliv Overseas BV (The Netherlands)
Autoliv Poland Sp zoo
Autoliv Romania SA
Autoliv Safety Technology Inc. (US)
Autoliv Sicherheitstechnik GmbH (Germany)
Autoliv Southern Africa Pty Ltd
Autoliv Stakupress GmbH (Germany)
Autoliv Sverige AB
Autoliv Thailand Ltd
Autoliv UK Holding Ltd
Marling BV (The Netherlands)
Mei-An Autoliv Co. (59% Taiwan)
Nanjing Hongguang Autoliv Vehicle Safety Co. Ltd. (50% China)
NSK Safety Technology (Thailand) Co. Ltd.
OEA Inc. (US)
Svensk Airbag AB
Van Oerle Alberton BV (The Netherlands)
Van Oerle Alberton Holding BV (The Netherlands)
Van Oerle Webco Pty Ltd (Australia)

COMPETITORS

AISIN World Corp.	Key Safety Systems
ASHIMORI INDUSTRY CO. LTD.	Kongsberg Automotive
	Magna International
Autocam	Mitsubishi Electric
Bosch Corp.	NFA
CASCO Products	Neaton Auto Products

DENSO
Delphi Automotive
  Systems
Ensign-Bickford
Gentex
Hella
Honeywell
  International
International Textile
  Group
Nihon Plast
Nippon Kayaku
Sequa
Special Devices
Toyoda Gosei
Toyota Boshoku
Valeo

HISTORICAL FINANCIALS

Company Type: Public

Income Statement				FYE: December 31
	REVENUE ($ mil.)	NET INCOME ($ mil.)	NET PROFIT MARGIN	EMPLOYEES
12/18	8,678	190	2.2%	67,000
12/17	10,382	427	4.1%	72,000
12/16	10,073	567	5.6%	70,300
12/15	9,169	456	5.0%	64,100
12/14	9,240	467	5.1%	60,000
Annual Growth	(1.6%)	(20.1%)	—	2.8%

2018 Year-End Financials

Debt ratio: 33.17%
Return on equity: 6.43%
Cash ($ mil.): 615
Current ratio: 1.15
Long-term debt ($ mil.): 1,609

No. of shares (mil.): 87
Dividends
  Yield: 3.5%
  Payout: 112.8%
Market value ($ mil.): 6,120

	STOCK PRICE ($) FY Close	P/E High/Low	PER SHARE ($) Earnings	Dividends	Book Value
12/18	70.23	73 32	2.18	2.46	21.62
12/17	127.08	27 20	4.87	2.38	46.39
12/16	113.15	20 15	6.42	2.30	41.68
12/15	124.77	25 19	5.17	2.22	39.22
12/14	106.12	21 17	5.06	2.12	38.63
Annual Growth	(9.8%)	—	(19.0%)	3.8%	(13.5%)

Automatic Data Processing Inc.

EXECUTIVES

Chb, John P Jones
Pres-Ceo*, Carlos A Rodriguez
Cfo, Jan Siegmund
Cto, Dermot J O'Brien
Chief Hr Officer, Sreeni Kutam
Cao-Corp Contrl, Brock Albinson
Corp V Pres-General Counsel-SE, Michael A Bonarti
Technology Consultant, Anthony Condegni
Senior Director Middleware Eng, Gary Ward
Senior Infrastructu, Hari Kalavakuri
Technologies Consultant I, Hugo Britto
Auditors: DELOITTE & TOUCHE LLP

LOCATIONS

HQ: Automatic Data Processing Inc.
One ADP Boulevard, Roseland, NJ 07068
Phone: 973 974-5000   **Fax:** 973 974-5390
Web: www.adp.com

COMPETITORS

Avatar Systems
CBIZ
Ceridian
Computer Sciences
  Corp.
Enertia Software
Global Payments
HP Enterprise Services
Insperity
Intuit
Oasis Outsourcing
Paychex
Reynolds and Reynolds
Total System Services
TriNet Group
Ultimate Software

HISTORICAL FINANCIALS

Company Type: Public

Income Statement				FYE: June 30
	REVENUE ($ mil.)	NET INCOME ($ mil.)	NET PROFIT MARGIN	EMPLOYEES
06/19	14,175	2,292	16.2%	58,000
06/18	13,325	1,620	12.2%	57,000
06/17	12,379	1,733	14.0%	58,000
06/16	11,667	1,492	12.8%	57,000
06/15	10,938	1,452	13.3%	55,000
Annual Growth	6.7%	12.1%	—	1.3%

2019 Year-End Financials

Debt ratio: 4.78%
Return on equity: 51.76%
Cash ($ mil.): 1,949
Current ratio: 1.05
Long-term debt ($ mil.): 2,002

No. of shares (mil.): 434
Dividends
  Yield: 0.0%
  Payout: 58.4%
Market value ($ mil.): 71,786

	STOCK PRICE ($) FY Close	P/E High/Low	PER SHARE ($) Earnings	Dividends	Book Value
06/19	165.33	32 23	5.24	3.06	12.44
06/18	134.14	38 28	3.66	2.52	7.88
06/17	102.46	27 22	3.85	2.24	8.94
06/16	91.87	28 22	3.25	2.08	9.83
06/15	80.23	29 23	3.05	1.95	10.31
Annual Growth	19.8%	—	14.5%	11.9%	4.8%

AutoNation, Inc.

AutoNation wants to instill patriotic fervor in the fickle car-buying public. The brainchild of entrepreneur Wayne Huizenga (Waste Management Blockbuster) AutoNation is the #1 auto dealer in the US (ahead of Penske Automotive Group and Sonic Automotive). The firm owns more than 370 new-vehicle franchises in 15 states and it conducts online sales through AutoNation.com and individual dealer websites. It sells 35 new brands of new vehicles. AutoNation acquires local retail brands and transitions them to the AutoNation name. In addition to auto sales AutoNation provides maintenance and repair services sells auto parts and finances and insures vehicles which together account for the majority of profits.

Operations

AutoNation divides the vehicle market into three segments: Domestic Import and Premium Luxury all of which generate around a third of sales each. Imports accounts for more than 35% of sales while Domestic brands represent more than 30%. Its core brands of new vehicles include Toyota Ford Honda Nissan and General Motors.

The Premium Luxury Segment which sells new vehicles manufactured primarily by Mercedes-Benz BMW and Lexus contributes more than 30% of AutoNation's sales.

Geographic Reach

AutoNation has more than 370 new-vehicle franchises in +15 US states. Florida Texas and California are its largest markets accounting for 26% 21% and 17% respectively .

Sales and Marketing

AutoNation sells vehicles through its online website and its stores.

Financial Performance

The company has reported an upward trend in revenues since 2011.

In fiscal 2016 sales increased a further 4% to $21.6 billion on the back of growth in all product categories including $260.8 million growth in new vehicle sales and $226.6 million growth in used vehicle sales. Growth in new car sales primarily came from contributions from acquired businesses; same store sales declined 3% due to lower unit sales partially offset by a shift towards higher-value vehicles such as trucks and sports utility vehicles.

Net income fell 3% to $430.5 million due to disruptive manufacturer marketing and a more competitive automotive retail environment.

Cash from operations increased 2% to $516.0 million due to a decrease in working capital requirements partially offset by a decrease in earnings.

Strategy

The auto dealer is banking on the caché of the AutoNation name to win sales and market share.

The company has invested and will continue to invest significantly in the AutoNation retail brand with the goals of enhancing its strong customer satisfaction and expanding its market share. It continues to make significant investments to build a seamless end-to-end customer experience in its stores and through its digital channels and to improve its ability to generate business through those channels.

A key element of the firm's business strategy is its diversified portfolio of 30-plus brands spanning imports premium luxury vehicles and domestic autos. Over the past decade AutoNation has increased the percentage of import and luxury cars it sells. It clusters dealerships within markets so that they can share inventory cross-sell to customers and reduce marketing costs — basically cutting and combining costs in an attempt to become the auto industry's Wal-Mart. As the economy improves AutoNation is looking for acquisition and new store opportunities.

In 2016 the company purchased 20 stores in Texas New York Colorado California and Maryland. It sold five Domestic stores and nine Import stores in the same year.

Hoping to capitalize on the possible takeover of self-driving cars in 2017 AutoNation signed a repair contract with Alphabet's self-drive unit Waymo. It will maintain and repair Waymo's Chrysler Pacific hybrid fleet as well as other brands that Waymo may develop in the future.

Mergers and Acquisitions

Historically AutoNation has been a driving force in the consolidation of the US car sales business. After an hiatus during the recession and credit crunch which put the brakes on acquisitions by mega dealers such as AutoNation the company is back in acquisition mode buying up around 20 stores and franchises each year.

In 2016 it acquired 20 stores in Texas New York Colorado California and Maryland. The acquisitions include Chrysler Dodge Jeep Ram Chevrolet Hyundai Mercedes-Benz Sprinter Jaguar Land Rover and BMW franchises.

HISTORY

AutoNation started in 1980 as Republic Resources which brokered petroleum leases did exploration and production and blended lubricants.

In 1989 after oil prices crashed and a stockholder group tried to force Republic into liquidation Browning-Ferris Industries (BFI) founder Thomas Fatjo gained control of the company and refocused it on a field he knew well — solid waste. He renamed the firm Republic Waste.

Michael DeGroote founder of BFI rival Laidlaw bought into Republic in 1990. (Fatjo left the next year.) DeGroote's investment funded more acquisitions. Republic moved into hazardous waste in 1992 just before the industry nosedived due to stringent new environmental rules. In 1994 Republic spun off its hazardous-waste operations as Republic Environmental Systems and Republic's stock began rising immediately.

That attracted the attention of Wayne Huizenga who had founded Waste Management and Blockbuster Video. To him Republic was not merely a midsized solid-waste firm. No Huizenga saw Republic as a publicly traded vehicle that could allow him to tap into the stock market to fund his latest project: an integrated nationwide auto dealer — a first for the highly fragmented and localized industry.

In 1995 Republic bought Hudson Management a trash business owned by Huizenga's brother-in-law and Huizenga bought a large interest in Republic. As a result Huizenga took control of Republic's board. The firm became Republic Industries and DeGroote stepped back from active management.

Huizenga's investment helped Republic acquire more waste businesses and his name brought a flood of new investors. The firm diversified with electronic security acquisitions but growth in this field faltered with a failed bid to buy market leader ADT in 1996. (Republic sold its security division to Ameritech in 1997.)

By 1996 Huizenga's still-separate auto concept AutoNation was operational with 55 automobile franchises and seven used-car stores. Republic bought Alamo Rent A Car and National Car Rental System and in 1997 AutoNation was bought by Republic. The combined company continued buying dealerships and car rental firms at a sizzling rate.

Republic spun off its solid-waste operations to the public in 1998 as Republic Services. That year Republic bought or agreed to buy 181 new-car franchises opened nine AutoNation USA dealerships and opened 62 CarTemps USA insurance-replacement locations.

Republic became AutoNation in 1999.

Having survived a market downturn in the late 2000s in 2013 the company began marketing its domestic and import stores under the AutoNation retail brand. The re-branding of the stores which previously operated under various local market retail brands (including Mike Shad in Jacksonville Florida and GO in Colorado) was completed that year. (The exception is the company's luxury dealership business which will continue to operate under their existing retail brands.) Using its website store signage and media presence the car dealer is working to increase consumer awareness of the AutoNation brand.

In 2013 the company acquired 12 franchises.

EXECUTIVES

Executive Vice President Secretary And General Counsel, Jonathan Ferrando
Chairman And Ceo, Michael J. (Mike) Jackson, age 71, $1,250,000 total compensation
Evp And Chief Marketing Officer, Marc Cannon, age 57
Evp And Cfo, Cheryl Miller, age 46, $596,875 total compensation
Evp Franchise Operations Mergers & Acquisitions And Corporate Real Estate, Donna Parlapiano, age 54, $532,084 total compensation
Evp General Counsel And Corporate Secretary, Coleman Edmunds
President Eastern Region, Jim Bender
Evp And Cto, Thomas M. (Tom) Conophy, age 58
President Western Region, Lance Iserman
President Central Region, Ron Ardisonne
Svp, Scott Arnold
Board Member, Alison Rosenthal
Board Member, Kaveh Khosrowshahi
Board Member, Tomago Collins
Auditors: KPMG LLP

LOCATIONS

HQ: AutoNation, Inc.
  200 SW 1st Avenue, Fort Lauderdale, FL 33301
Phone: 954 769-6000
Web: www.autonation.com

2017 Stores

	No.
Florida	5
Texas	47
California	39
Georgia	23
Colorado	15
Washington	16
Arizona	14
Nevada	11
Tennessee	8
Maryland	7
Illinois	7
Alabama	5
Ohio	4
New York	4
Virginia	2
Minnesota	1
Total	**253**

PRODUCTS/OPERATIONS

2017 Sales

	$ mil.	% of total
New vehicle	12,180	57
Used vehicle	4,878	23
Parts & services	3,398	16
Finance & insurance	939	4
Other	137	-
Total	**21**	**100**

2017 Sales

	$ mil.	% of total
Domestic	7,452	35
Import	6,873	32
Premium Luxury	6,832	32
Corporate & other	375	1
Total	**21,534**	**100**

COMPETITORS

Asbury Automotive	JM Family Enterprises
Brown Automotive	Lithia Motors
CarMax	Penske Automotive
Ed Morse Auto	Group
Group 1 Automotive	Potamkin Automotive
Hendrick Automotive	Sonic Automotive
Holman Enterprises	

HISTORICAL FINANCIALS

Company Type: Public

Income Statement

FYE: December 31

	REVENUE ($ mil.)	NET INCOME ($ mil.)	NET PROFIT MARGIN	EMPLOYEES
12/18	21,412	396	1.8%	26,000
12/17	21,534	434	2.0%	26,000
12/16	21,609	430	2.0%	26,000
12/15	20,862	442	2.1%	26,000
12/14	19,108	418	2.2%	24,000
Annual Growth	**2.9%**	**(1.4%)**	**—**	**2.0%**

2018 Year-End Financials

Debt ratio: 24.38%
Return on equity: 15.57%
Cash ($ mil.): 48
Current ratio: 0.86
Long-term debt ($ mil.): 1,926

No. of shares (mil.): 90
Dividends
  Yield: —
  Payout: —
Market value ($ mil.): 3,214

	STOCK PRICE ($) FY Close	P/E High/Low		PER SHARE ($) Earnings	Dividends	Book Value
12/18	35.70	14	8	4.34	0.00	30.17
12/17	51.33	13	9	4.43	0.00	25.88
12/16	48.65	14	10	4.15	0.00	22.95
12/15	59.66	17	14	3.89	0.00	21.20
12/14	60.41	17	13	3.52	0.00	18.29
Annual Growth	**(12.3%)**	**—**	**—**	**5.4%**	**—**	**13.3%**

AutoZone, Inc.

With more than 5600 stores in the US and Puerto Rico AutoZone is one of the nation's leading auto parts chains. It also has more than 550 stores in Mexico and about two dozen in Brazil. AutoZone stores sell hard parts (alternators engines batteries) maintenance items (oil antifreeze) accessories (car stereos floor mats) and non-automotive merchandise under brand names and private labels. AutoZone's commercial sales program distributes parts and other products to garages dealerships and other businesses. The company operates an electronic parts catalog Z-net that provide a wide range of information on parts for employees and customers.

Operations

AutoZone operates through one primary segment Auto Parts Stores which accounts for more than 95% of revenue. Leveraging a consistent store format each AutoZone store boasts between 85% and 90% of selling space — up to 40% to 45% of which is dedicated to hard parts inventory. Stores are outfitted with Z-net AutoZone's proprietary electronic catalog that gives employees advice and information for customers' vehicles down to the year make model and engine type.

Other revenue is generated by e-commerce operations (autozone.com and autoanything.com) and diagnostic and other software (provided through the company's ALLDATA business) used in automotive repair. The company also has a smartphone app through which customers can find and buy parts.

One class of similar products accounted for about an eighth of AutoZone's sales and it depends on one vendor for about 12 percent of its purchases.

Geographic Reach

Based in Tennessee AutoZone operates about 5600 AutoZone stores in the 50 US states the District of Columbia and Puerto Rico. Texas California Florida Ohio and Illinois are the company's largest markets and together account for more than a third of locations. The company's fast-growing subsidiary in Mexico AutoZone de México operates more than 560 stores. AutoZone also has stores in Brazil.

AutoZone has distribution centers in the US (Arizona California Georgia Illinois Ohio Pennsylvania Tennessee Texas and Washington) and Mexico; store support centers are in Tennessee as well as Mexico and Brazil. In addition the company has operations in China which support the sourcing efforts in Asia.

Sales and Marketing

AutoZone sells to do-it-yourself (DIY) consumers as well as repair garages dealers service stations and other commercial customers.

The company relies on targeted advertising and promotions to build its brand offer advice about the overall importance of vehicle maintenance and position its business as a great value. To drive traffic to its stores the retailer advertises on broadcast and Internet media. It works to educate consumers about which products they need through use of in-store signage and circulars as well as creative product placement and promotions.

Advertising expense for the company runs about $95 million a year.

Financial Performance

New locations drive revenue growth for AutoZone which has seen an average revenue increase of 5% per year since 2012 (similar to the 4% average location increase over the same period). Net income has also ticked up consistently since 2012 as the company keeps its net profit margin between 11%-12%.

In 2018 (ended August) the company reported revenue of $11.2 billion a company record and a 3.1% increase from $10.9 billion in 2017. New stores in the US provided $196.5 million while domestic same store sales rose about 2%. Domestic commercial sales increased $151.4 million about 7% year-to-year while auto parts sales rose 4% in 2018 from 2017 throughout the company.

AutoZone's net income increased 4% to about $1.3 billion in 2018 from 2017 boosted by a lower income tax bill due to the US Tax Cuts and Jobs Act. The company's net profit margin climbed to 12% in 2018 its highest in at least five years.

Cash at the end of 2018 was $218 million a decrease of about $75 million from the prior year. Cash from operations contributed $2.1 billion to the coffers while investing activities used about $522 million with increases the result of new distribution centers and additional investment in existing locations. Financing activities subtracted about $1.6 billion as AutoZone repaid about $250 million in debt and purchased about $1.6 billion in treasuries.

Strategy

AutoZone's core strategy includes expanding its store network and store inventory to meet customer needs. It added about 200 stores (net of closings) in fiscal 2018 (on top of 215 in 2017 and 205 in 2016) and is focusing on new-store development while also enhancing its existing stores and infrastructure. Nearly 50 of the new stores in 2018 were opened in Mexico and Brazil. The company also opened a distribution center in 2018.

With an eye on expanding inventory AutoZone is focused on hub and mega hub locations which offer inventory two to four times broader than typical stores. In 2018 it opened five hub stores for a total of nearly 195 and eight mega hub locations bringing that total to about 25. The company plans to have a total of 40 mega hub stores in operation over the next few years.

While AutoZone directly imports between 10% and 15% of parts many of its domestic vendors get supplies from overseas making the company subject to tariffs and other complications from international trade tensions.

Company Background

Joseph "Pitt" Hyde took over the family grocery wholesale business Malone & Hyde (established 1907) in 1968. He expanded into specialty retailing opening drugstores sporting goods stores and supermarkets but his fortunes began to race on Independence Day 1979 when he opened his first Auto Shack auto parts store in Forrest City Arkansas.

Using retailing behemoth Wal-Mart as a model Hyde concentrated on smaller markets in the South and Southeast emphasizing everyday low prices and centralized distribution operations. He stressed customer service to provide his do-it-yourself customers with expert advice on choosing parts. While a number of retailers have tried to copy Wal-Mart's successful model Hyde had an inside track: Before starting Auto Shack he served on Wal-Mart's board for seven years.

Auto Shack had expanded into seven states by 1980 and by 1983 it had 129 stores in 10 states. The next year Malone & Hyde's senior management with investment firm Kohlberg Kravis Roberts (KKR) took the company private in an LBO. Auto Shack continued to expand reaching 192 stores in 1984. The company was spun off to Malone & Hyde's shareholders in 1987 and Malone & Hyde's other operations were sold. The company changed its name to AutoZone in 1987 in part to settle a lawsuit with RadioShack.

To build its online presence AutoZone in 2013 acquired AutoAnything an online retailer of specialized automotive products.

HISTORY

Joseph "Pitt" Hyde took over the family grocery wholesale business Malone & Hyde (established 1907) in 1968. He expanded into specialty retailing opening drugstores sporting goods stores and supermarkets but his fortunes began to race on Independence Day 1979 when he opened his first Auto Shack auto parts store in Forrest City Arkansas.

Using retailing behemoth Wal-Mart as a model Hyde concentrated on smaller markets in the South and Southeast emphasizing everyday low prices and centralized distribution operations. He stressed customer service to provide his do-it-yourself customers with expert advice on choosing parts. While a number of retailers have tried to copy Wal-Mart's successful model Hyde had an inside track: Before starting Auto Shack he served on Wal-Mart's board for seven years.

Auto Shack had expanded into seven states by 1980 and by 1983 it had 129 stores in 10 states. The next year Malone & Hyde's senior management with investment firm Kohlberg Kravis Roberts (KKR) took the company private in an LBO. Auto Shack continued to expand reaching 192 stores in 1984. The company was spun off to Malone & Hyde's shareholders in 1987 and Malone & Hyde's other operations were sold. The company changed its name to AutoZone in 1987 in part to settle a lawsuit with RadioShack.

To build its online presence AutoZone in 2013 acquired AutoAnything an online retailer of specialized automotive products.

EXECUTIVES

Evp Finance Information Technology And Alldata And Cfo, William T. (Bill) Giles, age 60, $560,539 total compensation

Chairman President And Ceo, William C. (Bill) Rhodes, age 54, $1,000,000 total compensation

Svp Commercial, Larry M. Roesel, age 62, $425,308 total compensation

Svp Merchandising And Store Development, Mark A. Finestone, age 58, $430,154 total compensation

Evp Mexico Brazil Imc And Store Development, William W. Graves, age 59, $430,154 total compensation

Evp Store Operations Commercial And Loss Prevention, Thomas B. Newbern, age 57, $430,154 total compensation

Svp And Cio, Ronald B. (Ron) Griffin, age 66, $407,692 total compensation

Svp Marketing And E-commerce, Albert (Al) Saltiel, age 56

Svp General Counsel And Secretary, Kristen Wright

Vp It, Tony Dudek

Vice President Assistant General Counsel And Assistant Secretary, Maria Leggett

Information Technology Vice President, Jeff Nix

Vice President Merchandising, Bill Edwards

National Account Manager, Lee Fitts

Vice President Merchandising, John Lammers

Auditors: Ernst & Young LLP

LOCATIONS

HQ: AutoZone, Inc.
123 South Front Street, Memphis, TN 38103
Phone: 901 495-6500
Web: www.autozone.com

2018 Stores

	No.
US	5,618
Mexico	564
Brazil	20
Total	**6,202**

PRODUCTS/OPERATIONS

2018 Sales

	$ mil.	% of total
Auto Parts Locations	10,951	98
Other	269	2
Total	**11,221**	**100**

Selected Merchandise

Accessories
  Car stereos
  Floor mats
  Lights
  Mirrors
Hard Parts
  Alternators
  Batteries
  Brake shoes and pads
  Carburetors
  Clutches
  Engines
  Spark plugs
  Starters
  Struts
  Water pumps
Maintenance Items
  Antifreeze
  Brake fluid
  Engine additives
  Oil
  Power steering fluid
  Transmission fluid
  Waxes
  Windshield wipers
Other
  Air fresheners
  Dent filler
  Hand cleaner
  Paint
  Repair manuals
  Tools

Selected Brands
ALLDATA
AutoZone
Duralast
Duralast Gold
ProElite
SureBilt
Valucraft

COMPETITORS

Advance Auto Parts
Amazon.com
CARQUEST
Costco Wholesale
Fisher Auto Parts
Genuine Parts

Goodyear Tire & Rubber
O'Reilly Automotive
Pep Boys
Sears Holdings
Target Corporation
Wal-Mart

HISTORICAL FINANCIALS
Company Type: Public

Income Statement
FYE: August 31

	REVENUE ($ mil.)	NET INCOME ($ mil.)	NET PROFIT MARGIN	EMPLOYEES
08/19	11,863	1,617	13.6%	96,000
08/18	11,221	1,337	11.9%	90,000
08/17	10,888	1,280	11.8%	87,000
08/16	10,635	1,241	11.7%	84,000
08/15	10,187	1,160	11.4%	81,000
Annual Growth	3.9%	8.7%	—	4.3%

2019 Year-End Financials

Debt ratio: 53.18%
Return on equity: ***.***.**%
Cash ($ mil.): 176
Current ratio: 0.91
Long-term debt ($ mil.): 5,206

No. of shares (mil.): 24
Dividends
Yield: —
Payout: —
Market value ($ mil.): 26,482

	STOCK PRICE ($) FY Close	P/E High/Low		PER SHARE ($) Earnings	Dividends	Book Value
08/19	1,101.69	18	11	63.43	0.00	(71.30)
08/18	770.52	16	11	48.77	0.00	(59.06)
08/17	528.95	18	11	44.07	0.00	(51.32)
08/16	753.47	20	17	40.70	0.00	(61.39)
08/15	726.39	20	14	36.03	0.00	(55.49)
Annual Growth	11.0%	—	—	15.2%	—	—

Avangrid Inc

Auditors: KPMG LLP

LOCATIONS

HQ: Avangrid Inc
180 Marsh Hill Road, Orange, CT 06477
Phone: 207 629-1200
Web: www.avangrid.com

HISTORICAL FINANCIALS
Company Type: Public

Income Statement
FYE: December 31

	REVENUE ($ mil.)	NET INCOME ($ mil.)	NET PROFIT MARGIN	EMPLOYEES
12/18	6,478	595	9.2%	6,449
12/17	5,963	381	6.4%	6,570
12/16	6,018	630	10.5%	6,801
12/15	4,367	267	6.1%	6,809
12/14	4,594	424	9.2%	4,977
Annual Growth	9.0%	8.8%	—	6.7%

2018 Year-End Financials

Debt ratio: 19.74%
Return on equity: 3.94%
Cash ($ mil.): 36
Current ratio: 0.65
Long-term debt ($ mil.): 5,368

No. of shares (mil.): 309
Dividends
Yield: 3.4%
Payout: 90.8%
Market value ($ mil.): 15,478

	STOCK PRICE ($) FY Close	P/E High/Low		PER SHARE ($) Earnings	Dividends	Book Value
12/18	50.09	28	24	1.92	1.74	48.88
12/17	50.58	43	31	1.23	1.73	48.79
12/16	37.88	23	17	2.04	1.73	48.90
12/15	38.40	36	32	1.05	0.00	48.74
Annual Growth	6.9%	—	—	16.3%	—	0.1%

Avantor Inc

Auditors: Deloitte & Touche LLP

LOCATIONS

HQ: Avantor Inc
Radnor Corporate Center, Building One, Suite 200,
100 Matsonford Road, Radnor, PA 19087
Phone: 610 386-1700
Web: www.avantorsciences.com

HISTORICAL FINANCIALS
Company Type: Public

Income Statement
FYE: December 31

	REVENUE ($ mil.)	NET INCOME ($ mil.)	NET PROFIT MARGIN	EMPLOYEES
12/18	5,864	(86)	—	12,000
12/17	1,247	(112)	—	
12/16	691	(42)	—	
Annual Growth	191.3%	—	—	—

2018 Year-End Financials

Debt ratio: 69.86%
Return on equity: (-9.78%)
Cash ($ mil.): 184
Current ratio: 1.73
Long-term debt ($ mil.): 6,782

No. of shares (mil.): 132
Dividends
Yield: —
Payout: —
Market value ($ mil.): —

	STOCK PRICE ($) FY Close	P/E High/Low		PER SHARE ($) Earnings	Dividends	Book Value
12/18	0.00	—	—	(2.69)	0.00	6.08
12/17	0.00	—	—	(2.75)	0.00	7.31
Annual Growth	—	—	—	—	—	(8.8%)

Avery Dennison Corp

Avery Dennison has worked out how to make the most of a sticky situation. The company is a world-leader in sticky labels used by businesses to add their branding to products such as drinks food personal care items and pharmaceuticals. It also makes RFID tags for individual products. Its adhesives extend to vinyl wraps and specialty materials designed for digital imaging screen printing and sign-cutting applications. Under the Avery Dennison and Fasson brands it makes papers films and foils coated with adhesive. It also makes retail branding and security tags printer systems and fasteners as well as medical adhesive products. The California-based company gets 75% of its revenue from international customers.

Operations
Avery Dennison has three operating segments: Label and Graphic Materials (LGM) the largest at about 70% of sales; Retail Branding and Information Solutions (RBIS) which accounts for more than 20% of sales; and Industrial and Healthcare Materials (IHM) about 10% of sales.

The LGM segment makes pressure-sensitive adhesives (PSAs) which are sticky labels that are applied via pressure rather than heat or other means. Through the Fasson JAC and Avery Dennison brands the segment makes papers plastic films metal foils fabrics and specially coated backing papers and films. Other products include packaging materials roll-fed sleeves engineered films graphic imaging media and reflective materials

The RBIS segment designs manufactures and sells a variety of branding and information products and services. Branding items include creative services brand embellishments graphic tickets tags and labels and sustainable packaging. Among the RBIS products are item-level RFID tags.

The IHM segment sells branded tapes and fasteners pressure-sensitive medical devices and performance polymers.

Geographic Reach
Avery Dennison has wide geographic reach throughout its operations with about 180 manufacturing and distribution facilities in more than 50 countries and even geographic distribution of sales. The US is the company's biggest single-nation market accounting for nearly 25% of revenue. Asia is its largest regional market accounting for around 35% of revenue while Europe brings in more than 30%.

Sales and Marketing
Avery Dennison's major customers include advertising agencies distributors designers government agencies graphics vendors label converters architecture and building electronics and electrical OEMs package designers packaging engineers and manufacturers printers and sign manufacturers.

The RBIS segment sells a variety of branding and information products and services to retailers food service grocery pharmaceutical supply chains and transportation companies.

Avery Dennison also sells durable cast and reflective films to the construction automotive and fleet transportation market segments and reflective films for traffic and safety applications.

The company also sells directly and via third-party distributors and retailers.

Financial Performance
Building on two years of sales gains Avery Dennison'a revenue punched over the $7 billion mark(a company high) in 2018. The company's net income has fluctuated in recent years but it jumped to a company record in 2018.

The company's sales advanced to $7.1 billion in 2018 up about $500 million from 2017 led by high-value categories and emerging markets. The LGM segment grew about 8% despite significant raw material inflation. The RBIS segment's sales were up about 6% boosted by growth from RFID products (up 20% for the year). The IHM business posted a 17% sales increase in 2018 from 2017.

Avery Dennison delivered its highest net income of about $467 million in 2018 some $186 million more than 2017's figure. Besides higher sales the company had lower income taxes due to the US Tax Cuts and Jobs Act and a tax benefit from foreign tax planning as well as the impact of sales volume and mix.

The company's cash holdings were $232 million in 2018 compared to $224 million in 2017. Operations produced about $458 million in 2018 while investing activities used $232 million and financing activities used $208 million.

Strategy

Avery Dennison's growth strategy is based on expanding its presence in high-value and emerging markets. An example is its RFID business which has grown at a 20% rate in the past two years and the company expects that to continue for several years.

It also aims to return the IHM segment to growth and profitability by rebuilding customer relationships strengthening product pipeline and driving aggressive productivity improvements. It launched two new wound care technologies CHG (an antimicrobial agent) and TASA (Thin Absorbent Skin Adhesive).

The company's focus on emerging markets has helped drive sales in Asia particularly China. But Avery Dennison's performance in China could be affected by local economic conditions which had a negative impact in 2018 as well as US tariffs placed on goods made in China.

However acquisitions and heavy investments has presented the company with limited cash to fund new opportunities in the market or meet its short term debt obligations. Moreover Avery Dennison might be affected by a rapidly changing industry as customers move away from plastics and reduce waste in a more sustainable fashion. The company looks to build on its portfolio of sustainable products through research.

Mergers and Acquisitions

In 2017 the company acquired Yongle Tape Company for $190 million. Yongle is China's largest producer of cable harnessing and insulation tape and supplies both Chinese and global customers.

It also acquired Hanita Coatings for $75 million and Irish wound care company Finesse Medical in 2017.

HISTORY

Avery Dennison was created in 1990 by the merger of Avery International and Dennison Manufacturing. In 1935 Stanton Avery founded Kum-Kleen Products which would become Avery International. After a fire destroyed the plant's equipment in 1938 Avery who had renamed the company Avery Adhesives improved the machinery used in making the labels.

During and after WWII Avery Adhesives shifted toward the industrial market for self-adhesives. The company incorporated in 1946. At that time Avery Adhesives sold 80% of its production consisting of industrial labels to manufacturers that labeled their own products. The company lost its patent rights for self-adhesive labels in 1952 transforming the firm and the entire industry. As a result a new division was created — the Avery Paper Company (later renamed Fasson) — to produce and market self-adhesive base materials. Avery Adhesives went public in 1961.

Dennison was started in 1844 by the father-and-son team of Andrew and Aaron Dennison to produce jewelry boxes. By 1849 Aaron's younger brother Eliphalet Whorf (E.W.) was running the business and expanding it into tags labels and tissue paper. Dennison was incorporated in 1878 with $150000 in capital.

EXECUTIVES

Svp And Chief Human Resources Officer, Anne Hill, age 60, $512,787 total compensation
President Materials Group, Georges Gravanis, age 62, $523,775 total compensation

President And Ceo, Mitchell R. Butier, age 48, $988,333 total compensation
Svp And Cfo, Gregory S. (Greg) Lovins, age 46
Vp And Gm Global Commercial Retail Branding And Information Solutions, Michael Barton
Vice President Corporate Development, Stephen Keller
Vp And Assistant General Counsel Label And Graphic Materials Materials Group Graphic Solutions, Ken Schwartz
Vice President Strategy And Corporate Development, Danny Allouche
National Account Manager, Jay Siedel
Market Vice President, Gregoire Pastour
Vp Corporate Communications, Rob Six
Vice President And General Manager Label And Graphic Materials Europe, Jeroen Diderich
Vice President And General Manager Global Graphics And Reflective Solutions And Vice President Glo, Hassan Rmaile
Vp Marketing Materials Group North America, Shelley Woods
Vp Human Resources And Communications Retail Branding And Information Solutions, Deena Baker-Nel
Vice President And General Manager Emea And South Asia Region Retail Branding And Information Solut, Elif Kagitcibasi
Vice President Communications Label And Graphic Materials, Amy White
Vp Engineering Printer Solutions, Jeff Raymond
Vp Global Information Technology Label And Graphic Materials, Nathalie Haddad
Vice President Strategy And Mergers And Acquisitions, Henrik Kajueter
Vice President Human Resources, Anne Ceruti
Chairman, Dean A. Scarborough, age 64
Board Member, David Pyott
Board Member, Bradley Alford
Board Member, Julia Stewart
Board Member, Martha Sullivan
Board Member, Anthony Anderson
Board Member, Patrick Siewert
Auditors: PricewaterhouseCoopers LLP

LOCATIONS

HQ: Avery Dennison Corp
207 Goode Avenue, Glendale, CA 91203
Phone: 626 304-2000
Web: www.averydennison.com

2018 Sales

	$ mil.	% of total
Asia	2,473	35
Europe	2,251	31
US	1,625	23
Latin America	490	7
Other regions	319	4
Total	7,159	100

PRODUCTS/OPERATIONS

2018 Sales

	$ mil.	% of total
Label and Graphic Materials	4,851	68
Retail Branding and Information Solutions	1,613	22
Industrial and Healthcare Materials	694	10
Total	7,159	100

Selected Brands

Avery
Avery Dennison
Avery Graphics
Fasson

COMPETITORS

3M	LINTEC CORPORATION
Bostik	Newell Brands
Brady Corporation	Nitto Denko
Checkpoint Systems	

HISTORICAL FINANCIALS

Company Type: Public

Income Statement

FYE: December 29

	REVENUE ($ mil.)	NET INCOME ($ mil.)	NET PROFIT MARGIN	EMPLOYEES
12/18	7,159	467	6.5%	30,000
12/17	6,613	281	4.3%	30,000
12/16*	6,086	320	5.3%	—
01/16	5,966	274	4.6%	—
01/15	6,330	248	3.9%	25,000
Annual Growth	3.1%	17.1%	—	4.7%

*Fiscal year change

2018 Year-End Financials

Debt ratio: 37.98%	No. of shares (mil.): 84
Return on equity: 46.84%	Dividends
Cash ($ mil.): 232	Yield: 0.0%
Current ratio: 1.15	Payout: 38.0%
Long-term debt ($ mil.): 1,771	Market value ($ mil.): 7,526

	STOCK PRICE ($) FY Close	P/E High/Low		PER SHARE ($) Earnings	Dividends	Book Value
12/18	88.83	23	16	5.28	2.01	11.27
12/17	114.86	37	22	3.13	1.76	11.89
12/16*	70.22	22	16	3.54	1.60	10.48
01/16	62.66	22	17	2.95	1.46	10.73
01/15	51.79	20	16	2.60	1.34	11.79
Annual Growth	14.4%	—	—	19.4%	10.7%	(1.1%)

*Fiscal year change

Avis Budget Group Inc

Avis Budget Group (ABG) has a car rental brand for you. The company's core brands include: Avis Rent A Car which targets corporate and leisure travelers at the high end of the market; Budget Rent A Car and Payless Car Rental both marketed to those on a budget; and Zipcar a car-sharing service. The rental car operator operates through 5500 Avis and 4050 Budget branches across 180 countries in North America Europe Australia and New Zealand and generates nearly 70% of its revenue from its on-airport locations. Avis's Budget Truck is one of the leading truck rental businesses in the US.

HISTORY

Cendant began life through the 1997 merger of CUC International and HFS. A giant in hospitality HFS was cobbled together as Hospitality Franchise Systems by LBO specialist Blackstone Group in 1992. With brands including Days Inn Ramada and Howard Johnson HFS went public that year. In 1995 HFS bought real estate firm Century 21. The next year it added Electronic Realty Associates (ERA) and Coldwell Banker. Also in 1996 HFS acquired the Super 8 Motels brand as well as car-rental firm Avis (founded by Warren Avis in 1946 it went through a succession of owners until acquired by HFS). The next year HFS sold 75% of Avis' #1 franchisee to the public and later bought relocation service firm PHH.

In an attempt to leverage the power of his brands HFS CEO Henry Silverman began looking at direct marketing giant CUC International. CUC was founded in 1973 as Comp-U-Card America by Walter Forbes and other investors envisioning a computer-based home shopping network. During the 1980s CUC developed as a discount direct marketer and catalog-based shopping club. It went public in 1983 with 100000 members. CUC saw explosive growth as it signed up 7.6 million members between 1989 and 1993. In 1996 CUC acquired Rent Net an online apartment rental service and later bought entertainment software publishers Davidson & Associates and Sierra On-Line. In 1997 CUC bought software maker Knowledge Adventure and launched online shopping site NetMarket.

CUC and HFS completed their $14.1 billion merger in December 1997 with Silverman as CEO and Forbes as chairman. While the name Cendant was derived from "ascendant" the marriage quickly headed in the opposite direction. Accounting irregularities from before the merger that had inflated CUC's revenue and pretax profit by about $500 million were revealed in 1998. Cendant's stock price tumbled taking a $14 billion hit in one day. Forbes resigned that summer. Silverman quickly took action and began to sell off operations. Cendant Software National Leisure Group (now World Travel Holdings) National Library of Poetry and Match.com all were sold that year for a total of about $1.4 billion. The company also acquired Jackson Hewitt the US's #2 tax-preparation firm and UK-based National Parking.

Through 1999 the company continued to sell assets. Cendant sold its fleet business — including PHH Vehicle Management Services — to Avis Rent A Car for $5 billion and sold its Entertainment Publications unit the world's largest coupon book marketer and publisher to The Carlyle Group. Cendant later paid $2.8 billion in one of the largest shareholder class action lawsuit settlements. (Accounting firm Ernst & Young also settled with Cendant shareholders for $335 million.)

In 2000 Cendant introduced Move.com a relocation and real estate Internet portal. Also that year the company launched Cendant Internet Group to help cement its presence on the Web and bought the brand name and franchising rights of AmeriHost Inns from AmeriHost Properties. Later in 2000 cable programming company Liberty Media (now Liberty Interactive) invested $400 million in Cendant. The next year the company began licensing and outsourcing its Incentives and Marketing Services business (practically all of the businesses that made up the former CUC International) to Trilegiant a new company formed by the units' management.

In 2001 after selling Move.com to Homestore (later called Move) for $761 million Cendant sought to expand its travel holdings with a slew of acquisitions. Its purchases included timeshare resort firm Fairfield Communities ($690 million); travel services firm Galileo International ($2.4 billion); online travel reservation service Cheap Tickets ($425 million); and vacation timeshare marketer Equivest Finance ($100 million). In late 2001 Cendant cut some 6000 jobs to improve its bottom line and announced that during the next year or so it would cut an additional 10000 jobs and eliminate about 7% of its franchised hotels.

In 2002 the company sold its UK-based National Car Park unit which accounted for 3% of sales as part of its strategy to sell off noncore businesses. In June Cendant bought TRUST International from Bertelsmann and later that year purchased car rental company Budget Rent A Car for about $110 million then slashed costs by closing facilities and laying off more than 450 employees. The company also purchased Novasol AS which rented out private vacation homes in Northern Europe.

Cendant terminated its licensing and services agreements with Trilegiant in January 2004 and in February Sotheby's Holdings sold its 15 Sotheby's International Realty offices (along with the brand's licensing rights) to the company for about $100 million. In March Cendant's Jackson

Hewitt subsidiary filed for its IPO. In May the company purchased Dutch vacation rental company Landal Green Parks (LGP) for about $150 million. Also that month former chairman Walter Forbes and former vice chairman E. Kirk Shelton went on trial for federal fraud and conspiracy stemming from the pre-merger accounting irregularities. (Shelton was found guilty of multiple counts of fraud in early 2005.) In October CFO Ronald Nelson was named president taking over for Henry Silverman who remained chairman and CEO.

In 2004 Cendant acquired online travel firm Orbitz in a deal valued at about $1.25 billion. Quick on the heels of the Orbitz deal the company Cendant also purchased ebookers (a European online travel site now called Flightbookers) in a deal worth about $400 million and acquired two travel groups collectively known as Gullivers for about $1.1 billion.

As 2004 wound to a close Cendant completed the acquisition of the Ramada International Hotels & Resorts brand and franchising operations from Marriott International. Cendant already owned the rights to the brand and franchising operations in the US and Canada which included some 820 US properties and about 70 Canadian properties. In 2005 Cendant acquired the Wyndham hotel brand from Wyndham International Inc. for $101 million. The deal included the franchise agreements for 82 hotels and the management contracts for another 29 hotels but not the actual properties which were located in the US Mexico and the Caribbean. The next year Cendant acquired the Baymont Inn & Suites brand of limited-service midscale lodging from Blackstone's La Quinta Corporation (now LQ Management). The Baymont Inn & Suites brand covered 115 franchised properties; the properties themselves were not included in the deal.

Cendant in 2005 spun off its mortgage operations PHH Mortgage (formerly Cendant Mortgage) and fleet management (PHH Arval) businesses under the PHH Corporation umbrella. Also that year Cendant spun off Wright Express (payment processing and information services for fleet management) in an IPO and sold its marketing services division to Apollo Management for about $1.8 billion.

The divestitures that began in 2005 culminated in the unwinding of the Cendant conglomerate the next year. The company spun off its hotel and real estate operations and sold its travel services division in 2006 reconfiguring itself around its rental car businesses and renaming itself Avis Budget Group. Silverman became chairman and CEO of the company's real estate business Realogy and Nelson took over as chairman and CEO of the slimmed-down Avis Budget Group which took on its new name in September 2006.

Warren Avis the founder of Avis Rent A Car died in April 2007 at the age of 92. In October the company acquired a 48% stake in chauffeured transportation company Carey International for $60 million. (In 2009 due to losses at Carey it wrote down its investment in the company to zero.)

Avis Budget Group acquired Avis Europe plc in October 2011. The purchase followed ABG's withdrawal from its battle with rival Hertz to acquire Dollar Thrifty Automotive Group (DTG). Instead the company turned to Europe for growth by reuniting with Avis Europe which was legally separated from Avis in 1986. The deal created what ABG says is the largest publicly traded rental car business in the world.

In 2012 in continuing to bulk up its global operations after its purchase of Avis Europe ABG in 2012 acquired New Zealand's largest independently-owned car rental company Apex Car Rentals. The purchase added more than 4000 rental cars and strengthened Avis's position in New Zealand and Australia.

EXECUTIVES

President International, Mark J. Servodidio, age 54, $596,538 total compensation
Interim Cfo, Martyn R. Smith, age 64
Evp And Chief Marketing Officer, W. Scott Deaver, age 68
Ceo And Coo, Larry D. De Shon, age 60, $1,000,000 total compensation
Evp And Cio, Gerard Insall
Evp General Counsel And Chief Compliance Officer, Michael K. Tucker, age 61
President Americas, Joseph A. (Joe) Ferraro, age 62, $623,269 total compensation
Evp And Chief Human Resources Officer, Edward P. (Ned) Linnen, age 49
Evp And Chief Innovation Officer, Arthur Orduna
Vice President, Eric Schlanger
Vice President Us Sales Training, Barbara Kogen
Senior Vice President Of Fleet Services, Edward Gitlitz
Vice President Enterprise Applications, Steve Hoffman
Vice President Technical Operations Real Estate In, Jennifer Smith
Vice President Fleet Control, Neil Schamus
Vice President Human Resources, April Scavone
Vice President Tax, Izzy Martins
Vice President Information Technology, John Page
Senior Vice President, Joseph Siino
Vice President Area, Jeff Eisenbarth
Executive Vice President Strategy And Pricing, Scott Deaver
Vice President And Associate General Counsel, Rosalie Shoeman
Vice President Sales And Marketing, John Barrows
Vice President, Glenn Burke
Vice President Financial Planning And Analysis, David Crowther
Vp Shared Services Center, Larry Weinstein
Senior Vice President Global Digital Customer Experience, Neil Zamore
Vice President Supply Chain Americas, Mark Haeussler
Senior Vice President Management Information Services, Suzzane Wetherington
Vice President Fleet Services, Gregg Nierenberg
Cfo And Director, Ronald L. (Ron) Nelson, age 67
Board Member, Eduardo Mestre
Board Member, Robert Salerno
Board Member, Jeffrey Fox
Auditors: DELOITTE & TOUCHE LLP

LOCATIONS

HQ: Avis Budget Group Inc
6 Sylvan Way, Parsippany, NJ 07054
Phone: 973 496-4700
Web: www.avisbudgetgroup.com

2016 Locations

	AvisBudget	Americas
Company-operated	1,550	1,400
Licensees	700	650
International		
Company-operated	1,200	650
Licensees	2,050	1,350
Total	**5,550**	**4,050**

2016 Sales

	$ mil.	% of total
United States	5,674	66
All other countries	2,985	34
Total	**8,659**	**100**

2016 Sales

	$ mil.	% of total
Americas	6,121	71
International	2,538	29
Total	**8,659**	**100**

2016 Car Rental Sales

	% of total
On-Airport	70
Off-airport	30
Total	**100**

PRODUCTS/OPERATIONS

2016 Sales

	$ mil.	% of total
Vehicle rental	6,081	70
Others	2,578	30
Total	**8,659**	**100**

COMPETITORS

AMERCO	Penske Truck Leasing
Enterprise Rent-A-Car	Ryder System
Europcar	Sixt
Herc Holdings	

HISTORICAL FINANCIALS

Company Type: Public

Income Statement
FYE: December 31

	REVENUE ($ mil.)	NET INCOME ($ mil.)	NET PROFIT MARGIN	EMPLOYEES
12/18	9,124	165	1.8%	30,000
12/17	8,848	361	4.1%	31,000
12/16	8,659	163	1.9%	30,000
12/15	8,502	313	3.7%	30,000
12/14	8,485	245	2.9%	30,000
Annual Growth	**1.8%**	**(9.4%)**	**—**	**0.0%**

2018 Year-End Financials

Debt ratio: 71.98%
Return on equity: 33.43%
Cash ($ mil.): 615
Current ratio: 1.27
Long-term debt ($ mil.): 13,760

No. of shares (mil.): 75
Dividends
Yield: —
Payout: —
Market value ($ mil.): 1,699

	STOCK PRICE ($) FY Close	P/E High/Low	PER SHARE ($) Earnings	Dividends	Book Value
12/18	22.48	24 11	2.06	0.00	5.48
12/17	43.88	11 5	4.25	0.00	7.07
12/16	36.68	23 12	1.75	0.00	2.57
12/15	36.29	22 11	2.98	0.00	4.48
12/14	66.33	30 15	2.22	0.00	6.29
Annual Growth	**(23.7%)**	**— —**	**(1.9%)**	**—**	**(3.4%)**

Avnet Inc

If you need an electronic component Avnet probably has it. The company is one of the world's top distributors of electronic components (including connectors and semiconductors) enterprise computing and storage products and embedded subsystems with competitors Arrow Electronics and World Peace Group. It works with more than 1400 suppliers to provide some 2.1 million customers with parts and services. Customers include startups small and mid-sized businesses and big companies that produce electronics. Avnet has about 125 locations around the world and makes most of its sales to international customers. Semiconductors and related products comprise about 80% of Avnet's revenue.

Operations

Avnet is composed of two segments Electronic Components and Premier Farnell.

Electronic Components generates about 90% of revenue selling semiconductors embedded products and interconnect passive and electromechanical devices (IP&E). EC also offers design tools and engineering services to support product design as well as supply chain services to OEMs.

The Premier Farnell unit accounts for about 10% of revenue from distributing electronic components typically in small quantities primarily to support design engineers maintenance and test engineers and entrepreneurs as they develop technology products.

Additionally Avnet provides aftermarket services — from electronic product repair and refurbishment to asset recovery and reclamation — through a business unit called Avnet Integrated and it offers supply chain services including warehousing postponement and device programming through a unit called Avnet Logistics.

Geographic Reach

Avnet has a fairly even geographic spread of sales with each region contributing between about 25% to 40% of revenue. Customers in Asia account for about 40% of revenue with customers in EMEA providing about 35% and those in the Americas supplying about 25%.

Headquartered in Phoenix Arizona the company has warehousing integration operations and offices in Arizona and South Carolina in the US and overseas in Belgium Germany the UK and China.

Sales and Marketing

Avnet's customers include original equipment manufacturers electronic manufacturing services providers original design manufacturers systems integrators independent software vendors and value-added resellers.

Products from Texas Instruments account for more than 10% of Avnet's consolidated billings.

Financial Performance

Avnet's revenue fluctuated in a narrow range since 2014 before perking up in 2018 (ended June) from 2017. Sales of $19 billion in 2018 up 9% were boosted by the acquisition of Premier Farnell and the impact of foreign currency exchange rates. The Electronic Components segment's sales rose 6.5% in 2018 from higher sales in EMEA and Asia with declines in the Americas. Premier Farnell sales increased in all three regions due to the expansion of the products the segment carries and an investment in inventory to achieve a broader portfolio of products.

The company posted a net loss of $156 million in 2018 compared to net income of $525.3 million in 2017. Costs for restructuring pension payments and higher taxes in 2018 drove Avnet to the loss.

Avnet's cash and equivalents stood at $621.1 million in 2018 $215 million lower than its 2017 total. In 2018 the company generated $253 million in cash from operations and had $71.7 million from investing activities while using about $542 million in financing activities.

Strategy

As Avnet exited the technical services business with the sale of its Technology Solutions unit the company built up its digital offerings through the acquisitions of Premier Farnell MakerSource and Hackster.io. The company maintains that its digital ecosystem is one of the biggest online communities focused on delivering information and components to hardware developers. Its digital units provide information design tools support and community for the world of engineers including startups with the Hackster.io element.

To better integrate sales leads from Premier Farnell and Avnet the company is investing in advanced analytics. The company mines analytics to move highly qualified leads from the digital side to the company's marketing and sales teams so that they can offer tailored support to customers.

Operationally Avnet has reorganized its sales force in the Americas and established a program to improve HR programs compensation pricing and data analytics to increase the efficiency and effectiveness of its sales staff.

The company has taken steps to mitigate the impact of tariffs that the US has placed on good imported from China. It encourages supplies to use products not made in China when possible but 40% of its revenue is from that country.

Mergers and Acquisitions

Avnet has a strong history of using acquisitions to grow its geographic footprint across the globe. That practice continues to be a key part of its strategy today with Avnet seeking to acquire primarily smaller businesses in markets where it is trying to expand its presence or increase its scale.

In 2018 Avent bought Softweb Solutions which develops software for Internet of Things (IoT) applications. Terms were not disclosed. The deal formalizes a partnership that Avnet and Softweb have had for years adding software capabilities to the hardware that Avent sells for IoT systems.

In 2017 Avnet acquired Dragon Innovation which helps companies manage manufacturing processes with a cloud-based platform. The deal complements Avnet's digital strategy with the delivery of its services through software and access to subject matter experts matched to the customers' needs. It also adds to Avnet's design and supply chain capabilities beyond electronic components to include the finished product.

In 2016 Avnet bought Premier Farnell for about $900 million. Premier Farnell is a global distributor of electronic components and related products and should fortify Avnet's digital footprint. It offers products from companies ranging from Adam Electronics to Zeon Tech.

In November 2016 the company acquired California based Hackster Inc an online community platform which helps users globally learn how to design create and program Internet-connected hardware. The acquisition will enable company users to accelerate their hardware knowledge and time-to-market.

Company Background

Avnet got its start in 1921 when founder Charles Avnet sold parts for the new technology of the day radio. Over the years Avnet has adjusted with the times buying companies to address new markets while selling parts of the company to exit other markets.

EXECUTIVES

Vp And President Avnet Technology Solutions Emea, Graeme A. Watt
Ceo, William J. (Bill) Amelio
Svp Chief Human Resources Officer And Global Marketing And Communications, MaryAnn G. Miller, $540,000 total compensation
Svp And President Avnet Technology Solutions Global, Patrick Zammit, $488,400 total compensation
Vp And President Avnet Technology Solutions Americas, Jeff Bawol
President Avnet Electronics Marketing Americas, Chuck Delph
Cio, Kevin V. Summers
Svp And President Avnet Electronics Marketing Global, Gerald W. (Gerry) Fay, $600,000 total compensation
Svp And Chief Global Logistics And Operations Officer, Michael D. (Mike) Buseman
Vp And President Avnet Technology Solutions Asia Pacific, William Chu
Cfo, Thomas (Tom) Liguori
Vp And President Avnet Electronics Marketing Emea, Miguel Fernandez
Acting President Avnet Electronics Marketing Asia And Japan, Frederick Fu

Vice President Of Human Resources Ts Americas, Kaylene Moss
Senior Vice President And Chief People Officer, Ken Arnold
Vice President Sales, Brad Johnson
Vice President Sales And Operations, Sandra Scott
Vice President And Director Cable Assembly And Value Added Services, Jim Mooney
Vice President E Business Solutions, Michael Serago
Vice President And General Counsel, Cheree Mcalpine
Regional Vice President Of South Europe For Silica, Mario Orlandi
Senior Vice President, Dennis Losik
Vice President Of Marketing, Ivan Ho
Vice President Human Resources, Aaron Dean
Vice President Sales, Peter Rzonca
Vice President Global Operations, Derinda Ehrlich
Vice President, Ray Ramey
Vp Operations, Rich Fitzgerald
Vice President Global Program Management Office, Ellen Owens
Vice President Logistics Operations And Transportation, Lisa Kelley
Vice President Global Operations, Vincent Cellard
Vice President Sales Americas, Lou Lutostanski
Senior Vice President Global Programming Operations, Douglas Adams
Vice President Director Of Investorrelations, Vince Keenan
Vice President Global Trade Compliance, Robert Bowen
Vice President Information Systems, Bob Laurie
Senior Vice President Chief Human Resources Officer And Corporate Marketing And Communications, Maryann G Miller
Vice President Global Procurement And Administrative Services, James Azzinaro
Vice President, Philippe Fremont
Vice President Engineering And Technology, Jim Beneke
Vice President Of Global Technical Marketing, Vivian — Han
Vice President Global Contracts And Security, Joel Legin
Chairman, William H. (Bill) Schumann
Board Member, Mike Bradley
Auditors: KPMG LLP

LOCATIONS

HQ: Avnet Inc
2211 South 47th Street, Phoenix, AZ 85034
Phone: 480 643-2000
Web: www.avnet.com

2018 Sales

	$ mil.	% of total
Asia/Pacific	7,234	38
Europe Middle East and Africa	6,790	36
Americas	5,011	26
Total	**19,036**	**0**

PRODUCTS/OPERATIONS

2018 Sales by Operating Group

	$ mil.	% of total
Electronic Components	17,543	92
Premier Farnell	1,493	8
Total	**19,036**	**100**

2018 Sales by Product Category

	$ mil.	% of total
Semiconductors	14,890	78
Interconnect passive & electromechanical	3,468	18
Other	677	4
Total	**19,036**	**100**

Selected Products

Amplifiers
Analog Switch Multiplexer
Batteries
Capacitor
Circuit Protection
Communication
Data Conversion
Discrete
Displays
DSP
Embedded Boards
Enclosures Racks & Cabinets
Filter
Inductor
Interconnect
Interface
Kits And Tools
Lighting
Logic And Timing
Memory
Microcontrollers
Miscellaneous
Motors
Optoelectronics
Peripherals
Power Management
Power Supplies
Processor
Programmable Logic
Resistor
RF And Microwave
Sensors And Transducers
Software
Storage
Switches And Relays
Systems
Test & Measurement
Thermal Management
Transformer

COMPETITORS

Allied Electronics	Plexus
Arrow Electronics	Premier Farnell
Digi-Key	SYNNEX
Future Electronics	TTI Inc.
Heilind Electronics	Tech Data
Ingram Micro	WPG Holdings
N.F. Smith	

HISTORICAL FINANCIALS

Company Type: Public

Income Statement   FYE: June 29

	REVENUE ($ mil.)	NET INCOME ($ mil.)	NET PROFIT MARGIN	EMPLOYEES
06/19	19,518	176	0.9%	15,500
06/18*	19,036	(156)	—	15,400
07/17	17,439	525	3.0%	15,700
07/16	26,219	506	1.9%	17,700
06/15	27,924	571	2.0%	18,800
Annual Growth	**(8.6%)**	**(25.5%)**	**—**	**(4.7%)**

*Fiscal year change

2019 Year-End Financials

Debt ratio: 20.09%		No. of shares (mil.): 104	
Return on equity: 4.01%		Dividends	
Cash ($ mil.): 546		Yield: 0.0%	
Current ratio: 2.67		Payout: 50.3%	
Long-term debt ($ mil.): 1,419		Market value ($ mil.): 4,710	

	STOCK PRICE ($) FY Close	P/E High/Low		PER SHARE ($) Earnings	Dividends	Book Value
06/19	45.27	31	21	1.59	0.80	39.80
06/18*	42.89	—	—	(1.30)	0.74	40.45
07/17	38.88	12	9	4.08	0.70	42.10
07/16	40.27	12	10	3.80	0.68	36.84
06/15	42.09	11	9	4.12	0.64	34.58
Annual Growth	**1.8%**	—	—	**(21.2%)**	**5.7%**	**3.6%**

*Fiscal year change

AXOS BANK

EXECUTIVES

Ceo, Greg Garrabants
Sr V Pres-Cfo, Andrew Micheletti
Evp-Chief Credit Offr-Chief RE, Tom Constantine
Gen Counsel, Eshel Bar-Adon
Exec V Pres, Brian Swanson
Executive Vice-President, Adriaan Van Zyl
Vice-President, James Shoop
Assistant Vice-President, Joel Kodish
Facilities Manager, Dan Hager
Human Resources Manager, Maria Dews
Assistant Vice-President, Danielle Austin

LOCATIONS

HQ: AXOS BANK
4350 LA JOLLA VILLAGE DR, SAN DIEGO, CA
921221243
Phone: 858 350-6200
Web: WWW.AXOSBANK.COM

HISTORICAL FINANCIALS

Company Type: Private

Income Statement   FYE: December 31

	ASSETS ($ mil.)	NET INCOME ($ mil.)	INCOME AS % OF ASSETS	EMPLOYEES
12/17	8,908	150	1.7%	102
12/16	8,162	137	1.7%	—
12/15	6,656	104	1.6%	—
12/14	5,190	71	1.4%	—
Annual Growth	**19.7%**	**28.1%**	**—**	**—**

Axos Financial Inc

Formerly BofI Holding Axos Financial is the holding company for Axos Bank which provides consumers and businesses a variety of deposit and loan products via the internet. It conducts its business without any physical bank branches supporting its customers through a comprehensive online banking platform and the occasional physical retail locations of its partners. Most of its business originates in its home state of California though its operations attract customers from every US state. Founded in 2000 the company holds some $10.9 billion in assets more than $8.6 billion in deposits and a total portfolio of net loans and leases of about $9.1 billion.

Operations

Axos Financial operates through two segments: Banking Business and Securities Business.

The holding company's Banking Business division provides nearly all its revenue houses its online and concierge banking prepaid card mortgage vehicle and unsecured lending services. The Banking Business addresses consumers and small businesses through its online platform and over the phone. The segment also offers software products and consulting services for Chapter 7 bankruptcy and non-Chapter 7 trustees and fiduciaries cash management and commercial and industrial real estate loans.

Axos' Securities Business accounts for about 2% of revenue and provides broker-dealer and registered investment advisor services to its own clients and Banking Business clients.

More than 80% of Axos' revenue is generated by net interest income; non-interest income is derived mostly from banking and service fees. The bank's net loan and lease portfolio is dominated by single-family real estate: nearly 50% of its value is represented by mortgages; almost 10% comprises commercial specialty lender finance and construction loans secured by single-family real estate and warehouses. Some 20% is secured by multi-family real estate and another roughly 15% is made up of commercial and real estate loans.

Geographic Reach

San Diego California-based Axos Financial holds deposits from customers in every US state with large sources of balances in Florida and the Mid-Atlantic states. Around 70% of its mortgage portfolio is secured by real estate in California. Its next largest geographic segments by loan principal are New York and Florida each of which comprises less than 10%.

Sales and Marketing

Because the bank is branchless the traditional means of attracting customers?such as local advertising a physical bank presence community charity sponsorship?are not used. Rather the bank creates brand awareness through direct mail email digital marketing personal sales and print advertising. It also garners deposits through financial advisory companies and affinity partnerships.

Financial Performance

In recent years Axos Financial has experienced strong annual increases in revenue and in net income: each has added more than 170% since fiscal 2014. Net interest income?the company's greatest source of income?was boosted by its growing loan and lease portfolio particularly in residential real estate.

Axos posted revenue of $439.4 million in 2018 a 15% increase from 2017. A rise in the bank's net interest margin and a larger loan portfolio accounted for most of the gain. Banking and service fees pushed up non-interest income marginally. Net income rose 13% to $152.4 million on the strength of revenue.

The holding company depleted $20.6 million of its cash to end the year with $622.9 million. Operations generated $167.9 million and financing activities added $837.4 million entirely due to increased deposits. Axos used $1 Billion on investments?principally loans held for investment.

Strategy

Axos Financial's strategy is simply to grow its loan portfolio?and therefore its interest income?through new products expanded distribution channels leveraged data mining and acquisitions.

In 2018 the bank introduced two new products: factoring?in which a company sells its accounts receivable at a discount often to meet short term cash requirements?and its Universal Digital Bank online banking platform. The platform expands the bank's analytics and personalization capabilities enabling greater product cross-selling. It also facilitates development of in-house and third-party apps.

Axos is also growing through a spate of recent acquisitions. In 2019 the company received regulatory approval to acquire about $170 million in deposits from MWABank. That year the company also acquired financial advisor WiseBanyan Holdings gaining its digital wealth management platform and about $150 million in assets under management. Furthermore it expanded its service offerings and added about $35 million in yearly fee income through its purchase of clearing firm COR Clearing. In 2018 it bought Nationwide Building Society's banking and lending business?including $0.7 billion in checking savings and money

market accounts and $1.7 billion in time deposit accounts. It also acquired the trustee and fiduciary services business of Epiq Systems which encompasses its software and consulting services for Chapter 7 and non-Chapter 7 trustees and fiduciaries.

Mergers and Acquisitions

In 2019 Axos Financial took a step toward growing its deposit base when it received regulatory approval to acquire about $170 million in deposits from MWABank. That year the company also acquired financial advisor WiseBanyan Holdings gaining its digital wealth management platform and about $150 million in assets under management. Furthermore it expanded its service offerings and added about $35 million in yearly fee income through its purchase of clearing firm COR Clearing.

Axos bought Nationwide Building Society's banking and lending business?including $0.7 billion in checking savings and money market accounts and $1.7 billion in time deposit accounts?in 2018. It also acquired the trustee and fiduciary services business of Epiq Systems encompassing its software and consulting services for Chapter 7 and non-Chapter 7 trustees and fiduciaries.

Company Background

Axos Financial launched in 2000 as Bank of Internet USA as a digital bank offering checking accounts. The company went public in 2005 as BofI Holding. In 2018 after launching its Universal Digital Bank Platform BofI changed its name to Axos Financial in tandem with a listing on the NYSE.

EXECUTIVES

Evp And Cfo Bofi Holding Inc. And Bofi Federal Bank, Andrew J. Micheletti, age 62, $231,000 total compensation
President And Ceo Bofi Holding Inc. And Bofi Federal Bank, Gregory Garrabrants, age 48, $375,000 total compensation
Evp Specialty Finance And Chief Legal Officer Bofi Federal Bank, Eshel Bar-Adon, age 64, $250,000 total compensation
Evp And Chief Credit Officer Bofi Federal Bank, Thomas Constantine, age 57, $235,000 total compensation
Evp And Chief Lending Officer Bofi Federal Bank, Brian Swanson, age 39, $235,000 total compensation
Evp Chief Of Staff And Chief Performance Officer Bofi Federal Bank, Jan Durrans
Evp Chief Deposit Officer And Chief Marketing Officer Bofi Federal Bank, Eduardo Urdapilleta
Senior Vice President, Jason Kenoyer
Vice President Director Of Financial Reporting, Pete Bauer
First Vice President And Compliance Management, Sandy Hill
Senior Vice President Warehouse Lending And Loan Operations, Darin Sullivan
Vice President Construction Loan Manager, David Thomas
Assistant Vice President Product Delivery, Bryan Iv Hugh
Senior Vice President Risk, Justin Liang
Executive Vice President Director Of Deposits Development, Lane Elliott
Vice President Marketing, Dana Berry
Executive Vice President Human Resources, Mary Ciafardini
Chairman, Paul J. Grinberg, age 58
Vice Chairman, Nicholas A. Mosich
Board Member, James Court
Board Member, Edward Ratinoff
Board Member, James Argalas
Auditors: BDO USA, LLP

LOCATIONS

HQ: Axos Financial Inc
9205 West Russell Road, STE 400, Las Vegas, NV 89148
Phone: 858 649-2218
Web: www.bofiholding.com

PRODUCTS/OPERATIONS

2018 Sales

	$ mil.	% of total
Interest and dividend income:		
Loans and leases including fees	447	79
Investments	28	5
Interest expense	(106.6)	-
Non-interest income:		
Banking and service fees	47	11
Mortgage banking income	13	3
Gain on sale - other	5	1
Prepayment penalty fee income	3	1
Gain (loss) on sale of securities	(0.2)	-
Total	**455**	**100**

COMPETITORS

Ally Bank	ISN Bank
California Bank & Trust	MUFG Americas Holdings
Discover	PacWest Bancorp
E*TRADE Bank	San Diego County Credit Union
First IB	Scottrade
HSBC USA	

HISTORICAL FINANCIALS

Company Type: Public

Income Statement — FYE: June 30

	ASSETS ($ mil.)	NET INCOME ($ mil.)	INCOME AS % OF ASSETS	EMPLOYEES
06/19	11,220	155	1.4%	1,007
06/18	9,539	152	1.6%	801
06/17	8,501	134	1.6%	681
06/16	7,601	119	1.6%	647
06/15	5,823	82	1.4%	467
Annual Growth	**17.8%**	**17.0%**	**—**	**21.2%**

2019 Year-End Financials

Debt ratio: 1.51%	No. of shares (mil.): 61
Return on equity: 15.26%	Dividends
Cash ($ mil.): 857	Yield: —
Current ratio: —	Payout: —
Long-term debt ($ mil.): —	Market value ($ mil.): 1,666

	STOCK PRICE ($) FY Close	P/E High/Low	PER SHARE ($) Earnings	Dividends	Book Value
06/19	27.25	17 10	2.48	0.00	17.55
06/18	40.91	19 10	2.37	0.00	15.32
06/17	23.72	16 7	2.07	0.00	13.13
06/16	17.71	77 7	1.85	0.00	10.81
06/15	105.71	79 49	1.34	0.00	8.59
Annual Growth	**(28.7%)**	**— —**	**16.6%**	**—**	**19.5%**

Baker Hughes Company

Auditors: KPMG LLP

LOCATIONS

HQ: Baker Hughes Company
17021 Aldine Westfield Road, Houston, TX 77073-5101
Phone: 713 439-8600
Web: www.bakerhughes.com

Income Statement				FYE: December 31
	REVENUE ($ mil.)	NET INCOME ($ mil.)	NET PROFIT MARGIN	EMPLOYEES
12/18	22,877	195	0.9%	66,000
12/17	17,259	(73)	—	64,000
12/16	13,269	403	3.0%	34,000
12/15	16,688	(606)	—	—
12/14	19,191	1,840	9.6%	—
Annual Growth	4.5%	(42.9%)		

2018 Year-End Financials

Debt ratio: 12.07%
Return on equity: 1.21%
Cash ($ mil.): —
Current ratio: 1.66
Long-term debt ($ mil.): 6,285

No. of shares (mil.): 1,034
Dividends
  Yield: 0.0%
  Payout: 160.0%
Market value ($ mil.): 22,251

	STOCK PRICE ($) FY Close	P/E High/Low	PER SHARE ($)		
			Earnings	Dividends	Book Value
12/18	21.50	81 45	0.45	0.72	16.88
12/17	31.64	— —	(0.17)	0.35	13.03
Annual Growth	(9.2%)	— —	—	19.8%	6.7%

Ball Corp

The Ball Corporation produces sustainable metal beverage packaging and aerospace products. Ball's packaging revenue (90% of its net sales) is derived from a relatively few major beverage-producing companies and brands such as Coca-Cola Anheuser Busch InBev Molson Coors and Unilever. Additionally its aerospace segment provides an array of aerospace systems and services (such as spacecraft instruments and sensors and data solutions); 99% of these sales are to the US government. Ball Corporation operates through 85 locations in about 25 countries with the US its largest single market. In 2018 Ball divested its US steel food and steel aerosol packaging business to form a new joint venture named Ball Metalpack.

Operations

Ball Corporation divides its operations between five business segments. Its three beverage packaging segments ? North and Central America (about 40% of total revenue) Europe (more than 20%) and South America (about 15%) ? are all the leading provider of aluminum cans for soft drinks energy drinks beer and other beverages in their respective markets.

The company's aerospace segment (almost 10%) makes and sells aerospace and related products for the civil commercial and national security aerospace markets.

Geographic Reach

The company operates about 75 facilities spanning Asia Europe North America and South America. The US accounts for half of total revenues and more than 10% of sales come from Brazil.

Ball Corporation's headquarters as well as its aerospace segment offices are located in Broomfield CO. Regional offices for Europe are in Luton UK; Middle East and Asia operations are run out of Dubai and Hong Kong respectively; and South American offices are in Rio de Janeiro. Ball's R&D facilities are primarily located in Westminster Colorado.

Sales and Marketing

Ball's packaging revenue is derived primarily from long-term contracts with a relatively few customers. Anheuser-Busch InBev contributes about 15% of net sales. Other large accounts include Coca-Cola (more than 10% of revenue) Molson Coors (about 5%) and the US government (about 10%).

Financial Performance

Except for a dip in 2015 Ball's revenue has seen steady growth the last five years rising more than 35% between 2014 and 2018. Higher beverage packaging volumes across most geographies the acquisition of Rexam and a significant uptick in US defense contracts within the aerospace segment have been the chief growth drivers.

Sales in 2018 increased 6% to $11.6 billion compared to $11 billion in 2017. Growth in 2018 was fueled by higher volumes in the South America and Europe segments and increased pricing and optimized product mix in the North and Central America segment. Favorable exchange rates in the Europe segment and increased defense contracts within the aerospace division also boosted 2018 revenue.

Net income increased 21% to $454 million in 2018 compared to 2017 primarily due to higher sales in the Europe and North and Central America business units increased manufacturing efficiency and reduced business consolidation costs.

Cash at the end of 2018 was $728 million an increase of $269 million from the prior year. Cash from operations contributed $1.6 billion to the coffers while investing activities used $206 million mainly for capital expenditures. Financing activities used $1 billion primarily for repayment of long-term borrowings.

Strategy

Ball is continuing its "Drive for 10" vision ? a 10-year initiative established in 2011 which is focused on key levers underpinning its corporate strategy. Ball is focused on growing its existing business while also adding new products to its portfolio.

The company is streamlining processes and systems and increasing the sustainability of its beverage cans. In 2018 it is continuing with its global finance transformation projects by opening shared service centers in Serbia and Mexico. To tighten its beverage and food can operations it closed several plants in the US and one in Germany.

Other production optimization efforts included plans announced in 2019 to sell two steel aerosol packaging plants in Argentina. Late in 2018 Ball said it would sell its underperforming beverage can business in China for $225 million to China-based ORG Technology. Earlier in 2018 Ball divested its US steel food and steel aerosol packaging business to form a new joint venture named Ball Metalpack. Ball holds a 49% stake in Ball Metalpack; JV partner Platinum Equity controls 51%.

As consumer awareness about the environmental impacts of plastic packaging continues to increase Ball is well-positioned to offer aluminum container alternatives to plastic cartons and glass. More beverages ?- including sparkling waters wine and coffee ?- are making the move to cans. In the second half of 2018 Ball's North and Central America and Europe segments saw volumes grow nearly 7% as more of the company's customers migrated to aluminum packaging.

On the aerospace side Ball increased its contracted backlog by 25% to $2.2 billion in 2018. That year NASA selected Ball to design and develop the Wide Field Instrument which will contribute to the WFIRST space mission that aims to explore areas including dark matter exoplanets and infrared astrophysics.

Mergers and Acquisitions

In a sweeping move for the industry the company in mid-2016 acquired Rexam one of its biggest rivals for around $6.1 billion. The deal created the world's largest maker of food and beverage cans. As part of the stipulations to complete the deal Ball sold a dozen plants in Europe and two in Brazil. The company also completed the required sale of eight aluminum-can plants and related assets in the US to Ardagh Group for $3.4 billion. Further it shut down Rexam's London headquarters in late 2016.

Company Background

The Ball Corporation began in 1880 when Frank Ball and his four brothers started making wood-jacket tin cans to store and transport kerosene and other materials. In 1884 the company switched to tin-jacketed glass containers for kerosene lamps. The lamps however were soon displaced by Thomas Edison's electric light bulb.

The Ball brothers then learned that the patent to the original sealed-glass storage container (the Mason jar) had expired. By 1886 the brothers had entered the sealed-jar business and imprinted their jars with the Ball name.

The company began diversifying but a 1947 antitrust ruling prohibited it from buying additional glass subsidiaries. Ball decided to take advantage of the space race by buying Control Cells (aerospace science research) in 1957; that operation became Ball Brothers Research Corporation (later Ball Aerospace Systems Division).

Ball established its metal beverage-container business in 1969 when it bought Jeffco Manufacturing of Colorado. The operation soon won contracts to supply two-piece cans to Budweiser Coca-Cola Dr Pepper Pepsi and Stroh's Beer. Ball went public in 1973.

HISTORY

The Ball Corporation began in 1880 when Frank Ball and his four brothers started making wood-jacket tin cans to store and transport kerosene and other materials. In 1884 the company switched to tin-jacketed glass containers for kerosene lamps. The lamps however were soon displaced by Thomas Edison's electric light bulb.

The Ball brothers then learned that the patent to the original sealed-glass storage container (the Mason jar) had expired. By 1886 the brothers had entered the sealed-jar business and imprinted their jars with the Ball name. In their first year they made 12500 jars and sparked a patent war with the two reigning jar producers who asserted that they controlled the correct patents and threatened to sue. The Ball lawyers proved that the patents had expired and the jar remained Ball's mainstay for many years.

The company began diversifying but a 1947 antitrust ruling prohibited it from buying additional glass subsidiaries. Ball decided to take advantage of the space race by buying Control Cells (aerospace science research) in 1957; that operation became Ball Brothers Research Corporation (later Ball Aerospace Systems Division). The Soviets launched Sputnik that year igniting a massive US scientific effort in 1958 and Ball won federal contracts to make equipment for the US space program.

Ball established its metal beverage-container business in 1969 when it bought Jeffco Manufacturing of Colorado. The operation soon won contracts to supply two-piece cans to Budweiser Coca-Cola Dr Pepper Pepsi and Stroh's Beer.

EXECUTIVES

Svp And Cfo, Scott C. Morrison, age 56, $666,728 total compensation

Chairman President And Ceo, John A. Hayes, age 53, $1,238,615 total compensation

Svp Human Resources And Administration, Lisa A. Pauley, age 57, $464,443 total compensation

Svp And Coo Global Beverage Packaging, Daniel W. Fisher, age 46

Vp Technology, M. Andrew (Drew) Crouch

Vp General Counsel And Corporate Secretary, Charles E. Baker, age 61, $492,871 total compensation

Svp; President Ball Aerospace And Technologies, Robert D. (Rob) Strain, age 62

Vp Marketing And Corporate Affairs, James N. Peterson, age 50

Vice President Investor Relations, Ann Scott

Director Progam Development Chief Sales Officer, Jim Good

Vice President Operational Planning And Administra, Jim Curtin

Vice President Business Services, Gary Bybee

Vice President And General Manager Of Civil Space, Jim Oschmann

Vice President Sales, Bruce Doelling

Vice President, Art Morrissey

Vp Human Resources Metal Beverage Americas, John Olson

Vice President And General Manager, Stan Platek

Vice President, Roy Nelson

Vice President, Shelley B Petroy

Vice President Manufacturing, Rick Garske

Vice President Finance N.a. Metal Beverage Packaging Division, Rob Kim

Vice President Financial Reporting And Tax, Douglas Bradford

Vice President Corporate Strategy Marketing And Development, Dan Rabbitt

Vice President, Jason Myers

Senior Vice President Of International Sales, David Fredericks

Vice President Sales Telecomm Products, Tom Messler

Senior Business Intelligence Developer, Sean Foley

Vice President And General Manager Of National Security Space, Fred Doyle

Vp Regulatory Affairs, Fredrick Doyle

Vice President Talent, Andrew Stevens

Vice President Of Information Technology, Fernando Diaz

Programming Vice President, Alan Gans

Vice President Communications And Corporate Relations, Kathleen E Pitre

Vice President Supply Chain, Tom Schranz

Vice President And General Manager Systems Engineering Solutions Ball Aerospace And Technologies, W Daniel Gibson

Vp Engineering Ball Aerospace And Technologies, Michael Gazarik

Vice President And Treasurer, Jeffrey A Knobel

Vice President Global Business Services, Brian Gabbard

Vice President Information Technology And Services, Cheryl Martin

Vice President Of Operations, Richard Yelverton

Vice President, Vikki Schiff

Vp Of Engineering, Larry Wetzel

Vice President And General Manager, Debra D Facktor

Board Member, Chris Barkley

Board Member, Michael Cave

Board Member, Daniel Heinrich

Board Member, Cynthia Niekamp

Board Member, Cathy Ross

Board Member, Stuart Taylor

Auditors: PricewaterhouseCoopers LLP

LOCATIONS

HQ: Ball Corp
10 Longs Peak Drive, P.O. Box 5000, Broomfield, CO 80021-2510
Phone: 303 469-3131
Web: www.ball.com

2017 Sales

	$ mil.	% of total
US	5,496	50
Brazil	1,427	13
Other	4,060	37
Total	**10,983**	**100**

PRODUCTS/OPERATIONS

2017 Sales

	$ mil.	% of total
Beverage packaging North and Central America	4,178	38
Beverage packaging Europe	2,360	22
Beverage packaging South America	1,692	15
Food and aerosol packaging	1,138	10
Aerospace	991	9
Other	624	6
Total	**10,983**	**100**

Selected Products

Packaging
Aluminum beverage cans
Metal food containers and ends
Steel aerosol containers
Extruded aluminum aerosol containers
Aluminum slugs
Paint and general line cans
Aerospace and technologies
Aerospace hardware and components
Antennas and video tactical systems
Satellites and spacecraft
Space-based instruments and sensors
Radio frequency systems
Technical services

COMPETITORS

Amcor	Saint-Gobain
Arconic	Containers
Ardagh Group	Sequa
Crown Holdings	Silgan
Reynolds Food	Teledyne Technologies
Packaging	Tetra Laval
Rio Tinto Alcan	

HISTORICAL FINANCIALS

Company Type: Public

Income Statement — FYE: December 31

	REVENUE ($ mil.)	NET INCOME ($ mil.)	NET PROFIT MARGIN	EMPLOYEES
12/18	11,635	454	3.9%	17,500
12/17	10,983	374	3.4%	18,300
12/16	9,061	263	2.9%	18,450
12/15	7,997	280	3.5%	15,200
12/14	8,570	470	5.5%	14,500
Annual Growth	7.9%	(0.9%)	—	4.8%

2018 Year-End Financials

Debt ratio: 40.65%
Return on equity: 12.27%
Cash ($ mil.): 721
Current ratio: 0.96
Long-term debt ($ mil.): 6,510
No. of shares (mil.): 335
Dividends
Yield: 0.8%
Payout: 31.0%
Market value ($ mil.): 15,415

	STOCK PRICE ($) FY Close	P/E High/Low	PER SHARE ($) Earnings	Dividends	Book Value
12/18	45.98	38 27	1.29	0.40	10.31
12/17	37.85	76 35	1.05	0.37	11.26
12/16	75.07	99 77	0.82	0.26	9.82
12/15	72.73	75 59	1.00	0.26	4.40
12/14	68.17	41 28	1.65	0.26	3.77
Annual Growth	(9.4%)	— —	(6.0%)	11.4%	28.6%

Banc Of California Inc

Banc of California offers deposit and loan services at 35 branches in Southern California's Los Angeles Orange County and San Diego. Customers enjoy checking savings and money market accounts as well as mobile online and card payment services telephone banking automated bill payment safe deposit boxes direct deposit and wire transfers. Customers can also access their accounts through a nationwide network of 55000 surcharge-free ATMs. In addition to its branches the $9 billion-asset Banc of California operates around 70 mortgage loan production offices in California Arizona Oregon Indiana Idaho Nevada and Virginia.

Operations

Banc of California operates three core segments: Commercial Banking which offers commercial consumer and real estate secured loans as well as deposit accounts; Mortgage Banking which originates conforming SFR loans and sells the loans in the secondary market; and the Financial Advisory segment which purchases sells and manages SFR mortgage loans.

Unlike most retail banks Banc of California's income streams are less dependent on interest rates. The bank made 50% of its revenue from loan interest (including fees) during 2015 and another 5% from interest on investments. But it also made 29% of its revenue from its mortgage banking business while the rest came from other non-interest income sources.

Geographic Reach

The Irvine California-based bank has 90-plus banking locations in California including 35 branches in San Diego Orange Santa Barbara and Los Angeles Counties (as of mid-2016). It has 68 loan production offices in California Arizona Oregon Virginia Indiana Maryland Colorado Idaho and Nevada.

Sales and Marketing

The bank spent $6.2 million on advertising during 2015 or 23% more than in the prior year due to higher overall marketing costs tied to the bank's continued expansion.

Financial Performance

Banc of California's revenue has risen sevenfold since 2011 as a slew of bank acquisitions and organic growth have driven its loan and deposit business as well as its mortgage banking business.

The bank's revenue jumped 46% to $486.5 million during 2015 thanks to a 34% spike in loan interest income on more loan origination and loan and lease purchase activity; and thanks to a 52% rise in mortgage banking income as the bank originated and sold nearly twice as many mortgage loans on the secondary market than in 2014.

Strong revenue growth in 2015 caused Banc of California's net income to double to $62 million despite an uptick in salary and benefits cost that stemmed from additional hiring and commercial banking and mortgage banking expansion. The bank's operations used $45.24 million during the year or less than one-tenth as much cash as in 2014 mostly after adjusting its earnings for non-cash items related to proceeds of mortgage banking loans held-for-sale and proceeds from other loans held-for-sale.

Strategy

With its eye on becoming "California's Bank" Banc of California sometimes acquires smaller banks or bank branch networks to boost its loan and deposit business while expanding its branch network (mostly around California).

From 2010 through 2015 the bank has made seven acquisitions including three bank acquisitions (Gateway Bancorp Beach Business Bank and The Private Bank of California) and three other specialty financial firm acquisitions (Palisades Group which it divested in 2016; CS Financial; and Renovation Ready.)

Mergers and Acquisitions

In November 2014 the bank bought 20 branches in Southern California from Banco Popular North America (BPNA) along with $1.07 billion in loans and $1.08 billion in deposits for a total price of $24 million.

In January 2014 Banc of California purchased service contracts and intellectual property of RenovationReady a specialized loan services provider that served financial institutions and mortgage bankers that originated agency-eligible residential renovation and construction loan products.

Company Background

In 2012 it paid $15.5 million for Gateway Business Bank and $37 million for Beach Business Bank. The next year it took over The Private Bank of California for $25 million and bought The Palisades Group a residential mortgage investment advisory firm and specialty finance company CS Financial. In 2014 it announced plans to buy 20 branches of Banco Popular North America to reach California's Hispanic community.

In 2013 it sold eight branches to AmericanWest Bank in order to reshape its retail branch network to focus on servicing small - to midsized businesses and high net worth families.

EXECUTIVES

Evp Division General Counsel Lending, John F. Madden, age 58
Evp Enterprise Risk Analytics, Gilda Youdeem
Managing Director Institutional Banking And Fiduciary Services, Steven C. (Steve) Canup
Evp And Cfo Banc Of California Inc. And Banc Of California N.a., John A. Bogler
Evp And General Counsel Banking, Angelee J. Harris, age 49
Chief Investment Officer, Brian P. Kuelbs, age 56
Managing Director Community Banking, Gaylin D. Anderson
Vice Chairman And Evp, Jeffrey T. Seabold, age 52, $750,000 total compensation
President And Ceo, Douglas H. (Doug) Bowers, age 61
Chief Risk Officer, Hugh F. Boyle, age 59, $599,679 total compensation
Managing Director Warehouse Lending, Zoila Price
Evp And Chief Compliance Officer, Diane M. Summers
Evp Community Development, Gary S. Dunn
Evp And Cio, Ken Plummer
Evp Division General Counsel Banking, Manisha K. Merchant
Managing Director Construction Lending, Jim Fraser
Managing Director Cre Lending, Thomas Senske
Managing Director Sba Lending, Heather Endresen
Managing Director Commercial Banking, David Park
Chief Credit Officer, Paul Simmons
Managing Director Portfolio Lending, Julie Duong
Svp Operations, Robert Villaneda
Svp Marketing, Samantha Haugh
Managing Director Payment Solutions, Ben Kessler
Evp General Counsel And Secretary, John C. Grosvenor, age 69, $501,378 total compensation
Evp Private Banking, Jay D. Sanders
Vice President Client Service Officer, Christina Beltran
Vice President Credit Administration, Edward Massey
Executive Vice President, Chang Liu
Senior Vice President, Jerry Konzen

Vice President Information Technology Infrastructure, Len Tateyama
Assistant Vice President Credit Portfolio Manager, Aida Rodriguez
Vice President Deposit Operations Manager, Elizabeth Sevesind
Vice President, Justin Coleman
Senior Vice President National Sales Manager, Adam Liebross
Vice President Relationship Manager, Bryan Flores
Executive Vice President, Jim Wiegandt
Vp Sba Underwriter, Mike Choi
Vp, Cindy Crismer
Vice President Customer Service, Lori Ratzlaff
Vp Consumer Credit Administrator Portfolio Manager, Nathan Hennigan
Evp Ciso, Chris Forbes
Svp Relationship And Manager Commercial Real Estate Lending, Warren Ramsey
Senior Vice President Capital Markets, Charles Emley
Senior Business Intelligence Developer, Dabao Rinna
Vice President Business Transformation, Scott Swanson
Svp Portfolio Operations, Amber Mandir
Chairman, Robert D. Sznewajs, age 72
Board Member, Halle J Benett
Board Member, Bonnie G Hill
Board Member, Mary A Curran
Auditors: Ernst & Young LLP

LOCATIONS

HQ: Banc Of California Inc
  3 MacArthur Place, Santa Ana, CA 92707
Phone: 855 361-2262
Web: www.bancofcal.com

PRODUCTS/OPERATIONS

2013 Sales

	$ mil.	% of total
Interest and dividend income		
Loans including fees	116	53
Securities and others	3	2
Noninterest income		
Net gain on mortgage banking activities	68	31
Gain on sale of branches	12	6
Net gain on sale of loans	8	4
Loan servicing income	2	1
Customer service fees	1	1
Others	4	2
Total	**217**	**100**

COMPETITORS

American Business Bank	East West Bancorp
Bank of America	JPMorgan Chase
Bank of the West	MUFG Americas Holdings
BofI	PacWest Bancorp
California Bank & Trust	Pacific Mercantile
	Pacific Premier
City National	Simplicity Bancorp
Comerica	U.S. Bancorp

HISTORICAL FINANCIALS

Company Type: Public

Income Statement				FYE: December 31
	ASSETS ($ mil.)	NET INCOME ($ mil.)	INCOME AS % OF ASSETS	EMPLOYEES
12/18	10,630	45	0.4%	741
12/17	10,327	57	0.6%	738
12/16	11,029	115	1.0%	1,797
12/15	8,235	62	0.8%	1,710
12/14	5,971	30	0.5%	1,470
Annual Growth	**15.5%**	**10.7%**	**—**	**(15.7%)**

2018 Year-End Financials

Debt ratio: 1.63%	No. of shares (mil.): 50
Return on equity: 4.65%	Dividends
Cash ($ mil.): 391	Yield: 3.9%
Current ratio: —	Payout: 115.5%
Long-term debt ($ mil.): —	Market value ($ mil.): 674

	STOCK PRICE ($) FY Close	P/E High/Low		PER SHARE ($) Earnings	Dividends	Book Value
12/18	13.31	48	28	0.45	0.52	18.67
12/17	20.65	32	20	0.71	0.52	20.01
12/16	17.35	12	6	1.94	0.49	19.65
12/15	14.62	11	8	1.34	0.48	17.15
12/14	11.47	15	11	0.91	0.48	14.47
Annual Growth	**3.8%**	**—**	**—**	**(16.1%)**	**2.0%**	**6.6%**

BancFirst Corp. (Oklahoma City, Okla)

This Oklahoma bank wants to be more than OK. It wants to be super . BancFirst Corporation is the holding company for BancFirst a super-community bank that emphasizes decentralized management and centralized support. BancFirst operates more than 100 branches in more than 50 Oklahoma communities. It serves individuals and small to midsized businesses offering traditional deposit products such as checking and savings accounts CDs and IRAs. Commercial real estate lending (including farmland and multifamily residential loans) makes up more than a third of the bank's loan portfolio while one-to-four family residential mortgages represent about 20%. The bank also issues business construction and consumer loans.

Operations

The company operates three core units: metropolitan banks community banks and other financial service. Metropolitan and community banks offer traditional banking products such as commercial and retail lending and a full line of deposit accounts in the metropolitan Oklahoma City and Tulsa areas. Community banks consist of banking locations in communities throughout Oklahoma. Other financial services are specialty product business units including guaranteed small business lending residential mortgage lending trust services securities brokerage electronic banking and insurance.

The company's BancFirst Insurance Services arm sells property/casualty coverage while the bank's trust and investment management division oversees some $1.21 billion of assets on behalf of clients. Bank subsidiaries Council Oak Investment Corporation and Council Oak Real Estate focus on small business and property investments respectively.

Like other retail banks BancFirst makes the bulk of its money from interest income. More than 60% of its total revenue came from loan interest (including fees) during 2015 while another 2% came from interest on taxable securities. The rest of its revenue came from service charges on deposits (19% of revenue) insurance commissions (5%) trust revenue (3%) securities transactions (3%) and loan sales (1%).

Geographic Reach

BancFirst has 95 banking locations serving more than 52 communities across Oklahoma.

Sales and Marketing

The bank customers are generally small to medium-sized businesses engaged in light manufacturing local wholesale and retail trade commercial and residential real estate development and construction services agriculture and the energy industry.

BancFirst spent about $6.9 million for advertising and promotion during 2015 compared to $6.6 million in each of 2014 and 2013.

Financial Performance

BancFirst's annual revenues have risen 20% since 2011 thanks to continued loan asset and deposit growth (partly thanks to branch expansion). The company's annual profits have grown more than 40% over the same period as it's kept a lid on operating expenses and loan loss provisions.

BancFirst's revenue climbed 6% to $306.85 million during 2015 thanks to a combination of loan asset growth and gains on the sales of some of its securities.

Revenue growth in 2015 drove the company's net income up nearly 4% to $66.17 million. The bank's operating cash levels increased by almost 2% to $78.1 million with the rise in cash-based earnings.

Strategy

BancFirst's strategy focuses on providing a full range of commercial banking services to retail customers and small to medium-sized businesses in both the non-metropolitan trade centers and cities in the metropolitan statistical areas of Oklahoma. It operates as a 'super community bank' managing its community banking offices on a decentralized basis which permits them to be responsive to local customer needs. Underwriting funding customer service and pricing decisions are made by presidents in each market within the company's strategic parameters.

Mergers and Acquisitions

In October 2015 BancFirst purchased $196 million-asset CSB Banchsares and its Bank of Commerce branches in Yukon Mustang and El Reno in Oklahoma. The deal also added $148 million in new loan business and $170 million in deposits.

Company Background

The company has been buying smaller banks to expand in Oklahoma. In 2011 it acquired FBC Financial Corporation and its subsidiary bank 1st Bank Oklahoma with about five branches throughout the state. In 2010 BancFirst acquired Union Bank of Chandler Okemah National Bank and Exchange National Bank of Moore adding about another five branches. It acquired First State Bank Jones in 2009 to expand in eastern Oklahoma.

President and CEO David Rainbolt owns some 40% of BancFirst .

EXECUTIVES

Evp Investments Bancfirst, Robert M. Neville, age 63

Evp Financial Services Bancfirst, D. Jay Hannah, age 63

Evp Interim Cfo And Chief Risk Officer, Randy P. Foraker, age 63, $174,423 total compensation

Evp Human Resources Bancfirst, J. Michael Rogers, age 75

Evp And Cio Bancfirst, Scott Copeland, age 54

Sevp And Chairman Executive Committee, Dennis L. Brand, age 71, $525,000 total compensation

Vice Chairman And Ceo Council Oak Investment Corporation And Council Oak Real Estate Inc., William O. Johnstone, age 71, $200,000 total compensation

Evp And Chief Credit Officer Bancfirst, Roy C. Ferguson, age 72

Regional Executive Bancfirst, Karen James, age 63

President And Ceo Bancfirst, Darryl Schmidt, age 57, $350,000 total compensation

Regional Executive Bancfirst, David M. Seat, age 68

Evp And Cto Bancfirst, David Westman, age 63

Ceo, David R. Harlow, age 56, $325,000 total compensation

Regional Executive Bancfirst, Harvey G. Robinson, age 60

Evp Cfo And Treasurer, Kevin Lawrence, age 40, $214,231 total compensation

President Bancfirst Frederick, Jason McQueen

Evp And Chief Internal Auditor, Paul Fleming, age 68

Regional Executive Bancfirst, John Anderson, age 63

Senior Vice President Technologist, Stephen Florea

Executive Vice President, Debbie Kuykendall

Vice President, Tyler Smith

Senior Vice President, Patrick A Lippmann

Senior Vice President General Manager, Michael Kernan

Assistant Vice President Branch Manager, Desiree Raburn

Senior Vice President, Blane Allen

Senior Vice President Chief In, Scott Lewis

Senior Vice President Treasury Sales Director, Ashlea Briggs

Senior Vice President, Denise Duffle

Senior Vice President, Brian Renz

Vice President Lockbox Manager, Jennifer Seargent

Assistant Vice President, Tamara Reed

Vice President Financial Reporting, Chesney Whetstone

Assistant Vice President Network Services, Dian Joysizemore

Vice President Marketing, Ben Harrington

Vice President, Matt Harp

Executive Vice President, Sean Shadid

Vice President Consumer Lending, Shirley Myers

Senior Vice President Investments, Bob Neville

Senior Vice President, David Vinall

Executive Vice President, Janet W Gotwals

Senior Vice President, Kevin J Calabrese

Executive Vice President, Bob Winchester

Vice President, Delynn Rains

Assistant Vice President And Consumer Loan Officer, Jenny Gifford

Assistant Vice President, Scott Hofmann

Assistant Vice President Commercial Loan Officer, Mary Johnston

Senior Vice President Corporate Banking, Matt Crew

Senior Vice President, Mark C Demos

Senior Vice President, Trent Cronk

Vice Chairman, James R. Daniel, age 79

Vice Chairman, K. Gordon Greer, age 82

Chairman, David E. Rainbolt, age 63

Auditors: BKD, LLP

LOCATIONS

HQ: BancFirst Corp. (Oklahoma City, Okla)
101 N. Broadway, Oklahoma City, OK 73102-8405
Phone: 405 270-1086   **Fax:** 405 270-1089
Web: www.bancfirst.com

PRODUCTS/OPERATIONS

2015 Sales

	$ mil.	% of total
Interest		
Loans including fees	190	63
Securities	6	2
Interest-bearing deposit	4	1
Noninterest		
Service charges on deposits	57	18
Insurance commissions	14	5
Security transactions	9	3
Trust revenue	9	3
Income from sale of loans	2	1
Cash management	7	2
Other	5	2
Total	**306**	**100**

Selected Subsidiaries

BancFirst
  BancFirst Agency Inc. (credit life insurance)
  BancFirst Community Development Corporation
  Council Oak Investment Corporation (small business investments)
  Council Oak Real Estate Inc. (real estate investments)
Council Oak Partners LLC
BancFirst Insurance Services Inc.

COMPETITORS

Arvest Bank	Midland Financial
BOK Financial	Southwest Bancorp
Bank of America	UMB Financial
International Bancshares	Wells Fargo

HISTORICAL FINANCIALS

Company Type: Public

Income Statement

FYE: December 31

	ASSETS ($ mil.)	NET INCOME ($ mil.)	INCOME AS % OF ASSETS	EMPLOYEES
12/18	7,574	125	1.7%	1,906
12/17	7,253	86	1.2%	1,782
12/16	7,018	70	1.0%	1,773
12/15	6,692	66	1.0%	1,744
12/14	6,574	63	1.0%	1,688
Annual Growth	3.6%	18.5%		3.1%

2018 Year-End Financials

Debt ratio: 0.35%	No. of shares (mil.): 32
Return on equity: 14.99%	Dividends
Cash ($ mil.): 1,424	Yield: 2.0%
Current ratio: —	Payout: 30.2%
Long-term debt ($ mil.): —	Market value ($ mil.): 1,627

	STOCK PRICE ($) FY Close	P/E High/Low	PER SHARE ($) Earnings	Dividends	Book Value
12/18	49.90	17 13	3.76	1.02	27.69
12/17	51.15	40 18	2.65	0.80	24.32
12/16	93.05	42 23	2.22	0.74	22.49
12/15	58.62	32 26	2.09	0.70	21.01
12/14	63.39	33 25	2.02	0.65	19.65
Annual Growth	(5.8%)	— —	16.8%	11.9%	9.0%

BancorpSouth Bank (Tupelo, MS)

Like Elvis Presley BancorpSouth has grown beyond its Tupelo roots. It's the holding company for BancorpSouth Bank which operates some 290 branches in nine southern and midwestern states. Catering to consumers and small and midsized businesses the bank offers checking and savings accounts loans credit cards and commercial banking services. BancorpSouth also sells insurance and provides brokerage investment advisory and asset management services throughout most of its market area. Real estate loans including consumer and commercial mortgages and home equity construction and agricultural loans comprise approximately three-quarters of its loan portfolio. BancorpSouth has assets of $13 billion.

Geographic Reach

Mississippi-based BancorpSouth Bank operates in Alabama Arkansas Florida Illinois Louisiana Mississippi Missouri Tennessee and Texas. BancorpSouth's insurance and financial advisory businesses also operate in Illinois and Florida respectively.

Financial Performance

BancorpSouth reported net income of $94.1 million in 2013 an increase of 12% versus 2012. The decreased provision for credit losses was the primary factor contributing to the rise. Net interest revenue — the bank's primary source of revenue — fell 4% year over year to $$398.9 million the fourth consecutive year of decline. Net interest revenue declined because the decrease in interest expense was more than offset by the decrease in interest revenue as the yield on earning assets declined by a greater amount than that of interest-bearing liabilities. Noninterest income also declined on lower mortgage origination revenue in 2013 versus 2012.

Strategy

The regional bank has grown via the acquisition of other banks and insurance agencies and by opening new branches most recently in Texas and Louisiana. To reduce its reliance on interest-related revenue BancorpSouth hopes to diversify its revenue stream by increasing the amount it generates from mortgage lending insurance brokerage and securities activities. To this end subsidiary BancorpSouth Insurance Services has acquired small insurance agencies in Arkansas Missouri and Texas.

Mergers and Acquisitions

In 2014 BancorpSouth agreed to acquire Central Community Corp. the holding company for First State Bank Central Texas headquartered in Austin Texas. First State Bank operates 31 branches in Austin Round Rock Killeen and several other Central Texas communities. BancorpSouth has also agreed to purchase Ouachita Bancshares Corp. with a dozen branches in Louisiana. Both deals were announced in January 2014 and were expected to close promptly. However they've been delayed because BancorpSouth needs more time to get regulatory approvals and to meet "closing conditions necessary to complete" the mergers.

EXECUTIVES

Sevp Cfo And Treasurer, John G. Copeland, age 66
Evp And Corporate Secretary Bancorpsouth And Bancorpsouth Bank, Cathy S. Freeman, age 54
Chairman And Ceo Bancorpsouth Inc. And Bancorpsouth Bank, James D. (Dan) Rollins, age 60, $840,000 total compensation
Evp Bancorpsouth Inc. And Vice Chairman And Chief Lending Officer Bancorpsouth Bank, James R. Hodges, $382,500 total compensation
President And Coo, Chris A. Bagley, $495,000 total compensation
President Equipment Finance And Leasing, Kyle Gilliam
Sevp And General Counsel, Chuck Pignuolo, age 63
Executive Vice President, Clyde Guyse
Auditors: KPMG LLP

LOCATIONS

HQ: BancorpSouth Bank (Tupelo, MS)
One Mississippi Plaza, 201 South Spring Street,
Tupelo, MS 38804
Phone: 662 680-2000
Web: www.bancorpsouth.com

PRODUCTS/OPERATIONS

2016 Sales

	$ mil.	% of total
Interest		
Loans & leases	440	58
Securities	41	5
Deposits with other banks	1	-
Noninterest		
Insurance commissions	115	15
Deposit service charges	43	6
Mortgage lending	41	5
Credit card debit card and merchant fees	37	5
Wealth management	21	3
Other	19	3
Total	**762**	**100**

Selected Subsidiaries

BancorpSouth Bank
  BancorpSouth Insurance Services Inc.
  BancorpSouth Investment Services Inc.
  BancorpSouth Municipal Development Corporation
  Century Credit Life Insurance Company
  Personal Finance Corporation

COMPETITORS

BBVA Compass	Hancock Holding
Bancshares	Regions Financial
Capital One	Renasant
First Horizon	SunTrust
Great Southern Bancorp	Trustmark

HISTORICAL FINANCIALS

Company Type: Public

Income Statement

FYE: December 31

	ASSETS ($ mil.)	NET INCOME ($ mil.)	INCOME AS % OF ASSETS	EMPLOYEES
12/18	18,001	221	1.2%	4,445
12/17	15,298	153	1.0%	3,947
12/16	14,724	132	0.9%	3,998
12/15	13,798	127	0.9%	4,002
12/14	13,326	116	0.9%	3,820
Annual Growth	**7.8%**	**17.3%**	**—**	**3.9%**

2018 Year-End Financials

Debt ratio: 0.03%
Return on equity: 11.29%
Cash ($ mil.): 332
Current ratio: —
Long-term debt ($ mil.): —

No. of shares (mil.): 99
Dividends
  Yield: 2.3%
  Payout: 27.8%
Market value ($ mil.): 2,609

	STOCK PRICE ($) FY Close	P/E High/Low	PER SHARE ($) Earnings	Dividends	Book Value
12/18	26.14	16 11	2.23	0.62	22.10
12/17	31.45	20 16	1.67	0.14	18.97
12/16	31.05	22 13	1.41	0.45	18.40
12/15	23.99	20 15	1.33	0.35	17.58
12/14	22.51	21 16	1.21	0.25	16.69
Annual Growth	**3.8%**	**— —**	**16.5%**	**25.5%**	**7.3%**

Bank of America Corp

Among the United States' largest banks by assets (alongside JPMorgan Chase and Citigroup) ubiquitous Bank of America Corporation operates one of the country's most extensive branch networks with some 4300 locations and 16600 ATMs. The bank's core services include consumer and small business banking corporate banking credit cards mortgage lending and asset management. Its online banking operation counts more than 37 million active users and 28 million mobile users. Bank of America acquired Merrill Lynch in 2009 making it one of the world's leading wealth managers with about $2.4 trillion assets under management and boasting a beefed up trading and international businesses. Its US operations account for the vast majority of sales.

HISTORY

Bank of America predecessor NationsBank was formed as the Commercial National Bank in 1874 by citizens of Charlotte North Carolina. In 1901 George Stephens and Word Wood formed what became American Trust Co. The banks merged in 1957 to become American Commercial Bank which in 1960 merged with Security National to form North Carolina National Bank.

In 1968 the bank formed holding company NCNB which by 1980 was the largest bank in North Carolina. Under the leadership of Hugh McColl who became chairman in 1983 NCNB became the first southern bank to span six states.

NCNB profited from the savings and loan crisis of the late 1980s by managing assets and buying defunct thrifts at fire-sale prices. The company nearly doubled its assets in 1988 when the FDIC chose it to manage the shuttered First Republicbank then Texas' largest bank. The company renamed itself NationsBank in 1991.

In 1993 the company bought Chicago Research & Trading a government securities dealer and provider of oil and gas financing. A 1993 joint venture with Dean Witter and Discover to open securities brokerages in banks led to complaints that customers were not fully informed of the risks of some investments and that brokers were paying rebates to banking personnel for customer referrals. Dean Witter withdrew from the arrangement in 1994 and SEC investigations and a class-action lawsuit ensued. NationsBank settled the lawsuit for about $30 million the next year. (The company agreed to pay nearly $7 million to settle similar charges in 1998.)

NationsBank scooped up St. Louis-based Boatmen's Bancshares and Montgomery Securities (now Banc of America Securities) in 1997. The next year it bought Barnett Banks Florida's #1 bank.

Enter BankAmerica. Founded in 1904 as Bank of Italy BankAmerica had once been the US's largest bank but had fallen behind as competitors consolidated. The company's board of directors was pondering ways to become more competitive and in 1998 decided a merger was the best way. With the ink barely dry on its Barnett Banks deal NationsBank obliged.

After the merger the combined firm announced it would write down a billion-dollar bad loan to D.E. Shaw & Co. which followed the same Russian-investment-paved path of descent as Long-Term Capital Management. David Coulter (head of the old BankAmerica which made the loan) took the fall for the loss resigning as president; the balance of power shifted to the NationsBank side in 1999 when Kenneth Lewis took the post.

The Russian debacle and merger hiccups led the firm in early 1999 to reorganize and reduce overseas operations; it sold its private banking operations in Europe and Asia to UBS. Also that year it bought the recreational-vehicle financing unit of Associates First Capital (now part of Citigroup) 50% of Denver-based mutual fund firm Marsico Capital Management (it bought the rest in 2001) and BA Merchant Services. The bank also changed its name to Bank of America and began offering online banking through America Online. To avoid a court battle the bank settled charges that it retained proceeds from unclaimed bonds in California.

In 1999 the company earned the ire of labor officials for a program in which employees were recruited to maintain ATMs without being paid or provided supplies. EVP Frank Gentry who crafted the NationsBank/BankAmerica deal retired in 2000 signaling an end to the company's buying spree. Its focus turned inward as it set about the difficult integration of the two firms.

McColl retired as chairman in 2001. Later that year the company announced it would cease its subprime lending and car leasing operations.

In 2003 Bank of America's mutual fund chief Robert Gordon was among several employees who left the firm amidst a New York attorney general's investigation into hedge fund client Canary Capital Partners which allegedly had access to Bank of America's trading platform to make illegal after-hours trades of the company's erstwhile Nations Funds. Bank of America also paid $10 million for failing to provide documents to the SEC during its investigation of the scandal the largest-ever fine levied by the regulatory body for such an infraction.

The company sold its securities clearing and broker/dealer services units to ADP in 2004. In early 2005 the company struck a deal with regulators to implement tighter controls cut fees charged to investors exit the mutual fund clearing business and pay more than $500 million in fines including $140 million to settle complaints against FleetBoston. Also that year Bank of America remitted about another $460 million to settle investor claims that it did not adequately conduct due diligence when underwriting bonds of doomed telecom firm WorldCom in 2001 and 2002. (The claim involved 17 other investment banks as well; Citigroup paid more than $2.2 billion to clear itself of similar charges in late 2004).

Bank of America previously fattened up by purchasing northeastern banking behemoth Fleet-Boston for some $50 billion in 2004 and credit card giant MBNA for approximately $35 billion in cash and stock in early 2006. The latter deal roughly doubled the bank's credit card customer base (as well as its income from credit card fees) and gave the bank access to some 5000 organizations and institutions with which MBNA had affinity marketing relationships.

In early 2007 the company shed its venture capital arm BA Venture Partners (now Scale Venture Partners) to focus on middle-market private equity investments carried out by its BA Capital Investors unit.

In 2007 Bank of America bought U.S. Trust from Charles Schwab for more than $3 billion and acquired Chicago-based LaSalle Bank from Netherlands-based ABN AMRO for some $21 billion. Following the acquisition of U.S. Trust Bank of America merged the asset manager with its private banking and wealth management business to form U.S. Trust Bank of America Private Wealth Management. Prior acquisitions include credit card giant MBNA in 2006 a deal that doubled the bank's credit card customer base and its income from credit card fees.

In an effort to boost the economy and stimulate lending the US government in 2008 bought some $250 billion worth of preferred shares in the country's top banks. Approximately $45 billion of that was slated for Bank of America ($20 billion more than the original investment total). As a result of the government intervention US Treasury official (and so-called "pay czar") ordered then-CEO Lewis to receive no salary in 2009 and slashed compensation for other highly paid employees. Bank of America finished paying back the debt in late 2009.

As the global economy reeled from a credit freeze and subsequent recession in 2008 Bank of America added to its coffers by buying up troubled mortgage lender Countrywide Financial and investment bank Merrill Lynch. Countrywide had fallen on hard times as one of the hardest-hit victims of the subprime mortgage crisis. The deal was initially for $4 billion in stock but was finalized at around $2.5 billion as the economic climate sunk.

The Countrywide purchase made Bank of America the largest residential mortgage lender and servicer in the US. The company also settled a lawsuit contending that Countrywide engaged in deceptive lending practices. Bank of America agreed to pay more than $8 billion toward reductions on interest rates and principals of some 400000 troubled mortgage accounts. To avoid the stigma of the subprime loan crisis Countrywide was renamed Bank of America Home Loans in 2009.

Bank of America paid some $50 billion in stock to buy Merrill Lynch which had been crippled by the global credit crisis. Hoping to increase its upfront account fee revenues Bank of America began making a concerted push to cross-promote Merrill Lynch's wealth management business to the bank's affluent clients.

However the Merrill Lynch deal also brought its fair share of headaches. With the approval of Bank of America leadership the failed investment bank gave early bonuses worth billions to its executives prompting angry Bank of America shareholders and lawmakers to cry foul. The Securities and Exchange Commission slapped Bank of America with a $33 million fine for misleading shareholders about the bonuses. That fine was rejected by a federal judge in 2009 and the matter was ordered to go to trial. Bank of America ultimately agreed to pay $150 million in a settlement. In another Merrill Lynch-related settlement Bank of America agreed to pay $315 million in 2011 for claims that Merrill Lynch made false and misleading statements about its mortgage-backed securities sold to investors.

Then-CEO Ken Lewis in particular came under fire for not disclosing how bleak Merrill Lynch's financial condition was prior to the purchase; Lewis in turn said he had been implicitly pressured by the government to keep the troubles under wraps to prevent the deal from collapsing. A push to oust Lewis at the company's annual meeting in 2009 didn't pass but shareholders split the chairman and CEO positions to provide more accountability to the public. Director Walter Massey was named chairman and Lewis stepped down at the end of the year. Brian Moynihan the head of consumer and small business banking succeeded Lewis as CEO. Longtime Dupont CEO Charles Holliday took over as chairman in 2010 replacing the retiring Massey.

EXECUTIVES

Chairman And Ceo, Brian T. Moynihan, age 59, $1,500,000 total compensation
Chief Operations And Technology Officer, Catherine P. (Cathy) Bessant, age 58
Coo, Thomas K. (Tom) Montag, age 63, $1,000,000 total compensation
President Preferred And Small Business Banking And Co-head Consumer Banking, Dean C. Athanasia, age 52
President Retail Banking And Co-head Consumer Banking, Thong M. Nguyen, age 60
Vice Chairman And Head Global Wealth And Investment Management, Terence P. (Terry) Laughlin, age 64, $850,000 total compensation
Chief Risk Officer, Geoffrey S. Greener, age 54, $850,000 total compensation
Cfo, Paul M. Donofrio, age 58, $850,000 total compensation
Vice Chairman Global Wealth And Investment Management, John Thiel

Head Of Global Wealth And Retirement Solution, Andy Sieg
Vice President, Michael Young
Vice President, Victor Ward
Svp Consumer Information Security, Brian Metzner
Vice President;gwim Senior Credit Underwriter, Teri Berry
Information Technology Team Manager Assistant Vice President, Leo Kaplin
Vice President, Paul Mccormac
Assistant Vice President, Jennifer Satterthwaite
Vice President Operations Project Consultant, Carol Rogers
Vice President Financial Governance, Rob Edwards
Vice President Human Resources Manager, Michelle John
Senior Vice President, Richard H Vitale
Vice President Small Business Banker, Carlos Gonzalez
Senior Vice President, Greg Pinkerton
Senir Vice President Enterprise Business And Community Events, Lori Rianda
Vice President Senior Technology Manager Applications Programming, John Kwok
Vice President Technology Project Manager, Bruce Mills
Vice President Business Enablement, Amanda Hite
Vice President, Debbie Kirk
Vice President;gwim Senior Credit Underwriter, Erin H Grow
Svp Corporate Investments, Benjamin Tyner
Senior Vice President Leadership Development Executive, Stephanie Asbury
Vice President, Deborah Watson
Vice President, Myra Wardwell
Vice President Client Manager, Angela Meadows
Vice President, Teresa A Bednarski
Assistant Vice President;loan Administration Specialist, Annette Palmer
Vice President, John Waccard
Senior Vice President Business Executive Consumer Technology And Operations, Sudheer Omanakuttan
Senior Vice President Life Events Services, Sandra Agusti
Assistant Vice President Technology Audit Consultant, Marcela Sanchez
Vice President Head Of Business Lending, Marc Deville
Vice President Strategic Account Executi, Karen Fox
Vice President Of Information Technology, Parthasarathi Bhattacharya
Assistant Vice President;file Administrator Ii, Renee Beacham
Vice President, Prasad Pedireddi
Vice President Banking Center Manager, Peter Ackermann
Assistant Vice President;gwim Document Administrator, Kimberly Lewis
Senior Vice President Channel Strategy And Dev Man, Colleen Sims
Vice President Of Customer, Scott Prince
Vice President, Clay Walker
Vice President, Gene Werner
Vice President Human Resources, Stacey Moninski
Assistant Vice President; Application Development, Ganesh Natesan
Senior Vice President Business Control Manager Business Controls And Quality Assurance, Dan Peril
Vice President Senior Client Manager Commercial Real Estate Banking Cdb Bank Of America Merrill Lynch, Valerie Williams
Vice President Operations Manager, Lauren Glad
Senior Vice President, Erin De Avila
Vice President Supplier Diversity Development Manager, Ed Franklin

Vice President Program Manager Centralized Sales, Victor Shetti
Senior Vice President, Tim Gauvin
Senior Vice President Senior Project Manager, Terry Lomas
Vp Product Solutions Regional Leader, Sean Wright
Vice President, Patty Spooner
Vice President Senior Technology Manager Systems Engineer Anly, Albert Hansen
Assistant Vice President, William Pagano
Assistant Vice President;gwim Loan Monitoring Specialist, Jacquelyn Capers
Vice President Small Business Banker, Lenore Culpepper
Senior Vice President Business Development, Alfred Hamilton
Senior Vice President, Robert Maloney
Assistant Vice President;gwim Document Administrator, Lorita Cagle
Vice President Tech And Operations, Dean Osborne
Senior Vice President And Director, Sunil Movva
Vice Presideni Gt And O Innovation Innovation Lab Director, Alicia Jones
Senior Vice President, Thomas Gluckman
Senior Vice President, Stacey Ware
Vice President Senior Audit Consultant Corporate Audit Global Technology, Romelle K Parsons
Senior Vice President, Roy Woodham
Vice President Infrastructure, Chris Ritchie
Vice President; Supplier Manager, Vonshe Jenkins
Vice President Enterprise Data Services, Giovanni Simeone
Vice President Sales Process Integration, Jason Marsilio
Vice President Operational Risk, Shawn Otto
Senior Vice President Senior Credit Products Officer, Bill Franey
Senior Vice President, John Lenckos
Senior Vice President Quality And Reporting Manager, Belinda Eaton
Vice President Technology Architecture And Operations, Jim Drake
Vice President Small Business Card Services, Erin McCullen
Vice President Technology Manager, Steve Plair
Vice President Risk Technology, Lilian Okai
Senior Vice President Market Manager Pennsylvania Corporate Social Responsibility, Deborah O'brien
Vice President Marketing, Michele Ekarius
Vice President Ecommerce Channel Consultant, Jennifer Deisinger
Vice President Of Credit, Michael Boggess
Vice President Existing Customer Marketing Strategies, Alex Wisniewski Alex Wisniewski
Vice President Senior Credit Underwriter, Doug Wilson
Vice President Senior Technology Manager Apps Prog Erm Technology Group, Kalpesh Salot
Vp Business Support Manager, Melissa DiPento
Vice President Commercial Information Officer, Julie Smith
Senior Vice President, Joyce Taylor
Vice President, Amy Larch
Avp Assistant Manager, Corey Schissler
Vice President Unit Manager Corporation, Brian Greene
Vp; North Texas Project Manager, Wendy Morales
Assistant Vice President, Nikhil Nangia
Vp Card Marketing Strategy, Joel Stubblefield
Senior Vice President Portfolio Manager, Craig Murlless
Vice President, Alex Zhu
Senior Vice President Information Architecture Technolo, Michelle Boston
Assistant Vice President Intermediate Financial Analyst, Ryan Murtos
Vp Network Services Operations Governance, Steve Johnston

Vice President Small Business Banker, Tomas Jimenez
Assistant Vice President; Executive Support, Joe Louie
Svp Core Checking Product Manager, Kelly Dinda
Vice President Product Delivery Senior Officer Credit, Stuart Dudley
Vice President, Bill Onisick
Vice President Campus Recruiter, Marisa Witherspoon
Assistant Vice President Quantitative Operations Associate, Ankit Tanwar
Senior Card Account Manager Vice President, Janet Jernigan
Vice President; Operations Project Consultant, Charles Martinez
Vice President Consultant System Engineer, Prajwal Shetty Prajwal Shetty
Vice President; Team Manager Systems Engineering Doss Utility Platform Management, Ed Chaconas
Vice President Senior Operations Consultant, Sylvia Coats
Vice President, Manish Bhargava
Assistant Vice President Senior Marketing Programs Development Manager I, Marcia Carneiro
Vice President, Tracey Weaver
Vice President Competitive Research, Himani Bahl
Vice President, Shontell Knox
Vice President Global Information Security, Benjamin Tweel
Vice President Learning Performance Solutions, Jennifer Banker
Vice President Operations, Beth Law
Assistant Vice President Process Design Consultant, Jennifer Montgomery
Vice President, Julie Wallis
Process Design Consultant Vice President, Grisel Wallace
Vice President, Edwin Wegleitner
Vice President, Jon Whisman
Assistant Vice President; Senior Credit Support Associate, Gayle Sellitto
Senior Vice President, Laurin Titus
Vice President, Torivia Whiten
Vice President, Terrie Wilkerson
Vice President, Karla Wargo
Vice President, Mary Wahlin
Vice President, Wanda White
Vice President, Eileen Webb
Vice President, Marry Wanchik
Vice President, Beth Watson
Senior Vice President Of Organizational Development, Cynthia Bowman
Vice President Of Operations, Sethu Iyer
Assistant Vice President Business Support, Shannon Hart
Vice President Business Support Manager Strategic Portfolio Management (operational Risk), Brad Birkenholtz
Senior Vice President, Beth ONeill
Vice Presidentconsumer Products Strategic Analyst, Dave Ellison
Auditors: PricewaterhouseCoopers LLP

LOCATIONS

HQ: Bank of America Corp
Bank of America Corporate Center, 100 N. Tryon Street, Charlotte, NC 28255
Phone: 704 386-5681
Web: www.bankofamerica.com

2017 Sales by Region

	$ mil.	% of total
US	74,380	86
EMEA	7,907	9
Asia	3,405	4
Latin America	1,210	1
Total	**87,352**	**100**

PRODUCTS/OPERATIONS

2017 Sales

	$ mil.	% of total
Interest income	44,667	51
Non-interest income	42,685	49
Total	**87,352**	**100**

2017 sales

	% of total
Consumer Banking	39
Global Banking	22
Global Wealth & Investment Management	21
Global Markets	18
Total	**100**

Selected Products & Services

Capital raising and advisory
Card solutions
Equipment finance/leasing
Fraud prevention
Interest rate currency and commodity risk management
Investment solutions and management
Lending and financing
Liquidity management
Merchant services
Mergers and acquisitions
Payments/receivables management
Philanthropic management
Retirement and benefit plan services
Trade services

COMPETITORS

BB&T	JPMorgan Chase
Bank of New York Mellon	KeyCorp
	MUFG Americas Holdings
Capital One	Morgan Stanley
Citigroup	PNC Financial
Citizens Financial Group	RBC Financial Group
Goldman Sachs	State Street
HSBC	SunTrust
HSBC USA	U.S. Bancorp
	Wells Fargo

HISTORICAL FINANCIALS

Company Type: Public

Income Statement   FYE: December 31

	ASSETS ($ mil.)	NET INCOME ($ mil.)	INCOME AS % OF ASSETS	EMPLOYEES
12/18	2,354,507	28,147	1.2%	204,000
12/17	2,281,234	18,232	0.8%	209,000
12/16	2,187,702	17,906	0.8%	208,000
12/15	2,144,316	15,888	0.7%	213,000
12/14	2,104,534	4,833	0.2%	224,000
Annual Growth	2.8%	55.3%	—	(2.3%)

2018 Year-End Financials

Debt ratio: 9.11%—
Return on equity: 10.57%
Cash ($ mil.): 177,404
Current ratio: —
Long-term debt ($ mil.): —

Dividends
  Yield: 2.1%
  Payout: 20.6%
Market value ($ mil.): —

	STOCK PRICE ($) FY Close	P/E High/Low		PER SHARE ($) Earnings	Dividends	Book Value
12/18	24.64	12	9	2.61	0.54	27.44
12/17	29.52	18	14	1.56	0.39	25.97
12/16	22.10	15	7	1.50	0.25	26.54
12/15	16.83	13	11	1.31	0.20	24.68
12/14	17.89	50	40	0.36	0.12	23.15
Annual Growth	8.3%	—	—	64.1%	45.6%	4.3%

Bank of Hawaii Corp

Bank of Hawaii Corporation is the holding company for Bank of Hawaii (familiarly known as Bankoh) which has about 70 branches and 380-plus ATMs in its home state plus an additional dozen in American Samoa Guam Palau and Saipan. Founded in 1897 the bank operates through four business segments: retail banking for consumers and small businesses in Hawaii; commercial banking including property/casualty insurance for middle-market and large corporations (this segment also includes the bank's activities beyond the state); investment services such as trust asset management and private banking; and treasury which performs corporate asset and liability management services.

Operations

Bank of Hawaii operates through four segments including retail banking and commercial banking (which together account for about 85% of total net income) and investment services and treasury. The retail banking and commercial baking segments offer a range of financial products and services to consumers and small businesses and middle-market and large enterprises respectively. The company's investment services include private banking trust services and investment advisory services while the treasury segment includes corporate asset and liability management activities.

Bank of Hawaii generates nearly 60% of total revenue from interest and fees on loans. About 60% of its loan portfolio is made up of consumer loans (residential mortgage is the largest) with commercial loans accounting for the rest (commercial mortgage is the largest).

Geographic Reach

Bank of Hawaii provides a broad range of financial services and products to customers not only Hawaii but in Guam and other Pacific islands. Its principal offices are located in Honolulu.

Sales and Marketing

Bank of Hawaii spent about $6 million on advertising in 2017 and 2016 compared to $5.3 million in 2015.

Financial Performance

As Hawaii's real estate market continues to set records (in median sales prices for Oahu homes among other areas) Bank of Hawaii has seen consistent growth over the past five years with revenue up more than 15% since 2013. Net income has been on a similar trajectory rising just more than 20% during that time.

In 2017 the company reported revenue of $642.7 million which is up 5% from the prior year. The increase was powered by growth in the commercial and consumer lending portfolios as well as higher net interest margin; it was somewhat offset by a decline in noninterest income led by a nearly $7 million drop in mortgage banking income.

Net income rose 2% to $184.7 million in 2017 on the increase in revenue. The retail and commercial baking segments together account for 85% of total net income.

Cash at the end of fiscal 2017 was $447.8 million a decrease of $431.8 million from the prior year. Cash from operations contributed $175.1 million to the coffers while investing activities used $1 billion mainly because of net change in loans and leases and purchases of investment securities held-to-maturity. Financing activities provided another $415 million on a net change in deposits.

Strategy

A primary focus for Bank of Hawaii along with many other regional banks is modernizing and digitizing its business. It continues to renovate branches into what it calls the Branch of Tomorrow which includes updated technology interactive and private meeting spaces and more. In addition the company has introduced easy-deposit ATMs a Cardless Cash feature and enhancements to its mobile banking app.

Company Background

Bank of Hawaii traces its history to 1897 when businessman Peter Cushman Jones and friends Joseph Ballard Atherton and Charles Montague Cooke established a bank to serve the Hawaiian Islands. It was the first chartered and incorporated bank to do business in the Republic of Hawaii.

The company had branches on every major island in the archipelago by 1930. In 1971 it reorganized as a bank holding company.

EXECUTIVES

Sevp And Cfo, Dean Y. Shigemura
Chairman President And Ceo, Peter S. Ho, age 55, $776,077 total compensation
Vice Chairman And Chief Risk Officer, Mary E. Sellers, age 63, $427,565 total compensation
Vice Chairman Client Solutions Group, Sharon M. Crofts
Vice Chairman And Chief Administrative Officer, Mark A. Rossi, age 70, $433,776 total compensation
Vice Chairman; Chief Commercial Officer, Wayne Y. Hamano, $355,170 total compensation
Vice Chairman; Residential And Consumer Lending Group Manager, Derek J. Norris, age 69, $224,615 total compensation
Executive Vice President, Betty Brow
Senior Vice President, Galen Nakamura
Vice President, Rowell Comia
Vice President Of Operations, Andrew Boyles
Assistant Vice President And Operations Manager, Chris Onzuka
Vice President Loan And Deposit Operations, Linda Bernal
Senior Vice President, Kevin Baptist
Vice President Of Cash Management, Bernie Alama
Assistant Vice President And Grants Administrator, Paula Boyce
Senior Vice President And Contact Center Manager Operations, Doree J Ohelo
Vice President Of Lending, Cindy Okamura
Assistant Vice President Dealer Marketing Relationship Officer, Craig Ito
Vice President And Audit Consultant, Irene E B Kwan
Senior Vice President And Senior Audit Manager, James P Garcia
Vice President And Relationship Manager, Sean Rostron
Vice President Commercial Credit Manager, Rita Jugo
Vice President, Tom Guinan
Vice President And Commercial Banking Officer, Jenny Kajioka
Senior Vice President, Terri Okada
Vice President, Kathleen Bryan
Assistant Vice President, Gil Farias
Svp And Manager, Mark Tokito
Vice President And Assistant Service Manager, Tina Nakahara
Vice President, Toshiya Matsumoto
Assistant Vice President And Guam Residential Loan Manager, Calvin Hernandez
Vice President, Dean Uyeda
Vice President And West Oahu Isb Area Manager Of Bank Of Hawaii, Charleen Deuprey
Vice President, Edison Kobayashi
Assistant Vice President, Lynette Sakamoto
Executive Vice President Human Resources, Lester Stiefel
Senior Vice President And Manager, Steven Nakahara
Vice President, Miki Ikeda
Executive Vice President, David Oyadomari
Assistant Vice President And Compensation Manager, Kaleo Kekoolani
Senior Executive Vice President, Jill Higa
Executive Vice President, Edward Kim
Assistant Vice President And Customer Service Manager, Randi Yoshikawa
Vice President And Sales And Marketing And Client Development Manager, Dale Tanimoto
Senior Vice President, Brent Flygar
Senior Vice President, Ellen Mulholland
Senior Vice President Retail Deposits, Matt Emerson
Vice President, Malcom Lau
Financial Consultant And Vice President, Christopher Otto
Vice President And Manager Palau Island, Christina Michelsen
Senior Vice President, Shanae Souza
Senior Vice President, Kevin Sakamoo
Senior Vice President Director Of Corporate Security, Brian Ishikawa
Senior Operations Coordinator And Assistant Vice President, Melissa Poblete
Vice President, Randy Matsumoto
Vice President Private Client Services, Annalena Zanolini
Vice President, Rudy Alvior
Vice President Administration, Nelson Dang
Vice President, Paul Ramelb
Senior Vice President, Leilani Williams
Vice President, Natalie Fogle
Assistant Vice President And Senior Auditor, Jason Smith
Executive Vice President, Cynthia Wyrick
Vice President Business Banking, Gregory Knue
Senior Vice President Commercial Banking, Robert Mancini
Vice President And Private Wealth Advisor, Lisa Goo
Vice President Senior Portfolio Manager, Stephanie Nomura
Vice President, Janelle Higa
Vice President, Corey Shimabuku
Vice President, Jennifer Gershman
Vice President And Service Manager, Lisa Revilla
Vp And Manager Of International Commercial Banking, Robert Fortuna
Vice President, Amy Honda
Assistant Vice President Senior Consumer Loan Officer Dealer Indirect Lending Bank Of Hawaii, Cheryl Kaohi
Vice President Commercial Banking, Vincent Perez
Vp And Corporate Counsel, Val Ito
Vice President, Rosemarie Aquino
Assistant Vice President And Senior Auditor, Daniel Li
Vice President, Joseph Jaquay
Assistant Vice President Service Manager, Kimberly Holani
Vice President Commercial Banking Officer, Christopher Frost
Vice President, Gunjan Doshi
Vice President, Helene B Davis
Vice President, Holly Araki
Vice President And Manager Corporate Sourcing And Accounts Payable Department, Calla Oda
Senior Vice President, William Carpenter
Senior Vice President, Joel Tolentino
Vice President, Kawika Fiddler
Executive Vice President, Sheila Haunani Gomes
Vice President And Relationship Manager, Marissa Machida
Vice President Institutional Services, Keith Sato
Vice President And Real Estate Manager Corporate Facilities, Michael Taylor
Vice Chairman And Chief Strategy Officer, Kent T. Lucien, age 65
Vice Chairman, Donna A. Tanoue, age 65

Svp; **Manager Commercial Credit Underwriting And Analysis Pacific Islands Division Bank Of Hawaii,** James C. (Jim) Polk
Secretary, Jill Rotolo
Secretary, SHERRY SERRANO
Board Member, Pamela Moy
Board Member, ROBERT WO
Board Member, ROB NICHOLS
Board Member, Robert Huret
Board Member, Barbara Tanabe
Board Member, Mark Burak
Board Member, Clinton Churchill
Board Member, Raymond Vara
Board Member, Haunani Apoliona
Auditors: Ernst & Young LLP

LOCATIONS

HQ: Bank of Hawaii Corp
   130 Merchant Street, Honolulu, HI 96813
Phone: 888 643-3888
Web: www.boh.com

PRODUCTS/OPERATIONS

2017 Sales

	$ mil.	% of total
Net Interest Income		
Interest and Fees on Loans and Leases	370	48
Income on Investment Securities	128	21
Other	4	.
Interest Expense	(46.5)	.
Non-interest Income		
Trust and Asset Management	45	8
Mortgage Banking	13	2
Service Charges on Deposit Accounts	32	6
Fees Exchange and Other Service Charges	54	9
Investment Securities Gains Net	10	2
Annuity and Insurance	6	1
Bank-Owned Life Insurance	6	1
Other	15	2
Total	**642**	**100**

Selected Products/Services
Personal
Banking Products
Checking
Savings
Special Packages
Loans & Lines
Mortgages
Credit Cards
Debit Cards
Online & Mobile Banking
IRAs
Small Business
Banking Products
Checking
Savings
Special Packages
Credit Card
Debit Card
Loans & Leasing
Trade & International
Business Services
Online Banking
Corporate & Commercial
Checking
Savings
Cash Management
Loans & Leasing
International Trade Services
Business Needs

COMPETITORS

American Savings Bank
Australia and New
   Zealand Banking
Bank of America
Central Pacific
   Financial

First Hawaiian
HSBC
Territorial Bancorp
Westpac Banking

HISTORICAL FINANCIALS

Company Type: Public

Income Statement
FYE: December 31

	ASSETS ($ mil.)	NET INCOME ($ mil.)	INCOME AS % OF ASSETS	EMPLOYEES
12/18	17,143	219	1.3%	2,122
12/17	17,089	184	1.1%	2,132
12/16	16,492	181	1.1%	2,122
12/15	15,455	160	1.0%	2,200
12/14	14,787	163	1.1%	2,200
Annual Growth	3.8%	7.7%	—	(0.9%)

2018 Year-End Financials

Debt ratio: 0.06%	No. of shares (mil.): 41
Return on equity: 17.57%	Dividends
Cash ($ mil.): 327	Yield: 3.4%
Current ratio: —	Payout: 44.7%
Long-term debt ($ mil.): —	Market value ($ mil.): 2,794

	STOCK PRICE ($) FY Close	P/E High/Low		PER SHARE ($) Earnings	Dividends	Book Value
12/18	67.32	17	12	5.23	2.34	30.56
12/17	85.70	21	17	4.33	2.04	29.05
12/16	88.69	21	13	4.23	1.89	27.24
12/15	62.90	19	15	3.70	1.80	25.79
12/14	59.31	17	14	3.69	1.80	24.13
Annual Growth	3.2%	—	—	9.1%	6.8%	6.1%

Bank of Marin Bancorp

Bank of Marin supports the wealthy enclave of Marin County north of San Francisco. The bank operates more than 20 branches in the posh California counties of Marin Sonoma and Napa as well as in San Francisco and Alameda counties. Targeting area residents and small to midsized businesses the bank offers standard retail products as checking and savings accounts CDs credit cards and loans. It also provides private banking and wealth management services to high net-worth clients. Commercial mortgages account for the largest portion of the company's loan portfolio followed by business construction and home equity loans.

Geographic Reach
Bank of Marin has branches in Alameda Corte Madera Emeryville Greenbrae Mill Valley Napa Novato Oakland Petaluma San Francisco San Rafael Santa Rosa Sausalito Sonoma and Tiburon.

Sales and Marketing
Its customer base is made up of individuals small to midsized businesses professionals and not-for-profit organizations.

Financial Performance
The bank makes its money through interest income and non-interest income such as service charges and fees. Interest income accounts for almost 90% of overall revenues. The bank has seen its revenue levels fluctuate over the years and in 2013 revenues fell 5% to $68 million due to lower yields on investments and new loans with lower interest rates.

Mergers and Acquisitions
In 2013 the bank gained a branch in Alameda with the purchase of NorCal Community Bancorp the holding company of the Bank of Alameda.

EXECUTIVES

President Ceo And Director Bank Of Marin Bancorp And Bank Of Marin, Russell A. (Russ) Colombo, age 66, $400,355 total compensation
Evp Retail Banking Bank Of Marin, Peter Pelham, age 62, $214,725 total compensation
Evp And Cfo, Tani Girton, age 59, $239,500 total compensation
Evp And Chief Credit Officer Bank Of Marin, Elizabeth Reizman, age 60, $221,250 total compensation
Evp Commercial Banking Bank Of Marin, Timothy D. (Tim) Myers, age 48, $215,000 total compensation
Evp And Cio, James T. Burke, age 64
Chairman Bank Of Marin Bancorp And Bank Of Marin, Brian M. Sobel, age 64
Auditors: Moss Adams LLP

LOCATIONS

HQ: Bank of Marin Bancorp
   504 Redwood Boulevard, Suite 100, Novato, CA 94947
Phone: 415 763-4520
Web: www.bankofmarin.com

PRODUCTS/OPERATIONS

2015 Sales

	$ mil.	% of total
Interest income		
Interest and fees on loan	61	78
Interest on investment securities	7	10
Non-Interest income		
Wealth management & trust services	2	3
Service charges on deposit accounts	2	3
Debit card interchange fees	1	2
Others	3	4
Total	**78**	**100**

Selected Services
Business checking
Cash management
Credit cards
Floating home loans
Home equity lines
Lending
Online and mobile
Personal checking
Personal savings

COMPETITORS

Bank of America
Bank of the West
Citibank
Community Bank of the Bay
FNB Bancorp (CA)
First Republic (CA)

MUFG Americas Holdings
Patelco Credit Union
SVB Financial
U.S. Bancorp
Wells Fargo
Westamerica

HISTORICAL FINANCIALS

Company Type: Public

Income Statement
FYE: December 31

	ASSETS ($ mil.)	NET INCOME ($ mil.)	INCOME AS % OF ASSETS	EMPLOYEES
12/18	2,520	32	1.3%	305
12/17	2,468	15	0.6%	313
12/16	2,023	23	1.1%	262
12/15	2,031	18	0.9%	274
12/14	1,787	19	1.1%	278
Annual Growth	9.0%	13.3%	—	2.3%

2018 Year-End Financials

Debt ratio: 0.10%	No. of shares (mil.): 13
Return on equity: 10.64%	Dividends
Cash ($ mil.): 34	Yield: 3.0%
Current ratio: —	Payout: 74.7%
Long-term debt ($ mil.): —	Market value ($ mil.): 571

	STOCK PRICE ($)	P/E		PER SHARE ($)		
	FY Close	High/Low	Earnings	Dividends	Book Value
12/18	41.24	38 16	2.33	1.27	22.85
12/17	68.00	57 46	1.28	0.56	21.46
12/16	69.75	39 25	1.89	0.51	18.81
12/15	53.40	36 30	1.52	0.90	17.67
12/14	52.59	32 25	1.65	0.80	16.84
Annual Growth	(5.9%)	— —	9.1%	12.2%	7.9%

Bank of New York Mellon Corp

The Bank of New York Mellon (BNY Mellon) is one of the world's largest global asset servicing companies and a leader in asset management and corporate trust and treasury services. The firm boasts $35.5 trillion in assets under custody and administration and some $1.8 trillion in assets under management. BNY Mellon's state-chartered bank subsidiary Bank of New York Mellon offers asset issuer treasury broker-dealer and clearance and collateral services while its other main subsidiary BNY Mellon N.A. offers wealth management services. Alexander Hamilton a founding father of the US and icon of the US $10 bill helped establish in 1784 The Bank of New York which merged in 2007 with Pittsburgh?s Mellon Financial to form BNY Mellon.

HISTORY

In 1784 Alexander Hamilton (at 27 already a Revolutionary War hero and economic theorist) and a group of New York merchants and lawyers founded New York City's first bank The Bank of New York (BNY). Hamilton saw a need for a credit system to finance the nation's growth and to establish credibility for the new nation's chaotic monetary system.

Hamilton became US secretary of the treasury in 1789 and soon negotiated the new US government's first loan — for $200000 — from BNY. The bank later helped finance the War of 1812 by raising $16 million and the Civil War by loaning the government $150 million. In 1878 BNY became a US Treasury depository for the sale of government bonds.

The bank's conservative fiscal policies and emphasis on commercial banking enabled it to weather economic turbulence in the 19th century. In 1922 it merged with New York Life Insurance and Trust (formed in 1830 by many of BNY's directors) to form Bank of New York and Trust. The bank survived the crash of 1929 and remained profitable paying dividends throughout the Depression. In 1938 it reclaimed its Bank of New York name.

During the mid-20th century BNY expanded its operations and its reach through acquisitions including Fifth Avenue Bank (trust services 1948) and Empire Trust (serving developing industries 1966). In 1968 the bank created holding company The Bank of New York Company to expand statewide with purchases such as Empire National Bank (1980).

BNY relaxed its lending policies in the 1980s and began to build its fee-for-service side boosting its American Depositary Receipts business by directly soliciting European companies and seeking government securities business. The bank bought New York rival Irving Trust in a 1989 hostile takeover and in 1990 began buying other banks' credit card portfolios.

As the economy cooled in the early 1990s BNY's book of highly leveraged transactions and nonperforming loans suffered so the company sold many of those loans.

In the mid-1990s BNY bought processing and trust businesses and continued to build its retail business in the suburbs. It pared noncore operations selling its mortgage banking unit (and in 1998 moved its remaining mortgage operations into a joint venture with Alliance Mortgage); credit card business (1998); and factoring and asset-based lending operations (1999). In late 1997 and again in 1998 the bank tried to woo Mellon Bank (now Mellon Financial) into a merger but was rejected; it had better luck in 2006.

The growth of the firm's custody services accelerated in the late 1990s. In 1997 BNY bought operations from Wells Fargo Signet Bank (later part of First Union) and NationsBank (now Bank of America). By 1998 BNY had bought some two dozen corporate trust businesses. Two years later it acquired the trust operations of Royal Bank of Scotland and Barclays Bank.

During this period BNY also built its other operations largely through purchases. It bought the Bank of Montreal's UK-based fiscal agency business (1998) and Eastbrook Capital Management which manages assets for businesses and wealthy individuals (1999).

Scandal rocked the firm in 1999 when the US began investigating the possible flow of money related to Russian organized crime; the following year a former bank executive admitted to having laundered about $7 billion through BNY. The bank reached a non-prosecution agreement in the US in 2005 and four years later agreed to a $14 million settlement with Russia.

In 2000 BNY bought the corporate trust business of Dai-Ichi Kangyo Bank (now part of Mizuho Financial) and Harris Trust and Savings Bank. It also purchased a trio of securities clearing and processing firms in addition to hedge fund manager Ivy Asset Management. The next year BNY bought the corporate trust operations of U.S. Trust.

Purchases in 2002 included equity research firm Jaywalk institutional trader Francis P. Maglio & Co. and a pair of Boston-area asset managers for high-net-worth individuals Gannet Welsh & Kotler and Beacon Fiduciary Advisors. BNY bought Pershing from Credit Suisse First Boston in 2003.

Fallout from the money laundering scandal lingered. In 2006 the Federal Reserve accused the bank of not tightening its own controls to prevent a recurrence of illegal activity. But there were apparently no hard feelings between BNY and the federal government who tapped the company in 2008 to act as custodian for the US Treasury's $700 million Troubled Asset Relief Program (TARP) meant to provide liquidity to banks.

The Bank of New York jettisoned much of its traditional banking services for more lucrative fee-based securities and financial services swapping virtually all its retail branches in metropolitan New York for JPMorgan Chase's corporate trust business in 2006. Both units were valued at more than $2 billion each and JPMorgan Chase paid an additional $150 million in cash to make up the difference.

In 2007 Bank of New York merged with Mellon Financial to create BNY Mellon). It was the New York company's third attempt to acquire the Pittsburgh-based firm. The deal cemented the company's status as one of the largest securities servicing companies in the world and augmented its other areas of focus including asset management and corporate trust and treasury services.

The company followed that transaction with the sale of Mellon 1st Business Bank to U.S. Bancorp in 2008.

In 2009 the company acquired Insight Investment Management which specializes in liability-driven investment services fixed income products and alternative investments from Lloyds Bank for some $387 million. Also that year BNY Mellon bought analytics firm Portsmouth Financial Systems. The acquisition offered customers more transparency in structured credit portfolios.

In 2010 BNY Mellon sold one of the last remnants of Mellon Financial's banking operations the Florida-based Mellon United National Bank to Banco de Sabadell. Mellon had previously sold most of its retail business to Royal Bank of Scotland's US banking arm Citizens Financial Group in 2001. In 2015 looking to bolster its Investment Management business BNY bought New York-based Cutwater Asset Management which boasts some $23 billion in assets. The acquired company works closely with one of BNY Mellon's premier investment firms and leading European asset manager Insight Investment.In 2016 BNY Mellon bought California-based Atherton Lane Advisors one of the Menlo Park region's investment managers as well as its $2.5 billion in assets under management and 700 high net worth clients. The deal moved BNY into a key wealth market for a national and global expansion strategy.

EXECUTIVES

Chairman And Ceo, Gerald L. Hassell, age 67, $1,000,000 total compensation
Ceo Clearing Markets And Client Management, Thomas P. (Todd) Gibbons, age 62, $650,000 total compensation
Ceo Investment Management, Mitchell E. Harris, $625,000 total compensation
Sevp And General Counsel, J. Kevin McCarthy, age 55
Ceo Pershing, Lisa Dolly
Ceo Global Asset Servicing And Chairman Europe Middle East And Africa (emea), Hani Kablawi
Sevp And Chief Human Resources Officer, Monique R. Herena
Sevp And Head Client Service Delivery, Doug Shulman
Sevp And Chief Risk Officer, James S. (Jim) Wiener
Ceo Exchange Traded Funds, Jeff McCarthy
Chairman Asia Pacific, J. David Cruikshank
Ceo Issuer Services, Francis J. (Frank) La Salla
Ceo Alternative Investment Services (ais) And Structured Products, Chandresh Iyer
Sevp And Cio, Bridget E. Engle
Cfo, Michael P. Santomassimo
Ceo Bny Mellon Markets, Michelle M. Neal
Senior Vice President, John Weisenhorn
Assistant Vice President Systems And Technology, Rebecca Stalker
Vice President Relationship Manager, Mary Snyder
Vice President Director Of Sales, Donna Nemecek
Vice President, Larry Denbaum
Vice President, Robert Dawson
Assistant Vice President Systems, Kenneth Kenneth Newman Newman
Vice President Information Technology Manager, James Milella
Vice President Messaging Engineering, Anwar Ahmed
Vice President Information Technology, Joseph Aboulafia
Vice President, Keith Koble
Vice President Of Human Resources Business Partner, Louise Lisi
Senior Vice President And Director Of Employee Benefits, Robert Perego

Vice President, Patricia Gallagher
Vice President Business Analysis Quality, Lynn Leshe
Vice President Global Trade Finance Servs Div, Andrea Ratay
Vice President, Randolph Medrano
Vice President, Cary Jones
Vice President, Ellie Whalen
Vice President, Raymond Connery
Assistant Vice President, Jeffrey Roe
Vice President, Joseph Schnorr
Senior Vice President Legal Affairs, Bill Robinson
Vice President And Privacy Officer Mutual Funds Project Manager Asset Management Ops, Carla Wanzer
Vice President Of Information Technology, Gopinath Tatachar
Financial Analyst Vice President Corporate Trust, Evelina Lotte
Assistant Vice President Investments, Remy Quito
Vice President, Edward Dougherty
Assistant Vice President, John Rushmore
Vice President, David Sunderwirth
Assistant Vice President, Ann Lynch
Vice President, Gordon Wong
Vice President, Mary Milner
Vice President Customer Technology Solutions Delivery, Carl Hagelin
Vice President, Charles Baker
Vice President, Justin Verdesca
Vice President, Brian Stern
Assistant Vice President Information Security, Sam Dekay
Assistant Vice President, Panagiota Bouboulis
Vice President And Relationship Manager, Mark Hochgesang
Vice President, Brian Weddington
Vice President, Melinda Valentine
Assistant Vice President Business Services Group, Danny Wong
Vice President, Paul Angotta
Vice President, Elizabeth Wagner
Vice President, Claudia Leslie
Vice President, Brenda Stone
Vice President North American Banks Division, Joseph Barnes
Vice President, Reyne Macadaeg
Vice President Application Development, Brian Burton
Assistant Vice President, Glenn Obando
Vice President, Peter Helt
Assistant Vice President, Kerri Shenkin
Vice President, Paul Meskiewicz
Vice President, Rebecca Newman
Vice President, Derrick Cornelious
Vice President Relationship Manager Long Island Queens Brooklyn Regional Commercial Banking, Gail Rnian-bivona
Senior Vice President Customer Care, Bruce Falkin
Vice President, Larisa Turetsky
Vice President, Peter Holland
Executive Vice President, John Moore
Vice President Information Risk Management, Michael Lam
Vice President Of Information Solutions, Peter Farrell
Vice President Marketing Communications, Geraldine Lutzel
Vice President, David Cook
Vice President U S Corporate Banking, Mark O'Connor
Vice President, Lawrence Timmins
Vice President, Ron Giromonte
Vice President, Irene Kugel
Vice President, Carol Turi
Vice President, Joseph Sierra
Vice President Of Sales, Sarah Foster
Vice President Human Resources, Susan McFarlan
Vice President Of Information Technology Learning, Michael Dermody

Assistant Vice President Internal Audit, Maria Dolinski
Vice President Benefits Disbursements, Steve Coates
Vice President It Procurement Bank Of New York Mellon, Rich Castman
Assistant Vice President; Critical System Engineer, Dan Gaffney
Senior Vice President, Douglas Owen
Vice President Global Corporate Trust, Mike Maio
Vice President, Timothy Fitzgerald
Vice President, Wayne Ross
Assistant Vice President, Clarence Burleigh
Assistant Vice President, Karen O'Donohoe
Assistant Vice President Technology Global Markets And Ecommerce, Vadim Kazakevich
Assistant Vice President, Neil Grill
Assistant Vice President, Jeff Charmatz
Senior Vice President Chief Information Officer, Kurt Wetzel
Senior Vice President, James McTiernan
Assistant Vice President Corporate General Services, Patrick Koziol
Executive Vice President The Bank Of New York, John R Mohr
Executive Vice President The Bank Of New York, Thomas V Ford
Assistant Vice President Enterprise Bi Architect, Ron Van Der Laan
Vp Advanced Engineering, Matt Senken
First Vice President Operations Strategy Group, Mary Hannon
Vice President, Jeffrey Wolf
Vp Alternative Investment Services, Thomas Ryder
Vice President, Karen Manning
Executive Vice President The Bank Of New York, William Kerr
It Vice President Application Developer, John Metzger
Assistant Vice President Project Manager, Richard Ludwig
Vice President, Jean McNicholas Earley
Vice President, Kristine Gullo
Vice President Information Technology Asset, Karen Saxton
Middle Office Manager Vice President, Christopher Hart
Vice President, Sean Grace
Vice President, Rebecca Ryan
Middleware Specialist Iii Vice President, Mark Barnett
Vice President, Mitch Marburg
Vice President Corporate Events, Kat Fleming
Vice President Unix Specialist Systems Engineer, Shannon Hughes
Vice President Treasury Risk Management Within The Enterprise Audit Function, Francis Feola
Vice President Information Security, Donald Lorenz
Vice President, William Ewing
Vice President, Stacey Swentkowsky
Vice President, Heather Hinojosa
Vice President, Housto Earl Cockrell
Vice President And Cao, Joshua Tkalcevic
Vice President, Carolyn Lauro
Vice President Global Institutional Accounting, Dena Dojcak
Vice President Information Technology Project Manager, Steve Capizzi
First Vice President, Gordon Sapko
Vice President Itcollaborationservices, Courtney Kane
Board Member, Thomas J Mastro
Assistant Treasurer, Wendy Havener
Assistant Treasurer Of Information Security, Nicholas Aromando
Assistant Treasurer, Cheryl Baye
Assistant Treasurer, David Rocco
Assistant Treasurer, Daniel Giles
Assistant Treasurer, Nina Cheung

Assistant Treasurer, Denise Freytas
Assistant Treasurer, Marcus McGregor
Treasurer, Ruby Pizzini
Assistant Treasurer, Nicole Pelligra
Assistant Treasurer Asia Pacific Division, Xiaotong Jia
Auditors: KPMG LLP

LOCATIONS

HQ: Bank of New York Mellon Corp
240 Greenwich Street, New York, NY 10286
Phone: 212 495-1784
Web: www.bnymellon.com

PRODUCTS/OPERATIONS

2016 Revenue

	$ mil.	% of total
Investment servicing fees		
Asset servicing	4,244	27
Clearing services	1,404	9
Issuer services	1,026	7
Treasury services	547	3
Interest net	3,138	22
Investment management & performance fees	3,350	23
Foreign exchange & other trading revenue	701	4
Investment & other income	341	2
Financing-related fees	219	1
Distribution & servicing	166	1
Net securities gains	75	1
Income from consolidated investment management funds	26	-
Total	**15,237**	**100**

Selected Subsidiaries and Business Lines

BNY Capital Funding LLC - State of Organization: Delaware
BNY Capital Markets Holdings Inc. - State of Incorporation: New York
BNY Capital Resources Corporation - State of Incorporation: New York
BNY International Financing Corporation - Incorporation: United States
BNY Mellon Capital Markets LLC - State of Organization: Delaware
BNY Mellon Fund Managers Limited - Incorporation: England
BNY Mellon Global Management Limited - Incorporation: Ireland
BNY Mellon International Asset Management Group Limited - Incorporation: England
BNY Mellon International Asset Management (Holdings) Limited - Incorporation: England and Wales
BNY Mellon International Asset Management (Holdings) No. 1 Limited - Incorporation: England and Wales
BNY Mellon Investment Management Cayman Ltd. - Incorporation: Cayman Islands
BNY Mellon Investment Management EMEA Limited - Incorporation: England
BNY Mellon Investment Management Europe Holdings Limited - Incorporation: England
BNY Mellon Investment Management (Europe) Limited - Incorporation: England
BNY Mellon Investment Management (Jersey) Limited - Incorporation: Jersey
BNY Mellon Investment Servicing (US) Inc. - State of Incorporation: Massachusetts
BNY Mellon National Association - Incorporation: United States
BNY Mellon Securities Services (Ireland) Limited - Incorporation: Ireland
BNY Mellon Trust Company (Ireland) Limited - Incorporation: Ireland
BNYM GIS Funding I LLC - State of Organization: Delaware
BNYM GIS Funding III LLC - State of Organization: Delaware
BNYM GIS (UK) Funding II LLC - State of Organization: Delaware
Insight Investment Funds Management Limited - Incorporation: England
Insight Investment Management (Global) Limited - Incorporation: England
Insight Investment Management Limited - Incorporation: England
MAM (MA) Holding Trust - State of Incorporation: Massachusetts

MBC Investments Corporation - State of Incorporation: Delaware

Mellon Canada Holding Company - Incorporation: Canada

Mellon Overseas Investment Corporation - Incorporation: United States

Pershing Group LLC - State of Organization: Delaware

Pershing Holdings (UK) Limited - Incorporation: England

Pershing Limited - Incorporation: England

Pershing LLC - State of Organization: Delaware

Pershing Securities Limited - Incorporation: England

Standish Mellon Asset Management Company LLC - State of Organization: Delaware

The Bank of New York Mellon - State of Organization: New York

The Bank of New York Mellon (International) Limited - Incorporation: England

The Bank of New York Mellon (Luxembourg) S.A. - Incorporation: Luxembourg

The Bank of New York Mellon SA/NV - Incorporation: Belgium

The Dreyfus Corporation - State of Incorporation: New York

Walter Scott & Partners Limited - Incorporation: Scotland

COMPETITORS

Bank of America	JPMorgan Chase
Barclays	Morgan Stanley
BlackRock	Northern Trust
Charles Schwab	PNC Financial
Citigroup	Prudential
Credit Suisse (USA)	State Street
Deutsche Bank	U.S. Bancorp
Franklin Templeton	Wells Fargo
HSBC	

HISTORICAL FINANCIALS

Company Type: Public

Income Statement

FYE: December 31

	ASSETS ($ mil.)	NET INCOME ($ mil.)	INCOME AS % OF ASSETS	EMPLOYEES
12/18	362,873	4,266	1.2%	51,300
12/17	371,758	4,090	1.1%	52,500
12/16	333,469	3,547	1.1%	52,000
12/15	393,780	3,158	0.8%	51,200
12/14	385,303	2,567	0.7%	50,300
Annual Growth	(1.5%)	13.5%	—	0.5%

2018 Year-End Financials

Debt ratio: 8.04%	No. of shares (mil.): 960
Return on equity: 10.42%	Dividends
Cash ($ mil.): 88,000	Yield: 2.2%
Current ratio: —	Payout: 25.7%
Long-term debt ($ mil.): —	Market value ($ mil.): 45,207

	STOCK PRICE ($) FY Close	P/E High/Low	PER SHARE ($) Earnings	Dividends	Book Value
12/18	47.07	14 11	4.04	1.04	42.31
12/17	53.86	15 12	3.72	0.86	40.70
12/16	47.38	16 10	3.15	0.72	37.05
12/15	41.22	17 13	2.71	0.68	35.05
12/14	40.57	19 12	2.15	0.66	33.48
Annual Growth	3.8%	— —	17.1%	12.0%	6.0%

Bank OZK

Bank of the Ozarks is the holding company for the bank of the same name which has about 260 branches in Alabama Arkansas California the Carolinas Florida Georgia New York and Texas. Fo-

cusing on individuals and small to midsized businesses the $12-billion bank offers traditional deposit and loan services in addition to personal and commercial trust services retirement and financial planning and investment management. Commercial real estate and construction and land development loans make up the largest portion of Bank of the Ozarks' loan portfolio followed by residential mortgage business and agricultural loans. Bank of the Ozarks grows its loan and deposit business by acquiring smaller banks and opening branches across the US.

Operations

The bank makes three-fourths of its total revenue from interest income while the rest comes from fee-based sources. About 43% of Bank of the Ozark's total revenue came from non-purchased loan interest in 2014 while another 26% came from interest on purchased loans and a further 8% came from interest on its investment securities. The rest of its revenue came from service charges on deposit accounts (8% of revenue) mortgage lending income (1%) trust income (1%) and other non-recurring sources.

Geographic Reach

Bank of the Ozarks had 174 branches in eight states at the end of 2014 with 81 of them in Alabama and another 75 branches split among Georgia North Carolina and Texas. It has two loan offices in Houston and Manhattan that serve as an extension of the bank's Dallas-based Real Estate Specialties Group.

Sales and Marketing

The bank spent $3.03 million on advertising and public relations expenses in 2014 compared to $2.2 million and $4.09 million in 2013 and 2012 respectively.

Financial Performance

Bank of the Ozarks' annual revenues and profits have doubled since 2010 mostly as its loan assets have doubled from recent bank acquisitions spawning higher interest income.

The bank's revenue jumped 31% to $376 million during 2014 mostly thanks to strong purchased and non-purchased loan asset growth during the year from recent bank acquisitions. Its non-interest income grew 12% thanks to a 20% increase in deposit account service charges stemming from newly acquired deposit customers.

Strong revenue growth in 2014 boosted Bank of the Ozarks' net income by 30% to $119 million for the year. Its operating cash levels jumped 22% to $61 million during the year mostly thanks to higher cash earnings.

Strategy

Bank of the Ozarks continues its strategy of loan and deposit volume growth by acquiring smaller banks in new and existing geographic markets. It has also opened new branches and loan offices sparingly. During 2014 for example the bank opened retail branches in Bradenton Florida; Cornelius North Carolina; and Hilton Head Island South Carolina along with a new loan production office in Asheville North Carolina.

Mergers and Acquisitions

In July 2016 Bank of the Ozarks acquired Georgia-based Community & Southern Holdings and its Community & Southern Bank subsidiary. Adding some 45 branch locations in Georgia plus another in Florida it was the company's largest acquisition to-date.

Also in July 2016 the bank purchased C1 Financial along with its 32 C1 Bank branches on the west coast of Florida and in Miami-Dade and Orange Counties. The deal added $1.7 billion in total assets $1.4 billion in loans and $1.3 billion in deposits. This transaction was the bank's fifteenth acquisition in the past six years.

In August 2015 the bank purchased Bank of the Carolinas Corporation (BCAR) — and its eight

Bank of the Carolinas branches in North Carolina $345 million in total assets $277 million in loans and $296 million in deposits — for a total price of $65.4 million.

In February 2015 Bank of the Ozarks bought Intervest Bancshares Corporation and its seven Intervest National Bank branches in (five in Clearwater Florida and two more in New York City and Pasadena Florida) for $238.5 million. The deal added $1.5 billion in assets including $1.1 billion in loans and $1.2 billion in deposits.

In May 2014 it bought Arkansas-based Summit Bancorp Inc. and its 23 Summit Bank branches across Arkansas for $42.5 million though it closed more than a handful of them later in the year.

In March 2014 the company acquired Houston-based Bancshares Inc. and its subsidiary Omnibank N.A. for $21.5 million adding three branches in Houston Texas and a branch each in Austin Cedar Park Lockhart and San Antonio.

Company Background

The expansion strategy of Bank of the Ozarks - which had a mere five branches in Arkansas 20 years ago — centered on opening new locations in smaller communities in Arkansas. But with the financial crash the bank was able to expand to more states through a series of FDIC-assisted transactions to take over failed banks. It bought Chestatee State Bank First Choice Community Bank Horizon Bank Oglethorpe Bank Park Avenue Bank Unity National and Woodlands Bank.

Chairman and CEO George Gleason initially bought the bank more than three decades ago at age 25.

EXECUTIVES

Chief Credit Officer Bank Of The Ozarks, Darrel Russell, age 65, $252,308 total compensation

Chairman; Chief Executive Officer Of The Company And The Bank, George G. Gleason, age 65, $1,730,769 total compensation

President Leasing Division Bank Of The Ozarks, Scott Hastings, age 61, $181,925 total compensation

President Mortgage Division Bank Of The Ozarks, Gene Holman, age 71, $150,042 total compensation

President Trust And Wealth Management Division Bank Of The Ozarks, Rex Kyle, age 62, $241,674 total compensation

Vice Chairman; President Real Estate Specialties Group And Chief Lending Officer Bank Of The Ozarks, Dan Thomas, age 56, $1,242,308 total compensation

Cfo And Chief Accounting Officer Bank Of The Ozarks Inc. And Bank Of The Ozarks, Greg McKinney, age 51, $368,077 total compensation

Chief Operating Officer And Chief Banking Officer Of The Company And The Bank, Tyler Vance, age 44, $366,923 total compensation

President Western Division, Don Keesee

Senior Vice President Market Leader, Russell Hewatt

Senior Vice President Of Information Systems, Malcolm Hicks

Vice President Payment Systems, Paula Shaw

Senior Vice President, Chris Bragg

Senior Vice President Retail Banking Manager, Bob Moore

Vice President Regional Manager, Lisa Amato

Vice President Commercial Loan Officer, Austin Simpson

Vice President Lending, Erik Larson

Assistant Vice President Community Development Officer, Kimberly L Marshall

Vice President Marketing, Mark Greenhaw

Senior Vice President Treasury Management, Steve Woodruff

Assistant Vice President Branch Operations Manager, Fabian Garantiva

Senior Vice President Commercial Lender, Jeni Chokron
Vice President, Eric Teague
Senior Vice President, Ryan Tanner
Assistant Vice President Branch Manager, Pam Toney
Assistant Vice President Branch Manager, Derek Labrosse
Assistant Vice President Community Development Officer, Joann Smith
Executive Vice President, David Sarner
Executive Vice President, Martin Ball
Senior Vice President, Aram Zakian
Vice President Loan Officer, Dawn Speas
Vice President Treasury Management Wire Manager, Mona Kalchik
Auditors: PricewaterhouseCoopers LLP

LOCATIONS

HQ: Bank OZK
17901 Chenal Parkway, Little Rock, AR 72223
Phone: 501 978-2265   **Fax:** 501 978-2224
Web: www.bankozarks.com

PRODUCTS/OPERATIONS

2014 Sales

	$ mil.	% of total
Interest income		
Non-purchased loans and leases	162	43
Purchased loans	98	26
Investment securities	30	8
Non-interest income		
Service charges on deposit accounts	26	8
Other income from purchased loans net	14	4
Others	43	11
Total	**376**	**100**

Selected Services

Personal Banking
Apple PayChecking AccountsCredit CardsFree Bill PayFREE Debit CardsCustom Debit CardsEMV Chip CardsMobile BankingMortgage LoansMy Change KeeperOnline BankingOverdraft ProtectionPersonal LoansReloadable Spending CardsRetirement PlanningReorder ChecksSafe
Business Banking
Business ProductsApple Pay for BusinessDebit CardEMV Chip CardsBusiness Credit CardsChecking & Money MarketCommercial LoansExpress DepositMerchant ProcessingOnline BankingOverdraft ProtectionReorder ChecksTreasury Management Services
Online & Mobile Banking
Online BankingMobile BankingMobile DepositOnline Bill Pay
Wealth Management Services
Investment ProgramsFinancial PlanningCustomer Service

COMPETITORS

Arvest Bank	IBERIABANK
BOK Financial	JPMorgan Chase
BancorpSouth	Regions Financial
Bank of America	Simmons First
Bear State Financial	SunTrust
Cullen/Frost Bankers	Wells Fargo
Home BancShares	

HISTORICAL FINANCIALS

Company Type: Public

Income Statement				FYE: December 31
	ASSETS ($ mil.)	NET INCOME ($ mil.)	INCOME AS % OF ASSETS	EMPLOYEES
12/18	22,388	417	1.9%	2,563
12/17	21,275	421	2.0%	2,400
12/16	18,890	269	1.4%	2,315
12/15	9,879	182	1.8%	1,642
12/14	6,766	118	1.8%	1,479
Annual Growth	**34.9%**	**36.9%**	**—**	**14.7%**

2018 Year-End Financials

Debt ratio: 1.96%
Return on equity: 11.54%
Cash ($ mil.): 290
Current ratio: —
Long-term debt ($ mil.): —

No. of shares (mil.): 128
Dividends
  Yield: 3.4%
  Payout: 22.7%
Market value ($ mil.): 2,936

	STOCK PRICE ($) FY Close	P/E High/Low		PER SHARE ($) Earnings	Dividends	Book Value
12/18	22.83	16	7	3.24	0.80	29.32
12/17	48.45	17	12	3.35	0.37	26.98
12/16	52.59	21	13	2.58	0.63	23.02
12/15	49.46	26	15	2.09	0.55	16.19
12/14	37.92	46	20	1.52	0.47	11.37
Annual Growth	**(11.9%)**	**—**	**—**	**20.8%**	**14.0%**	**26.7%**

BankUnited Inc.

BankUnited is uniting the north and south again. It's the bank holding company for BankUnited N.A. which provides standard banking services to individuals and businesses through nearly 90 banking centers in about 15 Florida counties and five banking centers in the New York metro area. Deposit offerings include checking and savings accounts treasury management services and certificates of deposit. Commercial loans including multi-family residential mortgages account for some 80% of the bank's lending portfolio. In 2018 the company launched BankUnitedDirect an online division offering money market and CD accounts nationwide. BankUnited does not offer investment banking or wealth management services.

Sales and Marketing

BankUnited serves individuals growing companies and established middle-market companies. It markets its products through local television and radio ads digital and print ads and direct mail campaigns.

Financial Performance

BankUnited's revenue has been growing steadily for the last five years. Profits were relatively static until 2017 when they more than doubled. Cash flow has been somewhat volatile.

In 2017 revenue increased 14% to $1.1 billion as both interest and non-interest income grew. Interest on loans and securities rose while gains of sales of loans boosted non-interest income.

Net income rose 172% to $591 million that year. Part of that gain was due to a $327.9 million income tax benefit received.

The company ended 2017 with some $195 million in cash versus $448 million held at the end of 2016. Financing activities provided $1.9 billion in cash and operating activities provided $319 million. Investing activities used $2.5 billion in 2017 (the fifth straight year investments have used more than $2 billion).

Strategy

BankUnited has placed its bets on two large and growing markets — the Miami metro area and the Tri-State area of New York New Jersey and Connecticut. Because those geographic markets are so attractive though competition is fierce.

The company is also open to making strategic acquisitions of other financial firms or companies in complementary businesses.

Company Background

BankUnited was formed in 2009 following the demise of the former BankUnited FSB which collapsed under the weight of bad mortgages. A team of private investors bought BankUnited from the

FDIC injected $900 million in fresh capital and in 2011 took the company public via an initial public offering (IPO); it was the first IPO of a rescued bank during the economic crisis.

In February 2012 BankUnited acquired Herald National Bank for $65 million in cash and stock. At the time of the purchase BankUnited converted to a bank holding company. It also converted the charter of subsidiary BankUnited from a thrift to a national commercial bank. Herald National was merged into BankUnited in mid-2012.

EXECUTIVES

President New York Region, Joseph (Joe) Roberto, age 62, $300,000 total compensation
Chief Risk Officer, Mark P. Bagnoli, age 67
President And Ceo, Rajinder P. (Raj) Singh, age 48, $500,000 total compensation
Cfo, Leslie N. Lunak, age 62, $400,000 total compensation
Coo, Thomas M. Cornish, age 61, $500,000 total compensation
Cio, Julio Jogaib
Vice President Information Technology, William Hynes
Senior Vice President Commercial Real Estate, Robert Hummel
Assistant Vice President Portfolio Manager, Tracey Snow
Senior Vice President, Steven Hart
Vice President, Kenneth Lipke
Senior Vice President Commercial Private Banking, Corey Prinz
Executive Vice President, Cristina Di Mauro
Vice President, Laura Lowy
Vice President, Bill Williams
Vice President, Peter Dumelle
Senior Vice President, Elizabeth Claisse
Assistant Vice President, Pedro Garcia
Vice President, Susan Kay
Vice President Project Management Office, Janet Marotta
Senior Vice President Associate General Counsel, Alina Pastiu
Vice President Credit Officer, Patrick Rigney
Vice President Community Development Outreach, Naima Oyo
Vice President Treasury Management Relationship Manager Treasury Management, Mark Stevens
Vice President, Carol Hammond
Assistant Vice President Design And Development, Sonya Moro
Vice President, Sabine Bouchereau
Senior Vice President Corporate Finance, Cristina Frias
Senior Vice President Community Development Officer, Claire Raley
Vice President Banking Center Assistant Manager, Theresa Schuman
Vice President Electronic Banking, Juliana Tancrati
Vice President Commercial Banker, Jaime Fimiani
Vice President Accounting Department, Dorrett Boothe
Vice President Portfolio Analytics Manager, Matthew Crawford
Senior Vice President Bsa Officer, Scott Nathan
Senior Vice President Enterprise Stress Testing, Filippo Ghia
Senior Vice President Marketing And Public Relations, Mary Harris
Vice President Financial Center Manager, John Hernandez
Senior Vice President Corporate Banking, Joseph Disanti
Vice President Corporate Banking, Justin Allbright
Vice President And Business Banking, Jose Alonso
Vice President Relationship Manager, Patricia Lubian

Vice President Human Resources And Employee Relations, Ellen Gioia

Vice President Senior Relationship Manager, Daniel Vaccaro

Vice President Business Banking, Jason Costello

Vice President Commercial Banking, Ted Kunkel

Assistant Vice President Corporate Real Estate, Kristin Maresca

Vice President Banking Center Manager, Paige Homan

Vice President Commercial Real Estate, Jeremy Romine

Vice President Business Development Officer, Amy Rice

Senior Vice President Corporate Lending, Gerry Mcpartland

Senior Vice President, Michael Del Rocco

Vice President, Oleg Kochanov

Vice President, Wendy Spears

Senior Vice President Senior Credit Officer Commercial Real Estate, John Kenyon

Vice President Underwriter, Alexandra Tovar

Assistant Vice President, Gloria Persaud

Vice President Commercial And Consumer Loan Servic, Rebecca Thrasher

Vice President Corporate Portfolio Manager, Jeff Landroche

Vice President Business Banker, Timothy Byrnes

Senior Vice President Environmental Risk Manager, Michael Tartanella

Senior Vice President Business Banking Sales Manager, Gregory Milford

Vice President Banking Center Manager, Pat Kelly

Vice President Branch Sales Leader, Milton Price

Vice President, Monica Antongeorgi

Vice President Corporate Portfolio Manager, Thomas Mcgregor

Vice President Corporate Banking Division, Milciades Herrera

Senior Vice President, Tyson Carballo

Svp Commercial Real Estate Lender, Ellen Hoey

Executive Vice President, Gardner Semet

Senior Vice President Corporate Team Lead, Arthur Rhatigan

Vice President Corporate Portfolio Manager, Bradley Hendren

Senior Vice President, Larry Crowley

Vice President Operations Manager, Jose Alvarado

Vice President Corporate Banking, Jennifer Garcia-Barbon

Vice President Commercial Private Banker, Mike Smith

Vice President Business Development Officer, Marissa Ames

Vice President Private Client Team Lead, Thomas Pla

Vp, Tatiana Eyzaguirre

Vice President Commercial Underwriter Bankunited, Gregory O'Brien

Vice President Business Banking Lead Underwriter, Alexanders Saenz

Senior Vice President Corporate Team Leader, Christine Gerula

Assistant Vice President Project Administrator And Executive Assistant, Natalia Valenti

Assistant Vice President Financial Reporting, Niurka Hiott

Vice President, Guillermo Doria

Vp Corporate Portfolio Manager, Jasmine Varghese

Assistant Vice President, Shannie DeFreitas

Executive Vice President Mortgage Services, Ray Barbone

Vice President Doral Branch Sales Leader, Ralph Vasallo

Vice President Branch Sales Leader, Monica Ribeiro

Vice President Business Development Officer, Stephen Speer

Senior Vice President Team Leader, Thomas Riele

Senior Executive Vice President, Nick Bustle

Vice President, Dianne Brodie

Vice President; Business Banking, Jairo Cardona

Vice President Market Manager, Jeff Fusco

Senior Vice President, Brett Shulick

Vice President Business Banking Relationship Manager, Marshall Fulton

Avp Sba Loan Closer, Leslie Giannantoni

Executive Vice President Director Of Business Banking, Brian Clay

Svp Credit Review Group Manager, Nancy Lanzoni

Vp Credit Review Examination Manager, David Young

Vice President Retail And Small Business Banking, Sean Chaderton

Senior Vice President Senior Cre Credit Officer Florida Region, Raul Llanes

Vice President Business Banking Lead Underwriter, Larry Candelario

Senior Vice President Commercial Private Banking, Kelly Sleece

Vice President Relationship Manager, Larry Marchini

Assistant Vice President Branch Manager, Darlene Curti

Vice President Business Development Officer, Alan Hice

Senior Vice President, Benjamin Fisher

Senior Vice President Corporate Banking, Jackson Young

Vice President Business Banking, Richard Rippy

Vice President Business Development Officer, Jared Johnson

Senior Vice President Corporate Finance, Jorge Ray

Senior Vice President, Luis Garcia

Vice President Branch Sales Manager, Kathy Nemeth

Assistant Vice President Mortgage Warehouse Lending, Rosemarie Loparrino

Vice President Sba Underwriter, Scott Meckes

Executive Vice President New York, Ben Stacks

Vice President Sba Underwriter, Amy Luce

Vice President Senior Analyst Business Development Officer, Will Tinsley

Vice President, Lon Gopie

Vice President, Peter Hughes

Senior Vice President Of Government Institutional Banking Gib Team Leader For Private Client Svc, Emsley Hylton

Vice President Branch Manager, Sebastian Cannata

Senior Vice President, Steven Markowski

Vice President, Kevin Karstens

Svp Commercial Private Banking, Theonie Golden

Vice President Portfolio Manager, Noel Lassise

Vice President Credit Officer, Ward Burns

Executive Vice President, Michael Wilcox

Assistant Vice President Sba Loan Closer, Pannah Hem

Assistant Vice President Senior Servicing Portfolio Officer, Michael Castle

Chairman, John A. Kanas, age 72

Assistant Treasurer, Robert Treadwell

Vice Chairman Credit Risk Management, Jack Leonard

Board Member, Sanjiv Sobti

Board Member, Lynne Wines

Auditors: KPMG LLP

LOCATIONS

HQ: BankUnited Inc.
  14817 Oak Lane, Miami Lakes, FL 33016
Phone: 305 569-2000
Web: www.bankunited.com

COMPETITORS

BB&T	Ocean Bankshares
Bank of America	PNC Financial
Capital One	Regions Financial
Citibank	Signature Bank
Great Florida Bank	SunTrust

JPMorgan Chase	TD Bank USA
M&T Bank	Valley National
New York Community	Bancorp
Bancorp	Wells Fargo

HISTORICAL FINANCIALS

Company Type: Public

Income Statement

	ASSETS ($ mil.)	NET INCOME ($ mil.)	INCOME AS % OF ASSETS	EMPLOYEES
				FYE: December 31
12/18	32,164	324	1.0%	1,790
12/17	30,346	614	2.0%	1,763
12/16	27,880	225	0.8%	1,706
12/15	23,883	251	1.1%	1,741
12/14	19,210	204	1.1%	1,647
Annual Growth	13.8%	12.3%	—	2.1%

2018 Year-End Financials

Debt ratio: 1.25%
Return on equity: 10.92%
Cash ($ mil.): 382
Current ratio: —
Long-term debt ($ mil.): —

No. of shares (mil.): 99
Dividends
  Yield: 2.8%
  Payout: 28.0%
Market value ($ mil.): 2,968

	STOCK PRICE ($) FY Close	P/E High/Low		PER SHARE ($) Earnings	Dividends	Book Value
12/18	29.94	15	9	2.99	0.84	29.49
12/17	40.72	7	5	5.58	0.84	28.32
12/16	37.69	18	13	2.09	0.84	23.22
12/15	36.06	17	11	2.35	0.84	21.65
12/14	28.97	18	14	1.95	0.84	20.19
Annual Growth	0.8%	—	—	11.3%	(0.0%)	9.9%

Banner Corp.

Flagging bank accounts? See Banner Corporation. Banner is the holding company for Banner Bank which serves the Pacific Northwest through about 100 branches and 10 loan production offices in Washington Oregon and Idaho. The company also owns Islanders Bank which operates three branches in Washington's San Juan Islands. The banks offer standard products such as deposit accounts credit cards and business and consumer loans. Commercial loans including business agriculture construction and multifamily mortgage loans account for about 90% of the company's portfolio. Bank subsidiary Community Financial writes residential mortgage and construction loans.

Geographic Reach

Washington-based Banner Bank is focused on five primary markets in the Northwest: the Puget Sound region of Washington; the greater Portland Oregon market; Boise Idaho; and Spokane Washington. The fifth is the bank's historical base in the agricultural communities in the Columbia Basin region of Washington and Oregon.

Sales and Marketing

Banner Corp. reported advertising and marketing expenses of $6.9 million in 2013 versus $7.2 million in 2012. Banner Bank launched a redesigned website and new ad campaign in Boise Seattle and Portland and on social media in fall 2014.

Financial Performance

The regional bank holding company reported revenue of $223 million in 2013 an increase of 4% versus 2012. The rise in revenue was due to increased operating income as a result of gains on the sale of securities and a fee received from the termination of the bank's proposed acquisition of Home Federal Bancorp. The bank's growing customer base led to increased income from deposit fees and other service charges of $1.3 billion (5%) in 2013 versus the prior year. Net income declined 28% in 2013 versus 2012 to $46.6 million primarily due to higher provision for income tax expenses. After three consecutive years of losses (2008 thru 2010) the bank returned to profitability in 2011 and has remained profitable.

Banner Corp. has total consolidated assets of about $4.5 billion.

Strategy

Historically Banner Corp. has grown by acquisition. Since going public (in 1995) Banner has acquired about 10 commercial banks. Islanders Bank was acquired in 2007 the same year Banner acquired F&M Bank and NCW Community Bank of Wenatchee both also based in Washington. After the spate of acquisitions the company focused on opening branches. The company continues to look for acquisition opportunities with an eye on banks shut down by regulators.

In 2013 however a plan to merge with Home Federal Bancorp was terminated when that bank received a better offer from Cascade Bancorp. Also the company abandoned plans to buy Idaho Banking Company out of bankruptcy after being outbid.

Mergers and Acquisitions

In August 2014 Banner Bank acquired Siuslaw Financial Group the holding company for Siuslaw Bank the operator of 10 branches along the coast of Oregon. In June 2014 Banner Bank purchased six branches in Oregon from Sterling Savings Bank.

EXECUTIVES

Evp And Cfo Banner Corporation, Lloyd W. Baker, age 70, $260,724 total compensation

Evp Retail Banking And Administration, Cynthia D. (Cindy) Purcell, age 61, $289,038 total compensation

Evp And Chief Lending Officer Banner Corporation And Banner Bank, Richard B. Barton, age 75, $264,895 total compensation

President And Ceo, Mark J. Grescovich, age 54, $716,415 total compensation

Evp And Real Estate Lending Manager Banner Bank, Douglas M. Bennett, age 66, $236,174 total compensation

Evp And Cio, Steven W. (Steve) Rust, age 71

Evp Retail Products And Services, Gary W. Wagers, age 58

Evp And Commercial Executive East Region, M. Kirk Quillin, age 56

Evp And Commercial Executive West Region, James T. (Jim) Reed, age 56

Evp And Cfo Banner Bank, Peter J. Conner, age 53

Evp Human Resources, Kayleen Kohler

Evp And Mortgage Banking Director, Kenneth A. (Ken) Larsen, age 49

Evp And General Counsel Banner Bank, Craig Miller

Evp And Chief Risk Officer Banner Bank, Judy Steiner

Evp And Commercial Executive (south Region), Keith A. Western, age 63

Senior Vice President And Sba Manager, Walter Mclaughlin

Vice President Sr. Commercial Relationship Manager, Jeanne Walker

Assistant Vice President Training Manager, Terri Anderson

Vice President Credit Risk Manager, Heidi Collins

Vice Chairman Banner Corporation And Banner Bank, Jesse G. Foster, age 81

Chairman Banner Corporation And Banner Bank, Gary L. Sirmon, age 76

Auditors: Moss Adams LLP

LOCATIONS

HQ: Banner Corp.
10 South First Avenue, Walla Walla, WA 99362
Phone: 509 527-3636
Web: www.bannerbank.com

PRODUCTS/OPERATIONS

2016 Sales

	% of total
INTEREST INCOME:	
Loans receivable	75
Mortgage-backed securities	4
Securities and cash equivalents	3
NON-INTEREST INCOME:	
Deposit fees and other service charges	10
Mortgage banking operations	6
BOLI	1
Miscellaneous	1
Total	**100**

COMPETITORS

Bank of America	Sound Financial
Cascade Bancorp	U.S. Bancorp
Columbia Banking	Umpqua Holdings
FCA	Washington Federal
Glacier Bancorp	Wells Fargo
KeyCorp	

HISTORICAL FINANCIALS

Company Type: Public

Income Statement				FYE: December 31
	ASSETS ($ mil.)	NET INCOME ($ mil.)	INCOME AS % OF ASSETS	EMPLOYEES
12/18	11,871	136	1.2%	2,187
12/17	9,763	60	0.6%	2,128
12/16	9,793	85	0.9%	2,137
12/15	9,796	45	0.5%	2,143
12/14	4,723	54	1.1%	1,193
Annual Growth	25.9%	26.0%	—	16.4%

2018 Year-End Financials

Debt ratio: 1.96%	No. of shares (mil.): 35
Return on equity: 9.92%	Dividends
Cash ($ mil.): 272	Yield: 3.4%
Current ratio: —	Payout: 69.0%
Long-term debt ($ mil.): —	Market value ($ mil.): 1,882

	STOCK PRICE ($) FY Close	P/E High/Low	PER SHARE ($) Earnings	Dividends	Book Value
12/18	53.48	16 12	4.15	1.83	42.03
12/17	55.12	34 28	1.84	1.98	38.89
12/16	55.81	22 15	2.52	0.65	39.34
12/15	45.86	28 21	1.89	0.72	37.97
12/14	43.02	16 13	2.79	0.72	29.82
Annual Growth	5.6%	— —	10.4%	26.3%	9.0%

BANNER HEALTH

Banner Health is one of the largest secular not-for-profit health systems in the US. The organization operates about 30 acute-care hospitals (with roughly 4000 beds). It also operates clinics nursing homes clinical laboratories ambulatory surgery centers home health agencies and other health care-related organizations including physician practices and a captive insurance company. Banner Health participates in medical research in areas such as Alzheimer's disease and spinal cord injuries through its Banner Sun Health Research division. The company which has more than 400000 members provides services in seven states in the western US; its largest concentration of facilities is in Arizona.

Operations

Banner Health is one of the first not-for-profit hospital operators to reinsure its employees through its captive insurance company Samaritan Insurance Funding. By offering this service Banner Health is able to diversify its risk improve cash flow and lower life insurance costs by about half a million dollars a year.

The multi-specialty system also operates a health plan in Arizona for Medicare-eligible patients. Its MediSunONE plan includes Medicare and Medicare Part D. The company has joined forces with Aetna in what is called an accountable care collaboration (ACO). An ACO uses technology and a team-based approach to care for the hospital's patients. Doctors and hospitals assume accountability for patient outcomes and are rewarded financially for achieving higher quality greater efficiency and overall better patient outcomes. The partnership also includes a new product called Aetna Whole Health that allows Banner's patients access to a line of Aetna services including their own electronic patient record.

The system's specialty centers include Banner Alzheimer's Institute Banner Concussion Center Banner Heart Hospital and the Western States Burn Center. In addition Banner Health trains 270 doctors per year at Banner Good Samaritan and Northern Colorado Medical Center.

Banner Health also partners with M.D. Anderson Cancer Center to operate a comprehensive cancer center in Phoenix. Services include medical oncology radiation oncology surgical oncology pathology laboratory diagnostic imaging as well as other supportive clinical services. M.D. Anderson has clinical oversight for all aspects of care delivery.

Education looms large on Banner Health's list of priorities — the hospital operates one of the country's largest simulation education centers at its Banner Corporate Center-Mesa. Simulation education is an expanding field in which medical students use computerized mannequins to improve their surgical and medical skills. The school's research has paid off and with Scottsdale Healthcare Osborn Medical Center Banner Health invented the Sapien Transcatheter Heart Valve an artificial heart valve that can replace a diseased aortic heart valve without the open heart surgery that previously was required.

Geographic Reach

Banner Health operates in Alaska Arizona California Colorado Nebraska Nevada and Wyoming.

The system's Banner Health Network is a group of health care providers located in Arizona's Maricopa and Pinal counties.

Financial Performance

Banner Health's income is generally derived through three channels: third-party payers such as commercial insurance managed care agreements Medicare and Medicaid and a small portion of self-pay patients as well as by borrowing funds and receiving philanthropic donations.

Its revenues grew by 29% in 2015 from $5.4 billion to $7 billion; higher net patient service medical insurance premium and other revenues drove that increase. However rising expenses and a $49.3 million loss for ACO Banner Health Network led to a drop in net income which fell 65% to $83.7 million.

Strategy

The health system has grown through construction. Banner Health is nearly always engaged in some sort of construction renovation or upgrading at its numerous facilities. The organization has more than $1 billion in construction projects in progress or completed in recent years. The system has expanded its facilities at Banner Baywood Medical Center Banner Del E. Webb Medical Center Banner Desert Medical Center Banner Thunderbird Medical Center Cardon Children's Medical Center and McKee Medical Center.

In 2015 Banner Health opened a Fort Collins facility on a 28-acre campus with a two-story hospital featuring an emergency department a 24-bed inpatient unit labor and delivery rooms medical imaging women's services surgical services and lab services.

Also that year the system merged with the University of Arizona Health Network (now named Banner - University Medicine) as well as establishing a 30-year affiliation with the University of Arizona. The moves align with its strategy of combining health care provision with medical schools and academic training as well as expanding operations into new markets (in this case the Tuscon region). Banner Health hopes to both improve access to health care through a consumer-focused system and to provide opportunities for medical professionals to remain in Arizona. As part of the merger the company plans to build a new hospital and renovate an existing ambulatory campus.

In 2017 Banner Health restructured operations including cutting some 500 employees' positions. The move was part of its efforts to become more consumer-focused and included changes to its leadership lineup. Later that year after the restructuring was completed the company began recruiting to fill 1000 positions including spots for specialty nurses and physical and occupational therapists.

Mergers and Acquisitions

Banner Health does occasionally pick up a new hospital through acquisition. For instance in 2015 the company acquired The University of Arizona Health Network (now Banner - University Medicine). As a result University Medicine is the new academic medicine division of Banner Health which includes three academic medical centers: Banner - University Medical Center Tucson Banner - University Medical Center Phoenix and Banner - University Medical Center South.

In mid-2016 the company acquired more than 30 Arizona urgent-care centers from Urgent Care Extra. The centers to be rebranded under the Banner banner are among the expected 50 the company plans to have in Arizona by 2018.

In 2017 Banner Health acquired Medicare-certified home health agency SunLife Home Health which is based in Tucson Arizona. That deal allowed the system to expand its home care operations into southern Arizona.

Company Background

Banner Good Samaritan Medical Center first opened its doors as a 20-bed hospital in 1911. The medical center which is four months older than the state of Arizona marked its 100th anniversary in October 2011.

EXECUTIVES

Evp And Chief Administrative Officer, Ronald R. (Ron) Bunnell
President Ceo And Director, Peter S. Fine, age 67
Evp And Chief Clinical Officer, John Hensing
Evp University Medicine, Kathy Bollinger
Coo, Rebecca (Becky) Kuhn
Ceo Banner Estrella Medical Center, Tom Dickson
Cfo, Dennis L. Laraway

President Western Region, Jim Ferando
Ceo East Morgan County Hospital And Sterling Regional Medcenter, Linda Thorpe
President Arizona East Division, Todd S. Werner, age 51
Ceo Banner Baywood Medical Center And Banner Heart Hospital, Laura Robertson
Ceo Platte County Memorial Hospital And Community Hospital, Shelby Nelson
Ceo Banner Thunderbird Medical Center, Deb Krmpotic
Ceo Banner Research, Eric (Bill) Reiman
President Banner Health Network, Chuck Lehn
Ceo Banner Del E. Webb Medical Center And Banner Boswell Medical Center, Debbie Flores
Ceo University Medical Center Phoenix, Steve Narang
Ceo Banner Ironwood Medical Center And Banner Goldfield Medical Center, Sharon Lind
President And Ceo Banner Health Foundation And Banner Alzheimer's Foundation, Andy Kramer Petersen
Cio, Ryan Smith
Ceo Banner Casa Grande Medical Center, Rona Curphy
Ceo Banner Estrella Medical Center, Courtney Ophaug
Ceo Banner Gateway Medical Center Banner Md Anderson Cancer Center Banner Baywood Medical Center And Banner Heart Hospital, Lamont Yoder
Vp Post Acute Services And Ceo Banner Home Care/hospice, Lynn Rosenbach
Ceo Banner Lassen Medical Center, Catherine Harshbarger
Ceo Banner Churchill Community Hospital, Hoyt Skabelund
Ceo Washakie Medical Center, Jay Stallings
Ceo Ogallala Community Hospital, Drew Dostal
Ceo Banner Behavioral Health Hospital, Brian Beutin
Ceo Page Hospital, Brian Kellar
Interim Ceo Northern Colorado Service Area Including: Banner Fort Collins Medical Center Mckee Medical Center North Colorado Medical Center, Scott Baker
Vice President Materials Managerment, Doug Bowen
Vice President Of Information Technology, Frank Wallace
Vice President, Tony Blake
System Vice President Information Technology Business Services, Bryce Carder
Medical Director, Sathya Jyothinagaram
Medical Director, Carol Williams
Vice President Of Business Development, Christen Castellano
Cota L, Justin Ellis
Vice President, Robert Stern
Vice President Of Administration, Jason Armstrong
Director Of Pharmacy, Tina Peterson
Vice President, A Smith
Medical Director, Goodin Director
Director Of Nursing, Nancy Adamson
Vice Chair, Christopher H. (Chris) Volk
Chairman, Larry S. Lazarus
Secretary, Jennifer Manning
Secretary, Kathryn Mcswain
Auditors: ERNST & YOUNG LLP PHOENIX AZ

LOCATIONS

HQ: BANNER HEALTH
2901 N CENTRAL AVE # 160, PHOENIX, AZ 850122702
Phone: 602 747-4000
Web: WWW.BANNERHEALTH.COM

FEATURED SERVICES

Academic Medicine
Alzheimer's
Cancer
Heart
Insurance (Networks)
Maternity
Orthopedics
Pediatrics
Pharmacy
Physicians & Specialists
Research
Women's Health

COMPETITORS

Community Health Systems
Dignity Health
HCA
Inova
John C. Lincoln Health Network
Memorial Health System of East Texas
Northern Arizona Healthcare
Phoenix Children's Hospital
Poudre Valley Health System
Providence St. Joseph Health
Scottsdale Healthcare
Tenet Healthcare
Texas Health Resources
Wyoming Medical Center
Yuma Regional Medical Center

HISTORICAL FINANCIALS

Company Type: Private

Income Statement				FYE: December 31
	REVENUE ($ mil.)	NET INCOME ($ mil.)	NET PROFIT MARGIN	EMPLOYEES
12/18	8,519	64	0.8%	35,000
12/17	7,835	728	9.3%	—
12/16	7,633	309	4.1%	—
12/15	6,971	119	1.7%	—
Annual Growth	6.9%	(18.6%)	—	—

Bar Harbor Bankshares

Bar Harbor Bankshares which holds Bar Harbor Bank & Trust is a Maine -stay. Boasting $1.6 billion in assets the bank offers traditional deposit and retirement products trust services and a variety of loans to individuals and businesses through 15 branches in the state's Hancock Knox and Washington counties. Commercial real estate and residential mortgages loans make up nearly 80% of the bank's loan portfolio though it also originates business construction agricultural home equity and other consumer loans. About 10% of its loans are to the tourist industry which is associated with nearby Acadia National Park. Subsidiary Bar Harbor Trust Services offers trust and estate planning services.

Operations

Around 80% of the bank's loan assets are tied to real estate. About 41% of its loan portfolio was made up of residential real estate mortgages at the end of 2015 while another 37% was made up of commercial real estate mortgages. The rest of the portfolio was tied to commercial and industrial loans (8% of loan assets) home equity loans (5%) agricultural and farming loans (3%) commercial construction (3%) and other consumer loans (1%).

More than 80% of Bar Harbor's revenue comes from interest income. About 61% of its total revenue came from loan interest (including fees) during 2015 while another 25% came from interest income on investment securities. The remainder of its revenue came from trust and other financial services (6% of revenue) debit card service charges and fees (3%) deposit account service charges (1%) and other miscellaneous income sources.

Geographic Reach

The Bar Harbor Maine-based group operates 15 branches across the downeast midcoast and central regions of Maine more specifically in Bar Harbor Northeast Harbor Southwest Harbor Somesville Deer Isle Blue Hill Ellsworth Rockland Topsham South China Augusta Winter Harbor Milbridge Machias and Lubec.

Sales and Marketing

Bar Harbor serves individuals and retirees nonprofits municipalities as well as businesses that are vital to Maine's coastal economy including retailers restaurants seasonal lodging bio research laboratories.

Financial Performance

The group's annual revenues have risen more than 10% since 2011 as its loan assets have swelled over 35% to $990 million. Its profits have grown more than 30% over the same period as Bar Harbor has kept a lid on rising operating costs and as it's enjoyed low interest rates.

Bar Harbor's revenue climbed 4% to $64.2 million during 2015 mostly as its loan and other interest earning assets grew by more than 7%.

Revenue growth in 2015 drove the bank's net income up 4% to $15.15 million. Bar Harbor's operating cash levels spiked 31% to $20.33 million for the year mainly thanks to favorable working capital changes related to changes in other assets.

Strategy

Bar Harbor Bankshares looks to grow its loan and deposit business organically and through strategic bank acquisitions targeting the downeast midcoast and central Maine markets. It also continued in 2016 to focus on managing its operating expenses building upon its strong efficient ratio of 56.3% in 2015.

EXECUTIVES

Evp Business Banking Bar Harbor Bank & Trust, Gregory W. Dalton, age 59, $203,000 total compensation

Evp Retail Banking, Stephen M. Leackfeldt, age 62, $225,000 total compensation

Evp And Chief Risk Officer, Richard B. Maltz, $255,000 total compensation

Evp Cfo And Treasurer, Josephine Iannelli, age 47

President And Ceo Bar Harbor Bankshares And Bar Harbor Bank & Trust, Curtis C. Simard, age 48, $438,000 total compensation

Senior Vice President, Steve Gurin

Senior Vice President Internal Audit, Johanne Lapointe

Executive Vice President Regional President Of Nh Vt Of Bhbt, William Mciver

Chairman, David B. Woodside, age 67

Board Member, David Colter

Auditors: RSM US LLP

LOCATIONS

HQ: Bar Harbor Bankshares
 P.O. Box 400, 82 Main Street, Bar Harbor, ME 04609-0400
Phone: 207 288-3314
Web: www.bhbt.com

PRODUCTS/OPERATIONS

2015 sales

	$ mil.	% of total
Interest and dividend income		
Interest and fees on loans	39	61
Interest on securities	15	24
Dividends on FHLB stock	0	1
Non-interest income		
Trust and other financial services	3	6
Debit card service charges and fees	1	3
Net securities gains	1	2
Other operating income	1	2
Service charges on deposit accounts	0	1
Total	**64**	**100**

Selected Services

Retail Products and Services
Retail Brokerage Services
Electronic Banking Services
Commercial Products and Services

COMPETITORS

Bangor Savings Bank
Bank of America
Camden National
People's United Financial
TD Bank USA
The First Bancorp

HISTORICAL FINANCIALS

Company Type: Public

Income Statement

FYE: December 31

	ASSETS ($ mil.)	NET INCOME ($ mil.)	INCOME AS % OF ASSETS	EMPLOYEES
12/18	3,608	32	0.9%	445
12/17	3,565	25	0.7%	423
12/16	1,755	14	0.9%	186
12/15	1,580	15	1.0%	221
12/14	1,459	14	1.0%	223
Annual Growth	**25.4%**	**22.5%**	**—**	**18.9%**

2018 Year-End Financials

Debt ratio: 1.19%
Return on equity: 9.08%
Cash ($ mil.): 98
Current ratio: —
Long-term debt ($ mil.): —
No. of shares (mil.): 15
Dividends
 Yield: 3.5%
 Payout: 37.1%
Market value ($ mil.): 348

	STOCK PRICE ($) FY Close	P/E High/Low	PER SHARE ($) Earnings	Dividends	Book Value
12/18	22.43	14 10	2.12	0.79	23.87
12/17	27.01	28 15	1.70	0.75	22.96
12/16	47.33	30 18	1.63	0.73	17.19
12/15	34.42	22 18	1.67	0.67	17.10
12/14	32.00	24 15	1.63	0.60	16.40
Annual Growth	**(8.5%)**	**— —**	**6.7%**	**6.9%**	**9.8%**

BARCLAYS BANK DELAWARE

Spending money is a rewarding experience for holders of Barclays Bank Delaware cards. With co-branded credit cards from Barclays Bank Delaware (aka Barclaycard US) customers accumulate points that can be redeemed for air travel hotel stays and other perks. The company a division of Barclays issues Visa and MasterCard credit cards in addition to co-branded credit cards through partnerships with some 60 companies and institutions including Priceline Best Western L.L. Bean and BJ's Wholesale. Barclay's cards are ac-

cepted in more than 200 countries through some 600000 ATMs and banks worldwide. Founded as Juniper Financial in 2000; it became a part of Barclays in 2004.

Operations

The company creates customized co-branded credit card programs for some of the country's most successful travel entertainment retail and financial institutions.

Geographic Reach

Barclaycard US is part of a larger Barclaycard organization which operates internationally in 22 countries. In the Nordic region Barclaycard offers credit cards through Entercard a joint venture with Swedbank. In South Africa Barclaycard is offered through Absa. In total Barclaycard serves more than 21 million customers. Barclaycard US operates customer call centers in Delaware and Maine.

Sales and Marketing

Barclaycard US uses partnerships to expand its business. Some of its major partners include Barnes & Noble Frontier Airlines L.L. Bean Priceline.com Sallie Mae US Airways and Google.

Strategy

Barclaycard has been growing in recent years as the global economy improves. In 2014 the bank gained 3.6 million new customers and enjoyed Å 18.5 billion ($28.7 billion) worth of new and renewed lending to households in all regions.

Barclaycard continues to focus on next-generation payment technology in the UK South Africa and in the US with the goal of helping its customers adopt new digital platforms to pay using "tap and go" cards contactless stickers and smart phones. In 2012 the company started to promote mobile and online commerce by encouraging its cardholders in the US to save their card to Google Wallet which enables consumers to securely and easily shop online where they see the 'Google Wallet Buy' button or in-person using the Google Wallet mobile app.

Mergers and Acquisitions

In 2012 the company also signed an agreement Sallie Mae to acquire the $1.3 billion Upromise by Sallie Mae credit card portfolio from FIA Card Services.

EXECUTIVES

Managing Director Corporate Communications, Kevin M. Sullivan

Ceo, Amer Sajed

Cfo, Gerald (Jerry) Pavelich

Chief Credit Officer, Michael Mayer

Assistant Vp Strategic Cost Management, Glenn Watson

Vp Data Science And Advanced Analytics, Vishal Morde

LOCATIONS

HQ: BARCLAYS BANK DELAWARE
 100 S WEST ST, WILMINGTON, DE 198015015
Phone: 302 255-8000
Web: WWW.BARCLAYCARDUS.COM

PRODUCTS/OPERATIONS

Selected Card Partnerships

Ameriprise
Bank Atlantic
Barnes & Noble
BJ's
Frontier
L.L. Bean
US Airways
Best Western
Priceline.com
Payless
Travelocity
Virgin America

Alliance Data Systems
American Express
Bank of America
Capital One

Citibank
Discover
JPMorgan Chase

HISTORICAL FINANCIALS

Company Type: Private

Income Statement   FYE: December 31

	ASSETS ($ mil.)	NET INCOME ($ mil.)	INCOME AS % OF ASSETS	EMPLOYEES
12/14	25,012	239	1.0%	349
12/13	19,055	331	1.7%	—
12/08	12,418	20	0.2%	—
12/07	7,470	0	—	—
Annual Growth	18.8%	—	—	—

Baxter International Inc

A medical products manufacturer Baxter International is a leading producer of intravenous (IV) fluids and systems. It also makes infusion pumps pre-filled syringes biological sealants and inhaled anesthetics as well as dialyzers and other products for the treatment of end-stage renal disease (ESRD). In 2015 Baxter split its operations into two companies — one focused on biopharmaceuticals (Baxalta) and the other on medical products (Baxter).The company traces its roots back to 1931 when it was founded as an intravenous products maker.

HISTORY

Idaho surgeon Ralph Falk his brother Harry and California physician Donald Baxter formed Don Baxter Intravenous Products in 1931 to distribute the IV solutions Baxter made in Los Angeles. Two years later the company opened its first plant located outside Chicago. Ralph Falk bought Baxter's interest in 1935 and began R&D efforts leading to the first sterilized vacuum-type blood collection device (1939) which could store blood for weeks instead of hours. Product demand during WWII spurred sales above $1.5 million by 1945.

In 1949 the company created Travenol Laboratories to make and sell drugs. Baxter went public in 1951 and began an acquisition program the next year. In 1953 failing health caused both Falks to give control to William Graham a manager since 1945. Under Graham's leadership Baxter absorbed Wallerstein (1957); Fenwal Labs (1959); Flint Eaton (1959); and Dayton Flexible Products (1967).

In 1975 Baxter's headquarters moved to Deerfield Illinois. In 1978 the company debuted the first portable dialysis machine and had $1 billion in sales. Vernon Loucks Jr. became CEO two years later. Baxter claimed the title of the world's leading hospital supplier in 1985 when it bought American Hospital Supply (a Baxter distributor from 1932 to 1962). Offering more than 120000 products and an electronic system that connected customers with some 1500 vendors Baxter captured nearly 25% of the US hospital supply market in 1988. That year it became Baxter International.

In 1992 Baxter spun off Caremark (home infusion therapy and mail-order drugs) but kept a division that controlled 75% of the world's dialysis machine market.

In 1993 Baxter pleaded guilty (and was temporarily suspended from selling to the Veterans Administration) to bribing Syria to remove Baxter from a blacklist for trading in Israel.

The company entered the US cardiovascular perfusion services market in 1995 with the purchases of PSICOR and SETA. Baxter along with two other silicone breast-implant makers agreed to settle thousands of claims (at an average of $26000 each) from women suffering side-effects from the implants. The next year Baxter spun off its cost management and hospital supply business as Allegiance (sold to Cardinal Health in 1999).

Buys in 1997 boosted Baxter's presence in Europe and its share of the open-heart-surgery devices market. That year it agreed to pay about 20% of a $670 million legal settlement in a suit relating to hemophiliacs infected with HIV from blood products.

In response to concerns posed by shareholders Baxter in 1999 said it would phase out the use of PVC (polyvinyl chloride) in some products by 2010. In 2000 the firm spun off its underperforming cardiovascular unit as Edwards Lifesciences. To strengthen core operations it lined up a number of purchases including North American Vaccine.

Purchases in 2001 included the cancer treatment unit of chemicals firm Degussa. Also that year Baxter withdrew dialysis equipment from Spain and Croatia after patients who used its products died. It also ended production of two types of dialyzers that were sold there. As the number of deaths mounted to more than 50 in seven countries Baxter began facing lawsuits; it later settled with the families of many of the patients. In September 2002 the FDA issued a warning when several patients died after using Baxter's Meridian dialysis machines. The same year Baxter bought Fusion Medical to expand its BioScience unit.

Robert L. Parkinson Jr. took over as chairman and CEO in April 2004. Parkinson succeeded Harry M. Jansen Kraemer Jr. William Graham who remained on the Baxter board of directors as honorary chairman emeritus after his official retirement in 1996 died in 2006.

In 2005 the FDA seized Baxter's existing inventories of previously recalled 6000 Colleague Volumetric Infusion Pumps and nearly 1000 Syndeo PCA Syringe Pumps; the federal agency resorted to these measures after the company did not fix production and design problems with the pumps in a suitable amount of time after batches of the product had been recalled earlier that year.

Baxter's product troubles didn't end there. In 2008 Baxter halted production of heparin after hundreds of bad reactions (including several deaths) occurred in patients using the drug. Subsequent investigations focused on raw heparin supplied to Baxter by a Chinese factory which apparently added a cheaper ingredient into the drug which contaminated it. Heparin-related litigation continued for Baxter in following years.

In 2009 the company acquired the hemofiltration (renal replacement therapy) product line of Edwards Lifesciences in a $65 million deal.

To meet increasing demand Baxter also expanded its infusion systems portfolio that year by entering an agreement to distribute medical device maker SIGMA's Spectrum large volume infusion pumps domestically and internationally. The deal also gave Baxter a 40% stake in the company (with the option to buy the rest) as well as access to future products under development. In 2012 Baxter exercised its right to buy and paid $90 million in cash for the remaining 60% of the company.

The addition of the Spectrum system was especially helpful when the FDA ordered the company to recall all of its Colleague infusion pumps in the US market in 2010. Patients were given the option of receiving Spectrum pumps to replace the Colleague systems.

As part of restructuring efforts in 2010 the company sold its noncore US generic injectables business to Hikma Pharmaceuticals for about $112 million. Baxter divested the business to focus on its proprietary injectable formulation and packaging operations. The sale also included Baxter's manufacturing facility in New Jersey and a warehouse and distribution center in Tennessee.

The company grew its BioScience operations in 2010 by acquiring all of the hemophilia-related assets from privately-held Archemix in a deal worth up to $315 million. Archemix has products under development including a synthetic hemophilia treatment to improve the body's blood clotting capabilities. Then to jump into the bone grafting market the company spent some $330 million to acquire UK-based ApaTech which sells bone grafting materials in the US and Europe; the deal gave Baxter manufacturing and research facilities in Germany the UK and the US.

EXECUTIVES

Vice President Information Technology, Martin McBride
Corporate Vp And Cio, Paul E. Martin
Chairman And Ceo, José E. (Joe) Almeida, age 57, $1,300,000 total compensation
Corporate Vp Human Resources, Jeanne K. Mason, age 63, $540,192 total compensation
Corporate Vp And Cfo, James K. Saccaro, age 46, $644,415 total compensation
Corporate Vp And President Hospital Products, Brik V. Eyre, age 55, $618,533 total compensation
Corporate Vp And Chief Scientific Officer, Marcus Schabacker, age 55
Corporate Vp And President International, Paul Vibert, age 59
Corporate Vp And President Renal, Giuseppe Accogli, age 48, $514,028 total compensation
Vice President, Michael Baughman
Vp Marketing, Chandra Sekhar
Vice President Of Manufacturing, Manuel Domenech
Vice President Information Systems, Nicola Mayhew
Vice President Bioscience, Paul Grozier
Vice President Engineering, Ernest Shepard
Vice President Project Management Office (research And Development), Karen Marks
Vice President Manufacturing Strategy, Kathleen Warren
Global Vice President Application Services, Michael Hamill
Vice President Marketing, Cindy Huey
Senior Vice President Treasurer And Head Of Global Planning, Scott Bohaboy
Vice President Marketing User Services Hospital Products, Omar Khalil
Vice President, Darin Buser
Vice President Global Operations, Phil Batchelor
Associate Medical Director, Carol Schermer
National Sales Manager Inside Sales, Valarie Taulien
Vice President Sales For National Accounts, Gregg Boyer
Vice President, Laurie Hernandez
Vice President Human Resources, Mike Edicola
Vice President Talent Management, Irina Konstantinovsky
Vice President Talent Management, Steve King
Vice President Sales, Mike Canzoneri
Corporate Vice President And Chief Scientific Officer, Norbert Riedel
Vice President Of Global Research And Development, Noel Barrett
Vice President Sales, Joe Pudlo

Vice President Of Information Technology, Kurt Johnson
Vice President Corporate Audit, John Mccoy
Corporate Vice President And Cio, Karenann Terrell
Vice President Finance, Patrick Marschall
Human Resources Vice President Latin America, Paulo Bolgar
Vice President Employee Services, Faye Katt
Vice President Biosurgery Research And Development, Russ Holscher
Vice President Planning And Deployment, Prabir Sen-Gupta
Svp And Controller, Caroline Karp
Corporate Vice President Human Resources, Jeannie K Mason
Vice President Research And Development And Quality Information Technology, Andrew Worley
Vice President Global Business Development, Doerr David
Vice President, Robert Felicelli
Vice President Quality, Katherine Azuara
Vice President Head Global Business Development, Nicholas Manusos
Vp Environment Health And Safety And Sustainability, Art Gibson
Vice President Corporate Audit, Kim Roll-Wallace
Senior Vice President And Corporate Secretary, Ellen Mcintosh
Senior Vice President General Counsel, Sean Martin
Corporate Vice President Associate General Counsel And Corporate Secretary, Stephanie Shinn
Medical Director, Maggie Gellens
Vice President Of Digital Innovation, Jonathan Handler
Vice President Global Medical Affairs Hospital Products, Dheerendra Kommala
Vice President Meeting Programming And Design, Stasia L Ogden
Vice President Strategy Hospital Products, David H Roman
Vice President Global Engineering (baxter Global Operations), Bass William
Senior Vice President And President Emea, Cristiano Franzi
Senior Vice President Chief Science And Technology Officer, Sumant Ramachandra
Senior Vice President And President Apac, Andrew Frye
Vice President Supply Chain, Tyler Vassar
Vice President Strategic Initiatives And Business Development, Jay Saccaro
Senior Vice President Chief Accounting Officer, Brian Stevens
Corporate Vice President And Chief Information Off, Paul E Martin
Assistant Vice President Portfolio Management East, Michael Kosko
Vice President, Philippe Reale
Member Board Of Directors, James R Gavin
Board Member, Peter S Hellman
Board Member, John Forsyth
Board Member, Michael Mahoney
Board Member, Alexander Chen
Assistant Treasurer, Jeff Schaible
Board Member, Munib Islam
Auditors: PricewaterhouseCoopers LLP

LOCATIONS

HQ: Baxter International Inc
One Baxter Parkway, Deerfield, IL 60015
Phone: 224 948-2000   **Fax:** 847 948-2964
Web: www.baxter.com

2017 Sales

	$ mil.	% of total
US	4,510	42
Europe	2,731	26
Asia/Pacific	2,110	20
Latin America & Canada	1,210	12
Total	**10,561**	**100**

PRODUCTS/OPERATIONS

2017 Sales

	$ mil.	% of total
Renal	3,480	33
Medical delivery	2,698	26
Pharmaceuticals	1,883	18
Nutrition	882	8
Advanced surgery	707	7
Acute therapies	456	4
Others	455	4
Total	**10,561**	**100**

Selected Acquisitions

COMPETITORS

Becton Dickinson	Genzyme
CSL	Grifols
CSL Behring	Hospira
CareFusion	Kimberly-Clark Health
Fresenius Medical Care	Terumo

HISTORICAL FINANCIALS

Company Type: Public

Income Statement				FYE: December 31
	REVENUE ($ mil.)	NET INCOME ($ mil.)	NET PROFIT MARGIN	EMPLOYEES
12/18	11,127	1,624	14.6%	50,000
12/17	10,561	717	6.8%	47,000
12/16	10,163	4,965	48.9%	48,000
12/15	9,968	968	9.7%	50,000
12/14	16,671	2,497	15.0%	66,000
Annual Growth	(9.6%)	(10.2%)	—	(6.7%)

2018 Year-End Financials

Debt ratio: 22.23%
Return on equity: 19.20%
Cash ($ mil.): 1,832
Current ratio: 2.09
Long-term debt ($ mil.): 3,473
No. of shares (mil.): 513
Dividends
  Yield: 1.1%
  Payout: 24.5%
Market value ($ mil.): 33,766

	STOCK PRICE ($) FY Close	P/E High/Low		PER SHARE ($) Earnings	Dividends	Book Value
12/18	65.82	26	20	2.97	0.73	15.19
12/17	64.64	50	34	1.29	0.61	16.85
12/16	44.34	5	4	9.01	0.51	15.36
12/15	38.15	41	18	1.76	1.27	16.15
12/14	73.29	17	14	4.56	2.05	14.97
Annual Growth	(2.7%)	—	—	(10.2%)	(22.8%)	0.4%

BAYLOR SCOTT & WHITE HOLDINGS

EXECUTIVES

Exec Dir, Paul E Madeley
Auditors: PRICEWATERHOUSECOOPERS LLP DA

LOCATIONS

HQ: BAYLOR SCOTT & WHITE HOLDINGS
350 N SAINT PAUL ST # 2900, DALLAS, TX 752014234
Phone: 214 820-3151

HISTORICAL FINANCIALS

Company Type: Private

Income Statement				FYE: June 30
	REVENUE ($ mil.)	NET INCOME ($ mil.)	NET PROFIT MARGIN	EMPLOYEES
06/18	9,476	754	8.0%	1
06/17	9,084	630	6.9%	—
06/15	7,535	356	4.7%	—
Annual Growth	7.9%	28.4%	—	—

BCB Bancorp Inc

BCB Bancorp be the holding company for BCB Community Bank which opened its doors in late 2000. The independent bank serves Hudson County and the surrounding area from about 15 offices in New Jersey's Bayonne Hoboken Jersey City and Monroe. The bank offers traditional deposit products and services including savings accounts money market accounts CDs and IRAs. Funds from deposits are used to originate mortgages and loans primarily commercial real estate and multi-family property loans (which together account for more than half of the bank's loan portfolio). BCB agreed to acquire IA Bancorp in a $20 million deal in 2017.

EXECUTIVES

Pres-Ceo, Thomas M Coughlin
Chb, Mark D Hogan
V Chb, Joseph J Brogan
Cfo, Thomas P Keating
V Pres-General Counsel, John J Brogan
Board Member, Vincent Didomenico
Chief Information Officer, Wing Siu
Auditors: Wolf & Company, P.C.

LOCATIONS

HQ: BCB Bancorp Inc
104-110 Avenue C, Bayonne, NJ 07002
Phone: 201 823-0700
Web: www.bcb.bank

COMPETITORS

Bank of America	PNC Financial
City National Bancshares	Provident Financial Services
Hudson City Bancorp	Sterling Bank
Meridian Capital Group	Stewardship Financial
New York Community Bancorp	

HISTORICAL FINANCIALS

Company Type: Public

Income Statement				FYE: December 31
	ASSETS ($ mil.)	NET INCOME ($ mil.)	INCOME AS % OF ASSETS	EMPLOYEES
12/18	2,674	16	0.6%	365
12/17	1,942	9	0.5%	314
12/16	1,708	8	0.5%	353
12/15	1,618	7	0.4%	331
12/14	1,301	7	0.6%	327
Annual Growth	19.7%	21.9%	—	2.8%

2018 Year-End Financials

Debt ratio: 1.37%
Return on equity: 8.90%
Cash ($ mil.): 195
Current ratio: —
Long-term debt ($ mil.): —

No. of shares (mil.): 15
Dividends
Yield: 5.3%
Payout: 75.6%
Market value ($ mil.): 166

	STOCK PRICE ($) FY Close	P/E High/Low	PER SHARE ($) Earnings	Dividends	Book Value
12/18	10.47	16 10	1.01	0.56	12.60
12/17	14.50	22 16	0.75	0.56	11.73
12/16	13.00	21 16	0.63	0.56	11.63
12/15	10.40	18 14	0.69	0.56	11.91
12/14	11.73	17 14	0.81	0.54	12.18
Annual Growth	(2.8%)	— —	5.7%	0.9%	0.8%

Beacon Roofing Supply Inc

Not all products from Beacon Roofing Supply (BRS) are to be placed over your head. Along with roofing products Beacon distributes complementary building materials such as siding windows and waterproofing systems. One of North America's largest roofing materials distributors the company operates some 40 regional companies with 590 branches in the 50 US states and six Canadian provinces. BRS carries more than 90000 stock keeping units (SKUs) available for about 100000 customers. The company's customers include contractors home builders building owners and other resellers. Most of BRS's business involves reroofing existing homes because of age or weather damage.

Operations

Operating through one reportable segment BRS is focused on the wholesale distribution of building materials.

As the result of past purchases and its rapid growth rate acquisitive BRS operates its business under some 40 trade names. Its subsidiaries include Beacon Canada Beacon Roofing Supply Canada and Beacon Sales Acquisition. The residential and nonresidential roofing products BRS supplies to its customer base are sourced from companies such as Carlisle Johns Manville Malarkey Mid-States Asphalt and Owens Corning among others.

It caters to customers through 590 branch offices and a distribution infrastructure that has the capacity to make 2 million deliveries a year supported by a company-owned fleet of 2300 straight trucks 800 tractors and 1350 trailers. Typically each branch delivers roofing materials to customers within a two-hour radius; deliveries are made five days a week.

Residential roofing products comprise 45% of BRS' sales; nonresidential roofing products 25%; and siding waterproofing systems windows and other exterior building products 30%.

Geographic Reach

BRS enjoys a broad reach across the US serving mostly metropolitan areas in the 50 US states as well as half a dozen Canadian provinces. About 97% of the company's sales are in the US with the rest in Canada.

Sales and Marketing

BRS's customer base has grown to about 100000 home builders building owners resellers and contractors. The company's customers vary by end market with relatively small contractors in the residential market and small to large-sized contractors in the non-residential market.

BRS markets its products via its sales force newsletters direct mail social media and the internet.

Financial Performance

BRS has seen an upward trend in revenue over the last seven years.

In 2018 (ended September) sales jumped about 47% to $6.4 billion from 2017. While robust the increase was less than the 64% revenue jump in 2017 from 2016. A 400% increase in acquired market sales with a strong push from the Allied acquisition drove the overall growth of BRS's revenue in 2018 with existing market sales rising less than 1% year-to-year. Existing market sales suffered from comparison with previous years when more storm damage occurred. However the company saw higher selling prices across the company's major product lines and greater average sales volume for its complementary products. It also reported high demand in Florida and Texas following hurricanes Irma and Harvey.

BRS's net income slipped to $98.6 million in 2018 about $2.3 million less than the 2017 total of $100.9 million.

The company's cash rose to $138 million in 2018 from about $31 million in 2017. In 2018 operations generated $315 million while investing activities used $167 million and financing activities used about $40 million.

Strategy

Looking to increase its market share as one of the nation's top roofing materials distribution companies BRS is keenly focused on adding new names to its portfolio as it works to boost its bottom line. Acquisitions have been a key part of BRS's growth story. Since 2004 when it became a public company BRS has made nearly 50 acquisitions opened more than 80 new branches and broadened the scope of its product lines. In just 2018 the company acquired 215 branches and opened 3 new branches.

BRS made one of its biggest deals in 2018 buying Allied Building Products Corp. for about $2.9 billion. Allied distributed products from some 210 locations in more than 30 states. It had a strong presence in the populous states of New York New Jersey Florida and California as well as Hawaii and the upper Midwest.

Besides acquisitions BRS opens new operations in locations it doesn't serve with plans to open 10-15 branches in 2019. The new stores could focus on waterproofing insulation or interiors as well as roofing.

The company has expanded its online sales channels deploying technology to help contractors and consumers make purchases. BRS's Beacon Pro+ e-commerce portal introduced in 2017 enables online ordering and real time pricing and the capabilities to request and approve quotes and pay bills online. In 2018 the company rolled out Beacon 3D+ an application that allows residential customers to use their smartphone photos to generate a 3D models.

Mergers and Acquisitions

BRS acquired Allied Building Products Corp. for about $2.9 billion in 2018 adding significant geographic coverage in the US. Headquartered in East Rutherford New Jersey Allied was one of the country's largest exterior and interior building products distributors with some 210 locations in about 30 states in the US. Its major markets were New York New Jersey Florida California Hawaii and the upper Midwest.

Also in 2018 BRS acquired Tri-State Builder's Supply in Duluth Minnesota and Atlas Supply Inc. in the Pacific Northwest.

Company Background

BRS was started in 1928 in Charlestown Massachusetts one of the first distributors of commercial roofing materials in New England. In 1953 the company expanded its operations to a larger facility in Somerville and to Worcester and Lewiston Maine in the 1970s.

HISTORY

In 2014 BRS acquired All Weather Products Ltd. a distributor of residential roofing systems and related accessories with three branches in Canada; it also acquired Dallas-based Wholesale Roofing Supply a distributor of residential roofing materials.

In 2013 BRS relocated its corporate headquarters from Peabody Massachusetts to Herndon Virginia.

Adding to its roofing business the company in late 2012 acquired Pittsburgh-based McClure-Johnston Co. a distributor of residential and commercial roofing products; Ford Wholesale Co. of San Jose a distributor of residential and commercial roofing and related accessories; and Construction Materials Supply a distributor of mostly residential roofing products across Northern California.

The company bought Missouri-based Contractors Roofing & Supply Co. for about $14 million in 2012 as well as Southern California distributor Structural Materials which specializes in residential and commercial roofing products and operates six locations. It has also purchased Cassady Pierce a Pennsylvania-based distributor of roofing products for residential and commercial uses that logs some $52 million in sales each year. The deal gave BRS half a dozen locations in the Pittsburgh area. Concentrating on Canada BRS in 2011 acquired roofing distributor Enercon Products. With six locations in Western Canada Enercon extends from Edmonton to Vancouver giving BRS a presence in every major Canadian market.

BRS was formed in 1997 when investment firm Code Hennessy & Simmons acquired a controlling interest in Beacon Sales a commercial roofer founded in 1928.

EXECUTIVES

Divisional Vice President Sales Wset Division, John Massarelli
President And Ceo, Paul M. Isabella, age 63, $640,385 total compensation
Evp And Cfo, Joseph M. Nowicki, age 57, $440,419 total compensation
Evp Sales And Marketing, Jeff Willis
Svp, James I. MacKimm
Evp Acquisitions Operational Improvements Fleet And Safety; President Canada, John C. (Jack) Smith
Vp And Cio, Christopher (Chris) Nelson
Evp General Counsel And Secretary, Ross D. Cooper, age 54, $421,289 total compensation
Evp South Division, C. Munroe Best
Evp West Division, Kent C. Gardner
Evp East Division, C. Eric Swank
Evp And Chief Supply Chain Officer, Brendan P. Daly
Evp And Chief Human Resources Officer, Christopher Harrison
Vice President Internal Audit, Stephen Balogun
Regional Vice President North Texas, Mike Lyle
Vice President Credit, David Wrabel
Vice President Sales, Tommy Thompson
Regional Vice President, Dana Geisler
Vice President Finance West Division, Brian Richter
Vice President Human Resources West Division, David Chandler
Vice President And Associate General Counsel, Chuck Gartland
Chairman, Robert R. Buck, age 71
Auditors: Ernst & Young LLP

LOCATIONS

HQ: Beacon Roofing Supply Inc
505 Huntmar Park Drive, Suite 300, Herndon, VA 20170
Phone: 571 323-3939
Web: www.becn.com

2018 Sales

	$ mil.	% of total
Net sales		
US	6,239	97
Canada	179	3
Total	**6,418**	**100**

PRODUCTS/OPERATIONS

2018 Sales

	$ mil.	% of total
Residential roofing products	2,799	44
Non-residential roofing products	1,636	25
Complementary building products	1,983	31
Total	**6,418**	**100**

Selected Trade Names

Alabama Roofing Supply
Beacon Roofing Supply Canada Company
Beacon Sales Company
Best Distributing Company
Coastal Metal Service
Dealer's Choice
Enercon Products
Entrepot de la Toiture
Fowler & Peth
GLACO
Groupe Bedard
JGA Beacon
Lafayette Wood Works
Louisiana Roofing Supply
Mississippi Roofing Supply
North Coast Commercial Roofing Systems
Pacific Supply Company
Posi-Slope
Posi-Pentes
Quality Roofing Supply Company
The Roof Center
Roof Depot
Roofing and Sheet Metal Supply
RSM Supply
Shelter Distribution
Southern Roof Center
West End Lumber Company
West End Roofing Siding and Windows
Wholesale Roofing Supply
Residential roofing products
Asphalt shingles
Clay tile
Concrete tile
Felt
Gutters and downspouts
Metal edgings and flashings
Metal roofing
Nail base insulation
Nails and fasteners
Prefabricated flashings
Slate
Synthetic slate and tile
Ridges and soffit vents
Wood shingles and shakes
Non-residential roofing products
Asphalt
Built-up roofing
Cements and coatings
Commercial fasteners
Insulation—flat stock and tapered
Metal
Metal edges and flashings
Modified bitumen
Single-ply roofing
Skylights smoke vents and roof hatches
Complementary building products
Doors windows and millwork
Residential insulation
Vinyl siding
Waterproofing systems
Wood and fiber cement siding

COMPETITORS

84 Lumber
ABC Supply
BMC Stock
Do it Best
F.W. Webb
Guardian Building Products Distribution
HD Supply
Lowe's
PrimeSource Building
Sutherland Lumber

HISTORICAL FINANCIALS

Company Type: Public

Income Statement — FYE: September 30

	REVENUE ($ mil.)	NET INCOME ($ mil.)	NET PROFIT MARGIN	EMPLOYEES
09/19	7,105	(10)	—	8,147
09/18	6,418	98	1.5%	8,356
09/17	4,376	100	2.3%	5,406
09/16	4,127	89	2.2%	5,042
09/15	2,515	62	2.5%	3,366
Annual Growth	**29.6%**	—	—	**24.7%**

2019 Year-End Financials

Debt ratio: 40.65%
Return on equity: (-0.47%)
Cash ($ mil.): 72
Current ratio: 1.75
Long-term debt ($ mil.): 2,580

No. of shares (mil.): 68
Dividends
  Yield: —
  Payout: —
Market value ($ mil.): 2,299

	STOCK PRICE ($) FY Close	P/E High/Low		Earnings	PER SHARE ($) Dividends	Book Value
09/19	33.53	—	—	(0.51)	0.00	32.98
09/18	36.19	62	33	1.05	0.00	33.51
09/17	51.25	31	24	1.64	0.00	26.32
09/16	42.07	32	22	1.49	0.00	22.10
09/15	32.49	29	18	1.24	0.00	17.74
Annual Growth	**0.8%**	—	—	—	—	**16.8%**

Becton, Dickinson & Co

Don't worry you'll only feel a slight prick if Becton Dickinson (BD) is at work. The company's BD Medical segment is one of the top global manufacturers of syringes and other injection and infusion devices. BD Medical also makes IV catheters and syringes pre-fillable drug delivery systems self-injection devices for diabetes patients and related supplies such as anesthesia trays and sharps disposal systems. The BD Life Sciences segment makes products for the safe collection and transportation of diagnostic specimens; it also makes instruments and reagent systems that detect cancers infectious diseases and health care associated infections (HAIs). BD Interventional provides vascular urology oncology and surgical specialty products.

Operations

BD operates through three reportable segments: BD Medical (more than half of total revenue) BD Life Sciences (more than 25% of revenue) and BD Interventional (some 20% of revenue).

BD Medical specializes in the manufacturing of syringes catheters and injection devices. Sales of its safety devices have experienced growth in recent years especially in international markets. Other products include pre-filled syringes and diabetic pen needles.

BD Life Sciences operates in three key areas: pre-analytical systems diagnostic systems and biosciences. Its products include safety-engineered equipment for the collection of blood automated diagnostic platforms and cell analysis equipment.

BD Interventional also operates in three key areas: surgery peripheral intervention and urology and critical care. That segment's products include catheters stents and grafts.

Geographic Reach

BD has manufacturing marketing and warehousing operations in about 50 countries in the US; Europe the Middle East and Africa (EMEA); Greater Asia; Latin America; and Canada.

Though the company is working to increase international sales (especially in emerging markets) the US remains its largest segment accounting for about 55% of sales. The EMEA is BD's second-largest operating region accounting for about 20% of revenue. Asia brings in some 15% of revenue.

Sales and Marketing

BD's customers include entities in health care (including hospitals and pharmacies) drug development medical research (including academic and government labs) clinical research (such as reference labs and blood banks) and agricultural or food analysis. The company uses a direct sales force and independent representatives to market and distribute its products in the US and abroad. In the US products are sold primarily to distributors who then resell to end-users.

Financial Performance

With the exception of fiscal 2017 (ended September) BD's revenue has been climbing for the past few years. Growth has been driven by acquisitions of other companies including C. R. Bard purchased in late 2017. Net income on the other hand has been quite volatile especially as operating expenses have risen.

In fiscal 2018 revenue increased 32% to $16 billion thanks largely to the acquisition of Bard. Overall product sales increased 6% that year; all the BD Medical segment's units saw growth — especially the medication delivery business which had a 30% sales increase. Additionally the BD Life Sciences segment had higher sales in all three of its businesses (especially the diagnostic systems unit which grew 12%).

Despite the higher revenue net income fell 85% to $159 million in fiscal 2018. Operating costs and expenses increased 36% and the company's $862 million income tax provision further cut into the bottom line.

The company ended fiscal 2018 with $1.1 billion in net cash some $13.2 billion less than it had at the end of fiscal 2017. Operating activities provided $2.9 billion while investing activities (business acquisitions primarily) used $15.8 billion and financing activities used another $58 million.

Strategy

BD's growth strategies include focusing on its core lines of products developing platform extensions and new types of products acquiring companies to supplement organic growth and expanding further into emerging markets all while improving the effectiveness of its operations. Its disease management focus is centered on conditions including diabetes women's health and cancer and infectious disease. The company continually invests in research and development; it spent $1 billion on R&D in 2018 compared to $774 million in 2017.

Through the BD Medical segment BD has been cashing in on the increased emphasis on safety in health care delivery by introducing a number of safety-engineered devices that prevent accidental needle sticks (and thus exposure to infected blood). BD Life Sciences is doing the same growing through sales of its safety-engineered blood collection equipment including the BD Vacutainer system.

In addition to improving safety BD is working to improve drug delivery methods increasing the speed of disease diagnosis and advancing pharmaceutical research techniques. The company supplements its internal R&D programs by forming partnerships and conducting acquisitions.

BD has also divested non-core operations in recent years to focus its resources on its faster-growing operations. In 2018 the company sold its Advanced Bioprocessing business to Thermo Fisher Scientific. The sale should help its Life Sciences segment focus more on disease and therapy research and clinical diagnostics. Also that year the company sold French subsidiary Cardial (vascular grafts valvulotomes and surgical glue) to LeMaitre Vascular for $2 million.

After a 2018 recall of BD syringes the FDA released a warning letter to the company for failing to prevent equipment contamination at its Franklin Wisconsin manufacturing plant.

Mergers and Acquisitions

In mid-2018 BD acquired TVA Medical which develops minimally invasive vascular access products for patients with chronic kidney disease requiring hemodialysis.

BD made a big splash when it acquired US peer C. R. Bard for some $25 billion in late 2017. That purchase strengthened BD's oncology and surgery device portfolios as the company continues to expand beyond its diabetes care operations. Most of Bard's products were added to the BD Interventional operating segment. BD sold its global core needle biopsy devices business as well as a tissue market product under development as a condition for the deal.

Company Background

Maxwell Becton and Fairleigh Dickinson established medical supply firm Becton Dickinson and Company in New York in 1897. In 1907 the company moved to New Jersey and became one of the first US firms to make hypodermic needles.

During WWI Becton Dickinson (BD) made all-glass syringes and introduced the cotton elastic bandage. After the war its researchers designed an improved stethoscope and created specialized hypodermic needles.

After the deaths of Dickinson (1948) and Becton (1951) their respective sons Fairleigh Jr. and Henry took over. BD went public in 1963 to raise money for new expansion.

HISTORY

Maxwell Becton and Fairleigh Dickinson established a medical supply firm in New York in 1897. In 1907 the company moved to New Jersey and became one of the first US firms to make hypodermic needles.

During WWI Becton Dickinson (BD) made all-glass syringes and introduced the cotton elastic bandage. After the war its researchers designed an improved stethoscope and created specialized hypodermic needles. The company supplied medical equipment to the armed forces during WWII. Becton and Dickinson helped establish Fairleigh Dickinson Junior College (now Fairleigh Dickinson University) in 1942. The company continued to develop products such as the Vacutainer blood-collection apparatus its first medical laboratory aid.

After the deaths of Dickinson (1948) and Becton (1951) their respective sons Fairleigh Jr. and Henry took over. The company introduced disposable hypodermic syringes in 1961. BD went public in 1963 to raise money for new expansion. In the 1960s the company opened plants in Brazil Canada France and Ireland and climbed aboard the conglomeration bandwagon by diversifying into such businesses as industrial gloves (Edmont 1966) and computer systems (Spear 1968). BD also went on a major acquisition spree in its core

fields during the 1960s and 1970s buying more than 25 medical supply testing and lab companies by 1980.

Wesley Howe successor to Fairleigh Dickinson Jr. expanded the company's foreign sales in the 1970s. Howe thwarted a takeover by the diversifying oil giant Sun Company (now Sunoco) in 1978 and began to sell BD's non-medical businesses in 1983 ending with the 1989 sale of Edmont. Acquisitions including Deseret Medical (IV catheters surgical gloves and masks; 1986) sharpened BD's focus on medical and surgical supplies.

In the 1990s BD formed a number of alliances and ventures including a 1991 agreement to make and market Baxter International's InterLink needleless injection system which reduces the risk of accidental needle sticks and a 1993 joint venture with NeXagen (now part of Gilead Sciences) to make and market in vitro diagnostics. As tuberculosis reemerged in the US as a serious health threat the firm improved its TB-detection and drug-resistance test systems which cut testing time from as much as seven weeks to less than two.

In 1996 BD introduced GlucoWatch (a glucose monitoring device developed by Cygnus) and acquired the diagnostic business and brand name of MicroProbe (now Epoch Pharmaceuticals).

Previously known on Wall Street as a homely company that focused on cutting costs BD changed its image with a string of acquisitions beginning in 1997. The firm acquired PharMingen (biomedical research reagents) and Difco Laboratories (microbiology media) which broadened its product lines. BD also collaborated with Nanogen on diagnosis products for infectious disease.

EXECUTIVES

Chairman And Ceo, Vincent A. (Vince) Forlenza, age 66, $1,105,000 total compensation
Evp And President Global Health, Gary M. Cohen, age 61, $605,700 total compensation
Evp And General Counsel, Jeffrey S. Sherman, age 64, $560,333 total compensation
Evp Integrated Supply Chain Officer, Stephen (Steve) Sichak, age 61
Evp Cfo And Chief Administrative Officer, Christopher R. (Chris) Reidy, age 62, $746,568 total compensation
Evp Strategic Planning And Chief Marketing Officer, Nabil Shabshab, age 53
Evp And Chief Human Resource Officer, Linda M. Tharby, age 51
President, Thomas E. Polen, age 46, $651,000 total compensation
Evp; President Greater Asia, James Lim, age 54
President Pharmaceutical Systems, Alexandre Conroy, age 55, $530,334 total compensation
Evp And Chief Quality Officer, Pierre Boisier
Evp And President Life Sciences Segment, Alberto Mas, age 57
Evp Research And Development And Chief Medical Officer, Ellen R. Strahlman, age 61, $664,427 total compensation
Evp And Chief Regulatory Officer, Richard J. Naples
Vice President Global Supply Chain, Larry Smith
Vp Operations, Silvia Anselmino
Svp Corporate Finance Controller And Treasurer, John Gallagher
Senior Vice President Chief Intellectual Property Counsel And Assistant Secretary, David Highet
Svp Corporate Secretary And Associate General Counsel, Gary M Defazio
Vice President Finance, Jim Clark
Vice President Product Development Systems, James Down
Vice President Strategic Initiatives, Ben Verwer
Executive Vice President Global Operations Chief Supply Chain Officer, James Borzi
Vice President, J Natale

Vp Global Business Systems, Karen Baughman
Worldwide Vp Medical Affairs Diabetes Care, Larry Hirsch
Vice President Human Resources World Wide Businesses, Thomas Ruddy
Vp Hr Strategy And Service Delivery, Michael Tindall
Evp And Chief Regulatory Officer, Linda Peters
Senior Vice President Taxes, Antionette Segreto
Vice President Quality, Keith Alderman
Senior Vice President Global Shared Services And Business Processes, Michael Zill
Vice President Information Technology Global Operations, Robert Shannon
Evp And General Counsel, Samrat Khichi
Evp And President Interventional Segment, John Groetelaars
Evp And Chief Medical Officer, William Sigmund
Vice President Corporate Marketing, Carol Stone
Group Vice President, Sharon Luboff
Assistant Secretary, Patricia Walesiewicz
Assistant Secretary, David Singer
Assistant Secretary, Robert Thibeault
Auditors: Ernst & Young LLP

LOCATIONS

HQ: Becton, Dickinson & Co
1 Becton Drive, Franklin Lakes, NJ 07417-1880
Phone: 201 847-6800
Web: www.bd.com

2018 Sales

	$ mil.	% of total
US	8,769	55
EMEA	3,298	21
Greater Asia	2,460	15
Other	1,457	9
Total	**15,983**	**100**

PRODUCTS/OPERATIONS

2018 Sales by Segment

	$ mil.	% of total
Medical	8,616	54
Life Sciences	4,330	27
Interventional	3,037	19
Total	**15,983**	**100**

Selected Products

Medical
  Anesthesia needles and trays
  Hypodermic needles and syringes
  Intravenous catheters
  Insulin syringes and pen needles
  Prefillable drug-delivery systems
  Prefillable IV flush syringes
  Safety needles and syringes
  Sharps disposal systems
Diagnostics
  Bar-code systems for patient identification and data capture
  Blood culturing systems
  Cytology systems (for cervical cancer screening)
  Drug susceptibility systems
  Immunodiagnostic test kits
  Microorganism identification systems
  Molecular diagnostics (for infectious disease and hospital infection testing)
  Plated media
  Rapid diagnostic assays
  Safety-engineered blood collection devices
  Sample collection products
  Specimen management systems
Biosciences
  Cell culture media
  Cell sorters and analyzers
  Cell growth and screening products
  Cellular imaging systems
  Clinical and research laboratory software
  Diagnostic assays
  Labware (tubes pipettes Petri dishes etc.)
  Molecular biology reagents (for study of genes)
  Monoclonal antibodies (for biomedical research)
  Other research reagents

Abbott Labs
B. Braun Melsungen
Baxter International
Boston Scientific
Dako
Fresenius
Gen-Probe
Hologic

Hospira
Johnson & Johnson
Novo Nordisk
Roche Diagnostics
Terumo
Thermo Fisher
  Scientific
bioMérieux

HISTORICAL FINANCIALS

Company Type: Public

Income Statement

FYE: September 30

	REVENUE ($ mil.)	NET INCOME ($ mil.)	NET PROFIT MARGIN	EMPLOYEES
09/19	17,290	1,233	7.1%	70,093
09/18	15,983	311	1.9%	76,032
09/17	12,093	1,100	9.1%	41,933
09/16	12,483	976	7.8%	50,928
09/15	10,282	695	6.8%	49,517
Annual Growth	13.9%	15.4%	—	9.1%

2019 Year-End Financials

Debt ratio: 37.46%
Return on equity: 5.86%
Cash ($ mil.): 536
Current ratio: 1.18
Long-term debt ($ mil.): 18,081

No. of shares (mil.): 270
Dividends
  Yield: 1.2%
  Payout: 109.2%
Market value ($ mil.): 68,407

	STOCK PRICE ($) FY Close	P/E High/Low	PER SHARE ($) Earnings	Dividends	Book Value
09/19	252.96	66 52	3.94	3.08	77.95
09/18	261.00	423312	0.60	3.00	78.27
09/17	195.95	44 35	4.60	2.92	56.82
09/16	179.73	40 29	4.49	2.64	35.79
09/15	132.66	45 33	3.35	2.40	34.00
Annual Growth	17.5%	— —	4.1%	6.4%	23.1%

Bed, Bath & Beyond, Inc.

Bed Bath & Beyond (BBB) is the nation's #1 superstore domestics retailer with about 1000 BBB stores throughout the US Puerto Rico and Canada. The stores' floor-to-ceiling shelves stock better-quality (brand-name and private-label) goods in two main categories: domestics (bed linens bathroom and kitchen items) and home furnishings (cookware and cutlery small household appliances picture frames and more). BBB also operates more than 275 Cost Plus and World Market stores and four smaller specialty chains: about 125 buybuy Baby stores about 80 Christmas Tree Shops some 55 Harmon discount health and beauty shops and two One Kings Lane stores. California and Texas are its largest markets accounting for about 20% of its total stores.

Operations

BBB sells a wide assortment of domestics merchandise and home furnishings. Sales of home furnishings generate about 65% of the retailer's total revenue while domestic merchandise makes up about 35% of total revenue each year. Domestics merchandise includes categories such as bed linens and related items bath items and kitchen textiles while home furnishings include categories such as kitchen and tabletop items fine tabletop basic

housewares general home furnishings (including furniture and wall décor) consumables and certain juvenile products.Some of the company?s proprietary brands include Bee & Willow Home Wamsutta Olivia & Oliver SALT and Artisanal Kitchen Supply. BBB purchases substantially all of its merchandise in the US while the rest are purchased from importers. It also purchases a small amount of its merchandise directly from overseas sources. It has around 11200 suppliers with the ten largest accounting for approximately 15% of total purchases.

Geographic Reach

Nearly all of the New Jersey-based BBB's more than 1530 stores are in the US though around 60 of its stores are located across 10 Canadian provinces while three are in Puerto Rico. About 40% of the company's stores are in five US states: California Texas Florida New York and New Jersey. In Mexico BBB also has a joint venture with Mexican retailer Home & More where it currently operates some ten stores under the BBB banner.

Sales and Marketing

BBB prefers to locate its stores in strip malls and power strip shopping centers in suburban areas of medium and large-sized cities. It also places its stores near major off-price and conventional malls. The company?s marketing efforts include email mobile SMS social search digital display content and influencer marketing online affiliate programs and public relations efforts as well as traditional print media such as postcards newspaper inserts circulars and catalogs all of which sometimes include coupon offers.

Financial Performance

BBB has struggled to grow in recent years amid a fiercely competitive retail market. Its annual revenues have risen just 1% since 2014. Revenue decreased to $12 billion in 2018 an approximately 2% drop from the year prior. The decrease was driven in part by one week less in sales in 2018 compared to 2017 and a 1% decrease in comparable sales in 2018. Net loss was $137.2 million in 2018 a drop from net income of $424.9 million in 2017. Selling general and administrative expenses remained the same in fiscal 2018 at $3.6 billion. Cash on hand at the end of fiscal 2018 was $509 million. Cash provided by operating activities was $918.3 million in 2018 while investing activities used $509.7 million. Financing activities used another $238.6 million.

Strategy

Amid a competitive retail environment BBB is accelerating changes at the company designed to improve financial performance enhance its competitive position and improve its governance structure.

As part of a fleet optimization BBB announced in 2019 that it expected to close 60 stores in fiscal year 2020 to create a better balance between its physical and digital presence in the market. The company also announced a 7% reduction in corporate staff and a simplification of corporate structure in 2019 which included the elimination of the position of President and COO.

Private label brands is a growth opportunity for the company. BBB plans to launch six in-house brands by 2020. In 2019 the company launched a second private-label home furnishings brand called One Kings Lane Open House which is expected to have affordable pricing.

Seeking to improve the customer experience BBB is renovating stores to give them a more modern less cluttered feel with a better inventory assortment. The company is also enhancing its omnichannel capabilities through such initiatives as reserving online and picking up in-store purchasing online and returning in-store and online appointment scheduling for registry services.

HISTORY

Warren Eisenberg and Leonard Feinstein both employed by a discounter called Arlan's brainstormed an idea in 1971 for a chain of stores offering only home goods. They were betting that customers were in Feinstein's words interested in a "designer approach to linens and housewares." The two men started two small linens stores (about 2000 sq. ft) named bed n bath one in New York and one in New Jersey.

Expansion came at a fairly slow pace as the company moved only into California and Connecticut by 1985. By then the time was right for such a specialty retailer: Department stores were cutting back on their houseware lines to focus on the more profitable apparel segment and baby boomers were spending more leisure time at their homes (and more money on spiffing them up). Eisenberg and Feinstein opened a 20000-sq.-ft. superstore in 1985 that offered a full line of home furnishings. The firm changed its name to Bed Bath & Beyond (BBB) two years later in order to reflect its new offerings.

With the successful superstore format the company built all new stores in the larger design. BBB grew rapidly; square footage quadrupled between 1992 and 1996. The company went public in 1992. That year it eclipsed the size of its previous stores when it opened a 50000-sq.-ft. store in Manhattan. (It later enlarged this store to 80000 sq. ft.; the company's stores now average 42000 sq. ft.)

BBB's management has attributed its success in part to the leeway it gives its store managers who monitor inventory and have the freedom to try new products and layouts. One example often cited by the company is the case of a manager who decided to sell glasses by the piece instead of in sets. Sales increased 30% and the whole chain incorporated the practice.

The retailer opened 28 new stores in 1996 33 in 1997 (its first-ever billion-dollar sales year) and 45 in 1998.

In 1999 the company dipped a toe into the waters of e-commerce by agreeing to buy a stake in Internet Gift Registries which operates the WeddingNetwork website. The company later began offering online sales and bridal registry services. Keeping up its rapid expansion pace the company opened 70 stores in 1999 85 in 2000 and 95 in 2001.

In 2002 BBB acquired Harmon Stores a health and beauty aid retailer with 29 stores in three states. It acquired Christmas Tree Shops a giftware and household items retailer with 23 stores in six states for $200 million in 2003.

In March 2007 BBB acquired buybuy BABY which operates eight stores on the East Coast for $67 million. The retailer opened its first Canadian location in Ontario north of Toronto in December. In 2008 BBB added three more stores in Canada and its first locations in Mexico via a joint venture there under the Home & More banner.

In June 2012 the company bought Cost Plus which operates nearly 260 stores in 30 states under the World Market Cost Plus World Market and Cost Plus Imports banners for $495 million in cash.

In 2015 BBB acquired Of a Kind an e-commerce website that features specially commissioned limited edition items from emerging fashion and home designers.

In 2016 the company acquired online home goods retailer One Kings Lane Inc. in an all-cash deal. The deal the value of which was undisclosed bolstered BBB's furniture and home décor offerings in the online space. One Kings offers an extensive collection of designer and vintage furniture rugs kitchenware lighting and other décor for homes.

Also in 2016 the company acquired PersonalizationMall.com a online seller of personalized gifts for $190 in cash.In early 2017 it acquired Decorist an online interior design platform that provides personalized home design services. Decorist also offers photorealistic 3-D renderings of how items will look in their actual homes and offers additional online services.

EXECUTIVES

Coo, Eugene A. (Gene) Castagna, age 53, $1,928,846 total compensation
Vice President, Jim Brendle
Vice President, William Plate
Vice President Real Estate, Seth Geldzahler
Vice President Stores Midwest Region, Dana Pelan
Vice President, Patrick M Kelley
Vice President Supply Chain Logistics, Jeffrey Macak
President And Chief Merchandising Officer, Arthur (Art) Stark, age 64, $1,849,277 total compensation
Svp Stores, Matthew Fiorilli, age 62, $1,730,468 total compensation
Ceo, Steven H. (Steve) Temares, age 60, $3,967,500 total compensation
Cfo And Treasurer, Susan E. Lattmann, age 51, $1,021,154 total compensation
Vp And Cio, Robert Claybrook
Vp It, Trenton Parks
Vice President Of Ecommerce Merchandising, Cesar Garcia
Vice President Of Transportation, Doug Hanley
Vice President, Hiten Shroff
Vice President, John Mariani
Vice President Information Technology, Guy Miller
Vice President Customer Service, Hank Rinehardt
Vice President, Edward Kopil
Vice President Of Design And Development, Robert Caruso
Senior Vice President Of Sales, Josh Lighty
Vice President Stores, Glen Cary
Vice President Digital Marketing And Crm, Tom Kuypers
Vice President Visual Merchandising, Cindy Davis
Vice President Human Resources, Concetta Van Dyke
Vice President Finance, Jason Quint
Vp And Corporate Counsel, Michael Callahan
Regional Vice President, Bill Onksen
Executive Vice President Supply Chain, Jason Pankowski
Vice President, Lisa Cavanagh
Vice President, Chris Jackey
Vice President Store Operations, Christine Pirog
Vice President Information Technology, Bob Roe
Vice President Of Information Technology, Timothy Kirchner
Vice President Of Supply Chain, Jeff Macak
Vice President, Bill Plate
Vice President, George Elefther
Vice President Merchandise Control, Dave Denenberg
Vice President, Sal Dimino
Vp, Matt Mffiorilli
Vp Tax, Steven Taplits
Vice President Loss Prevention And Safety, Jim OConnor
Department Head, Morgan Biggs
Vice President Pmo, Andrea Arrowsmith
Vice President Portfolio Management, Jinny Uppal
Vp It Engineering, Justin Hill
Vp Risk Management, Manuel Homem
Co-chairman, Leonard (Lenny) Feinstein, age 82
Co-chairman, Warren Eisenberg, age 88
Board Member, Klaus Eppler
Board Member, Dean S Adler
Board Member, Patrick R Gaston
Board Member, Adam Heller
Auditors: KPMG LLP

LOCATIONS

HQ: Bed, Bath & Beyond, Inc.
650 Liberty Avenue, Union, NJ 07083
Phone: 908 688-0888 **Fax:** 908 810-8813
Web: www.bedbathandbeyond.com

2017 Stores

	No.
California	184
Texas	119
New York	101
Florida	96
New Jersey	91
Illinois	55
Ohio	49
Virginia	46
Massachusetts	44
Michigan	44
Pennsylvania	44
North Carolina	43
Arizona	42
Georgia	39
Washington	37
Colorado	35
Tennessee	29
Connecticut	25
Ontario Canada	25
Alabama	24
South Carolina	24
Indiana	23
Maryland	23
Missouri	23
Louisiana	20
Oregon	17
Utah	16
Wisconsin	16
Minnesota	15
Nevada	15
New Hampshire	14
Kansas	12
Alberta Canada	12
British Columbia Canada	12
Iowa	11
Kentucky	11
Idaho	10
New Mexico	10
Other	90
Total	**1,546**

PRODUCTS/OPERATIONS

2017 Stores

	No.
Bed Bath & Beyond	1,023
Cost Plus World Market	276
BABY Stores	113
Christmas Tree Shops	80
Harmon stores	54
Total	**1,546**

COMPETITORS

Amazon.com	Macy's
Art.com	Pier 1 Imports
Babies "R" Us	Ross Stores
Burlington Coat Factory	Sears
Children's Place	Sensational Beginnings
Container Store	TJX Companies
Dillard's	Target Corporation
Euromarket Designs	Tuesday Morning Corporation
Garden Ridge	Wal-Mart
Gymboree	Wayfair
Kmart	Williams-Sonoma

HISTORICAL FINANCIALS

Company Type: Public

Income Statement

FYE: March 2

	REVENUE ($ mil.)	NET INCOME ($ mil.)	NET PROFIT MARGIN	EMPLOYEES
03/19	12,028	(137)	—	62,000
03/18*	12,349	424	3.4%	65,000
02/17	12,215	685	5.6%	65,000
02/16	12,103	841	7.0%	62,000
02/15	11,881	957	8.1%	60,000
Annual Growth	**0.3%**	**—**		**0.8%**

*Fiscal year change

2019 Year-End Financials

Debt ratio: 22.65%	No. of shares (mil.): 132
Return on equity: (-5.05%)	Dividends
Cash ($ mil.): 508	Yield: 0.0%
Current ratio: 1.88	Payout: —
Long-term debt ($ mil.): 1,487	Market value ($ mil.): 2,207

	STOCK PRICE ($) FY Close	P/E High/Low		PER SHARE ($) Earnings	Dividends	Book Value
03/19	16.69	—	—	(1.02)	0.63	19.36
03/18*	21.83	14	6	3.04	0.58	20.56
02/17	41.04	11	8	4.58	0.38	18.59
02/16	48.99	15	8	5.10	0.00	16.34
02/15	74.66	15	11	5.07	0.00	15.75
Annual Growth	**(31.2%)**	—	—	—	—	**5.3%**

*Fiscal year change

Berkley (WR) Corp

Holding company W. R. Berkley offers an assortment of niche commercial property/casualty insurance across two segments — Insurance and Reinsurance. The Insurance segment comprising about 55 operating companies underwrites commercial insurance coverage including excess and surplus lines and admitted lines. It also develops self-insuring programs aimed at employers and employer groups. The Reinsurance segment allows insurance companies to pool their risks in order to reduce their liability. Berkley serves customers in 60 countries in the Americas Europe and the Asia/Pacific region.

Operations

Berkley's Insurance segment accounts for about 85% of the company's total revenue while the Reinsurance segment accounts for about 10%. The remainder is brought in by other operations.

In addition to insurance products Berkley offers a variety of fee-based services such as claims administrative and consulting services.

Geographic Reach

Berkley offers insurance and reinsurance through about 55 operating units in 60 nations in North America South America Europe Africa and the Asia/Pacific region.

Sales and Marketing

Berkley primarily serves small to midsized business customers. The insurer sells its high-risk coverage products directly and through retail and wholesale agents brokers and managing general agents to a wide variety of clients. The regional products business' offerings are sold through a network of brokers and commission-based independent agents.

Financial Performance

After seeing a revenue decline in 2015 Berkley has had slow but steady growth over the past three years. Net income has been more volatile since it fell 22% in 2015.

In 2018 revenue rose less than 1% to $7.72 billion. This was largely due to a less-than-1% increase in total premiums earned. Fee-related and other income which represent a much smaller category of revenue increased slightly that year. These gains were partially offset by lower investment income. And although insurance premiums written increased reinsurance premiums written declined.

Net income increased 17% to $640.7 million in 2018. It had fallen 9% in 2017 as a result of increased catastrophe losses in that record year of weather events. Catastrophe losses net of reinsurance recoveries totaled $105 million in 2018 (versus $184 million in 2017) resulting in a 1% drop in losses and loss expenses.

The company ended 2018 with $817.6 million in net cash about $130 million less than it had at the end of 2017. Operating activities provided $620.2 million while investing activities used $714.2 million and financing activities used $7.4 million.

Strategy

Strategically Berkley's decentralized structure promotes the development of specialized expertise in a range of areas and enables the company to adapt to cyclical market conditions and insulate itself from great risk. While the company has made a handful of acquisitions through the years it prefers to expand by forming new operating units after identifying needs in specific areas. In 2018 the company launched Berkley Healthcare which specializes in services and products for health care providers.

Other recent additions include firms specializing in cybersecurity and health care. In 2018 subsidiary Berkley One established a partnership with data defense services provider CyberScout to offer a suite of cyber solutions covering identity theft cyber bullying and system compromise. That same unit is also rolling out its platform serving high-net-worth customers in certain states; it is now active in about a dozen states.

The company focuses on growing world markets including Scandinavia South America Australia and the Asia/Pacific region. Additionally Berkley exits insurance lines as demand diminishes.

With the insurance market being so fragmented and new competitors entering the fray Berkley is under pressure to keep its prices down. This has led to a slowdown in premium growth for the company.

Company Background

Bill Berkley and a partner established investment management firm Berkley Dean & Company in 1967. The company went public as W.R. Berkley Corporation in 1973. Over the years it expanded through the formation of new companies as well as acquisitions.

EXECUTIVES

Evp Investments, James G. Shiel, age 59, $650,000 total compensation
Senior Vice President Insurance Risk Management, Robert Gosselink
Senior Vice President, Peter Kamford
Svp Underwriting, Michele Fleckenstein
Evp, C. Fred Madsen
Evp And Secretary, Ira S. Lederman, age 66, $650,000 total compensation
Evp, Eugene G. Ballard, age 66, $650,000 total compensation
President And Ceo, W. Robert (Rob) Berkley, age 46, $993,769 total compensation
Evp, Robert C. Hewitt, age 58
Evp, Philip S. Welt, age 60

Evp, Robert D. Stone, age 55
Evp, John K. Goldwater
Evp, William M. Rohde
Evp, Jeffrey M. (Jeff) Hafter
Evp, Lucille T. Sgaglione
Svp Cfo And Treasurer, Richard M. Baio, $497,981 total compensation
Evp, Kathleen M. Tierney
Vp And Chief Marketing Officer, Jonathan M. Levine
Svp And Cio, Richard M. Lowery
Evp, James P. Bronner
Svp And Chief Project Officer, Mir Mazhar
Evp, Kenneth P. Sroka
Vice President, Michael Harris
Evp, James Gilbert
Assistant Vice President And Corporate Actuary, Gene Zhang
Vice President, Nicholas Lang
Vice President Analytics, Robert McPherson
Assistant Vice President Of Application Developmen, Jim Leonardis
Vice President, Marie Gwin
Vp And Head Corporate Catastrophe Analysis, Robert Sabio
Executive Vice President, Ricardo Gonzalez
Vice President Actuarial And Data Analysis, Debbie Savoie
Executive Vice President, Steven Walsh
Senior Vice President Information Technology, Kevin H Ebers
Vp And Corporate Actuary, Jessica Somerfeld
Senior Vice President, C Madsen
Svp Business Shared Services, Kevin Ebers
Svp And Chief Corporate Actuary, Paul Hancock
Vice President, Carol La Punzina
Svp, Steven Taylor
Vice President, Beena Gadgil
Senior Vice President Enterprise Risk Management, Gillian James
Vice President, Joyce Krech
Vice President Marketing, John Bowen
Assistant Vice President Actuarial Analysis, Scott Jensen
Vice President And Corporate Controller, Andrea Kanefsky
Vice President Real Estate Operations, Jesse Faneuil
Senior Vice President Corporate Strategy And Development, Jared Abbey
Vice President Insurance Risk Management, Laura Goodall
Vice President Enterprise Risk Management, Trish Conway
Senior Vice President Marketing, Christoph Ritterson
Senior Vice President Customer Experience Berkley One, Susan Vella
Svp Insurance Risk Management, Melissa Emmendorfer
Senior Vice President Claims, Kevin Shea
Vice President Actuary, Dustin J Turner
Vice President Team Infrastructure, Mike Chang
Vice President Actuary, Dustin Turner
Senior Vice President, Tod Bolden
Vp International Network Manager, Brenda Menichillo
Chairman, William R. (Bill) Berkley, age 73
Assistant Secretary Human Resources, Donna Syko
Assistant Treasurer, George Richardson
Auditors: KPMG LLP

LOCATIONS

HQ: Berkley (WR) Corp
475 Steamboat Road, Greenwich, CT 06830
Phone: 203 629-3000
Web: www.wrberkley.com

PRODUCTS/OPERATIONS

2018 Sales

	$ mil.	% of total
Insurance	6,456	84
Reinsurance	1,600	8
Net investment gains	480	6
Corporate & other	154	2
Total	**7,718**	**100**

2018 Sales

	$ mil.	% of total
Net premiums earned	6,371	82
Net investment income	674	9
Revenue from non-insurance businesses	373	5
Net realized and unrealized gains on investments	154	2
Insurance service fees	117	2
Other	0	-
Total	**7,718**	**100**

Selected Property/Casualty Segments

Specialty (includes excess and surplus lines and admitted specialty lines)
Regional (commercial lines property/casualty)
Alternative markets (includes excess workers' compensation monoline workers' compensation accident and health and insurance services)
Reinsurance (facultative or treaty basis; participates in business written through Lloyd's of London)
International business (global underwriting)

COMPETITORS

AIG	Munich Re America
Allied World Assurance	Nationwide
American Financial Group	Swiss Re
Arch Capital	Transatlantic Reinsurance
Berkshire Hathaway	Travelers Companies
CNA Financial	White Mountains Insurance Group
Everest Re	

HISTORICAL FINANCIALS

Company Type: Public

Income Statement				FYE: December 31
	ASSETS ($ mil.)	NET INCOME ($ mil.)	INCOME AS % OF ASSETS	EMPLOYEES
12/18	24,895	640	2.6%	7,448
12/17	24,299	549	2.3%	7,722
12/16	23,364	601	2.6%	7,683
12/15	21,730	503	2.3%	7,621
12/14	21,716	648	3.0%	7,521
Annual Growth	3.5%	(0.3%)	—	(0.2%)

2018 Year-End Financials

Debt ratio: 11.20%
Return on equity: 11.81%
Cash ($ mil.): 817
Current ratio: —
Long-term debt ($ mil.): —
No. of shares (mil.): 182
Dividends
  Yield: 2.1%
  Payout: 41.8%
Market value ($ mil.): 13,525

	STOCK PRICE ($)	P/E		PER SHARE ($)		
	FY Close	High/Low	Earnings	Dividends	Book Value
12/18	73.91	24 20	3.33	1.39	29.72
12/17	71.65	25 21	2.84	1.03	29.69
12/16	66.51	20 15	3.12	1.01	27.76
12/15	54.75	22 18	2.58	0.31	24.87
12/14	51.26	16 11	3.24	0.95	24.14
Annual Growth	9.6%	— —	0.7%	10.0%	5.3%

Berkshire Hathaway Inc

Berkshire Hathaway is the holding company where Warren Buffett one of the world's richest men makes his money and spreads his risk. The company invests in a variety of industries from insurance and utilities to apparel and food and from building materials and furniture retailers to jewelry shops. Its core insurance subsidiaries include GEICO National Indemnity and reinsurance giant General Re. The company's other large holdings include Marmon Group McLane Company MidAmerican Energy and Shaw Industries. Buffett holds a significant stake in Berkshire Hathaway which owns a majority of more than 50 firms in all and has equity stakes in about a dozen others.

Operations

Berkshire Hathaway operates as a holding company with a highly decentralized structure without integrated business functions (such as sales marketing purchasing legal and human resources). Practicing a minimal day-to-day management leadership style the firm owns a diverse group of companies from a variety of industries with its core subsidiaries being insurance reinsurance freight rail transportation utilities and energy generation companies.

The insurance businesses constitute about three quarters of total revenue and are composed of over a dozen large providers that insure for example automobiles boats commercial buildings businesses workers? compensation and medical practices. Its most recognizable holding is GEICO (auto insurance). Sales and service revenues make up almost 70% of the insurance business revenue while another 20% comes from insurance premiums.

Lesser known to most are the company?s investment in other industries. Berkshire Hathaway's holdings include a railroad transportation company (Burlington Northern Santa Fe) a real estate business (Berkshire Hathaway Property Advisors) a carpet manufacturer (Shaw Industries) a wholesale distributor of consumer goods (McLane) a manufacturer of clay bricks (Acme Brick) a battery company (Duracell) and a specialty chemicals producer (Lubrizol). Berkshire Hathaway provides capital and financial guidance ensures the companies are well managed and then takes a back seat to allow company leadership to run the entities.

More than 15% of Berkshire Hathaway revenue comes from its railroad utilities and energy subsidiaries and about 5% comes from its finance and financial product companies.

Additionally the company invests its treasure trove of excess cash (typically more than $60 billion) in shares of public companies or in commercial debt which it usually holds for a few years. Recent investments were in Wrigley Kraft Heinz Dow and Phillips 66.

Geographic Reach

Omaha Nebraska-headquartered Berkshire Hathaway operates primarily in the US although it does provide insurance (and reinsurance) to clients in the Asia Pacific and Western Europe geographies.

Financial Performance

Buffett's famed investment vehicle enjoyed upward trends in revenue and profit over recent years highlighting the legendary investors' knack for choosing financially successful companies over the long term. It grew revenue from $107 billion in 2008 to more than $223 billion in 2016. Net income expanded almost fivefold from $5 billion in 2008 to almost $25 billion in 2016.

In 2016 Berkshire's revenue climbed 6% to a record-setting $223 billion on increases in insurance and financial product revenue which more than overcame a slip in revenue from its railroad utilities and energy businesses. Its insurance business especially through higher demand for GEICO?s auto policies grew 7% year over year. The firm's Finance and Financial Products business revenue shot up 36% with higher home sales volumes and a significant jump in the segment?s investment gains.

Net income was flat in 2016 versus the prior year. A jump in insurance losses & adjustments coupled with higher costs for sales and services ate into the higher revenue leaving the firm with a still highly profitable $24 billion.

Cash on hand at the end of 2016 was $28 billion a decrease of $39 billion from 2015. While operating activities provided $32 billion and financing activities offered an additional $13 billion of cash investing activities (primarily the purchase of US Treasury Bills) used more than $84 billion.

Strategy

Berkshire Hathaway seeks out large companies with consistent earnings easy-to-understand business models and like-minded leadership. Most acquisitions are made with cash and most firms retain their management after the transaction. Buffett and longtime business partner Charlie Munger attempt to run Berkshire like a small business albeit on a much larger scale. It operates as a collection of individual enterprises; Buffett and Munger largely keep their hands off portfolio companies' day-to-day operations but allocate capital and control risk.

In a letter to shareholders Buffett once declared "Our elephant gun has been reloaded and my trigger finger is itchy." Hunting big game (i.e. acquiring big companies) has become somewhat of a necessity for Berkshire Hathaway to continue its growth trajectory but the company benefits from not being married to any industry as it seeks out its quarry. Following its ?big game? investment strategy Berkshire entered new markets with the 2017 purchase of 38% of Pilot Flying J truck stop company and the $32 billion 2016 acquisition of aerospace components giant Precision Castparts. It plans to purchase a further 41% of Pilot Flying J in 2023 as part of a long-term move to acquire majority ownership. Berkshire?s holds non-majority investment stakes in Apple ($19 billion) Bank of America ($16 billion) and many other household name companies.

Company Background

Chairman and CEO Warren Buffett along with associates slowly accumulated a majority of shares in the Berkshire Hathaway textile company in the early 1960s. To stabilize revenues and reduce financial risks Buffett diversified the company with a purchase of Indemnity and National Fire & Marine Insurance Company in 1967. Thus began the long prosperous road towards profitability and dozens of acquisitions. Buffett still owns about 20% of Berkshire Hathaway's shares.

HISTORY

Warren Buffett bought his first stock — three shares of Cities Service — at age 11. In the 1950s he studied at Columbia University under famed investor Benjamin Graham. Graham's axioms: Use quantitative analysis to discover companies whose intrinsic worth exceeds their stock prices; popularity is irrelevant; the market will vindicate the patient investor.

In 1956 Buffett then 25 founded Buffett Partnership. Its $105000 in initial assets multiplied as the company bought Berkshire Hathaway (textiles 1965) and National Indemnity (insurance 1967). When Buffett nixed the partnership in 1969 because he believed stocks were overvalued value per share had risen 30-fold.

In late 2012 the firm also acquired Omaha-based online party supplier Oriental Trading Company.

Berkshire Hathaway's $28-billion purchase of ketchup giant H.J. Heinz in 2013 is also a textbook example of the firm's investment strategy as the firm and its investment partner Brazil's 3G Capital took the ketchup maker private to speed its transformation into a global food business.

EXECUTIVES

Chairman Bnsf Railway., Matthew K. (Matt) Rose, age 60

Svp And Cfo, Marc D. Hamburg, age 69, $1,550,000 total compensation

Chairman And Ceo, Warren E. Buffett, age 89, $100,000 total compensation

Head Of Reinsurance, Ajit Jain, age 67

Head Of Berkshire Hathaway Energy, Greg Abel

Svp Healthcare Professional Liability Berkshire Hathaway Specialty Insurance, Leo Carroll

Vice President Human Resources And Administration, Jennifer Johnson

Vice Chairman, Charles T. (Charlie) Munger, age 95

Board Member, Thomas Murphy

Treasurer And Controller, Janet Saar

Auditors: DELOITTE & TOUCHE LLP

LOCATIONS

HQ: Berkshire Hathaway Inc
3555 Farnam Street, Omaha, NE 68131
Phone: 402 346-1400
Web: www.berkshirehathaway.com

PRODUCTS/OPERATIONS

2016 sales

	$ mil.	% of total
Insurance and Other		
Sales and service revenues	119,489	53
Insurance premiums earned	45,881	21
Investment gains	5,128	2
Interest dividend and other investment income	4,725	2
Railroad Utilities and Energy	37,542	17
Finance and Financial Products		
Sales and service revenues	6,208	3
Investment gains	2,425	1
Interest dividend and other investment income	1,455	1
Derivative gains	751	0
Total	**223,604**	**100**

Subsidiaries and Selected Holdings
Acme Brick Company (bricks)
Applied Underwriters (workers' compensation)
Ben Bridge Jeweler (jewelry retailer)
Benjamin Moore (architectural and industrial paint)
Berkshire Hathaway Automotive
Berkshire Hathaway Energy Company
Berkshire Hathaway GUARD Insurance Companies
Berkshire Hathaway Homestate Companies
Berkshire Hathaway Life Insurance Company of Nebraska
BH Media Group (digital marketing publishing)
Boat U.S. (insurance)
Borsheim Jewelry Company (jewelry retailer)
Brooks (shoes)
The Buffalo News (newspaper)
Burlington Northern Santa Fe (railroad)
Business Wire Inc. (news service)
Central States Indemnity Co. of Omaha (credit and disability insurance)
Clayton Homes (manufactured housing and financing)
CORT Business Services Corp. (provider of rental furniture accessories and related services)
CTB International (manufacturer of equipment and systems for poultry hog and egg production)
The Fechheimer Brothers (uniforms and accessories)
FlightSafety International (high technology training to operators of aircraft and ships)
Forest River (recreational vehicles)
Fruit of the Loom (apparel)
Garan Inc. (apparel)
GEICO (property/casualty insurance)
General Re Corporation (property/casualty reinsurance)

H.H. Brown Shoe Company
Helzberg's Diamond Shops (jewelry retailer)
HomeServices of America (real estate services)
International Dairy Queen Inc. (licensing and servicing Dairy Queen Stores)
Johns Manville (building and equipment insulation)
Jordan's Furniture (retailing home furnishings)
Justin Brands (western footwear and apparel)
Kraft Heinz
Larson-Juhl
LiquidPower Speciality Products
Lubrizol (specialty chemicals)
Marmon Holdings (manufacturing and service)
McLane Company (wholesale distribution of groceries and non-food items)
MedPro Group (Med Pro; professional liability insurer)
MidAmerican Energy Holdings Company
  HomeServices of America Inc. (residential real estate brokerage)
  Kern River Gas Transmission Company
  Northern Electric
  Northern Natural Gas
  Pacific Power
  Rocky Mountain Power
  Yorkshire Electricity
MiTek (building components)
National Indemnity Company (specialty insurance)
Nebraska Furniture Mart (retailing home furnishings)
NetJets Inc. (fractional ownership programs for general aviation aircraft)
Oriental Trading Company (party supplies)
Pampered Chef Ltd. (kitchenware and housewares)
Precision Castparts Corp (aerospace parts manufacturer)
Precision Steel Warehouse (steel service center)
R.C. Willey Home Furnishings (home furnishings retailer)
Richline Group (jewelry manufacturer)
Scott Fetzer Company (manufacture and distribution of diversified products)
See's Candies (boxed chocolates and other confectionery products)
Shaw Industries (carpets and rugs)
Star Furniture Co. (home furnishings retailer)
TTI Inc. (electronics distribution)
United States Liability Insurance Group
XTRA Corporation (transportation equipment)

COMPETITORS

AEA Investors	Lincoln Financial
Allstate	Group
Apollo Global	Progressive
Management	Corporation
Bain Capital	State Farm
BlackRock	TPG
Blackstone Group	The Carlyle Group
CNA Financial	The Hartford
KKR	

HISTORICAL FINANCIALS

Company Type: Public

Income Statement · FYE: December 31

	STOCK PRICE ($) FY Close	P/E High/Low	PER SHARE ($) Earnings	Dividends	Book Value
12/18	306,000.00	1371 152	446.00	0.00	212,503
12/17	297,600.00	11	927,326.00	0.00	211,749
12/16	244,121.00	17	1314,645.00	0.00	172,108
12/15	197,800.00	15	1314,656.00	0.00	155,50
12/14	226,000.00	19	1412,092.00	0.00	146,185
Annual Growth	7.9%	—	— (32.9%)	—	9.8%

	ASSETS ($ mil.)	NET INCOME ($ mil.)	INCOME AS % OF ASSETS	EMPLOYEES
12/18	707,794	4,021	0.6%	389,000
12/17	702,095	44,940	6.4%	377,000
12/16	620,854	24,074	3.9%	367,700
12/15	552,257	24,083	4.4%	331,000
12/14	526,186	19,872	3.8%	316,000
Annual Growth	7.7%	(32.9%)	—	5.3%

2018 Year-End Financials

Debt ratio: 13.77%
Return on equity: 1.15%
Cash ($ mil.): 111,867
Current ratio: —
Long-term debt ($ mil.): —

No. of shares (mil.): 1
Dividends
  Yield: —
  Payout: —
Market value ($ mil.): 502,124

Berkshire Hills Bancorp Inc

EXECUTIVES

Ceo-Pres, Richard M Marotta
Chb, William J Ryan
Sr Exec V Pres, Sean A Gray
Sr Exec V Pres-Cfo, James M Moses
Vice President, Eric Navarra
Board Member, Williar Dunlaevy
Investment Manager, Adam Bronkella
Information Technology Directo, Genevieve Misiaszek
Vice President Relationship MA, Justin Priddle
Senior Vice President, Mary Cologero
Regional Training Manager, Stacey Browne
Auditors: Crowe LLP

LOCATIONS

HQ: Berkshire Hills Bancorp Inc
60 State Street, Boston, MA 02109
Phone: 800 773-5601
Web: www.berkshirebank.com

COMPETITORS

Bank of America	RBS Citizens Financial
Hudson City Bancorp	Group
KeyCorp	Sovereign Bank
Pathfinder Bancorp	TD Bank USA

HISTORICAL FINANCIALS

Company Type: Public

Income Statement · FYE: December 31

	ASSETS ($ mil.)	NET INCOME ($ mil.)	INCOME AS % OF ASSETS	EMPLOYEES
12/18	12,212	105	0.9%	1,917
12/17	11,570	55	0.5%	1,992
12/16	9,162	58	0.6%	1,731
12/15	7,831	49	0.6%	1,221
12/14	6,502	33	0.5%	1,091
Annual Growth	17.1%	33.1%	—	15.1%

2018 Year-End Financials

Debt ratio: 0.82%
Return on equity: 6.94%
Cash ($ mil.): 183
Current ratio: —
Long-term debt ($ mil.): —

No. of shares (mil.): 45
Dividends
  Yield: 3.2%
  Payout: 38.4%
Market value ($ mil.): 1,225

Berry Global Group Inc

	STOCK PRICE ($) FY Close	P/E High/Low	PER SHARE ($) Earnings	Dividends	Book Value
12/18	26.97	19 11	2.29	0.88	34.19
12/17	36.60	28 24	1.39	0.84	33.04
12/16	36.85	20 13	1.88	0.80	30.65
12/15	29.11	17 14	1.73	0.76	28.64
12/14	26.66	20 16	1.36	0.72	28.17
Annual Growth	0.3%	—	— 13.9%	5.1%	5.0%

With a portfolio that includes tapes tubes and trash bags Berry Global is a top maker of plastic products and engineered materials for customers across a broad range of industries. Its products include shrink wrap and other packaging films cloth and foil tapes plastic cups and lids components for diapers and other personal care items and prescription bottles. Key markets include the healthcare personal care and food and beverage industries. Berry Global operates worldwide but North America is by far its largest market. In July 2019 Berry Global completed the acquisition of plastic packaging company RPC Group for $6.5 billion.

Operations

Berry Global reports three operating segments: Engineered Materials; Health Hygiene and Specialties; and Consumer Packaging each contributing roughly a third of total revenue.

Engineered Materials manufactures tapes and adhesives polyethylene-based film products can liners printed films and laminated products.

The Health Hygiene and Specialties segment primarily consists of nonwoven specialty materials and films used in hygiene infection prevention personal care industrial construction and filtration applications.

The Consumer Packaging segment primarily consists of containers foodservice items closures overcaps bottles prescription containers and tubes.

Geographic Reach

Headquartered in Evansville Indiana Berry Global has some 130 manufacturing facilities primarily in North America but also in Europe the Middle East Asia and South America.

North America represents 80% of the company's sales.

Sales and Marketing

Berry Global sells its products to a very diverse customer base through a direct sales force and strategic distributors. Since many products are customized the sales team creates partnership with customers. The company's top ten customers account for 20% of total revenue.

Financial Performance

Berry Global's revenue has seen upward mobility increasing more than $2 billion in the last five years thanks to a string of acquisitions. In fiscal 2018 (ended September) the company reported net sales of $7.8 billion up 11% from the previous year. Acquisitions claimed the lion's share of revenue increase ($624 million) with the rest coming from organic sales ($92 million) and favorable impact of currency exchange ($58 million).

Berry has been profitable for five years straight but has enjoyed a sharp spike in the last couple of years. Profits increased 45% to $496 million in fiscal 2018 primarily due to a net income tax benefit of $19 million (compared to $109 million in expenses the prior year).

Cash holdings were at $381 million. Operations provided $1 billion offset by $1 billion going towards investment (mostly in acquisitions). Financial activities brought in $113 million.

Strategy

Enjoying half a decade of growing revenue and profits Berry Global is looking to turn competition up a notch. To that end the company is focusing on continuing strategic acquisitions on one hand and company restructuring to save money on the other.

In 2017-18 period Berry has shelled out $1.6 billion to acquire Laddawn Clopay AEP Industries and Adchem's tapes businesses. A major area of focus has been to expand its custom bag film and flexible packaging products as well as adhesive tapes.

The company is aiming to expand its complementary product lines especially in the technical film production sector. Taken in total the company expects to save more than $120 million in cost synergies. In particular the company has tremendously expanded its Health Hygiene & Specialties segment through inorganic growth ($365 million more in revenue in 2018).

Berry's continued growth is all the more impressive due to an already-crowded competitive landscape dominated by big producers including Silgan Aptar Reynolds 3M and Fitesa. The company's large and diverse customer base its scale and common customers across segments enables the company to minimize sales and marketing costs. However with current levels of healthy cash flow and reasonably costs of plastic resin the company will focus on paying down its considerable debts ($5.8 billion in long-term debt).

Mergers and Acquisitions

The board of plastic and recycled packaging company RPC in March 2019 unanimously recommended its shareholders accept an acquisition offer by Berry Global Group. Through the $6.5 billion deal Berry Global will gain more than 150 new manufacturing sites; about 25000 new employees; and RPC's more than 10000 customers. RPC's commercial activities span more than 30 countries; the company had net sales of $4.8 billion for the twelve months ended September 30 2018. The combined company will have revenue of $13 billion.

In 2018 Berry Global acquired Laddawn a manufacturer of blown polyethylene bags and films with a unique-to-industry e-commerce sales platform for $242 million. The company also completed its acquisition of Clopay for $475 million in November 2017. The acquisition is expected to bring $40 million in cost synergies while expanding Berry's reach in the elastic films and laminates business.

In 2017 Berry acquired Adchem Corp's tapes business for $49 million increasing its access to high performance adhesive tape business used in the automotive construction electronics and medical markets. Earlier that year the company completed the acquisition of AEP Industries for $791 million. AEP manufactures and markets flexible plastic packaging products with consumer industrial and agricultural applications.

Berry Global acquired UK-based RPC Group in 2019 for $6.5 billion. The deal expanded Berry's recycled and plastic packaging business and grew its geographic footprint.

Company Background

Berry Global was established in 1967 under the name of Imperial Plastics. In 1972 the injection molding company entered the container market and in 1983 Imperial plastics was purchased by Jerry Berry Sr. and renamed Berry Plastics. In 1988 it acquired some 40 companies. It began trading on the NYSE in 2012. In 2017 the company changed its name from Berry Plastics Group Inc. to Berry Global Inc.

EXECUTIVES

Vp Global Purchasing, Scott Farmer
Vp Corporate Development, Brett C. Bauer
Vp Finance And Business Planning, Rodgers K. Greenwalt
Cfo, Mark W. Miles, age 47, $453,380 total compensation
Chairman And Ceo, Thomas E. (Tom) Salmon, age 56, $499,617 total compensation
Evp Supply Chain, Terri Pitcher
Evp Human Resources, Ed Stratton
Evp General Counsel And Secretary, Jason K. Greene, age 48
President Engineered Materials, Curt L. Begle, age 43, $420,288 total compensation
President Flexible Packaging, Lawrence A. (Larry) Goldstein, age 56
Evp International, Jeffrey D. (Jeff) Thompson, age 47
Cio, Mark Freeman
President Health Hygiene And Specialties, Scott Tracey, age 51
President Consumer Packaging, Jean-Marc Galvez
Vp Hr, Jeffrey Bennett
Vice President Corporate Development, Ryan Ehlert
Auditors: Ernst & Young LLP

LOCATIONS

HQ: Berry Global Group Inc
101 Oakley Street, Evansville, IN 47710
Phone: 812 424-2904
Web: www.berryplastics.com

2018 Sales

	$ mil.	% of total
North America	6,474	82
Europe	807	11
South America	332	4
Asia	256	3
Total	**7,896**	**100**

PRODUCTS/OPERATIONS

2018 Sales

	$ mil.	% of total
Consumer Packaging	2,463	31
Health Hygiene & Specialties	2,734	35
Engineered Materials	2,672	34
Total	**7,869**	**100**

Selected Products

Rigid Plastics
  Bottles
  Containers
  Closures
  Foodservice items
  Housewares
  Overcaps
  Prescription vials
  Tubes
Engineered Materials
  Can liners
  Corrosion protection
  Polyethylene-based film products
  Specialty tapes and adhesives
Flexible packaging
  Custom films
  Flexible packaging products
  Printed bags
  Pouches

Selected Brands

Versalite
Color Scents
Ruffies
Polyken
Nashua
Reemay
Stopaq
Qubic

COMPETITORS

3M	Reynolds Food
AptarGroup	Packaging
Bemis	Silgan Plastics
Intertape Polymer	Tredegar

HISTORICAL FINANCIALS

Company Type: Public

Income Statement

	REVENUE ($ mil.)	NET INCOME ($ mil.)	NET PROFIT MARGIN	EMPLOYEES
09/19	8,878	404	4.6%	48,000
09/18	7,869	496	6.3%	24,000
09/17*	7,095	340	4.8%	23,000
10/16	6,489	236	3.6%	21,000
09/15	4,881	86	1.8%	16,000
Annual Growth	**16.1%**	**47.2%**	**—**	**31.6%**

FYE: September 28

*Fiscal year change

2019 Year-End Financials

Debt ratio: 69.01%
Return on equity: 26.57%
Cash ($ mil.): 750
Current ratio: 1.84
Long-term debt ($ mil.): 11,261

No. of shares (mil.): 132
Dividends
  Yield: —
  Payout: —
Market value ($ mil.): 5,202

	STOCK PRICE ($) FY Close	P/E High/Low	PER SHARE ($) Earnings	Dividends	Book Value
09/19	39.32	19 12	3.00	0.00	12.23
09/18	48.39	16 12	3.67	0.00	10.89
09/17*	56.65	22 16	2.56	0.00	7.73
10/16	43.85	24 15	1.89	0.00	1.79
09/15	30.29	51 32	0.70	0.00	(0.57)
Annual Growth	**6.7%**	**— —**	**43.9%**	**—**	**—**

*Fiscal year change

Best Buy Inc

Electronics giant Best Buy is preparing to outlast the competition with a compelling mix of products and services. The multinational retailer sells both products and services through more than 1200 stores in the US Canada and Mexico under the Best Buy Best Buy Express Magnolia Audio Video and Pacific Kitchen and Home Sales banners. Its stores sell a variety of electronic gadgets and wearables tablets movies music computers mobile phones and appliances. On the services side it offers installation and maintenance in-home consultations business accounts recycling and technical support. With 20000 staff members Best Buy's Geek Squad provides support for customers' technology products in a variety of ways online on the phone at customers' homes and at Best Buy store locations. The company also provides heath and safety technology solutions to aging customers through its GreatCall provider.

HISTORY

Tired of working for a father who ignored his ideas on how to improve the business (electronics distribution) Dick Schulze quit. In 1966 with a partner he founded Sound of Music a Minnesota home/car stereo store. Schulze bought out his partner in 1971 and began to expand the chain. While chairing a school board Schulze saw declining enrollment and realized his target customer group 15- to 18-year-old males was shrinking. In the early 1980s he broadened his product line and targeted older more affluent customers by offering appliances and VCRs.

After a 1981 tornado destroyed his best store (but not its inventory) Schulze spent his entire marketing budget to advertise a huge parking-lot sale. The successful sale taught him the benefits of strong advertising and wide selection combined with low prices. In 1983 Schulze changed the company's name to Best Buy and began to open larger superstores. The firm went public two years later.

Buoyed by the format change and the fast-rising popularity of the VCR Best Buy grew rapidly. Between 1984 and 1987 it expanded from eight stores to 24 and sales jumped from $29 million to $240 million. In 1988 another 16 stores opened and sales jumped by 84%. But Best Buy began to butt heads with many expanding consumer electronics retailers and profits took a beating.

To set Best Buy apart from its competitors in 1989 Schulze introduced the Concept II warehouse-like store format. Thinking that customers could buy products without much help Schulze cut payroll by taking sales staff off commission and reducing the number of employees per store by about a third. The concept proved to be such a hit in the company's home territory Minneapolis/St. Paul that it drove major competitor Highland Appliance to bankruptcy. Customers were happy but many of Best Buy's suppliers believing sales help was needed to sell products pulled their products from Best Buy stores. The losses didn't seem to hurt Best Buy; it took on Sears and Montgomery Ward in the Chicago market in 1989 and continued expanding.

In 1994 the company debuted Concept III an even larger store format. Best Buy opened 47 new stores in 1995 but found itself swimming in debt. Earnings plummeted in fiscal 1997 partly due to a huge PC inventory made obsolete by Intel's newer product. Best Buy started selling CDs on its website in 1997. That year it realized it had overextended itself with its expansion super-sized stores and financing promotions. Best Buy underwent a speedy massive makeover by scaling back expansion and doing away with its policy of "no money down no monthly payments no interest" (and next-to-no profits).

In 1999 Best Buy began to enter new markets (including New England) and introduced its Concept IV stores which highlighted digital products and featured stations for computer software and DVD demonstrations. Also in 1999 Best Buy formed a separate subsidiary for its online operations (BestBuy.com Inc.) and invested $10 million in consumer electronics information website etown.com (etown.com closed down in February 2001).

In 2000 Best Buy agreed to pay $88 million for Seattle-based Magnolia Hi-Fi a privately held chain of 13 high-end audio and video stores. In early 2001 Best Buy bought The Musicland Group (at the time operator of more than 1300 Sam Goody Suncoast On Cue and Media Play music stores) for about $425 million. The company began its international expansion in November 2002 with its $377 million acquisition of Future Shop Canada's leading consumer electronics retailer. Over the next year Best Buy opened eight of its own Best Buy stores in Ontario Canada.

In June 2002 Schulze turned over his responsibilities as CEO to vice chairman Brad Anderson; Schulze remained as chairman of the board. Best Buy acquired Geek Squad a computer support provider for $3 million the same year.

Best Buy shut down more than 100 Musicland stores (90 Sam Goody music stores and 20 Suncoast video stores) and laid off about 700 employees in January 2003; in June it sold the entire Musicland subsidiary (then about 1100 stores) to an affiliate of investment firm Sun Capital Partners. Three years later Best Buy purchased Pacific Sales Kitchen and Bath Centers which sells appliances and offers assistance on residential remodeling for $410 million.

Philip Schoonover a top executive in charge of customer segments defected to rival Circuit City in 2004. The company also dismissed Ernst & Young as its independent auditor after a former board member disclosed personal business dealings with the firm.

In 2006 the chain acquired home appliance and remodeling retailer Pacific Sales Kitchen and Bath Centers for about $410 million.

To facilitate its expansion in China Best Buy purchased a 75% stake in Jiangsu Five Star Appliance Co. in May 2006 and later opened the first Best Buy store in China in Shanghai.

To enhance its technology product offering for small businesses Best Buy in fiscal 2008 acquired Seattle-based Speakeasy a provider of broadband voice data and IT services. The deal valued at some $97 million made Speakeasy a wholly owned subsidiary that operates through the Best Buy for Business unit. Speakeasy CEO Bruce Chatterley as well as his management team was retained to run the Speakeasy operation once the deal closed. In a bid to add digital music downloads to its playlist Best Buy acquired a majority stake in Napster for about $127 million. The retailer's 2008 purchase of the music-swapping service included Napster's approximately 700000 digital entertainment subscribers.

In June 2008 Best Buy acquired a 50% stake in Carphone Warehouse's European and US retail interests for about $2.2 billion. In late October the company acquired digital music pioneer Napster for about $127 million via a tender offer for the firm's shares.

In early 2009 the retailer acquired the 25% of China's Jiangsu Five Star Appliance that it didn't already own. It also entered the Mexican market with its first store there.

CEO Brad Anderson retired in mid-2009 and COO and longtime employee Brian Dunn took over as CEO. Dunn's stint as chief executive lasted about three years. The 28-year company veteran stepped down in April 2012 handing his CEO title in the interim to board director Mike Mikan. In September 2012 the company named turnaround expert and Frenchman Hubert Joly to the position of CEO. Previously Joly served as head of T.G.I. Friday's and Radisson parent Carlson.In 2019 longtime Best Buy executive Corie Barry took over the company as CEO.

EXECUTIVES

Chairman And Ceo, Hubert Joly, age 60, $1,175,000 total compensation
Sevp And Chief Merchandising And Marketing Officer, R. Michael (Mike) Mohan, age 51, $833,654 total compensation
Sevp And President Multichannel Retail, Shari L. Ballard, age 52, $800,000 total compensation
President And Coo Best Buy Canada, Ron Wilson
Evp General Counsel And Secretary, Keith J. Nelsen, age 55, $650,000 total compensation
President Services, Trish Walker, age 52
Cfo, Corie S. Barry, age 44, $713,462 total compensation
Vice President Sales Operations, Chris Schmidt
Senior Vice President Loyalty And Membership And President Financial Services, Mark Williams
Senior Vice President Information Technology And Cio, Colleen Dunn
Svp Chief Administrative Officer Best Buy Canada, Philippe Arrata
Svp Merchandising Canada, Tony Sandhu
Vice President, John Schmidt

Senior Vice President Retail And Geek Squad Services Canada, Mat Povse
Senior Vice President Workforce Design, Damien Harmon
Board Member, Karen Mcloughlin
Board Member, Thomas Millner
Board Of Directors, Cindy Kent
Auditors: Deloitte & Touche LLP

LOCATIONS

HQ: Best Buy Inc
7601 Penn Avenue South, Richfield, MN 55423
Phone: 612 291-1000
Web: www.bestbuy.com

2017 Sales

	$ mil.	% of total
Domestic	36,248	92
International	3,155	8
Total	**39,403**	**100**

PRODUCTS/OPERATIONS

2018 U.S. Stores by Brand

	No.
Best Buy	
U.S. Best Buy	1,008
Mobile Stand-Alone Stores	257
Pacific Sales	28
Total	**1,293**

2018 Sales

	$ mil.	% of total
Domestic	38 662.9	92
International	3 498.8	8
Total	**42,151**	**100**

2018 International Stores by Brand

	No.
Canada	
Best Buy	134
Best Buy Mobile	51
Mexico	
Best Buy	25
Express	6
Total	**216**

2018 Sales by Domestic Category

	% of total
Products	
Consumer Electronics	33
Computing & Mobile Phones	45
Entertainment	8
Appliances	10
Services	4
Total	**100**

2018 Sales by International Category

	% of total
Products	
Computing & mobile phones	46
Consumer electronics	32
Entertainment	7
Appliance	8
Services	5
Other	2
Total	**100**

Selected Brands

Domestic
  Best Buy
  Best Buy Mobile
  Geek Squad
  Magnolia Audio Video
  Pacific Sales
International
  Canada
  Best Buy
  Best Buy Mobile
  Cell Shop
  Connect Pro
  Future Shop
  Geek Squad
  China
  Five Star

Europe
The Carphone Warehouse
The Phone House
Geek Squad
Mexico
Best Buy
Geek Squad

Selected Products

Consumer Electronics
  Audio
  Car stereos
  Home theater audio systems
  MP3 players
  Satellite radio systems
  Video
  Digital cameras and camcorders
  DVD players
  Televisions
Computing and mobile phones
  Computers
  Networking equipment
  Office furniture
  Printers
  Scanners
  Supplies
  Telephones
Entertainment
  CDs
  Computer software
  DVDs
  Subscription plans
  Video game hardware and software
Appliances
  Dishwashers
  Microwave ovens
  Refrigerators
  Stoves and ranges
  Vacuum cleaners
  Washers and dryers

COMPETITORS

ARTISTdirect	METRO AG
Amazon.com	MSN
Apple Inc.	MediaNet Digital
Audible Inc.	Myspace
Barnes & Noble	Office Depot
Brilliant Digital	OfficeMax
Entertainment	RadioShack
Brookstone	RealNetworks
Buy.com	Sears Holdings
Buzz Media	Sony Music
Conn's	Staples
Costco Wholesale	Systemax
Dell	Target Corporation
Fry's Electronics	Trans World
Gateway Inc.	Entertainment
HMV Retail	Wal-Mart
Hastings Entertainment	Yahoo!
Home Depot	eMusic.com
Lowe's	

HISTORICAL FINANCIALS

Company Type: Public

Income Statement   FYE: February 2

	REVENUE ($ mil.)	NET INCOME ($ mil.)	NET PROFIT MARGIN	EMPLOYEES
02/19	42,879	1,464	3.4%	125,000
02/18*	42,151	1,000	2.4%	125,000
01/17	39,403	1,228	3.1%	125,000
01/16	39,528	897	2.3%	125,000
01/15	40,339	1,233	3.1%	125,000
Annual Growth	1.5%	4.4%	—	0.0%

*Fiscal year change

2019 Year-End Financials

Debt ratio: 10.76%	No. of shares (mil.): 265
Return on equity: 42.44%	Dividends
Cash ($ mil.): 1,980	Yield: 0.0%
Current ratio: 1.18	Payout: 34.6%
Long-term debt ($ mil.): 1,332	Market value ($ mil.): 15,536

	STOCK PRICE ($) FY Close	P/E High/Low		PER SHARE ($) Earnings	Dividends	Book Value
02/19	58.47	16	9	5.20	1.80	12.44
02/18*	71.24	23	13	3.26	1.36	12.76
01/17	43.47	13	7	3.81	1.57	15.14
01/16	27.93	16	10	2.56	1.43	13.52
01/15	35.20	11	6	3.49	0.72	14.21
Annual Growth	13.5%	—	—	10.5%	25.7%	(3.3%)

*Fiscal year change

Big Lots, Inc.

One of North America's largest broadline close-out retailers Big Lots operates more than 1400 stores across the US. It sells a variety of brand-name products — including food and other consumables furniture housewares and decor seasonal items and toys — that have been overproduced returned discontinued or liquidated. Furniture represents the company's largest product line accounting for nearly a quarter of sales. Big Lots also has e-commerce operations and offers products via its website including some items only available online.

Operations

Big Lots sells merchandise in seven primary categories: furniture food consumables soft home seasonal hard home and electronics toys & accessories.

Furniture which includes upholstery mattresses case goods and ready-to-assemble items generates about a quarter of total sales. The food consumables (health items cosmetics plastics pet supplies) soft home (bedding frames rugs decor) and seasonal categories each account for about 15% of sales. The rest of sales is contributed by hard home (home appliances maintenance items) and electronics toys & accessories.

Geographic Reach

Big Lots has locations in nearly all US states with California Texas Florida and Ohio home to about a third of its stores and representing nearly 35% of sales.

The company boasts five regional distribution centers one each in Alabama California Oklahoma Ohio and Pennsylvania to receive process and distribute the majority of its merchandise to its retail locations across the US.

Sales and Marketing

Traditionally using television campaigns as its chief marketing channel Big Lots has shifted its marketing efforts to focus on capturing its customers' daily attention on mobile devices and digital media. It has significantly increased its presence in social and digital media outlets conducting entire campaigns on Facebook Instagram Pinterest Twitter and YouTube to drive increased brand awareness with its core customers and attract new customers.

In conjunction with those channels Big Lots still uses printed ad circulars in-store signage and television advertising to promote its brand and advertise special discounts in its stores.

Financial Performance

Amid store closures Big Lots has seen flat revenue over the past five years with growth between 0%-1%. Net income however has been trending upward a little more consistently during that time.

In fiscal 2017 (ended January 2018) the company reported revenue of $5.3 billion up 1% from the prior year. The increase is almost entirely because an extra week in the fiscal year as compared to 2016 offset by a net decrease of 16 stores.

Net income was $190 million that year up nearly 25% from fiscal 2016. Selling and administrative expenses and depreciation expense were both down in 2017 which combined with the slight uptick in revenue boosted the bottom line.

Cash at the end of fiscal 2017 was $51 million about the same as the prior year. Cash from operations contributed $250 million to the coffers while investing activities used $156 million mainly for capital expenditures. Financing activities used another $94 million for dividends to stockholders and treasury shares acquired.

Strategy

Big Lots is still focused on its Edit to Amplify strategy first introduced in 2013 and enhanced in 2016 to focus on merchandise categories it considers ownable and winnable. The company's attention investments and floor space are first dedicated to the segments it believes it can own (Furniture Seasonal) and next to the segments it believes it can win (Soft Home Food Consumables). Adjacent categories such as Hard Home and Electronics Toys & Accessories have been narrowed in recent years. (The bankruptcy of toy retailer Toys 'R' Us in 2018 caused Big Lots to rethink its decreased focus on toys at least temporarily as it looks to capture some of the holiday toy spending.)

The company's Store of the Future concept introduced in 2017 and scheduled to roll out over five to seven years (although not necessarily chain-wide) further emphasizes the Edit to Amplify strategy with more prominent positioning of those ownable and winnable categories and a revamped product mix.

As with many of its competitors Big Lots is also strengthening its e-commerce platform and omnichannel services. It was somewhat late to the e-commerce game first launching its platform in 2016. It has continued to expand and enhance its online offerings in the years since.

HISTORY

As a kid growing up in Columbus Ohio Russian-born Sol Shenk (pronounced "Shank") couldn't stand to pay full price for anything. His frugality blossomed into a knack for buying low and wholesaling. After a failed effort to make auto parts Shenk began the precursor to Consolidated Stores in 1967 backed by brothers Alvin Saul and Jerome Schottenstein.

The company started by wholesaling closeout auto parts and buying retailers' closeout items to sell to other retailers. By 1971 Shenk had branched into retailing selling closeout auto parts through a small chain of Corvair Auto Stores.

One of Shenk's sons suggested they devote space in the Corvair stores to closeout merchandise other than car parts. Sales surged and Shenk decided to sell the Corvair outlets and focus on closeout stores. The first Odd Lots opened in 1982. Consolidated grew more than 100% annually for the next three years. By 1986 the year after it went public the company was opening two stores a week in midsized markets around the Midwest.

Shenk found that people would buy anything as long as the price was right. Two years after the mania for Rubik's Cubes ended Odd Lots bought 6 million of the puzzles (once priced at $8) at 8 cents apiece marked them up 500% and sold them all.

By 1987 the company had nearly 300 Odd Lots/Big Lots stores. But runaway growth had created massive inventory shortages and losses as disappointed customers stopped browsing the company's sparsely stocked shelves. The woes coincided with a falling-out with the Schottensteins. Shenk retired in 1989.

Apparel and electronics retail executive William Kelley was named chairman and CEO the next year. Kelley returned Consolidated to its closeout roots and increased sales through acquisitions and creating new discount chains.

Consolidated doubled its size in 1996 with the $315 million purchase of more than 1000 struggling Kay-Bee Toys (now KB Toys) stores from Melville Corp. The expansion continued with the 1998 purchase of top closeout competitor Mac Frugal's Bargains - Closeouts. (Mac Frugal's had nearly bought Consolidated in 1989 before Consolidated board members vetoed the deal.) The $1 billion acquisition of Mac Frugal's gave Consolidated another 326 western stores under the Pic 'N' Save and Mac Frugal's names.

In 1999 Consolidated combined its online toy sales operations with those of BrainPlay.com to form KBkids.com. In mid-2000 Kelley was ousted as CEO handing the title over to CFO Michael Potter.

In December 2000 the company sold KB Toys (including KBkids.com) to a group led by KB management and global private equity firm Bain Capital for about $300 million. In mid-2001 the company changed its name to Big Lots and began converting all stores to that name to establish a national brand. Big Lots bought the inventory of bankrupt Internet home furnishings giant Living.com in June.

In 2002 the company completed converting 434 stores to the Big Lots banner including 380 stores previously operating under the names of Odd Lots Mac Frugal's and Pic 'N' Save. The name changes were part of a larger initiative to broaden the appeal of closeout retailing and to establish a unified national brand. During the year Big Lots opened 87 new stores and closed 42 others.

In 2003 Big Lots continued to remodel stores opened 86 new locations and closed 36 others. In 2004 the company opened about 100 new stores and continued to add furniture departments to its existing stores.

The company shuttered 174 stores in 2005 including 43 Big Lots Furniture stores and exited the frozen food business. Store closures continued in 2006 with a net loss of 25 locations.

In 2011 Big Lots acquired

EXECUTIVES

Evp Chief Merchandising And Operating Officer, Lisa M. Bachmann, age 57, $738,277 total compensation
Evp Human Resources And Store Operations, Michael A. (Mike) Schlonsky, age 52, $481,931 total compensation
Evp Chief Administrative Officer And Cfo, Timothy A. (Tim) Johnson, age 51, $578,317 total compensation
President Ceo And Director, David J. (Dave) Campisi, age 63, $1,092,308 total compensation
Svp And Cio, Stewart Wenerstrom, age 52
Senior Vice President Talent Management, Stella Keane
Regional Vice President, Mike Jasinowski
Vp Strategic Planning, Dan Yokum
Vice President Food Division, Michael PE Morales
Vice President Information Technology, Mike Demos
Vice President Of Merchandise Planning, Jay Caudill
Regional Vice President, Thomas R Myron
Vice President Of Ecommerce, Erica Fortune
Regional Vice President, Gary E Huber
Vice President Store Operations, Cathy DeLucia
Vp Advertising, Shelley Rubin
Vice President Merchandise Planning, Craig Hart

Senior Vice President Merchandising, Michelle Christensen
Senior Vice President General Counsel And Corporate Secretary, Rocky Robins
Vice President Investor Relations, Andrew D Regrut
Vice President In Store Marketing And Merchandise Presentation, Louis Dorado
Vice President Store Projects, Gary Null Hubr
Chairman, Philip E. Mallott, age 61
Board Member, Marla Gottschalk
Board Member, Nancy Reardon-sayer
Auditors: DELOITTE & TOUCHE LLP

LOCATIONS

HQ: Big Lots, Inc.
  4900 E. Dublin-Granville Road, Columbus, OH 43081
Phone: 614 278-6800   **Fax:** 614 278-6666
Web: www.biglots.com

2017 Locations

	No.
California	151
Texas	112
Florida	104
Ohio	96
North Carolina	72
Pennsylvania	67
New York	63
Georgia	53
Tennessee	47
Indiana	44
Other states	607
Total	**1,416**

PRODUCTS/OPERATIONS

2017 Sales

	$ mil.	% of total
Furniture	1,237	23
Food	824	16
Consumables	822	16
Soft Home	790	15
Seasonal	766	15
Hard Home	429	8
Electronics Toys & Accessories	403	7
Total	**5,271**	**100**

COMPETITORS

99 Cents Only	Michaels Companies
Amazon.com	OllieÂ's Bargain
BJ's Wholesale Club	Outlet
Costco Wholesale	Ross Stores
Dollar General	Sears
Dollar Tree	TJX Companies
Family Dollar Stores	Target Corporation
Five Below	Tuesday Morning
Fred's	Corporation
Jo-Ann Stores	Variety Wholesalers
Kmart	Wal-Mart

HISTORICAL FINANCIALS

Company Type: Public

Income Statement   FYE: February 2

	REVENUE ($ mil.)	NET INCOME ($ mil.)	NET PROFIT MARGIN	EMPLOYEES
02/19	5,238	156	3.0%	35,600
02/18*	5,270	189	3.6%	34,800
01/17	5,200	152	2.9%	35,100
01/16	5,190	142	2.8%	35,900
01/15	5,177	114	2.2%	36,100
Annual Growth	0.3%	8.2%	—	(0.3%)

*Fiscal year change

2019 Year-End Financials

Debt ratio: 18.49%	No. of shares (mil.): 40
Return on equity: 23.09%	Dividends
Cash ($ mil.): 46	Yield: 0.0%
Current ratio: 1.77	Payout: 31.3%
Long-term debt ($ mil.): 374	Market value ($ mil.): 1,254

	STOCK PRICE ($) FY Close	P/E High/Low	Earnings	PER SHARE ($) Dividends	Book Value
02/19	31.32	15 7	3.83	1.20	17.31
02/18*	57.74	14 10	4.38	1.00	15.97
01/17	48.67	17 11	3.32	0.84	14.70
01/16	38.78	18 13	2.80	0.76	14.67
01/15	45.91	24 12	2.06	0.51	14.92
Annual Growth	(9.1%)	— —	16.8%	23.9%	3.8%

*Fiscal year change

Biogen Inc

With its pipeline full of biotech drugs Biogen aims to meet the unmet needs of patients around the world. The biotech giant is focused on developing treatments in the areas of immunology and neurology. Its product roster includes best-selling drugs Tecfidera and Avonex (interferon) for the treatment of relapsing multiple sclerosis (MS); Tysabri a drug treatment for MS and Crohn's disease; and Fampyra which improves walking in adults with MS. Other products include Plegridy for MS. Founded in 1978 Biogen serves customers in more than 90 countries.

Operations

Biogen's top selling drug Tecfidera is sold in markets around the globe and accounts for around 35% of annual revenues. It is an oral therapy marketed in the US for the treatment of patients with relapsing forms of MS. It is sold in Europe for patients with relapsing-remitting MS (RRMS).

The firm's next-best seller Avonex (interferon) accounts for some 25% of revenues. A treatment to improve walking in adults with MS the Avonex pen is a single-use auto-injector version of the drug for once-weekly dosing.

Another top-selling global drug is Tysabri bringing in more than 15% of revenues. Despite the drug's troubled regulatory history — the drug can only be prescribed under a strict risk management plan due to the possible side effect of a rare brain condition — the company continues to pursue additional uses for the drug.

Rituxan sales conducted through a partnership with Genentech account for another 10% of sales and are classified as "unconsolidated joint business" revenues. In addition to non-Hodgkin's lymphoma and rheumatoid arthritis Rituxan is approved to treat leukemia follicular lymphoma and vasculitis.

Another drug MS treatment Fampyra (also known as Ampyra) is sold in partnership with Acorda Therapeutics. Biogen is also co-marketing Zinbryta another MS treatment in the US with AbbVie.

In addition to gaining revenue from the development and sales of its products (both directly and through partnerships) Biogen receives royalties on some patents it has licensed to other companies. For instance The Medicines Company pays royalties on sales of anticoagulant Angiomax.

Products in Biogen's pipeline include the anti-LINGO program for MS BAN2401 (in collaboration with Eisai) for Alzheimer's disease and STX-100 for idiopathic pulmonary fibrosis.

Geographic Reach

Biogen has offices in the US Australia Canada Japan the US and several European countries. It has direct sales operations in about 30 countries and operates through distribution partners in another 60 countries.

The US is Biogen's largest market bringing in more than 60% of total revenues. Europe follows with Germany alone representing more than 5% of revenues.

Sales and Marketing

Biogen primarily distributes its products in the US through wholesale pharmaceutical distributors mail-order specialty distributors and shipping service providers. Two wholesale distributors AmerisourceBergen and McKesson each bring in more than 10% of the firm's total revenues. Outside of the US distribution varies but includes wholesale pharmaceutical distributors and third-party distribution partners.

Avonex is marketed through Biogen's direct sales force to specialist physicians and hospitals in North America Europe and select other countries around the globe. The company also handles global marketing efforts for Tysabri. Genentech handles sales and marketing duties for Rituxan while marketing duties for Fampyra are split with Acorda (Biogen sells the drug in Europe and Canada).

In 2016 Biogen spent $106 million on advertising versus $108.6 million in 2015 and $92.9 million in 2014.

Financial Performance

Biogen's revenues and profits have steadily risen over the years as sales of its products have increased. In 2016 net revenue rose 6% to $11.4 billion largely due to higher sales of Tecfidera and Alprolix (which has since been spun off). Tecfidera sales rose 9% to $4 billion that year as sales in existing markets increased; the drug also continues to be launched in new markets boosting sales even further. Alprolix sales rose 45% to $333.7 million that year.

In 2016 net income increased 4% to $3.7 billion due to the higher revenue and a relatively low increase in operating expenses. Cash flow from operations rose 22% to $4.5 billion that year primarily due to higher earnings and positive changes in current liabilities.

Strategy

Biogen is the industry leader in multiple sclerosis treatments and in Europe it has a strong business in biosimilars (Benepali a biosimilar version of Enbrel and Flixabi a biosimilar of Remicade). It launched four new therapies during 2016 and the approval of spinal muscular atrophy treatment Spinraza that year should provide the company with its next blockbuster.

Biogen's pipeline of drug candidates is focused on treatments for central nervous system ailments including Alzheimer's MS amyotrophic lateral sclerosis (ALS) neuropathic pain and lupus. In addition to proprietary candidates the company has collaborative development candidates with Genentech Portola Pharmaceuticals (lupus and rheumatoid arthritis) and other drugmakers and it continuously looks to expand its pipeline through acquisitions and partnerships. R&D expenses totaled $1.97 in 2016 down from $2.01 billion in 2015.

The company has had its share of setbacks though. In 2019 it halted studies of its lead Alzheimer's treatment which spooked investors. In 2016 the company's anti-LINGO MS drug failed in mid-stage trials; Biogen is exploring additional studies for the treatment.

In early 2017 Biogen spun off its growing hemophilia operations into a separate publicly traded company named Bioverativ. That business' marketed products include Eloctate and Alprolix; the new firm continues its activities around the discovery and development of hemophilia therapies utilizing XTEN technology.

Mergers and Acquisitions

Biogen has expanded its operations through purchases of drug development firms as well as by purchasing commercialized and development-stage drugs. In 2019 the company struck a deal to buy London-based gene therapy startup Nightstar Therapeutics for $877 million. Nightstar is focused on treatments for inherited retinal disorders. Biogen is increasingly investing in the ophthalmology field.

HISTORY

Biogen Idec was formed out of the 2003 merger of IDEC Pharmaceuticals and Biogen.

The company began experiencing troubles with its lead product — Tysabri developed with partner Elan— soon after its formation. Sales were temporarily halted in 2005 after several patients died from a rare neurological condition. The companies were allowed to reintroduce Tysabri in 2006 (when it was also launched in Europe) under a strict risk management plan that insures sufficient doctor and patient education about risks and proper usage.

Activist investor Carl Icahn held a minority stake in the company for several years and kept a watchful eye over his investment. In 2007 he bullied the company to put itself up for sale but no buyer came through. Then he began a series of proxy battles in an attempt to stack the board with his own nominees to gain further control. By 2010 he had secured three seats on the board filled with his own representatives and resumed talks of seeing Biogen Idec broken into parts and/or sold to a larger pharmaceutical company.

Ichan's persistence might have contributed to the retirement of Biogen Idec's long-time CEO James Mullen in mid-2010 with George Scangos (former CEO of Exelixis) stepping in as Mullen's replacement. Scangos implemented sharp changes in late 2010 launching a reorganization plan aimed at reducing operational costs and increasing efficiencies. The plan included a 13% workforce reduction and a streamlining of R&D programs to focus primarily on neurological disease. Biogen Idec halted or licensed out its oncology and cardiovascular development programs and consolidated a number of US sites. As a sign that he was pleased with Mullen's work in early 2011 Icahn reduced his ownership stake and did not seek to gain control of more board seats; he sold his remaining interests in the firm in mid-2011.

EXECUTIVES

Evp Chief Legal Officer And Corporate Secretary, Susan H. Alexander, age 62, $697,721 total compensation

Evp And Cfo, Jeffrey D. (Jeff) Capello, age 54

Evp Human Resources, Kenneth A. (Ken) DiPietro, age 61, $648,023 total compensation

Ceo And Director, Michel Vounatsos, $519,231 total compensation

Evp And Head Of Research And Development, Michael D. (Mike) Ehlers, $491,827 total compensation

Evp Neurology Discovery And Development Center Neurodegeneration Therapeutic Area And Chief Medical Officer, Alfred W. Sandrock, age 61, $564,596 total compensation

Evp Pharmaceutical Operations And Technology, Paul McKenzie

Vp And Chief Accounting Officer And Interim Principal Financial Officer, Greg Covino, age 53

Evp And Head Of Global Marketing Market Access And Customer Innovation, Chirfi Guindo

Vice President Global Public Affairs, Katja Buller

Vice President Head Of Us Neurology Marketing And Field Operations, Dell Faulkingham

Vice President Customer Support, Janis Meyer

Vice President, Adam Adamson

Medical Director, Martha Fournier

Senior Vice President Translational Medicine And Technology, Timothy Harris

Vice President Sales And Field Operations, Todd Nichols

Medical Director Clinical Development, Mark Beatty

Vice President Of Quality, Sid Senroy

Senior Vice President Program Management, Johnathan Palmer

Vice President Global Commercial Strategy, Adrian Gottschalk

Vice President Treasurer, Michael Dambach

Executive Vice President Human Resources, Scott Handren

Executive Vice President Of Human Resources, Kenneth Dipetrio

Vice President Of Global Medical Affairs Biogen Idec's Avonex, Thorsten Eickenhorst

Vice President Managing Director, Simon Jordan

Vice President Research And Development Technology, Andrew Allen

Vice President Executive Director Biogen Idec Innovation Incubator, Rainer Fuchs

Vice President Medical Research, Bradley Maroni

Vice President Human Resources Worldwide Medical And Us Organization, Lauren Duprey

Associate Medical Director, Satish Eraly

Vice President Alzheimers Disease, Samantha Haeberlein

Senior Vice President Research And Early Development, Anirvan Ghosh

Vice President Legal Chief Employment Counsel, Jo A Taormina

Vp Neurology Research, Chris Henderson

Vice President And Ciso, Bob Litterer

Chairman, Stelios Papadopoulos, age 71

Abm, Karmon Warren

Abm, Don Benson

Auditors: PricewaterhouseCoopers LLP

LOCATIONS

HQ: Biogen Inc
225 Binney Street, Cambridge, MA 02142
Phone: 617 679-2000
Web: www.biogen.com

2017 Sales

	$ mil.	% of total
US	7,017	57
Europe	2,844	23
Asia	160	1
Other	332	3
Unconsolidated joint business	1,559	13
Other	360	3
Total	**12,273**	**100**

PRODUCTS/OPERATIONS

2017 Sales

	$ mil.	% of total
Products		
Tecfidera	4,214	34
Interferon	2,645	22
Tysabri	1,973	16
Spinraza	883	7
Benepali	370	3
Fampyra	91	1
Zinbryta	52	1
Eloctate	48	—
Fumaderm	39	—
Alprolix	26	—
Flixabi	9	—
Other products	360	3
Other	1,559	13
Total	**12,273**	**100**

Selected Products

Approved

Avonex (multiple sclerosis)
Fampyra (multiple sclerosis with Acorda Therapeutics)
Fumaderm (severe psoriasis in Germany only)
Rituxan (non-Hodgkin's lymphoma chronic lymphocytic leukemia follicular lymphoma rheumatoid arthritis vasculitis)
Tecfidera (multiple sclerosis)
Tysabri (multiple sclerosis Crohn's disease; with Elan Pharmaceuticals)

In development

GA101 (chronic lymphocytic leukemia non-Hodgkin's lymphoma)
Plegridy (PEGylated interferon beta 1a relapsing forms of multiple sclerosis)
Tysabri (secondary-progressive MS)

COMPETITORS

AbbVie	Johnson & Johnson
Abbott Labs	Merck KGaA
Amgen	Millennium: The Takeda
Bayer HealthCare	Oncology Company
Pharmaceuticals	Novartis
Bristol-Myers Squibb	Pfizer
Cephalon	Roche Holding
Genentech	Sanofi
Genmab	Teva
GlaxoSmithKline	UCB

HISTORICAL FINANCIALS

Company Type: Public

Income Statement — FYE: December 31

	REVENUE ($ mil.)	NET INCOME ($ mil.)	NET PROFIT MARGIN	EMPLOYEES
12/19	14,377	5,888	41.0%	7,400
12/18	13,452	4,430	32.9%	7,800
12/17	12,273	2,539	20.7%	7,300
12/16	11,448	3,702	32.3%	7,400
12/15	10,763	3,547	33.0%	7,350
Annual Growth	7.5%	13.5%	—	0.2%

2019 Year-End Financials

Debt ratio: 21.87%
Return on equity: 44.64%
Cash ($ mil.): 2,913
Current ratio: 1.72
Long-term debt ($ mil.): 4,459

No. of shares (mil.): 174
Dividends
　Yield: —
　Payout: —
Market value ($ mil.): 51,690

	STOCK PRICE ($) FY Close	P/E High/Low		PER SHARE ($) Earnings	Dividends	Book Value
12/19	296.73	11	7	31.42	0.00	76.60
12/18	300.92	18	12	21.58	0.00	66.12
12/17	318.57	29	21	11.92	0.00	59.63
12/16	283.58	19	13	16.93	0.00	56.23
12/15	306.35	31	17	15.34	0.00	42.88
Annual Growth	(0.8%)	—	—	19.6%	—	15.6%

BJ's Wholesale Club Holdings Inc

Auditors: PricewaterhouseCoopers LLP

LOCATIONS

HQ: BJ's Wholesale Club Holdings Inc
25 Research Drive, Westborough, MA 01581
Phone: 774 512-7400
Web: www.bjs.com

HISTORICAL FINANCIALS

Company Type: Public

Income Statement — FYE: February 2

	REVENUE ($ mil.)	NET INCOME ($ mil.)	NET PROFIT MARGIN	EMPLOYEES
02/19	13,007	127	1.0%	26,383
02/18*	12,754	50	0.4%	26,520
01/17	12,350	44	0.4%	—
01/16	12,467	24	0.2%	—
Annual Growth	1.4%	74.1%	—	—

*Fiscal year change

2019 Year-End Financials

Debt ratio: 56.58%
Return on equity: ***,***.**%
Cash ($ mil.): 27
Current ratio: 0.85
Long-term debt ($ mil.): 1,577

No. of shares (mil.): 137
Dividends
　Yield: —
　Payout: —
Market value ($ mil.): 3,635

	STOCK PRICE ($) FY Close	P/E High/Low		PER SHARE ($) Earnings	Dividends	Book Value
02/19	26.47	29	18	1.05	0.00	(1.47)
02/18*	0.00	—	—	0.54	8.31	(11.71)
Annual Growth	—	—	—	24.8%	—	—

*Fiscal year change

BlackRock Inc

With some $6.3 trillion in assets under management BlackRock is the world's largest public investment management firm. It specializes in equity and fixed income products as well as alternative and multi-class instruments which it invests in on behalf of institutional and retail investors worldwide. Clients include pension plans governments insurance companies mutual funds endowments foundations and charities. BlackRock also provides risk management services through BlackRock Solutions and is a leading provider of exchange-traded funds (ETFs) through iShares. The firm has offices in more than 30 countries. BlackRock serves around 90% of the Fortune 100 largest companies.

Operations

BlackRock manages some $6.3 trillion in assets through 135 investment teams. The BlackRock Solutions division provides risk management advisory and enterprise investment system services. iShares one of BlackRock's brands is a leading provider of exchange-traded funds (ETFs).

BlackRock's iShares is the world's largest ETF in the world with $1.3 trillion in assets under management.

BlackRock offers active and passive retail investment services. Mutual funds account for the majority of retail investment sums at around 80%. Retail has a US and an international arm.

The company possesses $3.4 trillion in institutional assets of which $2.3 trillion are index funds and $1.1 trillion active. Its clients consist of pensions foundations and endowments; official institutions; and financial and other institutions.

BlackRock's Asset Liability And Debt and Derivative Investment Network (or to use its snappier name Aladdin) is its enterprise resource management system which provides risk management portfolio management and trading and operation tools for other asset managers and institutional

investors. Aladdin is used by around 25000 investment professionals around the world.

Geographic Reach

New York-based BlackRock has more than 70 offices in more than 30 countries. The company makes more than 65% of its revenue in the Americas. Europe accounts for nearly 30% and the Asia-Pacific region 5%. BlackRock has clients and investments in more than 100 countries.

Sales and Marketing

BlackRock serves 15 out of the 25 largest endowments and foundation organizations in the US. It also serves around 90 of the Fortune 100 companies and more than 90% of the largest US retirement plans.

BlackRock focuses on establishing and maintaining its investment management relationships by marketing its services through financial professionals pension consultants third-party distribution relationships or directly to investors themselves.

Clients include tax-exempt institutions (defined benefit pension plans charities and foundations); official institutions (central banks sovereign wealth funds supranationals and other government entities); and taxable institutions (insurance companies financial institutions corporations and third-party fund sponsors and retail investors). Two-thirds of BlackRock's assets are pension plan assets.

Financial Performance

Thanks to a rising stock market and a growing investor base BlackRock has nearly quintupled its assets under management since 2007 — from $1.3 trillion to $6.3 trillion at the end of 2017 — which has led strong fee and advisory income growth over the past few years.

In fiscal 2017 revenue surged 12% to $12.5 billion due to growth in base fees performance fees and technology and risk management revenue. The strongest gains were in fees from iShares exchange-traded fundswhich added $570 million to revenue while higher demand for Aladdin added $82 million to the top line.

The 2017 US Tax Cuts and Jobs Act produced a tax benefit of $1.2 billion for BlackRock in 2017 helping net income swell 56% to $5.0 billion.

Cash from operations increased 72% to $3.8 billion mostly due to higher net income.

Strategy

Even powerful fund managers' jobs are not immune to the threat of automation. In 2017 BlackRock sacked seven portfolio managers as part of a wider shift away from active stock pickers and towards a robot-led quantitative approach. Amid relative market stability active fund managers are less able to beat the market than passive trackers. Investors pulled some $40 billion from actively managed funds during 2016. The robo-funds can be offered at a lower price than the more expensive hand-picked investment funds.

Part of the shift to automation includes the transfer of $1 trillion in assets under custody of State Street to JP Morgan in 2017. BlackRock hopes the move will cut operating expenses; JP Morgan has been investing in automation technology enabling the cheaper provision of services.

The company aims to drive customer growth in its Aladdin enterprise risk management system as well as its wider solutions business. Its goal is to grow Aladdin and other solutions to 30% of total revenue by 2022.

Mergers and Acquisitions

In 2019 BlackRock acquired alternative investment management software company eFront from Bridgepoint Advisers and eFront employees for $1.3 billion. BlackRock will combine eFront with Aladdin its investment management platform to allow users to manage portfolios across public and private asset classes including alternative assets. That year the firm also agreed to buy an 80% stake in Distributed Solar Development from GE.

GE's GE Renewable Energy unit will retain the remaining stake.

In 2017 BlackRock acquired First Reserve's equity infrastructure franchise First Reserve Energy Infrastructure Funds. The acquisition will help connect BlackRock's clients with energy infrastructure projects.

Company Background

BlackRock is led by CEO Laurence Fink who has overseen a string of major acquisitions in recent years expanding into private equity real estate energy and hedge funds as investors look to diversify beyond stock and bond funds.

Fink engineered a blockbuster merger with Barclays Global Investors (BGI) in 2009. In the deal which was several years in the making BlackRock bought Barclays Global Investors from UK banking giant Barclays for some $15 billion. The deal resulted in a new company operating under the BlackRock name. Barclays Bank retained a 20% stake in the combined firm but Fink remained in charge of the enterprise. The merger nearly tripled BlackRock's assets under management and propelled the company to the top of the international money management industry by enhancing its investment and risk management capabilities. The deal also gave BlackRock a much larger footprint outside the US and added more than 3500 new employees.

EXECUTIVES

President And Director, Robert S. (Rob) Kapito, age 62, $750,000 total compensation

Chairman And Ceo, Laurence D. (Larry) Fink, age 66, $900,000 total compensation

Senior Managing Director, Robert W. (Rob) Fairbairn, age 53, $350,000 total compensation

Senior Managing Director And Chief Risk Officer, Bennett W. Golub, age 61

Senior Managing Director And Global Head Of Multi-asset Strategies, J. Richard (Rich) Kushel, age 52, $500,000 total compensation

Senior Managing Director And Head Of Trading Liquidity And Investments Platform, Richard L. (Richie) Prager

Head Alladin Clien Business, Ryan D. Stork, age 47

Senior Managing Director Head Of Global Active Equities And Chairman Blackrock Alternative Investors, Mark Wiseman

Senior Managing Director And Global Head Of Ishares And Index Investments, Mark K. Wiedman

Senior Managing Director And Head Of Global Human Resources, Jeffrey A. Smith, age 48

Senior Managing Director Head Of The Americas Region And Global Head Of Blackrock Alternative Investors, Mark S. McCombe, age 53

Senior Managing Director And Head Of Europe Middle East And Africa (emea), David J. Blumer, age 50

Senior Managing Director And Cfo, Gary S. Shedlin, age 55, $500,000 total compensation

Senior Managing Director Coo And Global Head Blackrock Solutions, Rob L. Goldstein, age 45, $500,000 total compensation

Senior Managing Director And Global Head Business Operations And Technology, Derek K. Stein

Vice President, Ed Mallon

Vice President Human Resources, Katie Nedl

Vice President Database Administration, David Louie

Vice President, Marie McCarthy

Vice President Infrastructure Investment Group, Rael Mcnally

Vice President Institutional Sales Benelux, Norbert Van Veldhuizen

Vice President Technology, Rob Smith

Vice President Global Marketing, Laura Tyrholm

Vice President, Saba Anvar

Vice President, Robert Chiolan

Vice President, Vineet Gupta

Vice President, John Kent

Vice President Crm Database Marketing Manager, Sorin Tudor

Vice President, Piyush Naik

Vice President, Paul Horowitz

Vice President, Margaret Lassiter

Vice President, Duane Liedl

Senior Compliance Manager Vice President, Beth Moore

Vice President Corporate Communications, Farrell Denby

Vice President Us Wealth Advisory Strategy, Alissa Eisenberg

Vice President, Elizabeth Krow

Vice President, Viola Dunne

Vice President, Sherrika Fuller

Vice President Access And Identity Management, Nikhil Mathur

Vice President, Gina Forziati

Vice President And Technical Data Analyst, Wendy Knel

Vice President E Business Operations, Wendy Guthrie Harris

Vice President Hr Business Partner, Anna Kim

Vice President, Nigel Benson

Vice President, Jared Bilanin

Vice President, Chad Dziedzic

Vice President, Betsy Mathews

Vice President, Lisa Sanner

Vice President, Simon Chew

Vice President Business Development, Joe Ernst

Vice President, Dana Aurora

Vice President Finance, Roger Castoral

Vice President, Sharda Lekhraj

Vice President, Bridget Dean-Hammel

Vice President, Ryan Coulter

Vice President Sourcing, Michael Schnalzer

Vice President, Peter Hirsh

Vice President, Stephanie Rosen

Vice President, Brian Roberson

Vice President Fixed Income Portfolio Management Group, Sriram Reddy

Vice President Trader Portfolio Manager Cash Managment, Gene Meshechek

Vice President User Experience And Design, Devjit Basu

Vice President, David Kurapka

Vice President, Jeff Puntney

Vice President Event Management, Wendy Dooley

Vice President, Benjamin Cunningham

Vice President, Kelly Sanderson

Vice President Critical Infrastructure, Ed Cannon

Vice President, Prathima Nalluri

Vice President, Ned Rosenman

Vice President, Lauren Giametta

Vice President Market Research, Katie Herzog

Vice President, Amanda Huckle

Vice President, Susan Lapczynski

Vice President, Kumar Duvvuri

Vice President, Jeremy Jones

Vice President, Miranda Harrison

Vice President, Ying Li

Vice President Product Management, Jeff Lambert

Vice President, Patricia Belcher

Vice President Legal And Compliance, Danny Riemer

Vice President, David Curtin

Vice President, Ryan Shriber

Vice President, Sukhbir Gill

Vice President, Thomas Dara

Vice President Portfolio Manager, Brett Buchness

Vice President, Jeff Brown

Vice President Aladdin And Technology, Paul Dearman

Vice President Product Strategy Client Portfolio Management Global Credit, Jeremy Lee

Vice President, Diego Mora

Vice President Corporate Strategy, Theodore Bunzel

Vice President Media Services, Lisa Sturdivant

Vice President Us Board Governing Services, Danielle Costantino

Vice President, Vincent Dellaglio

Vice President, Julie Hoffman

Vice President Emea Retail Sales Strategy, Adam Riley

Vice President, Heinrich Schutze

Vice President, Joanne Mavra

Vice President Institutional Sales, Chantal Giles

Vp Of It, Geir Espeskog

Vice President, Davina Stickland

Vice President Financial Modeling Group (quantitative Finance), Remi Lefrancois

Vice President: Client Order Management, Suzanne Long

Vice President, Celia Chau

Vice President Internal Audit, Stella Yap

Vice President Director Account Management, Whitney Ehrlich

Vice President, Andrea Vigano

Vice President Investment Management Consultant, Robert Fakhry

Vice President Sma Portfolio Manager, David Dressel

Vice President, Kirsten Filosa

Vice President, Joe Plonski

Vice President, Nancy Dambrosio

Vice President Financial Institutions Group, Felipe Arguello

Vice President, Geraldine Santiago

Vice President Telecommunications, Sharad Pandey

Vice President Marketing Manager Benelux Ishares, Wouter Bruil

Vice President Product Management (digital), Jennifer Rector

Vice President Marketing, Danielle Ver Bruggen

Vice President Digital Marketing, Ritesh Joseph

Vice President Technology And Operations, Praveen Dasari

Vice President, Joanne Deignan

Vice President Blackrock, Brian Compton

Vice President Blackrock, Long Tran

Vice President Blackrock, Marc Chin

Vice President Blackrock, Raja Kurapati

Vice President, Sai Patnala

Vice President Blackrock, Scott Golub

Vice President, Rupkumar Radhakrishnan

Vice President Security Engineering, Rebecca Quinn

Vice President, Kevin Doody

Vice President Legal And Compliance, Eugene Drozdetski

Vice President, Ian Pinnavaia

Vice President Portfolio Compliance, Niranjan Nagarkar

Vice President, Simon Barr

Vice President, Sakthivel Thiyagarajan

Vice President, Jitesh Sampat

Vice President, Shankar Kasi Viswanatha Iyer

Vice President, Ray Szyjka

Vice President, Sumeet Nagar

Vice President, Neha Dhawan

Vice President, Atul Kumar

Vice President, Harish Kamath

Vice President, Torben Latza

Vice President, Junichiro Kato

Vice President, Henry Lee

Vice President, Mauricio Lara Espindola

Vice President, George Quilter

Vice President, Luke Holder

Vice President, James Mead

Vice President, Nancy Peirson

Vice President Treasury, Maureen Shearer

Auditors: Deloitte & Touche LLP

LOCATIONS

HQ: BlackRock Inc
55 East 52nd Street, New York, NY 10055
Phone: 212 810-5300
Web: www.blackrock.com

2017 Sales

	$ mil.	% of total
Americas	8,406	67
Europe	3,432	28
Asia/Pacific	653	5
Total	**12,491**	**100**

PRODUCTS/OPERATIONS

2017 Sales

	$ mil.	% of total
Investment advisory administration fees & securities lending		
Equity	5,722	46
Fixed income	2,921	23
Multi-asset class	1,181	10
Alternative investments	1,105	9
Cash management	558	5
Black Rock Solutions & advisory	755	6
Distribution fees	24	.
Other revenue	225	2
Total	**12,491**	**100**

COMPETITORS

Allianz Global	Federated Investors
Investors	Legg Mason
Bank of New York	Morgan Stanley
Mellon	Principal Global
Charles Schwab	State Street
Dimensional Fund	UBS
Advisors	Waddell & Reed

HISTORICAL FINANCIALS

Company Type: Public

Income Statement

FYE: December 31

	REVENUE ($ mil.)	NET INCOME ($ mil.)	NET PROFIT MARGIN	EMPLOYEES
12/18	14,198	4,305	30.3%	14,900
12/17	12,491	4,970	39.8%	13,900
12/16	11,155	3,172	28.4%	13,000
12/15	11,401	3,345	29.3%	13,000
12/14	11,081	3,294	29.7%	12,200
Annual Growth	6.4%	6.9%	—	5.1%

2018 Year-End Financials

Debt ratio: 3.12%
Return on equity: 13.41%
Cash ($ mil.): 6,302
Current ratio: 2.73
Long-term debt ($ mil.): 4,979

No. of shares (mil.): 157
Dividends
  Yield: 3.0%
  Payout: 45.2%
Market value ($ mil.): 61,890

	STOCK PRICE ($) FY Close	P/E High/Low	PER SHARE ($) Earnings	Dividends	Book Value
12/18	392.82	22 13	26.58	12.02	205.48
12/17	513.71	17 12	30.23	10.00	198.93
12/16	380.54	21 15	19.04	9.16	180.13
12/15	340.52	19 15	19.79	8.72	174.37
12/14	357.56	19 15	19.25	7.72	166.07
Annual Growth	2.4%	— —	8.4%	11.7%	5.5%

Blackstone Group Inc (The)

Throw a rock and you're bound to hit a Blackstone investment. The Blackstone Group is one of the world's largest real estate private equity and alternative asset managers in the world with around $540 billion in assets under management. Of the $540 billion private equity make up the firm's largest asset category with more than $170 billion under management and around 100 portfolio companies. Its real estate investment holdings constitute more than $150 billion making Blackstone one of the world's largest real estate investors. The firm manages investment vehicles including private equity funds funds of hedge funds and real estate funds. Clients include public and corporate pensions financial institutions and individuals.

Operations

The Blackstone Group is organized into four business segments: Private Equity Real Estate Credit and Hedge Fund Solutions.

The Private Equity segment produces more than 30% of revenue and typically holds interests in about 100 companies. It has some $170 billion in assets under management (about 75% of which are in the US) and has traditionally been involved in leveraged buyouts of developed companies investments in growth-oriented companies development projects and funding for smaller companies needing money and leadership to scale in fragmented industries.

The Real Estate segment is one of the largest real estate investment management operations in the world with $150 billion in assets under management. The operations focus on acquiring high quality well-located real estate that is under-managed and for sale at attractive prices. It then addresses property or business issues through active management and once the property reaches potential it sells the real estate. Its portfolio include retail residential industrial office and hotel properties. It generates nearly 30% of Blackstone revenue.

The company's Credit business GSO Capital Partners accounts for around 25% of revenue. It focuses on credit-oriented financial arrangements in alternative assets using senior and subordinated debt preferred stock and even common stock as vehicles for its investment. Credit has about $140 billion in assets under management.

Blackstone's Hedge Fund Solutions business primarily made up of Blackstone Alternative Asset Management (BAAM) has more than $80 billion in assets under management and makes just more than 15% of revenue. Its clients include public and corporate pension funds and high net worth individuals.

Geographic Reach

New York-based Blackstone Group has 25 offices worldwide in the Americas the Asia Pacific region and Europe. In the US the firm operates branches in Houston Los Angeles San Francisco Baltimore and Cambridge Massachusets. Its overseas offices are located in major cities around the world.

The firm holds real estate properties and portfolio (private equity) companies throughout the world. Investors also have a global presence.

Financial Performance

Over the past five years Blackstone's revenue has fluctuated ranging from a low of $4.1 billion in 2015 to a high during the period of $7.1 billion.

In 2018 revenue declined 5% to $6.8 billion from $7.1 billion in 2017 due to decreases investment income and incentive Fees partially offset by increases management and advisory fees and Other revenue.

Despite the revenue decline earnings for 2018 grew 5% from the prior year to $1.5 billion. Decreases in expenses including total compensation and benefits and fund expenses contributed to the increase. The firm also saw a lower income taxes in 2018 than in 2017.

Cash at the end of 2018 was $2.5 billion a decrease of $1.3 billion from the previous year. Financing activities used $1.3 billion mostly for distributions to unitholders and loan repayment. Investing activities used $116.5 million and operating activities contributed $45.7 million.

Strategy

Blackstone's four segments each follow a set of investment policies to achieve their respective financial objectives. Depending on market conditions and anticipated economic activity one segment might be more active than others. Prior to 2018 Blackstone's Real Estate segment participated in a slew of transactions continuing a multi-year upward trend; in 2018 and 2019 the firm shifted its investment activity to private equity.

Blackstone's legacy Private Equity division is known as a hands-on investor that builds up its portfolio companies' values before selling them off for large profits. After a slow-down in 2017 of M&A pursuits (mirroring a larger M&A trend in the US) Blackstone ramped up acquisitions in 2018 and 2019. A purchase of a majority stake in Thomson Reuters' Financial and Risk business for $20 billion — its largest dollar amount since the 2008 financial crisis — in 2018 along with agreements in 2019 to acquire stakes in Japan's AYUMI Pharmaceutical India's Essel Propack Ltd. and other companies signify a return to growth in its Private Equity division.

Mergers and Acquisitions

In mid-2019 Blackstone announced it reached an agreement to acquire CRH Europe Distribution the European building materials business of CRH plc Ireland's largest company.

Blackstone announced in early 2019 that it would acquire AYUMI Pharmaceutical which markets prescription acetaminophen analgesic drug Calonal in Japan. The acquisition is Blackstone's first Japanese control private equity investment. That same year it also acquired a controlling stake in India's Essel Propack Ltd the country's leading plastic packaging company. The deal should close for somewhere between $310 million and $460 million depending on how the deal plays out under Indian law.

In 2018 Blackstone acquired a majority stake in Thomson Reuters' Financial and Risk business for $20 billion. The deal marked Blackstone's largest acquisition since buyouts it made during the financial crisis of 2008.

Company Background

Founded in 1985 by industry veterans Peter Peterson and CEO Stephen Schwarzman the once-reclusive Blackstone went public in June 2007. The public offering which was a first among major US private equity firms valued Blackstone at upwards of $4 billion.

HISTORY

In 2013 the firm purchased the Hughes Center complex in Las Vegas for $347 million to eventually benefit from the region's rebound. Blackstone was also part of an investor group that bought Extended Stay Hotels owner HVM which was in bankruptcy. All of the hospitality investment activity helped bring in a dramatic rise in revenues in 2013.

In China following its strategy to invest in high-growth Chinese companies through its partnership with the Shanghai-Pudong district government a consortium led by Blackstone agreed in late 2013 to acquire China-based global consulting and technology services company Pactera Technology International Ltd. for about $600 million. The move marked Blackstone's foray into China's technology outsourcing industry a sector traditionally dominated by Indian firms.

In 2012 in capitalizing on the boom in energy markets Blackstone completed fundraising for its first energy-focused private equity fund Blackstone Energy Partners L.P. with total fund commitments of $2.4 billion. The firm also raised $13.3 billion for its seventh global real estate fund BREP VII making it the biggest real estate fund in the world. In 2013 Blackstone acquired secondary private fund of funds unit Strategic Partners Fund Solutions in a deal that added some $9.4 billion in assets under management.

Founded in 1985 by industry veterans Peter Peterson and CEO Stephen Schwarzman the once-reclusive Blackstone went public in June 2007. The public offering which was a first among major US private equity firms valued Blackstone at upwards of $4 billion.

EXECUTIVES

President And Coo, Hamilton E. (Tony) James, age 68, $350,000 total compensation
Chairman And Ceo, Stephen A. Schwarzman, age 72, $350,000 total compensation
Senior Managing Director And Head Of Private Equity Portfolio Operations, David L. (Dave) Calhoun, age 62
Senior Managing Director And Cfo, Michael S. Chae, age 50, $350,000 total compensation
Senior Managing Director Gso Capital Partners, Bennett J. Goodman, age 61
Senior Managing Director And Head Of Tactical Opportunities, David S. Blitzer, age 49
Senior Managing Director And Global Head Of Real Estate, Jonathan D. Gray, age 49
Senior Managing Director And Head Of Multi-asset Investing And External Relations, Joan Solotar, age 54, $350,000 total compensation
Vice Chairman And President And Ceo Blackstone Alternative Asset Management, J. Tomilson Hill, age 70, $350,000 total compensation
Global Head Of Private Equity, Joseph P. Baratta, age 48
Senior Managing Director And Chief Legal Officer, John G. Finley, age 62, $350,000 total compensation
Senior Managing Director And Cto, William Murphy
Chairman Asia-pacific, Christopher (Chris) Heady
Senior Managing Director And Head Of Energy Practice Gso Capital Partners, Dwight Scott, age 55
Senior Managing Director And Ceo Blackstone Insurance Solutions, Chris Blunt
Vice President, Brian Batten
Vice President Information Technology, Andrew Scott
Assistant Vice President Of Accounting, Scott Danna
Senior Vice President, Amy Blake
Vice President Credit Business, Juliann O'Sullivan
Svp Finance, Michael Davis
Assistant Vice President Information Technology, Garfield DeBarros
Vice President, John Wander
Vice President, Megan Chadderton
Vice President, Donald Purdy
Vice President, Jason Warner
Vp Innovations, Michael Scaturo
Vice President, John Tierney
Vice President Of Information Technology, Daniel Moy
Vice President, Ronald Lintag
Vice President Credit Business, Jimmy Wang
National Sales Manager For The Private Wealth Management Group, Joe Lohrer
Senior Vice President, Marlena Kaplan
Vice President, Brij Kalaria
Assistant Vice President, Robert Capparelli
Vice President, John Shields

Assistant Vice President, Vincent Barberesi
Vice President, Raphael Kiam
Assistant Vice President, Anna Fields
Assistant Vice President, Satie Prashaud
Assistant Vice President, Andrew Eichner
Vice President, Brett Chalanick
Assistant Vice President, Ryan Elman
Assistant Vice President, Alexander Brezden
Assistant Vice President, Michael Papera
Senior Vice President, Kaori Curran
Assistant Vice President, Sherilene Sibadan
Assistant Vice President, Kelly Yan
Vice President Private Equity Investor Relations And Business Development, Emily Ho
Vice President, John Miller
Vice President, Thomas Kali
Vice President, Kevin Kresge
Vice President, Stephen O'Connor
Vice President And Cao, Megan Mccann
Avp, Jason Drum
Vice President, Michael Batanian
Assistant Vice President, Michael Lacerda
Vice President, Bryan Shelby
Vice President, Katie Brackenbury
Assistant Vice President, Eric Meyer
Vice President Business Analyst, Cindy Hwang
Assistant Vice President, Sophie Chen
Vice President, Taylor Carvajal
Vice President, Jason Umlah
Assistant Vice President, Sara Slater
Vice President, Kuohsin Chen
Assistant Vice President, Joshua Wallin
Vice President, Brett Crandall
Assistant Vice President, Daniel Fromm
Vice President, Christian Vardeleon
Assistant Vice President, Frank Alleva
Vice President, Katherine Daco
Vice President, Emily Mathews
Senior Vice President Credit Businesses, Thomas Iannarone
Vice President, Kevin Gee
Vice President, Mike Wilcox
Vice President, Sudarshan Jain
Assistant Vice President, Ryan John
Vice President, Matthew Pedley
Vice President, Mark Tornga
Vice President, Michelle Harika
Vice President, Roberta Osborne
Senior Vice President Finance Group, Walter Dinsmore
Vice President Software Development, David Tanzer
Vice President, Adam Hermida
Senior Vice President, Sal Aloia
Assistant Vice President, Vinny Scutro
Vice President, Daniel Chang
Vice President, Thomas Procida
Vice President, Cooper Wright
Vice President, Michael Pierog
Vice President, Margaret Verdeschi
Vice President, Michael Amoroso
Vice President, Milca Beltre
Vice President Real Estate Debt Strategies, Damiano Buffa
Vice President, Marni Blivice
Assistant Vice President, Mai La
Senior Vice President Finance, Vijay Vithal Bharadia
Vice President Finance, Vinodh Krishnamoorthy
Vice President, Cj Brown
Senior Vice President Finance, Barbara Frank
Vice President, Richard Shih
Senior Vice President Real Estate Group, Judy Marcus
Vice President, Alex Horowitz
Assistant Vice President, Grant Bokerman
Assistant Vice President, James Fitzgerald
Assistant Vice President At Gso Capital Partners Lp, Samantha Fleary

Assistant Vice President Treasury Accounting, Tatiana Mirville
Vice President Hedge Fund Solutions, Sarah Acott
Vice President, Jennifer Chang
Senior Vice President, Martin Kamber
Assistant Vice President, Andrew Capitulo
Senior Vice President Treasury, Steven Swanson
Assistant Vice President, Matthew Moyer
Vice President, Natasha Gopaul
Vice President, Hannah Ellis
Vice President, Steven Cipolloni
Assistant Vice President, Jennifer Singh
Assistant Vice President, Kristen Hammonds
Assistant Vice President, Michael Walker
Vice President, Paul Bozgo
Vice President, Candice Sorbera
Vice President, Pat Hanna
Vice President Business Analyst, Kseniia Globa
Vice President, Brijesh Kalaria
Vice President, Bill Sheehan
Vice President, Ryan Chapman
Senior Vice President, Cathleen Becker
Vice President, Matt Weidemoyer
Vice President Manager Of Registration, Rebecca Stoehr
Vice President Servers And Application Infrastructure Engineering Lead, Glenn Wellington
Vice President Finance, Devyani Kamdar
Assistant Vice President, Amanda Lenok
Senior Vice President Blackstone Real Estate Debt Strategies Breds, Devi Ethiraj
Assistant Vice President, Kevin Burns
Vice President, Gerald Donaghy
Assistant Vice President, Larry Vodopivec
Senior Vice President, Sam Gleeson
Vice President In The Funds Of Funds Gro, Joseph Defalco
Auditors: DELOITTE & TOUCHE LLP

LOCATIONS

HQ: Blackstone Group Inc (The)
345 Park Avenue, New York, NY 10154
Phone: 212 583-5000
Web: www.blackstone.com

PRODUCTS/OPERATIONS

2018 Sales

	% of total
Management and Advisory Fees net	44
Total Investment Income	43
Interest and Dividend Revenue and Other	12
Incentive Fees	1
Total	**100**

Selected Investments

Allcargo
Alliant Insurance Services
AlliedBarton Security Services
Antares Restaurant Group
Apria Healthcare
Axis Capital
BankUnited
Bayview Asset Management
Biomet
Caesars Entertainment (formerly Harrah's Entertainment)
Catalent Pharma Solutions
Celanese
Center Parcs
Charter Communications
China Animal Healthcare Ltd.
China National Bluestar Group
CMS Computers Ltd.
Crestwood Midstream Partners
CTI Holdings
Cumulus Media Partners
DJO
Dili Group
eAccess
Emcure
Equity Office Properties

Extended Stay America
Freescale Semiconductor Group
Gates Corporation
Gateway Rail Freight Ltd.
Gerresheimer Group
Gokaldas Exports Limited
Gold Toe-Moretz
Houghton Mifflin
Imperial Home Décor
Independent Clinical Services
Intelenet Global Services
Intertrust
Klöckner Pentaplast
Leica Camera
Maldivian Air
Michaels Stores
Mivisa Envases S.A.U.
Monnet
Montecito
Moser Baer Energy
MTAR Technologies Private
Nuziveedu Seeds
Osum Oil Sands Corp.
PBF Energy
People's Choice TV
Performance Food Group
Pinnacle Foods Corporation
Polymer Group Inc.
RGIS Inventory Specialists
Sonalike International Tractors
SeaWorld Parks & Entertainment
Summit Materials
Stiefel Laboratories
SunGard
Team Health
Texas Genco
Tragus
TRW Automotive
UCAR
United Biscuits
Vivint Inc.
The Weather Channel
Western Integrated Networks

COMPETITORS

American Financial Group	Clayton Dubilier & Rice
Apollo Global Management	Goldman Sachs
Bain Capital	Investcorp
Berkshire Hathaway	KKR
BlackRock	The Carlyle Group

HISTORICAL FINANCIALS

Company Type: Public

Income Statement
FYE: December 31

	REVENUE ($ mil.)	NET INCOME ($ mil.)	NET PROFIT MARGIN	EMPLOYEES
12/18	6,833	1,541	22.6%	2,615
12/17	7,119	1,470	20.7%	2,360
12/16	5,125	1,039	20.3%	2,120
12/15	4,646	709	15.3%	2,060
12/14	7,484	1,584	21.2%	2,190
Annual Growth	(2.3%)	(0.7%)	—	4.5%

2018 Year-End Financials

Debt ratio: 34.41%
Return on equity: —
Cash ($ mil.): 2,545
Current ratio: 1.02
Long-term debt ($ mil.): 9,951

No. of shares (mil.): 663
Dividends
Yield: 0.0%
Payout: 107.0%
Market value ($ mil.): 19,770

	STOCK PRICE ($) FY Close	P/E High/Low		PER SHARE ($) Earnings	Dividends	Book Value
12/18	29.81	17	12	2.26	2.42	9.62
12/17	32.02	16	13	2.21	0.00	10.06
12/16	27.03	19	14	1.56	0.00	10.04
12/15	29.24	39	25	1.04	0.00	10.04
12/14	33.83	14	11	2.58	0.00	11.85
Annual Growth	(3.1%)	—	—	(3.3%)	—	(5.1%)

BNSF RAILWAY COMPANY

BNSF Railway operates one of the largest railroad networks in North America. A wholly-owned subsidiary of Burlington Northern Santa Fe itself a unit of Berkshire Hathaway the company provides freight transportation over a network of about 32500 route miles of track across some 30 US states and three provinces in Canada. BNSF Railway owns or leases a fleet of about 8000 locomotives. It also has some 25 intermodal facilities that help to transport agricultural consumer and industrial products as well as coal. In addition to major cities and ports BNSF Railway serves smaller markets in alliance with short-line partners.

Operations

BNSF Railway transports a wide range of products and commodities through its four main product segments.

The Consumer Products segment generates about 35% of revenue and consists of the Domestic Intermodal International Intermodal and Automotive business units. The Industrial Products segment provides about 25% of revenue and comprises five business units: Construction Products Petroleum Products Building Products Chemicals and Plastics Products and Food and Beverages.

Agricultural Products represents 20% of revenue and includes the transportation of commodities like corn wheat ethanol soybeans fertilizer oil seeds flour and other grains. The Coal business (less than 20%) is primarily BNSF's operations that originate from the Powder River Basin of Wyoming and Montana.

The company also generates about 5% of revenue from its wholly-owned non-rail logistics subsidiary BSNF Logistics LLC through logistics and transportation services such as storage as well as demurrage (detention fees for delays in loading and unloading of freight).

Geographic Reach

Headquartered in Fort Worth TX BNSF Railway's network spreads across about 30 US states and three Canadian provinces.

Sales and Marketing

BNSF Railway serves smaller markets by working closely with 200 shortline partners. It also forms marketing agreements with other rail carriers expanding the marketing reach for each railroad and its customers.

Financial Performance

BNSF has seen steady growth in recent years with revenue reaching $23.9 billion in 2018 a 12% increase compared with $21.4 billion in 2017. The increase in 2018 was mainly due to increased volume and increased rates per car as well as tight truck capacity in the transportation sector which converted some business from highway to rail.

Net income however plummeted to $5.2 billion less than half that of the previous year. This was primarily due to an increased tax liability as a result of the Tax Cuts and Jobs Act.

Cash at the end of fiscal 2018 was $2.0 billion about the same as the prior year. Cash from operations contributed $7.9 billion to the coffers while investing activities used $3.2 billion mainly for capital expenditures related to equipment purchases. Financing activities used another $4.7 billion primarily for cash distributions to its parent company.

Strategy

BNSF plans capital spending of about $3.5 billion in 2019 for network maintenance and replacement of assets to ensure safe and reliable operations. These include expansion and efficiency projects focused on key growth areas along its Southern and Northern Trancon routes. The company faces challenges in its supply chain environment with competition from improving productivity in the trucking industry. Another hurdle is consumers' expectations for quicker and quicker delivery as online shopping continues to grow. In response BSNF is focusing on providing consistent reliable and efficient transportation services to its customers.

Company Background

BNSF's traces its roots to 1849 when the Aurora Branch Railroad was founded in Illinois with 12 miles of track. Over the years additional rail lines were built including Atchison Topeka & Santa Fe;Burlington Northern; Chicago Burlington & Quincy; Frisco; Great Northern; Northern Pacific; and Spokane Portland & Seattle.

BNSF was created in 1995 when Burlington Northern Inc. (the parent company of Burlington Northern Railroad) merged with Santa Fe Pacific Corporation (parent company of the Atchison Topeka & Santa Fe Railway). The company was acquired by Berkshire Hathaway in 2010 and BNSF now operates as a subsidiary of that company.

EXECUTIVES

Evp And Coo, Carl R. Ice, age 62
Evp Law And Corporate Affairs, Roger Nober, age 54
Evp And Cfo, Julie A. Piggott
Evp And Chief Marketing Officer, Stevan B. Bobb
Evp Operations, Gregory C. Fox
Vice President Federal Government Affairs, Amy Hawkins
Executive Vice President Law And Government Affairs And Secretary, Jeffrey Moreland
Vice President Network Strategy, Dean Wise
Vice President Controller, Dannis Johnson
Chairman President And Ceo, Matthew K. (Matt) Rose, age 60
Auditors: DELOITTE & TOUCHE LLP FORT WO

LOCATIONS

HQ: BNSF RAILWAY COMPANY
2650 LOU MENK DR, FORT WORTH, TX 761312830
Phone: 800 795-2673
Web: WWW.BNSF.COM

PRODUCTS/OPERATIONS

2018 Sales

	$ mil.	% of total
Consumer Products	7,902	33
Industrial Products	5,967	25
Agricultural Products	4,697	20
Coal	4,012	17
Other revenues	1,277	5
Total	**23,855**	**100**

COMPETITORS

CSX	Kansas City Southern Railway
Canadian National Railway	Norfolk Southern
Canadian Pacific Railway	Union Pacific Railroad

HISTORICAL FINANCIALS

Company Type: Private

Income Statement
FYE: December 31

	REVENUE ($ mil.)	NET INCOME ($ mil.)	NET PROFIT MARGIN	EMPLOYEES
12/17	20,747	12,119	58.4%	41,000
12/16	19,278	4,260	22.1%	—
12/14	22,714	4,397	19.4%	—
12/13	21,552	4,271	19.8%	—
Annual Growth	(0.9%)	29.8%	—	—

BOARD OF EDUCATION OF CITY OF CHICAGO

EXECUTIVES

Pres, Frank Clark
Technology, James V Dispensa
Coordinator, Samantha Treworgy
Technology Manager, Denise Sangster
Auditors: MCGLADREY LLP CHICAGO ILLINO

LOCATIONS

HQ: BOARD OF EDUCATION OF CITY OF CHICAGO
42 W MADISON ST FL 2, CHICAGO, IL 606024309
Phone: 773 553-1600
Web: WWW.CPSBOE.ORG

HISTORICAL FINANCIALS

Company Type: Private

Income Statement   FYE: June 30

	REVENUE ($ mil.)	NET INCOME ($ mil.)	NET PROFIT MARGIN	EMPLOYEES
06/16	5,272	(381)		5,151
06/12	5,760	324	5.6%	—
06/11	5,660	238	4.2%	—
06/08	17	(0)	—	—
Annual Growth	103.8%	—	—	—

BOARD OF REGENTS OF THE UNIVERSITY SYSTEM OF GEORGIA

EXECUTIVES

Chancellor, Hank Huckaby
Director For Grants Accounting*, Jennifer Shaw
Procurement Staff, Michael Haun
Coordinator, Taylor Smith
Coordinator, Charlotte Stauffer
Customer Representativ, Justina Washington
Administrative Coordinator, Blair Witte
Director, Cherry Zhang
Ecampus Director, Christy Talley-Smith
Office Manager, Juanita D Ervin
Archival Manager, Kayla Barrett
Auditors: GREG S GRIFFIN ATLANTA GEORG

LOCATIONS

HQ: BOARD OF REGENTS OF THE UNIVERSITY
SYSTEM OF GEORGIA
270 WASHINGTON ST SW FL 7, ATLANTA, GA
303349009
Phone: 404 962-3050
Web: WWW.USG.EDU

HISTORICAL FINANCIALS

Company Type: Private

Income Statement   FYE: June 30

	REVENUE ($ mil.)	NET INCOME ($ mil.)	NET PROFIT MARGIN	EMPLOYEES
06/18	5,210	221	4.3%	40,000
06/17	5,100	57	1.1%	—
06/15	4,704	124	2.6%	—
06/11	0	0	—	—
Annual Growth	—	—	—	—

Boeing Co. (The)

Boeing is the world's largest aerospace company and one of only two major manufacturers (the other being Airbus) of 100-plus seat airplanes for the commercial airline industry. Its commercial jet aircraft models include the 737 narrow body; the fuel-efficient 737 MAX; the 747 767 and 777 wide bodies; and the 787 Dreamliner. Serving the military science and space and sea exploration sectors the company also produces KC-46 aerial refueling aircraft the AH-64 Apache helicopter the 702 family of satellites CST-100 Starliner spacecraft and the Echo Voyager unmanned undersea vehicle. Major customers include the US Department of Defense and NASA. Additionally Boeing provides aftermarket support as well as airplane financing and leasing services to both commercial and military customers.

Operations

Boeing's operations are divided into three business units: Commercial Airplanes (BCA); Defense Space & Security (BDS); and Boeing Global Services (BGS). Supporting these segments is Boeing Capital (BCC) its global financing operations.

Boeing Commercial Airplanes represents about 60% of sales and designs manufactures and services commercial jet aircraft for both passengers and cargo. More than 10000 Boeing-built commercial jetliners are in service worldwide which is almost half the world fleet. The company also offers the most complete family of freighters and about 90 percent of the world's cargo is carried onboard Boeing planes.

Defense Space & Security (about 25% of sales) provides design production modification service and support services for large-scale systems including missiles munitions aerial refuelers transporters and spacecraft.

Boeing Global Services generates more than 15% of sales. The division caters to aerospace and defense needs including supply chain and logistics management maintenance upgrades and conversions spare parts training systems and data analytics and digital services.

Geographic Reach

Boeing's principal operations are in the US Canada and Australia with some key suppliers and subcontractors located in Europe and Japan. Approximately 95% of its manufacturing warehousing engineering and administration facilities are located in the US. Boeing brings in about 45% of its revenue from the US about 25% from Asia 15% from Europe and about 10% from the Middle East.

Sales and Marketing

The main customer of Boeing's Defense Space & Security segment is the Department of Defense which generates about 85% of revenue (including foreign military sales through the US government).

Other significant BDS revenue is derived from NASA and customers in international defense markets civil markets and the commercial satellite market.

Financial Performance

Boeing's revenue has been trending upward over the past five years with a total increase of 11% since 2014.

The company's sales in 2018 surpassed the $100 billion mark for the first time with $101.1 billion in revenue an 8% increase over $94.0 billion in 2017. The increase was primarily due to increased 737 and 787 deliveries some non-US contract awards for fighter jets and satellites and higher parts revenue including the acquisition of aviation parts and services provider KLX Inc.

Along with increased sales net income jumped 24% to $10.5 billion in 2018 compared with $8.5 billion the previous year (net income also increased 68% in 2017 compared with 2016). Lower income tax expenses in 2018 contributed to the boost in profits.

Cash at the end of fiscal 2018 was $7.6 billion a decrease of $1.1 billion from the prior year. Cash from operations contributed $15.3 billion to the coffers while investing activities used $4.6 billion mainly for additions to property plant and equipment and acquisitions. Financing activities used another $11.7 billion for dividends to stockholders and the company's stock repurchase program.

Strategy

Boeing's growth strategy is centered around product initiatives including building more efficient airplanes developing smarter solutions for military customers and creating next-generation space exploration vehicles. It also aims to capture a larger share of the services market (it acquired parts and services provider KLX in 2018).

To house its manufacturing and R&D operations the company expanded its facilities outside the US with a new 737 Completion and Delivery Center in Zhoushan China and a fabrication factory in Sheffield UK. It also plans to open a new research center in Korea. New innovations are centered around additive manufacturing avionics data analytics and digital engineering technologies in its manufacturing and supply chain activities.

For its commercial and government aerospace customers Boeing launched a Disruptive Computing and Networks organization to develop advance computing and communications solutions. It also established Boeing NeXt a new organization focused on future mobility products such as high-speed aircraft and new spacecraft that could transport people and cargo to and from space.

In 2019 airlines worldwide grounded all Boeing 737 MAX passenger airliners after two crashes ? Indonesian Lion Air Flight 610 and Ethiopian Airlines Flight 302 ? killed 346 passengers aboard the 737 MAX aircraft. The crashes were attributed to issues with Boeing's new MCAS automated navigation system. The company has made software updates to the system and is working with the FAA to bring the 737s back into service.

Mergers and Acquisitions

Boeing achieves growth by acquiring businesses that focus on specific technology products and target the needs of emerging markets such as services.

In 2019 the company completed the acquisition of Houston Texas-based ForeFlight a leading provider of innovative mobile and web-based aviation applications. The acquisition of ForeFlight aligns with Boeing's growth strategy of complementing organic investments with targeted strategic investments that position the company for long-term growth.

In late 2018 it completed its acquisition of KLX Aerospace Solutions allowing the company to compete in the aerospace services market. KLX is a provider of aviation parts and services in the aerospace industry distributing products for approximately 2400 manufacturers and offers approximately 1 million catalog items. It will continue to operate from Miami with customer service centers located in more than 15 countries.

Also in 2018 it formed a partnership with Brazil-based Embraer to take over its commercial aircraft operations (Embraer's defense division and business jet unit were not part of the deal). Boeing acquired an 80% interest in the venture and expects costs synergies of about $150 million by 2020.

Another 2018 acquisition was small-satellite developer Millennium Space Systems based in El Segundo Calif. Millenium will operate as a subsidiary of Boeing Phantom Works and further adds to Boeing's investment in the aerospace market.

Company Background

The Boeing Company celebrated 100 years in business in 2016. Some of its first aircraft were used in World War I and the company began manufacturing commercial aircraft in 1919. The global aviation industry continued to grow even through The Great Depression and Boeing continued to deliver more commercial and military aircraft through the decades.

In 1947 Boeing set speed and distance records with its B-47 and its swept-back wings a design that would become standard on many commercial and military aircraft. Boeing also designed the first stage of the three-stage Saturn V rocket used for the Apollo space missions in the 1960s. The company went on to develop the Apache helicopter which is still in use today.

Most recently Boeing has been focused on future mobility products such as autonomous aircraft and next-generation space vehicles.

HISTORY

Bill Boeing who had already made his fortune in Washington real estate built his first airplane in 1916 with naval officer Conrad Westervelt. His Seattle company Pacific Aero Products changed its name to Boeing Airplane Company the next year. During WWI Boeing built training planes for the US Navy and began the first international air-mail service (between Seattle and Victoria British Columbia). The company added a Chicago-San Francisco route in 1927 and established an airline subsidiary Boeing Air Transport. The airline's success was aided by Boeing's Model 40A the first plane to use Frederick Rentschler's new air-cooled engine.

Rentschler and Boeing combined their companies as United Aircraft and Transport in 1929 and introduced the all-metal airliner in 1933. The next year new antitrust rules forced United Aircraft and Transportation to sell portions of its operations as United Air Lines and United Aircraft (later United Technologies). This left Boeing Airplane (as it was known until 1961) with the manufacturing concerns.

EXECUTIVES

Evp And Ceo Boeing Global Services, Stanley A. (Stan) Deal, age 55

Evp And General Counsel, J. Michael (Mike) Luttig, age 64, $903,673 total compensation

Svp Supply Chain And Operations, Patrick M. (Pat) Shanahan, age 57

Chairman President And Ceo, Dennis A. Muilenburg, age 55, $1,640,962 total compensation

President Phantom Works Boeing Defense Space And Security, Darryl W. Davis

Evp And President And Ceo Boeing Commercial Airplanes, Kevin G. McAllister, age 56, $92,308 total compensation

Svp Sales Asia Pacific And President Boeing India, Dinesh A. Keskar, age 65

Evp Business Development And Strategy And Cfo, Gregory D. (Greg) Smith, age 52, $911,442 total compensation

President Boeing Military Aircraft Boeing Defense Space And Security, Shelley K. Lavender, age 55

Svp And President Boeing International, Bertrand-Marc (Marc) Allen, age 45

Svp Information And Analytics And Cio, Theodore (Ted) Colbert, age 45

Svp Engineering And Cto, Gregory L. (Greg) Hyslop, age 60

President Boeing Capital Corporation, Timothy Myers

Evp And President And Ceo Defense Space And Security (bds), Leanne G. Caret, age 52

President Network And Space Systems, Jim Chilton

President Boeing Defense Space And Security Development (bds), Patrick (Pat) Goggin

Senior Vice President Commercial Sales And Marketing, Ihssane Mounir

Vice President Strategy Global Services, Dennis Floyd

Vice President Attack Helicopters And Mesa Senior Site Executive, Kim Smith

Boeing Vice President Of Leasing Sales, Bill Collins

Vice President, Mark Jenks

Vice President, Bernard Hensey

Vice President, Karen Tang

Vice President, Mark Bertrand

Vice President Legislative Affairs, Steve Bachmann

Regional Vice President, David Cazer

Vice President Of Strategic Development, Bill Bonadio

Vice President Human Resources, Grace Miller

Vice President Customer Support, Donald Ruhmann

Vice President Australia And Pacific Sales, Rick Westmoreland

Vice President Corporate Strategy, Rik Geiersbach

Vice President, Matt Wilks

Senior Vice President Gc, J M Luttig

Vp And Gm Supply Chain Commercial Airplanes, Elizabeth Lund

Vice President, James W Hoskinson

Vice President Federal Legislative Affairs Government Operations, Art Cameron

Vice President Of Supply Chain Rate Capability For Commercial Airplanes Supplier Management, Beth Anderson

Vice President Of Sales For Digital Division, Keith P White

Vice President Integrated Defense System, Gregory Laxton

Vice President Customer Support Americas, Larry Slate

Vice President Business Systems And Administration, Renee L Stober

Vp Communications, Gordon Johndroe

Vice President Airplane Development Engineering, Ed Petkus

Vice President Develop, John Roundhill

Vice President, Jay Byunn

Vice President And Managing Director, James Detwiler

Vice President Business Development, Christopher Raymond

Vp Intellectual Property Management Engineering Operations And Technology, Peter Hoffman

Vice President, Lynn Johnson

Vp Strategy Commercial Airplances, Sheila Remes

Vice President, Bruce Dennis

Vice President, Tobias Bright

Vice President Special Events, Lacey Jones

Vice President And General Manager For Supplier Management, Steve Schaffer

Vice President Of Sales And Marketing, Harry W Gray

Vice President Manufacturing Safety And Quality Commercial Airplanes, Walter Odisho

Vice President, Michael Sloup

Vice President Middle East Sales, Robert Johnstone

Vice President, Terry Kamm

Vice President Enterprise Strategy, Travis Sullivan

Vice President, Catherine J Pruss-Jones

Vice President Engineering, Russell E Shue

Vice President Supply Chain Boeing Global Services, Kenneth Shaw

Vice President For Government Affairs, Forey Hamilton

Vice President, Shelly Huff

Vp And Program Manager Boeing Global Broadband System, Bruce Chesley

Vice President And Program Manager C 130 Avionics Modernization Program, Michael Harris

Office Of The Vice President Of Engineering, Patricia Sandoval

Vice President, Steve Wallace

Vice President Corporate Audit, Bavan Holloway

Vice President, Elaine Milligan

Vp Human Resources, Wendy Livingston

Vice President Communications And Marketing, Ali T Mir

Vice President Transaction Services, Edward Bayne

Vice President Edelman Employee Engagement Practice, Nicole Silva

Vice President Of Decision Support, Rebecca Fasano

Vice President And Assistant General Counsel Boeing Commercial Airplanes, Matt Cooper

Svp Global Sales And Marketing Defense Space And Security, Thomas Bell

Vice President Government Operations, Greta Lundeberg

Senior Vice President Supplier Management, Jim Morris

Vice President Business And Supply Chain Systems, Lakshmi Eleswarpu

Vice President Total Rewards And Human Resources Analytics, Jon Fliss

Vice President Legislative Affairs Authorizations, Michael Waclawski

Executive Vice President, Terry White

Vice President, Jeremy Griffin

Vice President, Michael Fleming

Vice President Communications, Linda Mills

Vp Global Trade Controls, Sue Gainor

Vice President Navy Systems, Mike Manazir

Vice President And General Manager, Charles Toups

Vice President, Jeff Rice

Vice President Space Intelligence And Missile Defense Systems, Roger Teague

Vice President Information Technology Business Partners Defense Space And Security, Denise Russell Fleming

Vice President, Rob Borden

Vice President Sales, Rachel Lohmar

Vice Chairman, Raymond L. (Ray) Conner, age 63

Board Member, Brad Arbaugh

Assistant Treasurer, Ruud Roggekamp

Secretary, Bruce J Cadiz

Assistant Treasurer, Verett Mims

Assistant Treasurer Risk Management And Insurance, Michael Tarling

Board Member, Nancy J Kaatman

Board Member, Thi Tran

Treasurer, Roger Pullman

Svp Finance And Treasurer, David Dohnalek

Secretary, Chris Tavares

Treasurer, Laura LU

Chapter Treasurer, Daniel Hill

Office Of The Treasurer, Kim Rainey

Usglc Treasurer, Jefferson Hofgard

Treasurer, Melinda Donaldson

Board Member, David Good

Assistant Secretary, Teresa Loy
Treasurer, Gordon Yip
Secretary, Joseph S Lyons
Training Secretary, Gregory E Labus
Auditors: DELOITTE & TOUCHE LLP

LOCATIONS

HQ: Boeing Co. (The)
100 North Riverside Plaza, Chicago, IL 60606-1596
Phone: 312 544-2000
Web: www.boeing.com

2018 Sales

	$ mil.	% of total
US	44,676	44
Asia		
China	13,764	14
Other Asia	12,141	12
Europe	12,976	13
Middle East	9,745	10
Canada	2,583	3
Oceania	2,298	2
Africa	1,486	1
Latin American Caribbean & other	1,458	1
Total	**101,127**	**100**

PRODUCTS/OPERATIONS

2018 Sales

	$ mil.	% of total
Sales of products	90,229	89
Sales of services	10,898	11
Total	**101,127**	**100**

2018 Sales

	$ mil.	% of total
Commercial Airplanes	60,715	60
Defense Space & Security	23,195	23
Global Services	17,018	17
Boeing Capital	274	-
Adjustments	(75)	-
Total	**101,127**	**100**

Selected Products and Services

Commercial Airplanes
Products
  737 Next Generation (short-to-medium-range two-engine jet)
  747 (long-range four-engine jet)
  767 (medium-to-long-range two-engine jet)
  777 (long-range two-engine jet)
  Boeing Business Jet
  787 Dreamliner (in development; long-range super-efficient 200-250 passenger capacity)
  747-8 (in development;
Services
  Engineering modification and logistics
  Maintenance repair and overhaul
  Boeing Training & Flight Services
Defense Space & Security
Military Aircraft
  AH-64 Apache
  B-1B Lancer
  B-2 Spirit
  F/A-18 Hornet
  F-15E Strike Eagle
  F-22 Raptor
  T-45 Flight Training System
  A160 Hummingbird
  Harpoon
  Insitu
  C-17 Globemaster III
  CH-47D/F Chinook
  V-22 Osprey
Global Services & Support
  Integrated logistics
  Maintenance modifications and upgrades
  Training systems
  Government services
  Network & Space Systems
  Electronic and mission
  Cyber security
  Infrastructure
  Intelligence
  Logistics command and control
  Satellite and ground operations
  Space exploration

COMPETITORS

AgustaWestland
Airbus Group
BAE SYSTEMS
Dassault Aviation
Embraer
General Dynamics
Kaman
Leonardo

Lockheed Martin
Northrop Grumman
Raytheon
Rockwell Collins
Space Exploration Technologies
Thales
United Technologies

HISTORICAL FINANCIALS

Company Type: Public

Income Statement

FYE: December 31

	REVENUE ($ mil.)	NET INCOME ($ mil.)	NET PROFIT MARGIN	EMPLOYEES
12/19	76,559	(636)	—	161,100
12/18	101,127	10,460	10.3%	153,000
12/17	93,392	8,197	8.8%	140,800
12/16	94,571	4,895	5.2%	150,500
12/15	96,114	5,176	5.4%	161,400
Annual Growth	(5.5%)	—	—	(0.0%)

2019 Year-End Financials

Debt ratio: 20.43%
Return on equity: ***.***.**%
Cash ($ mil.): 9,485
Current ratio: 1.05
Long-term debt ($ mil.): 19,962

No. of shares (mil.): 562
Dividends
  Yield: 2.5%
  Payout: 126.6%
Market value ($ mil.): 183,373

	STOCK PRICE ($) FY Close	P/E High/Low		Earnings	Dividends	Book Value
12/19	325.76	—	—	(1.12)	8.22	(15.31)
12/18	322.50	22	16	17.85	6.84	0.60
12/17	294.91	22	12	13.43	5.68	0.60
12/16	155.68	20	14	7.61	4.36	1.32
12/15	144.59	21	17	7.44	3.64	9.50
Annual Growth	22.5%	—	—	—	22.6%	

BOK Financial Corp

With seven principal banking divisions in eight midwestern and southwestern states multi-bank holding company BOK offers a range of financial services to consumers and regional businesses. In addition to traditional deposit lending and trust services its banks provide investment management wealth advisory and mineral and real estate management services through a network of branches in Arizona Arkansas Colorado Kansas Missouri New Mexico Oklahoma and Texas. Brokerage subsidiary BOSC underwrites public private and municipal securities. BOK also owns electronic funds network TransFund and institutional asset manager Cavanal Hill.

Operations

BOK Financial operates through three primary segments: Commercial Banking Consumer Banking and Wealth Management. The Commercial Banking segment brings in more than 75% of BOK's total revenue with offerings including lending treasury and cash management and risk management products for small midsized and large companies. The Consumer Banking segment which brings in about 15% of total revenue is the retail arm providing lending and deposit services and all mortgage activities. The Wealth Management segment provides private bank and investment advisory services across all markets and it has more than $16 billion in assets under man-

agement. The segment is also engaged in trading and it underwrites state and municipal securities.

Geographic Reach

Most of Tulsa-based BOK Financial's locations are located in and around Tulsa; Oklahoma City; Dallas/Fort Worth; Houston; Albuquerque New Mexico; Denver; Phoenix; and Kansas City in Kansas and Missouri. The company's primary operations facilities lare in Tulsa; Oklahoma City; Dallas; and Albuquerque New Mexico.

Sales and Marketing

In 2017 BOK Financials spent $28.9 million on promotional costs versus $26.6 million in 2016 and $27.9 million in 2015.

Financial Performance

Thanks largely to the improving US economy BOK's revenues have been trending upward for the past five years. Net income has been somewhat more volatile but reached a peak in 2017.

Revenue increased 9% to $1.5 billion in 2017 as interest income increased 17%. Loan trading securities and interest-bearing cash and cash equivalents revenues saw significant growth that year. Asset management income also rose gaining some 20%. These increases were partially offset by a decline in mortgage banking revenue.

With the higher revenue plus certain lower operating expenses (including mortgage banking costs and insurance expenses) net income rose 44% to $331.1 million in 2017.

The company ended 2017 with $2.3 billion in net cash some $220 million less than it had at the end of 2016. Operating activities provided $214.9 million and investing activities provided $739.6 million. Financing activities used $1.2 billion.

Strategy

BOK emphasizes local decision-making at its flagship subsidiary Bank of Oklahoma and its operating divisions Bank of Albuquerque Bank of Arizona Bank of Arkansas Bank of Texas Colorado State Bank and Trust and Mobank. Commercial loans primarily to the energy services health care and wholesale and retail industries make up the majority of the company's loan portfolio. Commercial real estate residential mortgage car and consumer loans round out its lending activities.

The company is also focused on diversifying its revenue stream by growing its mortgage banking brokerage and wealth management operations.

With banking operations in several major oil- and natural gas-producing states more than 15% of the group's lending portfolio is in the energy sector. Because the energy industry has been challenged with low commodity prices BOK's energy-related charge-offs have grown significantly. In Q2 of 2018 net charge-offs reached $10.5 million — more than half of which was attributed to a single energy customer.

Mergers and Acquisitions

In October 2018 BOK Financial acquired financial services company CoBiz Financial which provides commercial banking and other financial services to businesses in Arizona and Colorado through its Colorado Business Bank and Bank of Arizona subsidiaries. The deal valued at $1 billion more than doubled BOK Financial's deposit market share in the two states.

EXECUTIVES

President And Ceo, Steven G. (Steve) Bradshaw, age 59, $484,275 total compensation
Evp And Cfo, Steven E. Nell, age 57, $439,354 total compensation
Evp Corporate Banking, Stacy C. Kymes, age 48
Chief Credit Officer, Marc C. Maun, age 61
Chairman And Ceo Bank Of Texas, Norman P. Bagwell, age 56, $403,054 total compensation

Evp And Chief Human Resources Officer, Stephen D. Grossi

Evp And Cio, Donald T. Parker

Evp Consumer Banking, Patrick E. Piper

Evp Wealth Management And Ceo Bosc. Inc., Scott B. Grauer

Ceo Oklahoma City Market, John Higginbotham

Assistant Vice President Process Consultant, Diana Pruitt

Assistant Vice President Finance And Administration, Lanny L Randolph

Senior Vice President Perf. Reporting And Analysis, Kent Rugeley

Vice President Credit Administration, Becky Keesling

Vice President Perf. Reporting And Analysis, Tamara Cobb

Senior Vice President And Chief Marketing Officer, Alan Nykiel

Senior Vice President, Guy Evangelista

Vice President Help Desk, Blu Bean

Vice President Production, Kathy Davis

Senior Vice President, Michael Bickel

Senior Vice President Information Technology, Jane Romine

Vice President, Alice Worthington

Vice President Middle Office Manager, John Williamson

Senior Vice President Credit Administration, Carol Cable

Senior Vice President, Lee Allen

Vice President Business Performance Measurement, Richard Hubbard

Vice President, Debi Briscoe

Senior Vice President Director Of Contact Center Operations, John Holt

Vice President, Lisa Albers

Vice President Marketing, Margot McKoy

Vice President, Candice Williams

Senior Vice President, Jill Hall

Senior Vice President, Jeff Sanders

Vice President, Mary Campbell

Vice President And Trust Officer, Claudia Cepeda

Vice President And Portfolio Manager, Tim Hopkins

Senior Vice President Director Of Business Banking, John Anderson

Vice President Risk Management, Don Mallory

Vice President Accounting Control Reporting, Ed Disney

Assistant Vice President Information Technology Project Manager, Lisa Porter Lisa Porter

Vice President Trust Officer Iii, Mary Thomason

Chairman, George B. Kaiser, age 76

Auditors: Ernst & Young LLP

LOCATIONS

HQ: BOK Financial Corp
Bank of Oklahoma Tower, Boston Avenue at Second Street, Tulsa, OK 74192
Phone: 918 588-6000
Web: www.bokf.com

PRODUCTS/OPERATIONS

2017 Sales

	% of total
Commercial Banking	76
Consumer Banking	7
Wealth Management	17
Total	**100**

Selected Banking Subsidiaries

Bank of Albuquerque National Association
Bank of Arizona National Association
Bank of Arkansas National Association
Bank of Oklahoma National Association
Bank of Texas National Association
Colorado State Bank & Trust
Mobank

COMPETITORS

BBVA Compass Bancshares	JPMorgan Chase
Bank of America	Regions Financial
Bank of the West	UMB Financial
Comerica	Wells Fargo
Commerce Bancshares	Zions Bancorporation
First National of Nebraska	

HISTORICAL FINANCIALS

Company Type: Public

Income Statement   FYE: December 31

	ASSETS ($ mil.)	NET INCOME ($ mil.)	INCOME AS % OF ASSETS	EMPLOYEES
12/18	38,020	445	1.2%	5,313
12/17	32,272	334	1.0%	4,930
12/16	32,772	232	0.7%	4,884
12/15	31,476	288	0.9%	4,789
12/14	29,089	292	1.0%	4,743
Annual Growth	**6.9%**	**11.1%**	**—**	**2.9%**

2018 Year-End Financials

Debt ratio: 16.83%	No. of shares (mil.): 72
Return on equity: 11.24%	Dividends
Cash ($ mil.): 1,143	Yield: 2.5%
Current ratio: —	Payout: 30.3%
Long-term debt ($ mil.): —	Market value ($ mil.): 5,289

	STOCK PRICE ($) FY Close	P/E High/Low	PER SHARE ($) Earnings	Dividends	Book Value
12/18	73.33	16 11	6.63	1.90	61.45
12/17	92.32	18 15	5.11	1.77	53.45
12/16	83.04	24 13	3.53	1.73	50.12
12/15	59.79	17 13	4.21	1.69	49.03
12/14	60.04	17 14	4.22	1.62	47.78
Annual Growth	**5.1%**	**— —**	**12.0%**	**4.1%**	**6.5%**

Booking Holdings Inc

Booking Holdings (formerly The Priceline Group) operates six of the world's leading online travel tools. Booking.com is its namesake and top brand and offers online reservation services for some 2.2 million properties — including hotels resorts apartments and homes — across 230-plus countries. The holding company also owns Priceline which features discount bookings for hotels cars airline tickets and vacation packages; other brands include Agoda KAYAK RentalCars and OpenTable. Booking Holdings generates revenues from commissions processing fees advertising and subscriptions. It was founded in 1997 and generates some 90% of sales outside the US.

Operations

Booking Holdings operates an online global travel services network. It works to connect customers looking to make travel reservations with providers of travel services worldwide including some 2.2 million hotels and accommodations.

Internationally the company offers a retail price-disclosed hotel and accommodation reservation service through global brands Booking.com (the world's largest online hotel and accommodation website) and Agoda.com (an online hotel reservation service with operations primarily in Asia). In the US it offers reservations via priceline.com brand for hotels rental cars airline tickets and vacations packages.

OpenTable allows consumers to set up restaurant reservations online and Rentalcars.com is a leading rental car reservation service.

More than 70% of Priceline Group's total revenue comes from agency revenue (commissions paid by travel service providers) while merchant revenue (service fees paid by travelers) and advertising revenue make up 20% and nearly 10% of its total sales respectively.

Geographic Reach

Connecticut-based Booking Holdings serves more than 230 countries. Its ownership of Amsterdam-based Booking.com means the company generates about 75% of its total revenue from the Netherlands. The US and other international markets together generate some 25% each.

Agoda.com is based in Bangkok Priceline and KAYAK are both headquartered in Connecticut OpenTable is based in San Francisco and Rentalcars.com is located in Manchester UK. Additional offices and data centers are located in the US UK Switzerland the Netherlands Germany Singapore and Hong Kong.

Sales and Marketing

Booking Holdings aggressively promotes its brands online relying on internet search engine (mostly Google) keyword purchases referrals from meta-search sites and travel research websites affiliate programs banner and pop-up advertisements and email campaigns to boost its business. The company is one of Google's biggest search marketing customers.

It spent $4.4 billion on performance marketing in 2018 compared to $4.1 billion and $3.5 billion the prior two years. Brand marketing which is a specific focus for the company increased to $509 million in 2018 compared to $435 million and $327 million in 2017 and 2016 respectively.

Financial Performance

Booking Holdings' annual revenue has grown more than 70% since 2014 thanks to the rising popularity of the online travel booking business. The company is also immensely profitable consistently posting profit margins of 20% or above.

In fiscal 2018 the company saw its sales hit $14.5 billion up 15% from the prior year. Gross bookings increased 14% resulting in solid growth across agency merchant and advertising and other revenue.

Net income jumped 71% that year compared to 2017 on revenue growth as well as a lower income tax expense related to the Tax Act of 2017 and the Netherlands Innovation Box Tax.

Cash at the end of 2018 was $2.6 billion an increase of $82 million from the prior year. Cash from operations contributed $5.3 billion to the coffers while investing activities added $2.2 billion from proceeds on the sale of investments. Financing activities used $7.4 billion primarily for a stock repurchase program.

Strategy

Booking Holdings' brands have historically operated independently of each other but the company is increasingly focused on bringing the brands together. The idea is to offer a full suite of travel services that can enable cross-selling and upselling opportunities before during and after travel. As an example in 2018 it began operating the Rentalcars.com business as part of Booking.com to provide transportation services to customers who made accommodation reservations through the namesake site. In addition Kayak leadership has taken responsibility for OpenTable and Agoda and Priceline are working more closely together.

Other elements of the company's strategy include a focus on the fast-growing Asian market (Booking Holdings invested some $500 million in Chinese ride-hailing firm DiDi Chuxing in 2018) and growing merchant revenue (which is paid by travelers). It has also indicated a continued interest in strategic acquisitions which is how it built itself into one of the world's leading online travel service giants.

Mergers and Acquisitions

In 2019 Booking Holdings acquired Washington DC-based Venga which operates a guest management platform for restaurants and other businesses. The business will improve the offerings of OpenTable for its more than 51000 restaurant partners.

The company purchased local activities software provider FareHarbor based in Denver Colorado in 2018. The software helps local tours and attractions bring their businesses online.

Company Background

Priceline founder Jay Walker launched a string of ventures before making the leap into e-commerce. In 1994 he founded Walker Digital an entrepreneurial think tank formed to develop business models that could germinate into new companies.

In 1996 Walker Digital found the impetus that would drive Priceline: Each day major airlines have more than 500000 empty seats. Walker's team reasoned that if the airlines were offered even a discounted price for these empty seats they'd jump at the chance to cut their losses. Based on that premise Walker Digital developed a "name your price" system and founded Priceline in 1997.

The company went public with a chart-busting IPO in 1999.

In April 2014 the company changed its name from Priceline.com to The Priceline Group to better reflect the growth of its business and all of its subsidiaries and brands including Booking.com priceline.com KAYAK OpenTable and others. Four years later it changed its name again — to Booking Holdings — reflecting its most important brand.

HISTORY

Priceline founder Jay Walker launched a string of ventures before making the leap into e-commerce. In 1994 he founded Walker Digital an entrepreneurial think tank formed to develop business models that could germinate into new companies.

In 1996 Walker Digital found the impetus that would drive Priceline: Each day major airlines have more than 500000 empty seats. Walker's team reasoned that if the airlines were offered even a discounted price for these empty seats they'd jump at the chance to cut their losses. Based on that premise Walker Digital developed a "name your price" system and founded Priceline in 1997.

The company launched its airfare service in 1998 and obtained financing from General Atlantic Partners and Paul Allen's Vulcan Ventures (now called Vulcan Northwest). That year it expanded into hotel reservations and added a car-buying service. Richard Braddock became chairman and CEO in 1998.

Priceline added home financing services to its offerings in 1999. The company went public with a chart-busting IPO later that year. Priceline also launched a rental car service. Branching into the retail arena it licensed its technology to WebHouse Club for use in selling grocery products. The company sued Microsoft in 1999 claiming that company's Expedia unit's name-your-own-price hotel reservation service violated Priceline's patent.

In 2000 the company licensed its business model to several international ventures including General Atlantic Partners' Priceline.com Europe (headed by Dennis Malamatinas former Burger King CEO) SOFTBANK's Priceline.com Japan (a deal that was later cancelled) MyPrice in Australia and New Zealand (also cancelled) and Asian conglomerate Hutchinson Whampoa. In collaboration

with Alliance Capital (now AllianceBernstein) Priceline created subsidiary pricelinemortgage to act as mortgage broker.

Daniel Schulman became CEO later that year. Jay Walker resigned as vice chairman at the end of 2000 after taking on the role of CEO at Walker Digital. After deciding it would probably never be profitable WebHouse Club shut down ending Priceline's foray into grocery sales. Known for its splashy ads Priceline dumped pop icon William Shatner as its TV spokesperson in favor of Sex and the City star Sarah Jessica Parker. (Shatner returned in 2002.) Later that year the company fired Schulman and reappointed Braddock as CEO.

In 2002 the company joined with National Leisure Group to offer cruises from its website. Later that year Priceline purchased the assets of discount travel site Lowestfare.com. It also announced plans to sell cars under a marketing agreement with Autobytel. In late 2002 Braddock passed his CEO responsibilities to president Jeffery Boyd. (Braddock remained as chairman.)

A handful of new international destinations (Australia Japan Indonesia Malaysia South Korea Taiwan) was added in 2003 to Priceline's hotel reservation service. In April 2004 chairman Richard Braddock (former president of Citicorp and one of the last remaining high-profile board members) resigned from the company. Director Ralph Bahna was then named chairman. The following month Priceline acquired most of Travelweb.com. That September it bought Active Hotels of Britain for about $161 million in cash. In December 2004 Priceline acquired the remaining stake in Travelweb for about $4 million.

EXECUTIVES

Ceo Priceline.com, Brett Keller, age 51
Evp General Counsel And Corporate Secretary, Peter J. Millones, age 49, $330,000 total compensation
Ceo, Glenn D. Fogel, age 57, $315,000 total compensation
Svp Cfo And Chief Accounting Officer, Daniel J. Finnegan, age 56, $315,000 total compensation
Ceo Agoda.com, Robert Rosenstein, age 52
Ceo Kayak, Steve Hafner
President And Ceo Booking.com, Gillian Tans, age 48, $498,356 total compensation
Ceo Rentalcars.com, Ian Brown
Ceo Opentable Inc., Christa Quarles
Senior Vice President Of It Operations Of Priceline.com, Ken Jones
Vice President Associate General Counsel, Brian Macdonald
Senior Vice President Global Infrastructure, Glen Dalgleish
Chairman, Jeffery H. (Jeff) Boyd, age 62
Board Member, Craig Rydin
Board Member, Tim Armstrong
Board Member, Mirian Graddick-weir
Board Member, Nicholas J Read
Auditors: DELOITTE & TOUCHE LLP

LOCATIONS

HQ: Booking Holdings Inc
800 Connecticut Avenue, Norwalk, CT 06854
Phone: 203 299-8000   **Fax:** 203 595-0160
Web: www.bookingholdings.com

2018 Sales

	$ mil.	% of total
The Netherlands	11,094	76
US	1,626	11
Other	1,807	13
Total	**14,527**	**100**

PRODUCTS/OPERATIONS

2018 Sales

	$ mil.	% of total
Agency	10,480	72
Merchant	2,987	21
Advertising and other	1,060	7
Total	**14,527**	**100**

Selected Products

Airline tickets
Cruises
Hotel rooms
Rental cars
Restaurant reservations
Vacation packages

Selected Brands

agoda.com
Booking.com
KAYAK
OpenTable
priceline.com
rentalcars.com

COMPETITORS

Airbnb	Facebook
Alibaba Group	Google
Amazon.com	Hotwire Inc.
American Express	Orbitz Worldwide
Apple Inc.	Travelocity
BCD Travel	TripAdvisor
Carlson Wagonlit	Yelp
Expedia	

HISTORICAL FINANCIALS

Company Type: Public

Income Statement				FYE: December 31
	REVENUE ($ mil.)	NET INCOME ($ mil.)	NET PROFIT MARGIN	EMPLOYEES
12/18	14,527	3,998	27.5%	24,500
12/17	12,681	2,340	18.5%	22,900
12/16	10,743	2,134	19.9%	18,500
12/15	9,223	2,551	27.7%	15,500
12/14	8,441	2,421	28.7%	12,700
Annual Growth	**14.5%**	**13.4%**		**17.9%**

2018 Year-End Financials

Debt ratio: 38.12%	No. of shares (mil.): 45
Return on equity: 39.89%	Dividends
Cash ($ mil.): 2,624	Yield: —
Current ratio: 2.36	Payout: —
Long-term debt ($ mil.): 8,649	Market value ($ mil.): 78,597

	STOCK PRICE ($) FY Close	P/E High/Low	PER SHARE ($) Earnings	Dividends	Book Value
12/18	1,722.42	26 19	83.26	0.00	192.52
12/17	1,737.74	43 31	46.86	0.00	232.31
12/16	1,466.06	37 23	42.65	0.00	199.64
12/15	1,274.95	29 20	49.45	0.00	177.29
12/14	1,140.21	30 22	45.67	0.00	164.96
Annual Growth	**10.9%**	**— —**	**16.2%**	**—**	**3.9%**

Booz Allen Hamilton Holding Corp.

Booz Allen Hamilton is a leading contractor for US Government defense and intelligence departments assisting in the fields of cyber security and intelligence operations. The firm which acts as prime contractor in nearly every instance generates billions in sales each year from the delivery of highly technical skills to the Department of Defense the National Security Agency the IRS and nearly every cabinet-level US Government department. It increasingly works with foreign governments and commercial clients as well. Investment firm The Carlyle Group owns a majority interest in the consulting firm which was founded in 1914. Booz Allen keeps a low profile despite its size but attracted unwanted attention in 2013 as the employer of whistleblower Edward Snowden.

Operations

Booz Allen Hamilton typically works under three contract types. Cost-Reimbursable Contracts which account for about 55% of revenue provide for the payment of costs racked up during the completion of a contract (up to a pre-determined ceiling) plus a fee. Under Time-and-Materials Contracts which account for around 25% of Booz Allen's sales the company bills its clients for each labor hour and material costs and out-of-pocket expenses. Under Fixed-Price Contacts which also account for 25% of sales the company works to a pre-determined price.

Booz Allen carries out contracts ranging from sub-$1 million to $10 million plus; the latter category accounts for the largest chunk of its sales at roughly 35% of the total.

Geographic Reach

Booz Allen's headquarters are located in McLean Virginia. The firm also has offices in Annapolis Junction Rockville and Laurel Maryland; San Diego California; Herndon Arlington and Alexandria Virginia; Charleston South Carolina; and Washington D.C.

Sales and Marketing

The majority (95%) of Booz Allen Hamilton's revenue comes from the US government. Defense clients including the US Army Navy/Marine Corps Air Force and Joint Combatant Commands account for around 45% of Booz Allen Hamilton's revenue. Intelligence agencies including the NSA National Geospatial-Intelligence Agency and National Reconnaissance Office account for another 25% of sales. Its other customers are mostly civil government clients (energy and environment financial services health homeland security) and global commercial clients (non-US governments and commercial entities in the Middle East North Africa and the Asia/Pacific region).

Financial Performance

Booz Allen Hamilton's revenue has grown strongly over the last five years. Profits are likewise trending upward albeit less predictably. In fiscal 2019 (ended March 31) the company's sales grew 9% to $6.7 billion — its best result as a public company. Booz Allen continues to benefit from continued increases in client demand allowing it to increase headcount and thus client staff labor. An increase in billable expenses provided an additional boost.

Net income rose 39% to $418.5 million in fiscal 2019 thanks to higher revenue and improved contract performance in addition to an $11.2 million expense reduction relating to its long-term disability plan liability.

Booz Allen's cash on hand fell $3.0 million during fiscal 2019 ending the year at $284.0 million. The company's operations generated $499.6 million while its investing activities used $89.2 million and its financing used $413.4 million. Booz Allen's main cash uses in fiscal 2019 were dividends and share repurchases ($367 million together) capital expenditures and net debt repayments.

Strategy

Booz Allen Hamilton's growth strategy is based on increasing the technical content of its services expanding in the commercial and international markets innovating on its capabilities and estab-

lishing a broad network of external partners and alliances. The strategy has been vindicated by strengthening backlog which reached new heights in 2019 and headcount growth in technical disciplines such as systems development cyber and analytics. Investment areas include machine intelligence and directed energy (high-energy lasers or microwaves) which are areas that the company expects to create integrated capabilities and drive demand in the long term. It also makes targeted acquisitions to expand capabilities.

HISTORY

Edwin Booz graduated from Northwestern University in 1914 with degrees in economics and psychology and started a statistical analysis firm in Chicago. After serving in the army during WWI he returned to his firm renamed Edwin Booz Surveys. In 1925 Booz hired his first full-time assistant George Fry and in 1929 he hired a second James Allen. By then the company had a long list of clients including U.S. Gypsum the Chicago Tribune and Montgomery Ward which was losing a retail battle with Sears Roebuck and Co.

In 1935 Carl Hamilton joined the partnership and a year later it was renamed Booz Fry Allen & Hamilton. The firm prospered well into the next decade by providing advice based on "independence that enables us to say plainly from the outside what cannot always be said safely from within" according to a company brochure.

During WWII the firm worked increasingly on government and military contracts. Fry opposed the pursuit of such work for consultants and left in 1942. The firm was renamed Booz Allen & Hamilton. Hamilton died in 1946 and the following year Booz retired (he died in 1951) leaving Allen as chairman. He successfully steered the firm into lucrative postwar work for clients such as Johnson Wax RCA and the US Air Force.

A separate company Booz Allen Applied Research Inc. (BAARINC) was formed in 1955 for technical and government consulting including missile and weaponry work as well as consulting with NASA. By the end of the decade Time had dubbed Booz Allen "the world's largest most prestigious management consultant firm." The partnership was incorporated as a private company in 1962 and in 1967 commissioner Pete Rozelle requested its services for the merger of the National Football League and American Football League.

When Allen retired in 1970 Charlie Bowen became the new chairman and the company went public. However as the economy stalled during the energy crisis spending for consultants plunged. Jim Farley replaced Bowen in 1975 and the company was taken private again in 1976. A turnaround was engineered and the firm was soon helping Chrysler through its 1979 bailout and developing strategies for the breakup of AT&T in 1984.

Booz Allen again experienced trouble in the 1980s after Farley instituted a competition to select his successor. Michael McCullough was eventually chosen in 1984 but the 10-month election process turned into a dogfight that pitted partner against partner taking an enormous toll on morale. McCullough began restructuring the firm along industry lines creating a department store of services in an industry characterized by boutique houses. The turmoil was too much and by 1988 nearly a third of the partners had quit.

William Stasior became chairman in 1991 and reorganized Booz Allen yet again splitting it down public and private sector lines. Allen died in 1992 the same year the firm moved to McLean Virginia. The company began privatization work in the former Soviet Union and in Eastern Europe in 1992 and continued to emphasize government business

including contracts with the IRS (1995) for technology modernization and with the General Services Administration (1996) to provide technical and management support for all federal telecommunications users.

In 1998 the company won a 10-year $200 million contract with the US Defense Department to establish a scientific and technical data warehouse. Ralph Shrader was appointed CEO in early 1999; Stasior retired as chairman later that year. Booz Allen acquired Scandinavian consulting firm Carta in 1999 and formed a venture capital firm for startups with Lehman Brothers in 2000. The company announced in late 2000 that it would spin off Aestix its e-commerce business but reconsidered amid a general economic slowdown and hostile IPO market. (The unit was integrated back into Booz Allen in 2002.)

Booz Allen saw an increase in work related to defense and national security after the terrorist attacks of September 11 2001. Engagements included work related to the reconstruction of Iraq (as a subcontractor on telecommunications projects managed by Lucent) and in 2003 Booz Allen was awarded a contract from the US Health Resources and Services Administration to help establish and operate a bioterrorism technical support center.

In 2008 Booz Allen spun off its commercial consulting business as an independent firm Booz & Company. The spinoff was part of a transaction in which investment firm The Carlyle Group acquired a controlling interest in the Booz Allen's government-related consulting business which retained the Booz Allen name.

Striving to alleviate debt Booz Allen launched an initial public offering on the New York Stock Exchange in November 2010.

EXECUTIVES

Executive Vice President And Chief People Officer, Betty Thompson

Evp Middle East And North Africa (mena), Nabih Maroun

Evp Digital Solutions, Gary D. Labovich

President And Ceo, Horacio D. Rozanski, age 51, $1,437,500 total compensation

Evp Justice And Homeland Security Business, Thad W. Allen

Evp Directed Energy Innovation, Henry A. (Trey) Obering

Evp Cfo And Treasurer, Lloyd W. Howell, age 57, $1,000,000 total compensation

Evp Chief Administrative Officer (cao) And Chief Information Security Officer (ciso), Joseph W. (Joe) Mahaffee, age 61, $765,000 total compensation

Evp Strategic Transformation, Michael M. (Mike) Thomas

Evp Homeland Security And Transportation, Patrick F. Peck, age 61

Evp Client Service Officer (cso) Justice Homeland Security And Transportation (jht), Fred K. Blackburn

Evp Digital Solutions, Gary C. Cubbage

Vp, Karen M. Dahut, age 55, $1,000,000 total compensation

Evp, Maria Darby

Evp Joint Combatant Command, Judith H. (Judi) Dotson

Evp Infrastructure And Military Health, Laurene (Laurie) Gallo

Evp Engineering And Science And C4isr Crosscut, Patricia Goforth

Evp Defense Business, Tom Greenspon

Vp, Gregory Harrison

Vp, David Kletter

Evp International Business, Christopher Ling

Evp Defense And Intelligence Group, Joseph (Joe) Logue, age 54, $1,250,000 total compensation

Evp Innovation Service Officer (iso) And Cyber Functional Service Officer (fso), Angela M. (Angie) Messer
Vp, Anthony (Tony) Mitchell
Vp, Susan L. Penfield
Evp Energy Business, Gary Rahl
Evp And Lead U.s. Defense And Military Intelligence And Operations, Joseph F. (Joe) Sifer
Evp Defense And Intelligence, Ted Sniffin
Evp Commercial Cyber Business, William (Bill) Stewart
Evp And Chief Personnel Officer, Elizabeth M. (Betty) Thompson, age 64
Evp Strategic Innovation Group (sig), Gregory G. (Greg) Wenzel
Evp Cyber Business, Christopher Pierce
Vp, Joan A. Dempsey
Evp Civil Health Business, Kristine Martin Anderson
Evp Chief Legal Officer And Secretary, Nancy J. Laben, age 57
Vp And Cio, Kevin Winter
Evp Energy Chemicals And Utilities, Walid Fayad
Evp Middle East And North Africa, Ramez Shehadi
Evp Command Control Communications Computers Intelligence Surveillance And Reconnaissance (c4isr), Steve Soules
Evp Army Market, Brian M. McKeon
Evp Digital Practice Middle East And North Africa (mena), Raymond Khoury
Vice President And Group Administrative Officer Defense And Intelligence Market, Joan Wolfle
Vice President, Kevin Vigilante
Senior Vice President, Charles S Hamilton
Senior Vice President Citizen Services, Shannon Fitzgerald
Vice President, Theodore Kraemer
Senior Vice President And Digital Analytics And Strategy Lead, Julie Mcpherson
Vice President Security Sector, Patricia Hanback
Vice President, Khalid Syed
Vice President Army Business, Jay Dodd
Vice President, Ralph Lawrence
Vice President, Lutfi Zakhour
Vice President, Adham Sleiman
Vice President, Donald Busson
Senior Vice President And Executive, Booz A Hamilton
Vice President Data Solutions And Machine Intelligence, Bryce Pippert
Vice President, Chris Pierce
Vice President Sales And Marketing, Scott Barr
Vice President, Ken Wiegand
Vice President Facility Infrastructure And Environment, Bob Miller
Vice President Technical Services, Felix Yao
Vice President Civil And Commercial Market, Marlene Aquino
Vice President Defense Market, Brian Pickerall
Vice President Of Information Technology, Joe Sifer
Vice President, John Druitt
Vice President, Scott Welles
Vice President, Rob Silverman
Vice President Defense Market, James Gibbons
Senior Vice President, Ken Mills
Executive Vice President Portfolio Strategic Projects, Matthew Calderone
Vice President Human Capital Management, Abe Zwany
Vice President And Lead Contracting Officer, Linda Asher
Senior Vice President Global Defense Group And Crosscut Market Strategy, Andrea Inserra
Vice President Enterprise Cloud Computing Business, Munjeet Singh
Senior Vice President U.s. Government Classified And National Geospatial Intelligence Agency, Kim Lynch
Vice President Digital Transformation Programs And Opportunities, Ralph Wade

Vice President Civil Health Business, John Peterson
Senior Vice President, Robert Smith
Vice President, Mark Hoffman
Senior Vice President And Cyber And Engineering Lead, Brad Medairy
Senior Vice President Nextgen Finance Modernization (ngfm) Program, Tim Lawrence
Vice President Civil Health Business, Travis Burd
Vice President Energy Environment And Infrastructure, Johnny Ayoub
Executive Vice President U.s. Commercial, Bill Phelps
Vice President Real Estate And Facilities Operations, Deane Edelman
Senior Vice President Technology Solutions, Natalie Givans
Vice President, Vincent Simpson
Vice President Law Enforcement, Bob Sogegian
Vice President Banking And Fintech Business Mena, Charles Habak
Senior Vice President Acquisition And Sustainment Efforts, Dick Johnson
Vice President Data Science And Advanced Analytics, Ezmeralda Khalil Sager
Vp And Corporate Group Administrative Officer, Jennifer Wagner
Vice President Air Force Military Intelligence And Cyber Business, Kim Bird
Senior Vice President Finance Energy And Economic Development, Mark Gamis
Senior Vice President Operations Practice Mena, Nadim Batri
Senior Vice President Health Business, Richard Crowe
Senior Vice President U.s. Air Force Clients, Rick Holley
Vice President Navy And Marine Corps Headquarters And Operations, Steve Moore
Vice President Finance Energy And Economic Development, Terence Mandable
Executive Vice President U.s. Navy And Marine Corps, Thomas Crabtree
Senior Vice President Army Market, Bill Schuler
Senior Vice President Cf And Ao, Sam Strickland
Senior Vice President, Fred Cipriano
Vice President, Chris Ellis
Senior Vice President And Director Of Center Cer, Wallave Angela
Vice President, Sam Porgess
Chairman, Ralph W. Shrader, age 75
Secretary, Jennifer Stingl
Auditors: Ernst & Young LLP

LOCATIONS

HQ: Booz Allen Hamilton Holding Corp.
8283 Greensboro Drive, McLean, VA 22102
Phone: 703 902-5000
Web: www.boozallen.com

PRODUCTS/OPERATIONS

2018 sales

	$ mil.	% of total
US Government		
Defense Clients	3,114	47
Intelligence Clients	1,566	23
Civil Clients	1,761	26
Global Commercial Clients	261	4
Total	**6,704**	**100**

2018 sales

	% of total
Prime contractor	92
Sub-contractor	8
Total	**100**

Selected Markets Served

Civil government
  Benefits and entitlements
  Federal finance
  International development and diplomacy
Defense
  Air Force
  Army
  Joint staff and combatant commands
  Navy and Marine Corps
  Office of the Secretary of Defense and defense agencies
  Space
Energy
Environment
Health
  Health informatics
  Health not-for-profit/nongovernmental organizations
  International public health
  US public health
Homeland security
Intelligence
Law enforcement
Not-for-profit/nongovernmental organizations
Transportation
  Aviation infrastructure
  Highways and automotive technology
  Passenger rail and mass transit

Selected Practice Areas

Assurance and resilience
Economic and business analysis
Information technology
Modeling and simulation
Organization and strategy
Supply chain and logistics
Systems engineering and integration

COMPETITORS

A.T. Kearney	IBM
Accenture	L3 Technologies
BAE SYSTEMS	Leidos
Bain & Company	Lockheed Martin
Boeing	MAXIMUS
Boston Consulting	ManTech
CACI International	McKinsey & Company
CSRA	Northrop Grumman
Capgemini	PA Consulting
Computer Sciences Corp.	PRTM Management
Deloitte Consulting	Raytheon
General Dynamics	SAIC
HP Enterprise Services	Unisys

HISTORICAL FINANCIALS

Company Type: Public

Income Statement

FYE: March 31

	REVENUE ($ mil.)	NET INCOME ($ mil.)	NET PROFIT MARGIN	EMPLOYEES
03/19	6,704	418	6.2%	26,100
03/18	6,171	305	4.9%	24,600
03/17	5,804	252	4.4%	23,300
03/16	5,405	294	5.4%	22,600
03/15	5,274	232	4.4%	22,500
Annual Growth	6.2%	15.8%	—	3.8%

2019 Year-End Financials

Debt ratio: 45.92%	No. of shares (mil.): 140
Return on equity: 68.05%	Dividends
Cash ($ mil.): 283	Yield: 0.0%
Current ratio: 1.44	Payout: 27.4%
Long-term debt ($ mil.): 1,701	Market value ($ mil.): 8,141

	STOCK PRICE ($) FY Close	P/E High/Low		PER SHARE ($) Earnings	Dividends	Book Value
03/19	58.14	20	13	2.91	0.80	4.82
03/18	38.72	19	15	2.05	0.70	3.87
03/17	35.39	23	16	1.67	0.62	3.85
03/16	30.28	16	12	1.94	0.54	2.76
03/15	28.94	19	13	1.52	1.46	1.25
Annual Growth	19.1%			— 17.6%	(14.0%)	40.1%

BorgWarner Inc

If suburbanites need four-wheel-drive vehicles to turbocharge their urban drive that's OK with BorgWarner. The company is a leading maker of engine and drivetrain products for the world's major automotive manufacturers. Products include turbochargers air pumps timing chain systems four-wheel-drive and all-wheel-drive transfer cases (primarily for light trucks and SUVs) and transmission components. Its largest customers include Volkswagen Ford and Daimler. The company nets more than 75% of its sales from outside the US.

Operations

BorgWarner's two operating segments are Engine Products (more than 60% of total sales) and drivetrain products (nearly 40% of sales). The Engine division manufactures products to optimize engines for fuel efficiency reduce emissions and enhance performance and includes turbochargers electric boosting systems engine timing systems ignition systems air management and cooling and controls. Its Remy business makes starter motors alternators and hybrid electric motors for OEMs. The Drivetrain unit provides automotive transmission components all-wheel drive torque transfer systems and rotating electrical devices. Turbochargers for light vehicles is the company's largest product line representing around 30% of sales.

Key divisions and units include BorgWarner TorqTransfer Systems BorgWarner Transmission Systems BorgWarner Morse TEC and BorgWarner BERU Systems. BorgWarner also operates seven joint ventures located in Japan China India and South Korea including NSK-Warner KK a leading producer of friction plates and one-way clutches in Japan and China.

Geographic Reach

BorgWarner operates more than 60 manufacturing and technical facilities in some 20 countries (including more than a dozen in the US and about half a dozen each in Germany China and South Korea).

Europe is by far BorgWarner's largest market: Germany accounts for roughly 20% of total sales; Hungary accounts for around 10% and other Europe 15%. The US generates around 25% of its sales and South Korea and China together represent some 25%.

Sales and Marketing

BorgWarner markets its products to OEMs of light vehicles (passenger cars sport-utility vehicles vans and light trucks) through separate sales teams for its two product divisions. Volkswagen and Ford each generate around 15% of the company's overall sales. Other key customers include Chrysler Nissan and General Motors.

Financial Performance

Aside from a misfire in 2015 BorgWarner's Engine and Drivetrain revenue has been turbocharged in recent years.

In fiscal 2017 revenue increased 8% to $9.8 billion due to higher sales of light vehicle turbochargers thermal products engine timing systems and stronger international commercial vehicle markets. In the Drivetrain segment BorgWarner sold more all-wheel drive systems and transmission components.

Net income rebounded in 2017 to $439.9 million after an $878.3 million asbestos-related lawsuit charge dragged 2016 net income down to just $118.5 million. Despite the improvement profitability remained below the levels seen in 2013-15 due to restructuring and merger and acquisition-related expenses.

Cash from operations increased 14% to $1.2 billion due to higher earnings.

Strategy

BorgWarner's product strategy puts it in a position to capitalize on growth in hybrid and electric vehicles while continuing to grow in the steadily declining combustion market. Its combustion products are increasingly being used on hybrids: Turbochargers with hybrid applications account for more than 10% of its order backlog. Its eBooster system improved the performance of both combustion vehicles and hybrids and it will supply the FUSO eCanter truck — the world's first all-electric light-duty truck — with its HV250 electric motor and eGearDrive transmission.

The company also grows via regular acquisitions including Sevcon in 2017 and Remy in 2016.

Mergers and Acquisitions

BorgWarner has been generating additional revenue over the years through the use of acquisitions.

In 2017 BorgWarner acquired Sevcon a British producer of electrification technologies with global operations. Its products include motor controllers battery chargers and uninterrupted power source system for electric and hybrid vehicles industrial medical and telecom applications. The purchase price was $10 million.

In a milestone transaction in late 2015 the company acquired Remy International for $1.2 billion. Remy is a global producer of rotating electrical components with key technologies and operations spanning 10 countries. The deal enhanced BorgWarner's rapidly developing powertrain electrification technology line.It sold the Remy light vehicle aftermarket business a year later.

HISTORY

BorgWarner traces its roots to the 1928 merger of major Chicago auto parts companies Borg & Beck (clutches) Warner Gear (transmissions) Mechanics Universal Joint and Marvel Carburetor. The newly named Borg-Warner Corporation quickly began buying other companies including Ingersoll Steel & Disc (agricultural blades and discs) and Norge (refrigerators).

EXECUTIVES

Vp General Counsel And Secretary, John J. Gasparovic, age 61, $477,250 total compensation
Vp; President And General Manager Borgwarner Transmissions Systems, Robin Kendrick, age 54, $406,250 total compensation
Vp Marketing Public Relations Communications And Government Affairs, Scott D. Gallett, age 53
Evp And Cfo, Ronald T. (Ron) Hundzinski, age 60, $665,750 total compensation
President And Ceo, James R. Verrier, age 56, $1,245,000 total compensation
Vp And President And General Manager Borgwarner Emissions Systems, Brady D. Ericson, age 47, $415,000 total compensation
Vp And President And General Manager Borgwarner Morse Systems, Joseph F. Fadool, age 52, $416,250 total compensation
Vp; President And General Manager Borgwarner Turbo Systems, Frédéric B. Lissalde, age 51, $606,630 total compensation
Vp And President And General Manager Borgwarner Powerdrive Systems, Stefan Demmerle, age 54, $442,750 total compensation
Vice President And Treasurer, Jan Bertsch
Vice President Of Operations, Todd Bennington
Vp Global Supply Management, Rob Deni
Vice President And Chief Compliance Officer, Laurene Horiszny
Vp Drivetrain It, Sandra Short

Vice President Global Supply Chain Management, Thomas Babineau
Vice President Global Supply Chain Management, Marco Caputo
Vice President Information Technology, Bernd Ruff
Vice President Human Resources, Shelley Bridarolli
Vice President And Treasurer, Tom Mcgill
Vice President Finance Emission Systems, Frederic Vaillant
Executive Vice President And Chief Financial Officer, Kevin Nowlan
Executive Vice President, Felecia Pryor
Chairman, Alexis P. Michas, age 61
Board Member, John McKernan
Secretary, Greg Dziegielewski
Board Member, Vicki Sato
Auditors: PricewaterhouseCoopers LLP

LOCATIONS

HQ: BorgWarner Inc
  3850 Hamlin Road, Auburn Hills, MI 48326
Phone: 248 754-9200
Web: www.borgwarner.com

2017 Sales

	$ mil.	% of total
United States	2,280	23
Europe		
Germany	1,652	17
Hungary	655	7
Other Europe	1,427	15
China	1,560	16
South Korea	877	9
Mexico	920	9
Other regions	425	4
Total	**9,799**	**100**

PRODUCTS/OPERATIONS

2017 Sales

	$ mil.	% of total
Engine	6,061	62
Drivetrain	3,790	38
Elimination	(52.4)	-
Total	**9,799**	**100**

Selected Products

Engine Group
  Air-control valves
  Chain tensioners and snubbers
  Complete engine induction systems
  Complex solenoids and multi-function modules
  Crankshaft and camshaft sprockets
  Diesel cabin heaters
  Diesel cold starting systems (glow plugs and instant starting systems)
  Electric air pumps
  Engine hydraulic pumps
  Exhaust gas-recirculation (EGR) coolers modules tubes and valves
  Fan clutches
  Fans and fan drives
  Front-wheel and four-wheel-drive chain and timing-chain systems
  High-temperature sensors (for exhaust gas aftertreatment systems)
  Ignition coils
  Intake manifolds
  On-off fan drives
  Single-function solenoids
  Throttle bodies
  Throttle position sensors
  Tire pressure sensors
  Transfer cases
  Turbochargers
Drivetrain Group
  Four-wheel-drive and all-wheel-drive transfer cases
  Friction plates
  One-way clutches
  Torque converter lock-up clutches
  Transmission bands

Selected Joint Ventures

BERU Korea Co. Ltd. (51% South Korea ignition coils and pumps)

Borg-Warner Shenglong (Ningbo) Co. Ltd. (70% China fans and fan drives)

BorgWarner TorqTransfer Systems Beijing Co. Ltd. (80% China transfer cases)

BorgWarner Transmission Systems Korea Inc. (60% South Korea transmission components)

BorgWarner United Transmission Systems Co. Ltd. (66% China transmission components)

BorgWarner-Vikas Emissions Systems India Private Limited (60% India EGR coolers)

Divgi-Warner Limited (60% India transfer cases and automatic locking hubs)

SeohanWarner Turbo Systems Ltd. (71% South Korea turbochargers)

COMPETITORS

American Axle & Manufacturing	Magna Powertrain
DENSO	Meritor
Dana	Mitsubishi Heavy Industries
Delphi Automotive Systems	Modine Manufacturing
GKN	NGK SPARK PLUG
Honeywell International	Renold
IHI Corp.	Robert Bosch
JTEKT	Schaeffler
Kolbenschmidt Pierburg	Tsubaki Nakashima
	Valeo
	Visteon

HISTORICAL FINANCIALS

Company Type: Public

Income Statement				FYE: December 31
	REVENUE ($ mil.)	NET INCOME ($ mil.)	NET PROFIT MARGIN	EMPLOYEES
12/18	10,529	930	8.8%	30,000
12/17	9,799	439	4.5%	29,000
12/16	9,071	118	1.3%	27,000
12/15	8,023	609	7.6%	30,000
12/14	8,305	655	7.9%	22,000
Annual Growth	6.1%	9.1%	—	8.1%

2018 Year-End Financials

Debt ratio: 20.93%
Return on equity: 23.44%
Cash ($ mil.): 739
Current ratio: 1.59
Long-term debt ($ mil.): 1,940

No. of shares (mil.): 208
Dividends
  Yield: 1.9%
  Payout: 15.3%
Market value ($ mil.): 7,233

	STOCK PRICE ($) FY Close	P/E High/Low		PER SHARE ($) Earnings	Dividends	Book Value
12/18	34.74	13	7	4.44	0.68	20.29
12/17	51.09	27	18	2.08	0.59	17.63
12/16	39.44	79	50	0.55	0.53	15.16
12/15	43.23	23	14	2.70	0.52	16.20
12/14	54.95	23	17	2.86	0.51	15.97
Annual Growth	(10.8%)	—	—	11.6%	7.5%	6.2%

Boston Private Financial Holdings, Inc.

Boston Private Financial Holdings (BPFH) is a holding company for firms engaged in wealth management and private banking including Boston Private Bank & Trust which operates branches in New England New York Los Angeles and the San Francisco Bay Area. (The bank sold its branches in the Pacific Northwest in 2013.) BPFH also owns four other wealth advisory and investment man-

agement firms. The company offers private banking wealth advisory investment management deposits and lending and trust services to wealthy individuals corporations and institutional clients. All told BPFH and its affiliates have more than $30 billion in managed or advised assets.

Operations

In addition to Boston Private Bank & Trust Co. BPFH's other affiliates include: investment advisory firms Anchor Capital Advisors and Dalton Greiner Hartman Maher & Co.; wealth managers Bingham Osborn & Scarborough and KLS Professional Advisors Group; as well as newly-acquired Banyan Partners a registered investment advisor. BPFH sold its majority-owned affiliate Davidson Trust Co. (DTC) in 2012. DTC was part of the holding company's wealth advisory business.

Financial Performance

Boston Private Financial Holdings (BPFH) reported revenue of $339.5 million in 2013 an increase of less than 1% versus 2012. The modest uptick was due to increased recurring fees from its investment management wealth advisory and private banking wealth management and trust businesses as well as other income and a gain on the sale of loans. Assets under management and advisory (AUM) increased 19% during 2013 due to $3.7 billion of market appreciation and $0.2 billion of net flows. All three of the BPFH's segments experienced gains in AUM.

Net income grew 32% in 2013 compared with 2012 to $70.5 million on a decline in interest expense on deposits partially offset by a 2% increase in average balance. The lower interest rate environment in the US has allowed the company's banking arm to lower interest rates on money markets accounts and certificates of deposit.

Strategy

Since its founding in 1987 Boston Private has had a voracious appetite for acquiring smaller trust companies private banks and wealth managers. While the firm put the brakes on its expansion and shifted strategies amid the economic recession. Indeed it divested about a half-dozen money management subsidiaries as way to raise capital and reduce risk. Also in 2011 the company consolidated its four banking charters into Boston Private Bank & Trust to simplify its structure and cut costs.

However with the economy and financial markets on the mend the company has resumed making acquisitions most recently to build its wealth management business.

Mergers and Acquisitions

In October 2014 Boston Private Bank & Trust Co. acquired Banyan Partners LLC an independent registered investment advisory firm based in Palm Beach Florida. With more than $4.5 billion in client assets Banyan has offices in Boston Miami Naples Atlanta Wisconsin Texas and California. The purchase furthered the bank's aim of expanding the reach and accelerating the development of its wealth management business.

In May 2013 Boston Private Bank & Trust sold three offices in the Pacific Northwest to focus on its banking business in California and New England. The bank recorded a $10.6 million pretax gain on the sale.

EXECUTIVES

Evp General Counsel Secretary And Chief Legal Officer, Margaret W. (Megan) Chambers, age 60, $360,000 total compensation
Evp Cfo And Chief Administrative Officer Boston Private Bank & Trust, Anne L. Randall
Ceo Private Banking Group; President Boston Private Bank & Trust Company, George G. Schwartz
Co-president Private Banking Group, James C. Brown
Evp Cfo And Chief Administrative Officer, David J. Kaye, age 55, $425,000 total compensation
Ceo; Ceo Boston Private Bank And Trust, Clayton G. (Clay) Deutsch, $675,000 total compensation
Evp And Chief Risk Officer, W. Timothy MacDonald, $350,000 total compensation
Ceo Boston Private Wealth Llc, Corey A. Griffin, $400,000 total compensation
Evp And Chief Human Resource Officer, Martha T. Higgins
President Boston Private Wealth Llc, Peter J. Raimondi
Co-president Private Banking Group, Torrance Childs
Evp Private Clients Group, Nicholas A.R. Hofer
Evp Commercial Banking Group, Robert J. Nentwig
Evp And Client Development Officer, Jacqueline S. Shoback
Svp And Chief Fiduciary Officer, Lynn Swenson
Assistant Vice President, Joe Lavigne
Senior Vice President Marketing, Allison Baird
Assistant Vice President Commercial Lending, Jonathan Willis
Vice President Manager Of Cred, Susan Tackitt
Senior Vice President, Mary Rohan
Vice President Residential Lending, Richard Little
Vice President Office Manager, Mark Connor
Senior Vice President Residential Lending, Rob Kinasewich
Vice President Commercial Real Estate, Andrew Garfinkle
Senior Vice President Northern California Deposit Sales Manager, John Delaney
Vice President And Residential Loan Officer, Maria Pineda
Vice President, William Massos
Senior Vice President Market Leader Residential Lending, Patrick Skovran
Vice President Certified Appraiser Residential Loan Officer, Rosa Amaya
Assistant Vice President Private Banking Relationship Officer, Ida Solari
Senior Vice President Venture And Private Equity Group West Coast Leader, Mark Shang
Vice President Commercial Banking, Sean Burke
Senior Vice President And Trust Officer, Jeanne Barrett
Senior Vice President Commercial Loan Officer Commercial Lending New England, George Carroll
Senior Vice President, Sherry Dewane
Executive Vice President General Counsel, Colleen Graham
Assistant Vice President, Gloria Stoneham
Vice President Chicago Territory, Scott Mortensen
Vice President, Peter Karp
Executive Vice President Human Resources, Pat Butler
Vice President Sales, Jeffrey Forbes
Vice President Of Real Estate, Sarah Abrams
Vice President Healthcare Life Sciences Solutions Sales, Jeff Forbes
Vice President Global Marketing, Lucian Lui
Vice President L1, Mark Hazel
Vice President Government Affairs, Theresa Pattara
Vice President Senior Project Manager, Ted Finnerty
Enterprise Architect Vice President, Christopher Green
Chairman, Stephen M. Waters, age 72
Board Member, Gloria Larson
Board Member, Mark Furlong
Board Member, Joseph Guyaux
Board Member, Kimberly Stevenson
Auditors: KPMG LLP

HQ: Boston Private Financial Holdings, Inc.
Ten Post Office Square, Boston, MA 02109
Phone: 617 912-1900
Web: www.bostonprivate.com

PRODUCTS/OPERATIONS

2015 Sales

	$ mil.	% of total
Interest and dividend income		
Loans	192	51
Mortgage-backed securities	10	3
Investment securities	9	2
Federal funds sold and other	1	1
Fees and other income		
Investment management & trust fees	45	12
Wealth advisory fees	50	14
Wealth management and trust fees	51	14
Other	13	3
Total	**374**	**100**

Selected Subsidiaries & Affiliates

Anchor Capital Advisors LLC
Bingham Osborn & Scarborough LLC
Boston Private Bank & Trust Company
Dalton Greiner Hartman Maher & Co. LLC
KLS Professional Advisors Group LLC

COMPETITORS

Bank of America	FMR
Brown Brothers	JPMorgan Chase
Harriman	Morgan Stanley
Central Bancorp	Sovereign Bank
Century Bancorp (MA)	TD Bank USA
Citigroup	TriState Capital
Citizens Financial	Wells Fargo
Group	

HISTORICAL FINANCIALS

Company Type: Public

Income Statement
FYE: December 31

	ASSETS ($ mil.)	NET INCOME ($ mil.)	INCOME AS % OF ASSETS	EMPLOYEES
12/18	8,494	80	0.9%	774
12/17	8,311	40	0.5%	925
12/16	7,970	71	0.9%	888
12/15	7,542	64	0.9%	890
12/14	6,797	68	1.0%	875
Annual Growth	5.7%	4.0%	—	(3.0%)

2018 Year-End Financials

Debt ratio: 1.25%	No. of shares (mil.): 83
Return on equity: 10.48%	Dividends
Cash ($ mil.): 127	Yield: 4.5%
Current ratio: —	Payout: 184.6%
Long-term debt ($ mil.): —	Market value ($ mil.): 884

	STOCK PRICE ($) FY Close	P/E High/Low	PER SHARE ($) Earnings	Dividends	Book Value
12/18	10.57	19 11	0.92	0.48	9.01
12/17	15.45	42 33	0.42	0.44	9.27
12/16	16.55	20 11	0.81	0.40	9.13
12/15	11.34	18 14	0.74	0.36	8.91
12/14	13.47	18 14	0.79	0.32	8.48
Annual Growth	(5.9%)	— —	—	3.9% 10.7%	1.5%

Boston Scientific Corp.

Boston Scientific makes medical supplies and devices used in interventional medical procedures. A leader in devices addressing heart conditions the firm focuses on manufacturing cardiovascular and cardiac rhythm management (CRM) products. It also makes devices used for electrophysiology endoscopy pain management (neuromodulation) urology and women's health. Its roughly 13000 diagnostic and treatment products — made in more than a dozen factories worldwide — include biopsy forceps catheters coronary and urethral stents defibrillators needles and pacemakers. Boston Scientific markets its products in about 130 countries but the US generates more than half of sales.

Operations

Boston Scientific operates in three primary segments: Cardiovascular Rhythm and Neuro and MedSurg.

Its largest segment Cardiovascular accounts for nearly 40% of annual revenues. That segment makes interventional cardiology products (coronary stents catheters guidewires) which account for more than 25% of the company's sales and peripheral intervention products (non-coronary vascular stents).

The Rhythm and Neuro segment (some 30% of revenue) makes implantable devices (pacemakers and implanted coronary defibrillators or ICDs) for cardiac rhythm management (20% of sales) as well as neuromodulation devices and electrophysiology devices.

The MedSurg segment (30% of revenue) makes devices for endoscopy (nearly 20% of sales) and urology and pelvic health. Endoscopy devices diagnose and treat pulmonary and gastrointestinal conditions through minimally invasive scopes and stent and needle systems.

Geographic Reach

Boston Scientific operates in around 40 countries and markets its products in some 130 nations around the world. Based in Marlborough Massachusetts it has seven manufacturing facilities in the US and nine manufacturing facilities abroad (in Ireland Costa Rica Malaysia Brazil Switzerland and Puerto Rico). The company also has physician training centers in France Germany Italy South Africa India Poland South Africa South Korea and Japan and it has research operations in China Costa Rica Germany India Ireland and Puerto Rico. It also has regional headquarters located in Singapore and France.

While the US is still Boston Scientific's largest single market international sales have grown to make up about 45% of total sales.

Sales and Marketing

Boston Scientific markets its products to some 35000 hospitals clinics outpatient facilities and medical offices around the world. In the US large group purchasing organizations (GPOs) hospital networks and other buying groups make up a significant portion of sales.

Boston Scientific markets products through direct forces in the US and European markets; it also uses dealers distributors and partners in certain countries.

Financial Performance

Boston Scientific's revenue has seen steady growth over the past five years increasing by 33% between 2014 and 2018. Net income has been in the black for the past three years (2016 2017 and 2018) after the company posted net losses in 2015 and 2014.

Revenue in 2018 climbed about 9% to some $9.8 billion due to strong growth in all three operating segments. MedSurg sales grew 10%

Rhythm and Neuro rose 8% and Cardiovascular rose 9%. Growth was fueled by the acquisitions of Symetis (2017) NxThera (2018) Claret (2018) and Augmenix (2018).

Net income climbed to a massive $1.6 billion in 2018 compared to $104 million in 2017 and $347 million in 2016 due to higher revenue and income tax benefits related to the US Tax Act.

The company ended 2018 with $829 million in cash down $188 million from 2017. Operating activities contributed $310 million while investing activities used $1.9 billion (mostly on acquisition expenses) and financing activities contributed $1.4 billion via an expanded credit line.

Strategy

Boston Scientific is focused on driving innovation in core markets expanding its global commercial presence and diversifying into additional areas of disease. Through product innovation the company aims to improve patient outcomes and accessibility while lowering medical costs. It strives to lead the market for minimally invasive medical devices that address unmet patient needs and reduce procedural trauma.

Introducing new products is essential in the medical device industry. The firm spends about 11% of revenue (about $1.1 billion in 2018) on R&D each year. Recent product launches include the Eluvia drug-eluting stent for peripheral artery disease; two Vercise brain stimulation systems for Parkinson's disease; and the LithoVue Empower retrieval device for kidney stones. R&D processes are costly so it is essential to gain regulatory approval for most product candidates.

The company supplements its internal R&D programs by collaborating with partners and by completing numerous small strategic acquisitions. It completed six transactions in 2018 to expand in cardiovascular rhythm pain management urology and other fields.

Boston Scientific looks to expand geographically especially in such emerging markets as China India and Brazil. Emerging markets account for more than 10% of total sales and have experienced double digit sales growth in recent years.

The company launched a global restructuring program in 2018 (to be completed in 2021) to improve efficiencies and operating performance. Through the plan Boston Scientific is optimizing its supply chain network to maximize manufacturing and distribution capacity. It is also establishing new functional capabilities to support business growth.

Like all medical equipment makers the company's performance is regularly impacted by product recall and liability issues. Device manufacturers also regularly face issues related to patent challenges and patent expirations.

Mergers and Acquisitions

In 2019 Boston Scientific completed the purchase of UK-based BTG which makes minimally-invasive devices targeting cancer and vascular diseases and specialty pharmaceuticals for $4.2 billion.

Earlier in 2019 the company acquired Veriflex a maker of a lumbar spinal stenosis device for $465 million. The deal expands Boston Scientific's pain management portfolio to include the only commercially-available minimally-invasive interspinous spacer.

In 2018 Boston Scientific acquired NxThera which makes the Rezum system for the treatment of enlarged prostrate in a deal valued at up to $406 million. It also purchased private firm Augmenix which makes the SpaceOAR Hydrogel System for side effects of prostate-cancer radiotherapy for $500 million; Securus Medical Group which makes imaging technology for use in heart rhythm procedures for $40 million; Claret (Sentinel cerebral embolic protection system) for up to $270 million; and nVision (women's health diagnostic devices) for up to $175 million.

In addition it acquired the 65% of Cryterion Medical it didn't already own for some $202 million in 2018; Cryterion is developing a single-shot cryoablation platform to treat atrial fibrillation.

Company Background

Boston Scientific traces its roots to the 1960s when co-founder John Abele bought a stake in surgical technology research firm Medi-tech. Abele teamed with Pete Nicholas in 1979 to form Boston Scientific for the purpose of acquiring Medi-tech.

The company expanded through product launches and acquisitions over the years. Purchases include Swiss company Symetis (transcatheter aortic valves 2017); Apama Medical (radiofrequency balloon catheter systems 2017); EndoChoice (infection control products 2016).

HISTORY

Many medical companies start near a hospital but Boston Scientific's roots sprouted at a children's soccer game where two dads found common ground. John Abele and Peter Nicholas had complementary interests: Wharton MBA Nichols wanted to run his own company; philosophy and physics graduate Abele wanted a job that would help people.

In 1979 the two men founded Boston Scientific to buy medical device maker Medi-Tech. (Abele had purchased a stake in Medi-tech in the 1960s.) Abele and Nicholas had to borrow half a million dollars from a bank and raise an additional $300000. Medi-Tech's primary product was a steerable catheter a soft-tipped device that could be maneuvered within the body. The catheter revolutionized gallstone operations in the early 1970s and Boston Scientific expanded on the success of the product. The company adapted it for a slew of new procedures for the heart lungs intestines and other organs.

Boston Scientific's sales were healthy in 1983 but the firm still lacked funds. It eagerly accepted $21 million from Abbott Laboratories in exchange for a 20% stake. New FDA regulations slowed product introduction and put a crimp in the company's growth.

Boston Scientific found a legal loophole in the late 1980s to avoid lengthy delays: The company described its products in the vaguest possible terms so upgraded devices were considered similar enough to predecessors to escape the in-depth scrutiny of the new approval process. Still Abele and Nicholas had to mortgage their personal properties to stay afloat before this linguistic legerdemain helped to clear government red tape.

Boston Scientific returned to profitability in 1991 and went public the next year buying back Abbott Laboratories' interest in the company as well.

Boston Scientific acquired a bevy of medical device companies throughout the late 1990s which expanded its range of cardiology products and doubled sales. Among them were SCIMED Life Systems Heart Technology Meadox Medicals EP Technologies and Symbiosis Target Therapeutics and Pfizer's catheter stent and angioplasty equipment business.

The company's Taxus drug-eluting stent was approved in the US in 2004 the second such device sold on the market. Major acquisitions in the 2000s included Guidant (with Abbott) and CryoCor.

EXECUTIVES

Chairman President And Ceo, Michael F. (Mike) Mahoney, age 54, $1,042,191 total compensation

Evp And President Rhythm Management, Joseph M. (Joe) Fitzgerald, age 55, $499,241 total compensation

Evp And Cfo, Daniel J. (Dan) Brennan, age 53, $544,421 total compensation

President Japan, Maulik Nanavaty, age 57

Evp And President Medical Surgery (medsurg), Michael P. (Mike) Phalen, age 60

Evp Chief Administrative Officer General Counseland Secretary, Timothy A. (Tim) Pratt, age 69, $640,017 total compensation

Evp And President Asia-pacific Middle East And Africa, Supratim Bose, age 66, $537,326 total compensation

Svp And President Endoscopy, David A. (Dave) Pierce, age 55

Svp And President Interventional Cardiology, Kevin J. Ballinger, age 46, $476,647 total compensation

Evp Operations, Edward F. Mackey, age 56, $410,548 total compensation

Svp Manufacturing And Supply Chain, John B. (Brad) Sorenson, age 51

Svp And President Europe, Eric Thépaut, age 57

Svp And President Endoscopy, Art Butcher

Evp And Global Chief Medical Officer, Ian Meredith

Svp And President Peripheral Interventions, Jeff Mirviss

Vice President Sales, Lee Sullivan

Vice President Government Affairs, Steve Lapierre

Vice President Marketing Science, Tom Robinson

Vice President Operations, Daniel Zaic

Vice President Communications And Progra, Marilee Grant

Vice President Of Sales, Mike Jones

Vice President Corporate Tax, Douglas Cronin

Vice President Of Sales, Allen Meacham

Vice President, Tatsuhiko Sato

Vice President Manager Director, Ru Zheng

Vice President Of Sales And Strategic Accounts, Samuel Conaway

Area Vice President Corporate Accounts, Ryan Farley

Vice President Global Marketing Endoscopy, Meghan Scanlon

Vp And Managing Director India, Prabal Chakraborty

Vice President Of Information Technology And General Superintendent, Neha Khera

National Sales Manager, Rahul Garg

Vice President Quality Neuromodulation, Patrick Crotteau

Executive Vice President Operations, Edward Macky

Svp And President Emea, Eric Thepaut

Svp And Cio, Jodi Eddy

Vp Information Systems, Benjamin Amel

Vice President Is Global Infrastructure Services, Tom Woehrle

Vice President Information Technology And Chief Digital Health Officer, David Feygin

Vice President Of Finance, David Inman

Auditors: Ernst & Young LLP

LOCATIONS

HQ: Boston Scientific Corp.
300 Boston Scientific Way, Marlborough, MA 01752-1234
Phone: 508 683-4000
Web: www.bostonscientific.com

PRODUCTS/OPERATIONS

Selected Products

Cardiovascular
Interventional Cardiology
PolarCath peripheral dilation system
PROMUS drug-eluting stents
TAXUS drug-eluting stents
VeriFLEX bare-metal stents
WALLSTENT carotid artery stents
Cardiac Rhythm Management (CRM)
ACUITY steerable ventricular leads
COGNIS cardiac resynchronization defibrillator
LATITUDE remote patient monitoring system
TELIGEN implantable cardiac defbrillator
Other cardiovascular
Cutting Balloon dilation device
FilterWire EZ embolic protection system
iLab ultrasound imaging catheter system
Maverick balloon catheters
Endoscopy
Radial Jaw 4 single-use biopsy forceps (gastrointestinal)
RX Biliary System (bile duct surgeries)
SpyGlass direct visualization system (pancreatic system)
Urology/Pelvic health
Genesys Hydro ThermAblator (endometrial ablation system)
Neuromodulation
Precision Spinal Cord Stimulation system (chronic pain)
Electrophysiology
Blazer Prime temperature ablation catheters

COMPETITORS

Abbott Labs	Hologic
American Medical Systems	Johnson & Johnson
	LeMaitre Vascular
Bard	Medtronic
Cook Group	ZOLL
Edwards Lifesciences	

HISTORICAL FINANCIALS

Company Type: Public

Income Statement				FYE: December 31
	REVENUE ($ mil.)	NET INCOME ($ mil.)	NET PROFIT MARGIN	EMPLOYEES
12/18	9,823	1,671	17.0%	32,000
12/17	9,048	104	1.1%	29,000
12/16	8,386	347	4.1%	27,000
12/15	7,477	(239)	—	25,000
12/14	7,380	(119)	—	24,000
Annual Growth	7.4%	—		7.5%

2018 Year-End Financials

Debt ratio: 33.60%
Return on equity: 21.24%
Cash ($ mil.): 146
Current ratio: 0.76
Long-term debt ($ mil.): 4,803
No. of shares (mil.): 1,384
Dividends
Yield: —
Payout: —
Market value ($ mil.): 48,931

	STOCK PRICE ($)	P/E	PER SHARE ($)		
	FY Close	High/Low	Earnings	Dividends	Book Value
12/18	35.34	32 21	1.19	0.00	6.30
12/17	24.79	373274	0.08	0.00	5.11
12/16	21.63	94 62	0.25	0.00	4.94
12/15	18.44	— —	(0.18)	0.00	4.69
12/14	13.25	— —	(0.09)	0.00	4.86
Annual Growth	27.8%	— —	—	—	6.7%

Bridge Bancorp, Inc. (Bridgehampton, NY)

Bridge Bancorp wants you to cross over to its subsidiary The Bridgehampton National Bank which operates about 25 branches on eastern Long Island New York. Founded in 1910 the bank offers traditional deposit services to area individuals small businesses and municipalities including checking savings and money market accounts and CDs. Deposits are invested primarily in mortgages which account for some 80% of the bank's loan portfolio. Title insurance services are available through bank subsidiary Bridge Abstract; wealth management services include financial planning estate administration and trustee services. Bridge Bancorp bought Hamptons State Bank in 2011 to fortify its presence on Long Island.

Geographic Reach

Bridgehampton New York-based Bridge Bancorp's market area is Suffolk County in eastern Long Island. The bank serves customers in the towns of East Hampton Southampton Southold and Riverhead. It also has branches in Brookhaven Babylon and Islip.

Financial Performance

The bank reported net income of $13.1 million in 2013 versus $12.8 million in 2012. Revenue increased 3% to $67.3 million on rising net interest income. Bridge Bancorp had total assets of $1.9 billion in 2013 an increase of 17% versus the prior year. Total deposits rose 9% in 2013 versus 2012 to $1.5 billion.

Mergers and Acquisitions

In February 2014 Bridge Bancorp acquired FNBNY Bancorp and its wholly-owned subsidiary the First National Bank of New York and converted its three branches to Bridgehampton National Bank (BNB) branches. The purchase expanded BNB's reach into Nassau County. Following the acquisition Bridge Bancorp's assets totaled approximately $2.1 billion with loans of approximately $1.1 billion and deposits of $1.7 billion with 26 branches throughout Long Island and one loan production office in Manhattan.

EXECUTIVES

President And Ceo, Kevin M. O'Connor, age 56, $300,000 total compensation
Evp And Chief Lending Officer, Kevin L. Santacroce, $180,000 total compensation
Svp And Cio, Thomas H. Simson, $175,000 total compensation
President Ceo And Director, Kevin OConnor
Chief Financial Officer, Adam Hall
Evp And Chief Retail Banking Officer, James J. Manseau, $235,000 total compensation
Senior Vice President And Regional Manager, Ralph Meyer
Vice Chairman, Dennis A. Suskind, age 76
Chairman, Marcia Z. Hefter, age 75
Board Member, Albert Mccoy
Board Member, Rudolph Santoro
Chief Financial Officer Executive Vice President Treasurer, John Mccaffery
Auditors: Crowe LLP

LOCATIONS

HQ: Bridge Bancorp, Inc. (Bridgehampton, NY)
2200 Montauk Highway, Bridgehampton, NY 11932
Phone: 631 537-1000
Web: www.bridgenb.com

COMPETITORS

Bank of America	JPMorgan Chase
Bank of New York Mellon	Suffolk Bancorp

HISTORICAL FINANCIALS

Company Type: Public

Income Statement   FYE: December 31

	ASSETS ($ mil.)	NET INCOME ($ mil.)	INCOME AS % OF ASSETS	EMPLOYEES
12/18	4,700	39	0.8%	473
12/17	4,430	20	0.5%	480
12/16	4,054	35	0.9%	477
12/15	3,781	21	0.6%	433
12/14	2,288	13	0.6%	348
Annual Growth	**19.7%**	**29.9%**	**—**	**8.0%**

2018 Year-End Financials

Debt ratio: 1.68%	No. of shares (mil.): 19
Return on equity: 8.88%	Dividends
Cash ($ mil.): 295	Yield: 3.6%
Current ratio: —	Payout: 98.9%
Long-term debt ($ mil.): —	Market value ($ mil.): 504

	STOCK PRICE ($) FY Close	P/E High/Low	Earnings	PER SHARE ($) Dividends	Book Value
12/18	25.49	19 12	1.97	0.92	22.93
12/17	35.00	37 29	1.04	0.92	21.78
12/16	37.90	19 13	2.00	0.92	21.36
12/15	30.43	22 17	1.43	0.92	19.62
12/14	26.75	23 20	1.18	0.92	15.03
Annual Growth	**(1.2%)**	**— —**	**13.7%**	**(0.0%)**	**11.1%**

Brighthouse Financial Inc

Auditors: DELOITTE & TOUCHE LLP

LOCATIONS

HQ: Brighthouse Financial Inc
11225 North Community House Road, Charlotte, NC 28277
Phone: 980 365-7100
Web: www.brighthousefinancial.com

HISTORICAL FINANCIALS

Company Type: Public

Income Statement   FYE: December 31

	ASSETS ($ mil.)	NET INCOME ($ mil.)	INCOME AS % OF ASSETS	EMPLOYEES
12/18	206,294	865	0.4%	1,260
12/17	224,192	(378)	—	1,260
12/16	221,930	(2,939)	—	1,100
12/15	226,725	1,119	0.5%	—
12/14	0	1,159	—	—
Annual Growth	**—**	**(7.1%)**		

2018 Year-End Financials

Debt ratio: 1.92%	No. of shares (mil.): 117
Return on equity: 5.98%	Dividends
Cash ($ mil.): 4,145	Yield: —
Current ratio: —	Payout: —
Long-term debt ($ mil.): —	Market value ($ mil.): 3,582

	STOCK PRICE ($) FY Close	P/E High/Low	Earnings	PER SHARE ($) Dividends	Book Value
12/18	30.48	9 4	7.21	0.00	122.67
12/17	58.64	— —	(3.16)	0.00	121.19
Annual Growth	**(15.1%)**	**—**	**—**	**—**	**0.3%**

Brighthouse Life Insurance Co - Insurance Products

EXECUTIVES

Chb-Pres-Ceo, Eric T Steigerwalt
V Pres-Cfo, Anant Bhalla
V Pres-Cao, Lynn A Dumais
Digital Marketing Analyst, Stacey Parmenter
Senior Vice President and Tax, Phyllis Zanghi
Head of Tax Planning, Sanjeev Doss
Strategic Relationship Manager, Sarah Shuck
Head of Brand Marketing, Yogini Biswas
Case Manager, Brianna White
Vp, Corey Overby
Account Management Vice Presid, Gretchen Bell
Auditors: DELOITTE & TOUCHE LLP

LOCATIONS

HQ: Brighthouse Life Insurance Co - Insurance Products
11225 North Community House Road, Charlotte, NC 28277
Phone: 980 365-7100
Web: www.metlife.com

HISTORICAL FINANCIALS

Company Type: Public

Income Statement   FYE: December 31

	ASSETS ($ mil.)	NET INCOME ($ mil.)	INCOME AS % OF ASSETS	EMPLOYEES
12/18	195,830	967	0.5%	—
12/17	212,045	(883)	—	—
12/16	199,273	(2,937)	—	—
12/15	202,362	839	0.4%	—
12/14	205,863	295	0.1%	—
Annual Growth	**(1.2%)**	**34.6%**	**—**	**—**

2018 Year-End Financials

Debt ratio: 0.22%	No. of shares (mil.): 0
Return on equity: 5.75%	Dividends
Cash ($ mil.): 3,494	Yield: —
Current ratio: —	Payout: —
Long-term debt ($ mil.): —	Market value ($ mil.): —

Bristol-Myers Squibb Co.

Pharmaceutical giant Bristol-Myers Squibb (BMS) treats an array of maladies through its vast lineup of therapies. The biopharmaceutical's blockbuster drugs include cancer treatment Opdivo rheumatoid arthritis treatment Orencia and Eliquis for stroke prevention. BMS also makes HIV treatments Reyataz and Sustiva. Most of the firm's sales come from products in the areas of oncology cardiovascular care immunology and virology. BMS has global research facilities and manufacturing plants mainly in the US and Europe and its products are marketed to health care practitioners hospitals and managed care providers in 100 countries. The firm is buying Celgene Corporation which makes blockbuster Revlimid for multiple myeloma for $74 billion.

HISTORY

Bristol-Myers Squibb is the product of a merger of rivals.

Squibb was founded by Dr. Edward Squibb in New York City in 1858. He developed techniques for making pure ether and chloroform; he turned the business over to his sons in 1891.

Sales of $414000 in 1904 grew to $13 million by 1928. The company supplied penicillin and morphine during WWII. In 1952 it was bought by Mathieson Chemical which in turn was bought by Olin Industries in 1953 forming Olin Mathieson Chemical. Squibb maintained its separate identity.

From 1968 to 1971 Olin Mathieson went through repeated reorganizations and adopted the Squibb name. Capoten and Corgard two major cardiovascular drugs were introduced in the late 1970s. Capoten was the first drug engineered to attack a specific disease-causing mechanism. Squibb formed a joint venture with Denmark's Novo (now Novo Nordisk) in 1982 to sell insulin.

William Bristol and John Myers founded Clinton Pharmaceutical in Clinton New York in 1887 (renamed Bristol-Myers in 1900) to sell bulk pharmaceuticals. The firm made antibiotics after the 1943 purchase of Cheplin Biological Labs. It began expanding overseas in the 1950s and eventually bought Clairol (1959); Mead Johnson (drugs infant and nutritional formula; 1967); and Zimmer (orthopedic implants 1972). Bristol-Myers launched new drugs to treat cancer (Platinol 1978) and anxiety (BuSpar 1986). That year it acquired biotech companies Oncogen and Genetic Systems.

The firm bought Squibb in 1989. In 1990 the new company bought arthroscopy products and implant business lines and joined Eastman Kodak and Elf Aquitaine to develop new heart drugs in 1993. Despite these initiatives earnings slipped. In 1994 company veteran Charles Heimbold became CEO and moved to increase profits. BMS in 1995 bought wound and skin care products firm Calgon Vestal Laboratories. Also that year the company along with fellow silicone breast implant makers 3M and Baxter International agreed to settle thousands of personal injury claims at an average of $26000 per claim.

Facing an antitrust suit filed by independent drugstores BMS and other major drugmakers agreed in 1996 to charge pharmacies the same prices as managed care groups for medications. That year the company formed a generic drug unit and launched Pravachol.

Over the next two years BMS tweaked its product line buying drug cosmetics and consumer products companies and brands. Having refined its product line the firm began a series of officer reassignments that were widely interpreted as an effort to find a successor for Heimbold who retired in 2001.

In 1999 the firm pulled its backing for EntreMed after the biotech had problems duplicating results for a cancer drug candidate. BMS helped market promising diabetes drug Avandia (from GlaxoSmithKline which ended the deal in 2002) and teamed with Millennium Pharmaceuticals to study the genetic makeup of tumors.

As the company entered the 21st century it began streamlining. It sold its Sea Breeze skin care brand (1999); Matrix Essentials hair care products unit (2000); and Clairol hair and personal care products business (2001). BMS also spun off its Zimmer orthopedic implant unit in 2001. More changes came in 2004: The firm sold its Mead Johnson Adult Nutritional business.

In 2002 BMS was dealt a blow when a judge ruled that the company had illegally blocked Mylan Labs and Watson Pharmaceuticals from selling generic versions of BuSpar.

The firm bought a 20% stake in ImClone to collaborate on the development of cancer drug Erbitux and to stay on top of the cancer drug market. Instead BMS found itself embroiled in the controversy over insider information and stock deals surrounding the biotech. Persistence paid off however; Erbitux was approved by the FDA in 2004.

During 2005 the company cleaned out parts of its medicine cabinet. Analgesics Excedrin and Bufferin had made the company a household name but in 2005 the company sold its US and Canadian consumer products operations to Novartis. The deal also meant saying goodbye to such brands as Comtrex (cold medications) Choice (blood sugar monitoring supplies) and Keri (lotions skin care). Sales for the its US and Canadian consumer products operations reached about $270 million in 2004.

That same year BMS sold Oncology Therapeutics Network which distributes cancer drugs to oncology doctors to private equity firm One Equity Partners. The unit had accounted for about 13% of sales in 2004.

As part of an agreement with the New Jersey US Attorney's office in 2005 to settle an investigation into inventory control and accounting practices the company split the role of chairman and CEO into two separate offices. Long-time BMS director James Robinson III was elected the company's new chairman with Peter Dolan in the CEO role. James Cornelius took over as CEO in 2006 and became chairman in 2008 bring the two roles back together.

While the patent expiration on blockbuster Plavix was still five years off in mid-2006 Canadian generics maker Apotex managed to flood the market with a generic version of Plavix for several weeks. The release of the drug followed bungled attempts by BMS to negotiate a deal with Apotex that would have kept it off the market. The debacle led to federal investigations into whether that deal violated anti-trust laws (among other things) and also resulted in the ouster of CEO Peter Dolan (replaced by James Cornelius). Though a judge put a halt to the manufacturing of the generic until the courts could straighten the whole thing out the short-term generic competition hurt Plavix sales to the tune of more than $1 billion. BMS ultimately wound up paying more than $150 million to settle lawsuits and agreed that it would report any future deals struck with generics makers.

The company announced a reorganizational plan in 2007 named the string-of-pearls strategy. As part of its efforts to remake itself into a purely biopharmaceutical player BMS began jettisoning its non-pharmaceutical businesses. During 2008 the company sold its Medical Imaging unit to private equity firm Avista Capital Partners for $525 million and Avista Capital Partners and Nordic Capital paid $4.1 billion to acquire BMS' ConvaTec ostomy and wound-care subsidiary. Then in 2009 the company divested its Mead Johnson subsidiary which sold Enfamil infant formula and other nutritional products for children.

EXECUTIVES

LOCATIONS

HQ: Bristol-Myers Squibb Co.
430 E. 29th Street, 14th Floor, New York, NY 10016
Phone: 212 546-4000 **Fax:** 212 546-4020
Web: www.bms.com

2017 Sales

	$ mil.	% of total
US	11,358	55
Europe	4,988	24
Other	3,877	18
Other revenues	553	3
Total	**20,776**	**100**

PRODUCTS/OPERATIONS

2017 Sales

	$ mil.	% of total
Prioritized brands		
Opdivo	4,948	24
Eliquis	4,872	23
Orencia	2,479	12
Sprycel	2,005	10
Yervoy	1,244	6
Emplicitti	231	1
Established brands		
Baraclude	1,052	5
Sustiva franchise	729	4
Reyataz franchise	698	3
Hepatitis C franchise	406	2
Other	2,112	10
Total	**20,776**	**100**

Selected Pharmaceuticals

Cardiovascular
Eliquis (atrial fibrillation with Pfizer)
Immunology
Nulojix (kidney rejection)
Orencia (rheumatoid arthritis)
Metabolism
Bydureon (type 2 diabetes)
Byetta (type 2 diabetes)
Neuroscience
Emsam (major depressive disorder)
Oncology
Erbitux (colorectal head and neck cancer with Lilly)
Sprycel (chronic myeloid leukemia with Otsuka)
Yervoy (metastatic melanoma)
Virology
Baraclude (chronic hepatitis B)
Reyataz (HIV)
Sustiva Franchise (includes Atripla and Sustiva for HIV with Gilead)

COMPETITORS

AbbVie	Johnson & Johnson
Allergan plc	Merck
Amgen	Mylan
Apotex	Novartis
AstraZeneca	Pfizer
Biogen	Roche Holding
Boehringer Ingelheim	Sandoz International
Eli Lilly	GmbH
Genentech	Sanofi
GlaxoSmithKline	Teva

HISTORICAL FINANCIALS

Company Type: Public

Income Statement FYE: December 31

	REVENUE ($ mil.)	NET INCOME ($ mil.)	NET PROFIT MARGIN	EMPLOYEES
12/18	22,561	4,920	21.8%	23,300
12/17	20,776	1,007	4.8%	23,700
12/16	19,427	4,457	22.9%	25,000
12/15	16,560	1,565	9.5%	25,000
12/14	15,879	2,004	12.6%	25,000
Annual Growth	9.2%	25.2%	—	(1.7%)

2018 Year-End Financials

Debt ratio: 21.01%		No. of shares (mil.): 1,624	
Return on equity: 38.18%		Dividends	
Cash ($ mil.): 6,911		Yield: 3.0%	
Current ratio: 1.61		Payout: 53.1%	
Long-term debt ($ mil.): 5,646		Market value ($ mil.): 84,416	

	STOCK PRICE ($) FY Close	P/E High/Low	PER SHARE ($) Earnings	PER SHARE ($) Dividends	PER SHARE ($) Book Value
12/18	51.98	23 16	3.01	1.60	8.64
12/17	61.28	107 77	0.61	1.56	7.23
12/16	58.44	29 18	2.65	1.14	9.72
12/15	68.79	75 61	0.93	1.49	8.55
12/14	59.03	51 39	1.20	1.45	8.94
Annual Growth	(3.1%)	— —	25.8%	2.5%	(0.9%)

BRIXMOR LLC

EXECUTIVES

MBR, Michael Carroll
Chief Financial Officer*, Tiffanie Fisher
MBR*, Steven F Siegel
MBR*, Leonard Brumberg
MBR*, Steve Splain
Pres*, Michael Pappagallo
Exec V Pres*, Dean Bernstein
Exec V Pres*, Timothy Bruce
Exec V Pres*, Steven Siegel
Director, Chris Reed
Project Manager, Stephen Herget
Auditors: ERNST & YOUNG LLP

LOCATIONS

HQ: BRIXMOR LLC
450 LEXINGTON AVE FL 13, NEW YORK, NY 100173956
Phone: 212 869-3000
Web: WWW.BRIXMOR.COM

HISTORICAL FINANCIALS

Company Type: Private

Income Statement FYE: December 31

	ASSETS ($ mil.)	NET INCOME ($ mil.)	INCOME AS % OF ASSETS	EMPLOYEES
12/08	4,157	(550)	—	442
12/07	5,702	(486)	—	—
Annual Growth	(27.1%)	—	—	—

Brookline Bancorp Inc (DE)

Boston-based Brookline Bancorp is the holding company for Brookline Bank Bank Rhode Island (BankRI) and First Ipswich Bank which together operate more than 50 full-service branches in eastern Massachusetts and Rhode Island. Commercial and multifamily mortgages backed by real estate such as apartments condominiums and office buildings account for the largest portion of the company's loan portfolio followed by indirect auto loans commercial loans and consumer loans. Established in 1997 as Brookline Savings Bank the bank went public five years later and changed its name to Brookline Bank in 2003.

Operations

Brookline Bancorp focuses its services and products to commercial enterprises. It offers commercial business and retail banking services such as cash management products on-line banking services consumer and residential loans and investment services. The holding company provides equipment financing through its Eastern Funding and Macrolease Corporation subsidiaries. Eastern Funding holds loans with higher-than-normal credit risk (and higher yields) due to the limited capital of its typical customers: coin-operated laundries dry cleaning businesses and convenience stores in the New York City metropolitan area.

Geographic Reach

Boston-based Brookline Bancorp operates primarily in Boston MA and Providence Rhode Island.

Financial Performance

Brookline Bancorp generated $263 million in interest & dividend income and another $32 million of non-interest income. Combined the $295 million of 2017 annual revenue exceeded the previous year's result by 12% aided heavily by the bank's one-time gain of $11 million on the sale of investment securities. Its loan portfolio grew 6% to $5.7 billion in 2017.

Despite the healthy improvement in revenue net income fell 4% to $50.5 million due in large part to an unusually high income tax bill triggered by the passing of the US Federal Tax Reform bill in late 2017.

Strategy

Brookline has grown from a sleepy suburban community savings bank to a publicly-traded commercial lender with loan volumes that put it among Massachusetts' top banks. Its operational approach of a holding company with local largely independent banks gives it certain advantages. The local banks are empowered to address local market needs whether in the form of products services or even interest rates on loans. This gives each bank the opportunity to build its own brand along with strong long-term relationships with commercial customers while leaving the corporate functions (IT risk management etc.) to the centralized holding company.

Mergers and Acquisitions

In 2018 the bank purchased for $264 million First Commons Bank N.A. to extend its reach into the western suburbs of Boston MA.

EXECUTIVES

President And Ceo, Paul A. Perrault, age 68, $715,000 total compensation
Coo, James M. Cosman, age 68, $265,000 total compensation
President And Ceo Bank Rhode Island, Mark J. Meiklejohn, age 55, $330,000 total compensation
Chief Risk Officer General Counsel And Secretary, Michael W. McCurdy, age 50
Chief Credit Officer, M. Robert Rose, age 67, $288,000 total compensation
President And Ceo The First National Bank Of Ipswich, Russell G. Cole, age 61
Cfo, Carl M. Carlson, age 55, $335,000 total compensation
Senior Vice President, Bill Mackenzie
Vice President Regional Manager, Cathy Pierce
Vice President, Tony Glazier
Vice President Of Commercial Lending, Tim Steiner
Vice President Underwriting And Operations, Gretchen Annese

Vice President, James Vallone
Vice President, Maryanne Bland
Vp Benefits And Payroll, Edgar Oteiza
Chairman, Joseph J. Slotnik, age 83
Treasurer, Reed H Whitman
Auditors: KPMG LLP

LOCATIONS

HQ: Brookline Bancorp Inc (DE)
131 Clarendon Street, Boston, MA 02116
Phone: 617 425-4600
Web: www.brooklinebancorp.com

PRODUCTS/OPERATIONS

2017 sales

	$ mil.	% of total
Interest and dividend income:		
Loans and leases	247	84
Debt securities	12	4
Marketable and restricted equity securities	3	1
Short-term investments	.4	-
Non-interest income:		
Deposit fees	10	3
Loan fees	1	-
Loan level derivative income net	2	1
Gain on sales of investment securities	11	4
Gain on sales of loans and leases held-for-sale	2	1
Other	4	2
Total	**295**	**100**

Selected Services

Personal
Checking
Savings
Borrowing
Investment Services
Business
Signature Business Banking
Business Checking Accounts
Business Savings
Business Lending
Business Online Banking
Cash Management
Service Center
Branch Locations
ATM Locations
Online Banking
Mobile Banking
Telephone Services
Mail Services
Order Checks
Order Foreign Currency
Overdraft Privilege Service

COMPETITORS

Bank of America
Berkshire Hills
 Bancorp
Boston Private
Central Bancorp
Century Bancorp (MA)

Citizens Financial
Group
Eastern Bank
Sovereign Bank
TD Bank USA

HISTORICAL FINANCIALS

Company Type: Public

Income Statement

FYE: December 31

	ASSETS ($ mil.)	NET INCOME ($ mil.)	INCOME AS % OF ASSETS	EMPLOYEES
12/18	7,392	83	1.1%	791
12/17	6,780	50	0.7%	765
12/16	6,438	52	0.8%	743
12/15	6,042	49	0.8%	718
12/14	5,799	42	0.7%	725
Annual Growth	**6.3%**	**18.1%**	**—**	**2.2%**

2018 Year-End Financials

Debt ratio: 1.84%	No. of shares (mil.): 80
Return on equity: 9.75%	Dividends
Cash ($ mil.): 89	Yield: 2.8%
Current ratio: —	Payout: 45.4%
Long-term debt ($ mil.): —	Market value ($ mil.): 1,108

	STOCK PRICE ($) FY Close	P/E High/Low	PER SHARE ($) Earnings	Dividends	Book Value
12/18	13.82	19 12	1.04	0.40	11.23
12/17	15.70	25 20	0.68	0.36	10.42
12/16	16.40	22 14	0.74	0.36	9.82
12/15	11.50	17 13	0.71	0.36	9.45
12/14	10.03	17 14	0.61	0.34	9.09
Annual Growth	**8.3%**	**—**	**14.3%**	**3.8%**	**5.4%**

Brunswick Corp.

Brunswick Corporation is a global manufacturer of marine recreation and fitness products. Its largest business segment marine engines makes outboard inboard and stern drive engines propellers and control systems. The company also makes pleasure craft offshore fishing boats and pontoons. Its fitness segment includes treadmills cross trainers stair climbers and stationary bicycles sold under the brands Life Fitness and Hammer Strength. It also has a 49% stake in marine financing company Brunswick Acceptance Company; a Wells Fargo subsidiary holds the other 51%. In 2019 the company agreed to sell its fitness segment to KPS Capital Partners for $490 million.

Operations

Brunswick has three operating segments: Marine Engine Boat and Fitness.

Marine generates some 55% of sales and manufactures and markets a full range of outboard sterndrive and inboard engines as well as marine parts and accessories.

The Boat segment accounts for some 25% of sales and designs manufactures and markets fiberglass pleasure boats yachts and sport yachts sport cruisers and sport boats as well as offshore fishing boats aluminum and fiberglass fishing boats pontoon boats utility boats deck boats inflatable boats and heavy-gauge aluminum boats.

The Fitness segment is the world's largest manufacturer of commercial fitness equipment and generates more than 20% of total revenue. It designs manufactures and markets a full line of cardiovascular fitness and strength equipment including treadmills total body cross-trainers stair climbers exercise bikes and strength-training equipment such as weight machines and free weights. Its brands are Life Fitness Cybex Hammer Strength SciFit and Indoor Cycling. The segment also includes games room equipment such as billiards tables. In 2019 the company agreed to sell the segment to KPS Capital Partners for $490 million.

Geographic Reach

Headquartered in Illinois Brunswick has manufacturing distribution warehouses sales offices and research and development facilities in some 14 countries across North America Europe and the Asia/Pacific region. The US generates some 70% of its total sales.

Sales and Marketing

Brunswick's marine engine segment's global sales network includes more than 6000 marine dealers distributors and marine retailers and service centers that sell its engines to end-users.

More than 2000 boat dealers and distributors market its lineup of boats. The business' largest

dealer MarineMax Inc has multiple centers and delivers more than 15% of the Boat segment's sales. The Boat segment includes a commercial and governmental sales unit that sells products to commercial customers as well as to the US government and state local and foreign governments.

The Fitness segment serves health clubs corporations schools and universities hotels professional sports teams and more. Its principal customer is Planet Fitness. Its sales division consists of a direct sales force domestic dealers and international distributors. Its products can be found in specialty retailers select mass merchants sporting goods stores and on the Life Fitness website.

Financial PerformanceNote: Brunswick provides revenue figures for continuing operations excluding revenue from units held for sale. In 2017 this included the Sea Ray business which had revenue of around $387 million and incurred a net loss of $40.9 million.In fiscal 2017 Brunswick's sales increased 9% to $4.5 billion due to increases in all segments. The Marine Engine segment grew sales of outboard engines and marine parts and accessories. Sales of higher horsepower engines performed particularly well. Boat segment sales were buoyed by higher aluminum and fiberglass outboard boat sales while the Fitness segment grew mostly internationally. Cross-segment international sales increased 10%.Net income fell 31% to $187.3 million due to higher impairment charges and pension settlement expenses partially offset by a tax benefit from the 2017 US Tax Cuts and Jobs Act.Cash from operations was largely unchanged in 2017 at $417.2 million down 1% due to an increase in working capital.

Strategy

Brunswick has been selling off various of its underperforming businesses in recent years due to unsatisfactory sales or profitability. In 2018 it made the decision to float its Fitness business which has struggled to find growth in the US. The next year it found a buyer in KPS Capital Partners which is paying $490 million for the segment. It also made the decision to sell its Sea Ray outboard engines business in 2017 although after no satisfactory offer to buy was received it is progressing with refocusing on its 25-40ft sports boat and cruiser product lines and will no longer make boats over 40ft. In 2014 it sold the AMF bowling business and in 2015 it sold its bowling products business.

Mergers and Acquisitions

Brunswick uses acquisitions to find additional revenue growth.

In 2017 Brunswick acquired Lankhorst Taselaar a Netherlands- and Germany-based marine parts and accessories distribution company for about $15 million. The acquisition augments the marine parts and accessories businesses through a broader product line and an expanded distribution network. Lankhorst Taselaar was combined into Brunswick's Marine Engine segment.

Recently it has pursued transactions to extend its international reach and beef up its Life Fitness portfolio. In 2016 the company obtained Payne's Marine Group of Victoria British Columbia a wholesale distributor of marine parts and accessories (P&A) in Canada. It also acquired Germany-based Indoor Cycling Group (ICG) for $54 million. Based in Nuremburg Germany ICG specializes in the design of indoor cycling equipment and is now part of the company's Life Fitness division. The company's third acquisition in 2016 was of Cybex International a maker of commercial fitness equipment for $195 million.

HISTORY

Swiss immigrant woodworker John Brunswick built his first billiard table in 1845 in Cincinnati. In 1874 he formed a partnership with Julius Balke and a decade later they teamed with H. W. Collender to form Brunswick-Balke-Collender Company.

Following Brunswick's death son-in-law Moses Bensinger became president. The company diversified into bowling equipment during the 1880s. Bensinger's son B. E. followed as president (1904) and led the company into wood and rubber products phonographs and records. (Al Jolson recorded "Sonny Boy" on the Brunswick label.) Brunswick went public after WWI.

By 1930 Brunswick focused on bowling and billiards sports that had seedy reputations during the 1920s and 1930s. When B. E. died in 1935 his son Bob became CEO and launched a massive promotional campaign to make his meal tickets respectable.

Bob's brother Ted succeeded him as CEO in 1954. Bowling equipment rival AMF introduced the first automatic pinsetter in 1952 and Brunswick followed four years later capturing the lead by 1958. Brunswick diversified adding Owens Yacht MacGregor (sporting goods 1958) Aloe (medical supplies 1959) Mercury (marine products 1961) and Zebco (fishing equipment 1961). The company adopted its present name in 1960.

To focus exclusively on its marine engine and boat business Brunswick sold all of its bowling operations in 2014 and 2015.

EXECUTIVES

Vice President, William Seeley

Vp And President South America Mercury Marine, William J. Gress

Svp And Cfo, William L. Metzger, age 57, $505,000 total compensation

Chairman And Ceo, Mark D. Schwabero, age 66, $971,154 total compensation

Vp And President Mercury Marine, John C. Pfeifer, age 53, $475,000 total compensation

Vp And Cto, David M. Foulkes

Vp And President Fitness Division, Jaime A. Irick, age 44

Vp And President Brunswick Boat Group, Huw S. Bower, age 44, $332,061 total compensation

Vp And Cio, Danielle Brown, age 49

Vp Finance, Bijoy Jha

Vice President Investor Relations, Ryan M Gwillim

Vice President New Business Development, Robert Staehle

Vice President And President Mercury Marine, Christopher Drees

Vice President, Michael Adams

Board Member, Jane Warner

Auditors: DELOITTE & TOUCHE LLP

LOCATIONS

HQ: Brunswick Corp.
26125 N. Riverwoods Blvd., Suite 500, Mettawa, IL 60045-3420
Phone: 847 735-4700
Web: www.brunswick.com

2017 Sales

	$ mil.	% of total
US	2,972	66
International	1,537	34
Total	**4,501**	**100**

PRODUCTS/OPERATIONS

2017 Sales

	$ mil.	% of total
Marine		
Marine Engine	2,631	55
Boat	1,103	23
Marine eliminations	(258.5)	-
Fitness	1,033	22
Total	**4,510**	**100**

Selected Products

Billiards
  Air hockey
  Billiards tables and accessories
Fitness
  Commercial equipment
Marine - Boats
  Boat parts and accessories
  Freshwater fishing and utility boats
  General recreation boats
  Motor yachts
  Pontoon and deck boats
  Rigid inflatable and inflatable boats
Marine - Engines
  Engine parts and accessories
  Inboard stern drive and jet drive engines
  Trolling motors
  Outboard engines

COMPETITORS

Cigarette Racing Team	Honda
Fountain Powerboat	Marine Products Corp.
Giant Manufacturing	Yamaha

HISTORICAL FINANCIALS

Company Type: Public

Income Statement

FYE: December 31

	REVENUE ($ mil.)	NET INCOME ($ mil.)	NET PROFIT MARGIN	EMPLOYEES
12/18	5,159	265	5.1%	16,038
12/17	4,510	146	3.2%	15,116
12/16	4,488	276	6.1%	14,415
12/15	4,105	241	5.9%	12,607
12/14	3,838	245	6.4%	12,165
Annual Growth	**7.7%**	**1.9%**		**7.2%**

2018 Year-End Financials

Debt ratio: 28.49%
Return on equity: 17.31%
Cash ($ mil.): 303
Current ratio: 1.50
Long-term debt ($ mil.): 1,179

No. of shares (mil.): 86
Dividends
  Yield: 1.6%
  Payout: 25.9%
Market value ($ mil.): 4,030

	STOCK PRICE ($) FY Close	P/E High/Low	PER SHARE ($) Earnings	Dividends	Book Value
12/18	46.45	23 14	3.01	0.78	18.24
12/17	55.22	39 30	1.62	0.69	16.94
12/16	54.54	18 13	3.00	0.62	16.12
12/15	50.51	22 18	2.56	0.53	14.11
12/14	51.26	20 15	2.58	0.45	12.64
Annual Growth	**(2.4%)**	**— —**	**3.9%**	**14.7%**	**9.6%**

Bryn Mawr Bank Corp

Bryn Mawr Bank Corporation stands atop a "big hill" in Pennsylvania. Bryn Mawr (which in Welsh translates as "big hill") is the bank holding company for Bryn Mawr Trust operates some 20 offices in Pennsylvania and Delaware. The bank offers traditional services as checking and savings accounts CDs mortgages and business and consumer loans in addition to insurance products equipment leasing investment management retirement planning tax planning and preparation and trust services. Founded in 1889 Bryn Mawr boasts more than $5 billion of assets under administration and management.

Operations

Bryn Mawr operates two business segments. Its Banking segment which makes up two-thirds of overall business provides commercial and retail banking services. The Wealth Management division which includes the Bryn Mawr Trust of Delaware and Lau Associates businesses makes up about one-third of the bank's overall revenue and provides a variety of custody investment management tax and brokerage services.

Broadly speaking the company generated 60% of its total revenue from interest and fees on loans and leases in 2014 while another 30% of its total revenue came from fees for wealth management services.

Bryn Mawr operated 19 full-service branches seven Life Care Community Offices five wealth offices and a full-service insurance agency in 2014.

Geographic Reach

The bank corporation has branches and offices across Montgomery Delaware Chester and Dauphin counties in Pennsylvania and New Castle county in Delaware.

Financial Performance

Bryn Mawr has enjoyed rising revenues and profits over the past several years reflecting strong growth in its loan business and wealth management business.

The bank's revenue rose by 4% to a record $131.23 million in 2014 mostly thanks to higher interest income from loans as it grew its loan assets by $153.9 million during the year. The company's Wealth Management services fees also grew by 5% thanks to new business acquisitions and solid market appreciation during the year which resulted in higher assets under management.

Higher revenue and a strong grip on costs in 2014 also boosted Bryn Mawr's net income by 14% to a record $27.84 million. Despite higher earnings the bank's operating cash declined by 6% to $37.68 million for the year as it made less in net proceeds from the sales of its loans held for resale.

Strategy

Bryn Mawr Bank Corporation continued to push its acquisition strategy in 2015 designed to broaden its service offerings boost its loan and deposit business and expand its branch network. The bank looks to strategically acquire smaller insurance businesses small to mid-sized banks and community banks wealth management companies and advisory and planning services firm that complement its existing businesses.

Besides acquisitions the company has been growing its wealth management business through marketing campaigns to raise brand awareness.

Mergers and Acquisitions

In April 2015 to grow its wealth management business the bank purchased Robert J. McAllister Agency which provides insurance and risk management solutions to individuals and businesses in the Philadelphia region.

In January 2015 Bryn Mawr acquired the Continental Bank Holdings and its Plymouth Meeting-based flagship Continental Bank adding some $433 million in loans and $480 million in deposits along with 10 full-service branches located in key markets in Montgomery Chester and Philadelphia counties.

In October 2014 Bryn Mawr bought the Rosemont Pennsylvania-based insurance agency Powers Craft Parker & Beard Inc. (PCPB) for $7 million to enhance its own insurance business among individuals and commercial clients.

In 2012 as part of a strategy to build its wealth management division the company acquired Davidson Trust adding some $1 billion in assets under management.

Company Background

In 2011 the company bought the private wealth management business of Hershey Trust Company for more than $14.5 million; that deal brought in approximately $1 billion of assets under management. In 2010 the company purchased First Keystone Financial adding about 10 bank branches in Pennsylvania and some $2.7 billion in trust and investment assets.

EXECUTIVES

Evp And Coo, Alison E. Gers, age 61, $250,000 total compensation

Evp And Chief Lending Officer Bryn Mawr Trust, Joseph G. (Joe) Keefer, age 60, $238,500 total compensation

President And Ceo, Francis J. Leto, age 59, $310,000 total compensation

Evp Secretary And Chief Risk Officer, Geoffrey L. Halberstadt

Cfo And Treasurer Bryn Mawr Bank Corporation; Evp Cfo And Treasurer Bryn Mawr Bank, Michael W. (Mike) Harrington, age 56

Evp Wealth Management Division, Harry R. Madeira

Senior Vice President Of Wealth Management Division, Rande Whitham

Senior Vice President Wealth Management, Barbara Pettit

Sr Vice President Market Leader, Tony Poluch

Assistant Vice President And Trust Advisor, Yvonne Lalime

Vice President Operations Manager Retail Credit Center Division, Mandy Payne

Senior Vice President Commercial Lending, Mike Bunn

Senior Vice President Operations, Mame Skelly

Vice President Wealth Management Division, J Keefer-Hugill

Assistant Vice President Trust Tax Advisor, John Fotiou

Vice President; Executive Vice President And Chief Administrative Officer Of The Bank, Alison Eichert

Vice President, Cheryl Howard

Vice President Small Business Account Lending Division, Douglas Whalen

Vice President, Sally Worrell

Vice President, Drew Smith

Vice President Relationship Manager, Shawn Williams

Vice President Director Of Investment Services, Bryan Andersen

Vice President Mortgage Division, Anne Stulpin

Vice President Comptrollers And Finance, Maral Kaloustian

Senior Vice President Managing Partner, Robert McLaughlin

Assistant Vice President And Senior Fiduciary Tax Acct, Amanda Decaria

Vice President, John Tucker

Svp And Relationship Manager, Joseph J Dimaio

Vice President And Trust Tax Advisor, Lisa Miles

Vice President Small Business Portfolio Manager, Kirsten Althoff

Assistant Vice President Service Manager Chadds Ford Branch, Leslie Paynter

Avp Recruitment Manager, Maria Delimitros

Svp And Chief Credit Officer, Liam Brickley

Senior Vice President Relationship Manager Bmt Wealth Management, Joanne Shallcross

Vice President Senior Mortgage Loan Officer, Patt Mcgowan

Senior Vice President And Director Of Facilities, Emanuel Ball

Senior Vice President Director Of Capital Markets, Mark Henderson

Senior Vice President Head Of Commercial And Industrial Banking, Jim Donovan

Senior Vice President Chief Investment Officer, Ernest E Cecilia

Senior Vice President Commercial, Dennis B Levasseur

Senior Vice President, Albert B Murphy

Senior Vice President, Ned Lee

Chairman, Britton H. Murdoch

Assistant Treasurer, Linda McLaughlin

Board Member, Michael Clement

Auditors: KPMG LLP

LOCATIONS

HQ: Bryn Mawr Bank Corp
801 Lancaster Avenue, Bryn Mawr, PA 19010
Phone: 610 525-1700
Web: www.bmtc.com

PRODUCTS/OPERATIONS

2014 Sales

	$ mil.	% of total
Interest		
Interest & fees on loans & leases	78	60
Investment securities	4	3
Cash & cash equivalents	0	-
Noninterest		
Fees for wealth management services	36	30
Service charges on deposits	2	2
Net gain on sale of residential mortgages	1	1
Loan Servicing and other fees	1	1
Other	5	3
Total	**131**	**100**

Selected Subsidiaries

Bryn Mawr Advisors Inc.
Bryn Mawr Asset Management Inc.
Bryn Mawr Brokerage Co. Inc.
Bryn Mawr Financial Services Inc.
Bryn Mawr Trust Company of Delaware
Joseph W. Roskos Co. Inc.
Lau Associates LLC
The Bryn Mawr Trust Company
 BMT Leasing Inc.
 BMT Mortgage Services Inc.
 BMT Settlement Services Inc.
 Insurance Counsellors of Bryn Mawr Inc.

COMPETITORS

Alliance Bancorp of Pennsylvania	Royal Bancshares
Firstrust Savings Bank	Sovereign Bank
PNC Financial	Wells Fargo

HISTORICAL FINANCIALS

Company Type: Public

Income Statement

FYE: December 31

	ASSETS ($ mil.)	NET INCOME ($ mil.)	INCOME AS % OF ASSETS	EMPLOYEES
12/18	4,652	63	1.4%	696
12/17	4,449	23	0.5%	680
12/16	3,421	36	1.1%	544
12/15	3,031	16	0.6%	530
12/14	2,246	27	1.2%	444
Annual Growth	**20.0%**	**23.0%**	**—**	**11.9%**

2018 Year-End Financials

Debt ratio: 2.58%	No. of shares (mil.): 20
Return on equity: 11.66%	Dividends
Cash ($ mil.): 48	Yield: 2.7%
Current ratio: —	Payout: 48.9%
Long-term debt ($ mil.): —	Market value ($ mil.): 694

	STOCK PRICE ($) FY Close	P/E High/Low		PER SHARE ($) Earnings	Dividends	Book Value
12/18	34.40	16	11	3.13	0.94	28.04
12/17	44.20	34	28	1.32	0.86	26.23
12/16	42.15	20	11	2.12	0.82	22.50
12/15	28.72	33	29	0.94	0.78	21.42
12/14	31.30	15	13	2.01	0.74	17.83
Annual Growth	**2.4%**		**—**	**11.7%**	**6.2%**	**12.0%**

Builders FirstSource Inc.

Builders FirstSource makes and sells building materials and manufactured components for homebuilders contractors remodelers and DIY consumers. It also offers construction-related services. The company's products and services?which include lumber windows and doors millwork installation and shell construction?are offered through some 400 locations across roughly 40 US states. Homebuilders such as Pulte Homes and Lennar are among its largest customers. Builders is the US' largest supplier of structural building products and services for new residential construction repair and remodeling.

Operations

Builders FirstSource operates through four geographic reporting segments: West (which provides about 30% of net sales) South (25%) Southeast (25%) and Northeast (20%).

By product category Builders' largest revenue generator is lumber and lumber sheet goods which account for nearly 40%. Windows doors and millwork provide almost 20% as do manufactured products. Roughly 10% derives from siding metal and concrete products; another 10% comes from what the company classifies as other building and product services?including cabinets hardware turnkey framing shell construction and design. Gypsum roofing and insulation brings in the remainder.

Geographic Reach

Based in Dallas Texas Builders FirstSource is active in about 40 US states. It serves about 75 of the country's top 100 metropolitan statistical areas.

Sales and Marketing

Builders FirstSource serves a range of customers from individual consumers to repair and remodel contractors to large homebuilders. Its top 10 customers account for more than 15% of sales and include large homebuilders such as D.R. Horton Pulte Homes Lennar Beazer Homes USA Hovnanian Enterprises Taylor Morrison Home and Toll Brothers.

The company markets its products and services through a locally focused sales force of some 1900.

Financial Performance

Huge gains by Builders FirstSource in 2015 (when it purchased building materials supplier ProBuild) and 2016 have driven a soaring increase in net sales of about 380% since 2014. The company's net income has been erratic: it fell to a loss in 2015 before rebounding in 2016?only to slide by about three-quarters the next year. 2018 saw net income reach a five-year high however.

Builders' net sales added 10% in 2018 to end the year at $7.7 billion; commodity price inflation boosted income as did greater sales volume in single-family and repair and remodel end markets. Declines in multifamily markets partially offset those additions.

The company's net income jumped a whopping 429% to $205 million in 2018 thanks mostly to greatly reduced net interest expense tied to debt transactions.

Builders depleted $48 million of its cash stores in 2018 to end the year with $10 million. Its operations provided $282.8 million. It invested a net $96.7 million in property plant and equipment; financing activities used $233.6 million primarily for revolving credit facility payments.

Strategy

An aggressive acquisition strategy—some three dozen companies since 1998—enabled Builders

FirstSource to become a construction powerhouse. It relies on its standing in the industry (particularly within the professional segment of the US residential building products market) to propel growth.

Amid continued improvement in the US housing market the company believes its "one-stop-shop" offering is a draw for homebuilders focused on competitive pricing on-site services and an expansive product portfolio. This is especially important as customers reduce supplier relationships in search of efficiencies. In addition Builders FirstSource continues to emphasize and invest in its value-added manufactured products category which helps drive efficiencies for its customer base.

Builders is also investing in operational efficiency initiatives to reduce its costs. It has incorporated fleet tracking and routing into its logistics systems developed an automated customer order entry and billing portal and implemented back-office accounts payable and receivable automation.

Since 2017 the company has also made the expansion of its sales force a focus. Through midyear it added more than 100 new sales associates and continues to plan additional hires.

Company Background
Builders FirstSource was founded in 1998 as BSL Holdings. It is the US' largest supplier of structural building products and services for new residential construction repair and remodeling.

EXECUTIVES

Svp And General Counsel, Donald F. McAleenan, age 64, $415,481 total compensation

President And Ceo, M. Chad Crow, age 51, $625,000 total compensation

Svp And Cfo, Peter Jackson

Vice President Treasury, Mark Cooper

Vice President, Gary Raven

Vice President Sales And Marketing, Randy Craine

Vice President Sales, Matt Liska

Vice President, Greg Turnage

Vice President Sales, Chris Lemly

Vice President Credit, Bart Roberts

Svp Investor Relations, Jennifer Pasquino

Vice President Human Resources, John Foley

Vice President, Kelly Kimbrel

Vice President Of Purchasing, Jeff Rettig

Vice President Credit Southeast Region, Liz Hummell

Vice President Development Seattle, Steve Yoon

Vice President Of Construction, Frank Navia

Vp Of Marketing, Kellie Hughes

Vice President Investor Relations, Binit Sanghvi

Chairman, Paul S. Levy, age 71

Board Member, Floyd F Sherman

Board Member, Kevin Kruse

Board Member, Daniel Agroskin

Auditors: PricewaterhouseCoopers LLP

LOCATIONS

HQ: Builders FirstSource Inc.
2001 Bryan Street, Suite 1600, Dallas, TX 75201
Phone: 214 880-3500   **Fax:** 214 880-3599
Web: www.bldr.com

2018 Sales

	$ mil.	% of total
West	2,461	32
South	2,051	27
Southeast	1,704	22
Northeast	1,340	17
Other	167	2
Total	**7,724**	**100**

PRODUCTS/OPERATIONS

2018 Sales

	$ mil.	% of total
Lumber and lumber sheet goods	2,902	37
Manufactured products	1,392	18
Windows doors and millwork	1,445	19
Siding metal and concrete products	697	9
Gypsum roofing and insulation	528	7
Other building products and services	758	10
Total	**7,724**	**100**

Selected Products

Building Materials
  Concrete
  Concrete block
  Decking
  Gypsum
  Paint
  Roofing
  Sheathing
Interior Items
  Builder hardware
  Cabinets
  Cabinet hardware
  Countertops
  Fireplaces
Lumber and Related Products
  Dimensional lumber
  Engineered wood
  Oriented strand board
  Plywood
  Pressure-treated lumber
Manufactured Components
  Floor trusses
  I-Joist floor systems
  Interior and exterior doors
  Open wall panels
  Roof trusses
  Stairs
Millwork
  Columns
  Custom millwork
  Interior and exterior doors
  Moldings
  Special-order millwork
  Windows
Tools
  Pneumatic tools
  Power tools

COMPETITORS

84 Lumber	HD Supply
Ace Hardware	Lowe's
BMC Stock	McCoy Corp.
BlueLinx	Menard
Boise Cascade Company	True Value
Carter Lumber	Universal Forest
CertainTeed	Products

HISTORICAL FINANCIALS

Company Type: Public

Income Statement   FYE: December 31

	REVENUE ($ mil.)	NET INCOME ($ mil.)	NET PROFIT MARGIN	EMPLOYEES
12/18	7,724	205	2.7%	15,000
12/17	7,034	38	0.6%	15,000
12/16	6,367	144	2.3%	14,000
12/15	3,564	(22)	—	14,000
12/14	1,604	18	1.1%	3,800
Annual Growth	**48.1%**	**83.4%**	**—**	**41.0%**

2018 Year-End Financials

Debt ratio: 53.65%
Return on equity: 42.20%
Cash ($ mil.): 10
Current ratio: 1.88
Long-term debt ($ mil.): 1,545
No. of shares (mil.): 115
Dividends
  Yield: —
  Payout: —
Market value ($ mil.): 1,256

	STOCK PRICE ($) FY Close	P/E High/Low		PER SHARE ($) Earnings	Dividends	Book Value
12/18	10.91	13	6	1.76	0.00	5.18
12/17	21.79	64	32	0.34	0.00	3.31
12/16	10.97	11	5	1.27	0.00	2.78
12/15	11.08	—	—	(0.22)	0.00	1.36
12/14	6.87	48	26	0.18	0.00	0.41
Annual Growth	**12.3%**	—	—	**76.8%**	—	**88.6%**

Burlington Northern & Santa Fe Railway Co. (The)

BNSF Railway operates one of the largest railroad networks in North America. A wholly-owned subsidiary of Burlington Northern Santa Fe itself a unit of Berkshire Hathaway the company provides freight transportation over a network of about 32500 route miles of track across some 30 US states and three provinces in Canada. BNSF Railway owns or leases a fleet of about 8000 locomotives. It also has some 25 intermodal facilities that help to transport agricultural consumer and industrial products as well as coal. In addition to major cities and ports BNSF Railway serves smaller markets in alliance with short-line partners.

Operations
BNSF Railway transports a wide range of products and commodities through its four main product segments.

The Consumer Products segment generates about 35% of revenue and consists of the Domestic Intermodal International Intermodal and Automotive business units. The Industrial Products segment provides about 25% of revenue and comprises five business units: Construction Products Petroleum Products Building Products Chemicals and Plastics Products and Food and Beverages.

Agricultural Products represents 20% of revenue and includes the transportation of commodities like corn wheat ethanol soybeans fertilizer oil seeds flour and other grains. The Coal business (less than 20%) is primarily BNSF's operations that originate from the Powder River Basin of Wyoming and Montana.

The company also generates about 5% of revenue from its wholly-owned non-rail logistics subsidiary BSNF Logistics LLC through logistics and transportation services such as storage as well as demurrage (detention fees for delays in loading and unloading of freight).

Geographic Reach
Headquartered in Fort Worth TX BNSF Railway's network spreads across about 30 US states and three Canadian provinces.

Sales and Marketing
BNSF Railway serves smaller markets by working closely with 200 shortline partners. It also forms marketing agreements with other rail carriers expanding the marketing reach for each railroad and its customers.

Financial Performance
BNSF has seen steady growth in recent years with revenue reaching $23.9 billion in 2018 a 12% increase compared with $21.4 billion in 2017. The increase in 2018 was mainly due to increased volume and increased rates per car as well as tight

truck capacity in the transportation sector which converted some business from highway to rail.

Net income however plummeted to $5.2 billion less than half that of the previous year. This was primarily due to an increased tax liability as a result of the Tax Cuts and Jobs Act.

Cash at the end of fiscal 2018 was $2.0 billion about the same as the prior year. Cash from operations contributed $7.9 billion to the coffers while investing activities used $3.2 billion mainly for capital expenditures related to equipment purchases. Financing activities used another $4.7 billion primarily for cash distributions to its parent company.

Strategy

BNSF plans capital spending of about $3.5 billion in 2019 for network maintenance and replacement of assets to ensure safe and reliable operations. These include expansion and efficiency projects focused on key growth areas along its Southern and Northern Trancon routes. The company faces challenges in its supply chain environment with competition from improving productivity in the trucking industry. Another hurdle is consumers' expectations for quicker and quicker delivery as online shopping continues to grow. In response BSNF is focusing on providing consistent reliable and efficient transportation services to its customers.

Company Background

BNSF's traces its roots to 1849 when the Aurora Branch Railroad was founded in Illinois with 12 miles of track. Over the years additional rail lines were built including Atchison Topeka & Santa Fe;Burlington Northern; Chicago Burlington & Quincy; Frisco; Great Northern; Northern Pacific; and Spokane Portland & Seattle.

BNSF was created in 1995 when Burlington Northern Inc. (the parent company of Burlington Northern Railroad) merged with Santa Fe Pacific Corporation (parent company of the Atchison Topeka & Santa Fe Railway). The company was acquired by Berkshire Hathaway in 2010 and BNSF now operates as a subsidiary of that company.

EXECUTIVES

Evp And Coo, Carl R. Ice, age 62
Evp Law And Corporate Affairs, Roger Nober, age 54
Evp And Cfo, Julie A. Piggott
Evp And Chief Marketing Officer, Stevan B. Bobb
Evp Operations, Gregory C. Fox
Vice President Federal Government Affairs, Amy Hawkins
Executive Vice President Law And Government Affairs And Secretary, Jeffrey Moreland
Vice President Network Strategy, Dean Wise
Vice President Controller, Dannis Johnson
Chairman President And Ceo, Matthew K. (Matt) Rose, age 60
Auditors: Deloitte & Touche LLP

LOCATIONS

HQ: Burlington Northern & Santa Fe Railway Co, (The) 2650 Lou Menk Drive, Fort Worth, TX 76131-2830
Phone: 800 795-2673
Web: www.bnsf.com

PRODUCTS/OPERATIONS

2018 Sales

	$ mil.	% of total
Consumer Products	7,902	33
Industrial Products	5,967	25
Agricultural Products	4,697	20
Coal	4,012	17
Other revenues	1,277	5
Total	**23,855**	**100**

COMPETITORS

CSX	Kansas City Southern
Canadian National Railway	Railway
Canadian Pacific Railway	Norfolk Southern
	Union Pacific Railroad

HISTORICAL FINANCIALS

Company Type: Public

Income Statement

FYE: December 31

	REVENUE ($ mil.)	NET INCOME ($ mil.)	NET PROFIT MARGIN	EMPLOYEES
12/17	20,747	12,119	58.4%	41,000
12/16	19,278	4,260	22.1%	41,000
12/15	21,401	4,915	23.0%	44,000
12/14	22,714	4,397	19.4%	48,000
12/13	21,552	4,271	19.8%	43,000
Annual Growth	**(0.9%)**	**29.8%**	**—**	**(1.2%)**

2017 Year-End Financials

Debt ratio: 1.74%	No. of shares (mil.): 0
Return on equity: 20.75%	Dividends
Cash ($ mil.): 516	Yield: —
Current ratio: 1.01	Payout: —
Long-term debt ($ mil.): 1,355	Market value ($ mil.): —

Burlington Stores Inc

Burlington Stores (dba Burlington Coat Factory) takes the "Brrr!" out of your life. The clothing retailer which made its name selling coats operates nearly 700 no-frills retail stores (averaging 70000 square feet) offering off-price current brand-name clothing in about 45 states plus Puerto Rico. Although it is one of the nation's largest coat sellers the stores also sells a full wardrobe of products including children's apparel bath items furniture gifts jewelry linens and shoes. Sister chains include a pair of higher-priced Cohoes Fashions shops a pair of Super Baby Depot stores and about ten MJM Designer Shoe stores. Burlington Stores was founded in 1972.

Operations

Almost all Burlington's sales are rung up at its Burlington Coat Factory Warehouse stores. Women's ready-to-wear apparel is its biggest earner at a quarter of sales followed by accessories and shoes (more than 20%) menswear (20%) youth and baby apparel (15%) home (15%) and coats (5%).

Its three other smaller businesses — Cohoes Fashions (off-price designer apparel) MJM Designer Shoe and Super Baby Depot — account for the rest. As its name suggests Super Baby Depot's two stores sell baby clothing accessories furniture and everything else a baby might need in the middle to higher price range. The company's MJM Designer Shoe sells brand names at significant discounts. Cohoes Fashions offers products similar to those offered by the mainline stores.

Geographic Reach

New Jersey-based Burlington has stores in 45 states and Puerto Rico. Its four primarily distribution centers which ship almost all its merchandise are located in Edgewater Park and Burlington New Jersey and San Bernardino and Redlands California. Three warehouses support its distribution centers.

Sales and Marketing

Burlington Coat Factory takes less of a markup than its department store competition and has lower profit margins than other clothing retailers. It buys the coats early in the season (up to five months before department stores) to lock in lower prices.

The company's marketing channels include TV direct mail email digital and social marketing and radio.

Financial Performance

Burlington Stores has recorded increasing revenue and profits over the last six years.

In fiscal 2019 (ended February 2) the company's sales grew 9% to $6.6 billion thanks to store openings and higher like-for-like sales partially offset by one less trading week than fiscal 2018 (which was a 53-week year). Burlington opened 46 net stores during the year taking the total to 675.

Net income grew 8% to $414.7 million due to higher sales and increased margins partially offset by an increase in income tax expenses. Burlington kept a lid on cost of sales which benefited from strong merchandise margins and store related costs which fell relative to sales.

Burlington's cash on hand fell $26.9 million during fiscal 2019 ending the year at $134.2 million. The company's operations generated $639.7 million offset by the $298.5 million used in its investing activities and $368.1 million used in its financing. Burlington's main cash uses in 2019 were capital expenditures (such as store openings) and share repurchases.

Strategy

Burlington's growth strategy is fairly simple: grow its store base refine its business model improve its customer segmentation and drive e-commerce growth.

Store openings are Burlington's main route to growth. The company has identified 1000 viable new store locations and has been adding 30-40 stores each year toward that goal. It reached 675 at the end of fiscal 2019 (ended February 2).

To refine its business model Burlington is reducing store inventories to accelerate inventory turnover and is deploying business intelligence systems to identify sell-through rates capitalize on the best performers and identify upcoming trends. These efforts are tied in with its goal of appealing more to its core demographic of women aged 25-49 with $25000-$100000 in household income. It hopes that by improving the attractiveness of its ready-to-wear clothing it will result in upsell across all categories increasing store performance.

HISTORY

Russian-Jewish immigrant Abe Milstein and a partner started coat wholesaler and manufacturer Milstein and Feigelson in 1924. Abe's son Monroe was a quick study. He graduated from New York University with a business degree in 1946 at age 19 and started his own coat and suit wholesaling business called Monroe G. Milstein Inc. His mother provided free labor at her son's company six days a week to keep the business alive. Abe ended his partnership in 1953 and joined his son's business.

Family relations were strained temporarily in 1972 when Monroe disregarded his father's advice not to buy a faltering coat factory outlet store in Burlington New Jersey. (Abe believed that his son did not have enough retailing experience.) Monroe however thought owning a retail store would provide a guaranteed sales outlet for their merchandise and he bought Burlington Coat Factory for $675000 (using $60000 of his wife Henrietta's savings). His company also adopted the Burlington Coat Factory Warehouse moniker as its own.

To become less dependent on the season-specific coat business the company soon expanded its merchandise mix by adding a children's division (started by Henrietta deceased in 2001) and subleased departments. It opened a second store in Long Island New York in 1975.

Settling a trademark dispute with fabric maker Burlington Industries in 1981 Burlington Coat Factory agreed to say in advertising — as it does to this day — that the two companies are not affiliated. The 31-store company went public two years later using the money it raised to open almost 30 stores that year. As part of its expansion in the 1980s Burlington Coat Factory opened stores in warmer climates such as Texas and Florida.

The firm tried to grow through acquisitions that decade but failed in its attempts to buy a number of department store retailers. It made a successful bid in 1989 for New York discount retailer Cohoes.

Burlington Coat Factory's sales topped the $1 billion mark for the first time in fiscal 1993. Also that year the company bought Boston-based off-price family apparel chain Decelle. It then opened its first store outside the US (in Mexico) and tried new stand-alone store concepts based on successful in-store departments such as Luxury Linens and Baby Depot. A warm winter in 1994 hurt the company: Profits fell by two-thirds and it sold off inventory for two years afterward.

The company pulled a line of men's parkas in late 1998 after a Humane Society investigation revealed that the coats were trimmed with hair from dogs killed inhumanely in China. Burlington Coat Factory launched a baby gift registry in 2000 and later that year opened a silk floral division in selected stores. In 2001 the company acquired 16 stores formerly occupied by bankrupt Montgomery Ward. Burlington Coat Factory began operating MJM Designer Shoes in fiscal 2002 opening nine of the stand-alone specialty shoe stores. The company closed its Decelle stores in 2003 but converted most of them to the Burlington Coat Factory and Cohoes names while launching 25 new stores in 2004 (most under the Burlington Coat Factory moniker).

In 2005 the company opened two Super Baby Depot stores. Burlington Coat Factory was acquired by the Boston-based private equity firm Bain Capital Partners in April 2006 for about $2.1 billion.

In fiscal year 2006 the company opened three MJM Designer Shoes stores. The company's two stand-alone Luxury Linens stores were shut down and instead operate as departments within Burlington Coat Factory stores.

In December 2008 Thomas Kingsbury was named president and CEO of Burlington Coat Factory Warehouse succeeding Mark Nesci who retired after 37 years with the retailer. Prior to joining the company Kingsbury was a SEVP at Kohl's.

In February 2010 the company changed its fiscal year end from May to January to better comply with its peers in the retail industry. In October Burlington Coat Factory agreed to pay $10 million to settle a long-running legal fight with Italian luxury goods maker Fendi over the sale of counterfeit handbags and other leather goods.

Burlington went public in 2013.

EXECUTIVES

Chairman President And Ceo, Thomas A. (Tom) Kingsbury, age 66, $1,164,257 total compensation
Cfo And Principal, Marc D. Katz, age 54, $654,400 total compensation
Evp General Counsel And Corporate Secretary, Janet L. Dhillon, age 56
Chief Merchandising Officer And Principal, Jennifer Vecchio, age 53, $677,195 total compensation

Chief Customer Officer And Principal, Fred Hand, age 55, $654,400 total compensation
Evp And Chief Marketing Officer, Hobart (Bart) Sichel, age 54, $326,923 total compensation
Evp Supply Chain Corporate Services And Asset Protection, Mike Metheny, age 52
Evp Merchandising, Rick Seeger, age 57, $629,826 total compensation
Evp Stores, Forrest David Coder
Evp Planning & Allocation And Merchandise Information Operations (mio), Eliot M. Rosenfield
Vp Merchandising Shoes And Accessories, Mario Gentile
Vp Planning And Design, Ronald Kaplan
Vp Ecommerce, Brian Questad
Regional Vice President, Marty Frent
Senior Vice President Real Estate Construction And Facilities, Gayle Aertker
Svp Profit Improvement, Pete Cupps
Vice President And Assistant Treasurer, Jeff Laub
Senior Vice President Visual Merchandise, Jean Marie Hill
Senior Vice President Planning And Allocation, Fran Jose
Vp Compensation Benefits And Hris, Anna Langenhan
Vice President Procurement, Jim Saurborn
Executive Vice President Human Resources, Joyce Manning
Vice President Planning And Allocation, Michael Cane
Vice President Vice President, Nancy Pickus
Vp Facilities, Shirley Culman
Vice President Store Administration, Steve Riley
Svp Stores Territory 5 South East U.s. And Puerto Rico, Troy Steiner
Vice President Advertising, Warren Johnson
Executive Vice President Supply Chain, Charlie Guardiola
Vice President Accounting Operations, Tony Hughes
Vp Store Operations And Customer Service, Susan Hilton
Vp And Assistant Secretary, Christopher Schaub
Vice President Chief Accounting Officer And Treasurer, Robert Lapenta
Regional Vice President, Richard Catapano
Evp Merchandising, Siiri Dougherty
Senior Vice President Gmm Ladies Apparel, Nancy Mair
Vice President Human Resources, Susan Katims
Svp Stores, Hank Wagner
Vice President, Andrew Milstein
Vp Divisional Merchandise Manager Housewares And Tabletop, Michael Kasprowicz
Auditors: Deloitte & Touche LLP

LOCATIONS

HQ: Burlington Stores Inc
2006 Route 130 North, Burlington, NJ 08016
Phone: 609 387-7800
Web: www.burlingtonstores.com

2017 Stores

	No.
Texas	67
California	66
Florida	46
New York	41
Illinois	34
Pennsylvania	33
New Jersey	31
Ohio	24
Georgia	19
Michigan	18
Virginia	18
Maryland	16
North Carolina	15
Massachusetts	14
Arizona	12
Indiana	12
Washington	12

Connecticut	11
Puerto Rico	11
Wisconsin	10
Missouri	9
Minnesota	8
South Carolina	8
Tennessee	8
Colorado	7
Louisiana	7
Nevada	7
Alabama	6
Arizona	5
Kansas	5
Kentucky	5
Rhode Island	5
Utah	5
Oregon	4
Delaware	3
Iowa	3
Mississippi	3
Nebraska	3
New Hampshire	3
New Mexico	3
Oklahoma	3
Arkansas	2
Idaho	2
Maine	2
North Dakota	1
South Dakota	1
Online Store	1
Total	**629**

PRODUCTS/OPERATIONS

2019 Sales

	% of total
Women's ready-to-wear apparel	23
Accessories & Footwear	22
Menswear	20
Youth Apparel/Baby	16
Home	14
Coats	5
Total	**100**

2019 Stores

	No.
Burlington Stores	661
MJM Designer Shoes	9
Cohoes Fashions	2
Super Baby Depot	2
Online Store	1
Total	**629**

Selected Store Banners

Burlington Coat Factory Warehouse (value-priced apparel accessories linens bath items gifts)
Cohoes Fashions (higher-priced apparel and accessories)
MJM Designer Shoes (designer and fashion shoes)
Super Baby Depot (baby clothing accessories furniture)

COMPETITORS

Ascena Retail	Nordstrom
Babies "R" Us	Payless ShoeSource
Bed Bath & Beyond	Ross Stores
Belk	Saks
Bon-Ton Stores	Sears
DSW	Stein Mart
Dillard's	TJX Companies
Kohl's	Target Corporation
Macy's	Wal-Mart

HISTORICAL FINANCIALS

Company Type: Public

Income Statement				FYE: February 2
	REVENUE ($ mil.)	NET INCOME ($ mil.)	NET PROFIT MARGIN	EMPLOYEES
02/19	6,668	414	6.2%	44,000
02/18*	6,110	384	6.3%	40,000
01/17	5,590	215	3.9%	40,000
01/16	5,129	150	2.9%	37,500
01/15	4,849	65	1.4%	34,000
Annual Growth	**8.3%**	**58.4%**	**—**	**6.7%**

*Fiscal year change

2019 Year-End Financials

Debt ratio: 32.04%
Return on equity: 203.13%
Cash ($ mil.): 112
Current ratio: 1.02
Long-term debt ($ mil.): 983

No. of shares (mil.): 67
Dividends
  Yield: —
  Payout: —
Market value ($ mil.): 11,540

	STOCK PRICE ($) FY Close	P/E High/Low		PER SHARE ($) Earnings	Dividends	Book Value
02/19	171.87	28	18	6.04	0.00	4.81
02/18*	115.75	23	14	5.48	0.00	1.28
01/17	80.91	29	16	3.01	0.00	(0.71)
01/16	53.73	30	20	1.99	0.00	(1.37)
01/15	49.89	58	27	0.87	0.00	(0.88)
Annual Growth	36.2%	—	—	62.3%	—	—

*Fiscal year change

Business First Bancshares Inc

Auditors: Hannis T. Bourgeois, LLP

LOCATIONS

HQ: Business First Bancshares Inc
  500 Laurel Street, Suite 101, Baton Rouge, LA 70801
Phone: 225 248-7600
Web: www.b1bank.com

HISTORICAL FINANCIALS
Company Type: Public

Income Statement				FYE: December 31
	ASSETS ($ mil.)	NET INCOME ($ mil.)	INCOME AS % OF ASSETS	EMPLOYEES
12/18	2,094	14	0.7%	333
12/17	1,321	4	0.4%	219
12/16	1,105	5	0.5%	208
12/15	1,076	4	0.4%	184
12/14	684	4	0.6%	—
Annual Growth	32.3%	36.7%	—	—

2018 Year-End Financials

Debt ratio: 1.19%
Return on equity: 6.41%
Cash ($ mil.): 96
Current ratio: —
Long-term debt ($ mil.): —

No. of shares (mil.): 13
Dividends
  Yield: 0.9%
  Payout: 30.7%
Market value ($ mil.): 320

	STOCK PRICE ($) FY Close	P/E High/Low		PER SHARE ($) Earnings	Dividends	Book Value
12/18	24.23	23	17	1.22	0.24	19.68
Annual Growth	—	—	—	—	—	—

Byline Bancorp Inc

Auditors: Moss Adams LLP

LOCATIONS

HQ: Byline Bancorp Inc
  180 North LaSalle Street, Suite 300, Chicago, IL 60601
Phone: 773 244-7000
Web: www.bylinebancorp.com

HISTORICAL FINANCIALS
Company Type: Public

Income Statement				FYE: December 31
	ASSETS ($ mil.)	NET INCOME ($ mil.)	INCOME AS % OF ASSETS	EMPLOYEES
12/18	4,942	41	0.8%	943
12/17	3,366	21	0.6%	844
12/16	3,295	66	2.0%	791
12/15	2,479	(14)	—	—
Annual Growth	25.8%	—	—	—

2018 Year-End Financials

Debt ratio: 0.74%
Return on equity: 7.43%
Cash ($ mil.): 121
Current ratio: —
Long-term debt ($ mil.): —

No. of shares (mil.): 36
Dividends
  Yield: —
  Payout: 1.9%
Market value ($ mil.): 605

	STOCK PRICE ($) FY Close	P/E High/Low		PER SHARE ($) Earnings	Dividends	Book Value
12/18	16.66	20	13	1.18	0.00	17.90
12/17	22.97	59	50	0.38	0.00	15.64
12/16	0.00			3.27	0.00	15.54
Annual Growth	—	—	—	(28.8%)	—	4.8%

Cadence Bancorporation

EXECUTIVES

Chb-Ceo, Paul B Murphy Jr
V Chb*, Joseph W Evans
Pres, Samuel M Tortorici
Exec V Pres-Cfo, Valerie C Toalson
Exec V Pres-General Counsel-SE, Jerry W Powell
Exec V Pres, David F Black
Evp, R H Holmes IV
Chief Talent Officer, Sheila E Ray
Auditors: Ernst & Young LLP

LOCATIONS

HQ: Cadence Bancorporation
  2800 Post Oak Boulevard, Suite 3800, Houston, TX 77056
Phone: 713 871-4000
Web: www.cadencebank.com

HISTORICAL FINANCIALS
Company Type: Public

Income Statement				FYE: December 31
	ASSETS ($ mil.)	NET INCOME ($ mil.)	INCOME AS % OF ASSETS	EMPLOYEES
12/18	12,730	166	1.3%	1,811
12/17	10,948	102	0.9%	1,206
12/16	9,530	65	0.7%	1,193
12/15	8,811	39	0.4%	—
12/14	0	44	—	—
Annual Growth	—	38.8%	—	—

2018 Year-End Financials

Debt ratio: 2.52%
Return on equity: 11.89%
Cash ($ mil.): 760
Current ratio: —
Long-term debt ($ mil.): —

No. of shares (mil.): 82
Dividends
  Yield: 3.2%
  Payout: 27.9%
Market value ($ mil.): 1,384

	STOCK PRICE ($) FY Close	P/E High/Low		PER SHARE ($) Earnings	Dividends	Book Value
12/18	16.78	16	8	1.97	0.55	17.43
12/17	27.12	22	16	1.25	0.00	16.25
Annual Growth	(11.3%)	—	—	12.0%	—	1.8%

Caesars Entertainment Corp

The palaces owned by this Caesar are part of a vast gaming empire. One of the world's largest gambling companies Caesars Entertainment Corporation owns and operates about 50 casinos mostly in the US and the UK. Properties include some of the biggest names on the Las Vegas Strip including Caesars Palace and Planet Hollywood. Operations which comprise hotels riverboat casinos and gaming establishments boast millions of square feet of casino space and thousands of hotel rooms. The company owns the World Series of Poker brand and tournaments through Caesars Interactive. Most revenue is generated in the US. Caesars has agreed to be acquired by Eldorado Resorts in a deal worth $17.3 billion.

HISTORY

William Harrah and his father founded their first bingo parlor in Reno Nevada in 1937. Using the income from that business Harrah opened his first casino Harrah's Club in downtown Reno in 1946. In 1955 and 1956 he bought several clubs in Stateline Nevada (near Lake Tahoe). Harrah built the company by using promotions to draw middle-class Californians to his clubs.

During the 1960s the entrepreneur expanded his operations in Lake Tahoe and in 1968 he built a 400-room hotel tower in Reno. Harrah's went public in 1971. After Harrah's death in 1978 the company expanded outside Nevada by building a hotel and casino in Atlantic City New Jersey.

Holiday Inns bought Harrah's in 1980 for about $300 million. The hotelier already owned a 40% interest in River Boat Casino which operated a casino next to a Holiday Inn in Las Vegas. When Holiday Inns acquired the other 60% of the casino/hotel in 1983 Harrah's took over its management. Holiday Inns became Holiday Corporation in 1985. The following year UK brewer Bass PLC put up $100 million for 10% of Holiday Corporation.

In 1990 Bass acquired the Holiday Inn hotel chain for $2.2 billion. The rest of Holiday Corporation including Harrah's was renamed Promus under chairman Michael Rose.

In the early 1990s Harrah's built a casino on Ak-Chin Indian land near Phoenix and opened riverboat casinos in Joliet Illinois; Shreveport Louisiana; and North Kansas City Missouri. In 1995 Promus spun off its hotel operations as Promus Hotel Corporation and changed the name of its casino business to Harrah's Entertainment. (Promus was acquired by Hilton Hotels later called Hilton Worldwide in 1999.)

Also in 1995 Harrah's gambled and lost. Big. Its New Orleans casino was shelved even before it was finished — a victim of Louisiana's Byzantine politics. Eager for the right to build what would be a $395 million 200000-sq.-ft. casino in the heart of the city Harrah's had made a number of ill-advised concessions to state and municipal officials. It agreed not to offer hotel rooms or food at the casino (forgoing about 20% of anticipated revenues) and promised to make an annual $100 million minimum payment to the state in addition to 19% of the casino's revenues. In the end the fiasco's price tag reached $900 million (only half of which went to casino construction costs) and Harrah's put the project into bankruptcy to stop the bleeding. (It resumed construction in 1999 and finally opened the casino at the end of the year.)

In 1997 Rose retired as chairman and was replaced by CEO Philip Satre. In 1998 Harrah's bought competitor Showboat with properties in Las Vegas and Atlantic City and management of a New South Wales Australia casino. A Louisiana Supreme Court ruling that year allowed the company to resume work on the New Orleans casino (albeit with a stake of less than 45% which was later increased to 63%). Harrah's also invested in Las Vegas-based National Airlines that year.

In early 1999 Harrah's bought Rio Hotel & Casino (also a partner in National Airlines) which operates one upscale casino on the Las Vegas Strip for about $525 million. In 2000 the company bought riverboat casino operator Players International for $425 million. Also that year Harrah's had to write off about $39 million in investments and loans to National Airlines which filed for bankruptcy. The company had a 48% stake in the airline.

Harrah's continued its acquisition streak in 2001 with the purchase of Harveys Casino Resorts with four locations in Colorado Iowa and Nevada for $675 million. (It sold the Colorado location in 2002.) The 452-room Harrah's Atlantic City hotel tower was opened in 2002. Also that year the company began construction of a second 800-room tower at its Atlantic City Showboat casino. Later in 2002 Harrah's acquired the shares of JCC Holding company it didn't already own for $54.1 million. It also acquired Louisiana Downs a Thoroughbred racetrack in Bossier City for $157 million. Harrah's subsequently turned Louisiana Downs into a full-blown casino.

In 2004 Harrah's acquired casino operator Horseshoe Gaming for $1.45 billion. The purchase added several properties to Harrah's portfolio (in Hammond Indiana; Bossier City Louisiana; and Tunica Mississippi). In order to gain regulatory approval for the purchase Harrah's later sold its Harrah's Shreveport casino to Boyd Gaming for $190 million. The sale was intended to limit Harrah's exposure in the Louisiana market.

The following year Harrah's completed a monster-sized deal the $9.4 billion acquisition of rival Caesars Entertainment Inc. which rocketed the company to the top of the gaming world. To appease regulators the company sold its Harrah's Tunica and East Chicago casinos to Colony Capital. In 2005 Harrah's bought the Imperial Palace one of the last few independent casinos on the Las Vegas Strip for $370 million.

The effects of Hurricane Katrina were felt at the company's Biloxi and Gulfport Mississippi locations which suffered extensive damage. Harrah's sold the Gulfport location such as it was and rebuilt the Biloxi site which re-opened in 2006. Also that year Harrah's acquired the remaining assets of Casino Magic Biloxi from Pinnacle Entertainment; Harrah's sold two subsidiaries that own businesses in Lake Charles Louisiana. In addition to the Casino Magic assets Pinnacle paid Harrah's some $25 million in the deal.

In 2006 Harrah's sold its Flamingo Laughlin hotel-casino and an undeveloped land parcel in Atlantic City to American Real Estate Partners. It also purchased casino operator London Clubs International for $586 million. London Clubs operates seven UK casinos as well as two in Egypt and one in South Africa.

The company acquired Macau Orient Golf one of only two golf courses in Macau China in 2007 for some $577 million. It subsequently re-branded the property Caesars Macau Golf. Caesars made the deal to enter the popular Chinese market joining rivals Las Vegas Sands Wynn Resorts and MGM Resorts International which already own casinos in Macau. In 2008 the company ceased to be a publicly traded company after being bought out by two private equity firms.

In 2010 Harrah's purchased the beleaguered Planet Hollywood Resort & Casino in Las Vegas. (The property is separate from Planet Hollywood International). Harrah's was attracted to Planet Hollywood proximity to its other resorts on the Strip as well as its strong brand name. The deal — the company's first new Vegas property since it bought Caesars Palace in 2005 — gave the firm its eighth connected property on the Strip's east side.

Also in 2010 the company filed to go public. However later that year it cancelled the IPO due to unfavorable market conditions and weak investor demand. In addition to its massive debt Harrah's lacked interest from investors due to the fact that its holdings are focused on domestic markets and the company has no plans to expand in the fast-growing Chinese market of Macau where its competitors have had much success.

After cancelling the IPO the company changed its name from Harrah's Entertainment to Caesars Entertainment Corporation. Though it continues to use the Harrah's brand at one of its bigger properties the company made the identity change to capitalize on the Caesar's name which it sees as "the world's preeminent and most respected casino brand."

The company went public in 2012 raising little more than $16 million in a small IPO.

EXECUTIVES

Evp Government Relations And Corporate Responsibility, Janis L. (Jan) Jones Blackhurst, age 71

President And Ceo, Mark P. Frissora, age 63, $1,976,923 total compensation

Evp General Counsel And Chief Regulatory And Compliance Officer, Timothy R. (Tim) Donovan, age 63, $703,990 total compensation

Global President, Thomas M. (Tom) Jenkin, age 64, $1,206,841 total compensation

President Global Development And Chief Development Officer, Marco A. Roca, age 54

President Hospitality, Robert J. (Bob) Morse, age 63, $854,845 total compensation

Evp Human Resources, Mary H. Thomas, age 52

Evp Public Affairs And Communications, Richard D. Broome, age 60

Cfo, Eric Hession, age 45, $703,990 total compensation

President International Development, Steven M. Tight, age 63

Evp And Cio, Les Ottolenghi, age 57

Evp Gaming And Interactive Entertainment, Christian Stuart

Vice President, John Maddox

Executive Vice President, Tariq Shaukat

Vice President Information Technology, Scott Campbell

Vice President Property Information Technology Operations, Mike LaPointe

Vice President And Assistant General Manager, Tracey Witchko

Vice President Finance, Jacqueline Beato

Vice President Of Human Resources, Jennifer Jennings

Vice President Risk Management, Brad Waldron

Vice President Of Finance, Brad Belhouse

Corporate Vp Customer Loyalty, Lisa Yahrling

Senior Vice President Partner And Channel Marketing, Annette Weishaar

Senior Vice President Development, Mike Salzman

Vice President, Diana Caballero

Regional Vp Marketing, Mary Riley

Vice President Of Global Infrastructure, Shawn Mcgovern

Senior Vice President And General Manager, Jonathan Jones

Regional Assistant Vice President Of Marketing, Renee Nadeau

Vice President Of Csa, Terry Byrnes

Vice President Of Slot Operations, Stephen Bimson

National Sales Manager, Sharon Goodspeed

Vice President, Mike Stratton

Vice President Marketing Operations, Marilyn Janssen

Vice President Tax, Craig Fjelsted

Vice President Email Marketing, Christopher Jenner

National Sales Manager, Jason Gaudet

Vice President Information Technology Development, Charley Paelinck

Vice President Of Strategic Data, Dave Kowal

Regional Vice President Human Resources, Lori Yeager

Vice President Of Hospitality Operations, Scott Lokke

National Sales Manager, Bre Glisan

Vice President And Associate Chief Counsel Employment Law, Jeffrey D Winchester

National Sales Manager, Teresa Hemphill

Vice President Of Procurement, Jessica Rosman

Vice President Of Player Development, Steve Moy

Vice President International Marketing, Bruce Bommarito

Vice President Hotel Operations, Steve Opdyke

Vice President Financial Assurance, Sam Rubenstein

Vice President Of Finance, Jim Janchar

National Sales Manager, Erick Harrell

Vice President And Executive Associate, Spyro Costopoulos

Vice President Of National Marketing, Joseph Watson

Vice President Player Development, Gerry Green

National Sales Manager, Misty Sparks

Citywide Vice President Latin Marketing, Joe Ripoll

Portfolio Vice President, Andrew Kesler

Vp Marketing Los Angeles Branch, Lynda Thipavong

Svp Chief Analytics Officer, Gene Lee

National Sales Manager, Judy Sereni

Vice President Of National Ticketing, Amy Graca

Vice President Human Resources, Colleen Moore

Vice President Of Human Resources, Melinda Mackey

Vice President Casino Operations, William Kelly

National Sales Manager, Peter Cancila

Vice President On Property Analytics, David Wolkoff

Vp Finance, Janae Sternberg

Senior Vice President Marketing And Chief Experience Officer, Michael Marino

Regional Vice President Government Relations, Joseph Tyrrell

Vp Entertainment Finance Planning And Analytics Caesars Entertainment, Rebecca Cates

Vice President Gaming Analytics, Nathan Armogan

Vice President Casino Marketing For Planet Hollywood Ballys Paris, Jim Korona

National Sales Manager, Grant Kehler

Vice President Government Relations, Karlos Lasane

Vice President Player Development, Sandra Zobrist

Vice President Of Human Resources And Property Develo, Ricky Busey

Vice President Of Total Rewards And Promotions, Matthew Bowers

National Sales Manager, September Gratton

National Sales Manager, David Diomedes

Vice President Casino Marketing, Eric Zilewicz

Vice President Of Finance Las Vegas Region, Boris Petkov

Vice President Chief Accounting Officer Caesars Entertainment Operating Company, Ken Kuick

Vice President Operations, JC Rieger

Vice President Assistant Controller, Kenneth Kuick

Corporate Vice President Of Human Resources, Jeff Wagner

Vice President Of Casino Operations Casino Marketing And Retail, Xenia Wunderlich

Vice President Of Environmental Compliance, Kathy Vailes

Vice President And Deputy General Counsel, Bill Buffalo

National Sales Manager, Stacey Purcell

Vice President Revenue Management, William Beine

Vice President Corporate Marketing, Joe Somma

Vice President Table Games, Dan Burdalski

Nnv Vice President Of Finance And Player Development, Bob Owens

Vice President Revenue Management, James Larsen

Vice President Asian Marketing, Ernest Wu

Vice President Of Hospitality Marketing, Jared Rapier

Vice President Information Technology Development, Mike Harty

Vice President Corporate Communications, Jennifer Forkish

National Sales Manager, Jennifer Flacke

Vice President National Marketing, Thomas Fiore

Vice President Of Food, Sean DiCicco

Regional Vice President Government Relations, Aj Baker

National Sales Manager, Jennifer Kishpaugh-stotz

Vice President Of Beverage, Ryan Voss

Vice President Customer Development, Rick Zeller

Vice President Information Technology Business Management, John Dermody

Vice President Enterprise Project Management And Strategic Initiatives, Rias Attar

National Sales Manager, Lester Robinson

National Sales Manager In Market, Andrea Romano

Vice President Of Corporate Hotel Operations, Christopher Najbicz

Assistant Vice President, Franco D'Angelo

Senior Vice President Aml And Ofac Officer, Benjamin Floyd

Evp Public Policy And Corporate Responsibility, Jan Jones Blackhurst

National Sales Manager, Kate Sklarski

Vp Advertising Digital Marketing And Ecommerce, Jeff Dekorte

National Sales Manager, Brian Crumby

Vice President Ess Credit, William Gormley

Svp Global It Infrastructure And Operations, Jay Fredericks

Vice President Information Technology, Pete Braitsch

Vice President Human Resources, Christina Krakowsky

National Sales Manager, Dawn Barth

Chairman, James Hunt

Board Member, Christopher Williams

Pac Treasurer, Lindsay Garcia

Auditors: DELOITTE & TOUCHE LLP

LOCATIONS

HQ: Caesars Entertainment Corp
One Caesars Palace Drive, Las Vegas, NV 89109
Phone: 702 407-6000
Web: www.caesars.com

2017 Sales

	$ mil.	% of total
Las Vegas	2,897	60
Other US	1,756	36
All Other	199	4
Total	**4,852**	**100**

PRODUCTS/OPERATIONS

2017 Sales

	$ mil.	% of total
Casino	2,865	52
Hotel Rooms	1,054	19
Food and Beverage	938	17
Other	626	11
Reimbursed Management Costs	48	1
Casino Promotional Allowances	(679)	-
Total	**4,852**	**100**

COMPETITORS

Boyd Gaming	Mashantucket Pequot
Isle of Capri Casinos	Station Casinos
Kerzner International	Tropicana
Las Vegas Sands	Entertainment
MGM Resorts	Trump Resorts
MGP	Wynn Resorts

HISTORICAL FINANCIALS

Company Type: Public

Income Statement				FYE: December 31
	REVENUE ($ mil.)	NET INCOME ($ mil.)	NET PROFIT MARGIN	EMPLOYEES
12/18	8,391	303	3.6%	66,000
12/17	4,852	(375)	—	65,000
12/16	3,877	(3,569)	—	31,000
12/15	4,654	5,920	127.2%	33,000
12/14	8,516	(2,783)	—	68,000
Annual Growth	(0.4%)	—	—	(0.7%)

2018 Year-End Financials

Debt ratio: 73.88%	No. of shares (mil.): 624
Return on equity: 9.36%	Dividends
Cash ($ mil.): 1,491	Yield: —
Current ratio: 1.13	Payout: —
Long-term debt ($ mil.): 18,858	Market value ($ mil.): 4,237

	STOCK PRICE ($) FY Close	P/E High/Low		PER SHARE ($) Earnings	Dividends	Book Value
12/18	6.79	33	13	0.41	0.00	5.21
12/17	12.65	—	—	(1.35)	0.00	4.71
12/16	8.50	—	—	(24.41)	0.00	(21.61)
12/15	7.89	0	0	40.26	0.00	6.81
12/14	15.69	—	—	(19.53)	0.00	(34.46)
Annual Growth	(18.9%)			—	—	—

Cambridge Bancorp

Cambridge Bancorp is the nearly $2 billion-asset holding company for Cambridge Trust Company a community bank serving Cambridge and the Greater Boston area through about a dozen branch locations in Massachusetts. It offers standard retail products and services including checking and savings accounts CDs IRAs and credit cards. Residential mortgages including home equity loans account for about 50% of the company's loan portfolio while commercial real estate loans make up more than 40%. The company also offers commercial industrial and consumer loans. Established in 1892 the bank also offers trust and investment management services.

Operations

The commercial bank operates a traditional retail banking line focused on lending as well as its Wealth Management Group which investment management and trust business. The bank had $1.8 billion in total assets and $2.4 billion in client assets under management at the end of 2015.

As with other retail banks Cambridge Bancorp makes the bulk of its revenue from interest income. About 58% of its total revenue came from loan interest during 2015 while another 10% came from interest on taxable and tax-exempt investment securities. The rest of its revenue came from wealth management income (24% of revenue) deposit account fees (3%) ATM/Debit card income (1%) and other non-interest income sources.

Geographic Reach

Cambridge Bancorp has 12 branches in Massachusetts in Cambridge Boston Belmont Concord Lexington Lincoln and Weston. It also has wealth management offices in Boston as well as in New Hampshire in Concord Manchester and Portsmouth.

Sales and Marketing

The company spent $2.38 million on marketing during 2015 up from $2.12 million in 2014.

Financial Performance

Cambridge's annual revenues and profits have been steadily rising over the past several years thanks to continued commercial real estate mortgage growth and as its Wealth Management business has nearly doubled its managed assets since 2011 spurring higher fee revenue.

The bank's revenue climbed 7% to $80.2 million during 2015 on 10% loan growth mostly driven by commercial real estate loans which spurred higher interest income. The company's wealth management business income grew 7% as its client assets continued to grow with new investor inflows.

Revenue growth in 2015 drove Cambridge Bancorp's net income up 5% to $15.7 million. The bank's operating cash levels rose 24% to $20 million for the year with an increase in cash-based earnings and favorable changes in working capital mostly related to a change in accrued interest receivable deferred taxes and other assets and liabilities.

Strategy

Cambridge Bancorp continued in 2016 to lean on the success of its commercial mortgage business though it plans to pivot more to commercial and industrial lending to diversify its commercial lending portfolio.

To better prepare for rising interest rates Cambridge Bancorp in 2015 and 2016 modified its commercial loan strategy from long-term fixed-rate loans (which are vulnerable to interest rate risk) to a new interest rate derivative product to offer an alternative long-term financing for its customers while helping the bank earn a variable rate of interest on its loans. For its consumer banking unit the bank in 2015 began a plan to sell the majority of its long-term residential mortgage production including secondary loans to the secondary market.

EXECUTIVES

Chairman President And Ceo, Denis K. Sheahan, age 53
Svp And Chief Investment Officer, James F. Spencer
Svp Commercial Real Estate Cambridge Trust, Martin B. Millane
Evp And Cio Cambridge Trust, Lynne M. Burrow
Evp And Head Of Wealth Management Cambridge Trust, Michael A. Duca
Evp And Consumer Banking Director Cambridge Trust, Thomas A. Johnson
Cfo, Michael Carotenuto
Svp And President Cambridge Trust Company Of New Hampshire, Susan Martore-Baker
Svp And Marketing Director, Robert N. Siegrist
Vp Finance, Patricia Hartnett
Vice President, Laura Mcgregor
Assistant Vice President And Tax Manager, Theresa Giglio
Assistant Vp Private Banking, Scott Mcgill
Avp Compliance Officer, Philip Pace
Assistant Vice President And Branch Manager, Fenton Martin
Vice President And Manager Of Community Business Development, Dina Scianna
Avp Hr Business Partner And Recruiter, Ashley Thomas
Auditors: KPMG LLP

LOCATIONS

HQ: Cambridge Bancorp
1336 Massachusetts Avenue, Cambridge, MA 02138
Phone: 617 876-5500
Web: www.cambridgetrust.com

PRODUCTS/OPERATIONS

2015 Sales

	% of total
Interest Income	
Interest on loans	58
Interest on taxable investment securities	7
Interest on tax exempt investment securities	3
Non-Interest Income	
Wealth Management Income	24
Deposits accounts fee	3
ATM/Debit card income	1
Bank Owned life insurance income	1
Gain on disposition on investment securities	1
Gain on loans held of sale	1
Other income	1
Loan related derivative income	
Total	100

Products/Services

Personal Banking
Checking
Savings CDs & IRAs
Online Banking
Mobile Banking
Mortgages
Home Equity
Credit Cards
Personal Loans
More Services
Business Banking
Checking & Savings
Commercial Lending
Commercial Real Estate
Cash Management
Remote Deposit Capture
Online Banking
Mobile Banking
Professional Services Program
More Services

Wealth Management
Investment Process
Investment Management
Fiduciary & Planning Services
Estate Settlement
Wealth Management Personnel
Forums
Online Access

COMPETITORS

Bank of America	Eastern Bank
Cambridge Financial	Middlesex Savings
Central Bancorp	Peoples Federal
Century Bancorp (MA)	Bancshares Inc.
Citizens Financial Group	

HISTORICAL FINANCIALS

Company Type: Public

Income Statement

	ASSETS ($ mil.)	NET INCOME ($ mil.)	INCOME AS % OF ASSETS	EMPLOYEES
12/18	2,101	23	1.1%	262
12/17	1,949	14	0.8%	247
12/16	1,849	16	0.9%	—
12/15	1,706	15	0.9%	—
12/14	1,573	14	0.9%	—
Annual Growth	7.5%	12.4%	—	—

FYE: December 31

2018 Year-End Financials

Debt ratio: —	No. of shares (mil.): 4
Return on equity: 15.16%	Dividends
Cash ($ mil.): 18	Yield: 2.3%
Current ratio: —	Payout: 41.3%
Long-term debt ($ mil.): —	Market value ($ mil.): 342

	STOCK PRICE ($) FY Close	P/E High/Low	PER SHARE ($) Earnings	Dividends	Book Value
12/18	83.25	16 13	5.77	1.96	40.67
12/17	79.80	24 17	3.61	1.86	36.24
12/16	62.29	15 11	4.15	1.84	33.36
12/15	47.40	13 11	3.93	1.80	31.26
12/14	46.50	13 10	3.78	1.68	29.50
Annual Growth	15.7%	— —	11.2%	3.9%	8.4%

Camden National Corp. (ME)

Camden National Corporation is the holding company for Camden National Bank which boasts nearly 45 branches in about a dozen Maine counties and provides standard deposit products such as checking and savings accounts CDs and IRAs. Commercial mortgages and loans make up 50% of its loan portfolio while residential mortgages make up another 40% and consumer loans constitute the remainder. Subsidiary Acadia Trust provides trust fiduciary investment management and retirement plan administration services while Camden Financial Consultants offers brokerage and insurance services. The largest bank headquartered in Maine Camden National Bank was founded in 1875 and once issued its own US currency.

Operations

About 63% of Camden National's total revenue came from loan interest (including fees) in 2014

while another 15% came from interest on its US government and sponsored enterprise obligations (investment securities). The rest of its revenue came from deposit account service charges (5%) other service charges and fees (5%) income from fiduciary services (4%) brokerage and insurance commissions (2%) and other miscellaneous income sources. The bank had a staff of 471 employees at the end of 2014.

Geographic Reach

Camden National has around 45 branches in 12 counties throughout Maine with one commercial loan office in Manchester New Hampshire. Its primary markets are in the counties of Androscoggin Cumberland Hancock Kennebec Knox Lincoln Penobscot Piscataquis Somerset Waldo Washington and York.

Sales and Marketing

The company offers deposit and loan services to consumers institutions municipalities non-profits and commercial customers.

Financial Performance

The company has struggled to consistently grow its revenues and profits in recent years mostly due to shrinking interest margins on loans amidst the low-interest environment.

Camden National's revenue dipped by 3% to $112.8 million in 2014 mostly because the bank in 2013 had collected a non-recurring $2.7 million gain from the sale of its five Franklin County branches and because its mortgage banking income fell by $1.1 million as it decided to retain most of its 30-year fixed rate residential mortgage production in 2014.

Despite revenue declines in 2014 the bank's net income jumped by 8% to $24.6 million mostly because in 2013 it had recorded a non-recurring $2.8 million goodwill impairment charge related to its financial services reporting unit. Camden's operating cash levels rose by 1% to $29.9 million for the year on higher cash earnings.

Strategy

The bank competes with larger financial institutions by emphasizing customer service to build customer loyalty and long-term relationships. It also sometimes pursues acquisitions of banks and branches in its target markets in Maine to grow its loan and deposit business.

Camden may also be expanding its franchise beyond Maine in future years. In 2014 it opened a commercial loan office in Manchester New Hampshire enabling it to serve more customers across northern New England.

Mergers and Acquisitions

In March 2015 Camden National Corporation agreed to purchase SBM Financial along with its subsidiary The Bank of Maine subsidiary. The deal expected to be completed in late 2015 would add $813 million in assets and make Camden National Bank Maine's largest community bank.

In late 2012 the bank acquired 15 full-service branches from Bank of America for $12 million.

EXECUTIVES

Vice President Risk Management, Steve Matteo
Evp Coo And Cfo, Deborah A. Jordan, age 53, $223,327 total compensation
Evp Retail Banking, June B. Parent, age 55, $189,248 total compensation
Evp Risk Management, Joanne T. Campbell, age 56, $124,585 total compensation
President And Ceo, Gregory A. (Greg) Dufour, age 58, $398,077 total compensation
Svp Information Technology, Scott Buckheit
Evp Commercial Lending, Timothy P. Nightingale, age 61, $213,846 total compensation
Vice President, Richard Nickerson

Vice President Compliance Manager, Jennifer Mazurek
Vice President, Cynthia Bergin
Vice President Information Security Manager, Anthony Mazzeo
Vice President Credit Risk Officer, Susan Weber
Vice President Loan Servicing, Mark Richards
Vice President Of Mortgage Operations, Paul Palmer
Senior Vice President Director Of Corporate Services, Susan Giffard
Vice President Commercial Portfolio Manager, Matthew Gilbert
Senior Vice President Commercial Lending Officer, Stephen Lawrence
Vice President Senior Trust Officer, Lauren Epstein
Chairman Camden National Corporation And Camden National Bank, Karen W. Stanley, age 73
Secretary, Diane Marion
Auditors: RSM US LLP

LOCATIONS

HQ: Camden National Corp. (ME)
2 Elm Street, Camden, ME 04843
Phone: 207 236-8821   Fax: 207 236-6256
Web: www.CamdenNational.com/healthprofunding

PRODUCTS/OPERATIONS

2014 Sales

	$ mil.	% of total
Interest		
Loans including fees	70	63
US government & agency securities	17	14
Other investments	0	1
Noninterest		
Service charges on deposit accounts & others	12	11
Income from fiduciary services	5	4
Brokerage and insurance commission	1	2
Other	5	5
Total	**112**	**100**

COMPETITORS

Bangor Savings Bank	People's United
Bar Harbor Bankshares	Financial
KeyCorp	TD Bank USA
Northeast Bancorp	The First Bancorp
Norway Bancorp	

HISTORICAL FINANCIALS

Company Type: Public

Income Statement   FYE: December 31

	ASSETS ($ mil.)	NET INCOME ($ mil.)	INCOME AS % OF ASSETS	EMPLOYEES
12/18	4,297	53	1.2%	634
12/17	4,065	28	0.7%	636
12/16	3,864	40	1.0%	631
12/15	3,709	20	0.6%	652
12/14	2,789	24	0.9%	471
Annual Growth	**11.4%**	**21.2%**	**—**	**7.7%**

2018 Year-End Financials

Debt ratio: 1.41%
Return on equity: 12.65%
Cash ($ mil.): 67
Current ratio: —
Long-term debt ($ mil.): —

No. of shares (mil.): 15
Dividends
  Yield: 3.0%
  Payout: 47.8%
Market value ($ mil.): 561

	STOCK PRICE ($) FY Close	P/E High/Low	PER SHARE ($) Earnings	Dividends	Book Value
12/18	35.97	14 10	3.39	1.10	27.95
12/17	42.13	26 20	1.82	0.92	25.99
12/16	44.45	19 11	2.57	0.80	25.30
12/15	44.09	26 21	1.73	0.80	23.69
12/14	39.84	19 16	2.19	0.72	22.00
Annual Growth	**(2.5%)**	**— —**	**11.6%**	**11.2%**	**6.2%**

CAMERON INTERNATIONAL CORPORATION

Cameron is a leading manufacturer provider and servicer of oil and gas industry equipment. The company makes products that control pressure at oil and gas wells including blowout preventers chokes controls wellheads measurement tools and valves. The company's products are used for offshore onshore and subsea applications. Cameron is a wholly owned subsidiary of oilfield product and services giant Schlumberger (a major provider of technology for reservoir characterization drilling production and processing services to the oil and gas industry).

Financial Performance

Cameron generates about 15% of Schlumberger's sales. The subsidiary's revenue declined 4% to $6.5 billion on lower sales for its OneSubsea and Valves & Measurements product segments. OneSubsea offers products and services for subsea oil and gas companies including wellheads subsea trees control systems and production system optimization. The company's Valves & Measurements products span valves and measurement systems for oil and gas flow for the upstream midstream and downstream sectors.

Strategy

To keep pace with rivals increasingly adopting automation technology Schlumbeger formed a joint venture in 2019 with Rockwell Automation to form Sensia. Sensia combines Cameron's sensor and measurement products with Rockwell's industrial automation technology and analytics capabilities. The new company's offerings will facilitate automated oilfield operations and connect equipment with software to gather data from sensors and devices. About two-fifths of the JV's revenue is expected to derive from North America.

EXECUTIVES

President Cameron Group, Olivier Le Peuch
Auditors: ERNST & YOUNG LLP HOUSTON TE

LOCATIONS

HQ: CAMERON INTERNATIONAL CORPORATION
4646 W SAM HOUSTON PKWY N, HOUSTON, TX 770418214
Phone: 713 939-2282
Web: WWW.SLB.COM

PRODUCTS/OPERATIONS

Selected Mergers and Acquisitions

COMPETITORS

ABB Inc.
Aker Solutions
Atlas Copco
CIRCOR International
Dresser-Rand
Dril-Quip
Ebara
FMC
Flotek
GE Oil
Ingersoll-Rand Industrial Technologies
McDermott
National Oilwell Varco
Weatherford International

HISTORICAL FINANCIALS

Company Type: Private

Income Statement   FYE: December 31

	REVENUE ($ mil.)	NET INCOME ($ mil.)	NET PROFIT MARGIN	EMPLOYEES
12/14	10,381	848	8.2%	23,000
12/13	9,838	724	7.4%	—
12/12	8,502	750	8.8%	—
Annual Growth	**10.5%**	**6.3%**	**—**	**—**

Campbell Soup Co

Soup boils down to M'm! M'm! Money! at the world's #1 soup maker Campbell Soup. The company's most popular selections among its extensive soup portfolio in the US include chicken noodle tomato and cream of mushroom. Campbell also makes many other simple foods snacks and beverages including SpaghettiOs canned pasta Pace picante sauce V8 beverages Aussie favorite Arnott's biscuits and Pepperidge Farm baked goods (including those popular tiny Goldfish crackers). Newer products for the soup company include Garden Fresh Gourmet salsas and dips and Bolthouse Farms carrots and organic baby foods. Campbell sells its products worldwide.

HISTORY

Campbell Soup Company began in Camden New Jersey in 1869 as a canning and preserving business founded by icebox maker Abram Anderson and fruit merchant Joseph Campbell. Anderson left in 1876 and Arthur Dorrance took his place. The Dorrance family assumed control after Campbell retired in 1894.

Arthur's nephew John Dorrance joined Campbell in 1897. The young chemist soon found a way to condense soup by eliminating most of its water. Without the heavy bulk of water-filled cans distribution was cheaper; Campbell products quickly spread.

In 1904 the firm introduced the Campbell Kids characters. Entering the California market in 1911 Campbell became one of the first US companies to achieve national distribution of a food brand. It bought Franco-American the first American soup maker in 1915.

The company's ubiquity in American kitchens made its soup can an American icon (consider Andy Warhol's celebrated 1960 print) and brought great wealth to the Dorrance family.

With a reputation for conservative management Campbell began to diversify acquiring V8 juice (1948) Swanson (1955) Pepperidge Farm (1961) Godiva Chocolatier (33% in 1966 full ownership in 1974) Vlasic pickles (1978) and Mrs. Paul's seafood (1982). It introduced Prego spaghetti sauce and LeMenu frozen dinners in the early 1980s.

Much of Campbell's sales growth in the 1990s came not from unit sales but from increasing its prices. In 1993 it took a $300 million restructuring charge and over the next two years it sold poor performers at home and abroad. John Sr.'s grandson Bennett Dorrance took up the role of vice chairman in 1993 becoming the first family member to take a senior executive position in 10 years.

Two years later Campbell paid $1.1 billion for Pace Foods (picante sauce) and acquired Fresh

Start Bakeries (buns and muffins for McDonald's) and Homepride (popular cooking sauce in the UK).

As part of its international expansion in 1996 the firm acquired Erasco a top German soup maker and Cheong Chan a food manufacturer in Malaysia. However back at home it sold Mrs. Paul's. In 1997 Campbell sold its Marie's salad dressing operations and bought Groupe Danone's Liebig (France's leading wet-soup brand). Also that year Dale Morrison a relative newcomer to the firm succeeded David Johnson as president and CEO. To reduce costs and focus on other core segments in 1998 Campbell spun off Swanson frozen foods and Vlasic pickles into Vlasic Foods International. (Vlasic later filed bankruptcy and was snapped up in a leveraged buyout.) In 1999 Campbell re-designed its soup can labels altering an American icon.

Morrison resigned abruptly as president and CEO in 2000; Johnson returned to the helm during the search for a permanent chief. In early 2001 Douglas Conant previously of Nabisco Foods joined Campbell as president and CEO. A fresh plan was introduced to spend up to $600 million on marketing product development and quality upgrades (at the expense of shareholder dividends). In 2001 Campbell also bought the Batchelors Royco and Heisse Tasse brands of soup as well as the OXO brand of stock cubes from Unilever for about $900 million. The deal made Campbell the leading soup maker in Europe. In 2003 Campbell bought Snack Foods Limited a leading snack food maker in Australia and Irish dry soup maker Erin Foods from Greencore.

Campbell reorganized its North American business in 2004 into the following units: US Soup Sauces and Beverages; Campbell Away From Home and Canada Mexico and Latin America; Pepperidge Farm; and Godiva Worldwide. (In response to dietary trends the company announced that year that it was removing all trans-fatty acids from its Pepperidge Farm breads.) The company retired the Franco-American brand in 2004; products that carried the brand (most notably Spaghetti-tiOs) now bear the Campbell brand. Also that year company chairman George M. Sherman retired and was replaced by Harvey Golub.

In 2006 Campbell sold its UK and Irish businesses to Premier Foods for about $870 million. Brands involved in the sale included Homepride sauces OXO stock cubes and Batchelors McDonnells and Erin soups.

In 2012 the company purchased Bolthouse Farms for about $1.55 billion from Madison Dearborn Partners. Bolthouse known for selling fresh carrots beverages and salad dressings was expected to further fuel Campbell's US beverage division which had benefited from the rising popularity of the V8 juice brand.

In fiscal 2013 Campbell expanded its access to manufacturing and distribution capabilities in Mexico for its beverages soups broths and sauces after it signed a deal with Grupo Jumex and Conservas La Costeñato. That year it also sold its European simple meals business closing facilities in Belgium France Germany and Sweden.

In August 2013 the soup giant acquired the Denmark-based baked snack maker Kelsen Group for $325 million.

In June 2013 it bought Plum Organics one of the top brands of organic baby food in the US. The company makes organic foods and snacks for babies toddlers and children a fast-growing premium food category. It hoped the purchase would bring a new generation of consumers to Campbell.

EXECUTIVES

Svp; President Global Snacks And Chief Customer Officer, Denise M. Morrison, age 65, $1,100,000 total compensation

Svp And Cfo, Anthony P. DiSilvestro, age 60, $642,500 total compensation

President Americas Simple Meals And Beverages, Mark R. Alexander, age 55, $696,667 total compensation

Svp And General Counsel, Adam G. Ciongoli, age 51, $700,000 total compensation

President Campbell Fresh, Edward L. (Ed) Carolan, age 50

President Global Biscuits And Snacks, Luca Mignini, age 56, $674,042 total compensation

Svp Global Research And Development And Quality, Carlos J. Barroso, age 60, $470,000 total compensation

President Campbell Soup Foundation, Kim Fremont Fortunato

Vp And Chief Technology And Information Officer, Francisco Fraga

Svp Integrated Global Services, Bethmara Kessler

Vice President Business Development Grea, John Shannon

Senior Vice President Global Sales, Alyssa Bansky

Senior Vice President Corporate Strategy, Emily Waldorf

Vice President Sales Us Retail, James Sterbenz

Vice President Fin Cna, Stan Polomski

Government Relations, Luz Alena

Vice President External Development, Roger Wilson

Vice President Initiatives And Network Optimization, Dave Parcher

Vp Of Talent Management Of Culture Of And Organizational Development, Heidi Manna

Vice President Corporate Responsibility And Chief Sustainability Officer, Dave Stangis

Svp Us Sales, Jim Sterbenz

Vp Of Corporate Audit, Kevin Blatcher

Vice President Taxes, Richard Landers

Vice President Global Talent And Change Management, David Walsh

Senior Vice President And Chief Legal And Public Affairs Officer, Ellen O Kaden

Vice President Global Procurement, Jose Turkienicz

Vice President Club Channel, Larry Daley

Vice President Global Procurement, Bob Frederick

Vice President Global Walmart, Ian Rowland

Vice President Global Indirect Procurement, Chris Calabretta

Vp Human Resources, Xavier Boza

Vp Business Operations, Rick Pifer

Chairman, Les C. Vinney, age 70

Board Member, Fabiola Arredondo

Auditors: PricewaterhouseCoopers LLP

LOCATIONS

HQ: Campbell Soup Co
1 Campbell Place, Camden, NJ 08103-1799
Phone: 856 342-4800   **Fax:** 856 342-3878
Web: www.campbellsoupcompany.com

2016 Sales

	$ mil.	% of total
US	6,437	81
Australia	590	7
Other	934	12
Total	**7,961**	**100**

PRODUCTS/OPERATIONS

2016 Sales

	$ mil.	% of total
Americas Simple Meals and Beverages	4,380	55
Global Biscuits and Snacks	2,564	32
Campbell Fresh	1,017	13
Total	**7,961**	**100**

2016 Sales

	$ mil.	% of total
Soup	2,690	34
Baked snacks	2,479	31
Other simple meals	1,702	21
Beverages	1,090	14
Total	**7,961**	**100**

Selected Brand Names

Domestic
  Away From Home
  Bolthouse Farms
  Campbell
  Ecce Panis
  Pace
  Pepperidge Farm
  Plum Organics
  Prego
  Select Harvest
  StockPot
  Swanson
  V8 and V8 Splash
  Wolfgang Puck
International
  Arnott's (Australia)

Selected Subsidiaries

Arnott's Biscuits Limited (Australia)
Bolthouse Holding Corp. (US)
Ecce Panis Inc.
Pepperidge Farm Incorporated
Players Group Limited (Australia)
Sinalopasta S.A. de C.V. (Mexico)
Stockpot Inc.

COMPETITORS

Associated British	Hanover Foods
Foods	Harry's Fresh Foods
B&G Foods	Heinz
Barbara's Bakery	Hormel
Baxters	Kellogg U.S. Snacks
Beech-Nut	Mondelez International
Big Heart Pet Brands	Morgan Foods
Bush Brothers	NORPAC
Canyon Creek Food	Nestlé
ConAgra	Odwalla
Dole Food	Pacific Coast
Frito-Lay	Producers
General Mills	Peter Rabbit Farms
Gerber Products	Red Gold
Golden Enterprises	Reily Foods
Grimmway Enterprises	Renée's Gourmet Foods
H. J. Heinz Limited	Snyder's-Lance
Hain Celestial	Walkers Snack Foods

HISTORICAL FINANCIALS

Company Type: Public

Income Statement

FYE: July 28

	REVENUE ($ mil.)	NET INCOME ($ mil.)	NET PROFIT MARGIN	EMPLOYEES
07/19	8,107	211	2.6%	19,000
07/18	8,685	261	3.0%	23,000
07/17	7,890	887	11.2%	18,000
07/16*	7,961	563	7.1%	16,500
08/15	8,082	691	8.5%	18,600
Annual Growth	**0.1%**	**(25.7%)**	**—**	**0.5%**

*Fiscal year change

2019 Year-End Financials

Debt ratio: 64.45%	No. of shares (mil.): 301
Return on equity: 17.15%	Dividends
Cash ($ mil.): 31	Yield: 0.0%
Current ratio: 0.58	Payout: 200.0%
Long-term debt ($ mil.): 7,103	Market value ($ mil.): 12,329

STOCK PRICE ($)		P/E	PER SHARE ($)		
	FY Close	High/Low	Earnings	Dividends	Book Value
07/19	40.96	62 46	0.70	1.40	3.66
07/18	40.94	62 38	0.86	1.40	4.53
07/17	52.85	22 18	2.89	1.40	5.44
07/16*	62.27	37 25	1.81	1.25	4.95
08/15	49.31	22 19	2.21	1.25	4.45
Annual Growth	(4.5%)	— —	(25.0%)	2.9%	(4.7%)

*Fiscal year change

CANDID COLOR SYSTEMS, INC.

EXECUTIVES

Pres-Ceo, Jack E Counts Jr
SEC-Treas, Beverly Ellis
Designer, David J Wall
Coo, Dan Hays

LOCATIONS

HQ: CANDID COLOR SYSTEMS, INC.
1300 METROPOLITAN AVE, OKLAHOMA CITY, OK 731082042
Phone: 405 947-8747
Web: WWW.CANDID.COM

HISTORICAL FINANCIALS

Company Type: Private

Income Statement				FYE: July 31
	REVENUE ($ mil.)	NET INCOME ($ mil.)	NET PROFIT MARGIN	EMPLOYEES
07/07	21,742	2,534	11.7%	300
07/05	22	1	8.3%	—
07/04	21	2	10.9%	—
07/03	21	1	9.4%	—
Annual Growth	467.2%	498.3%	—	—

Capital City Bank Group, Inc.

Capital City Bank Group is the holding company for Capital City Bank (CCB) which serves individuals businesses and institutions from some 70 branches in Florida Georgia and Alabama. CCB offers checking savings and money market accounts; CDs; IRAs; Internet banking; and debit and credit cards. Commercial real estate mortgages account for about 40% of its loan portfolio; residential real estate loans also hover near 40%. The bank also originates business loans and consumer loans including credit cards. Capital City also performs data processing services for other financial institutions in its market area.

Operations

In addition to its CCB bank subsidiary which accounts for about 94% of Capital City Bank Group's total revenue the holding company operates three other subsidiaries: Capital City Trust a provider of trust and asset management services; Capital City Banc Investments which offers investments retirement plans and life and long-term care insurance through an agreement with third-party provider INVEST Financial Corporation a subsidiary of Jackson National Life Insurance Company; and data processor Capital City Services Co.

Geographic Reach

Florida is CCB's largest market accounting for about 78% of its revenue. Georgia and Alabama account for 21% and 1% respectively.

Financial Performance

Capital City Bank Group's revenue has slid since the onset of the recession and housing crisis which battered the Florida market and during the uneven recovery. Revenue fell 5% in 2011 vs. 2010 marking the fourth consecutive year of decline. Indeed revenue plunged 74% between 2007 and 2011. However in 2011 the group returned to profitability with net income of $4.9 million following losses in 2010 and 2009.

Interest income decreased by 10% while non-interest income increased 4% in 2011 vs. 2010. Lower interest and fees on loans contributed to the decline in interest income. Growth in bank card and retail brokerage fees contributed to the rise in non-interest income.

Strategy

Capital City Bank Group was founded in 1982 to acquire six banks and has never looked back. While its growth has slowed the company has continued its acquisition strategy buying 15 banks since 1984; it has also expanded by opening new offices. However its home state of Florida was one of the hardest hit during the recession. High unemployment levels contributed to an increase in nonperforming loans in the bank's portfolio which in turn translated to net losses in 2009 and 2010. (Nonperforming loans totaled $75 million or 4.6% of the company's total loan portfolio at the end of 2011.) Capital City is focusing on diversifying its portfolio and reducing problem assets.

EXECUTIVES

Evp And Cfo, J. Kimbrough (Kim) Davis, age 65, $260,000 total compensation
Chairman President And Ceo, William G. (Bill) Smith, age 65, $350,000 total compensation
Credit Administration, Dale A. Thompson
Chief People Officer And President Capital Services Company, Bethany H. (Beth) Corum
President Capital City Banc Investments; President Capital City Trust Company, Bill Moor
President Leon County, Ed West
Residential Mortgage, Tom Allen
Commercial Banking, Ed Canup
Community Banking, Mitch Englert
Assistant Vice President, Lisa Elam
Assistant Vice President And Market Leader, Susan Terry
Vice President, Joel Ginaldi
Vice President, Cristie Garrett
Assistant Vice President, Janette Wagner
Vice President And Community Banker, Valerie Hoffler
Vice President Of Digital Engagement, Craig Ellard
Assistant Vice President Mis Analysis, Canington Carol
Vice President, Francis Rolfes
Vice President Marketing, Walter Hoskins
Assistant Vice President, Sylvia White
Business Banking Assistant Vice President, Myles Bradley
Assistant Vice President, Edie Frasier
Vice President, Karen C Meadows
Assistant Vice President And Community Banker, Janie Stewart
Vice President Information Security, Leanne Staalenburg
Vice President And Trust Officer, Angela Williamson
Assistant Vice President Business Banker, Terry Huiskens
Vice President, Alex Milton
Vice President, Courtney Armitage
Senior Vice President, Jim Scarboro
Vice President, Catherine Sherman
Vice President, Sterling Bryant
Vice President Auto Finance, Jim Philippou
Senior Vice President Human Resources Risk Manager, Pamela Gay
Assistant Vice President And Compliance Officer, Sheila D Reddick
Assistant Vice President, Francis M Rolfes
Senior Vice President, Lee Nichols
Vice President Of Human Resources, Linda Nwokeji
Senior Vice President, Brantley Henderson
Assistant Vice President, Yvonne Reed
Senior Vp, Sherry Thompson
Vice President, Stewart Wasson
Auditors: Ernst & Young LLP

LOCATIONS

HQ: Capital City Bank Group, Inc.
217 North Monroe Street, Tallahassee, FL 32301
Phone: 850 402-7821
Web: www.ccbg.com

PRODUCTS/OPERATIONS

2015 Sales

	$ mil.	% of total
Interest		
Loans including fees	73	55
Investment securities	5	5
Funds sold	0	-
Noninterest income		
Deposit fee	22	17
Bank card fees	11	8
Wealth management fees	7	6
Mortgage Banking fees	4	3
Data processing fees	1	1
Other	6	5
Total	133	100

COMPETITORS

Ameris	Regions Financial
BBX Capital	SunTrust
Bank of America	Thomasville Bancshares
Delta Community Credit Union	

HISTORICAL FINANCIALS

Company Type: Public

Income Statement				FYE: December 31
	ASSETS ($ mil.)	NET INCOME ($ mil.)	INCOME AS % OF ASSETS	EMPLOYEES
12/18	2,959	26	0.9%	819
12/17	2,898	10	0.4%	825
12/16	2,845	11	0.4%	853
12/15	2,797	9	0.3%	894
12/14	2,627	9	0.4%	937
Annual Growth	3.0%	29.7%	—	(3.3%)

2018 Year-End Financials

Debt ratio: 2.08%	No. of shares (mil.): 16
Return on equity: 8.94%	Dividends
Cash ($ mil.): 276	Yield: 1.3%
Current ratio: —	Payout: 30.7%
Long-term debt ($ mil.): —	Market value ($ mil.): 389

	STOCK PRICE ($) FY Close	P/E High/Low	PER SHARE ($) Earnings	Dividends	Book Value
12/18	23.21	17 14	1.54	0.32	18.07
12/17	22.94	41 28	0.64	0.24	16.73
12/16	20.48	32 19	0.69	0.17	16.34
12/15	15.35	31 26	0.53	0.13	15.99
12/14	15.54	30 22	0.53	0.09	15.62
Annual Growth	10.5%	— —	30.6%	37.3%	3.7%

CAPITAL INCOME BUILDER, INC.

EXECUTIVES

Pres, James B Lovelace

LOCATIONS

HQ: CAPITAL INCOME BUILDER, INC.
333 S HOPE ST FL 52, LOS ANGELES, CA 900713061
Phone: 213 486-9200
Web: WWW.CAPITALGROUP.COM

HISTORICAL FINANCIALS

Company Type: Private

Income Statement — FYE: October 31

	ASSETS ($ mil.)	NET INCOME ($ mil.)	INCOME AS % OF ASSETS	EMPLOYEES
10/18	102,648	(7,919)	—	2
10/16	100,286	2,628	2.6%	—
Annual Growth	1.2%	—	—	—

Capital One Financial Corp

Thanks to its "What's in Your Wallet" branding campaign Capital One Financial is one of the most recognizable issuers of Visa and MasterCard credit cards in the US. It also provides typical banking products such as checking and savings accounts and has a unit focused on auto financing. Furthermore it sells insurance and offers business and commercial banking services. Capital One holds some 45 million customer accounts in the US Canada and the UK and maintains a deposit portfolio worth roughly $250 billion. It boasts a banking network of hundreds of branches (mostly in about five US states) and maintains a strong online presence with its internet and mobile banking applications.

HISTORY

Capital One Financial is a descendant of the Bank of Virginia which was formed in 1945. The company began issuing products similar to credit cards in 1953 and was MasterCard issuer #001. Acquisitions and mergers brought some 30 banks and several finance and mortgage companies under the bank's umbrella between 1962 and 1986 when Bank of Virginia became Signet Banking.

Signet's credit card operations had reached a million customers in 1988 when the bank hired consultants Richard Fairbank and Nigel Morris (Fairbank is now chairman and CEO) to implement their "Information-Based Strategy." Under the duo's leadership the bank began using sophisticated data-collection methods to gather massive amounts of information on existing or prospective customers; it then used the information to design and mass-market customized products to the customer.

In 1991 — after creating an enormous database and developing sophisticated screening processes and direct-mail marketing tactics — Signet escalated the credit card wars luring customers from its rivals with its innovative balance-transfer credit card. The card let customers of other companies transfer what they owed on higher-interest cards to a Signet card with a lower introductory rate.

The new card immediately drew imitators (by 1997 balance-transfer cards accounted for 85% of credit card solicitations). After skimming off the least risky customers Fairbank and Morris began going after less desirable credit customers who could be charged higher rates. The result was what they call second-generation products — secured and unsecured cards with lower credit lines and higher annual percentage rates and fees for higher-risk customers.

The credit card business had grown to 5 million customers by 1994 but at a high cost to Signet which had devoted most of its resources to finding and servicing credit card holders. That year Signet spun off its credit card business as Capital One to focus on banking. (Signet was later acquired by First Union.)

The company moved into Florida and Texas in 1995 and into Canada and the UK in 1996; that year it established its savings bank mainly to offer products and services to its cardholders. In 1997 the company used this unit to move into deposit accounts buying a deposit portfolio from J. C. Penney. In 1998 the company began marketing its products to such clients as immigrants and high school students (whose parents must co-sign for the card). The company also expanded in terms of products and geography acquiring auto lender Summit Acceptance and opening a new office in Nottingham England.

In 1999 the firm's growth continued. The company stepped up its marketing efforts and was rewarded with significant boosts to its non-interest income and customer base. The next year the company launched The Capital One Place an Internet shopping site. In 2001 the company acquired AmeriFee which provides loans for elective medical and dental surgery; and PeopleFirst Inc. the nation's largest online provider of direct motor vehicle loans.

In response to industry-wide concern over subprime lending Capital One agreed in 2002 to beef up reserves on its subprime portfolio. Also in 2002 the company's UK operations proved profitable for the first time.

The company expanded into banking in 2005 and 2006 with the acquisitions of Hibernia and North Fork Bancorporation respectively. The deals gave it a boost in the banking sector expanding its presence both geographically in the Northeast and in the South and turning the company into one of the top bank holding companies in the US. The $13.2 billion stock-and-cash North Fork deal gave the company more than 300 bank branches in New York New Jersey and Connecticut.

The 2005 purchase of New Orleans-based Hibernia was a stock-and-cash transaction valued at some $5 billion nearly 10% less than the originally agreed-upon price. The transaction was delayed then renegotiated after Hurricane Katrina devastated Hibernia's home city. Hibernia which relocated to Houston adopted the Capital One moniker.

Capital One closed wholesale lender GreenPoint Mortgage Funding acquired as part of its acquisition of North Fork in 2007. The unit suffered from the credit woes that have plagued the subprime mortgage industry.

The company expanded its franchise into the Washington DC market in 2009 by buying Chevy Chase Bank for some $475 million in cash and stock.

In 2011 the company boosted its credit card business with the acquisition of GE Capital's $1.3 billion Hudson's Bay credit card portfolio tripling the number of Canadian customer accounts Capital One services. That year Capital One also acquired Kohl's existing $3.7 billion private-label credit card portfolio.

Capital One grew its US credit card business once again with the 2012 acquisition of HSBC's US card portfolio for some $2.6 billion.

In 2013 Capital One introduced its Capital One Quicksilver credit card offering cardholders a simple way to earn and redeem higher-than-average cash back rewards.

EXECUTIVES

General Counsel And Corporate Secretary, John G. Finneran, age 69, $1,016,538 total compensation
Chairman And Ceo, Richard D. (Rich) Fairbank, age 68
Senior Vice President Manager, Gerald Shepard
Head Of Finance And Corporate Development, Stephen S. (Steve) Crawford, age 54, $1,592,692 total compensation
Cfo, R. Scott Blackley, age 51, $617,769 total compensation
Cio, Robert M. Alexander, age 54
President Commercial Banking, Michael C. Slocum, age 62
Evp Europe, Sanjiv Yajnik, age 62, $962,654 total compensation
President Retail And Direct Banking, Jonathan W. Witter, age 49, $870,769 total compensation
Chief Enterprise Services Officer And Chief Of Staff To The Ceo, Frank G. LaPrade, age 52, $974,577 total compensation
Chief Risk Officer, Kevin S. Borgmann, age 47
President U.s. Card, Michael J. Wassmer, age 49
President International And Small Business Card, Christopher T. Newkirk, age 48
Vice President, Khary Scott
Vp Atm Kiosk Channel Management, Max Doerfler
Vice President Human Resources, Sammy Duff
Vice President, Ashish Tandon
Vice President Senior Associate General Counsel, Kathryn Hu
Assistant Vice President Information S, Carl Pomplon
Senior Vice President, Richard Amador
Vice President, Sonu Mittal
Vice President, Anthony Fermo
Vice President, Brad Dolbec
Executive Vice President, Murray Abrams
Senior Vice President, Roy Aksdal
Senior Vice President Senior Market Credit Executive, Lisa Spadafino
Vice President Human Resources, Guenet Beshah
Vice President Senior Director, John Walsh
Vp Digital Mobile It, Jeff Elgin
Vice President, Hamilton Blanton
Senior Vice President, James Wohn
Vice President, Ehab Awadallah
Vice President And Cra Business Development Officer, Lydia Jackson

Vice President Corporate Audit Services, Erika Ray
Vice President, Michael Lockery
Vice President Sales And Service Strategy, Shail Moorjani
Managing Vice President Treasury Balance, Jeffrey Kuzbel
Managing Vice President, Johan Gericke
Vice President, Shahram Elghanayan
Senior Vice President, John Blackwelder
Vice President Private Banking, Bob Sferrazza
Vice President And Senior Business Relationship Banker, Franklin Carrero
Vice President, Theresa Bedeau
Senior Vice President, Gregory Horstman
Vice President Underwriter, Lawrence Cannariato
Vice President Business Banking, Nate Hoffman
Senior Vice President, Bryan N Pynchon
Assistant Vice President Commercial Real Estate, Alexander Thezan
Managing Vice President, John Walker
Vice President Business Banking, Maria Brosnahan
Vice President Bank Project Management Office, Jonathan Topp
Vp Small Business Banking, Charles Middleton
Vice President, Kim Dean
Assistant Vice President, Carter King
Vice President, David P Blasini
Managing Vice President, Detelina Ivanova
Vice President Strategy, Sarah Strauss
Vice President Us Card, Emilia Lopez
Managing Vice President, Kara Lyons
Assistant Vice President Quality Assurance Manager, Gloria Stafford
Senior Vice President, Robbie Naquin
Vice President, Kader Ma
Senior Vice President, Ric Kearny
Senior Vice President Bank External Fraud Risk Management, Yu Huang
Vice President And Trust Officer, Jean Moncla
Vice President, Patrick Gemmell
Vice President Of Human Resources, Joel Martinez
Vice President Senior Audit Manager, Sandra Dato
Senior Vice President, Kristen Croxton
Vice President Investor Real Estate, Kevin Lemoine
Assistant Vice President, Lawren Allen
Assistant Vice President, Karen Eleser
Svp Commercial Real Estate, Jeff Wallace
Vice President Regional Executive North Tx North La, Laura Mathieu
Assistant Vice President, Hosai Akbarzadeh
Senior Vice President, Brian Hayes
Vice President, Sheikh Quddus
Vice President Corporate Security, Timothy Rigg
Vice President Regional Operations Manager, Farina Hanif
Vice President, Nathan Burlingame
Vice President Small Business Card, Jason Walker
Senior Vice President Origination, Brian Sykes
Assistant Vice President, Cristina Brum
Senior Vice President, Fran Nuchims
Vice President, Henriette Henriette Harris
Vp Hr, Rob Keeling
Assistant Vice President Loan Administrator, Terrie Harris
Vice President, Shelley Desilva
Senior Vice President, William Booth
Vice President, Billy Mcardle
Vice President, Ken Shah
Assistant Vice President Branch Manager, Jessica Kitzmann
Assistant Vice President, David Mialaret
Vice President Private Underwriter, Curtis Vincent
Senior Vice President, Enrico Panno
Senior Vice President, Tom Higgins
Assistant Vice President Manager, James Rocco
Vice President Business Banking, Fabian Martin
Vice President, Sal Fratanduono
Senior Vice President, Joshua Howes
Unit Manager Assistant Vice President, Michelle Jordan

Vice President, Bonnie Lowrimore
Vice President Senior Manager Strategy And Transformation, Aysun Cokyuksel
Assistant Vice President, Malcolm Ferrell
Vice President And Senior Trust Officer, Lorraine Gallagher
Assistant Vice President Merchant Services Sales Advisor, Diane Slatkin
Assistant Vice President Commercial Collateral Ser, Sheila Carmines
Senior Vice President, Jennifer Driscoll
Senior Vice President, Andrew Mahtaney
Assistant Vice President, Cindy Lau
Senior Vice President, Jonathan Wood
Vice President, Julianne Low
Assistant Vice President, Stanley Liu
Vice President Business Banker, Joshua Prejean
Assistant Vice President Commercial Banking, Diane Lee
Vice President, Haley Douds
Senior Vice President Managing Underwriter, Marlene Schwartz
Vp Branch Manager Iii, Yenisel Gamez
Vice President Managing Underwriter, Albert Lopez
Assistant Vice President, Milos Milosevic
Senior Vice President, Diane Dolce
Assistant Vice President, Roland Annan
Vice President Senior Manager, Kathleen Cavanaugh
Vice President Regulatory Relations, Morris Thompson
Vice President, Daniel Mouadeb
Vice President Senior Business Banker, Kirk Ranzino
Vice President Commercial Real Estate, Michael Monroe
Assistant Vice President, Kyle Anglin
Vice President, Staci Harvey
Vice President, Luis Otoya
Business Banker Vice President, Khadija Basir
Senior Vice President, Jon Oldham
Vice President Of Finance, Steve Braskamp
Vice President, Ilene O'Tero
Assistant Vice President Credit Support Specialist, Frank Di Lisio
Executive Vice President, Paul Widuch
Senior Vice President North Region Underwriting Manager, Chris Mclaughlin
Vice President, Ladan Karami
Assistant Vice President And Specialty Sales Process Manager, Darla Smith
Vice President Of Business Banking, Ryan Cash
Vice President Commerical Banking, Tom Shinn
Vice President Special Assets, Louis Ricchione
Vice President Account Management, Kenneth Hund
Vice President Capital One, Brent Reynolds
Auditors: Ernst & Young LLP

LOCATIONS

HQ: Capital One Financial Corp
1680 Capital One Drive, McLean, VA 22102
Phone: 703 720-1000
Web: www.capitalone.com

PRODUCTS/OPERATIONS

2018 Sales

	$ mil.	% of total
Interest		
Loans held for investment	24,728	76
Investment securities	2,211	7
Cash equivalents and other interest-earning assets	237	1
Interest Expense	4,301	-
Non-interest		
Interchange fees net	2,823	8
Service charges & other customer fees	1,585	5
Net securities gains (losses)	(209)	-
Others	1,002	3
Total	28	100

2018 Segment sales

	$ mil.	% of total
Credit card	17,687	63
Consumer banking	7,212	26
Commercial banking	2,896	10
Others	281	1
Total	**28,076**	**100**

2018 Loans

	% of total
Credit card	
Domestic credit card	43
International card business	4
Consumer banking	
Auto	23
Retail banking	1
Commercial banking	
Commercial and multifamily real estate	12
Commercial and industrial	17
Total	**100**

Selected Products

Auto Loans
Business Credit Cards
Commercial Banking
Investing
Personal Banking
Personal Credit Cards
Small Business Banking

COMPETITORS

Alliance Data Systems	GM Financial
American Express	HSBC USA
Bank of America	JPMorgan Chase
Citigroup	PNC Financial
Credit Acceptance	Regions Financial
Discover	Wells Fargo

HISTORICAL FINANCIALS

Company Type: Public

Income Statement FYE: December 31

	ASSETS ($ mil.)	NET INCOME ($ mil.)	INCOME AS % OF ASSETS	EMPLOYEES
12/18	372,538	6,015	1.6%	47,600
12/17	365,693	1,982	0.5%	49,300
12/16	357,033	3,751	1.1%	47,300
12/15	334,048	4,050	1.2%	45,400
12/14	308,854	4,428	1.4%	46,000
Annual Growth	4.8%	8.0%	—	0.9%

2018 Year-End Financials

Debt ratio: 15.81%
Return on equity: 11.98%
Cash ($ mil.): 13,186
Current ratio: —
Long-term debt ($ mil.): —

No. of shares (mil.): 467
Dividends
  Yield: 2.1%
  Payout: 13.5%
Market value ($ mil.): 35,355

	STOCK PRICE ($) FY Close	P/E High/Low		Earnings	PER SHARE ($) Dividends	Book Value
12/18	75.59	9	6	11.82	1.60	110.47
12/17	99.58	29	22	3.49	1.60	100.37
12/16	87.24	13	8	6.89	1.60	98.94
12/15	72.18	13	10	7.07	1.50	89.68
12/14	82.55	11	9	7.59	1.20	81.41
Annual Growth	(2.2%)	—	—	11.7%	7.5%	7.9%

Capitol Federal Financial Inc

Dorothy and Toto may not be in Kansas anymore but Capitol Federal Financial is. The holding company owns Capitol Federal Savings Bank the largest bank headquarted there. The savings bankÂ serves metropolitan areasÂ of the Sunflower StateÂ as well asÂ Kansas City Missouri throughÂ aboutÂ 45 branches includingÂ nearly aÂ dozen inside retail stores such as Target Price Chopper and Dillons. Serving consumers and commercial customers theÂ thrift offers standard servicesÂ such as mortgages and loans depositsÂ and retail investments. Its Capitol Agency affiliate sells life liability homeowners renters and vehicle insurance.

EXECUTIVES

Chairman President And Ceo, John B. Dicus, age 58, $581,484 total compensation

Evp Cfo And Treasurer, Kent G. Townsend, age 57, $303,991 total compensation

Evp And Chief Lending Officer, Rick C. Jackson, $163,690 total compensation

Evp Corporate Services, Carlton A Ricketts

Evp General Counsel, Natalie Haag

Evp Retail Operations, Frank H. Wright, $202,362 total compensation

Vice President Information Technology Delivery Systems, Tamara Vande Velde

Executive Vice President Retail Operations, Daniel Lehman

Vice President Security Business, Kevin Moore

First Vice President, Rodney Martin

Vice President, David Richardson

Vice President Consumer Lending Man, Mike Cast

Vice President Security, Ed Cox

Vice President, Wanda Espinosa

First Vice President: Mortgage Lending, Kevin Brittain

Vice President Information Technology Security And Risk, Steve Huff

First Vice President, Tara Van Houweling

First Vice President Director Of Marketing, Becky Moore

Assistant Vice President Network And Telecom Supervisor, Kevin Nelson

Vice President Deposit Services, Clint Devoe

Vice President Delivery Systems Manager, Travis Buchanan

First Vice President, Sarah Sanders

First Vice President, Joel Oliver

Vice President Chief Appraiser, Susan Sirridge

Vice President, Susan Fickler

Vice President, Debbie Wempe

Board Member, Jeffrey Johnson

Board Member, Reginald Robinson

Board Member, James Morris

Board Member, Michel Cole

Auditors: DELOITTE & TOUCHE LLP

LOCATIONS

HQ: Capitol Federal Financial Inc
700 South Kansas Avenue, Topeka, KS 66603
Phone: 785 235-1341
Web: www.capfed.com

PRODUCTS/OPERATIONS

2016 Sales

	$ mil.	% of total
Interest Income		
Loans receivable	243	75
Mortgage backed securities	29	9
FHLB stock	12	4
Cash and cash equivalents	9	3
Investment securities	5	2
Non-Interest Income		
Retail fees and charges	14	4
Income from bank-owned life insurance	3	1
Other non-interest income	5	2
Total	**324**	**100**

COMPETITORS

Bank of America
Commerce Bancshares
First Federal of Olathe
Landmark Bancorp
U.S. Bancorp
UMB Financial

HISTORICAL FINANCIALS

Company Type: Public

Income Statement

FYE: September 30

	ASSETS ($ mil.)	NET INCOME ($ mil.)	INCOME AS % OF ASSETS	EMPLOYEES
09/19	9,340	94	1.0%	773
09/18	9,449	98	1.0%	775
09/17	9,192	84	0.9%	708
09/16	9,267	83	0.9%	676
09/15	9,844	78	0.8%	691
Annual Growth	(1.3%)	4.8%	—	2.8%

2019 Year-End Financials

Debt ratio: 1.07%
Return on equity: 6.91%
Cash ($ mil.): 220
Current ratio: —
Long-term debt ($ mil.): —
No. of shares (mil.): 141
Dividends
Yield: 7.1%
Payout: 144.1%
Market value ($ mil.): 1,949

	STOCK PRICE ($) FY Close	P/E High/Low	PER SHARE ($) Earnings	Dividends	Book Value
09/19	13.78	21 18	0.68	0.98	9.45
09/18	12.74	21 17	0.73	0.88	9.85
09/17	14.70	27 21	0.63	0.88	9.90
09/16	14.07	23 19	0.63	0.84	10.13
09/15	12.12	22 20	0.58	0.84	10.33
Annual Growth	3.3%	— —	4.1%	3.9%	(2.2%)

Capstead Mortgage Corp.

Capstead Mortgage is a self-managed real estate investment trust (REIT) with holdings in mortgage-backed securities. It makes leveraged investments in single-family residential adjustable-rate mortgage securities issued and backed by government agencies such as Fannie Mae Freddie Mac and Ginnie Mae. It occasionally makes limited investments in credit-sensitive commercial mortgage assets as well. The REIT typically funds its investment activities through short-term borrowings or equity offerings. Founded in 1985 Capstead is one of the oldest publicly traded mortgage REITs in the US and manages an investment portfolio worth roughly $13.5 billion.

Operations

Dallas-based Capstead Mortgage buys and manages a large portfolio of short term federally backed residential mortgage investments which generate nearly all the company's revenue in the form of interest income. Capstead's nearly $13.5 billion investment portfolio is made up of almost exclusively short-duration ARM Agency Securities.

Unlike fixed-term securities that pay a static rate of interest short-duration ARM securities correspond with interest rate changes and are able to change their interest payments in a relatively short amount of time (e.g. If interest rates rise ARM securities can raise the rate of interest paid to security holders within a year or a few years.). These securities also have limited or no credit risk because payments are guaranteed by government agencies.

Financial Performance

Capstead Mortgage has struggled with declining revenues over the past few years largely due to depressed interest rates. Revenue fell below $100 million in 2016 and 2017. (By comparison the REIT generated $314 million and $400 million in 2009 and 2008 two of the company's strongest years ever.) Net income also fell under the $100-million-mark in 2016 and stayed there the following year.

Despite recovering interest rates revenue fell 11% to $87 million in 2017. Capstead's interest expenses outpaced interest income growth that year cutting into total revenue. The REIT also had lower average portfolio balances during the year.

With the lower revenue net income fell 4% to $79 million in 2017.

The company ended 2017 with $103.9 million in net cash an 83% increase over what it had at the end of 2016. Operating activities provided $212.1 million and financing activities provided $151.5 million. Investing activities used $316.4 million.

Strategy

By investing almost exclusively in short-duration ARM securities Capstead has an advantage in keeping its portfolio risk low even when interest rates change. Generally when interest rates rise traditional fixed-term mortgage securities fall in value as investors flock to securities that are paying higher interest. By contrast when interest rates rise short-duration ARM securities correspondingly raise their coupon rates (the percentage they pay in interest) relatively shortly afterward (within a few years or annually). This keeps the security values relatively steady — and keeps the volatility of Capstead's investments low even if interest rates rise.

In addition management believes that its investments are less risky than others because they are guaranteed by government-sponsored entities. The company is not immune to negative financing spreads though which could impact earnings.

Company Background

After its founding in 1985 Capstead was initially a conduit for nonconforming loans but adopted its current strategy in 2000 and now invests only in securities with implied AAA ratings.

HISTORY

Former Chairman and CEO Ronn Lytle formed Capstead Mortgage (originally called Lomas Mortgage Corp.) and took it public in 1985 to structure and manage mortgage investments. Lytle had previously been an SVP at mortgage banking firm Lomas & Nettleman Co. (later Lomas Mortgage USA) which provided initial funding and some management services.

In 1989 the firm became Capstead Mortgage and acquired Strategic Mortgage Investment. Capstead Mortgage entered the mortgage servicing business in 1992 and acquired Tyler Cabot Mortgage Securities Fund. The company severed its ties to Lomas after 1992.

As market conditions changed the company adjusted its strategy. In 1994 Capstead Mortgage stopped issuing collateralized mortgage obligations and instead began acquiring interest-only mortgage securities. In 1996 the investor reduced its commitment to adjustable-rate mortgage securities and increased its investments in interest-only mortgage securities.

By early 1998 the firm had serviced more than 400000 mortgage loans and developed a mortgage investment portfolio worth more than $10 billion. Capstead Mortgage even ventured into originating mortgages. With its servicing income threatened by prepayments the firm sold its mortgage servicing and writing operations that year.

In 1999 the company began rebuilding its investment portfolio which had lost value due to mortgage investment market conditions; it accepted a $51 million cash infusion from privately held real estate investor Fortress Investment in return for a share of Capstead Mortgage's stock.

The following year Capstead Mortgage sold off $1.4 billion in medium-term and fixed-rate securities opting instead to invest in adjustable-rate securities.

Capstead made its first direct investment in real estate in 2002 investing in a portfolio of seven senior living properties in Georgia Florida Ohio Virginia and Texas. It sold one property about five months after the purchase and the rest at the end of 2005.

EXECUTIVES

Evp And Chief Investment Officer, Robert R. Spears, age 57, $525,000 total compensation
President Ceo And Cfo, Phillip A. Reinsch, age 58, $420,000 total compensation
Chairman, Jack Biegler, age 75
Auditors: Ernst & Young LLP

LOCATIONS

HQ: Capstead Mortgage Corp.
8401 North Central Expressway, Suite 800, Dallas, TX 75225-4404
Phone: 214 874-2323
Web: www.capstead.com

PRODUCTS/OPERATIONS

2017 Sales

	$ mil.	% of total
Interest	361	100
Investment premium amortization	(128.8)	—
Interest expense	145	—
Total	**87**	**100**

COMPETITORS

AG Mortgage Investment Trust	Anworth Mortgage Asset
ARMOUR Residential REIT	Dynex Capital
Annaly Capital Management	MFA Financial
	Redwood Trust

Company Type: Public

Income Statement				FYE: December 31
	ASSETS ($ mil.)	NET INCOME ($ mil.)	INCOME AS % OF ASSETS	EMPLOYEES
12/18	12,186	50	0.4%	15
12/17	13,733	79	0.6%	13
12/16	13,576	82	0.6%	14
12/15	14,446	108	0.7%	14
12/14	14,389	140	1.0%	14
Annual Growth	(4.1%)	(22.8%)	—	1.7%

2018 Year-End Financials

Debt ratio: 90.90%
Return on equity: 4.36%
Cash ($ mil.): 60
Current ratio: —
Long-term debt ($ mil.): —
No. of shares (mil.): 85
Dividends
Yield: 7.3%
Payout: 144.1%
Market value ($ mil.): 569

	STOCK PRICE ($) FY Close	P/E High/Low		PER SHARE ($) Earnings	Dividends	Book Value
12/18	6.67	28	20	0.34	0.49	12.42
12/17	8.65	17	13	0.65	0.80	12.95
12/16	10.19	15	11	0.70	0.95	13.00
12/15	8.74	13	9	0.97	1.14	13.55
12/14	12.28	10	9	1.33	1.36	14.51
Annual Growth	(14.2%)	—	—	(28.9%)	(22.5%)	(3.8%)

Cardinal Health, Inc.

When your local pharmacy runs low on drugs or supplies it might just call Cardinal Health. The company is a top distributor of pharmaceuticals and other medical supplies and equipment in the US. Its pharmaceutical division provides supply chain services including branded generic and specialty pharmaceutical and OTC drug distribution. It also franchises Medicine Shoppe retail pharmacies. Cardinal's medical division parcels out medical laboratory and surgical supplies and provides logistics consulting and data management. Customers include retail pharmacies hospitals health care systems surgery centers nursing homes doctor's offices clinical labs and other health care businesses. The US accounts for the majority of Cardinal's sales.

HISTORY

Cardinal Health harks back to Cardinal Foods a food wholesaler named for Ohio's state bird. In 1971 Robert Walter then 26 and with the ink still fresh on his Harvard MBA acquired Cardinal in a leveraged buyout. He hoped to grow Cardinal by acquisitions but was frustrated when he found that the food distribution industry was already highly consolidated.

In 1980 Cardinal moved into pharmaceuticals distribution with the acquisition of Zanesville. It went public in 1983 as Cardinal Distribution and Walter began looking for more acquisitions. Cardinal soon expanded nationwide by swallowing other distributors. During the 1980s these purchases included two pharmaceuticals distributors headquartered in New York and a Massachusetts-based pharmaceuticals and food distributor.

In 1988 Cardinal sold its food group including Midland Grocery and Mr. Moneysworth to Roundy's and narrowed its focus to pharmaceuticals.

Drug distributors joined the rest of the pharmaceutical industry in its rush toward consolidation during the 1990s. Cardinal's acquisitions in those years included Ohio Valley-Clarksburg (1990 the Mid-Atlantic) Chapman Drug Co. (1991 Tennessee) PRN Services (1993 Michigan) Solomons Co. (1993 Georgia) Humiston-Keeling (1994 Illinois) and Behrens (1994 Texas).

One of Cardinal's most important acquisitions during this period was its cash purchase of Whitmire Distribution in 1994. Formerly Amfac Health Care Whitmire had been a subsidiary of Amfac one of Hawaii's "Big Five" landholders. When Amfac Health Care was spun off in 1988 its president Melburn Whitmire led a management group that acquired a majority interest. When Cardinal bought it Whitmire was the US's #6 drug wholesaler; the purchase bumped Cardinal up to #3. At that time the company changed its name to Cardinal Health and Melburn Whitmire became Cardinal's vice chairman.

In 1995 Cardinal made its biggest acquisition yet when it purchased St. Louis-based Medicine Shoppe International the US's largest franchisor of independent retail pharmacies. Founded by two St. Louis obstetricians in 1970 the Medicine Shoppe had 987 US outlets and 107 abroad at the time of its purchase by Cardinal (for $348 million in stock).

Over the next few years Cardinal continued to grow through acquisitions including automatic drug-dispensing system maker Pyxis pharmaceutical packaging company PCI Services and pharmacy management services company Owen Healthcare (which became Cardinal Health Pharmacy Management).

EXECUTIVES

Evp Customer Support Services And Cio, Patricia B. (Patty) Morrison, age 60
Chief Human Resources Officer, Pamela O. (Pam) Kimmet, age 60
President Nuclear Pharmacy Services, Tiffany P. Olson, age 60
Ceo And Director, Michael C. (Mike) Kaufmann, age 56, $721,311 total compensation
Ceo Medical Segment, Donald M. (Don) Casey, age 60, $671,311 total compensation
Chief Legal And Compliance Officer, Craig S. Morford, age 60, $531,311 total compensation
President Cardinal Health Specialty Solutions, Joseph I. DePinto, age 52
Ceo Pharmaceutical Segment, Jon Giacomin, age 54, $542,623 total compensation
Evp Global Sourcing, Craig Cowman
President Cordis, David J. Wilson
President Cardinal Health At Home, Steve Mason
President Global Commercial Solutions, Steve Blazejewski
Evp Strategy And Corporate Development, Michele Holcomb
Evp Deputy General Counsel And Corporate Secretary, Jessica L. Mayer
President Us Pharmaceutical Distribution, Debbie Weitzman
Cfo, Jorge M. Gomez
Svp Eit Shared Services, Scot Lindsey
Vice President, Kraig Corwin
Vice President General Manager Specialty Services Caridnal Health Specialty Solutions, Jennifer Fillman
Senior Vice President Global Sourcing, Stefan Grunwald
Pharmacy Manager, John Miller
Vice President, Marc Delorenzo
Vice President Account Management, Jennifer Ferrang
Vice President Customer Service Management, Susan Dixon

National Vice President Of Sales Laboratory
  Products, Angela Davis
Vice President And Associate General Counsel
  Finance, Rylan Rawlins
Vice President, Warren Hastings
Vice President, Sean Postol
Director Of Pharmacy, Norma Yeverino
Clinical Director, Steve Lundquist
Senior Vice President, Dennis Braun
Vice President And General Manager Cardinal
  Health Inventory Management Solutions, John
  Roy
Vice President Distribution Services, Paul Farnin
Vice President, John Sullivan
Director Of Pharmacy, Laurie Sobas
Pharmacy Manager, Melissa Christopher
Vice President Strategic Marketing And Product
  Management, David Mitchell
Vice President, Steve Peale
Vice President Of Sales, Andy Grant
Vice President Compensation, Melanie Filas
Manager Government Relations, Laura Padgitt
Senior Vice President Marketing Managed Care
  And Customer Solutions Pharmaceutical
  Distribution, Christi Pedra
Director Of Pharmacy Practice, Kevin Walker
Pharmacy Manager, Michael Wyant
Pharmacy Manager, Tally Townsend
Senior Vice President Of Ecommerce Enterprise
  Architecture And Chief Information Security
  Officer, Talvis Love
Pharmacy Manager, Sam Ling
Vice President, Ken Robinette
Director Of Pharmacy, Denise Payette
Vice President, Colleen McGuffin
Vice President, Jeff Brannon
Director Of Pharmacy Operations And Account
  Manager, Sue Raymoure
Pharmacy Manager, Gene Nickman
Vp Product Innovation And Strategy, Ben Stormer
Svp It, Annlea Rumfola
Vice President Human Resources, Ola Snow
Group Vice President Health Systems, Therese
  Grossi
Executive Vice President Packaging Service
  Group, Renard Pawlak
Pharmacy Manager, Sherry Miller
Director Of Pharmacy, Jay Dyer
Pharmacy Manager, Todd Lamb
Vice President, Sean Mcnally
Vice President, Chris Lanctot
Director Of Pharmacy, Todd Worsham
Pharmacy Manager, Bevan Callicott
Pharmacy Manager, Ann Shea
Director Of Pharmacy, Lynn Staggs
Vice President, Justin Schomaker
Pharmacy Manager, Mary Johnson
Pharmacy Manager, John Miano
Vice President And Executive Director Of
  Training, Lori Rivers
Pharmacy Manager, Arthur Bowman
Director Of Pharmacy, Sharon Greasheimer
Pharmacy Manager, Jeff Parrish
Vice President, Kendell Sherrer
Director Of Pharmacy, Rande Hempen
Pharmacy Manager, Jimmy Coker
Vice President Enterprise Information
  Technology, Cyndi Carter
Pharmacy Manager, Chad Walker
Vice President Of Marketing An, Erika Jurrens
Vice President, Luke Whitworth
Vp Health Systems, Craig Rothman
Senior Vice President Independent And Alternate
  Care Sales, Steve Lawrence
Vice President Enterprise Architecture And It
  Strategy, Jeff Greer
Pharmacy Manager, Abdul Kamara
Vice President Associate General Counsel, Cheryl
  Kahn

Vice President National Market Sales, Gregory
  Ewing
Pharmacy Manager, Matt Champ
Pharmacy Manager, Mark Wear
Vice President Strategic Account Management,
  Ken Rasbid
Vice President, Tina Lantz
Vp Human Resources, Bill Rozich
Vice President Operations, Martha Huston
Vice President Customer Service, Greg Stuart
Pharmacy Manager, Glenn Carmody
Pharmacy Manager, Kelli Love
Vice President, John Kilgour
Vice President Public Relations, Brett Ludwig
Vice President Sales, Ryan Schorr
Director Of Pharmacy, Anita Ward
Svp Government Relations, Sean Callinicos
Vice President Marketing, Michael Pintek
Pharmacy Manager, Gary Mantz
Senior Vice President General Counsel Medical
  Segment, Jennifer Spalding
Vice President Information Technology, Gregory
  Boggs
Vice President Investor Relations, Lisa Capodici
Clinical Director Infectious Diseases, Katherine
  Shea
Pharmacy Manager, Kevin Marsh
Global Medical Director Cordis, Ali Almedhychy
Svp Enterprise Corporate Accounts And
  Enterprise Marketing, Robert Rajalingam
Director Of Pharmacy, Carol Yuan
Senior Vice President General Manager Yong Yu,
  Elsie Lim
Vice President Engineering Fuse, Steve Langella
Vice President Community Relations, Jessie
  Cannon
Pharmacy Manager Radiation Safety Officer,
  Richard Medeiros
Evp Cio And Customer Support Services, Brian
  Rice
Vice President Enterprise Information
  Technology, Steven Callison
Vice President Of Tax, Hunter Scott
Chairman, George S. Barrett, age 64
Board Member, Colleen Arnold
Assistant Secretary To The Board, Elaine Natsis
Board Member, Calvin Darden
Auditors: Ernst & Young LLP

LOCATIONS

HQ: Cardinal Health, Inc.
  7000 Cardinal Place, Dublin, OH 43017
Phone: 614 757-5000
Web: www.cardinalhealth.com

2018 Sales

	$ mil.	% of total
US	132,526	97
Other	4,283	3
Total	**136,809**	**100**

PRODUCTS/OPERATIONS

2018 Sales by Segment

	$ mil.	% of total
Pharmaceutical	121,241	89
Medical	15,581	11
Corporate	(13)	-
Total	**136,809**	**100**

COMPETITORS

AmerisourceBergen	Medline Industries
Becton Dickinson	Owens & Minor
CVS	PharMerica
Deroyal Industries	Rite Aid
Franz Haniel	Thermo Fisher
Henry Schein	Scientific
McKesson	Walgreen

HISTORICAL FINANCIALS
Company Type: Public

Income Statement
FYE: June 30

	REVENUE ($ mil.)	NET INCOME ($ mil.)	NET PROFIT MARGIN	EMPLOYEES
06/19	145,534	1,363	0.9%	49,500
06/18	136,809	256	0.2%	50,200
06/17	129,976	1,288	1.0%	40,400
06/16	121,546	1,427	1.2%	37,300
06/15	102,531	1,215	1.2%	34,500
Annual Growth	**9.2%**	**2.9%**	**—**	**9.4%**

2019 Year-End Financials

Debt ratio: 19.61%	No. of shares (mil.): 299
Return on equity: 22.01%	Dividends
Cash ($ mil.): 2,531	Yield: 0.0%
Current ratio: 1.07	Payout: 42.1%
Long-term debt ($ mil.): 7,579	Market value ($ mil.): 14,083

	STOCK PRICE ($) FY Close	P/E High/Low		PER SHARE ($) Earnings	Dividends	Book Value
06/19	47.10	13	9	4.53	1.91	21.16
06/18	48.83	96	60	0.81	1.86	19.61
06/17	77.92	21	16	4.03	1.81	21.54
06/16	78.01	21	17	4.32	1.61	20.35
06/15	83.65	25	19	3.62	1.41	19.07
Annual Growth	**(13.4%)**	**—**	**—**	**5.8%**	**7.8%**	**2.6%**

Carmax Inc.

CarMax helps drivers find late-model used autos.
The US's largest specialty used-car retailer buys
reconditions and sells cars and light trucks through
more than 200 superstores in 100-plus television
markets (markets in which CarMax has a television
advertising presence). Typically selling vehicles that
are less than ten years old with less than 100000
miles CarMax sells more than 748000 used cars
per year. CarMax also operates two new-car franchises and sells older vehicles through more than
445000 in-store auctions each year at over 75
stores. Additionally it sells older cars and trucks
with higher mileage and offers vehicle financing
through its CarMax Auto Finance unit.

Operations

CarMax operates through two business segments: CarMax Sales Operations and CarMax Auto
Finance (CAF).

CarMax Sales Operations which sells more than
748000 used cars per year represents the nation's
largest used-car retailer. The company's finance
arm CarMax Auto Financing (CAF) offers financing solely to CarMax customers and finances about
50% of the company's retail vehicle unit sales. CAF
also services over 965000 customer accounts in
its $12.5 billion portfolio of managed receivables.

The company's used vehicle sales generate more
than 80% of total revenue wholesale vehicle sales
nearly 15% and other products and services less
than 5%.

Geographic Reach

While Richmond Virginia-based CarMax sells
cars in more than 40 US states its largest markets
are California Texas Florida North Carolina Georgia and Virginia which together account for nearly
half of store locations.

Its Auto Finance division operates out of Atlanta
Georgia.

Sales and Marketing

CarMax focuses on developing brand awareness
and detailing the advantages of shopping at its

stores. It reaches customers through TV and radio broadcasts carmax.com search engine optimization and online classified listings such as Pandora and Hulu. Additionally it looks to connect with consumers through Facebook Twitter and mobile apps.

CarMax's customers often take advantage of its transfer option which allows a customer to get a vehicle of their choice relocated to a more local CarMax store. About 35% of vehicles sold are transferred via customer request.

Financial Performance

CarMax has recorded consistently increasing net revenue over the last five-plus years as it has aggressively expanded its store base across the US.

In fiscal 2019 (ended February) revenue increased 6% to $18.1 billion. The growth can be attributed to used car sales which grew $780 million and wholesale vehicle sales which recorded $212 million growth. Used vehicle revenue was bumped up by a 4% increase in total unit sales driven primarily by new store openings. Wholesale revenue was positively impacted by growth in the store base increase in the appraisal buy rate and a boost in comparable store appraisal traffic.

Net income grew 26% to $842.4 million on the increased sales and a smaller provision for income taxes than in fiscal year 2018 as a result of the 2017 Tax Act.

Cash at the end of fiscal 2019 was $595.3 million an increase of 7% from the prior year. Cash from operations contributed $162.9 million to the coffers while investing activities subtracted $308.5 million mainly for capital expenditures. Financing activities added another $186 million.

Strategy

CarMax continues to adhere to its original strategy of providing a customer-friendly experience with competitive no-haggle prices and superior customer service offerings. Some of these offerings include the 7-day money-back guarantee and the vehicle transfer service which allows a customer to get a vehicle of their choice relocated from a distant CarMax store to a more local one.

CarMax has been rolling out its omni-channel buying experience for customers which allows customers to buy a car completely online from home in-store or an integrated combination of the two. The company plans to bring omni-channel options to the majority of customers by 2020 in part to better compete with online car dealers such as Carvana. In addition to increased competition from online-focused business models the company is facing a growing number car dealers who are adopting CarMax's popular no-haggle strategy and commitment to buy a customer's car even if the customer does not buy a car at the dealership.

Leveraging its successful "no-haggle" pricing business model CarMax has been aggressively expanding its geographic footprint over the past several years. The auto dealer has more than tripled its store count from 58 locations in 2005 to 203 stores in 2018. As a rule CarMax aims to average around 15 store openings each year.

Company Background

Looking for new retailing channels to conquer in 1993 Circuit City Stores began test-driving the used-car concept when it opened its first CarMax outlet in Richmond Virginia. Richard Sharp who also served as Circuit City's CEO became the chairman and CEO for CarMax Group.

A pioneer in the car industry CarMax offered computerized shopping play areas for children and no-haggle pricing. The company extended its geographical reach in 1995 and 1996. Circuit City spun off about 25% of CarMax to the public in 1997. Circuit City spun off CarMax as an independent company in 2002.

HISTORY

Looking for new retailing channels to conquer in 1993 Circuit City Stores began test-driving the used-car concept when it opened its first CarMax outlet in Richmond Virginia. Richard Sharp who was named Circuit City's CEO in 1986 became the chairman and CEO for CarMax Group as well.

A pioneer in the car industry CarMax offered computerized shopping play areas for children and no-haggle pricing. Competing car dealers criticized CarMax's TV ads which tarred rivals with a stereotype of sleaze and greed. Some dealers disputed CarMax's low-price claims.

The company extended its geographical reach into North Carolina Georgia and Florida in 1995 and 1996. In 1996 CarMax began selling new cars at an Atlanta store.

No longer riding it as a test-drive Circuit City spun off about 25% of CarMax to the public in 1997. The following year it moved into Illinois.

Also in 1998 CarMax bought a new-car Toyota dealership in Maryland and the multi-make Mauro Auto Mall of Wisconsin. It entered South Carolina that year and added a Georgia Mitsubishi dealership in early 1999. The company acquired two new-car franchises in the competitive Los Angeles market in mid-1999.

In mid-2001 Circuit City reduced its share in CarMax from 75% to about 65% having sold some stock to help remodel the company's electronics stores. Circuit City then spun off CarMax as an independent company in October 2002. President Austin Ligon took the CEO title at that time (Sharp remained chairman).

CarMax opened five superstores but sold four new-car dealerships in 2003.

EXECUTIVES

Vice President Marketing Carmax, Rob Sorenson
Region Vice President Merchandising Florida Region, William L McChrystal
Vice President, Rodney Baker
Vice President Investor Relations, Katharine Kenny
Region Vice President And General Manager Los Angeles Region, Vaughn Sigmon
Evp Strategy And Business Transformation, Edwin J. (Ed) Hill, age 59, $597,209 total compensation
Evp General Counsel And Secretary, Eric M. Margolin, age 66, $572,801 total compensation
Evp And Cfo, Thomas W. (Tom) Reedy, age 55, $699,039 total compensation
President Ceo And Director, William D. (Bill) Nash, age 50, $902,308 total compensation
Evp And Coo, William C. (Cliff) Wood, age 52, $699,039 total compensation
Svp And Chief Marketing Officer, James (Jim) Lyski, age 56
Svp And Cio, Shamim Mohammad, age 50
Svp Carmax Auto Finance, Jon G. Daniels, age 47
Vice President Human Resources, Peggy Philips
Vice President Of Information Technology, Michelle Ellwood
Vice President Operations, John Davis
Assistant Vice President Associate Relations, Greg Stewart
Assistant Vice President Consumer Finance, Rusty Jordan
Vice President Finance, Enrique Mayor-Mora
Assistant Vice President Compensation And Benefits, Chad Kulas
Regional Vice President Service Operations, Jason Lowery
Vice President, Patricia Gangwer
Legal Secretary, Kim Wickens
Vice President Deputy General Counsel, Ross Longood

Assistant Vice President Assistant Controller, Veronica Hinckle
Assistant Vice President Risk And Servicing Analytics, Kevin Duck
Vice President For The Atlanta Region, Kevin Cox
Avp Human Resources Services, Kim Ross
Vice President Treasurer, Tom Reedy
Regional Vice President, Chris Bartee
Vice President Financial Services And Products, Robert W Mitchell
Assistant Vice President Information Technology, Greg Shull
Vice President Program Vice President Program Management And Quality, Robert Adams
Sales Vice President, Ed Hill
Vice President Security And Ciso, Cherri Heart
Vp Marketing Analytics, Gautam Puranik
Regional Vice President Purchasing, Bryan Windsor
Vice President Information Technology, Steve Allocco
Vice President And Deputy General Counsel, Greg Fitzharris
Vice President Of Information Technology, Shamim Muhammad
Vice President Marketing, Rob Sorensen
Regional Vice President General Manager Xf Nashville Region, Dave Cantu
Avp Public Affairs And Communications, Trina Hoppin Lee
Vice President Regional Merchandising And Logistics, Tom Marcey
Chairman, Thomas J. (Tom) Folliard
Secretary, Williams Curtis
Auditors: KPMG LLP

LOCATIONS

HQ: Carmax Inc.
12800 Tuckahoe Creek Parkway, Richmond, VA 23238
Phone: 804 747-0422
Web: www.carmax.com

2017 Stores

	No.
California	23
Florida	16
Texas	16
Virginia	10
Georgia	9
Illinois	9
North Carolina	9
Tennessee	8
Maryland	6
Colorado	5
Ohio	5
Alabama	4
Massachusetts	4
Wisconsin	4
Arizona	3
Missouri	3
Nevada	3
Pennsylvania	3
South Carolina	3
Connecticut	2
Indiana	2
Kansas	2
Kentucky	2
Minnesota	2
Mississippi	2
New Jersey	2
New York	2
Oklahoma	2
Oregon	2
Delaware	1
Idaho	1
Iowa	1
Louisiana	1
Michigan	1
Nebraska	1
New Mexico	1
Rhode Island	1
Utah	1
Washington	1
Total	**173**

PRODUCTS/OPERATIONS

2017 Sales

	$ mil.	% of total
Used vehicles	13,270	84
Wholesale vehicles	2,082	13
Other sales & revenue	522	3
Total	**15,875**	**100**

COMPETITORS

Asbury Automotive	Holman Enterprises
AutoNation	Internet Brands
AutoTrader	JM Family Enterprises
Brown Automotive	KAR Auction Services
Cox Automotive	McCombs Enterprises
Danner Company	Penske Automotive
DriveTime Automotive	Group
Ed Morse Auto	Serra Automotive
Group 1 Automotive	Sonic Automotive
Hendrick Automotive	

HISTORICAL FINANCIALS

Company Type: Public

Income Statement

FYE: February 28

	REVENUE ($ mil.)	NET INCOME ($ mil.)	NET PROFIT MARGIN	EMPLOYEES
02/19	18,173	842	4.6%	25,946
02/18	17,120	664	3.9%	25,110
02/17	15,875	626	3.9%	24,344
02/16	15,149	623	4.1%	22,429
02/15	14,268	597	4.2%	22,064
Annual Growth	**6.2%**	**9.0%**	**—**	**4.1%**

2019 Year-End Financials

Debt ratio: 75.89%	No. of shares (mil.): 167
Return on equity: 25.25%	Dividends
Cash ($ mil.): 46	Yield: —
Current ratio: 2.45	Payout: —
Long-term debt ($ mil.): 13,806	Market value ($ mil.): 10,400

	STOCK PRICE ($) FY Close	P/E High/Low		PER SHARE ($) Earnings	Dividends	Book Value
02/19	62.10	17	12	4.79	0.00	20.04
02/18	61.92	21	15	3.60	0.00	18.45
02/17	64.54	21	14	3.26	0.00	16.66
02/16	46.26	24	14	3.03	0.00	14.92
02/15	67.11	25	15	2.73	0.00	15.11
Annual Growth	**(1.9%)**	—	—	**15.1%**	**—**	**7.3%**

Carolina Financial Corp (New)

EXECUTIVES

Pres-Ceo, Jerold L Rexroad
Exec V Pres-Cfo, William A Gehman III
Exec V Pres-SEC, M J Huggins III
Exec V Pres, David L Morrow
Auditors: Elliott Davis, LLC

LOCATIONS

HQ: Carolina Financial Corp (New)
288 Meeting Street, Charleston, SC 29401
Phone: 843 723-7700

HISTORICAL FINANCIALS

Company Type: Public

Income Statement

FYE: December 31

	ASSETS ($ mil.)	NET INCOME ($ mil.)	INCOME AS % OF ASSETS	EMPLOYEES
12/18	3,790	49	1.3%	773
12/17	3,519	28	0.8%	770
12/16	1,683	17	1.0%	441
12/15	1,409	14	1.0%	421
12/14	1,199	8	0.7%	394
Annual Growth	**33.3%**	**56.4%**	**—**	**18.4%**

2018 Year-End Financials

Debt ratio: 0.86%	No. of shares (mil.): 22
Return on equity: 9.45%	Dividends
Cash ($ mil.): 62	Yield: 0.8%
Current ratio: —	Payout: 11.0%
Long-term debt ($ mil.): —	Market value ($ mil.): 662

	STOCK PRICE ($) FY Close	P/E High/Low		PER SHARE ($) Earnings	Dividends	Book Value
12/18	29.59	20	12	2.26	0.25	25.70
12/17	37.15	22	16	1.73	0.17	22.61
12/16	30.79	21	11	1.42	0.13	13.00
12/15	18.00	12	9	1.48	0.11	11.63
12/14	13.99	48	15	0.88	0.09	9.64
Annual Growth	**20.6%**	—	—	**26.8%**	**30.0%**	**27.8%**

Carter Bank & Trust (Martinsville, VA)

Auditors: Yount, Hyde & Barbour, P.C.

LOCATIONS

HQ: Carter Bank & Trust (Martinsville, VA)
1300 Kings Mountain Road, Martinsville, VA 24112
Phone: 276 656-1776
Web: www.carterbankandtrust.com

HISTORICAL FINANCIALS

Company Type: Public

Income Statement

FYE: December 31

	ASSETS ($ mil.)	NET INCOME ($ mil.)	INCOME AS % OF ASSETS	EMPLOYEES
12/18	4,039	11	0.3%	992
12/17	4,112	(0)		963
12/16	4,505	15	0.4%	
12/15	4,893	39	0.8%	964
12/14	4,629	33	0.7%	957
Annual Growth	**(3.4%)**	**(22.8%)**		**0.9%**

2018 Year-End Financials

Debt ratio: —	No. of shares (mil.): 26
Return on equity: 2.74%	Dividends
Cash ($ mil.): 293	Yield: —
Current ratio: —	Payout: —
Long-term debt ($ mil.): —	Market value ($ mil.): 394

	STOCK PRICE ($) FY Close	P/E High/Low		PER SHARE ($) Earnings	Dividends	Book Value
12/18	15.00	44	32	0.45	0.00	16.60
12/17	17.55	—	—	(0.03)	0.00	16.46
12/16	13.29	23	20	0.61	0.30	16.55
12/15	13.50	9	8	1.49	0.40	16.24
12/14	12.70	10	9	1.27	0.40	15.15
Annual Growth	**4.2%**	—	—	**(22.8%)**	—	**2.3%**

Casey's General Stores, Inc.

Casey's provides convenience for small-town customers. One of the largest convenience store chains in the country Casey's General Stores owns some 2100 stores across 15-plus states primarily in the Midwest. Its stores most of which operate in areas with fewer than 5000 people offer gasoline prepared foods such as pizza and donuts and other food and nonfood items traditionally found in convenience stores. In addition to Casey's and Casey's General Store locations the company operates two tobacco stores two liquor stores and one grocery store. Gas sales account for about 60% of Casey's revenue.

Operations

Casey's generates some 60% of its revenue from fuel about 25% from grocery and other merchandise and more than 10% from prepared food and fountain drinks.

It has a broad selection of merchandise (from food staples to school supplies pet supplies and auto products) with stores typically stocking more than 3000 food and non-food items. The company sells nationally known brands as well as its own proprietary brands. Casey's has built up its selection of prepared foods over the years and now offers sandwiches and burgers pizza donuts chicken tenders and breakfast biscuits among other items.

Geographic Reach

Casey's operates stores in some 15 states including its largest markets — Iowa Illinois and Missouri — as well as Kansas Kentucky Minnesota Nebraska Wisconsin Indiana Michigan Ohio Oklahoma Arkansas Tennessee and the Dakotas.

It has distribution centers in Ankeny Iowa and Terre Haute Indiana.

Sales and Marketing

Casey's targets smaller communities by serving as both general and convenience stores including stocking a broader selection of products than typical of convenience stores.

Financial Performance

After falling for three years because of lower gas prices Casey's revenue has risen the past two years. Net income has been a little more sporadic but jumped significantly in fiscal 2018.

The comapny reported revenue of $8.4 billion in fiscal 2018 (ended April 2018) up 12% from the prior year. The results were driven by a rise in gas prices as well as more gas sold and an increase in grocery and other inside sales.

Net income that year jumped nearly 80% to $318 million from fiscal 2017 primarily as a result of a deferred tax benefit related to the 2017 Tax Act.

Cash at the end of fiscal 2018 was $53.7 million a decrease of $23 million from the prior year. Cash from operations contributed $419.8 million to the coffers while investing activities used $609.3 million mainly for capital expenditures. Financing activities provided $166.5 million primarily from long-term debt proceeds.

Strategy

In 2018 the year of Casey's 50th anniversary the company announced a long-term "Value Creation Plan." Key to that plan are three initiatives to improve store performance: its fleet car program price optimization and digital engagement.

Casey's has selected Fleetcor a provider of commercial payments services as a partner on its new commercial fuel card program. Fleetcor will handle all aspects of the program — which promises enhanced capabilities and convenience — from initial sales to payment processing billing and customer service. New card sales began in the summer of 2018 with existing customers being converted that fall.

The company has also selected partners for its price optimization initiative: PriceAdvantage for fuel optimzation and Dunnhumby for grocery items and other merchandise. Casey's with the help of its partners will use customer data as well as market data to centalize its pricing decisions to hopefully improve sales and margins across all categories. The rollout of this initiative is estimated to extend through fiscal 2020.

Lastly Casey's is looking to engage and interact with its customers through online and mobile channels as well as in stores. Plans include an enhanced website and revamped mobile app a new loyalty platform and in-store technology upgrades. As part of this initiative the company has staffed up in various marketing and digital functions and selected technology platforms from such heavyhitters as SAP MuleSoft and Salesforce.

Amid its "Value Creation Plan" the company continues opening or acquiring new stores. It ended fiscal 2018 with about 90 additional stores.

Mergers and Acquisitions

In fiscal 2018 Casey's acquired 26 stores of which it opened 20 (six will open in fiscal 2019). The comany will continue to acquire stores as the opportunity arises.

Company Background

Donald Lamberti who had run his family's grocery store founded Casey's General Stores with Kurvin C. "K. C." Fish. The men converted a gas station into the first Casey's convenience store in 1968. To expand and build brand recognition the company began franchising outlets two years later. By focusing on small towns the company avoided competition and expensive building and property costs. A significant growth spurt in 1979 took Casey's from 119 stores to 226. Fish retired the following year and the company went public in 1983.

EXECUTIVES

Svp And Cfo, William J. (Bill) Walljasper, age 58, $550,000 total compensation
Vp Marketing, Michael R. (Mike) Richardson, $195,000 total compensation
President And Ceo, Terry W. Handley, age 60, $770,000 total compensation
Svp General Counsel And Secretary, Julia L. (Julie) Jackowski, age 54, $530,000 total compensation
It Director, Rich Schappert
Svp Operations, John C. (Jay) Soupene, age 51
Vp Real Estate, Kirk Haworth
Board Director, David Lenhardt
Auditors: KPMG LLP

LOCATIONS

HQ: Casey's General Stores, Inc.
One SE Convenience Boulevard, Ankeny, IA 50021
Phone: 515 965-6100
Web: www.caseys.com

PRODUCTS/OPERATIONS

2018 Sales

	$ mil.	% of total
Fuel	5,146	61
Grocery & other merchandise	2,184	26
Prepared food & fountain	1,005	12
Other	55	1
Total	**8,391**	**100**

Selected Merchandise

Ammunition
Automotive products
Beverages
Food including fresh foods
Gasoline (self-service)
Health and beauty aids
Housewares
Pet products
Photo supplies
School supplies
Tobacco products

COMPETITORS

7-Eleven	Krause Gentle
Chevron	Kwik Trip
Couche-Tard	Martin & Bayley
Exxon Mobil	QuikTrip
Holiday Companies	Royal Dutch Shell
Hy-Vee	Thorntons Inc.

HISTORICAL FINANCIALS

Company Type: Public

Income Statement   FYE: April 30

	REVENUE ($ mil.)	NET INCOME ($ mil.)	NET PROFIT MARGIN	EMPLOYEES
04/19	9,352	203	2.2%	36,841
04/18	8,391	317	3.8%	37,205
04/17	7,506	177	2.4%	35,014
04/16	7,122	225	3.2%	34,997
04/15	7,767	180	2.3%	31,766
Annual Growth	**4.8%**	**3.1%**	**—**	**3.8%**

2019 Year-End Financials

Debt ratio: 36.86%
Return on equity: 15.22%
Cash ($ mil.): 63
Current ratio: 0.69
Long-term debt ($ mil.): 1,283

No. of shares (mil.): 36
Dividends
  Yield: 0.8%
  Payout: 21.6%
Market value ($ mil.): 4,853

	STOCK PRICE ($) FY Close	P/E High/Low		PER SHARE ($)		
				Earnings	Dividends	Book Value
04/19	132.35	25	17	5.51	1.16	38.42
04/18	96.60	15	11	8.34	1.04	34.47
04/17	112.07	30	24	4.48	0.96	30.71
04/16	112.00	22	14	5.73	0.88	27.74
04/15	82.18	20	14	4.62	0.80	22.51
Annual Growth	**12.7%**	**—**	**—**	**4.5%**	**9.7%**	**14.3%**

Caterpillar Inc.

EXECUTIVES

Chm-Ceo, D James Umpleby III
Cfo, Andrew R J Bonfield
Gen Counsel-Corp SEC, Suzette M Long
Cao, G Michael Marvel
Chief Hr Officer, Cheryl C Johnson
Chief Technology Officer, Karl Weiss
Vp, Legal Aftermarket Support, Tom Bluth
Mechanical Engineer, Alex Perez-Sandi
Latin America Marketing Manage, Alexandre Lima
Risk Management Team Member, Andrew Barger
Account Manager, Andy Diaz
Auditors: PricewaterhouseCoopers LLP

LOCATIONS

HQ: Caterpillar Inc.
510 Lake Cook Road, Suite 100, Deerfield, IL 60015
Phone: 224 551-4000
Web: www.caterpillar.com

COMPETITORS

ALSTOM	Komatsu
Atlas Copco	Kubota
Bombardier	Kuehne + Nagel
CNH Global	MAN
Charles Machine Works	Menlo Worldwide
Cummins	Mitsubishi Heavy
DEUTZ	Industries
DHL	Multiquip
Deere	Navistar International
Detroit Diesel	Nortrak
Doosan Infracore	Rolls-Royce
Dresser Inc.	Sandvik
GE	Sany Heavy Industry
GE Capital	Siemens Energy
GENCO Distribution	Sumitomo Heavy
System	Industries
Generac Holdings	Terex
Hitachi Construction	Tognum
Machinery	UPS Supply Chain
Hyundai Heavy	Solutions
Industries	Volvo
J C Bamford Excavators	Vossloh
Joy Global	Wartsila
Joy Mining	Weichai Power
Kawasaki Heavy	Wells Fargo Equipment
Industries	Finance
Kohler	Woods Equipment

HISTORICAL FINANCIALS

Company Type: Public

Income Statement   FYE: December 31

	REVENUE ($ mil.)	NET INCOME ($ mil.)	NET PROFIT MARGIN	EMPLOYEES
12/18	54,722	6,147	11.2%	104,000
12/17	45,462	754	1.7%	98,400
12/16	38,537	(67)	—	98,400
12/15	47,011	2,102	4.5%	105,700
12/14	55,184	3,695	6.7%	114,233
Annual Growth	**(0.2%)**	**13.6%**	**—**	**(2.3%)**

2018 Year-End Financials

Debt ratio: 46.56%
Return on equity: 44.33%
Cash ($ mil.): 7,857
Current ratio: 1.37
Long-term debt ($ mil.): 25,000

No. of shares (mil.): 575
Dividends
  Yield: 2.5%
  Payout: 31.9%
Market value ($ mil.): 73,134

	STOCK PRICE ($) FY Close	P/E High/Low		PER SHARE ($) Earnings	Dividends	Book Value
12/18	127.07	16	11	10.26	3.28	24.39
12/17	157.58	125	72	1.26	3.10	22.92
12/16	92.74	—	—	(0.11)	3.08	22.40
12/15	67.96	26	18	3.50	2.94	25.43
12/14	91.53	19	14	5.88	2.60	27.63
Annual Growth	8.5%	—	—	14.9%	6.0%	(3.1%)

Cathay General Bancorp

Cathay General Bancorp is the holding company for Cathay Bank which mainly serves Chinese and Vietnamese communities from some 30 branches in California and about 20 more in Illinois New Jersey New York Massachusetts Washington and Texas. It also has a branch in Hong Kong and offices in Shanghai and Taipei. Catering to small to medium-sized businesses and individual consumers the bank offers standard deposit services and loans. Commercial mortgage loans account for more than half of the bank's portfolio; business loans comprise nearly 25%. The bank's Cathay Wealth Management unit offers online stock trading mutual funds and other investment products and services through an agreement with PrimeVest.

Geographic Reach

California state-chartered Cathay Bank has branches in California Illinois Massachusetts New Jersey New York Texas and Washington. Overseas it has a branch in Hong Kong and offices in Shanghai and Taipei.

Financial Performance

The bank's revenue is on a downward trend. In 2012 revenue declined more than 5% vs. 2011 after posting a 3% decline in the previous annual comparison. Indeed between 2008 and 2012 revenue dipped by about 17% on lower interest income and dividend income. However the bank's profit picture is improving with net income up in 2012 for the third consecutive year.

Strategy

With 60% of its branches in California — a state hard hit by the downturn in the housing market — Cathay Bank's real estate secured loan portfolio has suffered as the value of the underlying collateral plummeted. In 2010 the company entered into a memorandum of understanding with the FDIC to reduce its concentration of commercial real estate loans improve its capital ratios reduce overall risk and strengthen asset quality. The moves have helped the company to cut its losses. The bank has also been successful growing deposits.

Mergers and Acquisitions

In 2016 Cathay Bank agreed to buy SinoPac Bancorp from Taiwan's Bank SinoPac for $340 million. SinoPac's Far East National Bank operates nine branches including five in Los Angeles. After the deal closes Cathay plans to close a number of branches. The transaction will help boost the company's balance sheet.

EXECUTIVES

Sevp And Coo, Irwin Wong, age 70, $339,777 total compensation

Evp And Chief Credit Officer Cathay Bank, Donald S. Chow, age 68, $312,615 total compensation
Evp Cfo And Treasurer, Heng W. Chen, age 67, $416,542 total compensation
Evp And General Manager East And Midwest Region Cathay Bank, Pin Tai, $424,900 total compensation
Evp And Chief Risk Officer Cathy Bank, Kim R. Bingham, age 62
Assistant Vice President Marketing, Chris Lu
Auditors: KPMG LLP

LOCATIONS

HQ: Cathay General Bancorp
777 North Broadway, Los Angeles, CA 90012
Phone: 213 625-4700
Web: www.cathaybank.com

2015 Branch offices

	No.
Southern California Branches	21
Northern California Branches	12
New York Branches	12
Illinois Branches	4
Washington Branches	3
Texas Branches	2
Massachusetts Branch	1
Nevada Branch	1
New Jersey Branch	1
Maryland Branch	1
Overseas Branch	1
Total	**59**

PRODUCTS/OPERATIONS

2015 sales

	$ mil.	% of total
Interest and Dividend income		
Loan receivable	427	88
Investment securities- taxable	21	4
Federal Home Loan Bank stock	3	1
Deposits with banks	1	—
Non-Interest income		
Securities losses net	(3.3)	-
Letters of credit commissions	5	1
Depository service fees	5	1
Other operating income	25	5
Total	**486**	**100**

Products/Services

Personal
Accounts
Checking Accounts
Savings Accounts
CDs
IRA CD
Debit Cards
Loans
Mortgage Loan
Home Equity Financing
Auto Loan
Credit Cards
Cathay Online Banking
Mobile Banking
Business/Commercial
Business Accounts
Business Checking Account
Business Savings Account
CDs
Cash Management Services
Merchant Deposit Capture
Zero Balance Account
Lockbox Service
Merchant Bankcard Services
Courier Deposit Service
Armored Transport Services
Cash Vault Services
Business Online Banking
Loans
Commercial Financing
Real Estate & Construction Financing
International Banking & Financing
Smart Capital Line
SBA Guaranteed Loan Program
Credit Cards

COMPETITORS

Bank of America	Grandpoint
Citibank	Hanmi Financial
East West Bancorp	Hope Bancorp
Far East National Bank	U.S. Bancorp

HISTORICAL FINANCIALS

Company Type: Public

Income Statement

FYE: December 31

	ASSETS ($ mil.)	NET INCOME ($ mil.)	INCOME AS % OF ASSETS	EMPLOYEES
12/18	16,784	271	1.6%	1,277
12/17	15,640	176	1.1%	1,271
12/16	14,520	175	1.2%	1,129
12/15	13,254	161	1.2%	1,122
12/14	11,516	137	1.2%	1,074
Annual Growth	**9.9%**	**18.5%**	**—**	**4.4%**

2018 Year-End Financials

Debt ratio: 1.23%
Return on equity: 13.28%
Cash ($ mil.): 600
Current ratio: —
Long-term debt ($ mil.): —

No. of shares (mil.): 80
Dividends
  Yield: 3.0%
  Payout: 36.2%
Market value ($ mil.): 2,699

	STOCK PRICE ($) FY Close	P/E High/Low		PER SHARE ($) Earnings	Dividends	Book Value
12/18	33.53	13	10	3.33	1.03	26.36
12/17	42.17	20	16	2.17	0.87	24.39
12/16	38.03	17	12	2.19	0.75	22.97
12/15	31.33	17	12	1.98	0.56	21.63
12/14	25.59	16	13	1.72	0.29	20.08
Annual Growth	**7.0%**	**—**	**—**	**18.0%**	**37.3%**	**7.0%**

CBRE Group Inc

As the world's largest commercial real estate services company by revenue CBRE Group provides property and facilities management leasing brokerage appraisal and valuation asset management financing and market research services from about 490 offices worldwide. Subsidiary Trammell Crow provides property development services for corporate and institutional clients primarily in the US. CBRE Global Investors manages real estate investments for institutional clients. The company garners about 60% of its revenue from the Americas. CBRE was founded in San Francisco in 1906 and by the 1940s grew to be one of the largest commercial real estate services firms in the western US.

HISTORY

Colbert Coldwell and Albert Tucker started real estate brokerage Tucker Lynch & Coldwell in 1906 in San Francisco. In 1922 the company expanded to Los Angeles where it began developing real estate in 1933 with a 60-acre subdivision in the burgeoning city.

Having profited from California's rapid growth in the 1950s and 1960s the firm expanded out of state. The partnership incorporated in 1962 as Coldwell Banker which went public in 1968. Sears Roebuck & Co. bought the company in 1981 for 80% above its market price. But by 1991 Sears had abandoned aims to become a financial services giant and sold Coldwell Banker's commercial operations to The Carlyle Group as CB Commercial Real Estate Services Group.

Free of Sears but $56 million in the red the company didn't return to profitability until 1993. Two years later it embarked on a shopping spree in real estate services buying tenant representatives Langon Rieder and Westmark Realty. In 1996 the company went public and bought mortgage banker L. J. Melody & Company (which was renamed CBRE | Melody); it purchased Koll Real Estate Services in 1997.

In 1998 the company widened its global scope with the acquisition of REI Limited the non-UK operations of Richard Ellis; it was renamed CB Richard Ellis Services. CB Richard Ellis also bought Hillier Parker May & Rowden (now operating in the UK as CB Hillier) a London-based provider of commercial property services.

CB Richard Ellis experienced a revenue crunch in 1999 and responded by restructuring its North American operations into three divisions (transaction financial and management services) and cutting management ranks by 30%. Growth continued in 1999 with the purchase of Pittsburgh-based Gold & Co. the addition of an office in Venezuela and a fat contract to manage more than 1100 locations for Prudential.

In 2000 the company committed significant resources to the Internet inking a deal to offer the lease management services of MyContracts.com and investing in Canadian real estate transaction tracker RealNet Canada.

A group of investors including then-CEO Ray Wirta chairman Richard Blum (and his BLUM Capital Partners) and Freeman Spogli took the company private in 2001. Blum Capital Partners bought the 60% of publicly traded CBRE that it did not already own forming CBRE Holding. Three years later the company went public once again.

In 2003 CBRE merged with top commercial real estate broker and property manager Insignia Financial. The next year the company changed its name to CB Richard Ellis Group and went public. It bought rival Trammell Crow in 2006 as well as a dozen or so other companies as it sought to fill in its holdings. The acquisitions deepened CBRE's outsourcing services especially project and facilities management for corporate and institutional clients in the US.

CBRE spun off former subsidiary Realty Finance Corporation in 2008 after the real estate investment trust continued to post losses in a troubled credit market.

Also in 2008 it opened its first offices in Bahrain and joined forces with Vanke to provide residential property management services in China. The following year CBRE expanded its existing UK-based investment banking business (advisory and restructuring services for real estate hospitality and gaming companies) to the Americas.

CBRE in 2011 made one of its largest deals in several years. The company bolstered its global real estate investment management business with the acquisition of ING Groep's real estate investment management operations for some $940 million. The Dutch firm's real estate investment management business in Asia and Europe was merged into CBRE Global Investors and more than doubled the size of the unit. The transaction also included US-based Clarion Real Estate Securities and interests in commercial real estate co-investments. (The ING deal helped boost CBRE's investment management revenue by more than 60% in 2012.)

In November 2012 CBRE acquired EA Shaw. a independent commercial and residential property partnership specializing in central London. The purchase significantly enhanced the firm's business in central London.

In 2013 CBRE acquired technical engineering services firm Norland Managed Services Ltd. which specialized in commercial buildings in the UK and Ireland and had a growing customer base in the US and Singapore.

The firm also in 2013 purchased The CAC Group a top commercial real estate services firm based in San Francisco. The move made CBRE the #1 provider of commercial property management and leasing in the market. CBRE also bought property and asset management specialist SOGES-MAINT-CBRE to build on its previous acquisitions in the Netherlands the Czech Republic Slovakia Poland Latvia and Lithuania. Additionally in 2013 CBRE acquired commercial real estate services business Resource Estate Partners and TPA Realty Services both based in Atlanta where it's working to boost its market share.

EXECUTIVES

President Ceo And Director, Robert E. (Bob) Sulentic, age 63, $990,000 total compensation
Ceo Global Workplace Solutions (gws), William F. (Bill) Concannon, age 63, $675,000 total compensation
President Americas Brokerage And Capital Markets, Christopher R. Ludeman
Cfo And Global Director Of Corporate Development, James R. (Jim) Groch, age 57, $770,000 total compensation
Global Group President Geographies, Calvin W. (Cal) Frese, age 63, $680,000 total compensation
Global President Debt And Structured Finance, Brian F. Stoffers
Ceo Asia Pacific, Steven A. (Steve) Swerdlow
Global Group President Lines Of Business & Client Care, Michael J. (Mike) Lafitte, age 58, $700,000 total compensation
Global Chief Investment Officer And Ceo Cbre Global Investors And Cbre Clarion Securities, T. Ritson Ferguson, age 59, $800,000 total compensation
Chairman Asia Pacific, Robert (Rob) Blain, age 64, $560,000 total compensation
Evp And General Counsel, Laurence H. Midler, age 54, $325,000 total compensation
Global Director Client Care, Tony Long
Ceo Trammell Crow Company., Matt Khourie
President Cbre Global Investors, Daniel (Danny) Queenan
Evp Global Brokerage And Sales Management, Laura OBrien
Ceo Americas, Jack Durburg
Ceo Cbre Europe Middle East And Africa (emea), Martin Samworth
Global President Occupier Advisory And Transaction Services, Whitley Collins
Global President Asset Services And Valuation And Advisory Services (vas), Mary Jo Eaton
President Cbre Southern California - Hawaii, Lewis Horne
Vice Chairman Capital Markets And Institutional Properties, Michael Hines
Chief Digital And Technology Officer, Chandra Dhandapani
Vice Chairman Cbre Capital Markets Debt And Structured Finance, Rocco Mandala
Senior Vice President Debt And Structured Finance, Peter Gineris
First Vice President, Erik Wanland
Senior Vice President, WALLY POLLOCK
Senior Vice President And Head Econic Incentive Solutions Group, Eric Stavriotis
Vice President, Benoit Poulin
Vice President, Charles Laginestra
Spqrea First Vice President, Ric Brandt
Senior Vice President, Gregg Haly
Evp Of Advisory And Transaction Of Chicago, Mark Pasquella

Senior Vice President, Bill Sheehy
First Vice President, John Hendricks
Senior Vice President, Steven Brabant
Sp Vice President, Robert Bunton
Senior Vice President Los Angeles, Richard Ratner
Executive Vice President, Jeffrey C Babikian
Senior Vice President, Ron McWherter
First Vice President, Don Weis
Senior Vice President, Cynthia Kamin
Senior Vice President, Mark Sprague
Vice President, Stacy Reid
First Vice President, Carl Shorett
Senior Vice President, Jim Koenig
Vice President, Brian Dooley
Vice President, Nancy Johnson
First Vice President, Taylor Hillenmeyer
First Vice President, Peter Mcguone
Senior Vice President, Trey Pennington
Vice President Information Technology, Mike Washington
Senior Vice President, Ned Burns
Senior Vice President, Bradley Gingerich
Vice President Senior, Mary O'Connor
Vice President, Brian Beaty
Executive Vice President, Sean Sullivan
Executive Vice President Managing Director, Jason Ruegg
Vice President, Mitchell Stravitz
Vice President, Neil Kolatkar
Executive Vice President, Thomas Bohlinger
Senior Vice President Partner, Kyle Juszczyszyn
Senior Vice President, Greg Geraci
Senior Vice President, Phillip Sample
Senior Vice President, Michael Shustak
Senior Vice President, Rod Apodaca
Senior Vice President Investment Properties, Alex Kozakov
Vice President, Justin Mohler
Senior Vice President, Cal Wessman
Executive Vice President, Sharon Kline
First Vice President, John Boote
First Vp Of Cincinnati, Kevin Torch
Vice President, Dorothy Chuang
Executive Vice President, George Good
Svp Leed Ap, Randall Koladis
Vice President, John Heffington
Vice President, Eric Greenfield
Senior Vice President Based, Daniel Woodward
Senior Vice President, Chris Caras
Senior Vice President, Mark McDermott
Senior Vice President, Alan Krueger
Vice President, Ben Bastian
Senior Vice President, Hyoung Chon
First Vice President, Michael Curran
Vice President, Neal Golub
Senior Vice President Of Industrial Properties, Mark Writt
Executive Vice President, Phil Brosseau
First Vice President, Daniel Brandel
Senior Vice President, Kurt Altvater
Senior Vice President, George Maragos
Vice President, Leonard Santoro
Vice President, Peter Dugan
Senior Vice President Partner, Rob Walles
Svp Retail Investments, Ian Schroeder
Vice President, Erik Parker
First Vice President, Bob Pielsticker
Senior Vice President, Randall Grimsman
Senior Vice President, Burke Weismann
Vice President, John Hamilton
Vice President, Matt Patyk
First Vice President, Dwayne Flynn
Vice President, Izzy Eichenstein
First Vice President, Lee Diamond
First Vice President, Steve Delaney
First Vice President, Patrick Wade
Vice President, Marta Villa
Executive Vice President, Jeffrey Shell
Vice President, Rabih Malaeb
Vice President Brokerage Services, Annah Moore

Vice President, Taylor Odegard
Senior Vice President, Brad Wilner
Senior Vice President, Carlos Vigon
Vice President, Joseph Orscheln
Senior Vice President, Nat Gambuzza
Vice President, Vincent Polce
Vice President, Michael Mccall
Senior Vice President, George Reid
Senior Vice President Global Corporate Services (gcs), Armando Nunez
Vice President, Michael P Wall
Senior Vice President, Clark Gore
Senior Vice President, Michael Wilson
Sp Vice President, William Kuntz
Mai Vice President, Mark Mediavilla
Lp Senior Vice President, Van Wehr
Senior Vice President, Joe Franco
Executive Vice President, Scott Prosser
Senior Vice President Institutional Properties Multifamily, Robert Dean
Vice President, Tommy Molin
Vice President Global Enterprise Systems, Will Wende
Senior Vice President, Jeremy Ballenger
Vice President, Tom Zorn
First Vice President, Will Lightfoot
Mai Vice President, Cheryl Scott
Vice President, Daniel Boring
Senior Vice President, James Flinn
Vice President, John Makowski
Senior Vice President, Mike Fahey
Executive Vice President, Jack Breard
Senior Vice President, Kevin Mclennan
Vice President Technical Sales, Kenna Brannon
Mai Vice President, Peter An
Vice President, Bennett Johnson
First Vice President, Annie Prupas
Senior Vice President, Martin Rolh
Senior Vice President, Michael Raffetto
Senior Principal Vice President, Timothy Jaeger
Vice President, Brian Myers
First Vice President, Mike Horne
First Vice President, John Krause
Vice President, Bill Leffier
Vice President, Marcus Cornelius
Senior Vice President, Larry Dinner
Auditors: KPMG LLP

LOCATIONS

HQ: CBRE Group Inc
400 South Hope Street, 25th Floor, Los Angeles, CA 90071
Phone: 213 613-3333
Web: www.cbre.com

2016 Sales

	$ mil.	% of total
Americas	7,226	55
Europe Middle East & Africa	3,917	30
Asia/Pacific	1,485	11
Global investment management	369	3
Development services	71	1
Total	**13,071**	**100**

2016 Sales

	$ mil.	% of total
US	6,917	55
UK	2,094	18
Other countries	4,059	27
Total	**13,071**	**100**

PRODUCTS/OPERATIONS

Selected Industries

CBRE Hotels
Data Centers
Energy & Sustainability
Golf & Resort Properties
Healthcare
Industrial & Logistics
Labor Analytics

Multifamily
Office
Public Institutions & Education
Residential
Retail
Alternative Investments Practice
Labor Analytics
Life Sciences

Selected Subsidiaries

CBRE Inc.
CBRE Capital Markets Inc.
CB/TCC LLC
CBRE Global Holdings SARL
CBRE Finance Europe LLP
CBRE Limited
CBRE Services Inc.
Norland Managed Services Ltd.
Trammell Crow Company LLC
CBRE Luxembourg Holdings SARL
CBRE Global Acquisition Company SARL
Relam Amsterdam Holdings
CBRE Limited Partnership

Selected service investors

Financing
Investment Administration
Investment Banking
Leasing & Advisory
Loan Servicing
Property Management
Property Sales
Valuation & Advisory

Selected services for occupiers

Facilities Management
Leasing & Advisory
Management Consulting
Project Management
Valuation & Advisory
Workplace

Selected Business Lines

Advisory & Transaction Services
Asset Services
Capital Markets
Global Workplace Solutions
Valuation & Advisory Services
Investment Management (CBRE Global Investors)
Development Services (Trammell Crow Company)
CB/TCC LLC
CBRE Finance Europe LLPCBRE Luxembourg Holdings SARLCBRE Global Acquisition Company SARLRelam Amsterdam HoldingsCBRE Limited Partnership

COMPETITORS

BGC Partners	Inland Group
Cassidy Turley	Jones Lang LaSalle
Colliers International	Lincoln Property
Colliers International Group	Marcus & Millichap
	Mitsui Fudosan
Cushman & Wakefield	Realogy Holdings
Eastdil Secured	Savills Studley

HISTORICAL FINANCIALS

Company Type: Public

Income Statement   FYE: December 31

	REVENUE ($ mil.)	NET INCOME ($ mil.)	NET PROFIT MARGIN	EMPLOYEES
12/18	21,340	1,063	5.0%	90,000
12/17	14,209	691	4.9%	80,000
12/16	13,071	571	4.4%	75,000
12/15	10,855	547	5.0%	70,000
12/14	9,049	484	5.4%	52,000
Annual Growth	**23.9%**	**21.7%**	**—**	**14.7%**

2018 Year-End Financials

Debt ratio: 23.03%
Return on equity: 23.74%
Cash ($ mil.): 777
Current ratio: 1.16
Long-term debt ($ mil.): 1,767
No. of shares (mil.): 336
Dividends
Yield: —
Payout: —
Market value ($ mil.): 13,490

	STOCK PRICE ($) FY Close	P/E High/Low		Earnings	PER SHARE ($) Dividends	Book Value
12/18	40.04	16	12	3.10	0.00	14.66
12/17	43.31	22	15	2.03	0.00	11.84
12/16	31.49	20	14	1.69	0.00	8.94
12/15	34.58	24	19	1.63	0.00	8.12
12/14	34.25	24	17	1.45	0.00	6.79
Annual Growth	**4.0%**	**—**	**—**	**20.9%**	**—**	**21.2%**

CBTX Inc

Auditors: Grant Thornton LLP

LOCATIONS

HQ: CBTX Inc
9 Greenway Plaza, Suite 110, Houston, TX 77046
Phone: 713 210-7600
Web: www.communitybankoftx.com

HISTORICAL FINANCIALS

Company Type: Public

Income Statement   FYE: December 31

	ASSETS ($ mil.)	NET INCOME ($ mil.)	INCOME AS % OF ASSETS	EMPLOYEES
12/18	3,279	47	1.4%	495
12/17	3,081	27	0.9%	462
12/16	2,951	27	0.9%	472
12/15	2,882	24	0.8%	—
Annual Growth	**4.4%**	**25.1%**	**—**	**—**

2018 Year-End Financials

Debt ratio: 0.05%
Return on equity: 10.13%
Cash ($ mil.): 382
Current ratio: —
Long-term debt ($ mil.): —
No. of shares (mil.): 24
Dividends
Yield: 0.6%
Payout: 14.3%
Market value ($ mil.): 732

	STOCK PRICE ($) FY Close	P/E High/Low		Earnings	PER SHARE ($) Dividends	Book Value
12/18	29.40	20	15	1.89	0.20	19.58
12/17	29.66	24	23	1.22	0.05	17.97
12/16	0.00	—	—	1.22	0.00	16.21
Annual Growth	**—**	**—**	**—**	**15.7%**	**(0.0%)**	**6.5%**

CDW Corp

Auditors: Ernst & Young LLP

LOCATIONS

HQ: CDW Corp
75 Tri-State International, Lincolnshire, IL 60069
Phone: 847 465-6000
Web: www.cdw.com

HISTORICAL FINANCIALS

Company Type: Public

Income Statement   FYE: December 31

	REVENUE ($ mil.)	NET INCOME ($ mil.)	NET PROFIT MARGIN	EMPLOYEES
12/18	16,240	643	4.0%	250
12/17	15,191	523	3.4%	250
12/16	13,981	424	3.0%	8,516
12/15	12,988	403	3.1%	8,465
12/14	12,074	244	2.0%	7,211
Annual Growth	**7.7%**	**27.3%**	**—**	**(56.8%)**

2018 Year-End Financials

Debt ratio: 44.76%
Return on equity: 65.68%
Cash ($ mil.): 205
Current ratio: 1.35
Long-term debt ($ mil.): 3,183

No. of shares (mil.): 147
Dividends
  Yield: 1.1%
  Payout: 21.0%
Market value ($ mil.): 11,971

	STOCK PRICE ($) FY Close	P/E High/Low	PER SHARE ($) Earnings	Dividends	Book Value
12/18	81.05	23 16	4.19	0.93	6.60
12/17	69.49	21 15	3.31	0.69	6.42
12/16	52.09	21 13	2.56	0.48	6.52
12/15	42.04	20 14	2.35	0.31	6.52
12/14	35.17	25 16	1.42	0.20	5.44
Annual Growth	23.2%	— —	31.1%	47.6%	5.0%

Celanese Corp (DE)

Celanese Corporation is a global technology and specialty materials company that manufactures building block chemicals like acetic acid and vinyl acetate monomers used in everything from inks and paints to agricultural products and chewing gum. The Texas-based also makes advanced plastics products such as precision molds for injection molding flame- and heat-resistance plastics and acetate film. Other products include acetate tow (used in cigarette filters) and industrial specialties like ethylene vinyl acetate.The company has dozens of industry-leading brands including polyacetal like Celcon and Hostaform thermoplastics under the GUR brand polyesters under Celanex and Impet brands Nylon under Nylfor Nimalid and Frianyl.

Operations

Celanese is one of the world's largest producers of acetyl products and a top global producer of engineered polymers.It operates through four business segments: Acetyl Intermediates Advanced Engineered Materials Consumer Specialties and Industrial Specialties.

Acetyl Intermediates bringing in around 40% of total company revenue produces acetic acid vinyl acetate monomer acetic anhydride and acetate esters. The segment's products are commonly used in colorants paints adhesives coatings and pharmaceuticals. It also produces organic solvents and intermediates for pharmaceutical agricultural and chemical products.

Advanced Engineered Materials worth more than 30% of sales makes high performance plastics mostly for automotive and medical applications.

Industrial Specialties accounts for 15% of sales and includes the emulsion polymers and EVA polymers businesses. The former's products find use in paints and coatings adhesives construction glass fiber textiles and paper. EVA polymers makes specialty ethylene vinyl acetate resins and compounds and low-density polyethylene for use in packaging lamination film hot melt adhesives auto parts and carpeting.

The Consumer Specialties segment brings in some 10% of sales and mostly makes acetate tow for use in cigarette filters. It also makes preservatives for the food and drink industries such as sorbic acid and potassium sorbate. It also makes Qorus and Sunett sweeteners.

Geographic Reach

Irving Texas-based Celanese has more than 30 production facilities across the world and 10 affiliate production sites.

Besides the US Celanese has properties plants or other operations in Belgium Brazil Canada China Germany Hungary Malaysia Mexico the Netherlands South Korea Sweden Singapore and the UK.

Germany account for around 30% of the company's sales followed by the US at 25%

Sales and Marketing

Celanese markets its products both directly to customers and through distributors. Sales to major global customers in a wide range of industries are usually made under multi-year contracts. The company serves a broad range of industries including consumer and industrial adhesives paints and coatings textiles food and beverage automotive applications consumer and medical applications performance industrial applications filter media paper and packaging chemical additives and construction applications.

Acetate tow is sold principally to the major tobacco companies that account for a majority of worldwide cigarette production. Customers of Clarifoil film include printers carton manufacturers retailers packaging buyers publishers designers and freezer door manufacturers. Food protection ingredients are primarily sold through regional distributors to small and medium sized customers and directly to large multinational customers in the food industry.

Financial Performance

In the last decade (2008-17) revenue at Celanese has hovered around the $5 billion to $6 billion mark. Although the company posted profits every year in that same period net income has fluctuated considerably between a low of $282 million (2008) and a peak of $1 billion (2013).

In 2017 Celanese revenue climbed some 15% to $6.1 billion stemming almost entirely from a 45% spike in additional volumes sold in the advanced engineered materials segment compared to the year prior. The growth was related SOFTER acquisition and the NILIT nylon compounding division.

Net income fell some 6% to $843 million mostly due to a year-over-year increase of some $90 million in SG&A costs and other charges. The $100 million SG&A spending increase comes from the merger acquisition and integration costs in the advanced engineered materials segment.

Celanese cash holdings decreased from $638 million in 2016 to $576 million in 2017. Operations generated $800 million. Investing activities used $550 million primarily in acquisitions and CAPEX. Financing took out a further $350 million due to a bulk purchase of treasury stocks costing some $500 million.

Strategy

The biggest advantage of Celanese is its continued name recognition across all the major industries on a global scale. It has over two-dozen high performance engineered materials that are readily recognized as top brands. The company maintains a large global production capacity. Its revenue stream also reflects an impressive geographic balance. This guards Celanese against sudden downturns as proven by its continued profitability despite a commodity price downturn in 2014-16 period.

The company spends top-dollar (averaging over $70 million a year) on research and innovation of new products and applications as well as an average CAPEX of $250 million in the 2015-17 period.

Ever expansive the company often acquires businesses with higher margins and lower exposure to price fluctuation. For example Celanese is pumping up its advanced materials business by making three acquisitions in 2015-18 period? SOFTER Nilit and Omni ? adding more nylon and thermoplastic end-products to its product lines.

Mergers and Acquisitions

In 2018 Celanese acquired Omni Plastics which specializes in custom compounding of various engineered thermoplastic materials. This particular material is in high demand in the automotive electrical and electronics consumer goods and industrial markets. The acquisition adds Celanese's compounding capacity in the Americas. The addition continues a recent trend of resin makers diversifying with compounding (both LyndondellBassel and Westlake Chemical pursued similar deals).

In 2017 Celanese acquired Nilit Plastics the nylon compounding division of Nilit an Israeli nylon manufacturer.

Company Background

Celanese Corporation was created in 2004 by the Blackstone Group which had acquired a majority share in Celanese AG turned it private and then flipped it in a 2005 public offering. Blackstone finally divested its remaining holdings in Celanese in 2007.

EXECUTIVES

Chairman And Ceo, Mark C. Rohr, age 67, $1,142,308 total compensation
Evp And Chief Administrative Officer, Lori A. Johnston, age 54, $475,000 total compensation
Evp And General Counsel, Peter G. Edwards, age 57
Evp And President Acetyl Chain And Integrated Supply Chain, Patrick D. (Pat) Quarles, age 51, $627,692 total compensation
Evp Coo And President Materials Solutions, Scott M. Sutton, age 54, $581,538 total compensation
Svp Finance And Cfo, Christopher W. (Chris) Jensen, age 52, $546,154 total compensation
Cio, Rajesh Nagarajan
Group Vice President Business Development, Jana Brimmer
Senior Vice President Engineered Materials, Patrick Schumacher
Vp And Chief Technology And Innovation Officer, Verghese Thomas
Vice President Global Sales Americas Region, John Caamano
Vice President Of Talent Development, Lisa Esparza
Vice President And Deputy General Counsel, Jay Felkins
Senior Vice President Supply Management, William Antonace
Senior Vice President Chief Financial Officer, Steven Sterin
Vice President Of Investor Relations, Jon Puckett
Vice President Manufacturing Engineered Materials, Christo Zemering
Vice President Cellulose Derivatives, Marcel V Amerongen
Vice President Europe Region, Amy Heber
National Accounts Manager, Jeff Clements
Vice President Business Service Management, Wade Nelson
Vice President Human Resources And Employment Law, Joseph Fox
Vice President Global Medical, Ik Khalil
Secretary, Pat Hurd
Board Member, John Wulff
Board Member, Kathryn Hill
Board Member, William Brown
Board Member, Edward Galante
Auditors: KPMG LLP

LOCATIONS

HQ: Celanese Corp (DE)
  222 W. Las Colinas Blvd., Suite 900N, Irving, TX 75039-5421
Phone: 972 443-4000
Web: www.celanese.com

2016 sales

	$ mil.	% of total
Germany	1,540	29
US	1,451	27
China	758	14
Singapore	745	14
Belgium	408	8
Canada	214	4
Mexico	150	2
Others	123	2
Total	**5,389**	**100**

PRODUCTS/OPERATIONS

2016 sales

	$ mil.	% of total
Advanced Engineered Materials	1,444	27
Acetyl Intermediates	2,441	45
Industrial Specialties	979	18
Consumer Specialties	929	17
Adjustments	(404)	-7
Total	**5,389**	**100**

Selected Products

Acetyl Intermediates
  Acetate esters
  Acetic acid
  Acetic anhydride
  Carboxylic acids
  Methanol
  Vinyl acetate monomer (VAM)
Industrial Specialties
  Emulsions
Consumer Specialties
  Acetate tow
  Sunett sweetener
Advanced Engineered Materials
  Polyacetal products (POM)
  Polyphenylene sulfide (Forton)
  UHMW-PE (GUR)

Selected Brand Names

AOPlus
BuyTiconaDirect
Celanex
Celcon
Celstran
Celvolit
Clarifoil
Compel
Erkol
GUR
Hostaform
Impet
Mowilith
Nutrinova
Riteflex
Sunett
Thermx
Vandar
Vectra
Vinamul

COMPETITORS

Asahi Kasei	Hexion
BASF SE	LANXESS
DSM	Methanex
Daicel Chemical	NutraSweet
Dow Chemical	Rhodia
Eastman Chemical	Solvay

HISTORICAL FINANCIALS

Company Type: Public

Income Statement   FYE: December 31

	REVENUE ($ mil.)	NET INCOME ($ mil.)	NET PROFIT MARGIN	EMPLOYEES
12/19	6,297	852	13.5%	7,714
12/18	7,155	1,207	16.9%	7,684
12/17	6,140	843	13.7%	7,592
12/16	5,389	900	16.7%	7,293
12/15	5,674	304	5.4%	7,081
Annual Growth	**2.6%**	**29.4%**	**—**	**2.2%**

2019 Year-End Financials

Debt ratio: 41.21%		No. of shares (mil.): 119	
Return on equity: 31.03%		Dividends	
Cash ($ mil.): 463		Yield: 1.9%	
Current ratio: 1.58		Payout: 33.2%	
Long-term debt ($ mil.): 3,409		Market value ($ mil.): 14,720	

	STOCK PRICE ($) FY Close	P/E High/Low		PER SHARE ($) Earnings	Dividends	Book Value
12/19	123.12	19	13	6.84	2.40	20.97
12/18	89.97	13	9	8.91	2.08	23.30
12/17	107.08	18	13	6.09	1.74	21.26
12/16	78.74	13	9	6.18	1.38	18.40
12/15	67.33	36	26	2.00	1.15	16.20
Annual Growth	**16.3%**	—	—	**36.0%**	**20.2%**	**6.7%**

Centene Corp

Centene provides managed care and related services in more than a dozen states under names such as Managed Health Services (Wisconsin and Indiana) Superior HealthPlan (Texas) and Buckeye Community Health Plan (Ohio). Centene provides services to some 12.3 million low-income elderly and disabled people receiving benefits from programs including Medicaid Supplemental Security Income (SSI) and state Children's Health Insurance Program (CHIP). Centene also offers specialty services in areas such as behavioral health (through Cenpatico) vision benefits (OptiCare) and pharmacy benefits management (US Script). Centene is buying Medicaid insurer WellCare for $17.3 billion.

Operations

Centene operates in two primary segments: Managed Care and Specialty Services.

The Managed Care segment provides services through Medicaid CHIP Long-Term Services and Supports (LTSS) LTC (long-term care) foster care and ABD (aged blind and disabled) programs. Centene's Medicaid contracts account for about 80% of total revenues. California accounts for about a fifth of revenues.

The Specialty Services segment is composed of companies offering a range of health care services and products to state programs health care organizations correctional facilities employer groups and other organizations. Offerings include telehealth advisory case management (CaseNet) and pharmacy services. Centene's Celtic Insurance subsidiary specializes in providing low-cost consumer-directed insurance policies to uninsured customers nationwide and its Bridgeway Health Solutions provides long-term care policies in select territories.

Geographic Reach

Centene serves hospitals and care facilities in more than 25 states including Arizona California Florida Louisiana and Texas. California and Texas are its two largest markets.

Sales and Marketing

Most of Centene's revenue comes under contract or subcontract with state Medicaid managed care programs. Its largest markets are California and Texas.

Financial Performance

Centene's revenue and net income have been rising significantly for the past five years as the company acquires other firms adds and retains state contracts and enters new business areas. Similarly net income has risen over the past few years.

Revenue grew 19% to $48.4 billion in 2017. The company's 2016 acquisition of Health Net boosted sales that year. Overall managed care membership increased 7% and premiums increased 22%. The company also secured numerous contracts with state corrections departments.

With the higher revenue net income rose 47% to $828 million in 2017. An increase in investment income and a decrease in income tax expenses also helped the bottom line.

The company ended 2017 with $4.1 billion in cash and cash equivalents a 4% increase from what it had at the beginning of the year. This was largely due to the higher earnings. Operating activities provided $1.5 billion in cash while investing activities (system enhancements and headquarters expansion) used $1.3 billion. Financing activities used another $82 million.

Strategy

Centene's primary growth strategies are to enter new markets and expand in existing markets via acquisitions and by gaining new contracts with state Medicaid agencies. The company is benefiting from the growing number of mandated managed care plans in states that are looking to control Medicaid spending. Since 2017 the firm has expanded its Medicare Advantage operations into more than a dozen existing states.

In addition to geographic expansion the company looks to grow its membership by adding new services in its existing state markets such as small business health plans and low-income individual plans. Centene has also done well in the challenging Affordable Care Act (ACA) exchange markets. It plans to enter the ACA markets in Pennsylvania North Carolina South Carolina and Tennessee in 2019.

The firm evaluates opportunities to grow in new fields such as health-related information technology and non-Medicaid health plans. It has a joint venture with MHM Services named Centurion which operates in the correctional facility managed care market; the company now plans to buy MHM and take full ownership of the Centurion venture.

Centene also occasionally divests or exits operations in smaller service areas to focus on its core growth regions. For example it exited the Arizona individual preferred provider organization (PPO) business in early 2017. The company has also lost certain contracts or market share where insurers have joined the Medicaid program.

Mergers and Acquisitions

Centene is buying Medicaid insurer WellCare in a $17.3 billion transaction. The deal will more than double Centene's Medicaid membership which will total more than 11 million.

The company bought not-for-profit insurer Fidelis Care for $3.75 billion in mid-2018. Fidelis offers Medicaid CHIP and other affordable coverage to some 1.6 million individuals. Through that deal the company gained entry to the New York market.

Also that year Centene acquired MHM Services which specializes in providing health care to correctional systems and other government agencies. The deal included MHM's 49% stake in the companies' Centurion joint venture which provides clinical programs for correctional systems. By investing in MHM Centene gained a more expansive presence in the correctional system health care market.

In another 2018 deal the company purchased Community Medical Holdings (dba Community Medical Group or CMG) an at-risk primary care provider serving more than 70000 patients in the Miami area. CMG provides health care and social services to Medicaid Medicare Advantage and Health Insurance Marketplace recipients. Centene is exploring the possibility of expanding CMG's business model into other areas.

EXECUTIVES

Vp It, Keith Bernier
Svp Products, Kevin J. Counihan
President And Coo, Cynthia J. (Cindy) Brinkley, age 59, $650,000 total compensation
Chairman And Ceo, Michael F. Neidorff, age 76, $1,500,000 total compensation
Evp Mergers & Acquisitions And Chief Strategy Officer, Jesse N. Hunter, age 43, $650,000 total compensation
Evp Markets, Christopher D. Bowers, age 63
Evp General Counsel And Secretary, Keith H. Williamson, age 66, $600,000 total compensation
Evp Cfo And Treasurer, Jeffrey A Schwaneke, age 44, $632,671 total compensation
Evp And Cio, Mark J. Brooks, age 49
Senior Vice President Operations Fl, William Kruegel
Vice President Of Actuarial Services, Don Killian
Vice President Of Finance, Trip Peeples
Vice President Hospital Operations, Michael Bailey
Corporate Vice President Business Development, Wade Rakes
Senior Vice President Patient Services, Susan Ekvall
Vice President Of Medical Affairs, David Harmon
Vice President Information Technology Security; Chief Information Security Officer, Dustin Wilcox
Vice President Medical Management, Kendra Case
Vice President Tax Services, Cynthia Lemons
Executive Vice President, Brandy Burkhalter
Vice President Operations, D Lewis
Vice President, Arvan Chan
Vice President Member And Provider Solutions, Scott Ireland
Senior Vice President Individual Business, Anand Shukla
Vice President Information Technology, Keith Hibbard
Director Of Pharmacy, Alicia Cyrus
Medical Director California Health And Wellness, Ramiro Zuniga
Medical Director, David Gilchrist
Vice President Actuarial Srvs And Risk Management, Steele Stewart
Vice President Of Business Development, Stacey Hull
Vice President Operations (health plans), Adam Peters
Vice President Internal Audit, Shannon Bagley
Senior Vice President Business Development, Debra Cooper
Vice President Of Human Resour, Jalie Cohen
Vice President Of Human Resources, Mary-Katherine Kutac
Vice President Information Technology, Steele Sloane
Regional Vice President, Alida Dodd
Vice President Of User Experience, Amy Poole-yaeger
Vice President Of Operations, Kristine Cusimano
Vice President Of Human Resources, Stephanie Hall
Vice President Of Payment Innovation, Ananth Lalithakumar
Vice President, Donald Pifer
Vice President And Director, Carolyn Thomas
Corporate Medical Director, Julianne Mazurek
Senior Vice President Government Relations, Jonathan Dinesman
Vice President Operations, James Sefcik
Vice President Operations, Stephanie Slaughter
Vice President Pharmacy Operations, Justin Weiss
Vice President Facility Management And Construction, Andrea Cruce
Vice President Of Enrollment Operations, Michael Boone
Vice President Medical Management, Marion Sustakoski

Vice President Of Medical Affairs, Ronald Charles
Medical Director, Randy Tompkins
Vice President Compliance, Jeff Torres
Director Of Pharmacy, James Frank Reynolds
Vice President Product Solutions, Lisa McClellan
Vice President Customer Service, Rodney Long
Vp It Envolve Pharmacy Solutions, Matt Merlo
Executive Vice President Health Plans, Rob Hitchcock
Vice President Marketing, John Howell
Director Of Pharmacy Operations, Martha Exton
Vice President, William Scheffel
Vice President Pharmacy Operations Federal Programs, Jeff Borowiecki
Vice President Of Organizational Development, Tony Myers
Vice President Of Medical Management New Business, Judy Bauer
Vice President Of Information Technology, Jamie Gilmore
Senior Vice President Boston, Chris Dycus
Vice President Of Finance, Nitin Jain
Vice President Medical Management Clinical Systems, Alice Stewart
Evp Sales And Account Management Envolve Pharmacy Solutions, Carmen Fontanez
Clinical Director, Rachel Blaising
Vice President Information Technology Operations Strategy And Business Development, Brian Holman
Senior Vice President And Chief Security Risk Officer, Louis Desorbo
Senior Vice President Of Medical Affairs, Marcus Wallace
Vice President Product Development Hemophilia Acariahealth, Charles Signorino
Vp Clinical Pharmacy Solutions Envolve Pharmacy Solutions, Laurie Amirpoor
Vice President Cenpatico Schools, Erik Ryan
Vp Business Knowledge And Informatics, Sigal Dor
Vp Data Analytics Cenpatico, Michael Grover
Vice President Compliance And Government Affairs, Terrica Miller
Senior Vice President Medicaid Solutions, Toby Douglas
Vice President Quality Buckeye Health Plan, Hagy Wegener
Vice President Innovation And Commercialization, Fredrik Engelhardt
Vice President Medical Management Um Superior Health Plan, Janice Wierschke
Vice President Of Operations, Jackie Shearer-adams
Vp Pharma Relations And Business Development Acariahealth, Steve Granzyk
Assistant Vice President Account Executive, Steven Merahn
Vice President Talent Acquisition, Dan Nielsen
Director Of Government Relations Coordinated Care Health Plan, Andrea Tull
Vice President Product Development, Jennifer Fortin
Vp Organizational Development And Training, Mike Josias
Vice President Of Product Performance, Abbie Lecoz
Vice President Legislative And Government Affairs Pennsylvania Health And Wellness, Norris Benns
Vice President, Ann Sciammacco
Vice President Marketing, John Rindlaub
Vice President Human Resources Operations, Jaclyn Pettinari
Vice President Medicare Programs, Michael Franks
Senior Vice President Health Plans, Chris Bowers
Vice President Medical Management, Roxanne Coulter
Vice President, Joyce Larkln
Vice President Legislative And Government Affairs, Shawn Furey

Svp Social Responsibility, Patrick J Frawley
Vice President Compliance, Krug Iris
Vice President External Relations, Jennifer Guy
Auditors: KPMG LLP

LOCATIONS

HQ: Centene Corp
7700 Forsyth Boulevard, St. Louis, MO 63105
Phone: 314 725-4477   **Fax:** 314 725-5180
Web: www.centene.com

PRODUCTS/OPERATIONS

2017 Sales

	$ mil.	% of total
Premiums	43,353	89
Premium tax & health insurer fee	2,762	6
Service	2,267	5
Total	**48,382**	**100**

2017 Sales by Segment

	$ mil.	% of total
Managed Care	45,842	79
Specialty Services	12,055	21
Adjustments	(9515)	—
Total	**48,382**	**100**

COMPETITORS

AMERIGROUP	Kaiser Foundation
Aetna	Health Plan
Anthem	Molina Healthcare
Blue Cross and Blue	Scott & White Health
Shield of Texas	Plan
CIGNA	UnitedHealth Group
Humana	WellCare Health Plans

HISTORICAL FINANCIALS

Company Type: Public

Income Statement				FYE: December 31
	REVENUE ($ mil.)	NET INCOME ($ mil.)	NET PROFIT MARGIN	EMPLOYEES
12/18	60,116	900	1.5%	47,300
12/17	48,382	828	1.7%	33,700
12/16	40,607	562	1.4%	30,500
12/15	22,760	355	1.6%	18,200
12/14	16,560	271	1.6%	13,400
Annual Growth	38.0%	35.0%	—	37.1%

2018 Year-End Financials

Debt ratio: 21.64%	No. of shares (mil.): 412
Return on equity: 10.13%	Dividends
Cash ($ mil.): 5,342	Yield: —
Current ratio: 1.00	Payout: —
Long-term debt ($ mil.): 6,648	Market value ($ mil.): 47,559

	STOCK PRICE ($) FY Close	P/E High/Low		PER SHARE ($) Earnings	Dividends	Book Value
12/18	115.30	64	43	2.26	0.00	26.47
12/17	100.88	43	24	2.35	0.00	19.75
12/16	56.51	43	29	1.72	0.00	17.14
12/15	65.81	81	35	1.44	0.00	8.96
12/14	103.85	92	48	1.13	0.00	7.36
Annual Growth	2.6%	—	—	19.1%	—	37.7%

CenterPoint Energy Resources Corp.

EXECUTIVES

Chb-pres-ceo, Scott M Prochazka
Senior Vice President Energy Services, Joseph Joe J Vortherms
Senior Vice President Gas Operations, Richard Rick A Zapalac
Auditors: DELOITTE & TOUCHE LLP

LOCATIONS

HQ: CenterPoint Energy Resources Corp.
1111 Louisiana, Houston, TX 77002
Phone: 713 207-1111
Web: www.centerpointenergy.com

HISTORICAL FINANCIALS

Company Type: Public

Income Statement | | | | FYE: December 31

	REVENUE ($ mil.)	NET INCOME ($ mil.)	NET PROFIT MARGIN	EMPLOYEES
12/18	7,343	208	2.8%	3,600
12/17	6,603	745	11.3%	3,613
12/16	4,454	245	5.5%	3,467
12/15	4,527	(912)	—	3,421
12/14	6,367	323	5.1%	4,581
Annual Growth	3.6%	(10.4%)	—	(5.8%)

2018 Year-End Financials

Debt ratio: 28.87%
Return on equity: 7.49%
Cash ($ mil.): 14
Current ratio: 1.32
Long-term debt ($ mil.): 2,371

No. of shares (mil.): 0
Dividends
Yield: —
Payout: 173.0%
Market value ($ mil.): —

CenterPoint Energy, Inc

CenterPoint Energy Inc. one of the largest public utilities in the US distributes natural gas and electricity to more than 6 million customers. Through subsidiary CenterPoint Energy Resources Corp this holding company distributes natural gas to 3.5 million customers in six states. The company's other major subsidiary Houston Electric distributes electricity that reaches 2.5 million customers in the Texas Gulf Coast region including Houston. Beyond these regulated distributions (that requires rate approval from regional authorities) CenterPoint Energy also sells gas directly to some 30000 customers across 30 US states. These customers range from large industries and utilities to municipalities and educational institutions. In addition to its portfolio of 54000 miles of power distribution lines and 76000 miles of gas distribution lines the holding company has a 54% equity investment in the master limited partnership Enable which maintains natural gas and crude oil infrastructure assets in three US states.

HISTORY

CenterPoint Energy's earliest predecessor Houston Electric Lighting and Power was formed in 1882 by a group including Emanuel Raphael

cashier at Houston Savings Bank and Mayor William Baker. In 1901 General Electric's financial arm United Electric Securities Company took control of the utility which became Houston Lighting & Power (HL&P). United Electric sold HL&P five years later; by 1922 HL&P ended up in the arms of National Power & Light Company (NP&L) a subsidiary of Electric Bond & Share (a public utility holding company that had been spun off by General Electric).

In 1942 NP&L was forced to sell HL&P in order to comply with the 1935 Public Utility Holding Company Act. As the oil industry boomed in Houston after WWII so did HL&P.

HL&P became the managing partner in a venture to build a nuclear plant on the Texas Gulf Coast in 1973. Construction on the South Texas Project with partners Central Power and Light and the cities of Austin and San Antonio began in 1975. In 1976 Houston Industries (HI) was formed as the holding company for HL&P.

By 1980 the nuke was four years behind schedule and over budget. HL&P and its partners sued construction firm Brown & Root in 1982 and received a $700 million settlement in 1985. (The City of Austin also sued HL&P for damages but lost.) The nuke was finally brought online in 1988 with the final cost estimated at $5.8 billion.

Meanwhile HI diversified into cable TV in 1986 by creating Enrcom (later Paragon Communications) through a venture with Time Inc. Two years later it bought the US cable interests of Canada's Rogers Communications. HI left the cable business in 1995 selling out to Time Warner.

Developing Latin fever HI joined a consortium that bought 51% of Argentinean electric company EDELAP in 1992. (However in 1998 HI sold its stake to AES.) On a roll HI acquired 90% of Argentina's electric utility EDESE (1995); joined a consortium that won a controlling stake in Light a Brazilian electric utility (1996); bought a stake in Colombian electric utility EPSA (1997); and bought interests in three electric utilities in El Salvador (1998). It also won a permit to develop and operate a natural gas system in Mexico (1998).

Back in the US HI acquired gas dealer NorAm for $2.5 billion in 1997. The next year it bought five generating plants in California from Edison International and laid plans to build merchant plants in Arizona (near Phoenix) Illinois Nevada (near Las Vegas in partnership with Sempra Energy) and Rhode Island. Overseas HI finished a power plant in India in 1998. It also bought a 65% interest in Colombian electric utilities Electricaribe and Electrocosta; EPSA bought about 55% of CET in Colombia and Light bought about 75% of Metropolitana (S o Paulo Brazil).

In 1999 HI became Reliant Energy and HL&P became Reliant Energy HL&P. That year the company bought a 52% stake in Dutch power generation firm UNA; it bought the remaining 48% the next year. Also in 2000 Reliant Energy paid Sithe Energies (now a part of Dynegy) $2.1 billion for 21 power plants in the mid-Atlantic states. It sold its operations in Brazil Colombia and El Salvador that year and transferred all of its nonregulated operations to subsidiary Reliant Resources. Reliant Energy also announced plans to spin off Reliant Resources that year.

Reliant Energy netted about $1.7 billion in 2001 from the sale to the public of nearly 20% of Reliant Resources. Later that year Reliant Resources announced that it would acquire US independent power producer Orion Power Holdings in a $4.7 billion deal; the deal was completed in 2002. Deregulation took effect in Texas that year and Reliant Energy transferred its retail power supply business to Reliant Resources.

As the finances of wholesale energy companies came under scrutiny in 2002 the SEC issued a

formal investigation into "round-trip" energy trades completed by Reliant Resources. These activities artificially inflated the company's trading volumes and led it to restate its 1999 2000 and 2001 financial results; it also reduced its energy marketing and trading workforce by about 35%.

Reliant Energy announced plans in 2001 to form a new holding company (CenterPoint Energy) for itself and Reliant Resources; it completed the name change in 2002.

CenterPoint Energy changed its name in 2002 in preparation for the spin-off of its 83% stake in Reliant Resources (now GenOn Energy) a global independent power producer and energy marketer; the spinoff was completed later that year. (Reliant Resources changed its name to Reliant Energy in 2004.) CenterPoint Energy transferred its nonregulated Texas retail power supply business to Reliant Resources before spinning off the unit.

EXECUTIVES

Evp And President Electric Division, Tracy B. Bridge, age 60, $481,250 total compensation
President Ceo And Director, Scott M. Prochazka, age 52, $996,525 total compensation
Svp Electric Utility Business, Kenneth M. Mercado
Svp Gas Operations, Richard A. (Rick) Zapalac
Evp And Cfo, William D. (Bill) Rogers, age 58, $485,000 total compensation
Svp Natural Gas Distribution, Scott E. Doyle
Svp Energy Services, Joseph J. (Joe) Vortherms
Svp Deputy General Counsel And Chief Ethics And Compliance Office, Carol Helliker
Vice President Audit Services, Kelly Gauger
Vice President And Treasurer, Carla Kneipp
Svp And Chief Human Resources Officer, Susan Ortenstone
Vp Regulatory And Government Affairs, Jason Ryan
Division Vp Operations Support And Technology, John Slanina
Vp Operations Support, Beverley Melchisedech
Vice President Marketing, Carol Burchfield
Vice President And Treasurer, Marc Kilbride
Vp Minnesota Operations, Brad Tutunjian
Svp Strategic Planning And Business Development, James Dumler
Vp Business Development, Michele Tihami
Vp Texas State Relations, Jeff Bonham
Vice President Gas Operations Louisiana And Mississippi, Trey Kuchar
Vp Corporate Communications And Community Relations, John Sousa
Senior Vice President Supply Chain, Leslie Alexander
Vice President Cmp Services, Rob Ellis
Vp Of Information Technology, Jessica Davis
Vice President Of Human Resources, Valencia Amenson
Vp Of Information Technology, Al Collins
Board Member, Susan Rheney
Chairman, Milton Carroll, age 68
Assistant Treasurer, Linda Geiger
Senior Secretary, Penny Hecox
Board Member, Peter Wareing
Secretary Iii, Jennifer Woodall
Vice Chairman, Jeremy Bloch
Board Member, John Somerhalder
Board Member, Scott Mclean
Board Member, Phillip Smith
Auditors: DELOITTE & TOUCHE LLP

LOCATIONS

HQ: CenterPoint Energy, Inc
1111 Louisiana, Houston, TX 77002
Phone: 713 207-1111
Web: www.centerpointenergy.com

PRODUCTS/OPERATIONS

2018 Sales

	$ mil.	% of total
Retail gas	4,161	39
Electric delivery	3,232	31
Wholesale gas	3,008	28
Energy products & services	156	2
Gas transportation & processing	32	-
Total	**10,589**	**100**

2018 Sales

	$ mil.	% of total
Energy Services	4,411	42
Electric Transmission & Distribution	3,232	30
Natural Gas Distribution	2,931	28
Other	15	-
Total	**10,589**	**100**

2018 Sales

	$ mil.	% of total
Utility	6,163	58
Non-utility	4,426	42
Total	**10,589**	**100**

COMPETITORS

AEP	Southern Company
AEP Texas Central	Southwestern Electric
AEP Texas North	Power
Ameren	Xcel Energy
OGE Energy	

HISTORICAL FINANCIALS

Company Type: Public

Income Statement   FYE: December 31

	REVENUE ($ mil.)	NET INCOME ($ mil.)	NET PROFIT MARGIN	EMPLOYEES
12/18	10,589	368	3.5%	7,977
12/17	9,614	1,792	18.6%	7,977
12/16	7,528	432	5.7%	7,727
12/15	7,386	(692)	—	7,505
12/14	9,226	611	6.6%	8,540
Annual Growth	3.5%	(11.9%)	—	(1.7%)

2018 Year-End Financials

Debt ratio: 33.93%
Return on equity: 5.77%
Cash ($ mil.): 4,231
Current ratio: 2.13
Long-term debt ($ mil.): 8,682

No. of shares (mil.): 501
Dividends
  Yield: 3.9%
  Payout: 150.0%
Market value ($ mil.): 14,149

	STOCK PRICE ($) FY Close	P/E High/Low	PER SHARE ($) Earnings	Dividends	Book Value
12/18	28.23	40 34	0.74	1.11	16.08
12/17	28.36	7 6	4.13	1.07	10.88
12/16	24.64	25 17	1.00	1.03	8.03
12/15	18.36	— —	(1.61)	0.99	8.05
12/14	23.43	18 15	1.42	0.95	10.58
Annual Growth	4.8%	— —	(15.0%)	4.0%	11.0%

CenterState Bank Corp

CenterState Banks is the holding company for CenterState Bank of Florida which serves the Sunshine State through about 60 branches. The bank offers standard deposit products such as checking and savings accounts money market accounts and CDs. Real estate loans primarily residential and commercial mortgages make up 85% of the company's loan portfolio while the rest is made up of business loans and consumer loans. The bank's correspondent division provides bond securities accounting and loans to small and mid-sized banks across the Southeast and Texas. It also sells mutual funds annuities and other investment products.

Operations

About 65% of CenterState Banks' total revenue came from loan interest in 2014 while another 10% came from interest on its investment securities. The rest of the bank's revenue came form correspondent banking capital markets revenue and related revenue (11%) deposit account service charges (5%) debit/ATM and merchant card fees (3%) wealth management fees (2%) and other miscellaneous income sources. The company had a staff of 785 employees by the end of 2014.

Geographic Reach

CenterState has nearly 60 branches across 20 counties in central southeast and northeast Florida. Its loan production offices are in Tampa Gainesville Crystal River and Ft. Meyers.

Sales and Marketing

CenterState offers consumer and commercial banking services to individuals businesses and industries across Florida.

Financial Performance

The company has struggled to consistently grow its revenues in recent years due to shrinking interest margins on loans amidst the low-interest environment. Its profits however have been rising thanks to declining loan loss provisions as its loan portfolio's credit quality has improved with higher property valuations in the strengthened economy.

CenterState had a breakout year in 2014 however with its revenue jumping 22% to $164.5 million thanks to higher interest income stemming from new loan business from its acquisitions of First Southern Bancorp and Gulfstream Bancshares during the year.

Higher revenue and stable costs in 2014 also drove the bank's net income higher by 6% to a record $12.96 million. CenterState's operating cash levels plummeted by 90% to $1.4 million after adjusting its earnings for non-cash items mostly related to the net proceeds from its trading securities sales.

Strategy

CenterState Banks continues to seek out additional acquisition opportunities to boost its loan and deposit business and expand into more markets across Florida. To this end the bank's 2014 acquisitions extended its reach into Broward Palm Beach and Martin counties for the first time while adding more than $1.3 billion in new deposits and over $600 million in new loan business to its books.

Struggling to grow its revenues the bank has also worked to become more efficient and profitable through selective branch closures. During 2014 the company closed seven smaller branches and a standalone drive-thru facility to free up resources for more profitable bank acquisitions.

Mergers and Acquisitions

CenterState is buying Platinum Bank Holding Company parent company of Platinum Bank for approximately $83.9 million. The acquisition will add seven banking branches in the Tampa-St. Petersburg-Clearwater and Lakeland-Winter Haven areas. It will also add some $584 million in assets.

In June 2014 CenterState purchased First Southern Bancorp which expanded its market reach into Broward County after adding a net of seven new branches. The deal also added some $600 million in new loan assets and $853 million in deposits.

In January 2014 the company expanded into Palm Beach and Martin counties after buying Gulfstream Bancshares and its four branches with $479 million in deposits.

EXECUTIVES

Senior Vice President Corporate Auditor, Wayne Stewart
Svp And Cfo, James J. Antal, age 68, $312,750 total compensation
President Ceo And Director Centerstate Banks Inc. And Centerstate Bank Of Florida, John Corbett, age 50, $420,250 total compensation
Corporate Chief Risk Officer, Daniel E. Bockhorst, $217,500 total compensation
Treasurer, Stephen Young, $278,333 total compensation
First Vice President Business Development, Chris Wright
Assistant Vice President Marketing And Business Development, Dana Townsend
Vice President, Todd Patrick
Vice President Commercial Lending, Dan Jackson
Senior Vice President And Commercial Lending Officer, Bill Daniels
Assistant Vice President Merchant Services Divison, Deborah Joyce
Assistant Vice President Business Analyst Ii, Chante Carlson
First Vice President, Stacey A Dunn
Senior Vice President And Director Of Operations, Darlene Bennett
Vice President, Stacy Byrd
Vice President Retail Market Manager, Bretta Christakos
Senior Vice President, Mark Tucker
Assistant Vice President Project Manager, Lexie Williams
Vice President Commercial Relationship Manager, Luis Gonzalez
First Vice President, Richard Skopick
Vice President Commercial Lender, Winn Keeton
Senior Vice President Commercial Banking, Garry Lubi
Senior Vice President Community President, Mark Stevens
First Vice President Prepaid Cards Division, Bruce Davidson
First Vice President, Doug Elmore
Senior Vice President, Scott Clemmons
Assistant Vice President Branch Manager, Denise Tarafa
Vice President Special Assets Team Lead, Idania Kestel
Vice President, Jim Hagerty
Vice President Commercial Relationship Manager, Ben Malik
Chairman, Ernest S. (Ernie) Pinner, age 71
Auditors: Crowe LLP

LOCATIONS

HQ: CenterState Bank Corp
  1101 First Street South, Suite 202, Winter Haven, FL 33880
Phone: 863 293-4710
Web: www.centerstatebanks.com

PRODUCTS/OPERATIONS

2011 Sales

	$ mil.	% of total
Interest		
Loans	65	36
Investment securities available for sale	15	9
Other	0	-
Noninterest		
Bargain purchase gain	57	31
Correspondent banking & bond sales	24	13
Service charges on deposit accounts	6	3
Net gain on sale of securities	3	2
Other	10	6
Total	**184**	**100**

BB&T
BBX Capital
Bank of America
Fifth Third
JPMorgan Chase

Regions Financial
Seacoast Banking
SunTrust
Wells Fargo

HISTORICAL FINANCIALS

Company Type: Public

Income Statement

FYE: December 31

	ASSETS ($ mil.)	NET INCOME ($ mil.)	INCOME AS % OF ASSETS	EMPLOYEES
12/18	12,337	156	1.3%	2,113
12/17	7,123	55	0.8%	1,200
12/16	5,078	42	0.8%	952
12/15	4,022	39	1.0%	784
12/14	3,776	12	0.3%	785
Annual Growth	34.4%	86.4%	—	28.1%

2018 Year-End Financials

Debt ratio: 3.19%
Return on equity: 10.88%
Cash ($ mil.): 367
Current ratio: —
Long-term debt ($ mil.): —

No. of shares (mil.): 95
Dividends
   Yield: 1.9%
   Payout: 22.7%
Market value ($ mil.): 2,013

	STOCK PRICE ($) FY Close	P/E High/Low		PER SHARE ($) Earnings	Dividends	Book Value
12/18	21.04	18	11	1.76	0.40	20.60
12/17	25.73	29	23	0.95	0.24	15.04
12/16	25.17	29	15	0.88	0.16	11.47
12/15	15.65	19	13	0.85	0.07	10.79
12/14	11.91	37	31	0.31	0.04	9.98
Annual Growth	15.3%	—	—	54.4%	77.8%	19.9%

Central Pacific Financial Corp

When in the Central Pacific do as the islanders do. This may include doing business with Central Pacific Financial the holding company for Central Pacific Bank which operates more than 35 branch locations and 110 ATMs across the Hawaiian Islands. Targeting individuals and local businesses the $5 billion bank provides such standard retail banking products as checking and savings accounts money market accounts and CDs. About 70% of the bank's loan portfolio is made up of commercial real estate loans residential mortgages and construction loans though it also provides business and consumer loans.

Operations

Central Pacific Financial operates through two core segments. The Banking Operations segment provides construction and real estate development loans commercial loans residential mortgage loans consumer loans trust services retail brokerage services and traditional banking products and services. The Treasury segment manages the company's investment securities portfolio and wholesale funding activities.

Boasting total assets of $5 billion Central Pacific Bank ranked as the fourth-largest bank by deposits in the state of Hawaii in 2014. The bank makes nearly 60% of its total revenue from interest and fees on loans and leases and nearly 20% from interest and dividends on its investment securities.

It makes about 10% on service charges on deposit accounts and other charges and fees while the small remainder of its revenue comes from a mix of loan servicing fees gains on sales of residential loans and foreclosed assets income from fiduciary activities and income from bank-owned life insurance.

Central Pacific Financial's other wholly-owned subsidiaries include CPB Capital Trust II; CPB Statutory Trust III; CPB Capital Trust IV; and CPB Statutory Trust V. Central Pacific Bank holds 50% stakes in Pacific Access Mortgage Gentry Home-Loans and Island Pacific HomeLoans.

Geographic Reach

Honolulu-based Central Pacific boasts more than 35 branches and 110 ATMs across Hawaii. The island of Oahu holds 28 branches while the Maui Hawaii and Kauai islands host the remaining branches.

Sales and Marketing

Central Pacific Financial spent $2.34 million on advertising in 2014 compared to $2.67 million and $3.52 million in 2013 and 2012 respectively.

Financial Performance

Central Pacific Financial's revenue performance has been mixed in recent years. Its mortgage banking business has suffered from lower residential mortgage origination volumes while its loan business has been growing at a healthy clip thanks to higher loan balances from added assets.

Following two years of modest top-line growth driven by growing loan business Central Pacific's revenue dipped by 1% to $193.63 million in 2014 as it collected lower net gains on sales of foreclosed assets and lower net gains on sales of residential mortgage loans. The bank's interest income from loans continued to grow however as the bank added more than $403 million in new loan assets.

Central Pacific's net income declined by 76% to $40.45 million in 2014 mostly because in 2013 the bank received a $112.25 million income tax benefit as it reversed a significant portion of its valuation allowance for its doubtful accounts from 2009. Beyond this non-recurring event the bank managed to cut its salaries and employee benefit expenses by 22% saving about $8 million for the year.

The bank's operating cash also fell by 15% during the year to $71.43 million primarily due to lower cash earnings.

Strategy

Central Pacific reiterated in 2015 that its strategy is to continue growing its loan business particularly focusing on providing more commercial loans and mortgages as well as construction loans and leases to small and mid-sized companies business professionals and real estate developers. Though its residential mortgage and consumer loans made up just 25% of its loan portfolio that year the bank will also continue its focus on extended those loans to more local homebuyers and individuals.

The bank's key to drumming up its commercial loan business has traditionally come from its community-oriented commercial real estate team and banking officers which are able to develop deep relationships with local communities and industries that they serve.

EXECUTIVES

President And Ceo, A. Catherine Ngo, age 59, $345,833 total compensation
Chairman, John C. Dean, age 72, $265,625 total compensation
Svp And Chief Marketing Officer Central Pacific Financial Corp. And Central Pacific Bank, Wayne H. Kirihara

Interim Vice Chairman And Coo, Denis K. Isono, age 68, $244,792 total compensation
Evp And Cio Central Pacific Financial Corp. And Central Pacific Bank, Lee Y. Moriwaki, age 60, $205,625 total compensation
Evp Cfo And Treasurer, David S. Morimoto, age 51, $201,208 total compensation
Evp Chief Legal Officer And Risk Management Division Manager Central Pacific Financial Corp. And Central Pacific Bank, K.C. (Glenn) Ching, age 60
Evp Community Banking Division Manager Central Pacific Financial Corp. And Central Pacific Bank, David W. Hudson, age 60, $220,000 total compensation
Svp And Commercial Real Estate Lending Division Manager Central Pacific Financial Corp. And Central Pacific Bank, Arnold D. Martines, age 54
Assistant Vice President And Commercial Branch Manager, Jolene Kiyono
Vice President, Joseph Miller
Vp Of Information Technology, Anna Hu
Vice President And Commercial Real Estate Officer, Keith Wakamura
Vice President And Senior Business Banking Officer, Stacey Suzui
Vice President, Michael Waring
Avp And Sr Mortgage Loan Officer, Juo Leung
Vice President And Manager Of The West Oahu Region, Susan Utsugi
Vice President And Commercial Branch Manager, Herman Chang
Senior Vice President And Senior Manager, Craig Taylor
Assistant Vice President, Jaysen Kim
Vice President, Francine Komine
Vice President Of Qc, Sheryl Kurizaki
Vice President And Corporate Communications Manager, Dean Kawamura
Vice President And Kihei Branch Manager, Pat Matsumoto
Senior Vice President, Garrett Grace
Board Member, Paul J Kosasa
Board Member, Earl Fry
Board Member, Wayne Kamitaki
Board Member, Saedene Ota
Auditors: KPMG LLP

LOCATIONS

HQ: Central Pacific Financial Corp
   220 South King Street, Honolulu, HI 96813
Phone: 808 544-0500   **Fax:** 808 531-2875
Web: www.centralpacificbank.com

PRODUCTS/OPERATIONS

2014 Sales

	$ mil.	% of total
Interest income		
Loans and leases	112	58
Securities	37	19
Non-interest income		
Other service charges and fees	11	6
Service Charges on deposit accounts	8	4
Loan Servicing fees	5	3
Others	18	10
Total	**193**	**100**

COMPETITORS

American Savings Bank
Bank of Hawaii
First Hawaiian

Mitsubishi UFJ
   Financial Group
Territorial Bancorp

HISTORICAL FINANCIALS

Company Type: Public

Income Statement
FYE: December 31

	ASSETS ($ mil.)	NET INCOME ($ mil.)	INCOME AS % OF ASSETS	EMPLOYEES
12/18	5,807	59	1.0%	844
12/17	5,623	41	0.7%	838
12/16	5,384	46	0.9%	837
12/15	5,131	45	0.9%	876
12/14	4,852	40	0.8%	841
Annual Growth	4.6%	10.1%	—	0.1%

2018 Year-End Financials

Debt ratio: 1.24%
Return on equity: 12.00%
Cash ($ mil.): 102
Current ratio: —
Long-term debt ($ mil.): —

No. of shares (mil.): 28
Dividends
  Yield: 3.3%
  Payout: 40.8%
Market value ($ mil.): 705

	STOCK PRICE ($) FY Close	P/E High/Low		PER SHARE ($) Earnings	Dividends	Book Value
12/18	24.35	16	12	2.01	0.82	16.97
12/17	29.83	24	20	1.34	0.70	16.65
12/16	31.42	21	12	1.50	0.60	16.39
12/15	22.02	18	13	1.40	0.82	15.77
12/14	21.50	20	16	1.07	0.36	16.12
Annual Growth	3.2%	—	—	17.1%	22.9%	1.3%

Century Bancorp, Inc.

Century Bancorp is the holding company for Century Bank and Trust which serves Boston and surrounding parts of northeastern Massachusetts from more than 25 branches. Boasting some $3.6 billion in total assets the bank offers standard deposit products including checking savings and money market accounts; CDs; and IRAs. Nearly two-thirds of its loan portfolio is comprised of commercial and commercial real estate loans. while residential mortgages and home equity loans make up around 30%. The bank also writes construction and land development loans business loans and personal loans. It offers brokerage services through an agreement with third-party provider LPL Financial.

Operations

Century Bank also provides cash management short-term financing and transaction processing services to municipalities in Massachusetts and Rhode Island. It offers automated lockbox collection services to its municipal customers as well as commercial clients. The bank also continues to open new branches in its traditional market area in metropolitan Boston.

The bank gets more than 80% of its revenue in the form of interest income (mostly from loans). It generated 32% of its total revenue from taxable loans in 2014 while another 18% came from nontaxable loans and 35% came from interest income on the bank's investment securities. On the noninterest side the bank made 8% of its overall revenue from service charges on deposit accounts 3% from lockbox fees and a negligible amount on brokerage commissions and gains on sales of securities or mortgage loans.

Geographic Reach

The bank operates more than 25 branches in 20 cities and towns across Massachusetts ranging from Braintree in the South to Andover in the northern part of the state.

Sales and Marketing

Most of Century Bank's business comes from small and medium-sized businesses needing commercial loans though the bank also serves retail customers as well as local governments and other institutions throughout Massachusetts.

The bank spent $1.79 million on advertising in 2014 compared to $1.75 million and $1.85 million in 2013 and 2012 respectively.

Financial Performance

Century Bancorp's revenues and profits have been steadily rising over the past few years thanks to increased loan business and declining loan loss provisions as its loan portfolio's credit quality has been improving in the strengthening economy.

The bank's revenue rose by more than 2% to a record $100.64 million in 2014 mostly as it collected more interest income from long-term securities and non-taxable loans during the year. The bank's earning securities assets grew by 8.5% during the year while the size of its loan business swelled by double-digits with increased tax-exempt lending and residential second mortgage lending; all of which boosted interest income during the year.

Higher revenue lower interest expenses on deposits and a continued dip in loan loss provisions in 2014 pushed Century's net income higher by 9% to a record $21.86 million. The bank's operating cash also grew by 7% to $22.39 million thanks to higher cash earnings.

Strategy

Century Bancorp has been growing organically through new branch openings and digital bank product launches in recent years. In 2014 for example the bank opened its new branch in Woburn Massachusetts and launched its all-new Century Bank Mobile App which boosted customer convenience and allowed the bank to better compete with larger banks with more expansive branch networks.

Showcasing its strong financial capitalization the bank received an "A" rating from the Standard and Poor's credit ratings agency in 2015 making Century Bank the only regional bank in the state to receive such a rating.

EXECUTIVES

Senior Vice President, Susan Delahunt
Evp Century Bank And Trust Company, Paul A. Evangelista, age 55, $337,614 total compensation
Evp Century Bank And Trust Company, David B. Woonton, age 63, $337,614 total compensation
President Ceo And Director, Barry R. Sloane, age 64, $569,207 total compensation
Cfo And Treasurer, William F. Hornby, age 52, $294,708 total compensation
Evp Century Bank And Trust Company, Linda Sloane Kay, age 57, $294,708 total compensation
Evp Century Bank And Trust, Brian J. Feeney, age 58, $294,708 total compensation
Vice President, Jim Smith
Senior Vice President, James Flynn
Vice President, Anna Gorska
Vice President, Nancy M Marsh
Senior Vice President, Brad Buckley
Senior Vice President Director Of Underwriting And Loan Review, Thomas Piemontese
Vice President, Bradford J Buckley
Senior Vice President, Deb Rush
Chairman, Marshall M. Sloane, age 92
Auditors: KPMG LLP

LOCATIONS

HQ: Century Bancorp, Inc.
400 Mystic Avenue, Medford, MA 02155
Phone: 781 391-4000
Web: www.centurybank.com

PRODUCTS/OPERATIONS

2014 Sales

	$ mil.	% of total
Interest		
Loans	50	50
Securities	2	3
Other	32	32
Noninterest		
Service charges on deposit accounts	8	8
Lockbox fees	3	3
Gains on sales of Mortgage loans	2	3
Other	1	1
Total	100	100

COMPETITORS

Boston Private	Eastern Bank
Brookline Bancorp	Middlesex Savings
Cambridge Financial	Peoples Federal
Capital Crossing	Bancshares Inc.
Central Bancorp	Sovereign Bank
Citizens Financial	
Group	

HISTORICAL FINANCIALS

Company Type: Public

Income Statement
FYE: December 31

	ASSETS ($ mil.)	NET INCOME ($ mil.)	INCOME AS % OF ASSETS	EMPLOYEES
12/18	5,163	36	0.7%	460
12/17	4,785	22	0.5%	447
12/16	4,462	24	0.5%	438
12/15	3,947	23	0.6%	438
12/14	3,624	21	0.6%	440
Annual Growth	9.3%	13.4%		1.1%

2018 Year-End Financials

Debt ratio: 4.62%
Return on equity: 12.92%
Cash ($ mil.): 342
Current ratio: —
Long-term debt ($ mil.): —

No. of shares (mil.): 5
Dividends
  Yield: 0.7%
  Payout: 10.1%
Market value ($ mil.): 377

	STOCK PRICE ($) FY Close	P/E High/Low		PER SHARE ($) Earnings	Dividends	Book Value
12/18	67.73	11	8	6.50	0.48	53.96
12/17	78.25	18	12	4.01	0.48	46.75
12/16	60.00	12	7	4.41	0.48	43.11
12/15	43.46	9	8	4.13	0.48	38.53
12/14	40.06	8	7	3.93	0.48	34.57
Annual Growth	14.0%	—	—	13.4%	(0.0%)	11.8%

CenturyLink Inc

CenturyLink provides cyber links throughout the country on one of the longest fiber networks in the US. Historically a regional wireline local and long-distance telephone provider it's connecting with the times by transforming into a broadband and network services provider for business residential and government clients. The company is the one of the largest US wireline telecom companies with about 450000 route miles of fiber optic cable globally and it's the incumbent local carrier in about 35 states. It spends around $3.5 billion a year on capital projects to build out its network. In 2017 CenturyLink and Level 3 Communications merged in a $34 billion deal.

Operations

CenturyLink operates in two main segments with the Business segment accounting for three-quarters of sales. The segment provides private line broadband Ethernet Voice over Internet Protocol (VoIP) network management services colocation and managed hosting and cloud hosting services for enterprise wholesale and governmental customers including other communication providers.

The Consumer segment about 25% of sales offers broadband wireless and video services including the Prism TV service. It also offers local and long-distance phone service as well as satellite TV through DirecTV and wireless service through Verizon.

The company's "other" segment which includes federal payments for serving rural areas accounts for the rest of revenue.

Aside from its global fiber optic cable operations CenturyLink's network includes about 910000 miles of copper plant; more than 360 colocation facilities and data centers globally; about 37500 route miles of subsea fiber optic cable systems; and more than 150000 Fiber On-net buildings.

Geographic Reach

CenturyLink operates a terrestrial and subsea fiber optic long-haul network throughout North America Europe Latin America and Asia Pacific which connects to its metropolitan fiber network operations. The company based in Monroe Louisiana also provides telephone services as an incumbent local telephone company in more than 35 states.

Sales and Marketing

CenturyLink reaches business customers through offices in major and secondary markets in the US and bigger markets in the some 60 countries in which it operates. Marketing to residential customers includes direct sales representatives inbound call centers telemarketing and third parties including retailers satellite television providers and digital marketing firms.

Financial Performance

Between 2014-2017 CenturyLink's revenue steadily inched lower a total of $439 million due to declining consumer sales.

In 2018 CenturyLink's revenue jumped 33% to $23.4 billion an increase of $5.8 billion from 2017 on the strength of the Level 3 acquisition. Revenue from CenturyLink's legacy operations dropped $935 million in 2018 from 2017 from lower voice and collaboration transport and infrastructure and IP and data services sales.

The company lost $1.5 million in 2018 reversing a $1.4 million profit in 2017. It had higher expenses in 2018 including a $170 million tax payment while it received a sizable tax benefit in 2017.

CenturyLink had $488 million in cash and equivalents in 2018 compared to $551 million in 2017. Operations generated $7 billion in 2018 while investing activities used $3.1 billion and financial activities used $4.1 billion.

The company has significant long-term debt of $35.6 billion and interest expense of about $1.5 billion (in 2018). The debt could limit its capability to respond to business opportunities and challenges.

Strategy

The network is at the heart of CenturyLink's business and its strategy. The company delivers video streaming applications and services related to the Internet of Things (IoT) and emerging technologies like virtual and augmented reality and

still-to-come 5G wireless technology over the network.

Already big with 265000-route miles of fiber in the US the network expanded with the addition of Level 3's 200000 route miles of fiber. In 2019 CenturyLink planned $500 million in additional capital expenditures which could reach $3.8 billion for the year for network expansion as well as building additions and digital initiatives.

CenturyLink moved to reduce its debt in 2019 reallocating capital to debt payments. The reduction should lower the company's cost of capital return cash to shareholders and provide flexibility to respond to market opportunities and interest rate changes. It also cut its dividend from $2.16 per share to $1 per share.

The consumer remains an integral part of CenturyLink's plans. The company is working to improve network speeds and the customer experience. It has invested in broadband to supply speeds of 100 Mbps to 1 Gbps to more service areas. The company also has simplified its pricing plans.

Mergers and Acquisitions

The $34 billion-dollar merger of CenturyLink and Level 3 Communications which closed in November 2017 created one of the largest telecommunications service providers in the US. The combined company's network connects more than 350 metro areas in the US and it has a presence in more than 60 countries. While each company has a nationwide network they say their combination brings together complementary assets and not result in less competition. With Level 3 carrying some $10 billion in net operating losses the combined company's tax bill should be lower freeing up cash flow for developing more infrastructure.

CenturyLink expanded its capabilities in IT services with the acquisition of SEAL Consulting a provider of SAP tools for enterprise business and technology needs.

In 2016 CenturyLink added a security element to its networking business with the acquisition in 2016 of netAura. The company specializes in engineering developing and consulting on managed security technologies.

EXECUTIVES

Evp Controller And Assistant Secretary, David D. Cole, age 61, $482,687 total compensation
President And Ceo, Glen F. Post, age 66, $1,250,000 total compensation
Senior Vice President Business Service Delivery And Operations, Todd Schafer
President Small And Mid-size Business (smb) And Ges/sled, Vernon L. Irvin, age 57
Evp And Cfo, Sunit S. Patel, age 57
Evp Chief Administrative Officer General Counsel And Secretary, Stacey W. Goff, age 53, $540,758 total compensation
Evp And Cto, Aamir Hussain, $496,049 total compensation
President Consumer Markets, Maxine L. Moreau, age 57
Evp Human Resources, Scott A. Trezise, age 50
President Global Accounts Management And International, Laurinda Y. Pang, age 49
Svp Cyber Engineering And Technology Services, William E. (Bill) Bradley
President Advanced Solutions Group And Chief Enterprise Relationship Officer, Gary Gauba
President And Coo, Jeffrey K. (Jeff) Storey
President Wholesale Indirect Channels And Alliances, Lisa Miller
President Strategic Enterprise Federal Government And Ges/sled, Ed Morche
Vice President Of Sales, Harman Steve
Vice President And General Counsel, Laurie Korneffel

Vice President Human Resources And Chief Diversity Officer, Richard Guidi
Vice President, Bruce Kipperman
Regional Vice President Project Management, Monte Johnson
Vice President And General Manager, Guy Gunther
Vice President Product Management, David Shacochis
National Account Manager, Frank Palazzo
Vice President Regional Reg And Legislative Affairs, William Hanchey
Vice President Of Corporate Development And Strategy, Kenneth Dunn
Vice President Compensation And Analytics, Jill Turner
Senior Vice President, Clay Bailey
Vice President Network Service Operations, Jeff Mitchell
Vice President Corporate Tax, Jon Robinson
Senior Vice President Product Development, Phillip Bronsdon
Vp Investor Relations, Tony Davis
Vice President Assistant General Counsel, Mark Stites
Regional Vice President, Ken Beck
Vice President Compensation And Benefits, Marina Pearson
Nw Region Vice President, Mark Reynolds
Vice President Investments And Operations, Shane Matson
Vice President Global Infrastructure Operations, Todd Miller
Vice President Of Information Systems, Adam Youmans
Area Vice President Global Markets, Mike Raney
Assistant Vice President, John Benedict
National Sales Manager, Jane Jensen
Svp Strategic Government, David Young
Regional Vice President Service Delivery, David Capote
Vice President, Vish Trichur
Vice President And General, Tim Sisneros
Chairman, Harvey P. Perry, age 74
Vice Chairman, W. Bruce Hanks, age 64
Secretary, Melissa Brocato
Treasurer, Steve Nolen
Auditors: KPMG LLP

LOCATIONS

HQ: CenturyLink Inc
100 CenturyLink Drive, Monroe, LA 71203
Phone: 318 388-9000   **Fax:** 318 789-8656
Web: www.centurylink.com

PRODUCTS/OPERATIONS

2018 Sales by Category

	$ mil.	% of total
Transport and Infrastructure	8,248	35
IP and Data Services	7,279	31
Voice and Collaboration	6,572	28
Regulatory	723	3
IT and Managed Services	621	3
Total	**23,443**	**100**

2018 Sales

	% of total
Business segment	74
Consumer segment	23
Other	3
Total	**100**

Selected Products & Services Local and long-distance voiceHigh-speed InternetMPLSPrivate line (including special access)Data integrationEthernetColocationManaged hosting

COMPETITORS

AT&T	Frontier
Cavalier Telephone	Communications
Comcast	Nsight
Cox Communications	Sprint Communications
DISH Network	Telephone & Data
Equinix	Systems
FairPoint	Time Warner Cable
Communications Inc.	Verizon
Farmers	XO Holdings
Telecommunications	

HISTORICAL FINANCIALS

Company Type: Public

Income Statement				FYE: December 31
	REVENUE ($ mil.)	NET INCOME ($ mil.)	NET PROFIT MARGIN	EMPLOYEES
12/18	23,443	(1,733)	—	45,000
12/17	17,656	1,389	7.9%	51,000
12/16	17,470	626	3.6%	40,000
12/15	17,900	878	4.9%	43,000
12/14	18,031	772	4.3%	45,000
Annual Growth	6.8%	—	—	0.0%

2018 Year-End Financials

Debt ratio: 51.33%
Return on equity: (-8.00%)
Cash ($ mil.): 492
Current ratio: 0.69
Long-term debt ($ mil.): 35,409

No. of shares (mil.): 1,080
Dividends
Yield: 14.2%
Payout: —
Market value ($ mil.): 16,365

	STOCK PRICE ($) FY Close	P/E High/Low		PER SHARE ($)		
				Earnings	Dividends	Book Value
12/18	15.15	—	—	(1.63)	2.16	18.36
12/17	16.68	12	6	2.21	2.16	21.97
12/16	23.78	28	19	1.16	2.16	24.52
12/15	25.16	26	15	1.58	2.16	25.86
12/14	39.58	31	21	1.36	2.16	26.42
Annual Growth	(21.3%)	—	—	—	(0.0%)	(8.7%)

Cerner Corp.

Cerner Corp. develops and sells software systems designed to help improve processes and eliminate errors and waste for organizations ranging from single-doctor practices to the pharmaceutical and medical device industries. Its software combines clinical financial and administrative information management applications including tools for managing electronic health records (EHRs). Complementary services include support and maintenance implementation and training remote hosting data analytics and transaction processing. The company's products are used by some 27500 facilities in more than 35 countries although the US is by far its largest market.

Operations

About a third of Cerner's revenue comes from professional services while managed services account for about 20% of sales. Another 20% comes from support and maintenance with about 20% of sales generated by the combination of licensed software subscriptions and technology sales.

The company offers its technologies on two main software platforms. The Cerner Millennium architecture includes integrated clinical financial and management information systems. It organizes and delivers information for physicians nurses laboratory technicians pharmacists front- and back-office professionals and consumers.

The HealtheIntent cloud-based platform is designed to grow with an institution's patient population while facilitating care for patient and provider. The HealtheIntent platform offers applications that can run on any EHR system (including those that aren't Cerner's) for gathering and processing data across the continuum of care.

Cerner's services segment is anchored by its CernerWorks managed services business which is designed to help customers spend more effectively. Other service products are Cerner ITWorks which helps customers manage IT functions and Cerner RevWorks which helps with customer revenue cycle functions.

Geographic Reach

Cerner's sales are heavily concentrated in the US (90%) with the rest from its international operations in about 35 countries. The Kansas City Missouri-based company has employees in about two dozen countries.

Sales and Marketing

Although hospitals and health systems account for most of sales Cerner's clients include physician groups and networks blood banks home health agencies laboratories managed care organizations pharmacies pharmaceutical manufacturers and public health organizations. The company markets its offerings directly via industry seminars and trade shows as well as by leveraging current customers for new leads in addition to upsell and cross-sell opportunities.

Financial Performance

Cerner Corp. has ridden a wave of spending for healthcare technology to post five years of revenue rising at a 12% annual rate.

In 2018 revenue increased 4% to $5.3 billion in 2018 compared to $5.1 billion in 2017 driven by an increase in professional services sales from stronger performance by Cerner ITWorks.

Profit fell to $630 million in 2018 a reduction of about $237 million from 2017. Cerner has higher operating expenses in 2018 from 2017 as it added workers to support revenue growth. It also had a lower tax rate in 2017 because of the US Tax Cuts and Jobs Act enacted in December 2017.

At $374 million Cerner's 2018 cash and equivalents rose about $3 million from 2017. Operations generated $1.4 billion in cash in 2018 while investing activities used $828.9 million and financing activities used $609.8 million.

Strategy

Cerner's fundamental strategy is to create organic growth by continuing to make large investments in R&D. With a strong foothold in many of its client markets part of the company's strategy is to sell additional products and services to its customers.

The company planned to cut costs by reducing headcount in 2019. It announced a Voluntary Separation Plan for US employees who meet a minimum level of combined age and tenure. The company expected to increase capital expenditures in 2019 to build facilities including its Innovations Campus office development in Kansas City.

To deal with consolidation in the healthcare industry Cerner created a group focused on its large clients that drive much of the consolidation. The group helps some customers deploy Cerner's EHR across acquired sites that are using another EHR as well as help them use HealtheIntent the cloud platform for health population applications.

Cerner is in the early stages of major contracts to provide healthcare IT services to the US Department of Defense and the Department of Veterans Affairs.

Cerner's geographic concentration puts it as the mercy of US healthcare policy which has experienced a level of instability in recent years as elected officials struggle to define who pays for what.

EXECUTIVES

Evp And Chief Of Staff, Jeffrey A. (Jeff) Townsend, age 55, $657,596 total compensation
Chairman And Interim Ceo, Clifford W. (Cliff) Illig, age 68
Evp And Cfo, Marc G. Naughton, age 63, $524,712 total compensation
President, Zane M. Burke, age 52, $657,596 total compensation
Evp And Coo, Michael R. (Mike) Nill, age 54, $657,596 total compensation
Vp And General Manager United Kingdom, Donald D. Trigg
Evp And Chief People Officer, Julia M. (Julie) Wilson, age 56
Vp And General Manager Academic/children's Northeast, Debbie Yantis
Vice President User Experience, Paul Weaver
Vice President Cerner Ambulatory, Julie Kay
Vice President Compensation And Benefits, Todd Downey
Vice President Population Health Accountable Care Strategy, Ray Herschman
Vice President, Ricky Stewart
Vice President, David Waltman
Auditors: KPMG LLP

LOCATIONS

HQ: Cerner Corp.
2800 Rockcreek Parkway, North Kansas City, MO 64117
Phone: 816 221-1024
Web: www.cerner.com

2018 Sales

	$ mil.	% of total
Domestic	4,730	88
Global	636	12
Total	**5,366**	**100**

PRODUCTS/OPERATIONS

2018 Sales

	$ mil.	% of total
Professional Services	1,811	34
Managed Services	1,154	21
Support & Maintenance	1,118	21
Licensed Software	613	11
Subscriptions	325	6
Technology Resale	245	6
Reimbursed Travel	97	2
Total	**5,366**	**100**

Selected Services

Population Health Management
Clinical Solutions
Open & Interoperable
Revenue Cycle Management

COMPETITORS

Accenture	InterSystems
Allscripts	MEDHOST
CPSI	McKesson
CareFusion	athenahealth
Dell	eClinicalWorks
Epic Systems	

HISTORICAL FINANCIALS
Company Type: Public

Income Statement
FYE: December 28

	REVENUE ($ mil.)	NET INCOME ($ mil.)	NET PROFIT MARGIN	EMPLOYEES
12/19	5,692	529	9.3%	27,400
12/18	5,366	630	11.7%	29,200
12/17	5,142	866	16.9%	26,000
12/16*	4,796	636	13.3%	24,400
01/16	4,425	539	12.2%	22,200
Annual Growth	6.5%	(0.5%)	—	5.4%

*Fiscal year change

2019 Year-End Financials
Debt ratio: 15.06%
Return on equity: 11.48%
Cash ($ mil.): 441
Current ratio: 2.04
Long-term debt ($ mil.): 1,038

No. of shares (mil.): 310
Dividends
  Yield: 0.0%
  Payout: 32.7%
Market value ($ mil.): 22,784

	STOCK PRICE ($) FY Close	P/E High/Low	Earnings	Dividends	Book Value
12/19	73.28	46 31	1.65	0.54	13.89
12/18	52.01	38 26	1.89	0.00	15.20
12/17	67.39	28 18	2.57	0.00	14.39
12/16*	47.37	36 25	1.85	0.00	11.92
01/16	60.17	48 36	1.54	0.00	11.38
Annual Growth	5.1%	— —	1.7%	—	5.1%

*Fiscal year change

CHALMETTE REFINING, L.L.C.

EXECUTIVES
Ceo, Thomas J Nimbley
Manager, Eric Beam

LOCATIONS
HQ: CHALMETTE REFINING, L.L.C.
500 W SAINT BERNARD HWY, CHALMETTE, LA 700434821
Phone: 504 281-1212
Web: WWW.CHALMETTEREFINING.COM

HISTORICAL FINANCIALS
Company Type: Private

Income Statement
FYE: December 31

	REVENUE ($ mil.)	NET INCOME ($ mil.)	NET PROFIT MARGIN	EMPLOYEES
12/07	5,647	364	6.4%	600
12/06	5,020	423	8.4%	
12/05	3,462	264	7.6%	
12/04	3,130	221	7.1%	
Annual Growth	21.7%	18.1%	—	—

HISTORICAL FINANCIALS
Company Type: Public

Income Statement
FYE: December 31

	REVENUE ($ mil.)	NET INCOME ($ mil.)	NET PROFIT MARGIN	EMPLOYEES
12/19	45,764	1,668	3.6%	95,100
12/18	43,634	1,230	2.8%	98,000
12/17	41,581	9,895	23.8%	94,800
12/16	29,003	3,522	12.1%	91,500
12/15	9,754	(271)	—	23,800
Annual Growth	47.2%	—	—	41.4%

2019 Year-End Financials
Debt ratio: 53.36%
Return on equity: 4.93%
Cash ($ mil.): 3,483
Current ratio: 0.52
Long-term debt ($ mil.): 75,578

No. of shares (mil.): 209
Dividends
  Yield: —
  Payout: —
Market value ($ mil.): 101,855

	STOCK PRICE ($) FY Close	P/E High/Low	Earnings	Dividends	Book Value
12/19	485.08	64 37	7.45	0.00	149.76
12/18	284.97	73 49	5.22	0.00	161.01
12/17	335.96	10 7	34.09	0.00	163.87
12/16	287.92	17 9	15.94	0.00	149.27
12/15	183.10	— —	(2.43)	0.00	(0.41)
Annual Growth	27.6%	— —	—	—	—

CFJ PROPERTIES LLC

EXECUTIVES
Chb, Crystal Call Maggelet
Exec Committee MBR*, Andre Lortz
Exec Committee MBR*, Richard D Peterson
Manager, Dale Rushton
Executive Committee MBR, Richard Peterson
Auditors: KPMG LLP SALT LAKE CITY UTAH

LOCATIONS
HQ: CFJ PROPERTIES LLC
5508 LONAS DR, KNOXVILLE, TN 379093221
Phone: 801 624-1000
Web: WWW.PEPPERONIGRILLNC.COM

HISTORICAL FINANCIALS
Company Type: Private

Income Statement
FYE: January 31

	REVENUE ($ mil.)	NET INCOME ($ mil.)	NET PROFIT MARGIN	EMPLOYEES
01/09	7,672	157	2.1%	6,250
01/07	6,769	50	0.7%	
01/06	6,166	48	0.8%	
Annual Growth	7.6%	47.7%	—	—

Charter Communications Inc (New)

Auditors: KPMG LLP

LOCATIONS
HQ: Charter Communications Inc (New)
400 Atlantic Street, Stamford, CT 06901
Phone: 203 905-7801
Web: www.charter.com

COMPETITORS

AT&T	Mediacom
Apple Inc.	Communications
Bright House Networks	Netflix
Cablevision Systems	RCN Corporation
Clearwire	Skype
Comcast	Sprint Communications
Cox Communications	Suddenlink
DIRECTV	Communications
DISH Network	T-Mobile USA
EarthLink	Time Warner Cable
Frontier	United Online
Communications	Verizon
Hulu	Vonage
Insight Communications	YouTube
LodgeNet	

Chemours Co (The)

Auditors: PricewaterhouseCoopers LLP

LOCATIONS
HQ: Chemours Co (The)
1007 Market Street, Wilmington, DE 19801
Phone: 302 773-1000
Web: www.chemours.com

HISTORICAL FINANCIALS
Company Type: Public

Income Statement
FYE: December 31

	REVENUE ($ mil.)	NET INCOME ($ mil.)	NET PROFIT MARGIN	EMPLOYEES
12/18	6,638	995	15.0%	7,000
12/17	6,183	746	12.1%	7,000
12/16	5,400	7	0.1%	7,000
12/15	5,717	(90)	—	8,100
12/14	6,432	400	6.2%	9,000
Annual Growth	0.8%	25.6%	—	(6.1%)

2018 Year-End Financials
Debt ratio: 53.95%
Return on equity: 106.19%
Cash ($ mil.): 1,201
Current ratio: 1.93
Long-term debt ($ mil.): 3,959

No. of shares (mil.): 170
Dividends
  Yield: 2.9%
  Payout: 15.4%
Market value ($ mil.): 4,819

	STOCK PRICE ($) FY Close	P/E High/Low	Earnings	Dividends	Book Value
12/18	28.22	10 5	5.45	0.84	5.94
12/17	50.06	14 5	3.91	0.12	4.70
12/16	22.09	674 78	0.04	0.12	0.55
12/15	5.36	— —	(0.50)	0.58	0.70
Annual Growth	51.5%	— —	—	9.7%	70.9%

Cheniere Energy Inc.

Cheniere Energy is a leading producer of liquefied natural gas (LNG) in the US exporting LNG to customers in 32 nations around the world. The company purchases natural gas and processes it into LNG and offers customers the option to load the LNG onto their vessels at its terminals or it delivers the LNG to regasification facilities around the world. The company has two terminals on the US Gulf Coast in various stages of development: its Sabine Pass liquefaction project in southwest Louisiana and its Corpus Christi liquefaction facility in South Texas. Nearly three quarters of revenue come from outside the US. Cheniere also has pipeline assets and operates an LNG and natural gas marketing business.

Operations

Cheniere's Sabine Pass project in southwest Louisiana has five liquefaction units or "Trains" as they are known in the LNG industry. When all Trains are completed (after its sixth Train is operational) its production capacity is expected to be approximately 27 million tonnes per annum (mtpa) of LNG. When its Corpus Christi liquefaction facility in South Texas is complete its aggregate production capacity is expected to be approximately 13.5 mtpa of LNG. The company has a contract with major engineering firm Bechtel for construction work.

Natural gas is transported to Cheniere's LNG facilities on third party pipelines as well as on pipelines Cheniere has constructed and owns and operates. Its pipelines include the Creole Trail a 94-mile pipeline interconnecting the Sabine Pass terminal with a number of large interstate pipelines; the Corpus Christi Pipeline a 23-mile pipeline that interconnect its Corpus Christi project with several inter- and intrastate natural gas pipelines; and the Midship Pipeline a new-build project that will connect new gas production from the Anadarko Basin in Oklahoma to Gulf Coast and Southeast markets once it is complete.

Its Cheniere Marketing subsidiary is developing a portfolio of contracts to monetize capacity at Sabine Pass and Creole Trail.

Nearly all the company's revenue (some 95%) comes from LNG sold at its terminals.

Geographic Reach

The Houston Texas-based Cheniere Energy derives substantially all of its revenue from facilities in Louisiana and Texas. Sales to customers in the US account for about 24% of revenue; South Korea about 20%; Ireland 15%; and India 13%.

In addition to offices in Cameron Louisiana and Gregory Texas the company has offices in Beijing London Singapore Tokyo and Washington DC.

Sales and Marketing

Approximately 80% of Cheniere's expected LNG production capacity either completed or under construction is contracted through long-term agreements with 18 customers. The remaining volumes of LNG are available to sell on the open market.

Cheniere is highly dependent on revenue from four major customers: BG Energy Korea Gas Corporation GAIL (India) and Naturgy LNG account for 18% 14% 19% and 13% of revenue respectively.

Financial Performance

Throughout the five-year period ending in 2018 Cheniere Energy reported year-over-year revenue growth as the company built more "Trains" (liquefaction units) and increased the volume of LNG it sold during the year. Between 2014 and 2017 the company reported losses as it invested big in build-out. Net income eventually swung to a profit in 2018.

The company reported nearly $8.0 billion in revenue in 2018 up from $5.6 billion in 2017. It had four Trains operational in 2018 versus two Trains operational during the prior year.

Net income was $471 million for the year versus a loss of $393 million in 2017. The increase was mostly attributable to growing income from operations due to additional Trains operating between the periods decreased loss on modification or extinguishment of debt and increased net derivative gain.

Cash at the end of 2018 was $3.16 billion. Cash from operations was $2.0 billion while investing activities used $3.7 billion primarily to fund construction of its Sabine Pass and Corpus Christi projects. Financing contributed $2.2 billion.

Strategy

The liquefaction of natural gas into LNG allows it to be shipped economically from areas of the world where natural gas is abundant and inexpensive to produce to other areas where natural gas demand and infrastructure exist to economically justify the use of LNG. Cheniere is one the top companies in developing and maintaining LNG terminals with premium access to existing pipeline infrastructure and deepwater shipping channels especially in the US Gulf Coast. (The Sabine Pass terminal is located in Cameron Parish Louisiana on the Sabine-Neches Waterway less than four miles from the Coast.) It has a global customer base that uses its sprawling infrastructure to conduct business through flexible competitive contracts. By 2020 Cheniere expects to be a top-5 global provider of LNG.

At its Sabine Pass project the company completed Train 5 (its fifth liquefaction unit) in February 2019. All regulatory approvals have been received to construct and operate Train 6 and a final investment decision was reached in June 2019. At the Corpus Christi Project Train 1 is in operation Train 2 is commissioning and is expected to be completed in the second half of 2019 and Train 3 is under construction with an expected completion date in the second half of 2021.

Cheniere is also constructing a 200-mile 36-inch interstate natural gas pipeline called the Midship Project to connect production from Oklahoma to Gulf Coast and Southeast markets.

Company Background

Cheniere Energy was founded in 1996. The company began developing its first LNG terminal in 1999 and was among the first companies to secure sites and commence development of new LNG terminals in North America. The company is particularly vulnerable to weather-related interruptions. While Hurricane Katrina in 2005 didn't directly hit its operations it significantly impacted workforce availability. Hurricanes Rita in 2005 Ike in 2008 and Harvey in 2017 all had a serious impact.

In February 2016 the Sabine Pass facility became the first to ship LNG from a commercial facility in the contiguous US. The company's Corpus Christi liquefaction facility in South Texas began operations in 2018.

EXECUTIVES

Svp International, Jean Abiteboul, age 67, $461,850 total compensation

Vp Human Resources, Ann Raden

President And Ceo, Jack A. Fusco, age 56

Vp Pipeline Operations, R. Keith Teague, age 54, $565,385 total compensation

Interim Special Advisor To Ceo, Neal A. Shear, $38,462 total compensation

Svp And Cfo, Michael J. Wortley, age 42, $565,385 total compensation

Svp And General Counsel, Greg W. Rayford, $565,385 total compensation

Vice President Trading Cheniere International (uk Establishment), Nicolas Zanen

Vice President Engineering, Darren Granger

Senior Vice President Policy Government And Public Affairs, Chris Smith

Vice President And Chief Security Risk Officer, Mitch Price

Vice President Investor Relations, Katie L Pipkin

Chairman, G. Andrea Botta, age 65

Board Member, David Kilpatrick

Auditors: KPMG LLP

LOCATIONS

HQ: Cheniere Energy Inc.
700 Milam Street, Suite 1900, Houston, TX 77002
Phone: 713 375-5000
Web: www.cheniere.com

PRODUCTS/OPERATIONS

2017 Sales

	$ mil.	% of total
LNG revenues	5,317	95
Regasification revenues	260	5
Other revenues	21	-
Other- related party	3	-
Total	**5,601**	**100**

Subsidiaries

Subsidiaries
Caldera LNG Holdings SpA Chile
Cheniere Cares Inc. Texas
Cheniere Chile SpA Chile
Cheniere CCH HoldCo I LLC Delaware
Cheniere CCH HoldCo II LLC Delaware
Cheniere Corpus Christi Holdings LLC Delaware
Cheniere Corpus Christi Pipeline L.P. Delaware
Cheniere Creole Trail Pipeline L.P. Delaware
Cheniere Energy Investments LLC Delaware
Cheniere Energy Operating Co. Inc. Delaware
Cheniere Energy Partners GP LLC Delaware
Cheniere Energy Partners LP Holdings LLC Delaware
Cheniere Energy Partners L.P. Delaware
Cheniere Energy Shared Services Inc. Delaware
Cheniere Field Services LLC Delaware
Cheniere GP Holding Company LLC Delaware
Cheniere Ingleside Marine Terminal LLC Delaware
Cheniere International Investments Holdings S.à.r.l Luxembourg
Cheniere International Investments S.à.r.l Luxembourg
Cheniere Land Holdings LLC Delaware
Cheniere Liquids LLC Delaware
Cheniere LNG Holdings GP LLC Delaware
Cheniere LNG O&M Services LLC Delaware
Cheniere LNG Terminals LLC Delaware
Cheniere Major Project Development LLC Delaware
Cheniere Marketing International HoldCo I L.P. Bermuda
Cheniere Marketing International HoldCo II Ltd. Bermuda
Cheniere Marketing International LLP United Kingdom
Cheniere Marketing LLC Delaware
Cheniere Marketing Ltd. United Kingdom
Cheniere Marketing PTE Ltd. Singapore
Cheniere Midship Holdings LLC Delaware
Cheniere Midstream Holdings Inc. Delaware
Cheniere Pipeline GP Interests LLC Delaware
Cheniere Pipeline Holdings LLC Delaware
Cheniere San Patricio Processing Hub LLC Delaware
Cheniere Southern Trail GP Inc. Delaware
Cheniere SPH Pipeline LLC Delaware
Cheniere Supply & Marketing Inc. Delaware
Concepción LNG Holding SpA Chile
Corpus Christi Liquefaction LLC Delaware
Corpus Christi Liquefaction Stage II LLC Delaware
Corpus Christi Liquefaction Stage III LLC Delaware
Corpus Christi LNG LLC Delaware
Corpus Christi Pipeline GP LLC Delaware
Corpus Christi Tug Services LLC Delaware
CQH Holdings Company LLC Delaware
CUI I LLC Delaware
Johnson Bayou Holdings LLC Delaware
Live Oak LNG Holdings LLC Delaware
Louisiana LNG Holdings LLC Delaware

Midship Holdings LLC Delaware
Midship Pipeline Company LLC Delaware
Nordheim Eagle Ford Gathering LLC Delaware
Sabine Pass Liquefaction LLC Delaware
Sabine Pass LNG-GP LLC Delaware
Sabine Pass LNG-LP LLC Delaware
Sabine Pass LNG L.P. Delaware
Sabine Pass Tug Services LLC Delaware

COMPETITORS

Ameren	PG&E Corporation
CMS Energy	Public Service
Calpine	Enterprise Group
DTE	Sempra Energy
Dominion Energy	TRII
Enbridge	TransCanada
ONEOK	

HISTORICAL FINANCIALS
Company Type: Public

Income Statement
FYE: December 31

	REVENUE ($ mil.)	NET INCOME ($ mil.)	NET PROFIT MARGIN	EMPLOYEES
12/18	7,987	471	5.9%	1,372
12/17	5,601	(393)	—	1,230
12/16	1,283	(609)	—	911
12/15	270	(975)	—	888
12/14	267	(547)	—	642
Annual Growth	133.7%	—	—	20.9%

2018 Year-End Financials

Debt ratio: 89.02%
Return on equity: ***,***.**%
Cash ($ mil.): 981
Current ratio: 2.43
Long-term debt ($ mil.): 28,236

No. of shares (mil.): 257
Dividends
  Yield: —
  Payout: —
Market value ($ mil.): 15,212

	STOCK PRICE ($) FY Close	P/E High/Low	PER SHARE ($) Earnings	Dividends	Book Value
12/18	59.19	37 27	1.90	0.00	(2.05)
12/17	53.84	— —	(1.68)	0.00	(7.42)
12/16	41.43	— —	(2.67)	0.00	(5.87)
12/15	37.25	— —	(4.30)	0.00	(3.83)
12/14	70.40	— —	(2.44)	0.00	(0.69)
Annual Growth	(4.2%)	— —	—	—	—

Cheniere Energy Partners L P

Cheniere Energy Partners a subsidiary of Cheniere Energy plans to be North America's biggest gas station — natural gas that is. The Sabine Pass LNG (liquefied natural gas) receiving terminal is one of North America's largest: It boasts 4 billion cu. ft. per day of regasification capacity as well as 13.5 billion cu. ft. of LNG storage capacity. All of the Sabine Pass LNG receiving terminal's capacity has already been contracted to Total Gas and Power North America Chevron and Cheniere Energy subsidiary Cheniere Marketing. In 2012 Blackstone agreed to invest $2 billion in the terminal's Sabine Pass liquefaction project. In 2016 Cheniere Energy bid to buy Cheniere Energy Partners before dropping the idea.

EXECUTIVES

Chairman Ceo And Director, Charif Souki, age 66
Svp And Director, Meg A. Gentle, age 44
Senior Vice President Engineering And Construction, Ed Lehotsky
Vice President Commercial Operations, Grant McCracken
Vice President Supply, Corey Grindal
Vice President And Treasurer, Lisa Cohen
Vice President, Azin Lotfi
Vice President Government Relations, Ankit Desai
Vice President Of Accounting, Len Travis
Vice President Commercial Operations, Patrick Yeater
Vice President Marketing Strategy, Davis Thames
Vice President Asia, Nicolas Zanen
Vice President, Gavin Garcia
Vice President, Brad Hitch
Vice President Business Development, Keith Little
Vice President, Katie Pipkin
Senior Vice President, Keith Teague
Vice President Communications, Eben Burnham-snyder
Vice President Strategy, Andrew Walker
Information Technology Vice President Policy And Governance, Khalid Makiya
Vice President, Jeffrey Zaruba
Board Member, Neal Shear
Auditors: KPMG LLP

LOCATIONS

HQ: Cheniere Energy Partners L P
  700 Milam Street, Suite 1900, Houston, TX 77002
Phone: 713 375-5000
Web: www.cheniere.com

COMPETITORS

AES	McMoRan Exploration
Chevron	Royal Dutch Shell
ConocoPhillips	Sempra Energy
Exxon Mobil	

HISTORICAL FINANCIALS
Company Type: Public

Income Statement
FYE: December 31

	REVENUE ($ mil.)	NET INCOME ($ mil.)	NET PROFIT MARGIN	EMPLOYEES
12/18	6,426	1,274	19.8%	—
12/17	4,304	490	11.4%	—
12/16	1,100	(171)	—	—
12/15	270	(318)	—	—
12/14	268	(410)	—	—
Annual Growth	121.1%	—	—	—

2018 Year-End Financials

Debt ratio: 89.38%
Return on equity: —
Cash ($ mil.): —
Current ratio: 2.21
Long-term debt ($ mil.): 16,066

No. of shares (mil.): 493
Dividends
  Yield: 6.0%
  Payout: 87.2%
Market value ($ mil.): 17,830

	STOCK PRICE ($) FY Close	P/E High/Low	PER SHARE ($) Earnings	Dividends	Book Value
12/18	36.10	16 11	2.51	2.19	1.62
12/17	29.64	— —	(1.32)	1.72	1.29
12/16	28.82	— —	(0.20)	1.70	1.29
12/15	26.07	— —	(0.43)	1.70	2.07
12/14	32.00	— —	(0.89)	1.70	3.28
Annual Growth	3.1%	— —	—	6.5%	(16.2%)

Chesapeake Energy Corp.

Chesapeake Energy is an exploration and production company with oil and gas assets across the US. The company one of the biggest natural gas producers in the US and the world has estimated proved reserves of some 6.8 trillion cu. ft. of natural gas equivalent (about 50% of the reserves are undeveloped). Chesapeake has exploration and production assets in Appalachia the Mid-Continent the Barnett Bossier and Haynesville shale plays and the Rockies. The company boasts 13200 producing oil and natural gas wells that turn out 520000 barrels of oil equivalent per day. Customers have included Valero Energy Corp. Royal Dutch Shell and BP.

Operations

Chesapeake's two sources of revenue are its production of oil natural gas and natural gas liquids (NGL) which accounts for about 50% of revenue and its marketing operations also 50% of revenue.

The oil natural gas and NGL operations explore for acquire develop and produce energy throughout the company's production areas. Within the segment natural gas and oil each account for about 45% of sales with NGLs providing 10%.

Chesapeake's marketing operations provide commodity price structuring securing and negotiating of services for gathering hauling processing and transportation and contract administration and nomination services. Marketing also aggregates volumes sold to intermediary markets end markets and pipelines.

Geographic Reach

Chesapeake Energy which is based in Oklahoma City Oklahoma has operations in the Marcellus - Northern Appalachian Basin in Pennsylvania; Haynesville in Northwestern Louisiana Eagle Ford in South Texas Brazos Valley in Southeast Texas Powder River Basin in Wyoming and the Mid-Continent - Anadarko Basin in northwestern Oklahoma.

Sales and Marketing

Chesapeake sells through market-sensitive short-term or spot price contracts. Natural gas and NGL production is sold to purchasers under percentage-of-proceeds contracts percentage-of-index contracts or spot price contracts. Valero Energy accounted for 10% of revenue in 2018.

Financial Performance

The overall downward trend of energy prices has reduced Chesapeake's revenue from about $23 billion in 2014 to $7.8 billion in 2016. Since then sales have resumed growing.

In 2018 revenue rose to $10.2 billion up about $735 million from 2017 driven by across-the-board increases from its revenue-producing units. Oil led the way with a 32% year-over-year increase while marketing revenue advanced 13%.

Profit slipped to $873 million in 2018 from $949 million the year before. The decrease came in spite of a $78 million reduction in production general and administrative and gathering processing and transportation expenses.

Chesapeake's coffers held $4 million in cash at the end of 2018 compared to $5 million in 2017. Operating activities generated $2 billion in 2018 while investing activities provided $185 million and financing activities used about $2.2 billion.

The company has a significant amount of debt about $8.6 billion and added another $1.4 billion with the acquisition of WildHorse in 2019. Paying down principal and interest could draw money away from other purposes such as operations and capital expenditures.

Strategy

Chesapeake Energy has been through the ups and downs of the oil-and-gas business over the years. Now the company is trying to adjust its operations and balance sheet to deliver sustained performance in a volatile industry.

In 2018 and 2019 Chesapeake engineered transactions to improve its asset mix. The company in 2018 sold $2.2 billion of proved and unproved properties including its Utica Shale properties in Ohio and used the proceeds to pay down debt (it paid off $2.6 billion in secured debt in 2018) and fund development.

In 2019 the company acquired WildHorse Resource Development Corp. and its oil-rich assets and merged it with its Brazos Valley operations. Chesapeake says the deal should provide further profitability and flexibility for the company.

Chesapeake has put new technologies in the field to improve operations. In the Eagle Ford South Texas area the company deployed a digital field technology to reduce down time resulting in a 17% reduction in controllable down volumes per day in 2018 (the equivalent of an additional 1100 barrels of oil sold per day). The company has expanded use of the technology to its other fields.

Mergers and Acquisitions

In 2019 Chesapeake bought WildHorse Resource for nearly $4 billion adding 20000 net acres in the Eagle Ford shale and Austin Chalk formations in Texas. Synergies will be around $280 million over the first five years the company said. However the deal came as a surprise to stockholders who expected further sell-offs to improve profitability. Investors have punished shares of peers like Denbury Concho Resources and Diamondback after similar merger announcements.

HISTORY

Aubrey McClendon (who grew up near Maryland's Chesapeake Bay) and Tom Ward had been non-operating partners in about 600 wells in Oklahoma before forming their own company in 1989 to develop new fields in Texas and Oklahoma during the 1990s. The firm went public in 1993. In 1995 the company acquired oil and gas acreage in Louisiana as well as Princeton Natural Gas an Oklahoma City-based gas marketing firm.

Oil finds in Louisiana and strong production from its Texas and Oklahoma wells helped lift Chesapeake's sales in 1996. That year it acquired Amerada Hess' (later renamed Hess) half of their joint operations in two Oklahoma fields. In 1997 chairman McClendon and president Ward acquired control of Chesapeake.

The company's success was based on its "growth through the drillbit" strategy — developing new wells. But after a 1997 loss Chesapeake modified its strategy and sought to grow by acquiring other companies. That year it bought energy company AnSon Production. Chesapeake subsequently bought oil and gas explorer-producer Hugoton Energy and energy company DLB Oil & Gas.

In 1998 the company acquired a 40% stake in Canadian oil producer Ranger Oil and paid Occidental Petroleum $105 million for natural gas reserves in the Texas Panhandle. Chesapeake then began to transform itself from a hotshot driller to an acquirer of natural gas properties almost tripling its proved reserves. The company suffered a huge loss that year in part from the acquisitions and continuing lower gas prices.

With gas prices soaring again the company continued its buying spree into 2000 when it agreed to buy midcontinent natural gas producer Gothic Energy for $345 million in stock and assumed debt. The deal closed in 2001. The company also

sold its Canadian assets that year in order to focus on its core US properties.

In 2002 Chesapeake acquired oil and gas producer Canaan Energy for about $118 million. Later that year the company announced plans to sell or trade its Permian Basin assets.

Chesapeake acquired in 2003 a 25% stake in Pioneer Drilling (which it subsequently sold). In 2004 the company acquired Barnett Shale assets from Hallwood Energy for $292 million. That year it also bought privately owned Concho Resources for $420 million. The next year the company acquired privately held BRG Petroleum which held assets of more than 450 wells with proved reserves of more than 275 billion cu. ft. of natural gas for $325 million.

In 2005 Chesapeake acquired 20% of Gastar Exploration (reduced to 15% by 2007). That year in a major move the company acquired Columbia Natural Resources for $2.2 billion.

To get better financial returns the company is selling assets to secure capital. Hurt by continuing low natural gas prices the company sold its midstream assets in 2012 and 2013 for $4.9 billion in three separate deals. As part of this move in 2012 the company sold its limited partner units and its general partner interests in Chesapeake Midstream Partners to Global Infrastructure Partners for $2 billion. That year the company also sold about $6.9 billion of its Permian basin properties in order to pay down debt.

To simplify its operations in 2012 Chesapeake spun off its oilfield service affiliate Chesapeake Oilfield Services.

In 2013 it also sold assets in the Northern Eagle Ford Shale and Haynesville Shale to an EXCO Resources subsidiary for $1 billion.

In 2013 the company sold its 50% undivided interest in 850000 acres in northern Oklahoma (its Mississippi Lime joint venture with Sinopec International Petroleum Exploration and Production) for $1.02 billion.

Other asset sales in 2013 included Granite Wash Midstream Gas Services (to a subsidiary of Mark-West Energy Partners for $252 million) and its interests in certain gathering system assets in Pennsylvania to Western Gas Partners for $134 million.

EXECUTIVES

Svp Information Technology And Cio, Cathlyn L. (Cathy) Tompkins, age 58
Evp And Cfo, Domenic J. (Nick) Dell'Osso, age 43, $725,001 total compensation
Evp Exploration And Production, Frank J. Patterson, age 60, $600,000 total compensation
Evp General Counsel And Corporate Secretary, James R. Webb, age 51, $625,000 total compensation
President And Ceo, Robert D. (Doug) Lawler, age 52, $1,300,000 total compensation
Evp Operations And Technical Services, M. Jason Pigott, age 45, $574,999 total compensation
Vice President And Division Controller Operations, Randy Goben
Vice President Drilling, Dave Bert
Vice President Marine Information Technology, Steve A Melton
Vice President Human Resources, James jay Hawkins
Vice President, Mandy Duane
Vice President Information Technology, Steve Evans
Vice President, Lacie Wilson
Vice President, Frank Gagliardi
Senior Vice President Information Technology And Cio, Cathy Tompkins
Vice President Environment Health And Safety, Brittany Benko
Vice President Performance Solutions, Chris Mitchel

Vice President Marketing, Sarika Jewell
Vp Land, Jim Dewbre
Evp And Cfo, Domenic Dell'osso Jr
Chairman, R. Brad Martin, age 67
Assistant Secretary, Anita Brodrick
Treasurer, Julian Carrillo
Auditors: PricewaterhouseCoopers LLC

LOCATIONS

HQ: Chesapeake Energy Corp.
6100 North Western Avenue, Oklahoma City, OK 73118
Phone: 405 848-8000
Web: www.chk.com

PRODUCTS/OPERATIONS

2018 Sales

	$ mil.	% of total
Oil natural gas and NGL	5,155	58
Marketing	5,076	42
Total	**10,231**	**100**

COMPETITORS

Adams Resources	Koch Industries Inc.
Anadarko Petroleum	Noble Energy
Apache	Occidental Petroleum
BP	Pioneer Natural
Chevron	Resources
ConocoPhillips	SandRidge Energy
Exxon Mobil	Southwestern Energy
Freeport-McMoRan Oil & Gas LLC	Unit Corporation

HISTORICAL FINANCIALS

Company Type: Public

Income Statement | | | | FYE: December 31

	REVENUE ($ mil.)	NET INCOME ($ mil.)	NET PROFIT MARGIN	EMPLOYEES
12/18	10,231	873	8.5%	2,350
12/17	9,496	949	10.0%	3,200
12/16	7,872	(4,401)	—	3,300
12/15	12,764	(14,685)	—	4,400
12/14	20,951	1,917	9.1%	5,500
Annual Growth	**(16.4%)**	**(17.9%)**	**—**	**(19.2%)**

2018 Year-End Financials

Debt ratio: 70.54%
Return on equity: ***,***.**%
Cash ($ mil.): 4
Current ratio: 0.57
Long-term debt ($ mil.): 7,341

No. of shares (mil.): 910
Dividends
  Yield: —
  Payout: —
Market value ($ mil.): 1,912

	STOCK PRICE ($) FY Close	P/E High/Low		Earnings	Dividends	Book Value
12/18	2.10	6	2	0.85	0.00	0.38
12/17	3.96	8	4	0.90	0.00	(0.55)
12/16	7.02	—	—	(6.45)	0.00	(1.63)
12/15	4.50	—	—	(22.43)	0.26	3.22
12/14	19.57	16	9	1.87	0.35	25.48
Annual Growth	**(42.8%)**			**(17.9%)**	**—**	**(65.1%)**

Chevron Corporation

Chevron has earned its stripes as the #2 integrated oil company in the US behind Exxon Mobil. Its global operations explore for and produce oil and oil equivalents refines them into various fuels and other end products and sells them through gas stations airport fuel depots and industrial channels. Chevron boasts more than 12 billion barrels of proved reserves produces about 3 million barrels of oil per day and has refining capacity for nearly 1.6 million barrels per day. The company sells refined products branded under the Chevron Texaco and Caltex names through nearly 8000 gas stations in the US and around 5000 outside the US.

HISTORY

Thirty years after the California gold rush a small firm began digging for a new product — oil. The crude came from wildcatter Frederick Taylor's well located north of Los Angeles. In 1879 Taylor and other oilmen formed Pacific Coast Oil attracting the attention of John D. Rockefeller's Standard Oil. The two competed fiercely until Standard took over Pacific Coast in 1900.

When Standard Oil was broken up in 1911 its West Coast operations became the stand-alone Standard Oil Company (California) which was nicknamed Socal and sold Chevron-brand products. After winning drilling concessions in Bahrain and Saudi Arabia in the 1930s Socal summoned Texaco to help and they formed Caltex (California-Texas Oil Company) as equal partners. In 1948 Socony (later Mobil) and Jersey Standard (later Exxon) bought 40% of Caltex's Saudi operations and the Saudi arm became Aramco (Arabian American Oil Company).

Socal exploration pushed into Louisiana and the Gulf of Mexico in the 1940s. In 1961 it bought Standard Oil Company of Kentucky (Kyso). The 1970s brought setbacks: Caltex holdings were nationalized during the OPEC-spawned upheaval and the Saudi Arabian government claimed Aramco in 1980.

In 1984 Socal was renamed Chevron and doubled its reserves with its $13 billion purchase of Gulf Corp. which had origins in the 1901 Spindletop gusher in Texas. Gulf became an oil power by developing Kuwaiti concessions but was hobbled when those assets were nationalized in 1975. After Gulf was rocked by disclosures that it had an illegal political slush fund Socal stepped in. The deal loaded the new company with debt and it cut 20000 jobs and sold billions in assets.

Chevron bought Tenneco's Gulf of Mexico properties in 1988 and in 1992 swapped fields valued at $1.1 billion for 15.7 million shares of Chevron stock owned by Pennzoil. It also moved into the North Sea in 1994.

In the 1990s Chevron gave its retailing units a tune-up. It allied with McDonald's (1995) to combine burger stands and gas stations in 12 western states. In addition the company sold 450 UK gas stations and a refinery to Shell (1997). Meanwhile Chevron sold its natural gas operation in 1996 for a stake in Houston-based NGC (later Dynegy ; sold in 2007) and it signed an onshore exploration contract in China the next year.

Poor economic conditions in Asia and slumping oil prices in 1998 forced Chevron to shed some US holdings including California properties. Looking for growth overseas in 1999 it bought Rutherford-Moran Oil increasing its interests in Thailand and Petrolera Argentina San Jorge Argentina's #3 oil company.

Chevron trimmed about 10% of its workforce in 1999 and 2000 in an effort to cut costs. As the rest of the industry consolidated Chevron discussed merging with Texaco but the talks collapsed in 1999. Later that year CEO Ken Derr retired and vice chairman Dave O'Reilly replaced him.

In 2000 Chevron formed a joint venture with Phillips Petroleum (later ConocoPhillips) that combined the companies' chemicals businesses as Chevron Phillips Chemical . That year talks with Texaco were revived and Chevron agreed to acquire its Caltex partner for about $35 billion in stock and about $8 billion in assumed debt. The deal completed in 2001 formed ChevronTexaco.

Part of the 2001 deal to acquire Texaco required Chevron to sell exclusive rights to the Texaco brand for a period of three years. A division of Royal Dutch Shell owned rights to the Texaco brand until 2004 and changed the name of the service stations to Shell. Once Chevron regained the rights to the Texaco name it revitalized the brand name by adding about 400 Texaco stations in the western US.

In 2002 ChevronTexaco divested its stakes in US downstream joint ventures Equilon (to Shell) and Motiva (to Shell and Saudi Aramco). It also sold part of a Gulf of Mexico pipeline and two natural gas plants in Louisiana to Duke Energy and its 12.5% stake in a natural gas liquids fractionator to Enterprise Products Partners. In 2004 ChevronTexaco sold 150 US natural gas and oil properties to XTO Energy for $912 million. The company changed its name to Chevron Corporation in 2005.

Chevron acquired Unocal in 2005 for more than $16 billion boosting its proved reserves by about 15%. Equally attractive to Chevron was the strategic position of Unocal's operations; at a time when industries are trying to get a foothold in China the reserves in Southeast Asia could easily be transported not only there but also to a surging India as well. Unocal's other operations easily supplied the US (from the Gulf of Mexico) and Europe (Caspian Sea) with gas and oil. Chevron bought a 5% stake in Indian refiner Reliance Petroleum for about $300 million in 2006. That year a company-led group of exploration firms announced a new successful oil strike in the Gulf of Mexico.

The company has also been growing its natural gas assets. In 2008 it announced plans to construct a $3.1 billion natural gas project in the Gulf of Thailand. The project will have the capacity to meet 14% of Thailand's natural gas needs.

Ultrapar acquired Chevron's Texaco-branded fuel distribution business in Brazil for $720 million in 2008 and the next year Chevron sold its Nigerian fuel marketing business.

A leading producer of viscous heavy oil in 2010 a Chevron-led consortium was awarded the rights to 40% of a heavy oil project in Venezuela's Orinoco Oil Belt.

In 2010 in the wake of the BP oil rig disaster in the Gulf of Mexico Chevron announced it was forming a $1 billion joint venture with Exxon Mobil Royal Dutch Shell and ConocoPhillips to create a rapid-response system capable of capturing and containing up to 100000 barrels of oil from an oil spill in water depths of 10000 feet.

Looking to develop a deepwater area unaffected by US regulations in 2010 the company acquired a 70% stake in three concessions in Liberia in West Africa. Other deepwater exploration asset acquisitions that year included purchases in China and the Turkish Black Sea.

In 2010 the company began to cut its US refining and marketing business staff by 20% and as part of this realignment it sold its 23% stake in Colonial Pipeline to a KKR affiliate.

In 2013 company acquired exploration interests in offshore Blocks EPP44 and EPP45 (more than 8 million acres in the Bight Basin off the South Australian coast).

Growing its LNG supply and export capacity in 2013 Chevron acquired a 50% operating interest in the Kitimat liquefied natural gas project and proposed Pacific Trail Pipeline and a 50% stake in 644000 acres of petroleum and natural gas rights in the Horn River and Liard Basins in British Columbia Canada. The company bought the assets from Apache for $405 million.

In a major move in 2011 Chevron acquired Atlas Energy in a $4.3 billion deal. The acquisition is part of the company's strategy of finding new reserves to replace reserves lost from declining fields. It also marked Chevron's move to become a major player in the prolific Marcellus Shale play in Pennsylvania where a number of majors are seeking to cash in on the improved drilling technology that has made the exploitation of unconventional gas finds more commercially viable. The purchase gave Chevron Atlas Energy's 850 billion cu. ft. of proved natural gas reserves and 80 million cu. ft. of daily natural gas production. It also complements Chevron's earlier acquisitions of shale gas assets in Canada Poland and Romania as well as its purchase of an additional 228000 acres in the Marcellus Shale from Chief Oil & Gas LLC and Tug Hill Inc. (The acquisitions added up to 5 trillion cubic feet of natural gas resources to Chevron's existing Marcellus Shale operations.)

An earlier chapter of Chevron's history reemerged in 2011 when the company was slapped with a bill for $18 billion in fines and charges by a court in Ecuador regarding environmental damages allegedly caused by Texaco (acquired in 2001) in the 1970s and 1980s. Chevron challenged the findings as illegitimate and unenforceable.

Restructuring its refinery and retail businesses to cut costs in 2011 Chevron sold its Chevron Ltd. UK unit which operated the Pembroke refinery to Valero for $730 million. In addition Valero agreed to pay more that $1 billion for other Chevron Ltd. assets including 1000 gas stations. That year Chevron also sold its fuels marketing and aviation businesses in 16 countries in the Caribbean and Latin America and some marketing businesses in five African countries.

In 2012 the company signed a 20-year deal with Tohoku Electric Power for the delivery of liquefied natural gas (LNG) from the Chevron-operated Wheatstone natural gas project in Australia.

Growing its shale assets in 2013 Chevron agreed to a $1.24 billion investment in YPF to help YPF develop the world's second-largest shale gas deposit and fourth-largest shale oil reservoir located in Argentina's Vaca Muerta region. In 2013 and 2012 the company also announced new exploration and production deals to expand its assets in China Kurdistan the Republic of Congo Surinam and the US.

In 2013 50%-owned affiliate GS Caltex opened a 53000-barrel-per-day gas oil fluid catalytic cracking unit at the Yeosu Refinery in South Korea.

The company consolidated the supply and trading functions in 2013 into a single supply and trading group within Chevron's Gas and Midstream organization.

EXECUTIVES

Vp And Cfo, Patricia E. (Pat) Yarrington, age 62, $1,073,242 total compensation

Chairman And Ceo, Michael K. (Mike) Wirth, age 59, $1,094,492 total compensation

Evp Downstream And Chemicals, Pierre R. Breber, age 54

Vp And General Counsel, R. Hewitt (Hew) Pate, age 57, $867,000 total compensation

Evp Technology Projects And Services, Joseph C. (Joe) Geagea, age 59, $906,367 total compensation

Evp Upstream, James W. (Jay) Johnson, age 60, $1,012,417 total compensation

Managing Director Chevron Nigeria Mid-africa, Clay Neff, age 57

Vice President Of Finance, Uriel Ose

Vice President, Elliott Ginger

Vice President, Petros Papazis

Vice President Marketing, Jeff Petro

Vice President, Marek Kacewicz

Vice President And General Cou, Wendy Daboval
Vice President Of Montgomery O, Julia Martin
National Account Manager, Steve Faggard
Assistant Vice President Information Technology Operations, Antonio Calombo
Vice President Of Membership, Yolanda Peria
Vice President Chevron Energy Solutions, Mark Emerson
Vice President Operations, Jill Seal
Vice President, Martin Donohue
Executive Vice President, Sandy Cab
Vice President, Sergey Kuznetsov
Vice President Finance, Brenda Young
National Account Manager, Marcella Love
Vice President, Nadine Barroca
Vice President, Jay Byers
Vice President, Francesca Fazzari
Vice President, Michael Murphy
Vice President, Jay Close
Vice President Of Marketing, Viviane Tonon
Vp And General Counsel, R Hewitt Pate
Vice President Of International Business Development And Gispro Sponsor, Hector Fajardo
Vice President, Amir Hidayat
Vice President Jv Managing Director, Leon De Bruyn
Vice Chairman Of The Board, Glenn F Tilton
Secretary, H Xun
Treasurer Chevron Stations, Ravinder Bhumbla
Secretary, Lawrence Febo
Assistant Secretary And Managing Counsel, Kari Endries
Board Member, Gary P Luquette
Auditors: PricewaterhouseCoopers LLP

LOCATIONS

HQ: Chevron Corporation
   6001 Bollinger Canyon Road, San Ramon, CA 94583-2324
Phone: 925 842-1000   Fax: 925 894-6017
Web: www.chevron.com

2018 sales

	$ mil.	% of total
US	83,289	44
International	107,939	56
Adjustments	(32326)	—
Total	**158,902**	**100**

PRODUCTS/OPERATIONS

2018 Sales

	$ mil.	% of total
Downstream	129,471	68
Upstream	60,713	32
Other	1,044	-
Adjustments	(32326)	-
Total	**158,902**	**100**

COMPETITORS

BP	Occidental Petroleum
ConocoPhillips	PEMEX
Devon Energy	PETROBRAS
Eni	Petr leos de
Exxon Mobil	Venezuela
Hess Corporation	Repsol
Imperial Oil	Royal Dutch Shell
Koch Industries Inc.	Sinopec Corp.
Marathon Petroleum	TOTAL

HISTORICAL FINANCIALS

Company Type: Public

Income Statement

	REVENUE ($ mil.)	NET INCOME ($ mil.)	NET PROFIT MARGIN	EMPLOYEES
				FYE: December 31
12/18	166,339	14,824	8.9%	48,600
12/17	141,722	9,195	6.5%	51,900
12/16	114,472	(497)	—	55,200
12/15	138,477	4,587	3.3%	61,500
12/14	211,970	19,241	9.1%	64,700
Annual Growth	(5.9%)	(6.3%)	—	(6.9%)

2018 Year-End Financials

Debt ratio: 13.57%
Return on equity: 9.80%
Cash ($ mil.): 10,292
Current ratio: 1.25
Long-term debt ($ mil.): 28,733

No. of shares (mil.): 1,902
Dividends
   Yield: 4.1%
   Payout: 57.8%
Market value ($ mil.): 207,010

	STOCK PRICE ($) FY Close	P/E High/Low	Earnings	Dividends	Book Value
			PER SHARE ($)		
12/18	108.79	17 13	7.74	4.48	81.22
12/17	125.19	26 21	4.85	4.32	77.77
12/16	117.70	— —	(0.27)	4.29	76.95
12/15	89.96	46 28	2.45	4.28	81.11
12/14	112.18	13 10	10.14	4.21	82.48
Annual Growth	(0.8%)	— —	(6.5%)	1.6%	(0.4%)

CHEVRON FEDERAL CREDIT UNION

EXECUTIVES

Pres-Ceo, James Mooney
Cfo*, Janet Lee
Officer, Wanda Quinto
Loan Officer, Melinda Schoppa
Business Officer R, Nancy Sung
Lending Sales Manager, Damon Nakano
Chief Operating Officer, Denis Murphy
Human Resources Specialist, Leticia Pinocci
Vice President of Marketing, Neil Sawyer
Manager, Roger Alvarado
Executive Vice President Execu, John Canavan

LOCATIONS

HQ: CHEVRON FEDERAL CREDIT UNION
   500 12TH ST STE 200, OAKLAND, CA 946074084
Phone: 888 884-4630
Web: WWW.CHEVRONFCU.ORG

HISTORICAL FINANCIALS

Company Type: Private

Income Statement

	ASSETS ($ mil.)	NET INCOME ($ mil.)	INCOME AS % OF ASSETS	EMPLOYEES
				FYE: December 31
12/17	3,163	30	1.0%	185
12/16	3,027	34	1.1%	—
12/15	2,748	26	1.0%	—
Annual Growth	7.3%	6.9%	—	—

CHEVRON PHILLIPS CHEMICAL COMPANY LP

EXECUTIVES

Ceo, Peter L Cella
Exec V Pres, Mark E Lashier
Sr V Pres, Ron Corn
Sr V Pres, Tim Hill
V Pres, Mitch Eichelberger
Coordinator, Aprile Turner
It Security, Mohit Chanana
Staff, Aaron Evitts
Human Resources Consultant, Susan Allen
Coordinator, Tom Shomette
Safety Manager, Carolyn Rogers
Auditors: ERNST & YOUNG LLP HOUSTON T

LOCATIONS

HQ: CHEVRON PHILLIPS CHEMICAL COMPANY LP
   10001 SIX PINES DR, THE WOODLANDS, TX 773801498
Phone: 832 813-4100
Web: WWW.CPCHEM.COM

HISTORICAL FINANCIALS

Company Type: Private

Income Statement

	REVENUE ($ mil.)	NET INCOME ($ mil.)	NET PROFIT MARGIN	EMPLOYEES
				FYE: December 31
12/17	7,919	841	10.6%	5,000
12/16	7,106	1,301	18.3%	—
12/15	7,990	2,020	25.3%	—
12/14	11,758	2,444	20.8%	—
Annual Growth	(12.3%)	(29.9%)	—	—

Chimera Investment Corp

This Chimera has the body of a mortgage real estate investment trust (REIT) but its head is that of its external manager FIDAC (Fixed Income Discount Advisory Company) a fixed-income investment management firm wholly-ownedÂ by Annaly Capital Management. Formed in 2007 Chimera invests in residential mortgage loans; residential mortgage-backed securities (RMBS) such as those guaranteed by government agencies Fannie Mae and Freddie Mac; real estate-related securities; and other assets including collateralized debt obligations or CDOs. The REIT went public in 2007 shortly after it was formed.

EXECUTIVES

Pres-Ceo, Matthew Lambiase
Non Exec Chb, Paul Donlin
Cfo, Robert Colligan
Coo, Choudhary Yarlagadda
Clo-SEC, Phillip J Kardis II
CIO, Mohit Marria
Auditors: Ernst & Young LLP

HQ: Chimera Investment Corp
520 Madison Avenue, 32nd Floor, New York, NY 10022
Phone: 212 626-2300
Web: www.chimerareit.com

COMPETITORS

Annaly Capital
Management
Capstead Mortgage
Impac Mortgage
Holdings

MFA Financial
Walter Investment
Management

HISTORICAL FINANCIALS

Company Type: Public

Income Statement   FYE: December 31

	ASSETS ($ mil.)	NET INCOME ($ mil.)	INCOME AS % OF ASSETS	EMPLOYEES
12/18	27,708	411	1.5%	38
12/17	21,222	524	2.5%	38
12/16	16,684	551	3.3%	38
12/15	15,344	250	1.6%	32
12/14	19,155	589	3.1%	—
Annual Growth	9.7%	(8.6%)	—	—

2018 Year-End Financials

Debt ratio: 31.09%
Return on equity: 11.22%
Cash ($ mil.): 47
Current ratio: —
Long-term debt ($ mil.): —

No. of shares (mil.): 187
Dividends
Yield: 11.2%
Payout: 102.0%
Market value ($ mil.): 3,333

	STOCK PRICE ($) FY Close	P/E High/Low		PER SHARE ($) Earnings	Dividends	Book Value
12/18	17.82	10	8	1.96	2.00	19.80
12/17	18.48	8	7	2.61	2.00	19.35
12/16	17.02	6	4	2.92	2.44	16.64
12/15	13.64	13	2	1.25	1.44	15.70
12/14	3.18	1	1	2.85	1.80	17.55
Annual Growth	53.9%	—	—	(8.9%)	2.7%	3.1%

Chipotle Mexican Grill Inc

US restaurant chain Chipotle Mexican Grill owns and operates more than 2500 quick-casual eateries popular for burritos tacos burrito bowls and salads. Chipotle offers a made-to-order menu from which customers can build a 1-1/4 pound burrito from a lineup that includes chicken steak barbecue or free-range pork as well as beans rice guacamole and various other veggies and salsas. The company claims that with extras its menu offers thousands of choices. Chipotle restaurants also serve soft tacos crispy tacos chips and salsa beer and margaritas. The company was founded in 1993 in Denver Colorado.

Operations

Chipotle's restaurants are found in strip centers malls and outlets downtown business districts and other populous retail areas. The company also has a presence at non-retail sites like airports military bases and train stations.

The chain operates various location types including end-cap locations (restaurants situated at the end of a line of retail outlets) free-standing buildings and in-line locations (in a line of retail outlets). At more than 1600 locations Chipotle's end-cap locations comprises the majority of the chain's nearly 2500 restaurants. Free-standing units number in the 400s while in-line units consist of about 350 locations. The average Chipotle restaurant is about 2500 square feet and seats about 60 people.

In addition to its Chipotle-branded restaurants the company also operates a few fast-casual Pizzeria Locale restaurants in Denver.

Geographic Reach

California-based Chipotle operates prominently in the US with locations in every US state except Alaska Hawaii and South Dakota. About one-third of Chipotle's restaurants are concentrated in California Texas and Ohio.

Outside the US the chain has a small international presence operating some 35 locations in Canada the UK France and Germany.

Sales and Marketing

Chipotle continues to distinguish itself from its competition by touting its focus on organically grown produce and naturally raised antibiotic free animal products. Many of its competitors — including Taco Bell — have followed its lead making Chipotle something of a trendsetter among its fast-food chain brethren.

Chipotle promotes its products through print outdoor transit and radio ads but it also incorporates digital advertising into the mix and conducts strategic promotions. It has a dedicated team of field marketing staff that connects its restaurants to local communities through fundraisers sponsorships and participation in local events. On the technology front the company attracts repeat customers through its Chipotle Rewards loyalty program accessed via a mobile app and offers mobile ordering and delivery.

The company's advertising and marketing expenses were approximately $111.7 million in 2018.

Financial Performance

Over the past five years Chipotle has battled through irregular revenue results driven mostly by highly publicized food safety concerns in 2015 and 2016. By 2017 revenue appeared to bounce back and settle into the company's more typical year-over-year climb.

In 2018 Chipotle's revenue rose 8% to $4.8 billion up from $4.4 billion in 2017. Driving the increase were higher sales from new locations as well as a 4% increase in comparable-restaurant sales. Higher menu prices helped bolster comparable sales.

Despite the higher revenue Chipotle's 2018 net income ($176.5 million) remained flat its bottom line curbed by higher labor costs (as a percentage of revenue) increases in general and administrative expenses and increases in depreciation and amortization.

Cash at the end of 2018 was $280.1 million an increase of $66 million from the prior year. Cash from operations contributed $621.5 million to the coffers while investing activities used $387.5 million mainly to fund purchases of leasehold improvements property and equipment. Financing activities used $166.5 million most of which went to acquire treasury stock.

Strategy

While very much a quick-service restaurant chain Chipotle has successfully differentiated itself from other fast-food brands by focusing on its distinctive customer experience and food quality. Most of the restaurants feature a minimalist interior designed to appeal to the young adult segment while the made-to-order system sets the brand apart from other fast-food chains. Chipotle restaurants serve a focused menu of burritos tacos burrito bowls (a burrito without the tortilla) and salads.

As part of its growth strategy the company has been investing heavily in technology to attract customers seeking to skip the line at its restaurants. It offers mobile ordering and in select markets mobile order pick-up lanes (called "Chipotlanes") and delivery services. The strategy has proven successful thus far as digital orders and delivery have been driving an uptick in sales in recent years. The company is well-positioned for future growth as it increases advertising and availability of these services.

Cost-cutting efforts have been front and center at Chipotle in recent years. Chipotle implemented a corporate restructuring strategy that included closing its New York New York corporate office consolidating operations at its Columbus Ohio office and moving its headquarters from Denver to Newport Beach California. The company expects to save up to $58 million as a result of its restructuring efforts.

Company Background

Chipotle was founded in 1993 in Denver by Steve Ells who served as the company's CEO until his resignation in 2017. Ells resigned in the wake of the company's notorious E. coli outbreak in 2015-2016 which resulted in a significant turn-around effort that included replacing management and winning back the public's trust through PR campaigns.

EXECUTIVES

Chairman And Ceo, M. Steven (Steve) Ells, age 54, $1,540,000 total compensation
Cfo, John R. (Jack) Hartung, age 62, $792,308 total compensation
Chief Digital Officer And Cio, Curtis (Curt) Garner
Vice President Information Technology, Elvir Ibrahimpasic
Vice President, Karin Alexander
Auditors: Ernst & Young LLP

LOCATIONS

HQ: Chipotle Mexican Grill Inc
610 Newport Center Drive, Suite 1300, Newport Beach, CA 92660
Phone: 949 524-4000
Web: www.chipotle.com

COMPETITORS

Chick-fil-A
Del Taco
El Pollo Loco
Fresh Enterprises
McDonald's
Moe's Southwest Grill

Panda Restaurant Group
Panera Bread
Qdoba Restaurants
Subway
Taco Bell

HISTORICAL FINANCIALS

Company Type: Public

Income Statement   FYE: December 31

	REVENUE ($ mil.)	NET INCOME ($ mil.)	NET PROFIT MARGIN	EMPLOYEES
12/19	5,586	350	6.3%	83,000
12/18	4,864	176	3.6%	73,000
12/17	4,476	176	3.9%	68,890
12/16	3,904	22	0.6%	64,570
12/15	4,501	475	10.6%	59,330
Annual Growth	5.5%	(7.4%)	—	8.8%

2019 Year-End Financials

Debt ratio: —
Return on equity: 22.41%
Cash ($ mil.): 480
Current ratio: 1.61
Long-term debt ($ mil.): —

No. of shares (mil.): 27
Dividends
Yield: —
Payout: —
Market value ($ mil.): 23,234

	STOCK PRICE ($) FY Close	P/E High/Low	PER SHARE ($) Earnings	Dividends	Book Value
12/19	837.11	67 35	12.38	0.00	60.64
12/18	431.79	83 40	6.31	0.00	52.04
12/17	289.03	80 43	6.17	0.00	48.68
12/16	377.32	684461	0.77	0.00	48.67
12/15	479.85	50 32	15.10	0.00	69.58
Annual Growth	14.9%	— —	(4.8%)	—	(3.4%)

CHRISTIAN BROTHERS INVESTMENT SERVICES, INC.

EXECUTIVES

Ceo, Jeffrey McCroy
Chief Investment Officer*, John W Geissinger
Marketing Staff, Miranda McCoy
Accountant, Alex Chan
Director, Dean Armstrong
Caia Director Institutional De, Sean McCaffrey
Associate Investment Advisor, Elizabeth Vella
Director, Diane Miller
Director, Julie Tanner

LOCATIONS

HQ: CHRISTIAN BROTHERS INVESTMENT SERVICES, INC.
20 N WACKER DR STE 2000, CHICAGO, IL
606063002
Phone: 312 526-3343
Web: WWW.CBISONLINE.COM

HISTORICAL FINANCIALS

Company Type: Private

Income Statement   FYE: December 30

	ASSETS ($ mil.)	NET INCOME ($ mil.)	INCOME AS % OF ASSETS	EMPLOYEES
12/11	2,079	100	4.8%	45
12/10	2,167	68	3.1%	—
12/09	1,863	0	—	—
12/05	2,191	0	—	—
Annual Growth	(0.9%)	—	—	—

CHS Inc

CHS is a major cooperative marketer of grain oilseed and energy resources in the US. It represents farmers ranchers and co-ops from the Great Lakes to Texas trading grain and selling farm supplies through its stores to members. The group processes soybeans for use in food and animal feeds and grinds wheat into flour. In addition to grain marketing it operates through joint ventures and a variety of business segments for the sale ofl soybean oil and crop nutrient products. CHS also provides insurance financial and risk-management services and operates petroleum refineries that sell Cenex-brand fuels lubricants and other energy products. The company does about 90% of its business in North America.

HISTORY

To help farmers through the Great Depression the Farmers Union Terminal Association (a grain marketing association formed in 1926) created the Farmers Union Grain Terminal Association (GTA) in 1938. With loans from the Farmers Union Central Exchange (later known as CENEX) and the Farm Credit Association the organization operated a grain elevator in St. Paul Minnesota. By 1939 GTA had 250 grain-producing associations as members.

GTA leased terminals in Minneapolis and Washington and built others in Wisconsin and Montana in the early 1940s. It then took over a Minnesota flour mill and created Amber Milling. GTA also began managing farming insurance provider Terminal Agency. In 1958 the association bought 57 elevators and feed plants from the McCabe Company.

Adding to its operations in 1960 GTA bought the Honeymead soybean plant. The next year the co-op acquired Minnesota Linseed Oil. In 1977 it acquired Jewett & Sherman (later Holsum Foods) which helped transform the company into a provider of jams jellies salad dressings and syrups.

In 1983 GTA combined with North Pacific Grain Growers a Pacific Northwest co-op incorporated in 1929 to form Harvest States Cooperatives. Harvest States grew in the early and mid-1990s by acquiring salad dressing makers Albert's Foods Great American Foods and Saffola Quality Foods; soup stock producer Private Brands; and margarine and dressings manufacturer and distributor Gregg Foods.

The company started a joint venture to operate the Ag States Agency agricultural insurance company in 1995. The next year the co-op's Holsum Foods division and Mitsui & Co.'s edible oils unit Wilsey Foods merged to form Ventura Foods a distributor of margarines oils spreads and other food products.

Harvest States merged in 1998 with Minnesota-based CENEX a 16-state agricultural supply co-op that had been founded in 1931 as Farmers Union Central Exchange. (Among CENEX's major operations was a farm inputs services marketing and processing joint venture with dairy cooperative Land O'Lakes formed in 1987.) CENEX CEO Noel Estenson took the helm of the resulting co-op Cenex Harvest States Cooperatives which soon formed a petroleum joint venture called Country Energy with Farmland Industries.

CHS members rejected a proposed merger with Farmland Industries in 1999. Also that year Cenex/Land O'Lakes Agronomy (it became Agriliance in 2000 when Farmland Industries joined the joint venture) bought Terra Industries' $1.7 billion distribution business (400 farm supply stores seed and chemical distribution operations partial ownership of two chemical plants).

CHS bought the wholesale propane marketing operations of Williams Companies in 2000 and the co-op paid $14 million for tortilla and tortilla chip maker Sparta Foods. Additionally Estenson retired that year and company president John Johnson took over as CEO. CHS launched an agricultural e-commerce site (Rooster.com) in conjunction with Cargill and DuPont in 2000. The site was shut down the next year however because of a lack of funds. Also in 2001 the cooperative became the full owner of Country Energy by purchasing Farmland Industries' share.

In 2002 CHS acquired Agway's Grandin North Dakota-based sunflower business and formed a wheat-milling joint venture (Horizon Milling) with Cargill. In 2003 the company changed its name from Cenex Harvest States Cooperatives to CHS Inc. and began trading on the NASDAQ. It used the proceeds from the stock offering to repay its short-term debts.

In 2004 CHS purchased all of bankrupt Farmland Industries' ownership of Agriliance thus giving CHS a 50% ownership of Agriliance (with Land O'Lakes owning the other 50%). With an eye to this growing energy sector CHS acquired a 28% ownership of ethanol producer and marketer US BioEnergy Corporation in 2005. Also that year it sold off its Mexican foods business and sold 81% of its 20% ownership of crop-nutrient manufacturer CF Industries in an initial public offering.

CHS and Land O'Lakes realigned the businesses of their 50-50 joint venture Agriliance in 2007 with CHS acquiring its crop-nutrients wholesale-products business and Land O'Lakes acquiring the crop-protection products business. Canadian ag cooperative La Coop f d r e purchased Agriliance's retail agronomy operation the following year. Adding to its lubricants offerings in 2007 the company acquired two Minnesota companies: Nor-Lakes Services Midwest and The Farm-Oyl Company. In 2008 it sold off all its remaining shares of CF.

Recognizing the growing demand for soy-based food products and in turn to increase shareholder value the company in 2008 acquired Legacy Foods maker of Ultra Soy and TSP brands of textured soybean products for use by both human food and pet food manufacturers. Legacy's operations are overseen by CHS's oilseed processing division.

On the energy front CHS became the sole owner of Provista Renewable Fuels Marketing in 2008 by purchasing US BioEnergy's 50% interest in the biofuels maker. (VeraSun Energy bought out US BioEnergy later that year.

In 2009 CHS acquired Winona River & Rail including 90000 tons of dry-fertilizer storage capacity a dedicated river dock and a 65-car railroad track capacity. The acquisition of the Minnesota operations bolstered the company's storage capacity and rail access in the midwestern and upper Mississippi River regions. Later that year it formed a joint venture with Russia's farm operation Agrico Group (called ACG) in order to manage the export and worldwide marketing of its wheat and feed grains. In turn it gave CHS access to the Russian grain market and improved its ability to serve its global customers.

Also in 2009 CHS formed another of its joint ventures this time at home. It joined with Nebraska's Central Valley Ag Cooperative (CVA) to form Advanced Energy Fuels to provide customers with an industry-leading fuel delivery system.

Beyond the US the company was part of a grain marketing joint venture (Multigrain A.G.) with Brazilian commodities-company PMG Trading and Mitsui. In 2011 CHS sold a nearly 45% stake in Multigrain to the Japanese firm for Â 47 billion yen (roughly $510 million). Mitsui which already owned about a 45% stake also bought PMG's interest. The deal marked one of the largest overseas farming investments made by a Japanese trading house.

Building on the success of its joint ventures in 2013 CHS formed a flouring-milling partnership with agri-giants Cargill and ConAgra called Ardent Mills. The newly-formed partnership was North America's largest flour miller with annual sales of more than $4 billion. CHS held 12% of Ardent Mills while ConAgra and Cargill each owned 44%.

EXECUTIVES

President And Ceo, Jay D. Debertin, $667,242 total compensation
Evp Business Solutions, Lisa Zell, $438,600 total compensation
Evp And Coo Country Operations, Lynden E. Johnson
Evp And Coo Ag Business And Enterprise Strategy, Shirley Cunningham, $593,983 total compensation
Evp And Cfo, Timothy Skidmore, $487,135 total compensation
Evp And Chief Human Resources Officer, Adam Holton
Evp And General Counsel, James (Jim) Zappa, $423,667 total compensation
Vice President And General Manager, Roger Baker
Vp Eastern Region Country Operation, Chris Cairo
Chairman, Daniel (Dan) Schurr
Second Vice Chairman, Jon Erickson
First Vice Chairman, Clinton J. (C.J.) Blew
Auditors: PricewaterhouseCoopers LLP

LOCATIONS

HQ: CHS Inc
5500 Cenex Drive, Inver Grove Heights, MN 55077
Phone: 651 355-6000
Web: www.chsinc.com

2018 Sales

	$ mil.	% of total
North America	29,475	90
EMEA	1,569	5
APAC	1,101	3
APAC	536	2
Total	**32,683**	**100**

PRODUCTS/OPERATIONS

2018 Sales

	$ mil.	% of total
Ag	25,052	81
Energy	8,068	19
Corporate and Other	64	-
Adjustments	(502.3)	-
Total	**32,683**	**100**

Selected Operations

Ag business
  Grain exporter
  Grain merchandising in Argentina
  Grain merchandising in Europe
  Grain merchandising in Spain
  Grain procurement and merchandising in Russia
  Grain procurement and merchandising in Ukraine
  Retail distribution of agronomy products
  Soybean procurement in Brazil
Corporate and Other
  Finance company
  Insurance agency
  Insurance brokerage
  Risk management products broker
Energy
  Crude oil transportation
  Finished product transportation
  Petroleum refining
Processing
  Food manufacturing and distribution
  Wheat milling in Canada
  Wheat milling in US

COMPETITORS

ADM	ConocoPhillips
Ag Processing Inc.	ExxonMobil Chemical
AmeriGas Partners	Flint Hills
CGC	GROWMARK
CITGO	JR Simplot
Cargill	Marathon Petroleum
Columbia Grain	Valero Energy
ConAgra	

HISTORICAL FINANCIALS
Company Type: Public

Income Statement
FYE: August 31

	REVENUE ($ mil.)	NET INCOME ($ mil.)	NET PROFIT MARGIN	EMPLOYEES
08/19	31,900	829	2.6%	10,703
08/18	32,683	775	2.4%	10,495
08/17	31,934	127	0.4%	11,626
08/16	30,347	424	1.4%	12,157
08/15	34,582	781	2.3%	12,511
Annual Growth	**(2.0%)**	**1.5%**	**—**	**(3.8%)**

2019 Year-End Financials

Debt ratio: 23.99%—
Return on equity: 9.90%
Cash ($ mil.): 211
Current ratio: 1.19
Long-term debt ($ mil.): 1,749
Dividends
Yield: 0.0%
Payout: —
Market value ($ mil.): —

	STOCK PRICE ($) FY Close	P/E High/Low	Earnings	PER SHARE ($) Dividends	Book Value
08/19	27.20	— —	(0.00)	1.88	(0.00)
08/18	28.21	— —	(0.00)	1.88	(0.00)
08/17	29.51	— —	(0.00)	1.88	(0.00)
08/16	31.22	— —	(0.00)	1.88	(0.00)
08/15	27.28	— —	(0.00)	0.84	(0.00)
Annual Growth	**(0.1%)**	**— —**	**—**	**22.3%**	**—**

Cigna Corp (New)

EXECUTIVES

Pres-Ceo, David Cordani
Exec V Pres-Chief Marketing of, Lisa Bacus
Exec V Pres-Chief Information, Mark Boxer
Exec V Pres-General Counsel, Nicole Jones
Chief Clinical Officer, Steve Miller
Exec V Pres-Chief Human Resour, John Murabito
Exec V Pres-Cfo, Eric Palmer
Pres Government Bus, Brian C Evanko
Pres Strategy, Segment & Sol, Christopher J Hocevar
Pres Intl Markets, Jason D Sadler
Pres US Markets, Michael W Triplett
Auditors: PricewaterhouseCoopers LLP

LOCATIONS

HQ: Cigna Corp (New)
900 Cottage Grove Road, Bloomfield, CT 06002
Phone: 860 226-6000   **Fax:** 860 226-6741
Web: www.cigna.com

HISTORICAL FINANCIALS
Company Type: Public

Income Statement
FYE: December 31

	ASSETS ($ mil.)	NET INCOME ($ mil.)	INCOME AS % OF ASSETS	EMPLOYEES
12/18	153,226	2,637	1.7%	73,800
12/17	61,753	2,237	3.6%	46,000
12/16	59,360	1,867	3.1%	41,000
12/15	57,088	2,094	3.7%	39,300
12/14	55,896	2,102	3.8%	37,200
Annual Growth	**28.7%**	**5.8%**	**—**	**18.7%**

2018 Year-End Financials

Debt ratio: 26.67%
Return on equity: 9.63%
Cash ($ mil.): 3,855
Current ratio: —
Long-term debt ($ mil.): —
No. of shares (mil.): 380
Dividends
Yield: 0.0%
Payout: 0.3%
Market value ($ mil.): 72,345

	STOCK PRICE ($) FY Close	P/E High/Low	Earnings	PER SHARE ($) Dividends	Book Value
12/18	189.92	21 15	10.54	0.04	107.71
12/17	203.09	24 15	8.77	0.04	56.30
12/16	133.39	20 16	7.19	0.04	53.42
12/15	146.33	21 12	8.04	0.04	46.91
12/14	102.91	13 9	7.83	0.04	41.55
Annual Growth	**16.6%**	**— —**	**7.7%**	**(0.0%)**	**26.9%**

Cincinnati Financial Corp.

Cincinnati Financial Corporation (CFC) provides a wide range of insurance products and services primarily in the midwestern and southeastern US. Its flagship firm Cincinnati Insurance (operating through four subsidiaries) sells commercial property liability excess and surplus auto bond and fire insurance. Personal lines include homeowners auto and liability products. The Cincinnati Insurance companies also sell life and disability coverage and annuities. Other CFC subsidiaries include CFC Investment (leasing and financing services) CSU Producers Resources (excess and surplus lines brokerage) and Cincinnati Global Underwriting (global specialty insurance).

Operations

CFC operates through five segments: Commercial Lines Insurance Personal Lines Insurance Excess and Surplus Lines Insurance Life Insurance and Investments.

The Commercial Lines Insurance segment which accounts for about 60% of total revenue provides commercial property/casualty coverage including auto workers' compensation and management liability.

The Personal Lines Insurance segment accounting for about 25% of sales writes personal auto homeowners fire watercraft umbrella and other property/casualty policies.

The Life Insurance Excess and Surplus Lines and Investment income segments each account for about 5% of revenue.

Primary operating unit Cincinnati Insurance has two standard property/casualty subsidiaries: Cincinnati Casualty and Cincinnati Indemnity. Its Cincinnati Specialty Underwriters Insurance unit underwrites excess and surplus property/casualty policies while Cincinnati Life Insurance provide annuities and life insurance. The four subsidiaries are known as the Cincinnati Insurance Companies.

The CFC Investment unit provides commercial financing leasing and real estate services to its independent insurance agents and their clients while the CSU Producers Resources business offers insurance brokerage services to independent agencies.

The company's Cincinnati Global Underwriting unit formerly MSP Underwriting is a London-based specialty insurance firm acquired in 2019.

Geographic Reach

CFC markets its policies in more than 40 states but does most of its business in the Midwest and Southeast US. The company writes about 15% of its business in Ohio and it is strong in Illinois Indiana Georgia North Carolina and Pennsylvania. It is licensed in 49 states and Washington DC.

Sales and Marketing

CFC maintains a force of more than 1700 field associates who provide local service to distributing independent agencies and policy holders.

The company's commercial lines segment targets primarily small to mid-sized businesses though it is working to expand its services for larger companies. CFC has tied its growth to expanding the territories in which it markets and to increasing the number of new agencies with which it strikes new relationships.

Financial Performance

CFC revenue climbed steadily between 2014 and 2017 but declined in 2018. Overall sales increased 9% over the past five years. Net income fluctuated in the $500 million to $1 billion range between 2014 and 2017 but dropped below $300 million in 2018.

Revenue declined nearly 6% to $5.4 billion in 2018 due to investment losses caused by unfavorable changes in equity security values despite growth in property/casualty premiums.

Net income also declined in 2018 dropping about 73% to $287 million due to a sizable decrease in net investment gains after taxes resulting from an accounting change. The sharp drop was also caused by the absence of a sizable tax benefit reported in 2017 from US tax reform efforts.

The company ended 2018 with $784 million in cash up $127 million from 2017. Operating activities contributed $1.2 billion while investing activities used $451 million (mostly fixed maturity purchases) and financing activities used $603 million on shareholder dividends share repurchases and contract holder fund withdrawals.

Strategy

To reduce its reliance on traditional insurance offerings CFC is adding new types of coverage and expanding its products into new markets. For example it extended its personal lines business into eight new states between 2015 and 2018. It is also offering coverage for high-net-worth individuals in a growing number of states and it is expanding its reinsurance operations. During 2018 the company brought on new field associates to expand sales of management liability and surety products.

Like other property/casualty insurers the company has struggled with an increase in catastrophe losses in recent years from wildfires hurricanes and other weather or man-made events. The company is also vulnerable to changes in the frequency and severity of auto losses — which have been rising across the industry. In addition to diversifying its product offerings the firm is working to counteract potential negative impacts of these trends by improving its underwriting activities and pricing practices via predictive analytics and using technology tools to improve driver safety practices.

Supporting independent agents is of key importance to CFC and the firm works to provide modern technology tools and marketing resources to boost agent sales. Towards this end it seeks to attract and retain skilled associates provide exceptional field service and improve efficiencies via enhanced online portals and workflow tools for billing and claims processes. The company is also adding new agencies to its distribution network.

CFC's investment portfolio largely consists of stable assets such as fixed-maturity and equity security investments. This long-term investment strategy serves to maintain stable reserves over longer timeframes which can result in short-term investment return volatility.

Mergers and Acquisitions

In 2019 the company expanded internationally through the purchase of MSP Underwriting a London-based specialty insurance firm from Munich Re for some Â 102 million. MSP Underwriting has since been renamed Cincinnati Global Underwriting. The purchase included management of Lloyd's Syndicate 318 through its Beaufort Underwriting Agency unit.

Company Background

Cincinnati Insurance was founded by the Schiff brothers in 1950 to offer property/casualty insurance to homeowners and small businesses. In 1968 Cincinnati Financial Corporation was formed as a holding company for the insurance operation; CFC went public in 1969.

The company expanded into real estate and life insurance services in the 1970s. It focused on personal lines in the 1960s and 1970s but grew its commercial offerings in the 1980s and 1990s.

HISTORY

Jack Schiff spent three years with the Travelers Company before he joined the Navy in WWII. He returned to Cincinnati to start his own independent insurance agency in 1946 and was joined by his younger brother Robert; both were Ohio State graduates whose affection for the Buckeyes led them in later years to close company banquets with the school fight song. The brothers incorporated Cincinnati Insurance with $200000 from investors in 1950.

Under Harry Turner the company's first president the company offered property/casualty insurance to small businesses and homeowners through its network of agents. By 1956 the company had spread into neighboring Kentucky and Indiana. During the next decade Cincinnati Insurance expanded its products and network adding auto burglary and commercial all-risk lines and enlisting agents throughout the Midwest.

In 1963 Turner took the chairman's seat and Jack Schiff became president introducing a more aggressive leadership style. In 1968 the company reorganized forming Cincinnati Financial Corporation as a holding company for the insurance operation and went public in 1969. CFC used the money to pay off debts and buy new businesses forming two subsidiaries: CFC Investment Company in 1970 to deal in commercial real estate and financing; and Queen City Indemnity (later named The Cincinnati Casualty Company) in 1972 to offer direct-bill personal policies.

By 1973 operations included The Life Insurance Company of Cincinnati Queen City Indemnity and fellow Cincinnati giant Inter-Ocean Insurance Company. That year Jack Schiff added CEO to his title.

CFC continued to grow throughout the 1970s with a new emphasis on independent investments. In 1982 Cincinnati Financial veteran Robert Morgan became president and CEO. The company's conservative roots and investment base helped it shake off the early-1980s recession and a string of natural disasters that left many other insurers dangling in the wind.

Also during the 1980s the company started to shift its focus from personal to commercial lines. In 1988 it reorganized its life insurance subsidiaries under the Cincinnati Life banner and formed The Cincinnati Indemnity Company to offer workers' compensation and personal insurance.

EXECUTIVES

Executive Vice President Of The Cincinnati Insurance Company, Jacob Scherer

President Ceo And Director, Steven J. Johnston, age 59, $960,814 total compensation

Vice President Commercial, Anthony Henn

Svp Cfo And Treasurer, Michael J. (Mike) Sewell, age 55, $784,665 total compensation

Svp Chief Investment Officer Assistant Secretary And Assistant Treasurer, Martin F. Hollenbeck, age 59, $646,808 total compensation

Assistant Vice President Bond And Executive Risk, Ted W Doughman

Vice President, Matt Laws

Vice President, David Sloan

Assistant Vice President Government Relations Of, Scott Gilliam

Vice President, Gary J Kline

Senior Vice President And Senior Marketing Officer, Glenn Nicholson

Assistant Vice President Information Technology, Michael Hingsbergen

Vice President Commercial Lines The Cincinnati Insurance Company, Bill Thomas

Vice President Marketing, Mark McBeath

Vice President Information Technology, Rich Mathews

Assistant Vice President For Education, BradleyBrad Delaney

Vice President Of Personal Lines, Stephen Leibel

Assistant Vice President Information Technology, Kim Beckman

Executive Vice President Human Resources, Greg Ziegler

Vice President Human Resources, BRIAN WOOD

Vice President, Allen Matheny

Vice President Marketing, Mike Terrell

Vice President Sales And Marketing, Duane Swanson

Assistant Vice President, Frank Obermeyer

Vice President Information Technology, Todd Taylor

Assistant Vice President Headquarters Claims, William Gregory

Vice President And Chief Information Security Officer, Mike Dockery

Senior Vice President Chief Underwriter The Cincinnati Life Insurance Company, Brad Behringer

Executive Vice President Of Sales And Marketing, Jay Sherer

Vice President Financial Planning And Analysis, Tony Dunn

Executive Vice President, Blake D Slater

Assistant Vice President Commercial Lines Proper, David E McKinney

Vice President, Frederick Ferris

Svp And Treasurer, Theresa Hoffer

Vice President Target Markets, Steve Spray

Assistant Vice President, Tony Henn

Vice President Commercial Lines Director Of Underwriting, Rick Ferris

Vice President Reinsured Assumed, Claudio Ronzitti

Vice President, Gary Givler

Executive Vice President, Jf Scherer

Vice President Field Claims, Charles Robinson

Vice President Personal Lines, Joseph Kinsey

Vice President Corporate Comminications, Elizabeth Ertel

Vp And Director Product Management, Steve Ventre

Vice President Reinsured Assumed, John Davis

Vice President Reinsured Assumed, James Faust

Vice President Reinsured Assumed, Paul Lestourgeon

Assistant Vice President Headquarters Claims, John Crow

Vp And Director Risk Management, Vicki Hill

Vice President Reinsurance Assumed, James Hole

Assistant Vice President For Education, Bradley Delaney

Vice President Director Of Risk Management, Vicki Walno

Legal Secretary, Megan VanLeuven

Region Vice President, Pat Luchtel

Avp Pricing Analytics, Daniel F Henke

Avp Commercial Lines, Matthew R Burrows

Vp Commercial Lines, David J Selembo

Senior Vice President Of The Cincinnati Insurance Company, William Heuvel

Vice President Premium Audit Manager, Tim Morris

Chairman, Kenneth W. (Ken) Stecher, age 72

Assistant Secretary It, James Dawes

Assistant Secretary Manager Life And Health Claims, Ann Binzer

Secretary, Glenda Keith

Assistant Treasurer, Kevin Smith

Board Member, John Steele

Secretary, Linda Campbell

Secretary, Sean Givler

Board Member, BRENDA GAGNON

Board Member, William Bahl

Assistant Treasurer, William Loftis

Board Member, Kenneth Lichtendahl

Board Member, Thomas Schiff

Assistant Secretary Process Developmenteducation, David Pierce

Secretary Commercial Lines The Cincinnati Insurance Company, Pamela Cooper

Assistant Secretary It Support Services, Kevin Heslin

Assistant Secretary Headquarters Claims The Cincinnati Insurance Company, Dale Prisco

Board Member, David Osborn

Board Member, Douglas Skidmore

Auditors: DELOITTE & TOUCHE LLP

LOCATIONS

HQ: Cincinnati Financial Corp.
6200 S. Gilmore Road, Fairfield, OH 45014-5141
Phone: 513 870-2000
Web: www.cinfin.com

PRODUCTS/OPERATIONS

2017 Sales

	$ mil.	% of total
Earned premiums	4,954	86
Net investment income	609	11
Realized investment gains	148	3
Fees	16	-
Other	5	-
Total	**5,732**	**100**

2017 Sales

	$ mil.	% of total
Commercial lines	3,170	55
Personal lines	1,246	22
Investment income	757	13
Life insurance	237	4
Excess & surplus	210	4
Other	112	2
Total	**5,732**	**100**

Selected Subsidiaries

CFC Investment Company
CSU Producer Resources Inc.
The Cincinnati Insurance Company
  The Cincinnati Casualty Company
  The Cincinnati Indemnity Company
  The Cincinnati Life Insurance Company
  The Cincinnati Specialty Underwriters Insurance Company

COMPETITORS

American Financial Group	Progressive Corporation
CNA Financial	Selective Insurance
Erie Indemnity	The Hartford
Farmers Group	Travelers Companies
Indiana Insurance	Westfield Insurance

Ohio Casualty   Zurich American
OneBeacon

HISTORICAL FINANCIALS
Company Type: Public

Income Statement
FYE: December 31

	ASSETS ($ mil.)	NET INCOME ($ mil.)	INCOME AS % OF ASSETS	EMPLOYEES
12/18	21,935	287	1.3%	4,999
12/17	21,843	1,045	4.8%	4,925
12/16	20,386	591	2.9%	4,754
12/15	18,888	634	3.4%	4,493
12/14	18,753	525	2.8%	4,305
Annual Growth	**4.0%**	**(14.0%)**	**—**	**3.8%**

2018 Year-End Financials

Debt ratio: 3.95%	No. of shares (mil.): 162
Return on equity: 3.57%	Dividends
Cash ($ mil.): 784	Yield: 2.7%
Current ratio: —	Payout: 121.1%
Long-term debt ($ mil.): —	Market value ($ mil.): 12,604

	STOCK PRICE ($) FY Close	P/E High/Low	PER SHARE ($) Earnings	Dividends	Book Value
12/18	77.42	47 38	1.75	2.12	48.11
12/17	74.97	13 11	6.29	2.50	50.29
12/16	75.75	22 15	3.55	1.92	42.94
12/15	59.17	16 13	3.83	2.30	39.21
12/14	51.83	16 14	3.18	1.76	40.15
Annual Growth	**10.6%**	**— —**	**(13.9%)**	**4.8%**	**4.6%**

Cintas Corporation

Cintas has a uniform approach to business. The top uniform supplier in the US Cintas boasts more than 1 million clients and some 5 million people wear its garb each day. Cintas which sells leases and rents uniforms operates over 480 facilities in more than 330 cities; it leases over half of them. Besides offering shirts jackets slacks and footwear the company provides clean-room apparel and flame-resistant clothing. Other products offered by Cintas include uniform cleaning first-aid and safety products and clean-room supplies. Richard Farmer founded the company in 1968. Cintas is run by his son CEO Scott Farmer.

Operations

The company has two segments: Uniform Rental and Facility Services and First Aid and Safety Services. Uniform Rental and Facility Services which accounts for more 80% of total consists of the rental and servicing of uniforms and other garments including flame resistant clothing mats mops and shop towels and other ancillary items. In addition to these rental items it provides restroom cleaning services and supplies and carpet and tile cleaning services. First Aid and Safety Services which accounts for about 10% of sales consists of first aid and safety products and services. The remainder of Cintas' businesses (around 10% of sales) consist primarily of Fire Protection Services and its Direct Sale business.

Geographic Reach

Cincinnati-based Cintas operates over 480 facilities including five manufacturing plants and about a dozen distribution centers in over 330 cities. It serves businesses in North America Asia Europe and Latin America. The company has approximately 11400 local delivery routes.

Sales and Marketing

Cintas provides its products and services to more than 1 million businesses of all sizes. Cintas uses its corporate website www.cintas.com as a channel for routine distribution of important information including news releases analyst presentations and financial information.

Financial Performance

Cintas has seen robust revenue growth in recent years. Its annual revenues have risen more than 54% since 2016. Revenue increased to $6.4 billion in 2019 an approximately 21% increase from the year prior. The increase was driven by organic growth as well as acquisitions.

Net income was $843 million in fiscal year 2019 an increase from $481 million in fiscal year 2018. Selling general and administrative expenses grew 3% in fiscal 2019 to $63.9 million.

Cash provided by operating activities was $1 billion in fiscal 2019 while investing activities used $235.6 million. Financing activities used another $873.3 million.

Strategy

Cintas' strategy for adding to its customer base includes investing in its sales force across all business segments as well expanding geographically.

Beyond its dominant position in uniform rental and sales Cintas is looking to emerging businesses such as First Aid and Safety Services for growth. While still relatively small representing 9% of sales the business is growing through acquisitions and the introduction of new services. It is looking to increase its penetration with existing customers and by broadening its customer base to include business segments to which it has not historically served. It will also continue to identify additional product and service opportunities for its current and future customers.

The company pursues the strategy of broadening its customer base in several ways. Cintas has a national sales organization introducing all of its products and services to prospects in all business segments. Its broad range of products and services allows its sales organization to consider any type of business a prospect. It also broadens its customer base through geographic expansion especially in its first aid and safety and fire protection businesses.

Mergers and Acquisitions

In 2017 Cintas acquired rival G&K Services a top-five uniform rental company for $2.2 billion. The acquisition bolsters Cintas' business customer base broadens its service areas and strengthens its route operations. G&K Services now operates as a subsidiary of the company.

Company Background

In 1929 onetime animal trainer boxer and blacksmith Richard "Doc" Farmer started a business of salvaging old rags cleaning them and then selling them to factories. Farmer later began renting the rags to his customers. He would pick up the dirty rags clean them and return them to the factory. By 1936 the Acme Overall & Rag Laundry had established itself in Cincinnati with plans to convert an old bathhouse into a laundry. Farmer along with his adopted son Herschell suffered a setback from flood damage in 1937 but the family rebuilt and continued to grow the business.

HISTORY

In 1929 onetime animal trainer boxer and blacksmith Richard "Doc" Farmer started a business of salvaging old rags cleaning them and then selling them to factories. Farmer later began renting the rags to his customers. He would pick up the dirty rags clean them and return them to the factory. By 1936 the Acme Overall & Rag Laundry had established itself in Cincinnati with plans to convert an old bathhouse into a laundry. Farmer along with his adopted son Herschell suffered a setback from flood damage in 1937 but the family rebuilt and continued to grow the business.

Doc Farmer died in 1952 and Herschell assumed command of the company. Five years later Herschell turned the reins over to his 23-year-old son Richard who immediately moved Acme into the uniform rental market and the company blossomed. Throughout the 1960s the company grew enormously aided by Richard's innovative leadership. (Acme was the first to use a polyester-cotton blend that lasted twice as long as normal cotton work uniforms.) Through a holding company Richard established a string of uniform plants in the Midwest starting with a factory in Cleveland in 1968. Four years later the company changed its name to Cintas.

At this time the company began tapping into the new corporate identity market pushing the idea that uniforms convey a sense of professionalism and present a cleaner safer image. The company began to custom-design the uniforms adding logos and distinctive colors. This aspect of the business compelled Cintas to expand to help accommodate its national clients; by 1972 the company had offices throughout Ohio and in Chicago Detroit and Washington DC. By 1975 Cintas was operating in 13 states.

The company went public in 1983. For the rest of the 1980s Cintas rode the wave of consolidation in the uniform rental industry making a slew of acquisitions. The company also expanded from its blue-collar base into the service industry and began to supply uniforms to hotels restaurants and banks. By the early 1990s Cintas was a presence in most major US cities and its share of the US market had climbed to about 10%. Farmer turned over the title of CEO to president Robert Kohlhepp in 1995. That year the company acquired Cadet Uniform Services a Toronto uniform rental business for $41 million.

Scott Farmer Richard's 38-year-old son was named president and COO in 1997. That year Cintas made a number of acquisitions including Micron-Clean Uniform Service and Canadian firms Act One Uniform Rentals and DW King Services. The company also moved into the first aid supplies industry with its purchase of American First Aid and added clean-room garments to its expanding list of uniform rentals. In 1998 Cintas acquired uniform rental company Apparelmaster as well as Chicago-based Uniforms To You a $150 million design and manufacturing company. In an effort to expand its corporate uniform business the company acquired rival Unitog in 1999 for about $460 million.

As part of the integration of Unitog in 2000 Cintas closed several of Unitog's uniform rental operations distribution centers and manufacturing plants. The company also established first aid supplies and safety equipment unit Xpect. In 2002 Cintas purchased Omni Services marking its largest acquisition to date.

Cintas purchased more than 10 document management businesses and three first-aid and fire protection businesses in fiscal 2009.

In fiscal 2013 it launched its AR Red Suiting Collection (made with renewable-sourced fiber) as well as its Signature Series line of designer soap and toilet paper dispensers and related products.

EXECUTIVES

President And Coo, J. Phillip Holloman, age 64, $643,966 total compensation

Chairman And Ceo, Scott D. Farmer, age 60, $1,000,000 total compensation

Svp Secretary And General Counsel, Thomas E. Frooman, age 52, $499,550 total compensation

Vp Finance And Cfo, J. Michael (Mike) Hansen, age 51, $360,000 total compensation

Vp And Treasurer, Paul F. Adler, age 48, $250,000 total compensation

Vice President Communications, Michelle Goret

National Account Manager, John Shannon

Regional Vice President, Greg Eling

Senior Vice President Operations, Dave Pollack

National Account Manager, Eric Wermes

Vice President Product Development, David Mesko

Vice President Corporate Development, Mike Mahoney

Vice President And Marriott Lodging Uniforms And Services, Donna L Williams

National Account Manager Global Accounts And Strategic M, Jacqueline Nopka

Board Member, Jim Johnson

Board Of Directors, Melanie Barstad

Board Member, Lynn Burton

Board Member, Robert Coletti

Board Member, Jamie Johnson

Auditors: Ernst & Young LLP

LOCATIONS

HQ: Cintas Corporation
6800 Cintas Boulevard, P.O. Box 625737, Cincinnati, OH 45262-5737
Phone: 513 459-1200   **Fax:** 513 573-4030
Web: www.cintas.com

PRODUCTS/OPERATIONS

2016 sales

	$ mil.	% of total
Uniforms Rental & Facility Services	3,777	77
First aid and safety services	461	9
All others	665	14
Total	**4,905**	**100**

Selected Products and Services

Clean-room supplies
Entrance mats
Fender covers
Fire protection
First aid and safety products and services
Linen products
Mops
Restroom supplies
Towels
Uniform cleaning
Uniform rental and sales

COMPETITORS

ARAMARK	NCH
Alsco	Superior Uniform Group
Angelica Corporation	UniFirst
Iron Mountain Inc	

HISTORICAL FINANCIALS

Company Type: Public

Income Statement   FYE: May 31

	REVENUE ($ mil.)	NET INCOME ($ mil.)	NET PROFIT MARGIN	EMPLOYEES
05/19	6,892	884	12.8%	45,000
05/18	6,476	842	13.0%	41,000
05/17	5,323	480	9.0%	42,000
05/16	4,905	693	14.1%	35,000
05/15	4,476	430	9.6%	32,000
Annual Growth	**11.4%**	**19.7%**	**—**	**8.9%**

2019 Year-End Financials

Debt ratio: 38.32%	No. of shares (mil.): 103
Return on equity: 29.41%	Dividends
Cash ($ mil.): 96	Yield: 0.9%
Current ratio: 1.98	Payout: 25.6%
Long-term debt ($ mil.): 2,537	Market value ($ mil.): 22,912

	STOCK PRICE ($) FY Close	P/E High/Low		PER SHARE ($) Earnings	Dividends	Book Value
05/19	221.83	28	19	7.99	2.05	29.07
05/18	182.25	24	16	7.56	1.62	28.37
05/17	125.88	28	20	4.38	1.33	21.85
05/16	94.80	15	13	6.21	1.05	17.68
05/15	86.09	23	17	3.63	1.70	17.30
Annual Growth	**26.7%**	**—**	**—**	**21.8%**	**4.8%**	**13.9%**

Cisco Systems Inc

Cisco Systems is leading maker of the network gear — routers switches and servers as well as software — that moves information around the internet and corporate networks. The company which has dominated the market for internet protocol-based networking equipment also makes security devices internet conferencing systems and other networking equipment for businesses and government agencies. Software that controls networks has become an increasing focus for Cisco which also provides consulting services. Most sales come from customers in the Americas. Cisco's primary customers are large enterprises and telecommunications service providers but it also sells products designed for small businesses.

Operations

Cisco offers products and services in four categories.

The company's infrastructure platforms which generate about 60% of its revenue consist of switching routing wireless and data center products that provide networking capabilities and transport and store data.

Applications which account for more 10% of revenue are primarily software-related offerings that run on the company's networking and data center platforms. The applications include collaboration offerings (unified communications Cisco TelePresence and conferencing) as well as AppDynamics and Internet of Things software.

The Security product category about 5% of revenue includes network security cloud and email security identity and access management advanced threat protection and unified threat management products.

The Other Products category 1% of revenue consists of cloud and system management products.

The Services segment about 25% of revenue provides service and support for customers including technical support.

Cisco contracts with independent third-party companies to make printed-circuit boards conduct in-circuit testing assemble products and make repairs.

Geographic Reach

Cisco does well in the US and the Americas which account for some 60% of its sales. Internationally Cisco runs up against competitors like Huawei and Nokia which have strongholds in Asia and Europe respectively. Cisco gets about 25% of its revenue from customers in the Europe Middle East and Africa region and customers in the Asia/Pacific China and Japan region supply about 15%.

Cisco's headquarters is in San Jose California and it has regional headquarters in Amsterdam and Singapore. The company has significant operations in Australia Belgium China Germany India Japan Mexico Poland and the UK.

Financial Performance

Cisco's revenue has trended higher in the past five years with some fluctuations on the way. The company's net income has followed a similar pattern.

In 2019 (ended July) revenue rose about 5% to $51.9 billion about $2.6 billion higher than the $49.3 billion recorded in 2018. Much of the growth in 2019 came from product revenue in the US where total revenue increased $1.9 billion. Sales in China however fell 16%. Sales in Security and Applications were up 16% and 15% respectively and the Infrastructure Platforms segment's sales were 7% higher. Service revenue ticked 2% higher year-over-year.

Net income for 2019 jumped to $11.6 billion compared to $110 million in 2018 when taxes took a cut of about $12.9 billion (due to the US Tax Cuts and Jobs Act). Higher sales a 15% reduction in general and administrative costs and a lower tax rate combined to produce the stronger 2019 bottom line which was more in line with past years' profits.

In 2019 Cisco had about $11.7 billion in cash compared to $8.9 billion in 2018. Its operations generated $15.8 billion in 2019 and investing activities provided $14.8 billion while financing activities used $27.9 billion (including $20.7 billion spent to repurchase stock).

Strategy

Cisco has been a hardware company making the switches and routers and other devices that transfer information. But it is building up its software offerings for cloud computing and software-defined networks (SDN). Telecom service providers in particular are moving toward SDN to program their networks. In response Cisco is shifting its business to more of a subscription and software-based model. To address the emergence of SDN the company offers its Application Centric Infrastructure (ACI) which delivers centralized application-driven policy automation management and visibility of both physical and virtual environments as a single system. The system is composed of Cisco's Nexus 9000 portfolio of switches improved versions of its NX-OS operating system and the Application Policy Infrastructure Controller (APIC).

In another software-related strategy the company?s Cisco DNA Center a centralized management dashboard for its intuitive network and ETA are available through subscriptions on the Cisco Catalyst 9000 Series Switches. Such moves get Cisco closer to cloud-managed products and services across its networking portfolio. In 2019 (ended July) subscriptions accounted for 70% of Cisco's software revenue 12% higher than 2018.

The company is using artificial intelligence (AI) and machine learning tools to make products smarter and increase automation and security. Cisco introduced an AI network analytics capability which provides more visibility and insights across an entire enterprise network.

Cisco maintains a healthy level of cash that allows it to make several acquisitions a year and invest in research and development as well as pay dividends and buy back shares.

Slowing economic growth and trade tensions reduced Cisco's revenue in China 16% in 2019. Cisco believes it is a short-term situation and that its sales will rebound in China.

Mergers and Acquisitions

Cisco regularly acquires companies to expand technologies and fill gaps.

Cisco agreed to buy Voicea which provides meeting transcription voice search and meeting highlights to add to its Webex portfolio of products. Voicea's technology blends artificial intelligence and automated speech recognition to provide digital notes from meetings. The deal was expected to close in Cisco's quarter that ends Oct. 31 2019.

In 2019 Cisco agreed to buy Acacia Communications which designs and manufactures high-speed optical interconnect technologies for about $2.6 billion. The deal allows Cisco to amplify its switching routing and optical networking products to address customer demanding for faster transmission of data. Acacia would join Cisco's Optical Systems and Optics business. The transaction was expected to close in second half of Cisco's 2020 fiscal year.

In 2019 Cisco acquired privately-held Luxtera which uses silicon photonics to make chips with optics capabilities for faster transmission for about $660 million. Cisco bought Luxtera's technology to increase the speed and capacity that its networking equipment can provide for webscale and enterprise data centers service provider market segments and other customers.

Also in 2018 Cisco acquired Duo Security a developer of security software for about $2.3 billion. Duo develops two-factor authentication software which helps companies keep track of employees as they log in from multiple devices such as a computer at the office or a phone from home. The deal deepens Cisco's software portfolio and strengthens its security offerings.

EXECUTIVES

Senior Vice President Cisco Research And Advanced Development, Joel Bion
Senior Vice President Operations Processes And Systems, Randy Pond
Senior Vice President, Bruce Klein
Senior Vice President Cloud And Managed Services Partner Organization, Edison Peres
Vice President, Ross Fowler
Senior Vice President Sports And Entertainment Solutions Group Sesg, David Holland
Evp And Chief Development Officer, Pankaj S. Patel, $749,135 total compensation
Evp Worldwide Sales And Field Operations, Chris Dedicoat, $691,490 total compensation
Svp Cloud Services And Platforms; Cto, Zorawar Biri Singh
Chairman And Ceo, Charles H. (Chuck) Robbins, age 53, $1,172,115 total compensation
President Asia Pacific, Owen Chan
Svp And Chief Operations, Rebecca J. Jacoby
Svp And General Manager Collaboration Technology Group, Rowan M. Trollope
President Cisco Capital, Kristine A. (Kris) Snow, age 59
President Latin America Theater, Jordi Botifoll
President Smart+connected Communities And Deputy Chief Globalization Officer, Anil Menon
Svp And General Manager Cisco Security Solutions, Bryan Palma
Evp And Cfo, Kelly A. Kramer, $749,135 total compensation
Svp And Cio, Guillermo Diaz
Svp And Chief Marketing Officer, Karen Walker
President Cisco India And Saarc, Sameer Garde
Vice President Director Of Technology, Jerry Tonies
Vice President, Mark Gorman
Senior Vice President Marketing For The Insieme Business Unit, Soni Jiandani
Vice President Sales, Bejoy Antony
Vp Sales Strategy And Planning, Stephen Sinclair
Vice President Cisco Systems China, Hanh Tu
Segment Vice President, Chuck Look
Vice President Middle East And Turkey Operat, Mike Weston
Vice President, Tony Bates
Senior Vice President Data Center, Luca Cafiero
Vice President Of Engineering Network Software And, Greg – Lavender

Regional Vice President Northeast, Mei Ling
Vice President Of Sales And Marketing, Joseph Bonney
It Vice President Of Switching Hardware, Scott Scheeler
Vice President Finance, Ken Mesuda
Svp, Brett Wingo
Vice President Corporate Marketing Cisco Canada, Willa Black
Vice President Sales, Hunter Haverty
Vice President Emerging Markets, Milo Schacher
Executive Vice President General Sales Manager, Lily Zhou
Vice President Marketing South Florida Commercial, Amanda Silva
Vice President Of Service Provider Marketing, Suraj Shetty
Vice President, Tom Wilburn
Vice President Sales, Anant Deshpande
Vp Sales, Marylou Maco
Vice President And General Manager Cloud And Virtualization Group, Thomas Wyatt
Vice President Sales, Rajesh Shetty
Vice President Corporate Development, Rob Salvagno
Vp Gm, Steve Slattery
Vice President, Arcangelo Fanelli
Executive Vice President And Chief People Officer, Francine Katsoudas
Vice President, Bruce Laird
National Sales Manager, Femy Fonacier
Vice President Of Operations, Paris Arey
Vp.business Operations, Denise Peck
Vice President Product Management And Marketing, Tuqiang Cao
Vice President Canadian Services Operations, Derek Mak
Vice President Law And Deputy General, Van Dang
Vice President Product Management, Kaustubh Das
Vice President Of Engineering, Jeffrey Allison
Vice President, Tae Yoo
Vice President Corporate Affairs, Amy Christen
Vice President Market Development, Paul Bosco
Vice President Marketing Manager, Donna Cox
Vp Sales, Pankaj Lulla
Vice President And General Manager, Gene Quon
Senior Vice President Sales, Steve Ficklin
Vice President Corporate Development And Cisco Investments, Derek Idemoto
Vice President Marketing And Business Development, Aaron Stu
Vp Hr, Fred Schultz
Vice President Of Product Management, Gennady Sirota
Vice President Global Iot Service Operations, Cliff Johnson
Vice President Plant, Don McClaughlin
Senior Vice President, David Chai
Vice President Marketing Cisco Systems, Ranajoy Punja
Vp And Deputy General Counsel, Lynn Easterling
Vice President Global Video And Connected Life Solutions, Stephen Silva
Vice President Enterprise And Mid Market Solutions Marketing, Paul McNab
Vice President And Ct0, Bret Hartman
Vice President Of Innovation, Gordon Feller
Senior Vice President Software, John Brigden
Regional Vice President Cisco Systems Administrator, Mark Guerrazzi
Vice President Communications Software, Todd Murray
Vice President Us Partner Sales, Geoff Fancher
Vp Advanced Services Us Public Sector, Mike Solomita
Svp And Gm Cloud Platform And Solutions Group, Kip Compton
Vice President Sales, Bernadette Wightman
Vice President Marketing Cloud Services, Peder Ulander

It Vice President, Steve Lang
Vp Marketing, Christoph Caspar
Vice President Advanced Services, Flint Brenton
Senior Vice President, David Yen
Senior Vice President Manager Of Scott Scheeler, Ravikrishna Cherukuri
Vice President Cyber Security Global Government Solutions Group, Yvon Le Roux
Vice President Sales Industry, Jan Schlosser
Vice President Finance At Cisco, Ted Hull Ted Hull
Vice President Marketing Service Provider, Yeshwant Shetty
Vice President Engineering, Donald Williams
Vice Presidentproduct Management, Steve Chazin
Executive Vice President, Randall Pond
Area Vice President Us Sales, Georges Antoun
Vice President Of Talent, Annmarie Neal
Vpam Small Business Fl South North Carolina South Carolina, Richard Hinkley
Vpss Flexpod, Cesar Hurtado
Vp Global Services, Jerome Katz
Vice President And Business Development, Mitch Null Zenger
Vice President, Jeanne Beliveau-dunn
Vice President Systems Engineering, Michael Koons
Area Vice President Enterprise Sales, Mark Houska
Vice President Customer Value Chain Management, David Ashley
Senior Vice President And Chief Strategy Officer, Anuj Kapur
Vice President Engg Routing Tech Grp, Bill Jennings
Vice President Software Engineeting, Richard Heaton
Vice President Sales, Clarence Jasin
Vice President Of Marketing, Thomas Hooker
Vice President Federal Operations, Ed McCrossen
Vice President Customer Value Chain Management, Jeff Devine
Vice President New Business Ventures, Sanjay Pol
Vice President Finance Operations, Debbie Normington
Area Vice President Us Sales, Roxann Swanson
Vice Presidentibsg, Richard Cantwell
Vice President Finance, Phil Roush
Vice President Of Corporate Portfolio Management A, Inder Singh
Vice President Information Technology Customer Strategy And Success, Lance Perry
Vice President Broker, Rajeev Grover
Senior Vice President Human Resources And Talent Acquisition, Jill Larsen
Vice President Engineering Network Software And Systems, Amit S Phadnis
Vice President Of Marketing, Andy Blackburn
Vice President Of Software Engineering, Ramesh Bodapati
Vice President Sales, Timothy Hannon
Vice President Sales And Purchasing, Peter Buchmeier
Senior Vice President Advanced Services, Parvesh Sethi
Vice President Of Sales North America, Michael Trahtenhertz
Vice President, Marie Higa
Vice President Sales And Marketing, Leon Baranovsky
Vice President Sales, Jeff Towson
Kfir Pravda Imtc Vice President Of Marketing, Cary Bryan
Vice President, Cathleen Ashley
Area Vice President Commercial Sales S, David Ruggiero
Vice President Subscriber Networks Sector, Robert Beebe
Executive Vice President, David Harrison
Vice President Engineering, John Wakerly
Vice President Consumer Marketing, Ken Wirt

Vice President World Wide Supply Chain Management, Steve Darendinger
Vice President And General Manager Sales And Busin, Ruma Balasubramanian
Vice President Marketing, Paul Buteaux
Vice President Systems Engineering, Maria Cannon
Vp Social Media, Joe Diodati
Vice President Marketing Smb, Joseph Puthussery
Vice President Central And Eastern Europ, Kaan Terzioglu
Auditors: PricewaterhouseCoopers LLP

LOCATIONS

HQ: Cisco Systems Inc
  170 West Tasman Drive, San Jose, CA 95134
Phone: 408 526-4000
Web: www.cisco.com

2019 sales

	$ mil.	% of total
Americas	30,927	60
Europe the Middle East& Africa	13,100	25
Asia-Pacific regionJapan & China	7,877	15
Total	**51,904**	**100**

PRODUCTS/OPERATIONS

2019 sales

	$ mil.	% of total
Infrastructure Platforms	30,191	58
Applications	5,803	11
Security	2,730	5
Other Products	281	1
Services	4,352	9
Total	**51,904**	**100**

Selected Products

Access servers
Blade servers
Cable modems
Cables and cords
Content delivery devices
Customer contact software
Digital video recorders
Ethernet concentrators hubs and transceivers
Interfaces and adapters
Network management software
Networked applications software
Optical platforms
Power supplies
Routers
Security components
Switches
Telephony access systems
Television set-top boxes
Video networking
Virtual private network (VPN) systems
Voice integration applications
Wireless networking

Selected Acquisitions

COMPETITORS

AWS	Huawei Technologies
Arista Networks	Juniper Networks
Broadcom	Lenovo
Check Point Software	LogMeIn
Citrix Systems	Motorola Mobility
CommScope	NSN
Dell	Nutanix
Extreme Networks	Palo Alto Networks
F5 Networks	Symantec
Fireye	VMware
Fortinet	
Hewlett Packard Enterprise	

HISTORICAL FINANCIALS

Company Type: Public

Income Statement   FYE: July 27

	REVENUE ($ mil.)	NET INCOME ($ mil.)	NET PROFIT MARGIN	EMPLOYEES
07/19	51,904	11,621	22.4%	75,900
07/18	49,330	110	0.2%	74,200
07/17	48,005	9,609	20.0%	72,900
07/16	49,247	10,739	21.8%	73,700
07/15	49,161	8,981	18.3%	71,833
Annual Growth	**1.4%**	**6.7%**	**—**	**1.4%**

2019 Year-End Financials

Debt ratio: 25.22%—
Return on equity: 30.36%
Cash ($ mil.): 11,750
Current ratio: 1.51
Long-term debt ($ mil.): 14,475

Dividends
  Yield: 0.0%
  Payout: 52.1%
Market value ($ mil.): —

	STOCK PRICE ($) FY Close	P/E High/Low	PER SHARE ($) Earnings	Dividends	Book Value
07/19	56.53	22 15	2.61	1.36	7.90
07/18	42.57	23151519	0.02	1.24	9.36
07/17	31.52	18 15	1.90	1.10	13.27
07/16	30.53	14 11	2.11	0.94	12.64
07/15	28.40	17 13	1.75	0.80	11.74
Annual Growth	**18.8%**	**— —**	**10.5%**	**14.2%**	**(9.4%)**

CIT Group Inc (New)

A stalwart in the big-business landscape for over a century CIT Group is a financial holding company that offers lending leasing debt restructuring equipment financing and advisory services to small- and mid-sized businesses in such industries as energy health care retail communications manufacturing IT services and sports. It operates a physical branch network in southern California and spans the US with its online banking platform. Founded in 1908 CIT expanded is consumer presence with the 2015 acquisition of OneWest.

HISTORY

Henry Ittleson founded CIT Group as Commercial Credit and Investment Trust in St. Louis in 1908. Initially financing horse-drawn carriages it moved to New York in 1915 as Commercial Investment Trust (CIT) to participate in one of the milestones of modern consumer debt: Its auto financing program launched in collaboration with Studebaker was the first of its kind.

CIT diversified into industrial financing during the 1920s and went public in 1924 on the NYSE. Cars remained a strong focus though: When Ford Motor Co. ran into difficulties in 1933 it sold financing division Universal Credit Corp. to CIT. CIT continued to expand into industrial financing incorporating its industrial business as CIT Financial Corp. in 1942.

During the post-WWII boom CIT began financing manufactured home sales and offering small loans. In 1964 it consolidated factoring operations into Meinhard-Commercial Corp. By the end of the 1960s the firm started to retreat from auto financing focusing instead on industrial leasing factoring and equipment financing.

In 1980 RCA bought CIT seeking to buy financing to develop its other businesses. RCA found the debt from the purchase unwieldy however and sold

CIT to Manufacturers Hanover Bank (Manny Hanny) in 1984. The bank bought CIT to expand outside its home state of New York: Though it could not open banks out of state Manny Hanny could still offer financial services through CIT which became The CIT Group in 1986.

Manny Hanny executives tried to bring aggressive management to staid top-heavy CIT. The company sold its Inventory Finance division in 1987 divested the consumer loan business in 1988 and consolidated the Meinhard-Commercial and Manufacturers Hanover factoring units in 1989. By then Manny Hanny was cash-strapped over losses incurred from foreign loans so it sold a 60% stake in CIT to The Dai-Ichi Kangyo Bank of Japan.

CIT gave Dai-Ichi entrée into US financial services and it began expanding CIT's range of services again including equity investment (1990) credit finance (from its purchase of Fidelcor Business Credit in 1991) and venture capital (1992). CIT also reentered the consumer loan market (including home equity lending) with a new Consumer Finance group (1992).

In 1995 Chemical Bank (Manny Hanny's successor; now part of JPMorgan Chase) sold an additional 20% share to Dai-Ichi bumping the Japanese bank's holdings to 80% and arranging to sell its remaining shares to Dai-Ichi. In 1997 instead of Dai-Ichi buying the rest of Chase's shares CIT bought them and spun them off to the public. In 1998 Dai-Ichi reduced its stake.

In 1999 CIT bought Newcourt Credit Group North America's #2 equipment finance and leasing firm; it also bought Heller Financial's commercial services unit. In 2000 the firm worked on integrating Newcourt and sold its Hong Kong consumer finance unit.

Tyco International bought CIT in 2001 renaming the new subsidiary Tyco Capital. Under Tyco's umbrella it sold its manufactured home loan portfolio to Lehman Brothers and recreational vehicle portfolio to Salomon Smith Barney in an effort to exit noncore businesses. Tyco however expanded too far too fast and the next year announced an about-face on its financial services subsidiary deciding to spin off the division and return it to its CIT identity.

Jeff Peek took the reins of the company from longtime chairman and CEO Al Gamper in 2004.

CIT Group's Student Loan Xpress unit was one of several companies in the student-lending industry that came under investigation for business practices in 2007. It discontinued its private student loans that year and in 2008 it stopped originating government-guaranteed student loans.

Amid losses the company also exited the consumer finance business to focus on commercial lending. In 2008 it sold its home loan unit to Lone Star Funds and its manufactured housing portfolio to Vanderbilt Mortgage and Finance. The previous year it sold its construction lending unit to Wells Fargo and its 30% stake in Dell Financial Services to Dell.

CIT was hit hard in the economic recession which nearly shut down the credit markets. The company struggled to stay afloat as liquidity levels sank (a situation exacerbated as nervous customers drew on their credit lines). It exited money-losing businesses sold units and secured $3 billion from company bondholders including PIMCO and Oaktree Capital. The company also converted to a bank holding company enabling it to access government bailout funds. Still struggling CIT filed for Chapter 11 in November 2009. The restructuring lasted six weeks and helped the company eliminate more than $10 billion in debt. None of CIT's operating subsidiaries were included in the bankruptcy.

Jeffrey Peek who oversaw CIT's untimely expansion activities stepped down as CEO in early 2010. He was succeeded by John Thain who has also led Merrill Lynch and New York Stock Exchange. No stranger to turning ailing companies around Thain is credited with bringing the NYSE into the modern era with electronic trading. He also merged NYSE with Euronext establishing the first trans-Atlantic exchange.

EXECUTIVES

President Cit Rail, George D. Cashman, age 65

Evp And Cfo, John J. Fawcett

Evp And Head Of Technology And Operations, Denise M. Menelly, age 57, $253,846 total compensation

Evp And Chief Marketing And Communications Officer, Gina M. Proia, age 47

President Cit Commercial Finance, James L. (Jim) Hudak, age 55, $503,526 total compensation

Evp And Chief Risk Officer, Robert C. Rowe, age 58

Evp General Counsel And Corporate Secretary, Stuart Alderoty, age 60

President Cit Real Estate Finance, Matthew E. (Matt) Galligan, age 65

Chairman And Ceo; President And Ceo Cit Bank, Ellen R. Alemany, age 63, $883,333 total compensation

Evp And Chief Strategy Officer, Kelley Morrell, age 39

President Consumer Banking Cit Business Capital And California, Steven (Steve) Solk, age 64

Evp And Chief Human Resources Officer, James J. (Jim) Duffy, age 64

President Aviation Lending, Jennifer Villa Tennity

Managing Director Aerospace Defense And Government Services, John Heskin

Senior Vice President, John Edel

Vice President, Julianne Allen

Vice President Strategic Marketing, Ann Crater

Vice President And Information Technology Manager Receibable Systems, Mike Noonan

Vice President Capital Equipment Finance, Bruce Fabian

Assistant Vice President Credit Scoring, Xiaoman Wang

Vice President Dealer Service, Rob Sureda

Vice President, Jeff Rushnak

Senior Vice President Bsa Aml And Ofac Sanctions Compliance Head, Michelle Goodsir

Vice President Credit Risk Management, Ari Romanoff

Vice President, George Fikaris

Vice President Threat And Vulnerability Management Information, Roman Brozyna

Senior Vice President National Manager, Kenneth Wendler

Vice President, Joel Wolitzer

Vice President National Accounts Manager, Mike Loconsolo

Senior Vice President Rail Finance, Jeffrey Lytle

Vice President, Kristin Appelbaum

Vice President, Ronald Gibney

Executive Vice President Chief Credit And Risk Officer Corporate Credit Risk Management, Nancy Foster

Vice President Aml Compliance, Rachel Benjamin

Assistant Vice President, Joshua Hare

Assistant Vice President, Rosalyn Jones

Vice President, Sohail Khan

Assistant Vice President, Soheir Krauss

Vice President, Debra Brown

Assistant Vice President Sales Support, Haley Werle

Vice President, Patricia Matos

Vice President, David Howson

Vice President, Kai Liang

Vice President, William Riggin

Vice President, Jim Condina

Senior Vice President, Eugene Schwartz

Sales Support Manager Assistant Vice President, James Bailey

Vice President Consumer Finance Operations, Krista Neal

Vice President Employment Human, Tammy Haynie

Vice President Sales, Thomas Gonnella

Vice President Finance, Frederick Rick

Operation Manager Vice President, Marvin Daniel

Assistant Vice President, Adam Schacter

Executive Vice President And Treasurer, Glenn Alan Votek

Vice President Applications Management, Martin Herman

Vice President Leveraged Finance, Nicole Rapport

Vp Sales, Enrique Sosa

Vice President, Diane Harris

Vice President Project And Service Management, Russell Hansen

Vice President Facility Operations, Vincent Sorrentino

Vice President (architect), Santosh Kulkarni

Senior Vice President, Joseph Florio

Vice President, Daniel Bernstein

Assistant Vice President Content Marketing, Saryia Green

Assistant Vice President, Munindra Nath

It Assistant Vice President Tech Operations, Gabby Lopez

Senior Vice President And Head Of Investor Relations, Barbara Callahan

Vp Consumer And Business, Lionel Eppes

Svp And Gm Locomotives, Ken Pierson

Evp, Kenneth Brause

Svp Financial Operations, Ed Sperling

Svp Internal Audit, Jacque Breslauer

Assistant Vice President, Robert Hensel

Assistant Vice President Hr Operations, Jennifer Hodsden

Vice President Account Executive, Vernon Wells

Vice President Information Technology .net Enterprise Architecture, Harvey Orloff

Assistant Vice President Human Resources Project Management Office Project Manager, Janine Santangelo

Vp Corporate Treasury Services, Jay D'auria

Senior Vice President Head Of Consumer And Internet Banking Technology, Kedar Sathe

Vice President Of Factoring Operations For Ny Region, Sam Macrillo

Vp Business Development Franchise Strategy, Christopher Wren

Vice President Capital Markets, Elias Uribe

Avp, Rebecca Wong

Avp Sox, Liana Balseiro

Vp Regulatory Compliance And Controls, Nathan Lai

Avp Compliance Aml Edd, Cynthia Hernandez

Evp And Chief Strategy Officer, Kennth Mcphail

Vice President And Business Development Officer Commercial Services, Nicholas Nunnari

Vice President, Manesh Chandwani

Assistant Vice President, Oscar Menendez

Vice President Financial Analytics And Modeling, Cynthia Kim

Avp Treasury Controllers, Robert Bickerstaff

Assistant Vice President Accounts Payable, Warren Allen

Assistant Vice President Third Party Management, Jennifer Terribile

Vice President, William Sheridan

Assistant Vice President Accounting Manager, Irene Yang

Vp Underwriting, Matt Ensley

Assistant Vice President Aml And Sanctions Program Strategy, Mark DiGaetani

Vp Of Business Development Of Technology Of Equipment Finance, Mike Hampton

Avp Audit Manager, Patricia Hennessy

Senior Vice President Of Information Technology, Fred Mistretta
Executive Vice President, Mark Links
Vice President Account Executive, Jeffrey Kremberg
Vp; Fraud Prevention Manager, Elizabeth Goff
Senior Vice President Corporate Strategy, Emmelene Lee
Vice President Sales And Business Development, Mark Hall
Senior Vice President Chief Information, Stephen Schwimmer
Vice President Marketing, Veru Narula
Vice President, Kenneth Nwele
Vice President Corporate Social Responsibility, Darrah Feldman
Executive Vice President, Donal Ratigan
Vice President And Senior Counsel, Danny Park
Board Member, William Freeman
Auditors: DELOITTE & TOUCHE LLP

LOCATIONS

HQ: CIT Group Inc (New)
11 West 42nd Street, New York, NY 10036
Phone: 212 461-5200
Web: www.cit.com

2016 Sales

	$ mil.	% of total
US	2,755	89
Europe	139	5
Rest of the world	198	6
Total	**3,093**	**100**

PRODUCTS/OPERATIONS

Products and Services

Account receivables collection
Acquisition and expansion financing
Asset management and servicing
Asset-based loans
Cash management and payment services
Credit protection
Debt restructuring
Debt underwriting and syndication
Deposits
Enterprise value and cash flow loans
Equipment leases
Factoring services
Financial risk management
Import and export financing
Insurance services
Letters of credit / trade acceptances
Merger and acquisition advisory services
Residential mortgage loans
Secured lines of credit
Small Business Administration loans

Sales 2016

	$ mil.	% of total
Commercial Banking	2,546	79
Consumer Banking	382	12
Non-Strategic Portfolios	26	1
Corporate & Other	252	8
Total	**3,207**	**100**

2017 Sales

	$ mil.	% of total
Interest income		
Interest & fees on loans	1,638	58
Other interest and dividends	197	4
Non-interest income		
Rental income on operating leases	1,007	33
Other income	364	5
Total	**3,207**	**100**

COMPETITORS

Ally Financial	ILFC
Citigroup	JPMorgan Chase
Comerica	ORIX
Deutsche Bank	Zions Bancorporation
First Republic (CA)	

HISTORICAL FINANCIALS

Company Type: Public

Income Statement

FYE: December 31

	ASSETS ($ mil.)	NET INCOME ($ mil.)	INCOME AS % OF ASSETS	EMPLOYEES
12/18	48,537	447	0.9%	3,678
12/17	49,278	468	1.0%	4,167
12/16	64,170	(848)	—	4,410
12/15	67,498	1,056	1.6%	4,900
12/14	47,880	1,130	2.4%	3,360
Annual Growth	**0.3%**	**(20.7%)**	**—**	**2.3%**

2018 Year-End Financials

Debt ratio: 9.31%
Return on equity: 6.91%
Cash ($ mil.): 1,795
Current ratio: —
Long-term debt ($ mil.): —

No. of shares (mil.): 100
Dividends
  Yield: 2.1%
  Payout: 22.7%
Market value ($ mil.): 3,862

	STOCK PRICE ($) FY Close	P/E High/Low		PER SHARE ($) Earnings	Dividends	Book Value
12/18	38.27	15	10	3.61	0.82	58.92
12/17	49.23	18	14	2.80	0.61	55.73
12/16	42.68	—	—	(4.20)	0.60	49.50
12/15	39.70	9	7	5.67	0.60	54.61
12/14	47.83	9	7	5.96	0.50	50.13
Annual Growth	**(5.4%)**	—	—	**(11.8%)**	**13.2%**	**4.1%**

CITGO PETROLEUM CORPORATION

CITGO Petroleum is the fifth-largest independent refiner in the US. It refines and markets petroleum products including transportation fuels lubricants and petrochemicals. It markets CITGO branded gasoline through about 5300 independent retail outlets in about 30 US states mainly east of the Rockies. CITGO Petroleum owns oil refineries in Illinois Louisiana and Texas. The company has the refining capacity to process more than 749000 barrels of crude oil per day. It markets more than 600 types of lubricants and sells over 13 billion gallons of refined products annually. CITGO Petroleum is the operating subsidiary of PDV America itself a subsidiary of Venezuela's national oil company PDVSA.

Operations

CITGO has a total refining capacity of about 749000 barrels of crude oil per day. It operates through three US refineries in Texas Illinois and Louisiana.

The company's TriCLEAN TOP TIER gasoline is sold to independent marketers who sell motor fuels at CITGO branded retail outlets. CITGO Lubricants provides a line of agricultural automotive and industrial lubricants as well as oil and greases and private label lubricants. Lubricants are manufactured through blending and packaging plants located across the US with products marketed under the CITGO Mystik and Clarion brands. CITGO's petrochemicals and solvents business provides products such as adhesives paints and coatings.

CITGO also offers its loyalty program Club CITGO which offers special savings and rewards such as free coffee and snacks through its downloadable Club CITGO app.

Geographic Reach

Headquartered in Houston TX CITGO operates three refineries in Lemont IL; Corpus Christi TX; and Lake Charles LA and three lubricant blending plants in Cicero (IL) Oklahoma City and Atlanta. The company stores and distributes its petroleum products through several locations across the US. The CITGO Terminal Facilities & Pipeline network comprises three fully-owned pipelines six jointly-owned pipelines and approximately 50 petroleum product terminals.

Sales and Marketing

The company markets automotive fuels to independent marketers which sell to nearly 5300 CITGO branded retail outlets in the US and markets jet fuel directly to airlines. CITGO produces a variety of agricultural automotive industrial and private label lubricants which are sold to independent distributors mass marketers and industrial customers across the US and in 41 countries around the world.

Financial Performance

With a focus on safety and operational performance CITGO generated $851 million in net income in 2018 a significant increase compared with prior years. The company's oil refining processing capacity increased 8% from 2017 to 2018 allowing CITGO to increase exports to 206000 barrels per day in 2018 up 4 percent relative to 2017. The company was also able to increase volumes and capture higher margins in international markets with improvements to its logistics operations.

Strategy

The company is currently working to cut ties with its Venezuelan parent company Petroleos de Venezuela SA (PDVSA). CITGO Petroleum is being hampered by US sanctions imposed on PDVSA (still controlled by socialist President Nicolas Maduro) possibly preventing it from refinancing a revolving credit and term loan to generate cash. CITGO has stopped making payments to PDVSA ended subscriptions to corporate services and email communications and is avoiding mentioning PDVSA in any of its marketing materials. The company has also shut down PDVSA Services its procurement subsidiary that operated from CITGO's headquarters.

Company Background

CITGO was founded in 1910 by pioneer oilman Henry L. Doherty. First named Cities Service Company the company was one of the first to supply gas and electric utility services in the Midwest. It provided the electricity that lit the Statue of Liberty for the first time in 1916 and during World War II supplied much of the fuel used by US armed forces and its allies.

In 1928 the company was the first to discover the Oklahoma City Pool one of the most productive oil fields in the US. During the 1950s Cities Service began exploration in the Middle East. As part of a joint venture it also was the first company to discover oil in the Gulf of Mexico in 1952.

In 1965 Cities Service introduced its new name and marketing brand CITGO which used the first part of its former name ending with "GO" which represents energy and the company's forward-thinking culture. It added the CITGO Quik Mart convenience store platform to its gas stations in 1972.

In 1983 CITGO was acquired by 7-Eleven operator Southland Corporation. Three years later Petr leos de Venezuela S.S. (PDVSA) purchased a 50% stake in the company and in 1990 became wholly owned by PDVSA.

EXECUTIVES

Chairman, Alejandro Granado
Vp Finance And Treasurer, Maritza Villanueva
Vp Refining And General Manager Lake Charles Manufacturing Complex, Eduardo Assef
Vp Supply And Marketing, Gustavo Vel ˙squez
Vp And General Manager Lemont Refinery, Jim Cristman
Vice President General Manager, Tomeu Vadell
Vice President And General Manager Corpus Christi Refinery, Randy Flowers
Vice President Manager Director, Bob Pennington
Vice President Supply Marketing, Fernando Valera
Vice President Finance, Jose Pereira
National Account Manager, Jason Williams
Auditors: KPMG LLP HOUSTON TEXAS

LOCATIONS

HQ: CITGO PETROLEUM CORPORATION
1293 ELDRIDGE PKWY, HOUSTON, TX 770771670
Phone: 832 486-4000
Web: WWW.CITGO.COM

PRODUCTS/OPERATIONS

Selected Products

Fuels
TriCLEAN Gasoline
Premium Diesel
Lubricants
CITGO
Mystik
Clarion
Petrochemicals and Solvents

COMPETITORS

Anadarko Petroleum	Exxon Mobil
Apache	Holly Energy Partners
BP	Shell Oil Products
CVR	Sunoco
Chevron	Valero Energy
ConocoPhillips	

HISTORICAL FINANCIALS

Company Type: Private

Income Statement   FYE: December 31

	REVENUE ($ mil.)	NET INCOME ($ mil.)	NET PROFIT MARGIN	EMPLOYEES
12/17	24,100	715	3.0%	4,000
12/16	19,914	234	1.2%	—
/ 0	0	0	—	—
Annual Growth	—	—	—	—

Citigroup Inc

This is the Citi that never sleeps. One of the largest financial services firms known to man Citigroup (also known as Citi) has some 200 million customer accounts and serves clients around the globe. It offers deposits and loans (mainly through Citibank) investment banking brokerage wealth management and other financial services. Trading in more than 160 countries and with approximately 142 million Citi-branded credit cards in circulation worldwide few other banks can equal Citigroup's global reach. Hit hard by the 2008 financial crisis Citi has been refocusing on its orig-

inal mission — traditional banking. Citi has some $1.9 trillion in assets and some $1 trillion in deposits. Citigroup generates some 45% of its sales from North America.

HISTORY

Empire builder Sanford "Sandy" Weill who helped build brokerage firm Shearson Loeb Rhoades sold the company to American Express (AmEx) in 1981. Forced out of AmEx in 1985 Weill bounced back in 1986 buying Control Data's Commercial Credit unit.

Primerica caught Weill's eye next. Its predecessor American Can was founded in 1901 as a New Jersey canning company; it eventually expanded into the paper and retail industries before turning to financial services in 1986. The firm was renamed Primerica in 1987 and bought brokerage Smith Barney Harris Upham & Co.

Weill's Commercial Credit bought Primerica in 1988. In 1993 Primerica bought Shearson from AmEx as well as Travelers taking its name and logo.

Weill set about trimming Travelers. He sold life subsidiaries and bought Aetna's property/casualty business in 1995. In 1996 he consolidated all property/casualty operations to form Travelers Property Casualty and took it public. The next year Travelers bought investment bank Salomon Brothers and formed Salomon Smith Barney Holdings (now Citigroup Global Markets).

Weill sold Citicorp chairman and CEO John Reed on the idea of a merger in 1998 in advance of the Gramm-Leach-Bliley act which deregulated the financial services industry in the US. By the time the merger went through a slowed US economy and foreign-market turmoil brought significant losses to both sides. The renamed Citigroup consolidated in 1998 and 1999 laying off more than 10000 employees. So many executives (including co-chairmen and co-CEOs Weill and Reed) were paired through "co" titling that the company was dubbed "the ark."

In 1999 Citigroup moved deeper into subprime lending. Also that year former Treasury Secretary Robert Rubin joined Citigroup as a co-chairman.

In 2000 Reed retired and the company bought the investment banking business of British firm Schroders. Citigroup also bought subprime lender Associates First Capital (now part of CitiFinancial) for approximately $27 billion to expand its consumer product lines and its international presence. The deal however also brought Citigroup federal scrutiny regarding perceived predatory lending tactics. In 2001 the company bought New York-based European American Bank from ABN AMRO and purchased Grupo Financiero Banamex one of Mexico's biggest banks.

The company parlayed the $4 billion it netted from the 2002 spinoff of 20% of Travelers Property Casualty (it distributed most of the remaining stock to Citigroup shareholders) into a $5.8 billion purchase of California-based Golden State Bancorp the parent of the then-third-largest thrift in the US Cal Fed.

Also that year Citigroup paid some $215 million to settle federal allegations that Associates First Capital made customers unwittingly purchase credit insurance by automatically billing for the service. The agreement was one of the largest consumer-protection settlements ever.

The company also became embroiled in the Enron mess as regulators scrutinized short-term loans that Citigroup floated to the energy trader and were possibly used by Enron in transactions with offshore entities to mask debt and inflate cash flow figures. Citigroup neither confirmed nor denied allegations that it helped fudge Enron's books but in 2003 remitted more than $100 million ear-

marked to pay victims who lost money because of Enron's malfeasance.

A landmark ruling by the SEC in 2003 implied that Citigroup issued favorable stock ratings to companies in exchange for investment banking contracts (predictably the company neither confirmed nor denied the allegations). Also as part of the ruling erstwhile star analyst Jack Grubman agreed to pay some $15 million in fines for his overly rosy stock reports and accepted a lifetime ban from working in the securities industry. Citigroup forked over $400 million in fines the largest portion of a total of some $1.4 billion levied against 10 brokerage firms regarding conflicts of interest between analysts and investment bankers.

Amid the investigations Citigroup separated its stock-picking and corporate advisory businesses creating a retail brokerage and equity research unit called Smith Barney. In the SEC's 2003 ruling such a "Chinese Wall" between bankers and analysts was later made mandatory at all firms. Still Citigroup raked in net profits of nearly $18 billion (on revenues in excess of $94 billion) in 2003 one of the largest-ever yearly takes in US corporate history.

In 2004 the company — while admitting no wrongdoing — paid $2.65 billion to investors who were burned when WorldCom went bankrupt amid an accounting scandal. (Citigroup was one of the lead underwriters of WorldCom stocks and bonds.) The settlement was one of the largest ever for alleged securities fraud and compelled Citigroup to set aside an additional $5 billion to cover legal fees for this case and others involving Enron and spinning. The company eventually paid $2 billion in mid-2005 to investors who lost money on publicly traded Enron stocks and bonds again settling the matter while denying it broke any laws. Enron shareholders had argued that Citigroup helped Enron to set up offshore companies and shady partnerships to exaggerate the energy trader's cash flow.

In Japan where Citigroup is one of the leading foreign banks regulators pulled the plug on the company's private banking operations in 2004 after determining that Citigroup misled customers regarding the sale of certain structured bonds. The closures led to the forced resignation of three top executives in the company's asset management and private banking units about a month later.

Citigroup sold The Travelers Life and Annuity Company (now MetLife Life and Annuity Company of Connecticut) plus most of its international insurance business to MetLife in 2005. Later that year a convoluted deal with Legg Mason netted Citigroup that company's retail brokerage and capital markets business (and $1.5 billion of Legg Mason stock) in exchange for most of Citigroup's asset management and mutual fund division; Citigroup concurrently sold Legg Mason's capital markets operations to Stifel Financial.

Seeking growth internationally Citigroup was part of a consortium that acquired a controlling stake in Guangdong Development Bank in 2006. Also that year the company opened more than 800 bank branches and consumer finance offices outside the US.

Weill ended years of speculation in 2003 by anointing corporate and investment bank head Chuck Prince as his successor. Weill retired as chairman in 2006 and Prince assumed that title as well. Prince resigned in 2007 as Citigroup dealt with losses on mortgage-related securities and other investments.

Prince was succeeded by Vikram Pandit a Morgan Stanley veteran who came to Citigroup when it acquired hedge fund and private equity manager Old Lane Partners in 2007. Pandit was at Citigroup only a few months before he was named CEO but during that time he oversaw the company's alternative investments and led its institutional clients group. The following year Citigroup disbanded Old Lane and wound up its flagship fund.

Citigroup further expanded its fund services operations via its 2007 acquisition of BISYS. As part of the deal the company sold BISYS' insurance services division to investment firm J.C. Flowers & Co.

Also that year it picked up remnants of the sub-prime mortgage collapse when it acquired ACC Capital Holding's wholesale mortgage origination operations as well as the servicing rights to some $5 billion in home loans. It also bought ABN AMRO Mortgage Group and shelled out more than $1 billion to buy Egg one of the largest online-only banks in the world from Prudential plc. The deal boosted its UK consumer operations by adding some 3 million customers.

The company sold its trademark red umbrella logo back to insurance firm Travelers which began using the symbol nearly 150 years before. Citigroup acquired the iconic logo when it bought the insurance company in 1993 and held onto it after it spun off Travelers in 2002. But the company ultimately decided that customers associated the umbrella with insurance and sold it in 2007.

In order to shore up its balance sheet Citigroup sold some 5% of itself to the Abu Dhabi Investment Authority a Middle Eastern sovereign fund for $7.5 billion in 2007. It later raised more than $12 billion by selling preferred shares to investors including a Singapore government-owned investment fund former CEO Sandy Weill and Saudi investor Prince Al-Walid bin Talal who owns roughly 5% stake of Citigroup.

Citigroup bought a majority stake in one of Japan's largest brokerages Nikko Cordial in 2007. It acquired the remaining shares of Nikko Cordial in early 2008 and merged it with Citigroup Japan Holdings to form Nikko Citi Holdings.

In 2008 Citigroup sold several of its commercial finance lines to GE Capital. It sold its German consumer banking business to French bank Groupe Cr dit Mutuel.

As the global credit crisis mounted in 2008 the US government injected some $700 billion into the nation's banking industry including $45 billion investment in Citigroup. It further stepped in to aid the faltering bank by backing more than $300 in loans and securities to boost confidence in the bank and protect its investments. In exchange the government took a 34% stake in Citigroup. The company received approval to pay the funds back in 2009 and the government began reducing its ownership.

Citigroup shed numerous noncore operations (grouped into its new Citi Holdings division) to raise money to repay the government bailout funds. In 2009 it sold Japanese brokerage Nikko Cordial (nowSMBC Nikko) and other parts of Nikko Citi Holdings for $8.7 billion to Sumitomo Mitsui Financial Group. Also in 2009 Citigroup combined its Smith Barney and Quilter wealth management units with those of Morgan Stanley to create Morgan Stanley Smith Barney taking a 49% of the combined firm.

Sales in 2010 include its $1.93 billion Canadian MasterCard portfolio (to CIBC) a $3.5 billion real estate loan portfolio (to JPMorgan Chase) a $3.2 billion auto loan portfolio (to Santander) and a $1.6 billion portfolio of retail credit card assets (to GE). In 2011 it sold a $1.7 billion private equity portfolio to AXA. Also in 2010 the company spun off Primerica in an IPO selling remaining shares by 2011.

Furthermore Citigroup exited the student loan business in the wake of federal legislation eliminating subsidies for private lenders: It sold its 80% stake in Student Loan Corporation and much of its private student loans portfolio to Discover Financial Services and Sallie Mae. The company also sold three hedge fund businesses with a combined $4.2 billion in assets under management to New York-based SkyBridge Capital.

The firm began withdrawing from the consumer lending business in Europe by selling its Egg UK credit card business to Barclays in 2011 and its UK/Ireland Diners Club business to Affiniture Cards in 2012.

EXECUTIVES

Ceo Citibank N.a., Barbara J. Desoer, age 66
Ceo North America, William J. (Bill) Mills, age 63
President Citigroup Inc. And Ceo Institutional Clients Group, James A. (Jim) Forese, age 56, $500,000 total compensation
Ceo, Michael L. Corbat, age 58, $1,500,000 total compensation
Global Head Markets And Securities Services, Paco Ybarra
Cfo, John C. Gerspach, age 66, $500,000 total compensation
Ceo Global Consumer Banking, Stephen Bird, age 52, $499,623 total compensation
Ceo Citi Holdings, Francesco Vanni d'Archirafi
Head Operations And Technology, Don Callahan, age 62, $500,000 total compensation
Evp Global Public Affairs, Edward Skyler, age 45
Ceo Latin America, Jane Fraser, age 51, $500,000 total compensation
Ceo Europe Middle East And Africa, James C. Cowles, age 63
Ceo Citi Cards, Jud Linville
Ceo Asia Pacific, Francisco A. Aristeguieta Silva, age 53
Chief Risk Officer, Bradford Hu, age 55
Ceo Citi Mexico And Banco Nacional De México (banamex), Ernesto Torres Cantu
Assistant Vice President, George Gilbert
Assistant Vice President And Business Information Security Officer, Veena Srinivasan
Senior Vice President Asset Management, Gustav Gollisz
Vice President, Charan Singh
Avp, Jennifer Chen
Vp Finance, Don Lee
Senior Vice President, Ryan McCaughey
Senior Vice President Global Portfolio Management, Mary Imbriale-Holubec
Assistant Vice President Senior Compliance Analyst Global Wealth Management, Renato Lima
Senior Vice President Network Architect, David Gubitosi
Assistant Vice President, Melissa Alomar
Vice President Application Development Senior Manager Global Equities, Peter Micciche
Senior Vice President, Andres Rodriguez
Senior Vice President, Peter Sullivan
Svp Marketing Program Director, Chad Steinwolf
Senior Vice President, Lynn Wuller
Senior Vice President, Linda Basher
Vice President, Savio Fernandes
Vice President, Michael Mandell
Senior Vice President Investment Finance, Greg Zann
Senior Vice President, Charles Walker
Vice President Business Initiatives, Raj Mohan
Vp Control Administrator, Dawn Patak
Senior Vice President Storage Engineering, Eliot Wilson
Senior Vice President, Fabricio Calderon
Vice President, Joseph Pasciak
Vice President Information Technology Risk Management, Ram Kumar
Vice President, Mayank Shah
Senior Vice President, Nareg Dermanuelian
Information Technology Management: Vice President, Jeffrey Bray
Sr Vice President, Bhupesh Kokate
Assistant Vice President, Brendan Toomey
Vice President, Rajeshwar Bhakey
Vice President Depositary Receipt Services, Victor Martinez
Senior Vice President Relationship Manager, Betty Silfa
Relationship Manager Svp, Edia Cruz
Senior Vice President, Dheepa Krishnamoorthy
Vice President Client Executive, Keri Reed
Vice President, Charles Benjamin
Vice President Finance, Ryan Hall
Assistant Vice President Equity Derivatives Trading, Peter Plevritis
Assistant Vice President, Sam Dyson
Assistant Vice President, Donna Chan
Svp Risk Management, Cheri Bockhorst
Vice President, Brian Gelok
Vp Latam Gts Financial Analyst, Noelia Ozuna
Associate Vice President, Cesar Tobar
Assistant Vice President Cpb Technology, Elizabeth Reen
Senior Vice President, Chris Cralle
Assistant Vice President, Kenzel Fleming
Vice President Treasury, Austin Holbrook
Senior Vice President Compliance, Joseph Morgo
Vice President, Brad Randlett
Senior Vice President Manager Of Regulatory Reporting Department For Derivatives (otc And Et), Yanina Kulchitskaya
Assistant Vice President, Anthony Thomas
Senior Vice President, Frank Zhang
Vice President Crm Process Manager, Brian Lilly
Senior Vice President, Harim Shon
Assistant Vice President Recovery Senior Supervisor Litigation, John Linnenbrink
Senior Vice President, Tim Walter
Assistant Vice President At Citi Loan Syndications Group, Christopher Romanelli
Assistant Vice President, Timothy Seaton
Vice President, Kyle Moeller
Vice President, Donna McCafferty
Vice President, Kevin Vee
Senior Vice President, Vikram Mago
Vice President, Beth Mcabee
Vice President, Sibylle Baker
Vice President Customer Engagement Risk, Pankaj Agarwal
Assistant Vice President, David Broad
Senior Vice President, Diana Alfonso
Vp Global Pmo, Eric Moon
Vice President Sales Development Counsultant Cit, Leta Bajraktari
Vp Information Systems, Harsh Goyal
Assistant Vice President, Sharon Eng
Senior Vice President, Ranjeet Jha
Assistant Vice President, Cherry Tam
Vice President And Senior Quality Assurance, Stella Zhang
Vice President Securities Country Manager, Yogendra Shah
Vice President, Elizabeth Clancey
Senior Vice President Remedial Management Senior Manager, Bernadette Walsh
Vice President, Donna Rhodes
Vice President Executive Recruiter, Carlos Fernandez
Vice President And Compliance Officer, Yolette Mazile
Assistant Vice President, Darrell Drake
Senior Vice President, Patrick Defeciani
Executive Vice President, Mark Morgenlender
Vice President Client Development, Michael Vaughan
Vice President Technology, James Carney
Vice President, Jodi Rodgers
Assistant Vice President Transaction Services, Zirley Moyette
Vice President, Dawn Cato
Assistant Vice President, Noreen Hanson

Vice President Compensation Manager, Lauren Geer

Assistant Vice President Change Management Shift Manager, Patrick Davis

Vice President Infrastructure Senior Manager, Keith Skoog

Senior Vice President Global Strategic Operations, Jason Marchese

Vice President, Joseph Stanz

Vice President Of Market Research Glob, Tim Teran

Senior Vice President, Hao Hu

Assistant Vice President, Laurence Evans

Vp Financial Center Manager, Arthur Lucien

Assistant Vice President, Anuja Raval

Vice President, Patrick Kosiek

Vice President, Divya Rai

Vice President, William Schwarz

Quantitative Analyst Vp, Katya Zulaica

Vice President, Santhosh Babu

Vice President Marketing, Reema Butala

Vice President Relationship Manager Commercial Banking, Madison Murphy

Avp, Errol Rathjen

Vice President, Imran Hirani

Senior Vice President Risk Management, Peter You

Vice President, Henry Palmer

Assistant Vice President, John Yiovanakos

Senior Vice President, Cathleen Bok

Vice President, Pei Wang

Avp Senior Client Service Officer, Frances Argento

Vice President, Marc Silva

Assistant Vice President, Ron Helm

Vice President, Julian Stippig

Vice President, Andrea Vaswani

Vice President E Citi Director, Joan Haffenreffer

Vice President Information Technology, Diane Papenberg

Vice President Of Marketing, Kathleen Desiderio

Senior Vice President Citi Cards, Ron Guggenheimer

Vice President Risk Management, Alice Dymally

Assistant Vice President, Suleman Khan

Assistant Vice President Local Advanced, Mary Chin

Vice President, Eric Levine

Vice President, Nicholas Woomer

Assistant Vice President, Teri Kennedy

Assistant Vice President Mutual Funds And Annuities, Jamie Catalano

Senior Vice President Treasury Capital Markets, Pascal Weel

Vice President, Edward Montero

Auditors: KPMG LLP

LOCATIONS

HQ: Citigroup Inc
388 Greenwich Street, New York, NY 10013
Phone: 212 559-1000
Web: www.citigroup.com

PRODUCTS/OPERATIONS

2017 Sales

	$ mil.	% of total
Net Interest	44,687	63
Non-interest		
Commissions & fees	12,939	18
Principal transactions	9,168	13
Administration & other fiduciary fees	3,079	4
Realized gains on sales of investments	778	1
Other	861	1
Adjustments	(63)	-
Total	**71,449**	**100**

2017 Sales

	% of total
Institutional Clients Group	50
Global Consumer Banking	46
Corporate/Other	4
Total	**100**

2017 Sales

	% of total
North America	47
Asia	20
Latin America	14
EMEA	15
Corporate/Other	4
Total	**100**

Selected Products

Banamex
Bill Consolidation
Checking
Citi Cards
Citi Private Bank
CitiMortgage
Commercial Real Estate Loans
Home Equity
Mortgages
Online Banking
Personal Loans
Savings
Student Loans

COMPETITORS

American Express	Goldman Sachs
Bank of America	HSBC
Bank of New York	JPMorgan Chase
Mellon	Mizuho Financial
Barclays	U.S. Bancorp
Capital One	UBS
Deutsche Bank	USAA
FMR	Wells Fargo
GE	

HISTORICAL FINANCIALS

Company Type: Public

Income Statement

FYE: December 31

	ASSETS ($ mil.)	NET INCOME ($ mil.)	INCOME AS % OF ASSETS	EMPLOYEES
12/18	1,917,383	18,045	0.9%	204,000
12/17	1,842,465	(6,798)	—	209,000
12/16	1,792,077	14,912	0.8%	219,000
12/15	1,731,210	17,242	1.0%	231,000
12/14	1,842,530	7,313	0.4%	241,000
Annual Growth	**1.0%**	**25.3%**	**—**	**(4.1%)**

2018 Year-End Financials

Debt ratio: 12.10%—
Return on equity: 9.09%
Cash ($ mil.): 188,105
Current ratio: —
Long-term debt ($ mil.): —

Dividends
  Yield: 2.9%
  Payout: 23.0%
Market value ($ mil.): —

	STOCK PRICE ($) FY Close	P/E High/Low	Earnings	PER SHARE ($) Dividends	Book Value
12/18	52.06	12 7	6.68	1.54	82.85
12/17	74.41	— —	(2.98)	0.96	78.11
12/16	59.43	13 7	4.72	0.42	81.20
12/15	51.75	11 9	5.40	0.16	75.12
12/14	54.11	26 21	2.20	0.04	69.62
Annual Growth	**(1.0%)**	**— —**	**32.0%**	**149.1%**	**4.4%**

Citizens Financial Group Inc (New)

Paper plastic or coin? No matter — Citizens Financial Group can handle it all. The company's main operating subsidiary is consumer bank Citizens Bank which spans some 1150 branches across eleven US states in the Northeast and the Midwest and boasts more than $150 billion in assets. The bank's branches are often found in supermarkets and offer standard retail and commercial services as well as investment services insurance employer-sponsored retirement plans student loans and vehicle lending. Citizens Financial also operates a network of non-branch banking offices.

Operations

Citizens Financial offers customers mortgage lending auto lending student lending and commercial banking services. Altogether its portfolio includes 1150 branches 130 non-branch offices and 3300 ATMs.

The bank operates two segments: Consumer Banking which serves individuals and counts for more than 60% of the bank's total revenue; and Commercial Banking which serves businesses and accounts for some 35% of revenue.

Interest income accounts for more than three-quarters of Citizens' revenue.

Geographic Reach

Rhode Island-based Citizens Financial operates branches in New England the Mid-Atlantic and the Midwest. Its largest markets are Boston Philadelphia Providence and Pittsburgh.

Sales and Marketing

Citizens Financial's customers include individuals small businesses middle-market companies large corporations and institutions. Its business clients typically operate out of the healthcare technology franchise and energy sectors.

Financial Performance

Citizens Financial has grown its revenue and profits more or less consistently since 2013. In fiscal 2017 the bank's net revenue (net interest income plus noninterest income) rose 9% to $5.7 billion as a $7.9 billion increase in interest-earning assets pushed up net interest income 11% to $4.2 billion. Total assets grew $2.8 billion to $152.3 billion while deposits expanded $5.3 billion to $115.1 billion.

Net income grew strongly in 2017 up 59% to $1.7 billion. A significant chunk of the growth was a one-time effect of the 2017 US Tax Cuts and Jobs Act worth $340 million; the rest of the increase came from stronger overall operating performance and higher interest rates.

The company's cash position weakened in 2017 with cash on hand falling $672 million to $3.0 million.

Strategy

Citizen Financial's growth strategy is based outperforming its rivals in terms of customer relationships. The company is leveraging analytics to target customers with customized products and offers with the goal of winning expanding and retaining customer relationships. It is working to increase convenience by investing in its digital channels (online mobile ATM) while implementing a more personal in-branch experience with "Citizens Checkup" consultations.

Citizens Financial is also tightening its focus on the Mass Affluent and Affluent customer segments which have higher growth potential. To do so the company is working on its Wealth Management business which includes improving its advice services (including digital advice) and product suite and services.

The company has been leaning on student lending and installment loans in recent years to drive growth. The group has launched several new products including student loan refinancing partnered with Apple on iPhone upgrade financing and launched a new credit card.

Company Background

In September 2014 Royal Bank of Scotland (RBS) sold a 25% ownership interest or 140 million shares of the regional US bank for $21.50 each (below the company's expected range of $23 to $25 per share). The deal which valued Citizens Financial Group (CFG) at $3 billion was one of the largest bank IPOs on record. In October 2015 RBS sold its remaining stake (the last 20.9% of Citizens common stock) for $23.38 per share raising some $2.6 billion.

After being bought by RBS in 1988 Citizens Financial went on an acquisition spree making more than two dozen deals. In 2000 and through later years the company gobbled up Mellon's retail banking network Medford Bancorp and Port Financial in Massachusetts and Pennsylvania's Commonwealth Bancorp and Thistle Group Holdings among others. The company expanded into the Midwest by buying superregional bank Charter One in 2004. Following its acquisition of Charter One its largest deal yet Citizens Financial retained the Charter One Bank name in Midwestern markets but converted the bank's branches to Citizens Bank in New York and Pennsylvania. That was the company's last major acquisition however.

Like many banks the company was hamstrung by the mortgage crisis. It posted a nearly $1 billion loss in 2008 as its nonperforming loans roughly doubled. The developments compelled the company to re-evaluate its acquisition strategy and it has reversed its field: Citizens Financial sold 18 of its branches in northern New York to Community Bank System in 2008 and all 65 Charter One branches in Indiana to Old National Bancorp the following year. The company also pegged certain operations as noncore including its dealer finance program and portions of its auto lending business. In 2012 Citizens Financial unloaded more branches selling nearly 60 supermarket locations to People's United Financial. In 2013 it opted to unload its Chicago branches.

In 2015 RBS sold its remaining stake in Citizens Financial.

EXECUTIVES

Evp And Cfo, John F. Woods, age 54
Evp And Chief Risk Officer, Malcolm D. Griggs, age 58
Vice Chairman Commercial Banking, Donald H. (Don) McCree, age 57, $700,000 total compensation
Evp General Counsel And Chief Legal Officer, Stephen T. (Steve) Gannon, age 66, $600,000 total compensation
Vice Chairman Consumer Banking, Brad L. Conner, age 57, $700,000 total compensation
Chairman And Ceo, Bruce Van Saun, age 61, $1,487,000 total compensation
Chief Marketing Officer And Head Of Consumer Strategy, Beth Johnson
Head Of Technology Services, Brian OÂ'Connell
President Citizens Bank Rhode Island, Keith Kelly
Evp And Head Of Business Services, Mary Ellen Baker, age 60
Senior Vice President, Anthony Watson
Svp Hr, Joanna Robbins
Senior Vice President, Lawrence Bigelow
Vice President Senior Risk Manager, Pat Coutu
Chief Sales Officer, Chauncey Holden
Executive Vice President, Carol-Lynn Saliba
Executive Vice President, Sean Rowles
Senior Vice President, Michael Stank
Senior Vice President, James McLaughlin
Senior Vice President, Sheryl Medeiros
Vice President, Diane Yalch
Senior Vice President, John Cooper
Senior Vice President, Kathryn Gallagher
Executive Vice President, Paul Howard
Svp And Head Consumer And Regional Operations, Jeff Leblanc
Assistant Vice President Portfolio Manager, Laurie Charest
Executive Vice President, Kenneth Deveaux
Svp Head Operations Supply Chain Services, Alison Sorel
Senior Vice President, Claire Smith
Senior Vice President, Dave Howe
Vice President, Dave Mewkalo
Assistant Vice President, Sylvia Castro
Evp Head Investor Relations, Ellen Taylor
Executive Vice President, Cindy Erickson
Senior Vice President, Steven Girard
Senior Vice President, Jeffrey LeBlanc
Senior Vice President, Susan Baker Shipley
Senior Vice President, F Gorham Brigham
Senior Vice President, Michael Brown
Senior Vice President, Gillian Cairns
Senior Vice President, Peter Camilleri
Executive Vice President, Craig Campbell
Senior Vice President, Dwayne Finney
Senior Vice President, Paul Flynn
Executive Vice President, Peter Galligan
Executive Vice President, Neil Grassie
Senior Vice President, Michael Hall
Executive Vice President, Paul Hanlon
Senior Vice President, William Harris
Executive Vice President, Kathryn Hinderhofer
Executive Vice President, Cynthia Jerome-Resnick
Senior Vice President, Thomas King
Executive Vice President, Margaret Marty
Senior Vice President, Daniel May
Senior Vice President, Paul McKinnon
Senior Vice President, James Morris
Senior Vice President, Michael Palinkos
Senior Vice President, Gregory Suchy
Senior Vice President, Carol Townsend
Senior Vice President, Michael Williams
Senior Vice President, Stephen Wilus
Vp Workforce Operations, Isabel Dealmeida
Vice President, Deven Dittrich
Vice President Solutions Architecture, Santosh Sinha
Senior Vice President Human Resources Analytics, Melissa Arronte
Senior Vice President Strategy And Architecture, Saumitra Pande
Assistant Vice President Information Technology Security And Infrastructure Management, Joe Prest
Senior Vice President, Louis Noppenberger
Senior Vice President Credit Products Manager, Mark Walker
Assistant Vice President Branch Manager, Anna Clune
Senior Vice President Business Development, John Lim
Senior Vice President, Edward Kloecker
Vice President, Biagio Maffettone
Assistant Vice President Sales Manager, Maria Esposito
Vice President, Jeff Hoepf
Vice President Senior Strategy Consultant Private Wealth Management, Joe Savoca
Senior Vice President Professionals Banking, Jay Benegal
Vp, Adrienne Bain
Vice President Flex Staffing Program, Cheryl Rebello
Senior Vice President, Christopher Hallee
Senior Vp Chief Architect, James Mitcheson
Board Member, Wendy A Watson
Auditors: DELOITTE & TOUCHE LLP

LOCATIONS

HQ: Citizens Financial Group Inc (New)
One Citizens Plaza, Providence, RI 02903
Phone: 401 456-7000   **Fax:** 401 455-5927
Web: www.citizensbank.com

2017 Branches

	Nos
Pennsylvania	340
Massachusetts	246
New York	133
Ohio	103
Michigan	93
Rhode Island	78
New Hampshire	66
Connecticut	41
Delaware	23
Vermont	16
New Jersey	11
Total	**1,150**

PRODUCTS/OPERATIONS

2017 Sales

	$ mil.	% of total
Interest income		
Interest on loans & fees	4,249	66
Investment securities	625	10
Others	46	1
Non-interest income		
Service charges & fees	517	8
Card fees	233	3
Trust & investment services fees	158	2
Capital markets fees	194	3
Letter of credit & loan fees	121	2
Others	320	5
Net security impairment loss	(7)	-
Total	**6,454**	**100**

Sales 2017

	% of total
Consumer Banking	62
Commercial Banking	34
Others	4
Total	**100**

COMPETITORS

Bank of America	M&T Bank
Bank of New York	PNC Financial
Mellon	People's United
Citigroup	Financial
Fifth Third	Sovereign Bank
HSBC USA	TD Bank USA
Huntington Bancshares	U.S. Bancorp
JPMorgan Chase	Wintrust Financial
KeyCorp	

HISTORICAL FINANCIALS

Company Type: Public

Income Statement   FYE: December 31

	ASSETS ($ mil.)	NET INCOME ($ mil.)	INCOME AS % OF ASSETS	EMPLOYEES
12/18	160,518	1,721	1.1%	18,100
12/17	152,336	1,652	1.1%	17,600
12/16	149,520	1,045	0.7%	18,000
12/15	138,208	840	0.6%	17,700
12/14	132,857	865	0.7%	18,310
Annual Growth	**4.8%**	**18.8%**	**—**	**(0.3%)**

2018 Year-End Financials

Debt ratio: 4.31%
Return on equity: 8.38%
Cash ($ mil.): 4,222
Current ratio: —
Long-term debt ($ mil.): —
No. of shares (mil.): 466
Dividends
  Yield: 3.3%
  Payout: 27.8%
Market value ($ mil.): 13,854

	STOCK PRICE ($) FY Close	P/E High/Low		PER SHARE ($) Earnings	Dividends	Book Value
12/18	29.73	14	8	3.52	0.98	44.67
12/17	41.98	13	10	3.25	0.64	41.30
12/16	35.63	19	9	1.97	0.46	38.57
12/15	26.19	18	15	1.55	0.40	37.22
12/14	24.86	16	14	1.55	0.10	35.30
Annual Growth	**4.6%**	**—**	**—**	**22.8%**	**76.9%**	**6.1%**

City Holding Co.

"Take Me Home Country Roads" may be the (unofficial) state song of West Virginia but City Holding hopes all roads lead to its City National Bank of West Virginia subsidiary which operates more than 80 branches in the Mountaineer State and in neighboring areas of southern Ohio eastern Kentucky and northern Virginia. Serving consumers and regional businesses the nearly $4 billion bank offers standard deposit products loans credit cards insurance trust and investment services. Residential mortgages and home equity loans constitute more than half of City Holding's $2.5 billion loan portfolio though the bank also writes commercial industrial commercial mortgage and installment consumer loans.

Operations

City National Bank (CNB) operates four main business divisions: Commercial banking Consumer Banking Mortgage Banking and Wealth Management and Trust Services.

Commercial Banking provides traditional banking products commercial and industrial loans and different kinds of real estate loans to corporations and other business customers. Consumer Banking provides deposit products installment loans and real estate loans and lines of credit. The bank's Mortgage Banking division offers fixed and adjustable-rate mortgages construction financing production of conventional and government-backed mortgages secondary marketing and mortgage servicing.

Wealth Management and Trust Services offers personal trust and estate administration investment management and investment and custodial services for commercial and individual customers. This includes management of investment accounts for individuals employee benefit plans and charitable foundations.

Altogether the company earned 62% of its total revenue from interest and fees on loans in 2014 plus another 7% from interest on its investment securities. About 14% of revenue came from service charges 8% came from bankcard revenue and 2% came from trust and investment management fee income.

Geographic Reach

City boasts around 80 branches in four US states including more than 55 branches in West Virginia nearly 15 in Virginia around 10 in Kentucky and less than a handful of branches in Ohio.

Sales and Marketing

The bank spent $3.27 million on advertising in 2014 compared to $2.67 million and $2.59 million in 2013 and 2012 respectively.

Financial Performance

City Holding's revenues and profits have mostly been on the uptrend in recent years as the bank has grown its loan business through acquisitions.

The bank's revenue dipped by 4% to $188.29 million in 2014 mostly because it generated less in loan interest due to an expected drop in accretion from fair value adjustments related to its recent Virginia Savings Bank and Community Bank acquisitions. Interest margins also shrank amidst the low interest environment which caused further headwinds to interest income. The bank did have some bright spots with 16% growth in trust and investment fee income and 11% growth in bankcard revenue as it continued to push those services.

Despite lower revenue in 2014 City Holdings net income jumped by 10% to $52.96 million – the highest its profit has been since 2007. The rise was mostly thanks to a combination of a non-income based tax rebate (non-recurring) decreased

legal and professional fees from lower legal settlements a $2.7 million decline in loan loss provisions as the credit quality of the bank's loan portfolio improved and a $1.3 million reduction in interest expense on deposits.

City's operating cash fell to $53.35 million despite higher earnings during the year primarily because the bank used more of its cash toward purchasing assets and generated less net cash proceeds from its loans held for sale.

Strategy

City Holding's flagship subsidiary City National Bank has been growing its loan business and branch network in target markets through acquisitions in recent years. In mid-2015 for example the bank agreed to acquire three bank branches in Lexington Kentucky from American Founders Bank boosting CNB's presence in the state to 11 branches while adding $164.2 million in new deposits and $125 billion in performing loans to its books.

Beyond buying just select branches the bank has also been known to buy smaller community banks outright in its target markets.

To free up resources for more investment in its core business City National sold its insurance operations to The Hilb Group in early 2015 netting an after-tax gain of $5.80 million.

Mergers and Acquisitions

In January 2013 City Holding acquired Community Financial Corporation holding company of the 11-branch Community Bank in Virginia.

In 2012 the company entered a new market in Virginia through its acquisition of Virginia Savings Bank which had five branches in the northern part of the state.

EXECUTIVES

Evp Marketing Human Resources And Retail Banking, Craig G. Stilwell, age 63, $330,000 total compensation

President And Ceo, Charles R. (Skip) Hageboeck, age 56, $500,000 total compensation

Evp Commercial Banking, John A. DeRito, age 69, $250,000 total compensation

Cfo, David L. Bumgarner, age 54, $207,000 total compensation

Cio, Jeffrey D. (Jeff) Legge, $175,000 total compensation

Assistant Vice President And Trust Officer, John Chandler

Vice President Of Risk Management, Kevin Thomas

Executive Vice President Customer Service, Jack Cavender

Vice President, Madison Sayre

Vice President Of Customer Service, John Kelly

Vice President Information Technology, Vince Workman

Senior Vice President Manager, Ron Mccloud

Vice President Business Development, Sharon Hughes

Vice President, Keith Unger

Vice President Human Resources, Lillian Komata

Senior Vice President Information Technology, Abigal Scott

Senior Vice President Chief Administrative Officer And Chief Information Officer Of The Company And, Jeff Legge

Vice President, Clara Mullins

Assistent Vice President, Christina Pocrnich

Avp, Pat Davis

Vice President Commercial Relationship Manager, Sherry Houck

Vice President, Debbie Holcomb

Avp And Branch Manager, Massie Schemmel

Assistant Vice President And Branch Manager, Ora Muth

Chairman, C. Dallas Kayser, age 67

Board Member, John Elliot

Board Member, Tracy Hylton

Board Member, Sharon Rowe

Auditors: Crowe LLP

LOCATIONS

HQ: City Holding Co.
25 Gatewater Road, Charleston, WV 25313
Phone: 304 769-1100
Web: www.bankatcity.com

PRODUCTS/OPERATIONS

2014 Sales

	$ mil.	% of total
Interest		
Loans including fees	116	62
Investment securities & other	13	7
Noninterest		
Service charges	265	14
Bankcard revenue	15	8
Other	171	9
Total	**188**	**100**

COMPETITORS

1st West Virginia Bancorp	Huntington Bancshares
BB&T	Ohio Valley Banc
Fifth Third	Premier Financial Bancorp
First Community Bancshares	United Bankshares
	WesBanco

HISTORICAL FINANCIALS

Company Type: Public

Income Statement

FYE: December 31

	ASSETS ($ mil.)	NET INCOME ($ mil.)	INCOME AS % OF ASSETS	EMPLOYEES
12/18	4,899	70	1.4%	891
12/17	4,132	54	1.3%	839
12/16	3,984	52	1.3%	847
12/15	3,714	54	1.5%	853
12/14	3,461	52	1.5%	889
Annual Growth	9.1%	7.2%	—	0.1%

2018 Year-End Financials

Debt ratio: 0.08%	No. of shares (mil.): 16
Return on equity: 12.69%	Dividends
Cash ($ mil.): 122	Yield: 2.8%
Current ratio: —	Payout: 43.1%
Long-term debt ($ mil.): —	Market value ($ mil.): 1,119

	STOCK PRICE ($) FY Close	P/E High/Low		PER SHARE ($) Earnings	Dividends	Book Value
12/18	67.59	18	14	4.49	1.91	36.29
12/17	67.47	21	17	3.48	1.75	32.17
12/16	67.60	20	12	3.45	1.71	29.25
12/15	45.64	15	12	3.53	1.66	27.62
12/14	46.53	14	12	3.38	1.57	25.79
Annual Growth	9.8%	—	—	7.4%	5.0%	8.9%

Civista Bancshares Inc

First Citizens Banc Corp. is the holding company for The Citizens Banking Company and its Citizens Bank and Champaign Bank divisions which together operate more than 30 branches in northern Ohio. The banks offer such deposit products as checking and savings accounts and CDs in addition to trust services. They concentrate on real estate lending with residential mortgages and commercial mortgages each comprising approximately 40% of the company's loan portfolio. The Citizens Banking Company's Citizens Wealth Management division provides financial planning brokerage insurance and investments through an agreement with third-party provider UVEST (part of LPL Financial).

EXECUTIVES

Vice President And Commercial Lender, John Desanto
Auditors: S. R. Snodgrass, P.C.

LOCATIONS

HQ: Civista Bancshares Inc
100 East Water Street, Sandusky, OH 44870
Phone: 419 625-4121

COMPETITORS

Fifth Third	PNC Financial
Huntington Bancshares	U.S. Bancorp
KeyCorp	

HISTORICAL FINANCIALS

Company Type: Public

Income Statement				FYE: December 31
	ASSETS ($ mil.)	NET INCOME ($ mil.)	INCOME AS % OF ASSETS	EMPLOYEES
12/18	2,138	14	0.7%	432
12/17	1,525	15	1.0%	350
12/16	1,377	17	1.3%	337
12/15	1,315	12	1.0%	326
12/14	1,213	9	0.8%	303
Annual Growth	15.2%	10.4%	—	9.3%

2018 Year-End Financials

Debt ratio: 1.38%	No. of shares (mil.): 15
Return on equity: 5.85%	Dividends
Cash ($ mil.): 42	Yield: 1.8%
Current ratio: —	Payout: 40.5%
Long-term debt ($ mil.): —	Market value ($ mil.): 272

	STOCK PRICE ($) FY Close	P/E High/Low		PER SHARE ($) Earnings	Dividends	Book Value
12/18	17.42	23	15	1.02	0.32	19.16
12/17	22.00	16	13	1.28	0.25	18.09
12/16	19.43	10	5	1.57	0.22	16.49
12/15	12.83	8	7	1.17	0.20	15.96
12/14	10.28	11	7	0.85	0.19	15.04
Annual Growth	14.1%	—	—	4.7%	13.9%	6.2%

Clorox Co (The)

Although Clorox may be best known for its namesake bleach the leading consumer and professional products maker has a plethora of market-leading brands. It sells laundry and cleaning items (Formula 409 Pine-Sol Green Works) as well as dressings and sauces (Hidden Valley KC Masterpiece Soy Vay) charcoal (Kingsford Match Light) plastic wrap and containers (Glad) and cat litters (Fresh Step Scoop Away). Other items include filtration systems (Brita) dietary supplements (Rainbow Light Natural Vitality) and personal care items (Burt's Bees). Clorox makes and sells its products worldwide although the US accounts for the most revenue by far.

HISTORY

Known first as the Electro-Alkaline Company The Clorox Company was founded in 1913 by five Oakland California investors who put up $100 apiece to make bleach using water from salt ponds around San Francisco Bay. The next year the company registered the brand name Clorox (the name combines the bleach's two main ingredients chlorine and sodium hydroxide). At first the company sold only industrial-strength bleach but in 1916 it formulated a household solution.

With the establishment of a Philadelphia distributor in 1921 Clorox began national expansion. The company went public in 1928 and built plants in Illinois and New Jersey in the 1930s; it opened nine more US plants in the 1940s and 1950s. In 1957 Procter & Gamble (P&G) bought Clorox. The Federal Trade Commission raised antitrust questions and litigation ensued over the next decade. P&G was ordered to divest Clorox and in 1969 Clorox again became an independent company.

Following its split with P&G the firm added household consumer goods and foods acquiring the brands Liquid-Plumr (drain opener 1969) Formula 409 (spray cleaner 1970) Litter Green (cat litter 1971) and Hidden Valley (salad dressings 1972). Clorox entered the specialty food products business by purchasing Grocery Store Products (Kitchen Bouquet 1971) and Kingsford (charcoal briquettes 1973).

Henkel a large West German maker of cleansers and detergents purchased 15% of Clorox's stock in 1974 as part of an agreement to share research. Beginning in 1977 Clorox sold off subsidiaries and brands such as Country Kitchen Foods (1979) to focus on household goods.

During the 1980s Clorox launched a variety of new products including Match Light (instant-lighting charcoal 1980) Tilex (mildew remover 1981) and Fresh Step (cat litter 1984). Clorox began marketing Brita water filtration systems in the US in 1988 (adding Canada in 1995). In 1990 it paid $465 million for American Cyanamid's household products group including Pine-Sol cleaner and Combat insecticide. (It sold Combat and Soft Scrub to Henkel in 2004.)

Clorox left the laundry detergent business in 1991 (begun in 1988) after it was battered by heavyweights P&G and Unilever. Household products VP Craig Sullivan became CEO the next year (stepping down in December 2003). In 1993 Clorox dumped its frozen food and bottled water operations. It began marketing its liquid bleach in Hungary through a Henkel subsidiary in 1994 and also bought S.O.S soap pads from Miles Inc.

A string of acquisitions brought the company into new markets as it built on existing brands. Clorox bought Black Flag and Lestoil in 1996 and car care product manufacturer Armor All in 1997. With its 1999 purchase of First Brands — for about $2 billion in stock and debt — Clorox added four more brands of cat litter and diversified into plastic products (Glad).

Despite adding 115 new products in 2000 the company said it would put more emphasis on core brands going forward; it pushed its struggling Glad brand with more trade promotions and coupons.

Clorox in January 2001 announced a joint venture with Bombril Brazil's leading name in steel wool to form Detergentes Bombril; however Clorox canceled the agreement in April 2001 claiming that various conditions of the deal had not been met. A year later Clorox further distanced itself from the Brazilian market selling its SBP insecticides business to Reckitt Benckiser. In 2002 Clorox announced that due to the difficult economic environment in the region it was selling its Brazil business.

In 2003 it jumpstarted a joint venture with Procter & Gamble to take advantage of P&G's manufacturing acumen to improve its Glad products. P&G received a 10% stake in Glad. Clorox also sold its Jonny Cat Litter business to Oil-Dri Corporation of America and Black Flag operations in 2003.

In January 2004 Robert Matschullat the company's nonexecutive chairman replaced Sullivan upon his retirement. Matschullat stepped down as chairman and became a director in January 2005; he passed the title to Jerry Johnston. Matschullat reclaimed the titles of chairman and CEO on an interim basis when Johnston suffered a heart attack and retired in 2006. Former Coca-Cola executive Donald Knauss was named chairman and CEO in late 2006; Matschullat remained a director.

Chemical giant Henkel once owned nearly 30% of Clorox but Clorox bought it back in 2004 through an asset swap valued at $2.8 billion. The transaction involved Henkel's purchase of Clorox's 20% stake in Henkel Iberica a joint venture between the two firms operating in Portugal and Spain. Henkel also bought Clorox's stake in a pesticide company.

In late 2004 though P&G boosted its share in the joint venture (with $133 million) from 10% to 20% which is the maximum it can invest according to the agreement.

In 2010 Clorox began to explore strategic alternatives for its $300-million-in-sales car-care brands (Armor All STP) culminating in their sale to private equity firm Avista Capital Partners for $780 million.

EXECUTIVES

Evp General Counsel And Corporate Affairs, Laura Stein, age 58, $582,050 total compensation
Chairman And Ceo, Benno Dorer, age 55, $976,154 total compensation
Evp And Cfo, Stephen M. (Steve) Robb, age 54, $576,846 total compensation
Evp Product Supply Enterprise Performance And It, James Foster, age 56
Svp And Chief Innovation Officer, Denise Garner, age 55
Svp And Cio, Manjit Singh, age 49
Svp International Division, Michael Costello, age 52
Svp; General Manager Specialty Division, Jon Balousek, age 50
Evp And Coo, Dawn Willoughby, age 50, $515,154 total compensation
Svp And Chief Marketing Officer, Eric Reynolds, age 48
Vice President Consumer Insights, Raj Rajaratnam
Senior Vice President And Chief Product Supply Officer, Andy Mowery
Vice President Digital Consumer Experience, Doug Milliken
Vice President And General Manager Waste Management Glad Brands And Brita Brand, Ed Huber
Vp Finance, Theo Razzouk
Svp And Chief Customer Officer, Matt Laszlo
Vp Hr Strategic Consulting, Hilda West
Vice President Of Product Supply Global Sourcing And Supply Chain Design, Greg Ginsburg
Vice President Associate General Counsel, Mark Danis
National Account Manager, Valerie Varin
Vice President Global Risk Management, Laura Cisi
Auditors: Ernst & Young LLP

LOCATIONS

HQ: Clorox Co (The)
1221 Broadway, Oakland, CA 94612-1888
Phone: 510 271-7000
Web: www.thecloroxcompany.com

2019 Sales

	$ mil.	% of total
US	5,281	85
Foreign	933	15
Total	**6,214**	**100**

PRODUCTS/OPERATIONS

2019 Sales

	$ mil.	% of total
Cleaning	2,109	34
Household	1,870	30
Lifestyle	1,265	20
International	970	16
Total	**6,214**	**100**

Selected Food-Related Products

Brita
Glad
Glad Press 'n Seal
GladWare
Hidden Valley
K.C. Masterpiece

Selected Household & Professional Cleaning Products

Aplicare
Clorox
Clorox 2
Clorox Clean-Up
Clorox Disinfecting Wipes
Clorox Dispatch
Clorox FreshCare
Clorox Healthcare
Clorox Oxi Magic
Clorox ReadyMop
Clorox Toilet Bowl Cleaner
Formula 409
Formula 409 Carpet Cleaner
Green Works
Handi-Wipes
HealthLink
Lestoil
Liquid-Plumr
Pine-Sol
S.O.S
Stain Out
Tilex
ToiletWand
Tuffy
Ultra Clorox Bleach

Selected International Products

Agua Jane (bleach Uruguay)
Ant Rid (insecticides)
Arela (waxes)
Astra (disposable gloves)
Bluebell (cleaners)
Chux (cleaning tools)
Clorisol (bleach)
Clorox Gentle (color-safe bleach)
Glad (containers)
Glad-Lock (resealable bags)
Guard (shoe polish)
Gumption (cleaners)
Home Mat (insecticides)
Home Keeper (insecticides)
Javex (bleach Canada)
Mono (aluminum foil)
Nevex (bleach Venezuela)
OSO (aluminum foil)
Prestone (coolant)
Selton (insecticides)
S.O.S (cleaners)
Super Globo (bleach)
XLO (sponges)
Yuhanrox (bleach)

Selected Specialty Products

BBQ Bag
Burt's Bees
EverClean
EverFresh
Fresh Step
Fresh Step Scoop
Kingsford
Match Light
Rain Dance
Scoop Away
Son of a Gun!
Tuff Stuff

COMPETITORS

Alticor	Procter & Gamble
Blistex	Reckitt Benckiser
Church & Dwight	S.C. Johnson
Colgate-Palmolive	Seventh Generation
Kiehl's	The Dial Corporation
Kiss My Face	Tupperware Brands
Lancaster Colony	Unilever UK
Newman's Own	

HISTORICAL FINANCIALS

Company Type: Public

Income Statement

FYE: June 30

	REVENUE ($ mil.)	NET INCOME ($ mil.)	NET PROFIT MARGIN	EMPLOYEES
06/19	6,214	820	13.2%	8,800
06/18	6,124	823	13.4%	8,700
06/17	5,973	701	11.7%	8,100
06/16	5,761	648	11.2%	8,000
06/15	5,655	580	10.3%	7,700
Annual Growth	**2.4%**	**9.0%**	**—**	**3.4%**

2019 Year-End Financials

Debt ratio: 52.44%
Return on equity: 127.63%
Cash ($ mil.): 111
Current ratio: 0.91
Long-term debt ($ mil.): 2,287
No. of shares (mil.): 125
Dividends
  Yield: 0.0%
  Payout: 60.7%
Market value ($ mil.): 19,244

	STOCK PRICE ($) FY Close	P/E High/Low		PER SHARE ($) Earnings	Dividends	Book Value
06/19	153.11	26	20	6.32	3.84	4.45
06/18	135.25	23	18	6.26	3.48	5.67
06/17	133.24	26	21	5.33	3.20	4.20
06/16	138.39	27	21	4.92	3.08	2.30
06/15	104.02	25	19	4.37	2.96	0.92
Annual Growth	**10.1%**	**—**	**—**	**9.7%**	**6.7%**	**48.4%**

CMS Energy Corp

Michigan relies on CMS Energy. The energy holding company's regulated utility subsidiary Consumers Energy serves 1.8 million electricity and 1.8 million natural gas customers. It has electric generating capacity of 5800 MW and purchases an additional 2700 MW from third party electricity providers. Another subsidiary CMS Enterprises operates the non-regulated businesses of CMS Energy and is an operator of independent power generating plants. CMS Enterprises' independent power plants (coal- gas- and biomass-fired) have a capacity of 1200 MW and are located in Michigan North Carolina and Wisconsin.

HISTORY

In the late 1880s W. A. Foote and Samuel Jarvis formed hydroelectric company Jackson Electrical Light Works in Jackson Michigan. After building plants in other Michigan towns Foote formed utility holding company Consumers Power. In 1910 the firm merged with Michigan Light to create Commonwealth Power Railway and Light (CPR&L) and began building a statewide transmission system.

Foote died in 1915 and after nine years of acquisitions successor Bernard Cobb sold the rail systems and split CPR&L into Commonwealth Power (CP) and Electric Railway Securities. In 1928 Cobb bought Southeastern Power & Light (SP&L) and merged CP with Penn-Ohio Edison to form Allied Power & Light. Commonwealth and Southern (C&S) was then created as the parent of Allied and SP&L.

In 1932 future GOP presidential nominee Wendell Willkie took the helm and became a national political figure by opposing the Public Utility Holding Company Act of 1935 which began 60 years of regulated monopolies. Consumers Power was divested from C&S after WWII.

Consumers brought a nuclear plant on line in 1962 and the next year began buying Michigan oil and gas fields. In 1967 it formed NOMECO (now CMS Oil and Gas) to guide its oil and gas efforts.

The completion of the Palisades nuke in 1971 began a 13-year run of chronic problems and lengthy shutdowns. Cost overruns and an environmental lawsuit killed the firm's third nuke (Midland) in 1984 — after $4.1 billion was spent.

A rate hike and new CEO William McCormick set the firm on a new path in 1985. McCormick formed a subsidiary to develop and invest in independent power projects in 1986 and created holding company CMS (short for "Consumers") Energy the next year. CMS Gas Transmission was formed in 1989.

Midland Cogeneration Venture (CMS Energy and six partners) completed converting Midland to a natural gas-fueled cogeneration plant in 1990 and CMS Energy wrote off $657 million from its losses at the former nuke. It regained profitability in 1993.

McCormick split the utilities into electric and gas divisions in 1995 and also issued stock for its gas utility and transmission businesses Consumers Gas Group. The next year CMS Energy formed an energy marketing arm.

In 1996 and 1997 CMS Energy invested in power plants in Morocco and Australia and bought a stake in a Brazilian electric utility. The next year it began developing a gas-fired plant in Ghana and won a bid to build a plant in India. CMS Energy also bought gas gathering and processing firms Continental Natural Gas and Heritage Gas Services in 1998.

Michigan's public service commission (PSC) issued utility restructuring orders in 1997 and 1998 but in 1999 the state Supreme Court ruled that the PSC lacked restructuring authority. Facing less-favorable proposed legislation CMS Energy and DTE Energy moved to implement competition per the PSC's guidelines.

CMS Energy bought Panhandle Eastern Pipe Line from Duke Energy for $2.2 billion in 1999. It also grabbed a 77% stake in another Brazilian utility and began building its Powder River Basin gas pipeline. In 2000 the company partnered with Marathon Ashland Petroleum (now Marathon Petroleum) and TEPPCO to operate a pipeline transporting refined petroleum from the US Gulf Coast to Illinois. Later that year CMS Energy announced plans for an IPO for its CMS Oil and Gas unit; however the IPO was withdrawn in 2001.

CMS Energy agreed in 2001 to sell Consumers' high-voltage electric transmission assets to independent transmission operator Trans-Elect for about $290 million; the deal which was the first of its kind in the US was completed in 2002. That year the company sold its Equatorial Guinea (West Africa) oil and gas assets to Marathon Oil for about

$1 billion. Also that year McCormick stepped down amid controversy over "round trip" power trades that artificially inflated the company's sales and trading volume; CMS Energy later announced that it would restate its 2000 and 2001 financial results to eliminate the effects of the trades.

Later in 2002 the company exited the exploration and production business. It sold CMS Oil and Gas' North American and African assets to private French energy firm Perenco for $167 million and it sold the unit's Colombian properties to Spanish energy firm Compa 'ia Espa 'ola de Petr "leos (Cepsa) for $65 million. CMS Energy sold its CMS Panhandle companies which together operated an 11000-mile pipeline system to Southern Union for $1.8 billion in 2003.

CMS Energy's nonregulated operations grew to account for more than half of sales in 2001 and 2002; however as the wholesale power marketing industry has experienced a downturn the company has refocused on its regulated energy distribution operations. The company has exited the speculative wholesale energy-trading business which was conducted through its CMS Energy Resource Management (formerly CMS Marketing Services and Trading) unit; it has sold its wholesale natural gas trading book to Sempra Energy and has sold its electricity trading book to Constellation Energy Commodities Group (formerly Constellation Power Source).

In 2013 The Utility Workers Union of America signed a new five-year labor agreement with Consumers Energy under which the union will assume a leading role in training employees at Michigan's largest electric and gas utility.

That year Consumers Energy teamed up with global IT services provider HCL Technologies to open the Michigan Technology Development Center in Jackson Michigan. HCL provides IT services for Consumers Energy at the center.

EXECUTIVES

Vice Chairman Cms Energy And Consumers Energy, Thomas J. (Tom) Webb, age 67, $705,000 total compensation

Vp Governmental And International Affairs Cms Energy And Consumers Energy, David G. Mengebier, age 62, $375,000 total compensation

Svp Energy Resources, Daniel J. (Dan) Malone, age 58, $490,000 total compensation

Svp And General Counsel, Catherine M. Reynolds, age 61, $516,667 total compensation

Evp And Cfo Cms Energy And Consumers Energy, Rejji P. Hayes, age 44

Svp Customer Experience And Cio, Brian F. Rich, age 44

President And Ceo, Patricia K. (Patti) Poppe, age 51, $775,000 total compensation

Svp Operations, Garrick Rochow

Vice President, Hillary Hogarth

Director Of Health And Safety, Shajahan Kamalbatcha

Senior Vice President, John Butler

Vp Enterprise Project Management And Environmental Services Consumers Energy, Dennis Dobbs

Vice President, Thomas Miller

Senior Vice President Strategy And Business Planning Cms Energy And Consumers Energy., Venkat Rao

Vp Electric Grid Integration Consumers Energy, Timothy Sparks

Senior Vice President Finance, Tim Kowaleski

Vice President Treasurer And Investor Relations, Srikanth Maddipati

Vice President Rates And Regulation Consumers Energy, Michael Torrey

Vp Human Resources, Catherine Hendrian

Vice President Of Information Technology, David Luck

Chairman, John G. Russell, age 62

Board Member, Myrna Soto

Assistant Treasurer, Thomas Cox

Assistant Secretary, Georgine Hyden

Auditors: PricewaterhouseCoopers LLP

LOCATIONS

HQ: CMS Energy Corp
One Energy Plaza, Jackson, MI 49201
Phone: 517 788-0550
Web: www.cmsenergy.com

PRODUCTS/OPERATIONS

2017 Sales

	$ mil.	% of total
Electric utility	4,448	68
Gas utility	1,774	27
Enterprises	229	3
Other reconciling items	132	2
Total	**6,583**	**100**

Selected Subsidiaries

Consumers Energy Company (electric and gas utility)
CMS Capital
  EnerBank USA (banking services)
CMS Enterprises Company (nonutility holding company)
EnerBank USA

COMPETITORS

AEP	Progress Energy
Alliant Energy	Resources Corp.
Calpine	SCANA
Con Edison	SEMCO ENERGY
DTE	TECO Energy
Edison International	WEC Energy
NextEra Energy	Xcel Energy
NiSource	

HISTORICAL FINANCIALS

Company Type: Public

Income Statement

FYE: December 31

	REVENUE ($ mil.)	NET INCOME ($ mil.)	NET PROFIT MARGIN	EMPLOYEES
12/19	6,845	680	9.9%	8,789
12/18	6,873	657	9.6%	8,625
12/17	6,583	460	7.0%	7,952
12/16	6,399	551	8.6%	7,366
12/15	6,456	523	8.1%	7,804
Annual Growth	**1.5%**	**6.8%**	**—**	**3.0%**

2019 Year-End Financials

Debt ratio: 49.03%	No. of shares (mil.): 283
Return on equity: 13.92%	Dividends
Cash ($ mil.): 140	Yield: 2.4%
Current ratio: 0.86	Payout: 69.8%
Long-term debt ($ mil.): 12,027	Market value ($ mil.): 17,838

	STOCK PRICE ($) FY Close	P/E High/Low	PER SHARE ($) Earnings	Dividends	Book Value
12/19	62.84	27 20	2.39	1.53	17.68
12/18	49.65	23 18	2.32	1.43	16.78
12/17	47.30	31 25	1.64	1.33	15.77
12/16	41.62	23 18	1.98	1.24	15.23
12/15	36.08	20 17	1.89	1.16	14.21
Annual Growth	**14.9%**	**— —**	**6.0%**	**7.2%**	**5.6%**

CNA Financial Corp

CNA Financial is an umbrella organization for a wide range of insurance providers including Continental Casualty and Continental Insurance. It primarily provides commercial policies such as workers' compensation auto and general liability. CNA also sells specialty insurance including professional liability (accountants lawyers architects) and vehicle warranty service contracts. The firm offers commercial surety bonds (through CNA Surety) risk management claims administration and information services. Its products are sold by independent agents and brokers in the US and through partners abroad. Holding company Loews which is controlled and run by the Tisch family owns 90% of CNA.

Operations

CNA Financial operates through three core property/casualty segments and two non-core segments. Its property/casualty segments are Specialty (more than 40% of revenue) Commercial (35%) and International (10%) while non-core business segments are Life & Group and Corporate & Other.

The Specialty segment provides professional financial and specialty products and services through independent agents brokers and managing general underwriters. The Commercial segment includes products sold to small and mid-market organizations primarily through an independent agency distribution system; it also sells commercial insurance and risk management products to large corporations primarily through insurance brokers. The International segment offers management and professional liability products and services outside of the US; distribution is via a network of brokers independent agencies and managing general underwriters. The segment also sells on the Lloyd's marketplace.

Most of CNA Financial's non-core insurance products are in run-off including a few remaining life annuity and pension products as well as accident and health insurance.

Geographic Reach

CNA is headquartered in Chicago and has offices throughout the US (Arizona Florida New York South Dakota and Pennsylvania) and Canada; it also has locations in Europe.

Sales and Marketing

In the US independent agents and brokers market CNA products to customers including businesses of all sizes other insurers associations and professionals while partners handle the coverage abroad. The group primarily targets companies in the health care manufacturing education financial services and construction industries.

Financial Performance

CNA's revenue fell in 2015 but has been rebounding since then. Net income has been somewhat more turbulent but overall has been trending upward.

In 2018 revenue increased 6% to $10.1 billion. This was largely due to changes in the federal corporate income tax rate change. Excluding the positive impact of those changes CNA's core property/casualty income fell some $158 million. Much of that decline was due to lower net investment income for both the Specialty and Commercial segments. Furthermore the International segment reported a loss of $19 million. On the other hand CNA had lower catastrophe losses that year.

Investment earnings also impacted net income which fell 10% to $813 million in 2018. Additionally increased property losses and professional liability losses in the UK drove profits down.

The company ended 2018 with $310 million in net cash $45 million less than it had at the end of 2017. Operating activities provided $1.2 billion while financing activities (primarily dividends paid) used $1.1 billion and investing activities used another $177 million.

Strategy

CNA has renewed its focus on underwriting discipline and on attracting and developing talent. Those efforts paid off in 2018 when the company saw 13% new business growth. It is also strengthening its technological capabilities and in 2018 it outsourced the management of its IT infrastructure to Atos which should free up some cash for business development.

The company's largest segment Specialty has maintained a strong performance and the Commercial segment has also seen growth but CNA's smaller International segment has been marred by property and professional liability losses. In 2019 CNA began exiting certain underperforming lines in its Lloyd's portfolio. That move will lower premium volume but should improve the segment's combined ratio which totaled 107% in 2018. (A combined ratio of more than 100% is the result of an insurer having more losses and expenses than earned premiums.)

Company Background

Merchant Henry Bowen along with a group of investors established Continental Insurance in the 1880s. In 1897 a group of Midwestern investors formed Continental Casualty. Both Continentals rose to the challenges presented by the World Wars and the Depression; they entered the 1950s ready for new growth.

In the 1960s Continental Insurance added interests in Diners Club and Capital Financial Services; in 1968 it formed holding company Continental Corp. Meanwhile Continental Assurance (which had formed its own holding company CNA Financial) went even farther afield adding mutual fund consumer finance nursing home and residential construction companies.

Both companies suffered losses arising from Hurricane Andrew in 1992 but CNA which had done some housecleaning in the 1970s was better able to deal with the blow than Continental which entered the 1990s in need of restructuring.

The two companies merged in 1995 to become one of the US's top 10 insurance companies.

EXECUTIVES

Evp General Counsel And Secretary, Jonathan D. (Jon) Kantor, age 63, $800,000 total compensation
President And Coo Cna Specialty, Mark I. Herman, age 60, $675,000 total compensation
Evp And Cfo, D. Craig Mense, age 67, $825,000 total compensation
President And Ceo Cna Canada, Nick Creatura
Chief Executive Hardy, David J. (Dave) Brosnan, age 56
Evp And Chief Underwriting Officer, Douglas M. (Doug) Worman
Evp Worldwide Property And Casualty Claim, Andrew J. Pinkes, age 56
Chairman And Ceo, Dino E. Robusto, age 60, $114,103 total compensation
Evp And Chief Actuary, Larry A. Haefner, age 62, $367,628 total compensation
President Worldwide Field Operations, Timothy J. (Tim) Szerlong, age 66, $700,000 total compensation
President Long Term Care, Albert J. (Al) Miralles, age 49
President And Coo Cna Commercial, Kevin Leidwinger, age 55
Evp Technology And Operations, Joseph (J.) Merten
Svp And Northeastern Zone Officer, Jim Romanelli
Senior Vice President And Western Zone Officer, Steve Marohn

Vice President Boston Branch, Tom Allen
Svp Financial Institutions And Management Liability Cna Specialty, Paul Larson
Senior Vice President Construction, Song Kim
Senior Vice President And Chief Procurement Officer, Doug Kortfelt
Avp Professional Liability, Michelle Aliperti-urbielewicz
Vp Underwriting, Ryann Elliott
Vp Private And Not For Profit, Dominic Senese
Svp And Chief Marketing Officer, Jennifer Livingstone
Svp Healthcare, Brice Dymtrow
Svp Of Underwriting Services, Katie Wilson
Board Member, Don Randel
Board Member, Michael Bless
Board Member, Andre Rice
Auditors: DELOITTE & TOUCHE LLP

LOCATIONS

HQ: CNA Financial Corp
 151 N. Franklin, Chicago, IL 60606
Phone: 312 822-5000   **Fax:** 312 822-6419
Web: www.cna.com

PRODUCTS/OPERATIONS

2018 Sales by Segment

	$ mil.	% of total
Specialty		
Management & professional	2,440	24
Warranty & alternative risks	1,169	11
Surety	571	6
Commercial		
Middle market	2,045	20
Small business insurance	472	5
Other commercial insurance	1,061	10
Life & Group	1,333	13
International		
Hardy	441	4
Europe	363	4
Canada	255	3
Corporate & Other	39	-
Adjustments	(55)	-
Total	**10,134**	**100**

Selected Solutions

Business interruption
Cargo (ocean marine)
CNA connect
CNA paramount
Commercial auto
Commercial general liability
Cyber liability
Directors & officers (d&o)
Employment practices liability (epl)
Epack extra
Equipment breakdown
Fidelity and crime insurance
Inland marine
International
Kidnap ransom and extortion
Professional liability (errors & omissions)
Property
Surety
Umbrella liability
Warranty
Workers' compensation

COMPETITORS

AIG
American Financial Group
Berkshire Hathaway
Everest Re
Liberty Mutual
Nationwide
Old Republic
The Hartford
Travelers Companies
United Fire
W. R. Berkley
Zurich Insurance Group

HISTORICAL FINANCIALS

Company Type: Public

Income Statement

FYE: December 31

	ASSETS ($ mil.)	NET INCOME ($ mil.)	INCOME AS % OF ASSETS	EMPLOYEES
12/18	57,152	813	1.4%	6,100
12/17	56,567	899	1.6%	6,300
12/16	55,233	859	1.6%	6,700
12/15	55,047	479	0.9%	6,900
12/14	55,566	691	1.2%	6,900
Annual Growth	0.7%	4.1%	—	(3.0%)

2018 Year-End Financials

Debt ratio: 4.69%	No. of shares (mil.): 271
Return on equity: 6.93%	Dividends
Cash ($ mil.): 310	Yield: 7.4%
Current ratio: —	Payout: 110.7%
Long-term debt ($ mil.): —	Market value ($ mil.): 11,985

	STOCK PRICE ($) FY Close	P/E High/Low		PER SHARE ($)		
			Earnings	Dividends	Book Value
12/18	44.15	18 14	2.98	3.30	41.32
12/17	53.05	17 12	3.30	3.10	45.15
12/16	41.50	13 9	3.17	3.00	44.25
12/15	35.15	25 19	1.77	3.00	43.50
12/14	38.71	17 14	2.55	2.00	47.39
Annual Growth	3.3%	— —	4.0%	13.3%	(3.4%)

CNB Financial Corp. (Clearfield, PA)

CNB Financial is the holding company for CNB Bank ERIEBANK and FCBank. The banks and subsidiaries provide traditional deposit and loan services as well as wealth management merchant credit card processing and life insurance through nearly 30 CNB Bank- and ERIEBANK-branded branches in Pennsylvania and nine FCBank branches in central Ohio. Commercial industrial and agricultural loans make up more than one-third of the bank's loan portfolio while commercial mortgages make up another one-third. It also makes residential mortgages consumer and credit card loans. The company's non-bank subsidiaries include CNB Securities Corporation Holiday Financial Services Corporation and CNB Insurance Agency.

Operations

Commercial industrial and agricultural loans made up 36% of the bank's $16.74 billion loan portfolio at the end of 2015 while commercial mortgages made up another 33%. The rest of the portfolio was made up of residential mortgages (15% of loan assets) consumer (14%) overdrafts (less than 1%) and credit card loans (less than 1%).

The group makes more than 80% of its revenue from interest income. About 70% of its revenue came from loan interest during 2015 while another 15% came from interest income from taxable and tax-exempt securities. The remainder of its revenue came from deposit account service charges (4% of revenue) wealth and asset management fees (3%) and other miscellaneous income sources.

Geographic Reach

Clearfield Pennsylvania-based CNB Financial serves clients in its home state as well as in Ohio.

CNB Financial serves a specific market area such as the Pennsylvania counties of Cambria Cameron Centre Clearfield Crawford Elk Erie Indiana Jefferson McKean and Warren.

Sales and Marketing

The group serves individuals businesses government and institutional customers.

CNB Financial has been increasing its advertising spend in recent years. It spent $1.6 million during 2015 up from $1.5 million and $1 million in 2014 and 2013 respectively.

Financial Performance

CNB Financial's revenues have risen more than 30% since 2011 as its loan assets have nearly doubled to $1.58 billion. The firm's profits have grown nearly 50% over the same period as low-interest rates and declining loan loss provisions have lowered operating costs.

The group's revenue climbed 1% to $102 million during 2015 thanks to a modest rise in interest income stemming mostly from 16% loan asset growth.

Despite revenue growth in 2015 CNB Financial's net income dipped 4% to $22.2 million mostly due to nearly 10% rise in salary and employee benefit costs from new hires and more expensive benefits. The group's operating cash levels jumped 16% to $34 million for the year thanks to favorable working capital changes related to accrued interest payables and other liabilities.

Strategy

CNB Financial has been acquiring other banks and opening branches in new geographic markets in recent years to boost its loan and deposit business. As a sign of success the bank noted that its assets have nearly doubled in size since 2009 from $1.16 billion to $2.29 billion at the end of 2015.

Toward its branch expansion plans the group's ERIEBANK brand entered Ohio by opening a loan production office there in 2014 with plans to open another by the end of 2016. After opening an FCBank branch in Dublin Ohio in 2014 the group in 2016 also continued to push its FCBank brand which has been enjoying double-digit loan and deposit business growth in the Columbus and Lancaster regions in Ohio. It plans to open a new FCBank branch in Worthington Ohio by the end of 2016.

Mergers and Acquisitions

In 2016 CNB looked expanded into Northeast Ohio after buying Mentor Ohio-based Lake National Bank — and its $152 million in assets — for nearly $25 million. Lake National Bank's operations were folded into ERIEBANK's operations when the transaction closed.

In 2013 extending its reach in Ohio CNB Financial acquired FC Banc Corp. for $41.6 million. The deal gave CNB Financial Farmers Citizens Bank which serves the northern Ohio communities of Bucyrus Cardington Fredericktown Mount Hope and Shiloh as well as the greater Columbus Ohio area.

Company Background

In 2012 CNB Financial acquired an Ebensburg Pennsylvania-based consumer discount company which brought with it a loan portfolio valued at about $1 million.

EXECUTIVES

Evp Human Resources, Mary Ann Conaway
Sevp And Chief Credit Officer Cnb Bank, Mark D. Breakey, age 60, $211,000 total compensation
President And Ceo, Joseph B. Bower, age 55, $458,000 total compensation
Sevp And Coo Cnb Bank, Richard L Greslick, age 43, $221,000 total compensation

Evp Cfo And Treasurer Cnb Bank And Treasurer Principal Financial Officer And Principal Accounting Officer Cnb Financial Corporation, Brian W. Wingard, age 45, $210,000 total compensation
Evp And Chief Commercial Banking Officer Cnb Bank, Joseph E. Dell, age 63, $211,000 total compensation
Evp Customer Experience, Leanne D. Kassab
Assistant Vice President Of Mortgage Lending, Eileen Ryan
Avp Human Resources, Shannon Irwin
Vice Presidents Commercial Banking, Joseph Yaros
Assistant Vice President Compliance, Kylie Ogden
Vice President, Andrew Roman
Senior Vice President Chief Lending Officer, Jeffrey Alabran
Executive Vice President Coo, Rich Greslick
Senior Vice President Of Operations, Vincent C Turiano
Vice President Information Technology, Bonnie Garito
Chairman, Peter F. Smith, age 64
Board Member, Jeffrey Powell
Board Member, Robert Montler
Board Member, Deborah Pontzer
Auditors: Crowe LLP

LOCATIONS

HQ: CNB Financial Corp. (Clearfield, PA)
1 South Second Street, P.O. Box 42, Clearfield, PA 16830
Phone: 814 765-9621
Web: www.cnbbank.bank

PRODUCTS/OPERATIONS

2015 Sales

	$ mil.	% of total
Interest and Dividend Income		
Loans including fees	71	70
Securities		
Taxable	11	10
Tax-exempt	3	4
Dividends	0	1
Non-Interest Income		
Wealth and asset management fees	3	3
Service charges on deposit accounts	4	4
Other service charges and fees	3	3
Other revenues	4	5
Total	102	100

Selected Services

Checking
Credit cards
Loans
Savings

COMPETITORS

AmeriServ Financial
CBT Financial
Citizens Financial Group
First Commonwealth Financial

M&T Bank
Northwest Bancshares
PNC Financial
S&T Bancorp

HISTORICAL FINANCIALS

Company Type: Public

Income Statement — FYE: December 31

	ASSETS ($ mil.)	NET INCOME ($ mil.)	INCOME AS % OF ASSETS	EMPLOYEES
12/18	3,221	33	1.0%	556
12/17	2,768	23	0.9%	528
12/16	2,573	20	0.8%	507
12/15	2,285	22	1.0%	454
12/14	2,189	23	1.1%	426
Annual Growth	10.1%	9.9%	—	6.9%

2018 Year-End Financials

Debt ratio: 9.80%
Return on equity: 13.31%
Cash ($ mil.): 45
Current ratio: —
Long-term debt ($ mil.): —

No. of shares (mil.): 15
Dividends
Yield: 2.9%
Payout: 36.4%
Market value ($ mil.): 349

	STOCK PRICE ($) FY Close	P/E High/Low	PER SHARE ($) Earnings	Dividends	Book Value
12/18	22.95	15 10	2.21	0.67	17.28
12/17	26.24	19 13	1.57	0.66	15.98
12/16	26.74	20 12	1.42	0.66	14.64
12/15	18.03	12 11	1.54	0.66	14.01
12/14	18.50	12 10	1.60	0.66	13.09
Annual Growth	5.5%	— —	8.4%	0.4%	7.2%

CNO Financial Group Inc

Have a modest but stable income? Graying at the temples? CNO Financial Group finds that especially attractive and has life insurance and related products targeted at you and millions of others. With a focus on middle-income working families and seniors the holding company's primary units include Bankers Life and Casualty which provides Medicare supplement life annuities and long-term care insurance; Washington National which offers specified disease insurance accident insurance life insurance and annuities; and Colonial Penn which offers life insurance to consumers. The company also offers reinsurance. CNO Financial operates nationwide.

Operations

CNO operates through four segments: Bankers Life Washington National Colonial Penn and Long-term care in run-off. The Bankers Life segment accounts for about 70% of CNO's annual revenue and the Washington National segment accounts for more than 20%. Colonial Penn (nearly 10%) and Long-term care in run-off (1%) round out the group's sales.

CNO has some 3.5 million policies in force including third-party policies sold by its Bankers Life agents.

Geographic Reach

With operations throughout the US (including the District of Columbia and certain protectorates) CNO counts Florida Pennsylvania California and Texas among its largest markets. Together the four states account for more than a quarter of CNO's total premiums.

Sales and Marketing

CNO's largest segment Bankers Life sells products through its own team of around 4000 career agents; it also markets Medicare Advantage plans through distribution arrangements with Humana and United HealthCare. The Washington National segment uses a combination of brokers independent agents and worksite marketing programs. The smaller Colonial Penn segment sells policies through direct sales efforts including television advertising direct mail telemarketing and online sales campaigns.

The group's career agent distribution channel brings in the bulk of its business representing some three-fourths of premiums collected. Independent producers account for more than 15% of collected premiums and direct marketing accounts for some 10%.

CNO leases around 275 sales offices.

Financial Performance

CNO had steady single-digit growth until the 2014 sale of Conseco Life Insurance which brought revenue down for a couple of years. Revenue has been rising since but net income has been more turbulent.

In 2017 revenue increased 8% to $4.3 billion. This was largely due to increases in insurance policy and investment income but was partially offset by a decline in fees and other income. Subsidiary Bankers Life had higher collected premium and annuity account values that year. Washington National also had a strong year gaining a record in new annualized premium. Colonial Penn had a reduction in new annualized premium.

Despite the higher revenue in 2017 net income fell 51% to $175.6 million as operating expenses (primarily insurance policy benefits paid) and income tax expenses both rose.

The company ended 2017 with $578.4 million in net cash $100 million more than it had at the end of 2016. Operating activities provided $613.1 million in cash while financing activities used $274 million and investing activities used $239.6 million.

Strategy

CNO believes its target markets of seniors and middle-income families are often overlooked and underserved giving the company opportunity in the senior market which is expected to double over the next decade. One of its strategies is to market Medicare Supplement insurance which is popular among its target customers and cross-sell discretionary products such as life insurance and annuities.

A major priority is growth across a number of areas including broadening its product portfolio revamping its distribution channels to increase efficiency and reach and deepening its reach within certain of its target demographics. For example in 2016 the company launched its own broker-dealer (Bankers Life Securities) and registered investment advisor (Bankers Life Advisory Services) subsidiaries. Those financial services units are a direct response to Middle America 's increasing concern with financial security in retirement when health care costs typically increase.

The company is working to lower its relative exposure to the long-term care business which pose a higher level of tail risk. It stopped selling home health care long-term policies and comprehensive and nursing home long-term care policies with benefits exceeding three years. In 2018 CNO ceded the legacy (prior to 2003) comprehensive and nursing home long-term care policies of subsidiary Bankers Life and Casualty to Wilton Reassurance Company.

To increase profits CNO is working to reduce unnecessary costs across the entire organization while expanding its number of locations. It also works to attract and retain talented employees in part by offering professional development opportunities. For example it is dedicated to increasing the number of career agents holding a securities license which has already helped assets under administration and assets under management grow.

Company Background

In 2010 the company changed its name from Conseco to CNO Financial Group to reflect a broader identity. (The firm also sought to distance itself from historical financial instabilities associated with the Conseco brand.) The name change came after several years' worth of management efforts to conserve capital reduce complexity and debt and sequester or divest less profitable operations.

HISTORY

CNO Financial evolved from Security National an Indiana insurance company formed in 1979 by Stephen Hilbert. The former encyclopedia salesman and Aetna executive believed most insurance companies were bloated and the industry itself overcrowded as well as ripe for consolidation by a smart lean organization.

In 1982 the company began a growth-by-acquisition strategy with the purchase of Executive Income Life Insurance (renamed Security National Life Insurance). The next year it bought Consolidated National Life Insurance and renamed the expanded company Conseco.

The firm went public in 1985 using the proceeds to fund an acquisitions spree that included Lincoln American Life Insurance Lincoln Income Life (sold in 1990) Bankers National Life Insurance Western National Life Insurance (sold in 1994) and National Fidelity Life Insurance.

In 1990 the company formed Conseco Capital Partners (with General Electric and Bankers Trust) to finance acquisitions without seeming to burden the parent company with debt. This device financed the purchase of Great American Reserve and the 1991 acquisition of Beneficial Standard Life. The former Conseco bought Bankers Life Insurance in 1992 then sold 67% of the firm the next year. Also in 1993 the company formed the Private Capital Group to invest in non-insurance companies.

In 1994 the company tried to acquire the much larger Kemper Corp. but shied away from the debt load that the $2.6 billion deal would have entailed. The aborted deal cost $36 million in bank and accounting fees and spelled the end of the company's relationship with Merrill Lynch which had underwritten the company's IPO when a Merrill Lynch analyst downgraded its stock after the fiasco.

Meanwhile Private Capital's success led the company to form Conseco Global Investments. Other investments included stakes in racetrack and riverboat gambling operations in Indiana.

In 1996 and 1997 the firm absorbed eight life health property/casualty and specialty insurance companies and raised its interest in American Life Holdings to 100%.

Itching to move beyond insurance in 1998 the company bought Green Tree Financial the US's #1 mobile home financier. Charges of Green Tree's own fuzzy accounting practices helped torpedo the company's quest for a federal thrift charter. But the troubles had just begun. The mobile home finance industry took a dive as customers refinanced at lower rates and prepayments slammed Green Tree Financial reducing Conseco's earnings.

The company tried to recoup in 1999 by launching an ad campaign portraying the company as the "Wal-Mart of financial services." It also continued the acquisition spree. But Green Tree Financial (renamed Conseco Finance that year) couldn't stanch the flow of red ink: Buyers grew wary of the quality of the finance unit's loan securities and changes in accounting methods cost the parent company a $350 million charge against earnings for 1999.

In 2002 due to its financial woes the NYSE suspended trading in the company and its stock was moved to the OTC. The company also filed for Chapter 11 protection. As part of the reorganization agreement it agreed to sell Conseco Finance. The company's insurance operations were not subject to the Chapter 11 agreement.

In 2003 it finally unloaded the Conseco Finance unit to investor group CFN Investment Holdings and General Electric Co.'s consumer finance unit for $1 billion. The company emerged from bankruptcy in September 2003.

The company agreed to pay a fine of $6.3 million in 2008 after an investigation determined that its long-term care insurance business Conseco Senior Health had wrongly denied claims and mishandled complaints and that some sales and marketing practices at Banker's Life did not comply with industry standards. To put what it could in the past in late 2008 the firm spun off its closed block of long-term care insurance. The new entity was named Senior Health Insurance Company of Pennsylvania and consisted entirely of policies in run-off.

EXECUTIVES

Ceo And Director, Gary C. Bhojwani, age 51, $517,307 total compensation

Evp Coo And Cto, Bruce K. Baude, age 55, $559,487 total compensation

Chief Investment Officer And President 40|86 Advisors, Eric R. Johnson, age 59, $500,000 total compensation

Evp Human Resources, Susan L. (Sue) Menzel, age 53

President Bankers Life And Casualty Company, Scott L. Goldberg, age 48

Evp And Chief Actuary, Christopher J. (Chris) Nickele, age 63, $416,667 total compensation

Evp And General Counsel, Matthew J. (Matt) Zimpfer, age 52

Evp And Cfo, Erik M. Helding, age 46, $357,813 total compensation

President Washington National, Mike Heard

President Colonial Penn, Joel Schwartz

Avp Technical Services, Gevan Arnett

Senior Vice President Underwriting And New Business, David Vega

Vp Application Delivery, Sean Fallon

Vice President, Gregory Turner

Vice President Compensation And Benefits, Grace Brothers

Vice President Finance And Administration Bankers Life, Doug Williams

Vice President Product Marketing, Dana Allen

Vice President Operations, Ken Kueber

Assistant Vice President Internet T Senior Director Customer Service, Ming Tong

Vice President Corporate Development, Adam Auvil

Executive Vice President Government Relations, William Fritts

Vp Corporate Tax, David Humm

Vice President Product Management, Greg Turner

Vice President Valuation, Tim Bischof

Vp Operational Risk And Performance Management, Tricia Borcherding

Vice President Human Resources Services, Mark Rawas

Senior Vice President Enterprise Operations, Jean Linnenbringer

Vp Distribution Planning Bankers Lilfe, Robert Yates

Vp And General Auditor, Tom Kleyle

Vice President, Purushothaman Arivukkarasu

Svp Of Sales And Distribution Of Bankers Life, Nathan Richardson

Chairman, Neal C. Schneider, age 75

Assistant Treasurer, Paul Podgorny

Board Member, Charles Jacklin

Auditors: PricewaterhouseCoopers LLP

LOCATIONS

HQ: CNO Financial Group Inc
11825 N. Pennsylvania Street, Carmel, IN 46032
Phone: 317 817-6100
Web: www.cnoinc.com

PRODUCTS/OPERATIONS

2017 Sales

	$ mil.	% of total
Insurance policy income	2,647	61
General account assets	1,285	30
Policyholder & reinsurer accounts & other special-purpose portfolios	265	6
Net realized investment gains excluding impairment losses	77	2
Fee revenue & other	48	1
Adjustments	(27.1)	–
Total	**4,297**	**100**

2017 Sales by Segment

	% of total
Bankers Life	67
Washington National	23
Colonial Penn	8
Long-term care in run-off	1
Corporate	1
Total	**100**

COMPETITORS

Aflac	MetLife
Allstate	Mutual of Omaha
Colonial Life & Accident	New York Life
	Northwestern Mutual
Gerber Life	Torchmark
MassMutual	

HISTORICAL FINANCIALS

Company Type: Public

Income Statement

FYE: December 31

	ASSETS ($ mil.)	NET INCOME ($ mil.)	INCOME AS % OF ASSETS	EMPLOYEES
12/18	31,439	(315)	—	3,300
12/17	33,110	175	0.5%	3,300
12/16	31,975	358	1.1%	3,400
12/15	31,125	270	0.9%	3,500
12/14	31,184	51	0.2%	4,200
Annual Growth	0.2%	—	—	(5.9%)

2018 Year-End Financials

Debt ratio: 12.66%
Return on equity: (-7.67%)
Cash ($ mil.): 656
Current ratio: —
Long-term debt ($ mil.): —

No. of shares (mil.): 162
Dividends
  Yield: 2.6%
  Payout: —
Market value ($ mil.): 2,414

	STOCK PRICE ($) FY Close	P/E High/Low	PER SHARE ($) Earnings	Dividends	Book Value
12/18	14.88	— —	(1.90)	0.39	20.78
12/17	24.69	25 18	1.02	0.35	29.05
12/16	19.15	10 7	2.01	0.31	25.82
12/15	19.09	15 11	1.39	0.27	22.49
12/14	17.22	80 65	0.24	0.24	23.06
Annual Growth	(3.6%)	— —	—	12.9%	(2.6%)

COASTAL FEDERAL CREDIT UNION

EXECUTIVES

Chb, Joan Nelson
Chb*, Richard S Bloom
SEC-Treas*, William F Smith
Exec V Pres*, Chuck Purvis
Exec V Pres-Coo*, Kris Kovacs

R Vpres,cfo*, Brad Miller
R Vp Chief ADM Offcr*, Brenda Hooks
Corporate Communications Staff, Michael Doi
Technology, Mike Day
Vice-President, David Jacobs
Account Manager, Marta Guzman

LOCATIONS

HQ: COASTAL FEDERAL CREDIT UNION
  1000 SAINT ALBANS DR, RALEIGH, NC 276097347
Phone: 919 420-8000
Web: WWW.COASTAL24.COM

HISTORICAL FINANCIALS

Company Type: Private

Income Statement

FYE: December 31

	ASSETS ($ mil.)	NET INCOME ($ mil.)	INCOME AS % OF ASSETS	EMPLOYEES
12/08	2,087	2	0.1%	400
12/07	1,881	13	0.7%	—
12/06	46	0	—	—
Annual Growth	566.5%	—	—	—

COBANK, ACB

You could say CoBank is dependent on its rural customers and vice versa. A member of the Farm Credit System (which is regulated by the FCA) the $110 billion cooperative bank provides seasonal and wholesale loans to agribusinesses as well as to rural power water and communications cooperatives across the US. The bank also leases vehicles farming equipment and agricultural facilities through various Farm Credit System affiliates. Its core agribusiness customers range from local and regional farmers' cooperatives to multinational food companies. It has counted Land O' Lakes Blue Diamond Almonds and National Beef as among its larger customers. Formed in 1989 CoBank merged with US AgBank in early 2012.

Operations

CoBank operates three main business segments: Strategic Relationships Agribusiness and Rural Infrastructure. Its Strategic Relationships loans made up 50% of its $80 billion loan portfolio at the end of 2014 while Agribusiness and Rural Infrastructure made up another 30% and 20% respectively.

About 76% of CoBank's total revenue came from loan interest in 2014 while another 16% came from interest income on investment securities. The rest of its revenue came from fee income (5% of revenue) prepayment income (1%) and other miscellaneous sources.

Geographic Reach

Based in Colorado the bank operates 15 regional offices throughout the US including locations in Iowa Georgia Texas Connecticut Kansas Missouri and Kentucky. It also has an international office in Singapore.

Sales and Marketing

CoBank mainly serves clients in rural America in the agribusiness water communications and power sectors.

Financial Performance

CoBank's annual revenues and profits have been rising over the past several years thanks to steady loan asset growth across all three of its target loan types (Strategic Relationships Agribusiness and Rural Infrastructure).

The bank's revenue jumped 5% to $2.2 million during 2014 mostly thanks to higher average loan volume and increased earnings from a strengthened balance sheet. CoBank's lending business grew with food and agribusiness customers Farm Credit Association customers and rural energy and communications customers which all in turn contributed to its top-line growth.

Revenue growth in 2014 drove CoBank's net income up 6% to $904.3 million for the year. The bank's operating cash levels dipped 2% to $883.1 million during the year due to unfavorable working capital changes related to accrued interest balance changes.

EXECUTIVES

Cfo, David P. Burlage
Chief Risk Officer, Lori L. O'Flaherty
Coo, Ann Trakimas
Evp Banking Services Group, Antony M. Bahr
Svp And Cio, James R. Bernsten
Evp Regional Agribusiness Banking Group, Amy H. Gales
Central Region President Regional Agribusiness Banking Group, Mike Hechtner
Chief Credit Officer, Daniel Key
Evp Corporate Agribusiness Banking Group, Jonathan B. Logan
Southern Region President Regional Agribusiness Banking Group, Lynn Scherler
Svp And Manager Communications Division, Robert F. (Rob) West
Eastern Region President Regional Agribusiness Banking Group, David Sparks
Western Region President Regional Agribusiness Banking Group, Leili Ghazi
Ceo, Robert B. Engel, $880,000 total compensation
President, Mary E. McBride
Chief Banking Officer; Member Management Executive Committee, Thomas Halverson
Vp And Managing Counsel Legal And Loan Processing Division, Chris Clayton
President Farm Credit Leasing, Mike Romanowski
Svp Power Energy And Utilities Banking Division, Todd E. Telesz
Svp Electric Distribution Water And Community Facilities, Nivin Elgohary
Vice President And Managing Counsel, Christian Clayton
Vice President Lead Relationship Manager, David James
Vice President And Lead Relationship Manager, Natalya Rivkin
Vice President Energy Banking, Allison Dunn
Vice President, Kevin Oliver
Vice President, Marshall Essig
Vice President Policy And Public Affairs, Sarah Tyree
Regional Vice President, Catherine Roddick
Senior Vice President, Matt Cammer
Vice President And Executive D, Matthew Brill
Vice President, Richard Dill
Second Vice Chair, Kevin A. Still
First Vice Chair, Daniel T. (Dan) Kelley
Chairman, Everett M. Dobrinski
Auditors: PRICEWATERHOUSECOOPERS LLP DE

LOCATIONS

HQ: COBANK, ACB
  6340 S FIDDLERS GREEN CIR, GREENWOOD VILLAGE, CO 801114951
Phone: 303 740-6527
Web: WWW.COBANK.COM

COMPETITORS

AgFirst	Northwest Farm Credit
AgStar	Rabo AgriFinance
AgriBank	Wells Fargo
Bank of America	
Farm Credit Services of Mid-America	

HISTORICAL FINANCIALS

Company Type: Private

Income Statement				FYE: December 31
	ASSETS ($ mil.)	NET INCOME ($ mil.)	INCOME AS % OF ASSETS	EMPLOYEES
12/15	117,470	936	0.8%	500
12/14	107,428	904	0.8%	—
12/10	67,700	818	1.2%	—
12/09	58,160	565	1.0%	—
Annual Growth	12.4%	8.8%	—	—

Coca-Cola Co (The)

The Coca-Cola Company is the #1 nonalcoholic beverage company in the world as well as one of the world's most recognizable brands. It is home to more than 500 beverage brands some 20 of those billion-dollar-brands including four of the top five soft drinks: Coca-Cola Diet Coke Fanta and Sprite. In addition to soft drinks it markets waters juice drinks energy and sports drinks dairy and plant-based beverages and ready-to-drink teas and coffees. Other top brands include Minute Maid Powerade Dasani Honest Tea and vitaminwater. With the world's largest beverage distribution system Coca-Cola reaches thirsty consumers in more than 200 countries. Nearly 65% of its sales comes from outside the US.

HISTORY

Atlanta pharmacist John Pemberton invented Coke in 1886. His bookkeeper Frank Robinson named the product after two ingredients coca leaves (later cleaned of narcotics) and kola nuts. By 1891 druggist Asa Candler had bought The Coca-Cola Company and within four years the soda-fountain drink was available in all states; it was in Canada and Mexico by 1898.

Candler sold most US bottling rights in 1899 to Benjamin Thomas and John Whitehead of Chattanooga Tennessee for $1. The two designed a regional franchise bottling system that created more than 1000 bottlers within 20 years. In 1916 Candler retired to become Atlanta's mayor; his family sold the company to Atlanta banker Ernest

Woodruff for $25 million in 1919. Coca-Cola went public that year.

The firm expanded overseas and introduced the slogans "The Pause that Refreshes" (1929) and "It's the Real Thing" (1941). To keep WWII soldiers in Cokes at a nickel a pop the government built 64 overseas bottling plants. Coca-Cola bought Minute Maid in 1960 and began launching new drinks — Fanta (1960) Sprite (1960) TAB (1963) and Diet Coke (1982).

In 1981 Roberto Goizueta became chairman. Four years later with Coke slipping in market share the firm changed its formula and introduced New Coke which consumers soundly rejected (thus Coca-Cola Classic was born). In 1986 it consolidated the US bottling operations it owned into Coca-Cola Enterprises and sold 51% of the new company to the public. Goizueta also engineered the company's purchase of Columbia Pictures in 1982. (Columbia earned Coke a $1 billion profit when it sold the studio to Sony in 1989.)

In 1995 it bought Barq's root beer. Goizueta died of lung cancer in 1997; while he was at the helm the firm's value rose from $4 billion to $145 billion. Douglas Ivester the architect of Coca-Cola's restructured bottling operations succeeded him. An agreement to buy about 30 Cadbury Schweppes beverage brands — including Canada Dry Dr Pepper and Schweppes — outside the US and France was scaled down because of antitrust concerns. Completed in 1999 the deal also excluded Canada much of continental Europe and Mexico. (Cadbury in 2008 spun off its beverage division which became Dr Pepper Snapple Group.)

A battered Ivester resigned in 2000; president and COO Douglas Daft was named chairman and CEO. Coca-Cola began its largest cutbacks ever slashing nearly 5000 jobs and later agreed to pay nearly $193 million to settle a race-discrimination suit filed by African-American workers.

To fortify its portfolio in the fast-growing noncarbonated drinks segment Coca-Cola acquired Mad River Traders (teas juices sodas) and Odwalla (juices and smoothies) in 2001. The company also bought a 35% interest (San Miguel Corporation owned the rest) in bottler Coca-Cola Philippines from Coca-Cola Amatil. (In 2005 Coke bought the remaining percentage of the Philippine bottler.) The company announced the creation of a huge beverage and snack distribution joint venture with Procter & Gamble but the multibillion-dollar operation fell apart before it could begin. Coca-Cola also announced that it would invest $150 million to build bottling facilities in China.

In 2002 Coca-Cola introduced Vanilla Coke its biggest new product launch since the disastrous New Coke debacle. The company also secured distribution rights to Danone's Evian brand in North America and paid about $128 million when it formed a joint venture (CCDA Waters LLC) with Danone to produce market and distribute Danone's bottled water in the North America (including Dannon and Sparkletts brands under license). Also in 2002 Steven Heyer president and COO of Coca-Cola Ventures and Coca-Cola Latin America was named Coca-Cola's new president and COO. (The company's former president Jack Stahl had left after a reorganization in 2001.)

As part of the restructuring initiated by Daft in 2000 another 1000 employees (half in Atlanta) were laid off in 2003 after the company decided to combine several business units under the Coca-Cola North America umbrella. The company laid off 2800 employees worldwide in 2003.

Those layoffs led one former employee to sue claiming the soft drink maker improperly accounted for funds discriminated against minorities and in 2000 rigged test marketing of frozen Coca-Cola at a Virginia Burger King. Coca-Cola said it does not violate general accounting principles and

does not discriminate. However the company said it had already disciplined employees involved in the Burger King tests and Coke executive Thomas Moore who led the fountain drinks division responsible for the questionable tests resigned. Coke also agreed to pay Burger King as much as $21 million to settle the matter. Coke said in 2003 it would reduce its revenue by $9 million to make up for accounting errors from the fountain drinks division that managed the troubled tests. Coke later settled its dispute with the former employee who first raised concerns about Coke's conduct agreeing to pay $500000 in severance and legal costs.

Later in 2003 trouble broke out for the company overseas. Claims surfaced in India that both Coke and Pepsi bottled in that country contain traces of DDT malathion and other pesticides that exceed government limits. Both Coke and Pepsi denied the reports in a joint press conference. Government labs cleared the colas saying the drinks were safe but not before both soft drink companies saw sales dip by as much as 50% in a two-week period.

Trying to boost the younger consumer's interest in its flagship cola Coca-Cola launched new marketing and ad campaigns in 2003. Efforts included changing graphics on Coke bottles and cans back to a more traditional look. However Coca-Cola took the opposite tactic to spur interest in Sprite unveiling Sprite Remix a tropical-flavored version of the soft drink. Minute Maid unveiled Minute Maid Premium Heart Wise which claims to lower cholesterol as long as people consistently drink two glasses a day.

Coca-Cola rolled out a lime version of its Diet Coke in 2004. (The non-diet version came out in 2005.) The flavor joined diet cherry lemon and vanilla. In making the announcement Coca-Cola said it also had reformulated its lemon flavor so that it tastes "lighter." Also in 2004 Coke opened an online music store in the UK called MyCokemusic.com. A month later Coke began selling its Dasani bottled water in the UK and 19 other countries. Later in 2004 the company recalled Dasani water in Europe because of elevated levels of bromate. In addition Daft retired as Coca-Cola's chairman and CEO in 2004 and former Coca-Cola HBC CEO E. Neville Isdell replaced him.

Responding to the growing awareness by consumers of health problems associated with obesity and inactive lifestyles in 2004 Coca-Cola created The Beverage Institute for Health & Wellness a beverage research and educational operation which the company hopes will lead to the creation of more healthful beverage products.

Having introduced Minute Maid products in Russia in 2004 Coke furthered its juice presence in the country with the 2005 purchase of Russian juice maker Multon. Coke bought the company in conjunction with Coca-Cola Hellenic Bottling Co. Later that year Coke began test marketing a Mountain Dew-like drink named Vault in Alabama North Carolina and Tennessee. (Surge a previous Mountain Dew competitor tried by Coke failed in testing.) In 2005 the company announced the phasing out of Vanilla Coke and introduction of Black Cherry Coke.

In 2005 Coke bought Danone's 49% stake in their North American bottled-water venture for about $100 million. The joint venture never turned a profit during its three-year run but Coke hopes full ownership of the Dannon and Sparkletts brands will prove profitable. Coke still shares North American import and marketing rights of Danone's premier water brand Evian which although the world's top-selling bottled water has seen declining in US sales.

The company's rivalry with PepsiCo goes beyond soda to juice products (Coca-Cola's Minute Maid vs. PepsiCo's Tropicana) bottled water

(Dasani vs. Aquafina) and other noncarbonated products. Feeling pressure to stay competitive with these faster selling beverages Coca-Cola introduced an energy drink Full Throttle in 2005.

Also in 2005 Coke also announced a revamping of its global marketing team announcing the retirement of Sandy Allen president of its European division. In an effort to expand its international product offerings later that same year it acquired Brazilian juice maker Sucos Mais for some $48 million.

New drinks introduced in 2006 included Vault (a Mountain Dew knock-off). That year Blak a coffee-flavored Coke (with half the calories and twice the caffeine of a regular Coke that was in development for two years) was first test-marketed in France and subsequently introduced in the US. (The pricey soda — $1.99 for an 8-ounce bottle — was discontinued in the US in 2007 due to poor sales.)

Boosting its drinks in the reduced-calorie category in 2006 the company introduced a so-called "calorie-burning" drink called Enviga a green-tea-based drink. It is marketed through a joint venture with Nestl . (The joint venture called Beverage Partners Worldwide primarily focuses on black tea drinks.)

The company also launched a new line of premium coffee and tea beverages called Far Coast in 2006. The drinks were launched in Canada along with Far Coast concept stores where consumers can taste test the flavors. The company expanded its reach into coffee further with a deal with coffeehouse chain Caribou Coffee. Coca-Cola and Caribou created a new line of ready-to-drink iced coffee beverages.

In 2013 Coca-Cola opened a new bottling plant in Myanmar as part of a planned $200 million investment during the next five years there which also includes adding more than 22000 jobs during that time period.

In 2013 it bought ZICO Beverages a maker of ZICO Pure Premium Coconut Water.

Growing its distribution network in 2013 The Coca-Cola Company bought Sacramento Coca-Cola Bottling Company the sixth-largest independent Coca-Cola bottler in the nation that serves nine northern California counties.

EXECUTIVES

Evp And President Bottling Investments And Supply Chain, Irial Finan, age 62, $908,108 total compensation

Evp And President Coca-cola North America, J. Alexander M. (Sandy) Douglas, age 58, $698,091 total compensation

Evp And Chief Marketing Officer, Marcos de Quinto, age 60, $778,379 total compensation

President Europe Middle East And Africa (emea), Brian J. Smith, age 63

Svp And Cio, Barry N. Simpson, age 58

President And Ceo, James R. Quincey, age 55, $923,625 total compensation

Evp And Cfo, Kathy N. Waller, age 61, $749,365 total compensation

President Coca-cola Refreshments North America, Paul Mulligan

Vice President Of Operations National Di, Kraig Adams

Svp And Cto, Ed Hays, age 60

Svp And Chief Customer And Commercial Leadership Officer, Julie Hamilton, age 53

President Asia Pacific Group, John Murphy, age 57

President West Africa, Peter Njonjo

President South And East Africa, Kelvin Balogun

Svp And President The Mcdonald's Division, Craig Williams

President Latin America Group, Alfredo Rivera, age 57

President Coca-cola Ltd., Shane Grant

President Coca-cola South Pacific, Vamsi Mohan

Vp Connections Plng, Katie Miller

Sr Vp, Brent Hastie

Vice President Retail Channel Strategy A, Kelly Marr

Vice President Contact Centers, Glenn Gemmill

Vice President Marketing, Allison Higbie

Vice President Sales National Accounts Cr, Dean McKillip

Vp Business Planning, Todd Ryan

Vp Finance Us Region Sales, Greg Blumeyer

Vice President Strategic Partnership Marketing, Bruce Mcdonald

Vice President And Controller, Larry Mark

Vice President Sales, David Schuh

Vice President Flavor Supply, Bernard Mcguinness

Vice President National Sales, Scott Woodburn

Vice President Government Relations, Connell Stafford

Vice President Of Tamacc, Ish Arebalos

Vice President Sprite Flavors, Kim Venkatesh

Vice President Environment, Jefferson Seabright

Vice President Retail Marketi, Diane Wallace

Vice President, Matthew T Echols

Vice President Convenience Retail Channel Ccr, Jay J Ard

Vice President Nrs Customer Level I, Patricia Herrick

Vice President Finance, Mark Eppert

Global Vice President And General Manager (coca Cola Freestyle Division), Chris Hellmann

Vice President U S Sales Walmart Custome, Brian Sappington

Vice President Qse, Mary Tarver

Vice President National Retail Sales Spe, Steve Paccone

Vice President Field Service, Patrick Plunkett

Vp Commercial Leadership, Andrew Buckingham

Vice President Sales Bu, Doug C Herrington

Chairman, Muhtar Kent, age 66

Assistant Secretary, Fiona K Payne

Auditors: Ernst & Young LLP

LOCATIONS

HQ: Coca-Cola Co (The)
One Coca-Cola Plaza, Atlanta, GA 30313
Phone: 404 676-2121 **Fax:** 404 676-6792
Web: www.coca-colacompany.com

2018 Sales

	$ mil.	% of total
US	11,344	36
Other countries	20,512	64
Total	**31,856**	**100**

2018 Sales

	$ mil.	% of total
North America	11,768	36
Europe Middle East & Africa	7,702	24
Asia Pacific	5,197	16
Latin America	4,014	12
Bottling Investments	3,771	12
Corporate	105	-
Eliminations	(701)	-
Total	**31,856**	**100**

PRODUCTS/OPERATIONS

2018 Sales

	$ mil.	% of total
Concentrate operations	20,457	64
Finished product operations	11,399	36
Total	**31,856**	**100**

Selected Brands

Sparkling Beverages
  Core sparkling
    Barq's
    Coca-Cola
    Coca-Cola Zero/Coke Zero

Diet Coke/Coca-Cola Light
Fanta
Fresca
Inca Kola
Lift
Schweppes
Sprite
Thums Up
Energy drinks
  Burn
  Nos
  Real Gold
Still Beverages
  Coffee & teas
    Ayataka teas
    Dogadan teas
    Georgia coffees
    Leão/Matte Leão teas
    Nestea teas
    Sokenbicha teas
  Juices and juice drinks
    Cappy
    Del Valle
    Dobriy
    Hi-C
    Minute Maid
    Minute Maid Pulpy
    Simply
  Other still beverages
    glaceau vitaminwater
    Fuze
  Sports drinks
    Aquarius
    Powerade
  Waters
    Bonaqua/Bonaqa
    Ciel
    Dasani
    Ice Dew
    Kinley
    ZICO Pure Premium Coconut Water

COMPETITORS

Danone	Monster Beverage
Dole Food	Naked Juice
Dr Pepper Snapple	Nestlé
Group	PepsiCo
IZZE	Red Bull
Kirin Holdings Company	Suntory Holdings
Kraft Heinz	Unilever PLC
Mondelez International	Wonderful Company

HISTORICAL FINANCIALS

Company Type: Public

Income Statement   FYE: December 31

	REVENUE ($ mil.)	NET INCOME ($ mil.)	NET PROFIT MARGIN	EMPLOYEES
12/18	31,856	6,434	20.2%	62,600
12/17	35,410	1,248	3.5%	61,800
12/16	41,863	6,527	15.6%	100,300
12/15	44,294	7,351	16.6%	123,200
12/14	45,998	7,098	15.4%	129,200
Annual Growth	**(8.8%)**	**(2.4%)**	**—**	**(16.6%)**

2018 Year-End Financials

Debt ratio: 52.34%—
Return on equity: 37.79%
Cash ($ mil.): 8,926
Current ratio: 1.05
Long-term debt ($ mil.): 25,364

Dividends
  Yield: 3.2%
  Payout: 104.0%
Market value ($ mil.): —

	STOCK PRICE ($) FY Close	P/E High/Low		Earnings	PER SHARE ($) Dividends	Book Value
12/18	47.35	33	28	1.50	1.56	3.98
12/17	45.88	164	139	0.29	1.48	4.01
12/16	41.46	31	27	1.49	1.40	5.38
12/15	42.96	26	22	1.67	1.32	5.91
12/14	42.22	28	23	1.60	1.22	6.94
Annual Growth	**2.9%**		**— —**	**(1.6%)**	**6.3%**	**(13.0%)**

Cognizant Technology Solutions Corp.

Cognizant Technology Solutions is aware of the desire to shift business processes to digital technologies and it wants to help. To help customers make the switch the information technology outsourcing company provides intelligent systems automation cloud technologies and cyber security tools. In more traditional IT services Cognizant offers application maintenance business intelligence data warehousing software and systems development and integration and re-engineering services for legacy systems. The company targets companies in financial services health care manufacturing retail and logistics. Most of Cognizant's software development centers and employees are in India.

Operations
Cognizant's financial services business brings in about 35% of revenue followed by the healthcare segment about 30% the products and resources unit about 20% and its communications media and technology operation more than 10%.

The company also offers digital services consulting application development systems integration application testing application maintenance infrastructure services and business process services. Additionally it develops licenses implements and supports proprietary and third-party software products and platforms for the healthcare industry.

Geographic Reach
Cognizant headquartered in Teaneck New Jersey has offices and operations in more than 75 cities including New York London Paris Melbourne Singapore and Sao Paulo in more than 35 countries.

Although it has operations worldwide Cognizant relies heavily on its North American customers (mostly those in the US) which generate more than 75% of its revenue. Combined Europe and the UK constitute the next biggest market accounting for more than 15% of sales.

Sales and Marketing
Cognizant markets and sells through its direct sales force which operates from offices in the US and around the world. The sales process can last between two months to a year depending on the products or services under negotiation.

Cognizant's 10 biggest customers account for about 15% of its revenue.

Financial Performance
Cognizant's revenue marched steadily higher for the past five years rising at an annual rate of 11%. After two years of lower net income profit jumped in 2018.

In 2018 revenue rose to $16.1 billion a 9% increase from $14.8 billion in 2017 with higher sales in each business segment and geographic market. Work to integrate digital technologies into customers' workflows and higher customer spending on discretionary projects helped drive sales higher.

At $2.1 billion Cognizant's 2018 profit was 40% higher than 2017. The company had higher income from operations in 2018 and paid less in taxes in 2018 than 2017.

Cash and equivalents stood at $1.1 billion in 2018 compared to $1.9 billion in 2017. In 2018 operations generated $2.6 billion while investing and financing activities used $1.6 billion and $1.7 billion respectively.

Strategy
Cognizant has aligned its operations to pursue its digital strategy. The company's Digital Business area helps customers design and implement digital

business models while the Digital Operations area provides digital tools for managing customers' business processes. The Cognizant Digital Systems and Technology area helps with their digital IT operations. The company reported that digital-related revenue rose 30% in 2018 and accounts for about 30% of revenue compared to 27% in 2017.

Cognizant has made acquisitions to beef up its digitization expertise and capabilities and to bolster its healthcare offerings. In 2017 and into 2018 the company made five deals to address those areas. The company plans to allocate 25% of its free cash flow for acquisitions that add to its digital capabilities and expand its geographic footprint.

Cognizant offers a mix of on-site and near-shore and offshore service. Unlike competitors that provide no on-site assistance Cognizant typically locates technical and account management teams at its customers' locations with development work handled at dedicated development centers offshore. This boosts Cognizant's bottom line by taking advantage of lower labor costs while maintaining a closer connection with its customers.

Cognizant works in a competitive business where margins are thin and companies try to keep costs low. The industry's practice of short-term contracts with customers makes it easy for customers to move to other service providers. Some of Cognizant's competitors are bigger companies with more resources which can make a difference in hiring employees and bidding for acquisitions.

Mergers and Acquisitions
With recent acquisitions Cognizant has expanded its reach in international markets while adding to its digital capabilities.

In 2019 Cognizant agreed to acquire Zenith Technologies a life sciences manufacturing technology services company headquartered in Cork Ireland. Zenith uses digital technologies to manage control and optimize drug and medical device production. The deal extends Cognizant's services offerings for connected biopharmaceutical and medical device manufacturers. The transaction was expected to close in the 2019 third quarter.

Cognizant acquired Advanced Technology Group (ATG) a consultant on Salesforce.com implementations in 2018. Cognizant cited ATG's quote-to-cash capabilities in making the acquisition. ATG's customers include financial services healthcare communications and technology organizations.

In 2018 Cognizant acquired Bolder Healthcare Solutions a developer of revenue cycle management software for healthcare facilities and physician practices. The deal helps Cognizant expand its healthcare and its digitization efforts.

The 2017 acquisition of TMG Health which provides business process services to Medicare and Medicaid markets was another move to build on healthcare.

The deal for Zone made in 2017 brought a UK-based digital agency specializing in customer experience digital strategy and content creation into Cognizant.

Cognizant also made inroads in the UK and Europe with the acquisition of Netcentric in 2017. Based in Zurich Netcentric's customers include Allianz Mercedes-Benz Swisscom and UBS. It offers services for personalizing customer interaction.

In another 2017 transaction Cognizant acquired Brilliant Service a Japan-based company that develops intelligent products. The acquisition adds to Cognizant's digital service offerings in Japan and expands its presence in Osaka and Tokyo.

Company Background
Cognizant Technology Solutions began as an in-house technology center for Dun & Bradstreet in 1994 and was spun off from D&B in 1996. Two years later Cognizant reorganized and spun off its market research operations into two public companies IMS Health and Nielsen Media Research in order to focus on IT services.

EXECUTIVES

President, Rajeev (Raj) Mehta, age 52, $574,100 total compensation

Evp Strategy And Marketing, Malcolm Frank, age 53, $417,000 total compensation

Executive Vice Chairman Cognizant India, Ramakrishnan Chandrasekaran, age 61, $152,925 total compensation

Cfo, Karen McLoughlin, age 54, $426,500 total compensation

Ceo And Director, Francisco D'Souza, age 50, $664,300 total compensation

Coo, Srinivasan Veeraghavachary

Evp And President Global Industries And Consulting, Ramakrishna Prasad Chintamaneni, age 49, $417,250 total compensation

Evp And President Global Client Services, Dharmendra Kumar Sinha, age 56, $356,504 total compensation

Assistant Vice President Global Information Technology Merger And Acquisition Infrastructure Build Outs, Ramesh Lakshminarayan

Vp And Head Global Corporate Strategy, Pascal Aguirre

Associate Vice President Legal, Rohan Sukhdeo

Avp Analytics And Information Management, Jay Warren

Assistant Vice President Projects, Ronald Trella

Vice President Corp. Comm., Richard Lacroix

Senior Vice President Of Marketing, Robert Painter

Vice President, Curtis Girod

Assistant Vice President Business Development, James Burton

Assistant Vice President Healthcare, Gopal Iyer

Avp And Partner Digital Strategy, John Mcvay

Assistant Vice President Projects, Norma Hauer

Vice Chairman, Lakshmi Narayanan, age 66

Chairman, John E. Klein, age 77

Board Member, John N Fox

Auditors: PricewaterhouseCoopers LLP

LOCATIONS

HQ: Cognizant Technology Solutions Corp.
Glenpointe Centre West, 500 Frank W. Burr Blvd., Teaneck, NJ 07666
Phone: 201 801-0233   **Fax:** 201 801-0243
Web: www.cognizant.com

2018 Sales

	$ mil.	% of total
North America	12,293	76
Europe		
United Kingdom	1,274	10
Rest of Europe	1,563	6
Other	995	6
Total	**16,125**	**100**

PRODUCTS/OPERATIONS

Selected Services
Application design development integration and re-engineering
  Complex custom systems development
  Customer relationship management (CRM)
  Data warehousing/Business intelligence (BI)
  Enterprise resource planning (ERP)
  Software testing services
IT consulting and technology services
  Business and knowledge process consulting
  IT strategy consulting
  Program management consulting
  Technology consulting
Outsourcing services
  Application maintenance
  Business and knowledge process outsourcing
  Cloud
  CRM and ERP maintenance

Custom application maintenance
IT infrastructure outsourcing
Mobility

2018 Sales

	$ mil.	% of total
Financial services	5,845	36
Health care	4,668	30
Products and Resources	3,415	21
Communications Media and Technology	2,197	13
Total	**16,125**	**100**

2018 Sales

	$ mil.	% of total
Consulting and Technology Services	9,309	59
Outsourcing Services	6,816	42
Total	**16,125**	**100**

Industries

Industries
Banking & Financial Services
Communications
Consumer Goods
Education
Energy & Utilities
Healthcare
Information Services
Insurance
Life Sciences
Manufacturing
Media & Entertainment
Retail
Technology
Transportation & Logistics
Travel & Hospitality

COMPETITORS

Accenture	Genpact
Atos	HCL Technologies
Capgemini	IBM Global Services
Computer Sciences	Infosys
Corp.	Tata Consultancy
EPAM	Wipro

HISTORICAL FINANCIALS

Company Type: Public

Income Statement   FYE: December 31

	REVENUE ($ mil.)	NET INCOME ($ mil.)	NET PROFIT MARGIN	EMPLOYEES
12/18	16,125	2,101	13.0%	281,600
12/17	14,810	1,504	10.2%	260,000
12/16	13,487	1,553	11.5%	260,200
12/15	12,416	1,623	13.1%	221,700
12/14	10,262	1,439	14.0%	211,500
Annual Growth	12.0%	9.9%	—	7.4%

2018 Year-End Financials

Debt ratio: 4.68%
Return on equity: 19.02%
Cash ($ mil.): 1,161
Current ratio: 3.12
Long-term debt ($ mil.): 736

No. of shares (mil.): 577
Dividends
Yield: 1.2%
Payout: 32.5%
Market value ($ mil.): 36,628

	STOCK PRICE ($) FY Close	P/E High/Low	PER SHARE ($) Earnings	Dividends	Book Value
12/18	63.48	23 17	3.60	0.80	19.80
12/17	71.02	30 20	2.53	0.45	18.14
12/16	56.03	25 19	2.55	0.00	17.64
12/15	60.02	26 19	2.65	0.00	15.23
12/14	52.66	45 18	2.35	0.00	12.70
Annual Growth	4.8%	— —	11.3%	—	11.7%

Colgate-Palmolive Co.

Colgate-Palmolive takes a bite out of grime. The company is a top global maker and marketer of toothpaste (it has more than 40% of the global market) and soap and cleaning products. Colgate-Palmolive also offers pet nutrition products through subsidiary Hill's Pet Nutrition which makes Science Diet Ideal Balance and Prescription Diet pet foods. Many of its oral care products fall under the Colgate brand and include toothbrushes mouthwash and dental floss. Its Tom's of Maine unit covers the natural toothpaste niche. Personal and home care items include Ajax brand household cleaner Palmolive dishwashing liquid Softsoap shower gel and Sanex and Speed Stick deodorants. The company has operations in 80-plus countries and sells its products in more than 200 countries.

HISTORY

William Colgate founded The Colgate Company in Manhattan in 1806 to produce soap candles and starch. Colgate died in 1857 and the company was passed to his son Samuel who renamed it Colgate and Company. In 1873 the company introduced toothpaste in jars and in 1896 it began selling Colgate Dental Cream in tubes. By 1906 Colgate was making 160 kinds of soap 625 perfumes and 2000 other products. The company went public in 1908.

In 1898 Milwaukee's B. J. Johnson Soap Company (founded 1864) introduced Palmolive a soap made of palm and olive oils rather than smelly animal fats. It became so popular that the firm changed its name to The Palmolive Company in 1916. Ten years later Palmolive merged with Peet Brothers a Kansas City-based soap maker founded in 1872. Palmolive-Peet merged with Colgate in 1928 forming Colgate-Palmolive-Peet (shortened to Colgate-Palmolive in 1953). The stock market crash of 1929 prevented a planned merger of the company with Hershey and Kraft.

During the 1930s the firm purchased French and German soap makers and opened branches in Europe. Colgate-Palmolive-Peet introduced Fab detergent and Ajax cleanser in 1947 and the brands soon became top sellers in Europe. The company expanded to Asia in the 1950s and by 1961 foreign sales were 52% of the total.

Colgate-Palmolive introduced a host of products in the 1960s and 1970s including Palmolive dishwashing liquid (1966) Ultra Brite toothpaste (1968) and Irish Spring soap (1972). During the same time the company diversified by buying approximately 70 other businesses including Kendall hospital and industrial supplies (1972) Helena Rubinstein cosmetics (1973) Ram Golf (1974) and Riviana Foods and Hill's Pet Products (1976). The strategy had mixed results and most of these acquisitions were sold in the 1980s.

Reuben Mark became CEO of Colgate-Palmolive in 1984. The company bought 50% of Southeast Asia's leading toothpaste Darkie in 1985; it changed its name to Darlie in 1989 following protests of its minstrel-in-blackface trademark. Both Palmolive automatic dishwasher detergent and Colgate Tartar Control toothpaste were introduced in 1986. That year Colgate-Palmolive purchased the liquid soap lines of Minnetonka the most popular of which is Softsoap. In 1992 the company bought Mennen maker of Speed Stick (the leading US deodorant).

Increasing its share of the oral care market in Latin America to 79% in 1995 Colgate-Palmolive acquired Brazilian company Kolynos (from Wyeth

for $1 billion) and 94% of Argentina's Odol Saic. The company also bought Ciba-Geigy's oral hygiene business in India increasing its share of that toothpaste market. At home however sales and earnings in key segments were dismal so in 1995 Colgate-Palmolive began a restructuring that included cutting more than 8% of its employees and closing or reconfiguring 24 factories in two years.

The company introduced a record 602 products in 1996 and continued to expand its operations in countries with emerging economies. In 1997 Colgate-Palmolive took the lead in the US toothpaste market for the first time in 35 years (displacing P&G).

In 1999 the company sold the rights to Baby Magic (shampoos lotions oils) in the US Canada and Puerto Rico to Playtex Products retaining the rights in all other countries. Two years later the company sold its heavy-duty laundry detergent business in Mexico (primarily the Viva brand) to Henkel one of Europe's leading detergent producers.

In 2002 Colgate-Palmolive introduced a teeth-whitening gel Simply White to compete with rival P&G's Crest Whitestrips. The company saw success that year when its Hill's Pet Nutrition subsidiary launched new specialty foods for cats and dogs; one of its dog foods reportedly slows brain aging in canines.

In late 2004 Colgate-Palmolive implemented a four-year restructuring plan. Its three primary objectives were to increase profit reallocate resources to promising growth areas and leverage global market efficiencies. It implemented the plan by reducing its global workforce by some 12% closing about 25 of its 78 factories and focusing on core units. Colgate-Palmolive also built new state-of-the-art plants to produce toothpaste in the US and Poland. The company believed that its savings estimated at $500 million altogether would allow it to fund investments in its key businesses as well as provide for new product development.

By selling its North American laundry detergent brands in 2005 Colgate-Palmolive began focusing on the high-margin pearly whites (with bite) of its portfolio — oral care and pet care. The company's purchase of natural oral-care products maker Tom's of Maine in 2006 marked its effort to target the natural niche. It bought some 84% of the firm for about $100 million.

Chairman and CEO Reuben Mark handed over the title of CEO to then-president and COO Ian Cook in July 2007 and the title of chairman to Cook in January 2009; Mark retired at the end of 2008.

Colgate-Palmolive in early 2010 sold its Code 10 brand which boasted about a 10% market share. Indian consumer goods maker Marico acquired the Malaysian hair-styling name; the move was intended to allow Colgate-Palmolive to focus on its oral personal and pet care businesses.

EXECUTIVES

Cfo, Dennis J. Hickey, age 70, $910,000 total compensation
Chairman President And Ceo, Ian M. Cook, age 67, $1,309,000 total compensation
Vp Global Hr, Laura Flavin
Vice President, Malcolm Williams
President Global Oral Care, Suzan F. Harrison
Vp And General Manager Colgate South Pacific, Chris E. Pedersen
President Colgate Mexico, Ricardo (Ricky) Ramos
Chief Supply Chain Officer, Michael A. (Mike) Corbo
President Colgate Latin America, Panagiotis Tsourapas
Coo Global Innovation And Growth And Hill's Pet Nutrition, Noel R. Wallace

President And Ceo Hill's Pet Nutrition, Peter Brons-Poulsen
President Hill's International, P. Justin Skala, age 60, $734,333 total compensation
Vp And General Manager Colgate U.s., Derek A. Gordon
Vp Colgate-latin America, Bernal Saborio
Vp And Controller, Henning Jakobsen, age 59
President Colgate-africa/eurasia, Jean-Luc Fischer
Vp And General Manager Colgate Central Europe East, Wojciech Krol
Vp And General Manager Colgate Brazil, Andrea Lagioia
Vp Global Research And Development, Patricia Verduin, age 59
President Colgate-north America, Juan Pablo Zamorano
Vp And General Manager Colgate Latin America, Massimo Poli
Vp; General Manager Colgate-venezuela, Ruben Young
President Colgate Asia Pacific, Vinod Nambiar
Vp And General Manager Colgate-north Africa Middle East, Burc Cankat
Vp And General Manager Colgate Northern Europe, Philip Durocher
Cio, Mike Crowe
Vp And General Manager Colgate India And South Asia, Issam Bachaalani
President Colgate Europe, Prabha Parameswaran
Vp And General Manager Colgate-philippines, Arvind Sachdev
Vp Hill's Pet Nutrition-eurasia, David Scharf
Vp And General Manager Colgate Central Europe West, Dany Schmidt
Vp And General Manager Greater China, Stephen Lau
Vp And General Manager Colgate North America, Bill Van de Graaf
Vp And Gm Colgate Andina Region, Hector Pedraza
Chief Information And Business Services Officer, Thomas (Tom) Greene
Vp And General Manager Global Toothbrush Division, Christopher Rector
Vp And General Manager Colgate-north America, Anne-Marie Motte
Vp And General Manager Colgate-north America, Julie Dillon
Vp And General Manager Tom's Of Maine, Nancy Pak
Vp And General Manager Colgate Western Europe, Andrew Shepard
Vp And General Manager Colgate South Africa, Orlando Tenorio
Vp And General Manager Global Personal Care, John Hazlin
Vp And General Manager Colgate Southern Cone, Adriana Leite
Vp And General Manager Hawley & Hazel, Eddie Niem
Vice President Global Information Technology, Paul McGarry
Vice President Global Oral Care, Jay Jayaraman
Vp Global Insights, Richard Thorogood
Vice President Colgate Latin America, Pablo Mascolo
Vice President Sourcing, Katherine Freeley
Vice President Deputy General Counsel Operations, Rosemary Nelson
Vp Safety Sustainability And Supply Chain Strategy, Ann Tracy
Vice President Global Supply Chain, Warren Pruitt
Vice President Global Legal, Peter Graylin
Vp, Paolo Rossetto
Vp Enterprise Risk Management, Elise Halvorson
Vp Global Marketing, Dan Wish
Vp Global Finance, Scott Cain
Vp, Mauro Watanabe
National Account Manager, Jenny Squier
Vp, Chad D Riley

Vice President Worldwide Shopper Marketing, Steve Fogarty
Vice President Global Information Technology, Marianne Delorenzo
Vice President Colgate Africa Middle East, Robert Tatera
Vice President, Tom Boyd
Vice President Seni, Andrea Bernard
Vp And Corporate Treasurer, Elaine Paik
Vp Global Legal, Nina Huffman
Vp And Gm Colgate Eurasia, Alan Wolpert
Vice President Ethics And Compliance, Bob Holland
Vp Colgate North America, Pascal Montilus
Vp Chief Business Services Officer, Stephane Lionnet
Vp Hill's Pet Nutrition Japan, Joy Klemencic
Vp Global Information Technology, David Foster
Vp, Valerie Haliburton
Vp Colgate Europe, Vangelis Spyridakos
Svp Chief Of Staff, John J Huston
Vice President Global Research And Development, Daniel Bagley
National Account Manager, Ray Runyan
Senior Vice President Investor Relations, Jon Simon
National Account Manager, Susan Siao
Vice President Colgate Latin America, Jose Fernando Serrano
Vice President And General Manager Colgate Southern Europe, Riccardo Ricci
Senior Vice President Investor Relations, John Faucher
Vice President Global Legal, Lisa Mather
Vice President Hill 's Pet Nutrition, Donald Beatty
Vp Global Legal, Charalabos Klados
Vice President Corporate Audit, Gregory Malcolm
Vp Global It, Javier Llinas
Vice President Colgate Asia Pacific, Iain Kielty
Vice President Colgate Africa Eurasia, Godfrey Nthunzi
Vice President Colgate Europe And Africa Eurasia, Robert Hofmann
Vp Colgate Asia Pacific, Raymond Ho
Vp Global Human Resources, Lynne Tapper
Vp Global Legal, Cliff Wilkins
Vice President Colgate Africa Eurasia, Debashish Roy
Vice President Hill 's Pet Nutrition, Michele Ross
Vice President Colgate Mexico, Diana Geofroy
Vice President And General Manager Colgate Central America, Francisco Munoz
Vice President Global Sustainability And Environmental Health And Safety, Lori Michelin
Vice President And Gm Colgate Cace, Shekar Bharatwaj
Senior Vice President General Counsel, Andrew Hendry
Vice President, Danielle Koffer
Vp Global Marketing Communications, Maria Elisa Carvajal
Vp Global Research And Development, Constantina Christopoulou
Vice President Colgate Latin America, Kim Faulker
Vp Chief Security Officer, Nancy Rolph
Vice President Colgate Latin America, Jose Fernando Fernando Serrano
Vp Global Research And Development, Angel Dario Belalcazar
Executive Vice President Chief Growth And Strategy Officer, P Justin Skala
Vp And Gm, Maria Paula Capuzzo
Vp Chief Business Services Officer, Stephanie Lionnet
Vp And Gm Colgate Greater China, Winnie Wong
Vp Chief Communications Officer, Paula David
Executive Vice President Strategic Business Operations Customer And Partner Engagement Salesforce.com Inc., Lisa M Edwards

Executive Vice President Chief Growth And Strategy Officer, Peter Skala
President Colgate Europe, Franck J. Moison, age 66
Board Member, Stephen Sadove
Board Member, Crystal Harris
Assistant Treasurer, Eric Warren
Board Member, John Bilbrey
Board Member, Lorrie Norrington
Board Member, James Maiorana
Auditors: PricewaterhouseCoopers LLP

LOCATIONS

HQ: Colgate-Palmolive Co.
300 Park Avenue, New York, NY 10022
Phone: 212 310-2000   **Fax:** 212 310-3284
Web: www.colgatepalmolive.com

2017 Sales

	$ mil.	% of total
Oral personal & home care		
Latin America	3,887	25
North America	3,117	20
Asia Pacific	2,781	18
Europe	2,394	16
Africa/Eurasia	983	6
Pet nutrition	2,292	15
Total	**15,454**	**100**

PRODUCTS/OPERATIONS

2017 Sales

	$ mil.	% of total
Oral personal & home care	13,162	85
Pet nutrition	2,292	15
Total	**15,454**	**100**

Selected Brands

Home Care
  Ajax
  Fabuloso
  Murphy Oil Soap
  Palmolive
  Suavitel
Oral Care
  Colgate
Personal Care
  Afta
  Irish Spring
  Sanex
  Skin Bracer
  Softsoap
  Speed Stick
Pet Nutrition
  Prescription Diet
  Science Diet

COMPETITORS

Avon	Johnson & Johnson
Campbell Soup	Kimberly-Clark
Church & Dwight	Kraft Heinz
Clorox	Nestlé
ConAgra	Nu Skin
Estée Lauder	Philips Oral
General Mills	Procter & Gamble
GlaxoSmithKline	Reckitt Benckiser
Hain Celestial	Sun Products
Henkel	Unilever NV

HISTORICAL FINANCIALS

Company Type: Public

Income Statement   FYE: December 31

	REVENUE ($ mil.)	NET INCOME ($ mil.)	NET PROFIT MARGIN	EMPLOYEES
12/18	15,544	2,400	15.4%	34,500
12/17	15,454	2,024	13.1%	35,900
12/16	15,195	2,441	16.1%	36,700
12/15	16,034	1,384	8.6%	37,900
12/14	17,277	2,180	12.6%	37,700
Annual Growth	**(2.6%)**	**2.4%**	**—**	**(2.2%)**

2018 Year-End Financials

Debt ratio: 52.35%
Return on equity: ***,***.**%
Cash ($ mil.): 726
Current ratio: 1.14
Long-term debt ($ mil.): 6,354

No. of shares (mil.): 862
Dividends
  Yield: 2.7%
  Payout: 60.3%
Market value ($ mil.): 51,361

	STOCK PRICE ($) FY Close	P/E High/Low	PER SHARE ($) Earnings	Dividends	Book Value
12/18	59.52	28 21	2.75	1.66	(0.12)
12/17	75.45	34 28	2.28	1.59	(0.07)
12/16	65.44	27 23	2.72	1.55	(0.28)
12/15	66.62	47 39	1.52	1.50	(0.33)
12/14	69.19	30 25	2.36	1.42	1.26
Annual Growth	(3.7%)	— —	3.9%	4.0%	—

COLORADO HOUSING AND FINANCE AUTHORITY

EXECUTIVES

Ceo, Cris A White
Chief Operating Officer*, Jaime Gomez
Cfo*, Patricia Hippe
Int Gen Coun*, Charles L Borgman
Manager, Aaron Fuerst
Program Compliance Officer, Alyssa Swenson
Manager, Beth Truby
Senior Developer, Bill Spencer
Director, Dana Pearce
Asset Management Officer, Darcey Borzileri
Program Compliance Officer, Davina Ray
Auditors: CLIFTON & GUNDERSON LLP GREEN

LOCATIONS

HQ: COLORADO HOUSING AND FINANCE AUTHORITY
  1981 BLAKE ST, DENVER, CO 802021229
Phone: 303 297-2432
Web: WWW.CHFAINFO.COM

HISTORICAL FINANCIALS

Company Type: Private

Income Statement				FYE: December 31
	ASSETS ($ mil.)	NET INCOME ($ mil.)	INCOME AS % OF ASSETS	EMPLOYEES
12/18	2,354	52	2.2%	150
12/17	2,192	52	2.4%	—
12/16	2,037	24	1.2%	—
12/09	3,671	(15)	—	—
Annual Growth	(4.8%)	—	—	—

Columbia Banking System Inc

Columbia Banking System (CBS) is the roughly $13 billion-asset holding company for Columbia Bank. The regional community bank has about 150 branches in Washington from Puget Sound to the timber country in the southwestern part of the state as well as in northern Oregon and Idaho. Targeting retail and small to medium-sized business customers the bank offers standard retail services such as checking and savings accounts CDs IRAs credit cards loans and mortgages. Commercial and multifamily residential real estate loans make up about 45% of the company's loan portfolio while business loans make up another 40%.

Financial Performance

Bolstered by consistent growth in its loan and securities portfolio caused by acquisitions and organic growth Columbia Banking System (CBS) has seen rising revenue each of the last five years to yield an overall expansion of more than 50%; net income fared even better?more than doubling in that time as the bank consolidated physical branches.

The holding company increased its revenue 22% to $565.9 million in 2018 on a large increase in CBS's loan and securities portfolios following its 2017 acquisition of Pacific Continental the parent company of Pacific Continental Bank?which had $2.9 billion in assets.

CBS's net income rose 53% to $172.9 million on the strength of its revenue gains and a lower income tax provision caused by US tax reform.

The company used $64.9 million of its cash in 2018 to end the year with $277.6 million. Operations provided $237.2 million and financing activities?primarily Federal Home Loan Bank advances?generated $203.9 million. CBS used $506 million on investments which mainly comprised purchases of debt securities available for sale.

Strategy

Columbia Banking System (CBS) has grown its loan and securities base recently through a major acquisition while reducing its costs by consolidating physical branches and adopting digital banking technologies.

In 2017 CBS acquired Pacific Continental for $644.8 million. Pacific Continental is the holding company for Pacific Continental Bank which had 14 branches in Oregon and Washington. The purchase gave CBS $2.9 billion in assets (including $1.9 billion in loans) and $2.1 billion in deposits.

Amid the rising popularity of digital banking CBS consolidated one branch in 2017 and seven branches in 2018. It has plans to consolidate a further three branches in 3Q19. The company's 2018 digital banking initiatives include programs to enable digital commercial business and healthcare banking; use data to drive its workforce; upgrade its digital enterprise workflows; and expand its base of employees with expertise in the digital environment. CBS's Columbia Connect platform allows retail customers to deposit checks pay bills transfer funds or locate physical branches or ATMs via internet-connected devices.

Company Background

Columbia Banking System took advantage of the rash of bank failures in past years to increase its presence in the Pacific Northwest region. It added more than 30 branches in 2010 when it acquired most of the deposits and assets of failed banks Columbia River Bank and American Marine Bank a week apart. In similar transactions in 2011 it acquired most of the operations of the failed institutions Summit Bank First Heritage Bank and Bank of Whitman. Those deals added more than a dozen branches in Washington.

EXECUTIVES

Evp And Chief Credit Officer, Andrew L. (Andy) McDonald, age 60, $298,000 total compensation
Evp And Cfo, Clint E. Stein, age 48, $345,000 total compensation
Ceo, Hadley S. Robbins, age 62, $369,827 total compensation
Evp And General Counsel, Kumi Yamamoto Baruffi, age 49
Evp And Chief Human Resources Officer, David C. (Dave) Lawson, age 61, $247,500 total compensation
Vice President, Michael Drake
Vice President Fiduciary Officer, Barbara Root
Senior Vice President And Manager, Kathy Peterman
Senior Vice President Team Leader, Chris Gruenfeld
Vice President, Chris Bohl
Vice President Appraisal Review, Michael Munson
Vice President Senior Financial Advisor With Cb Financial, John Brunk
Vice President Operations, Avery Johnson
Vice President Professional Banking Officer, Chris Frankovich
Vice President, Thomas Poole
Vice President Commercial Banking Officer, Antoine White
Vice President, Harold Boucher
Vice President Private Banking Relationship Manager, Donna Himpler
Avp Wealth Advisor, Ron Polluconi
Vice President Branch Manager, Deb Wilding
Vice President Branch Manager, Rob Stewart
Vice President District Manager, Ryan Munsey
Vice President, Melissa Case
Assistant Vice President Residential Loan Officer, Alan Day
Vice President, Stephen Maffett
Vice President, Windy Rudd
Vice President, Cameron Moorehead
Vice President Private Banking Officer, Amy Mullins
Senior Vice President, Jan Furey
Vice President Lakewood Branch Mangaer, Melissa Missall
Vice President, Tom Kirkwood
Vice President, Kai Neizman
Senior Vice President Cash Management Manager, Janice Phillips
Vice President Branch Manager, Amy Hart
Cfp Assistant Vice President Private Banking Officer, Nori Roman
Assistant Vice President Senior Residential Loan Officer, Lorry Gilbreath
Senior Vice President Private Banking Officer, Vince Martinez
Assistant Vice President Senior Residential Loan Officer, Wanda Hemenway
Vice President Manager, Debbie Patterson
Senior Vice President Real Estate Group Manager, Kevin Conklin
Assistant Vice President Marketing Creative Manager Marketing, Bryan Habeck
Vice President Professional Banking Officer, Debbie Woodrich
Vice President And Treasury Management Sales Officer, Janis Watford
Senior Vice President Chief Accounting Officer, Brock Lakely
Svp, Michael Evans
Vice President Branch Manager Iii, Alfredo Aguilar
Vice President, Chris Skandalis
Vice President Market Manager, Suzanne Vanamburgh
As Vice President Business Development Officer, Derek Rawnsley
Chairman, William T. Weyerhaeuser, age 76
Board Member, David Dietzler
Board Member, Ford Elsaesser
Board Member, John Folsom
Board Member, Thomas Hulbert
Board Member, Mark Finkelstein
Board Member, Elizabeth Seaton
Auditors: DELOITTE & TOUCHE LLP

LOCATIONS

HQ: Columbia Banking System Inc
1301 A Street, Tacoma, WA 98402-2156
Phone: 253 305-1900
Web: www.columbiabank.com

2018 Branches

	No.
Washington	74
Oregon	62
Idaho	14
Total	**150**

PRODUCTS/OPERATIONS

2018 Revenue

	% of total
Net Interest Income	
Loans	73
Taxable securities	10
Tax-exempt securities	2
Non-interest Income	15
Total	**100**

COMPETITORS

BECU	JPMorgan Chase
Bank of America	KeyCorp
Banner Corp	U.S. Bancorp
Heritage Financial	Washington Federal
HomeStreet	Wells Fargo

HISTORICAL FINANCIALS

Company Type: Public

Income Statement				FYE: December 31
	ASSETS ($ mil.)	NET INCOME ($ mil.)	INCOME AS % OF ASSETS	EMPLOYEES
12/18	13,095	172	1.3%	2,137
12/17	12,716	112	0.9%	2,120
12/16	9,509	104	1.1%	1,819
12/15	8,951	98	1.1%	1,868
12/14	8,578	81	1.0%	1,844
Annual Growth	**11.2%**	**20.7%**	**—**	**3.8%**

2018 Year-End Financials

Debt ratio: 0.27%
Return on equity: 8.68%
Cash ($ mil.): 277
Current ratio: —
Long-term debt ($ mil.): —

No. of shares (mil.): 73
Dividends
  Yield: 2.7%
  Payout: 58.7%
Market value ($ mil.): 2,658

	STOCK PRICE ($) FY Close	P/E High/Low	PER SHARE ($)		
			Earnings	Dividends	Book Value
12/18	36.29	20 14	2.36	1.14	27.76
12/17	43.44	25 19	1.86	0.88	26.70
12/16	44.68	25 15	1.81	1.53	21.55
12/15	32.51	21 15	1.71	1.34	21.52
12/14	27.61	19 16	1.52	0.94	21.38
Annual Growth	**7.1%**	**— —**	**11.6%**	**4.9%**	**6.7%**

Columbia Financial Inc

Auditors: KPMG LLP

LOCATIONS

HQ: Columbia Financial Inc
19-01 Route 208 North, Fair Lawn, NJ 07410
Phone: 800 522-4167
Web: www.columbiabankonline.com

HISTORICAL FINANCIALS

Company Type: Public

Income Statement				FYE: December 31
	ASSETS ($ mil.)	NET INCOME ($ mil.)	INCOME AS % OF ASSETS	EMPLOYEES
12/18	6,691	22	0.3%	663
12/17*	5,766	3	0.1%	—
09/17	5,429	31	0.6%	679
09/16	5,037	32	0.7%	
Annual Growth	**15.3%**	**(16.9%)**	**—**	**—**
*Fiscal year change

2018 Year-End Financials

Debt ratio: 2.39%
Return on equity: 3.15%
Cash ($ mil.): 42
Current ratio: —
Long-term debt ($ mil.): —

No. of shares (mil.): 115
Dividends
  Yield: —
  Payout: —
Market value ($ mil.): 1,772

	STOCK PRICE ($) FY Close	P/E High/Low	PER SHARE ($)		
			Earnings	Dividends	Book Value
12/18	15.29	88 74	0.20	0.00	8.39
12/17*	0.00	— —	(0.00)	0.00	
47,207,000.00					
Annual Growth	**—**	**— —**	**—**	**—**	**—**
(100.0%)
*Fiscal year change

Comcast Corp

EXECUTIVES

Chb-Pres-Ceo, Brian L Roberts
Sr Exec V Pres-Cfo, Michael J Cavanagh
Sr Exec V Pres, Stephen B Burke
Sr Exec V Pres, David L Cohen
Sr Exec V Pres, David N Watson
Sr V Pres-Cao-Contrl, Daniel C Murdock
Sr Exec V Pres-General Counsel, Thomas J Reid
Vp-Sales & Marketing, Kristeen Cominiello
Reg Svp-Big South Region, Jason Gumbs
Vp-Finance & Business Operatio, Marcos Vicente
Vp-Engineering, Jeff Votaw
Auditors: DELOITTE & TOUCHE LLP

LOCATIONS

HQ: Comcast Corp
One Comcast Center, Philadelphia, PA 19103-2838
Phone: 215 286-1700
Web: www.comcastcorporation.com

COMPETITORS

21st Century Fox	ITC^DeltaCom
AT&T	Insight Communications
Blockbuster	Liberty Interactive
Cablevision Systems	Netflix
Charter Communications	RCN Corporation
Cox Communications	Time Warner Cable
DIRECTV	ValueVision Media
DISH Network	Verizon
Disney	Viacom
EarthLink	Xanadoo

HISTORICAL FINANCIALS

Company Type: Public

Income Statement				FYE: December 31
	REVENUE ($ mil.)	NET INCOME ($ mil.)	NET PROFIT MARGIN	EMPLOYEES
12/19	108,942	13,057	12.0%	190,000
12/18	94,507	11,731	12.4%	184,000
12/17	84,526	22,714	26.9%	164,000
12/16	80,403	8,695	10.8%	159,000
12/15	74,510	8,163	11.0%	141,000
Annual Growth	**10.0%**	**12.5%**	**—**	**7.7%**

2019 Year-End Financials

Debt ratio: 38.80%—
Return on equity: 16.92%
Cash ($ mil.): 5,500
Current ratio: 0.84
Long-term debt ($ mil.): 97,765

Dividends
  Yield: 1.8%
  Payout: 30.3%
Market value ($ mil.): —

	STOCK PRICE ($) FY Close	P/E High/Low	PER SHARE ($)		
			Earnings	Dividends	Book Value
12/19	44.97	16 12	2.83	0.82	18.17
12/18	34.05	17 12	2.53	0.92	15.82
12/17	40.05	16 7	4.75	0.47	14.77
12/16	69.05	39 30	1.79	0.68	11.35
12/15	56.43	39 32	1.62	0.49	10.70
Annual Growth	**(5.5%)**	**— —**	**15.0%**	**13.9%**	**14.2%**

COMENITY BANK

World Financial Network National Bank (WFNNB) will take credit for the credit it extends. The company is the private-label and co-branded credit card banking subsidiary of Alliance Data Systems. Along with affiliate World Financial Capital Bank the company underwrites cards on behalf of more than 85 businesses. The company's largest clients include apparel retailers L Brands and Redcats USA. WFNNB oversees about 120 million cardholder accounts and roughly $4 billion in receivables. Private equity giant Blackstone planned to acquire parent Alliance Data Systems for more than $6 billion but that deal was terminated in 2008.

EXECUTIVES

Pres, Timothy King
Computer Operations, Mike Schick
Project Manager, Connie Murphy
Information Technology, Paul Wroten
Client Sales Manager, Stacey Siak
Director Financial Planning, Don Borowy
Client Sales Manager, Jennifer Staten
Marketing Staff, Jeffrey Fasino
Administrative Assistant, Kurt Fraczkowski
Senior Vice President Chief Co, Michael F Swallow

LOCATIONS

HQ: COMENITY BANK
1 RIGHTER PKWY STE 100, WILMINGTON, DE 198031533
Phone: 614 729-4000

COMPETITORS

American Express	Citigroup
Bank of America	Target Receivables
Barclays Bank Delaware	

HISTORICAL FINANCIALS

Company Type: Private

Income Statement				FYE: December 31
	ASSETS ($ mil.)	NET INCOME ($ mil.)	INCOME AS % OF ASSETS	EMPLOYEES
12/14	9,149	389	4.3%	200
12/13	7,453	350	4.7%	—
12/05	332	10	3.2%	—
12/03	672	88	13.2%	—
Annual Growth	26.8%	14.4%	—	—

Comerica, Inc.

Comerica is the holding company for Comerica Bank which has nearly 440 branches primarily in five US states and in Canada and Mexico. The company is organized into three main segments. The Business Bank division is the largest offering loans deposits and capital markets products to small- and middle-market businesses multinational corporations and government clients. The Retail Bank serves consumers while the Wealth Management arm provides fiduciary services investment management and advisory and retirement services. Comerica categorizes its securities portfolio and asset and liability management under an additional Finance segment. The company boasts total assets of about $70 billion and deposits of over $55 billion.

Operations

Comerica generates more than 65% of its revenue from loan interest and fees. It derives between 5% and 10% of its revenue from each of investment securities interest card fees deposit account service charges and fiduciary income. Business Bank is the company's largest segment accounting for about 85% of its net interest income while Wealth Management generates another 10%. The rest comes from the Retail Bank segment.

The bulk of Comerica's portfolio is made up of commercial loans which represent about two-thirds of the total. Commercial mortgages make up about 20%; real estate construction lending comprises some 5%.

Comerica's net income is heavily weighted in its Business Bank segment—it provides about 85% of the total. Wealth Management and the Retail Bank provide some 10% and 5% respectively. The Business Bank division offers loans deposits and capital markets products to small- and middle-market businesses multinational corporations and government clients. The Retail Bank serves consumers while the Wealth Management arm provides fiduciary services investment management and advisory and retirement services. Comerica categorizes its securities portfolio and asset and liability management under an additional Finance segment.

Geographic Reach

Comerica operates around 550 locations including about 440 bank branches. Its other facilities offer trust services loan production and other financial services. California and Michigan each represent about 30% of the holding company's net income; Texas provides about 20%. Arizona Florida and Canada contribute the remainder. Comerica has roughly 190 branches in Michigan 120 in Texas 100 in California and 25 in its other markets.

Sales and Marketing

Beyond retail customers Comerica caters to small- and middle-market businesses multinational corporations and government entities and others operating in the energy automotive production and real estate industries. Middle-market clients represent more than half of its loan portfolio.

Financial Performance

Comerica's revenue has grown by a third in the last five years thanks mainly to higher short-term rates most of those years. Despite reductions in 2015 and 2016 net income has more than doubled in that period due to increased net interest income the last two years particularly in 2018.

Overcoming a decrease in average earning assets (interest-bearing deposits and average investment securities) the holding company's revenue grew 5% to $3.3 billion in 2018; loan interest and fees drove most of the gains. Net income rose by 66% on the strength of the company's net interest income expansion and?to a lesser extent?a reduced income tax provision.

Comerica's cash stores lost $1.3 billion in 2018 to end the year at $4.6 billion. Operations contributed $1.6 billion while investment and financing activities used $1.2 billion and $1.7 billion respectively. Net change in loans primarily accounted for investment loss; reductions from financings were mostly attributable to common stock repurchases and net change in deposits.

Strategy

Comerica is primarily concerned with controlling its risk exposure. The holding company is reducing risk associated with real estate loans (which comprise about 25% of its total portfolio) by monitoring commercial real estate borrowers and adopting a conservative loan-to-value ratio strategy. Its real estate construction loans are primarily made to long-time customers with good historical completion rates.

Comerica's management is also grappling with the issue of a sharp deterioration in the performance of loans to the beleaguered oil industry. While some US banks are under pressure from oil weakness Comerica has relatively large exposure to the industry.

To deal with the issue the company is cutting costs to free up cash in preparation for heavy losses. Its GEAR Up program has consisted of layoffs renegotiated vendor contracts a reduction in bank branches lower executive bonuses and technology outsourcing. It has also reduced lending to oil drillers.

Company Background

Elon Farnsworth founded Comerica precursor Detroit Savings Fund Institute in 1849 to serve Michigan clients. The company changed its name to Comerica in 1982. The holding company expanded into the Florida and Texas markets in 1982 and 1988 respectively.

HISTORY

Comerica traces its history to 1849 when Michigan governor Epaphroditus Ransom tapped Elon Farnsworth to found the Detroit Savings Fund Institute. At that time Detroit was a major transit point for shipping between Lakes Huron and Erie as well as between the US and Canada. The bank grew with the town and in 1871 became Detroit Savings Bank.

By 1899 Detroit was one of the top 10 US manufacturing centers and thanks to a group of local tinkerers and mechanics that included Henry Ford was on the brink of even greater growth. Detroit Savings grew also fueled by the deposits of workers whom Ford paid up to $5 a day. Detroit Savings was not however the beneficiary of significant business with the auto makers; for corporate banking they turned first to eastern banks and then to large local banks in which they had an interest.

Detroit boomed during the 1920s as America went car-crazy but after the 1929 crash Detroiters defaulted on mortgages by the thousands. By 1933 Michigan's banks were in such disarray that the governor shut them down three weeks prior to the federal bank holiday. Detroit Savings was one of only four Detroit banks to reopen. None of the major banks associated with auto companies survived.

A few months later Manufacturers National Bank backed by a group of investors that included Edsel Ford (Henry's son) was founded. Although its start was rocky Manufacturers National was on firm footing by 1936; around the same time Detroit Savings Bank renamed itself the Detroit Bank to appeal to a more commercial clientele.

WWII and the postwar boom put Detroit back in gear. In the 1950s and 1960s both banks thrived. In the 1970s statewide branching was permitted and both banks formed holding companies (DETROITBANK Corp. and Manufacturers National Corp.) and expanded throughout Michigan. As they grew they added services; when Detroit's economy was hit by the oil shocks of the 1970s these diversifications helped them through the lean years.

DETROITBANK opened a trust operation in Florida in 1982 to maintain its relationship with retired customers and renamed itself Comerica to be less area-specific. Manufacturers National also began operating in Florida (1983) and made acquisitions in the Chicago area (1987). Comerica went farther afield buying banks in Texas (1988) and California (1991).

Following the national consolidation trend in 1992 Comerica and Manufacturers National merged (retaining the Comerica name) but did not fully integrate until 1994 when the new entity began making more acquisitions. To increase sales and develop its consumer business the company reorganized in 1996. It sold its Illinois bank and its Michigan customs brokerage business and acquired Fairlane Associates to expand its property/casualty insurance line.

As part of its strategy to have operations in all three NAFTA countries Comerica opened a bank in Mexico in 1997 and one in Canada in 1998. That year it dropped $66 million for the naming rights to the Detroit Tigers' baseball stadium which opened as Comerica Park in 2000. It also started a Web-based payment system for its international trade business.

To fortify its business lending operations in California Comerica bought Imperial Bancorp in 2001. At the beginning of 2002 chairman Eugene Miller handed the CEO reins to Ralph Babb who had been CFO. Later that year Babb became chairman as well.

EXECUTIVES

Chairman President And Ceo Comerica Incorporated And Comerica Bank, Ralph W. Babb, age 70, $1,265,000 total compensation

Evp And President Comerica Bank (california Market), Judith S. Love, age 62

Evp And Chief Risk Officer Comerica Incorporated And Comerica Bank, Michael H. Michalak, age 61

Evp And Director Of Operations Services, Paul R. Obermeyer, age 61

Evp Governance Regulatory Relations And Legal Affairs Comerica Incorporated And Comerica Bank, John D. Buchanan, age 55, $573,846 total compensation

President Comerica Incorporated And Comerica Bank, Curtis C. Farmer, age 56, $700,000 total compensation

Evp And Cfo, Muneera S. Carr, age 51

Evp And President Comerica Bank Michigan Market, Michael T. Ritchie, age 50

Evp And Chief Human Resources Officer Comerica Incorporated And Comerica Bank, Megan D. Burkhart, age 47

Evp And Chief Credit Officer, Peter W. Guilfoile, age 58

Evp And President Comerica Bank Texas Market, Peter L. Sefzik, age 43

Evp And General Auditor, Christine Moore

Assistant Vice President Senior Systems Engineer, David Walker

Vice President Texas Market, Greg Wilcox

Vice President, Cindy Morgan

Vice President Financial Systems Support, William Grace

Senior Vice President, Melanie Rice

Vice President And Senior Trust, Joan Dindoffer

Assistant Vice President Information Systems, Ken Lootens

Vice President Cbo, Angela Knight

Vice President Human Resources Staffing, Dan Dunn

Assistant Vice President Relationship Manager, Dave Sullivan

Vice President, Daniel Roesner

Vice President, Jenal Zak

Vice President Marketing, Jason Logan

Vice President, Brian Miller

Vice President, Kelly McConnell

Assistance Vice President, Daphne Berry

Senior Vice President, Geoff Payne

Vice President, Jake Friemel

Assistant Vice President, Steve Hattey

Vice President Relationship Manager, Brad Bell

Vice President Western Market, Peter Wentworth

Vice President, Thomas Jones

Vice President, Padmanabhan Karatha

Assistant Vice President Texas Market, Marc Farmer

Senior Vice President Group Manager Stemmons, David A Milton

Vice President, Rhonda D Dantzler

Vice President Private Banking, Gary J Beyer

Treasury Management Vice President, Danette R Hames

Vice President Liquidity Risk Management, Brittany Butler

Vice President Middle Market Banking, Bryan L Johnston

Vice President, Marc P Abello

Vice President, Lynn M Ris

Vice President Business Consulting Manager, Kristin Class

Vice President, Lesley B Higginbotham

Vice President And Alternate Group Manager Commercial Real Estate, Cynthia V Porter

Banking Center Manager And Assistant Vice President, Alfonso J Ugarte

Vice President, Debbie Tuftee

Vice President, Doreen Boelstler

Assistant Vice President Treasury Management, Pamela G Porter

Vice President, Nancy Blake

Vice President, Kristy Denby

Vice President, Linda Vance

Vice President Estate Administration, Angela W Aycock

Vice President Lakeshore District, Christopher Scott

Banking Center Manager Assistant Vice President, Teresa Nolasco

Vice President, John Mckee

Vice President U S. Banking Midwest, Mark Leveille

Vice President, Fred Hoops

Banking Center Manager Vice President, Gordon McKinley

Banking Center Manager Assistant Vice President, Lisa Thompson

Vice President, Rodney Thompson

Vice President, Cynthia Walters

Vice President Agm, Matthew Breight

Vice President, Matt Maberry

Vice President, Ann Day-Salo

Vice President National Developers, Casey Stevenson

Vice President, Raffi Khelghatian

Assistant Vice President, Christopher Hoffman

Vice President, Lorraine Jackman

Senior Vice President And Director Compensation, Sarah Stratton

Banking Center Manager Assistant Vice President, Henry Tran

Vice President Retail Prod Management, John MacMillan

Senior Vice President And Assistant General Counsel, Terrance Henderson

Vice President, Rona Khan

Senior Vice President Texas Market North Texas Region Manager, Barry Brundage

Senior Vice President Midwest Region Commercial Real Estate Finance, James Preston

Vice President Business Banking, Karen Gladney

Vice President, Kathy Pitton

Vice President Product Development, William Anderson

Senior Vice President, Dan Evans

Vice President, Tom O'connell

Vice President, Peter Kennedy

Assistant Vice President, Bryndon Skelton

Vice President, Michael Mccarty

Vice President U S Banking Midwest, Brandon Welling

Vice President Regional Banking Officer Financial Services Division, Laura Reyes

Vice President And Senior Counsel, Marinda Little

Senior Vice President Division Finance Officer Wim, Sajid Siddiqi

Vice President, Madhuri Bandla

Vice President, Evan Huckabay

Vice President, Teresa Bosco

Vice President, Maribeth Gomez

Vice President And Senior Counsel, Jennifer Perry

Vice President Private Banking, Todd Goodhue

Vice President Sba Portfolio Management, Mario Nava

Vice President, Barry Carroll

Vice President, Cheryl Degraff

Assistant Vice President, Ian Patterson

Vice President Alternate Group Manager, Charles Mccarroll

Senior Vice President, David Ohanian

Vice President And Human Resources Counsel, Von Hays

Vice President Project Manager, Grey Cole

Vice President Of Enterprise Project Management Office, Paul Gustafson

Vice President, Elizabeth Alvarado

Assistant Vice President Relationship Manager, Sara Trogdon

Vice President Texas Market, Jim Young

Vice President, Laith Francis

Assistant Vice President Finance, Haiyan Li

Vice President International Finance, Carlos Capetillo

Vice President, Douglas Smith

Senior Vice President, Dennis Gilkerson

Banking Center Manager Assistant Vice President, Vanessa Ochoa

Vice President Ets Server Engineering, Alex Gonzalez

Svp Credit Administration, Scott Wineman

Vice President And Banking Center Manager Iv, Linda K Landers

Assistant Vice President, Joe Fisher

Vice President Institutional Sales, Rick Clancy

Vice President, Craig Weingarden

Vice President, Brian Fitzgerald

Senior Vice President Asset Quality Review, Edward Gwilt

Assistant Vice President, Megan Trapp

Vice President, Dennis Black

Vice President And Alternate Group Manager, Rob Gray

Assistant Vice President Branch Manager, Anna Quijano

Vice President Relationship Manager, Erik McKay

Vice President, Danny Sanchez

Assistant Vice President Learning, Scott Blackman

Vp Fraud Strategy And Compliance Manager, Sharry Fealk

Senior Vice President And Group Manager, Pete Fitzpatrick

Vice President Regional Sales Manager, Stephanie Sealey

Svp Private Banking, Debbie Ludwig

Vice President Commercial Banking Officer, Adan Gonzalez

Vice President Business Banking, Derek Aten

Banking Center Manager Assistant Vice President, Jasko Korajkic

Vice President, Crystal Dennis

Vice President Ii, Garth Gorrall

Vice President, Abigail Soper

Vice President Relationship Manager, Rebecca Callahan

Vice President, Embry Fura

Vice President, James Dox

Banking Center Manager Assistant Vice President, Rachel Svoboda

Vice President Information Security Engineer, Dave Frank

Vice President, Marcia Mazany

Vice President, John Graham

Vice President Director Of Product Risk Control, Shelly Gannaway

Vice President Treasury Management Consultant, Brock Poe

Assistant Vice President Retail Product Manager, Jon Long

Business Relationship Manager Vice President, Robert Yates

Vice President, Paul Debono

Auditors: Ernst & Young LLP

LOCATIONS

HQ: Comerica, Inc.
Comerica Bank Tower, 1717 Main Street, MC 6404, Dallas, TX 75201
Phone: 214 462-6831
Web: www.comerica.com

2018 Banking Centers

	No.
Michigan	193
Texas	122
California	96
Other Markets	
Arizona	17
Florida	7
Canada	1
Total	**436**

Selected Markets

Arizona
California
Colorado
Florida
Illinois
Michigan
Nevada
Ohio
Texas
Washington

PRODUCTS/OPERATIONS

2018 Sales

	$ mil.	% of total
Net Interest Income		
Fees on Loans	2,262	61
Investment securities	265	7
Short-term investments	92	3
Interest expense	(267)	-
Noninterest income		
Card fees	244	7
Service charges on deposit accounts	211	6
Fiduciary income	206	6
Other noninterest income	315	10
Total	**3,328**	**100**

2018 Sales

	% of total
Business Bank	85
Wealth Management	10
Retail Bank	5
Total	**100**

Selected Subsidiaries

Comerica Bank
Comerica Bank & Trust National Association
Comerica Capital Advisors Incorporated
Comerica Financial Incorporated
Comerica Holdings Incorporated
Comerica Insurance Group Inc.
Comerica Insurance Services Inc.
Comerica Investment Services Inc.
Comerica Investments LLC
Comerica Leasing Corporation
Comerica Merchant Services Inc.
Comerica Securities Inc.
Wilson Kemp & Associates Inc.
World Asset Management Inc.

COMPETITORS

Bank of America	Regions Financial
Citigroup	SVB Financial
Cullen/Frost Bankers	SunTrust
Fifth Third	TCF Financial
Huntington Bancshares	U.S. Bancorp
JPMorgan Chase	Wells Fargo
MUFG Americas Holdings	

HISTORICAL FINANCIALS

Company Type: Public

Income Statement				FYE: December 31
	ASSETS ($ mil.)	NET INCOME ($ mil.)	INCOME AS % OF ASSETS	EMPLOYEES
12/18	70,818	1,235	1.7%	8,051
12/17	71,567	743	1.0%	8,190
12/16	72,978	477	0.7%	8,149
12/15	71,877	521	0.7%	9,103
12/14	69,190	593	0.9%	9,115
Annual Growth	0.6%	20.1%	—	(3.1%)

2018 Year-End Financials

Debt ratio: 3.76%	No. of shares (mil.): 160
Return on equity: 15.97%	Dividends
Cash ($ mil.): 4,561	Yield: 2.6%
Current ratio: —	Payout: 25.5%
Long-term debt ($ mil.): —	Market value ($ mil.): 10,996

	STOCK PRICE ($) FY Close	P/E High/Low		PER SHARE ($) Earnings	Dividends	Book Value
12/18	68.69	14	9	7.20	1.84	46.89
12/17	86.81	21	15	4.14	1.09	46.07
12/16	68.11	26	11	2.68	0.89	44.47
12/15	41.83	18	14	2.84	0.83	43.03
12/14	46.84	16	13	3.16	0.79	41.35
Annual Growth	10.0%	—	—	22.9%	23.5%	3.2%

Commerce Bancshares Inc

Commerce Bancshares owns bank branch operator Commerce Bank. The financial institution boasts a network of more than 360 locations across several US states including Missouri Kansas Illinois Oklahoma and Colorado. The bank focuses on retail and commercial banking services such as deposit accounts mortgages loans and credit cards. Commerce Bank also runs a wealth management division that offers asset management trust private banking brokerage and estate planning services and also manages proprietary mutual funds. As part of its operations Commerce Bank has subsidiaries devoted to insurance leasing and private equity investments.

Operations

The company operates three main segments: Consumer Commercial and Wealth.

The Commercial segment which collects roughly 65% of the bank's total revenue provides corporate lending merchant and commercial bank card products leasing and international services as well as business and government deposit and cash management services. Fixed income investments are sold to individuals and institutional investors through the segment's Capital Markets Group.

Another 20% of bank revenue is generated through the Consumer segment which includes the retail branch network consumer installment lending personal mortgage banking and consumer debit and credit bank card activities. It provides services through a network of more than 200 full-service branches a 400-machine ATM network and alternative delivery channels such as extensive online banking and telephone banking services.

The remaining bank revenue (around 15%) comes from the Wealth segment which manages investments with a market value of $20.4 billion and administers an additional $14.8 billion in non-managed assets provides traditional trust and estate tax-planning services brokerage services and advisory and discretionary investment portfolio management services targeted to personal and institutional corporate customers. The Wealth segment also manages Commerce Bank's proprietary mutual funds.

Broadly speaking interest income from the bank's portfolio of loans make up more than 40% of total revenue. Roughly 60% of the portfolio is comprised of commercial loans (mostly business real estate loans but also construction and land loans and other business-related loans). Personal banking loans make up the remaining 40% of the portfolio and mostly include real estate loans and consumer lines of credit but also consumer credit cards revolving home equity loans and some overdraft lines of credit.

Geographic Reach

Commerce Bancshares through its Commerce Bank business operates more than 360 branch banks in five central US states with major focus in Peoria and Bloomington Illinois; St. Louis; Kansas City and Wichita Kansas; Denver; Tulsa Oklahoma; Nashville; Cincinnati; and Dallas. The bank also has commercial offices in Cincinnati Nashville and Dallas. The company's two largest markets include St. Louis and Kansas City. To this end the cities serve as the central hubs for its operation.

Sales and Marketing

The bank spent $14.2 million on marketing in fiscal 2013 down 6% from $15.1 million in 2012 and down 15% from the $16.8 million it spent on marketing in 2011.

Financial Performance

In the recent low interest environment Commerce Bancshares has seen its revenue slowly decline over the past few years from declining interest income from its loans and investment securities. In fiscal 2013 revenue fell by $8.9 million to $1.08 billion as the bank earned lower rates on investment securities and loans (from smaller interest margins) despite higher loan balances and lower rates paid on deposits. The bank was able to offset some of its revenue losses by earning $18.8 million more from bank card transaction trust and brokerage fees.

The bank's net income also dipped by $8.4 million (or 3%) to $261 million in 2013. This is mostly from the drop in revenue but also because the bank paid $6 million more toward employee salaries and benefits (from higher salaries) and $4.4 million more toward data processing and software expenses as bank card processing costs went up. Profits are still up significantly from the bank's recovery period in 2009 and 2010 when it earned $169.1 million and $221.7 million respectively.

The amount of cash provided from operations fell for the third straight year to $360.9 million in 2013 down 6% from the $383.1 million provided in 2012. This was primarily because of lower net income but also because it paid $11.7 million more toward its income tax obligations than in the prior year.

Unlike its revenue and earnings Commerce's assets have been growing. Total loans were $10.96 billion in 2013 representing an increase of $1.13 billion or 11% over balances in 2012. While loan assets have increased across the board business loan assets contributed the most growing by $580.5 million in 2013 to a total of $3.7 billion. Deposit assets also rose by 4% to $19.05 billion in 2013.

Strategy

Commerce Bancshares serves its local retail markets through relationship banking and high touch service. It works to grow its core revenue by expanding new and existing customer relationships leveraging improved technology and enhancing customer satisfaction. To respond to changes in consumer banking preferences the bank will work to improve its distribution strategy by de-emphasizing the central role of traditional branch banking and providing more customers access to its services through ATMs call centers mobile and house lines internet. It will also work to develop new products and focus on expense reductions wherever possible to improve the company's bottom line.

To grow its commercial business segment which already provides two-thirds of all bank revenue Commerce plans to invest in distinctive lower-risk/higher return businesses to increase its loan business. In addition it intends to deepen its relationships with existing commercial customers and provide more products to them to increase profitability while taking on little additional risk or cost.

Thanks to higher brokerage and trust fees Commerce Bancshares' Wealth division saw the largest segment revenue growth in 2013. The bank is optimistic that its new hires in the division will contribute to higher sales productivity over the next few years particularly in the institutional and St. Louis Family Office. In addition management believes that the improving US economy and booming stock market will improve investor confidence and M&A activity which should help grow the segment in the years ahead.

Mergers and Acquisitions

Commerce Bancshares in May 2013 inked a merger agreement with Summit Bancshares whereby Summit merged into a wholly-owned subsidiary of Commerce Bancshares. The transaction valued at approximately $40.6 million consisted entirely of Commerce Bancshares' stock and added more than $200 million in new loans to the bank's portfolio. The deal significantly boosted Commerce Bank's foothold in the Tulsa Oklahoma market and allowed it to enter the Oklahoma City market.

EXECUTIVES

Svp; Director Operations And Information Services, Robert J. Rauscher, age 61
Cfo, Charles G. (Chuck) Kim, age 59, $415,080 total compensation
Evp Commercial Line Of Business; President And Coo Commerce Bank Kansas City Region, Kevin G. Barth, age 59, $408,705 total compensation
Evp; Chief Human Resources Officer And Director Internal Support Services, Sara E. Foster, age 59
Chairman And Ceo, David W. Kemper, age 68, $896,073 total compensation
Evp Trust Line Of Business; President The Commerce Trust Company A Division Of Commerce Bank, V. Raymond (Ray) Stranghoener, age 68, $235,900 total compensation
Evp; Chief Credit Officer And Chief Risk Officer, Daniel D. Callahan
Svp; Director Commercial Card And Merchant Services, Jeff Burik
Svp; Director Community Bank Administration, Michael J. Petrie
President And Coo, John W. Kemper, $462,287 total compensation
Senior Vice President, Patricia R Kellerhals
Vice President Marketing Support, Christopher Schildz
Vice President, Jason Boyer
Vice President, Paul Zietlow
Vice President Private Client Group, Joe Morris
Vice President Of Human Resources, Betty Maes
Vice President Commercial Marketing, Liz Lewis
Assistant Vice President Regional Marketing, Jenny Stanley
Vice President, Jeffrey Turner
Vice President, Joe Mccaddon
Vice President Marketing Product Manager, Winona Murray
Assistant Vice President Commercial Banking, Tom Whooley
Vice President Regional Retail Sales Manager, Jen Bradley
Senior Vice President Retail And Small Business Group Manager, Robin Wandschneider
Assistant Vice President, Ron Nesemeyer
Vice President, Trishia Baker
Assistant Vice President Information Tec, Andy Frank
Senior Vice President And Director Operations, Eric Rauscher
Vice President Business Banking Relationship Manager, Rob Gillespie
Vice President Of Investment Banking, Michael Hartmann
Vice President Branch Management, Robert Henson
Vice President Treasury Sales, Chuck Peterson
Senior Vice President, Dee Joyner
Vice President Server Operations Manager Information Technology, Wanda Edgmond
Senior Vice President, Mark Tankesley
Senior Vice President, John Blakeney
Assistant Vice President Information Technology Manager, Chad Boline
Vice President, Clive Veri
Vice President, Susan McGee
Vice President Of Information Technology, Allan Smith
Vice President Commercial Lending, Pam Hill
Vice President And Director Of Finance, Duane Locher
Assistant Vice President, Timothy Gillock
Executive Vice President, Gaylyn McGregor

Svp Private Client Manager, Thomas Durfee
Vice President, Ron Koenig
Vice President Information Technology, Thomas Cook
Vice President, Craig Duerksen
Vice President, Joel Hubbard
Assistant Vice President, Wilkerson Kurtis
Assistant Vice President Business Line Systems Manager, Kevin Belloma
Vice President, JO Hicks
Vice President, Barbara Mccaslin
Vice President, Lance Wright
Senior Vice President, Gordon Roewe
Vice President, Bernice Hodge
Senior Vice President, Nick Fafoglia
Vice President Finance, Lynn McLaughlin
Svp Director Private Banking Credit, Kyle Rosborg
Vice President, Garth Kilburn
Vice President, Brendan Carmichael
Senior Vice President, Brian Mallak
Senior Vice President, Len Metzger
Vice President Commercial Card Services, Rob Perdue
Vice President, Gerald Mckay
Assistant Vice President Small Business Banking Specialist, Darin Crump
Vice President Senior Relationship Manager, Lee Tilghman
Assistant Vice President, Andrew Fogt
Vice President Team Leader, Matt Dority
Vice President Business Banking Center Manager, Jamie Huch
Vice President Business Development, Brent Miller
Vice President, Bruce Talen
Assistant Vice President Branch Manager Iv, Hank Koehly
Senior Vice President, Joe Williams
Executive Vice President Chief Credit Officer Risk Manager, Robert Matthews
Assistant Vice President, Keturah Green
Assistant Vice President, Melissa Caputo
Vice President, Jim Watson
Vice President, Jack Stapleton
Vice President National Accounts, Venus Vega
Assistant Vice President, Cole Higginbotham
Assistant Vice President Small Business Banking, Sonya Tandy
Assistant Vice President Small Business Banking, Donald Reynolds
Assistant Vice President, Angela Wright-Jones
Senior Vice President, Michael Boehn
Vp Business Transformation Program Manager, Stacy Regnier
Vice President Of Information Technology, Ken Isbell
Senior Vice President Commercial Loan Servicing, Jeremy Allen
Vice President Private Banking Officer, Ami Slader
Executive Vice President, Doug Neff
Vice President Senior Account Executive, Cindy Horan Horan
Vice President Business Banking, Todd Norton
Vice President Of Information Technology, James G Smith
Assistant Vice President, Jason Ward
Vice President, David Langley
Vice President And Director Marketing (western Region), Terri Hurd
Vice President Senior Financial Planner, Kimberly Bridges
Vp Senior Account Executive Commercial Payments, Amanda Wengert
Vice President National Account Executive, Michael Venditto
Svp Private Client Wealth Advisor, Beth Kinzel
Svp Healthcare, Richard Heise
Vice Chairman, Seth M. Leadbeater, age 68
Vice Chairman, Jonathan M. Kemper, age 66
Board Member, Karen L Daniel
Auditors: KPMG LLP

LOCATIONS

HQ: Commerce Bancshares Inc
1000 Walnut, Kansas City, MO 64106
Phone: 816 234-2000 **Fax:** 816 234-2369
Web: www.commercebank.com

2016 Sales by Market

	% of total
Kansas City	32
St. Louis	28
Other regions	40
Total	**100**

PRODUCTS/OPERATIONS

2016 Sales

	$ mil.	% of total
Interest Income		
Interest and fees on loans	490	42
Interest on investment securities	207	18
Interest on long-term securities purchased under agreements to resell	13	1
Interest on loans held for sale	1	0
Interest on federal funds sold and short-term securities purchased under agreements to resell	0	0
Interest on deposits with banks	1	0
Non-Interest Income		
Bank card transaction fees	181	15
Trust fees	121	10
Deposit account charges and other fees	86	7
Consumer brokerage services	13	1
Loan fees and sales	11	1
Capital market fees	10	1
Other	48	4
Total	**1,187**	**100**

Selected Services

Commercial Banking
  Financing
  Treasury Services
  Commercial Card Products
  Merchant Services
  International Services
  Capital Markets
  Investment Management
  Corporate Trust
Personal Banking
  Checking Accounts
  Savings Accounts
  Money Market Accounts & CDs
  Borrowing Solutions & Loans
  Mortgages
  Credit Cards
  Check Cards & Prepaid Cards
  Online Banking Services & Mobile Banking
Small Business Banking
  Small Business Checking Accounts
  Small Business Online Services
  Small Business Loans
  Business Credit Cards & Check Cards
  Business Resource Center
  Merchant Services
Wealth Management
  The Commerce Trust Company
  Investment Management
  Private Banking Services
  Financial Advisory Services
  Trust Services
  Institutional Trust Services
  Corporate Trust
  Brokerage Services
  Insurance Services

Selected Subsidiaries

Capital for Business Inc.
CBI-Kansas Inc.
CFB Partners LLC
CFB Venture Fund L.P.
Clayton Financial Corp.
Clayton Holdings LLC
Clayton Realty Corp.
Commerce Bank National Association
Commerce Brokerage Services Inc.
Commerce Insurance Services Inc.
Commerce Investment Advisors Inc.
Commerce Mortgage Corp.
Illinois Financial LLC
Illinois Realty LLC
Tower Redevelopment Corporation

COMPETITORS

BOK Financial
Bank of America
Bank of the West
Capitol Federal
 Financial
Dickinson Financial
First Banks
First National of
 Nebraska
Great Western Bancorp
INTRUST
U.S. Bancorp
UMB Financial
Wells Fargo

HISTORICAL FINANCIALS

Company Type: Public

Income Statement   FYE: December 31

	ASSETS ($ mil.)	NET INCOME ($ mil.)	INCOME AS % OF ASSETS	EMPLOYEES
12/18	25,463	433	1.7%	4,869
12/17	24,833	319	1.3%	4,857
12/16	25,641	275	1.1%	4,877
12/15	24,604	263	1.1%	4,859
12/14	23,994	261	1.1%	4,866
Annual Growth	1.5%	13.4%	—	0.0%

2018 Year-End Financials

Debt ratio: 0.03%
Return on equity: 15.35%
Cash ($ mil.): 1,224
Current ratio: —
Long-term debt ($ mil.): —

No. of shares (mil.): 116
Dividends
 Yield: 1.6%
 Payout: 24.8%
Market value ($ mil.): 6,590

	STOCK PRICE ($) FY Close	P/E High/Low		PER SHARE ($) Earnings	Dividends	Book Value
12/18	56.37	20	15	3.60	0.90	25.08
12/17	55.84	23	20	2.62	0.82	24.22
12/16	57.81	26	17	2.25	0.78	23.39
12/15	42.54	23	19	2.11	0.74	19.96
12/14	43.49	23	20	2.05	0.71	18.93
Annual Growth	6.7%	—	—	15.2%	6.1%	7.3%

Commercial Metals Co.

EXECUTIVES

Chb-Pres-Ceo, Barbara R Smith
Exec V Pres-Coo, Tracy L Porter
V Pres-Cfo, Paul J Lawrence
V Pres-Gen Counsel-Corp SEC, Paul K Kirkpatrick
V Pres-Cao, Adam R Hickey
Director, Aaron Baker
Mobile Communications Supervis, Betty Schriewer
Manager, Bill Isom
Network Engineer, Brett Koger
Manager, Jerry Garrison
Global Delivery Manage, Sheila Barnett
Auditors: DELOITTE & TOUCHE LLP

LOCATIONS

HQ: Commercial Metals Co.
 6565 North MacArthur Blvd., Irving, TX 75039
Phone: 214 689-4300   **Fax:** 214 689-5886
Web: www.cmc.com

COMPETITORS

AK Steel Holding
 Corporation
BHP Billiton
Blue Tee
Connell LP
David J. Joseph
Gerdau Ameristeel
Indel
Roanoke Bar Division
 Ryerson
Schnitzer Steel
Severstal North
 America
Simec
Steel Dynamics
Tube City IMS

Keywell
Metals USA
Mueller Industries
Nucor
OmniSource
Quanex Building
 Products
United States Steel
Universal Forest
 Products
Worthington Industries

HISTORICAL FINANCIALS

Company Type: Public

Income Statement   FYE: August 31

	REVENUE ($ mil.)	NET INCOME ($ mil.)	NET PROFIT MARGIN	EMPLOYEES
08/19	5,829	198	3.4%	11,524
08/18	4,643	138	3.0%	8,900
08/17	4,569	46	1.0%	8,797
08/16	4,610	54	1.2%	8,388
08/15	5,988	141	2.4%	9,126
Annual Growth	(0.7%)	8.7%	—	6.0%

2019 Year-End Financials

Debt ratio: 33.11%
Return on equity: 12.71%
Cash ($ mil.): 192
Current ratio: 2.99
Long-term debt ($ mil.): 1,227

No. of shares (mil.): 117
Dividends
 Yield: 0.0%
 Payout: 28.9%
Market value ($ mil.): 1,848

	STOCK PRICE ($) FY Close	P/E High/Low		PER SHARE ($) Earnings	Dividends	Book Value
08/19	15.67	13	8	1.66	0.48	13.77
08/18	21.60	22	15	1.17	0.48	12.76
08/17	18.89	61	37	0.39	0.48	12.10
08/16	15.52	38	27	0.47	0.48	11.93
08/15	15.70	15	11	1.20	0.48	11.41
Annual Growth	(0.0%)	—	—	8.5%	(0.0%)	4.8%

COMMONSPIRIT HEALTH

Formed in 2019 through the merger of Catholic hospital systems Catholic Health Initiatives and Dignity Health CommonSpirit Health is a $29 billion not-for-profit organization with more than 140 hospitals in 21 states. Its hospitals range from large urban medical centers (many with educational and research programs) to small hospitals in rural areas. The company also operates clinics long-term care assisted-living and senior residential facilities (totaling more than 700 health care facilities) and provides home-based care services. The system is sponsored by nearly 20 different congregations of nuns. CommonSpirit is the largest not-for-profit health system in the US.

Operations

CHI's network includes acute-care hospitals including academic and teaching facilities rural facilities with critical-care access nursing colleges home-health agencies community health services organizations long-term care facilities assisted-care and residential senior homes research and development programs and labs. The company has about 25000 physicians and advanced practice clinicians.

Geographic Reach

CHI operates in Arkansas California Colorado Indiana Iowa Kansas Kentucky Minnesota Nebraska Nevada New Jersey New Mexico North Dakota Ohio Oregon Pennsylvania South Dakota Tennessee Texas Washington and Wisconsin — 21 states in all.

Strategy

The 2019 merger of California-based Dignity Health and Colorado-based Catholic Health Initiatives that resulted in the creation of CommonSpirit Health was just one of several health system transactions in a time of rising M&A activity. The systems joined forces to strengthen their operations enabling them to provide better care for more people. The combined system's operating goals include expanding its clinical capabilities shifting to providing care outside of the hospital investing in technology addressing social determinants of health and maintaining an experienced workforce.

Mergers and Acquisitions

After years of discussions CHI and Dignity Health merged in early 2019. The combined health system CommonSpirit Health is the largest not-for-profit hospital system in the US. The size of the system allows for it to provide expanded care to patients through such methods as virtual appointments a broader range of clinical programs and advanced technologies. The new organization with 142 hospitals in 21 states is headquartered in Chicago. Individual hospitals continue to operate under their existing names.

HISTORY

In 1860 the Sisters of St. Francis established a hospital in Philadelphia laying the foundation for a larger health care organization. In 1981 Franciscan Health System was formally established to be a national holding company for Catholic hospitals and related organizations. By the mid-1990s the system consisted of 12 member and two affiliate hospitals and 11 long-term-care facilities located in the mid-Atlantic states and the Pacific Northwest.

Sisters of Charity of Cincinnati and the Sisters of St. Francis Perpetual Adoration of Colorado Springs co-sponsored The Sisters of Charity Health Care Systems incorporated in 1979 as a multi-institutional health care network. By the mid-1990s the system included 20 hospitals in Colorado Kentucky Nebraska New Mexico and Ohio.

Three congregations collaborated to form Catholic Health Corporation in 1980 one of the first such health care partnerships between religious communities within the Roman Catholic Church in the US. By 1996 this coalition operated 100 health care facilities in 12 states.

The development of modern managed care health care systems put pressure on the smaller Catholic hospital operations so the three systems established Catholic Health Initiatives (CHI) in 1996 as a national entity serving five geographic regions. Patricia Cahill a lay health care veteran who previously served the Archdiocese of New York was appointed president and CEO of CHI. The following year CHI absorbed the 10-hospital Sisters of Charity of Nazareth Health Care System based in Bardstown Kentucky (founded in a log cabin in 1812).

That year CHI continued to seek new partnerships to improve efficiency. With Alegent Health it formed provider network Midwest Select with nearly 200 hospitals marketing discounted rates to businesses. CHI allied with the Daughters of Charity to form for-profit joint venture Catholic Healthcare Audit Network to provide operational financial compliance and information systems audits as well as due diligence reviews. CHI also joined insurance joint venture NewCap Insurance with the Daughters of Charity and Catholic Health East; the firm allowed CHI to operate independently of commercial insurers.

CHI made a secular tie-in with the University of Pennsylvania Health System in 1998 whereby the university's system would offer care through five Catholic hospitals (CHI made plans to transfer these hospitals to Catholic Health East in 2001). The next year CHI announced its first loss due to lackluster performance in the Midwest. During 2000 the company responded by streamlining operations and changing management resulting in a positive bottom line. In 2001 it sold three hospitals in Pennsylvania one in Delaware and one in New Jersey to Catholic Health East.

EXECUTIVES

President And Chief Executive Officer, Kevin E. Lofton, age 64

President Enterprise Business Lines And Cfo, J. Dean Swindle

Svp Divisional Operations (texas), Michael H. Covert

Svp Marketing And Communications, Joyce M. Ross

Executive Vice President Mission, Thomas R. Kopfensteiner

Svp Divisional Operations And Ceo Chi Memorial (tennessee), Larry Schumacher, age 61

Svp Legal Services And General Counsel, Mitch H. Melfi

Interim Svp And Coo, Paul W. Edgett

Evp Chief Administrative Officer And Chief Human Resources Officer, Patricia G. (Pat) Webb

Svp Divisional Operations And Ceo Chi Health (nebraska And Southwest Iowa), Cliff A. Robertson

Senior Vice President And Division Executive Officer, Jeffrey S. Drop

Svp And Chief Nursing Officer, Kathleen D. Sanford

Svp Divisional Operations And Ceo Mercy Health Network (iowa), David H. Vellinga

Svp Divisional Operations And Ceo Chi Franciscan Health (tacoma), Ketul J. Patel

Svp And President And Ceo Kentuckyone Health, Ruth W. Brinkley

Ceo Chi St. Alexius Health, Matt Grimshaw, age 44

Interim Evp Operations, Anthony Jones

Svp And Chief Medical Officer, Robert J. Weil

Senior Vice President And Chief Medical Officer, Stephen L Moore

Divisional Assistant Vice President Information Technology Business Relationship, Debbie Mullins

Vp Governance And Administrative Services, Ellen Barton

Vice President Contracting Supply Chain, Susan Schrupp

Director Of Medical Records, Becki Thompson

Senior Vice President Divisional Operationsceo, Robert Ratzi

Vice President Human Resource Business Practices, Thomas Sams

Vice President Of Operations, Dan Bjerknes

Vice President Supply Chain Data Analytics, Kevin Kakuda

Vice President Corporate Responsibility, Susan Shiflett

Vice President Clinical Operations And Physician Leadership Development, Manoj Pawar

Vice President Of Patient Care, Deb Haagenson

Vice President Outreach, Ellen Lee

Director Of Pharmacy, Sandy Jacobson

Director Of Pharmacy, Nicki Bohl

Director Of Pharmacy, Marian Rhoads

Senior Vice President Performance Excellence, Robert Strickland

Vice President Of Nursing, Heike Duban

Vice President Corporate Responsibility, Betsy Wade

Senior Vice President Strategy Development, Meta Dooley

Vice President And Medical Director National Cardiovascular Service Line, Jerome Granato

Vice President Care Management, Chris Stanley

Svp Ciso, Sheryl Rose

Vice President Strategic Planning And Alignment, Tim Moran

Vice President Of Finance, Christy Spitser

Vice President, Deeanna Opstedahl

Vice President Operational Finance Mercy Medical Center, Joseph Ruark

Vice President Clinic, Marilyn Mcginley

Vp Business Intelligence, Deborah Odell

National Vp Supply Chain Operations Procurement, John Frye

Vp Finance, Brent Schmidt

Auditors: ERNST & YOUNG LLP DENVER CO

LOCATIONS

HQ: COMMONSPIRIT HEALTH
444 W LAKE ST STE 2500, CHICAGO, IL 606060097
Phone: 312 741-7000
Web: WWW.CATHOLICHEALTHINITIATIVES.ORG

COMPETITORS

Adventist Health System Sunbelt Healthcare
Allina Hospitals
Ascension Health
Baptist Health
Baptist Health (Arkansas)
BryanLGH Medical Center
Denver Health and Hospital Authority
Exempla Healthcare
HCA
Life Care Centers
Memorial Health System (Colorado)
Methodist Health System
OhioHealth
Tenet Healthcare
Universal Health Services

HISTORICAL FINANCIALS

Company Type: Private

Income Statement   FYE: June 30

	REVENUE ($ mil.)	NET INCOME ($ mil.)	NET PROFIT MARGIN	EMPLOYEES
06/18	14,982	222	1.5%	72,500
06/17	15,547	128	0.8%	—
06/16	15,942	(703)	—	—
06/07	7,731	902	11.7%	—
Annual Growth	6.2%	(12.0%)	—	—

Community Bank System Inc

Community Bank System is right up front about what it is. The holding company owns Community Bank which operates about 195 branches across upstate New York and northeastern Pennsylvania where it operates as First Liberty Bank and Trust. Focusing on small underserved towns and non-urban markets the bank offers standard products and services such as checking and savings accounts certificates of deposit and loans and mortgages to consumer business and government clients. Boasting over $11.0 billion in assets the bank's loan portfolio consists of mostly business loans residential mortgages and consumer loans. Community Bank System's subsidiaries offer employee benefit services wealth management and insurance products and services.

Operations

Community Bank System operates three business segments. The Banking segment which made up 83% of the company's total revenue during 2015 provides lending and deposit services to individuals businesses and municipalities. Employee Benefit Services (12% of revenue) offers trust investment fund retirement plan actuarial healthcare consulting and other administrative services through Benefit Plan Administrative Services (BPAS). The All Other segment (5% of revenue) includes its Wealth Management (operating through Community Investment Services) and Insurance businesses (operating through CBNA Insurance Agency).

Nearly 70% of the company's revenue comes from interest income. About 49% of its revenue came from loan interest during 2015 while another 19% came from interest on taxable and nontaxable investments. The rest of its revenue came from deposit service fees (14% of revenue) employee benefit services (12%) wealth management and insurance services (5%) and other banking revenues (1%).

Geographic Reach

Community Bank System operated 194 branches and six back-office operating facilities in 36 counties in upstate New York and six counties in northeastern Pennsylvania at the end of 2015.

Sales and Marketing

The bank has been ramping up its advertising spend in recent years. It spent $3.6 million on advertising during 2015 up from $3.2 million and $3.0 million in 2014 and 2013 respectively.

Financial Performance

Community Bank System's annual revenues have been slowly trending higher since 2013 despite a decline in loan interest mostly as it's been building its non-interest related business lines. Meanwhile its net income has risen more than 15% as it's had to pay less in interest expenses on deposits amidst the low interest environment.

The bank's revenue grew 2% to $382.92 million during 2015 thanks to a combination of employee benefit services business growth from new customers and expanding business relationships with existing customers as well as from new service offerings; higher interest income from loans and taxable investments as such interest-earning asset balances grew modestly; and a 13% jump in wealth management and insurance services revenue stemming from the acquisition of OneGroup from the Oneida Financial Group acquisition.

Despite revenue growth in 2015 Community's net income dipped less than 1% to $91.23 million for the year due to costs related to the Oneida acquisition. The company's operating cash levels shrank 5% to $116.46 million mostly due to unfavorable working capital changes related to deferred income tax provisions and changes in other assets and liabilities.

Strategy

Community Bank System looks to continue building its loan and deposit business as well as its non-interest service lines organically and through strategic acquisitions of other banks and financial companies. The financial company in 2015 began exploring expansion opportunities into neighboring markets in eastern Ohio upper New England and New Jersey and in 2017 acquired Northeast Retirement Services (NRS) for around $146 million. NRS provides institutional transfer agency master recordkeeping services custom target date fund administration trust product administration and customized reporting services to institutional clients.

Mergers and Acquisitions

Community Bank System acquired Kinderhook Bank in 2019 for $93.4 million. Kinderhook has 11 offices in five New York counties (including in the Capital District of upstate New York) and holds nearly $640 million in assets and about $560 million in deposits. The deal extends Community

Bank's reach into the Capital District markets.

In spring 2017 Community Bank acquired Vermont-based Merchants Bancshares. Merchants operates nearly 35 branches and has assets in excess of $1.8 billion; the acquisition will expand Community Bank's operations into Vermont and western Massachusetts.

Company Background

In mid-2012 the bank purchased about 20 branches in upstate New York from HSBC. The deal which was made to satisfy antitrust concerns regarding First Niagara's purchase of 195 branches in New York from HSBC strengthened Community Bank Systems' geographic footprint.

In 2011 the company bought bank holding company The Wilber Corporation adding about 20 locations in the Catskills Mountains region of central New York.

In 2011 expanding its trust and benefits administration business it bought retirement plan administrator CAI Benefits which has offices in New York and Northern New Jersey.

EXECUTIVES

Evp And Cfo, Scott A. Kingsley, age 54, $422,500 total compensation

President Ceo And Director, Mark E. Tryniski, age 58, $725,000 total compensation

Evp And Chief Banking Officer, Brian D. Donahue, age 63, $350,000 total compensation

Cto, J. Michael Wilson, age 48

Svp Retail Banking Sales And Marketing, Harold M. (Harry) Wentworth, age 54

Svp And Chief Investment Officer, Joseph J. Lemchak, age 57

President Pennsylvania Banking, Robert P. Matley, age 67

Svp Municipal Banking Director, Joseph E. Sutaris, age 51

Svp And Senior Commercial Lending Officer Northern New York, Nicholas S. (Nick) Russell, age 51

Svp And Chief Credit Administrator, Stephen G. Hardy, age 64

Evp And General Counsel, George J. Getman, age 62, $375,000 total compensation

Svp And Chief Risk Officer, Paul J. Ward

Svp And Chief Credit Officer, Joseph Serbun, $248,107 total compensation

Assistant Vice President Marketing An, Mary K Barnette

Executive Vice President Marketing, Aaron Kurtz

Senior Vice President Commercial Banking, Joe Tomko

Executive Vice President Marketing, Deborah Fitch

Vice President Marketing, Art Gentry

Executive Vice President Marketing, Barbara Call

Vice President And Manager Financial Analysis, Robert Frost

Vice President Director Mortgage Lending, George J Burke

Vice President And Information Technology Manager, James Wilson

Senior Vice President, Marlene Walker

Vice President Administration, Eric Wollman

Finance Senior Vice President, Richard Heidrick

Vice President Commercial, Dave Unberger

Vice President Of Human Resources, Denise Cooper

Vice President Information Technology, Brian Montalbano

Vice President And Marketing Director, Blake Boyer

Vice President Commercial Banker, Allison Mosher

Assistant Vice President Cash Management Sales Officer, Lindsay Horn

Vice President Commercial Banking, Craig Stevens

Assistant Vice President, Melissa Peryea

Vice President Farm Loan Manager, Edward Ward

Vice President Commercial Relationship Officer, Michael Moore

Vp Commercial Banking Officer, Edward Michalek

Vp Commercial Loan Officer, Christopher Humphrey

Vp Br Manager, Diane Easton

Vp Commercial Banking Officer, Richard Ferrari

Vp, Russell Williamson

Senior Vice President, Richard Kazmerick

Senior Vice President, Edward Nork

Vice President Client Service, Kevin Wade

Assistant Vice President Loan Ptflo Ofc Assistant, William Giglio

Svp Regional Executive, Jeffrey Levy

Vice President For Finance, Richard Halberg

Chair, Sally A. Steele, age 63

Board Member, Raymond Pecor

Auditors: PricewaterhouseCoopers LLP

LOCATIONS

HQ: Community Bank System Inc
5790 Widewaters Parkway, DeWitt, NY 13214-1883
Phone: 315 445-2282
Web: www.communitybankna.com

PRODUCTS/OPERATIONS

2015 Sales

	$ mil.	% of total
Interest Income:		
Interest and fees on loans	187	49
Taxable investments	52	14
Nontaxable investments	19	5
Noninterest		
Deposit service fees	52	14
Employee benefit services	45	12
Wealth management	20	5
Other	5	1
Total	**382**	**100**

Selected Subsidiaries & Affiliates

Benefit Plans Administrative Services Inc.
Benefit Plans Administrative Services LLC
Brilie Corporation
CBNA Insurance Agency Inc.
CBNA Preferred Funding Corp.
CBNA Treasury Management Corporation
Community Bank N.A. (also dba First Liberty Bank & Trust)
Community Investment Services Inc.
First of Jermyn Realty Company
First Liberty Service Corporation
Flex Corporation
Hand Benefit & Trust Company
Hand Securities Inc.
Harbridge Consulting Group LLP
Nottingham Advisors Inc.
Town & Country Agency LLC
Western Catskill Realty Inc.

COMPETITORS

Arrow Financial	Financial Institutions
Bank of America	HSBC USA
Canandaigua National	JPMorgan Chase
Chemung Financial	KeyCorp
Citizens Financial Group	M&T Bank
	NBT Bancorp
Elmira Savings Bank	

HISTORICAL FINANCIALS

Company Type: Public

Income Statement   FYE: December 31

	ASSETS ($ mil.)	NET INCOME ($ mil.)	INCOME AS % OF ASSETS	EMPLOYEES
12/18	10,607	168	1.6%	2,933
12/17	10,746	150	1.4%	2,874
12/16	8,666	103	1.2%	2,499
12/15	8,552	91	1.1%	2,490
12/14	7,489	91	1.2%	2,182
Annual Growth	9.1%	16.6%	—	7.7%

2018 Year-End Financials

Debt ratio: 0.94%	No. of shares (mil.): 51
Return on equity: 10.07%	Dividends
Cash ($ mil.): 211	Yield: 2.4%
Current ratio: —	Payout: 44.4%
Long-term debt ($ mil.): —	Market value ($ mil.): 2,988

	STOCK PRICE ($) FY Close	P/E High/Low	PER SHARE ($) Earnings	Dividends	Book Value
12/18	58.30	20 16	3.24	1.44	33.43
12/17	53.75	20 16	3.03	1.32	32.26
12/16	61.79	27 15	2.32	1.26	26.96
12/15	39.94	20 15	2.19	1.22	26.06
12/14	38.13	18 15	2.22	1.16	24.24
Annual Growth	11.2%	— —	9.9%	5.6%	8.4%

Community Health Systems, Inc.

Community Health Systems (CHS) owns or leases about 100 hospitals — mostly in rural areas or small cities — in about 20 states. Its hospitals (which house roughly 18000 beds) typically operate as part of larger regional networks or act as the sole or primary acute health care provider in a service area. Facilities offer a variety of medical surgical and emergency services; CHS also operates a couple of stand-alone rehabilitation or psychiatric facilities. The CHS network also includes physician practices urgent care clinics surgery centers cancer and imaging centers and occupational medicine clinics.

Operations

CHS operates through a single segment — hospital operations. The segment's holdings include inpatient centers and their related outpatient care facilities.

Altogether CHS employs some 2000 physicians and 1000 other licensed practitioners.

Geographic Reach

Headquartered in Franklin Tennessee CHS has hospitals in about 20 states with its largest market concentrations in Florida Indiana Tennessee and Texas.

Sales and Marketing

CHS receives about 60% of its revenue from commercial insurance companies. Nearly 40% of sales come from Medicare and Medicaid reimbursements and a small portion of revenue comes from self-pay patients.

Financial Performance

CHS reported growing revenue in 2014 and 2015 as it continued its acquisitive strategy but the company saw declining sales in 2016 2017 and 2018 as it conducted extensive hospital divestitures. Net income hovered at around $100 to $150 million in 2014 and 2015 but then the company reported sharp net losses from 2016 through 2018 due to lower revenue and higher operating expenses (including severance payments and surgical supply purchases).

Revenue in 2018 declined 8% to some $14.2 billion primarily due to lost revenues from hospital divestitures. Same-store revenue (from hospitals owned in both 2017 and 2018) increased nearly 3% due to improved pricing despite a slight decline in same-store inpatient admissions.

The company reported a net loss of $788 million in 2018 an improvement over a staggering $2.5 billion loss in 2017. The 2018 net loss primarily stemmed from goodwill and asset impairment charges for hospitals sold or up for sale in addition to a charge related to a change in how the company estimates bad debt provisions.

The company ended 2018 with $196 million in cash down $367 million from 2017. Operating activities contributed $274 million while investing activities used $245 million (property and equipment purchases and other investments) and financing activities used $396 million on debt payments.

Strategy

CHS has been shedding noncore assets in light of its financial struggles. The company is divesting underperforming or noncore hospitals as it focuses on its stronger holdings. In 2018 it sold 11 hospitals for a total of some $405 million and shuttered three hospitals and it continued to divest facilities into 2019. Historically CHS has expanded via aggressive hospital acquisitions especially in growing non-urban markets. It expects to ultimately return to that strategy and has continued to make some small acquisitions in the meantime primarily of outpatient care locations.

Beyond its portfolio optimization efforts the firm is focused on becoming a market leader or increasing market share in the communities where it operates. Efforts in this area include strengthening regional networks expanding outpatient care facilities to increase patient access points recruiting skilled primary and specialty physicians and connecting episodes of care for patients. The company acquired 43 physician practices in 2018.

Additionally CHS is standardizing and centralizing operations (such as billing collections and procurement) across its facilities to improve efficiency and contain costs. All the while the company emphasizes patient safety and quality of care through systematic improvements that improve physician and patient satisfaction. Efforts in this area include monitoring clinical outcomes evidence-based training programs error-prevention tools and leveraging technology to promote information sharing and clinical best practices.

Company Background

Community Health Systems (CHS) was founded in 1985 and went public in 1991. The company was reincorporated in Delaware in 1996 when it was acquired by investment firm Forstmann Little & Co. It also moved its headquarters from Houston to Nashville Tennessee that year.

In 2014 CHS added some 70 hospitals through the acquisition of Health Management Associates (HMA). CHS conducted an IPO in 2000.

In 2016 the company spun off nearly 40 of its hospitals along with its Quorum Health Resources unit (a provider of management services to non-affiliated hospitals) forming a new public company named Quorum Health Corporation. In 2017 it sold 30 hospitals for a total of some $1.7 billion. Also that year CHS sold an 80% stake in its home health and hospice operations to Almost Family for $128 million.

HISTORY

Community Health Systems (CHS) was founded in 1985.

In 1996 it was acquired by investment firm Forstmann Little & Co. in a leveraged buyout transaction worth some $1.1 billion. It also moved its headquarters from Houston to Nashville Tennessee that year.

CHS once again became a public entity through an IPO in 2000. It engaged is engaged in a flurry of acquisition activity of small regional hospitals each year following its IPO.

However CHS limited its purchases somewhat after plunking down $7 billion in 2007 to acquire Triad Hospitals (and its more than 50 hospitals).

After conducting integration efforts at the former Triad hospitals CHS fully resumed its acquisition activity when it purchased five hospitals during 2010 including the Marion Regional Hospital in South Carolina the Forum Health (later Valley-Care) hospitals in Ohio and the Bluefield Hospital in West Virginia.

Buoyed by those purchases CHS launched a campaign to acquire fellow hospital operator and rival Tenet in late 2010 in a deal worth some $7.3 billion in cash stock and debt. However after much back and forth between the firms — including lawsuits and hostile tender offers — CHS halted its acquisition attempts the following year due to a lack of response from Tenet's shareholders and board members.

CHS instead completed several smaller purchases that year including the acquisition of the Mercy Health Partners Scranton operations in Pennsylvania from Catholic Health Partners. The company also purchased Tomball Regional Medical Center (TRMC) located near Houston.

As part of its periodic practice of divesting noncore centers in 2011 it sold two Oklahoma facilities SouthCrest Hospital and Claremore Regional Hospital to Ardent Health Services' Hillcrest HealthCare System unit for an undisclosed price. It also sold a Texas hospital Cleveland Regional Medical Center that year to New Directions Health Systems.

EXECUTIVES

Vice President Of Facilities Management, Gordon Carlisle

Vice President Practice Management Division I Operations, Todd Hill

Evp And Cfo, W. Larry Cash, age 71, $850,000 total compensation

Chairman And Ceo, Wayne T. Smith, age 73, $1,600,000 total compensation

President Division Ii Operations, Michael T. Portacci, age 61, $663,341 total compensation

Svp Operations, Martin G. (Marty) Schweinhart, age 64

Svp Corporate Communications Marketing And Public Affairs, Tomi Galin

President And Coo, Tim L. Hingtgen, age 52, $655,007 total compensation

Svp And Chief Purchasing Officer, Tim G. Marlette

President Division Iii Operations, P. Paul Smith, age 56

Svp And Cio, Manish Shah

President Division Iv Operations, John W. McClellan

Chief Quality Officer; President Clinical Services, Lynn T. Simon, age 56

President Division I Operations, Martin J. Bonick, age 46

Svp And Chief Nursing Officer, Pamela T. Rudisill

Cfo, Thomas J. (Tom) Aaron

Radiology Director, Lex Weatherly

Interim Vice President Commonwealth Health Regional Service Center, Marilee Bruns

Vice President Of Finance, Lynne Mitchell

Vice President And Associate General Counsel, Jesse Neil

Vp Dir Finance, James Wright

Senior Vice President Of Managed Care, Richard T Willis

Senior Vice President Corporate Compliance And Privacy Officer, Andrea Bosshart

Vice President Of Finance, Nicole Slaughter

Vice President And Chief Strategy Officer, Wesley Littrell

Executive Vice President, Larry Cash

Director Of Health, Lisa Naylor

Director Of Pharmacy, Marshall Robbins

Senior Vice President Internal Audit, Mark Buford

Vice President Of Operations, Matt Hayes

Senior Vice President Financial Services, Michael Lynd

Vice President, Terry Hendon

Vice President Division Operations, Christopher Costello

Director Of Surgery Services, Craig Hiott

Medical Director, Scott Wagner

Clinic Manager, Amanda Anderton

Vice President, Laurence Bludau

Vice President Of Human Resource, Sam Pettit

Vice President Physician Business Services, Dan Adkins

Vice President Of Information Technology, Byung Kang

Senior Vice President, Ken Hawkins

Vice President; Associate General Counsel Division Iv, Carol Hendry

Senior Vice President Human Resources, Ronald Shafer

Vice President Operations, David Fikse

Vice President Case Management And Appeals, Terri Yancey

Senior Vice President And Chief Human Resources Officer, James M Hayes

Auditors: Deloitte & Touche LLP

LOCATIONS

HQ: Community Health Systems, Inc.
4000 Meridian Boulevard, Franklin, TN 37067
Phone: 615 465-7000
Web: www.chs.net

PRODUCTS/OPERATIONS

2017 Sales

	% of total
Managed care & other third-party payors	54
Medicare	23
Self-pay	13
Medicaid	10
Total	**100**

COMPETITORS

Adventist Health System Sunbelt Healthcare
Adventist Health System West
Ascension Health
Banner Health
CHRISTUS Health
Carolinas HealthCare System
Catholic Health Initiatives
Dignity Health
Encompass Health
HCA
LifePoint Health
Mercy Health
SSM Health Care
SunLink Health Systems
Sutter Health
Tenet Healthcare
Texas Health Resources
Trinity Health (Novi)
Universal Health Services
University Health Services
WellStar Health System

HISTORICAL FINANCIALS

Company Type: Public

Income Statement   FYE: December 31

	REVENUE ($ mil.)	NET INCOME ($ mil.)	NET PROFIT MARGIN	EMPLOYEES
12/18	14,155	(788)	—	87,000
12/17	15,353	(2,459)	—	95,000
12/16	18,438	(1,721)	—	120,000
12/15	19,437	158	0.8%	137,000
12/14	18,639	92	0.5%	167,000
Annual Growth	(6.6%)	—	—	(15.0%)

Community Trust Bancorp, Inc.

Community Trust Bancorp is the holding company for Community Trust Bank one of the largest Kentucky-based banks. It operates 70-plus branches throughout the state as well as in northeastern Tennessee and southern West Virginia. The bank offers standard services to area businesses and individuals including checking and savings accounts credit cards and CDs. Loans secured by commercial properties and other real estate account for nearly 70% of the bank's portfolio which also includes business consumer and construction loans. Subsidiary Community Trust and Investment Company provides trust estate retirement brokerage and insurance services through a handful of offices in Kentucky and Tennessee.

Operations

Community Trust Bancorp's lending activities include making commercial construction mortgage and personal loans. It also offers lease-financing lines of credit revolving lines of credit term loans and other specialized loans including asset-backed financing.

Some 69% of Community Trust Bancorp's portfolio of loans is secured real estate (36% of which consists of commercial real estate).

Geographic Reach

Kentucky-based Community Trust Bancorp operates more than 70 banking locations across Kentucky West Virginia and Tennessee. Its trust offices are located in Kentucky and Tennessee.

Sales and Marketing

Community Trust Bancorp specializes in serving both small and medium-sized businesses.

Financial Performance

Despite weak loan demand Community Trust Bancorp has grown its revenue from 2009 to 2011 followed by a marginal decline in 2012. Thanks to a decline in both interest expenses and provisions for loan losses Community Trust Bancorp has seen its net income rise during the past five years.

While Community Trust Bancorp logged marginal decreases (1%) in revenue in fiscal 2012 vs. 2011 the financial institution posted net income increases of 16% to $45 million during the reporting period.

Mergers and Acquisitions

Community Trust Bancorp bought LaFollette First National Corporation the holding company for First National Bank of LaFollette for some $16 million. The 2010 acquisition gave the company its first four bank branches and first trust office in Tennessee.

Community Trust is considering additional acquisitions of smaller competitors. It also grows by opening new branches.

EXECUTIVES

Chairman President And Ceo And Chairman Community Trust Bank, Jean R. Hale, age 73, $548,077 total compensation

Evp And Cfo Community Trust Bancorp And Evp And Treasurer Community Trust Bank, Kevin J. Stumbo, age 59, $231,539 total compensation

Evp And Secretary Community Trust Bancorp President And Ceo Community Trust Bank And Vp Community Trust And Investment Company, Mark A. Gooch, age 61, $397,000 total compensation

Evp Community Trust Bancorp And Evp And Chief Credit Officer Community Trust Bank, James J. (Jim) Gartner, age 78

Evp Community Trust Bancorp And Evp Operations Community Trust Bank, James B. (Jim) Draughn, age 60, $241,231 total compensation

Evp Community Trust Bancorp And Evp And South Central Region President Community Trust Bank, Ricky D. Sparkman, age 56

Evp Community Trust Bancor And Evp And Eastern Region President Community Trust Bank, Richard W. (Rick) Newsom, age 64

Evp Community Trust Bancorp And Evp And President Central Kentucky Region Community Trust Bank Inc., Larry W. Jones, age 72, $249,231 total compensation

Evp Community Trust Bancorp And Evp And Chief Internal Audit And Risk Officer Community Trust Bank, Steven E. (Steve) Jameson, age 62

Evp Community Trust Bancorp And Evp And President North East Region Community Trust Bank Inc., D. Andrew Jones, age 56

Evp Community Trust Bancorp And President And Ceo Community Trust And Investment Co., Andy D. Waters, age 53

Evp Community Trust Bancorp Inc. And Evp And Senior Staff Attorney Community Trust Bank Inc., C. Wayne Hancock, age 44

Svp Facilities Manager, Brian Hatmaker

Executive Vice President, David Jones

Board Member, James E Mcghee

Board Member, Anthony St Charles

Auditors: BKD, LLP

LOCATIONS

HQ: Community Trust Bancorp, Inc.
346 North Mayo Trail, Pikeville, KY 41501
Phone: 606 432-1414
Web: www.ctbi.com

PRODUCTS/OPERATIONS

2016 Sales

	$ mil.	% of total
Interest income		
Interest and fees on loans	133	69
Interest and dividends on securities	12	6
Noninterest income		
Service charges on deposit accounts	24	13
Gains on sales of loans	1	1
Trust and wealth management income	9	5
Loan related fees	4	2
Bank owned life insurance	2	1
Brokerage revenue	1	1
Securities gains (losses)	0	—
Other noninterest income	3	2
Total	195	100

Selected Products & Services

Business Banking
  Business CDs
  Business Checking
  Corporate Services
  Lending
  Merchant Services
  Online Services
  Savings & Money Market
Financial Services
Personal Banking
  Card Services
  CDs & IRAs
  Consumer Loans
  Home Equity
  Interest Checking
  Mobile Banking
  Mortgages
  Personal Checking
  Savings & Money Market
Wealth & Trust Management

COMPETITORS

BB&T
Fifth Third
Home Federal
Premier Financial
Bancorp

Republic Bancorp
U.S. Bancorp

HISTORICAL FINANCIALS

Company Type: Public

COMMUNITYBANK OF TEXAS NATIONAL ASSOCIATION

EXECUTIVES

Prin, George Casseb
Fo*, Donna Dillon
Senior Executive Vice Presiden, Robert Pigott

HISTORICAL FINANCIALS
Company Type: Private

Income Statement				FYE: December 31
	ASSETS ($ mil.)	NET INCOME ($ mil.)	INCOME AS % OF ASSETS	EMPLOYEES
12/17	3,079	28	0.9%	60
12/16	2,950	28	1.0%	—
12/15	2,881	25	0.9%	—
12/14	2,629	23	0.9%	—
Annual Growth	5.4%	6.2%	—	—

COMPUTER SCIENCES CORPORATION

Computer Sciences Corporation (CSC) has been one of the world's leading providers of systems integration and other information technology services. It offers application development data center management communications and networking development IT systems management and business consulting. It also provides business process outsourcing (BPO) services in such areas as billing and payment processing customer relationship management (CRM) and human resources. CSC boasts 2500 clients in more than 70 countries. In 2017 CSC merged with the Enterprise Services segment of Hewlett-Packard Enterprise to form DXC Technology Co. This report is based on CSC's last year as an independent company.

Change in Company Type
DXC is the result of mixing and matching of downsizing and upsizing corporate units. Computer Sciences Corp. spun out its government service unit several years ago which reduced CSC's revenue. Hewlett Packard Enterprise Services was part of Hewlett Packard Enterprise one of two companies created with Hewlett-Packard split up. The combination of HP Enterprise Services and CSC began in 2016 and concluded in April 2017 when DXC formally began operations. The new company is expected to have annual revenue of about $26 billion. This report reflects the final year of CSC as an independent company.

Operations
Prior to the creation of DXC CSC conducted business in through Global Business Services (GBS) and Global Infrastructure Services (GIS). GBS (55% of revenue) addresses key business challenges such as consulting applications services and software. GIS (45% of revenue) provides IT infrastructure services such as managed and virtual desktop solutions unified communications and collaboration services data center management cyber security and cloud-based offerings.

Geographic Reach
CSC has major operations throughout North America Europe Asia and Australia. The company has clients in more than 70 countries. About 40% of sales are made in the US and about 20% are in the UK the second biggest market.

Sales and Marketing
CSC's clients have included AboveNet Communications Deutsche Telekom DirecTV Vodafone and Ryman Hospitality Properties (formerly Gaylord Entertainment).

Financial Performance
After seven straight years of revenue declines CSC's sales rebounded in 2017 (ended March) to $7.6 billion a 7% increase from 2016. The increase was driven by the Global Business Services unit's business processing services offerings and contributions from recent acquisitions in the Digital Applications business. The Global Infrastructure Services unit posted a small revenue increase from new business and sales from acquisitions.

CSC lost about $123 million in 2017 down from a $251 million profit in 2016 mainly due to large restructuring charges.

Cash flow from operating activities rose to $978 million in 2017 from $802 million in 2016. The increase flowed from an increase in trade payables and a decrease in net account receivables.

Strategy
After going through corporate breakups DXC Technology bets that bigger will be better and stronger in competing in the worldwide market for IT services. The companies have a wide footprint and with some $26 billion in annual revenue and will have some weight to throw around. A question will be if the company can effectively compete with companies that provide similar services such as Cognizant WiPro Accenture IBM Global Service and Dell Technologies.

DXC has bulked up to ride the wave of digital transformation that its customers and potential customers are going through. The company's range of services could lead customers from legacy systems to private or public or hybrid cloud systems.

Mergers and Acquisitions
In 2016 CSC acquired Xchanging plc provider of technology-enabled business services for $633 million. Xchanging brings its Xuber software which is used by commercial insurance companies around the world.

Also in 2016 CSC acquired Aspediens a European provider in the service-management sector and a preferred partner of ServiceNow. The deal extended CSC's reach in software-as-a-service in Europe.

EXECUTIVES

Vice President, Debbie Granberry
Vice President Finance Corporate Development And Corporate Treasurer, Charles Diao
Vice President Finance And Administration, Frank Sossi
Vice President Of Global Human Resources And Trans, Mike Darcy
Division Director Deputy Vice President General Manager, Richard Morrow
Managing Director India And Global Head Workforce Management, Sreehanth Krishnan Arimanithaya
Senior Vice President And General Manager Security, Art Wong
Vice President Sales, Robb Maltempo
Vice President And General Manager Global Insurance, Phil Ratcliff
Vice President Global Pricing, Mike Brocato
Vice President, Brad Canel
Senior Vice President Federal Government Solutions, John Kavanaugh
Vp Corporate Communications, Caryn Kboudi
Svp Of Leasing, Michelle Waak
Auditors: DELOITTE & TOUCHE LLP MCLEAN

LOCATIONS

HQ: COMPUTER SCIENCES CORPORATION
1775 TYSONS BLVD STE 1000, TYSONS, VA 221024284
Phone: 703 245-9675
Web: WWW.DXC.TECHNOLOGY

2017 Sales

	$ mil.	% of total
United States	2,986	40
United Kingdom	1,482	19
Australia	921	12
Other Europe	1,594	21
Other International	624	8
Total	**7,607**	**100**

PRODUCTS/OPERATIONS

2017 Sales

	$ mil.	% of total
Global Business Services	4,173	55
Global Infrastructure Services	3,434	45
Total	**7,607**	**100**

Selected Service Areas
Application outsourcing
Business process outsourcing
Customer relationship management
Data hosting
Enterprise application integration
Knowledge management
Management consulting
Risk management
Security
Supply chain management

Selected Solutions
Application Services
Big Data & Analytics
Business & Technology Consulting
Cloud Solutions & Services
Cybersecurity
Industry Software & Solutions
Infrastructure Services
Managed Services & Outsourcing
Mobility Solutions

COMPETITORS
ADP
Accenture
Atos
Booz Allen
CACI International
CIBER
Capgemini
Cognizant Tech Solutions
Computacenter
Convergys
Dell
Deloitte Consulting
Dimension Data
General Dynamics Information Technology
Getronics
HCL Technologies
Honeywell International
IBM Global Services
Infosys
Leidos
ManTech
NTT Data
Northrop Grumman
Siemens AG
Tata Consultancy
Tech Mahindra
Unisys
Wipro
Wipro Technologies

HISTORICAL FINANCIALS

Company Type: Private

Income Statement | | | | FYE: March 31

	REVENUE ($ mil.)	NET INCOME ($ mil.)	NET PROFIT MARGIN	EMPLOYEES
03/17*	7,607	(100)	—	66,000
04/16	7,106	263	3.7%	—
04/15	12,173	7	0.1%	—
03/14	12,998	690	5.3%	—
Annual Growth	(16.4%)	—	—	—

*Fiscal year change

Conagra Brands Inc

ConAgra Foods fills the refrigerators freezers and pantries of most households. The company makes and markets name-brand packaged and frozen foods that are sold widely across the US including in Wal-Mart stores. ConAgra's cornucopia of America's best-known brands includes Banquet Birds Eye Chef Boyardee Egg Beaters Healthy Choice and Marie Callender. Around 50 factories scattered across the Midwest New England and Sunbelt regions of the US as well as Canada Mexico and India manufacture ConAgra's many products. ConAgra began as a flour-milling company in Nebraska in 1919 and over the decades transformed into a consumer goods company.

HISTORY

Alva Kinney founded Nebraska Consolidated Mills in 1919 by combining the operations of four Nebraska grain mills. It did not expand outside Nebraska until it opened a mill and feed processing plant in Alabama in 1942.

Consolidated Mills developed Duncan Hines cake mix in the 1950s. But Duncan Hines failed to raise a large enough market share and the company sold it to Procter & Gamble in 1956. Consolidated Mills used the proceeds to expand opening a flour and feed mill in Puerto Rico the next year. In the 1960s while competitors were moving into prepared foods the firm expanded into animal feeds and poultry processing. By 1970 it had poultry processing plants in Alabama Georgia and Louisiana. In 1971 the company changed its name to ConAgra (Latin for "in partnership with the land"). During the 1970s it expanded into the fertilizer catfish and pet accessory businesses.

Poorly performing subsidiaries and commodity speculation caused ConAgra severe financial problems until 1974 when Mike Harper a former Pillsbury executive took over. Harper trimmed properties to reduce debt and had the company back on its feet by 1976. ConAgra stayed focused on the commodities side of the business but was thus tied to volatile price cycles. In 1978 it bought United Agri Products (agricultural chemicals).

ConAgra moved into consumer food products in the 1980s. It bought Banquet (frozen food 1980) and within six years had introduced almost 90 new products under that label. Other purchases included Singleton Seafood (1981) Armour Food Company (meats dairy products frozen food; 1983) and RJR Nabisco's frozen food business (1986). ConAgra became a major player in the red meat market with the 1987 purchases of E.A. Miller (boxed beef) Monfort (beef and lamb) and Swift Independent Packing.

Confident it had found the right path ConAgra continued with acquisitions of consumer food makers including Beatrice Foods (Orville Redenbacher's popcorn Hunt's tomato products) in 1991. In 1997 the company agreed to pay $8.3 million to settle federal charges of wire fraud and watering down grain. That year ConAgra named vice chairman and president Bruce Rohde as CEO; he became chairman in 1998. Also in 1998 the company bought GoodMark Foods maker of Slim Jim and Nabisco's Egg Beaters and table spread unit(Parkay). ConAgra bought Holly Ridge Foods (pastries) in 1999 and announced a major restructuring.

ConAgra bought Emerge an agricultural and land-use information software provider from Litton Industries in 2000. It also acquired Seaboard's poultry division and refrigerated meat alternatives maker Lightlife (Tofu pups Smart Dogs) before buying major brand holder International Home Foods from HM Capital Partners (known as Hicks Muse Tate & Furst at the time) for about $2.9 billion. The company then became ConAgra Foods.

During 2001 the company drew SEC attention and was forced to restate earnings for the previous three years due to accounting no-no's in its United Agri Products division.

In 2002 the USDA forced ConAgra to recall 19 million pounds of ground beef because of possible E. coli contamination making it the second-largest food recall in US history. (The largest recall occurred in 1997 when Hudson Foods later purchased by Tyson Foods withdrew 35 million pounds of beef.) Later in 2002 ConAgra sold its fresh beef and pork processing business — one of the largest in the US — to Booth Creek Management and HM Capital Partners and it was renamed Swift & Company Swift & Company. (Swift was acquired by Brazilian beef giant JBS in 2007.)

In 2003 the company began supplying packaged meat products for grilling to George Foreman Foods which sells them via its Web site. That year it sold its Bumble Bee canned seafood business to members of Bumble Bee management and private investment firm Centre Partners Management and its blue cheese brands (Treasure Cave Nauvoo) to Canada's Saputo Inc. for undisclosed prices. It also sold its chicken processing business to Pilgrim's Pride for a stock and cash deal worth about $550 million in 2003.

Also in 2003 ConAgra agreed to pay $1.5 million in cash and job offers to settle an EEOC lawsuit charging bias against disabled workers at the company's California-based Gilroy Foods plant. The agreement involves the largest disability settlement in the agriculture industry. The dispute dated back to 1999 when Gilroy Foods then owned by Basic Vegetable Products (ConAgra bought the facility in 2000) after a strike failed to recall disabled workers who were on leaves of absence due to illness or pregnancy or who had a history of illness or injury.

In keeping with its strategy to focus on its branded and value-added food business in 2003 ConAgra sold United Agri Products to Apollo Management for stock and securities. The deal was worth about $600 million. In 2004 it sold its minority interest in the beef and pork processing operations of Swift Foods to HM Capital Partners. The deal was worth $194 million. ConAgra also sold Swift's feedlot operations to Smithfield Foods for an undisclosed amount.

ConAgra sold its turkey hatchery and breeding business to Ag Forte in 2004. It sold its Canadian and US crop inputs businesses and its Spanish feed and Portuguese poultry businesses that year as well. In addition it sold Casa de Oro Foods (the US's third-largest tortilla maker) to the Plaza Belmont Fund II. Also that year ConAgra introduced Golden Cuisine a line of frozen meals designed for

seniors. The company began manufacturing and supplying Golden Cuisine to Meals On Wheels which distributes the meals which are formulated for seniors to the homebound elderly. That year ConAgra also introduced a high-fiber flour called Ultragrain that has the taste and texture of refined flour but the nutrition of whole grain.

In 2005 ConAgra sold its remaining 15 million shares of Pilgrim's Pride to that company for about $480 million. That year CEO Bruce Rhode retired. His replacement was former chairman and CEO of PepsiCo Beverages and Foods North America Gary Rodkin who began a company-wide restructuring. The company reorganized its business structure from three channels to two: Foodservice was merged with Food Ingredients and became ConAgra Foods Commercial ; the ConAgra Retail channel remained the same.

ConAgra agreed to pay a $14 million shareholder settlement in 2005 regarding a lawsuit claiming fictitious sales and mis-reported earnings at its former subsidiary United Agri Products.

In a move to demonstrate its commitment to the humane treatment of animals in 2006 ConAgra urged its poultry suppliers to consider slaughtering chickens in a more humane manner called controlled-atmosphere killing. The process which ConAgra has only suggested to its suppliers is approved by the People for the Ethical Treatment of Animals.

Rodkin continued the company redo focusing on portfolio trimming when in early 2006 he announced plans to sell a large part of ConAgra's refrigerated-meats business. The brands involved in the sale include some of the company's best-known: Armour Butterball and Eckrich. (The Brown 'N Serve Healthy Choice Hebrew National Pemmican and Slim Jim brands were not included in the portfolio reduction.) It sold its Cook's ham business to Smithfield Foods for $260 million that year.

Not long after that it agreed to sell of the rest of its refrigerated meats business that it had for sale to Smithfield as well. The deal which became final in October 2006 cost Smithfield $571 million in cash. That same month it sold its Butterball Turkey unit to Carolina Turkeys for $325 million. (Carolina subsequently changed its company name to Butterball LLC .)

Divesting almost faster than one can keep track of one day after the Butterball deal was completed ConAgra sold its MaMa Rosa's Pizza operations to investment firm the Plaza Belmont Management Group. (MaMa Rosa's is refrigerated — not frozen pizza — and competes in a different market than other pizzas albeit frozen powerhouses such as Di Giorno Tombstone or Tony's .)

In another move to improve long-term operating performance ConAgra announced its intention to sell off its seafood and domestic and imported cheese businesses. To that end the company sold its surimi business including the Louis Kemp brand to Trident Seafoods and its Singleton Seafood and Meridian Seafood to Singleton Fisheries. It sold its specialty and imported cheese operation Swissrose International to investment company Fairmount Food Group. Late in 2006 the company sold its oat-milling business to investment companies Sequel Holdings and Falcon Investment Advisors.

The company added to its Lamb Weston branded potato products with the 2008 acquisition of Watts Brothers. With operations in Washington and Oregon Watts is a vegetable-processing company that has annual sales of some $100 million. It has retail foodservice and industrial customers throughout the US as well as in Mexico Japan China and other Far East countries. The deal also included Watts' organic dairy fertilizer cold storage packaging and agricultural farming businesses.

In early 2007 salmonella was found in some of the company's Peter Pan and Great Value (a Wal-Mart product) brands of peanut butter forcing a nationwide recall of the peanut butter bearing the product code involved. Salmonella food poisoning was linked to some 600 people in 47 states. No deaths related to the peanut better were confirmed. The recall eventually included products made as far back as October 2004. ConAgra shut down the Sylvester Georgia plant that was involved in the outbreak and reopened it in Augusts 2007 having spent $15 million on renovation which included repairing the roof installing new equipment and creating a manufacturing process that better separated raw materials from the finished peanut butter.

Just two months later the company voluntarily stopped production at the Missouri plant that makes its Banquet and generic brands of frozen turkey and chicken pot pies after learning that the were linked to some 140 cases of salmonella in 30 states. ConAgra did not recall the pies but offered mail-in refunds and store returns. The USDA began an investigation and advised consumers not to eat the pies.

As part of its strategy to add to its brand-name offerings in 2007 ConAgra acquired Alexia Foods a maker of natural frozen potatoes appetizers and artisan breads for about $50 million in cash. Later that year the company paid a penalty of $45 million in the wake of SEC charges that alleged the company had misreported its profits for the fiscal years 1999 2000 and 2001.

The company acquired Lincoln Snacks Company in 2007. Lincoln's well-known brands such as Fiddle Faddle and Poppycock extended ConAgra's name-brand lineup which is in line with company strategy. That year it also announced the removal of the chemicals from its microwave popcorn products that are suspected of causing lung ailments in popcorn-plant workers.

ConAgra sold its trading and merchandising operations (ConAgra Trade Group) in 2008 to a group of investors that included the Ospraie Special Opportunities Fund for $2.8 billion. The sale was part of the company's long-term strategy to exit the commodities business and concentrate on its consumer food products. Saying it couldn't give the brand the attention it needs in 2008 the company sold its Knott's Berry Farm jam and jelly business to J. M. Smucker .

In a tragedy that made the evening news three ConAgra workers were killed and some 40 were injured in an explosion and fire at a company Slim Jim manufacturing plant in Garner North Carolina in June 2009. It was later determined that the blast was caused by a natural-gas leak. ConAgra partnered with the United Way forming the Garner Plant Fund that raised money to assist the victims and their families. The company also continued to pay workers salaries while the plant remained closed for investigation. ConAgra was fined $106000 by the government in 2010 and the plant was eventually closed.

During 2010 ConAgra unloaded its Gilroy Foods & Flavors business-to-business unit to Olam International for $250 million. The sale excluded Gilroy's seasonings and flavors businesses.

In 2011 ConAgra Foods made an unsolicited takeover bid to buy Ralcorp Holdings a leading maker of private-label snack foods cereals and condiments. After proffering an initial bid of $82 per share ConAgra ultimately offered $94 (valuing Ralcorp at more than $5 billion). However Ralcorp spurned all bids saying they were not in the best interests of shareholders.

In May 2012 the company completed the acquisition of Odom's Tennessee Pride the #2 producer of frozen breakfast sandwiches in the US.

In January 2013 ConAgra completed its $6.8 billion purchase of Ralcorp Holdings.

In September 2013 it purchased the frozen dessert producer business of Harlan Bakeries which made frozen fruit pies cream pies pastry shells and loaf cakes.

In early 2013 ConAgra acquired Ralcorp the nation's #1 maker of private-label food in a deal valued at about $6.8 billion (including debt). The combined company was expected to generate $18 billion in sales and made ConAgra the largest private-brand packaged foods business in North America with annual private brand sales of about $4.5 billion a year. The private brands segment makes private-label ready-to-eat cereals cereal bars snack mixes cookies crackers and other products for retailers under their own brand names.

EXECUTIVES

Senior Vice President And Chief Litigation Counsel, Leo Knowles

Evp General Counsel And Corporate Secretary, Colleen Batcheler, age 45, $521,635 total compensation

Evp And Cfo, John F. Gehring, age 58, $643,269 total compensation

Ceo, Sean M. Connolly, $1,100,000 total compensation

President Consumer Foods, Thomas M. (Tom) McGough, age 54, $636,538 total compensation

Evp And President Sales, Derek De La Mater

President Commercial Foods, Tom Werner, $438,654 total compensation

Evp And Chief Supply Chain Officer, Dave Biegger

Evp And Chief Human Resources Officer, Charisse Brock

Cio, Mindy Simon

Vp Talent Effectiveness, Tresia Nwamadi

Vice President Research And Development, Richard McArdle

Vp Research And Development Packaging, Eric Sinz

Senior Vice President Insights And Analytics, Bob Nolan

Vice President Product Readiness, Mark Evans

Vice President Customer Development, Michael Fitzpatrick

Vice President Information Technology, Scott Tylski

Vice President Business Development, Keith Chapman

Vice President Marketing, Mike Veal

Vice President Sustainable Development, Gail Tavill

Division Vp West, Wes Upchurch

Vice President Human Resources, Kelly Schaefer

Vice President General Manager, Taylor Strubell

Vice President Of Marketing, Andy Johnston

Vice President Assistant Treasurer, Scott Schneider

Vice President Research Quality And Innovation, Christian Rhynalds

Vice President General Manager Spicetec, Mark Duffy

Senior Vice President Marketing, Karen E Carey

Vice President Internal Audit, Allen Cooper

Senior Vice President Supply Chain, Mike Tracy

Senior Vice President Procurement, Dk Singh

Vice President Corporate Real Estate And Facilities, James Doyle

Vice President Finance, Teresa Wallfred

Vice President Program Management, Mark Grohe

Vice President Manufacturing, Charlie Gorman

Vice President Marketing, Karl Sears

Vice President Transportation And Warehousing, Ken Smith

Senior Vice President Sales, Bill Tragos

Vice President Supply Chain Integration, Craig Weiss

Senior Vice President Strategy And Business Development, Brian Davison

Vice President Finance Enterprise Procurement, Scott Luther

Vice President Program Implementation, Joe McSharry

Vp Enterprise Deployment, Jim Blakemore

Vice President Customer Facing Lead Ralcorp Integration, Dave Dobronski

Vice President Procurement, Bob Hellem

Vice President Precision Marketing, Delu Jackson

Vice President International Finance, Denise Hansen

Vice President Engineering, Jim Prunesti

Vice President Sales Kroger Team, Jeremy Attal

Chairman, Steven F. (Steve) Goldstone, age 74

Board Member, Jennifer Hudson

Vp And Treasurer And Chief Risk Officer, Johan Nystedt

Auditors: KPMG LLP

LOCATIONS

HQ: Conagra Brands Inc
222 West Merchandise Mart Plaza, Suite 1300, Chicago, IL 60654
Phone: 312 549-5000
Web: www.conagrabrands.com

PRODUCTS/OPERATIONS

2018 sales

	$ mil.	% of total
Grocery & Snacks	3,279	34
Refrigerated & Frozen	2,804	30
International	793	8
Foodservice	934	10
Pinnacle Foods	1,727	18
Total	**9,538**	**100**

Selected Brands

Commercial foods
  ConAgra Mills
  Lamb Weston
  Spicetec Flavors & Seasonings
Consumer foods
  Act II
  Alexia
  Banquet
  Bertolli
  Blue Bonnet
  Chef Boyardee
  DAVID Seeds
  Egg Beaters
  Healthy Choice
  Hebrew National
  Hunt's
  Marie Callender's
  Odom's Tennessee Pride
  Orville Redenbacher's
  PAM
  Peter Pan
  P.F. Chang's
  Reddi-wip
  Slim Jim
  Snack Pack
  Swiss Miss
  Van Camp's
  Wesson

COMPETITORS

American Pop Corn	Jenny Craig
B&G Foods	Kellogg
Big Heart Pet Brands	Link Snacks
Boulder Brands	MOM Brands
Bush Brothers	Manischewitz Company
Campbell Soup	McCain Foods
Clorox	McIlhenny
Eden Foods	Monterey Gourmet Foods
Frito-Lay	Mott's
General Mills	Nestlé
Gilster-Mary Lee	Newman's Own
Goya	Nutrisystem
H. J. Heinz Limited	Pinnacle Foods
Hain Celestial	Schwan's
Hanover Foods	Seneca Foods

Heinz
Hormel
Inventure foods
J-OIL MILLS
JR Simplot

Slim-Fast
Smucker
Snappy Popcorn
Weaver Popcorn Company

HISTORICAL FINANCIALS
Company Type: Public

Income Statement				FYE: May 26
	REVENUE ($ mil.)	NET INCOME ($ mil.)	NET PROFIT MARGIN	EMPLOYEES
05/19	9,538	678	7.1%	18,000
05/18	7,938	808	10.2%	12,400
05/17	7,826	639	8.2%	12,600
05/16	11,642	(677)	—	20,900
05/15	15,832	(252)	—	32,900
Annual Growth	(11.9%)	—	—	(14.0%)

2019 Year-End Financials
Debt ratio: 48.07%
Return on equity: 12.30%
Cash ($ mil.): 236
Current ratio: 1.28
Long-term debt ($ mil.): 10,655

No. of shares (mil.): 486
Dividends
  Yield: 0.0%
  Payout: 55.9%
Market value ($ mil.): 14,014

	STOCK PRICE ($) FY Close	P/E High/Low		PER SHARE ($) Earnings	Dividends	Book Value
05/19	28.83	25	14	1.52	0.85	15.19
05/18	37.41	20	16	1.98	0.85	9.41
05/17	39.03	33	23	1.46	0.90	9.58
05/16	45.29	—	—	(1.56)	1.00	8.48
05/15	38.61	—	—	(0.60)	1.00	10.57
Annual Growth	(7.0%)	—	—	—	(4.0%)	9.5%

Conduent Inc

Auditors: PricewaterhouseCoopers LLP

LOCATIONS
HQ: Conduent Inc
  100 Campus Drive, Suite 200, Florham Park, NJ 07932
Phone: 844 663-2638
Web: www.conduent.com

HISTORICAL FINANCIALS
Company Type: Public

Income Statement				FYE: December 31
	REVENUE ($ mil.)	NET INCOME ($ mil.)	NET PROFIT MARGIN	EMPLOYEES
12/18	5,393	(416)	—	82,000
12/17	6,022	181	3.0%	90,000
12/16	6,408	(983)	—	96,000
12/15	6,662	(414)	—	93,700
12/14	6,938	(81)	—	—
Annual Growth	(6.1%)	—	—	—

2018 Year-End Financials
Debt ratio: 23.46%
Return on equity: (-11.83%)
Cash ($ mil.): 756
Current ratio: 1.64
Long-term debt ($ mil.): 1,512

No. of shares (mil.): 211
Dividends
  Yield: —
  Payout: —
Market value ($ mil.): 2,246

	STOCK PRICE ($) FY Close	P/E High/Low		PER SHARE ($) Earnings	Dividends	Book Value
12/18	10.63	—	—	(2.06)	0.00	15.92
12/17	16.16	21	16	0.83	0.00	17.44
Annual Growth	(9.9%)	—	—	—	—	(2.3%)

ConnectOne Bancorp Inc (New)

ConnectOne Bancorp (formerly Center Bancorp) is the holding company for ConnectOne Bank which operates some two dozen branches across New Jersey. Serving individuals and local businesses the bank offers such deposit products as checking savings and money market accounts; CDs; and IRAs. It also performs trust services. Commercial loans account for about 60% of the bank's loan portfolio; residential mortgages account for most of the remainder. It also has a subsidiary that sells annuities and property/casualty life and health coverage. The former Center Bancorp acquired rival community bank ConnectOne Bancorp in 2014 and took that name.

Geographic Reach
ConnectOne has 24 branches in Bergen Essex Hudson Manhattan Mercer Monmouth Morris and Union Counties in New Jersey.

Mergers and Acquisitions
In 2019 ConnectOne Bancorp agreed to acquire online business lending marketplace company BoeFly. BoeFly connects franchisors and small business owners with lenders and loan brokers in the US and has facilitated more than $5 billion in financing transactions. BoeFly's online platform and client network will enhance and expand ConnectOne's Small Business Adminstration (SBA) line of business.

EXECUTIVES
Vice President, Lisa Wagner
Vice President, William Tierney
Auditors: Crowe LLP

LOCATIONS
HQ: ConnectOne Bancorp Inc (New)
  301 Sylvan Avenue, Englewood Cliffs, NJ 07632
Phone: 201 816-8900
Web: www.centerbancorp.com

COMPETITORS
BCB Bancorp
Bank of America
Citizens Financial Corp.
Fulton Financial
Hudson City Bancorp
Investors Bancorp
JPMorgan Chase
Kearny Financial
Lakeland Bancorp

New York Community Bancorp
Oritani Financial
PNC Financial
Provident Financial Services
Sovereign Bank
Valley National Bancorp
Westamerica

HISTORICAL FINANCIALS
Company Type: Public

Income Statement				FYE: December 31
	ASSETS ($ mil.)	NET INCOME ($ mil.)	INCOME AS % OF ASSETS	EMPLOYEES
12/18	5,462	60	1.1%	—
12/17	5,108	43	0.8%	—
12/16	4,426	31	0.7%	—
12/15	4,016	41	1.0%	—
12/14	3,448	18	0.5%	—
Annual Growth	12.2%	34.3%		

2018 Year-End Financials
Debt ratio: 13.34%
Return on equity: 10.23%
Cash ($ mil.): 172
Current ratio: —
Long-term debt ($ mil.): —

No. of shares (mil.): 32
Dividends
  Yield: 1.6%
  Payout: 16.1%
Market value ($ mil.): 597

	STOCK PRICE ($) FY Close	P/E High/Low		PER SHARE ($) Earnings	Dividends	Book Value
12/18	18.47	17	9	1.86	0.30	18.99
12/17	25.75	21	16	1.34	0.30	17.63
12/16	25.95	26	15	1.01	0.30	16.62
12/15	18.69	16	13	1.36	0.30	15.87
12/14	19.00	25	21	0.79	0.30	15.03
Annual Growth	(0.7%)	—	—	23.9%	(0.0%)	6.0%

ConocoPhillips

EXECUTIVES
Ceo, Ryan M Lance
Chb-Ceo*, J J Mulva
Exec V Pres-Cfo-Treas*, John A Carrig
V Pres*, Matt Fox
Executive Assistant, Carol Riddell
Counsel, Hans Holmen
Human Resources, Honorata Krzysiak
Director, Mark Frick
Finance Manager, Paul Rusch
Director, Scott Fretheim
Coordinator, Tiffany A Deis
Auditors: Ernst & Young LLP

LOCATIONS
HQ: ConocoPhillips
  925 N. Eldridge Parkway, Houston, TX 77079
Phone: 281 293-1000
Web: www.conocophillips.com

HISTORICAL FINANCIALS
Company Type: Public

Income Statement				FYE: December 31
	REVENUE ($ mil.)	NET INCOME ($ mil.)	NET PROFIT MARGIN	EMPLOYEES
12/18	38,727	6,257	16.2%	10,800
12/17	32,584	(855)	—	11,400
12/16	24,360	(3,615)	—	13,300
12/15	30,935	(4,428)	—	15,900
12/14	55,517	6,869	12.4%	19,100
Annual Growth	(8.6%)	(2.3%)	—	(13.3%)

2018 Year-End Financials

Debt ratio: 21.39%
Return on equity: 20.01%
Cash ($ mil.): 5,915
Current ratio: 1.80
Long-term debt ($ mil.): 14,856

No. of shares (mil.): 1,138
Dividends
  Yield: 1.8%
  Payout: 21.8%
Market value ($ mil.): 70,976

	STOCK PRICE ($) FY Close	P/E High/Low		PER SHARE ($) Earnings	Dividends	Book Value
12/18	62.35	15	10	5.32	1.16	28.06
12/17	54.89	—	—	(0.70)	1.06	26.00
12/16	50.14	—	—	(2.91)	1.00	28.27
12/15	46.69	—	—	(3.58)	2.94	32.17
12/14	69.06	16	11	5.51	2.84	42.16
Annual Growth	(2.5%)	—	—	(0.9%)	(20.1%)	(9.7%)

Consolidated Edison Co. of New York, Inc.

Consolidated Edison Company of New York (Con Edison of New York) keeps the nightlife pulsing in The Big Apple. The utility a subsidiary of Consolidated Edison distributes electricity throughout most of New York City and Westchester County. The company distributes electricity to 3.4 million residential and business customers in New York City; it also delivers natural gas to about 1.1 million customers. The utility also provides steam services to 1703 customers in portions of the New York metropolitan area. Con Edison of New York owns and operates more than 133900 miles of overhead and underground power distribution lines.

Operations

The company has three segments: electric gas and steam — which contributed 79% 15% and 6% of total revenues in 2015.

Its assets include more than 4300 miles of gas distribution mains a gas liquefaction and storage facility and electric and steam generating stations. It also owns a range of power transmission assets which are operated by the New York Independent System Operator. Con Edison of New York's electric generating facilities consist of plants located in New York City with an aggregate capacity of 724 MW.

The company's distribution system had a transformer capacity of 29762 MVA with 36929 miles of overhead distribution lines and 97286 miles of underground distribution lines. The underground distribution lines represent the single longest underground electric delivery system in the United States.

Geographic Reach

Con Edison of New York has distribution facilities throughout New York City and Westchester County and operates manufactured gas plants at 51 sites.

Sales and Marketing

Con Edison of New York delivers electricity to state and municipal customers of NYPA and economic development customers of municipal electric agencies. Its customers include residential commercial industrial public authorities retail choice customers.

Financial Performance

In fiscal 2015 its net revenues decreased by 4% due to the lower gas steam and electric sales.

Revenues from electric decreased due to lower purchased power expenses and lower fuel ex-

penses offset in part by higher revenues from the electric rate plan.

Con Edison of New York's gas revenues declined due to a decrease in gas purchased for resale expenses offset in part by higher revenues from the gas rate plan (reflecting higher delivery volumes attributable to oil-to-gas conversions). However revenues from steam increased due primarily to higher fuel expenses and higher revenues from the steam rate plan offset by the weather impact on revenues and lower purchased power costs.

In fiscal 2015 net income increased by 2% due to lower gas purchased for resale and purchased power.

Cash from operating activities increased by 16% due to lower income taxes paid net of refunds received offset in part by increased pension contributions.

Strategy

In 2016 Con Edison of New York filed a request with the New York State Public Service Commission for an electric rate increase of $482 million. It also entered into an agreement to sell certain electric transmission projects to NY Transco.

The company (in 2015) partnered with Drive Electric Vehicle Research Forward to help promote electric vehicles.

In 2014 Con Edison of New York was in the middle of a four-year $1 billion storm hardening program in the wake of 2012's Superstorm Sandy. Investments include the installation of 3000 devices that isolate and clear temporary faults on overhead electric systems and more than 150 smart switches that minimize outages caused by fallen trees. More than a mile of flood walls and 260 pieces of submersible equipment also have been installed. For its efforts the utility was named as the winner of the 2014 Outstanding System Reliability Award by the PA Consulting Group. The award recognizes the PA Consulting Group ReliabilityOne regional award recipient that demonstrated superior annual system-wide reliability performance for its customers. Con Edison of New York was also named best in the Northeast Region.

Company Background

Citing a 20% growth rate during the 2000s Con Edison of New York in 2011 spent almost $1.8 billion ($2 billion in 2010) to upgrade the company's aging electrical delivery systems (new high-voltage transmission cables) in New York City and surrounding areas. In 2010 Con Edison of New York and sister company Orange and Rockland also received $200 million in federal grants to install smart grid technology (automated more efficient meters and other systems) across their service area. By mid-2011 the company had also supported the installation of 8.5 MW of solar power units across its service region.

EXECUTIVES

Chairman And Ceo, Kevin Burke, age 69, $1,107,200 total compensation
Svp And Cro, Robert N. Hoglund, age 58, $584,200 total compensation
President Of Consolidated Edison Company Of New York; Inc., Craig S. Ivey, age 56
President And Ceo Orange And Rockland Utilities Inc., John T. McAvoy, age 58
Owner, Linda Goldberg
Auditors: PricewaterhouseCoopers LLP

LOCATIONS

HQ: Consolidated Edison Co. of New York, Inc.
  4 Irving Place, New York, NY 10003
Phone: 212 460-4600

COMPETITORS

Commerce Energy Group	New York Power
Delmarva Power	Authority
Green Mountain Energy	Public Service
Integrys Energy	Enterprise Group
Services	Rochester Gas and
NYSEG	Electric
National Grid USA	

HISTORICAL FINANCIALS

Company Type: Public

Income Statement

FYE: December 31

	REVENUE ($ mil.)	NET INCOME ($ mil.)	NET PROFIT MARGIN	EMPLOYEES
12/18	10,680	1,196	11.2%	13,685
12/17	10,468	1,104	10.5%	14,010
12/16	10,165	1,056	10.4%	13,531
12/15	10,328	1,084	10.5%	13,393
12/14	10,786	1,058	9.8%	13,200
Annual Growth	(0.2%)	3.1%	—	0.9%

2018 Year-End Financials

Debt ratio: 32.83%
Return on equity: 9.44%
Cash ($ mil.): 818
Current ratio: 0.80
Long-term debt ($ mil.): 13,676

No. of shares (mil.): 235
Dividends
  Yield: —
  Payout: 70.7%
Market value ($ mil.): —

Consolidated Edison Inc

Utility holding company Consolidated Edison (Con Edison) is the night light for the city that never sleeps. Con Edison's main subsidiary Consolidated Edison Company of New York distributes electricity to 3.5 million residential and business customers in a 660-mile service territory centered on New York City. It delivers natural gas to about 1.1 million customers and operates the country's largest steam distribution service to deliver energy to parts of Manhattan. Subsidiary Orange and Rockland Utilities serves more than 300000 electric and gas customers in New York and New Jersey. Con Edison also owns or operates renewable energy facilities and advises large clients on energy efficiency programs.

HISTORY

Several professionals led by Timothy Dewey formed The New York Gas Light Company in 1823 to illuminate part of Manhattan. In 1884 five other gas companies joined New York Gas Light to form the Consolidated Gas Company of New York.

Thomas Edison's incandescent lamp came on the scene in 1879 and The Edison Electric Illuminating Company of New York was formed in 1880 to build the world's first commercial electric power station (Pearl Street) financed by a group led by J.P. Morgan. Edison supervised the project and in 1882 New York became the first major city with electric lighting.

Realizing electricity would replace gas Consolidated Gas acquired electric companies including Anthony Brady's New York Gas and Electric Light Heat and Power Company (1900) which joined Edison's Illuminating Company in 1901 to form the New York Edison Company. More than 170 purchases followed including that of the New York Steam Company (1930) a cheap source of steam for electric turbines.

The Public Utility Holding Company Act of 1935 ushered in the era of regulated regional monopolies. The next year New York Edison combined its holdings to form the Consolidated Edison Company of New York (Con Ed).

Con Ed opened its first nuclear station in 1962. By then Con Ed had a reputation for inefficiency and poor service and shareholders were angry about its slow growth and low earnings. Environmentalists joined the grousers in 1963 when Con Ed began constructing a pumped-storage plant in Cornwall near the Hudson River. Charles Luce a former undersecretary with the Department of Interior was recruited to rescue Con Ed in 1967. He added power plants and beefed up customer service.

In the 1970s inflation and the energy crisis drove up oil prices (Con Ed's main fuel source) and in 1974 Luce withheld dividends for the first time since 1885. He persuaded the New York State Power Authority to buy two unfinished power plants saving Con Ed $200 million. In 1980 Luce ended the Cornwall controversy and donated the land for park use. He retired in 1982.

The utility started buying power from various suppliers and in 1984 began a two-year price freeze a boon to rate-hike-weary New Yorkers. The New York State Public Service Commission didn't approve another rate increase until 1992.

In 1997 Con Ed government officials consumer groups and other energy firms outlined the company's deregulation plan which included the formation of the Consolidated Edison Inc. holding company (known as Con Edison) and a power marketing unit in 1998. The next year Con Edison sold New York City generating facilities to KeySpan Northern States Power and Orion Power for a total of $1.65 billion.

Also in 1999 Con Edison bought Orange and Rockland Utilities for $790 million to increase its New York base and expand into New Jersey and Pennsylvania. In an effort to push into New England the company that year agreed to buy Northeast Utilities (NU since renamed Eversource Energy) for $3.3 billion in cash and stock and $3.9 billion in assumed debt. But the deal broke down in 2001. NU accused Con Edison of improperly trying to renegotiate terms while Con Edison accused NU of concealing information about unfavorable power supply contracts.

Con Edison's Indian Point Unit 2 nuclear plant was shut down temporarily in 2000 after a radioactive steam leak; later that year it agreed to sell Indian Point Units 1 and 2 to Entergy for $502 million. The sale was completed in 2001. That year Con Edison also incurred an estimated $400 million in costs related to emergency response and asset damage from the September 11 terrorist attacks on New York City.

In 2013 Con Edison announced plans to make it easier and less expensive for customers to convert from heating oil to lower cost natural gas in Manhattan and the Bronx. Its gas infrastructure expansion program includes investing a $100 million on new mains regulators and other upgrades in several neighborhoods.

It also plans to develop 25 MW of solar energy resources in New York City by the end of 2015. The solar power generated in the New York project would annually offset about 16000 tons of carbon dioxide.

EXECUTIVES

Senior Vice President Public Affairs, Frances Resheske
Vice President Human Resources, Claude Trahan, age 68
President And Ceo Con Edison Transmission Inc., Joseph P. Oates, age 58
Svp And Cfo Con Edison And Cecony, Robert N. Hoglund, age 58, $721,242 total compensation
Chairman And Ceo Coned And Cecony, John T. McAvoy, age 58, $1,220,767 total compensation
President Consolidated Edison Company Of New York Inc. (cecony), Timothy P. Cawley, age 54, $409,033 total compensation
Svp And General Counsel Consolidated Edison And Cecony, Elizabeth D. Moore, age 64, $608,017 total compensation
President And Ceo Con Edison Clean Energy Businesses Inc., Mark Noyes, age 54
Office Of The Vice President Central Engineering, Laurens Irizarry
Vice President Of Retail Commodity, Bob Anderson
Vice President Education, Michelle Anderson-Ioague
Auditors: PricewaterhouseCoopers LLP

LOCATIONS

HQ: Consolidated Edison Inc
4 Irving Place, New York, NY 10003
Phone: 212 460-4600
Web: www.conedison.com

PRODUCTS/OPERATIONS

2018 Sales

	$ mil.	% of total
Electric	8,612	70
Gas	2,327	19
Non-utility	767	6
Steam	631	5
Total	**12,337**	**100**

2018 sales

	$ mil.	% of total
CECONY	10,680	87
Clean Energy Business	891	7
O&R (Orange and Rockland)	763	6
Con Edison Transmissino	4	-
Other	-1 -	
Total	**12,337**	**100**

Selected Subsidiaries

Consolidated Edison Inc. (Con Edison)
Consolidated Edison Company of New York Inc. (CECONY)
Con Edison Clean Energy Businesses Inc.
  Consolidated Edison Development Inc.
  Consolidated Edison Energy Inc.
Consolidated Edison Solutions Inc.
Con Edison Transmission Inc.
  Consolidated Edison Transmission LLC (CET Electric)
  Consolidated Edison Gas Pipeline and Storage LLC (CET Gas)
Orange and Rockland Utilities Inc. (O&R)
Pike County Light & Power Company
Rockland Electric Company (RECO)

COMPETITORS

AEP	PPL Corporation
Avangrid	Public Service
CH Energy	Enterprise Group
Green Mountain Energy	South Jersey
NSTAR	Industries
National Fuel Gas	USPowerGen
National Grid USA	

HISTORICAL FINANCIALS

Company Type: Public

Income Statement

FYE: December 31

	REVENUE ($ mil.)	NET INCOME ($ mil.)	NET PROFIT MARGIN	EMPLOYEES
12/18	12,337	1,382	11.2%	15,307
12/17	12,033	1,525	12.7%	15,591
12/16	12,075	1,245	10.3%	14,960
12/15	12,554	1,193	9.5%	14,806
12/14	12,919	1,092	8.5%	14,601
Annual Growth	(1.1%)	6.1%	—	1.2%

2018 Year-End Financials

Debt ratio: 35.18%
Return on equity: 8.60%
Cash ($ mil.): 895
Current ratio: 0.62
Long-term debt ($ mil.): 17,495

No. of shares (mil.): 321
Dividends
  Yield: 3.7%
  Payout: 64.7%
Market value ($ mil.): 24,544

	STOCK PRICE ($) FY Close	P/E High/Low	PER SHARE ($) Earnings	Dividends	Book Value
12/18	76.46	19 16	4.42	2.86	52.11
12/17	84.95	18 15	4.94	2.76	49.74
12/16	73.68	20 15	4.12	2.68	46.88
12/15	64.27	18 14	4.05	2.60	44.55
12/14	66.01	18 14	3.71	2.52	42.94
Annual Growth	3.7%	— —	4.5%	3.2%	5.0%

CONSOLIDATED GRAIN & BARGE COMPANY

EXECUTIVES

Ceo, Kevin D Adams
V Pres*, Gregory Beck
Auditors: KPMG LLP NEW ORLEANS LA

LOCATIONS

HQ: CONSOLIDATED GRAIN & BARGE COMPANY
1127 HWY 190 E SERVICE RD, COVINGTON, LA 704334929
Phone: 985 867-3500

HISTORICAL FINANCIALS

Company Type: Private

Income Statement

FYE: May 31

	REVENUE ($ mil.)	NET INCOME ($ mil.)	NET PROFIT MARGIN	EMPLOYEES
05/17	6,430	16	0.3%	2,000
05/16	5,759	21	0.4%	
05/14	7,093	44	0.6%	
05/12	5,996	50	0.8%	
Annual Growth	1.4%	(20.4%)	—	

Constellation Brands Inc

Constellation Brands is a leading wine beer and spirits company in North America. The company is the world's largest premium wine producer offering more than 100 brands sourced from the world's premier wine-growing regions; brands include Robert Mondavi Clos du Bois and Meiomi. On the beer front Constellation holds the exclusive license to produce import and sell Mexican beer giant Grupo Modelo's Corona and Modelo brand in the US; it also owns a number of small-scale craft beer brands. Spirits the company's smallest business includes the premium spirits Black Velvet whiskey and SVEDKA vodka. Brothers Richard and Robert Sands control the company which was founded by the late Marvin Sands.

Operations

Constellation Brands reports its business in two main segments: Beer and Wine & Spirits. The beer segment accounting for nearly two-thirds of group revenue has an exclusive license to import and sell Grupo Modelo's Corona Modelo and other brands. Wine & Spirits accounting for the remaining third of revenue covers a wide range of wine and spirits over a spectrum of price points. Wine brands include Charles Smith Wines Meiomi and Ruffino while spirits brands include SVEDKA a Swedish import and the largest imported vodka brand in the US.

Geographic Reach

New York-based Constellation Brands has operations in the US Mexico New Zealand Italy and Canada and sells its products in roughly 100 countries. That being said the company gets virtually all its revenue from two countries: its generates over 90% of its sales in the US and most of the rest comes from Canada. The company is also a leading wine company in New Zealand.

Sales and Marketing

Constellation Brands staffs in-house marketing sales and customer service teams to increase its sales. These teams deploy a variety of marketing strategies conducting market research consumer and trade advertising price promotions point-of-sale materials event sponsorship on-premise promotions and public relations activities.

The company owns 18 of the top 100 wine brands in the US. Its top 20 wine and spirit brands termed "Focus Brands" received a large share of the company's sales and marketing spend.

Financial Performance

Constellation Brands' has recorded strong revenue and profit growth over the last five years and it boasts enviable margins.

In fiscal 2019 (ended February 28) the company's sales grew 7% to $8.9 billion as the Beer category grew 12% and Spirits 5% partially offset by a 1% fall in Wine. Growth in the Beer category was a result of broad-based volume growth in its Mexican beer portfolio as well as higher prices in select markets.

Net income jumped 49% to $3.5 billion in fiscal 2019 thanks to a surge in income from cannabis company Canopy its share in which grew from 10% to 38%. Gross margins were flat and income tax grew substantially due to the one-off benefit of the US Tax Cuts and Jobs Act recorded in the previous financial year.

Constellation Brands' cash on hand grew $3.3 million during fiscal 2019 ending the year at $93.6 million. The company's operations generated $2.2 billion and its financing yielded $2.6 billion offset by the $4.8 billion used in investing activities. The

bulk of its investing cash was the $4 billion spent on growing its stake in Canopy; its other main cash uses were capital expenditures dividends and share repurchases. It also issued debt worth $3.7 billion to support its investment program.

Strategy

Constellation Brands is in the process of up-scaling its beer wine and spirits portfolio and has been buying up small-scale producers of high-quality craft beer and fine wines. The acquisitions present opportunities to improve profit margins create operating efficiencies and invest in expanded distribution. Constellation is also branching out into a new sector — cannabis — via its non-controlling investment in Canopy. It spent $4 billion on increasing its stake in the company from 10% to 38% in 2018.

Besides acquisitions Constellation is investing heavily in expanding its Mexican beer portfolio which has been performing strongly. It has more than tripled the production capacity of its Nava Brewery since it was purchased in 2013 and will invest $900 million in capacity expansion in its Obregon brewery acquired from Modelo in 2016. It is also constructing a brewery in Baja California just over the southern border with California.

The flipside of its investments and portfolio additions is a significantly increased debt load which Constellation is addressing by off-loading lower-margin businesses. To deleverage its balance sheet the company sold around 30 low-margin wine and spirits brands for $1.7 billion in 2019.

Mergers and Acquisitions

Constellation has been through a heavy-acquisition period as it reshapes its portfolio towards premium brands.

In 2018 Constellation acquired two craft beer companies Four Corners a Texas-based craft brewer and Funky Buddha Brewery a Florida craft producer. It also acquired Schrader Cellars a producer of limited-production fine wines. The three acquisitions cost $149.8 million.

Looking to make a move in the nascent cannabis industry Constellation spent $4 billion on increasing its stake in Canopy from 10% to 38%.

HISTORY

Marvin Sands the son of winemaker Mordecai (Mack) Sands exited the Navy in 1945 and entered distilling by purchasing an old sauerkraut factory in Canandaigua New York. His business Canandaigua Industries struggled while making fruit wines in bulk for local bottlers in the East. Aiming at regional markets the company began producing its own brands two years later. Marvin opened the Richards Wine Cellar in Petersburg Virginia in 1951 and put his father in charge of the unit. In 1954 Marvin developed his own brand of "fortified" wine — boosted by 190-proof brandy — and named it Richards Wild Irish Rose after his son Richard.

The company slowly expanded buying a number of small wineries in the 1960s and 1970s. It went public in 1973 changing its name to Canandaigua Wine. A year later the company expanded to the West Coast thus gaining access to the growing varietal market.

Canandaigua continued to grow through acquisitions and new product introductions in the early 1980s. In 1984 when wine coolers became popular the company introduced Sun Country Coolers doubling sales to $173 million by 1986.

The short-lived wine cooler fad made Canandaigua realize that its distribution network could handle more volume so it began looking for additional brands. After a flurry of acquisitions in the late 80s and 90s the company changed its name in 1997 to Canandaigua Brands.

Founder Marvin Sands died in 1999. His son Richard who had been CEO since 1993 succeeded his father as chairman. In 2000 the firm changed its name to Constellation Brands.

In June 2013 Constellation Brands completed its acquisition of Grupo Modelo's US beer business from Anheuser-Busch InBev for approximately $5.23 billion. The transaction included full ownership of Crown Imports LLC which provided Constellation with complete independent control of all aspects of the US commercial business; a state-of-the-art brewery in Nava (Piedras Negras) Mexico; and an exclusive perpetual brand license in the US to import market and sell Corona and the Modelo brands. The deal gave Constellation ownership of six of the top 20 imported beer brands in the US.

EXECUTIVES

President And Ceo, Robert S. (Rob) Sands, age 60, $1,310,383 total compensation

Evp And Coo, William A. (Bill) Newlands, age 60

Evp And General Counsel, Thomas J. (Tom) Mullin, age 68, $497,663 total compensation

Evp And President Beer, F. Paul Hetterich, age 56, $600,000 total compensation

Evp And President Wine And Spirits Division, Christopher (Chris) Stenzel, age 51

Evp And Chairman Beer, William F. (Bill) Hackett, age 67, $607,046 total compensation

Svp And Cio, Joseph D. (Joe) Bruhin

Evp And Chief Human Resources Officer, Thomas M. (Tom) Kane, age 58

Evp And Cfo, David Klein, age 55, $600,000 total compensation

Vp Americas Region, Erwin Petznek

Vice President Strategic Accounts, Mark Elder

Vice President, Jennifer Murray

Senior Vice President Human Resources Wine + Spirits Division, Melina Param

Vice President Deputy General Counsel Mexico, Abdon Hernandez

National Account Manager, ED Corbett

National Account Manager, Jorey Newcomb

Vice President Corporate Indirect Procurement, Charlie Shikany

Vice President And Controller, Deb Price

Senior Vice President Public Affairs, Ginny Clark

Vice President Strategic Accounts, Phil Parker

National Account Manager, Stephen Civello

Vice President Assistant Treasurer, Sandy Dominach

Vice President Marketing Luxury Brands, Michelle Perry

Vice President Human Resources Operations, Dan Towner

Vice President Events Sponsorship Field Marketing, Rene Ramos

Vp And Deputy General Counsel, Barb Laverdi

Vp Finance Controller, Darrell Hearne

Svp Finance Wine + Spirits Division, Lisa Schnorr

Vice President Chief Winemaker, Chris Millard

Senior Vice President Operations, Martin Van Der Merwe

National Account Manager, Chris Beletti

National Account Manager, Eric Ramey

National Account Manager, Paul Hays

Vice President Associate General Counsel, Brian Bennett

Vice President On Premise, Scott Waters

Vice President National Accounts, Shawn Keller

National Account Manager, Fred Ashenbrenner

Senior Vice President Corporate Communications, Michael McGrew

Senior Vice President Human Resources, Julie Bassett

Vice President Of Sales, William Renspie

Senior Vice President Operations Beer Division, Michael Othites

Vice President And Associate General Counsel, K
Kristann Carey
National Account Manager, Matt Pinchera
Senior Vice President General Counsel Beer
Division, Jeffrey LaBarge
National Sales Manager, Frank Labar
Vp Associate General Counsel, Dana Wood
Svp Controller, Tom Mccorry
Vp Data Solutions, Brian Berlin
Svp Production Wine + Spirits Division, Sam
Glaetzer
Svp Chief Growth Officer And Chief Of Staff,
Mallika Monteiro
Vp Marketing Innovation, John Seethoff
Executive Vice President And President Beer
Division, Paul Hetterich
Svp Public Affairs, Matt Stanton
Chairman, Richard Sands, age 68
Board Member, Annie Johnson
Auditors: KPMG LLP

LOCATIONS

HQ: Constellation Brands Inc
207 High Point Drive, Building 100, Victor, NY 14564
Phone: 585 678-7100
Web: www.cbrands.com

2019 Sales

	$ mil.	% of total
US	7,894	97
International	221	3
Total	**8,116**	**100**

PRODUCTS/OPERATIONS

2019 Sales

	$ mil.	% of total
Beer	5,202	64
Wine	2,532	31
Spirit	381	5
Total	**8,116**	**100**

Selected Subsidiaries and Operations

Constellation Spirits Inc.
Constellation Wines U.S.
Crown Imports LLC (beer)
Vincor International Inc. (wine Canada)

Selected Brands

Wine
  Black Box
  Clos du Bois
  Estancia
  Franciscan Estate
  Inniskillin
  Kim Crawford
  Mark West
  Mount Veeder
  Nobil
  Robert Mondavi
  Ruffino
  SIMI
  Wild Horse
Beer
  Corona Extra
  Corona Light
  Modelo Especial
  Negra Modelo
  Pacifico
Spirits
  SVEDKA Vodka

COMPETITORS

Andrew Peller	Lion
Anheuser-Busch InBev	MillerCoors
Bacardi	Patr n Spirits
Beam Suntory	Pernod Ricard
Boston Beer	SABMiller
Bronco Wine Co.	Scheid Vineyards
Brown-Forman	Sebastiani Vineyards
Carlsberg	Taittinger
Diageo	Terlato Wine
E. & J. Gallo	Treasury Wine Estates
GIV	Trinchero Family
Halewood	Estates
Heineken	W.J. Deutsch
Jackson Family Wines	Willamette Valley
Korbel	Vineyards
LVMH	Wine Group

HISTORICAL FINANCIALS

Company Type: Public

Income Statement
FYE: February 28

	REVENUE ($ mil.)	NET INCOME ($ mil.)	NET PROFIT MARGIN	EMPLOYEES
02/19	8,116	3,435	42.3%	9,800
02/18	7,585	2,318	30.6%	9,600
02/17	7,331	1,535	20.9%	8,700
02/16	6,548	1,054	16.1%	9,000
02/15	6,028	839	13.9%	7,200
Annual Growth	**7.7%**	**42.2%**	**—**	**8.0%**

2019 Year-End Financials

Debt ratio: 46.58%
Return on equity: 33.36%
Cash ($ mil.): 93
Current ratio: 1.16
Long-term debt ($ mil.): 11,759

No. of shares (mil.): 191
Dividends
  Yield: 1.7%
  Payout: 16.8%
Market value ($ mil.): 32,357

	STOCK PRICE ($) FY Close	P/E High/Low	Earnings	Dividends	Book Value
02/19	169.16	13 8	17.57	2.96	65.62
02/18	215.48	19 13	11.55	2.08	42.06
02/17	158.81	22 18	7.52	1.60	35.41
02/16	141.43	28 20	5.18	1.24	32.89
02/15	114.72	26 18	4.17	0.00	29.66
Annual Growth	**10.2%**	**— —**	**43.3%**	**—**	**22.0%**

Consumers Energy Co.

Consumers Energy Company makes sure that energy consumers in Michigan have the power to crank up their heaters and the gas to fire up their stoves. The company's operating area includes all 68 counties of Michigan's lower peninsula. All told Consumers Energy (the primary operating unit of CMS Energy) has a generating capacity of more than 5600 MW (primarily fossil-fueled) and distributes electricity to 1.8 million customers and natural gas to 1.8 million customers. Included in the utility's arsenal of power production is electricity generated from coal natural gas wind and hydroelectric power plants. Utility customers are a mix of residential commercial and diversified industrial clients.

Operations

Consumers Energy is the regulated utility subsidiary of CMS Energy.

Electric utility operations (70% of revenue) include the generation purchase distribution and sale of electricity. It owns some dozen power generation facilities and purchased some 2700 MW from third parties. It shuttered seven of its smaller coal-fired plants in 2016 and is replacing some of the lost capacity with gas-fired facilities. The company's electric distribution system has more than 60000 miles of electric lines.

Its gas utility operations (30%) include the purchase transmission storage distribution and sale of natural gas. The gas distribution system delivers roughly 350 billion cubic feet of natural gas per year

Geographic Reach

Consumers provides electric service to 275 cities and villages in 61 counties in Michigan. Principal cities served are Battle Creek Bay City Cadillac Flint Grand Rapids Jackson Kalamazoo Midland Muskegon and Saginaw.

Consumers gas business purchases about 5% of its gas from Canadian sources and the rest from US suppliers including several along the US Gulf Coast. It serves a 13000-square mile area that includes more than 200 cities and villages. More than one half of its customers are in metro Detroit.

Sales and Marketing

The company serves 1.8 million electric customers and 1.8 million gas customers in Michigan's Lower Peninsula.

The company serves residential commercial industrial and other customers. Though it is a regulated utility Consumers Energy is open to electricity competition in its service area at a rate of up to 10% of its previous year's retail sales. Gas competition also exists from Gulf Coast companies as well as alternative fuels such as propane oil and electricity.

Financial Performance

Consumers Energy's overall revenue decreased by almost 2% (reflecting lower gas prices and sales volumes) in 2016 to $6.1 billion and its net income increased by about 4% to $616 million.

From a net income perspective electric operating revenues increased by $122 million reflecting $91 million from rate increases and a $62 million increase in sales due to favorable weather. These increases were partially offset by a $25 million net decrease in securitization revenue and a $6 million drop in other revenue.

Gas operating revenue increased by $15 million reflecting $33 million from a 2016 rate increase offset partially by an $18 million decrease in sales due to milder winter weather.

Net cash provided by operating activities dropped from $1.8 million to $1.7 million. This decline was due to lower customer collections offset partially by higher income tax payments to CMS Energy lower post-retirement benefits contributions and higher net income.

Strategy

Addressing new regulatory mandates Consumers is making big changes its energy generation mix mostly from coal to natural gas. In 2016 after retiring seven of its smaller coal-fired plants (representing 950 MW of capacity) the percent of power coming from the black commodity dropped from 79% to 58%. That same year Consumers adjusted a Power Purchase Agreement (PPA) with an Entergy nuclear plant to terminate the agreement in May 2018 four years ahead of schedule. The lost capacity will be replaced with the output of Consumers' 2015-acquired 540 MW gas-fueled plant in Jackson MI along with a reduction in consumer demand updated PPA agreements and power from renewable energy sources.

Consumers informed state regulators in 2017 that it is interested in acquiring an additional gas-fired electricity plant in Michigan. As well the utility broke ground on its third wind energy project Cross Winds Energy Park II in Tuscola County. Phase I is expected to have 19 turbines capable of generating 44 MW of electricity and will commence service in early 2018. When completed it will have more than 80 wind turbines and 155 MW of energy production (enough to serve 60000 residents).

Consumers gas business is working on a $610 million 5-year project to replace 78 miles of gas pipe dating to the 1940s and located in Saginaw Genesee and Oakland counties. Construction began in mid-2017 and will continue until the end of 2022. Additional capital is being deployed to address anticipated growth installing new pipes to serve an increase of nearly 8000 new business customers and 2500 residential customers in its service area.

To improve its bottom line and the efficiency of its operations and in an effort to stem the tide of commercial and residential customers jumping ship for other electricity providers Consumers Energy is looking at options to reform its rate structures.

The company is being guided by its "Balanced Energy Initiative" a comprehensive 20 year plan (introduced in 2007). The plan calls for the utility to develop new power plants increase the efficiency of its operations and expand its renewable energy projects.

Consumers anticipates a continued rise in industrial production in its service territory will drive its total electric deliveries to increase annually by 0.5% through 2021. Excluding the impacts of energy efficiency programs the company expects its total electric deliveries to increase by 1% a year over the same time period. It also expects that its gas deliveries will remain stable through 2021 reflecting growth in gas demand being offset by energy efficiency and conservation activities.

The company's planned base capital investments of $4.6 billion in 2017 include $2.6 billion to preserve electric utility reliability and capacity and $2 billion at the gas utility to sustain the delivery system and enhance pipeline integrity.

Between 2012 and 2017 the company installed smart meters (advanced meters that allow customers to have better control over their energy use) across its electric power distribution system.

EXECUTIVES

Evp And Cfo, Thomas J. (Tom) Webb, age 67, $695,000 total compensation

Svp Energy Resources, Daniel J. (Dan) Malone, age 58, $465,000 total compensation

Svp, John M. Butler, age 55, $470,000 total compensation

Svp Customer Experience And Cio, Brian F. Rich, age 44

President And Ceo, Patricia K. (Patti) Poppe, age 51, $430,000 total compensation

Vice President Electric Operations Consumers Energy, GUY C PACKARD

Vice President Of Consumers Energy Company, GREGORY M SALISBURY

Vice President Public Affairs, Roger Curtis

Chairman, John G. Russell, age 62

Auditors: PricewaterhouseCoopers LLP

LOCATIONS

HQ: Consumers Energy Co.
One Energy Plaza, Jackson, MI 49201
Phone: 517 788-0550
Web: www.consumersenergy.com

PRODUCTS/OPERATIONS

2016 Sales

	$ mil.	% of total
Electric	4,379	72
Gas	1,685	28
Total	**6,064**	**100**

COMPETITORS

DTE Electric	SEMCO ENERGY
DTE Gas Company	We Energies
Indiana Michigan Power	Xcel Energy

HISTORICAL FINANCIALS
Company Type: Public

Income Statement   FYE: December 31

	REVENUE ($ mil.)	NET INCOME ($ mil.)	NET PROFIT MARGIN	EMPLOYEES
12/19	6,376	743	11.7%	8,253
12/18	6,464	705	10.9%	8,121
12/17	6,222	632	10.2%	7,496
12/16	6,064	616	10.2%	7,366
12/15	6,165	594	9.6%	7,394
Annual Growth	**0.8%**	**5.8%**	**—**	**2.8%**

2019 Year-End Financials

Debt ratio: 31.37%
Return on equity: 10.14%
Cash ($ mil.): 11
Current ratio: 1.09
Long-term debt ($ mil.): 7,124

No. of shares (mil.): 84
Dividends
  Yield: 0.0%
  Payout: 79.8%
Market value ($ mil.): 9,209

	STOCK PRICE ($) FY Close	P/E High/Low	Earnings	Dividends	Book Value
12/19	109.50	— —	(0.00)	4.50	92.00
12/18	101.50	— —	(0.00)	4.50	82.28
12/17	103.96	— —	(0.00)	4.50	77.15
12/16	102.90	— —	(0.00)	4.50	70.62
12/15	97.00	— —	(0.00)	4.50	65.95
Annual Growth	**3.1%**	**— —**	**—**	**(0.0%)**	**8.7%**

Core Mark Holding Co Inc

One of the nation's leading convenience store distributors Core-Mark Holding supplies packaged consumables (including cigarettes and other tobacco products candy snacks grocery items perishables nonalcoholic beverages and health and beauty aids) to about 43000 retail locations. Traditional convenience stores are the company's primary customer but it also serves mass merchandisers; supermarkets; drug liquor and specialty stores; college campuses and casinos. Cigarettes and other tobacco products are Core-Mark's top sellers generating more than three-fourths of net sales. The company operates primarily in the US serving customers in all 50 US states; it also has customers in five Canadian provinces.

Operations

Core-Mark offers some 58000 products. Cigarettes account for about two-thirds of its revenue with other tobacco products bringing in an additional 10%. Food — including fast food candy snacks groceries beverages and fresh products — generates some 20% of revenue and non-food products such as health and beauty aids and general merchandise contributes the rest.

The company purchases brand name and private label products from approximately 5800 suppliers and manufacturers in the US and Canada. Two suppliers — Altria Group (parent of Philip Morris USA) and R.J. Reynolds Tobacco Company — together account for about 55% of total purchases.

Geographic Reach

Westlake Texas-based Core-Mark operates in the US where it generates more than 90% of its revenue. The company's remaining revenue comes from Canada.

It operates a network of 30-plus distribution centers in the US and Canada (excluding two distribution facilities it operates as a third-party logistics provider). More than two dozen of its distribution centers are located in the US and the rest are in Canada.

The company has information technology offices in Plano Texas and Richmond British Columbia.

Sales and Marketing

Core-Mark's primary customer base consists of traditional convenience stores including major national and super-regional convenience store operators as well as independently owned convenience stores. Other customers include grocery stores cigarette and tobacco shops drug and liquor stores hotel gift shops military exchanges college and corporate campuses casinos and airport concessions. Of its 43000 customer locations some 55% are chains and 45% are independents.

Canadian convenience store operator Murphy U.S.A is Core-Mark's largest customer representing more than 10% of sales. Candy sales to retail giant Walmart accounts for about a third of the company's total candy sales. Other customers include Seven-Eleven Rite Aid Speedway and Circle K.

Financial Performance

Acquisitions and organic growth have pushed Core-Mark's revenue up 59% since 2014. Net income has a little more sporadic but is still up 7% during that time.

In 2018 the company reported revenue of $16.4 billion up 5% from the prior year. Sales of food and non-food products rose 13% because of the acquisition of distributor Farner-Bocken and the addition of Walmart as a customer as well as increased orders from existing customers. Cigarette sales on the other hand were flat as an increase in the average price was offset by an ongoing general decline in cigarette consumption.

Net income was also up that year jumping 36% to $45.5 million on the rise in revenue.

Cash at the end of 2018 was $27.3 million a decrease of $14.3 million from the prior year. Cash from operations contributed $211.2 million to the coffers while investing activities used $24.4 million mainly for capital expenditures. Financing activities used another $203.2 million for line of credit repayments.

Strategy

Core-Mark's strategy includes both organic growth and acquisitions.

As consumer tastes change the company is focused on expanding its fresh food and meal replacement capabilities which has grown at an average rate of 13% annually over the past five years. It is investing in chill docks and tri-temp trailers which enables the delivery of a broad range of chilled items. In addition it is partnering with strategically-located dairies kitchens bakeries and other entities to offer a greater selection of premium items such as fried chicken fresh pizza sandwiches and wraps cut fruit doughnuts and bread.

Continued investment in and growth of Core-Mark's Vendor Consolidation Initiative (VCI) and Focused Marketing Initiative (FMI) are also key elements of its strategy. VCI capitalizes on the fragmented convenience store supply chain by consolidating deliveries from disparate product segments. For the company's independent customers FMI offers pricing strategy category insights and marketing services to increase sales and profitability.

Since 2010 Core-Mark has expanded its distribution network product selection and customer base via six acquisitions. It has also added three primary distribution centers.

Company Background

The company's roots reach back to 1888 when it was known as Glaser Bros. a family-run candy and tobacco distribution business in San Francisco.

EXECUTIVES

Svp And Cfo, Christopher M. (Chris) Miller, age 58, $312,885 total compensation

President And Coo, Scott E. McPherson, age 49, $296,640 total compensation

Ceo And Director, Thomas B. Perkins, age 60, $515,412 total compensation

President Core-mark Canada, Eric J. Rolheiser, age 48

Svp Us Distribution-west, Christopher K. (Chris) Hobson, age 50, $270,375 total compensation

Svp Us Distribution East, William G. Stein, age 49, $263,718 total compensation

Chairman, Randolph I. Thornton, age 73

Auditors: Deloitte & Touche LLP

LOCATIONS

HQ: Core Mark Holding Co Inc
1500 Solana Boulevard, Suite 3400, Westlake, TX 76262
Phone: 940 293-8600
Web: www.core-mark.com

2018 Sales

	$ mil.	% of total
US	14,844	91
Canada	1,494	9
Corporate	56	—
Total	**16,395**	**100**

PRODUCTS/OPERATIONS

2018 Sales

	$ mil.	% of total
Cigarettes	10,974	67
Food	1,659	10
Candy	992	6
Fresh	474	3
Other tobacco products	1,387	9
Health beauty & general	711	4
Beverages	191	1
Equipment/other	5	—
Total	**16,395**	**100**

COMPETITORS

AMCON Distributing	H. T. Hackney
Associated Food	McLane
C&S Wholesale	Performance Food Group
Coca-Cola	SUPERVALU
Eby-Brown	Sobeys
Frito-Lay	Southco Distributing
GSC Enterprises	SpartanNash

HISTORICAL FINANCIALS

Company Type: Public

Income Statement

FYE: December 31

	REVENUE ($ mil.)	NET INCOME ($ mil.)	NET PROFIT MARGIN	EMPLOYEES
12/18	16,395	45	0.3%	8,087
12/17	15,687	33	0.2%	8,413
12/16	14,529	54	0.4%	7,688
12/15	11,069	51	0.5%	6,655
12/14	10,280	42	0.4%	5,933
Annual Growth	**12.4%**	**1.6%**	**—**	**8.1%**

2018 Year-End Financials

Debt ratio: 20.78%
Return on equity: 8.11%
Cash ($ mil.): 27
Current ratio: 1.89
Long-term debt ($ mil.): 346

No. of shares (mil.): 45
Dividends
 Yield: 1.7%
 Payout: 43.1%
Market value ($ mil.): 1,063

	STOCK PRICE ($) FY Close	P/E High/Low	PER SHARE ($) Earnings	Dividends	Book Value
12/18	23.25	40 18	0.99	0.41	12.41
12/17	31.58	60 37	0.72	0.37	12.03
12/16	43.07	79 28	1.17	0.33	11.48
12/15	81.94	81 47	1.11	0.28	10.71
12/14	61.93	101 47	0.92	0.23	9.99
Annual Growth	**(21.7%)**	**— —**	**2.0%**	**15.5%**	**5.6%**

Corning Inc

Once known for kitchenware and lab products Corning Incorporated makes a diverse range of glass and ceramic products for optical communications mobile consumer electronics display technology automotive and life sciences markets. Its products include damage-resistant cover glass for mobile devices precision glass for advanced displays optical fiber and automotive emissions control products to name a few. Corning's signature Gorilla Glass cover glass for mobile devices is known for surviving high and repeated drops. The company operates more than 100 manufacturing and processing facilities in around 15 countries. More than half of its sales come from the Asia Pacific region.

Operations

Corning operates in five segments. Its largest segment Optical Communications accounts for more than 35% sales and is classified into two main product groups?carrier network and enterprise network. The carrier network group consists primarily of products and solutions for optical-based communications infrastructure for services such as video data and voice communications. The enterprise network group consists of optical-based communication networks.

Display Technologies which manufactures glass substrates primarily for flat panel liquid crystal displays brings in about 30% of sales.

The Specialty Materials business about 15% of sales manufactures products that provide more than 150 material formulations for glass glass ceramics and fluoride crystals for various customer needs. It is powered by superstar product Gorilla Glass which is used in consumer electronics devices such as notebook computers mobile phones and TVs.

Environmental Technologies (substrates and filters for automotive and diesel products) and Life Sciences (glass and plastic equipment for labs and other scientific applications) each account for around 10% of sales.

Geographic Reach

Corning's US-based customers generate more than 30% of its revenue. The Asia-Pacific region accounts for more than half of sales with China representing about 25% and Korea more than 10%.

The company operates more than 100 manufacturing and processing facilities in 15 countries. Its display glass manufacturing operations are in South Korea Japan Taiwan and China.

Its optical fiber manufacturing facilities are in North Carolina China and India. Cabling operations are mainly in North Carolina Germany Poland and China. Its hardware and equipment products are produced in Texas and Arizona in the US and in other facilities worldwide. Corning's Specialty Materials segment includes Gorilla Glass

which is manufactured in Kentucky South Korea Japan and Taiwan.

Corning manufactures ceramic substrates and filter products for its Environmental Technologies segment in New York Virginia China Germany and South Africa. Products for its Life Sciences segment are made in several US states as well as in Mexico France Poland and China.

Sales and Marketing

Corning's display glass products within the Display Technologies segment are sold to customers directly using the company's manufacturing facilities throughout Asia. Products such as optical-based communication networks within its Optical Communications segment are sold to businesses governments and individuals for their own use.

The Environmental Technologies segment sells its products worldwide to catalyzers and manufacturers of emission control systems who then sell to automotive and diesel vehicle or engine manufacturers. Products in the Life Sciences segment are marketed globally primarily through distributors to pharmaceutical and biotechnology companies academic institutions hospitals and government entities.

Financial Performance

Corning's revenue has seen a general upward trend in revenue with incrementally larger increases in sales over the last three years.

The company posted net sales of $11.3 billion in 2018 a 12% increase compared with $10.1 billion in 2017. Growth in 2018 was driven by sales increases in all its divisions: Optical Communications was up $123 million Environmental Technologies $43 million the Life Sciences segment $22 million and Specialty Materials $12 million.

Profits soared to more than $1 billion in 2018 compared with a $497 million loss the previous year. Profits in 2018 were unhindered by the large income tax provision incurred the previous year?$2.2 billion due to the Tax Cuts and Jobs act. Income before taxes was actually 9% lower in 2018 due to higher expenses and the negative impact of foreign currency translation.

Cash at the end of fiscal 2018 was $2.4 billion a decrease of $2.0 billion from the prior year. Cash from operations contributed $2.9 billion to the coffers while investing activities used $2.9 billion including capital expenditures for the expansion of manufacturing facilities in China and the acquisition of 3M's Communication Markets Division (CMD) for $841 million. Financing activities used another $2.0 billion for dividends to stockholders and the company's stock repurchase program.

Strategy

Corning is fueling growth by leveraging its capabilities around current trends such as 5G wireless communication smart cars connected homes and augmented reality. The company continues to develop technologies in its Optical Communications business for applications such as fiber to the home hyperscale data centers and in-building networks. Larger TV sizes specifically in China are benefiting Corning's Display Technologies division with increased shipments in Gen 10.5 LCD glass. The company plans to build on this trend with innovations in higher resolution screens and a wider color gamut that improves picture quality.

In Mobile Consumer Electronics Corning signed an agreement with WaveOptics in late 2018 to supply high-performance augmented reality optics for its mobile devices. Smartphone manufacturers are also adding glass on the backside of smartphones doubling the amount of glass needed for each unit and foldable smartphones which could use Corning's ultra-thin bendable glass are becoming more popular.

In its Automotive business the company is investing in Gorilla Glass for automobiles with expanded manufacturing capacity coming online in 2019.

Corning's Valor Glass product has the potential to drive further growth in the Life Sciences segment as customers move toward the FDA certification required to use the damage- and break-resistant Valor Glass product in pharmaceutical packaging applications.

Mergers and Acquisitions

Corning Inc.'s recent acquisitions have been made to strengthen its Optical Communications business. In mid-2018 the company acquired 3M's Communications Markets Division which consists of optical fiber and copper passive connectivity tools. The 3M operations will be part of Corning's Optical Communications unit. The 3M assets expand Corning's reach in global markets and its high-bandwidth portfolio.

In mid-2017 the company acquired SpiderCloud Wireless Inc. a provider of in-building wireless technologies. SpiderCloud's products would help extend the Corning's fiber optic cables in building networks. "With the acquisition of SpiderCloud Wireless we believe our combined product solutions will help drive optical convergence and enable the advantages of fiber-deep architectures within the Enterprise Local Area Network." said Clark S. Kinlin executive vice president Corning Optical Communications.

Company Background

Amory Houghton started Houghton Glass in Massachusetts in 1851 and moved it to Corning New York in 1868. By 1876 the company renamed Corning Glass Works was making several types of technical and pharmaceutical glass. In 1880 it supplied the glass for Thomas Edison's first light bulb. Other early developments included the red-yellow-green traffic light system and borosilicate glass (which can withstand sudden temperature changes) for Pyrex oven and laboratory ware.

By 1945 the company's had introduced the first mass-produced television tubes freezer-to-oven ceramic cookware (Pyroceram Corning Ware) and car headlights. After WWII Corning emphasized consumer product sales and expanded globally. In the 1970s the company pioneered the development of optical fiber and auto emission technology (now two of its principal products).

EXECUTIVES

Chairman And Ceo, Wendell P. Weeks, age 60, $1,337,740 total compensation

Vice Chairman And Corporate Development Officer, Lawrence D. (Larry) McRae, age 61, $731,971 total compensation

Svp And Cfo, R. Tony Tripeny, age 60, $504,808 total compensation

Evp And Corning Innovation Officer, Martin J. (Marty) Curran, age 60

Evp Corning Optical Telecommunications, Clark S. Kinlin, age 59

President Corning Glass Technologies (cgt), James P. Clappin, age 62, $686,538 total compensation

Evp Corning Technologies And International, Eric S. Musser, age 60

Svp Corporate Research, David L. Morse, age 67, $631,010 total compensation

Vice President Sales And Marketing, Aparna Krishnamurthy

Vice President Treasurer, Melinda Lee

Vice President Of Sales, Duncan Rogers

Vice President Flat Glass Photovoltaics Program, Marc Giroux

Vice President New Opportunity Development New Business Development, Robert Ritchie

Vice President Technology, Claudio Mazzali

Vice President, Susan Ford

Vice President Of Sales, Eric Marinakis

Vice President Of Product Management, Jeff Kunst

Division Vice President, John Sharkey

Vice President Of Chemical Engineering, Thomas Capek

Management Vice President, Thomas Appelt

Senior Vice President, Alan Eusden

Vice President, Adriane Brown

Vice President Sales, Kevin Hussey

Vice President, Robert France

Senior Vice President Global Benefits And Compensation, John P MacMahon

Vice President Carrier Market Development, Robert Whitman

Senior Vice President Science And Technology, Jean-pierre Mazeau

Vice President Of Communications, Daniel Collins

Vice President Corporate Controller, Ed Schlesinger

Vice President Tax, Jude Lemke

Vice President Commercial Technology, Bill Cune

Vice President Marketing And Technical Support, Dave Purwin

Vice President Global Commercial Operations, J David Johnson

Vice President And Gm Corning Life Sciences, Richard Eglen

Vice President, David Watson

Senior Vice President And General Manager, Mike Bell

Vice President Strategy Corning Optical Communications And Corporate Development, Steve Miller

Division Vice President And Commercial Director, Thomas Lynch

Vice President Of Finance, Rob Hutton

National Sales Manager, Ryan Ehrhart

Vice President And Director, Ishak Waguih S

Vice President Financial Services And Assistant Treasurer, Jill Baker

Vice President Communications And Technology, Hank Blackwood

Treasurer, Chris Strykowski

Treasurer, Lee Starnes

Assistant Treasurer, Rob Vanni

Us Treasurer, Ida Meadows

Secretary, Kathy McClure

Auditors: PricewaterhouseCoopers LLP

LOCATIONS

HQ: Corning Inc
One Riverfront Plaza, Corning, NY 14831
Phone: 607 974-9000
Web: www.corning.com

2018 Sales

	$ mil.	% of total
North America		
United States	3,569	31
Canada	296	3
Mexico	53	-
Asia Pacific		
China	2,716	24
Korea	1,259	11
Taiwan	921	8
Japan	415	4
Other	436	4
Europe		
Germany	451	4
Other	905	8
All other	377	3
Total	**11,398**	**100**

PRODUCTS/OPERATIONS

2018 Sales

	$ mil.	% of total
Optical Communications	4,192	37
Display Technologies	3,276	29
Specialty Materials	1,479	13
Environmental Technologies	1,289	11
Life Sciences	946	8
All Other	216	2
Total	**11,398**	**100**

Selected Products

Display technologies
  Liquid crystal displays (LCD)
  Organic light-emitting diode (OLED) displays
Telecommunications
  Optical fiber and cable
  Optical networking components
Environmental technologies
  Industrial and stationary emissions products
  Mobile emissions and automotive catalytic converter products
Life sciences
  Genomics and laboratory equipment
Specialty Materials
  Gorilla Glass
Other
  Polarized glass
  Semiconductor materials

COMPETITORS

Asahi Glass	Nippon Electric Glass
CommScope	Nippon Sheet Glass
Dai Nippon Printing	Prysmian
Eppendorf	SCHOTT
Heraeus Holding	Thermo Fisher
IBIDEN	Scientific
NGK INSULATORS	

HISTORICAL FINANCIALS

Company Type: Public

Income Statement

FYE: December 31

	REVENUE ($ mil.)	NET INCOME ($ mil.)	NET PROFIT MARGIN	EMPLOYEES
12/18	11,290	1,066	9.4%	51,500
12/17	10,116	(497)	—	46,200
12/16	9,390	3,695	39.4%	40,700
12/15	9,111	1,339	14.7%	35,700
12/14	9,715	2,472	25.4%	34,600
Annual Growth	3.8%	(19.0%)	—	10.5%

2018 Year-End Financials

Debt ratio: 21.81%
Return on equity: 7.23%
Cash ($ mil.): 2,355
Current ratio: 2.12
Long-term debt ($ mil.): 5,994

No. of shares (mil.): 788
Dividends
  Yield: 2.3%
  Payout: 63.7%
Market value ($ mil.): 23,805

	STOCK PRICE ($) FY Close	P/E High/Low		PER SHARE ($)		
				Earnings	Dividends	Book Value
12/18	30.21	30	22	1.13	0.72	17.50
12/17	31.99	—	—	(0.66)	0.62	18.30
12/16	24.27	7	5	3.23	0.54	19.32
12/15	18.28	25	16	1.00	0.48	16.63
12/14	22.93	13	9	1.73	0.40	16.94
Annual Growth	7.1%	—	—	(10.1%)	15.8%	0.8%

Costco Wholesale Corp

Operating more than 760 membership warehouse stores Costco is the nation's largest wholesale club operator (ahead of Wal-Mart's SAM'S CLUB). Primarily under the Costco Wholesale banner it serves nearly 95 million cardholders in some 45 US states Washington DC and Puerto Rico and about 10 other countries. Stores offer discount prices on some 3700 products (many in bulk packaging) ranging from alcoholic beverages and appliances to fresh food pharmaceuticals and tires. Certain club memberships also offer products and services such as car and home insurance real estate services and travel packages. Costco generates most of its sales in the US.

Operations

Costco generates revenue from five major product categories: food & sundries hardlines fresh food softlines and ancillary. It generates about 40% of its revenue from food & sundries which includes dry and packaged foods groceries snacks candy alcoholic and nonalcoholic beverages and cleaning supplies. Another 15% each stem from hardlines (major appliances electronics hardware garden & patio items) and fresh foods (meat produce deli bakery). Softline product sales (apparel and small appliances) account for about 10% of sales with the ancillary gas and pharmacy operations bringing in the last 20%.

To shop at Costco customers must be members — a policy the company believes reinforces customer loyalty and provides a steady source of fee revenue (to the tune of about 2% of yearly sales). Three types of annual memberships are available: Business ($60 each) Gold Star ($60 for individuals and their spouses) and Executive ($120 allows members to purchase products and services including insurance mortgage services and long-distance phone service at reduced rates). Costco also operates the e-commerce site costco.com which offers products not found in its stores.

Geographic Reach

More than 70% of Costco's revenues come from the US while about 15% stem from Canada. The majority of its stores are located in the US and Puerto Rico although about 100 are in Canada. Other markets include Mexico the UK Japan Korea Taiwan Australia France Iceland and Spain. Costco operates in Taiwan and Korea through majority-owned subsidiaries.

Sales and Marketing

Costco uses several marketing and promotional tactics to reach existing and prospective members. It typically promotes new warehouse openings sends direct mail pieces to potential new members and employs a regular direct-marketing program. The program which targets existing members to promote selected merchandise consists of The Costco Connection magazine coupon mailers handouts and promotional emails to members.

The company sells products in China through Alibaba's Tmall site. Other e-commerce businesses such as Google Express Instacart and Jet.com offer Costco products for delivery via their online services.

Financial Performance

Costco's revenues and profits have seen robust growth over the past several years as the company has expanded its store count and in-store amenities. Revenue is up 25% since fiscal 2014 (ended August) and net income is up more than 50%.

In fiscal 2018 the company reported revenue of $142 billion up 10% from the prior year driven by sales at newly opened warehouses and a 9% spike in comparable sales. Changes in gasoline prices contributed positively thanks to a 19% increase in the average sales price per gallon. In addition membership fees increased by 10% in 2018 due to membership sign-ups at existing and new warehouses and an annual fee increase.

Net income that year jumped 17% to $3.1 billion primarily due to the higher revenues as well as a jump in interest income.

Cash at the end of fiscal 2018 was $6 billion an increase of about $1.5 billion from the prior year. Cash from operations contributed $5.8 billion to the coffers while investing activities used $2.9 billion mainly for property and equipment. Financing activities used another $1.3 billion primarily for stock buyback and dividends paid.

Strategy

Costco aims to offer its members a broad range of high-quality merchandise at consistently lower prices than they can find elsewhere. To keep inventory costs low its merchandising strategy is to limit certain items to fast-selling models sizes and colors. By doing this Costco can limit its number of stock keeping units (SKUs) to about 3700 per warehouse enabling it to hold significantly fewer items than other discount retailers supermarkets and supercenters. Its product lines are not static however as it continues to expand its own Kirkland Signature brand (which grew more than 10% in fiscal 2018).

Along with merchandise management Costco is focused on expansion. It has opened more than 100 new wholesale clubs in the last five years and has plans for about 25 new locations in 2019 including its first store in China. In addition the company has plans to relocate four warehouses in 2019 to more ideal spots within existing markets and it continues to add gas stations and other ancillary services to existing locations.

As is the case with many retailers the warehouse giant is also investing in digital initiatives as consumer preferences and technological advancements alter the landscape. The company's ecommerce sales jumped more than 30% in fiscal 2018 amid improved online ordering capabilities ecommerce product showcases and grocery delivery. Continued focus on digital/tech initiatives is key for Costco as the competition is intense from traditional warehouse clubs and grocery stores as well as discount grocers such as Aldi and of course from online behemoth Amazon.

Company Background

In 1983 the first Costco warehouse location was opened in Seattle; it went public in 1985.

A decade after the opening of that first club Costco merged with a rival chain (Price Club) to form Price/Costco. It eventually changed its name to Costco later that decade.

Price Club's first location opened in 1976 in a converted airplane hangar in San Diego. It originally served only small businesses but soon found its engine for growth by serving non-business members as well.

HISTORY

From 1954 to 1974 retailer Sol Price built his Fed-Mart discount chain into a $300 million behemoth selling general merchandise to government employees. Price sold the company to Hugo Mann in 1975 and the next year with son Robert Rick Libenson and Giles Bateman opened the first Price Club warehouse in San Diego to sell in volume to small businesses at steep discounts.

Posting a large loss its first year prompted Price Club's decision to expand membership to include government utility and hospital employees as well as credit union members. In 1978 it opened a second store in Phoenix. With the help of his father Sol's other son Laurence began a chain of tire-mounting stores (located adjacent to Price Club outlets on land leased from the company and using tires sold by the Price Clubs).

The company went public in 1980 with four stores in California and Arizona. Price Club moved into the eastern US with its 1984 opening of a store in Virginia and continued to expand including a joint venture with Canadian retailer Steinberg in 1986 to operate stores in Canada; the first Canadian warehouse opened that year in Montreal.

Two years later Price Club acquired A. M. Lewis (grocery distributor Southern California and Arizona) and the next year it opened two Price Club Furnishings offering discounted home and office furniture.

Price Club bought out Steinberg's interest in the Canadian locations in 1990 and added stores on the East Coast and in California Colorado and British Columbia. However competition in the East from ensconced rivals such as SAM'S CLUB and PACE forced the closure of two stores two years later. A 50-50 joint venture with retailer Controladora Comercial Mexicana led to the opening of two Price Clubs in Mexico City one each in 1992 and 1993.

Price Club merged with Costco Wholesale in 1993. Founded in 1983 by Jeffrey Brotman and James Sinegal (a former EVP of Price Company) Costco Wholesale went public in 1985 and expanded into Canada.

In 1993 Price/Costco opened its first warehouse outside the Americas in a London suburb. Merger costs led to a loss the following year and Price/Costco spun off its commercial real estate operations as well as certain international operations as Price Enterprises (now Price Legacy). In 1995 the company launched its Kirkland Signature brand of private-label merchandise. Two years later the company changed its corporate name to Costco Companies.

Costco began online sales and struck a deal to buy two stores in South Korea in 1998 and opened its first store in Japan in 1999. Under industrywide pressure over the way members-only chains record fees Costco took a $118 million charge for fiscal 1999 to change accounting practices. That year the company made yet another name change to Costco Wholesale (emphasizing its core warehouse operations).

In 2000 the company purchased private retailer Littlewoods' 20% stake in Costco UK increasing Costco's ownership to 80%. Costco began expanding into the Midwest in 2001 as part of plans to open 40 new clubs a year including ones in China.

During fiscal 2002 Costco opened 29 new warehouse clubs. In December 2002 the retailer opened its first home store — called Costco Home — in Kirkland Washington stocked with mostly high-end furniture. A second Costco Home store opened in Tempe Arizona in December 2004.

Costco increased its equity interest in Costco Wholesale UK in October 2003 to 100% when it purchased Carrefour Nederland's 20% stake.

In 2006 Costco began offering more than 200 generic prescription medicines (100 count) for $10 or less. The following year Costco.com logged sales in excess of $1 billion.

In July 2009 Costco shuttered its two Costco Home stores which were located in Washington and Arizona. The retailer cited the weak economy and market for home furnishings and the fact that the concept didn't fit with its expansion plans for their closure. In August the company opened its first warehouse club in Australia.

CEO Jim Sinegal stepped down in 2012 after more than 20 years at the helm. Sinegal who together with chairman Jeffrey Brotman founded Costco in 1983 handed the reins to Craig Jelinek a 28-year veteran and former president and COO of the company.

In 2012 Costco bought the remaining 50% stake in Costco Mexico for $789 million from its joint venture partner Controladora Comercial Mexicana.

EXECUTIVES

Svp Operations, Roger A. Campbell

Evp Costco Wholesale Industries, Timothy L. Rose, age 66

Evp Information Systems, Paul G. Moulton, age 68, $602,519 total compensation

Evp Administration And Human Resources, Franz E. Lazarus, age 72

Evp And Coo Eastern And Canadian Divisions, Joseph P. (Joe) Portera, age 67, $645,297 total compensation

President And Ceo, W. Craig Jelinek, age 67, $699,810 total compensation

Evp And Coo Southwest And Mexico Divisions, Dennis R. Zook, age 70, $642,618 total compensation

Evp And Cfo, Richard A. Galanti, age 63, $712,888 total compensation

Evp International, James P. (Jim) Murphy, age 66

Evp And Coo Northern Division And Midwest Region, John D. McKay, age 62

Svp And General Manager Northeast Region, Jeffrey R. Long

Svp And General Manager Midwest Region, John B. Gaherty

Svp And General Manager Mexico, Jaime Gonzalez

Evp And Coo Merchandising, Douglas W. (Doug) Schutt, age 60

Svp And General Manager Bay Area Region, Jeffrey Abadir

Svp And General Manager Northwest Region, Mario Omoss

Svp And General Manager San Diego Region, Yoram Rubanenko

Svp And General Manager Eastern Canada Region, Pierre Riel

Svp And General Manager Los Angeles Region, Caton Frates

Svp And General Manager Western Canada Region, Russ Miller

Pharmacy Manager, Hassan Awada

Vice President Operations Southesat Region, Julie Cruz

Senior Vice President E Commerce And Publishing, Don Burdick

Assistant Vice President Finance And Investor Relations, Jeff Elliott

Pharmacy Manager, Jeff Mrowczynski

Pharmacy Manager, Jai Abraham

Vice President, Todd Thull

Senior Vice President General Manager Europe, Stephen Pappas

Assistant Vice President Information Systems, Tim Bowersock

Assistant Vice President Risk Management, Dellanie Fragnoli

Senior Vice President Merchandising Fresh Foods, Jeffrey Lyons

Executive Vice President Human Resources Retension And Talent Recruiting, Brenda Colgate

Pharmacy Manager, Bill Jones

Senior Vice President General Manager Bay Area Region, Jeff Abadir

Vice President Merchandise Accounting Controller, Joseph Grachek

Vice President Member Services, Mona Silva

Vice President Member Services, Colleen Johnson

Board Member, Susan Decker

Board Member, John Meisenbach

Board Member, Jeffrey Raikes

Auditors: KPMG LLP

LOCATIONS

HQ: Costco Wholesale Corp
999 Lake Drive, Issaquah, WA 98027
Phone: 425 313-8100
Web: www.costco.com

2018 Sales

	$ mil.	% of total
US	102,286	72
Canada	20,689	15
Other	18,601	13
Total	**141,576**	**100**

PRODUCTS/OPERATIONS

2018 Sales

	$ mil.	% of total
Sales	138 434	98
Membership fees	3,142	2
Total	**141,576**	**100**

2018 Sales

	% of total
Food & Sundries (dry & institutionally packaged candy snacks beverages cleaning products)	41
Hardlines (major appliances electronics health & beauty hardware garden & patio)	16
Fresh food (meat bakery deli & produce)	14
Softlines (apparel small appliances)	11
Ancillary (pharmacy fuel)	18
Total	**100**

COMPETITORS

Amazon.com	Office Depot
BJ's Wholesale Club	Safeway
Best Buy	Sam's Club
Big Lots	Staples
Dollar General	Target Corporation
Dollar Tree	Wal-Mart
Home Depot	Walgreens Boots
Kroger	

HISTORICAL FINANCIALS

Company Type: Public

Income Statement   FYE: September 1

	REVENUE ($ mil.)	NET INCOME ($ mil.)	NET PROFIT MARGIN	EMPLOYEES
09/19	152,703	3,659	2.4%	254,000
09/18	141,576	3,134	2.2%	245,000
09/17*	129,025	2,679	2.1%	231,000
08/16	118,719	2,350	2.0%	218,000
08/15	116,199	2,377	2.0%	205,000
Annual Growth	**7.1%**	**11.4%**	—	**5.5%**

*Fiscal year change

2019 Year-End Financials

Debt ratio: 15.03%
Return on equity: 26.17%
Cash ($ mil.): 8,384
Current ratio: 1.01
Long-term debt ($ mil.): 5,124

No. of shares (mil.): 439
Dividends
  Yield: 0.0%
  Payout: 29.5%
Market value ($ mil.): 129,584

	STOCK PRICE ($) FY Close	P/E High/Low		PER SHARE ($) Earnings	Dividends	Book Value
09/19	294.76	36	23	8.26	2.44	34.67
09/18	233.13	33	22	7.09	2.14	29.21
09/17*	158.24	30	23	6.08	8.90	24.65
08/16	163.93	32	26	5.33	1.70	27.61
08/15	139.95	29	22	5.37	6.51	24.24
Annual Growth	**20.5%**	—	—	**11.4%**	**(21.8%)**	**9.4%**

*Fiscal year change

Coty, Inc.

For perfume giant Coty the sweet smell of success is on retail shelves worldwide. The company is one of the leading makers of fragrances and beauty products for men and women across the globe. Its lineup ranges from moderately priced scents and cosmetics sold by mass retailers to prestige fragrances and premium skincare products found in department stores and upscale boutiques. Coty also make hair and nail care products for professional salons. The company's 75-plus owned or licensed brands include some of the world's most well-known including COVERGIRL Max Factor philosophy Escada Calvin Klein and Stetson. It generates most of its revenue outside North America. With a history that dates to 1904 Coty has used acquisitions to power its growth.

Operations

Coty divides its activities among three product segments: consumer beauty luxury and professional beauty.

The consumer beauty segment accounts for about 40% of total revenue and includes color cosmetics retail hair coloring and styling products body care products and mass fragrances. Brands include Clairol CoverGirl Max Factor Rimmel and Sally Hansen.

The company generates another 40% of revenue from the prestige fragrances premium skincare and premium cosmetics of its luxury segment which includes Burberry Calvin Klein Escada and philosophy among its brands.

With brands such as Sassoon Professional and Clairol Professional Coty generates the remainder of its revenue with sales to hair and nail salons and salon professionals.

The company generates about 40% of revenue from its licensed brands.

Geographic Reach

Truly a global company Coty generates nearly 70% of revenue outside North America; Europe accounts for about 45%.

It has offices in more than 35 countries and distributes products in some 150 countries. The company's major facilities are located in Brazil China France Germany Mexico Monaco Russia Spain Switzerland Thailand the UK and the US.

Sales and Marketing

Coty's products are sold in retail stores from drug stores to prestige boutiques as well as through hair and nail salons and travel retail sales channels such as duty-free shops airlines cruise ships and other tax-free zones. The company also has an e-commerce presence. Its top retailer Wal-mart accounts for about 5% of total revenue.

The company has dedicated sales and marketing teams in most of its major markets and seeks to attract customers via traditional media in-store and in-salon displays digital and social media and collaborations product placements and events. Celebrity endorsers are also key for Coty; recent ad campaigns have included Lupita Nyong'o Kate Moss Jake Gyllenhaal Gwen Stefani and Jared Leto.

Advertising and promotional costs for fiscal years 2019 2018 and 2017 were $1.9 billion $2.2 billion and $1.9 billion respectively.

Financial Performance

Although Coty's revenue fell in fiscal 2019 acquisitions have driven its strong growth over the past five years with revenue doubling since fiscal 2015. Net income has been less consistent with substantial losses in three of the last five years.

In fiscal 2019 (ended June 2019) the company reported revenue of $8.6 billion down 8% from the prior year. The decrease was driven by category weakness competition and supply chain issues that resulted in a 4% decline in unit volume in Consumer Beauty; other factors included the impact from foreign currency exchange and the termination or divestiture of some licenses (Guess Playboy Cerruti).

An asset impairment charge related to the Consumer Beauty business resulted in a huge loss of $3.8 billion that year compared to losses of about $170 million and $420 million in 2018 and 2017.

Cash at the end of fiscal 2019 was $380.4 million an increase of $18.2 million from the prior year. Cash from operations contributed $639.6 million to the coffers while investing activities used $454 million mainly for capital expenditures. Financing activities used another $160.3 million primarily for dividend payments.

Strategy

Coty's growth strategy which includes a Turnaround Plan announced in mid-2019 is focused on the areas of core brands and innovation digital transformation and emerging market expansion.

The company is putting its energy and investment dollars behind its strongest brands which include some of the world's most recognizable beauty names (CoverGirl Clairol Gucci Calvin Klein Burberry) as well as the smaller brands positioned for growth (Bourjois Chloe). In addition to relaunches of select brands it has discarded about a dozen brands (GUESS Cerruti Playboy) as part of a portfolio rationalization and has announced plans to divest its multi-level marketing business Younique. With core brands as the foundation Coty is introducing new product lines as part of its innovation initiative. The focus on stabilizing core brands is especially critical for its consumer beauty business which excluding the impact of acquisitions has been on the decline.

On the digital transformation front the company is investing in talent acquisition data and product management systems and in-house content creation capabilities as it works to grow e-commerce capabilities. Coty launched a digital accelerator program in mid-2018 that allows tech start-ups to present at quarterly summits and earn the opportunity to work with Coty's vendor brands. It also introduced a personal beauty assistant app for the Amazon Echo that year.

Lastly growth in emerging markets in Latin America and Asia particularly are key to Coty's strategy. An acquisition moved the company into Brazil where it continues to gain market share. Although currently a small market for Coty China is a major focus. In 2018 the company had a successful launch of the Tiffany brand in China where it also has a business partnership with Asian e-commerce giant Alibaba. Mexico and the Middle East are also target markets.

Mergers and Acquisitions

Coty has kickstarted revenue added new product categories and moved into new geographies through major acquisitions over the past several years.

In fiscal 2019 it completed the final steps of the integration of the P&G Beauty Business which was originally acquired in 2016. The P&G deal included the CoverGirl and Max Factor cosmetics brands and the Hugo Boss and Gucci fragrance brands. Valued at a hefty $11.4 billion the move bolstered Coty's market presence as a beauty products company ranking it third behind LOréal and Unilever. Its geographic presence was also significantly expanded.

Company Background

Coty was founded in Paris in 1904 after François Coty created his first perfume La Rose Jacqueminot.

EXECUTIVES

President Global Markets, Edgar O. Huber
Svp General Counsel And Secretary, Jules P. Kaufman, age 61, $525,000 total compensation
Svp Global Research And Development And Chief Scientific Officer, Ralph Macchio, age 62
Chairman And Interim Ceo, Lambertus J. H. (Bart) Becht, age 62
Evp And Cfo, Patrice de Talhouet, age 53, $784,100 total compensation
Evp Supply Chain, Mario Reis, age 59, $609,560 total compensation
Evp Category Development, Camillo Pane, age 49, $592,320 total compensation
Vice President Marketing, Lori Singer
Global Vp It, Joan Luzzi
Vice President Corporate Finance, Leah Zaslavsky
Senior Vice President American Fragrances Coty Prestige, Catherine Walsh
Vice President Marketing, Trent Hurst
Vice President Global Marketing (coty Presitige Skincare), Rachel Shelowitz

Svp Global Deputy General Counsel, Joseph Conklin
Vice President Corporate Finance, Jerome Estampes
Vice President Marketing, Laura Weinstein
Vice President Sales, David Russell
Vice President Sales National Accounts, Mary Vanpraag
Senior Vice President Human Resources, Gtraudmarie Lacassagne
Vice President Infrastructure Services, Glen Dalgleish
Senior Vice President Global Supply Chain, Franco Valenti
Vice President Global Information Technology, Natalie Elgart
Public Relations Corporate Communications International Vice President Vice President Public Relations And Communications, Isabelle Mical
Vp Supply Chain, German Alonso
Sr Vp Us Sales, Brian Falcone
Senior Vice President Global Ecommerce, Sean Foster
Senior Vice President Human Resources, Raul Valentin
Vice President Human Resources, Keri-Lynne Shaw
Vice President Global Influencer Marketing (philosophy), Andy Fouche
Vice President Global Marketing (marc Jacobs And Alexander Mcqueen Fragrances), Renaud Salmon
Vice President Influencer Marketing And Communications, Cheryl Dixon
National Account Manager, Carolyn Goodwin
Vice President Legal Patents, David Joyal
Senior Vice President Sales, Michaelene Roark
Vp Of Covergirl Sales Strategy + Consumer Beauty Commercial Integration, Alanna Watson
Vice President Ecommerce, Jean-paul Jansen
Vp Category And Global Trade Marketing Color Cosmetics, Jose Palacios
Vp Qvc Marketing Philosophy, Joan Pellegrino
Vp Sales Specialty Channel, Denise Greco
Auditors: DELOITTE & TOUCHE LLP

LOCATIONS

HQ: Coty, Inc.
350 Fifth Avenue, New York, NY 10118
Phone: 212 389-7300
Web: www.coty.com

2019 Sales

	$ mil.	% of total
Europe	3,777	44
North America	2,656	31
ALMEA (Asia Latin America Middle East Africa)	2,214	25
Total	**8,648**	**100**

PRODUCTS/OPERATIONS

2019 Sales

	$ mil.	% of total
Consumer Beauty	3,539	41
Luxury	3,294	38
Professional Beauty	1,814	21
Total	**8,648**	**100**

Selected Brands by Segment

Consumer Beauty
  Adidas
  Beckham
  Beyonce
  Clairol
  CoverGirl
  Jovan
  Max Factor
  Rimmel
  Sally Hansen
  Stetson
Luxury
  Balenciaga
  Burberry

  Calvin Klein
  Chloe
  Escada
  Gucci
  Joop!
  Marc Jacobs
  Miu Miu
  philosophy
  Stella McCartney
  Tiffany & Co.
Professional Beauty
  Clairol Professional
  ghd
  Kadus Professional
  Sassoon Professional
  Wella Professionals

COMPETITORS

Avon	LVMH
Body Shop	Markwins International
Chanel	Mary Kay
Elizabeth Arden Inc	Nu Skin
Estée Lauder	Parlux Fragrances
Inter Parfums	Revlon
L'Oréal	

HISTORICAL FINANCIALS

Company Type: Public

Income Statement   FYE: June 30

	REVENUE ($ mil.)	NET INCOME ($ mil.)	NET PROFIT MARGIN	EMPLOYEES
06/19	8,648	(3,784)	—	19,000
06/18	9,398	(168)	—	20,000
06/17	7,650	(422)	—	22,000
06/16	4,349	156	3.6%	10,060
06/15	4,395	232	5.3%	8,100
Annual Growth	**18.4%**	—	—	**23.8%**

2019 Year-End Financials

Debt ratio: 43.38%	No. of shares (mil.): 754
Return on equity: (-56.33%)	Dividends
Cash ($ mil.): 340	Yield: 0.0%
Current ratio: 0.94	Payout: —
Long-term debt ($ mil.): 7,469	Market value ($ mil.): 10,106

	STOCK PRICE ($) FY Close	P/E High/Low	PER SHARE ($) Earnings	Dividends	Book Value
06/19	13.40	— —	(5.04)	0.50	6.08
06/18	14.10	— —	(0.23)	0.50	11.79
06/17	18.76	— —	(0.66)	0.65	12.45
06/16	25.99	73 48	0.44	0.25	1.07
06/15	31.97	49 24	0.64	0.20	2.69
Annual Growth	**(19.5%)**	— —	—	**25.7%**	**22.6%**

CrossFirst Bankshares Inc

Auditors: BKD, LLC

LOCATIONS

HQ: CrossFirst Bankshares Inc
11440 Tomahawk Creek Parkway, Leawood, KS 66211
Phone: 913 312-6822
Web: www.crossfirstbankshares.com

HISTORICAL FINANCIALS

Company Type: Public

Income Statement

FYE: December 31

	ASSETS ($ mil.)	NET INCOME ($ mil.)	INCOME AS % OF ASSETS	EMPLOYEES
12/18	4,107	19	0.5%	360
12/17	2,961	5	0.2%	—
Annual Growth	38.7%	234.9%	—	—

2018 Year-End Financials

Debt ratio: 0.02%
Return on equity: 5.04%
Cash ($ mil.): 216
Current ratio: —
Long-term debt ($ mil.): —

No. of shares (mil.): 45
Dividends
Yield: —
Payout: —
Market value ($ mil.): —

	STOCK PRICE ($) FY Close	P/E High/Low		PER SHARE ($) Earnings	Dividends	Book Value
12/18	0.00	—	—	0.47	0.00	10.88
12/17	0.00	—	—	0.12	0.00	9.36
/0.00	—		—(0.00)	0.00	(0.00)	
Annual Growth	—			—	—	—

Crown Castle International Corp (New)

Auditors: PricewaterhouseCoopers LLP

LOCATIONS

HQ: Crown Castle International Corp (New)
1220 Augusta Drive, Suite 600, Houston, TX 77057-2261
Phone: 713 570-3000
Web: www.crowncastle.com

COMPETITORS

American Tower	NextG
CellXion	PlastiComm Industries
Global Tower LLC	SBA Communications
LCC International	TowerCo LLC
Microwave Transmission Systems	VelociTel

HISTORICAL FINANCIALS

Company Type: Public

Income Statement

FYE: December 31

	REVENUE ($ mil.)	NET INCOME ($ mil.)	NET PROFIT MARGIN	EMPLOYEES
12/18	5,423	671	12.4%	5,000
12/17	4,355	444	10.2%	4,500
12/16	3,921	356	9.1%	3,200
12/15	3,663	1,520	41.5%	2,700
12/14	3,689	390	10.6%	2,400
Annual Growth	10.1%	14.5%	—	20.1%

2018 Year-End Financials

Debt ratio: 50.88%
Return on equity: 5.51%
Cash ($ mil.): 277
Current ratio: 0.87
Long-term debt ($ mil.): 16,575

No. of shares (mil.): 415
Dividends
Yield: 3.9%
Payout: 319.0%
Market value ($ mil.): 45,081

	STOCK PRICE ($) FY Close	P/E High/Low		PER SHARE ($) Earnings	Dividends	Book Value
12/18	108.63	87	75	1.34	4.28	29.00
12/17	111.01	113	84	1.01	3.90	30.37
12/16	86.77	108	82	0.95	3.61	20.96
12/15	86.45	20	17	4.42	3.35	21.24
12/14	78.70	81	66	1.04	0.82	20.12
Annual Growth	8.4%	—	—	6.5%	51.1%	9.6%

Crown Holdings Inc

Crown Holdings is a leading global manufacturer of consumer packaging products including steel and aluminum food and beverage cans. Its portfolio includes aerosol cans and various metal vacuum closures marketed under brands Liftoff SuperEnd and Easylift as well as specialty packaging products such as novelty containers and industrial cans. Crown also supplies can-making equipment and parts. Its roster of customers has included Coca-Cola SC Johnson Unilever Friesland Campina and Procter & Gamble. Crown traces its historical roots all the way back to 1892. Nearly three-quarters of its net sales is generated outside the US.

Operations

Crown is focused on growing on a global scale and has divided its business along geographic lines. The company's reportable segments are Americas Beverage (accounting for about 30% of net sales) European Food (nearly 20%) European Beverage (nearly 15%) and Asia Pacific (more than 10%). The company makes steel and aluminum food and beverage cans glass bottles steel crowns and metal vacuum closures.

Crown also has a Transit Packaging segment which is further divided into industrial solutions protective solutions and equipment and tools. Industrial solutions include products such as steel strap plastic strap and industrial film used in the steel and lumber industries and in corrugated boxes food and beverage goods and agriculture products. Protective solutions are products like airbags edge protectors and honeycomb products that protect goods during transport. The equipment and tools business includes items used in manufacturing applications to apply things like strap and film. The Transit Packaging segment accounts for approximately 15% of revenue.

The company's non-reportable segments include its North American food can and aerosol can businesses its European aerosol and promotional packaging business and its tooling and equipment operations in the US and UK. These account for about 10% of total sales.

By product Crown's metal beverage cans business accounts for about half of total revenue while metal food cans represent about 20%. Metal packaging and other products account for the remaining revenue.

Geographic Reach

Crown operates around 240 plants in more than 45 countries some in Brazil Spain Mexico Belgium Germany India Sweden and Switzerland among others. About 75% of sales come from outside the

US. The Americas Beverage division has nearly 50 operating facilities. The European division 60 and the Asia Pacific division 30. Transit Packaging operates approximately 100 facilities. The company also has three can-making equipment and spare part operations in the US and the UK.

Crown's US headquarters is stationed in Yardley Pennsylvania while its European headquarters is in Baar Switzerland. In addition its Asia Pacific headquarters resides in Singapore. It has additional research facilities in Alsip Illinois and Wantage England.

Sales and Marketing

Crown markets and sells products to customers through its own sales and marketing staffs. In some instances contracts with customers are centrally negotiated but products are ordered through and distributed directly by its local facilities. Its top 10 global customers collectively represent about 30% of its overall revenue.

Customers include Anheuser-Busch InBev Coca-Cola Keurig Dr Pepper Heineken Molson Coors Pepsi-Cola and Refresco among others.

Financial Performance

The company's revenues have been up and down in recent years. After two years of decline Crown Holding's sales in 2017 started to improve and in 2018 the acquisition of Signode Industrial Group boosted revenue by $1.8 billion to $11.2 billion. This represents a 28% increase compared with $8.7 billion in 2017. Other factors driving growth were higher sales unit volumes in global beverage sales and favorable foreign currency translation.

The company posted net income of $439.0 in 2018 up 36% from $323.0 million in 2017 mainly due to a lower provision for income tax expense in 2018.

Cash at the end of fiscal 2018 was $659 million an increase of $224 million from the prior year. Cash from operations contributed $571 million to the coffers while investing activities used $3.8 billion mainly for the acquisition of Signode. Financing activities provided $3.5 billion primarily from proceeds of long-term debt to finance the Signode acquisition.

Strategy

Crown grows its businesses in specific international growth markets while improving its operations and results in more mature markets through disciplined pricing and improvements in manufacturing and productivity. However with international expansion Crown like its rivals risks exposure to unfavorable foreign-currency exchange rates of the euro pound sterling and Canadian dollar as well as cyclical consumer spending on food and beverages. Its net sales are also impacted by the rise or decrease in the cost of aluminum and steel which is passed on to customers.

However the company believes that technological innovation will help mitigate for usual risks and cycles. Not content with making containers the same old way Crown Holdings operates research development and engineering centers in the US and the UK. Its mission is to design cost-efficient manufacturing processes reduce material content while maintaining freshness and develop new products with the application of new technologies. One of the company's key strategies is to drive sales by offering a number of different can sizes.

Crown is specifically targeting Southeast Asia and Mexico as regions ripe with growth opportunities. In 2018 the company opened new manufacturing facilities in Myanmar and expanded existing capacity at its plant in Cambodia. In Mexico it began operations at a new glass factory to serve the expanding beer market in the region. In Brazil it plans to begin operations at a new beverage can plant. Crown has also been building new plants and expanding its European operations in Spain and Italy.

Mergers and Acquisitions

In 2018 Crown purchased transit packaging provider Signode Industrial Group from Carlyle Group for $3.9 billion. Signode is based in Illinois and has operations in 40 countries across six continents. It sells its products in some 60 countries. The acquisition broadens and diversifies Crown's customer base.

HISTORY

Formed as Crown Cork & Seal Co. (CC&S) of Baltimore in 1892 the company was consolidated into its present form in 1927 when it merged with New Process Cork and New York Patents. The next year CC&S expanded overseas and formed Crown Cork International. In 1936 CC&S acquired Acme Can and benefited from the movement at the time from home canning to processed canning. A decade later the company launched its new product in 1946 — the first aerosol can.

EXECUTIVES

President Ceo And Director, Timothy J. Donahue, age 57, $915,000 total compensation

Svp And Cfo, Thomas A. Kelly, age 60, $575,000 total compensation

Evp Corporate Technology And Regulatory Affairs And President Crown Packaging Technology, Daniel A. Abramowicz

Evp And Coo, Gerard H (Jerry) Gifford, age 64, $600,000 total compensation

President Crown Aerosol Packaging North America, C. Anderson (Andy) Bolton

President Crown Food Packaging North America Crown Closures And Specialty Packaging, James D. (Jim) Wilson

President Americas Division, Djalma Novaes, age 58, $510,000 total compensation

President Crown Beverage Packaging South America, Wilmar Arinelli

President Crown Beverage Packaging Mexico, Abel Coello Quintanilla

President Crown Beverage Packaging North America, Timothy J. (Tim) Lorge

President Asia Pacific, Robert H. Bourque, age 49, $302,413 total compensation

President Crown Europe, Didier Sourisseau, age 53

Vice President Health And Safety European Division, Eddy Geelen

Division Vice President, George Fernandez

Vice President Planning And Development, Torsten Kreider

Vice President Operations North America Beverage Division, Doug Pyer

Vice President, Randall Chaffins

Regional Vice President Sales, Michelle Hinton

Vice President, Joseph Pierce

V.p. Of Operations, Ken Tutin

Vice President Sales, Ralph Menichini

Executive Vice President, Ronald Thoma

Vp Ir And Corporate Affairs, Thomas Fischer

Vice President Commercial Food Europe, Olivier Aubry

Vice President Labor And Employee Relations, Vince Pepenelli

Vp And Controller Europe, Inigo D'ornellas

Divisional Vice President Of Sales, Greg Wise

Chairman, John W. Conway, age 73

Board Member, Josef Muller

Board Member, Arnold Donald

Vice Chairman, Hans Loliger

Board Member, Aaron Miller

Board Member, Caesar Sweitzer

Board Member, Jim Turner

Auditors: PricewaterhouseCoopers LLP

LOCATIONS

HQ: Crown Holdings Inc
770 Township Line Road, Yardley, PA 19067
Phone: 215 698-5100
Web: www.crowncork.com

2018 Sales

	$ mil.	% of total
US	3,018	27
Mexico	763	7
Brazil	732	7
UK	685	6
Spain	666	6
Other regions	5,287	47
Total	**11,151**	**100**

PRODUCTS/OPERATIONS

2018 Sales

	$ mil.	% of total
Metal beverage cans & ends	5,551	50
Metal food cans & ends	2,452	22
Transit packaging	1,800	16
Other metal packaging	884	8
Other products	464	4
Total	**11,151**	**100**

2017 Sales

	$ mil.	% of total
Americas beverage	3,282	29
European food	1,982	18
European beverage	1,489	13
Asia Pacific	1,316	12
Transit Packaging	1,800	16
Non-reportable segments	1,282	12
Total	**11,151**	**100**

Selected Products

Metal packaging
  Aerosol cans
  Beverage cans
  Closures and caps
  Crowns
  Ends
  Food cans
Plastics packaging
Other products
  Can making equipment and spares

Selected Markets

Food and beverage
Health and beauty
Household / Industrial
Luxury Goods
Promotional
Construction
Agriculture

COMPETITORS

Amcor	Berry Global
AptarGroup	Metal Container
Arconic	Corporation
Ardagh Group	Owens-Illinois
BWAY	Silgan
Ball Corp.	Sonoco Products

HISTORICAL FINANCIALS

Company Type: Public

Income Statement

FYE: December 31

	REVENUE ($ mil.)	NET INCOME ($ mil.)	NET PROFIT MARGIN	EMPLOYEES
12/18	11,151	439	3.9%	33,000
12/17	8,698	323	3.7%	24,000
12/16	8,284	496	6.0%	24,000
12/15	8,762	393	4.5%	24,000
12/14	9,097	387	4.3%	23,000
Annual Growth	5.2%	3.2%	—	9.4%

2018 Year-End Financials

Debt ratio: 56.95%	No. of shares (mil.): 135
Return on equity: 57.09%	Dividends
Cash ($ mil.): 607	Yield: —
Current ratio: 1.04	Payout: —
Long-term debt ($ mil.): 8,517	Market value ($ mil.): 5,619

	STOCK PRICE ($) FY Close	P/E High/Low		PER SHARE ($) Earnings	Dividends	Book Value
12/18	41.57	18	12	3.28	0.00	6.93
12/17	56.25	26	22	2.38	0.00	4.48
12/16	52.57	16	12	3.56	0.00	2.62
12/15	50.70	20	16	2.82	0.00	1.03
12/14	50.90	19	14	2.79	0.00	0.86
Annual Growth	(4.9%)	—	—	4.1%	—	68.7%

CSX Corp

EXECUTIVES

Pres-Ceo, James M Foote
Chb*, Edward J Kelly III
V Chb*, Paul C Hilal
Exec V Pres Oprs, Edmond L Harris
Exec V Pres-Clo-Sec, Nathan D Goldman
Exec V Pres-Chief ADM Officer, Mark K Wallace
V Pres-Contrl, Angela C Williams
Svp-Cso, Farrukh A Bezar
Evp-Cfo, Kevin Boone
Contractor, Shawn Trexler
Administrator, Sridhar Raman
Auditors: Ernst & Young LLP

LOCATIONS

HQ: CSX Corp
500 Water Street, 15th Floor, Jacksonville, FL 32202
Phone: 904 359-3200
Web: www.csx.com

COMPETITORS

APL Logistics	Hub Group
Burlington Northern	J.B. Hunt
Santa Fe	Norfolk Southern
Canadian National	Pacer International
Railway	Schneider National
Canadian Pacific	Union Pacific
Railway	Washington Companies

HISTORICAL FINANCIALS

Company Type: Public

Income Statement

FYE: December 31

	REVENUE ($ mil.)	NET INCOME ($ mil.)	NET PROFIT MARGIN	EMPLOYEES
12/18	12,250	3,309	27.0%	22,500
12/17	11,408	5,471	48.0%	24,000
12/16	11,069	1,714	15.5%	27,000
12/15	11,811	1,968	16.7%	29,000
12/14	12,669	1,927	15.2%	31,511
Annual Growth	(0.8%)	14.5%	—	(8.1%)

2018 Year-End Financials

Debt ratio: 40.18%	No. of shares (mil.): 818
Return on equity: 24.27%	Dividends
Cash ($ mil.): 858	Yield: 1.4%
Current ratio: 1.34	Payout: 11.9%
Long-term debt ($ mil.): 14,739	Market value ($ mil.): 50,834

	STOCK PRICE ($)	P/E		PER SHARE ($)		
	FY Close	High/Low	Earnings	Dividends	Book Value
12/18	62.13	20 13	3.84	0.88	15.35
12/17	55.01	10 6	5.99	0.78	16.53
12/16	35.93	21 12	1.81	0.72	12.58
12/15	26.13	19 12	2.00	0.70	12.07
12/14	36.68	20 13	1.92	0.63	11.25
Annual Growth	14.1%	— —	18.9%	8.7%	8.1%

Cullen/Frost Bankers, Inc.

One of the largest independent bank holding companies in Texas Cullen/Frost Bankers owns Frost Bank and other financial subsidiaries through a second-tier holding company The New Galveston Company. The community-oriented bank serves individuals and local businesses as well as clients in neighboring parts of Mexico through 120-plus branches in Texas metropolitan areas. It offers commercial and consumer deposit products and loans trust and investment management services mutual funds insurance brokerage and leasing. Subsidiaries include Frost Insurance Agency Frost Brokerage Services Frost Investment Advisors and investment banking arm Frost Securities. Cullen/Frost has total assets of $26.5 billion.

Geographic Reach

San Antonio-based Cullen/Frost Bankers has branches throughout Texas including the Austin Corpus Christi Dallas Fort Worth Houston Permian Basin the Rio Grande Valley and San Antonio regions.

Financial Performance

Cullen/Frost reported revenue of $945.3 million in 2013 an increase of 3% versus 2012 on increased interest income on loans and deposits and an increase in trust and investment management fees. Net income was $237.9 a flat comparison with the prior year. 2013 marked the third consecutive year of rising revenue following a dip in 2010. The bank's fortunes are rising along with the thriving energy and technology sectors in Texas.

Strategy

Cullen/Frost has built its insurance business through acquisitions in recent years; since 2009 it has bought agencies in Dallas Houston San Antonio and San Marcos that provide group employee benefit plans. The company continues to seek out acquisition opportunities while it also looks for ways to expand and diversify within its existing markets. To reduce its reliance on interest rate spreads Cullen/Frost wants to grow its income from fees such as insurance commissions trust investment fees and service charges on deposit accounts.

Mergers and Acquisitions

In June 2014 Frost Bank acquired Odessa Texas-based Western National Bank (WNB) increasing its presence in the oil-rich Permian Basin Midland and Odessa markets in West Texas. Seven of WNB's eight branches were converted to the Frost name (an office in San Antonio was closed) increasing the number of Frost branches statewide to more than 120. The acquisition of WNB added $1.8 billion in assets $1.6 billion in deposits and $668 million in total loans to Cullen/Frost. The purchase of WNB was the first time in nearly seven years that Frost acquired another bank.

EXECUTIVES

Chairman And Ceo, Phillip D. Green, age 64, $565,000 total compensation
President Frost Bank; Evp Frost Wealth Advisors, Patrick B. (Pat) Frost, age 59, $485,000 total compensation
President, Paul H. Bracher, age 62, $500,000 total compensation
Evp And Cfo, Jerry Salinas, $400,000 total compensation
Vice President, Stephanie Conti
Vice President Of Marketing, Bobby Jacob
Vice President Of Marketing, Linda Hopkins
Vice President Of Marketing, Howard Kasanoff
Senior Vice President It, Harvey Gutierrez
Vice President And Senior Real Property Appraiser, Michael L Cleary
Senior Executive Vice Presiden, William Sirakos
Senior Vice President Director Of Investor Relatio, Greg Parker
Vice President Of Finance, Vicki Ball
Senior Vice President, David Hamilton
Executive Vice President, Mark Freeman
Senior Vice President Treasury Management, Darlene Selsor
Executive Vice President, John Robb
Vice President, Hilary Stull
Senior Vice President, John Hind
Vice President Of Operation, Cliff McCauley
Vice President Of Finance, Gregory Dreier
Senior Vice President, Dan Taaffe
Vice President, Oscar Molina
Senior Vice President, Cliff Perez
Senior Vice President, Cathy Garison
Senior Vice President, Vennesa Starr
Vice President, Jonathan Pursch
Senior Vice President, Clay Cary
Senior Vice President, Casey Maxfield
Vice President Executive Benni, Darleen Schauer
Senior Vice President, Jill Stacy
Vice President Sales, Talal Tay
Vice President, Julius Eccell
Vice President Of Marketing, Wendy Erickson
Vice President Of Finance, Wayne Baker
Vice President Marketing, Ericka Pullin
Senior Vice President, Michael S Cain
Senior Vice President, Mark Seeberger
Senior Vice President, Edward Porras
Senior Vice President, James Valdez
Senior Vice President, Scott Tellkamp
Assistant Vice President, Kelly Shanteau
Senior Vice President, David Seitze
Vice President Of Operation, Erica Noriega
Senior Vice President Capital Markets, Mark Brell
Senior Vice President, Tara Menchaca
Senior Vice President, Roger Lind
Vice President Administration, Gary Roney
Vice President, Teresa Woods
Vice President, Clay Jones
Vice President Of Information Technology, Diane Madalin
Senior Vice President Project Manager, Terrie Ramirez
Senior Vice President, Leigh Olejer
Vice President Collections, Alan McCabe
Vice President, Floyd Wilson
Senior Vice President, Michael Nutter
Senior Vice President, Mike Davis
Vice President Of Employee Benefits, Tony Zavala
Vice President Of Finance, Andrea Knight
Senior Vice President, Carl Mclaughlin
Vice President, Maro Rodriguez
Vice President, Susan Carruthers
Regional Vice President, Lorraine Neff
Senior Vice President, Olga Harrison
Executive Vice President, Gary Mcknight
Assistant Vice President, Austin Burns
Assistant Vice President, Hope S Molina
Vice President, Matt Badders
Senior Vice President Institutional Trust Administration, Steven A Klein
Senior Vice President, Terry Frank
Senior Vice President, Letty Dominguez
Vice President Of Finance, Mark Cranmer
Senior Vice President Community Leader, Jeff Fuller
Vice President Technology Infrastructure, Robert Jacobs
Senior Vice President Wealth Advisor Private Trust, John Sands
Vice President Mineral Asset Management Frost Banking Investments, Robert Turnbull
Senior Vice President Compliance, Jan Robertson
Senior Vice President Corporate Banki, Susie Howell
Senior Vice President Capital Markets, Victor Quiroga
Vice President Of Marketing, Daryl Hoffmann
Executive Vice President, Sue Turnage
Senior Vice President Workout Officer, Jennifer Crabtree
Senior Vice President Of Investment Division, Jeanne Glorioso
Senior Vice President North Texas Sales Manager Public Finance, Shirley Cox
Assistant Vice President Of Network Engineering, Danny Leal
Senior Vice President Application Support, Jeff Sanders
Senior Vice President, Shannon Watt
Assistant Vice President, Elsie Boone
Senior Vice President Investments, Linnie Phebus
Executive Vice President Marketing, Debbie Danmeter
Vice President, Ben Kavanagh
Senior Vice President, Carol Lampier
Assistant Vice President, Beth Pence
Assistant Vice President Employee Benefits, Brenda Smith
Senior Vice President, Gina Prill
Executive Vice President, Richard Foster
Assistant Vice President, Rene Ramirez
Senior Vice President, Melissa Adams
Vice President Of Finance, Vance Arnold
Vice President Energy Finance, Alex Zemkoski
Vice President, Duncan Morrow
Senior Vice President Special Assets, Betsy Gleiser
Vice President Of Marketing, John Greenwood
Executive Vice President Compliance Manager, Cindy Reeves
Senior Vice President Compliance, Verna Fletcher
Senior Executive Vice President, James Allen
Executive Vice President, Louis Barton
Senior Vice President, Stacy L Flores
Senior Vice President Of Private Trust Services, Debbie Eippert
Senior Vice President, Mark Ritter
Assistant Vice President, Mariela Hernandez
Vice President, Ken Orsburn
Assistant Vice President, Patricio Perez
Assistant Vice President, Lauren Urban
Assistant Vice President Commercial Banking, Jennifer Grimes
Assistant Vice President, Yolanda Gonzales
Vice President, Michael Aubuchon
Vice President, Van C Carter
Vice President, Anna Sanchez
Senior Vice President, Brent Bike
Vice President, Anabell Rodriguez
Vice President Corporate Banking Frost Banking Investments, Luke Healy
Vice President Equipment Leasing And Finance, Laura Eckhardt
Vice President, Sallie Newman
Vice President, Margaret Velasquez
Vice President, Gwen Dominic

Assistant Vice President, Justin Steinbach
Assistant Vice President, Samuel Lopez
Vice President, Laura Pinto
Senior Vice President, Carole Kilpatrick
Assistant Vice President, Karla Riley
Vice President Intl Private Banking, Elvia Daley
Assistant Vice President, Trey McCord
Senior Vice President, Anthony White
Vice President Sales, Linda Wileman
Vice President Sba Loan Coordinator, Kathy Raia
Senior Vice President Trust Internal Audit,
 Deanna Rankin
Vice President, Allison Byers
Senior Vice President, Lou Kissling
Sr. Vice Pres., Barbara Kelly
Vice President In Human Resources Department,
 Janet Lane
Vice President, Albert Shannon
Executive Vice President And General Counsel,
 Stanley McCormick
Executive Vice President, Chas Mella
Senior Vice President, James Winton
Vice President, Sherry Mcgillicuddy
Senior Vice President, Kaye Carpenter
Vice President, Ileana Payne
Vice President Business Services, Gloria Kopycinski
Auditors: Ernst & Young LLP

LOCATIONS

HQ: Cullen/Frost Bankers, Inc.
 111 W. Houston Street, San Antonio, TX 78205
Phone: 210 220-4011   Fax: 210 220-5578
Web: www.frostbank.com

PRODUCTS/OPERATIONS

2016 Sales

	$ mil.	% of total
Interest		
Loans including fees	458	40
Securities	313	28
Interest-bearing deposits	16	1
Federal funds sold and resell agreements	0	-
Non-interest		
Trust and investment management fees	104	9
Service charges on deposit accounts	81	7
Insurance commissions & fees	47	4
Interchange and debit card transaction fees	21	2
Other charges commissions and fees	39	4
Net gain (loss) on securities transactions	15	1
Other	41	4
Total	**1,138**	**100**

2016 Sales

	% of total
Banking	88
Frost Wealth Advisors	12
Total	**100**

Selected Subsidiaries

Carton Service Corporation
Cullen BLP Inc.
Cullen/Frost Capital Trust II
Frost Bank
Frost Brokerage Services Inc.
Frost Insurance Agency Inc.
Frost Investment Advisors Inc.
Main Plaza Corporation
Tri-Frost Corporation

COMPETITORS

BBVA Compass
 Bancshares
Bank of America
Broadway Bancshares
Capital One
Comerica
Extraco
First Financial
 Bankshares
International
 Bancshares

JPMorgan Chase
Lone Star Bank
PlainsCapital
Prosperity Bancshares
Texas Capital
 Bancshares
Wells Fargo
Woodforest Financial

Income Statement   FYE: December 31

	ASSETS ($ mil.)	NET INCOME ($ mil.)	INCOME AS % OF ASSETS	EMPLOYEES
12/19	34,027	443	1.3%	4,659
12/18	32,292	454	1.4%	4,370
12/17	31,747	364	1.1%	4,270
12/16	30,196	304	1.0%	4,217
12/15	28,567	279	1.0%	4,211
Annual Growth	4.5%	12.3%	—	2.6%

2019 Year-End Financials

Debt ratio: 0.69%
Return on equity: 12.19%
Cash ($ mil.): 3,431
Current ratio: —
Long-term debt ($ mil.): —

No. of shares (mil.): 62
Dividends
 Yield: 2.8%
 Payout: 39.6%
Market value ($ mil.): 6,128

	STOCK PRICE ($) FY Close	P/E High/Low	Earnings	Dividends	Book Value
12/19	97.78	15 12	6.84	2.80	62.42
12/18	87.94	17 12	6.90	2.58	53.49
12/17	94.65	18 15	5.51	2.25	51.95
12/16	88.23	19 9	4.70	2.15	47.30
12/15	60.00	19 14	4.28	2.10	46.63
Annual Growth	13.0%	—	12.4%	7.5%	7.6%

Cummins, Inc.

EXECUTIVES

Chb-Ceo, N Thomas Linebarger
Pres-Coo, Livingston L Satterthwaite
V Pres-Cfo, Patrick J Ward
Cto, Jim Fier
V Pres-Chief ADM Officer, Marya M Rose
V Pres-Gen Counsel, Sharon R Barner
V Pres-Corp Controller, Christopher C Clulow
Vp-Chief Information Officer, Sherry A Aaholm
Vp Global Supply Chain & Mfg, Peter W Anderson
Group Vp China & Russia, Steven M Chapman
Vp-Chief Hr Officer, Jill E Cook
Auditors: PricewaterhouseCoopers LLP

LOCATIONS

HQ: Cummins, Inc.
 500 Jackson Street, P.O. Box 3005, Columbus, IN
 47202-3005
Phone: 812 377-5000   Fax: 812 377-4937
Web: www.cummins.com

COMPETITORS

BorgWarner
Briggs & Stratton
 Power Products
CLARCOR
Caterpillar
China Yuchai
DENSO
DEUTZ
Detroit Diesel
Donaldson Company
Eaton
Emerson Electric
Fiat
Ford Motor
Hino Motors
Honeywell
 International
Illinois Tool Works

Ingersoll-Rand
Isuzu
Kohler
MAN
Mack Trucks
Mitsubishi Heavy
 Industries
Navistar International
Parker-Hannifin
Regal Beloit
Robert Bosch
Tenneco
Textron
Tognum
UD Trucks
Volvo
W.W. Grainger
Weichai Power

Income Statement   FYE: December 31

	REVENUE ($ mil.)	NET INCOME ($ mil.)	NET PROFIT MARGIN	EMPLOYEES
12/18	23,771	2,141	9.0%	62,610
12/17	20,428	999	4.9%	58,600
12/16	17,509	1,394	8.0%	55,400
12/15	19,110	1,399	7.3%	55,200
12/14	19,221	1,651	8.6%	54,600
Annual Growth	5.5%	6.7%	—	3.5%

2018 Year-End Financials

Debt ratio: 12.99%
Return on equity: 29.31%
Cash ($ mil.): 1,303
Current ratio: 1.54
Long-term debt ($ mil.): 1,597

No. of shares (mil.): 158
Dividends
 Yield: 3.3%
 Payout: 33.7%
Market value ($ mil.): 21,115

	STOCK PRICE ($) FY Close	P/E High/Low	Earnings	Dividends	Book Value
12/18	133.64	15 10	13.15	4.44	46.51
12/17	176.64	30 23	5.97	4.21	43.81
12/16	136.67	18 10	8.23	4.00	40.87
12/15	88.01	19 11	7.84	3.51	42.27
12/14	144.17	18 14	9.02	2.81	42.53
Annual Growth	(1.9%)	—	9.9%	12.1%	2.3%

Customers Bancorp Inc

Customers Bancorp makes it pretty clear who they want to serve. Boasting some $8.5 billion in assets the bank holding company operates about 15 branches mostly in southeastern Pennsylvania but also in New York and New Jersey. It offers personal and business checking savings and money market accounts as well as loans certificates of deposit credit cards and concierge or appointment banking (they come to you seven days a week). Around 95% of the bank's loan portfolio is made up of commercial loans while the rest consists of consumer loans. It was formed in 2010 as a holding company for Customers Bank which was created in 1994 as New Century Bank.

Operations

Customers Bancorp operates two main business lines: Commercial Lending and Consumer Lending. Its Commercial Lending business provides commercial and industrial loans small and middle-market business banking and small business administration (SBA) loans multi-family and commercial real estate loans and commercial loans to mortgage originators. Its Consumer Lending division mostly makes local market mortgage loans and home equity loans. More than 95% of the bank's loan portfolio was made up of commercial loans at the end of 2015 while the rest consisted of consumer loans.

Broadly speaking the bank makes roughly 90% of its revenue from interest income. About 66% of its revenue came from loan interest during 2015 while another 19% came from interest loans held for sale and 4% came from interest on investment securities. The remainder of its revenue came from mortgage warehouse transactional fees (4%) and other miscellaneous and non-recurring sources.

Geographic Reach

The bank had 14 branches at the end of 2015 including nine in Philadelphia and Southeastern

Pennsylvania; four in Berks County Pennsylvania; one in Westchester County New York; and one in Mercer County New Jersey. It also had a handful of additional offices in Boston; New York City; Portsmouth New Hampshire; Providence Rhode Island; and Suffolk County New York.

Sales and Marketing

Customers Bancorp's customers include private businesses business customers non-profits and consumers. Its commercial lending division typically makes loans to companies with revenues between $1 million to $50 million needing between $0.5 million to $10 million in credit.

The bank has been ramping up its advertising spend in recent years. It spent $1.48 million on advertising in 2015 up from $1.33 million and $1.27 million in 2014 and 2013 respectively.

Financial Performance

The bank's annual revenues have nearly quadrupled since 2011 as its loan assets have more than tripled (its loan assets reached $5.45 billion by of the end of 2015). Meanwhile growing revenues strong cost controls and low interest rates have pushed the bank's annual profits up almost 15-fold over the same period.

Customers Bancorp's revenue jumped 29% to $277.5 million during 2015 mostly as its average balance of interest-earning loan and securities assets rose by 31% to $6.7 billion for the year.

Revenue growth in 2015 drove the bank's net income up 36% to $58.5 million. Customer Bancorp's operating cash levels declined sharply to $356.6 million for the year as the bank originated more loans held for sale than it actually sold.

Strategy

With its eye on becoming the leading regional bank holding company Customers Bancorp continued in 2016 to focus on expanding its market share with its high-touch personalized Concierge Banking services and its "high-tech" BankMobile offerings which include remote account opening remote deposit capture and mobile banking. The BankMobile and online banking channels allow Customers Bancorp to slow expensive branch-expansion plans and cut operating costs significantly while giving customers faster access to banking services.

But even with digital banking the bank occasionally opens new branches (and selectively acquire others) to grow its loan and deposit business. In January 2016 it opened and replaced an existing branch in Hamilton New Jersey onto Route 33 in the same city. In June 2015 Customers opened a new Long Island location in Mellville New York to expand its private and commercial banking services to local clients there.

Mergers and Acquisitions

In December 2015 Customers Bank expanded its deposit business and added 2 million new student customers after buying the One Account Student Checking and Refund Management Disbursement Services business from higher education refund disbursement provider Higher One Inc for $42 million.

Company Background

In late 2011 Customers purchased Berkshire Bancorp and picked up five branches in Berks County Pennsylvania for about $11.3 million.

EXECUTIVES

Chairman And Ceo, Jay S. Sidhu, age 67, $300,000 total compensation
President And Coo, Richard A. Ehst, age 73, $225,000 total compensation
Executive Vice President President Of Community Banking, Warren Taylor, age 61, $190,000 total compensation
Evp And Chief Credit Officer, Thomas Jastrem

Evp And Chief Administrative Officer, Jim Collins
Evp And Chief Lending Officer, Timothy D. Romig
Evp And President Special Assets Group, Robert A. White
Evp And Cfo, James D. Hogan
Evp And Director Multi-family And Investment Cre Lending, Kenneth A. Keiser
Senior Vice President, Randy Hanks
Vice President, Michael Mccarrie
Vice President, John Gerhart
Assistant Vice President And Appraisal Review Officer, Richard Nagy
Senior Vice President, Mary Moffitt
Vice President, Margaret Donovan
Senior Vice President Credit O, Barbara Bergman
Senior Vice President, William Hirst
Vice President Of Operations, Richard Kirk
Vice President Government Guaranteed Lending, Lisa Kennedy
Vice President Government Guaranteed Lending, Michele Vervlied
Assistant Vice President Capital Markets, Dana Galvin
Vice President, Scott Gates
Assistant Vice President And Assistant Branch Manager, Lisa Gearheart
Assistant Vice President Sox Internal Control Manager, Frank Bommentre
Senior Vice President, Kevin Cornwall
Assistant Vice President, Terry Meehan
Assistant Vice President And Portfolio Manager, Christopher Haley
Senior Vice President Facilities And Security, James Zardecki
Vice President Commercial Lending, John Camero
Manager Deposit Operations Vice President, Natasha Alexander
Senior Vice President Ne Director Of Pla, Paula Pais
Vice President And Government Guaranteed Lender, Jennifer Mason
Senior Vice President Commercial Finance Group, Sam Smith
Vice President Sales And Industrial Group, Kurt Kolesha
Vice President Government Guaranteed Lending Sba And Usda, Mario Campbell
Vice President And Government Guaranteed Lender, Jennifer Mckay
Vice President, Joanne Jolin
Vice President, Laura Simon
Senior Vice President Commercial Real Estate Lending, Stephen King
Senior Vice President Regional Chief Lending Officer, Robert Fischer
Vice President Small Business Lending, Martin Hernandez
Assistant Vice President Collateral Manager, Donna Abel
Vice President, Kimberly Miller
Business Development Officer Vice President, Sunita Raina
Senior Vice President, Veder Reddick
Vice President Commercial Lending, Brett V Long
Vice President Insurance Risk Management, Antonette Tumminello
Senior Vice President Senior Credit Officer, Clifford Gaysunas
Senior Vice President, Samuel H Smith
Senior Vice President Audit Director, Brion Watson
Vice President Lead Corporate Counsel, Michael Detommaso
Vice President Special Assets Financial Reporting, Doan Dang
Assistant Vice President And Lead Information Technology Auditor, Patrick Direnzo
Executive Vice President And Deputy Credit Officer, Andrew Bowman
Vice President Special Assets Group, Kathy Hansen

Vice President, Kimberly Stack
Senior Vice President Director Of Mortgage Servicing, Debra Hutchinson
Assistant Vice President, John Chung
Vice President, Diane Billman
Vice President, Keith Munley
Vice President Consumer Lending Compliance, Matt Kachurka
Vice President And Senior Analyst, Joann Zerbo
Avp Portfolio Manager, Chris Lacroix
Vice President, Lucia Deangelo
Senior Vice President Commercial Deposit Services Manager, Lary Snow
Auditors: DELOITTE & TOUCHE LLP

LOCATIONS

HQ: Customers Bancorp Inc
1015 Penn Avenue, Suite 103, Wyomissing, PA 19610
Phone: 610 933-2000
Web: www.customersbank.com

PRODUCTS/OPERATIONS

2015

	$ mil.	% of total
Interest income		
Loans receivable including fees	182	66
Loans held for sale	51	19
Investment securities	10	4
Other	5	2
Non interest income		
Mortgage warehouse transnational fees	10	4
Bank-owned life insurance	7	3
Gains on sales of loans	4	1
Deposit fees	0	0
Mortgage loan and banking income	0	0
Gain (loss) on sale of investment securities	(0.09)	0
Other	4	1
Total	**277**	**100**

Products include

Equipment Loans
Mortgage Warehouse Loans
Multi-Family And Commercial Real Estate Loans
Residential Mortgage Loans
Small Business Loans

COMPETITORS

Bank of America	Huntington Bancshares
Capital One	JPMorgan Chase
Citigroup	KeyCorp
Comerica	PNC Financial
Fifth Third	U.S. Bancorp
HSBC	Wells Fargo

HISTORICAL FINANCIALS

Company Type: Public

Income Statement

FYE: December 31

	ASSETS ($ mil.)	NET INCOME ($ mil.)	INCOME AS % OF ASSETS	EMPLOYEES
12/18	9,833	71	0.7%	827
12/17	9,839	78	0.8%	765
12/16	9,382	78	0.8%	739
12/15	8,401	58	0.7%	517
12/14	6,825	43	0.6%	426
Annual Growth	9.6%	13.5%	—	18.0%

2018 Year-End Financials

Debt ratio: 2.37%	No. of shares (mil.): 31
Return on equity: 7.64%	Dividends
Cash ($ mil.): 62	Yield: —
Current ratio: —	Payout: —
Long-term debt ($ mil.): —	Market value ($ mil.): 564

	STOCK PRICE ($) FY Close	P/E High/Low	PER SHARE ($) Earnings	Dividends	Book Value
12/18	18.20	18 9	1.78	0.00	30.86
12/17	25.99	17 12	1.97	0.00	29.35
12/16	35.82	15 9	2.31	0.00	28.26
12/15	27.22	15 9	1.96	0.00	20.59
12/14	19.46	14 11	1.55	0.00	16.57
Annual Growth	(1.7%)	— —	—	3.5%	16.8%

CVB Financial Corp

CVB Financial is into the California Vibe Baby. The holding company's Citizens Business Bank offers community banking services to primarily small and midsized businesses but also to consumers through nearly 50 branch and office locations across central and southern California. Boasting more than $7 billion in assets the bank offers checking money market CDs and savings accounts trust and investment services and a variety of loans. Commercial real estate loans account for about two-thirds of the bank's loan portfolio which is rounded out by business consumer and construction loans; residential mortgages; dairy and livestock loans; and municipal lease financing.

Operations
In addition to its 40 business financial centers CVB operates seven Commercial Banking Centers (CBCs). The CBCs operate primarily as sales offices and focus on business clients professionals and high-net-worth individuals. The bank also has three trust offices.

Citizens Business Bank provides auto and equipment leasing and brokers mortgage loans through its Citizens Financial Services Division; CitizensTrust offers trust and investment services.

Overall the bank made 63% of its total revenue from interest income on loans and leases in 2014 with another 24% of total revenue coming from interest income on the bank's investment securities. About 5% of total revenue came from service charges on deposit accounts and 3% came from trust and investment services income.

Geographic Reach
CVB Financial has 40 Business Financial Centers located in the Inland Empire Los Angeles County Orange County San Diego County and the Central Valley regions in California.

Sales and Marketing
CVB Financial provides services to companies from a variety of industries including: industrial and manufacturing dairy and livestock agriculture education nonprofit entertainment medical professional services title and escrow government and property management.

Financial Performance
CVB's revenue has been in decline in recent years due to shrinking interest margins on loans amidst the low-interest environment. The firm's profits however have been rising thanks to declining loan loss provisions as its loan portfolio's credit quality has been improving in the strengthening economy.

CVB enjoyed a breakout year in 2014 with revenue rebounding by 12% to $289.32 million mostly thanks to higher interest income as the bank grew its loan and lease assets by 7% during the year and grew its investment security assets by 18%. Most of its loan growth came from commercial real estate loans while SFR mortgage loans consumer loans and construction loans also helped boost the company's top line. The bank's non-interest income also jumped by 44% during the year thanks to a $6 million gain on loans held-for-sale and a net $3.6 million decrease in its FDIC loss sharing asset.

Higher revenue and a $16.1 million loan loss provision recapture in 2014 also drove the bank's net income higher by 9% to $104.02 million.

Despite higher earnings for the year CVB's operating cash levels shrank by 22% to $87.70 million as the bank used more cash toward employee payments and income taxes.

Strategy
CVB Financial continues to seek out acquisitions of smaller banking trust and investment companies to grow its loan and deposit business as well as its geographic reach in key markets in (mostly Southern) California. With its 2014 acquisition of American Security Bank for example CVB boosted its assets by 6% to over $7 billion while adding branches in more than a handful of key markets in Southern California.

Remaining profitable throughout the economic downturn CVB Financial credits its success in part to its strict loan underwriting standards. The bank targets family-owned or other privately held businesses with annual revenues of up to $200 million with the goal of maintaining its client relationships for decades.

Mergers and Acquisitions
In March 2014 CVB Financial through its Citizens Business Bank (CBB) subsidiary purchased Southern California-based American Security Bank (the flagship subsidiary of American Bancshares) for a total of $57 million. The deal would add American Security Bank's $431 million in assets and boost CBB's branch presence across key markets in Newport Beach Corona Laguna Niguel Lancastar Victorville and Apple Valley.

In 2016 CVB Financial agreed to buy the $416 million-asset Valley Commerce Bancorp the holding company for Valley Business Bank. Valley Business has four banking locations in California's Visalia Tulare Fresno and Woodlake.

Company Background
In 2009 CVB Financial healthier than most California banks acquired the failed San Joaquin Bank after the FDIC took it over. The deal added five branches banking centers in the Bakersfield area.

EXECUTIVES

Evp And General Counsel Cvb Financial Corporation And Citizens Business Bank, Richard H. Wohl, age 60

President And Ceo Cvb Financial And Citizens Business Bank, Christopher D. (Chris) Myers, age 56, $800,000 total compensation

Evp And Cfo, E. Allen Nicholson, age 52

Evp And Cio, Elsa I. Zavala

Evp And Dairy And Livestock Industries Group Manager Citizens Business Bank, G. Larry Zivelonghi

Svp And Regional Manager Citizens Business Bank, Ted J. Dondanville

Svp And Regional Manager Citizens Business Bank, David A. Brager, $300,000 total compensation

Evp And Coo Citizens Business Bank, David C. Harvey, $300,000 total compensation

Evp; Head Citizenstrust, R. Daniel Banis

Evp And Chief Risk Officer Citizens Business Bank, Yamynn De Angelis

Evp Ventura/santa Barbara, Donald R. Toussaint

Executive Vice President, Daniel Banis

Vice President Relationship Manager, Nadine Ortega

Senior Vice President, Michael D Stain

Vice President Relationship Manager, Jason Gould

Vice President Senior Product Manager, John Outwater

Vice President Administration, Joe Pacis

Senior Vice President, Robert Peccini

Senior Vice President, John Stenz

Vice President And Relationship Manager, Maria Padilla

Evp Of Cfo, Allen Nicholson

Vice President Specialty Service Officer Commercial Banking Group, Martha Ponce

Vice President Special Assets Portfolio Manager, Bruce Adams

Vp And Special Assets Portfolio Manager, Verona Chion

Vice President Center Manager, Pamela Gaspar

Vice President Credit Officer, Frank Yu

Vice Chairman, George A. Borba, age 86

Chairman, Raymond V. OÀ'Brien

Auditors: KPMG LLP

LOCATIONS

HQ: CVB Financial Corp
701 North Haven Ave., Suite 350, Ontario, CA 91764
Phone: 909 980-4030
Web: www.cbbank.com

Selected Branch Locations
Fresno County
Kern County
Los Angeles County
Madera County
Orange County
Riverside County
San Bernardino County
Tulare County

PRODUCTS/OPERATIONS

2014 Sales

	$ mil.	% of total
Interest		
Loans including fees	181	62
Investment securities	68	24
Other	2	1
Noninterest		
Service charges on deposit accounts	15	5
Trust & investment services	8	3
Bankcard services	3	1
BOLI income	2	1
Other	10	3
Adjustments	(3.6)	-
Total	**289**	**100**

COMPETITORS

Bank of America	Popular Inc.
Bank of the West	Provident Financial
City National	Holdings
Comerica	U.S. Bancorp
JPMorgan Chase	Wells Fargo
MUFG Americas Holdings	

HISTORICAL FINANCIALS

Company Type: Public

Income Statement

FYE: December 31

	ASSETS ($ mil.)	NET INCOME ($ mil.)	INCOME AS % OF ASSETS	EMPLOYEES
12/18	11,529	152	1.3%	—
12/17	8,270	104	1.3%	—
12/16	8,073	101	1.3%	—
12/15	7,671	99	1.3%	—
12/14	7,377	104	1.4%	—
Annual Growth	**11.8%**	**9.9%**	**—**	**—**

2018 Year-End Financials

Debt ratio: 0.22%	No. of shares (mil.): 140
Return on equity: 10.41%	Dividends
Cash ($ mil.): 171	Yield: 2.7%
Current ratio: —	Payout: 50.9%
Long-term debt ($ mil.): —	Market value ($ mil.): 2,832

STOCK PRICE ($) FY Close	P/E High/Low		PER SHARE ($) Earnings	Dividends	Book Value
12/18	20.23	20 15	1.24	0.56	13.22
12/17	23.56	26 21	0.95	0.52	9.70
12/16	22.93	25 15	0.94	0.36	9.15
12/15	16.92	20 16	0.93	0.48	8.68
12/14	16.02	17 14	0.98	0.40	8.29
Annual Growth	6.0%	— —	6.1%	8.8%	12.4%

CVR Energy Inc

CVR Energy refines and markets high value transportation fuels to retailers railroads and farm cooperatives and other refiners/marketers in Kansas Oklahoma and Illinois. Located within 100 miles of Cushing Oklahoma (a major crude oil trading and storage hub) the company's two oil refineries?in Coffeyville Kansas and Wynnewood Oklahomórepresent close to a quarter of the region's refining capacity. Through a limited partnership the company also produces and distributes ammonia and ammonium nitrate to farmers in Illinois Iowa Kansas Nebraska and Texas.

Company Background

CVR Energy was formed in September 2006 as a subsidiary of Coffeyville. Its nitrogen business held an IPO in 2011 for $350 million followed by Refining IPO fetching $90 million in 2013.

EXECUTIVES

President And Ceo, John J. (Jack) Lipinski, age 68, $950,000 total compensation

Evp Refining Operations, Robert W. Haugen, age 61, $315,000 total compensation

Cfo And Treasurer, Susan M. Ball, age 56, $360,000 total compensation

Vice President Of Capital Projects, Dennis Mccleary

Senior Vice President, John Walter

Vice President, Wyatt Jernigan

Vice President Technical Services, John Huggins

Vice President, Gina Bowman

Vice President Capital Projects, James Rowe

Vp Human Resources, Alicia Skalnik

Vice President Refined Products, Michael Puddy

Vice President Logistics, Reed Copeland

Vice President Of Finance, Jay Finks

Executive Vice President, Bill White

Vice President Investor Relations Cvr Gp, Wes Harris

Senior Vice President, Puddy Michael

Vice President Economics And Planning, David LLandreth

Senior Vice President, Pat Quinn

Chairman, Carl C. Icahn

Board Member, Bob Alexander

Board Member, Stephen Mongillo

Board Member, James Strock

Auditors: Grant Thornton LLP

LOCATIONS

HQ: CVR Energy Inc
2277 Plaza Drive, Suite 500, Sugar Land, TX 77479
Phone: 281 207-3200
Web: www.cvrenergy.com

PRODUCTS/OPERATIONS

2017 Sales

	$ mil.	% of total
Petroleum	5,664	95
Nitrogen Fertilizer	330	5
Intersegment elimination	(6.6)	-
Total	**5,988**	**100**

COMPETITORS

CF Industries	Koch Industries Inc.
CHS	Phillips 66
ConocoPhillips	Terra Nitrogen
Flint Hills	Valero Energy
HollyFrontier	

HISTORICAL FINANCIALS

Company Type: Public

Income Statement   FYE: December 31

	REVENUE ($ mil.)	NET INCOME ($ mil.)	NET PROFIT MARGIN	EMPLOYEES
12/18	7,124	289	4.1%	1,450
12/17	5,988	234	3.9%	1,440
12/16	4,782	24	0.5%	1,487
12/15	5,432	169	3.1%	1,332
12/14	9,109	173	1.9%	1,298
Annual Growth	(6.0%)	13.5%	—	2.8%

2018 Year-End Financials

Debt ratio: 29.95%
Return on equity: 26.70%
Cash ($ mil.): 668
Current ratio: 2.61
Long-term debt ($ mil.): 1,167

No. of shares (mil.): 100
Dividends
  Yield: 7.2%
  Payout: 80.1%
Market value ($ mil.): 3,466

STOCK PRICE ($) FY Close	P/E High/Low		PER SHARE ($) Earnings	Dividends	Book Value
12/18	34.48	15 9	3.12	2.50	12.39
12/17	37.24	14 6	2.70	2.00	10.58
12/16	25.39	141 45	0.28	2.00	9.88
12/15	39.35	25 17	1.95	2.00	11.33
12/14	38.71	25 18	2.00	5.00	11.38
Annual Growth	(2.9%)	— —	11.8%	(15.9%)	2.2%

CVS Health Corporation

CVS Health Corp. is a leading pharmacy benefits manager with nearly 92 million plan members as well as the nation's largest drugstore chain (topping Walgreens). It runs more than 9900 retail and specialty drugstores. In addition to its stand-alone pharmacy operations the company operates CVS locations inside Target stores and runs a prescription management company Caremark Pharmacy Services. The company also offers walk-in health services through its retail network of MinuteClinics that are located in around 1100 CVS stores. In late 2018 CVS acquired health insurer Aetna in a $70 billion megadeal which adds traditional health insurance plans serving some 38 million people to its operations.

HISTORY

Brothers Stanley and Sid Goldstein who ran health and beauty products distributor Mark Steven branched out into retail in 1963 when they opened up their first Consumer Value Store in Lowell Massachusetts with partner Ralph Hoagland.

The chain grew rapidly amassing 17 stores by the end of 1964 (the year the CVS name was first used) and 40 by 1969. That year the Goldsteins sold the chain to Melville Shoe to finance further expansion.

Melville had been founded in 1892 by shoe supplier Frank Melville. Melville's son Ward grew the company creating the Thom McAn shoe store chain and later buying its supplier. By 1969 Melville had opened shoe shops in Kmart stores (through its Meldisco unit) launched one apparel chain (Chess King sold in 1993) and purchased another (Foxwood Stores renamed Foxmoor and sold in 1985).

In 1972 CVS bought the 84-store Clinton Drug and Discount a Rochester New York-based chain. Two years later when sales hit $100 million CVS had 232 stores — only 45 of which had pharmacies. The company bought New Jersey-based Mack Drug (36 stores) in 1977. By 1981 CVS had more than 400 stores.

CVS's sales hit $1 billion in 1985 as it continued to add pharmacies to many of its older stores. In 1987 Stanley's success was recognized company-wide when he was named chairman and CEO of CVS's parent company which by then had been renamed Melville.

CVS bought the 490-store Peoples Drug Stores chain from Imasco in 1990 giving it locations in Maryland Pennsylvania Virginia West Virginia and Washington DC. CVS created PharmaCare Management Services in 1994 to take advantage of the growing market for pharmacy services and managed-care drug programs. Pharmacist Tom Ryan was named CEO that year.

With CVS outperforming Melville's other operations in 1995 Melville decided to concentrate on the drugstore chain. By that time Melville's holdings had grown to include discount department store chain Marshalls and furniture chain This End Up both sold in 1995; footwear chain Footaction spun off as part of Footstar in 1996 along with Meldisco; the Linens 'n Things chain spun off in 1996; the Kay-Bee Toys chain sold in 1996; and Bob's Stores (apparel and footwear) sold in 1997.

Melville was renamed CVS in late 1996. Amid major consolidation in the drugstore industry in 1997 CVS — then with about 1425 stores — paid $3.7 billion for Revco D.S. which had nearly 2600 stores in 17 states mainly in the Midwest and Southeast. The next year the company bought Arbor Drugs (200 stores in Michigan later converted to the CVS banner) for nearly $1.5 billion.

CVS opened about 180 new stores and relocated nearly 200 in 1998 as it shifted from strip malls to freestanding stores. (It also closed nearly 160 stores.) Stanley retired as chairman in 1999 and was succeeded by Ryan.

In 1999 the company bought online drugstore pioneer Soma.com renamed CVS.com. It also launched the CVS ProCare pharmacy to serve customers in need of complex drug therapies. A year later CVS bought Stadtlander Pharmacy of Pittsburgh from Bergen Brunswig (now AmerisourceBergen) for $124 million.

In early 2001 Wolverine Equities paid $288 million for 96 stores which CVS said it would continue to operate. In 2001 CVS opened 43 stores in new markets including Miami and Fort Lauderdale Florida; Las Vegas; and Dallas Houston and Fort Worth Texas. As part of a strategic restructuring begun in 2001 CVS closed more than 200 stores and moved others from strip malls to freestanding locations.

In July 2002 CVS was among the winning bidders for the remaining assets of bankrupt rival Phar-Mor. CVS acquired the majority of Phar-Mor's prescription lists. In October CVS named

KB Toys as the exclusive toy supplier to its drugstores. CVS opened 266 new stores in 2002 and another 150 new stores in 2003.

In April 2003 specialty pharmacy division CVS ProCare changed its name to PharmaCare Specialty Pharmacy.

With those store closings behind it the drugstore chain began opening stores in Minneapolis the 10th-largest drugstore market in the US in 2004. CVS opened about 10 stores in the Los Angeles area in 2004 marking the drugstore chain's return to Southern California after a 12-year absence. CVS is also targeting other high-traffic markets including Chicago Florida Las Vegas Phoenix and Texas for expansion.

In July 2004 CVS completed the acquisition of 1260 Eckerd stores Eckerd Health Services (which included Eckerd's $1 billion mail order and pharmacy benefits management businesses) and three distribution centers from J. C. Penney Company for $2.15 billion. The acquisition of the Eckerd stores (622 in Florida) gave CVS more stores than archrival Walgreen. CVS completed the conversion of Eckerd stores in Alabama Arizona Colorado Florida Kansas Louisiana Mississippi Missouri New Mexico Oklahoma and Texas to its own banner within about a year.

In June 2005 CVS agreed to pay $110 million to settle a shareholders' lawsuit filed in 2001 that alleged the company had made misleading statements to artificially raise its stock price and violated accounting practices. CVS denied the charges and said the settlement was "purely a business decision."

In June 2006 CVS completed the acquisition of some 700 stand-alone Sav-On and Osco drugstores from Albertson's. CVS was part of a consortium that bought the nation's #2 supermarket chain and split it up amongst themselves. The transaction gave CVS access to Southern California and key Midwest markets. In September the company purchased the retail-based health clinic operator MinuteClinic for an undisclosed amount. The acquisition allowed CVS to provide in-store care to its customers for minor ailments.

In March 2007 CVS changed its name to CVS Caremark Corporation following its acquisition of the pharmacy benefits manager Caremark RX after months of bidding between CVS and Express Scripts. Ultimately CVS paid about $26.5 billion for Caremark. In November CEO Ryan added the chairman's title to his job description following the retirement of Mac Crawford.

In October 2008 CVS Caremark acquired Longs Drug Stores for about $2.9 billion. Longs Drug operates 521 pharmacies in California Hawaii Nevada and Arizona. The purchase included Long's Rx America subsidiary a pharmacy benefits management service to more than 8 million members. Also in 2008 the company opened about 190 new retail pharmacies.

In 2008 CVS settled a lawsuit regarding drug-switching allegations for $36.7 million. The company had been accused of switching Medicaid customers to a more expensive capsule form of Zantac from a tablet form; CVS denied the allegations.

In June 2009 CVS agreed to pay almost $1 million to settle allegations stemming from the sale of expired OTC medications infant formula and dairy products.

CVS Caremark in early 2011 won a contract to administer Aetna's retail pharmacy network. CVS Caremark is managing both purchasing and prescription filling for Aetna's mail-order and specialty pharmacy operations. Prior to his retirement in May 2011 Ryan assumed the title of non-executive chairman in March when Larry Merlo took over as president and CEO of CVS.

In 2012 CVS opened drugstores in four new states: Arkansas Colorado Oregon and Washington.

In September 2014 the company changed its name to CVS Health Corporation to reflect its broader commitment to health care. The corporate name change coincided with the cessation of tobacco sales at its retail stores in September.

EXECUTIVES

Evp Health Plans, Tracy L. Bahl, age 56
Vp Pharmacy Affairs, Papatya Tankut
President And Ceo, Larry J. Merlo, age 63, $1,630,000 total compensation
Evp; President Cvs/pharmacy, Helena B. Foulkes, age 54, $950,000 total compensation
Evp And Cio, Stephen J. Gold, age 60
Evp And Chief Human Resources Officer, Lisa Bisaccia, age 63
Svp And Chief Marketing Officer, Norman de Greve
Evp Specialty Pharmacy Cvs/caremark, Alan M. Lotvin, age 57
Evp And Chief Medical Officer, Troyen A. Brennan, age 65, $637,500 total compensation
Evp And Head Of Retail Operations, Scott Baker
Evp And Coo, Jonathan C. Roberts, age 63, $950,000 total compensation
Evp And Cfo, David M. (Dave) Denton, age 54, $850,000 total compensation
Evp And Associate Chief Medical Officer; President Cvs/minuteclinic, Andrew J. (Andy) Sussman, age 53
Evp Sales And Marketing Cvs/caremark, J. David Joyner, age 54
Evp Chief Health Strategy Officer And General Counsel, Thomas M. Moriarty, age 56, $750,000 total compensation
Evp Enterprise Strategy And Corporate Development, Joshua (Josh) Flum
Evp And President Omnicare, Robert O. (Rocky) Kraft, age 49
Vp Workforce Strategies And Chief Diversity Officer, David Casey
Vice President Sales And Marketing, Harry Boysen
Vice President Sales, Edward Devaney
Executive Vice President Sales, Rima Parikh
Vice President Store Operations, Chris Cox
Vice President Corporate Communications, Karen Brown
Executive Vice President Sales, James Parasole
Pharmacy Manager, Sara Pivarunas
Vice President Strategic Procurement, Anna M Umberto
Senior Vice President Investor Relations, Michael McGuire
Senior Vice President Chief Compliance Officer, John Buckley
Pharmacy Manager, Vijay Patel
Senior Vice President Chief Accounting Officer Controller, James Clark
Senior Vice President Tax, John Kennedy
Enterprise Analytics Manager Vice President Is Applications, Bob Darin
Pharmacy Manager, Kim Nguyen
Senior Vice President Trade Relations, Gary Loeber
Pharmacy Manager, Brian Jackson
Pharmacy Manager, Michael Brito
Pharmacy Manager, Komal Patel
Pharmacy Manager, JoAnne Tran
Pharmacy Manager, Deanne Medouris
Pharmacy Manager, James Przybylowicz
Pharmacy Manager, Harsh Patel
Vice President And Ciso, Frank Price
Vice President Pharma Procurement, Debra Farrell
Senior Vice President Logistics And Supply Chain, Ron Link
Vp Specialty Pharmacy Technology And Project Management Office, Eric Rel

Vice President Information Technology, Dawn Pagano
Senior Vice President Enterprise Product Innovation And Development, Anita Allemand
Svp Government And Public Affairs, Melissa Schulman
Pharmacy Manager, Benjamin King
Senior Vice President Payer Relations And Managed Care Cvs Pharmacy, Tom Gibbons
Vice President Retail Pharmacy Systems, Dennis MacQuarrie
Vice President Clinical Services Operations, Julie Sheer
Sales Vice President, Joel Helle
Executive Vice President Client Relations Chronic Sales, Pat Morgan
Pharmacy Manager, Joseph Morasutti
Vice President, Shannon Penberthy
Senior Vice President Assistant General Counsel, Elizabeth Ferguson
Vice President, Joan O'Rourke
Vice President, Stephen Holodak
Pharmacy Manager, Mariam Al-Khudhair
Pharmacy Manager, Gary Weaver
Pharmacy Manager, Ashlie Miller
Vice President Health Plan Sales At Cvs Caremark, Michelle Manolovic
Svp Investor Relations, Nancya R Christal
Evp Cvs Health And President Omnicare, C Daniel Haron
Executive Vice President Sales And Account Services, John Joyner
Pharmacy Manager, Joshua Jacobs
Vice President Corporate Finance, John Shamshoian
Chairman, David W. (Dave) Dorman, age 65
Board Member, Jean-pierre Millon
Board Member, Nancy-ann Deparle
Board Member, William Weldon
Board Member, Richard Bracken
Board Member, Tony White
Auditors: Ernst & Young LLP

LOCATIONS

HQ: CVS Health Corporation
One CVS Drive, Woonsocket, RI 02895
Phone: 401 765-1500 **Fax:** 401 762-2137
Web: www.cvshealth.com

PRODUCTS/OPERATIONS

2018 Sales

	$ mil.	% of total
Products	183,910	95
Premiums	8,184	4
Services	1,825	1
Net investment income	660	-
Total	**194,579**	**100**

2018 Sales

		$ mil.	% of total
Pharmacy services		134,128	60
Retail/LTC Segment		83,989	37
Health care benefits		5,549	3
Corporate and other	606		
Adjustments		(29693)	
Total		**194,579**	**100**

COMPETITORS

Anthem	OptumRx
Blue Cross	PharMerica
CIGNA	Prime Therapeutics
Express Scripts	Rite Aid
Humana	Wal-Mart
MedImpact	Walgreen
Medicare & Medicaid Services	

HISTORICAL FINANCIALS

Company Type: Public

Income Statement

FYE: December 31

	REVENUE ($ mil.)	NET INCOME ($ mil.)	NET PROFIT MARGIN	EMPLOYEES
12/18	194,579	(594)	—	295,000
12/17	184,765	6,622	3.6%	246,000
12/16	177,526	5,317	3.0%	250,000
12/15	153,290	5,237	3.4%	243,000
12/14	139,367	4,644	3.3%	217,800
Annual Growth	8.7%	—	—	7.9%

2018 Year-End Financials

Debt ratio: 37.38%
Return on equity: (-1.24%)
Cash ($ mil.): 4,059
Current ratio: 1.03
Long-term debt ($ mil.): 71,444

No. of shares (mil.): 1,295
Dividends
  Yield: 3.0%
  Payout: —
Market value ($ mil.): 84,848

	STOCK PRICE ($) FY Close	P/E High/Low		PER SHARE ($) Earnings	Dividends	Book Value
12/18	65.52	—	—	(0.57)	2.00	44.96
12/17	72.50	13	10	6.44	2.00	37.17
12/16	78.91	22	15	4.90	1.70	34.71
12/15	97.77	24	20	4.63	1.40	33.78
12/14	96.31	25	16	3.96	1.10	33.30
Annual Growth	(9.2%)	—	—	—	16.1%	7.8%

Dacotah Banks Inc.

EXECUTIVES

Ceo, Richard Westra
Pres, Michael Hollan
SEC, Kenneth L Gosch
Cfo, Chad Bergan
Sr V Pres, Joe Senger
Sr V Pres, Robert Fouberg
Dir, Tom Heisler
Sr V Pres, Bob Compton
V Pres, Steven Schaefer
V Pres, Kent Edson
Pres Market Faulkton, SD, Dwight Hossle
Auditors: Eide Bailly LLP

LOCATIONS

HQ: Dacotah Banks Inc.
  401 South Main Street, Suite 212, P.O. Box 1496,
  Aberdeen, SD 57402-1496
Phone: 605 225-4850   **Fax:** 605 225-4929
Web: www.dacotahbank.com

HISTORICAL FINANCIALS

Company Type: Public

Income Statement

FYE: December 31

	ASSETS ($ mil.)	NET INCOME ($ mil.)	INCOME AS % OF ASSETS	EMPLOYEES
12/18	2,577	28	1.1%	—
12/17	2,406	17	0.7%	—
12/16	2,297	22	1.0%	—
12/08	1,588	14	0.9%	—
12/07	1,391	12	0.9%	441
Annual Growth	5.8%	7.5%	—	—

2018 Year-End Financials

Debt ratio: 1.24%
Return on equity: 9.84%
Cash ($ mil.): 168
Current ratio: —
Long-term debt ($ mil.): —

No. of shares (mil.): 14
Dividends
  Yield: 0.0%
  Payout: 18.7%
Market value ($ mil.): 729

	STOCK PRICE ($) FY Close	P/E High/Low		PER SHARE ($) Earnings	Dividends	Book Value
12/18	51.01	22	12	2.51	0.47	20.70
12/17	33.00	25	18	1.57	0.43	19.17
12/16	28.25	135	12	2.07	0.40	18.20
12/08	147.00	118	105	1.32	0.23	13.34
12/07	150.00	142	121	1.13	0.22	12.20
Annual Growth	(9.3%)	—	—	7.5%	7.1%	4.9%

DAIRY FARMERS OF AMERICA, INC.

Dairy Farmers of America (DFA) is one of the world's largest dairy cooperatives with nearly 15000 member farmers across the US. Millions of cows belonging to member farmers produce 64 billion pounds of milk a year (roughly 30% of milk production in the US) which DFA markets. Along with fresh and shelf-stable fluid milk the co-op produces cheese butter dried milk powder and other dairy products for industrial wholesale and retail customers. It also offers contract manufacturing services. The co-op owns more than 40 manufacturing plants nationwide. DFA whose profits are shared based on member contribution is a major supplier to dairy giant Dean Foods as well as joint venture partners such as Hiland Dairy.

Operations

DFA owns more than 40 manufacturing plants nationwide. The facilities are focused on several functions and product categories including consumer cheese and butter consumer fluid ingredient cheese and protein and contract manufacturing.

The company's brands include Borden and Cache Valley for consumer cheese; Keller's Creamery Plugra Breakstone's Falfurrias and Hotel Bar for butter; and other dairy products under Sport Shake (sports beverage) La Vaquita (queso) Kemps Guida's Dairy and Dairy Maid Dairy.

Geographic Reach

DFA is based in Kansas City Missouri and divides the US into seven areas: Central (which shares the main headquarters) Mideast (Medina OH) Mountain (Salt Lake City UT) Northeast (East Syracuse NY) Southeast (Knoxville TN) Southwest (Grapevine TX) and Western (Corona CA).

Sales and Marketing

DFA's customers include big names in the dairy food and retail businesses including Hiland Dairy Borden supermarket giant Kroger Dean Foods Kraft Foods Nestle and many others.

Financial Performance

In 2017 DFA reported revenue of $14.7 billion up nearly 10% from the prior year due to unit sales growth as well as higher milk prices.

Net income that year was $127.4 million.

Strategy

In a statement that could be written about most companies across most industries DFA's strategic focus is on technology and innovation. In late 2018 it invested in SomaDetect a startup that promotes artificial intelligence as a way for dairy farmers to more closely monitor herd health and improve

milk quality. Also that year it partnered with startup ripe.io to evaluate the usefulness of blockchain technology in the food supply chain.

As far as product innovation DFA introduced a new cheese brand (Craigs Creamery) in early 2019 and invested in a whey protein-infused yogurt (MOPRO) in 2018.

The cooperative also continues to invest in its facilities expanding existing plants and acquiring new ones.

Mergers and Acquisitions

In late 2018 DFA agreed to purchase a St. Paul Minnesota facility from Canada-based dairy cooperative Agropur which will expand DFA's extended shelf-life capabilities and introduce aseptic processing (sterilization techniques to produce items that don't need refrigeration) into its business portfolio.

Company Background

DFA was established in 1998 by leaders of four of the nation's leading milk cooperatives: Associated Milk Producers Mid-America Dairymen Milk Marketing and Western Dairymen Cooperative.

HISTORY

Mid-America Dairymen (Mid-Am) the largest of the cooperatives that merged to form Dairy Farmers of America (DFA) was born in 1968. At that time several Midwestern dairy co-ops banded together to attack common economic problems such as reduced government subsidies price drops resulting from a rising milk surplus dealer consolidation and improvements in production processing and packaging. The merging organizations — representing 15000 dairy farmers — were Producers Creamery Company (Springfield Missouri) Sanitary Milk Producers (St. Louis) Square Deal Milk Producers (Highland Illinois) Mid-Am (Kansas City Missouri) and Producers Creamery Company of Chillicothe (north central Missouri).

During the early 1970s Mid-Am struggled with internal restructuring. Most dairy farmers and co-ops were hit hard by the energy crisis and the government's decision to allow increased dairy imports in 1973 the same year the US Justice Department filed an antitrust suit against Mid-Am. (A judge cleared the co-op 12 years later.)

In 1974 Mid-Am lost almost $8 million on revenues of $625 million chalked up to record-high feed prices a weakened economy a milk surplus and a massive inventory loss. Co-op veteran Gary Hanman was named CEO that year. Over the next two years Mid-Am cut costs sold corporate frills downsized management and began marketing more of its own products under the Mid-America Farms label thus reducing dependency on commodity sales.

Mid-Am expanded its research and development efforts throughout the 1980s. The co-op opened its services to farmers in California and New Mexico in 1993 and a series of mergers in 1994 and 1995 nearly doubled its size. In 1997 it purchased some of Borden's dairy operations including rights to the valuable Elsie the Cow and Borden's trademarks.

Wary of falling milk prices Mid-Am merged with Western Dairymen Cooperative Milk Marketing and the Southern Region of Associated Milk Producers at the end of 1997 to form DFA. Hanman moved into the seat of CEO at the new co-op. DFA began a series of joint ventures with the #1 US dairy processor Suiza Foods (now Dean Foods). DFA added California Gold (more than 330 farmers 1998) and Independent Cooperative Milk Producers Association (730 dairy farmer members in Michigan and parts of Ohio and Indiana 1999). In another joint venture with Suiza in early 2000 DFA sold its 50% stake in the US's #3 fluid milk processor Southern Foods in exchange for 34% of a new company named Suiza Dairy Group.

After mollifying the government's antitrust fears DFA acquired the butter operations of Sodiaal North America in 2000. It then molded all its butter businesses into a new entity Keller's Creamery. However another acquisition did not fare as well. The same year DFA acquired controlling interest in Southern Belle Dairy only to have the merger challenged three years later by the Department of Justice. Arguing that the merger formed a monopoly in school milk sales in several states the Department of Justice filed suit which a federal judge later dismissed.

During 2001 the cooperative went in with Land O'Lakes 50/50 to purchase a cheese plant from Kraft. Later in the year as Suiza Foods acquired Dean Foods (and took on its name) DFA sold back its stake in Suiza Dairy Group to the new Dean Foods. DFA then teamed up with a group of dairy investors to form a new 50/50 joint venture National Dairy Holdings which received 11 processing plants from Dean Foods as part of the exchange for Suiza Dairy.

EXECUTIVES

Senior Adviser; President Affiliate Division, Alan J. Bernon, age 64
Coo Northeast Area, Gregory I. (Greg) Wickham
President Ceo And Director, Richard P. (Rick) Smith
Evp; President Global Dairy Products Group, Mark Korsmeyer
Svp Finance, David Meyer
Executive Vice President Of Commercial Operations, Doug Glade
Vice President Sales And Marketing Global Ingredients, Lavonne Dietrich
Vice Chairman, Bill Siebenborn
Chairman, Randy Mooney
Vice Chairman, Wayne Palla
Vice Chairman, George Mertens
Auditors: KPMG LLP KANSAS CITY MO

LOCATIONS

HQ: DAIRY FARMERS OF AMERICA, INC.
1405 N 98TH ST, KANSAS CITY, KS 661111865
Phone: 816 801-6455
Web: WWW.DFAMILK.COM

PRODUCTS/OPERATIONS

Selected Products and Brands
Consumer brands
  Borden cheese
  Breakstone's butter
  Cache Valley cheese
  Keller's Creamery butter
  Plugrá butter
  Sport Shake energy milk shake
Contract manufacturing
  Cheese dips
  Cheese powders & flavors
  Coffee-based flavored drinks
  Instant formula
  Sour cream
  Sports drinks
Dairy ingredients
  Cheeses (American & Italian)
  Nonfat dry milk powder
  Skim milk powder
  Sweetened condensed milk

COMPETITORS

Arla Foods
Associated Milk Producers
Berkeley Farms
California Dairies Inc.
Glanbia plc
Great Lakes Cheese
HP Hood
Humboldt Creamery
Lactalis
Land O'Lakes
ConAgra
Darigold Inc.
Dean Foods
Farmland Dairies
Foremost Farms
Friendship Dairies
Garelick Farms
Marathon Cheese
Mayfield Dairy Farms
Northwest Dairy
Prairie Farms Dairy
Quality Chekd
Sargento

HISTORICAL FINANCIALS
Company Type: Private

Income Statement · FYE: December 31

	REVENUE ($ mil.)	NET INCOME ($ mil.)	NET PROFIT MARGIN	EMPLOYEES
12/15	13,803	98	0.7%	7,000
12/14	17,856	48	0.3%	—
12/13	12,826	58	0.5%	—
12/12	12,082	(126)	—	—
Annual Growth	4.5%	—	—	—

Dana Inc

EXECUTIVES

Pres-Ceo Chb, James K Kamsickas
Non Exec Chb, Keith E Wandell
Exec V Pres-Cfo, Jonathan M Collins
Exec V Pres, Mark E Wallace
Sr V Pres-Gen Counsel-Sec, Douglas H Liedberg
V Pres-Cao, James D Kellett
Pres Off-Highway-Motion System, Aziz S Aghili
Pres Power Technologies, Dwayne E Matthews
Pres Light Vehicle Driveline, Robert D Pyle
Accounts Payable, Carolyn Jackson
Engineer, Charlie Estes
Auditors: PricewaterhouseCoopers LLP

LOCATIONS

HQ: Dana Inc
3939 Technology Drive, Maumee, OH 43537
Phone: 419 887-3000   **Fax:** 419 887-5200
Web: www.dana.com

COMPETITORS

AISIN World Corp.
American Axle & Manufacturing
AxleTech International
Boler
BorgWarner
Carraro
Chrysler
DENSO
ElringKlinger
Federal-Mogul
Freudenberg-NOK
GKN
Hitachi Automotive Systems Americas
Magna International
Mahle International
Mark IV
Martinrea International
Meritor
Metaldyne
Modine Manufacturing
Neapco
Tower International
Valeo
Visteon
Wanxiang
ZF Friedrichshafen

HISTORICAL FINANCIALS
Company Type: Public

Income Statement · FYE: December 31

	REVENUE ($ mil.)	NET INCOME ($ mil.)	NET PROFIT MARGIN	EMPLOYEES
12/18	8,143	427	5.2%	20,900
12/17	7,209	111	1.5%	30,100
12/16	5,826	640	11.0%	24,900
12/15	6,060	159	2.6%	23,100
12/14	6,617	319	4.8%	22,600
Annual Growth	5.3%	7.6%	—	(1.9%)

2018 Year-End Financials
Debt ratio: 30.13%
Return on equity: 36.22%
Cash ($ mil.): 510
Current ratio: 1.66
Long-term debt ($ mil.): 1,755
No. of shares (mil.): 144
Dividends
  Yield: 2.9%
  Payout: 13.7%
Market value ($ mil.): 1,972

	STOCK PRICE ($) FY Close	P/E High/Low		PER SHARE ($) Earnings	Dividends	Book Value
12/18	13.63	12	4	2.91	0.40	9.30
12/17	32.01	46	24	0.71	0.24	6.99
12/16	18.98	5	2	4.36	0.24	8.04
12/15	13.80	23	13	0.99	0.23	4.85
12/14	21.74	12	9	1.84	0.20	6.50
Annual Growth	(11.0%)	—	—	12.1%	18.9%	9.3%

Danaher Corp

Danaher is a diversified industrial and medical conglomerate whose products test analyze and diagnose. Its subsidiaries design manufacture and market products and offer services geared to worldwide professional medical and dental industrial and commercial markets. Danaher operates through four segments: Life Sciences Diagnostics (research and clinical tools) Environmental & Applied Solutions (turbine pumps and air/water analysis and treatment equipment) and Dental (orthodontic bracket systems and lab products). It has facilities in more than 60 countries and generates 35% of sales from customers in the US.

Operations
Built largely through acquisitions Danaher's four business segments reflect a well-balanced portfolio. Top segments Life Sciences and Diagnostics account for about a third of revenue each. The Life Sciences segment's products include mass spectrometry; cellular analysis and lab automation; filtration; and microscopy. The Diagnostics segment offers clinical lab critical care and anatomical pathology. The remaining revenue comes from the Dental and Environmental & Applied Solutions units.

Key Danaher subsidiaries include Beckman Coulter X-Rite EskoArtwork Linx Printing Technologies Sybron Dental Specialtiesand Trojan Technologies.

Geographic Reach
Danaher has around 260 manufacturing and distribution facilities worldwide. About 110 are in the US spread over more than 25 states; another 150 locations are in 30 countries throughout Asia Europe North America South America and Australia. The company generates about 40% of its revenue from North America primarily the US (more than 35% of sales). Western Europe represents a quarter of sales while the countries Dana-

her terms its "high-growth markets" including countries in Eastern Europe the Middle East Africa Latin America and the Asia/Pacific region together bring in 30% of sales.

Financial Performance

Danaher Corp.'s sales have risen strongly over the past five years as it has expanded its portfolio through acquisitions offset by a few spinoffs.

In 2018 the company's revenue grew 9% to $19.9 billion thanks to contributions from acquired businesses in the Life Sciences and Environmental & Applied Solutions segments in addition to strong organic growth in both high-growth and development markets and currency tailwinds.

By segment the fastest-growing was the Life Sciences segment which overtook Diagnostics as Danaher's biggest contributor to sales. Life Sciences witnessed strong demand for mass spectrometers in China wider Asia and North America particularly in the clinical applied and pharmaceutical end markets. The Diagnostics and Environmental & Applied Solutions segments also grew strongly buoyed by demand for Danaher's infectious disease products and analytic instrumentation products respectively. Only in the Dental segment were sales muted.

Net income growth was also positive at around 6% with Danaher posting a net profit of $2.7 billion. Higher sales were partially offset by higher income taxes.

Danaher's cash on hand grew $157.5 million during 2018 ending the year at $787.8 million. The company's operations generated $4.0 billion partially offset by the $2.9 billion used in investing activities and the $797.4 million used in its financing. Danaher's main cash uses in 2018 were acquisitions ($2.2 billion) and dividends ($433.4 million).

Strategy

Even after spending some $20 billion to buy Cepheid Pall and Nobel Biocare in the past several years Danaher Corp. is still in acquisition mode. Thanks to its strong operating cash flow and ability to borrow in large tranches Danaher is in a position to continue even accelerate its acquisition spending. In 2019 it agreed to buy GE Life Science's Biopharma for a whopping $21.4 billion. Before that in 2018 it bought two companies for a not-insubstantial $2.2 billion the bulk of which was spent on IDT a manufacturer of customer DNA and RNA oligonucleotides; and in 2017 the company bought 10 companies (for a measly $386 million) to fill in product gaps in some cases and to expand to adjacent markets in others. Danaher's total debt is high pushing $10 billion but the company's sound financials make its debt level serviceable.

If the most recent deals work out half as well as the big acquisitions have then it will be money well spent. Danaher has reported that the acquisitions have played a significant role in its rising revenue in terms of products sold as well as in geographies were sales are made. The company's sales in emerging markets are rising sharply particularly China which has grown from representing less than 9% of sales in 2014 to 12% in 2018.

On the flipside Danaher is spinning off three companies within its Dental business as a separate entity Envista in the second half of 2019. The Dental segment has witnesses a steady decline in sales in recent years and Danaher needs cash to fund its extensive acquisition program.

Mergers and Acquisitions

In 2019 Danaher agreed to buy General Electric's BioPharma unit for about $21.4 billion. The biopharma business makes instruments and software that support the research and development of pharmaceuticals and is part of GE's healthcare segment. Danaher plans to slot the acquisition and its $3 billion annual sales as a stand-alone operat-

ing company within its $6.5 billion Life Sciences segment. The transaction is expected to close in the 2019 fourth quarter.

In 2018 Danaher acquired IDT (Integrated DNA Technologies) for $2.1 billion. IDT makes custom DNA and RNA oligonucleotides for customers in the academic and biopharma research biotech agriculture clinical diagnostics and pharmaceutical development end-markets. IDT has sales of around $2.1 billion.

In 2017 Danaher acquired 10 companies for a total of close to $390 million in cash. The acquisitions complement businesses in the Life Sciences Dental and Environmental & Applied Solutions segments.

HISTORY

Danaher (from the Celtic word dana meaning "swift flowing") is named for a fishing stream off the Flathead River in Montana. The term is also an appropriate description of the spotlight-averse Rales brothers. The two have proven to be fishers not only of trout but also of companies buying underperforming companies with strong market shares and recognizable brand names.

Once dubbed "raiders in short pants" by Forbes Steven and Mitchell Rales began making acquisitions in their 20s. In 1981 they bought their father's 50% stake in Master Shield a maker of vinyl building products. The brothers bought tire manufacturer Mohawk Rubber the following year. In 1983 they acquired control of publicly traded DMG a distressed Florida real-estate firm; the next year they sold DMG's real estate holdings and folded Mohawk and Master Shield into the company which they renamed Danaher.

EXECUTIVES

Evp And Cfo, Daniel L. Comas, age 55, $862,357 total compensation
President And Ceo, Thomas P. Joyce, age 58, $1,100,000 total compensation
Evp Diagnostics And Dental, William K. (Dan) Daniel, age 54, $730,144 total compensation
Svp Human Resources, Angela S. Lalor, age 53, $603,986 total compensation
Evp Life Sciences, Rainer M. Blair, age 54
Vice President Of Business Development For Product Iden, Pasha Fedorenko
Vice President, Craig Overhage
Global Vice President Human Resources Water Qua, Larry Byrnes
Vp Danaher Business Systems, Brian Burnett
Corporate Vice President And Chief Financial Officer Asia, Samuel Liao
Vice President Compensation, Joe Cavallaro
Vice President Internal Audit, Christopher Sandberg
Vice President And Bu Manager, Raj Karanam
Vice President And Chief Counsel Mergers And Acquisitions, Attila Bodi
Vp Investor Relations, Matthew Gugino
National Sales Manager, Jim White
Vice President Business Development And Strategy Dental, Mischa Reis
Vice President Sales (tektronix Division), Eben Jenkins
Vice President, Daniel Rakas
Vice President Dbso, Michael Weatherred
Chairman, Steven M. Rales, age 67
Board Member, Donald Ehrlich
Board Member, Alan Spoon
Board Member, Teri List-stoll
Board Member, Elias A Zerhouni
Auditors: Ernst & Young LLP

LOCATIONS

HQ: Danaher Corp
2200 Pennsylvania Avenue, N.W., Suite 800W, Washington, DC 20037-1701
Phone: 202 828-0850   **Fax:** 202 828-0860
Web: www.danaher.com

2018 Sales

	$ mil.	% of total
United States	7,374	37
China	2,357	12
Germany	1,247	6
Japan	918	5
All other	7,995	40
Total	**19,893**	**100**

2018 sales

	%
North America	39
Nigh-growth markets	31
Western Europe	24
Other developed markets	6
Total	**0**	**100**

PRODUCTS/OPERATIONS

2018 Sales

	$ mil.	% of total
Diagnostics	6,257	31
Life Sciences	6,471	33
Environmental & Applied Solutions	4,319	22
Dental	2,844	14
Total	**18,329**	**100**

2018 Sales

	$ mil.	% of total
Research and medical products	12,686	64
Dental products	2,844	14
Analytical and physical instrumentation	2,437	12
Product identification	1,925	10
Total	**19,839**	**100**

COMPETITORS

ABB	National Instruments
Advantest	Parker-Hannifin
Bosch Rexroth Corp.	PerkinElmer
Datamax-O'Neil	Rockwell Automation
Emerson Electric	SPX
GE	Schneider Electric
Greenlee Textron	Siemens Water
Hitachi	Technologies
Johnson & Johnson	Snap-on
Medical	Stanley Black and
Keysight	Decker
Labfacility	Thermo Fisher
Makita	Scientific
Mettler-Toledo	Wayne

HISTORICAL FINANCIALS

Company Type: Public

Income Statement

FYE: December 31

	REVENUE ($ mil.)	NET INCOME ($ mil.)	NET PROFIT MARGIN	EMPLOYEES
12/18	19,893	2,650	13.3%	71,000
12/17	18,329	2,492	13.6%	67,000
12/16	16,882	2,553	15.1%	62,000
12/15	20,563	3,357	16.3%	81,000
12/14	19,913	2,598	13.0%	71,000
Annual Growth	(0.0%)	0.5%	—	0.0%

2018 Year-End Financials

Debt ratio: 20.36%	No. of shares (mil.): 701
Return on equity: 9.72%	Dividends
Cash ($ mil.): 787	Yield: 0.6%
Current ratio: 1.47	Payout: 17.1%
Long-term debt ($ mil.): 9,688	Market value ($ mil.): 72,339

	STOCK PRICE ($)	P/E	PER SHARE ($)		
	FY Close	High/Low	Earnings	Dividends	Book Value
12/18	103.12	29 24	3.74	0.64	40.22
12/17	92.82	26 22	3.53	0.56	37.84
12/16	77.84	28 21	3.65	0.57	33.23
12/15	92.88	20 17	4.74	0.54	34.49
12/14	85.71	24 19	3.63	0.40	33.19
Annual Growth	4.7%	— —	0.7%	12.5%	4.9%

Darden Restaurants, Inc.

You could call this company Olive Darden. After all Darden Restaurants' spot as the No. 1 casual-dining company has been fueled by its Olive Garden chain of nearly 850 Italian-themed restaurants. But Darden is more than garden operating more than 1750 restaurants in the US and Canada. Its other concepts are LongHorn Steakhouse The Capital Grille (upscale steakhouse) Bahama Breeze (Caribbean food and drinks) Eddie V's (seafood) Yard House (American food) and Seasons 52 (casual grill and wine bar). The company added Cheddar's Scratch Kitchen chain to its menu in 2017. Most of the company's restaurants cater to families in suburban locations. Overall Darden restaurants serve about 390 million guests a year.

Operations

Darden's Olive Garden restaurants dish up about 50% the company's revenue followed by Long-Horn Steakhouse locations providing about 20% of revenue. Another 20% of revenue comes from the Other segment composed of the Yard House Bahama Breeze Cheddars and Seasons 52 restaurants. Darden's fine-dining segment of Capital Grille and Eddie V's restaurants with higher-priced menus (steak and seafood entrees in the $30-$50 range) provides less than 10% of revenue.

The company runs 850 Olive Garden restaurants about 500 LongHorn Steakhouses some 70 Yard House locations about 60 Capital Grilles 40 each Seasons 52 and Bahama Breeze and 20 Eddie V's restaurants.

Geographic Reach

Darden operates more than 1750 restaurants in the US and Canada. The three most populous US states have the most Darden locations: Florida about 200 Texas more than 180; and California more than 100. The company operates restaurants in all 50 states and the District of Columbia as well as six in Canada.

Sales and Marketing

Olive Garden has come to epitomize the chain restaurant experience. Olive Garden offers a version of Italian cuisine designed for mass appeal and affordability.

Darden spends heavily on research and development to roll out a succession of new menu items that are heavily promoted through television advertising. The chains also use discount pricing and special offers to win business against the competition which includes Applebee's Chili's (operated by Brinker International) and Outback Steakhouse (OSI Restaurant Partners).

Financial Performance

Darden's revenue has increased six years in a row rising at a 6% annual rate over that time.

In 2018 (ended May) sales rose 12% to $8.1 billion from $7.2 billion in 2017 driven by the strongest sales increases in each brand in at least four years. Sales at Olive Garden which accounts for half of revenue rose about 4% for the year. Overall the company benefited from the acquisition of Cheddar's a 2.3% increase in same-store sales and sales from 40 new company-owned restaurants.

Net income rose to $596 million in 2018 a 24% increase from $479 million in 2017. Food and beverage costs were lower as a percent of sales but labor costs increased as a percent of sales due to wage-rate inflation and the impact of Cheddar's higher labor costs compared to Darden's legacy brands.

Darden finished 2018 with $147 million in cash compared to $233 million in 2017. Cash from operations totaled $1 billion in 2017. Investing and financing activities in 2018 used $451 million and $636 million respectively.

Strategy

Darden has built its dining empire without the aid of franchising a strategy that allows the company the highest degree of control for maintaining food and service quality. The major downside is the cost of operating and maintaining all those restaurants. The company is constantly focused on improving margins by negotiating lower prices for food and other ingredients.

One cost that's hard to contain is labor. The national unemployment rate has been below 4% leading to competition between employers for workers. Darden's labor costs increased 15% in 2018 from 2017. The company said it has raised pay for its workers (it has some 180000 overall) and it provides health insurance benefits and retirement plan contributions.

Darden has invested in technology to strengthen its marketing and analytics capabilities. Its efforts include an online and mobile ordering system for Olive Garden and LongHorn Steakhouse and developing customer relationship management programs data analytics and data-driven marketing.

Darden is looking outside of the US for growth including plans to develop Olive Garden and Long-Horn Steakhouse locations in Brazil Colombia the Dominican Republic Panama and Puerto Rico. Most of the company's international growth emphasis has been on its Olive Garden and LongHorn Steakhouse chains.

Mergers and Acquisitions

In 2017 Darden acquired the Cheddar's casual dining chain from private equity firms L Catteron and Oak Investment Partners among other owners. The $780 million deal brings some 160 locations across more than two dozen states to Darden.

EXECUTIVES

Ceo And Director, Eugene I. (Gene) Lee, age 58, $953,750 total compensation
Svp And Chief Human Resources Officer, Danielle Kirgan, $378,462 total compensation
Evp And President Olive Garden, David C. (Dave) George, age 63, $576,539 total compensation
Svp And Cfo, Ricardo (Rick) Cardenas, age 51, $474,539 total compensation
President Yard House, Michael (Mike) Kneidinger
Vp Operations The Capital Grille, Brian Foye
President Longhorn Steakhouse, Todd Burrowes, $442,211 total compensation
Svp And Cio, Chris Chang
President The Capital Grille And Eddie V's, John Martin
Senior Vice President Division, Sam Pereira
Svp Corporate Controller, John Madonna
Vice President Of Finance, Mark Cooper
Senior Vice President Human Resource Olive Garden, Paula Manchester
Vice President, Kathy Janiga
Senior Vice President Division, Paula Britton
Senior Vice Presiden, Amy Hagedoorn
Executive Vice President Marketing, Salli Setta
Vice President Quality Assurance, Ana Hooper
Svp And Treasurer, Bill White
Senior Vice President Corp Marketing, Angela Simmons
Senior Vice President Strategy And Insights, Ali Charri
Vice President Communications, Justin Sikora
Senior Vice President Franchising And President International Operations, Michael Beacham
Svp And Chief Development Officer, Rich Renninger
Vice President Culinary Operations Olive Garden, Timothy Blaise
Executive Vice President Of Ma, Jose Duenas
Vice President, Carlito Jocson
Senior Vice President Financial Planning Analysis And Treasure, Raj Vennam
Vice President Enterprise Beverage Strategy And Innovation, Helen Mackey
Executive Vice President Of Marketing, Debby Shimick
Vice President Of Division, Anthony Morrow
Svp Development, Joe Mutti
Vice President Of Division, Summara Jones
Senior Vice President, Mike Vale
Chairman, Charles M. (Chuck) Sonsteby
Secretary, Stephanie Talamas
Board Member, Margaret Atkins
Treasurer, Pommels Craig
Auditors: KPMG LLP

LOCATIONS

HQ: Darden Restaurants, Inc.
1000 Darden Center Drive, Orlando, FL 32837
Phone: 407 245-4000
Web: www.darden.com

PRODUCTS/OPERATIONS

Restaurant Brands
Bahama Breeze
Eddie V's
LongHorn Steakhouse
Olive Garden
The Capital Grille
Yard House
Seasons 52
Cheddar's Scratch Kitchen

2018 Sales

	$ mil.	% of total
Olive Garden	4,082	51
LongHorn Steakhouse	1,703	21
Fine Dining	575	7
Other Business	1,720	21
Total	**8,080**	**100**

COMPETITORS

Bob Evans	DineEquity
Brinker	Hooters
Carlson Restaurants	OSI Restaurant
Cheesecake Factory	Partners
Cracker Barrel	Perkins & Marie
Denny's	Callender's

Income Statement				FYE: May 26
	REVENUE ($ mil.)	NET INCOME ($ mil.)	NET PROFIT MARGIN	EMPLOYEES
05/19	8,510	713	8.4%	184,514
05/18	8,080	596	7.4%	180,656
05/17	7,170	479	6.7%	178,729
05/16	6,933	375	5.4%	150,000
05/15	6,764	709	10.5%	150,000
Annual Growth	5.9%	0.1%	—	5.3%

2019 Year-End Financials

Debt ratio: 15.74%	No. of shares (mil.): 123
Return on equity: 31.19%	Dividends
Cash ($ mil.): 457	Yield: 0.0%
Current ratio: 0.61	Payout: 52.7%
Long-term debt ($ mil.): 927	Market value ($ mil.): 14,788

	STOCK PRICE ($) FY Close	P/E High/Low		PER SHARE ($) Earnings	Dividends	Book Value
05/19	120.13	22	15	5.69	3.00	19.44
05/18	87.88	21	16	4.73	2.52	17.77
05/17	87.95	23	16	3.80	2.24	16.76
05/16	67.48	25	18	2.90	2.10	15.47
05/15	65.54	13	8	5.47	2.20	18.42
Annual Growth	16.4%	—	—	1.0%	8.1%	1.4%

DaVita Inc

DaVita performs dialysis treatments for patients suffering from end-stage renal disease (ESRD or chronic kidney failure). The firm is one of the US' largest providers of dialysis — its administrative services reach more than 200000 patients through 2600 outpatient centers across the US. The company also offers home-based dialysis services as well as inpatient dialysis in some 900 hospitals. It operates two clinical laboratories that specialize in routine testing of dialysis patients and serve the company's network of clinics.

Operations

DaVita's Kidney Care (dialysis and related lab and support services) division became its sole operating segment following the divestiture of its DaVita Medical Group unit in 2019.

Dialysis and lab services account for more than 90% of the company's revenues. DaVita and its main competitor Fresenius Medical Care each serve nearly 40% of all US outpatient dialysis patients. Fresenius is one of DaVita's largest dialysis product and equipment suppliers.

A portion of DaVita's dialysis and lab-related revenues comes from administering specialty pharmaceuticals to patients receiving dialysis. Those pharmaceuticals include vitamin D iron supplements and EPO ?- which is used during dialysis to treat anemia (a common complication). Amgen is the only company that manufactures EPO; to buffer against price fluctuations or shortages DaVita has a multi-year agreement with Amgen to secure its supply of EPO at discounted pricing.

The company sold its DaVita Medical Group (DMG) unit (formerly known as HealthCare Partners or HCP) to UnitedHealth Group's Optum unit for $4.3 billion in 2019; DMG's Nevada operations were sold to Intermountain Healthcare as part of the transaction. DMG provides integrated health care services and manages medical care offices in California Colorado Florida Nevada New Mexico and Washington.

Geographic Reach

California Texas and Florida are home to about 30% of all DaVita dialysis centers though the firm has locations in more than 45 US states and Washington DC. The company divested its DaVita Medical Group (DMG) unit in 2019 which operated and managed medical groups and physician practice networks in California Colorado Florida Nevada New Mexico and Washington.

The company has a long-term strategy to expand into overseas markets through acquisitions and partnerships. The company has established a presence in nine countries in Europe Latin America the Middle East and the Asia-Pacific region through roughly 250 outpatient dialysis centers. Germany Poland Malaysia Brazil and Saudi Arabia together account for about 85% of DaVita's outpatient dialysis centers outside of the US.

Sales and Marketing

Almost 90% of DaVita's dialysis patients are covered by government-based health plans including Medicare and Medicaid making DaVita particularly vulnerable to changes in government reimbursement rates (which are regularly under threat of being lowered by state and federal governments facing budget pressures).

Financial Performance

Davita's revenue has risen steadily since 2014; increased sales volume and payment rates at its existing and acquired dialysis centers have driven an overall expansion of more than 20%. Net income has shifted erratically in the last five years dropping more than 60% in 2015 (due mostly to higher medical claim and hospital expenses from senior Medicaid members) bouncing back to a peak the following year on strong revenue performance and declining the next two years.

The company's revenue added 5% to $11.4 billion in 2018 thanks to greater calcimimetics administration Medicare bad debt revenue and treatment volume.

Davita's net income slid 76% to $159 million that year as it failed to contain patient care and other costs — particularly those for calcimimetics greater headcount and a new 401(k) matching program.

The company used $103.5 million of its cash in 2018 to end the year with $415.4 million. Operating activities generated $1.8 billion. The company used $1 billion on investments (mainly property and equipment) and $625.3 million on financing activities (mostly treasury stock purchases).

Strategy

DaVita sold its DaVita Medical Group (DMG) segment to UnitedHealth in 2019 for $4.3 billion. The move allowed it to focus on its core kidney care business; however the company is still exploring other business avenues in healthcare. That same year it launched its CKD EHR by Epic product. Epic is the most widely used electronic health records (EHR) platform; DaVita's CKD EHR uses Epic's network to share nephrology data between healthcare providers irrespective of the EHR program they use enabling enhanced population health management and risk stratification models.

DaVita primarily grows through acquisitions. In 2017 the company purchased Pacific Northwest independent physician association Northwest Physicians Network (NPN). That buy gave DaVita 1000 primary and specialty care physicians. The next year NPN partnered with medical and community service groups in Pierce County Washington to test a program whereby patients who call frequently call 911 are referred to NPN which then refers the patient to case management services.

The company also seeks partnerships to improve its client experience. In 2018 DaVita began its Transplant Waitlist Support Program in collaboration with the University of Chicago. The program reduces the chance a kidney transplant patient will be passed up due to outdated contact information by electronically sharing patient data between DaVita and transplant centers.

Mergers and Acquisitions

In 2017 DaVita bought Colorado-based Renal Ventures for $415 million. Renal Ventures operates 36 dialysis clinics in six states; it also has units that operate infusion and vascular centers. That year it also purchased Pacific Northwest independent physician association Northwest Physicians Network (NPN). That buy gave DaVita 1000 primary and specialty care physicians.

HISTORY

Hospital chain National Medical Enterprises (NME now Tenet) formed Medical Ambulatory Care in 1979 to run its in-hospital dialysis centers. The unit bought other centers in NME's markets. In 1994 the subsidiary's management backed by a Donaldson Lufkin & Jenrette — now Credit Suisse First Boston (USA) — investment fund bought the dialysis business and renamed it Total Renal Care (TRC).

To become a leader in its consolidating field TRC began buying other centers and soon added clinical laboratory and dialysis-related pharmacy services and home dialysis programs. It went public in 1995.

The next year the firm added 66 facilities 32 from its acquisition of Caremark International's dialysis business. In 1997 TRC expanded abroad buying UK-based Open Access Sonography (vein care) and partnering with UK-based Priory Hospitals Group.

In 1998 TRC bought Renal Treatment Centers nearly doubling its size. But the acquisition costs caused a loss that year and sparked shareholder lawsuits (settled in 2000) over alleged misleading statements. The firm also became embroiled in a reimbursement dispute with Florida's Medicare program. Problems continued into 1999 as the company struggled to meld operations. The company took a charge to cover a billing shortfall and chairman and CEO Victor Chaltiel and COO/CFO John King resigned. New management began improving billing procedures and took other cost-cutting measures.

The company changed its name in 2000 to DaVita an Italian phrase loosely translated as "he/she gives life." It also sold its international operations to competitor Fresenius.

In 2005 the company acquired Gambro's US dialysis operations for about $3 billion adding some 565 dialysis clinics to its operations. To meet FTC requirements for the deal DaVita sold about 70 clinics to RenalAmerica a company founded by former Gambro Healthcare executive Michael Klein.

In 2007 DaVita expanded its health care offerings by acquiring a majority stake in HomeChoice Partners a provider of home infusion services. The company added about 80 new centers through acquisitions in 2009.

DaVita significantly widened its domestic network of dialysis centers when it acquired regional dialysis chain DSI Renal for $690 million in 2011. To secure approval for the deal from the FTC DaVita agreed to divest 30 clinics but overall the acquisition added more than 100 dialysis centers to its holdings.

Elsewhere around the world DaVita entered Germany with the 2011 purchase of DV Care. It also expanded into the Middle East through the acquisition of a majority stake in Lehbi Care a leading Riyadh-based kidney care company with three clinics.

The company has also been looking to branch out into new areas of health care including medical practice management a mission it accomplished through the 2012 purchase of private medical group management firm HealthCare Partners through a merger transaction worth some $4.4 billion.

Following the deal the company changed its legal name from DaVita to DaVita HealthCare Partners to reflect its broadened operations; the dialysis division continues to operate under the DaVita name while HealthCare Partners operates as an independent subsidiary of DaVita HealthCare Partners. The two companies both count California and Florida as key markets and DaVita HealthCare Partners has used HealthCare Partners' integrated care model to help it offer a wider range of health care services.

Internationally the company entered China in 2012 through a joint venture to provide dialysis services with Chinese biotech company 3SBio.

EXECUTIVES

Executive Chair Davita Medical Group, Charles G. (Chuck) Berg, age 62
Chairman And Ceo, Kent J. Thiry, age 63, $1,273,077 total compensation
Cfo, Joel Ackerman, age 54
Group Vp Purchasing And Public Affairs, LeAnne M. Zumwalt, age 60, $400,000 total compensation
Chief Compliance Officer, Jeanine M. Jiganti, age 60
Chief Accounting Officer, James K. (Jim) Hilger, age 57, $375,000 total compensation
Ceo Davita Kidney Care, Javier J. Rodriguez, age 48, $865,385 total compensation
Chief Medical Officer Davita Kidney Care, Allen R. Nissenson, age 72
President Colorado Springs Health Partners, Oraida Roman
Ceo Davita International, Robert Lang
Director Of Pharmacy Operations, Randy Ferreter
Medical Director, John Burns
Vice President, Rebecca Griggs
Vice President And Associate General Counsel, David Witek
Vice President Revenue Management, David Corlett
Senior Vice President Strategy, James Rechtin
Vp Operations, Ray Follett
Vice President Integration, Douglas Allen
Division Vice President, Brandon King
Director Of Clinical Services, Cicely Gibson
Vice President Corporate Development, Scott Lloyd
Vice President Finance, Chitra Goswami
Vice President Revenue Operations, Chad Hull
Vice President, Stuart Bachelder
Director Of Clinical Services, Karla Close
Vice President, Maxwell Larson
Vice President Federal Government Affairs, Joelle Thornhill
Division Vice President, Vanessa Pfeiffer
Division Vice President Crossroads Division, Roxanne Ramoutar
Group Medical Director, Mihran Naljayan
Vice President Divisional, Debbie Wolfe
Board Member, Paul Diaz
Auditors: KPMG LLP

LOCATIONS

HQ: DaVita Inc
  2000 16th Street, Denver, CO 80202
Phone: 720 631-2100
Web: www.davita.com

PRODUCTS/OPERATIONS

2018 Revenues by Payer

	% of total
Government-based programs	
Medicare and Medicare-assigned plans	59
Medicaid and Managed Medicaid	6
Other government-based programs	4
Commercial	31
Total	**100**

2018 Dialysis Revenues

	% of total
Outpatient hemodialysis centers	79
Peritoneal dialysis and home-based hemodialysis	16
Hospital inpatient hemodialysis	5
Total	**100**

2016 Sales

	$ mil.	% of total
US dialysis and related lab services	10,335	90
Other - Ancillary services and strategic initiatives	1,196	10
Adjustments	(127.2)	-
Total	**11,404**	**100**

Selected Operations

Astro Hobby West Mt. Renal Care Limited Partnership
Austin Dialysis Centers L.P.
Beverly Hills Dialysis Partnership
Brighton Dialysis Center LLC
Capital Dialysis Partnership
Carroll County Dialysis Facility L.P.
Central Carolina Dialysis Centers LLC
Chicago Heights Dialysis LLC
Continental Dialysis Center Inc.
Dallas-Fort Worth Nephrology L.P.
Dialysis of Des Moines LLC
Dialysis Specialists of Dallas Inc.
Downriver Centers Inc.
Downtown Houston Dialysis Center L.P.
Durango Dialysis Center LLC
DVA Healthcare of Maryland Inc.
East End Dialysis Center Inc.
Elberton Dialysis Facility Inc.
Empire State DC Inc.
Greenwood Dialysis LLC
Hawaiian Gardens Dialysis LLC
HealthCare Partners LLC
HuntingtonPark Dialysis LLC
Indian River Dialysis Center LLC
Jedburg Dialysis LLC
Kidney Centers of Michigan L.L.C.
Lincoln Park Dialysis Services Inc.
Mason-Dixon Dialysis Facilities Inc.
Middlesex Dialysis Center LLC
Natomas Dialysis
Nephrolife Care (India) Pte. Ltd.
North Colorado Springs Dialysis LLC
Open Access Lifeline LLC
Palomar Dialysis LLC
Physicians Choice Dialysis of Alabama LLC
Physicians Dialysis of Houstin LLP
Renal Life Link Inc.
Renal Treatment Centers Inc.
RMS Lifeline Inc.
Rocky Mountain Dialysis Services LLC
Shining Star Dialysis Inc.
Soledad Dialysis Center LLC
Summit Dialysis Center L.P.
Tortugas Dialysis LLC
Total Renal Care Inc.
Total Renal Laboratories Inc.
Total Renal Research Inc.
TRC West Inc.
Tulsa Dialysis Center LLC
Upper Valley Dialysis L.P.

COMPETITORS

Apria Healthcare	Lincare Holdings
Critical Care Systems	Molina Healthcare
International	Permanente Medical
Dialysis Clinic Inc	Groups
FMCNA	Quest Diagnostics
Gentiva	U.S. Renal Care
LabCorp	UnitedHealth Group

HISTORICAL FINANCIALS

Company Type: Public

Income Statement
FYE: December 31

	REVENUE ($ mil.)	NET INCOME ($ mil.)	NET PROFIT MARGIN	EMPLOYEES
12/18	11,404	159	1.4%	77,700
12/17	10,876	663	6.1%	74,500
12/16	14,745	879	6.0%	70,300
12/15	13,781	269	2.0%	60,400
12/14	12,795	723	5.7%	57,900
Annual Growth	**(2.8%)**	**(31.5%)**	**—**	**7.6%**

2018 Year-End Financials

Debt ratio: 52.86%
Return on equity: 3.80%
Cash ($ mil.): 323
Current ratio: 1.72
Long-term debt ($ mil.): 8,172
No. of shares (mil.): 166
Dividends
  Yield: —
  Payout: —
Market value ($ mil.): 8,562

	STOCK PRICE ($) FY Close	P/E High/Low	PER SHARE ($) Earnings	Dividends	Book Value
12/18	51.46	86 52	0.92	0.00	22.26
12/17	72.25	21 15	3.47	0.00	25.70
12/16	64.20	18 13	4.29	0.00	23.89
12/15	69.71	66 53	1.25	0.00	23.22
12/14	75.74	23 18	3.33	0.00	23.98
Annual Growth	**(9.2%)**	**— —**	**(27.5%)**	**—**	**(1.8%)**

DCP Midstream LP

DCP Midstream is one of the largest natural gas gatherers in North America and also the top producer and a primary marketer of natural gas liquids (NGLs). It also engages in natural gas compressing treating processing transporting and selling. DCP Midstream also transports and sells NGLs and distributes propane wholesale. The company operates natural gas gathering and transmission systems (64000 miles of pipe) in 16 states (including Arkansas Louisiana Oklahoma and Texas) 12 fractioning facilities four NGL pipelines and seven propane storage terminals. DCP Midstream Partners LP merged with DCP Midstream LLC in 2017 to become DCP Midstream LP.

Operations

DCP Midstream has two reportable segments: Gathering and Processing (G&P) and Logistics and Marketing (L&M).

G&P comprises the gathering compressing treating and procession of natural gas; the production and fractionation of NGLs; and recovering condensate. It generated 40% of sales. L&M transports trades markets and stores natural gas and NGLs and brings in 60% of total sales.

Geographic Reach

DCP Midstream operates assets in more that 15 states in the continental US: Alabama Arkansas Colorado Kansas Louisiana Maine Massachusetts Michigan New Mexico Oklahoma Texas and Wyoming and others.

The company's logistics and marketing activities take place in Colorado Kansas Louisiana Michigan Oklahoma New Mexico and Texas while its gathering and processing operations are conducted through around 50 facilities spread across the North Permian Midcontinent and South of the US.

An NGL storage facility which holds ethane propane and butane is located in Marysville Michigan and has access to Marcellus Utica and Canadian NGLs.

The natural gas supply for its gathering pipelines and processing plants is derived primarily from natural gas wells located in Colorado Louisiana Michigan Oklahoma Texas Wyoming and New Mexico.

Sales and Marketing

DCP Midstream's customers include multi-national petrochemical and refining companies natural gas marketers and commodity producers.

The company typically sells propane to propane distributors under annual sales agreements.

Financial Performance

DCP Midstream's sales are closely tied to oil prices. Oversupply from OPEC nations and the fracking boom in the US cratered oil prices — and DCP's revenue — in 2015-16. Prices have been rising since and so has DCP's revenue.

In 2018 the company's sales grew 19% to $9.4 billion. The Logistics & Marketing business was the main growth driver buoyed by higher NGL and crude prices and higher gas and NGL sales volumes partially offset by lower natural gas prices and unfavorable commodity derivative activity. The Gathering & Processing segment grew albeit at a slower rate thanks to higher prices increased drilling in the Eagle Ford system as the impact of Hurricane Harvey on the previous year's results.

Net income grew 29% to $302 million due to higher earnings from affiliate companies partially offset by higher loss on financing activities.

DCP's cash on hand fell $155 million during 2018 ending the year at just $1 million. It appears to be a deliberate decision on behalf of the company to maintain low cash reserves instead using investing the cash generated by its operations. DCP's operations generated $662 million and its financing yielded $128 million during 2018 while its investing activities used $945 million. The company's main cash uses were capital expenditures investments in affiliates and dividends. It issued debt to increase liquidity.

Strategy

DCP Midstream's investment programs target plant construction and expansion as well as the pipeline operations of its unconsolidated affiliates Sand Hills and Southern Hills. In 2019 it plans to spend around $700-900 million in total with around $100 million on maintenance and $700 million on expansion. Expansions include the O'Connor 2 plant in the DJ Basin the construction of the Gulf Coast Express pipeline the Front Range and Texas Express expansions and the extension of the Southern Hills pipeline into the DJ Basin.

In 2019 DCP sold subsidiary Gas Supply Resources a propane wholesale business that operates seven natural gas liquids terminals in the Eastern US for $90 million to NGL Energy Partners.

Company Background

In 2013 DCP Midstream bought a 47% stake in an Eagle Ford joint venture from the owner of its general partner for $626 million bringing its ownership interest in the joint venture to 80%.

In 2012 DCP Midstream acquired the Texas-based Crossroads processing plant and gathering system from Penn Virginia Resource Partners for $63 million. The bolt-on acquisition allows the company to expand its market position in East Texas and provide services to drillers in the Haynesville shale and Cotton Valley regions.

In 2011 DCP Midstream acquired the Seaway Products Pipeline Co. from ConocoPhillips. The pipeline now called Southern Hills Pipeline and being converted to NGL service is expected to be operational by mid-2013. It will provide NGL access from the Midcontinent to the Texas Gulf Coast.

Expanding in Michigan in 2009 the company acquired gas gathering and treating assets for $45.1 million. In 2010 it acquired a 350-mile interstate natural gas liquids pipeline system in Colorado's Denver-Julesburg Basin from Buckeye Partners for $22 million.

In 2010 DCP Midstream moved to extend its Northeast wholesale propane business into the MidAtlantic region acquiring UGI's Atlantic Energy for $49 million. That year it also purchased of NGL storage company Marysville Hydrocarbon Holdings (in Michigan) for about $95 million.

In terms of the company's origins the D in DCP Midstream Partners (formerly Duke Energy Field Services) is for Duke Energy; the CP ConocoPhillips. These two energy majors formed DCP Midstream Partners in 2005. Following the spinoff of Spectra Energy from Duke Energy in 2007 Spectra Energy assumed Duke Energy's 50% holding in DCP.

EXECUTIVES

Group Vp And Chief Environmental Health And Safety Officer, Jerry Barnhill, age 57
Group Vp And Chief Transformation Officer, Bill Johnson
President Commercial, Don Baldridge, age 49, $182,077 total compensation
Chairman President And Ceo, Wouter T. van Kempen, age 49
Group Vp And Cfo, Sean P. OÂ'Brien, age 49
President Asset Operations, Brian Frederick
Group Vp And Cfo, Sean O'brien
Vice President, Paul Kennedy
Vice President Of Quality Information Technology And Regulatory Affairs, Rusty Bondeson
Executive Vice President, Richard Cargile
Group Vice President Human Resources Public Affr Faculty, Chris Lewis
Executive Vice President, Mark Borer
Vice President Procurement, Bill Prentice
Vice President Of Information Technology, Quay Chan
Vice President Of Information Technology, Susie Sjulin
Vice President Of Information Technology, William Johnson
Vice President Of Technology Systems, Timothy Yearous
Vice President Of Information Systems, Lori Martinez
Vice President, Mark Krabbe
Vp Engineering, Chris Root
Vice President Corporate Development And Strategic Planning, Rob Sadler
Senior Vice President Information Technology Infrastructure, Craig McCarty
Vice President Of Operations, Richard Valley
Vice President And Deputy General Counsel, Steve Van Hooser
Vice President Of It, Peter Wright
Senior Paralegal And Assistant Secretary, Stacey Metcalfe
Treasurer, Evelyn Kastner
Auditors: DELOITTE & TOUCHE LLP

LOCATIONS

HQ: DCP Midstream LP
370 17th Street, Suite 2500, Denver, CO 80202
Phone: 303 595-3331
Web: www.dcpmidstream.com

PRODUCTS/OPERATIONS

2018 Sales

	$ mil.	% of total
Logistics & Marketing	9,014	61
Gathering & Processing	5,843	39
Intersegment eliminations	(5035)	-
Total	**9,822**	**100**

2018 Sales

	$ mil.	% of total
Sales of natural gas propane NGLs and condensate	9,374	95
Transportation processing and other	489	5
Trading and marketing (losses) gains net	(41)	
Total	**9,822**	**100**

COMPETITORS

BP NGL	Martin Midstream
Crestwood Midstream	Partners
Partners LP	SandRidge Energy
Enterprise Products	Williams Companies
Kinder Morgan	XTO Energy
Magellan Midstream	

HISTORICAL FINANCIALS

Company Type: Public

Income Statement

				FYE: December 31
	REVENUE ($ mil.)	NET INCOME ($ mil.)	NET PROFIT MARGIN	EMPLOYEES
12/18	9,822	298	3.0%	—
12/17	8,462	229	2.7%	—
12/16	1,497	312	20.8%	—
12/15	1,898	228	12.0%	—
12/14	3,642	423	11.6%	7
Annual Growth	**28.1%**	**(8.4%)**	**—**	**—**

2018 Year-End Financials

Debt ratio: 37.20%
Return on equity: —
Cash ($ mil.): 1
Current ratio: 0.67
Long-term debt ($ mil.): 4,782

No. of shares (mil.): 143
Dividends
  Yield: 11.7%
  Payout: 511.4%
Market value ($ mil.): 3,796

	STOCK PRICE ($) FY Close	P/E High/Low		PER SHARE ($)		
				Earnings	Dividends	Book Value
12/18	26.49	75	42	0.61	3.12	50.71
12/17	36.33	97	69	0.43	3.12	51.69
12/16	38.38	24	10	1.64	3.12	22.67
12/15	24.67	52	23	0.91	3.12	24.16
12/14	45.43	20	15	2.84	3.01	26.27
Annual Growth	**(12.6%)**	**—**	**—**	**(31.9%)**	**0.9%**	**17.9%**

Dean Foods Co.

Dean Foods is the nation's largest milk bottler. The company markets fluid milk ice cream cultured dairy products and beverages (juices teas and bottled water) under more than 50 local regional and private-label brands including DairyPure Borden Pet Country Fresh Meadow Gold and TruMoo a leading national flavored milk brand. Dean Foods owns and operates a number of smaller regional dairy companies including Friendly's Berkeley Farms and Garelick Farms. The company distributes dairy products across the US from regional manufacturing facilities.

Operations

About 70% of Dean Foods' revenue comes from its fluid milk while ice cream products account for about 15%. The rest of the company's sales come from fresh cream cultured products extended shelf-life dairy and other products and other beverages. The company's heavy reliance on fluid milk puts it at the mercy of milk prices consumer demand and competition. Changes in any of those forces could affect the company's operations.

The company has a wide reach around the US operating more than 60 production facilities around the country. It ships most of its products directly to stores in a fleet of refrigerated trucks. It buys milk produced by more than 930000 cows from some 4350 farms.

Geographic Reach

Dean Foods rings up 99% of its sales in the US where it operates manufacturing facilities in 32 states (and distributes across all 50 states). The company's nationwide manufacturing and distribution capacity could be strengths as it tries to roll out products such as Friendly's and Mayfield ice creams across bigger regions and countrywide.

Outside of the US the dairy giant has some operations in Europe.

Sales and Marketing

Dean Foods markets its products through advertising and other promotions including media coupons trade shows and other promotional activities. The company has significantly increased its advertising spending in the past several years to drive consumer awareness of its national brands.

Dean Foods' customers include food retailers distributors foodservice operators educational institutions (some 32500 schools) and governmental entities throughout the US. Walmart and its subsidiaries including Sam's Club is the company's largest customer accounting for more than 15% of revenue. The next four biggest customers account for less than 20% of sales.

The company's products are sold primarily on a local or regional basis through local and regional sales forces although some national customer relationships are coordinated by a centralized corporate sales department.

Financial Performance

After a couple years of declining revenue Dean Foods' sales inched up 1% in 2017 from 2016. The rise was attributed to higher prices for fluid milk which were caused by higher commodity prices. The company also had contributions from the Friendly's and Mayfield ice cream acquisitions. Increases were offset to a degree by lower fluid milk volume from overall category softness and reductions in private label fluid milk volume due to competitive pressures. Dean Foods also blamed an increase in retailers investing more in their own private label products.

Dean Foods' profit fell to about $61 million in 2017 from about $120 million in 2016. The company had higher expenses for several items in 2018 including increased commodity prices costs associated with closing facilities and reorganization and impairment charges for long-lived assets.

The company's cash and cash equivalents fell to $16.5 million in 2017 from $18 million in 2016. It had lower cash from operations because of reduced operating income and a discretionary payment made to the company-sponsored pension plan.

Strategy

Dean Foods is trying to move into higher margin products such as ice cream to lessen its dependence on low-margin milk products particularly private-label products. The transition has been interrupted however by rising milk prices declining demand and looming competition from Walmart the company's biggest customer.

Dean Foods looks to its size and scale to provide flexibility to serve customers the country with private label and branded products. The company counts on its national brands such as DairyPure TruMoo Organic Valley and Friendly's to win space in grocery dairy sections. It began selling extensions of the brands such as DairyPure cottage cheese that includes a mix-in product as well as DairyPure sour cream.

Another challenge on the horizon is Wal-Mart's construction of its own dairy processing plant in Indiana. The plant is to supply dairy products to some 600 stores in the Midwest. Walmart will shift an estimated 90 million gallons of production from Dean to the plant in 2018 and 2019 reducing Dean's annual volume by about 4%. Dean will continue to supply Walmart in other parts of the country.

Dean Foods is responding to these challenges with cost cutting measures plant closures and the shift to a more profitable product mix. In a program the company calls OPEX 2020 it plans to cut expenses to bring them into line with revenue and give the company flexibility to respond the market opportunities and challenges.

With fluid milk volumes declining Dean Foods believes a switch to more profitable branded products and reducing its large-format private label business will provide higher gross margins. Increased sales of products such as ice cream and cottage cheese is to improve profitability.

Dean Foods' strengthened its ice cream offerings with the 2016 acquisition of Friendly's. Friendly's bolstered Dean Foods' market position in the Northeast US and provides a platform for nationwide expansion. Dean Foods also is looking to expand the Mayfield Creamery product line in the southern US. Another step to sell higher margin products is Dean's 50-50 production and distribution partnership with Organic Valley and its line of organic dairy products.

Mergers and Acquisitions

In 2016 the company bolstered its ice cream product lineup after it acquired Friendly's Ice Cream's retail and manufacturing ice cream business for $155 million in cash. Prior to the acquisition Friendly's made and distributed a variety of ice cream products; it also operates a restaurant chain in the northeastern US that was not part of the acquisition. The Friendly's brand complements Dean's line-up of ice cream brands including Mayfield and Dean's Country Fresh.

HISTORY

Investment banker Gregg Engles formed a holding company in 1988 with other investors including dairy industry veteran Cletes Beshears to buy the Reddy Ice unit of Dallas-based Southland (operator of the 7-Eleven chain). The company also bought Circle K's Sparkle Ice and combined it with Reddy Ice. By 1990 it had acquired about 15 ice plants.

The company changed its name to Suiza Foods when it bought Suiza Dairy in 1993 for $99 million. The Puerto Rican dairy was formed in 1942 by Hector Nevares Sr. and named for the Spanish word for "Switzerland." By 1993 it was Puerto Rico's largest dairy controlling about 60% of the island's milk market.

Suiza Foods bought Florida's Velda Farms manufacturer and distributor of milk and dairy products in 1994. The company went public in 1996 the same year it bought Swiss Dairy (dairy products California and Nevada) and Garrido y Compañ a (coffee products Puerto Rico).

The company became one of the largest players in the North American dairy industry through its acquisitions in 1997. It paid $960 million for Morningstar (Lactaid brand lactose-free milk Second Nature brand egg substitute) which — like Suiza Foods itself — was a Dallas-based company formed in 1988 through a Southland divestiture. The company entered the Midwest with its $98 million purchase of Country Fresh and the Northeast with the Bernon family's Massachusetts-based group of dairy and packaging companies including Garelick Farms and Franklin Plastics (packaging).

Suiza Foods strengthened its presence in the southeastern US in 1998 with its $287 million acquisition of Land-O-Sun Dairies operator of 13 fluid-dairy and ice-cream processing facilities. Also that year Suiza Foods purchased Continental Can (plastic packaging) for about $345 million and sold Reddy Ice to Packaged Ice for $172 million.

After settling an antitrust lawsuit brought by the US Department of Justice in 1999 Suiza Foods bought dairy processors in Colorado Ohio and Virginia. That year Suiza Foods combined its US packaging operations with Reid Plastics to form Consolidated Containers retaining about 40% of the new company.

In 2001 Suiza Foods announced it had agreed to purchase rival Dean Foods for $1.5 billion and the assumption of $1 billion worth of debt. Dean Foods had begun as Dean Evaporated Milk founded in 1925 by Sam Dean a Chicago evaporated-milk broker. By the mid-1930s it had moved into the fresh milk industry. The company went public in 1961 and was renamed Dean Foods in 1963.

Suiza Foods completed the acquisition and took on the Dean Foods name later in 2001. The new Dean Foods bought out Dairy Farmers of America's interest in Suiza Dairy and merged it with the "old" Dean's fluid-dairy operations to create its internal division Dean Dairy Group.

Along with the purchase of "old" Dean came a 36% ownership of soy milk maker WhiteWave and in 2002 Dean Foods purchased the remaining 64% for approximately $189 million. By the end of the year Dean had sold off some smaller businesses (boiled peanuts and contract hauling) and its Puerto Rico operations for $119 million in cash.

EXECUTIVES

Ceo, Ralph P. Scozzafava, age 60, $850,000 total compensation

Evp General Counsel Corporate Secretary And Government Affairs, Russell F. Coleman

Evp And Chief Human Resources Officer, Kimberly (Kim) Warmbier, age 57, $432,000 total compensation

Svp Logistics, S. Craig McCutcheon, age 58

Evp Supply Chain, Brad Cashaw, age 55, $343,674 total compensation

Interim Cfo, Scott K. Vopni, age 51

Vice President National Accounts, Tom Arcand

Vice President Human Resources, Toni Potvin

Vice President Director Manager, Joan Salyers

Vice President Business Development Group, Christopher Anderson

Group Vice President Sales, Ed Hinson

Vp Tax, Stu Hueber

Vice President Legal Departmet, Karen Hess

Vice President Sales, Terry Dana

Vice President Finance, Kim Lechner

Vp Of It Infrastructure, Thomas Ehrman

Vice President And General Manager Lamb Weston Ret, Michael Smith

Vice President General Manager, Bill Riley

Vice President Research And Development Fresh Dairy Direct, Kathleen Dacunha

Vice President, Scott Toth

Vice President Director Manager, Abi Rasti

Senior Vice President And Credit Manager, Ed Gorden

Vice President Sales South Region, Marvin Monroe

Vice President Prc, Gary Tritt

Vice President Corporate Development, Steve Schultz

Vice President Tax Planning, Shan Luton

Vice President Legal, Mark Niermann

Vice President Of Finance, Tim Jones

Vice President, David Hurst

National Account Manager, Hunter Jarvis

Vice President Foodservice And C Store Sales, Shawn Mcguire

Vice President Of Sales National Accounts, Tim Heil

Vice President Ehs, Mark Longmier

Chairman, Jim L. Turner, age 73

Assistant Treasurer, Edgar Deguia
Auditors: Deloitte & Touche LLP

LOCATIONS

HQ: Dean Foods Co.
2711 North Haskell Avenue, Suite 3400, Dallas, TX 75204
Phone: 214 303-3400
Web: www.deanfoods.com

2017 Sales

	% of total
Domestic	99
Foreign	1
Total	**100**

PRODUCTS/OPERATIONS

2017 Sales

	$ mil.	% of total
Fluid milk	5,316	68
Ice cream	1,108	14
Fresh cream	389	5
Cultured	282	4
Other beverages	291	4
Extended shelf life and other dairy products	196	2
Other	213	3
Total	**7,795**	**100**

2017 Fresh Dairy Direct Sales

	% of total
Private-label brands	51
Company brands	49
Total	**100**

Selected Brands

Alpro (Europe)
Alta Dena
Berkeley Farms
Borden (licensed)
Brown Cow
Brown's Dairy
Dean's
Friendly's
Garelick Farms
Gandy's
Hershey's (licensed)
Horizon Organic
Knudsen (licensed)
LAND O'LAKES (licensed)
Mayfield Creamery
Oak Farms
Over the Moon
Pet (licensed)
Provamel (Europe)
Robinson Dairy
Silk
Swiss Premium
Tru Moo
Tuscan
WhiteWave

Selected Products

Bottled waters
Eggnog
Eggs
Cottage cheese
Half-and-half
Ice cream
Juice
Milk
Pudding
Sour cream
Soymilk
Whipping cream

COMPETITORS

Associated Milk Producers
Aurora Organic Dairy
Ben & Jerry's
Blue Bell
Brewster Dairy
California Dairies Inc.
ConAgra
Crystal Farms Refrigerated Distribution Company

Dairy Farmers of America
Danone
Darigold Inc.
Dreyer's
Foster Dairy Farms
Galaxy Nutritional Foods
Grupo LALA
H-E-B
HP Hood
Hain Celestial
Hiland Dairy
Lactalis
Lifeway Foods
Maryland & Virginia Milk Producers
Mondelez International
National Dairy
Nestlé USA
Northwest Dairy
Organic Valley
Prairie Farms Dairy
Quality Chekd
Rockview Dairies
Stonyfield Farm
Tillamook County Creamery Association
Vitasoy International
Wal-Mart

HISTORICAL FINANCIALS

Company Type: Public

Income Statement

FYE: December 31

	REVENUE ($ mil.)	NET INCOME ($ mil.)	NET PROFIT MARGIN	EMPLOYEES
12/18	7,755	(326)	—	15,000
12/17	7,795	61	0.8%	16,000
12/16	7,710	119	1.6%	17,000
12/15	8,121	(8)	—	16,960
12/14	9,503	(20)	—	17,246
Annual Growth	**(5.0%)**	**—**	**—**	**(3.4%)**

2018 Year-End Financials

Debt ratio: 42.78%
Return on equity: (-68.18%)
Cash ($ mil.): 24
Current ratio: 1.30
Long-term debt ($ mil.): 905

No. of shares (mil.): 91
Dividends
  Yield: 7.8%
  Payout: —
Market value ($ mil.): 348

	STOCK PRICE ($) FY Close	P/E High/Low	Earnings	PER SHARE ($) Dividends	Book Value
12/18	3.81	— —	(3.58)	0.30	3.31
12/17	11.56	32 13	0.67	0.36	7.20
12/16	21.78	17 12	1.31	0.36	6.74
12/15	17.15	— —	(0.09)	0.28	5.97
12/14	19.38	— —	(0.22)	0.28	6.67
Annual Growth	**(33.4%)**	**— —**	**—**	**1.7%**	**(16.0%)**

Deere & Co.

EXECUTIVES

Chb-Ceo, Samuel R Allen
Pres-Coo*, John C May
Sr V Pres-Cfo, Ryan D Campbell
Sr V Pres-Chief ADM Officer, Marc A Howze
Sr V Pres-General Counsel, Mary K W Jones
Electrical Engineer, Patrick Smith
Project Manager, Rebecca Jungwirth
Operations Manager Employee SE, Teresa Woodworth
Pres, John Deere Fin-CIO, Rajesh Kalathur
Parts Sales, Jason Duffey
Manager Financial, Jeff Vandecasteele
Auditors: DELOITTE & TOUCHE LLP

LOCATIONS

HQ: Deere & Co.
One John Deere Place, Moline, IL 61265
Phone: 309 765-8000   **Fax:** 309 765-9929
Web: www.johndeere.com

COMPETITORS

AGCO
Buhler Industries
CNH Global
Caterpillar
Great Plains Manufacturing
Honda
Komatsu
Kubota

Mahindra
Navistar International
Terex
Toro Company
Uzel Makina Sanayi
Valmont Industries
Volvo
Woods Equipment

HISTORICAL FINANCIALS

Company Type: Public

Income Statement

FYE: November 3

	REVENUE ($ mil.)	NET INCOME ($ mil.)	NET PROFIT MARGIN	EMPLOYEES
11/19*	39,258	3,253	8.3%	73,489
10/18	37,357	2,368	6.3%	74,413
10/17	29,737	2,159	7.3%	60,476
10/16	26,644	1,523	5.7%	56,800
10/15	28,862	1,940	6.7%	57,200
Annual Growth	**8.0%**	**13.8%**	**—**	**6.5%**

*Fiscal year change

2019 Year-End Financials

Debt ratio: 62.09%
Return on equity: 28.20%
Cash ($ mil.): 3,857
Current ratio: 0.69
Long-term debt ($ mil.): 30,229

No. of shares (mil.): 313
Dividends
  Yield: 0.0%
  Payout: 29.9%
Market value ($ mil.): 55,147

	STOCK PRICE ($) FY Close	P/E High/Low	Earnings	PER SHARE ($) Dividends	Book Value
11/19*	176.11	17 13	10.15	3.04	36.45
10/18	133.00	23 18	7.24	2.58	35.45
10/17	133.25	20 13	6.68	2.40	29.70
10/16	88.30	18 15	4.81	2.40	20.71
10/15	78.00	17 13	5.77	2.40	21.29
Annual Growth	**22.6%**	**— —**	**15.2%**	**6.1%**	**14.4%**

*Fiscal year change

Delek US Holdings Inc (New)

EXECUTIVES

Chb-Pres-Ceo, Ezra Uzi Yemin
Exec V Pres-Cfo*, Kevin L Kremke
Exec V Pres-Coo*, Frederec Green
Exec V Pres-Cco*, Avigal Soreq
Exec V Pres Hr*, Donald N Holmes
Unknown, Blake Waterson
Project Coordinator, Alexandra Dalton
Director Financial and SEC Rep, Heather Denham
Project Director, Randy Goodspeed
Manager of Training, Bob Gonzales
Help Desk Manager, Gary McCullough
Auditors: Ernst & Young LLP

LOCATIONS

HQ: Delek US Holdings Inc (New)
7102 Commerce Way, Brentwood, TN 37027
Phone: 615 771-6701
Web: www.delekus.com

COMPETITORS

7-Eleven	Motiva Enterprises
CITGO	Murphy Oil
Chevron	Publix
ConocoPhillips	Racetrac Petroleum
Costco Wholesale	The Pantry
Cumberland Farms	Wal-Mart
Exxon Mobil	Winn-Dixie
Gate Petroleum	

HISTORICAL FINANCIALS

Company Type: Public

Income Statement   FYE: December 31

	REVENUE ($ mil.)	NET INCOME ($ mil.)	NET PROFIT MARGIN	EMPLOYEES
12/18	10,233	340	3.3%	3,717
12/17	7,267	288	4.0%	3,941
12/16	4,197	(153)	—	1,326
12/15	5,762	19	0.3%	4,584
12/14	8,324	198	2.4%	4,361
Annual Growth	5.3%	14.4%	—	(3.9%)

2018 Year-End Financials

Debt ratio: 30.96%
Return on equity: 20.72%
Cash ($ mil.): 1,079
Current ratio: 1.45
Long-term debt ($ mil.): 1,751

No. of shares (mil.): 78
Dividends
  Yield: 2.9%
  Payout: 24.3%
Market value ($ mil.): 2,536

	STOCK PRICE ($) FY Close	P/E High/Low		PER SHARE ($) Earnings	Dividends	Book Value
12/18	32.51	15	7	3.95	0.96	20.93
12/17	34.94	9	5	4.00	0.30	20.44
12/16	24.07	—	—	(2.49)	0.60	16.01
12/15	24.60	128	70	0.32	0.60	18.56
12/14	27.28	11	8	3.35	1.00	17.49
Annual Growth	4.5%	—	—	4.2%	(1.0%)	4.6%

Dell Technologies Inc

Auditors: PricewaterhouseCoopers LLP

LOCATIONS

HQ: Dell Technologies Inc
One Dell Way, Round Rock, TX 78682
Phone: 800 289-3355
Web: www.delltechnologies.com

HISTORICAL FINANCIALS

Company Type: Public

Income Statement   FYE: February 1

	REVENUE ($ mil.)	NET INCOME ($ mil.)	NET PROFIT MARGIN	EMPLOYEES
02/19	90,621	(2,310)	—	157,000
02/18	78,660	(3,728)	—	145,000
02/17*	61,642	(1,672)	—	138,000
01/16	50,911	(1,104)	—	
01/15	54,142	(1,221)	—	
Annual Growth	13.7%	—	—	—

*Fiscal year change

2019 Year-End Financials

Debt ratio: 47.86%
Return on equity: (-90.11%)
Cash ($ mil.): 9,676
Current ratio: 0.80
Long-term debt ($ mil.): 49,201

No. of shares (mil.): 719
Dividends
  Yield: —
  Payout: —
Market value ($ mil.): 35,698

	STOCK PRICE ($) FY Close	P/E High/Low	PER SHARE ($) Earnings	Dividends	Book Value
02/19	49.65	— —	(6.04)	0.00	(6.35)
Annual Growth	—		—	—	—

Delta Air Lines Inc (DE)

Delta Air Lines is one of the world's largest airlines by traffic. Through its regional carriers the company serves about 300 destinations in about 50 countries and it operates a mainline fleet of 800-plus aircraft as well as maintenance repair and overhaul (MRO) and cargo operations. The airline serves more than 180 million customers each year and offers more than 15000 daily flights. Delta is a founding member of the SkyTeam marketing and code-sharing alliance (airlines extend their networks by selling tickets on flights) which includes carriers Air France KLM and Alitalia. Customers from the US account for approximately 70% of sales.

Operations

Delta divides its operations into two chief segments: airline and refinery. The airline segment which accounts for 90% of Delta's sales provides scheduled air transportation for passengers and cargo throughout the US and around the world and other ancillary airline services including maintenance and repair services for third parties.

The refinery segment provides jet fuel to the airline segment from its own production and through jet fuel obtained via agreements with third parties. The costs included in the refinery segment are primarily for the benefit of the airline segment.

By product type economy/coach tickets accounts for about half of total revenue while business cabin and premium tickets generate about 30%. Loyalty travel awards travel-related services cargo and other services accounts the remainder.

Geographic Reach

Atlanta Georgia-based Delta operates from hubs in Amsterdam Atlanta Boston Detroit London-Heathrow Los Angeles Mexico City Minneapolis-St. Paul New York-LaGuardia New York-JFK Paris-Charles de Gaulle Salt Lake City S o Paulo Seattle Seoul-Incheon and Tokyo-Narita. The US market is its largest representing about 70% of net sales.

Delta directly owns an oil refinery in Pennsylvania operated by subsidiary Monroe Energy. Monroe which supplies a large chunk of Delta's jet fuel is loss-making and Delta execs are having a hard time finding a willing buyer.

Sales and Marketing

Delta's tickets are sold through various distribution channels including telephone reservations Delta.com and traditional brick and mortar and online travel agencies. Delta annual advertising budget is around $270 million.

Financial Performance

Aside from a slowdown in 2016 Delta Air Line's revenue has been growing steadily. In 2018 sales growth accelerated to 8% Delta's best performance by far for a number of year. Total revenue of $44.4 billion was boosted by higher passenger revenue

in all three regions (Atlantic Latin America and Pacific) and growth in the aircraft maintenance business and loyalty program. High points were strong yield (revenue per mile) growth in Europe as it leveraged its alliance partners hubs in Amsterdam London and Paris while its Latin America recovered after a particularly bad hurricane season in 2017.

Delta's net income grew 23% to $3.9 billion but remains below levels reported in 2016 and 2015. The increase in 2018 arose from a much lower tax expense in 2018 partially offset by a decrease in operating profits as expenses (particularly fuel) grew faster than sales. Fuel costs can vary year-by-year and represent around a fifth to a quarter of Delta's annual costs. Intense competition in the airline industry means Delta cannot always pass on higher fuel prices to customers impact the bottom line.

Delta's cash position strengthened during 2018 ending the year $895 million higher at $2.7 billion. It generated $7.0 billion from its operations while investing activities used $4.4 billion and financing activities used $1.7 billion. Delta's primary cash uses during the year were investments in flight equipment and ground property long-term debt repayments stock repurchases and dividend payouts.

Strategy

The airline industry is fueled by strategic alliances that allow individual carriers to extend their service without physically flying into new territory. Delta's alliance with SkyTeam extends the airline's reach to more than 900 destinations in 170-plus countries around the globe. The company gets a boost in global coverage with airlines around the world coming aboard the SkyTeam alliance. Delta has five joint ventures with foreign carriers.

To boost its position in the important region of China Delta acquired a 3% stake in China Eastern one of the leading airlines in China. The move allows Delta and China Eastern to compete more effectively on routes between the US and China and provided more travel options for customers in both countries.

Looking to Europe Delta has joint ventures with Air France-KLM and Alitalia and plans to build its presence in its strategically advantaged hubs in London Paris and Amsterdam while de-emphasizing higher Europe point-of-sale markets. It also holds a 49% equity investment in Virgin Atlantic which improved its presence in London one of Delta's largest revenue markets from the US.

Targeting the Asia/Pacific region for growth in 2018 Delta and Korean Air formed a joint venture creating a combined network serving more than 290 destinations in the Americas and more than 80 in Asia. The increase in scale between the carriers includes expanded codesharing in the trans-Pacific market joint sales and marketing initiatives in Asia and the US and co-location at key hubs.

Delta also has JVs with Virgin Australia serving Australia and New Zealand and Mexican airline Aeroméxico which includes a joint MRO operation in Queretaro (in addition to trans-border flights between the US and Mexico).

Strong demand and investment in its operations led to Delta upgrading Boston airport to hub status only the second airport after Atlanta to achieve that designation on the East Coast of the US. Capacity through Boston will increase roughly 15% in 2019 serving Amsterdam Dublin Edinburgh Lisbon and London. The move will ruffle feathers in JetBlue's boardroom which has a roughly 30% share of Boston traffic.

HISTORY

Delta Air Lines was founded in Macon Georgia in 1924 as the world's first crop-dusting service

Huff-Daland Dusters to combat boll weevil infestation of cotton fields. It moved to Monroe Louisiana in 1925. In 1928 field manager C. E. Woolman and two partners bought the service and renamed it Delta Air Service after the Mississippi Delta region it served. About 80 years later Delta became one of the world's largest airlines by traffic after its $2.8 billion acquisition of Northwest Airlines in 2008.

EXECUTIVES

Executive Vice President Human Resources And Labor Relations, Michael Campbell

Senior Vice President New York, Gail Grimmett

Ceo, Edward H. (Ed) Bastian, age 61, $741,669 total compensation

President, Glen W. Hauenstein, age 58, $604,997 total compensation

Evp And Cfo, Paul A. Jacobson, age 47, $525,000 total compensation

Sevp And Coo, Wayne G. (Gil) West, $617,977 total compensation

Evp And Chief Human Resources Officer, Joanne Smith

Svp And Cio, Rahul Samant

Evp Global Sales; President International, Steve Sear

Evp And Chief Legal Officer, Peter W. Carter, $500,000 total compensation

Vp In Flight Field Operations, James Sarvis

Vice President Corporate Real Estate, Shane Jones

Vice President Of Communications, Bridget Carey

Vp State And Local Government Affairs, Jeff Davidman

Svp Network Planning, Joe Esposito

Svp Global Sales, Bob Somers

Executive Vice President And Chro, Anne Smith

Vice President Marketing, Lidia Chiang

Senior Vice President Operations And Customer Center, Dave Holtz

Vice President And Chief Accounting Officer, Craig Meynard

Vice President Of Application, Richard Stone

Vice President, Cherylope Taylor

Vp Customer Experience Integration, Charisse Evans

Vice President Global Human Resources Services, Chris Collins

Vice President And Treasurer, Kenneth Morge

Assistant Vice President Corporate Communications, Jonathan Kennedy

Vice President, Patrick Redahan

Vice President Technical Services, Mark Benson

Assistant Vice President Retail Information Technology, Timothy W Harms

Sevp And Coo, Gil West

Svp Hr, Rob Kight

Vice President Information Systems, Robert Olson

Senior Vice President Delta Connection, Don Bornhurst

Senior Vice President Delta Connection, Donald Bornhorst

National Account Manager, Laura Cascino

Vice President, Shreve Lee

Department Head, Mandell Pressley

Senior Vice President Flight Operations, Steve Dickson

Vice President Of Global Diversity And Community Affai, Jerome Miller

Vice President Global Distribution And Digital Strategy, Rhonda Crawford

Svp Supply Chain Management And Fleet Strategy, Greg May

Aa To Vice President, Keila Workley

Vice President Of Business Operations, Thomas E Schull

Regional Vice President, Wynetta Mccrary

Vp Strategic Alliance, Piero Ceschia

Svp Global Alliances, Nat Pieper

Regional Vice President, Richard R Marr

Vp Airport Customer Service Detroit, John Fechushak

Vp Customer Engagement And Loyalty And Ceo Delta Vacations, Sandeep Dube

Aa To Executive Vice President, Mary Mitchell

Senior Vice President And Deputy General Counsel, Matthew Knopf

Vice President Channel Technology, Matthew Matt Cincera

Aa To Senior Vice President, Laurie Jones

Aa To Senior Vice President, Maylin Fischer

Vice President Mergers And Acquisitions, Terrance Schwartz

Senior Vice President Finance And Controller, Bryan Treadway

Vp Total Rewards And It Human Resources, Greg Tahvonen

Svp Worldport Operations, Greg Kennedy

Vp Latin America And Alliances Americas, Nicolas Ferri

Vp Sales Operations And Development, Kristen Shovlin

Vp Of It Infrastructure And Reliability, Dan Blanchard

Vp Reservation Sales And Customer Care, Victoria Forbes-roberts

Svp Legal Regulatory And International, Christine Wilson

Svp Delta Technical Operations, Don Mitacek

Vp Transatlantic, Roberto Ioriatti

Vice President Information Technology Revenue Technology And Data Analytics, Matt Schrag

Vp Airport Operations New York Jfk International Airport, Hussein Berry

Senior Vice President Europe Middle East Africa And India, Corneel Koster

Executive Vice President, Jim O'brien

Vice President Of Sales Mro Services, Sonny Stern

Senior Vice President Safety Engineering And Compliance, Kimberly Hill

Vice President Of Operations, Lora Sarah

Vice President Sales Latin America, Paul R Jones

Senior Vice President Central Region, Trevor O Pickle

Atg Vice President Fld Stns Xy, Kristin K Rice

Atg Vice President Human Resources Xy, Jannie Richardson

Vpcorp Audit, Brandi Thomas

Atg Vice President Fld Stns Xy, Kristin Rice

Vice President Sales Latin America, Paul Jones

National Account Manager, John Matthews

Vp Seattle, Tony Gonchar

Vpp Safety Coordinator, Ron Etchison

Svp Of Network Planning, Bob Cortelyou

Senior Vice President Supply Chain Manag, Gregory May

Vice President Of Business Operations, Helen Zhang

Vp Head Of Supply Chain Management, Heather Ostis

Svp Finance And Controller And Principal Accounting Officer, William Carroll

Chairman, Francis S. (Frank) Blake, age 69

Spec Acs Safetysecretarycompl, Clifton Jackson

Spec Acs Safetysecretarycompl, Abhishek Chauhan

Board Member, Kathy Waller

Board Member, Sergio Rial

Board Member, Jeanne Jackson

Board Member, Allan Carter

Auditors: Ernst & Young LLP

LOCATIONS

HQ: Delta Air Lines Inc (DE)
Post Office Box 20706, Atlanta, GA 30320-6001
Phone: 404 715-2600
Web: www.delta.com

2018 Sales

	$ mil.	% of total
Domestic	31,233	70
Atlantic	7,042	16
Latin America	3,181	7
Pacific	2,982	7
Total	**44,438**	**100**

PRODUCTS/OPERATIONS

2018 sales

	$ mil.	% of total
Tickets - Main Cabin	21,196	48
Ticket - business cabin and premium products	13,754	31
Loyalty travel awards	2,651	6
Travel-related services	2,154	5
Cargo	865	2
Other	3,818	8
Total	**44,438**	**100**

2018 Sales

	$ mil.	% of total
Airline	43,890	89
Refinery	5,458	11
Intersegment Sales/Other	(4910)	-
Total	**44,438**	**100**

Selected Aircraft TypeB-717-200B-737-700B-737-800B-737-900ERB-747-400B-757-200B-767-300B-777-200ERE190-100MD-88

COMPETITORS

Air Canada	Lufthansa
AirTran Airways	Qantas
American Airlines Group	SAS
British Airways	Singapore Airlines
Cathay Pacific	Southwest Airlines
Japan Airlines	United Continental
JetBlue	Virgin Atlantic Airways

HISTORICAL FINANCIALS

Company Type: Public

Income Statement — FYE: December 31

	REVENUE ($ mil.)	NET INCOME ($ mil.)	NET PROFIT MARGIN	EMPLOYEES
12/18	44,438	3,935	8.9%	89,000
12/17	41,244	3,577	8.7%	87,000
12/16	39,639	4,373	11.0%	84,000
12/15	40,704	4,526	11.1%	83,000
12/14	40,362	659	1.6%	80,000
Annual Growth	**2.4%**	**56.3%**	**—**	**2.7%**

2018 Year-End Financials

Debt ratio: 27.42%
Return on equity: 28.52%
Cash ($ mil.): 1,565
Current ratio: 0.34
Long-term debt ($ mil.): 14,054

No. of shares (mil.): 679
Dividends
  Yield: 2.6%
  Payout: 26.3%
Market value ($ mil.): 33,929

	STOCK PRICE ($) FY Close	P/E High/Low		PER SHARE ($) Earnings	Dividends	Book Value
12/18	49.90	11	8	5.67	1.31	20.13
12/17	56.00	11	9	4.95	1.02	19.67
12/16	49.19	9	6	5.79	0.68	16.81
12/15	50.69	9	7	5.63	0.45	13.93
12/14	49.19	62	35	0.78	0.30	10.68
Annual Growth	**0.4%**	**—**	**—**	**64.2%**	**44.6%**	**17.2%**

Devon Energy Corp.

As an independent energy company Devon explores develops and produces oil gas bitumen and NGLs onshore the US and Canada. It is especially focused in developing projects in the Delaware Basin and STACK assets. Devon also owns Enlink an MLP with substantial midstream operations in the US but agreed to sell it in 2018. The company manages some 6500 net wells with about 200 mmboe in annual production.

HISTORY

Larry Nichols (a lawyer who clerked for US Supreme Court Chief Justice Earl Warren) and his father John founded Devon Energy in 1969. John Nichols was a partner in predecessor company Blackwood and Nichols an oil partnership formed in 1946.

In 1981 the company bought a small stake in the Northeast Blanco Unit of New Mexico's San Juan Basin. To raise capital Devon formed the limited partnership Devon Resource Investors and took it public in 1985. In 1988 Devon consolidated all of its units into a single publicly traded company.

The firm increased its stake in Northeast Blanco in 1988 and again in 1989 ending up with about 25%. By 1990 Devon had drilled more than 100 wells in the area and had proved reserves of 58 billion cu. ft. of natural gas.

During the 1990s the company launched a major expansion program using a two-pronged strategy: acquiring producing properties and drilling wells in proven fields. In 1990 it bought an 88% interest in six Texas wells; two years later Devon snapped up the US properties of Hondo Oil & Gas. After its 1994 purchase of Alta Energy which operated in New Mexico Oklahoma Texas and Wyoming Devon had proved reserves of more than 500 billion cu. ft. of gas.

Between 1992 and 1997 the company also drilled some 840 successful wells. Buoyed by new seismic techniques that raise the odds of finding oil Devon devoted more resources to pioneering fields in regions where it already had expertise.

Continuing its buying spree Devon bought Kerr-McGee's onshore assets in 1997. Two years later it bought Alberta Canada-based Northstar for $775 million creating a company with holdings divided almost evenly between oil and gas.

Also in 1999 Devon grabbed its biggest prize when it purchased PennzEnergy of Houston in a $2.3 billion stock-and-debt deal that analysts called a bargain. PennzEnergy spun off from Pennzoil in 1998 dates back to the Texas oil boom after WWII. In addition to new US holdings the deal gave Devon a number of international oil and gas assets in such places as Azerbaijan Brazil Egypt Qatar and Venezuela.

On a roll Devon in 2000 bought Santa Fe Snyder for $2.35 billion in stock and $1 billion in assumed debt. The deal increased Devon's proved reserves by nearly 400 million barrels of oil equivalent.

In 2001 the company agreed to a major deal to supply Indonesian natural gas to Singapore. It also made an unsuccessful bid for rival Barrett Resources that was trumped by a bid from Williams Companies. Undaunted that year Devon acquired Anderson Exploration for $3.4 billion in cash and $1.2 billion in assumed debt. It also purchased Mitchell Energy & Development for $3.1 billion in cash and stock and $400 million in assumed debt.

As part of its strategy to refocus on core operations in 2002 the company sold its Indonesian

assets to PetroChina for $262 million. By mid-year the company had raised about $1.2 billion through the disposition of oil properties worldwide.

Over this decade Devon Energy bought its way into the big leagues as a North American producer through a series of multibillion-dollar acquisitions of oil and gas producers including Ocean Energy in 2003 for $3.5 billion and US-based Chief Holdings LLC in 2006 for $2.2 billion.

In 2007 Devon began to divest all of its assets in West Africa. It sold its oil and gas business in Egypt to Dana Petroleum for $375 million and its Gabon assets for $206 million. In 2008 it sold its oil and gas business in C "te d'Ivoire to Afren plc for $205 million and in Equatorial Guinea (to that country's national oil company GE Petrol) for $2.2 billion.

In 2010 it sold most of its remaining international assets to BP for $7 billion. As part of this deal BP sold undeveloped oil sand leases in Canada to Devon Energy for $500 million and formed a joint venture with the company to exploit them. The company also sold its Panyu field offshore China to China National Offshore Oil for $515 million.

Consolidating its North American assets to just its onshore properties In 2010 Devon Energy sold its stakes in the Cascade Jack and St. Malo fields in the Gulf of Mexico (about 200 million barrels of estimated recoverable reserves) to AP Moller-Maersk's oil unit for $1.3 billion. It also sold its remaining Gulf of Mexico shelf assets to Apache for $1 billion.

In 2012 it sold its last international offshore asset in Angola for about $71 million.

Boosting its financial resources in 2012 Devon Energy secured a commitment from Sinopec International Petroleum Exploration & Production for the Chinese company to invest $2.2 billion in exchange for one-third of Devon's interest in five new joint venture plays in the Tuscaloosa Marine Shale Niobrara Mississippian Ohio Utica Shale and the Michigan Basin.

That year it also closed a similar $1.4 billion joint venture deal with Sumitomo Corp. to develop 650000 net acres in the Cline Shale and the Midland-Wolfcamp Shale in West Texas.

In 2013 it combined all of its midstream assets with the assets of the former Crosstex Energy Inc. and Crosstex Energy L.P. to form EnLink Midstream LLC and EnLink Midstream Partners LP. The creation of EnLink improves the diversification and growth of midstream holdings while preserving Devon's capital for its core business.

In a cost savings move in 2013 the company closed its office in Houston and consolidated its US personnel into a single operations group at its corporate headquarters in Oklahoma City.

EXECUTIVES

Assistant Controller, R. Alan Marcum, age 52, $550,000 total compensation

President And Ceo, David A. (Dave) Hager, age 63, $1,275,000 total compensation

Evp And General Counsel, Lyndon C. Taylor, age 61, $625,000 total compensation

Vp And Cio, Ben Williams, age 47

Coo, Tony D. Vaughn, age 62, $735,192 total compensation

Svp Canadian Operations And President Devon Canada, Rob Dutton, age 49

Vp Southern Business Unit, Gregg Jacob, age 58

Vp Anadarko Basin Business Unit, Todd Moehlenbrock, age 54

Vp Delaware Basin Business Unit, Frank Schroeder, age 48

Svp Exploration And Production, Richard A. (Rick) Gideon, age 43

Svp Exploration And Production, Kevin Lafferty, age 44

Vp Rockies Business Unit, John Raines, age 36

Evp And Cfo, Jeff L. Ritenour, age 45

Svp Exploration And Production, David G. Harris, age 45

Vice President Supply Chain And Marketing, Mike Dionisio

Senior Vice President Human Resources, Tana Cashion

Vice President, Curtis Kantenberger

Vice President And Associate General Counsel, Connie Burnett

Vp Of Information Technology, Patty Bingham

Assistant To Rick Gideon Senior Vice President Of Us Operations, Heather Powell

Senior Vice President Communications And Investor Relations, Howard Thill

Vp Policy And Government Affairs, Rebecca Rosen

Vp And Cio, Benjamin Williams

Executive Vice President Land, Dan Higdon

Evp Administration, R Alan Marcum

Chairman, John Richels, age 68

Auditors: KPMG LLP

LOCATIONS

HQ: Devon Energy Corp.
333 West Sheridan Avenue, Oklahoma City, OK 73102-5015
Phone: 405 235-3611
Web: www.devonenergy.com

2017 Sales

	% of total
US	53
EnLink	36
Canada	11
Total	**100**

PRODUCTS/OPERATIONS

2017 Sales

	$ mil.	% of total
Marketing & midstream	8,642	62
Upstream	5,307	38
Total	**13,494**	**100**

COMPETITORS

Abraxas Petroleum	Exxon Mobil
Apache	Hess Corporation
BP	JKX
Bonanza Creek	Jones Energy
Cabot Oil & Gas	Marathon Oil
Chesapeake Energy	Occidental Petroleum
Chevron	Royal Dutch Shell
ConocoPhillips	Williams Companies
EOG	XTO Energy
Encana	

HISTORICAL FINANCIALS

Company Type: Public

Income Statement

FYE: December 31

	REVENUE ($ mil.)	NET INCOME ($ mil.)	NET PROFIT MARGIN	EMPLOYEES
12/18	10,734	3,064	28.5%	2,900
12/17	13,949	898	6.4%	4,900
12/16	12,197	(3,302)	—	5,000
12/15	13,145	(14,454)	—	6,600
12/14	19,566	1,607	8.2%	6,600
Annual Growth	(13.9%)	17.5%	—	(18.6%)

2018 Year-End Financials

Debt ratio: 30.39%	No. of shares (mil.): 449
Return on equity: 33.23%	Dividends
Cash ($ mil.): 2,414	Yield: 1.3%
Current ratio: 1.99	Payout: 9.0%
Long-term debt ($ mil.): 5,785	Market value ($ mil.): 10,120

DHPC TECHNOLOGIES, INC.

EXECUTIVES

Pres, Joseph Aletta
V Pres-Ops & Program MGT*, John Antonino
V Pres Engr*, Richard Gifford
Controller*, Robert Jansen
Director, Robert Lake
Engineer, Tom Tokash
Senior Consultant, Dan Glasel
Engineer, Kevin Sullivan
Engineer, Daniel Vance
Associate, David Gandarillas
Chief Scientist, Frank Barone

LOCATIONS

HQ: DHPC TECHNOLOGIES, INC.
10 WOODBRIDGE CENTER DR, WOODBRIDGE, NJ 070951152
Phone: 732 791-5400
Web: WWW.DHPCTECH.COM

HISTORICAL FINANCIALS

Company Type: Private

Income Statement · FYE: May 11

	REVENUE ($ mil.)	NET INCOME ($ mil.)	NET PROFIT MARGIN	EMPLOYEES
05/17*	38,584	1,320	3.4%	150
12/09	11	1	9.0%	—
12/07	6	1	29.2%	—
06/06	1,726	0	0.0%	—
Annual Growth	32.6%	179.9%	—	—

*Fiscal year change

Dick's Sporting Goods, Inc

Dick's Sporting Goods sells a full range of sports and outdoor merchandise from A (adidas cleats) to uh Y (Yeti coolers). The company's some 730 namesake stores across the US feature sporting goods apparel and footwear for leisure pursuits ranging from football golf and cycling to hunting and camping. In addition to well-known brand names Dick's carries exclusive brands such as Walter Hagen Second Skin and Top-Flite. The company also operates about 95 Golf Galaxy and some three dozen Field & Stream stores as well as associated e-commerce sites.

Operations

Dick's reports through three primary merchandise categories: hardlines apparel and footwear. Hardlines which includes equipment and gear is the largest segment and accounts for about 45% of sales. Apparel and footwear bring in about 35% and 20% respectively.

The company purchases merchandise from some 1200 vendors including Nike (its largest) which represents nearly 20% of the total. Beyond Nike and other well-known national and international brands it sells products under its private-label brands such as Cobra (youth golf sets) Field & Stream Fitness Gear Lady Hagen and Quest. Dick's own brands contribute about 15% of sales.

Geographic Reach

Dick's has a total of about 860 stores in 45-plus US states; its largest markets are California Florida New York North Carolina Ohio Pennsylvania and Texas which together account for nearly 40% of total stores.

It also has distribution centers in Goodyear Arizona; Atlanta Georgia; Plainfield Indiana; Conklin New York; and Smithton Pennsylvania and a customer support center in Coraopolis Pennsylvania.

Sales and Marketing

Dick's generates about 85% of sales through its network of retail stores with the remainder coming from its e-commerce sites. The company is focused on developing its omni-channel offering designed to serve customers however they prefer to shop - in stores online or through a combination of both.

It markets its products through traditional channels such as newspaper and direct mail pieces but is increasingly moving toward digital and personalized appeals enabled by its customer marketing database and ScoreCard loyalty program. Its Dick's Team Sports HQ business is a digital platform for youth sports meant to cultivate current and future customers.

Dick's spent $322 million on advertising in fiscal 2018 compared to $330 million in 2017 and $305 million in 2016.

Financial Performance

Dick's has seen robust growth over the past decade with revenue nearly doubling during that time as it expands its network of stores. Net income has generally grown over those 10 years but has been a little more sporadic.

In fiscal 2018 (ended January 2019) the company reported revenue of $8.4 billion down 2% from the prior year. Same-store sales fell 3% that year amid declines in the outdoor equipment and electronics categories as well as the hunt category which has been hurt by the company's decision to no longer sell assault-style firearms. New stores which have been powering Dick's for several years were not enough to offset the same-store sales decline.

Net income also fell that year declining 1% to $319.9 million primarily because of the drop in revenue.

Cash at the end of fiscal 2018 was $113.7 million an increase of $12.4 million from the prior year. Cash from operations contributed $712.8 million to the coffers while investing activities used $198.2 million for capital expenditures. Financing activities used another $502.1 million for dividends to stockholders and Dick's stock repurchase program.

Strategy

Dick's is operating in a highly competitive tough retail environment at a time when foot traffic in stores is on the decline as more consumers turn to Amazon and other online destinations for purchases. For that reason the company has made improving its omni-channel and e-commerce capabilities a key element of strategy alongside more traditional initiatives such as expanding its store network and boosting sales of its private-label brands.

E-commerce sales as a percent of total revenue grew about 2.5% in fiscal 2018 (to 15%) considerably better than the less than half a percentage point of growth the previous year. In 2019 Dick's is looking to improve its shipping and fulfillment functions (with new fulfillment centers in New York and California) and provide faster online checkout improved page responsiveness and new content.

Dick's also continues to expand its store network although at a slower pace; it has plans for seven new Dick's Sporting Goods locations in 2019 and two new Golf Galaxy stores. The company is hoping to expand in markets left underserved by competitors such as Sports Authority who have gone out of business or entered bankruptcy. It has added more than 200 locations since fiscal 2013.

Lastly Dick's continues to focus on its private-label brands which it feels is a differentiator and competitive advantage. The growth of the private-label business outpaced the company average in fiscal 2018 when it hit nearly $1.2 billion in sales. The company expects private brands to outpace the average again in 2019 as it invests in marketing design and technology behind key brands such as CALIA; it also plans to introduce new private brands.

Company Background

Dick's was founded in 1948 when Dick Stack father of company chairman and CEO Edward Stack opened a bait and tackle shop. Edward joined the business full-time in 1977 and became CEO in 1984 when the company only had two locations.

In 1999 the company changed its name from Dick's Clothing and Sporting Goods to Dick's Sporting Goods. It went public in 2002.

EXECUTIVES

V Pres-controller, Oliver Joseph
Chairman And Ceo, Edward W. (Ed) Stack, age 64, $1,000,000 total compensation
Cto, Paul J. Gaffney, age 48
Evp And Cfo, Lee J. Belitsky, age 58, $541,983 total compensation
President, Lauren R. Hobart, age 50, $520,000 total compensation
Evp And Chief Merchant, Keri Jones
Svp Information Technology And Cio, Kurt J. Schnieders
Evp And Chief Strategy Officer, Michele B. Willoughby, age 53, $538,024 total compensation
Svp Operations, Don Germano
Vp Ecommerce Merchandising, Joe Pietropola
Regional Vice President, Tom Mcalorum
Vice President Business Systems And Procurement, Miles Mewhertre
Vp Leadership And Organizational Development, Patty Beard
Regional Vice President, Dave Shappee
Senior Vice President Retail Operations, George Hill
Senior Vice President Operations, Donald Germano
Senior Vice President Supply Chain, George Giacobbe
Vice President Total Rewards, Todd Lombardi
Vice President Of Store Planning Construction And Purchasing, Scott Blyze
Svp Organizational Productivity, Joseph Oliver
Vice President Of Logistics And Vendor Relations, Terri Seagroatt
Vp Strategy And Innovation, Ryan Eckel
Vice President Retail Technology, Dave Lammers
Vp Tax, Todd Hipwell

Vice President Of Marketing, Tom Hassett
Svp Real Estate, Dave Barnes
Svp General Counsel And Secretary, John Hayes
Vice President Of Brand Marketing, Ryan Eckle
Vice President Customer Innovation Technology, Rafeh Massod
Vice President Of Product Development Softlines, Meredith Laginess
Vp Data Science Analytics And Crm, Vimal Kohli
Vice Chairman, William J. (Bill) Colombo, age 63
Board Member, Lawrence Schorr
Auditors: DELOITTE & TOUCHE LLP

LOCATIONS

HQ: Dick's Sporting Goods, Inc
345 Court Street, Coraopolis, PA 15108
Phone: 724 273-3400
Web: www.DICKS.com

2018 Locations

	No.
California	67
Pennsylvania	52
Texas	53
Florida	54
Ohio	50
New York	49
North Carolina	42
Virginia	34
Illinois	34
Michigan	28
Georgia	24
Indiana	21
Massachusetts	21
New Jersey	22
Tennessee	20
Other states	288
Total	**858**

PRODUCTS/OPERATIONS

2018 Sales

	% of total
Hardlines	43
Apparel	35
Footwear	20
Other	2
Total	**100**

Selected Categories

Archery
Backpacking
Baseball
Basketball
Boating
Bowling
Camping
Cycling
Exercise
Fishing
Football
Golf
Hockey (ice and roller)
Hunting
In-line skating
Lacrosse
Optics/telescopes
Paintball
Racquetball/squash
Running
Skateboarding
Snow sports
Soccer
Tennis
Volleyball
Water sports

COMPETITORS

Academy Sports	L.L. Bean
Amazon.com	REI
Big 5	Sears
Cabela's	Sportsman's Warehouse
Costco Wholesale	Target Corporation
Finish Line	Wal-Mart
Foot Locker	Zumiez
Hibbett Sports	

HISTORICAL FINANCIALS

Company Type: Public

Income Statement

FYE: February 2

	REVENUE ($ mil.)	NET INCOME ($ mil.)	NET PROFIT MARGIN	EMPLOYEES
02/19	8,436	319	3.8%	40,700
02/18*	8,590	323	3.8%	45,200
01/17	7,921	287	3.6%	40,500
01/16	7,270	330	4.5%	37,200
01/15	6,814	344	5.1%	37,600
Annual Growth	**5.5%**	**(1.8%)**	**—**	**2.0%**

*Fiscal year change

2019 Year-End Financials

Debt ratio: 1.43%
Return on equity: 16.68%
Cash ($ mil.): 113
Current ratio: 1.41
Long-term debt ($ mil.): 54

No. of shares (mil.): 93
Dividends
  Yield: 0.0%
  Payout: 27.7%
Market value ($ mil.): 3,308

	STOCK PRICE ($) FY Close	P/E High/Low		PER SHARE ($) Earnings	Dividends	Book Value
02/19	35.25	12	9	3.24	0.90	20.29
02/18*	31.49	18	8	3.01	0.68	18.84
01/17	51.31	24	14	2.56	0.61	17.49
01/16	39.08	21	12	2.83	0.55	16.01
01/15	51.65	20	14	2.84	0.50	15.51
Annual Growth	**(9.1%)**	**—**	**—**	**3.3%**	**15.8%**	**6.9%**

*Fiscal year change

DIGNITY HEALTH

Dignity Health has steadily grown to become the hospital provider in the state of California and the fifth-largest health system in the US. The not-for-profit health care provider operates a network of 40 acute-care facilities located in the Golden State and to a lesser extent in Arizona and Nevada. Those facilities house 8300 acute care beds as well as 600 skilled nursing beds. Dignity Health provides home health and hospice services through agencies in California and Nevada. It also operates more than 670 emergency and specialty clinics imaging centers and medical labs as well as managed care and wellness programs. Dignity Health is the official health care provider of the San Francisco Giants. In 2019 Dignity merged with Denver-based hospital group Catholic Health Initiatives to create CommonSpirit Health the largest not-for-profit health system in the US.

Change in Company Type

In 2019 Dignity Health and Catholic Health Initiatives joined forces to become CommonSpirit Health which operates more than 700 care sites and some 40 hospitals. It also has research programs home health operations and living communities. After the combination Dignity Health operates as part of CommonSpirit.

Operations

Dignity Health offers inpatient outpatient subacute and home health care services as well as physician services through affiliates including Dignity Health Medical Foundation. Through another affiliate U.S. HealthWorks Dignity Health provides occupational health and urgent care services in about 20 additional states.

Geographic Reach

Dignity Health operates some 680 hospitals urgent care centers clinics emergency rooms and specialty care centers in California Nevada and Arizona. It has some 540 facilities in California 85 in Arizona and 60 in Nevada.

Strategy

Although Dignity Health combined with Catholic Health Initiatives in 2019 to become part of the larger CommonSpirit Health system it continues to pursue its own strategic goals. Those include improving quality of care in a just work environment implementing clinical and administrative changes to cut costs and expanding operations in existing markets and new markets. For example it broke ground on a $215 million campus expansion in downtown Los Angeles in early 2019. In another project it is embarking on a multi-million dollar expansion of a campus in Chandler Arizona.

The system is also working to establish more wellness programs and increasingly provide ambulatory and non-urgent care in order to improve the overall health of the communities it serves. In late 2018 it acquired six urgent care centers from San Francisco-based Golden Gate Urgent Care.

In 2018 Dignity Health joined forces with Concentra to operate urgent care centers. Concentra acquired Dignity subsidiary U.S. HealthWorks operator of about 250 urgent care centers and onsite clinics in 21 states. The combined urgent care operator which operated more than 550 urgent care centers is majority owned by Concentra; Dignity holds a 20% stake. The deal allowed the companies to standardize best practices while reaching more patients as rising demand for urgent care centers brings more business to their operators.

Mergers and Acquisitions

After years of discussions Dignity Health and Catholic Health Initiatives merged in early 2019. The combined health system named CommonSpirit Health and with 142 hospitals in 21 states is the largest not-for-profit hospital system in the US. The size of the new system allows for it to provide expanded care to patients through such methods as virtual appointments a broader range of clinical programs and advanced technologies. The new organization is headquartered in Chicago. The group's hospitals continue to operate under their existing names.

Company Background

Dignity Health traces its roots to 1857. The Sisters of Mercy Catholic order was established in Dublin in 1831. In the 1850s eight Sisters arrived in San Francisco and began caring for residents with cholera typhoid and influenza. They established St. Mary's Hospital now that city's oldest continuously operating hospital. The order merged operations with another community of Sisters of Mercy in 1986 to create Catholic Healthcare West. The combined system had one retirement home and 10 hospitals throughout California.

The system changed its name to Dignity Health in early 2012 as part of a governance restructuring program. While the firm remained a not-for-profit organization with Catholic roots and its Catholic hospitals continued to be sponsored by their founding congregations (and governed by the Catholic health care directives) the parent organization itself was no longer an official ministry of the Catholic church. In 2019 Dignity Health joined forces with Catholic Health Initiatives to create CommonSpirit Health the nation's largest not-for-profit health system.

HISTORY

Dignity Health formerly Catholic Healthcare West (CHW) traces its roots to 1857 when the Sisters of Mercy founded St. Mary's Hospital in San Francisco. The order expanded in that area and in 1986 two different communities of the Sisters of Mercy merged their hospitals into an organization with one retirement home and 10 hospitals from the Bay Area to San Diego. Declining membership in Roman Catholic religious orders combined with consolidation in the field led the orders to see merger as their only route to survival.

CHW continued to add facilities including AMI Community Hospital in Santa Cruz California in 1990. Since CHW already owned the area's only other acute care hospital Dominican Santa Cruz Hospital CHW in 1993 was ordered not to acquire any more acute care hospitals in Santa Cruz County without FTC approval.

As the trend to managed care became a stampede in the 1990s CHW moved more into preventive care and began reigning in costs through productivity improvement plans. It continued to add hospitals including tax-supported institutions trying to compete with national for-profit systems.

The network increased its medical clout in 1994 by allying with San Diego-based Scripps one of the state's largest HMO systems. In 1995 the Daughters of Charity Province of the West realigned its six-hospital operation with CHW. The next year the Dominican Sisters (California) the Dominican Sisters of St. Catherine of Siena (Wisconsin) and the Sisters of Charity of the Incarnate Word allied their California hospitals with CHW. New community hospitals included Bakersfield Memorial Sierra Nevada Memorial (Grass Valley) Sequoia Hospital (Redwood City) and Woodland Healthcare.

Charity and cost-consciousness clashed in 1996 when union members staged a walkout to protest nonunion outsourcing of vocational nursing housekeeping and kitchen jobs. This dispute was settled but CHW continued to be a target for union organizers with a bitter battle against the Service Employees International Union (SEIU) starting in 1998.

The year 2000 brought CHW more problems with labor relations: SEIU argued that the organization was resistant to unionization. Continued losses led the organization to implement major restructuring the following year as its 10 regional divisions were consolidated into four.

The company parted ways with one of its sponsoring organizations the Franciscan Sisters of the Sacred Heart of Frankfort Illinois in 2003. The sponsorship ended when CHW closed St. Francis Medical Center of Santa Barbara. However the hospital operator that fiscal year posted its first operating profit in seven years.

The company changed its name from Catholic Healthcare West (CHW) to Dignity Health in early 2012 as part of a governance restructuring program. While the firm remained a not-for-profit organization with Catholic roots and its Catholic hospitals continued to be sponsored by their founding congregations (and governed by the Catholic health care directives) the parent organization itself was no longer an official ministry of the Catholic church.

The company's rebranding and restructuring aimed to give it more flexibility to pursue its growth strategy of widening its presence into additional regions of the US while lowering the overall cost of care (a desire of most large hospital operators as the US government works to reform its ailing health system). At the time of the governance shift Dignity Health operated 25 Catholic hospitals and 15 non-Catholic hospitals.

EXECUTIVES

Evp Sponsorship Mission Integration And Philanthropy, Bernita McTernan
President And Ceo, Lloyd H. Dean
Evp And Chief Human Resources Officer, Darryl L. Robinson
Evp And Chief Administrative Officer, Elizabeth Shih
Sevp And Coo, Marvin O'Quinn
Sevp And Cfo, Daniel J. Morissette
Sevp And Chief Strategy Officer, Charles P. Francis
Evp And Cio, Deanna L. Wise
Evp And Chief Medical Officer, Robert L. Wiebe
Evp And General Counsel, Rick Grossman
Evp Sponsorship And Mission Integration, Elizabeth Keith
Vice President, Adam Berman
Vice President, Jeff Land
Senior Vice President And Chief Strategy Officer, Charlie Francis
Vice President Epmo And Performance Excellence, Joan Beach
Vice President Population Health, Julie Bietsch
Vice President Chief Strategy Officer, Joe Diefenderfer
Clinical Director, Pat Britt
Vice President Ambulatory Services, Margie Roper
Vp Strategic Market Development, Gary Spaugh
Senior Vice President Of Philanthropy, Fred Najjar
Director Of Radiology, Richard Siegel
Associate Medical Director, Albert Tejada
Medical Director Nicu And Pediatrics, Madhu Bhogal
Director Of Pharmacy, Jason Glick
Vice President, Kathleen Sullivan
Physical Therapy, Robert Zvada
Vice President Employee And Labor Relations, Scott Fuller
Medical Director, Christina Kwasnica
Director Of Pharmacy, Reed Howe
Senior Vice President Of Operations For Bay Area Service Area, Todd Strumwasser
Vice President Chief Strategy Office, Jordan Wright
Vice President Communications And Public Relations, Marie Kennedy
Vice President Mission Integration, Margaret McBride
Professor; Vice President Research, Ron Lukas
Medical Director, Javier Cardenas
Vice President Medical Affairs, Sahin Yanik
Director Of Pharmacy, Patty Womack
Vice President Employer Relationships, Duncan Ross
Vice President Patient Care Services Cne, Sherie Ambrose
Vice President Of Philanthropy, Jessa Brooks
Vp Of Strategy And Business Development, Isaac Lin
Vice President Marketing Communications, Jennifer Fagnani
Chairman, Caretha Coleman
Vice Chair, Judy Carle
Medical Secretary, Ann Vong
Auditors: DELOITTE & TOUCHE LLP SAN FRA

LOCATIONS

HQ: DIGNITY HEALTH
185 BERRY ST STE 300, SAN FRANCISCO, CA 941071773
Phone: 415 438-5500

Selected Facilities

Arizona
Barrow Neurological Institute (Phoenix)
Chandler Regional Medical Center
Mercy Gilbert Medical Center
St. Joseph's Hospital and Medical Center (Phoenix)
California
Arroyo Grande Community Hospital
Bakersfield Memorial Hospital
California Hospital Medical Center (Los Angeles)
Community Hospital of San Bernardino
Dominican Hospital (Santa Cruz)
French Hospital Medical Center (San Luis Obispo)
Glendale Memorial Hospital and Health Center
Marian Medical Center (Santa Maria)
Mark Twain St. Joseph's Hospital (San Andreas)

Mercy General Hospital (Sacramento)
Mercy Hospital of Bakersfield
Mercy Hospital of Folsom
Mercy Medical Center Merced Community Campus
Mercy Medical Center Merced Dominican Campus
Mercy Medical Center Mt. Shasta
Mercy Medical Center Redding
Mercy San Juan Medical Center (Carmichael)
Mercy Southwest Hospital (Bakersfield)
Methodist Hospital of Sacramento
Northridge Hospital Medical Center
Oak Valley Hospital (Oakdale)
Saint Francis Memorial Hospital (San Francisco)
Sequoia Hospital (Redwood City)
Sierra Nevada Memorial Hospital (Grass Valley)
St. Bernardine Medical Center (San Bernardino)
St. Elizabeth Community Hospital (Red Bluff)
St. John's Pleasant Valley Hospital (Camarillo)
St. John's Regional Medical Center (Oxnard)
St. Joseph's Behavioral Health Center (Stockton)
St. Joseph's Medical Center (Stockton)
St. Mary Medical Center (Long Beach)
St. Mary's Medical Center (San Francisco)
Woodland Healthcare
Nevada
St. Rose Dominican Hospital Rose de Lima Campus (Henderson)
St. Rose Dominican Hospital San Martín Campus (Las Vegas)
St. Rose Dominican Hospital Siena Campus (Henderson)

PRODUCTS/OPERATIONS

Sponsoring Organizations
Congregation of the Dominican Sisters of St. Catherine of Siena of Kenosha (Kenosha Wisconsin)
Congregation of the Sisters of Charity of the Incarnate Word (Houston Texas)
Sisters of Mercy of the Americas West Midwest Community (Omaha Nebraska; formerly Auburn Regional Community of the Sisters of Mercy and Burlingame Regional Community of the Sisters of Mercy in California)
Sisters of St. Dominic Congregation of the Most Holy Rosary (Adrian Michigan)
Sisters of St. Francis of Penance and Christian Charity St. Francis Province (Redwood City California)
Sisters of the Third Order of St. Dominic Congregation of the Most Holy Name (San Rafael California)

COMPETITORS

Adventist Health System West
Banner Health
Community Health Systems
Community Hospital of the Monterey Peninsula
Ensign Group
HCA
John C. Lincoln Health Network
John Muir Health
Loma Linda University Medical Center
Memorial Health Services
Prospect Medical
Providence St. Joseph Health
Salinas Valley Memorial
Shasta Regional Medical Center
Stanford Health Care
Sutter Health
Tenet Healthcare
UCSF Medical
Universal Health Services
VITAS Healthcare

HISTORICAL FINANCIALS
Company Type: Private

Income Statement

	REVENUE ($ mil.)	NET INCOME ($ mil.)	NET PROFIT MARGIN	EMPLOYEES
06/09	8,957	(799)	—	55,494
06/08	8,401	169	2.0%	—
Annual Growth	6.6%	—	—	—

FYE: June 30

Dillard's Inc.

Sandwiched between retail giants such as Macy's and discount chains such as Kohl's Dillard's is rethinking its strategy and trimming its store count. The department store chain operates about 290 locations in some 30 US states covering the Sunbelt and the central US. Its stores primarily cater to middle- and upper-middle-income women selling name-brand and private-label merchandise with a focus on apparel and home furnishings. Founded in 1938 by William Dillard family members through the W. D. Company control the company

Operations

Dillard's' largest product category is ladies' apparel with more than 20% of sales followed by men's apparel and accessories (15%) ladies' accessories and lingerie (15%) shoes (15%) and cosmetics (nearly 15%). Children's apparel home and furniture and construction bring in the remainder. Most of its stores are located in suburban shopping malls and open-air centers. Customers may also purchase merchandise online at the company's e-commerce website which features online gift registries and a variety of other services. Dillard's exclusive brand lines include Antonio Melani Gianni Bini GB Roundtree & York and Daniel Cremieux.Beyond department stores Dillard's owns CDI Contractors a Little Rock Arkansas-based construction firm that was started to build and remodel Dillard's' stores.

Geographic Reach

Texas and Florida are the Arkansas-based department store chain's two largest markets accounting for about a third of total stores. The company operates about 290 Dillard's stores including over 25 clearance centers representing nearly 50 million square feet of space in about 30 states.

Financial Performance

Dillard's has seen uneven revenues in recent years. Its annual revenues have fallen more than 4% since 2015.

Revenue increased to $6.5 billion in 2018 a 1% increase from the year prior. The slight increase was driven by a 2% increase in comparable store sales and significantly higher sales of home goods and furniture.

Net income was $170 million in fiscal year 2018 a drop from $221 million in fiscal year 2017. Selling general and administrative expenses grew slightly in fiscal 2018 to $1.6 billion.

Cash provided by operating activities was $367.2 million in fiscal 2018 while investing activities used $127.7 million. Financing activities used another $303 million.

Strategy

Traditional department store chains have struggled in recent years and Dillard's has not been immune to the challenging retail environment.

While other department store chains have made some radical changes to reach modern customers Dillard's is known for maintaining its traditional format at a high quality level offering on-trend fashions and investing in superior customer service. The company has a loyal older customer base that has remained true to the chain which has helped it during the downturn.

Customers have increasingly high expectations around digital offerings and Dillard's offers an e-commerce website and has made investments into developing a more robust omnichannel experience.

Looking to reduce costs Dillard's has continued to close underperforming stores in recent years.

HISTORY

At age 12 William Dillard began working in his father's general store in Mineral Springs Arkansas. After he graduated from Columbia University in 1937 the third-generation retailer spent seven months in the Sears Roebuck manager training program in Tulsa Oklahoma.

With $8000 borrowed from his father William opened his first department store in Nashville Arkansas in 1938. Service was one of the most important things he had to offer he said and he insisted on quality — he personally inspected every item and would settle for nothing but the best. William sold the store in 1948 to finance a partnership in Wooten's Department Store in Texarkana Arkansas; he bought out Wooten and established Dillard's the next year.

Throughout the 1950s and 1960s the company became a strong regional retailer developing its strategy of buying well-established downtown stores in small cities; acquisitions in those years included Mayer & Schmidt (Tyler Texas; 1956) and Joseph Pfeifer (Little Rock Arkansas; 1963). Dillard's moved its headquarters to Little Rock after buying Pfeifer. When it went public in 1969 it had 15 stores in three states.

During the early 1960s the company began computerizing operations to streamline inventory and information management. In 1970 Dillard's added computerized cash registers which gave management hourly sales figures.

The chain continued acquiring outlets (more than 130 over the next three decades including stores owned by Stix Baer & Fuller Macy's Joske's and Maison Blanche). In a 1988 joint venture with Edward J. DeBartolo Dillard's bought a 50% interest in the 12 Higbee's stores in Ohio (buying the other 50% in 1992 shortly after Higbee's bought five former Horne's stores in Ohio).

In 1991 Vendamerica (subsidiary of Vendex International and the only major nonfamily holder of the company's stock) sold its 8.9 million shares of Class A stock (25% of the class) in an underwritten public offering.

Dillard's purchase of 12 Diamond stores from Dayton Hudson in 1994 gave it a small-event ticket-sales chain in the Southwest which it renamed Dillard's Box Office. A lawsuit filed by the FTC against Dillard's that year claiming the company made it unreasonably difficult for its credit card holders to remove unauthorized charges from their bills was dismissed the following year.

Dillard's continued to grow; it opened 11 new stores in 1995 and 16 more in 1996 (entering Georgia and Colorado). The next year it opened 12 new stores and acquired 20 making its way into Virginia California and Wyoming.

William retired in 1998 and William Dillard II took over the CEO position while brother Alex became president. The company then paid $3.1 billion for Mercantile Stores which operated 106 apparel and home design stores in the South and Midwest. To avoid redundancy in certain regions Dillard's sold 26 of those stores and exchanged seven others for new Dillard's stores. The assimilation of Mercantile brought distribution problems that cut into earnings for fiscal 1999. In late 2000 with a slumping stock price and declining sales Dillard's said it would de-emphasize its concentration on name-brand merchandise and offer deep discounts on branded items already in stock. Despite these efforts sales and earnings continued to slide in 2001.

Founder and patriarch William Dillard (the company's guiding force) died in February 2002. Son William II became chairman of the company which has been family-controlled for half a century. Dillard's opened four new stores and closed nine in 2002. Sales declined 3% versus the previous year.

In 2003 Dillard's shuttered 10 stores and opened five new store locations.

In November 2004 Dillard's completed the sale of Dillard National Bank the retailer's credit card portfolio to GE Consumer Finance for about $1.1 billion (plus debt). Dillard's had said it would use the proceeds to reduce debt repurchase stock and to achieve general corporate purposes.

In the spring of 2005 Dillard's shuttered the last of 16 home and furniture stores acquired when the department store chain acquired Mercantile Stores Co. in 1998. Hurricanes Katrina Rita and Wilma took a toll on Dillard's in 2005 interrupting business in about 60 of the company's stores at various times.

In August 2008 Dillard's purchased the 50% stake in the Arkansas-based construction firm CDI Contractors that it didn't already own for about $9.8 million. CDI is a general contactor that also builds stores for Dillard's. In November Dillard's announced 500 job cuts including about 60 at headquarters.

Amid falling sales and rising investor discontent Dillard's bowed to pressure from hedge funds Barington Capital Group and Clinton Group and appointed four new directors in April 2008 to avoid a proxy fight.

In February 2012 Dillard's acquired Acumen Brands an e-commerce company located in Fayetteville Arkansas.

EXECUTIVES

Evp, Drue Matheny, age 72, $735,000 total compensation

Evp, Mike Dillard, age 67, $735,000 total compensation

President, Alex Dillard, age 69, $1,000,000 total compensation

Chairman And Ceo, William (Bill) Dillard, age 74, $1,000,000 total compensation

Svp Co-principal Financial Officer And Principal Accounting Officer, Phillip R. Watts, age 56, $500,000 total compensation

Svp And Co-principal Financial Officer, Chris B. Johnson, age 47, $500,000 total compensation

Regional Vice President, Michael Hubbell

Vice President Advertising, Christine Rowell

Corporate Vice President Mdse And Ecomm, Sara Byrne

Upper Management Vice President, Kristin Jacobson

Assistant Vice President For Sponsored Programs, Theodore Callier

Vice President, Mike Shields

Vice President Accounting, Steve Gelwix

Executive Vice President And Director, Drue Corbusier

Vice President Advertising, Roger Williams

Vice President Merchanising, Mike McNiff

Vice President Merchandising St Louis Division, Mark Killingsworth

Vice President Sales Promotion, Louise Platt

Vice President District Manager, Bill Hite

Vp Mens, Gianni Duarte

Corporate Vice President Stores, Brant Musgrave

Svp, Denise Mahaffy

Assistant Vice President, Brian Gibbs

Secretary, Suzanne Stewart

Secretary, Shirley Wallace

Operations Secretary, Carole Kreider

Store Secretary, Joanie Byrd

Board Member, Lee Hastings

Treasurer, Kent Burnett

Board Member, Frank Mori

Board Member, Robert Connor

Board Member, Nick White

Auditors: KPMG LLP

LOCATIONS

HQ: Dillard's Inc.
 1600 Cantrell Road, Little Rock, AR 72201
Phone: 501 376-5200
Web: www.dillards.com

2017 Stores

	No.
Texas	58
Florida	42
Arizona	17
Louisiana	15
North Carolina	14
Ohio	14
Georgia	12
Oklahoma	10
Tennessee	10
Alabama	9
Missouri	9
Arkansas	8
Colorado	7
South Carolina	7
Kansas	6
Kentucky	6
Mississippi	6
New Mexico	6
Virginia	6
Iowa	5
Nevada	5
Utah	4
California	3
Illinois	3
Indiana	3
Nebraska	3
Idaho	2
Montana	2
Wyoming	1
Total	**293**

PRODUCTS/OPERATIONS

2017 Sales

	% of total
Ladies' apparel	22
Men's apparel & accessories	17
Shoes	16
Ladies' accessories & lingerie	16
Cosmetics	14
Juniors' & children's apparel	8
Home & furniture	4
Construction segment	3
Total	**100**

COMPETITORS

Abercrombie & Fitch	Macy's
American Eagle	Mattress Firm
Outfitters	Neiman Marcus
Ann Taylor	Nordstrom
Bed Bath & Beyond	Sears
Belk	Stein Mart
Bon-Ton Stores	TJX Companies
Burlington Coat	Tailored Brands
Factory	Talbots
Caleres	Target Corporation
Eddie Bauer LLC	The Gap
Foot Locker	Tuesday Morning
J. Crew	Corporation
Kohl's	Von Maur
Lands' End	Walgreen

HISTORICAL FINANCIALS

Company Type: Public

Income Statement   FYE: February 2

	REVENUE ($ mil.)	NET INCOME ($ mil.)	NET PROFIT MARGIN	EMPLOYEES
02/19	6,503	170	2.6%	39,000
02/18*	6,422	221	3.4%	40,000
01/17	6,418	169	2.6%	40,000
01/16	6,754	269	4.0%	40,000
01/15	6,780	331	4.9%	40,000
Annual Growth	(1.0%)	(15.4%)	—	(0.6%)

2019 Year-End Financials

Debt ratio: 16.57%	No. of shares (mil.): 26
Return on equity: 10.08%	Dividends
Cash ($ mil.): 123	Yield: 0.0%
Current ratio: 1.90	Payout: 6.4%
Long-term debt ($ mil.): 567	Market value ($ mil.): 1,729

	STOCK PRICE ($) FY Close	P/E High/Low		PER SHARE ($) Earnings	Dividends	Book Value
02/19	65.61	16	9	6.23	0.40	63.70
02/18*	63.68	11	6	7.51	0.34	60.77
01/17	54.65	18	11	4.93	0.28	53.41
01/16	70.41	21	9	6.91	0.26	49.98
01/15	113.60	16	11	7.79	0.24	49.02
Annual Growth	(12.8%)	—	—	(5.4%)	13.6%	6.8%

*Fiscal year change

Dime Community Bancshares, Inc

Dime Community Bancshares is in a New York state of mind. It is the holding company for Dime Community Bank (formerly The Dime Savings Bank of Williamsburgh) which boasts $4.5 billion in assets and operates more than 25 branches in Brooklyn Queens and the Bronx as well as Nassau County on Long Island. Founded in 1864 the bank provides standard products and services including checking savings retirement money market and club accounts accounts. Multifamily residential and commercial real estate loans comprise the vast majority of the bank's loan portfolio. Subsidiary Dime Insurance Agency (formerly Havemeyer Investments) offers life policies fixed annuities and wealth management services.

Operations

Multifamily residential real estate loans accounted for 80% of Dime Savings' $4 billion loan portfolio in 2014; most of these were secured by properties in Brooklyn Queens and Manhattan. Another 18% of the portfolio was made up of commercial real estate loans. The community-oriented bank believes that multifamily residential and mixed-use loans in the New York City area produce higher yields than securities with similar maturities.

The bank generated 93% of its total revenue from interest income on loans secured by real estate in 2014 while interest on mortgage-backed securities service charge fees mortgage banking income and other miscellaneous fees made up the rest of revenues.

Geographic Reach

The Brooklyn-based bank operates 25 branches in New York City in the boroughs of Brooklyn Queens and the Bronx as well as in Nassau County in New York.

Sales and Marketing

Dime Community's primary lending area is in the New York Metro area though its total lending area spans 50 miles from its headquarters' radius.

Financial Performance

Dime Community's revenue has been in decline in recent years due to shrinking interest margins on loans amidst the low-interest environment. The firm's profits however have been rising since 2012 thanks to declining loan loss provisions as its loan portfolio's credit quality has improved with the strengthened economy.

Dime's revenue dipped by less than 1% to $182 million in 2014 as the bank's interest income continued to decline on shrinking interest margins on both real estate loans and mortgage-backed securities. The bank blamed fierce mortgage refinancing competition for much of the 49 basis point-reduction of interest yields on its loan portfolio which led to lower interest income.

Despite lower revenue in 2014 the company's net income rose by nearly 2% to $44.25 million thanks to a continued decline in the provision for loan losses. Dime Community's operating cash fell by 23% to $47.26 million during the year due to lower cash earnings.

Strategy

Dime Community Bancshares has been moving toward digital banking channels that are quickly taking the industry by storm allowing the bank to slow expensive branch-expansion plans and cut operating costs significantly while giving customers faster access to banking services. In 2014 as part of its eBanking platform initiative to expand into online banking mobile banking bill pay and remote deposit the bank launched its Dime Mobile Banking platform which allowed customer to deposit checks pay bills transfer funds and check account balances and status from their smartphones.

EXECUTIVES

Evp And Chief Risk Officer, Timothy B. King, age 60, $342,000 total compensation
President And Ceo, Kenneth J. Mahon, age 68, $550,000 total compensation
Secretary, Lance J. Bennett, age 67
Sevp Business Banking, Stuart H. Lubow, age 61
Sevp And Coo, Robert S. Volino, age 47
Evp And Cto, Timothy K. Lenhoff, age 61
Evp And Chief Retail Officer, William E. Brown, age 52
Evp And Chief Administrative Officer, Anthony J. Rose, age 48
Evp Business Banking, Conrad J. Gunther, age 72
Principal Financial Officer Dime Community Bancshares Inc. And Dime Community Bank, James L. Rizzo
Vice President, Tom Dippolito
Vice Chairman, Michael P. Devine, age 72
Chairman, Vincent F. Palagiano, age 78
Auditors: Crowe LLP

LOCATIONS

HQ: Dime Community Bancshares, Inc
 300 Cadman Plaza West, 8th Floor, Brooklyn, NY 11201
Phone: 718 782-6200
Web: www.dime.com

PRODUCTS/OPERATIONS

2014 Sales

	$ mil.	% of total
Interest		
Loans secured by real estate	169	93
Mortgage-backed securities	0	1
Other	2	1
Noninterest		
Service charges & other fees	3	2
Bank-owned life insurance	1	1
Other	4	2
Total	**182**	**100**

COMPETITORS

Astoria Financial	HSBC
Carver Bancorp	JPMorgan Chase
Citigroup	Valley National
First of Long Island	Bancorp
Flushing Financial	

Income Statement | | | | FYE: December 31

	ASSETS ($ mil.)	NET INCOME ($ mil.)	INCOME AS % OF ASSETS	EMPLOYEES
12/18	6,320	51	0.8%	443
12/17	6,403	51	0.8%	421
12/16	6,005	72	1.2%	386
12/15	5,032	44	0.9%	388
12/14	4,497	44	1.0%	409
Annual Growth	8.9%	3.8%	—	2.0%

2018 Year-End Financials

Debt ratio: 19.60%
Return on equity: 8.54%
Cash ($ mil.): 147
Current ratio: —
Long-term debt ($ mil.): —

No. of shares (mil.): 36
Dividends
  Yield: 3.3%
  Payout: 38.6%
Market value ($ mil.): 613

	STOCK PRICE ($) FY Close	P/E High/Low		PER SHARE ($) Earnings	Dividends	Book Value
12/18	16.98	16	12	1.38	0.56	16.69
12/17	20.95	16	13	1.38	0.56	16.00
12/16	20.10	10	8	1.97	0.56	15.11
12/15	17.49	15	12	1.23	0.56	13.22
12/14	16.28	14	11	1.23	0.56	12.47
Annual Growth	1.1%	—	—	2.9%	(0.0%)	7.5%

HISTORICAL FINANCIALS
Company Type: Public

Income Statement | | | | FYE: December 31

	ASSETS ($ mil.)	NET INCOME ($ mil.)	INCOME AS % OF ASSETS	EMPLOYEES
12/18	109,553	2,742	2.5%	16,600
12/17	100,087	2,099	2.1%	16,500
12/16	92,308	2,393	2.6%	15,549
12/15	86,936	2,297	2.6%	15,036
12/14	83,126	2,323	2.8%	14,676
Annual Growth	7.1%	4.2%	—	3.1%

2018 Year-End Financials

Debt ratio: 24.85%
Return on equity: 24.90%
Cash ($ mil.): 13,299
Current ratio: —
Long-term debt ($ mil.): —

No. of shares (mil.): 331
Dividends
  Yield: 2.5%
  Payout: 19.2%
Market value ($ mil.): 19,549

	STOCK PRICE ($) FY Close	P/E High/Low		PER SHARE ($) Earnings	Dividends	Book Value
12/18	58.98	10	7	7.79	1.50	33.58
12/17	76.92	14	11	5.42	1.30	30.43
12/16	72.09	13	7	5.77	1.16	29.13
12/15	53.62	13	10	5.13	1.08	26.74
12/14	65.49	14	11	4.90	0.92	24.79
Annual Growth	(2.6%)	—	—	12.3%	13.0%	7.9%

Discover Financial Services

EXECUTIVES

Pres-Ceo, Roger C Hochschild
Chb*, Lawrence A Weinbach
Evp-Cfo*, John T Greene
Exec V Pres-Cro, Brian D Hughes
Exec V Pres-CIO, Glenn P Schneider
Exec V Pres-Chief Hr & ADM Off, R Andrew Eichfeld
Clo-Gen Coun, Wanji Walcott
Project Manager, Michael Tatevosian
Programmer Analyst, Patrick McKeown
Storage Manager, Paul Goodine
Consultant, Raymond Tan
Auditors: Deloitte & Touche LLP

LOCATIONS

HQ: Discover Financial Services
  2500 Lake Cook Road, Riverwoods, IL 60015
Phone: 224 405-0900
Web: www.discover.com

COMPETITORS

Ally Financial	JPMorgan Chase
American Express	MasterCard
Bank of America	Sallie Mae
Capital One	USAA
Citigroup	Visa Inc
First Data	Wells Fargo

Discovery Inc

Discovery allows viewers to go on safari without ever having to leave their couch. The company is the world's #1 provider of non-fiction TV programming with about 20 cable TV networks that together reach approximately 4 billion subscribers in more than 220 countries. Properties include the Discovery Channel Animal Planet Oprah Winfrey Network (OWN) and The Learning Channel (TLC). Discovery also operates digital streaming services and publishes online content through Discovery.com and AnimalPlanet.com. It gained Food Network HGTV and Travel Channel when it acquired Scripps Networks in 2018 creating a powerhouse of unscripted entertainment brands. The US accounts for about 60% of revenue.

HISTORY

John Hendricks a history graduate who wanted to expand the presence of educational programming on TV founded Cable Educational Network in 1982. Three years later he introduced the Discovery Channel. Devoted entirely to documentaries and nature shows the channel premiered in 156000 US homes. After dodging bankruptcy (it had $5000 cash and $1 million in debt to the BBC) within a year the Discovery Channel had 7 million subscribers and a host of new investors including Cox Communications and TCI (later AT&T Broadband). It expanded its programming from 12 hours to 18 hours a day in 1987.

Discovery continued to attract subscribers reaching more than 32 million by 1988. The next year it launched Discovery Channel Europe to more than 200000 homes in the UK and Scandinavia. The company began selling home videos in 1990 and entered the Israeli market. The following year Discovery Communications Inc. (DCI) was formed to house the company's operations and it bought The Learning Channel (TLC founded

1980). The company revamped TLC's programming and in 1992 introduced a daily six-hour commercial-free block of children's programs. The next year it introduced its first CD-ROM title In the Company of Whales based on the Discovery Channel documentary.

DCI increased its focus on international expansion in 1994 moving into Asia Latin America the Middle East North Africa Portugal and Spain. The next year the company introduced its website and began selling company merchandise such as CD-ROMs and videos. DCI solidified its move into the retail sector in 1996 with the acquisition of The Nature Company and Scientific Revolution chains (renamed Discovery Channel Store). Also that year it launched its third major cable channel Animal Planet.

The company continued expanding internationally throughout the mid-1990s establishing operations in Australia Canada India New Zealand and South Korea (1995); Africa Brazil Germany and Italy (1996); and Japan and Turkey (1997). DCI also added to its stable of cable channels with the purchase of 70% of the Travel Channel from Paxson Communications (later ION Media Networks) in 1997. (It acquired the remaining 30% interest in 1999.) The company's 1997 original production "Titanic: Anatomy of a Disaster" attracted 3.2 million US households setting a network ratings record.

The following year DCI and the BBC launched Animal Planet in Asia through a joint venture and agreed to market and distribute new cable channel BBC America. It also bought CBS 's Eye on People renaming the channel Discovery People (DCI shut the channel down in 2000). DCI spent $330 million launching its new health and fitness channel Discovery Health in 1999 and formed partnerships with high-speed online service Road Runner (to provide interactive information and services to Road Runner customers) and Rosenbluth Travel (to provide vacation packages based on DCI programming).

DCI reorganized its Internet activities into one unit called Discovery.com in 2000 with plans to eventually take it public. Later that year the Discovery Channel set back-to-back records with the two highest-rated documentaries ever on cable "Raising the Mammoth" (10.1 million people) and "Walking With Dinosaurs" (10.7 million people). In 2001 the company cut about 50 jobs as part of a restructuring. Later that year Discovery Communications struck a three-year deal to lease time from NBC on Saturday mornings (paying $6 million per season) to show its Discovery Kids programs.

In 2002 the company launched a 24-hour high-definition television network called Discovery HD Theater. Two years later founder John Hendricks relinquished his CEO duties (he remained chairman). President Judy McHale replaced him.

DCI started off 2005 by rebranding its aviation-themed Discovery Wings channel as the Military Channel. Later that year former majority owner Liberty Media placed its stake in DCI into a new company called Discovery Holding which it then spun off to Liberty shareholders.

Early in 2007 former NBC Universal Cable executive David Zaslav was named CEO replacing McHale. DCI later bought out 25%-partner Cox Communications in exchange for $1.3 billion in cash along with such assets as the Travel Channel and Antenna Audio. It also began shuttering its chain of Discovery Channel Stores as part of a cost-cutting effort.

Joint venture partners Discovery Holding and Advance/Newhouse (an affiliate of Advance Publications) combined their stakes in Discovery Communications in 2008 spinning off DCI as a public company.

Over the next few years DCI worked diligently to launch new networks targeting a diverse selection of audience segments. In 2010 it rolled out The Hub a channel targeting kids ages 2-11. Another 50/50 joint venture with toy maker Hasbro The Hub offers programming based on many of Hasbro's popular brands including G.I. Joe Scrabble Tonka and Transformers.

In early 2011 the company helped launch OWN talk show host Oprah Winfrey's new network and 3net one of the first networks dedicated to providing 3D programming 24 hours a day.

EXECUTIVES

President Ceo And Director, David M. Zaslav, age 60, $3,000,000 total compensation
Group President Discovery Channel Animal Planet And Science Channel, Rich Ross, age 58
President Own: Oprah Winfrey Network And Harpo Studios, Erik Logan
Chief Commercial Officer, Paul (Guyardo) Guagliardo, age 55, $1,400,000 total compensation
Group President Investigation Discovery American Heroes Channel And Destination America, Henry S. Schleiff, age 70
Evp And Head International Business Operations Discovery Networks International, John Honeycutt
President Discovery Networks International, Jean-Briac (JB) Perrette, $1,381,557 total compensation
President And Managing Director Discovery Networks Asia-pacific, Arthur Bastings
President And Ceo Discovery Education, Bill Goodwyn
President International Development Digital And Discovery Nordics, Michael (Mike) Lang, age 54
Evp Global Communications And Corporate Affairs, David C. Leavy
Chief Development Distribution And Legal Officer, Bruce L. Campbell, age 52, $1,544,423 total compensation
President And General Manager Tlc, Nancy Daniels
President And Managing Director Discovery Networks Latin America/u.s. Hispanic And Canada, Enrique R. (Henry) Mart nez
Chief Human Resources And Global Diversity Officer, Adria Alpert-Romm, age 64, $801,058 total compensation
President And Managing Director Discovery Networks Central & Eastern Europe Middle East And Africa, Kasia Kieli
Cfo, Gunnar Wiedenfels
Ceo Eurosport, Peter Hutton
President Domestic Distribution, Eric Phillips
President And Managing Director Discovery Networks Southern Europe, Marinella Soldi
President International Content Group, Susanna Dinnage
Vice President Operations And Prod Development Partnerships, Kevin Malone
Vice President Operations, Toni Herbert
Vice President Financial Planning And Analysis, Matthew Deprey
Executive Vice President Advertising Sales Mtv Networks Kids And Family Group, Jim Perry
Carrie D Storer Senior Vice President Human Resources And Compliance Legal, Carrie Storer
Senior Vice President Of Operations, Veronica Cajigas
Vice President, John Saag
Vice President, Michela Giorelli
Senior Vice President Investor Relations, Craig Felenstein
Senior Vice President Distribution, Meg Lowe
Senior Vice President Us Media Operations, Don Johnson
Vice President Strategy And Account Management, Todd Richards
Chairman, Robert J. (Bob) Miron, age 82
Auditors: PricewaterhouseCoopers LLP

LOCATIONS

HQ: Discovery Inc
  8403 Colesville Road, Silver Spring, MD 20910
Phone: 240 662-2000
Web: www.discoverycommunications.com

PRODUCTS/OPERATIONS

2017 Sales

	$ mil.	% of total
Distribution	3,474	51
Advertising	3,073	45
Other	326	4
Total	**6,873**	**100**

2017 Sales

	$ mil.	% of total
US networks	3,434	50
International networks	3,281	48
Education & other	158	2
Corporate & adjustments	(2)	-
Total	**6,873**	**100**

Selected Mergers and Acquisitions
FY2012
Revision3 ($30 million; San Francisco CA; digital video provider)

Selected Operations
Cable channels
  Animal Planet
  Discovery Channel
  Discovery Kids
  Investigation Discovery
  Planet Green
  Science Channel
  TLC (The Learning Channel)
Commerce and education
  Discovery Education
  DiscoveryStore.com
Business and Brands
U.S. Networks
Discovery Networks International
Discovery Education
Discovery Commerce
Discovery Digital Media
Revision3
Discovery Enterprises International
Discovery Studios

COMPETITORS

A&E Networks	NBCUniversal
AMC Networks	PBS
CBS Corp	Turner Broadcasting
Disney	Viacom
E! Entertainment Television	

HISTORICAL FINANCIALS
Company Type: Public

Income Statement
FYE: December 31

	REVENUE ($ mil.)	NET INCOME ($ mil.)	NET PROFIT MARGIN	EMPLOYEES
12/18	10,553	594	5.6%	9,000
12/17	6,873	(337)	—	7,000
12/16	6,497	1,194	18.4%	7,000
12/15	6,394	1,034	16.2%	7,000
12/14	6,265	1,139	18.2%	6,800
Annual Growth	13.9%	(15.0%)	—	7.3%

2018 Year-End Financials
Debt ratio: 52.37%
Return on equity: 9.14%
Cash ($ mil.): 986
Current ratio: 1.06
Long-term debt ($ mil.): 15,185
No. of shares (mil.): 523
Dividends
  Yield: —
  Payout: —
Market value ($ mil.): 12,963

	STOCK PRICE ($) FY Close	P/E High/Low	PER SHARE ($) Earnings	Dividends	Book Value
12/18	24.74	39 24	0.86	0.00	16.00
12/17	22.38	— —	(0.59)	0.00	12.07
12/16	27.41	15 12	1.96	0.00	13.29
12/15	26.68	22 16	1.58	0.00	13.30
12/14	34.45	54 19	1.66	0.00	12.75
Annual Growth	(7.9%)	— —	(15.2%)	—	5.8%

DISH Network Corp

DISH Network believes entertainment (and news and sports) is a dish best served from the sky and over the internet. The company is one of the biggest pay-TV providers in the US serving about 12 million household subscribers as well as hotels motels and other commercial accounts. Programming includes premium movies on-demand video service regional and specialty sports local and international channels and pay-per-view in addition to basic video programming. Its relatively new Sling TV offering provides streaming video over the internet. DISH generates almost all sales in the US.

Operations

DISH Network's revenue comes from its satellite and streaming pay-TV subscriptions. The satellite service relies on satellite dishes that are set up on customers' structures (homes and commercial buildings) to receive signals. Signals reach those dishes from the 11 satellites that DISH owns or leases orbiting some 22300 miles above the equator. (DISH Network added another nine satellites in 2019 in a deal with EchoStar.) The company also leases set-top boxes and video recorders to subscribers.

The Sling streaming service is transmitted over the internet and is geared to consumers who don't subscribe to cable or satellite services. Sling-branded pay-TV services consist of live streaming programming for US and international markets.

Among DISH Network's assets is a range of radio spectrum for wireless service. The company spent some $21 billion over the past decade to amass the spectrum holdings.

Geographic Reach

While virtually all of DISH Network's revenue is from US customers the company gets a fraction of sales from Canada and Mexico. The company based in the Denver suburb of Englewood operates 10 call centers in seven states. Its major digital broadcast operations facilities are in Cheyenne Wyoming and Gilbert Arizona.

Sales and Marketing

DISH Network gains new subscribers through third parties including national retailers and telecommunications firms local and regional electronics stores and small satellite retailers among other channels. Of its 12 million subscribers about 10 million are DISH customers and two million are Sling subscribers.

Financial Performance

DISH Network's revenue peaked in 2015 after seven years of steady growth. Revenue has declined in the past three years with the loss of subscribers in the face of increasing competition from streaming video services.

The company's revenue dropped 5% to $13.6 billion in 2018 from 2017 due to a net loss of 932000 subscribers. Sling TV gained about 200000 subscribers in 2018 about half a million subscribers less than signed up in 2017. The monthly average revenue per user (for satellite and Sling TV) fell to $85.46 in 2018 from $86.43 in 2017 because Sling TV's lower cost was averaged into the cost of satellite TV service.

Net income fell to $1.5 billion in 2018 from $2.1 billion in 2017 when the company had a tax benefit in 2017 that was not repeated in 2018.

The holdings of cash and equivalents in DISH Network's coffers slid to $887 million in 2018 from $1.4 billion in 2017. Operations provided $2.5 billion in 2018 while investing activities used $1.9 billion and financing activities used $1.1 billion.

Strategy

DISH Network is going over the heads of telecommunications companies to build a network for 5G wireless service. The fifth generation of wireless networks 5G is supposed to be much faster than its predecessors unlocking myriad applications. DISH Network has spent $21 billion over 10 years to stockpile wireless spectrum licenses that it would deploy for a 5G-capable network. DISH Network's narrow band network is to focus on service for devices connected to the Internet of Things sensors and other devices that collect and transmit data from weather readings to communications between driverless cars. The company plans to start the network in 2020.

In programming DISH Network has focused much of its attention on its Sling TV packages aimed at customers who have cut their subscription to cable and satellite TV services. The company expanded its Sling packages to offer consumers more choices: The Sling TV Blue service offers streaming over multiple devices while the original service now Sling TV Orange streams to one device.

While Sling TV has helped DISH Network is it enough to enable it to compete with increasingly fierce rivals? Rival pay-TV services have added content arms to supplement their distribution assets. Satellite TV provider DirecTV has the backing of giant telecom AT&T which added the Time Warner news and entertainment offerings (such as HBO CNN and TNT) through an acquisition. Cable provider Comcast is taking advantage of its NBCUniversal division to bolster its offerings. Furthermore the Netflix Hulu YouTube and Amazon.com's Prime video streaming services have put pressure on DISH Network and its pay-TV colleagues.

DISH added to its satellite capacity in 2019 spending $800 million (all in stock) for nine broadcast satellites from EchoStar.

Mergers and Acquisitions

DISH added to its satellite fleet with the purchase of assets from EchoStar. DISH paid $800 million in stock for nine direct broadcast satellites licensing for the 61.5-degree orbital slot and some real estate properties. In a 2017 deal with EchoStar DISH bought set-top box development Sling TV technology software development employees and US satellite TV ground infrastructure.

In 2018 Dish acquired Parkifi a developer of sensors for parking lots. Parkifi adds experience in connecting low-powered sensors with the cloud to DISH.

Company Background

Charlie Ergen a former financial analyst for Frito-Lay founded a Denver company called Echosphere a retailer of large-dish C-band satellite TV equipment with his wife Cantey and James DeFranco in 1980. Echosphere which preceded DISH Network evolved into a national manufacturer and distributor which in 1987 began its move toward the new direct broadcast satellite (DBS) delivery system. It filed for a DBS license and set up subsidiary EchoStar Communications Corporation to build launch and operate DBS satellites. In 1992 the FCC granted the company an orbital slot.

By 1994 Echosphere was the US's largest distributor of conventional home satellite equipment but the future clearly rested with DBS and EchoStar. A 1995 reorganization renamed the firm EchoStar Communications; the Echosphere distributor business became a subsidiary. EchoStar also created the DISH (Digital Sky Highway) Network brand aiming for an easier-to-remember name than its rivals' "DSS" and "USSB."

EXECUTIVES

Evp Strategic Planning, Bernard L. (Bernie) Han, age 54, $500,000 total compensation
Evp Sales And Distribution And Director, James (Jim) DeFranco, age 67, $374,640 total compensation
Chairman And Ceo, Charles W. (Charlie) Ergen, age 65, $1,000,000 total compensation
Evp Corporate Development, Thomas A. (Tom) Cullen, age 59, $450,000 total compensation
President And Coo, W. Erik Carlson, age 49, $515,000 total compensation
Evp General Counsel And Secretary, R. Stanton Dodge, age 51, $296,155 total compensation
Evp And Cto, Vivek Khemka, age 46
Evp Operations, John W. Swieringa, age 41
Evp Customer Acquisition And Retention, Brian V. Neylon, age 53
Svp And Cfo, Steven E. (Steve) Swain, age 51, $357,539 total compensation
Evp Marketing Programming And Media Sales, Warren W. Schlichting, age 57, $372,885 total compensation
Svp And Cio, Rob Dravenstott
Svp And Chief Marketing Officer, Jay Roth
Vice President Corporate Development, Theodore Henderson
Vice President Sales, Christopher Samuelson
Vice President, Melissa Gonzalez
National Sales Manager, Jessica Palframan
Vice President Of Finance, Kevin Gelston
National Account Manager, Brett Temple
Vice President Human Resources, Aaron Lapoint
National Account Manager, Brian Cox
National Accounts Manager, Christopher Guthery
National Sales Manager, Milena Bontcheva
Marketing Vice President, Alfredo Rodriguez
National Sales Manager, Perry Crider
National Sales Manager, Carlene Attick
National Sales Manager, Andrew Hirko
Senior Vice President And Deputy General Counsel, Jeffrey Blum
Vp Partner Marketing, Bassil Khatib
Vice President Corporate Communications, Bob Toevs
Vice President Of Corporate Initiatives, Rex Povenmire
National Account Manager, Laura Haessler
Vice President Human Resources, Rob Fuchs
Senior Vice President Sec, David K Moskowitz
Svp Manufacturing, Jim Larocque
Vice President, Jim Defranco
Senior Vice President Of Sales, Carlos Barberi
Vice President Of Sales And Marketing, Michael Kinner
Vice President Of Marketing, Shathabi Ravindra
Vice President, Jeff Anderson
Vice President Operations, Jeremy Mccarty
Vice President Hardwareengineering, Mark Gomez
Senior Vice President Supply Chain And Operations, Gareth Hughes
Vp Engineering, Terry Pattison
Vice President And Associate General Counsel, Katzin Lawrence R
National Sales Manager Strategic Channels, Josh Rogers
Senior Vice President Product Developmen, Rao Paddy
Treasurer, Jason Kiser
Auditors: KPMG LLP

LOCATIONS

HQ: DISH Network Corp
9601 South Meridian Boulevard, Englewood, CO 80112
Phone: 303 723-1000   **Fax:** 303 723-1499
Web: www.dishnetwork.com

2018 Sales

	$ mil.	% of total
United States	13,578	100
Canada and Mexico	43	-
Total	**13,621**	**100**

PRODUCTS/OPERATIONS

2018 Sales

	$ mil.	% of total
Subscriber-related revenue	13,456	99
Equipment sales and other revenue	165	1
Total	**13,621**	**100**

COMPETITORS

AT&T	Grande Communications
Altice USA	Hulu
Amazon.com	Netflix
Charter Communications	Roku
Comcast	Time Warner Cable
Cox Communications	Verizon
DIRECTV	YouTube

HISTORICAL FINANCIALS

Company Type: Public

Income Statement				FYE: December 31
	REVENUE ($ mil.)	NET INCOME ($ mil.)	NET PROFIT MARGIN	EMPLOYEES
12/18	13,621	1,575	11.6%	16,000
12/17	14,391	2,098	14.6%	17,000
12/16	15,094	1,449	9.6%	16,000
12/15	15,068	747	5.0%	18,000
12/14	14,643	944	6.5%	19,000
Annual Growth	(1.8%)	13.6%	—	(4.2%)

2018 Year-End Financials

Debt ratio: 49.54%	No. of shares (mil.): 467
Return on equity: 20.28%	Dividends
Cash ($ mil.): 887	Yield: —
Current ratio: 0.69	Payout: —
Long-term debt ($ mil.): 13,810	Market value ($ mil.): 11,683

	STOCK PRICE ($) FY Close	P/E High/Low		PER SHARE ($) Earnings	Dividends	Book Value
12/18	24.97	15	7	3.00	0.00	18.37
12/17	47.75	15	10	4.07	0.00	14.87
12/16	57.93	19	13	3.05	0.00	9.97
12/15	57.18	49	35	1.61	0.00	5.92
12/14	72.89	39	26	2.04	0.00	4.36
Annual Growth	(23.5%)	—	—	10.1%	—	43.3%

Disney (Walt) Co. (The)

EXECUTIVES

Chb-Ceo, Robert A Iger
Sr Exec V Pres-Cfo, Christine M McCarthy
Sr Exec V Pres-Gen Counsel-Sec, Alan N Braverman
Sr Exec V Pres-Cso, Kevin A Mayer
Sr Exec V Pres-Chief Hr Office, M Jayne Parker
Senior Vice President, Dorothy Attwood

HISTORICAL FINANCIALS

Company Type: Public

Income Statement   FYE: September 28

	REVENUE ($ mil.)	NET INCOME ($ mil.)	NET PROFIT MARGIN	EMPLOYEES
09/19	69,570	11,054	15.9%	223,000
09/18	59,434	12,598	21.2%	201,000
09/17*	55,137	8,980	16.3%	199,000
10/16	55,632	9,391	16.9%	195,000
10/15	52,465	8,382	16.0%	185,000
Annual Growth	7.3%	7.2%	—	4.8%

*Fiscal year change

2019 Year-End Financials

Debt ratio: 24.22%
Return on equity: 16.11%
Cash ($ mil.): 5,418
Current ratio: 0.90
Long-term debt ($ mil.): 38,129

No. of shares (mil.): 1,783
Dividends
  Yield: 0.0%
  Payout: 26.5%
Market value ($ mil.): 231,719

	STOCK PRICE ($) FY Close	P/E High/Low		PER SHARE ($) Earnings	Dividends	Book Value
09/19	129.96	22	15	6.64	1.76	49.85
09/18	116.94	14	12	8.36	1.68	32.78
09/17*	98.57	20	16	5.69	1.56	27.23
10/16	92.86	21	15	5.73	1.42	27.09
10/15	103.00	25	17	4.90	1.81	26.81
Annual Growth	6.0%	—	—	7.9%	(0.7%)	16.8%

*Fiscal year change

Dollar General Corp

Dollar General commands the field of discount general merchandise. The fast-growing retailer boasts some 14500 discount stores in some 45 US states mostly in the South the Midwest and the Southwest. It generates more than 75% of its sales from consumables (including refrigerated shelf-stable and perishable foods) and more than 10% from seasonal items. The stores also offer household products (cleaning supplies and health and beauty aids) and apparel. Dollar General targets low- middle- and fixed-income shoppers pricing

items at $10 or less. The no-frills stores typically measure about 7400 sq. ft. and are in small towns that are off the radar of giant discounters.

HISTORY

J. L. Turner was 11 when his father was killed during the 1890s in a Saturday night wrestling match. This forced J. L. to drop out of school and work on the family farm which was weighted by a mortgage. By his 20s J. L. who never learned to read well was running an area general store. Experiencing some success he branched out and purchased two stores of his own. They failed but J. L. rebounded going to work for a wholesaler. With the onset of the Depression J. L. found he could buy out the inventories of failing merchants for next to nothing using short-term bank loans that were quickly repaid.

In 1939 J. L. was joined by his son Cal. The two each put up $5000 to start a new Scottsville Kentucky-based dry goods wholesaling operation called not surprisingly J.L. Turner & Son. It was not until 1945 when the company experienced a glut of women's underwear that it expanded into retail. J.L. Turner & Son sold off the dainties in their first store located in Albany Kentucky. Within a decade the company was operating 35 stores. In 1956 J.L. Turner & Son introduced its first experimental Dollar General Store — all items priced less than a dollar — in Springfield Kentucky. Like the company's first stores the dollar store concept would grow: Dollar General Stores numbered 255 a decade later.

Cal Jr. J. L.'s 25-year-old grandson joined the family business in 1965 and became a director in 1966. The company changed its name to Dollar General and went public two years later. In 1977 Cal Jr. was named president and CEO. That year Dollar General acquired Arkansas-based United Dollar Stores.

The early 1980s saw Dollar General continue its acquisition-powered growth. The company bought INTERCO's 280-store P.N. Hirsch chain and the 203-store Eagle Family Discount chain in 1983 and 1985 respectively. To cope with expanded distribution demands Dollar General opened an additional distribution center in Homerville Georgia in 1986 to help out the original Scottsville facility. The acquisitions led by Cal Jr.'s brother Steve ended up costing the company dearly; Dollar General's 1987 stock price dropped nearly 85%. The next year they also cost Steve his job: He was forced out by the company's new chairman Cal Jr. In addition to ousting Steve Cal Jr. replaced more than half of Dollar General's executives in 1988. The retailer began moving toward everyday low pricing (la Wal-Mart) in the late 1980s.

Growth from then on was powered by internal expansion. In 1990 the company operated nearly 1400 stores; by 1995 it had more than 2000. To accommodate the growth Dollar General built a third distribution center in Ardmore Oklahoma in 1995 and another in South Boston Virginia in 1997.

While continuing to focus on small towns and neighborhoods Dollar General has expanded beyond the Southeast and Midwest opening its first stores in New York and New Jersey in 2001. In 2004 the company opened more than 700 locations and expanded into Arizona New Mexico and Wisconsin.

In April 2005 the company settled a Securities and Exchange Commission investigation into the circumstances that resulted in a $100 million earnings restatement for the years 1998 through 2000 with payment of a $10 million civil penalty.

To support its growth Dollar General opened a new distribution center in South Boston (its ninth)

in 2006 and one in Union County South Carolina in mid-2005. Also in 2006 the retailer expanded its warehouse in Ardmore Oklahoma.

In July 2007 Dollar General was taken private by Kohlberg Kravis & Roberts GS Capital Partners (an affiliate of Goldman Sachs) and Citi Private Equity an investment arm of Citigroup in a deal valued at $7.3 billion.

In November 2009 the company went public with an offering valued at $716 million. The fast-growing chain opened its 9000th store in late July 2010.

Dollar General in August 2014 bid $78.50 per share for its smaller rival Family Dollar Stores. The all-cash offer which valued Family Dollar at about $9.7 billion topped a standing offer for Family Dollar from Dollar Tree of $74.50 in cash and stock. The addition of Family Dollar's 8200 stores would solidify Dollar General's standing as the largest in its industry. By July 2015 however Dollar Tree had prevailed in the bid and completed its acquisition that month. Before Dollar Tree's triumph Dollar General revealed that it may have had to sell between 1500 and 4000 stores prior to the deal closing in order to comply with regulators.

EXECUTIVES

LOCATIONS

HQ: Dollar General Corp
100 Mission Ridge, Goodlettsville, TN 37072
Phone: 615 855-4000   **Fax:** 615 855-5527
Web: www.dollargeneral.com

No. of stores in 2018

	No.
Texas	1,413
Georgia	827
Florida	825
North Carolina	787
Ohio	755
Tennessee	733
Alabama	720
Other states	8,549
Total	**14,609**

PRODUCTS/OPERATIONS

2018 Sales

	$ mil.	% of total
Consumables	18,054	77
Seasonal	2,837	12
Home Products	1,400	6
Apparel	1,178	5
Total	**23,471**	**100**

Selected Merchandise

Basic apparel
Cleaning supplies
Dairy products
Frozen foods
Health and beauty aids
Housewares
Packaged foods
Seasonal goods
Stationery

COMPETITORS

99 Cents Only	Kroger
ALDI	Lidl
Big Lots	Rite Aid
CVS	TJX Companies
Costco Wholesale	Target Corporation
Dollar Tree	Variety Wholesalers
Family Dollar Stores	Wal-Mart
Fred's	Walgreen
Kmart	

HISTORICAL FINANCIALS

Company Type: Public

Income Statement

FYE: February 1

	REVENUE ($ mil.)	NET INCOME ($ mil.)	NET PROFIT MARGIN	EMPLOYEES
02/19	25,625	1,589	6.2%	135,000
02/18	23,470	1,538	6.6%	129,000
02/17*	21,986	1,251	5.7%	121,000
01/16	20,368	1,165	5.7%	113,400
01/15	18,909	1,065	5.6%	105,500
Annual Growth	**7.9%**	**10.5%**	**—**	**6.4%**

*Fiscal year change

2019 Year-End Financials

Debt ratio: 21.70%
Return on equity: 25.41%
Cash ($ mil.): 235
Current ratio: 1.55
Long-term debt ($ mil.): 2,862

No. of shares (mil.): 259
Dividends
  Yield: 1.0%
  Payout: 19.4%
Market value ($ mil.): 29,854

	STOCK PRICE ($) FY Close	P/E High/Low	PER SHARE ($) Earnings	Dividends	Book Value
02/19	115.04	20 14	5.97	1.16	24.73
02/18	99.44	19 12	5.63	1.04	22.80
02/17*	73.14	22 15	4.43	1.00	19.64
01/16	75.06	21 15	3.95	0.88	18.76
01/15	67.06	20 15	3.49	0.00	18.82
Annual Growth	**14.4%**	**— —**	**14.4%**	**—**	**7.1%**

*Fiscal year change

Dollar Tree Inc

Dollars may not grow on trees but Dollar Tree brings in the green. The fast-growing company operates more than 15000 Dollar Tree and Family Dollar discount stores across the US and in five provinces in Canada. The stores carry a mix of housewares toys seasonal items food health and beauty aids and books. At Dollar Tree shops most goods are priced at $1 or less while Family Dollar merchandise is usually less than $10. The stores are generally located in high-traffic strip centers and malls often in midsized cities and small towns.

Operations

Dollar Tree reports its operations through the Dollar Tree and Family Dollar brands. Each brand generates about half of the company's overall revenue.

The Dollar Tree division built around merchandise at the $1 price point has about 7000 stores with an average of some 8000-10000 sq. ft. of sales space. Family Dollar operates through nearly 8200 stores which are a bit smaller at 6000-8000 sq.ft. of sales space; it offers competitively priced merchandise often less than $10.

From a product standpoint the consumables category (candy food health and beauty products household paper products) accounts for about 60% of sales; variety merchandise (toys housewares gifts) electronics and seasonal offerings bring in the rest.

Geographic Reach

Dollar Tree operates stores across the US. Its largest markets are Texas Florida Ohio North Carolina and California which together account for about a third of locations. It has some 225 stores in Canada with about half in Ontario.

The Dollar Tree segment has about a dozen distribution centers in the US two distribution centers in Canada and a store support center in Chesapeake Virginia. The Family Dollar segment has more than 10 distribution centers across the US and a store support center in Matthews North Carolina (which is being moved to Virginia in late 2019).

Sales and Marketing

The Dollar Tree brand primarily serves middle income customers in suburban locations with Family Dollar serving lower income customers in urban and rural locations.

The company's advertising costs totaled $100 million in fiscal 2018 (ended January 2019) compared to $106 million in 2017 and $60 million in 2016.

Financial Performance

Dollar Tree saw its revenue nearly double in fiscal 2016 as a result of the acquisition of Family Dollar and the growth has only continued as the company opens new stores each year. Net income sank the year of the acquisition but had been rising until 2018 when it plummeted because of goodwill impairment. The company took on quite a bit of debt related to the Family Dollar acquisition although it has been reduced by about 40% in the past three years.

In fiscal 2018 (ended January 2019) the company reported record revenue of $22.8 billion up 3% from the prior year. The results were driven by new stores as well as an increase of nearly 2% in same-store sales (powered by the Dollar Tree segment). The weak spot financially for Dollar Tree is the flat same-store sales for Family Dollar (0.1% in 2018); the company has struggled to get that brand growing at a faster clip.

Net income fell from $1.7 billion in fiscal 2017 to a loss of $1.6 billion in 2018. The steep drop was primarily the result of a $2.7 billion goodwill

impairment charge based on a reassessment of the Family Dollar segment.

Cash at the end of fiscal 2018 was $446.7 million a decrease of $651.1 million from the prior year. Cash from operations contributed $1.8 billion to the coffers while investing activities used $816.7 million mainly for capital expenditures. Financing activities used another $1.6 billion for payments on long-term debt primarily.

Strategy

Fast-growing Dollar Tree opens hundreds of new locations each year. In fiscal 2018 it opened more than 400 new stores and relocated or expanded another 70 locations and plans similarly sized initiatives in fiscal 2019. The company envisions some 26000 stores across North America ultimately.

With its strong store portfolio Dollar Tree is focused on adding new merchandise options and refreshing locations. It has been adding coolers and freezers to its Dollar Tree stores (more than 450 in 2018) to boost the consumables business including frozen and refrigerated foods and more directly compete with convenience and grocery stores. In addition the company has introduced Snack Zones which provides easy access to immediately consumable goods to hundreds of stores. Within the Family Dollar brand Dollar Tree is investing in renovation with some 500 stores revamped in 2018 and another 1000 planned for the following year; improvements include more productive endcaps more beverage and snack offerings updated hair care assortments and in some stores expanded adult beverages.

Unlike many retailers dollar stores are a bit more immune to competitive pressure from Amazon and other online sites. For that reason the company has not had to invest in building a robust omnichannel experience with e-commerce platforms and apps. It is however cutting costs as it works to jumpstart the stalled Family Dollar business. In late 2018 Dollar Tree announced it would close Family Dollar's North Carolina corporate office and eliminate about 200 jobs as a result (the other 700 positions will be relocated to the company's Virginia headquarters).

Company Background

In 1953 K. R. Perry opened a variety store in Norfolk Virginia called Ben Franklin; it was later renamed K&K 5&10. By 1970 Perry and two other men established a mall concept store called K&K Toys also in Virginia although it eventually grew to some 130 locations along the East Coast. A third chain Only $1.00 was started in 1986 with stores located alongside K&K Toys stores.

K&K Toys was sold in the early 1990s to KB Toys and proceeds from the sale were used to expand the dollar store chain. By 1995 that chain Only $1.00 had become Dollar Tree and gone public.

Dollar Tree expanded through new store openings and acquisitions culminating in the 2015 purchase of North Carolina-based Family Dollar for about $9 billion.

EXECUTIVES

Chief Supply Chain Officer, Gary A. Maxwell, age 57

Cfo, Kevin S. Wampler, age 56, $690,385 total compensation

President Ceo And Director, Gary M. Philbin, age 62, $1,121,154 total compensation

Cio, Joshua R. (Josh) Jewett, age 49

President And Coo Family Dollar Stores, Duncan C. Mac Naughton, age 57, $61,538 total compensation

Chief Administrative Officer, Michael (Mike) Matacunas, age 52, $537,500 total compensation

Chief Merchandising Officer, Robert H. (Bob) Rudman, age 68, $740,385 total compensation
President And Coo Dollar Tree, Michael Witynski, age 56
Vice President Treasurer, Roger Dean
Svp Store Operations, Tom Mcaloon
Chairman, Bob Sasser, age 67
Board Member, Stephanie Stahl
Auditors: KPMG LLP

LOCATIONS

HQ: Dollar Tree Inc
500 Volvo Parkway, Chesapeake, VA 23320
Phone: 757 321-5000
Web: www.dollartree.com

2018 Canadian Stores

	No.
Ontario	110
British Columbia	49
Alberta	37
Saskatchewan	16
Manitoba	13
Total	**225**

2018 US Stores

	No.
Texas	1,622
Florida	1,107
Ohio	757
North Carolina	721
California	725
Georgia	665
New York	641
Michigan	628
Pennsylvania	622
Other states	7,524
Total	**0** **15,012**

PRODUCTS/OPERATIONS

2018 Sales

	% of total
Consumables	62
Other	38
Total	**100**

2018 Sales

	$ mil.	% of total
Dollar Tree	11,712	51
Family Dollar	11,111	49
Total	**22,823**	**100**

Selected Products

Books
Candy
Cards
Food
Gifts
Health and beauty care products
Housewares
Party goods
Personal accessories
Seasonal goods
Stationery
Toys

COMPETITORS

99 Cents Only	OllieÂ's Bargain
ALDI	Outlet
Big Lots	Rite Aid
CVS	SUPERVALU
Dollar General	Savers Inc.
Five Below	Target Corporation
Fred's	Wal-Mart
Kmart	Walgreen

HISTORICAL FINANCIALS

Company Type: Public

Income Statement

FYE: February 2

	REVENUE ($ mil.)	NET INCOME ($ mil.)	NET PROFIT MARGIN	EMPLOYEES
02/19	22,823	(1,590)	—	182,100
02/18*	22,245	1,714	7.7%	176,100
01/17	20,719	896	4.3%	176,800
01/16	15,498	282	1.8%	167,800
01/15	8,602	599	7.0%	90,000
Annual Growth	**27.6%**	**—**	**—**	**19.3%**

*Fiscal year change

2019 Year-End Financials

Debt ratio: 31.59%
Return on equity: (-24.88%)
Cash ($ mil.): 422
Current ratio: 2.05
Long-term debt ($ mil.): 4,265

No. of shares (mil.): 238
Dividends
 Yield: —
 Payout: —
Market value ($ mil.): 23,020

	STOCK PRICE ($) FY Close	P/E High/Low	PER SHARE ($) Earnings	Dividends	Book Value
02/19	96.69	— —	(6.66)	0.00	23.70
02/18*	108.83	16 9	7.21	0.00	30.26
01/17	74.05	26 19	3.78	0.00	22.82
01/16	81.32	66 48	1.26	0.00	18.76
01/15	71.10	25 17	2.90	0.00	8.68
Annual Growth	**8.0%**	**— —**	**—**	**—**	**28.6%**

*Fiscal year change

Dominion Energy Inc (New)

Dominion Energy dominates the American energy market as one of its top producers and transporters of electricity and natural gas. It serves some 6 million utility and retail energy customers across 12 US states with a special concentration in Ohio Virginia West Virginia and Pennsylvania. The company boasts an impressive energy portfolio with approximately 26000 MW of generating capacity as well as one of the largest underground natural gas storage systems with 1 trillion cu. ft. capacity. Formerly Dominion Resources the company changed its name to Dominion Energy in 2017.

HISTORY

In 1781 the Virginia General Assembly established a group of trustees including George Washington and James Madison to promote navigation on the Appomattox River. The group (named the Appomattox Trustees) formed the Upper Appomattox Company in 1795 to secure its water rights. The company eventually began operating hydroelectric plants on the river and by 1888 it had added a steam-powered plant to its portfolio.

The Virginia Railway and Power Company (VR&P) led by Frank Jay Gould purchased the Upper Appomattox Company (which had changed its name) in 1909. The next year the firm acquired several electric and gas utilities as well as some electric streetcar lines.

In 1925 New York engineering company Stone & Webster acquired VR&P. The company became known as Virginia Electric and Power Company (Virginia Power) and was placed under Engineers

Public Service (EPS) a new holding company. Virginia Power purchased several North Carolina utilities following its acquisition.

During the 1930s the Depression (and the popularity of the automobile) led the company to exit the trolley business. The Public Utility Holding Company Act of 1935 (repealed 2005) which ushered in an era of regulated utility monopolies forced EPS to divest all of its operations except Virginia Power. However the utility soon merged with the Virginia Public Service Company thus doubling its service territory.

The company added new power plants to keep up with growing customer demand in the 1950s. Always an innovator it also built an extra-high-voltage transmission system the first in the world.

In the 1970s Virginia Power's first nuclear plants became operational. By 1980 however the firm was near bankruptcy. That year William Berry who had completed a 23-year rise through the ranks to become president canceled two other nuclear units. He also became an early supporter of competition in the electric utility industry. In 1983 he formed Dominion Resources as a parent company for Virginia Power and halted nearly all plant construction. Two additional subsidiaries were soon formed: Dominion Capital in 1985 and Dominion Energy in 1987.

In 1990 the year Thomas Capps took over as CEO Dominion sold its natural gas distribution business and in 1995 Dominion Energy began developing natural gas reserves through joint ventures and by purchasing three natural gas exploration and production companies.

The company acquired UK utility East Midlands Electricity in 1997. However after it was hit by a hefty windfall tax by the newly elected Labour Party and its hopes for mergers with other UK utilities were dashed it sold East Midlands to PowerGen just 18 months after acquiring it.

In 1999 Dominion prepared for energy deregulation through reorganization. It separated its electricity generation activities from its transmission and distribution operations. In 2000 Dominion bought Consolidated Natural Gas (CNG) for $9 billion making it one of the largest fully integrated gas and electric power companies in the US; it then sold CNG's Virginia Natural Gas to AGL Resources and the two firms' combined Latin American assets to Duke Energy.

Virginia Power moved to head off state and federal lawsuits in 2000 by agreeing to spend $1.2 billion over 12 years to reduce pollution from coal-fired plants. The company also agreed to pay $1.3 billion for Eversource Energy's Millstone nuclear power complex that year (the deal closed in 2001). Also in 2000 Dominion changed its brand name from Dominion Resources to just Dominion and rebranded several of its subsidiaries as well.

In 2001 Dominion bought exploration and production company Louis Dreyfus Natural Gas for about $1.8 billion in cash and stock and $500 million in assumed debt; the acquisition added 1.8 trillion cu. ft. of natural gas equivalent to Dominion's proved reserves. The company also sold the assets of its financial services unit Dominion Capital that year.

The following year Dominion purchased a 500-MW Chicago power plant from US power producer Mirant (now GenOn Energy)for $182 million and it purchased the Cove Point LNG (liquefied natural gas) import facility from The Williams Companies for $217 million.

Dominion began to prepare for power deregulation implemented in most of its service territories by expanding its nonregulated electric operations. The company also divested its non-US operations to focus on its businesses in the Northeast Mid-Atlantic and Midwest. In 2004 it sold its telecom business to private firm Elantic Networks. The firm completed the acquisition of three fossil-fueled plants (2800 MW) from USGen New England a subsidiary of National Energy & Gas Transmission for $656 million in 2005. That was the same year Dominion purchased the 550-MW Kewaunee nuclear plant from WPS Resources subsidiary Wisconsin Public Service and Alliant Energy subsidiary Wisconsin Power & Light for $220 million.

At the end of 2006 Dominion Exploration & Production had proved reserves of 6.5 trillion cu. ft. of natural gas equivalent. The next year Dominion began to dismantle the unit selling its offshore operations in the Gulf of Mexico to Eni; its assets in Alabama Michigan and Texas to Loews Corp.; its Mid-Continent operations to Linn Energy; and operations in the Rocky Mountain and Gulf Coast regions to XTO Energy. Dominion Resources pocketed almost $14 billion from the sales.

To free up cash and hone its business focus the company has sold most of its exploration and production operations in recent years. In 2010 the company sold its remaining Appalachian exploration and production assets to CONSOL Energy for about $3.5 billion. The acquisition doubled CONSOL's natural gas reserves to 3 million cu. ft. (In 2007 Dominion sold the bulk of its oil and gas exploration and production assets — excluding its Appalachian operations because at the time they offered less risk — for nearly $14 billion.)

In a related move Dominion agreed to sell its Appalachian gas distribution companies The Peoples Natural Gas Company and Hope Gas located in Pennsylvania and West Virginia to investment firm SteelRiver Infrastructure Partners for $910 million. After receiving approval from Pennsylvania the deal was rejected in late 2009 by West Virginia saying the terms of the agreement were not in the public interest. The company then sold just Peoples Natural Gas to SteelRiver in 2010 for $780 million.

Dominion's divestments allow it to concentrate its efforts on its core power generation and gas and electricity distribution businesses along with its trading and marketing activities.

In 2012 Dominion announced plans to sell three fossil fuel-fired merchant power stations (one in Massachusetts and two in Illinois) as part of its transition to cleaner burning and renewable power plants.

On the gas side of the business in 2012 Dominion and Caiman Energy II LLC formed a $1.5 billion joint venture (Blue Racer Midstream LLC) to provide midstream services to natural gas producers operating in the Utica shale in Ohio and portions of Pennsylvania.

In 2013 Dominion Virginia Power put the Altavista Power Station into commercial operation with renewable biomass as its fuel the first of three such stations to be converted from coal to biomass.

EXECUTIVES

Ceo Dominion Generation Group, Paul D. Koonce, age 59, $680,138 total compensation
Evp Dominion Resources And Consolidated Natural Gas; President And Ceo Dominion Energy, Thomas F. Farrell, age 64, $1,502,372 total compensation
Vp Corporate Strategy And Chief Risk Officer, Simon Hodges
Evp And Cfo, Mark F. McGettrick, age 61, $850,055 total compensation
Evp; Ceo Dominion Generation Group, David A. Christian, age 64, $680,138 total compensation
President And Chief Nuclear Officer Dominion Nuclear, David A. Heacock, age 61, $528,098 total compensation
President And Ceo Dominion Virginia Power, Robert M. (Bob) Blue, age 51

Svp And Cio, P. Rodney Blevins
President And Ceo Dominion Energy, Diane G. Leopold, age 52
President Dominion Questar, Craig C. Wagstaff
Svp Operations Engineering And Construction, Scot C. Hathaway
Svp Corporate Affairs And Chief Legal Officer, Mark O. Webb, age 54
President Dominion Midstream Operations, Paul F. Ruppert
Vice President State And Electric Public Policy, William Murray
Vice President Of Information Technology, Kris Morelli
Vice President Nuclear Operations, Daniel G Stoddard
Senior Vice President, Barbara Roland
Senior Vice President Pipeline Customer Service And Business Development, Donald Raikes
Vice President Government Affairs, Daniel Weekley
Vice President Customer Service Dominion Virginia Power, Charlene Whitfield
Senior Vice President Distribution, Edward Ed Baine
Vice President Nuclear Engineering, Mark Sartain
Vp And Chief Security Officer, Adam S Lee
Vp Corporate Communications, Gregory A Hitt
Board Member, William Barr
Auditors: DELOITTE & TOUCHE LLP

LOCATIONS

HQ: Dominion Energy Inc (New)
120 Tredegar Street, Richmond, VA 23219
Phone: 804 819-2000   **Fax:** 804 775-5819
Web: www.dom.com

PRODUCTS/OPERATIONS

2016 Sales

	$ mil.	% of total
Dominion Generation	6,757	55
Dominion Energy	2,766	22
DVP	2,233	18
Corporate and Other	602	5
Adjustments & Eliminations	(621)	
Total	**11,737**	**100**

2016 Sales

	$ mil.	% of total
Electric Sales	8,867	76
Gas transportation and Storage	1,636	14
Gas Sales	854	7
Other	380	3
Total	**11,737**	**100**

Selected Subsidiaries and Business Units

Dominion Generation Corporation (power plant management)
Dominion Energy (energy marketing gas and power transmission)
 Dominion Transmission Inc. (natural gas pipelines)
Dominion Virginia Power
 Consolidated Natural Gas
 Dominion East Ohio (or The East Ohio Gas Company gas distribution)
 Dominion Hope (or Hope Gas Inc. West Virginia gas distribution)
 Dominion North Carolina Power (or Virginia Electric and Power Company electricity distribution)
 Dominion Retail Inc. (retail energy marketing)
 Virginia Electric and Power Company (electricity distribution)

COMPETITORS

AEP	Exelon
CenterPoint Energy	Koch Industries Inc.
Duke Energy	NiSource
Entergy	Piedmont Natural Gas

HISTORICAL FINANCIALS

Company Type: Public

Income Statement   FYE: December 31

	REVENUE ($ mil.)	NET INCOME ($ mil.)	NET PROFIT MARGIN	EMPLOYEES
12/18	13,366	2,447	18.3%	21,300
12/17	12,586	2,999	23.8%	16,200
12/16	11,737	2,123	18.1%	16,200
12/15	11,683	1,899	16.3%	14,700
12/14	12,436	1,310	10.5%	14,400
Annual Growth	**1.8%**	**16.9%**		**10.3%**

2018 Year-End Financials

Debt ratio: 40.49%
Return on equity: 13.14%
Cash ($ mil.): 268
Current ratio: 0.67
Long-term debt ($ mil.): 31,144
No. of shares (mil.): 681
Dividends
 Yield: 4.6%
 Payout: 89.3%
Market value ($ mil.): 48,664

	STOCK PRICE ($) FY Close	P/E High/Low	PER SHARE ($) Earnings	Dividends	Book Value
12/18	71.46	21 17	3.74	3.34	29.53
12/17	81.06	18 15	4.72	3.04	26.58
12/16	76.59	23 20	3.44	2.80	23.26
12/15	67.64	25 20	3.20	2.59	21.25
12/14	76.90	36 28	2.24	2.40	19.75
Annual Growth	**(1.8%)**	— —	**13.7%**	**8.6%**	**10.6%**

Domtar Corp

Auditors: PricewaterhouseCoopers LLP

LOCATIONS

HQ: Domtar Corp
234 Kingsley Park Drive, Fort Mill, SC 29715
Phone: 803 802-7500
Web: www.domtar.com

HISTORICAL FINANCIALS

Company Type: Public

Income Statement   FYE: December 31

	REVENUE ($ mil.)	NET INCOME ($ mil.)	NET PROFIT MARGIN	EMPLOYEES
12/18	5,455	283	5.2%	10,000
12/17	5,157	(258)	—	10,000
12/16	5,098	128	2.5%	10,000
12/15	5,264	142	2.7%	9,850
12/14	5,563	431	7.7%	9,800
Annual Growth	**(0.5%)**	**(10.0%)**	—	**0.5%**

2018 Year-End Financials

Debt ratio: 17.34%
Return on equity: 11.27%
Cash ($ mil.): 111
Current ratio: 2.03
Long-term debt ($ mil.): 853
No. of shares (mil.): 62
Dividends
 Yield: 4.9%
 Payout: 38.8%
Market value ($ mil.): 2,210

STOCK PRICE ($)	P/E	PER SHARE ($)		
FY Close	High/Low	Earnings	Dividends	Book Value
12/18	35.13	12 8	4.48	1.74	40.34
12/17	49.52	— —	(4.11)	1.66	39.60
12/16	39.03	21 15	2.04	1.65	42.76
12/15	36.95	21 16	2.24	1.60	42.20
12/14	40.22	17 5	6.64	1.40	45.15
Annual Growth	(3.3%)	— —	(9.4%)	5.6%	(2.8%)

Donnelley (RR) & Sons Company

If you can read it RR Donnelley & Sons (RRD) can print it (and digitize distribute and market it too). The company is evolving from a provider of printing services to a full-on communications services firm. Its primary offerings fall under the Business Services category and include commercial print packaging labels and forms as well as supply chain management and business process outsourcing. RRD also has a Marketing Services segment which produces direct mail in-store marketing materials and creative campaigns. The company has operations in more than 30 countries but most revenue comes from the US.

Operations

RR Donnelley's (RRD's) Business Services segment accounts for more than 80% of the company's sales while its Marketing Solutions segment accounts for the remaining 20%.

Commercial printing products and branded materials such as manuals publications brochures business cards flyers post cards posters and promotional items accounts for more than a third of the company's Business Services segment's revenue. Packaging ranging from rigid boxes to in-box print materials for clients in consumer electronics life sciences cosmetics and consumer packaged goods industries account for about 12% of the segment's revenue. The remaining revenue comes from statements labels forms supply chain management and business process outsourcing. This Business Services segment includes all RRD's operations in Asia Europe Canada and Latin America.

Direct marketing — including audience segmentation creative development program testing print production postal optimization and performance analytics for large-scale direct mail programs— accounts for nearly half of Marketing Solutions' net sales. Digital print and fulfillment accounts for 40% of Marketing Solutions while creative services and other related services account for the remainder.

Geographic Reach

RR Donnelley headquartered in Chicago operates about 215 facilities in the US and nearly 90 facilities in Asia Europe Canada and Latin America.

The US accounts for about 75% of the company's revenue while Asia accounts for about 15% and Europe contributes more than 5%. Other countries and regions generate the remainder.

Sales and Marketing

RR Donnelley claims more than 50000 customers including 95 of the Fortune 100 companies. The company?s five largest clients account for about 10% of sales.

Financial Performance

Since 2015 RR Donnelley (RRD) has reported losses while revenue has held steady hovering between $6.8 billion and $6.9 billion during the last five fiscal years. The company has felt pressure from declines in commercial print and forms products continued price pressures in most parts of its business and highly competitive market conditions.

Revenue in 2018 was $6.8 million a decrease of about 2% from 2017. The disposition of RRD's Print Logistics business contributed to the decline as did lower volume in commercial print due to market trends and lower specialty card sales as well as price pressures. The decreases were offset by higher volume primarily in packaging the remaining logistics business and direct marketing.

RRD recorded a loss of about $11 million in 2018 an improvement over the 2017 loss of $34 million. The company has initiated several restructuring actions to reduce costs including closing manufacturing facilities and reorganizing or consolidating some operations.

The company had $404 million in cash at the end of 2018. Cash generated by operations was $203.5 million. Cash used in investing was $7.4 million and cash used in financing was $77.2 million.

Strategy

RR Donnelley (RRD) is implementing strategic initiatives across each of its segments to reduce its overall cost structure and enhance productivity primarily through consolidations reorganizations integrations of operations and streamlining of administrative and support activities. It divested its Print Logistics business in 2018 to focus on its strategic transformation as a marketing and business communications company.

In 2018 RRD reduced its reporting structure from three internally based segments (Variable Print Strategic Services and International) to two outwardly focused segments (Business Services and Marketing Solutions). RRD made the change to organize operations by common strategic purposes help it better meet the rapidly changing needs of its customers and allow stakeholders to better assess the company's progress.

RRD?s business markets are fiercely competitive with larger companies and smaller regional firms vying for customers? attention. The competition forces prices lower. Bigger firms buying smaller ones could increase price pressures as remaining competitors lower prices.

Company Background

RR Donnelley was once even bigger than it is now before it split itself up into three separate publicly traded companies in 2016. The breakup of the $11.7 billion conglomerate was conducted to "maximize shareholder value" by creating more focused companies. RR Donnelley kept the business communications and business process outsourcing holdings as the largest surviving entity with $7 billion in sales and 42000 employees. The other two entities include LSC Communications a $3.7 billion 22000-employee company serving magazine catalog and book publishers; and Donnelley Financial Solutions which has 3500 workers and $1.05 billion in sales and focuses on critical financial investment and legal communications.

EXECUTIVES

Evp And Cfo, Terry D. Peterson, age 54, $168,750 total compensation
Ceo, Daniel L. (Dan) Knotts, age 55, $781,250 total compensation
Evp And Chief Administrative Officer, Thomas M. Carroll, age 53, $450,000 total compensation
Cio, Ken O'Brien
Evp Global Markets, John P. Pecaric, age 53, $396,250 total compensation

Evp Domestic Operations, Glynn Perry
President Dls, Charles Fattore
Vice President Sales, Robert Eaton
Senior Vice President Sales, James Martin
Senior Vice President, Kim Yates
Vice President Of Lending, Maureen Lein
Executive Vice President Director, Chris Harder
Chairman, John C. (Jack) Pope, age 69
Treasurer, Douglas Rees
Auditors: DELOITTE & TOUCHE LLP

LOCATIONS

HQ: Donnelley (RR) & Sons Company
35 West Wacker Drive, Chicago, IL 60601
Phone: 312 326-8000
Web: www.rrd.com

2017 sales

	$ mil.	% of total
U.S	5,233	75
Asia	857	12
Europe	455	7
Other	394	6
Total	**6,939**	**100**

PRODUCTS/OPERATIONS

2017 Sales

	$ mil.	% of total
Variable Print	3,113	45
Strategic Services	1,765	25
International	2,060	30
Total	**6,939**	**100**

2017 Sales

	$ mil.	% of total
Product	5,326	77
Services	1,613	23
Total	**6,939**	**100**

Selected Operations

US print and related services
  Book (consumer religious educational and specialty and telecommunications)
  Direct mail (content creation database management printing personalization finishing and distribution in North America)
  Directories (yellow and white pages)
  Logistics (consolidation and delivery of printed products; expedited distribution of time-sensitive and secure material; print-on-demand warehousing and fulfillment services)
  Magazine catalog and retail inserts
  Short-run commercial print (annual reports marketing brochures catalog and marketing inserts pharmaceutical inserts and other marketing retail point-of-sale and promotional materials and technical publications)
International
  Business process outsourcing
  Global Turnkey Solutions (product configuration customized kitting and order fulfillment)

Selected Capabilities:

Digital
Print
Consulting & Execution
Logistics & supply chain
Industry solutions

COMPETITORS

Accenture	Merrill
Arandell	Penn Lithographics
Capgemini	Quad/Graphics
Cenveo	St Ives
Dai Nippon Printing	St. Joseph Communications
Deluxe Corporation	Taylor Corporation
EBSCO	Toppan Printing
Harte-Hanks	Transcontinental Inc.
IBM Global Services	Valassis
Infosys	
M & F Worldwide	

HISTORICAL FINANCIALS

Company Type: Public

Income Statement   FYE: December 31

	REVENUE ($ mil.)	NET INCOME ($ mil.)	NET PROFIT MARGIN	EMPLOYEES
12/18	6,800	(11)	—	39,500
12/17	6,939	(34)	—	42,700
12/16	6,895	(495)	—	44,360
12/15	11,256	151	1.3%	68,400
12/14	11,603	117	1.0%	68,000
Annual Growth	(12.5%)	—	—	(12.7%)

2018 Year-End Financials

Debt ratio: 57.45%
Return on equity: ***,***,**%
Cash ($ mil.): 370
Current ratio: 1.35
Long-term debt ($ mil.): 1,875

No. of shares (mil.): 70
Dividends
  Yield: 8.5%
  Payout: —
Market value ($ mil.): 279

	STOCK PRICE ($) FY Close	P/E High/Low		PER SHARE ($) Earnings	Dividends	Book Value
12/18	3.96	—	—	(0.16)	0.34	(3.69)
12/17	9.30	—	—	(0.49)	0.56	(3.10)
12/16	16.32	—	—	(7.09)	0.14	(1.51)
12/15	14.72	9	7	2.19	3.12	9.81
12/14	16.81	12	8	1.77	3.12	8.92
Annual Growth	(30.3%)	—	—	(42.5%)		—

Dover Corp

Dover operates in three segments: engineered systems (products for printing and identification transportation waste handling and industrial markets); fluids (fluid handling products for retail fueling oil and gas chemical and hygienic markets); and refrigeration and food equipment (systems and products serving the commercial refrigeration and food service industries). It generates more than 45% of revenue outside the US. Dover traces its historical roots back to 1947. In mid-2018 Dover spun off its former energy segment — equipment used in the extraction and handling of oil and gas ?- as Apergy Corporation.

Operations

Dover operates through three segments: Engineered Systems Fluids and Refrigeration and Food Equipment.

The Engineered Systems segment accounts for around 40% of total revenue and is divided into two sub-segments: Printing and Identification and Industrials. The Printing and Identification division makes precision marking and coding digital textile printing and soldering and dispensing equipment. The Industrials unit serves the vehicle service industrial automation and waste and recycling sectors with products such as light and heavy-duty vehicle lifts vehicle diagnostics and module automation components such as clamps conveyors and pick-and-place machinery.

Fluids (about 40% of revenue) makes products to handle fluids in the retail fueling chemical hygienic oil and gas and industrial markets. Products include pumps coupling systems fuel and chemical dispensing equipment and hydrodynamic bearings and reciprocating compressor components.

Refrigeration & Food Equipment generates about 20% of sales and includes the kind of fridges found in supermarkets and convenience stores as well as heat exchangers used in industrial applica-

tions and climate control. Food equipment offerings include commercial foodservice equipment wash systems kitchen ventilation systems conveyors and beverage can-making machinery.

Geographic Reach

Dover has a significant worldwide presence and operates in Australia Brazil Canada China Eastern Europe France Germany India Malaysia Mexico the Middle East the Netherlands Switzerland Sweden the UK and the US.

The US generates more than 50% of Dover's revenue while Europe accounts for about 25%. Other countries in the Americas generate around 10% as does the Asia/Pacific region.

Sales and Marketing

Dover sells directly to customers as well as through a network of distributors. It caters to the supermarket industry including big-box retail and convenience stores the commercial/industrial refrigeration industry institutional and commercial food service and food production markets and beverage can-making industries.

Its products are sold to national dealership networks original equipment manufacturers national multi-shop operations groups independent repair and service shops large national accounts and government/transit customers through a network of distributors and channel partners.

Financial Performance

Dover's revenue has seen steady growth the last three years rising 16% between 2016 and 2018. The company's Fluids segment has been the chief growth driver.

Sales in 2018 increased nearly 3% to $7 billion compared to $6.8 billion in 2017. Growth in 2018 was led by organic growth in Dover's Fluids and Engineered Systems segments. A favorable pricing environment also boosted revenue.

Net income decreased 30% to $570.3 million in 2018 compared to 2017 primarily due to lower earnings from continued operations.

Cash at the end of 2018 was $396.2 million a decrease of $357.8 million from the prior year. Cash from operations contributed $789.2 million to the coffers while investing activities used $245.5 million mainly for capital expenditures. Financing activities used $897.8 million primarily for repurchases of common stock.

Strategy

Dover relies on a steady stream of divestitures and acquisitions as its principal means for growth. It goes for bolt-ons that enhance existing businesses (through global reach or products strategy) or more rarely larger standalone businesses that provide synergies or bring innovative technologies in growth spaces.

Between 2016 and 2018 Dover spent $1.7 billion across 10 such purchases. On the other hand in the same period it sold several businesses for $583 million. In mid-2018 Dover also spun off its former energy segment — equipment used in the extraction and handling of oil and gas ? as Apergy Corporation.

Mergers and Acquisitions

Dover's acquisition activity is significant.

In mid-2019 Dover acquired All-Flo Pump Company which was rolled into the Pump Solutions Group (PSG) unit within Dover's Fluids segment. All-Flo is a manufacturer of specialty air-operated double-diaphragm (AODD) pumps used in a wide range of industrial applications. The addition of All-Flo enhances PSG's lineup of AODD pumps and expands its geographic and channel reach.

Earlier in 2019 Dover bought Belanger Inc. a leading manufacturer of vehicle wash equipment and systems. Belanger adds to the vehicle wash systems operations of Dover's Fluids segment.

In 2018 it acquired Ettlinger Group a German manufacturer of filtering solutions for the recycling industry. The company opens Dover to the virgin

and higher-growth recycled plastics processing market and enhances the company's Fluids segment. Also in 2018 Dover acquired Rosario Handel a Dutch manufacturer of decorator and base coating machinery used in the production of drink food and aerosol cans. The deal beefs up the company's Refrigeration & Food Equipment segment.

Company Background

George Ohrstrom a New York stockbroker formed Dover in 1955 and took it public that year. Originally headquartered in Washington DC Dover consisted of four companies: C. Lee Cook (compressor seals and piston rings) Peerless (space-venting heaters) Rotary Lift (automotive lifts) and W.C. Norris (components for oil wells). In 1958 Dover made the first of many acquisitions and entered the elevator industry by buying Shepard Warner Elevator.

HISTORY

George Ohrstrom a New York stockbroker formed Dover in 1955 and took it public that year. Originally headquartered in Washington DC Dover consisted of four companies: C. Lee Cook (compressor seals and piston rings) Peerless (space-venting heaters) Rotary Lift (automotive lifts) and W.C. Norris (components for oil wells). In 1958 Dover made the first of many acquisitions and entered the elevator industry by buying Shepard Warner Elevator.

EXECUTIVES

Vp; President And Ceo Dover Fluids, William W. (Bill) Spurgeon, age 61, $650,000 total compensation

President And Ceo, Robert A. (Bob) Livingston, age 65, $1,030,000 total compensation

President And Ceo Dover Energy, Sivasankaran (Soma) Somasundaram, age 54, $502,000 total compensation

Svp And Cfo, Brad M. Cerepak, age 60, $670,000 total compensation

President And Ceo Dover Engineered Systems, C. Anderson Fincher, age 48, $530,000 total compensation

President And Ceo Refrigeration And Food Equipment, William T. Bosway

President Dover Business Services, S. Gary Kennon

Vice President Communications, Adrian Sakowicz

Vice President Global Human Resources, Cynthia Wells

Executive Vice President, James Moyle

Vp Tax, Anthony Kosinski

Vice President Internal Audit, Cynthia Boumann

Vice President And Deputy General Counsel, Alison Rhoten

Vice President Human Resources, David Schmit

Corporate Vice President Human Resources, Rich Cooper

Vice President Sales (institutional Accounts), Beth Hammer

Vp And Associate Counsel Global Regulatory Affairs, Beverly Wyckoff

Vice President Software Engineering, Sreedhar Patnala

Vice President Corporate Development, Andrey Galiuk

Chairman, Michael F. (Mike) Johnston, age 71

Board Member, Stephen Wagner

Board Member, Stephen Todd

Vice President Treasurer, James Moran

Board Member, Keith Wandell

Auditors: PricewaterhouseCoopers LLP

LOCATIONS

HQ: Dover Corp
  3005 Highland Parkway, Downers Grove, IL 60515
Phone: 630 541-1540
Web: www.dovercorporation.com

2017 Sales

	$ mil.	% of total
Americas		
United States	4	57
Other Americas	735	9
Europe	1,504	19
Asia	774	10
Other	391	5
Total	**6,830**	**100**

PRODUCTS/OPERATIONS

2017 Sales

	$ mil.	% of total
Engineered Systems	2,576	33
Fluids	2,250	29
Refrigeration & Food Equipment	1,599	20
Energy	1,406	18
Intra-segment eliminations	(1.3)	-
Total	**6,794**	**100**

Selected Brands

Engineered Systems
Caldera
Destaco
JK Group

Fluids
CPC
Dover Fueling Solutions
Hydro

Energy
Accelerated
Cook Compression
Dover Artifical Lift
Refrigeration & Food Equipment
Anthony
Belvac
Hillphoenix

COMPETITORS

Alfa Laval	Middleby
Brother Industries	Navistar
Carlisle Companies	Oshkosh Truck
Crane Co.	PACCAR
Danaher	Paul Mueller
Danfoss	RAKON LIMITED
Dayco Products	SPX
Domino Printing	Schlumberger
Fortive	Sequa
Franklin Electric	Siemens AG
Gardner Denver	Smith Bits
Hussmann International	Snap-on
IDEX	Swagelok
Illinois Tool Works	Tatung
Ingersoll-Rand	Thermador Groupe
KEMET	Vesuvius
KSB AG	Wastequip
Kaydon	Weatherford
Lufkin Industries	International
Manitowoc	Zebra Technologies

HISTORICAL FINANCIALS

Company Type: Public

Income Statement
FYE: December 31

	REVENUE ($ mil.)	NET INCOME ($ mil.)	NET PROFIT MARGIN	EMPLOYEES
12/18	6,992	570	8.2%	24,000
12/17	7,830	811	10.4%	29,000
12/16	6,794	508	7.5%	29,000
12/15	6,956	869	12.5%	26,000
12/14	7,752	775	10.0%	27,000
Annual Growth	(2.5%)	(7.4%)	—	(2.9%)

2018 Year-End Financials

Debt ratio: 37.82%		No. of shares (mil.): 144	
Return on equity: 15.95%		Dividends	
Cash ($ mil.): 396		Yield: 2.6%	
Current ratio: 1.37		Payout: 50.6%	
Long-term debt ($ mil.): 2,943		Market value ($ mil.): 10,282	

	STOCK PRICE ($) FY Close	P/E High/Low	Earnings	PER SHARE ($) Dividends	Book Value
12/18	70.95	28 18	3.75	1.90	19.11
12/17	100.99	19 15	5.15	1.82	28.31
12/16	74.93	24 16	3.25	1.72	24.45
12/15	61.31	14 10	5.46	1.64	23.51
12/14	71.72	21 15	4.59	1.55	22.70
Annual Growth	(0.3%)	—	(4.9%)	5.2%	(4.2%)

Dow Inc

Auditors: DELOITTE & TOUCHE LLP

LOCATIONS

HQ: Dow Inc
  2211 H.H. Dow Way, Midland, MI 48674
Phone: 989 636-1000
Web: www.dow.com

HISTORICAL FINANCIALS

Company Type: Public

Income Statement
FYE: December 31

	REVENUE ($ mil.)	NET INCOME ($ mil.)	NET PROFIT MARGIN	EMPLOYEES
12/19	42,951	(1,359)	—	36,500
12/18	60,278	4,499	7.5%	37,000
12/17	55,508	466	0.8%	—
12/16	48,158	4,318	9.0%	—
Annual Growth	(3.7%)	—	—	—

2019 Year-End Financials

Debt ratio: 28.08%		No. of shares (mil.): 741	
Return on equity: (-6.73%)		Dividends	
Cash ($ mil.): 2,367		Yield: 3.8%	
Current ratio: 1.57		Payout: —	
Long-term debt ($ mil.): 15,975		Market value ($ mil.): 40,582	

	STOCK PRICE ($) FY Close	P/E High/Low	Earnings	PER SHARE ($) Dividends	Book Value
12/19	54.73	— —	(1.84)	2.10	18.26
12/18	0.00	— —	(0.00)	0.00	
268,310,000.00					
Annual Growth	—	—	—	(99.6%)	

DTE Electric Company

Ford Motors is not the only powerhouse operating in Detroit — DTE Electric is another. The utility (formerly known as Detroit Edison) generates and distributes electricity to 2.2 million customers in Michigan mainly around Detroit with expansion north to Lake Huron and east to Ann Arbor. The company a unit of regional power player DTE Energy has more than 11000 MW of generating capacity from its interests in primarily fossil-fueled nuclear and hydroelectric power plants. It operates more than 46000 circuit miles of distribution lines and owns and operates more than 670 distribution substations.

Operations

The largest electric utility in Michigan DTE Electric has a 1 million utility poles 671 distribution substations and 430600 line transformers.

The utility operates nine fossil fuel-(coal and oil) fired generating plants and one nuclear power plant (which accounts for 30% of Michigan's nuclear power output). It also co-owns a hydroelectric pumped storage plant with Consumers Energy.

Geographic Reach

The company serves customers across a 7600-sq. ml. service area in southeastern Michigan.

Financial Performance

Reflecting a stronger economy and growing demand in 2012 DTE Electric's revenues increased by 3% to $5.3 billion due to an 8% jump in residential segment sales 11% growth in commercial segment revenues and a 13% increase in industrial segment sales. Net income increased 11% in 2012 due to stronger sales and a 13% jump in other income.

The company has seen consistent revenue growth over the past five years.

Strategy

To meet the state requirements for reducing carbon emissions in 2009 the company announced plans to add 1200 MW of renewable power by 2015 half through contracts with third-parties and the remainder through its own renewable energy projects (primarily wind farms). In 2011 the company was working on developing a 200 MW wind farm.

In 2010 the company began operating a 60-kW solar energy plant in Scio Township in Washtenaw County the first installation to produce power for the grid under DTE Electric's SolarCurrents program. Its 270 solar panels include 60 that track the sun's movement.

EXECUTIVES

Sr V Pres-Cfo, Peter B Oleksiak
Cao, Donna M England
Senior Electrical Super, Bryan Fowler
Strategic Category Manager, Michelle Underwood
Operations Analyst, Georgetta Davis
Mechanical Engineer, Emily Yatch
Engineer, Mohammed Jalil
Auditors: PricewaterhouseCoopers LLP

LOCATIONS

HQ: DTE Electric Company
  One Energy Plaza, Detroit, MI 48226-1279
Phone: 313 235-4000
Web: www.dteenergy.com

PRODUCTS/OPERATIONS

2016 Sales

	$ mil.	% of total
Residential	2,477	47
Commercial	1,754	34
Industrial	654	12
Interconnection sales	50	1
Other	290	6
Total	**5,225**	**100**

COMPETITORS

Consumers Energy	WEC Energy
Indiana Michigan Power	Xcel Energy

Company Type: Public

Income Statement   FYE: December 31

	REVENUE ($ mil.)	NET INCOME ($ mil.)	NET PROFIT MARGIN	EMPLOYEES
12/19	5,224	716	13.7%	4,900
12/18	5,298	664	12.5%	4,900
12/17	5,102	601	11.8%	4,700
12/16	5,225	622	11.9%	4,600
12/15	4,900	544	11.1%	4,500
Annual Growth	1.6%	7.1%	—	2.2%

2019 Year-End Financials

Debt ratio: 30.67%
Return on equity: 10.24%
Cash ($ mil.): 12
Current ratio: 0.74
Long-term debt ($ mil.): 6,552

No. of shares (mil.): 138
Dividends
 Yield: —
 Payout: 68.9%
Market value ($ mil.): —

DTE Energy Co

DTE Energy provides Detroit with a reliable spark. The holding company's main subsidiary DTE Electric (formerly Detroit Edison) distributes electricity to some 2.2 million customers in southeastern Michigan. The utility's power plants have a generating capacity of more than 11600 MW. The company's DTE Gas unit distributes natural gas to 1.3 million customers throughout Michigan. DTE Energy runs non-regulated businesses in gas storage & pipelines power & industrial operations and energy trading which together have a presence in more than 15 US states.

HISTORY

DTE Energy's predecessor threw its first switch in 1886 when George Peck and local investors incorporated the Edison Illuminating Company of Detroit. Neighboring utility Peninsular Electric Light was formed in 1891 and both companies bought smaller utilities until they merged in 1903 to form Detroit Edison. A subsidiary of holding company North American Co. Detroit Edison was incorporated in New York to secure financing for power plants.

Detroit's growth in the 1920s and 1930s led the utility to build plants and buy others in outlying areas. Detroit Edison acquired Michigan Electric Power which had been divested from its holding company under the Public Utility Holding Company Act of 1935 and was itself divested from North American in 1940.

The post-WWII boom prompted Detroit Edison to build more plants most of them coal-fired. In 1953 it joined a consortium of 34 companies to build Fermi 1 a nuclear plant brought on line in 1963. Still strapped for power Detroit Edison built the coal-fired Monroe plant which began service in 1970. In 1972 Fermi 1 had a partial core meltdown and was taken off line.

Detroit Edison began shipping low-sulfur Montana coal through its Wisconsin terminal in 1974 which reduced the cost of obtaining the fuel. The next year it began building another nuke Fermi 2. The nuke had cost more than $4.8 billion by the time it went on line in 1988. That year the utility began its landfill gas recovery operation (now DTE Biomass Energy).

A recession pounded automakers in the early 1990s leading to cutbacks in electricity purchases.

In 1992 Congress passed the Energy Policy Act allowing wholesale power competition. In 1993 a fire shut down Fermi 2 for almost two years. Michigan's public service commission (PSC) approved retail customer-choice pilot programs for its utilities in 1994. Detroit Edison and rival Consumers Energy (now CMS Energy) took the PSC to court.

DTE Energy became Detroit Edison's holding company in 1996. The next year it formed DTE Energy Trading (to broker power) and DTE-Co-Energy (to provide energy-management services and sell power to large customers). It also formed Plug Power with Mechanical Technology to develop fuel cells that convert natural gas to power without combustion.

In 1997 and 1998 the PSC bolstered by state court decisions issued orders to restructure Michigan's utilities. The transition to retail competition began in 1998. That year DTE Energy and natural gas provider Michigan Consolidated Gas (MichCon) began collaborating on some operations including billing and meter reading. DTE and GE formed a venture to sell and install Plug Power fuel cell systems.

A higher court shot down the PSC's restructuring orders in 1999 but DTE Energy and CMS Energy decided to implement customer choice using PSC guidelines. That year the US Department of Energy selected DTE Energy to install the world's first super power-cable which could carry three times as much electricity as conventional copper. Also in 1999 DTE Energy agreed to acquire MCN Energy MichCon's parent.

In 2000 DTE Energy formed subsidiary International Transmission (ITC) to hold Detroit Edison's transmission assets; the next year ITC joined the Midwest Independent System Operator which began to manage ITC's network. It also completed its $4.3 billion purchase of MCN Energy in 2001. Full deregulation of Michigan's electricity market was completed in 2002. International Transmission was sold in 2003 to affiliates of Kohlberg Kravis Roberts and Trimaran Capital Partners for $610 million.

In 2007 it sold its Michigan Antrim Shale gas exploration and production assets to Atlas Energy Resources (which later was acquired by Chevron) for about $1.3 billion. That year due to the expiration of synthetic fuel production tax credits DTE Energy exited the synfuels business. In 2010 it sold its rail service unit (DTE Rail Services) to FreightCar America for $23 million.

In 2012 DTE Energy signed a deal with Spectra Energy and Enbridge to jointly develop the NEXUS Gas Transmission system a 250-mile long pipeline project to transport the growing supplies of Ohio Utica shale gas to markets in Michigan Ohio and Ontario.

To raise cash to pay down debt and to focus on its core businesses in 2012 the company sold its Unconventional Gas Production business (88000 acres of gas and oil production assets in the western Barnett and Marble Falls shale areas of Texas) for $255 million.

In 2013 the company opened the northern portion of the Bluestone Project. The 44.5 mile pipeline (which interconnects with Millennium Pipeline in New York) transports up to 600000 million cu. ft. per day to both the Millennium Pipeline in Broome County New York and the Tennessee Gas Pipeline in Susquehanna County Pennsylvania. (The southern portion of Bluestone interconnects with Tennessee Pipeline).

In 2013 DTE Energy has reached an agreement to sell its historic Marysville Power Plant (an idled coal-fired plant on the St. Clair River) to Commercial Development Company.

EXECUTIVES

Svp And General Counsel, Bruce Peterson
Chairman And Ceo, Gerard M. Anderson, $1,293,519 total compensation
President Dte Gas And Oil And Dte Gas Resources, Richard L. Redmond, age 62
Chairman And President Dte Energy Foundation, Faye A. Nelson, age 66
President And Coo Dte Electric, Trevor F. Lauer, age 55
President Dte Gas Storage Pipelines And Processing, Gerardo (Jerry) Norcia, $650,926 total compensation
Vp Gas Sales And Supply Michigan Consolidated Gas Company, Mark W. Stiers, age 57
President Dte Energy Services, David Ruud, age 52
President Dte Biomass Energy, Mark Cousino
Svp And Cfo, Peter B. Oleksiak, age 53, $553,519 total compensation
President Dte Energy Trading, Steven Mabry
Vp And Cio, Steve Ambrose
President Dte Gas Stprage And Pipelines, David Slater
President Dte Energy Foundation, Lynette Dowler
Executive Vice President Major Enterprise Projects, Ron May
Vp And Cio, Steven Ambrose
Vp And Chief Tax Officer, Joann Chavez
Vice President Dte Methane Resources, Jan Stewart
Vice President Regulatory Affairs, Daniel Brudzynski
Senior Vice President Distribution Operations, Heather Rivard
Vice President Distribution Operations, Marco Bruzzano
Vp Business Planning And Development, Irene Dimitry
Vp Commercial And Strategy, Chuck Conlen
Vp Environmental Management And Resources, Skiles Boyd
Senior Vice President Commercial Develop, Gregg Russell
Vice Chairman And Chief Administrative Officer, David E. (Dave) Meador, age 62
Board Member, David Thomas
Secretary, Francesca Racz
Auditors: PricewaterhouseCoopers LLP

LOCATIONS

HQ: DTE Energy Co
 One Energy Plaza, Detroit, MI 48226-1279
Phone: 313 235-4000
Web: www.dteenergy.com

PRODUCTS/OPERATIONS

2017 Sales

	$ mil.	% of total
Electric utility	5,102	38
Gas utility	1,388	11
Energy trading	4,277	32
Power & industrial products	2,089	16
Gas storage & pipeline	453	3
Adjustments	(704)	-
Corporate and Other	2	-
Total	**12,607**	**100**

2017 Sales

	$ mil.	% of total
Utility	6,434	51
Non-utility	6,173	49
Total	**12,607**	**100**

HISTORICAL FINANCIALS

Company Type: Public

Income Statement				FYE: December 31
	REVENUE ($ mil.)	NET INCOME ($ mil.)	NET PROFIT MARGIN	EMPLOYEES
12/19	12,669	1,169	9.2%	10,700
12/18	14,212	1,120	7.9%	10,600
12/17	12,607	1,134	9.0%	10,200
12/16	10,630	868	8.2%	10,000
12/15	10,337	727	7.0%	10,000
Annual Growth	5.2%	12.6%	—	1.7%

2019 Year-End Financials

Debt ratio: 41.66%
Return on equity: 10.67%
Cash ($ mil.): 93
Current ratio: 0.77
Long-term debt ($ mil.): 15,935

No. of shares (mil.): 192
Dividends
  Yield: 2.9%
  Payout: 64.6%
Market value ($ mil.): 24,962

	STOCK PRICE ($) FY Close	P/E High/Low		PER SHARE ($)		
				Earnings	Dividends	Book Value
12/19	129.87	21	17	6.31	3.85	60.73
12/18	110.30	19	15	6.17	3.59	56.27
12/17	109.46	18	15	6.32	3.36	53.03
12/16	98.51	21	16	4.83	3.06	50.22
12/15	80.19	23	18	4.05	2.84	48.88
Annual Growth	12.8%	—	—	11.7%	7.9%	5.6%

Duke Energy Carolinas LLC

Auditors: Deloitte & Touche LLP

LOCATIONS

HQ: Duke Energy Carolinas LLC
526 South Church Street, Charlotte, NC 28202-1803
Phone: 704 382-3853

HISTORICAL FINANCIALS

Company Type: Public

Income Statement				FYE: December 31
	REVENUE ($ mil.)	NET INCOME ($ mil.)	NET PROFIT MARGIN	EMPLOYEES
12/18	7,300	1,071	14.7%	—
12/17	7,302	1,214	16.6%	—
12/16	7,322	1,166	15.9%	—
12/15	7,229	1,081	15.0%	—
12/14	7,351	1,072	14.6%	—
Annual Growth	(0.2%)	(0.0%)	—	—

2018 Year-End Financials

Debt ratio: 27.37%—
Return on equity: 9.30%
Cash ($ mil.): 33
Current ratio: 0.89
Long-term debt ($ mil.): 10,933

Dividends
  Yield: —
  Payout: —
Market value ($ mil.): —

Duke Energy Corp

Duke Energy is one of the top electric power holding companies in the US serving about 7.7 million retail customers in six US states covering some 95000 square miles of service area in the Southeast and Midwest. Its substantial coal nuclear and natural gas assets generate around 50000 MW of electricity. The company also serves about 1.6 million natural gas customers through 60000 miles of pipelines. Duke Energy's rate-regulated utilities serve customers in the Carolinas Florida Ohio Indiana and Kentucky. The company also owns some renewable energy assets like wind and solar farms.

HISTORY

Surgeon Gill Wylie founded Catawba Power Company in 1899; its first hydroelectric plant in South Carolina was on line by 1904. The next year Wylie and James "Buck" Duke (founder of the American Tobacco Company and Duke University's namesake) formed Southern Power Company with Wylie as president.

In 1910 Buck Duke became president of Southern Power and organized Mill-Power Supply to sell electric equipment and appliances. He also began investing in electricity-powered textile mills which prospered as a result of the electric power and continued to bring in customers. He formed the Southern Public Utility Company in 1913 to buy other Piedmont-region utilities. Wylie died in 1924 the same year the company was renamed Duke Power; Buck Duke died the next year.

Growing after WWII the company went public in 1950 and moved to the NYSE in 1961. It also formed its real estate arm Crescent Resources in the 1960s. Insulating itself from the 1970s energy crises Duke invested in coal mining and three nuclear plants the first completed in 1974.

In 1988 Duke began to develop power projects outside its home region and it also bought neighboring utility Nantahala Power and Light. The next year it formed a joint venture with Fluor's Fluor Daniel unit to provide engineering and construction services to power generators. Mill-Power Supply was sold in 1990.

By the 1990s Duke had moved into overseas markets acquiring an Argentine power station in 1992. It also tried its hand at telecommunications creating DukeNet Communications in 1994 to build fiber-optic systems and in 1996 it joined oil giant Mobil to create a power trading and marketing business. As the US power industry traveled toward deregulation Duke also sought natural gas operations. It targeted PanEnergy which owned a major pipeline system in the eastern half of the US. Duke Power bought PanEnergy in 1997 to form Duke Energy Corporation.

Seeing an opportunity in 1998 Duke formed Duke Communication Services to provide antenna sites to the fast-growing wireless communications industry. It also acquired a 52% stake in Electroquil an electric power generating company in Guayaquil Ecuador. That year it purchased a pipeline company in Australia from PG&E; it also bought three PG&E power plants to compete in California's deregulated electric utility marketplace.

Duke merged its pipeline business Duke Energy Trading and Transport with TEPPCO Partners and acquired gas processing operations from Union Pacific Resources. It sold Panhandle Eastern Pipe Line and gas-related assets in the Midwest to CMS Energy in 1999 to reduce operations in the region and made plans to build a pipeline extending from Alabama to Florida (completed in 2002).

To further enhance natural gas operations in other regions Duke bought El Paso's East Tennessee Natural Gas pipeline unit in 2000 and a 20% stake in Canadian 88 Energy; it also purchased $1.4 billion in South American generation assets including assets from Dominion Resources and the gas trading operations of Mobil (now Exxon Mobil) in the Netherlands. Also in 2000 Duke and Phillips Petroleum (now ConocoPhillips) merged their gas gathering and processing and NGL operations into Duke Energy Field Services.

In 2001 Duke announced the $8 billion acquisition of Westcoast Energy; the purchase which was completed in 2002 added more than a million natural gas customers and 6900 miles of gas pipeline in Canada. That year Duke sold its Duke Engineering & Services unit to Framatome ANP and its DukeSolutions unit to Ameresco. Duke Energy Field Services purchased Chevron's 33% stake in Discovery Producer Services which operates a Gulf of Mexico gas pipeline and nearby processing facilities.

Duke set out to sell $1.5 billion in assets in 2003 to focus on core operations. The company sold its Empire State Pipeline subsidiary to National Fuel Gas for $240 million and sold its stakes in the Alliance Pipeline Alliance Canada Marketing and the Aux Sable refinery to Enbridge and Fort Chicago Energy Partners for $245 million. Also that year Duke sold its stake in Foothills Pipe Lines to TransCanada for $181 million and it sold $300 million in renewable energy facilities to privately owned Highstar Renewable Fuels.

In 2004 the company sold an Indonesian power plant to Freeport-McMoRan in a $300 million deal and it sold its 30% interest in the Vector Pipeline to Enbridge and DTE Energy for $145 million. It also sold the assets of its merchant finance business (Duke Capital Partners) and its stake in Canadian 88 Energy (now Esprit Exploration). Following this trend in 2005 Duke Energy sold its 620-MW Grays Harbor facility (Washington) to an affiliate of Invenergy for $21 million.

In 2006 Duke sold a 50% stake in its real estate subsidiary Crescent Resources to Morgan Stanley Real Estate. That year the company bought an 825-MW power plant in Rockingham County North Carolina from Dynegy for $195 million.

In a major industry power move in 2006 the company bought energy provider Cinergy in a $9 billion stock swap. Reorganizing its business lines to focus on its US power businesses that year Duke Energy sold its commercial marketing and trading businesses to Fortis and in 2007 it spun off its natural gas transmission business as Spectra Energy. The company also exited the European energy marketing business; it also left the proprietary (third-party) energy trading business in North America (primarily made up of Duke Energy North America or DENA sold to LS Power Equity Partners for a reported $1.5 billion). Duke also wound down its energy-trading joint venture with Exxon Mobil.

In 2008 Duke moved to strengthen its alternative energy assets by buying wind energy producer Catamount Energy for about $240 million plus assumed debt. Catamount had about 500MW of renewable energy in operation.

That year as part of its refocusing on its energy businesses the company stopped reporting on its Crescent Resources unit (a joint venture with Morgan Stanley Real Estate Fund which manages land holdings and develops real estate projects).

It acquired its first solar project Blue Wing Solar now a 14-MW solar farm in San Antonio from juwi solar in January 2010.

That year it formed a partnership with Integrys Energy Services and Smart Energy Capital to build solar projects across the US. In 2010 Duke Energy also teamed up with Areva to build a $250 million biomass-fueled power plant in Shelton in Washington state.

To raise cash that year Duke Energy sold its 50% stake in DukeNet communications to investment firm Alinda Capital Partners for $137 million.

Boosting its role in the transmission sector in 2011 Duke Energy formed a transmission utility joint venture with American Transmission. Duke-American Transmission Co. builds owns and operates new power transmission infrastructure across North America.

Through its Duke Energy Renewables unit in 2011 the company acquired the Shirley Wind Power Project a 20-MW wind farm in Wisconsin from Central Hudson Energy Group. The project has a 20-year contract to sell its output to Wisconsin Public Service Corp.

In late 2011 the Renewables unit acquired three commercial solar projects in southwestern North Carolina. It bought the photovoltaic projects from ESA Renewables and the power from each solar farm is sold through Blue Ridge Mountain EMC to the Tennessee Valley Authority. The unit has four other commercial solar farms in North Carolina all located outside of Duke Energy's regulated service territories in the state. That year it also snapped up two solar farms in Arizona (in Ajo and Bagdad) from Recurrent Energy doubling its portfolio of commercial solar projects in operation and expanding its footprint further into the western US.

Not neglecting its international growth markets in 2012 Duke Energy International acquired CGE Group's Iberoamericana de Energ a Ibener S.A. subsidiary in Chile including hydroelectric generating assets with 140 MW capacity for $415 million. Chile is Duke's the fourth largest non-US country in terms of generating capacity.

In a major US expansion in 2012 Duke acquired Progress Energy in a $32 billion deal. The acquisition created a more than $100 billion enterprise with the US' largest regulated customer base and was aimed at securing major costs savings in fuel purchasing power generating plant operations and other economies of scale benefits.

In 2012 Duke had almost 1300 MW of wind and solar powered plants in operation.

Growing its solar footprint in California in 2013 Duke Energy Renewables acquired a 4.5 MW solar project the largest solar generation facility in San Francisco from solar project developer Recurrent Energy. That year it also bought the 21-megawatt Highlander solar power projects in Twentynine Palms California. All told Duke Energy Renewables has more than 100 MW of solar generating capacity (16 solar farms in the US).

EXECUTIVES

Evp And Cfo, Steven K. Young, age 59, $625,000 total compensation

Svp Global Risk Management And Insurance And Chief Risk Officer, Keith G. Butler, age 59

Evp Chief Legal Officer And Corporate Secretary, Julie S. Janson, age 54, $520,833 total compensation

Evp; President Natural Gas Business, Franklin H. Yoho, age 60

Svp And Chief Distriution Officer, Michael A. Lewis, age 57

Evp Market Solutions And President Carolinas Region, Lloyd M. Yates, age 58, $661,458 total compensation

Chairman President And Ceo, Lynn J. Good, age 59, $1,291,667 total compensation

Evp And President Midwest And Florida, Douglas F. (Doug) Esamann, age 61

Evp And Coo, Dhiaa M. Jamil, age 62, $737,500 total compensation

President Duke Energy Indiana, Melody Birmingham-Byrd

Vp Foundation And Community Affairs, Alisa Mcdonald

State President North Carolina, David B. Fountain

State President Ohio And Kentucky, James P. (Jim) Henning

Svp And Chief Nuclear Officer, John W. (Bill) Pitesa

Vp And Cio, Christopher B. (Chris) Heck

Evp Administration And Chief Human Resources Officer, Melissa H. Anderson, age 54

State President South Carolina, Kodwo Ghartey-Tagoe

State President Florida, Harry K. Sideris

Svp Financial Planning And Analysis, Bill Currens

Vp Legal And Assistant Corporate Secretary, David Maltz

Vp Investor Relations, Michael Callahan

Vice President Of Marketing, Jack Farley

Vice President Human Resources Business Partners, Jim O'Connor

Vice President, David Litchfield

Executive Vice President, John McArthur

Vp Call Center Operations, Dennis Gowan

Vice President Finance, Bill Dickey

Vice President, Angeline Clinton

Vice President Business Development, John Upchurch

Site Vice President, Dave Baxter

Vice President, John Stowell

Senior Vice President Government Relations, David Dave Marventano

Vp Legal, Bob Ringel

Vice President Internal Audit And Chief Ethics And Compliance Officer, Jeffrey Stone

Senior Vice President Business Development And Strategy Infrastructure, Robert Bob Prieto

Vice President Nuclear Oversight, Joseph Donahue

Vice President Asset Management, Ron Snead

Vp Corporate Public Affairs, Hilda Pinnix-ragland

Vice President, Arthur Raymond

Vice President Talent Management, Lisa Marcuz

Vice President Litigation, Vijay Bondada

Svp State And Federal Regulatory Legal Support, R Alexander Glenn

Vp Community Relations And Economic Development, Laura Boisvert

Vice President And Chief Ethics And Compliance Officer, Sandra Wyckoff

Svp Corporate Development, Karl Newlin

Vice President Crescent Communities, John Roach

Board Member, Daniel Dimicco

Pac Treasurer, William Mayhew

Board Member, Robert Davis

Board Member, Charles Moorman

Board Member, Carlos Saladrigas

Board Member, Tom Skains

Board Member, William Kennard

Board Member, Theodore Craver

Board Of Directors, Marie Mckee

Board Member, Austin Mckee

Auditors: Deloitte & Touche LLP

LOCATIONS

HQ: Duke Energy Corp
550 South Tryon Street, Charlotte, NC 28202-1803
Phone: 704 382-3853
Web: www.duke-energy.com

PRODUCTS/OPERATIONS

2018 Sales

	$ mil.	% of total
Electric Utilities and Infrastructure	22,273	90
Gas Utilities and Infrastructure	1,881	8
Commercial Renewables	477	2
Other	89	-
Eliminations	(199)	-
Total	**24,521**	**100**

2018 Sales

	$ mil.	% of total
Regulated electric	22,097	90
Regulated natural gas	1,773	7
Nonregulated electric and other	651	3
Total	**24,521**	**100**

COMPETITORS

AEP	PG&E Corporation
AES	Piedmont Natural Gas
Avista	SCANA
CenterPoint Energy	Southern Company
Entergy	TVA
Exelon	Williams Companies

HISTORICAL FINANCIALS

Company Type: Public

Income Statement

FYE: December 31

	REVENUE ($ mil.)	NET INCOME ($ mil.)	NET PROFIT MARGIN	EMPLOYEES
12/18	24,521	2,666	10.9%	30,083
12/17	23,565	3,059	13.0%	29,060
12/16	22,743	2,152	9.5%	28,798
12/15	23,459	2,816	12.0%	29,188
12/14	23,925	1,883	7.9%	28,344
Annual Growth	0.6%	9.1%	—	1.5%

2018 Year-End Financials

Debt ratio: 39.85%	No. of shares (mil.): 727
Return on equity: 6.23%	Dividends
Cash ($ mil.): 442	Yield: 4.2%
Current ratio: 0.65	Payout: 96.6%
Long-term debt ($ mil.): 51,123	Market value ($ mil.): 62,740

	STOCK PRICE ($) FY Close	P/E High/Low		PER SHARE ($) Earnings	Dividends	Book Value
12/18	86.30	24	19	3.76	3.64	60.27
12/17	84.11	21	18	4.36	3.49	59.63
12/16	77.62	28	23	3.11	3.36	58.62
12/15	71.39	22	16	4.05	3.24	57.74
12/14	83.54	33	25	2.66	3.15	57.81
Annual Growth	0.8%	—		9.0%	3.6%	1.0%

DXC Technology Co

Auditors: DELOITTE & TOUCHE LLP

LOCATIONS

HQ: DXC Technology Co
1775 Tysons Boulevard, Tysons, VA 22102
Phone: 703 245-9675
Web: www.dxc.technology

HISTORICAL FINANCIALS

Company Type: Public

Income Statement

FYE: March 31

	REVENUE ($ mil.)	NET INCOME ($ mil.)	NET PROFIT MARGIN	EMPLOYEES
03/19	20,753	1,257	6.1%	130,000
03/18	24,556	1,751	7.1%	150,000
03/17	7,607	(123)	—	—
Annual Growth	65.2%	—	—	—

Debt ratio: 25.06%
Return on equity: 10.10%
Cash ($ mil.): 2,899
Current ratio: 0.96
Long-term debt ($ mil.): 5,470

No. of shares (mil.): 268
Dividends
  Yield: 0.0%
  Payout: 17.0%
Market value ($ mil.): 17,262

| | STOCK PRICE ($) | P/E | | PER SHARE ($) | |
	FY Close	High/Low	Earnings	Dividends	Book Value
03/19	64.31	23 11	4.47	0.76	42.48
03/18	100.53	17 11	6.04	0.72	47.26
03/17	0.00	— —	(0.88)	0.00	(0.00)
/0.00	—	—	(0.00)	0.00	(0.00)
Annual Growth	—	—	—	—	—

E*TRADE Financial Corp

Known for its brokerage services E*TRADE Financial provides products tools services and advice to individual investors and stock plan participants wanting to manage their own investments. For corporate clients it offers market making trade clearing and employee stock option plan administration services. Subsidiary E*TRADE Bank provides deposits savings and credit cards online and from some 30 financial centers in major US cities. Its other units include E*TRADE Financial Corporate Services — an equity compensation plan management software and services company for corporate customers — and E*TRADE Securities — a broker-dealer that offers mutual funds options fixed income products exchange-traded funds and portfolio management services.

Operations

While E*TRADE Financial operates one unified segment its core brokerage business is split into five product areas: trading investing banking and cash management corporate services and advisor services.

The company's digital trading products cover investment vehicles including US equities exchange-traded funds options bonds futures and non-proprietary mutual funds for self-directed investors and active traders. It also provides margin solutions including calculators and requirement lookup and analysis.

E*TRADE's investing offerings span four portfolio types — core blend dedicated and fixed income — and tools like mutual fund and exchange-traded fund screeners time frame- and risk tolerance-based ETF and mutual fund portfolios and educational and editorial content.

The firm's E*TRADE Bank unit's banking and cash management services facilitate account transfers online and mobile bill payments and mobile check deposits. Products include savings accounts and credit borrowed against securities.

Through its Equity Edge Online platform the company provides corporate services to public and private companies such as employee stock plan administration (multi-currency settlement and delivery tax calculation and 10b5-1 plan design and implementation) accounting and reporting tools and SEC filing.

E*TRADE's Liberty technology is the major vehicle for its advisor services. Those offerings range from modeling and rebalancing to reporting and practice management.

Geographic Reach

New York-based E*TRADE Financial has roughly 30 E*TRADE Bank branch offices across the US. E*TRADE's websites are accessible in Europe the Middle East the Asia-Pacific region and the US.

Sales and Marketing

E*TRADE Financial sells and provides customer support from its branches online and by telephone. Its financial advisors also promote the firm's products and services. The company serves investors traders advisors and stock plan participants and administrators.

Financial Performance

Despite a moderate decrease in 2015 when the company terminated $4.4 billion of legacy wholesale funding obligations to reduce its funding costs E*TRADE Financial's revenue has added about 70% in the last five years. Net income has rocketed some 260% in that time thanks particularly to gains in 2016 (following the 2015 terminations) and 2018.

The company's revenue increased 21% to $2.9 billion in 2018 primarily due to increased average interest-earning assets and margins. Fees service charges and commissions also drove up revenue.

Net income shot up 71% to $1.1 billion that year on the strength of E*TRADE's revenue and a lower income tax expense caused by US tax reform.

The firm added $1.5 billion to its cash holdings in 2018 to end the year with $3.3 billion. Operating activities generated $1.7 billion. Financing activities provided $45 million; common stock repurchases trust preferred securities payments and decreases in Federal Home Loan Bank advances largely offset increased deposits. Investment spend — primarily purchases of held-to-maturity securities — was $190 million.

Strategy

E*TRADE Financial's strategy is centered on adding new products and services to its lineup while improving its existing offerings.

In 2019 the company made three adjustments to its Core Portfolios a group of non-proprietary exchange-traded funds that range in strategy from conservative to aggressive growth. Clients can now invest with a minimum of $500 in six to eight ETFs. The portfolios' cash allocations were also adjusted to 1%. The company also expanded its Power E*TRADE active trader platform to include paper trading (moneyless trading strategy experimentation) new alerts (such as dollar amount triggers) equity and options orders saving and automatic intraday technical pattern recognition.

The previous year the firm introduced the E*TRADE Advisor Network referral initiative which links independent financial advisors to potential wealth management clients not being fully served by E*TRADE's in-house capabilities. Furthermore it launched an automated 10b5-1 trading plan online dashboard and added greater than 120 no-load no-transaction fee mutual funds.

The company acquired one million retail brokerage accounts in 2018 from Capital One Financial for $109 million. The accounts had $15.4 billion in total assets including $1.6 billion in cash.

Mergers and Acquisitions

In 2018 E*TRADE acquired Trust Company of America (TCA) a custodian of independent investment advisors that it supports with tehcnology solutions consultative services and back-office operations. TCA had $18.3 billion in institutional assets under custody at the time of the purchase.

Company Background

A disastrous decision to move more strongly into banking (originally aiming to triple its loan business) just as the credit crisis struck down banks and lenders around the world led to large losses at the company. The firm was forced to hoard reserves to counter loan losses and exited both its wholesale lending and direct lending operations. The company also shuttered its institutional brokerage business. Its strategy to do improve results revolves around focusing on its online brokerage business and enhancing its position in retirement and investing while continuing to mitigate credit losses in its loan portfolio.

HISTORY

In 1982 physicist William Porter created Trade Plus an electronic brokerage service for stockbrokers; clients included Charles Schwab & Co. and Fidelity Brokerage Services. A decade later subsidiary E*TRADE Securities became CompuServe's first online securities trader.

In 1996 E*TRADE moved from the institutional side to retail when it launched its website. Christos Cotsakos (a Vietnam and FedEx veteran) became CEO and took the firm public. But there were problems: E*TRADE covered $1.7 million in customer losses and added backup systems after computer failure stymied user access. In 1997 it formed alliances with America Online and BANK ONE and ended the year with 225000 accounts.

The firm began to position itself globally in 1997 and 1998 opening sites for Australian Canadian German Israeli and Japanese customers. It offered its first IPO (Sportline USA) in 1997. Volume grew as Internet trading increased but technical glitches dogged E*TRADE. In 1999 day trading became fashionable and the company began running ads promoting prudent trading to counter criticism that online trading fosters a get-rich-quick mentality.

The company also continued to add services. In 1999 it teamed with Garage.com to offer affluent clients venture capital investments in young companies and launched online investment bank E*OFFERING with former Robertson Stephens & Co. chairman Sanford Robertson. (E*TRADE sold its stake in the bank to Wit Soundview — which later became SoundView Technology Group — the next year.) It also bought TIR Holdings which executes and settles multi-currency securities transactions.

Retail banking was a major focus in 2000. The company bought Telebanc Financial (now E*TRADE Financial) owner of Telebank an online bank with more than 100000 depositors and started E*TRADE Bank which offers retail banking products on the E*TRADE website. To provide clients with "real-world" access to their money it bought Card Capture Services an operator of more than 9000 ATMs across the US.

Continuing to expand its global reach E*TRADE bought the part of its E*TRADE UK joint venture it didn't already own; acquired Canadian firm VERSUS Technologies a provider of electronic trading services; and teamed with UBS Warburg to allow non-US investors to buy US securities without needing to trade in dollars. Later its E*Trade International Capital announced plans to offer IPOs to European investors.

In 2001 E*TRADE entered consumer lending when it bought online mortgage originator LoansDirect (now E*TRADE Mortgage). Also that year the company bought online brokerage Web Street and moved to the NYSE. In late 2002 E*TRADE Bank purchased Ganis Credit Corp. (a US-based unit of Germany's Deutsche Bank) to boost its consumer finance business.

E*TRADE purchased the online trading operations of Tradescape in mid-2002. The deal which cost E*TRADE $280 million was hashed out the previous April — just days after rival Ameritrade announced its acquisition of online brokerage Datek.

Cotsakos resigned in early 2003 days after the company issued a gloomy forecast (he also had been criticized for his 2001 pay of $80 million although he subsequently gave up about $20 million). He was replaced by company president Mitch

Caplan who had been viewed as instrumental in the company's effort to integrate brokerage and banking operations.

In 2005 E*TRADE bought US-based online brokerage Harris direct from Bank of Montreal as well as the former J.P. Morgan Invest unit BrownCo which served experienced online traders. The acquisitions expanded its client base and helped the company to keep pace with TD Ameritrade (the result of the 2006 merger of rivals Ameritrade and TD Waterhouse).

E*TRADE built its wealth management operations in 2005 and 2006 by purchasing several money managers including Boston-area investment advisory firm Kobren Insight Management.

After E*TRADE got snared in the subprime mortgage crisis in 2007 Caplan stepped down. He was replaced in 2008 by Donald Layton a former executive with JPMorgan Chase.

Layton retired the following year. Company director Robert Druskin took over as chairman while Steven Freiberg became CEO. Freiberg was formerly a co-CEO of Citigroup's global consumer operations.

To raise additional cash it sold its Canadian operations to Scotiabank for more than $440 million in 2008. The following year it raised some $733 million in three separate stock offerings and exchanged another $1.7 billion in debt for convertible debentures.

EXECUTIVES

Chief Brokerage Officer, Michael J. Curcio, age 57, $450,000 total compensation

Ceo, Karl A. Roessner, age 51, $800,000 total compensation

Evp And Chief Administrative Officer, Michael E. Foley, age 67, $592,308 total compensation

Evp And Cfo, Michael A. Pizzi, $484,615 total compensation

Evp And Chief Risk Officer, Ellen Koebler

Vp Systems Engineering, Ray Hiltbrand

Svp Principal Accounting Officer And Controller, Brent Simonich

Vp Head Of Innovation Lab, Jeanne Jang

Svp And Head Of Operational Risk Third Party Oversight And It Risk, Lisa Peternel

Senior Vice President Of Relationship Management, Carrie Kovac

Vice President Strategic Accounts, Wylie Ewing

Chairman, Rodger A. Lawson, age 72

Auditors: Deloitte & Touche LLP

LOCATIONS

HQ: E*TRADE Financial Corp
11 Times Square, 32nd Floor, New York, NY 10036
Phone: 646 521-4300
Web: www.etrade.com

PRODUCTS/OPERATIONS

2018 Sales

	$ mil.	% of total
Interest Income	2,009	66
Interest Expense	(163)	-
Noninterest Income		
Commissions	498	16
Fees and Service Charges	431	14
Gains on Loans and Securities Net	53	3
Other Revenue	45	1
Total	**2,873**	**100**

Selected Subsidiaries

E*TRADE Bank (federally chartered savings bank)
E*TRADE Clearing LLC (clearing house)
E*TRADE Securities LLC (registered broker-dealer)
G1 Execution Services LLC (registered broker-dealer and market maker)

COMPETITORS

Charles Schwab	ShareBuilder
FMR	Siebert Financial
Morgan Stanley	TD Ameritrade
Scottrade	UBS Financial Services

HISTORICAL FINANCIALS

Company Type: Public

Income Statement

FYE: December 31

	ASSETS ($ mil.)	NET INCOME ($ mil.)	INCOME AS % OF ASSETS	EMPLOYEES
12/18	65,003	1,052	1.6%	4,000
12/17	63,365	614	1.0%	3,600
12/16	48,999	552	1.1%	3,600
12/15	45,427	268	0.6%	3,400
12/14	45,530	293	0.6%	3,200
Annual Growth	**9.3%**	**37.7%**		**5.7%**

2018 Year-End Financials

Debt ratio: 2.17%	No. of shares (mil.): 246
Return on equity: 15.59%	Dividends
Cash ($ mil.): 3,344	Yield: 0.3%
Current ratio: —	Payout: 4.2%
Long-term debt ($ mil.): —	Market value ($ mil.): 10,816

	STOCK PRICE ($) FY Close	P/E High/Low	PER SHARE ($) Earnings	Dividends	Book Value
12/18	43.88	17 11	3.88	0.14	26.62
12/17	49.57	23 15	2.15	0.00	25.98
12/16	34.65	18 10	1.98	0.00	22.89
12/15	29.64	34 24	0.91	0.00	19.90
12/14	24.26	25 19	1.00	0.00	18.58
Annual Growth	**16.0%**	**— —**	**40.3%**	**—**	**9.4%**

Eagle Bancorp Inc (MD)

For those nest eggs that need a little help hatching holding company Eagle Bancorp would recommend its community-oriented EagleBank subsidiary. The bank serves businesses and individuals through more than 20 branches in Maryland Virginia and Washington DC and its suburbs. Deposit products include checking savings and money market accounts; certificates of deposit; and IRAs. Commercial real estate loans represent more than 70% of its loan portfolio while construction loans make up another more than 20%. The bank which has significant expertise as a Small Business Administration lender also writes business consumer and home equity loans. EagleBank offers insurance products through an agreement with The Meltzer Group.

Operations

Like other retail banks Eagle Bancorp makes the bulk of its money from loan interest. About 86% of its total revenue came from loan interest (including fees) during 2015 while another 4% came from interest on investment securities. The rest of its revenue came from deposit account service charges (2% of revenue) and non-recurring income sources.

The bank has two direct subsidiaries: Bethesda Leasing LLC which holds the bank's foreclosed real estate (owned and acquired); and Eagle Insurance Services LLC which provides commercial and retail insurance products through a referral arrangement with insurance broker The Meltzer Group.

Geographic Reach

The Bethesda Maryland-based bank operates 21 branches in Maryland Virginia and Washington DC (as of mid-2016) including nine in Northern Virginia seven in Montgomery County and five in the District of Columbia.

Sales and Marketing

Eagle Bancorp serves local businesses professional clients individuals sole proprietors small and medium-sized businesses non-profits and investors. Other clients are from the healthcare accountant and attorney markets.

The bank spent $2.7 million on marketing and advertising during 2015 up 38% from the $2 million it spent in 2014 mostly due to higher digital and print advertising and sponsorship costs.

Financial Performance

Eagle Bancorp's annual revenue has more than doubled since 2011 mostly thanks to strong loan growth with the addition of new branches. Meanwhile its net income has more than tripled as the bank has kept a lid on credit loss provisions and overhead costs.

The bank's revenue jumped 33% to $279.8 million during 2015 largely thanks to a rise in interest income as its loan assets grew 16%.

Strong revenue growth in 2015 coupled with an absence of merger expenses drove Eagle Bancorp's net income up 55% to $84.1 million. The bank's operating cash levels spiked 66% to $98.5 million for the year thanks to a strong rise in cash-based earnings.

Strategy

The company has been focused on growing within its existing markets. Its strategy for further growth includes continuing to seek opportunities to open or acquire new banking locations while waiting out record low interest rates. Eagle's strict loan underwriting standards — it didn't write subprime residential mortgages and didn't buy securities backed by subprime mortgages — has helped it have fewer problem loans the downfall for many banks.

Beyond its core lending and deposit businesses Eagle Bancorp continues to expand its other product offerings as well. In 2015 it introduced a Full Service Equipment Leasing program which provided alternative and convenient financing for all types of business equipment for customers.

Mergers and Acquisitions

In November 2014 Eagle Bancorp significantly expanded its presence in Northern Virginia after it purchased Fairfax County-based Virginia Heritage. The deal added six Virginia Heritage Bank branches (renamed as EagleBank) in northern Virginia along with $917.4 million in assets — including $715 million in loans and $737 million in deposits.

EXECUTIVES

Evp; Sevp And Coo Eaglebank, Susan G. Riel, age 70, $478,806 total compensation

Chairman President And Ceo; Chairman And Ceo Eaglebank; President Ronald D. Paul Cos., Ronald D. Paul, age 64, $863,565 total compensation

Evp; Evp And Chief Credit Officer Eaglebank, Janice L. Williams, age 62, $391,758 total compensation

Evp And General Counsel Eagle Bancorp And Eaglebank, Laurence E. Bensignor, age 63

Evp; Evp And Chief Lending Officer Commercial Real Estate Eaglebank, Antonio F. Marquez, age 61, $368,256 total compensation

Evp; Evp And Chief Lending Officer Commercial And Industrial Eaglebank, Lindsey S. Rheaume, age 59

Evp And Cfo, Charles D. Levingston, age 39

Vice President, Joan Grant

Vice President Special Assets, Jodee Lichtenstein

Senior Vice President Commercial Banking Team Leader, Derek Whitwer
Vice President, Linda Dawkins
Vice President Facilities Operations Manager, Shawn Cox
Vice Chairman Of The Board Of Company And Bank, Norman Pozez
Vice President Treasurer, Scott Clark
Auditors: Dixon Hughes Goodman LLP

LOCATIONS

HQ: Eagle Bancorp Inc (MD)
7830 Old Georgetown Road, Third Floor, Bethesda, MD 20814
Phone: 301 986-1800
Web: www.eaglebankcorp.com

PRODUCTS/OPERATIONS

Selected Subsidiaries

EagleBank

Bethesda Leasing LLC
Eagle Insurance Services LLC
Fidelity Mortgage Inc.
Eagle Commercial Ventures LLC

COMPETITORS

BB&T	OBA Financial Services
Bank of America	PNC Financial
Capital One	Sandy Spring Bancorp
M&T Bank	SunTrust

HISTORICAL FINANCIALS

Company Type: Public

Income Statement   FYE: December 31

	ASSETS ($ mil.)	NET INCOME ($ mil.)	INCOME AS % OF ASSETS	EMPLOYEES
12/18	8,389	152	1.8%	470
12/17	7,479	100	1.3%	466
12/16	6,890	97	1.4%	469
12/15	6,076	84	1.4%	434
12/14	5,247	54	1.0%	427
Annual Growth	12.4%	29.4%	—	2.4%

2018 Year-End Financials

Debt ratio: 2.59%
Return on equity: 14.79%
Cash ($ mil.): 309
Current ratio: —
Long-term debt ($ mil.): —

No. of shares (mil.): 34
Dividends
  Yield: —
  Payout: —
Market value ($ mil.): 1,675

	STOCK PRICE ($) FY Close	P/E High/Low		PER SHARE ($) Earnings	Dividends	Book Value
12/18	48.71	15	10	4.42	0.00	32.25
12/17	57.90	23	17	2.92	0.00	27.80
12/16	60.95	22	15	2.86	0.00	24.77
12/15	50.47	22	13	2.50	0.00	22.07
12/14	35.52	18	15	1.95	0.00	20.60
Annual Growth	8.2%	—	—	22.7%	—	11.9%

East West Bancorp, Inc

East West Bancorp banks in both hemispheres of the world. It's the holding company for East West Bank which provides standard banking services and loans through more than 130 branches in major US metropolitan areas and about 10 offices across in China Hong Kong and Taiwan. Boasting $29 billion in assets East West Bank focuses on making commercial and industrial real estate loans which account for the majority of the company's loan portfolio. Catering to the Asian-American community it also provides international banking and trade financing to importers/exporters doing business in the Asia/Pacific region. East West Bank offers multilingual service in English Cantonese Mandarin Vietnamese and Spanish.

Operations

East West Bancorp operates two business segments. The commercial banking segment (which generated 62% of its total revenue in 2014) includes commercial industrial and commercial real estate primarily generates commercial and industrial real estate loans and offers a wide variety of international finance and trade services and products. The retail banking segment (33% of total revenue) focuses primarily on retail operations through the East West Bank's branch network. The bank also offers insurance products through East West Insurance.

Broadly speaking the bank made 93% of its revenue from loan interest (including fees) in 2014 and another 7% from interest on investment securities investment in Federal Home Loan Bank and Federal Reserve Bank Stock and short-term investments. It had a staff of roughly 2700 employees at the end of 2014.

Geographic Reach

East West's bank network in the US is mainly in California (in and around Los Angeles the San Francisco Bay area Orange County and Silicon Valley) and in the Atlanta Boston Houston New York and Seattle metropolitan areas. Internationally the bank has five branches in Hong Kong and Greater China (Shanghai Shantou and Shenzhen) and five representative offices in Beijing Chongqing Guangzhou Xiamen and Taiwan.

Sales and Marketing

East West Bancorp caters its banking and loan business to companies in the manufacturing wholesale trade and service sectors.

Financial Performance

The bank has struggled to consistently grow its revenues in recent years due to shrinking interest margins on loans amidst the low-interest environment. Its profits however have been rising thanks to declining loan loss provisions as its loan portfolio's credit quality has improved with higher property valuations in the strengthened economy.

East West had a breakout year in 2014 as its revenue climbed by 17% to $1.14 billion mostly thanks to an increase in non-covered loan volumes. Higher revenue in 2014 drove East West Bancorp's net income higher by 16% to $342.5 million. Lower income tax provisions resulting from additional purchases of affordable housing partnerships and tax-credited investments also help pad the bank's bottom line.

The bank's operating cash levels dipped by 8% to $392.9 million mostly due to unfavorable working capital changes related to accrued interest receivables and other asset balances.

Strategy

East West Bancorp's long-term vision reiterated in 2015 is to "serve as the financial bridge between the United States and Greater China" by reaching more customers with its cross-border products and capabilities. Its full-service branches in Greater China offer traditional letters of credit and trade finance between businesses while also providing the bank a way to serve existing clients and establish new business relationships.

Toward its international expansion plans the company opened two new branches in Greater China's Shenzhen and Shanghai Pilot Free Trade Zone during 2014 which would better position it to help its customers and facilitate their financial needs between Greater China and the US.

The bank may also occasionally pursue acquisitions of other banks to broaden its market reach and grow its loan and deposit business.

Mergers and Acquisitions

In 2014 East West Bancorp expanded its presence in Texas and California after it purchased Metrocorp along with its 19 MetroBank and Metro United Bank branches in the Houston Dallas and San Diego markets. The deal also added $1.7 billion in assets and $1.4 billion in new loan assets.

Company Background

East West Bancorp was founded in 1998.

In 2009 the company acquired more than 60 branches and most of the banking operations of larger rival United Commercial Bank which had been seized by regulators. The deal gave East West Bank about 40 more California branches plus some 20 additional US locations beyond the state.

EXECUTIVES

Evp Chief Risk Officer General Counsel And Secretary East West Bancorp And East West Bank, Douglas P. Krause, age 63, $403,090 total compensation
Chairman And Ceo East West Bancorp And East West Bank, Dominic Ng, age 60, $1,000,000 total compensation
Vice Chairman East West Bancorp And East West Bank, John M. Lee, age 87
Evp And Head Of International And Commercial Banking, Andy Yen, age 61, $370,977 total compensation
Evp And Cfo East West Bancorp And East West Bank, Irene H. Oh, age 41, $403,090 total compensation
Evp And Chief Credit Officer East West Bank, Albert Sun, age 64
President And Coo East West Bancorp And East West Bank, Gregory L. Guyett, age 55
Evp Head Of U.s. Eastern And Texas Regions And Head Of Consumer And Business Banking, Wendy Cai-Lee
First Vice President And Customer Communications Manager, Manni Liu
Senior Vice President Industry Manager, Victor Owens
Senior Vice President, Frances Ng
Senior Vice President, Bennett Chui
Vice President, Samsonz Lam
First Vice President Relationship Manager, Steve Reichmuth
Vice President Assistant Branch Manager El Monte, Fiona Yao
Vice President Bm, Betty Liaw
Vice President Business Development Officer, Ellen Chiang
Senior Vice President, Mary Wei
Avp Loan Portfolio Manager, Sheng-ta Tsai
Avp Loan Documentation And Funding, Jacquelynn Forte
Assistant Vice President Credit Analyst, Joseph Au
Senior Vice President Head Of Special Assets, Stuart Bonomo
Vice President Portfolio Manager Commercial Real Estate Eastern Region, Akmar Wallace
Vice President Tms Sales Consultant Ii, Stacy So
First Vice President, Johnny Cheng
First Vice President Head Of Information Technology Operations, Bill Likes
First Vice President Loan Support Manager, Peggy Donovan
First Vice President Interest Rates And Foreign Exchange, Supat Tipayamongkol
Vice President Commercial Banking, Ricky Lam
Senior Vice President, Andrew Stein
Avp Tax Supervisor, Sophia Xie

Vice President Financial Planning Manager, Nia Chen
Senior Vice President, Al Cheng
Assistant Vice President, Elvira Valenzuela
Abm, Sophia Lam
Auditors: KPMG LLP

LOCATIONS

HQ: East West Bancorp, Inc
135 North Los Robles Ave., 7th Floor, Pasadena, CA 91101
Phone: 626 768-6000
Web: www.eastwestbank.com

PRODUCTS/OPERATIONS

2011 Sales

	$ mil.	% of total
Commercial lending	619	57
Retail banking	358	33
Other & adjustments	112	10
Total	**1,091**	**100**

COMPETITORS

Bank of America	Hanmi Financial
Bank of East Asia	Hope Bancorp
Cathay General Bancorp	JPMorgan Chase
Citibank	U.S. Bancorp
City National	Wells Fargo
Comerica	

HISTORICAL FINANCIALS

Company Type: Public

Income Statement

FYE: December 31

	ASSETS ($ mil.)	NET INCOME ($ mil.)	INCOME AS % OF ASSETS	EMPLOYEES
12/18	41,042	703	1.7%	3,200
12/17	37,150	505	1.4%	3,000
12/16	34,788	431	1.2%	2,873
12/15	32,350	384	1.2%	2,833
12/14	28,738	342	1.2%	2,709
Annual Growth	**9.3%**	**19.7%**	**—**	**4.3%**

2018 Year-End Financials

Debt ratio: 0.36%
Return on equity: 17.03%
Cash ($ mil.): 3,372
Current ratio: —
Long-term debt ($ mil.): —

No. of shares (mil.): 144
Dividends
　Yield: 1.9%
　Payout: 20.3%
Market value ($ mil.): 6,310

	STOCK PRICE ($) FY Close	P/E High/Low		PER SHARE ($) Earnings	Dividends	Book Value
12/18	43.53	15	8	4.81	0.86	30.52
12/17	60.83	18	14	3.47	0.80	26.58
12/16	50.83	17	9	2.97	0.80	23.78
12/15	41.56	17	13	2.66	0.80	21.70
12/14	38.71	16	13	2.38	0.72	19.85
Annual Growth	**3.0%**	**—**	**—**	**19.2%**	**4.5%**	**11.3%**

Eastman Chemical Co

Eastman Chemical Company is a major international producer of acetate tow for cigarette filters. From manufacturing sites in the US and six European countries (including the UK Germany and France) it also turns out chemicals fibers plastics rubber materials polymers and solvents. Eastman's products include such items as food and medical packaging films and toothbrushes. Its end markets include transportation building and construction tobacco consumer durables food and agriculture and health and wellbeing. The company was once part of film giant Eastman Kodak.

HISTORY

Eastman Chemical went public in 1994 but the company traces its roots to the 19th century. George Eastman after developing a method for dry-plate photography established the Eastman Dry Plate and Film Company in 1884 in Rochester New York (the name was changed to Eastman Kodak in 1892).

In 1886 Eastman hired scientist Henry Reichenbach to help create and manufacture new photographic chemicals. As time passed Reichenbach and the company's other scientists came up with chemicals that were either not directly related to photography or had uses in addition to photography.

Eastman bought a wood-distillation plant in Kingsport Tennessee in 1920 and formed the Tennessee Eastman Corporation to make methanol and acetone for the manufacture of photographic chemicals. The company by this time called Kodak introduced acetate yarn and Tenite a cellulose ester plastic in the early 1930s. During WWII the company formed Holston Defense to make explosives for the US armed forces.

Kodak began to vertically integrate Tennessee Eastman's operations during the 1950s acquiring A. M. Tenney Associates Tennessee Eastman's selling agent for its acetate yarn products in 1950. It also established Texas Eastman opening a plant in Longview to produce ethyl alcohol and aldehydes raw materials used in fiber and film production. At the end of 1952 Kodak created Eastman Chemical Products to sell alcohols plastics and fibers made by Tennessee Eastman and Texas Eastman. Also that year Tennessee Eastman developed cellulose acetate filter tow for use in cigarette filters. In the late 1950s the company introduced Kodel polyester fiber.

Kodak created Carolina Eastman Company in 1968 opening a plant in Columbia South Carolina to produce Kodel and other polyester products. It also created Eastman Chemicals Division to handle its chemical operations.

In the late 1970s Eastman Chemicals Division introduced polyethylene terephthalate (PET) resin used to make containers. It acquired biological and molecular instrumentation manufacturer International Biotechnologies in 1987.

Eastman Chemicals Division became Eastman Chemical Company in 1990. In 1993 it exited the polyester fiber business. When Kodak spun off Eastman Chemical in early 1994 the new company was saddled with $1.8 billion in debt.

Eastman's 1996 earnings were reduced when oversupply lowered prices for PET. Eastman opened plants in Argentina Malaysia and the Netherlands in 1998.

Eastman added to its international locations in 1999 by opening a plant in Singapore and an office in Bangkok. It also bought Lawter International (specialty chemicals for ink and coatings) with locations in Belgium China and Ireland. In 2000 the company began restructuring into two business segments (chemicals and polymers) and acquired resin and colorant maker McWhorter Technologies.

In 2001 Eastman acquired most of Hercules' resins business. In November the company announced that it had postponed plans to split into two companies (one focusing on specialty chemicals and plastics the other concentrating on polyethylene plastics and acetate fibers) until mid-2002 due to the weak economy. In early 2002 the company announced that it had cancelled those plans altogether and would operate the two as separate divisions.

The following year Eastman announced it would split off part of its coatings adhesives specialty polymers and inks (CASPI) segment. The division had been underperforming and had been hit particularly hard by the high costs of raw materials and a general overcapacity in the marketplace. Eastman sold a portion of CASPI to investment firm Apollo Manageme

EXECUTIVES

Evp And Cfo, Curtis E. (Curt) Espeland, age 54, $736,887 total compensation
Chairman And Ceo, Mark J. Costa, age 52, $1,102,895 total compensation
Svp And Chief International Ventures Officer, Michael H. K. Chung, age 65
Svp And Cto, Stephen G. (Steve) Crawford, age 54, $484,892 total compensation
Evp And Chief Commercial Officer, Brad A. Lich, age 51, $611,007 total compensation
Svp Chief Manufacturing And Engineering Officer, Mark K. Cox, age 53
Vp And Cio, Keith Sturgill
Evp Additives Functional Products And Chemical Intermediates, Lucian Boldea
Senior Vice President Fibers And Global Supply Chain, Richard Johnson
Vice President, Don Cleek
Vice President Global Public Affairs And Policy, Etta Clark
National Sales Manager, Vince Volk
Vice President And General Manager, Burt Capel
Corporate Medical Director, Ibrahim Heiba
Vp Ir, Gregory Riddle
Vice President Director Of Information Technology Risk Management, Rick Noller
Vice President Information Technology, Michael Stoltz
Board Member, Julie Holder
Auditors: PricewaterhouseCoopers LLP

LOCATIONS

HQ: Eastman Chemical Co
　200 South Wilcox Drive, Kingsport, TN 37662
Phone: 423 229-2000
Web: www.eastman.com

2016 Sales

	$ mil.	% of total
US & Canada	4,025	45
Europe Middle East & Africa	2,305	24
Asia/Pacific	2,163	25
Latin America	515	6
Total	**9,008**	**100**

PRODUCTS/OPERATIONS

2016 Sales

	$ mil.	% of total
Additives & Functional Products	2,979	33
Chemical Intermediates	2,534	28
Advanced Materials	2,457	27
Fibers	992	11
Other	46	1
Total	**9,008**	**100**

Selected Brands and Products

ABALYN rosin resins
ABITOL hydroabietyl alcohols
ADMEX plasticizers
ASPIRA family of resins
BENZOFLEX plasticizers
BIOEXTEND high performance additives
CADENCE resins for calendered films
CELLOLYN synthetic resins
CHROMSPUN acetate yarn
CRYSTEX insoluble sulfur

CYPHREX microfibers
DRESINATE rosin soaps
DURASTAR polymer
DYMEREX rosins
EASTAPURE electronic chemicals
EASTAR copolyesters
EASTEK polymer dispersion
EASTMAN AQ polymers
EASTMAN cellulose esters
EASTMAN coalescents
EASTMAN G polymers
EASTMAN low volatile pure monomer resins
EASTMAN NPG glycol
EASTMAN plasticizers
EASTMAN solvents
EASTMAN TXIB formulation additive
EASTOFLEX amorphous polyolefins
EASTOTAC resins
ECDEL elastomers
EMBRACE family of resins
ENDEX hydrocarbon resins
ENERLOGIC low-e window film
ESTRON acetate yarn
FLEXVUE film
FORAL hydrogenated rosins
FORALYN hydrogenated rosin esters
FORMULAONE high performance auto tint
GILA DIY window film
HUPER OPTIK & DESIGN film
IQUE film
KRISTALEX hydrocarbon resins
LLUMAR window film
METALYN rosin esters
NANOLUX film
NEOSTAR elastomer
OPTIFILM family of products
PAMOLYN fatty acids
PENTALYN synthetic resins
PERENNIAL WOOD
PERMALYN resins
PICCO hydrocarbon resins
PICCOLASTIC hydrocarbon resins
PICCOTAC hydrocarbon resins
PICCOTEX hydrocarbon resins
PLASTOLYN hydrocarbon resins
POLY-PALE rosin resins
PROBENZ sodium benzoate
PROVISTA copolymer
REGALITE hydrocarbon resins
REGALREZ hydrocarbon resins
SAFLEX PVB polymers
SANTOFLEX antidegradants
SKYDROL aviation hydraulic fluids
SKYKLEEN solvents
SOLUS performance additive
SPECTAR copolyester
STAYBELITE-E hydrogenated rosins
SUN-X film
SUSTANE SAIB
TACOLYN resin dispersions
TENITE cellulosics
TENOX antioxidants
TEXANOL ester alcohol
THE GLASS POLYMER
THERMINOL heat transfer fluids
TiGLAZE copolyester
TMPD glycol
TRITAN copolyester
VANCEVA PVB polymers
VELATE coalescents
VISTA window film
V-KOOL film
XIR coated PET

Selected Mergers and Acquisitions

COMPETITORS

Akzo Nobel	DSM
BASF SE	Dow Chemical
Celanese	ExxonMobil Chemical
Clariant	Huntsman Corp
DIC Corporation	Solvay

HISTORICAL FINANCIALS
Company Type: Public

Income Statement
FYE: December 31

	REVENUE ($ mil.)	NET INCOME ($ mil.)	NET PROFIT MARGIN	EMPLOYEES
12/18	10,151	1,080	10.6%	14,500
12/17	9,549	1,384	14.5%	14,000
12/16	9,008	854	9.5%	14,000
12/15	9,648	848	8.8%	15,000
12/14	9,527	751	7.9%	15,000
Annual Growth	1.6%	9.5%	—	(0.8%)

2018 Year-End Financials

Debt ratio: 38.56%	No. of shares (mil.): 139
Return on equity: 19.28%	Dividends
Cash ($ mil.): 226	Yield: 3.1%
Current ratio: 1.82	Payout: 30.4%
Long-term debt ($ mil.): 5,925	Market value ($ mil.): 10,215

	STOCK PRICE ($) FY Close	P/E High/Low		PER SHARE ($) Earnings	Dividends	Book Value
12/18	73.11	14	9	7.56	2.30	41.53
12/17	92.64	10	8	9.47	2.09	37.81
12/16	75.21	13	10	5.75	1.89	30.95
12/15	67.51	15	11	5.66	1.66	26.67
12/14	75.86	18	14	4.97	1.45	23.62
Annual Growth	(0.9%)	—	—	11.1%	12.2%	15.2%

EATON CORPORATION

EXECUTIVES

Chair-Ceo, Craig Arnold
Cfo, Richard Fearon
Exec V Pres, Mark McGuire
Sr V Pres-SEC, Thomas Moran
Sr V Pres-Contrl, Billie Rawot
Sr V Pres Corp Devt & Treas, David Foster
Senior Engineer, Fred James
Manager, Gordon Harmon
Sales Manager, Jim Lago
Executive Officer, Matt Greene
Coordinator, Sandy Benzin
Auditors: ERNST & YOUNG LLP CLEVELAND

LOCATIONS

HQ: EATON CORPORATION
1000 EATON BLVD, CLEVELAND, OH 441226058
Phone: 440 523-5000
Web: WWW.EATON.COM

HISTORICAL FINANCIALS
Company Type: Private

Income Statement
FYE: December 31

	REVENUE ($ mil.)	NET INCOME ($ mil.)	NET PROFIT MARGIN	EMPLOYEES
12/15	6,925	821	11.9%	736
12/14	6,990	170	2.4%	—
Annual Growth	(0.9%)	382.9%	—	—

eBay Inc.

eBay is a well-known e-commerce platform for online auctions and boasts more than 179 million users and some 1.2 billion listings globally. Trading goods every second of every day eBay offers an online forum for buying and selling merchandise worldwide from fine antiques to the latest video games. It generates revenue through listing and selling fees and through advertising. The company also sells tickets to concerts sporting events and other entertainment via its StubHub platform and provides online classified listings via its Classifieds platform. eBay is available across digital platforms including mobile. Some 60% of its sales are outside the US.

HISTORY

Pierre Omidyar created a flea market in cyberspace when he launched online auction service Auction Web on Labor Day weekend in 1995. Making a name for itself largely through word of mouth the company incorporated in 1996 the same year it began to charge a fee to auction items online. That year it enhanced its service with Feedback Forum (buyer and seller ratings).

The company changed the name to eBay in 1997 and began promoting itself through advertising. By the middle of that year eBay was boasting nearly 800000 auctions each day and Benchmark Capital came on board as a significant financial backer.

Margaret ("Meg") Whitman a former Hasbro executive replaced Omidyar as CEO in early 1998. EBay made a blockbuster debut as a public company later that year. The company moved closer to household name status the same year by launching a national ad campaign and inking alliance deals with AOL and WebTV.

eBay showed its acquisitive streak in 1999 with purchases of Alando (online auctions in Germany) and Billpoint (person-to-person credit card technology). It also made one of its first investments in an outside company with the purchase of 6% of TradeOut.com an online seller of corporate surplus materials. The company set the jewel in its 1999 acquisition crown when it acquired upscale auction house Butterfield & Butterfield (now just Butterfields). eBay also expanded down under through a joint venture with Australia-based ecorp (formerly PBL Online). A bit of the bloom came off the rose in 1999 when online service interruptions (one "brownout" in June persisted for 22 hours) revealed a chink in eBay's armor. The company called its top 10000 users to convey its apologies and pledged to improve its website's performance.

In 2000 eBay agreed to develop person-to-person and merchant-to-person auction sites for Disney's GO Network began distributing information through wireless products and joined with banking giant Wells Fargo to offer eBay sellers the option of accepting online checks. Also that year the US Department of Justice began an investigation to determine if eBay had violated antitrust laws in its dealings with competitors. In other legal news a class-action lawsuit was filed against the company claiming that eBay was an auctioneer and therefore must authenticate the items on its site. (A trial court dismissed the case in early 2001.)

Also in 2000 the company expanded into Japan through eBay Japan with computer firm NEC acquiring 30% of the Japanese subsidiary and eBay owning the rest; it also launched Canadian and Austrian sites. In addition eBay took an equity stake in online used-car dealer AutoTrader.com and launched a co-branded used-car auction website and it acquired online trading community Half.com.

eBay strengthened its European position in 2001 through the purchase of French Internet auction firm iBazar. It also launched sites in Ireland New Zealand and Switzerland. eBay made a deal that year to provide its e-commerce capabilities to Microsoft developers and to add business-to-business auctions to its consumer operations. In addition the company began offering virtual storefronts for retailers to sell fixed-price items and purchased auctioneer of foreclosed property HomesDirect. In late 2001 eBay sold its iBazar's Brazilian subsidiary to MercadoLibre Latin America's leading auction site in exchange for a 19.5% stake (now 18%) in MercadoLibre.

Disappointed with the performance of eBay Premiere (fine art and other high-end merchandise) in 2002 the company partnered with Sotheby's in a deal that moved Sotheby's entire online business into the eBay website replacing eBay Premiere (Sotheby's later pulled out of the deal citing lagging sales). eBay also sold its traditional auction house Butterfields and shuttered its eBay Japan operations after its dismal performance in that market. In 2003 the company continued to grow through acquisitions with its purchases of EachNet (after acquiring a minority stake in the Chinese e-commerce company in 2002) FairMarket and Internet Auction.

In 2004 eBay took several steps toward diversifying its business. It expanded its international presence through acquisitions in China and India and spent heavily to establish operations there. Three years later eBay shifted its China strategy entering into a joint venture with Chinese Internet gaming firm TOM Online.

The company purchased about a 25% stake in online classifieds provider craigslist and announced plans to offer a music downloading service. Overall in 2004 more than 60% of eBay's new registered users were in the international business.

2005 was a particularly acquisitive year for eBay. That year it picked up Internet listing site Rent.com for about $415 million. Then eBay's international classifieds group Kijiji (Swahili for "village") acquired London-based Gumtree.com and Spain's LoQUo.com a community-based listings website that operates sites for several Spanish cities alongside ones for France Germany Norway Portugal and the UK. Kijiji next acquired opusforum a local classifieds website based in Germany for an undisclosed sum.

Later in 2005 eBay closed on three major deals. It acquired Shopping.com — a provider of online comparison shopping and consumer reviews with sites in France the UK and the US — for about $635 million. It also purchased PayPal VeriSign's payment gateway business for about $370 million. Also in 2005 eBay acquired start-up online telecom service provider Skype of Luxembourg for nearly $3 billion. Skype's Web-based software allowed its 220 million registered users to make phone calls over the Internet. The acquisition proved costly however. eBay took about $1.5 billion in Skype-related charges in the third quarter of 2007.

Keeping the acquisitions rolling in 2006 eBay snatched up the leading Swedish online auctioneer Tradera.com for $48 million; eBay made the purchase to strengthen its Swedish trading opportunities in the future. Later in 2006 Internet powerhouse Yahoo! and eBay entered an agreement to join forces on advertising Web searches online payments (through eBay's PayPal platform) and a co-branded toolbar. Key elements of the arrangement's design included Yahoo! providing advertisements throughout eBay's site and the integration of PayPal into Yahoo!'s e-commerce infrastructure.

eBay bought German auction management software company Via-Online in 2007. Via-Online operated sales tool Afterbuy.com and eBay made the deal to ramp up support for its Germany sellers. Looking to diversify its online marketplace operations also that year eBay acquired ticket seller StubHub for about $310 million. The company followed that up with the significant $900 million purchase of Bill Me Later in 2008.

In 2008 eBay settled its long-running patent dispute with MercExchange agreeing to buy the three MercExchange patents it had been accused of violating. MercExchange had sued eBay in 2001 claiming that eBay's "Buy It Now" option infringed on its patent technology. A federal judge ruled that eBay should pay MercExchange $30 million in damages in the case. Terms of the settlement were not disclosed.

Later in 2008 eBay announced it would end its arrangement with LiveAuctioneers.com that allowed customers to participate in live auctions hosted by other companies. eBay said ending the deal allowed it to better concentrate on growing listings in its core product.

To encourage further growth in its auctions the company reduced fees and rolled out an improved matching feature in 2008. The feature implemented a ranking system that took into account time remaining feedback scores quality of listing pictures and other criteria.

Whitman who led eBay for a decade stepped down as president and CEO of the company in 2008. She was succeeded by John Donahoe who previously led the company's highest revenue-producing unit eBay Marketplaces. Also that year eBay acquired the California-based visual media company VUVOX Network to further develop rich media capabilities in the eBay marketplace.

In a program that ran through the bulk of 2009 eBay partnered with resurrected automaker General Motors to sell new cars online. Prospective buyers could place bids for vehicles from more than 225 GM dealers in California at gm.ebay.com. The program did not move as many cars as anticipated however prompting the automaker to halt sales and shift its attention to marketing. eBay in 2009 paid about $1 billion for a majority stake (99.2%) in Gmarket a leading online marketplace in South Korea.

eBay also sold a majority of Skype in 2009. Four years after investing in the service eBay acknowledged that Skype did not complement the rest of its operations. It sold off a 70% stake in Skype to investors led by the private-equity firm Silver Lake in a deal involving $1.9 billion in cash and a $125 million note. As part of the agreement eBay retained a 30% interest in the Skype. (eBay had purchased Skype for nearly $3 billion but in 2007 it took a write-down for about half that amount.) eBay sold its share in Skype to Microsoft in 2011.

In 2010 eBay acquired popular German shopping site Brands4Friends for about $200 million. It made the deal to become a leading online fashion destination in Europe. The company continued its shopping spree in Germany the following year when it bolstered PayPal assets by acquiring the German company BillSAFE adding over 15 million accounts. The deal gave eBay purchase-on-invoice capabilities that are popular to merchants and consumers in Austria German the Netherlands and Switzerland.

eBay bought mobile software application developer Critical Path in 2010. Critical Path had worked with eBay to develop several of its applications for Apple's iPhone. The acquisition doubled the size of eBay's mobile team which is working to capitalize on the growing numbers of consumers who are shopping on their smart phones.

In its largest acquisition since purchasing Skype in 2011 eBay bought GSI Commerce a provider of

such services as website development and maintenance order fulfillment and digital advertising for $2.4 billion.

In 2012 eBay sold Rent.com to PRIMEDIA. eBay spun off PayPal in 2015.

EXECUTIVES

President And Ceo, Devin N. Wenig, age 52, $1,000,000 total compensation

President Stubhub, Scott Cutler

Svp And General Counsel, Marie Oh Huber, age 58, $389,462 total compensation

Svp Ebay North America, Harry A. (Hal) Lawton, age 45, $650,000 total compensation

Svp And Cto, Stephen (Steve) Fisher, age 54, $625,000 total compensation

Svp And Cfo, Scott F. Schenkel, age 51, $650,000 total compensation

Svp Global Operations, Wendy Jones

Svp Ebay Europe, Paul Todd

Svp Ebay Asia Pacific, Jay Lee

Svp And Chief Product Officer, Raymond J. (R.J.) Pittman, age 49, $580,000 total compensation

Svp And Chief People Officer, Kristin Yetto

Senior Vice President Operations, Ryan Downs

Vice President Ebay Fashion, Michael Mosser

Vice President Ebay Customer Service Solutions And Technology, Scott Murray

Executive Vice President, Molly Smith

Vice President Core Product Experience, Mohan Patt

Vice President Of Data, Zoher Karu

Vice President Deputy General Counsel Head Of Legal Americas And Global Product And Technology, Karin Schwab

Vice President Talent Acquisition Management And Development, Lou Sanchez

Senior Vice President Information Technology, Andre Tozzi

Vice President Mobile Products, Kevin Hurst

Vice President Sales, Todd Pearson

National Account Manager, Jessica Schrenker

Vp Engineering, Louis Perrochon

Vice President Product Development, Jay Hanson

Senior Vice President Finance Chief Financial Officer, Bob Swan

Vice President Of Engineering, Dane Glasgow

Vice President, Don Albert

Vice President Global Customer Experience Ebay Europe, Jean-marc Codsi

Vice President Investor Relations, Thomas Hudson

Vice President Legal, John Muller

Vice President Of Compensation Benefits And Human Resources, Robin Colman

Vice President Information Technology, Omar Jabbar

Vice President Human Resources Business Partner, Donna Zontos

Vice President Engineering, Japjit Tulsi

Vp It, Rami Mazid

Vice President New Product Development, Bora Chung

Vice President And General Manager Classifieds Incubator Markets And Global Operation, Chris Prill

Vice President And General Manager Selling Experience, Sunil Rajasekar

Vice President B2c And Seller Experience, Bob Kupbens

Vice President Finance And Chief Audit Executive, Meeta Sunderwala

Chairman, Thomas J. (Tom) Tierney, age 65

Board Member, Logan Green

Board Member, Fred Anderson

Board Member, Pierre M Omidyar

Auditors: PricewaterhouseCoopers LLP

LOCATIONS

HQ: eBay Inc.
2025 Hamilton Avenue, San Jose, CA 95125
Phone: 408 376-7008
Web: www.ebay.com

2018 Sales

	$ mil.	% of total
US	4,373	41
Germany	1,591	15
UK	1,481	14
South Korea	1,195	11
Rest of world	2,106	19
Total	**10,746**	**100**

PRODUCTS/OPERATIONS

2018 Sales

	$ mil.	% of total
Net transaction revenues:		
Marketplace	7,416	69
StubHub	1,068	10
Marketing services and other revenues:		
Marketplace	1,225	11
Classifieds	1,022	10
StubHub Corporate and other	15	-
Total	**10,746**	**100**

COMPETITORS

Alibaba.com	HSN
Amazon.com	Naspers
Buy.com	Overstock.com
Costco Wholesale	Spectrum Group
Digital River	Tickets.com
Etsy	Wal-Mart
Facebook	Wayfair
Google	

HISTORICAL FINANCIALS

Company Type: Public

Income Statement
FYE: December 31

	REVENUE ($ mil.)	NET INCOME ($ mil.)	NET PROFIT MARGIN	EMPLOYEES
12/19	10,800	1,786	16.5%	13,300
12/18	10,746	2,530	23.5%	14,000
12/17	9,567	(1,016)	—	14,100
12/16	8,979	7,266	80.9%	12,600
12/15	8,592	1,725	20.1%	11,600
Annual Growth	5.9%	0.9%	—	3.5%

2019 Year-End Financials

Debt ratio: 42.70%
Return on equity: 39.03%
Cash ($ mil.): 975
Current ratio: 1.16
Long-term debt ($ mil.): 6,738

No. of shares (mil.): 796
Dividends
  Yield: 1.5%
  Payout: 25.5%
Market value ($ mil.): 28,744

	STOCK PRICE ($) FY Close	P/E High/Low		PER SHARE ($) Earnings	Dividends	Book Value
12/19	36.11	20	13	2.09	0.56	3.61
12/18	28.07	18	10	2.55	0.00	6.86
12/17	37.74			(0.95)	0.00	7.84
12/16	29.69	5	3	6.35	0.00	9.70
12/15	27.48	46	17	1.42	0.00	5.55
Annual Growth	7.1%	—	—	10.1%	—	(10.2%)

Ecolab Inc

Ecolab cleans up by cleaning up. The company offers cleaning sanitation pest-elimination and maintenance products and services to the energy healthcare hospitality and industrial sectors among others. Its cleaning and sanitizing operations serve hotels schools commercial and institutional laundries and quick-service restaurants. Other units focus on products for textile care water care healthcare food and beverage processing and pest control. It also makes chemicals used in water treatment for industrial processes including in the paper and energy industries. The US is Ecolab's largest market accounting for more than 50% of revenue.

Operations

Ecolab provides cleaning and sanitizing programs and products equipment repair and pest elimination for markets such as food service food and beverage processing chemical processing oil and gas production healthcare government and education and textile care.

Ecolab's chemicals and services are used in water treatment pollution control oil and gas steelmaking papermaking mining and other industrial processes. It is also one of the top suppliers of chemical dishwashing products to institutions in the US.

Ecolab has three operating segments: Global Industrial (consisting of the Global Water Global Food & Beverage Global Paper and Global Textile Care operating units); Global Institutional (Global Institutional Global Specialty and Global Healthcare operating units); and Global Energy (operating under the Nalco Champion name).

The Global Industrial segment (accounting for more than 35% of sales) provides water treatment and cleaning and sanitizing services to large industrial clients in the chemical commercial laundry food manufacturing and paper industries. Global Institutional also generates around 35% of sales and Global Energy accounts for about 25% of sales.

Geographic Reach

St. Paul Minnesota-based Ecolab has broad reach across the world operating in more than 170 countries. The US accounts for about 50% of the company's total revenue. Europe accounts for about 20% the Asia/Pacific region around 15%; Latin America less than 10% the Middle East and Africa 5% and Canada 5%.

Sales and Marketing

Ecolab serves customers in a range of segments including buildings and facilities chemical processing education facility care food and beverage processing food retail foodservice government healthcare lodging and oil and gas.

Some of Ecolab's products are sold to distributors agents or licensees. Deliveries to customers are made from manufacturing plants and a network of distribution centers and third-party logistics service providers using common carriers Ecolab's own delivery vehicles and distributors' vehicles.

Financial Performance

After hitting a peak of $14.3 billion in revenue in 2014 Ecolab's sales tailed off in the next two years. But Ecolab's revenue grew in 2017 and again in 2018 when it posted record revenue through organic growth and contributions from acquisitions.

In 2018 revenue rose 6% to about $14.7 billion up about $900 million from 2017 driven by higher sales in each segment and geographic region. Overall Ecolab sold more products and services at higher prices in 2018 compared to 2017. Acquisitions also contributed to the company's sales increase.

Net income slipped to $1.4 billion in 2018 from $1.5 billion in 2017 due to charges for restructuring acquisition-related activities and the company's commitment to the Ecolab Foundation.

Ecolab had about $294 million in cash in 2018 compared to $211 million the year before. In 2018 operations generated $2.3 billion while investing activities used about $1 billion and financing activities used about $1.2 billion.

The company has a sizable debt load of about $7 billion which could require diverting cash flow from operations to pay principal and interest. That could reduce the amount of money available for acquisitions and capital investment as well as limit its flexibility in reacting to changes in business and market conditions.

Strategy

Acquisition has been a growth engine for Ecolab spreading its reach and expanding line of products and services to provide water processing management to food and beverage hospitality and laundry customers worldwide. In 2018 and 2019 the company extended its offerings and enlarged its footprint in Europe with the acquisitions of Holchem in Germany and Bioquell in the UK.

Ecolab's 2020 growth strategy rests on integrating digital into its back end and products and positioning the company as a desirable destination for talent. To reach those goals Ecolab is restructuring to simplify and automate processes and tasks reduce complexity and management layers consolidate facilities and focus on long-term growth areas. The company expects savings to total $325 million by 2021.

The company plans to spin off its Upstream Energy business composed of the WellChem and Oil Field Chemicals businesses into an independent publicly traded company by mid-2020. The upstream business has an increasingly different business model than the rest of Ecolab and the company believes that two more focused companies would better serve their customers. The upstream business had sales of about $2.4 billion in 2018.

With trade tensions in global markets Ecolab may suffer from higher raw material costs needed for its products that include an array of organic and inorganic chemicals.

Mergers and Acquisitions

In 2019 Ecolab closed on its acquisition of Bioquell a provider of hydrogen peroxide vapor biodecontamination systems and services for the life sciences and healthcare industries. Based in the UK Bioquell's 2017 sales were approximately Â 29 million.

Ecolab acquired food hygiene and cleaning products firm Holchem Group in 2018. The company serves food and beverage and food service customers in Ireland the U.K. and mainland European countries. It made $56 million in revenue last year. Financial details were not disclosed.

In 2017 Ecolab acquired Laboratoires Anios from co-owners Bertrand and Thierry Letartre and private investment company Ardian for about $800 million. Anios is a European manufacturer and marketer of hygiene and disinfection products for the healthcare food service and food and beverage processing industries. Based in Lille France Anios has a presence in more than 85 countries. Anios' innovative product line expands the solutions Ecolab can offer while also providing a complementary geographic footprint.

Also in 2017 the company acquired Abednego Environmental Services a Novi Michigan-based provider of water services for automotive customers. The acquisition adds to the suite of products and services Ecolab provides to automobile manufacturers to re-cycle water reduce energy use and reduce waste.

HISTORY

Salesman Merritt Osborn founded Economics Laboratory in 1924 as a specialty chemical maker; its first product was a rug cleaner for hotels. It added industrial and institutional cleaners and consumer detergents in the 1950s. The company went public in 1957. By 1973 it had been organized into five divisions: industrial (cleaners and specialty chemical formulas) institutional (dishwasher products sanitation formulas) consumer (dishwasher detergent and laundry aids coffee filters floor cleaners) food-processing (detergents) and international (run by future CEO Fred Lanners).

EXECUTIVES

Chairman And Ceo, Douglas M. (Doug) Baker, age 61, $1,187,500 total compensation

Cfo, Daniel J. (Dan) Schmechel, age 59, $581,250 total compensation

Evp And Cio, Stewart H. McCutcheon

President And Coo, Thomas W. (Tom) Handley, age 64, $581,250 total compensation

Evp General Counsel And Assistant Secretary, Michael C. McCormick

Evp; President Global Institutional, Michael A. (Mike) Hickey, age 57, $543,125 total compensation

Evp And Cto, Larry L. Berger, age 58

Evp; President International Regions, Christophe Beck, age 51, $548,125 total compensation

Vp And General Manager Healthcare North America, Paul B. Chaffin

Evp; President International Regions, Timothy P. Mulhere, age 56

Evp Human Resources, Laurie M. Marsh, age 55

Evp; President Global Energy, Stephen M. (Steve) Taylor, age 57, $518,818 total compensation

Evp; President Global Services And Specialty, Roberto D. (Bobby) Mendez

Evp General Counsel And Secretary, James J. (Jim) Seifert, age 62

Evp And President Europe, Darrell Brown

Evp Global Textile Care, Andreas Weilinghoff

Evp And President Global Food And Beverage And Global Healthcare, Jill S. Wyant, age 47

Evp And Chief Supply Chain Officer, Alex Blanco, age 58, $450,000 total compensation

Svp Global Marketing And Communications, Elizabeth A. (Beth) Simermeyer

Svp And President Middle East And Africa, Vishal Sharma

Evp; President Asia Pacific, Sean Toohey

Evp And General Manager Global Food And Beverage, Nicholas (Nick) Alfano

Svp And President Latin America, John Guttery

Evp And Gm Global Food And Beverage, Nick Alfano

Assistant Vice President Corporate Accounts, Cargile Kelly

Vp Global Technology Licensing, Srinivas Somayajula

Executive Vice President And Chief Information Officer, Anil Arcalgud

Vice President Human Resources Talent, Sue Metcalf

Avp Global Foodservice, Rob Sloan

Vp Corporate Sustainability, Emilio Tenuta

Senior Vice President External Relations, Michael Monahan

Vice President Institutional Global Corporate Accounts Finance, William Fiedler

Senior Vice President And Corporate Controller, Bryan Hughes

Vice President Food Safety And Public Health, Ruth Petran

Vp Global It Business, Chris Vitek

Vice President Business Development, Jeremiah Keehn

Senior Vice President And President Middle East And Africa, Arjan Boogaards

Senior Vice President And General Manager Global Healthcare, Gergely Sved

Executive Vice President And President Greater China, Connell Zhang

Vice President Supply Chain, Jose Luis Josan

Assistant Vice President Area Sales, George Panas

Board Member, Stephen Chazen

Auditors: PricewaterhouseCoopers LLP

LOCATIONS

HQ: Ecolab Inc
1 Ecolab Place, St. Paul, MN 55102
Phone: 800 232-6522
Web: www.ecolab.com

2018 Sales

	$ mil.	% of total
United States	7,748	53
Europe	2,858	19
Asia Pacific excluding Greater China	1,239	8
Latin America	906	6
MEA	519	4
Canada	687	5
Greater China	709	4
Total	**14,668**	**100**

PRODUCTS/OPERATIONS

2018 Sales

	$ mil.	% of total
Global Industrial	5,462	37
Global Institutional	5,204	35
Global Energy	3,501	23
Other	877	5
Effect of foreign currency translation	(378.1)	2
Total	**14,668**	**100**

Selected Services

Equipment Care
Facility Cleaning
Food Retail Solutions
Food Safety Specialties
Foodservice Water Management
Front and Back of House
Housekeeping — Guest Rooms
HVAC Performance Services
Laundry
Pest Elimination
Pool and Spa
Restaurants
Water Safety
Water Treatment

COMPETITORS

3M Purification	ISS A/S
Ashland	Medline Industries
Chemed	Rollins Inc.
Diversey	STERIS
GE Water and Process Technologies	ServiceMaster
Healthcare Services	Zep Inc.

HISTORICAL FINANCIALS

Company Type: Public

Income Statement

FYE: December 31

	REVENUE ($ mil.)	NET INCOME ($ mil.)	NET PROFIT MARGIN	EMPLOYEES
12/18	14,668	1,429	9.7%	49,000
12/17	13,838	1,508	10.9%	48,400
12/16	13,152	1,229	9.3%	47,565
12/15	13,545	1,002	7.4%	47,000
12/14	14,280	1,202	8.4%	47,430
Annual Growth	**0.7%**	**4.4%**	**—**	**0.8%**

2018 Year-End Financials

Debt ratio: 35.10%
Return on equity: 18.30%
Cash ($ mil.): 114
Current ratio: 1.27
Long-term debt ($ mil.): 6,301

No. of shares (mil.): 287
Dividends
  Yield: 1.1%
  Payout: 34.6%
Market value ($ mil.): 42,395

	STOCK PRICE ($) FY Close	P/E High/Low		PER SHARE ($) Earnings	Dividends	Book Value
12/18	147.35	32	26	4.88	1.69	27.82
12/17	134.18	26	23	5.13	1.52	26.33
12/16	117.22	30	24	4.14	1.42	23.65
12/15	114.38	36	29	3.32	1.34	23.35
12/14	104.52	29	24	3.93	1.16	24.40
Annual Growth	**9.0%**	**—**	**—**	**5.6%**	**10.0%**	**3.3%**

Edison International

Edison International is a major power provider in California through its Southern California Edison (SCE) subsidiary which distributes electricity to 5.1 million customers in central coastal and southern California. The utility's system consists of more than 12600 miles of transmission lines and some 91400 miles of distribution lines. SCE also has about 6900 MW of generating capacity from interests in nuclear hydroelectric fossil-fueled and solar power plants and it buys and sells power wholesale. Through its Edison Energy subsidiary Edison International owns and operates additional solar power projects.

HISTORY

In 1896 a group including Elmer Peck and George Baker organized West Side Lighting to provide electricity in Los Angeles. The next year the company merged with Los Angeles Edison Electric which owned the rights to the Edison name and patents in the region and Baker became president. Edison Electric installed the first DC-power underground conduits in the Southwest.

John Barnes Miller took over the top spot in 1901. During his 31-year reign the firm bought many neighboring utilities and built several power plants. In 1909 it took the name Southern California Edison (SCE).

SCE doubled its assets by buying Southern California electric interests from rival Pacific Light & Power in 1917. However in 1912 the City of Los Angeles had decided to develop its own power distribution system and by 1922 SCE's authority in the city had ended. A 1925 earthquake and the 1928 collapse of the St. Francis Dam severely damaged SCE's facilities.

SCE built 11 fossil-fueled power stations (1948-1973) and moved into nuclear power in 1963 when it broke ground on the San Onofre plant with San Diego Gas & Electric (brought online in 1968). It finished consolidating its service territory with the 1964 purchase of California Electric Power. In the late 1970s SCE began to build solar geothermal and wind power facilities.

Edison Mission Energy (EME) was founded in 1986 to develop buy and operate power plants around the world. The next year investment arm Edison Capital was formed as well as a holding company for the entire group SCEcorp. EME began to build its portfolio in 1992 when it snagged a 51% stake in an Australian plant and bought hydroelectric facilities in Spain. In 1995 it bought UK hydroelectric company First Hydro; it also began building plants in Italy Turkey and Indonesia.

The 1994 Northridge earthquake that cut power to a million SCE customers was nothing compared to the industry's seismic shifts. In 1996 SCEcorp became the more worldly Edison International.

California's electricity market opened to competition in 1998 and the utility began divesting SCE's generation assets; it sold 12 gas-fired plants. Overseas EME picked up 25% of a power plant being built in Thailand and a 50% stake in a cogeneration facility in Puerto Rico.

SCE got regulatory approval to offer telecom services in its utility territory in 1999. That year EME snapped up several plants in the Midwest from Unicom for $5 billion. Overseas it purchased two UK coal-fired plants from PowerGen (which it sold to American Electric Power in 2001 for $960 million). The next year EME CEO Edward Muller (who had held the post since 1994) abruptly resigned and Edison bought Citizens Power from the Peabody Group.

In 2000 SCE got caught in a price squeeze brought on in part by deregulation. Prices on the wholesale power market soared but the utility was unable to pass along the increase to customers because of a rate freeze. The company gained some prospect of relief in 2001 when California's governor signed legislation to allow a state agency to buy power from wholesalers under long-term contracts. In addition the California Public Utilities Commission (CPUC) approved a substantial increase in retail electricity rates and the Federal Energy Regulatory Commission approved a plan to limit wholesale energy prices during periods of severe shortage in 11 western states.

To reduce debt Edison International agreed to sell its transmission grid to the state for $2.8 billion. While the California legislature debated the agreement however the CPUC announced a settlement in which SCE would be allowed to keep its current high rates in place until its debts are paid off. The settlement which was approved in 2002 eliminated the need for the sale of the company's transmission grid.

Also in 2001 the company sold most of its Edison Enterprises businesses including home security services unit Edison Select which was sold to ADT Security Services.

In 2004 Edison International committed to taking a lead position in developing comprehensive national programs to reduce greenhouse gas emissions primarily carbon dioxide.

In 2006 SCE signed the largest wind energy deal ever completed by a US utility providing for 1500 MW of wind power from plants in the Tehachapi area of California.

EME marketed energy in the US and Turkey and had interests in more than 40 power plants in the US and one in Turkey that gave it a net physical generating capacity of about 10780 MW. EME filed for bankruptcy protection in 2012 citing high operating losses due to low realized energy and capacity prices high fuel costs and low generation at its Midwest Generation plants.

In 2013 SCE decided to permanently retire Units 2 and 3 of its San Onofre Nuclear Generating Station. Unit 2 was taken out of service January 2012 for a planned routine outage. Unit 3 was also taken offline a few weeks later after station operators found a small leak in a tube inside a steam generator.

In 2013 Edison Energy acquired SoCore Energy a Chicago-based solar portfolio development and commercial rooftop installation company focusing on the solar energy needs of multisite retailers REITs and industrial clients and bought a minority stake in Clean Power Finance a financial services and software provider for the solar industry.

In 2016 Edison International subsidiary SoCore Energy acquired equity interests in about 20 community solar garden development projects in Minnesota as part of the SunEdison bankruptcy proceedings. The price was $80 million.

EXECUTIVES

President Edison Energy, Ronald L. Litzinger, age 60, $600,000 total compensation
President Ceo And Director, Pedro J. Pizarro, age 54, $836,782 total compensation
Vp And Cio Southern California Edison, Todd L. Inlander
Ceo Southern California Edison Company (sce), Kevin M. Payne, age 58, $421,171 total compensation
Svp Commercial Operations Edison Energy And President Edison Transmission Llc, Steven D. Eisenberg
Evp And Cfo, Maria Rigatti, age 55, $392,891 total compensation
Evp And General Counsel, Adam S. Umanoff, age 59, $548,391 total compensation
President Socore Energy, Rob Scheuermann
President Southern California Edison (sce), Ronald O. Nichols, age 65
Vp Operational Finance Sce, Chris Dominski
Vice President, Weston Williams
Vice President Regulatory Operations, Akbar Jazayeri
Senior Vice President Human Resources, John Kelly
Svp Government Affairs Edison International And Sce, Gaddi Vasquez
Vp And Corporate Controller, Aaron Moss
Senior Vice President, Drew Murphy
Vice President Local Public Affairs Sce, Christopher Thompson
Vice President Strategic Planning Edison International, Oded Rhone
Vice President Of Distribution, Gregory Ferree
Vice President Of Investor Relations, Sam Ramraj
Chairman, William P. (Bill) Sullivan, age 69
Board Member, Linda Stuntz
Board Member, James Morris
Board Member, Michael Camunez
Auditors: PricewaterhouseCoopers LLP

LOCATIONS

HQ: Edison International
2244 Walnut Grove Avenue, P.O. Box 976, Rosemead, CA 91770
Phone: 626 302-2222
Web: www.edisoninvestor.com

PRODUCTS/OPERATIONS

Selected Subsidiaries
Edison Energy (solar power activities)
Southern California Edison Company (SCE electric utility)

COMPETITORS

AES	NV Energy
Avista	NextEra Energy
Berkshire Hathaway Energy	PG&E Corporation
CMS Energy	PacifiCorp
Calpine	Portland General Electric
Constellation Energy Group	Sacramento Municipal Utility
Electricité de France	Sempra Energy
Los Angeles Water and Power	

HISTORICAL FINANCIALS

Company Type: Public

Income Statement				FYE: December 31
	REVENUE ($ mil.)	NET INCOME ($ mil.)	NET PROFIT MARGIN	EMPLOYEES
12/18	12,657	(423)	—	12,574
12/17	12,320	565	4.6%	12,521
12/16	11,869	1,311	11.0%	12,390
12/15	11,524	1,020	8.9%	12,768
12/14	13,413	1,612	12.0%	13,690
Annual Growth	(1.4%)	—	—	(2.1%)

2018 Year-End Financials

Debt ratio: 27.21%
Return on equity: (-3.82%)
Cash ($ mil.): 144
Current ratio: 0.62
Long-term debt ($ mil.): 14,632

No. of shares (mil.): 325
Dividends
  Yield: 4.2%
  Payout: —
Market value ($ mil.): 18,496

	STOCK PRICE ($) FY Close	P/E High/Low		Earnings	PER SHARE ($) Dividends	Book Value
12/18	56.77	—	—	(1.30)	2.43	32.10
12/17	63.24	48	37	1.72	2.23	35.82
12/16	71.99	20	14	3.97	1.98	36.82
12/15	59.21	22	18	3.10	1.73	34.89
12/14	65.48	14	9	4.89	1.48	33.64
Annual Growth	(3.5%)	—	—	—	13.1%	(1.2%)

EDUCATIONAL FUNDING OF THE SOUTH, INC.

Reading is fundamental but funding is crucial to higher education. That's where Educational Funding of the South comes in. Known as Edsouth the not-for-profit public benefit corporation provides student loan funding by purchasing loans from originators. Nearly 500 lending institutions participate in one or more of Edsouth's educational loan programs. Edsouth is one of the nation's largest holders of student loans. The organization was founded in 1988. Formerly known as Volunteer State Student Funding Corporation it changed its name to Educational Funding of the South in 1996.

EXECUTIVES

Ceo, Ron Gambill
Chief Operating Officer, Eric Stewart
Auditors: KRAFT CPAS NASHVILLE TENNESS

LOCATIONS

HQ: EDUCATIONAL FUNDING OF THE SOUTH, INC.
12700 KINGSTON PIKE, KNOXVILLE, TN 379340917
Phone: 865 342-0684
Web: WWW.EDSOUTH.ORG

COMPETITORS

Bank of America
Brazos Higher Education Service Corp.
College Loan Corporation
Discover
JPMorgan Chase
Nelnet
Sallie Mae

HISTORICAL FINANCIALS

Company Type: Private

Income Statement   FYE: September 30

	ASSETS ($ mil.)	NET INCOME ($ mil.)	INCOME AS % OF ASSETS	EMPLOYEES
09/12*	2,924	(20)	—	3
12/06	4,223	252	6.0%	—
12/05	4,484	26	0.6%	—
12/04	3,881	30	0.8%	—
Annual Growth	(3.5%)	—	—	—

*Fiscal year change

EMCOR Group, Inc.

Electrical and mechanical construction specialist EMCOR Group is one of the world's largest specialty construction firms. It designs installs operates and maintains complex mechanical and electrical systems. These include systems for power generation and distribution lighting water and wastewater treatment voice and data communications fire protection plumbing and heating ventilation and air-conditioning (HVAC). EMCOR also provides facilities services including management and maintenance support. Through some 75 subsidiaries and joint ventures the company serves a range of commercial industrial institutional and utility customers.

Operations

EMCOR Group operates four main business segments based on service type that together account for 96% of company revenue: Mechanical Construction and Facilities; Electrical Construction and Facilities; Building Services; and Industrial Services. It also operates a building services business in the UK accounting for the remaining 4%.

The Mechanical Construction and Facilities division generates some 40% of total sales. It makes systems for central air refrigeration and cleanroom process ventilation; fire protection; plumbing and piping; controls and filtration; water and wastewater treatment and central plant heating and cooling; cranes and rigging; and steel-related work.

EMCOR's Electrical Construction and Facilities division (around 25% of sales) handles and installs systems for electrical power; on-premise electrical and lighting systems; low-voltage systems such as fire alarm security and process control; voice and data communication; roadway and transit lighting; and fiber optic lines.

The US Building Services business (around 25% of revenue) offers operation maintenance and services for everything from a company's electrical and mechanical systems for commercial and government sites to janitorial services landscaping and snow removal services.

The Industrial Services segment (10% of sales) provides industrial and maintenance services such as refinery turnaround planning and engineering; specialty welding; overhaul and maintenance; and refinery and petrochemical plant maintenance and services.

The UK Building Services operation supports and maintains customers' facilities including commercial and government sites in the UK.

Geographic Reach

More than 95% of Norwalk Connecticut-based EMCOR's revenue comes from work performed in the US. The remainder is derived from the UK.

Sales and Marketing

Some of EMCOR's largest institutional industrial and commercial projects include water treatment plants hospitals correctional facilities research labs manufacturing plants oil refineries data centers hotels shopping malls and office buildings.

Large projects (those larger than $10 million) account for around 30% of total sales. These are often multi-year projects.

Projects of less than $10.0 million account for 70% of sales. These smaller value projects are often one-off in nature such as a modification or construction to serve a specific purpose and are less dependent on the wider construction market.

Financial Performance

EMCOR's revenue and profits have grown steadily in recent years.

After an impressive 2016 in fiscal 2017 EMCOR's sales growth slowed to 2% although total sales of $7.7 billion was still a company record.

Growth was uneven across EMCOR's operating units as $320 million growth in US mechanical construction and $125 million growth in electrical construction was offset by contractions in US building services and US industrial services. The US mechanical construction segment was boosted by higher revenue from healthcare commercial and hospitality construction projects as well as contributions from acquired businesses. In EMCOR's UK business a $14.4 million revenue increase included an unfavorable exchange rate impact of $15.9 million as the Brexit vote dragged on the pound sterling.

Net income grew 25% to $227.2 million largely due to a tax benefit from the 2017 US Tax Cuts and Jobs Act as well as higher revenue.

Cash from operations increased 39% to $366.1 million due to higher net income and improved cash from accounts payable.

Strategy

EMCOR has grown by diversifying its services and expanding geographically within the US. With the US economy on the upswing EMCOR is reaping the benefits of being a more efficient operator. The company has continued its longstanding practice of building out its portfolio of services through acquisitions.Recently this has included three small purchases in 2017 and a larger purchase in 2016.

Mergers and Acquisitions

In 2019 EMCOR agreed to acquire Batchelor & Kimball a leading provider of mechanical construction and maintenance services. The acquisition strengthens EMCOR?s position in mechanical construction and maintenance services and broadens its capabilities across the South and Southeast regions.

In 2017 EMCOR made three bolt-on acquisitions: one company that provides fire protection and alarms in the Southern region of the US; one that provides millwright services for manufacturers across the US; and one that offers mobile mechanical services in the Western US. The first two were combined into EMCOR's US mechanical construction and facilities services segment and the third into its US building services segment.

In 2016 EMCOR bought Ardent Services and subsidiary Rabalais Constructors providers of electrical and instrumentation services to the energy infrastructure market in North America for $205 million. Ardent is active in the US industrial and refinery electrical and instrumentation service business. It includes refiners petrochemical companies midstream operators integrated oil companies and other energy operators.

HISTORY

EMCOR's forerunner Jamaica Water Supply Co. was incorporated in 1887 to supply water to some residents of Queens and Nassau Counties in New York. In 1902 it bought Jamaica Township Water Co. and by 1906 it was generating revenue — reaching $1.6 million by 1932. Over the next 35 years the company kept pace with the population of its service area.

In 1966 the enterprise was acquired by Jamaica Water and Utilities which then bought Sea Cliff Water Co. In 1969 and 1970 it acquired Welsbach (electrical contractors) and A to Z Equipment (construction trailer suppliers); it briefly changed its name in 1974 to Welsbach Corp. before becoming Jamaica Water Properties in 1976.

Diversification proved unprofitable however and in 1977 Martin Dwyer and his son Andrew took over the management of the struggling firm. Despite posting million-dollar losses in 1979 it was profitable by 1980.

The Dwyers acquired companies in the electrical and mechanical contracting security telecommunications computer energy and environmental businesses. In 1985 Andrew Dwyer became president and the firm changed its name the next year to JWP.

Between 1986 and 1990 JWP acquired more than a dozen companies including Extel (1986) Gibson Electric (1987) Dynalectric (1988) Drake & Scull (1989) NEECO and Compumat (1990) and Comstock Canada (1990).

In 1991 JWP capped its strategy of buying up US computer systems resellers by acquiring Businessland. It then bought French microelectronics distributor SIVEA. Later that year JWP bought a 34% stake in Resource Recycling Technologies (a solid-waste recycler).

JWP's shopping spree extended the firm's reach but the company began to struggle when several sectors turned sour. A price war in the information services business and a weak construction market led to a loss of more than $600 million in 1992. That year president David Sokol resigned after questioning JWP's accounting practices. He turned over to the SEC a report that claimed inflated profits.

Cutting itself to about half its former size the company sold JWP Information Services in 1993. (JWP Information Services later became ENTEX Information Services which was acquired by Siemens in 2000.) However JWP continued to struggle and in early 1994 it filed for bankruptcy. Emerging from Chapter 11 protection in December 1994 the reorganized company took the name EMCOR. That year Frank MacInnis former CEO of electrical contractor Comstock Group stepped in to lead EMCOR.

In 1995 the SEC using Sokol's information charged several former JWP executives with accounting fraud claiming they had overstated profits to boost the value of their company stock and their bonuses. EMCOR later reached a non-monetary settlement with the SEC. The company sold Jamaica Water Supply and Sea Cliff in 1996; it also achieved profitability that year.

Focusing on external growth EMCOR acquired a number of firms in 1998 and 1999 including Marelich Mechanical Co. and Mesa Energy Systems BALCO Inc. and the Poole & Kent group of mechanical contracting companies based in Baltimore and Miami. To meet increased demands for facilities services in 2000 EMCOR consolidated the operations of three of its mechanical contractors (BALCO J.C. Higgins and Tucker Mechanical) into one company EMCOR Services which operates in New England.

That year about six years after emerging from bankruptcy EMCOR began trading on the New York Stock Exchange. In 2002 EMCOR bought 19 subsidiaries from its financially troubled rival Comfort Systems USA including its largest unit Shambaugh & Son. Later that year it expanded its facilities services operations with the acquisition of Consolidated Engineering Services (CES) an Archstone-Smith subsidiary that operated in 20 states.

EMCOR broadened its facilities services operations by acquiring the US facility management services unit of Siemens Building Technologies in 2003; in 2005 it added Fluidics Inc. a mechanical services company based in Philadelphia.

In 2007 EMCOR acquired FR X Ohmstede Acquisitions Co. a leading provider of aftermarket maintenance and repair services and replacement parts for oil refinery equipment.

The company added to its industrial services operations by acquiring South Carolina-based facilities maintenance provider MOR PPM in 2008.

In 2009 EMCOR bought LT Mechanical of North Carolina a leading plumbing and mechanical contractor. The following year it bought Pennsylvania-based engineering and facilities services firm Scalise Industries broadening its mechanical services business.

EXECUTIVES

Evp And Cfo, Mark A. Pompa, age 55, $670,000 total compensation
Evp Shared Services, R. Kevin Matz, age 61, $530,000 total compensation
Ceo Emcor Uk, Keith Chanter, age 60
President Ceo And Director, Anthony J. (Tony) Guzzi, age 54, $1,071,000 total compensation
Vp Marketing And Communications, Mava K. Heffler
President And Ceo Emcor Construction Services, Michael J. (Mike) Parry, age 70
President And Ceo Emcor Building Services, Michael P. (Mike) Bordes
President And Ceo Emcor Industrial Services And Ohmstede, Bill Reid
Executive Vice President, Shelly Cammaker
Vice President Of Sales And Marketing Emcor Group Inc, Jeff Budzinski
Vice President Information Systems And Technology, Peter Baker
Vice President Massachusetts Operations, Gary Picco
Senior Vice President Information Systems And Technology Building Services, Timothy Reed
Vice President, Charlie Hadsell
Vice President And Controller, William Feher
Vice President Facility Services, Anthony Scalise
Chairman, Stephen W. Bershad, age 77
Auditors: Ernst & Young LLP

LOCATIONS

HQ: EMCOR Group, Inc.
301 Merritt Seven, Norwalk, CT 06851-1092
Phone: 203 849-7800
Web: www.emcorgroup.com

PRODUCTS/OPERATIONS

Selected Services
EMCOR Construction Services
Electrical Construction
Mechanical Construction
Fire Protection
EMCOR Building Services
EMCOR Facilities Services
EMCOR Mechanical Services
EMCOR Government Services
EMCOR Energy Services
Customer Solutions Centers
EMCOR Industrial Services
Turnarounds
Heat Exchangers
Towers
Refractory

2017 Sales

	$ mil.	% of total
United States mechanical construction and facilities services	2,994	39
United States building services	1,812	23
United States electrical construction and facilities services	1,837	24
United States industrial services	801	10
Less intersegment revenues	-99.7	0
United Kingdom building services	340	4
Total	**7,687**	**100**

Selected Operations

Mechanical and Electrical Construction
  Building plant and lighting systems
  Data communications systems
  Electrical power distribution systems
  Energy recovery
  Heating ventilation and air-conditioning (HVAC) systems
  Lighting systems
  Low-voltage systems (alarm security communications)
  Piping and plumbing systems
  Refrigeration systems
  Voice communications systems
Facilities Services
  Facilities management
  Installation and support for building systems
  Mobile maintenance and service
  Program development and management for energy systems
  Remote monitoring
  Site-based operations and maintenance
  Small modification and retrofit projects
  Technical consulting and diagnostic services

Selected Subsidiaries

Dyn Specialty Contracting Inc.
EMCOR Construction Services Inc.
EMCOR-CSI Holding Co.
EMCOR Facilities Services Inc.
EMCOR Group (UK) plc
EMCOR International Inc.
EMCOR (UK) Limited
EMCOR Mechanical/Electrical Services (East) Inc.
  EMCOR (UK) Limited
FR X Ohmstede Acquisitions Co.
MES Holdings Corporation

COMPETITORS

ABM Industries	Johnson Controls Power
AECOM	Solutions
APi Group	Jones Lang LaSalle
ARAMARK	Limbach Facility
CBRE Group	Services
Comfort Systems USA	MYR Group
Cushman & Wakefield	MasTec
Dycom	Quanta Services
Fluor	Schneider Electric
Hoffman Corporation	Siemens AG
Honeywell	Sodexo USA
International	SteelFab
IES Holdings	Trane Inc.
ISS GROUP LIMITED	Tutor Perini
Jacobs Technology	

HISTORICAL FINANCIALS

Company Type: Public

Income Statement   FYE: December 31

	REVENUE ($ mil.)	NET INCOME ($ mil.)	NET PROFIT MARGIN	EMPLOYEES
12/18	8,130	283	3.5%	33,000
12/17	7,687	227	3.0%	32,000
12/16	7,551	181	2.4%	31,000
12/15	6,718	172	2.6%	29,000
12/14	6,424	168	2.6%	27,000
Annual Growth	**6.1%**	**13.9%**	**—**	**5.1%**

2018 Year-End Financials

Debt ratio: 7.23%
Return on equity: 16.61%
Cash ($ mil.): 363
Current ratio: 1.38
Long-term debt ($ mil.): 279
No. of shares (mil.): 55
Dividends
  Yield: 0.5%
  Payout: 6.6%
Market value ($ mil.): 3,342

	STOCK PRICE ($) FY Close	P/E High/Low	PER SHARE ($) Earnings	Dividends	Book Value
12/18	59.69	17 12	4.85	0.32	31.09
12/17	81.75	22 16	3.82	0.32	28.46
12/16	70.76	24 14	2.97	0.32	25.64
12/15	48.04	19 15	2.72	0.32	24.18
12/14	44.49	19 15	2.52	0.32	22.48
Annual Growth	**7.6%**	**— —**	**17.8%**	**(0.0%)**	**8.4%**

Emerson Electric Co.

EXECUTIVES

Chb-Ceo, David N Farr
Pres, Michael H Train
Sr Exec V Pres-Cfo, Frank J Dellaquila
Exec V Pres-Coo, Steven J Pelch
Sr V Pres-Cmo, Katherine Button Bell
Sr V Pres-General Counse-SEC, Sara Y Bosco
V Pres-Cao-Contrl, Michael J Baughman
Evp Automation Solutions, Lal Karsanbhai
Evp Commercial & Residential, Robert T Sharp
Svp Planning & Dev't, Mark J Bulanda
Vp-Engineering, Justin King
Auditors: KPMG LLP

LOCATIONS

HQ: Emerson Electric Co.
8000 W. Florissant Avenue, P.O. Box 4100, St. Louis, MO 63136
Phone: 314 553-2000
Web: www.emerson.com

COMPETITORS

ABB	McDermott
AMETEK	NEC
Cooper Industries	Parker-Hannifin
Cummins	Power-One
Dana Holding	Raytheon
Danaher	Rexnord
Dresser Inc.	Rockwell Automation
Eaton	Rolls-Royce
Endress + Hauser	SPX
GE	Siemens AG
Hitachi	Sino-American
Honeywell	Electronic
International	Snap-on
Illinois Tool Works	Stanley Black and
Ingersoll-Rand	Decker
Interpump	TE Connectivity
Invensys	Tecumseh Products
Johnson Controls	Toshiba
Kinetek	Trippe Manufacturing
Lennox	United Technologies
Mark IV	Yokogawa Electric

HISTORICAL FINANCIALS

Company Type: Public

Income Statement   FYE: September 30

	REVENUE ($ mil.)	NET INCOME ($ mil.)	NET PROFIT MARGIN	EMPLOYEES
09/19	18,372	2,306	12.6%	88,000
09/18	17,408	2,203	12.7%	87,500
09/17	15,264	1,518	9.9%	76,500
09/16	14,522	1,635	11.3%	103,500
09/15	22,304	2,710	12.2%	110,800
Annual Growth	**(4.7%)**	**(4.0%)**	**—**	**(5.6%)**

Debt ratio: 27.91%   No. of shares (mil.): 611
Return on equity: 26.85%   Dividends
Cash ($ mil.): 1,494   Yield: 2.9%
Current ratio: 1.19   Payout: 55.6%
Long-term debt ($ mil.): 4,277   Market value ($ mil.): 40,892

	STOCK PRICE ($) FY Close	P/E High/Low	PER SHARE ($) Earnings	Dividends	Book Value
09/19	66.86	21 15	3.71	1.96	13.46
09/18	76.58	23 17	3.46	1.94	14.22
09/17	62.84	27 21	2.35	1.92	13.59
09/16	54.51	22 17	2.52	1.90	11.77
09/15	44.17	16 11	3.99	1.88	12.34
Annual Growth	10.9%	— —	(1.8%)	1.0%	2.2%

Employers Holdings Inc

Because workers' compensation is nothing to gamble with small business owners can turn to Employers Holdings. The Reno-based holding company provides workers' compensation services including claims management loss prevention consulting and care management to small businesses in low and medium hazard industries including retailers and restaurants. The company provides workers' compensation through its Employer Insurance Company of Nevada (EICN) and Employers Compensation Insurance Company. Employers Holdings also operates Employers Assurance and Employers Preferred Insurance Company both of which also offer workers' compensation.

Geographic Reach
While Employers Holdings distributes its products in more than 35 states and the District of Columbia more than half of its premiums come from California.

Sales and Marketing
Employers Holdings uses a network of more than 5100 independent agencies to brings its wares to the public; these agencies bring in about three-fourths of the company's in-force premiums. The company also markets its products through brokers and local trade groups and associations. Furthermore it markets its products along with ADP's payroll services in several states. Employers Holdings is forging additional distribution partners in other markets.

Financial Performance
Employers Holdings' revenue has been relatively stable for the past few years. In fiscal 2016 revenue rose 4% to $779.8 million. That change was primarily driven by gains on investments as premiums earned saw just a modest increase.

The higher revenue and a drop in losses and loss adjustments led to higher profits that year. Employers Holdings' net income which has been recovering since taking a bit of a dip in 2013 increased 13% to $106.7 million in 2016. This in turn led to a 5% increase in operating cash flow which totaled $122.8 million.

Strategy
Employers Holdings targets small businesses as there are fewer competitors in that space. The firm operates in low-to-medium hazard industries to keep its losses under control. Its top sectors served include restaurants the clerical side of physician offices automobile service or repair centers and colleges (professional employees and clerical). The company also spreads its risk around and is not dependent upon any one customer for a significant portion of its income. Similarly although California is the firm's largest market it focuses on expanding geographically to diversify its revenue stream.

Additionally Employer Holdings is investing in its IT infrastructure to improve customer service increase efficiency and expand its operating capacity.

EXECUTIVES

President And Ceo, Douglas D. Dirks, $927,569 total compensation
Evp Chief Legal Officer And General Counsel, Lenard T. Ormsby, $485,708 total compensation
Evp Corporate And Public Affairs, Ann W. Nelson, $354,501 total compensation
Evp And Chief Administrative Officer, John P. Nelson, $334,391 total compensation
Evp And Coo, Stephen V. Festa, $488,299 total compensation
Evp And Cio, Tracey L. Berg
Svp And Chief Underwriting Officer, Lawrence S. (Larry) Rogers
Evp And Cfo, Michael S. Paquette, age 56
Vice President Deputy General Counsel, Mary Lynn
Vice President, Jim Werbeckes
Vice President Human Resources, Chris Mclauchlin
Vice President Of Treasury And Investments, Matthew Hendricksen
Vice President Customer Support, Dennis Dix
Vice President, Sam King
Senior Vice President Chief Data And Analytics Officer, Tom Warden
Vice President Claims, David Macy
Chairman, Michael D. (Mike) Rumbolz, age 66
Auditors: Ernst & Young LLP

LOCATIONS

HQ: Employers Holdings Inc
10375 Professional Circle, Reno, NV 89521
Phone: 888 682-6671

2015 Premiums In-force
	% of total
California	57
others	43
Total	**100**

PRODUCTS/OPERATIONS

2015 Sales
	$ mil.	% of total
Net premiums earned	690	91
Net investment income	72	9
Realized losses on investments	(10.7)	—
Other income	0	—
Total	**752**	**100**

Selected Products & Services
Claims Management
Fraud Prevention
Loss Control
Loss Run Report
Managed Care Services
PrecisePay (Pay-As-You-Go)
Premium Audit
Return to Work Program
Safety Promotion Programs
Workers' Compensation Insurance

Selected Subsidiaries
AmSERV Inc.
EIG Services Inc.
Elite Insurance Services Inc.
Employers Assurance Company
Employers Compensation Insurance Company
Employers Group Inc.
Employers Insurance Company of Nevada
Employers Occupational Health Inc.
Employers Preferred Insurance Company
Pinnacle Benefits Inc.

COMPETITORS

AMERISAFE
AmTrust Financial
Baldwin & Lyons
Berkshire Hathaway
CNA Financial
Donegal
EMC Insurance
Liberty Mutual
Meadowbrook Insurance
Navigators
ProAssurance
RLI

Republic Indemnity
Safety Insurance
SeaBright Insurance
Selective Insurance
State Auto Financial
State Compensation Insurance Fund
The Hartford
TowerGroup
Travelers Companies
United Fire
Zurich Insurance Group

HISTORICAL FINANCIALS

Company Type: Public

Income Statement   FYE: December 31

	ASSETS ($ mil.)	NET INCOME ($ mil.)	INCOME AS % OF ASSETS	EMPLOYEES
12/18	3,919	141	3.6%	704
12/17	3,840	101	2.6%	672
12/16	3,773	106	2.8%	693
12/15	3,755	94	2.5%	716
12/14	3,769	100	2.7%	709
Annual Growth	1.0%	8.8%	—	(0.2%)

2018 Year-End Financials

Debt ratio: 0.51%   No. of shares (mil.): 32
Return on equity: 14.38%   Dividends
Cash ($ mil.): 101   Yield: 1.9%
Current ratio: —   Payout: 18.8%
Long-term debt ($ mil.): —   Market value ($ mil.): 1,375

	STOCK PRICE ($) FY Close	P/E High/Low	PER SHARE ($) Earnings	Dividends	Book Value
12/18	41.97	11 9	4.24	0.80	31.08
12/17	44.40	16 12	3.06	0.60	29.07
12/16	39.60	12 7	3.24	0.36	26.16
12/15	27.30	10 7	2.90	0.24	23.62
12/14	23.51	10 6	3.14	0.24	21.81
Annual Growth	15.6%	— —	7.8%	35.1%	9.3%

Energy Transfer LP

Energy Transfer LP (ET) transfers natural gas and other energy resources through its massive network of US-based pipelines. The company's operations occur primarily through primary subsidiary Energy Transfer Operating LP (ETO) and Sunoco LP although it has interests in a number of LPs and other subsidiaries. The company operates pipelines that transport natural gas natural gas liquids refined products and crude oil across the US. It also owns and operates associated terminalling storage and fractionation facilities. Energy Transfer LP generates about 30% of revenue through a 35% stake in Sunoco LP. In 2019 the company agreed to acquire SemGroup Corporation for $5 billion.

Operations
Energy Transfer (ET) reports financial results according to its major investments in Energy Transfer Partners Sunoco LP and Lake Charles LNG.

Its largest segment is Energy Transfer Operating LP (ETO). ETO gathers processes compresses treats and transports natural gas. These midstream services occur in some of the most prolific shale plays in the US such as Eagle Ford Marcellus Utica

Bone Spring and Avalon. ETO is one of the largest movers of natural gas in the country and does so through its 71000 miles of pipeline. It also possesses a controlling interest in a limited partnership that owns and operates a logistics business consisting of crude oil natural gas liquids (NGLs) and refined products pipelines.

Its investment in Sunoco LP brings in some 35% of revenue. Sunoco LP operates almost 50000 gas stations and convenience stores in the Eastern US. It produces revenue through fuel sales which typically top 2.5 billion gallons in a given year. It generates a few billion dollars from merchandise sales in its gas station convenience stores. Sunoco sells about 5 billion gallons of fuel wholesale through nearly 8000 dealers distributors and commercials customers. In 2017 this segment's pipeline and product terminals were merged into the ETO entity.

Lake Charles LNG generates a small amount of total revenue by storing and re-gasifying natural gas in its facility in Lake Charles LA.

Geographic Reach

Dallas TX is home to Energy Transfer Operating's and Energy Transfer's headquarters. ETO along with the recently merged pipeline and terminal assets of Sunoco have significant operations in Texas Louisiana Oklahoma West Virginia Pennsylvania and New York. Its pipelines reach as far as North Dakota Arizona and Idaho.

The Sunoco LP subsidiary is headquartered in Philadelphia PA and operates nearly 5000 gas stations in 26 states mostly in the Eastern US and Texas.

Sales and Marketing

Energy Transfer via Energy Transfer Operating sells natural gas to utilities industrial consumers other marketers and pipeline companies. Its Sunoco segment sells gasoline and diesel in addition to a broad mix of merchandise such as groceries fast foods and beverages at its convenience stores. A sizable portion of Sunoco's gasoline and diesel sales are to wholesale customers.

Financial Performance

In recent years Energy Transfer's revenue growth has been excellent rising from a $5.4 billion low in 2009 to a $55.7 billion peak in 2014 (driven by the Sunoco acquisition) before sliding back to $37.5 billion in 2016. Net income was rangebound between 2010 and 2013 ($200 million - $300 million) before spiking to $1.2 billion in 2015 and then falling in 2016.

In 2016 revenue decreased 11% to $37.5 billion due to a 20% fall in crude oil sales and lower refined product sales both partially offset by higher NGL sales.

Net income in 2016 fell 17% to $983 million the result aided by a $954 million windfall from a noncontrolling interest adjustment. Without the adjustment net income from operations came in at a paltry $41 a 96% plummet from the prior year. Although in dollar terms operating expenses fell when viewed as a percent of revenue the expenses did not fall in line with revenue and therefore had a negative effect on earnings. Included in expenses was a goodwill impairment loss exceeding $1.0 billion.

Cash available at the end of 2016 was $483 million a decrease of $123 million from 2015. Large uses of cash came from $8.0 billion of capital expenditures and a $1.6 billion outlay for acquisitions. Operations contributed $3.4 billion to cash and financing activities added almost $6.0 billion mainly through issuance of debt and notes.

Strategy

Energy Transfer has been busy in recent years. Its strategy is playing out through partnership restructuring divestitures capital raises and the build out of several midstream projects.

Announced in 2016 and closed in early 2017 ET orchestrated a merger of its two primary subsidiaries ? Energy Transfer Partners and the midstream assets of its Sunoco LP ? into a surviving entity that kept the Energy Transfer Partners name. The deal cleans up its partnership structure and is anticipated to help with credit ratings going forward. Operational synergies are expected to be minimal.

Sunoco LP has been on an acquisition spree since 2014 spending over $700 million between then and mid-2017. Its retail acquisitions brought on board more than 120 new gas stations from previous owners Pico Petroleum Aziz Quick Stops Valentine Stores Denny Oil Aloha Petroleum among others. It purchased a wholesaler in the US Northeast and obtained midstream assets in Alabama Hawaii and Texas.

To help raise capital for its acquisitions and project expenses ET sold in late 2017 half of its interests in ET Rover Pipeline to Blackstone Energy Partners for approximately $1.6 billion. ET through its ETO subsidiary will remain operator of the Marcellus and Utica shale Rover Pipeline. ETO sold off partial interests in its Bakken holdings in late 2016 for $2 billion. ETO also issued perpetual preferred stock in late 2017 raising $1.5 billion.

ET is building out its already expansive midstream network of assets. In the Permian Basin it brought online an additional 600 mm cubic feet/day in processing capacity and anticipates 200 mmcf/d more by mid-2018. Its Mariner East system in the Marcellus Shale is receiving capital to expand its NGLs transport line from Ohio & Western Pennsylvania to the Marcus Hook Industrial Complex on the Eastern Atlantic coast. ET is also expanding its Mont Belvieu fractionation facility adding more than 250 mmbpd capacity by mid 2019. In total the company spent about $4.0 billion on capital expenditures in 2016 and is on track to spent $3.5 billion in 2017.

Mergers and Acquisitions

In 2019 Energy Transfer agreed to acquire fellow pipeline and energy infrastructure firm SemGroup Corporation in a transaction valued at $5 billion. The deal would enhance Energy Transfer's midstream infrastructure connectivity increases the company's crude oil and natural gas liquids (NGL) infrastructure and adds direct pipelines to the Houston Ship Channel and the Nederland Terminal.

Company Background

In 2012 Energy Transfer Equity bought diversified gas player Southern Union for $9.4 billion (including $3.7 billion in debt). The acquisition made Energy Transfer Equity one of the largest natural gas infrastructure companies in the US.

That year the company also completed a $2 billion merger of a wholly owned Energy Transfer Partners subsidiary with and into Southern Union subsidiary CrossCountry Energy LLC which owns an indirect 50% interest in Citrus Corp. the owner of the Florida Gas Transmission pipeline system. After the merger CrossCountry Energy remained as the surviving entity a wholly owned subsidiary of Energy Transfer Partners.

In 2010 Energy Transfer Equity acquired the general partner stake of Regency Energy Partners and sold a 49.9% stake in its Midcontinent Express Pipeline to that company. The move was seen as a way for the company to diversify its general partner operations with the aim of getting a better return for shareholders. Regency Energy Partners focuses on the gathering processing marketing and transportation of natural gas and natural gas liquids in Arkansas Kansas Louisiana and Texas.

Energy Transfer Equity was formed in 2002 as La Grange Energy a Texas limited partnership. In early 2005 it changed its name to Energy Transfer

Company. In August 2005 it converted from a Texas limited partnership to a Delaware limited partnership and became Energy Transfer Equity.

EXECUTIVES

President, John W. McReynolds, age 67, $577,280 total compensation

Cfo, Thomas E. (Tom) Long, age 63, $454,154 total compensation

Evp And General Counsel, Thomas P. Mason, age 62, $571,729 total compensation

President And Coo Etp, Marshall S. (Mackie) McCrea, $1,009,231 total compensation

Evp And Head Tax, Bradford D. (Brad) Whitehurst, $503,354 total compensation

Vice President Operations, Robert Truesdell

Senior Vice President Commercial Operations Allegheny Region, Alan Vaina

Vp Engineering, Rodney Rogers

Vice President Human Resources And Administration, Robert M Kerrigan

Vice President Human Resources, Gene Weldon

Vice President Market Services, Bradley Holmes

Vice President Executive Operations, Laura Whitfield

Vice President Engineering, Charles Frey

Senior Vice President Commercial Operations, Mario Rivera

Senior Vice President Commercial Operations, Brian Beebe

Vice President Engineering, Chris Sonneborn

Vice President Commercial Operations, Glenn Emery

V.p. Operations, Jim Kerns

Vice President Procurement Fleet Budget, Kelly Henry

Assistant Treasurer, Debbie Gomez

Auditors: Grant Thornton LLP

LOCATIONS

HQ: Energy Transfer LP
 8111 Westchester Drive, Suite 600, Dallas, TX 75225
Phone: 214 981-0700
Web: www.energytransfer.com

PRODUCTS/OPERATIONS

2016 Sales

	$ mil.	% of total
Investment in ETP	21,827	58
Investment in Sunoco LP	15,698	41
Investment in lake Charles LNG	197	1
Adjustments	(218)	-
Total	**37,504**	**100**

2016 Sales

	$ mil.	% of total
Refined product sales	14,020	37
Crude sales	6,766	18
NGL sales	4,841	13
Gathering transportation and other fees	4,172	11
Natural gas sales	3,619	10
Other	4,086	11
Total	**37,504**	**100**

Selected Subsidiaries and Operating Units

EASTERN GULF CRUDE ACCESS LLC
ETP- Energy Transfer Partners L.P.
ETP GP- Energy Transfer Partners GP L.P. the general partner of ETP
ETP LLC- Energy Transfer Partners L.L.C. the general partner of ETP GP
Holdco- ETP Holdco Corporation
Regency GP- Regency Energy Partners GP LP the general partner of Regency
Regency LLC- Regency Energy Partners GP LLC the general partner of Regency GP
Regency- Regency Energy Partners LP
Southern Union- Southern Union Company
Sunoco Logistics- Sunoco Logistics Partners L.P.
Sunoco- Sunoco Inc.

COMPETITORS

AmeriGas Partners	Exxon Mobil
Atmos Energy	Ferrellgas Partners
Chevron	Kinder Morgan
Crestwood Midstream	Magellan Midstream
Partners LP	ONEOK
DCP Midstream Partners	Star Gas Partners
Enbridge	Suburban Propane

HISTORICAL FINANCIALS

Company Type: Public

Income Statement
FYE: December 31

	REVENUE ($ mil.)	NET INCOME ($ mil.)	NET PROFIT MARGIN	EMPLOYEES
12/18	54,087	1,694	3.1%	11,768
12/17	40,523	954	2.4%	29,486
12/16	37,504	995	2.7%	30,992
12/15	42,126	1,189	2.8%	30,078
12/14	55,691	633	1.1%	27,605
Annual Growth	(0.7%)	27.9%	—	(19.2%)

2018 Year-End Financials

Debt ratio: 52.16%—
Return on equity: —
Cash ($ mil.): 419
Current ratio: 0.73
Long-term debt ($ mil.): 43,373

Dividends
Yield: 9.2%
Payout: 106.0%
Market value ($ mil.): —

	STOCK PRICE ($) FY Close	P/E High/Low	Earnings	Dividends	Book Value
12/18	13.21	17 10	1.15	1.22	7.85
12/17	17.26	23 18	0.83	1.15	(1.11)
12/16	19.31	21 4	0.92	1.14	(1.62)
12/15	13.74	63 10	1.11	1.02	(0.89)
12/14	57.38	146 69	0.58	0.75	0.61
Annual Growth	(30.7%)	— —	18.9%	12.9%	89.1%

Energy Transfer Operating LP

Energy Transfer Operating (ETO) is the main operating subsidiary of diversified energy asset firm Energy Transfer LP. ETO's crude oil segment (about 30% of sales) operates more than 9500 miles of pipelines that provide crude transportation services to oil markets in the Southwest Midwest and Northeast US. The NGL and Refined Products segment (20% of sales) operates about 4700 miles of natural gas liquids (NGL) pipelines and fractionation facilities. The company's midstream activities (nearly 15% of sales) include the gathering compression and treating of natural gas. Other operations include more than 28000 miles of interstate and intrastate natural gas pipelines and an LNG import terminal and regasification facility in Louisiana. The company derives about 30% of revenue through a 35% stake in Sunoco LP.

EXECUTIVES

Ceo, Kelcy L Warren
Pres-Coo, Matthew S Ramsey
L.P., Gen Ptnr, Energy T GP
Auditors: Grant Thornton LLP

LOCATIONS

HQ: Energy Transfer Operating LP
  8111 Westchester Drive, Suite 600, Dallas, TX 75225
Phone: 214 981-0700
Web: www.energytransfer.com

PRODUCTS/OPERATIONS

2011 Sales

	% of total
Crude oil acquisition & marketing	92
Terminal facilities	4
Crude oil pipelines	3
Refined product pipelines	1
Total	**100**

COMPETITORS

Buckeye Partners	Magellan Midstream
CITGO	Marathon Petroleum
Enbridge Energy	Plains All American
Enterprise Products	Pipeline
Kinder Morgan Energy	RKA Petroleum
Partners	TransMontaigne
Kinder Morgan	TransMontaigne
Management	Partners

HISTORICAL FINANCIALS

Company Type: Public

Income Statement
FYE: December 31

	REVENUE ($ mil.)	NET INCOME ($ mil.)	NET PROFIT MARGIN	EMPLOYEES
12/18	54,087	3,020	5.6%	11,768
12/17	29,054	2,081	7.2%	506,829
12/16	9,151	705	7.7%	2,575
12/15	10,486	393	3.7%	2,500
12/14	18,088	291	1.6%	2,250
Annual Growth	31.5%	79.5%	—	51.2%

2018 Year-End Financials

Debt ratio: 45.80%—
Return on equity: —
Cash ($ mil.): 418
Current ratio: 0.73
Long-term debt ($ mil.): 37,853

Dividends
Yield: 2.0%
Payout: —
Market value ($ mil.): —

EnLink Midstream LLC

Auditors: KPMG LLP

LOCATIONS

HQ: EnLink Midstream LLC
  1722 Routh St., Suite 1300, Dallas, TX 75201
Phone: 214 953-9500
Web: www.enlink.com

HISTORICAL FINANCIALS

Company Type: Public

Income Statement
FYE: December 31

	REVENUE ($ mil.)	NET INCOME ($ mil.)	NET PROFIT MARGIN	EMPLOYEES
12/18	7,699	(13)		1,449
12/17	5,739	212	3.7%	1,494
12/16	4,252	(460)		1,472
12/15	4,452	(355)		1,432
12/14	3,500	126	3.6%	1,148
Annual Growth	21.8%	—	—	6.0%

2018 Year-End Financials

Debt ratio: 41.43%
Return on equity: (-0.72%)
Cash ($ mil.): 100
Current ratio: 0.81
Long-term debt ($ mil.): 4,031

No. of shares (mil.): 181
Dividends
Yield: 11.1%
Payout: —
Market value ($ mil.): 1,721

	STOCK PRICE ($) FY Close	P/E High/Low	Earnings	Dividends	Book Value
12/18	9.49	— —	(0.07)	1.06	9.54
12/17	17.60	17 13	1.17	1.02	10.64
12/16	19.05	— —	(2.56)	1.02	10.45
12/15	15.09	— —	(2.17)	0.99	13.92
12/14	35.56	77 55	0.55	0.63	16.91
Annual Growth	(28.1%)	— —	—	13.9%	(13.3%)

Entergy Corp

Entergy is into energy. The integrated utility holding company's subsidiaries distribute electricity to some 2.9 million customers in four southern states (Arkansas Louisiana Mississippi and Texas) and provide natural gas to about 200000 customers in Louisiana. The company has interests in regulated and non-regulated power plants in North America that have a combined generating capacity of about 30000 MW. Entergy is also one of the largest nuclear power generators in the US (nearly 9000 MW). The company's regulated utilities have little retail competition as they are deemed by state regulators as the sole providers of electricity in their service areas.

Operations

The company operates two business segments: Utility and Wholesale Commodities.

The Utility segment produces 85% of revenue by generating transmitting distributing and selling electric power to customers in its regulated service areas in the US Gulf States region. The segment is composed of several regulated utility companies including: Entergy Arkansas Inc. Entergy Louisiana LLC Entergy Mississippi Inc. Entergy New Orleans Inc. and Entergy Texas. Four nuclear power plant sites with capacity of some 5200 MW are owned and operated by corporations that roll up into this segment. It also runs a small natural gas distribution business. Of its generation capacity about 65% is from gas oil and hydroelectric sources about 25% is from nuclear and the rest comes from coal-fired plants.

Entergy Wholesale Commodities segment produces 15% of total revenue through its ownership and operation of nuclear power plants (nearly 4200 MW of capacity) and fossil fuel plants (some 400 MW of capacity) and the sale of its electricity on the wholesale market. It also provides management services to Nebraska's Cooper Nuclear Station (800 MW of capacity). More than 90% of this segment's generation portfolio is nuclear-sourced.

Geographic Reach

Entergy's Utility segments operates power plants in Arkansas Mississippi and its headquarters in Louisiana. It provides power to customers in those states plus Texas. Entergy New Orleans distributes and transports natural gas within New Orleans and Louisiana through approximately 2500 miles of gas pipeline.

The Wholesale Commodities segment has power plants and customers in New York Michigan Massachusetts Nebraska Arkansas and Louisiana.

Sales and Marketing

Entergy delivers electricity to about 700000 customers in Arkansas about 1.3 million in Louisiana some 450000 in Mississippi and some 450000 in Texas. It provides natural gas to about 100000 customers in New Orleans and nearly another 100000 throughout the rest of Louisiana. Entergy's retail business (mostly through the regulated utility companies) generates some 40% of sales volume from industrial businesses nearly 25% from commercial enterprises more than 25% from residential and the rest from government agencies wholesale and other customers.

Entergy Wholesale Commodities segment sells both energy and capacity from its nuclear plants to retail power providers utilities electric power co-operatives power trading organizations and other power generation companies. These customers include Consolidated Edison and Consumers Energy companies from which Entergy purchased plants with the promise to continue providing energy to them. It also sells to transmission-sharing entities such as ISO New England NYISO and MISO.

The company's regulated utilities have little retail competition as they are deemed by state regulators as the sole providers of electricity in their service areas.

Financial Performance

In recent years Entergy's revenue remained steadfast within a range of $10 billion and $12 billion with a $12.5 billion peak in 2014. Net income over the same period has generally been going down with sharp decreases in 2015 and 2016.

In 2017 revenue crept up 2% to $11 billion thanks to $412 million addition in electric sales increases offset by a 10% fall in competitive business segment sales.

Net income improved from a loss of $565 million in 2016 to a profit of $425 million in 2017. The turnaround in performance was primarily due to a YOY reduction of $2.3 billion in special charges relating to asset write-offs.

Cash holdings at the end of 2017 reduced to $781 million from $1.2 billion the year prior. Operations generated a net inflow of $2.6 billion in cash which was more than offset by $3.8 billion used in investing activities. Financial activities brought in a net cash inflow of $810 million thanks to a net issuance of $1.4 billion in new debt.

Strategy

Entergy wants to expand its investments in regulated utility firms while winding down all its wholesale commodities businesses. The company plans to invest around $10 billion between 2017 and 2019 in utilities almost half of it earmarked for distribution and transmission upgrades. Generation plants will get some 45% of the pot.

The company recently completed the Ninemile 6 plant at the Union Power Station and received approval for work on its St. Charles Lake Charles and Montgomery County Power Stations. The company also joined the MISO transmission-sharing agreement to expand its own network. Finally it is awaiting approval to build a new New Orleans Power Station.

Entergy's Wholesale Commodities business has run into significant headwinds in recent years. The shale boom has resulted in nuclear power being pricier than plants running on shale-sourced natural gas. The New York state is also pressuring the company to decommission its Indian Point Energy Center by 2021. Other nuclear plants await similar fates.

Company Background

Entergy has had a colorful and varied start in the beginning of the 20th Century. Its roots can be traced back to Arkansas Power & Light (1913) New Orleans Public Service Inc (1922) Louisiana Power & Light and Mississippi Power & Light (both formed in 1927). In 1949 these four companies along with other utilities were combined into a Maine holding company Electric Power and Light. In 1949 after a small phase when the unified company was dissolved a new holding company Middle South Utilities emerged that year to take over the four utilities' assets. In 1989 following a badly botched construction plan of two nuclear facilities (behind schedule and over budget)- whereby

Middle South tried to pass on the costs to customers but eventually settled the disputes— the company changed its name to Entergy to distance itself from the controversy.

HISTORY

Arkansas Power & Light (AP&L founded in 1913) consolidated operations with three other Arkansas utilities in 1926. Also that year New Orleans Public Service Inc. (NOPSI founded in 1922) merged with two other Big Easy electric companies. Louisiana Power & Light (LP&L) and Mississippi Power & Light (MP&L) were both formed in 1927 also through consolidation of regional utilities.

AP&L LP&L MP&L NOPSI and other utilities were combined into a Maine holding company Electric Power and Light which was dissolved in 1949. A new holding company Middle South Utilities emerged that year to take over the four utilities' assets.

In 1971 the company bought Arkansas-Missouri Power. In 1974 it brought its first nuclear plant on line and formed Middle South Energy (now System Energy Resources) to develop two more nuclear facilities Grand Gulf 1 and 2. Unfortunately Grand Gulf 1 was completed behind schedule and about 400% over budget. When Middle South tried to pass on the costs to customers controversy ensued. Construction of Grand Gulf 2 was halted and the CFO Edwin Lupberger took charge in 1985. Two years later nuke-related losses took the company to the brink of bankruptcy.

The company moved to settle the disputes by absorbing a $900 million loss on Grand Gulf 2 in 1989. To distance itself from the controversy Middle South changed its name to Entergy. In 1991 NOPSI settled with the City of New Orleans over Grand Gulf 1 costs.

That year Entergy anticipating deregulation branched out into nonregulated industries and looked abroad for growth opportunities. In 1993 a consortium including Entergy acquired a 51% interest in Edesur a Buenos Aires electric utility. In 1995 Entergy agreed to buy a 20% stake in a power plant under construction in India but the state government soon halted the project accusing the participating US companies of exploiting India.

Entergy completed its acquisition of CitiPower an Australian electric distributor in 1996 and the next year it bought the UK's London Electricity.

But diversification had drained funds. Lupberger resigned in 1998 and a new management team began selling noncore businesses such as CitiPower and London Electricity. NYMEX began trading electricity futures in 1998 using Entergy and Cinergy as contract-delivery points.

EXECUTIVES

Vice President Regulatory Policy, Jay Lewis
Group President Utility Operations, Theodore H. (Theo) Bunting, age 61, $607,806 total compensation
Chairman And Ceo, Leo P. Denault, age 60, $1,191,462 total compensation
Svp And Coo, Paul D. Hinnenkamp
Evp, Roderick K. (Rod) West, age 51, $654,514 total compensation
President And Ceo Entergy Mississippi Inc, Haley R. Fisackerly, $248,346 total compensation
Evp Nuclear Operations And Chief Nuclear Officer, A. Christopher (Chris) Bakken, $426,990 total compensation
Evp And Cfo, Andrew S. (Drew) Marsh, age 46, $553,284 total compensation
President And Ceo Entergy New Orleans Inc, Charles Rice
President And Ceo Entergy Arkansas Inc., Rick Riley

Evp And General Counsel, Marcus V. Brown, age 57, $563,208 total compensation
President And Ceo Entergy Texas Inc, Sallie Rainer
President And Ceo Entergy Louisiana Llc And Entergy Gulf States Louisiana L.l.c., Phillip R. May
Evp Shared Services And Human Resources; Chief Diversity Officer, Don Vinci
Vice President Information Technology Entergy Corp., Robyn Murhammer
Senior Vice President Of Nuclear Business Development, Randy Hutchinson
Vice President, Charles Fink
Vice President Performance Management, Jeanne Kenney
Vice President, Bill Abler
Vice President Of Marketing, Liz Gaiennie
Vp Regulatory And Governmental Affairs Entergy Texas, Deanna Rodriguez
Vice President Asset Management, Rose Albarado
Vice President Nuclear Decommissioning, Steven Scheurich
Vice President, William Maguire
Group Vice President Corporate Communications, Necole Merritt
Vice President, Demetric Mercadel
Vp Customer Experience, Ed Melendreras
Site Vice President Vermont Yankee, Chris Wamser
Vice President Engineering, Mike Knight
Svp Nuclear Strategy And Operations Entergy Nuclear, Donna Jacobs
Evp And Cao, Donald Vinci
Svp And Chief Accounting Officer, Alyson Mount
Vice President, Michael Twornay
Vice President Federal Governmental Affairs, Daniel Turton
Vice President Finance, Bob Cushman
Site Vice President, Bob Smith
Vp Customer Experience Strategy Entergy Services, Tracie Boutte
Vice President Of Governmental Affairs, Kenneth Theobalds
Vice President Critical Infrastructur, Chris Peters
Vice President And Associate Broker, Mike Wilson
Senior Vice President Human Resources Chro And Chief Diversity Officer, Andrea Rowley
Vp Customer Operations Support, Shawn Corkran
Executive Vice President Nuclear Operations; Chief Nuclear Officer Entergy Nuclear, Chris Bakken
Vp External Affairs Wholesale, Mike Twomey
Vice President Energy Technology And Analytics, Raiford Smith
Vp Regulatory Affairs Entergy Mississippi, Bob Grenfell
Vice President Transmission Asset Management, Michael Vaughan
Site Vice President Grand Gulf Nuclear Station, Kevin Mulligan
Executive Vice President Of External Ope, Seth Block
Secretary, Kim Leddy
Secretary, Gwen Hymel
Secretary, Julie Mullet
Secretary, Cheryl Morse
Board Member, Perry Rodrigue
Board Member, Charles E Watkins
Secretary Iii, Sandra Bailey
Senior Secretary, Cynthia Washington
Board Of Directors, Dave McElwee
Senior Secretary, Linda Lay
Board Member, Kirkland Donald
Board Member, Doris Minter
Senior Secretary, Marie Montanarello
Secretary, Karla Jones
Senior Secretary, Shirley Halliburton
Board Member, Blanche L Lincoln
Board Member, Stuart Levenick
Board Member, Karen Puckett
Auditors: Deloitte & Touche LLP

LOCATIONS

HQ: Entergy Corp
    639 Loyola Avenue, New Orleans, LA 70113
Phone: 504 576-4000
Web: www.entergy.com

PRODUCTS/OPERATIONS

2017 Sales

	$ mil.	% of total
Utility	9,417	85
Entergy Wholesale Commodities	1,656	15
Eliminations	(0.1)	-
Total	**11,074**	**100**

2017 Sales

	$ mil.	% of total
Electric	9,278	84
Competitive businesses	1,656	15
Natural gas	1,389	1
Total	**11,074**	**100**

Selected Subsidiaries

Entergy Arkansas Inc. (electric utility)
Entergy Louisiana LLC. (electric utility)
Entergy Mississippi Inc. (electric utility)
Entergy New Orleans Inc. (electric and gas utility)
Entergy Nuclear Inc. (nuclear plant operation)
Entergy Operations Inc. (plant management and
    maintenance for Entergy utilities)
Entergy Services Inc. (management services for Entergy
    utilities)
System Energy Resources Inc. (plant management and
    supply to Entergy utilities)
System Fuels Inc. (fuel storage and delivery to Entergy
    utilities)

COMPETITORS

AEP	Oncor Electric
Atmos Energy	Delivery
CenterPoint Energy	Southern Company
OGE Energy	

HISTORICAL FINANCIALS

Company Type: Public

Income Statement				FYE: December 31
	REVENUE ($ mil.)	NET INCOME ($ mil.)	NET PROFIT MARGIN	EMPLOYEES
12/18	11,009	862	7.8%	13,688
12/17	11,074	425	3.8%	13,504
12/16	10,845	(564)	—	13,513
12/15	11,513	(156)	—	13,579
12/14	12,494	960	7.7%	13,393
Annual Growth	(3.1%)	(2.6%)	—	0.5%

2018 Year-End Financials

Debt ratio: 37.56%	No. of shares (mil.): 189
Return on equity: 10.00%	Dividends
Cash ($ mil.): 480	Yield: 4.1%
Current ratio: 0.54	Payout: 77.3%
Long-term debt ($ mil.): 15,538	Market value ($ mil.): 16,272

	STOCK PRICE ($) FY Close	P/E High/Low	PER SHARE ($) Earnings	Dividends	Book Value
12/18	86.07	19 15	4.63	3.58	47.94
12/17	81.39	38 31	2.28	3.50	45.37
12/16	73.47	— —	(3.26)	3.42	46.25
12/15	68.36	— —	(0.99)	3.34	53.67
12/14	87.48	17 12	5.22	3.32	57.53
Annual Growth	(0.4%)	— —	(3.0%)	1.9%	(4.5%)

Enterprise Bancorp, Inc. (MA)

Enterprise Bancorp caters to more customers than just entrepreneurs. The holding company owns Enterprise Bank and Trust which operates more than 20 branches in north-central Massachusetts and southern New Hampshire. The $2 billion-asset bank offers traditional deposit and loan products specializing in lending to businesses professionals high-net-worth individuals and not-for-profits. About half of its loan portfolio is tied to commercial real estate while another one-third is tied to commercial and industrial and commercial construction loans. Subsidiaries Enterprise Investment Services and Enterprise Insurance Services provide investments and insurance geared to the bank's target business customers.

Operations

More than 50% of Enterprise Bancorp's $1.86 billion loan portfolio was tied to commercial real estate loans at the end of 2015 while commercial and industrial and commercial construction loans made up another 25% and 11% of the bank's loan assets. The rest of the bank's portfolio was tied to residential mortgages (9% of loan assets) home equity loans and lines of credit (4%) and consumer loans (less than 1%).

Nearly 80% of the bank's total revenue comes from loan interest while investment advisory fees and deposit and interchange fees each make up another 5%.

Geographic Reach

The Lowell Massachusetts-based bank operated 23 branches mostly located in the greater Merrimack Valley and North Central regions of Massachusetts and Southern New Hampshire at the end of 2015.

Sales and Marketing

Enterprise spent $2.7 million on advertising and public relations during 2015 down from $2.9 million in 2014.

Financial Performance

The bank's annual revenues have risen more than 40% since 2011 as its loan assets have swelled by 50% to $1.86 billion. Meanwhile its net income has grown more than 50% as it's kept a lid on loan loss provisions and operating costs.

Enterprise Bancorp's revenue climbed 8% to $98.4 million during 2015 thanks to 11% loan asset growth driven by a "seasoned" lending team a sales and service culture and geographic market expansion. Commercial construction loans grew the fastest rate during the year though all loans grew albeit at a slightly slower rate.

Revenue growth in 2015 drove the bank's net income up 10% to $16.1 million despite higher salary and employee benefit expenses. Enterprise Bancorp's operating cash levels nearly doubled to $25.7 million for the year largely thanks to positive changes in working capital mainly related to pre-paid expenses and other assets.

Strategy

Enterprise Bancorp has traditionally expanded its loan and deposit business by opening new branches rather than by acquiring other banks. Enterprise hopes to take advantage of the trend to switch from larger banks to smaller community-oriented institutions. The company has also invested in upgrading its branches and operations systems.

EXECUTIVES

Evp And Cfo Enterprise Bancorp And Enterprise Bank And Trust, James A. (Jim) Marcotte, age 61, $194,806 total compensation
Ceo Enterprise Bancorp And Enterprise Bank And Trust, John P. (Jack) Clancy, age 61, $400,000 total compensation
President Enterprise Bancorp And Enterprise Bank And Trust, Richard W. (Dick) Main, age 71, $258,918 total compensation
Evp And Coo Enterprise Bank And Trust, Stephen J. Irish, age 64, $194,804 total compensation
Svp And Chief Commercial Lender, Brian H. Bullock, age 61
Svp And Chief Commercial Real Estate Lender, Steven R. Larochelle, age 55
Svp And Sales Manager, Chester J. (Chet) Szablak, age 61
Vice President, Paul Rousseau
Vice Chairman Enterprise Bancorp And Enterprise Bank And Trust, Arnold S. Lerner, age 89
Chairman Enterprise Bancorp And Enterprise Bank And Trust, George L. Duncan, age 78
Auditors: RSM US LLP

LOCATIONS

HQ: Enterprise Bancorp, Inc. (MA)
    222 Merrimack Street, Lowell, MA 01852
Phone: 978 459-9000

PRODUCTS/OPERATIONS

2015 Sales

	$ mil.	% of total
Interest and dividend income:		
Loans and loans held for sale	77	79
Investment securities	5	5
Other interest-earning assets	0	-
Non-interest income:		
Investment advisory fees	4	5
Deposit and interchange fees	4	5
Net gains on sales of investment securities	1	2
Income on bank-owned life insurance net	0	1
Gains on sales of loans	0	1
Other income	2	3
Total	**98**	**100**

Products and Services

Lending Products:
Residential Loans
Home Equity Loans and Lines of Credit
Consumer Loans
Credit Risk and Allowance for Loan Losses
Deposit Products:
Cash Management Services
Product Delivery Channels
Investment Services
Insurance Services

COMPETITORS

Bank of America	Peoples Federal
Citizens Financial	Bancshares Inc.
Group	Sovereign Bank
Eastern Bank	TD Bank USA

HISTORICAL FINANCIALS

Company Type: Public

Income Statement				FYE: December 31
	ASSETS ($ mil.)	NET INCOME ($ mil.)	INCOME AS % OF ASSETS	EMPLOYEES
12/18	2,964	28	1.0%	508
12/17	2,817	19	0.7%	482
12/16	2,526	18	0.7%	468
12/15	2,285	16	0.7%	426
12/14	2,022	14	0.7%	412
Annual Growth	10.0%	18.5%	—	5.4%

2018 Year-End Financials

Debt ratio: 0.50%
Return on equity: 11.86%
Cash ($ mil.): 63
Current ratio: —
Long-term debt ($ mil.): —

No. of shares (mil.): 11
Dividends
  Yield: 1.8%
  Payout: 27.2%
Market value ($ mil.): 377

	STOCK PRICE ($) FY Close	P/E High/Low		PER SHARE ($) Earnings	Dividends	Book Value
12/18	32.16	17	12	2.46	0.58	21.80
12/17	34.05	23	18	1.66	0.54	19.97
12/16	37.56	22	12	1.70	0.52	18.72
12/15	22.85	16	13	1.55	0.50	17.38
12/14	25.25	18	12	1.44	0.48	16.35
Annual Growth	6.2%	—	—	14.3%	4.8%	7.5%

Enterprise Financial Services Corp

Enterprise Financial Services wants you to boldly bank where many have banked before. It's the holding company for Enterprise Bank & Trust which mostly targets closely-held businesses and their owners but also serves individuals in the St. Louis Kansas City and Phoenix metropolitan areas. Boasting $3.8 billion in assets and 16 branches Enterprise offers standard products such as checking savings and money market accounts and CDs. Commercial and industrial loans make up over half of the company's lending activities while real estate loans make up another 45%. The bank also writes consumer and residential mortgage loans. Bank subsidiary Enterprise Trust offers wealth management services.

Operations

Enterprise Trust the company's wealth management unit targets business owners wealthy individuals and institutional investors providing financial planning business succession planning and related services. The unit also invests in Missouri state tax credits from funds for affordable housing development which it then sells to clients and others.

About 82% of Enterprise Financial's total revenue came from loan interest (including fees) in 2014 while another 7% came from interest on its taxable and tax-exempt investment securities. The rest of its revenue came from wealth management income (4%) service fees (3%) gains on state tax credits (1%) and other miscellaneous income sources. The bank had a staff of 452 full-time employees at the end of 2014.

Geographic Reach

Enterprise Bank & Trust operates eight banking locations in or around Kansas City six banking locations and a support center in the St. Louis area and two banking locations in the Phoenix metro area.

Financial Performance

The company has struggled to consistently grow its revenues in recent years mostly due to shrinking interest margins on its loans amidst the low-interest environment. Its profits however have mostly trended higher thanks to declining loan loss provisions as its loan portfolio's credit quality has improved with higher property valuations in the strengthened economy.

Enterprise Financials' revenue fell by 9% to $148.4 million in 2014 mostly due to double-digit declines in interest income as its purchased credit-impaired (PCI) loan balances and accelerated payments declined and as interest margins on its loans continued to shrink. The bank's portfolio loan balances increased however helping to offset some of its interest income decline.

Lower revenue and higher loan loss provisions (it received a loan loss benefit of $642 thousand in 2013) in 2014 caused the bank's net income to dive 18% to $27.2 million. Enterprise Financial's operating cash levels rose by 7% to $31.5 million despite lower earnings for the year mostly thanks to favorable changes in its working capital related to a $12-million change in other asset balances.

Strategy

Enterprise Financial Services planned in 2015 to continue its long-term strategy of keeping a "relationship-oriented distribution and sales approach"; growing its fee income and niche businesses; practicing "prudent" credit and interest rate risk management; and using advanced technology and controlled-expense growth. The company added that it planned on "operating branches with larger average deposits and employing experienced staff who are compensated on the basis of performance and customer service."

Though it just had two branches in Phoenix in 2015 the bank believes the fast-growing Phoenix market offers long-term growth opportunities for the company with its underlying demographic and geographic factors. Indeed at the end of 2014 the market had over 90000 privately-held businesses and 80000-plus households each with investable assets of more than $1 million.

Mergers and Acquisitions

In 2017 Enterprise Financial Services completed the acquisition of Jefferson County Bancshares the holding company of Eagle Bank and Trust Company in Missouri. The deal added 13 branches in metropolitan St. Louis and Perry County Missouri. The acquisition expanded EFS's assets to nearly $5 billion.

Company Background

In a restructuring move Enterprise Financial Services sold life insurance arm Millennium Brokerage in 2010 five years after investing in the company.

EXECUTIVES

President Enterprise Bank And Trust, Scott R. Goodman, age 55, $318,150 total compensation
Evp And Cfo, Keene S. Turner, age 39, $333,125 total compensation
Ceo, James B. Lally, age 51, $331,342 total compensation
Chief Credit Officer Enterprise Bank & Trust, Douglas N. Bauche, age 50, $253,270 total compensation
Senior Vice President Trust Officer, Steven Ray
Senior Vice President Relationship Manager, Tim Barringhaus
Senior Vice President Treasury Management, Rhonda Harrelson
Vice President Operations, Colleen Shea
Senior Vice President Treasury Management, Mark Lawson
Vice President Treasury Management, Shirley Jacobs
Senior Vice President, Debbie Barstow
Vice President Relationship Manager, Brian Bonfanti
Vice President Treasury Management, Beth Selanders
Senior Vice President, Tim Kelley
Executive Vice President Wholesale, Greg Willert
Vice President Finance, Matt Eusterbrock
Chairman, John S. Eulich, age 68
Auditors: Deloitte and Touche LLP

LOCATIONS

HQ: Enterprise Financial Services Corp
150 North Meramec, Clayton, MO 63105
Phone: 314 725-5500
Web: www.enterprisebank.com

PRODUCTS/OPERATIONS

2011 Sales

	$ mil.	% of total
Interest		
Loans including fees	130	79
Securities	11	7
Other	0	1
Noninterest		
Wealth management	6	4
Service charges on deposit accounts	5	3
Gain on state tax credits net	3	2
Other service charges and fee income	1	1
Other	4	3
Adjustments	(3.5)	-
Total	**161**	**100**

Selected Acquisitions

COMPETITORS

BOK Financial	Midwest BankCentre
Bank of America	Pulaski Financial
Commerce Bancshares	U.S. Bancorp
First Clover Leaf Financial	Wells Fargo

HISTORICAL FINANCIALS

Company Type: Public

Income Statement

FYE: December 31

	ASSETS ($ mil.)	NET INCOME ($ mil.)	INCOME AS % OF ASSETS	EMPLOYEES
12/18	5,645	89	1.6%	650
12/17	5,289	48	0.9%	635
12/16	4,081	48	1.2%	479
12/15	3,608	38	1.1%	459
12/14	3,277	27	0.8%	452
Annual Growth	14.6%	34.6%	—	9.5%

2018 Year-End Financials

Debt ratio: 2.13%
Return on equity: 15.48%
Cash ($ mil.): 194
Current ratio: —
Long-term debt ($ mil.): —

No. of shares (mil.): 22
Dividends
  Yield: 1.2%
  Payout: 12.2%
Market value ($ mil.): 858

	STOCK PRICE ($) FY Close	P/E High/Low		PER SHARE ($) Earnings	Dividends	Book Value
12/18	37.63	15	10	3.83	0.47	26.47
12/17	45.15	22	18	2.07	0.44	23.76
12/16	43.00	18	10	2.41	0.41	19.31
12/15	28.35	16	10	1.89	0.26	17.53
12/14	19.73	15	12	1.35	0.21	15.94
Annual Growth	17.5%	—	—	29.8%	22.3%	13.5%

Enterprise Products Partners L.P.

Enterprise Products Partners has the energy to go the distance. The limited partnership's primary operating subsidiary Enterprise Products Operating LLC (EPO) is a leading player in the North

American midstream services to producers and consumers of natural gas natural gas liquids (NGL) crude oil petrochemicals and refined products. Operations include natural gas processing NGL fractionation petrochemical services and crude oil transportation. It owns some 50000 miles of pipelines 14 billion cu. ft. of natural gas storage and 260 million barrels of storage for NGLs refined products and crude oil. It owns some 27 natural gas processing plants and 18 deep water docks used to export product. The hub of EPO's business is Houston's Mont Belvieu refinery complex.Substantially all of the company's consolidated revenues are earned in the US and derived from a wide customer base.

Operations

Enterprise has four business segments: NGL Pipelines and Services Crude Oil Pipelines and Services Petrochemical and Refined Products Services Natural Gas Pipelines and Services.

The NGL Pipelines and Services segment produces some 45% of overall revenue with its natural gas processing plants and related natural gas liquid (NGL) marketing activities. At the core of its business are 25 processing plants that collect natural gas and remove NGLs and impurities in preparation for transportation and eventual end-user purchase. It owns nearly 20000 miles of NGL pipelines NGL and related product storage facilities and 15 NGL fractionators. The segment also includes the company's NGL import and LPG export terminal operations. NGL marketing activities use a fleet of roughly 800 railcars to deliver feedstocks to its facilities and distribute NGLs to customers throughout the US and Canada.

Crude Oil Pipelines & Services brings in about 30% of revenue and includes about 6000 miles of crude oil pipelines and related operations crude oil storage and marine terminals and crude oil marketing activities. Of its pipelines the Seaway pipeline is notable in that it connects the Cushing OK crude oil hub (major industry hub where price settlement for West Texas Intermediate (WTI) occurs) with markets in southeast Texas.

The Petrochemical and Refined Products Services segment is engaged in petrochemical and refined products transportation and services. It fractionates propylene to create the building blocks of carpet fibers molded plastic parts for appliances cars and medical products and packaging film. It accounts for approximately 15% of revenue.

Natural Gas Pipelines and Services segment includes 19000 miles of pipeline used to gather and transport natural gas from shale plays Eagle Ford Haynesville Barnett Permian and others. It leases underground salt dome natural gas storage facilities in Texas and Louisiana. The segment is also home to natural gas marketing activities. It accounts for approximately 10% of revenue.

Geographic Reach

Houston TX-based Enterprise Products operates the vast majority of its facilities in Texas along the Gulf Coast with particular emphasis in the Mont Belvieu refinery and transport complex. Key locations from which it gathers natural gas and crude oil include Colorado Louisiana New Mexico Texas and Wyoming. It has a presence in shale plays: Eagle Ford Haynesville Barnett Permian Piceance San Juan and Greater Green River supply basins. Its NGL pipelines extend throughout the US Midwest and Gulf Coast including states such as Georgia New York Oklahoma and Minnesota.

Sales and Marketing

Enterprise Products sells product and services to refineries industrial companies commercial customers and regional natural gas processing plants. It generates much of its revenue from fees calculated by the volume of product it transports. Vitol accounted for more than 10% of the company's revenue. The company also performs significant intersegment sales.

Financial PerformanceRevenue increased some 30% to $29 billion. The $6 billion increase came primarily due to the higher sales price as well as higher volumes sold of crude oil natural gas petrochemicals refined products and octane additives.Net income increased more than 10% to $2.8 billion primarily from higher gross income (revenue increased more than expenses) as well as a $60 million increase in equity income of unconsolidated affiliates.Cash holdings reduced drastically from $417 million in 2016 to $70 million at the end of 2017. Operations generated $4.7 billion in cash inflows offset by $3.3 billion for investment and a further $1.7 billion in financing activities. CAPEX was $3.1 billion for 2017.

Strategy

Enterprise's strategy is focused on building and managing an integrated network of midstream energy assets (including salt domes and fractionation and natural gas processing plants) to take advantage of growing US market demand for natural gas NGLs crude oil and refined products.

The company's business strategies are to capitalize on expected increases in the production of natural gas NGLs and crude oil from development activities in various US production basins. Part of this strategy involves expansion through growth capital projects. It plans to continue to expand its assets through the construction of new facilities and to capitalize on expected increases in natural gas NGL and crude oil production resulting from development activities in the Rocky Mountains Mid-Continent Northeast and US Gulf Coast regions including the Niobrara Barnett Eagle Ford Permian Haynesville Marcellus and Utica Shale plays.

Enterprise began commercial service in 2016 on approximately $2.2 billion of growth capital projects. The projects included its Morgan's Point Ethane Export Terminal Waha and South Eddy natural gas processing facilities and the completion of over 2 MMBbls of additional crude oil storage capacity at terminals in Houston and Mont Belvieu.

The company has approximately $6.7 billion of growth capital projects scheduled to be completed by 2020 including two processing facilities the Midland-to-Sealy segment of its Midland-to-ECHO Pipeline System and a joint venture-owned dock infrastructure project in Corpus Christi designed to accommodate crude oil volumes. In early 2017 it purchased assets from bankrupt Azure Midstream to extend its capabilities in East Texas and Northern Louisiana.

To raise cash to both weather the market downturn and fund capital expenditures Enterprise sold its entire Offshore Pipelines & Services segment to Genesis Energy for $1.5 billion. It also raised $2.5 billion with a secondary offering of its stock units.

Mergers and Acquisitions

In 2017 Enterprise Products purchased the midstream business and assets of bankrupt Azure Midstream which has operations in East Texas and Northern Louisiana. Enterprise gained nearly 1000 miles of natural gas gathering pipelines and three natural gas processing facilities.

Company Background

The company is investing heavily in serving shale plays especially the Eagle Ford in South Texas and is building midstream facilities to serve the surge in natural gas production. In 2012 it opened a fifth NGL fractionator at its Mont Belvieu facility to process Eagle Ford hydrocarbons and a fifth in 2012.

That year Enterprise joined Enbridge Energy Partners and Anadarko Petroleum in advancing development of the Texas Express Pipeline by the companies' joint venture. The 20-inch diameter pipeline will extend about 580 miles from Skellytown Texas to the Mont Belvieu NGL fractionation complex. The pipeline also provides access to other producers in several regions: West Texas the Rocky Mountains southern Oklahoma and the Mid-continent area.

In 2010 in a move to increase its footprint in the lucrative Haynesville/Bossier Shale play Enterprise acquired two natural gas gathering and treating systems in northwest Louisiana and East Texas from M2 Midstream LLC for $1.2 billion.

In a major expansion move in 2009 the company acquired rival TEPPCO Partners L.P. in a $26 billion all-stock deal which boosted its pipelines and oil refined products and NGL storage capacity. The TEPPCO Partners purchase made the company the largest publicly traded energy partnership in the US. The expanded company's assets include 60 liquid storage terminals 25 natural gas storage facilities 17 fractionation facilities and six offshore hub platforms.

That year the company acquired Enterprise GP Holdings which controlled the general partner of Enterprise. The $8 billion deal was aimed at reducing long-term capital costs and simplifying the business structure of Enterprise Products Partners.

The family of Chairman Dan Duncan controls a 35% stake in Enterprise.

EXECUTIVES

President, W. Randall (Randy) Fowler, age 63, $521,178 total compensation

Ceo, A. James (Jim) Teague, age 73, $800,000 total compensation

Evp Commercial, William (Bill) Ordemann, age 60, $451,150 total compensation

Svp And Cfo, Bryan F. Bulawa, age 50

Svp And Cio, Paul G. Flynn

Evp Operations And Engineering, Graham W. Bacon, age 55, $375,000 total compensation

Svp Commercial, Brent Secrest

Vice President Gulf Coast Gathering Processing And Transportation, Rockey Storie

Vice President, Tony Chovanec

Vp Internal Audit, Charles Stovall

Senior Vice President, Daniel Boss

Vp Government Affairs, Delbert Fore

Vice President Crude Oil Pipelines And Terminals, Greg Mills

Vice President Planning And Analysis, Randy Scheirman

Svp Regulatory Affairs, Craig Murray

Senior Vice President, Charles Brabson

Vice President Deputy General Counsel Assistant Secretary, Stephanie Hildebrandt

Senior Vice President, Anthony C Chovanec

Svp General Counsel And Secretary, Harry Weitzel

Svp Accounting And Risk Control, R Daniel Boss

Svp Of Government Affairs And Public Relations, James A Cisarik

Executive Vice President Operations, Christopher Cragg

Vice President Commercial Activity And Business Development, Terrance Mcgill

Vice President Engineering, Matt Isom

Chairman, Randa D. Williams, age 57

Auditors: Deloitte & Touche LLP

LOCATIONS

HQ: Enterprise Products Partners L.P.
  1100 Louisiana Street, 10th Floor, Houston, TX 77002
Phone: 713 381-6500
Web: www.enterpriseproducts.com

2016 Sales

	$ mil.	% of total
NGL Pipelines & Services	10,242	45
Crude Oil Pipelines & Services	6,515	28
Petrochemical & Refined Products Services	3,721	16
Natural Gas Pipelines & Services	2,543	11
Total	**23,022**	**100**

COMPETITORS

Anadarko Petroleum	Kinder Morgan
CenterPoint Energy	Magellan Midstream
Crestwood Midstream	ONEOK
Partners LP	Occidental Petroleum
Dominion Energy	Plains All American
Duke Energy	Pipeline
Enbridge	Spectra Energy
Energy Transfer Equity	TRII
Exxon Mobil	Williams Companies

HISTORICAL FINANCIALS

Company Type: Public

Income Statement   FYE: December 31

	REVENUE ($ mil.)	NET INCOME ($ mil.)	NET PROFIT MARGIN	EMPLOYEES
12/18	36,534	4,172	11.4%	—
12/17	29,241	2,799	9.6%	—
12/16	23,022	2,513	10.9%	—
12/15	27,027	2,521	9.3%	—
12/14	47,951	2,787	5.8%	—
Annual Growth	**(6.6%)**	**10.6%**	**—**	**—**

2018 Year-End Financials

Debt ratio: 45.95%—
Return on equity: —
Cash ($ mil.): 344
Current ratio: 0.85
Long-term debt ($ mil.): 24,678

Dividends
Yield: 6.9%
Payout: 89.7%
Market value ($ mil.): —

	STOCK PRICE ($) FY Close	P/E High/Low	PER SHARE ($) Earnings	Dividends	Book Value
12/18	24.59	16 12	1.91	1.72	10.92
12/17	26.51	23 18	1.30	1.67	10.43
12/16	27.04	25 16	1.20	1.59	10.41
12/15	25.58	29 17	1.26	1.51	10.08
12/14	36.12	53 21	1.47	1.43	9.32
Annual Growth	**(9.2%)**	**— —**	**6.8%**	**4.6%**	**4.0%**

EOG Resources, Inc.

Large-scale shale is the Holy Grail for oil prospector EOG Resources. It engages in exploration development and marketing of natural gas and crude oil originating in the Eagle Ford Shale and Barnett Shale in Texas and the Bakken formation in North Dakota. Of its 2.5 million boe reserves EOG holds 1.3 million barrels in crude oil and condensates with a roughly 4.3 billion cubic feet of natural gas. The US is the company's largest market.

Operations

EOG is the biggest operator (by volume produced) in the lucrative Eagle Ford Shale play in South Texas. The company also has a presence in the Delaware Basin owning about 160000 net acres in the Leonard Shale and over 345000 net acres in the Wolfcamp Shale. Additionally EOG

has acreage in the Wolfcamp Shale within the Midland Basin.

Sales of crude oil and crude condensates account for around 55% of total sales natural gas sales account for roughly 10% and NGLs (natural gas liquids) over 5%.

EOG also conducts gas gathering processing and marketing which together bring in nearly 30% of the company's sales. It sells oil and natural gas in local downstream markets transported either by pipeline or truck.

EOG operates its own sand mine and sand processing plants in Hood County Texas to reduce costs and to help fulfill EOG's sand needs for its well completion operations in Texas.

Geographic Reach

EOG has a presence in three major shale plays of the US- the Eagle Ford Shale and Barnett Shale in Texas and the Bakken Formation in North Dakota. Though most of its assets are in the US EOG also has operations in Canada offshore Trinidad the UK North Sea and East Irish Sea and the Sichuan Basin in China.

The US accounts for over 95% of the company's proved reserves.

Sales and Marketing

EOG sells two major products—wellhead crude oil & condensates and natural gas. To sell beyond its local market EOG markets these products to downstream customers via extensive pipelines. Crude is also distributed by rail and truck. Its major sales points include Midwest the Permian Basin Cushing Oklahoma St. James Louisiana and other Gulf Coast locations.

The company's Trinidad natural gas operations were sold to the National Gas Company of Trinidad and Tobago while its Chinese natural gas operations were sold to PetroChina.

Financial Performance

EOG has seen revenue climb from $4.8 billion in 2009 to a peak of $12.6 billion by 2014 only to fall drastically to $5.5 billion by 2016. Though EOG has posted handsome profits (typically north of $1 billion) on most years a severe commodity price downturn led to a two-year loss of $5.6 billion in the 2015-16 period.

In 2017 revenue climbed an impressive 47% to $11.2 billion mostly coming from a 45% increase in wellhead crude oil and condenstate revenue higher composite average prices ($1.1 billion) plus higher production ($815 million). Natural gas revenue went up 24% to $922 million due to higher prices as well.

Net income shot up from a loss of $1.1 billion to a net profit of $2.6 billion. This was primarily due to a $2.1 billion improvement in operating income followed by an almost $1.5 billion YOY increase in income tax benefit for 2017.

Cash holdings declined $765 million to $834 million at the end of 2017. Operations generated $4.2 billion which was offset by $3.9 billion used for investments (mostly in additions of new oil & gas properties) plus $1 billion of outflows to financing activities (primarily in debt repayments).The company was able to reduce its debt by some $950 million during 2017 and its outstanding debt was just over $6 billion at the year end.

Strategy

EOG has recovered nicely from a rough commodity price downturn when it lost $5.6 billion in two short years (2015-16). Since then buoyed by recovering oil and gas prices Trump administration tax cuts and operational excellence the company has reported expectation-beating financial and production levels in the 2017-18 period. The key to its success has been two-fold— avoiding acquisition-driven growth and successful diversification into the Powder River Basin. EOG followed that with the spin-off of its UK business to Lon-

don-based Tailwind Energy an oil and gas venture. This includes the Conwy oil field a 25% non-operated interest in the Columbus gas development project and other minor asset interests in the North Sea.

Since EOG has been acquisition averse it has only focused on low-cost exploration acreage as opposed to purchasing higher-cost acreage where oil has already been discovered. This has allowed EOG to maintain nearly $1 billion in cash holdings while only having some $6 billion in debt.

One of its biggest strategic gambles was exploring the Powder River Basin in Wyoming. South Texas' Eagle Ford shale remains EOG's top producing region and the company also has significant presence in the Permian Basin. And yet while most of its peers were keen to boost output at the Permian Basin of West Texas recognizing pipeline limitations creating a bottleneck EOG wanted to diversify.

It focused on E&P at the Powder Basin as early as 2015 which paid off initially with the discovery of the Turner formation. However the true jackpot came in 2018 when the company announced the stunning discovery of the Mowry and Niobrara shale plays in the Basin which holds some 1.9 billion BOE of recoverable resources a more than tenfold increase for EOG.

The company has also had an equally excellent production run. With a $6 billion capital spending budget EOG is aiming to complete 720 wells by the end of the year 20 more than originally expected. It also reported a record 415000 boe/day production rate up 27 percent from a year ago. It has also made considerable progress lowering costs and improving well performance which helps explain the company's $4.8 billion in revenue by September.

Mergers and Acquisitions

In 2016 EOG acquired Yates Petroleum Corporation Abo Petroleum Corporation MYCO Industries Inc. and certain other entities (collectively Yates) in a deal valued at $2.5 billion.

HISTORY

In 1987 Enron formed Enron Oil & Gas from its existing InterNorth and Houston Natural Gas operations to concentrate on exploration for oil and natural gas and their production. Enron maintained full ownership until 1989 when it spun off 16% of Enron Oil & Gas to the public raising about $200 million. Later offerings reduced its holdings to just over 50%.

Enron Oil & Gas in 1992 was awarded a 95% working interest in three fields off Trinidad that previously had been held by government-owned companies. Two years later the company assumed the operations of three drilling blocks off Bombay (including the Tapti field) as well as a 30% interest in them. Natural gas prices fell in the winter of 1994 causing Enron Oil & Gas to focus its 1995 drilling on crude oil exploitation and the enhancement of its natural gas reserves. Natural gas prices rebounded in 1996. That year Enron Oil & Gas was awarded a 90% interest in an offshore area of Venezuela. In 1997 the company inked a 30-year production contract with China. The company made a major discovery of natural gas in offshore Trinidad in 1998. That year Mark Papa succeeded Forrest Hoglund as CEO (Papa became chairman in 1999).

In 1999 Enron traded most of its remaining stake in Enron Oil & Gas to the company in exchange for Enron Oil & Gas' operations and assets in India and China. Consequently the company changed its name from Enron Oil & Gas to EOG Resources.

The next year EOG won contracts to develop properties in Canada's Northwest Territories. It also moved into the Appalachian Basin in 2000 through the acquisition of Somerset Oil & Gas. Buoyed by a strong performance that year the company increased its capital spending on North American exploration by more than 30% and in 2001 it bought Energy Search a small natural gas exploration and production company that operated in the Appalachian Basin.

EXECUTIVES

Chairman And Ceo, William R. Thomas, age 67, $925,000 total compensation
President And Coo, Gary L. Thomas, age 70, $835,000 total compensation
Svp And Chief Information And Technology Officer, Sandeep Bhakhri
Vp Human Resources Administration, Patricia L. Edwards
Evp And Cfo, Timothy K. Driggers, age 58, $480,000 total compensation
Vp And General Manager Corpus Christi, Kenneth E. Dunn
Evp Exploration And Production, Lloyd W. (Bill) Helms, age 61, $470,000 total compensation
Vp Drilling, Robert C. Smith
Vp And General Manager San Antonio, Sammy G. Pickering
Evp Exploration And Production, David W. Trice, age 48
Vp And General Manager International, J. Pat Woods
Vp And General Manager Midland, Ezra Y. Yacob
Svp Operations, John J. Boyd
Vp Land, Steven D. Wentworth
Evp General Counsel And Corporate Secretary, Michael P. Donaldson, $475,000 total compensation
Vp And General Manager Oklahoma City, Nathan J. Andrews
Vp And General Manager Corpus Christi, Kenneth D. Marbach
Vp And General Manager Denver, Kenneth W. Boedeker
Vp And General Manager Artesia, Reese T. Lantrip
Vp And Treasurer, Robert West
Vice President And Gm Midlands, Jeff Leitzell
Vice President Of Information Technology, Jim Coleman
Vice President Investor And Public Relations, David Streit
Vp Government Relations, Eric Dille
Vice President Engineering, Cory Helms
Senior Vice President And Chief Accounting Officer, Ann Janssen
Vice President, Steve Wentworth
Vice President, Sara Miller
Vp Audit, Kevin Hanzel
Vp Of Drlling, Bobby Smith
Vice President Executive Exploration, Charles Sheppard
Vice President Business Development, Joe Korenek
Vice President Exploration, Charlie Sheppard
Vp And Gm International, J Pat Woods
Vice President, Rosemary Bussell
Treasurer Eog Resources, Lorraine Baline
Auditors: DELOITTE & TOUCHE LLP

LOCATIONS

HQ: EOG Resources, Inc.
1111 Bagby, Sky Lobby 2, Houston, TX 77002
Phone: 713 651-7000
Web: www.eogresources.com

2017 sales

	$ mil.	% of total
United States	10,872	97
Trinidad	284	3
Other International	51	-
Total	**11,208**	**100**

PRODUCTS/OPERATIONS

2017 sales

	$ mil.	% of total
Crude oil & condensate	6,256	55
Natural Gas Liquids	729	7
Natural Gas	921	8
Gains on Mark-to-Market Commodity Derivative Contracts	19	-
GatheringProcessing and Marketing	3,298	29
Gains on Asset DispositionsNet	(99.1)	-
OtherNet	81	1
Total	**11,208**	**100**

COMPETITORS

Anadarko Petroleum	Occidental Petroleum
Chevron	Parsley Energy LLC
ConocoPhillips	Pioneer Natural
Enerplus	Resources
Newfield Exploration	Royal Dutch Shell
Oasis Petroleum	

HISTORICAL FINANCIALS
Company Type: Public

Income Statement
FYE: December 31

	REVENUE ($ mil.)	NET INCOME ($ mil.)	NET PROFIT MARGIN	EMPLOYEES
12/18	17,275	3,419	19.8%	2,800
12/17	11,208	2,582	23.0%	2,664
12/16	7,650	(1,096)	—	2,650
12/15	8,757	(4,524)	—	2,760
12/14	18,035	2,915	16.2%	3,000
Annual Growth	**(1.1%)**	**4.1%**	**—**	**(1.7%)**

2018 Year-End Financials

Debt ratio: 17.93%
Return on equity: 19.18%
Cash ($ mil.): 1,555
Current ratio: 1.36
Long-term debt ($ mil.): 5,170

No. of shares (mil.): 580
Dividends
Yield: 0.8%
Payout: 12.8%
Market value ($ mil.): 50,584

	STOCK PRICE ($) FY Close	P/E High/Low		PER SHARE ($) Earnings	Dividends	Book Value
12/18	87.21	22	14	5.89	0.76	33.39
12/17	107.91	24	19	4.46	0.67	28.15
12/16	101.10	—	—	(1.98)	0.67	24.24
12/15	70.79	—	—	(8.29)	0.67	23.54
12/14	92.07	35	15	5.32	0.51	32.30
Annual Growth	**(1.3%)**			**2.6%**	**10.3%**	**0.8%**

EQUINOR MARKETING & TRADING (US) INC.

Check the stats. Oil. Hundreds of thousands of barrels of oil gasoline and more. Statoil Marketing & Trading is a wholesaler of oil and petroleum products. The company is the US trading arm of StatoilÂ the leading Scandinavian oil and gas enterprise. Statoil Marketing & Trading delivers about 600000 barrels a day in the form of crude oil gasoline liquefied petroleum gas (LPG) propane and butane to the North American market. In addition to supplying Norwegian crude the company trades crude oil from Africa South America and North America.Â Statoil Marketing & Trading sells itÂ oil products primarilyÂ to customers in Northeastern Canada the US East Coast and Gulf Coast.

EXECUTIVES

Senior Vice President, Thore Kristiansen
Vice President Human Resources, Shild Larsen
Vice President Human Resources Services, Siv Oftedal
Vice President Operations Subsea, Rune Aase
Vice President Legal, Paul Owen
Vice President Project Management, Erik Westad
Vice President Project Management, Johnny Wollberg
Vice President Quality, Magne Ottera
Vice President, Sverre Serck-hanssen
Vice President Operations, Atle Kjenes
Vice President Project Management, Kjell Eide
Vice President Operations, Lars Hier
Vice President Of Supply Chain, Mauro Andrade
Vice President Operations, Dag Johnsgaard
Vp Tax, Tom Geczik
Executive Vice President Technology Projects And Drilling, Anders Opedal
Vice President Communications, Nathaniel Teti
Vice President Drilling And Well Engineering, Erik Kirkemo
Auditors: KPMG LLP STAMFORD CONNECTICU

LOCATIONS

HQ: EQUINOR MARKETING & TRADING (US) INC.
120 LONG RIDGE RD 3EO1, STAMFORD, CT 069021839
Phone: 203 978-6900
Web: WWW.EQUINOR.COM

COMPETITORS

Global Partners	Irving Oil Limited
Gulf Oil	Shell Oil
Hess Corporation	Tauber Oil

HISTORICAL FINANCIALS
Company Type: Private

Income Statement
FYE: December 31

	REVENUE ($ mil.)	NET INCOME ($ mil.)	NET PROFIT MARGIN	EMPLOYEES
12/17	9,874	(28)	—	5
12/16	5,984	(259)	—	—
12/15	6,947	(132)	—	—
12/14	12,075	(140)	—	—
Annual Growth	**(6.5%)**	**—**	**—**	**—**

Equitable Holdings Inc

Auditors: PricewaterhouseCoopers LLP

LOCATIONS

HQ: Equitable Holdings Inc
1290 Avenue of the Americas, New York, NY 10104
Phone: 212 554-1234
Web: www.axa.com

HISTORICAL FINANCIALS

Company Type: Public

Income Statement
FYE: December 31

	ASSETS ($ mil.)	NET INCOME ($ mil.)	INCOME AS % OF ASSETS	EMPLOYEES
12/18	220,797	1,820	0.8%	7,800
12/17	235,648	850	0.4%	7,500
12/16	216,614	1,272	0.6%	—
12/15	0	333	—	—
Annual Growth	—	76.1%	—	—

2018 Year-End Financials

Debt ratio: 2.00%	No. of shares (mil.): 528
Return on equity: 13.31%	Dividends
Cash ($ mil.): 5,639	Yield: 1.5%
Current ratio: —	Payout: 7.9%
Long-term debt ($ mil.): —	Market value ($ mil.): 8,795

	STOCK PRICE ($) FY Close	P/E High/Low		PER SHARE ($) Earnings	Dividends	Book Value
12/18	16.63	7	5	3.27	0.26	26.22
12/17	0.00	—	—	1.51	0.00	24.04
Annual Growth	—	—	—	29.4%	—	2.9%

Equity Bancshares Inc

Auditors: Crowe LLP

LOCATIONS

HQ: Equity Bancshares Inc
7701 East Kellogg Drive, Suite 300, Wichita, KS 67207
Phone: 316 612-6000
Web: www.equitybank.com

HISTORICAL FINANCIALS

Company Type: Public

Income Statement
FYE: December 31

	ASSETS ($ mil.)	NET INCOME ($ mil.)	INCOME AS % OF ASSETS	EMPLOYEES
12/18	4,061	35	0.9%	627
12/17	3,170	20	0.7%	526
12/16	2,192	9	0.4%	415
12/15	1,585	10	0.6%	297
12/14	1,175	8	0.8%	262
Annual Growth	36.3%	41.3%		24.4%

2018 Year-End Financials

Debt ratio: 0.45%	No. of shares (mil.): 15
Return on equity: 8.63%	Dividends
Cash ($ mil.): 197	Yield: —
Current ratio: —	Payout: —
Long-term debt ($ mil.): —	Market value ($ mil.): 557

	STOCK PRICE ($) FY Close	P/E High/Low		PER SHARE ($) Earnings	Dividends	Book Value
12/18	35.25	19	14	2.28	0.00	28.87
12/17	35.41	22	18	1.62	0.00	25.62
12/16	33.64	34	19	1.07	0.00	22.09
12/15	23.39	16	15	1.54	0.00	20.37
Annual Growth	10.8%	—	—	10.3%	—	9.1%

EQUITY ONE, INC.

LOCATIONS

HQ: EQUITY ONE, INC.
1 INDEPENDENT DR STE 114, JACKSONVILLE, FL 322025005
Phone: 212 796-1760

COMPETITORS

Agree Realty	Kimco Realty
AmREIT	Kite Realty
CBL & Associates Properties	Realty Income
	Regency Centers
DDR	Vornado Realty
EDENS	Weingarten Realty

HISTORICAL FINANCIALS

Company Type: Private

Income Statement
FYE: December 31

	ASSETS ($ mil.)	NET INCOME ($ mil.)	INCOME AS % OF ASSETS	EMPLOYEES
12/16	3,494	72	2.1%	155
12/14	3,262	61	1.9%	—
12/13	3,354	88	2.6%	—
12/12	3,502	7	0.2%	—
Annual Growth	(0.1%)	78.2%	—	—

Eversource Energy

The largest energy delivery company in New England Eversource Energy serves roughly four million electric and gas customers via its six distinct utility companies in Connecticut Massachusetts and New Hampshire. Eversource delivers its energy through about 630000 overhead and underground lines and covers over 3300 square miles of natural gas distribution. Its electricity-focused utility companies include Public Service Company of New Hampshire (PSNH) The Connecticut Light and Power Company and NSTAR Electric Company. Eversource's gas utilities are NSTAR Gas and Yankee Gas which supply natural gas to about 295000 customers in central and eastern Massachusetts and about 235000 customers in Connecticut respectively. The company also operates a water utilities subsidiary Eversource Aquarion Holdings in Connecticut Massachusetts and New Hampshire.

HISTORY

In 1966 three old intertwined New England utilities merged. One was The Hartford Electric Light Company (HELCO) founded in 1883 by Austin Dunham in Hartford Connecticut. In 1915 the company signed the first power exchange agreement in the US with Connecticut Power (CP) which HELCO acquired in 1920.

The second founded in 1886 was Western Massachusetts Electric (WMECO) which merged with Western Counties in the 1930s to become WMECO. The third was Connecticut Light and Power (CL&P). Founded as Rocky River Power in 1905 it took the CL&P name in 1917. In 1929 it built the US's first large-scale pumped-storage hydroelectric plant.

In the 1950s HELCO formed Yankee Atomic Electric with CL&P WMECO and others to build an experimental nuclear reactor. In 1965 members of the group began jointly building the Connecticut Yankee nuke (on line in 1968). After years of cooperation CL&P HELCO and WMECO merged in 1966 and Northeast Utilities (NU) was born. It was the first multistate utility holding company created since the Public Utility Holding Company Act of 1935 had broken up the old utility giants. Holyoke Water Power joined NU the following year.

The 1970s energy crisis spurred NU to continue building nukes including Maine Yankee Vermont Yankee and two Millstone units. But by the 1980s construction delays had raised the cost of the final unit Millstone 3.

Regulators forced CL&P to spin off its gas utility Yankee Energy System in 1989. The next year NU acquired bankrupt utility Public Service Company of New Hampshire (PSNH) and its new Seabrook nuke. (PSNH emerged from bankruptcy in 1991.)

The 1995 shutdown of Millstone 1 began NU's nuclear troubles. In 1996 regulators closed all of its nukes except Seabrook because of safety concerns and NU mothballed Connecticut Yankee. The next year Michael Morris replaced CEO Bernard Fox who left after federal regulators ordered NU to comply with regulations and fix management problems — NU managers had routinely retaliated against whistleblowers — the first time a utility had been given such an order. New managers came in including a former whistleblower but NU couldn't avoid a record-setting $2.1 million fine. NU received permission to restart the Millstone units in 1998-99. But it had to absorb the $1 billion in power replacement associated with the shutdown.

Meanwhile as deregulation loomed NU created a retail marketer (now Select Energy) and a telecommunications arm (Mode 1 Communications) in 1996. Two years later retail competition began in Massachusetts and deregulation legislation was passed in Connecticut (deregulation went into effect there in 2000).

In 1999 NU sold its Massachusetts plants to New York's Consolidated Edison and auctioned off its non-nuclear plants in Connecticut to its subsidiary Northeast Generation and Northern States Power (now Xcel Energy). NU agreed to plead guilty to 25 federal felony counts and pay $10 million in penalties for polluting water near Millstone and lying to regulators.

That year Consolidated Edison agreed to buy NU for $3.3 billion in cash and stock and $3.9 billion in assumed debt. The deal broke down in 2001 however; Con Edison charged NU with misrepresenting information about power-supply contracts and NU charged Con Edison with improperly attempting to renegotiate the terms of the acquisition.

Bringing an old family member home NU bought Yankee Energy System for $679 million in 2000. Later that year Dominion Resources which had helped NU restart Millstone 2 and Millstone 3 (Millstone 1 had been taken out of service) agreed to buy the Millstone complex for $1.3 billion. The sale closed in 2001.

Also in 2001 NU subsidiary Select Energy bought Niagara Mohawk's energy marketing unit NU sold the distribution business of its Holyoke Water Power utility to the City of Holyoke for $18 million and retail electric competition began in New Hampshire. The company agreed to sell CL&P's 10% stake in the Vermont Yankee nuclear facility to Entergy in 2001; the deal was completed the following year.

NU sold its 40% interest in the Seabrook Nuclear Generating facility in 2002 to FPL Group.

In 2006 NU sold nonregulated subsidiary Select Energy which marketed and traded energy to wholesale and retail customers to Hess Corporation. That year the company also sold its competitive generation assets in Connecticut and Massachusetts to Energy Capital Partners for $1.34 billion.

In 2007 Connecticut Light and Power Company completed the installation of electric service to Yankee Gas Services Company's new liquefied natural gas facility in Waterbury.

To give better access and service to its customers in 2009 NU relocated its headquarters from Berlin Connecticut to a larger building in downtown Hartford.

The 2012 acquisition of NSTAR (with 1.1 million power and 300000 gas customers) for $4.2 billion boosted the financial resources of Eversource to pay for planned transmission projects aimed at bringing cleaner power from northern New England and Canada to population centers in southern New England. The "merger of equals" (NSTAR and Eversource) created a major energy player in the US Northeast which serves more than half the total utility customers in New England. NSTAR shareholders hold about 44% of the expanded company.

EXECUTIVES

Evp And Coo, Werner J. Schweiger, age 59, $592,108 total compensation

Evp And General Counsel, Gregory B. Butler, age 61, $514,494 total compensation

President And Ceo, James J. (Jim) Judge, age 63, $959,690 total compensation

Evp Enterprise Energy Strategy And Business Development Eversource Energy And Eversource Service, Leon J. (Lee) Olivier, age 71, $1,232,250 total compensation

Evp Customer And Corporate Relations Eversource Energy And Eversource Service, Joseph R. (Joe) Nolan, age 55, $419,364 total compensation

Evp Human Resources And Information Technology Eversource Energy And Eversource Service, Christine M. (Chris) Carmody, age 56

Svp And Cfo, Philip J. (Phil) Lembo, age 63, $439,208 total compensation

Vp Internal Audit And Security, Ron Smith

Vice President Energy Supply, James Daly

Evp And Cfo, Phillip Lembo

Vp New Hampshire Generation, William Smagula

Vp Engineering New Hampshire, Paul Ramsey

Svp Regulatory Affairs And Chief Communications Officer, Jim Hunt

Vice President New Hampshire Electric Operations, Joseph Purington

Vice President Communications, Beth Foley

Vice President Electric System Operations, Michael Hayhurst

Chairman, Thomas J. (Tom) May, age 72

Board Member, Dennis Harrington

Secretary, Richard Morrison

Auditors: DELOITTE & TOUCHE LLP

LOCATIONS

HQ: Eversource Energy
300 Cadwell Drive, Springfield, MA 01104
Phone: 800 286-5000
Web: www.eversource.com

PRODUCTS/OPERATIONS

2018 Sales

	$ mil.	% of total
Retail Tariff Sales		
Residential	4,439	52
Commercial	3,028	36
Industrial	442	5
Wholesale Transmission Revenue	264	3
Wholesale Market Sales Revenue	241	3
Other Revenue from Contracts with Customers	81	1
Reserve for Revenue Subject to Refunds	(24.3)	-
Alternative Revenue Programs	(46.1)	-
Other Revenue	21	-
Total	**8,448**	**100**

2018 Sales

	$ mil.	% of total
Electric distribution	6,957	67
Electric transmission	1,286	12
Natural gas distribution	1,022	10
Water distribution	212	2
Other	936	9
Eliminations	(1965.8)	-
Total	**8,488**	**100**

Selected Subsidiaries & Affiliates

The Connecticut Light and Power Company (CL&P eletric utility)
NSTAR Electric Company (electric utility)
NSTAR Gas Company (natural gas utility)
Public Service Company of New Hampsire (PSNH electric utility)
Western Massachusetts Electric Company (WMECO electric utility)
Yankee Gas Services Company (natural gas utility)

COMPETITORS

Avangrid	NiSource
Con Edison	Public Service
Green Mountain Power	Enterprise Group
National Grid	Unitil
New Hampshire Electric	

HISTORICAL FINANCIALS

Company Type: Public

Income Statement

FYE: December 31

	REVENUE ($ mil.)	NET INCOME ($ mil.)	NET PROFIT MARGIN	EMPLOYEES
12/18	8,448	1,033	12.2%	7,998
12/17	7,751	988	12.7%	8,084
12/16	7,639	942	12.3%	7,762
12/15	7,954	878	11.0%	7,943
12/14	7,741	819	10.6%	8,248
Annual Growth	**2.2%**	**6.0%**	**—**	**(0.8%)**

2018 Year-End Financials

Debt ratio: 38.26%
Return on equity: 9.15%
Cash ($ mil.): 108
Current ratio: 0.56
Long-term debt ($ mil.): 12,832
No. of shares (mil.): 316
Dividends
  Yield: 3.1%
  Payout: 62.1%
Market value ($ mil.): 20,610

	STOCK PRICE ($) FY Close	P/E High/Low		PER SHARE ($) Earnings	Dividends	Book Value
12/18	65.04	22	16	3.25	2.02	36.25
12/17	63.18	21	17	3.11	1.90	34.98
12/16	55.23	20	17	2.96	1.78	33.80
12/15	51.07	20	16	2.76	1.67	32.64
12/14	53.52	22	16	2.58	1.57	31.47
Annual Growth	**5.0%**	**—**	**—**	**5.9%**	**6.5%**	**3.6%**

Exchange Bank (Santa Rosa, CA)

Exchange Bank serves personal and business customers from some 20 branch offices throughout Sonoma County California. It also has a branch in nearby Placer County. The bank provides standard products including checking and savings accounts Visa credit cards online banking and a variety of real estate business and consumer loans. It also offers investment services such as wealth management personal trust administration employee benefits plans and individual retirement accounts. Effective early 2014 Exchange Bank is on its eighth president since its inception in 1890. The Doyle Trust which was established by co-founder Frank Doyle owns a majority of the bank.

Operations

Exchange Bank's lending activity is concentrated in Sonoma County. Commercial real estate loans represent more than half of its loan portfolio. Exchange Bank believes it will continue to benefit from growth in the local technology and biomedical industries and lower unemployment increased tourism and a decline in commercial real estate vacancies in Sonoma County.

Geographic Reach

Based in Santa Rosa California Exchange Bank operates primarily in Sonoma County but also in Placer and Contra counties.

Sales and Marketing

Exchange Bank counts some 25000 customers among its clients serving them through about 20 branch offices. It caters to customers online as well through its website which in fiscal 2013 earned 1.5 million customer visits.

Financial Performance

Revenue dropped 4% in fiscal 2013 to $85.9 million as compared to $89.1 million in 2012. Exchange Bank attributes the decrease to lower interest income resulting from a decline in interest received on term loans offset in part by increased interest on securities. From $12.26 million in 2012 the firm's net income grew some 28% to $15.73 million. Exchange Bank points to noteworthy drops in the provision for loan and lease losses and a decrease in interest and non-interest income for the net income gains.

EXECUTIVES

Vice President, Jason Hinde
Auditors: KPMG LLP

LOCATIONS

HQ: Exchange Bank (Santa Rosa, CA)
545 Fourth Street, Santa Rosa, CA 95401
Phone: 707 524-3301
Web: www.exchangebank.com

COMPETITORS

Bank of America	U.S. Bancorp
First Northern	Wells Fargo
JPMorgan Chase	Westamerica
MUFG Americas Holdings	

HISTORICAL FINANCIALS

Company Type: Public

Income Statement

FYE: December 31

	ASSETS ($ mil.)	NET INCOME ($ mil.)	INCOME AS % OF ASSETS	EMPLOYEES
12/18	2,653	38	1.5%	—
12/17	2,584	19	0.8%	—
12/16	2,179	21	1.0%	—
12/15	2,062	21	1.0%	—
12/14	1,887	17	0.9%	—
Annual Growth	**8.9%**	**21.4%**	**—**	**—**

2018 Year-End Financials

Debt ratio: —
Return on equity: 17.72%
Cash ($ mil.): 197
Current ratio: —
Long-term debt ($ mil.): —

No. of shares (mil.): 1
Dividends
Yield: 2.3%
Payout: 22.5%
Market value ($ mil.): 283

	STOCK PRICE ($) FY Close	P/E High/Low		PER SHARE ($) Earnings	Dividends	Book Value
12/18	165.00	9	7	22.46	3.85	135.08
12/17	152.00	14	11	11.38	3.40	118.53
12/16	125.00	11	6	12.54	2.80	110.35
12/15	89.00	7	6	12.27	2.20	100.98
12/14	84.00	8	7	10.25	1.55	93.37
Annual Growth	18.4%	—	—	21.7%	25.5%	9.7%

Exelon Corp

Exelon is lighting up the utility industry with high-powered energy generation and extensive electricity delivery. The utility holding company does enough of both to be designated one of the largest in the US. Its Exelon Generation subsidiary holds power-generating assets of almost 35000 MW (some 20000 MW is produced at 23 nuclear plants). Exelon distributes electricity and gas to 10 million customers in Illinois Maryland the District of Columbia Delaware New Jersey and Pennsylvania through its regulated utility companies. Its Constellation subsidiary provides energy products and services to 2.2 million business customers. In a major expansion Exelon acquired three regulated utilities for $7.1 billion in 2016

HISTORY

Thomas Dolan and local investors formed the Brush Electric Light Company of Philadelphia in 1881 to provide street and commercial lighting. Competitors sprang up and in 1885 Brush merged with the United States Electric Lighting Company of Pennsylvania to form a secret "electric trust" or holding company. Dolan became president in 1886 and bought four other utilities.

In 1895 Martin Maloney formed Pennsylvania Heat Light and Power to consolidate the city's electric companies. By the next year it had acquired among other businesses Columbia Electric Light Philadelphia Edison and the electric trust. In 1899 a new firm National Electric challenged Maloney by acquiring neighboring rival Southern Electric Light. Before retiring Maloney negotiated the merger of the two firms forming Philadelphia Electric in 1902.

Demand rose rapidly into the 1920s fueled in part by the company's promotion of electric appliances. In 1928 the year after it completed the Conowingo Hydroelectric Station Philadelphia Electric was absorbed by the much larger United Gas Improvement. United Gas avoided large layoffs during the Depression but passage of the Public Utility Holding Company Act (PUHCA) in 1935 sounded its death knell. (PUHCA was repealed in 2005.) In 1943 the SEC forced United Gas to divest Philadelphia Electric.

Philadelphia Electric built several plants in the 1950s and 1960s in response to a postwar electricity boom. A small experimental nuclear reactor was completed at Peach Bottom Pennsylvania in 1967 and in 1974 the company placed two nuclear units in service at the plant. The Salem (New Jersey) nuke (Unit 1) followed in 1977. The company relied on these plants during the OPEC oil crisis. Another one Limerick Unit 1 began operations in 1986 and Unit 2 went on line in 1990 but the Peach Bottom plant was shut down from 1989 to 1991 because of management problems (later resolved).

The company began reorganizing in 1993 and changed its name the next year to PECO Energy Company. It also sold Maryland retail subsidiary Conowingo Power retaining the hydroelectric plant. In 1995 rival PP&L rejected PECO's acquisition bid citing PECO's nuclear liabilities.

A year later PECO teamed with AT&T Wireless to offer PCS in Philadelphia (service was launched in 1997). EnergyOne a national venture formed in 1997 by PECO UtiliCorp United (now Aquila) and AT&T offered consumers a package of power phone and Internet services on one bill. However the slow deregulation process caused the venture to fail.

PECO also joined with British Energy in 1997 to form AmerGen hoping to buy nukes at rock-bottom prices from utilities eager to unload them. AmerGen purchased three nuclear facilities in 1999 and 2000: Unit 1 of the Three Mile Island (Pennsylvania) facility; a plant in Clinton Illinois; and an Oyster Creek (New Jersey) location.

In 1999 PECO announced plans to acquire Chicago's Unicom the parent company of Commonwealth Edison (ComEd). After the deal was completed in 2000 the combined company took the name Exelon and established its headquarters in Chicago.

Pennsylvania's utility markets were fully deregulated in 2000. To expand its power generation business Exelon that year bought 49.9% of Sithe Energies for $682 million. In 2001 Exelon agreed to buy two gas-fired power plants (2300 MW) in Texas from TXU for $443 million; the deal was completed in 2002.

Also in 2002 Exelon purchased Sithe Energies' stakes in six New England power plants with 2000 MW of capacity (plus 2400 MW under construction) for $543 million plus the assumption of $1.15 billion in debt. The company also sold its Philadelphia PCS venture interest to former partner AT&T Wireless Services (now part of AT&T Mobility). Sithe Energies was sold to Dynegy in 2005 for $135 million.

To focus on core utility operations the company sold its infrastructure construction business InfraSource and its facility and infrastructure management business Exelon Solutions. Exelon then completed the sale of its interest in telecommunications joint venture PECO TelCove which provides voice and data services to its partner TelCove and sold its district heating and cooling division (Thermal Chicago).

In 2008 in a move to expand its geographic reach Exelon made a $6.2 billion bid to buy NRG Energy. Though the offer to buy NRG met with resistance Exelon had kept up its pursuit of the company. Toward the end of 2008 it announced an exchange offer for NRG's shares. By the expiration date of the offer early the next year it had acquired just more than 50% of those shares. In addition to announcing another extension of the offer Exelon said it hoped NRG's Board would allow it to do due diligence and begin negotiations for an acquisition. But an NRG proxy vote rejection in 2009 led Exelon to terminate its offer.

In 2010 in a bid to grow its renewable energy segment and lower its carbon emissions the company acquired wind power developer John Deere Renewables for about $860 million. The deal added 735 MW of operating wind power capacity (and 230 MW under development) to Exelon's generation assets.

To meet stricter environmental regulations the company has been bulking up its non-fossil fuel generating assets. Growing its cleaner-burning plant fleet in Texas in 2011 the company bought Wolf Hollow a 720 MW combined-cycle natural gas-fired power plant in north Texas from Sequent Wolf Hollow for $305 million.

Expanding its green energy assets that year the company also acquired Antelope Valley Solar Ranch One from First Solar. The 230-MW solar power project is under development in northern Los Angeles County. The $1.4 billion investment complements Constellation Energy's solar power holdings and marks Exelon's first move into the California merchant power market.

In 2012 the company bought Constellation Energy in a $7.9 billion stock deal. The acquisition part of an industry-wide consolidation trend gives Exelon access to Constellation's major retail operations in Maryland enabling it to grow its retail profile.

The US Department of Justice required Exelon and Constellation to divest three electricity generating plants in Maryland to proceed with the merger. It contended that combining the companies' assets would potentially enable the merged firm to raise wholesale electricity prices and reduce output.

As part of the integration of Constellation Energy's assets in 2013 Exelon announced that three commercial nuclear power plants operated by the Constellation Energy Nuclear Group in New York and Maryland will be integrated into the Exelon Generation nuclear fleet.

EXECUTIVES

President And Ceo, Christopher M. (Chris) Crane, age 60, $1,255,515 total compensation

Svp And Chief Information And Digital Officer, Mike Koehler, age 52

President Exelon Power, Ronald J. (Ron) DeGregorio, age 56

Evp; Coo Excelon Generation, Michael J. Pacilio, age 58

Sevp And Cfo, Jonathan W. (Jack) Thayer, age 47, $784,802 total compensation

President And Ceo Comed, Anne R. Pramaggiore, age 60

Sevp And Chief Commercial Officer And President And Ceo Exelon Generation, Kenneth W. (Ken) Cornew, age 53, $857,477 total compensation

Evp And Ceo Constellation, Joseph (Joe) Nigro, age 54

Sevp And Chief Strategy Officer, William A. (Bill) Von Hoene, age 65, $831,350 total compensation

President And Ceo Pepco Holdings, David M. (Dave) Velazquez, age 60

President And Chief Nuclear Officer Exelon Nuclear, Bryan C. Hanson, age 53

Evp; President And Ceo Peco, Craig L. Adams, age 66

Ceo Baltimore Gas And Electric, Calvin G. Butler, age 49

Evp And Chief Enterprise Risk Officer, Paymon Aliabadi, age 56

Evp Governmental And Regulatory Affairs And Public Policy, Joseph Dominguez, age 55

Sevp And Ceo Exelon Utilities, Denis P. OÂ'Brien, age 58, $800,378 total compensation

Evp Corporate Operations, M. Bridget Reidy

Senior Vice President State Governmental And Regulatory Affairs, David Fein

Senior Vice President Operations Support, Christopher Mudrick

Vice President Corporate Affairs, Melissa Sherrod

Vpres Clinton Power Station, Mark Newcomer

Vice President And Deputy General Counsel Employment And Benefits, Susan Rider

Vice President, Dean Hengst

Vice President Nuclear Oversight, Edward Callan

Senior Vice President And Chro, Amy Best
Vice President And Deputy General Counsel, Nina Jezic
Svp Investor Relations, Daniel Eggers
Vp Tech Services And Smart Grid And Smart Meter Peco Energy, John Mcdonald
Senior Vice President Corporate Affairs Philanthropy And Customer Engagement, Maggie Fitzpatrick
Vice President Engineering And Project Management, Michelle Blaise
Vice President Regulatory Policy And S, Michael Guerra
Site Vice President, Garey Stathes
Vice President, Formica Vivian
Vice President Of Distribution Operations, William Mcbride
Vice President Finance Exelon Nuclear, Jeanne Jones
Vp And Cso, Kevin Perkins
Senior Vice President Corporate Controller, Fabian Souza
Vice President, Marlow Colvin
Vice President, William Scott
Senior Vice President Operations, Daniel Enright
Senior Vice President Exelon Generation And President Exelon Power, John Barnes
Vice President Marketing, Richard Gwebster
Executive Assistant To M Bridget Reidy Executive Vice President Corporate Operations, Griffith Evan
Site Vice President, Tracey Gorham
Vice President Market Risk And Analytics, Daniel Scobell
Vice President Supply Chain, Ed Jandacek
Chairman, Mayo A. Shattuck, age 64
Board Member, Brian Boggetto
Secretary Iv, Maria Boweolsen
Secretary Work Center And Projects Anlst, Charles Steven
Auditors: PricewaterhouseCoopers LLP

LOCATIONS

HQ: Exelon Corp
10 South Dearborn Street, P.O. Box 805379, Chicago, IL 60680-5379
Phone: 800 483-3220
Web: www.exeloncorp.com

PRODUCTS/OPERATIONS

2016 Sales

	$ mil.	% of total
Generation	17,751	54
ComEd	5,254	16
PECO	2,994	9
BGE	3,233	10
PHI	3,643	11
Other	(1515)	-
Total	**31,360**	**100**

2016 Sales

	$ mil.	% of total
Competitive businesses revenues	16,324	52
Rate-regulated utility revenues	15,036	48
Total	**31,360**	**100**

Selected Operating Units Subsidiaries and Affiliates

Exelon Energy Delivery
Baltimore Gas and Electric (BGE electric and gas utility)
Commonwealth Edison Company (ComEd electric utility)
PECO Energy Company (PECO electric and gas utility)
Pepco Holdings LLC (PHI)
Potomac Electric Power Company (Pepco electric utility)
Delmarva Power & Light Company (DPL electric and gas utility)
Atlantic City Electric Company (ACE electric utility)
Exelon Generation Company LLC
   Constellation
   Exelon Power
   Exelon Hydro

Exelon Solar
Exelon Wind
Exelon Power Team
Exelon Energy (nonregulated retail power sales)
Exelon Nuclear (nuclear power generation)
Exelon Transmission Company

COMPETITORS

AES	FirstEnergy
Alliant Energy	Green Mountain Energy
Ambit Energy	Jersey Central Power & Light
Ameren	
American Transmission	NextEra Energy
Dominion Energy	PPL Corporation
Duke Energy	Public Service
Duquesne Light Holdings	Electric and Gas
	UGI

HISTORICAL FINANCIALS
Company Type: Public

Income Statement

			FYE: December 31

	REVENUE ($ mil.)	NET INCOME ($ mil.)	NET PROFIT MARGIN	EMPLOYEES
12/18	35,985	2,010	5.6%	33,383
12/17	33,531	3,770	11.2%	34,621
12/16	31,360	1,134	3.6%	34,396
12/15	29,447	2,269	7.7%	29,762
12/14	27,429	1,623	5.9%	28,993
Annual Growth	**7.0%**	**5.5%**	**—**	**3.6%**

2018 Year-End Financials

Debt ratio: 30.52%	No. of shares (mil.): 968
Return on equity: 6.63%	Dividends
Cash ($ mil.): 1,349	Yield: 3.0%
Current ratio: 1.17	Payout: 66.6%
Long-term debt ($ mil.): 34,465	Market value ($ mil.): 43,665

	STOCK PRICE ($) FY Close	P/E High/Low		PER SHARE ($) Earnings	Dividends	Book Value
12/18	45.10	23	17	2.07	1.38	31.77
12/17	39.41	11	8	3.97	1.31	30.99
12/16	35.49	30	22	1.22	1.26	27.96
12/15	27.77	15	10	2.54	1.24	28.25
12/14	37.08	20	14	1.88	1.24	26.52
Annual Growth	**5.0%**	**—**	**—**	**2.4%**	**2.7%**	**4.6%**

Exelon Generation Co LLC

Exelon Generation Company has built an excellent reputation by generating electricity. The company a subsidiary of Exelon Corporation is one of the largest electric wholesale and retail power generation companies in the US. In 2013 Exelon Generation had a generation capacity of more than 44560 MW (primarily nuclear but also fossil-fired and hydroelectric and other renewable energy-based plants). Subsidiary Exelon Nuclear operates the largest fleet of nuclear power plants in the US. Exelon Generation's Exelon Power unit oversees a fleet of more than 100 fossil- and renewable-fueled plants (more than 15875 MW of capacity) in Illinois Maryland Massachusetts Pennsylvania and Texas.

Operations

The company operates as an integrated business leveraging its owned and contracted electric gen-

eration capacity to market and sell power to wholesale and retail customers. It has ownership interests in eleven nuclear generating stations currently in service consisting of 19 units with an aggregate of 17263 MW of capacity. It also owns a 50% interest in CENG a joint venture with EDF. CENG is governed by a board of ten directors five of which are appointed by Generation and five by EDF.

Geographic Reach

The Mid-Atlantic represents operations in the eastern half of PJM and accounted for 37% of Exelon Generation's generating capacity in 2013; Midwest (western half of PJM the entire US footprint of MISO 34%); New England (the operations within the ISO-NE 8%); New York (ISO-NY 3%); ERCOT (Texas) 12%; and Other areas 6%).

The Mid-Atlantic region includes Pennsylvania New Jersey Maryland Virginia West Virginia Delaware the District of Columbia and parts of North Carolina. Midwest includes portions of Illinois Indiana Ohio Michigan Kentucky and Tennessee; and the United States footprint of MISO excluding MISO's Southern Region which covers all or most of North Dakota South Dakota Nebraska Minnesota Iowa Wisconsin and the remaining parts of Illinois Indiana Michigan and Ohio not covered by PJM; and parts of Montana Missouri and Kentucky.New England represents the operations within ISO-NE covering the states of Connecticut Maine Massachusetts New Hampshire Rhode Island and Vermont. New York represents the operations within ISO-NY which covers the state of New York in its entirety. ERCOT represents operations within Electric Reliability Council of Texas covering most of the state of Texas. "Other Regions" is an aggregate of other geographic regions not considered individually significant.

Sales and Marketing

Exelon Generation's customers include distribution utilities municipalities cooperatives financial institutions and commercial industrial governmental and residential customers in competitive markets. The company also sells natural gas and renewable energy and other energy-related products and services and engages in natural gas exploration and production activities.

Financial Performance

The company's revenues increased by 8% in 2013 primarily due to increased capacity prices and higher nuclear volume partially offset by lower realized energy prices higher nuclear fuel costs and lower mark-to-market gains.

Net income increased by 90% in 2013 primarily due to higher revenues net of purchased power and fuel expense lower operating and maintenance expense and higher earnings from Exelon Generation's interest in CENG; partially offset by impairment of certain generating assets and higher depreciation costs property taxes and interest expenses.

Strategy

Exelon Generation leverages owned and contracted electric generation capacity to market and sell power wholesale. The company's integrated business operations include the physical delivery and marketing of power obtained through its generation capacity and through long-term intermediate-term and short-term contracts. Exelon Generation maintains an effective supply strategy through ownership of generation assets and power purchase and lease agreements. The company has also contracted for access to additional generation through bilateral long-term power agreements.

Exelon Generation's electricity generation strategy is to pursue opportunities that provide generation to load matching and that diversify the generation fleet by expanding Generation's regional and technological footprint. The company leverages its energy generation portfolio to ensure delivery of energy to both wholesale and retail customers under long-term and short-term contracts and in wholesale power markets.

In 2012 a subsidiary of Exelon Generation sold three coal-fired plants (Brandon Shores and H.A. Wagner generating station in Anne Arundel County Maryland and the C.P. Crane plant in Baltimore County Maryland) to Raven Power Holdings LLC a subsidiary of Riverstone Holdings LLC to comply with certain of the regulatory approvals required by the company's merger with Constellation Energy for net proceeds of $371 million which resulted in a pre-tax loss of $272 million.

Exelon Nuclear operates the largest nuclear fleet in the US (10 stations with 17 nuclear units) and has about 20% of the industry's total capacity. Exelon Generation has submitted an application to the Nuclear Regulatory Commission to build a new nuclear generating facility in Texas. The company hasn't made the decision to build the facility but wanted to get a start on the potentially onerous process. The last license to result in the construction of a new nuclear facility in the US was granted in 1973. However the Fukushima nuclear plant disaster in early 2011 placed nuclear power expansion plans under serious scrutiny from regulators.

Mergers and Acquisitions
In a major move to grow its retail operations in 2012 parent Exelon Corporation bought Constellation Energy in a $7.9 billion stock deal. The purchase of Constellation Energy (which gets 17% of its power from nuclear plants) helped the company boost its nuclear-generated power plant assets.

Company Background
Growing its cleaner-burning plant fleet in Texas in 2011 Exelon Corporation bought the 720 MW capacity Wolf Hollow plant in north Texas from Sequent Wolf Hollow for $305 million.

In 2010 to grow its renewable energy unit the company acquired wind power developer John Deere Renewables for about $860 million. The purchase adds 735 MW of operating wind power capacity to its generation capacity.

EXECUTIVES

MBR, John W Rowe
MBR, John Young
MBR-Ceo, Christopher M Crane
Chm, Mayo A Shattuck III
Svp, Bryan Hanson
Paralegal, Jenifer Newman
Svp, Generation Development, Thomas S O'Neill
Svp, Doyle N Beneby
Svp and President and Chief Nu, Bryan C Hanson
Senior Supervisor, Leah Dawes
Technician, Brian Higgins
Auditors: PricewaterhouseCoopers LLP

LOCATIONS

HQ: Exelon Generation Co LLC
300 Exelon Way, Kennett Square, PA 19348-2473
Phone: 610 765-5959
Web: www.exeloncorp.com

PRODUCTS/OPERATIONS

2013 Sales

	$ mil.	% of total
Mid-Atlantic	5	33
Midwest	4	27
New England	1	8
ERCOT	1	8
Other Regions	1	6
New York	0	5
Others	2	13
Total	**15**	**100**

COMPETITORS

AES	Duke Energy
AMP	NextEra Energy
Buckeye Power	Wolverine Power Supply
CMS Energy	

HISTORICAL FINANCIALS

Company Type: Public

Income Statement

FYE: December 31

	REVENUE ($ mil.)	NET INCOME ($ mil.)	NET PROFIT MARGIN	EMPLOYEES
12/18	20,437	370	1.8%	14,110
12/17	18,466	2,694	14.6%	15,011
12/16	17,751	496	2.8%	14,717
12/15	19,135	1,372	7.2%	14,512
12/14	17,393	835	4.8%	14,370
Annual Growth	**4.1%**	**(18.4%)**	**—**	**(0.5%)**

2018 Year-End Financials

Debt ratio: 19.42%	No. of shares (mil.): 968
Return on equity: 2.76%	Dividends
Cash ($ mil.): 750	Yield: —
Current ratio: 1.46	Payout: —
Long-term debt ($ mil.): 7,887	Market value ($ mil.): —

Expedia Group Inc

Expedia a market leader in online travel services (with rival Booking Holdings) is often the go-to online trip-planner. It offers tools that allow users to book airline tickets hotel reservations car rentals cruises and vacation packages. Expedia's portfolio of brands could fill a boutique hotel. They include flagship Expedia.com online travel bookers Travelocity and Orbitz accommodations manager Hotels.com vacation rental site HomeAway travel discounter Hotwire hotel meta-searcher Trivago luxury package provider Classic Vacations and several sites focused on international destinations. More than 1 million hotels and alternative accommodations properties can be booked through Expedia. Some 45% of sales come from customers in the US.

Operations
Expedia operates through four segments: Core OTA (online travel agency) Trivago HomeAway and Egencia.

Core OTA accounts for roughly 80% of Expedia's total revenue and includes the brands Hotwire and Hotels.com. Trivago which generates 10% of total revenue is a hotel price-comparison platform that scans prices across 400 booking websites. HomeAway offers vacation rentals through HomeAway.com VRBO and Vacationrentals.com and also brings in some 10% of revenue. Egencia the smallest segment at 5% of sales is a full-service travel management company that offers travel products and services to businesses and their corporate travelers.

Expedia has three principal revenue sources: Lodging (70% of sales) Air fares (8% of sales) and Advertising and Media (10%). The remaining approximately 15% of sales arise from car rental insurance destination services and fees from corporate customers.

Geographic Reach
Based in Bellevue Washington Expedia has offices throughout the Americas Europe and Asia/Pacific region and operates in about 200 countries. The company operates call centers around the world including outsourced centers in the Philippines El Salvador Egypt and India.

The US accounts for about 55% of revenue.

Sales and Marketing
"Hotel? Trivago" is a refrain familiar to millions thanks to Expedia's extensive Trivago advertising campaigns on television radio print and online. Expedia's selling and marketing spend is massive among the largest of any company in the world. It spends roughly half its annual sales on selling and marketing each year (as does arch-rival Booking) much of it with Google.

Financial Performance
Expedia has traveled a long way in the past decade with revenue rising from $2.6 billion in 2007 to more than $11 billion in 2018.

Sales grew 12% to $11.2 billion in 2017 thanks to strong growth in its core Online Travel Agency businesses and Homeway. Trivago saw sales fall 8% while the smaller Egencia unit grew 16%. By type lodging air and other assorted revenue sources all strengthened but advertising revenue growth slowed sharply from 33% in 2017 to 2% in 2018.

Expedia's net income which grew 7% to $406 million in 2018 lags far behind rival Booking Holdings which reported net income of $4.0 billion in 2018. The growth came from higher revenue operating performance being equal.

Expedia's cash position fell $212 million during 2018 ending the year at $2.7 billion. Its operations generated $2.0 billion while investing activities used $559 million and financing activities used $1.5 billion. The company's main cash uses in 2018 were capital expenditures investments debt repayments and stock repurchases.

Strategy
Expedia's goal is to generate two-thirds of its revenue outside the US. International customers accounted for 45% of revenue in 2018 up significantly from 21% in 2008 (although flat on 2017). Building its image globally and expanding its brand portfolio have been key in its efforts to reach a wide slice of consumers (including budget-conscious luxury and business travelers). Expedia has grown internationally with the acquisition of several online travel sites around the world. It also records huge advertising spend to win eyeballs online and compete with Booking and Airbnb shelling out more than $5 billion each year. The strategy has helped revenue grow powerfully but at the expense of profits which are marginal at best.

Expedia is seeing increasing traffic from mobile sources which the company has embraced due to the incremental growth offered by shorter booking windows and higher customer engagement resulting from cross-device usage. Expedia's apps have overtake taken desktops/laptops as traffic sources and the company has steadily integrated new functions into its apps such as voice search chatbots and using messaging apps for customer support. Mobile channels also help drive traffic acquisition increased wallet share and repeat customers.

Mergers and Acquisitions
Expedia isn't shy about acquiring parts of the travel planning experience that it doesn't already have. The approach has brought some well-recognized travel sites under its corporate umbrella.

In 2019 Expedia agreed to acquire Liberty Expedia a holding company whose main interest is a 16% stake in Expedia itself. Liberty Expedia also owned Bodybuilding.com via subsidiary Vitalize. The acquisition improves Expedia's corporate governance and meaningfully reduces its share count.

In late 2018 Expedia made two acquisition Pillow and ApartmentJet which both are active in the short-term rental market going toe-to-toe with Airbnb. Pillow helps multifamily building landlords supervise usership of their property while helping them comply with local regulations. ApartmentJet does much the same thing helping landlords list their apartments and run checks on potential guests.

Company Background
Originally a division of Microsoft Expedia was sold to IAC/InterActiveCorp which acquired the computer maker's majority stake in 2002 and the minority interest it did not already own in 2003. Two years later IAC spun off Expedia into a separate publicly traded firm.

EXECUTIVES

President Ecommerce Platform, J. Tucker Moodey
President Hotwire Group, Henrik V. Kjellberg, age 49
President Hotels.com And Ean, Johan Svanstrom, age 48
President Expedia Lodging Partner Services, Cyril Ranque
President Egencia, Rob Greyber
President Ceo And Director, Mark D. Okerstrom, $750,000 total compensation
Evp General Counsel And Secretary, Robert Dzielak, $575,000 total compensation
President Brand Expedia Group, Aman Bhutani, age 43
Chief People Officer, Nikki Krishnamurthy
President Homeaway, John Kim
Svp And General Manager Expedia Affiliate Network, Ariane Gorin
Vice President Of Employee Engagement, Kristin Graham
Senior Vice President Marketing Packages And Canada, Sean C Shannon
Senior Vice President Sales, Bruce Freeman
Vice Chairman, Victor A. Kaufman, age 75
Chairman, Barry Diller, age 77
Auditors: Ernst & Young LLP

LOCATIONS

HQ: Expedia Group Inc
333 108th Avenue N.E., Bellevue, WA 98004
Phone: 425 679-7200
Web: www.expediainc.com

2018 Sales

	$ mil.	% of total
United States	6,202	55
All other countries	5,021	45
Total	11,223	100

PRODUCTS/OPERATIONS

2018 Sales

	$ mil.	% of total
Core OTA (online travel agency)	8,760	78
trivago	691	6
HomeAway	1,171	11
Egencia	601	5
Total	11,223	100

2018 Sales

	$ mil.	% of total
Merchant	5,950	53
Agency	3,010	27
Advertising and media	1,092	11
HomeAway	1,171	9
Total	11,223	100

BRANDS

BRANDS
CarRentals.com
Classic Vacations
Egencia
Expedia
Expedia Affiliate Network (EAN)
Expedia CruiseShipCenters
Expedia Local Expert
Expedia Media Solutions
HomeAway
Hotels.com
Hotwire
Orbitz
SilverRail
Traveldoo
Travelocity
trivago
Wotif Group

SELECTED SUBSIDIARIES

Classic Vacations LLC
Cruise LLC
EAN.com LP
Egencia France SAS
Egencia LLC
EXP Holdings Luxembourg S.A.
Expedia Asia Holdings Mauritius
Expedia do Brasil Agencia de Viagens e Turismo Ltda.

COMPETITORS

Airbnb	Prestige Travel
American Express	Priceline
BCD Travel	Sabre
Carlson Wagonlit	Travelport
Concur Technologies	TripAdvisor
GetThere	Uniglobe Travel
Google	WorldRes
Pegasus Solutions	ebookers.com

HISTORICAL FINANCIALS

Company Type: Public

Income Statement — FYE: December 31

	REVENUE ($ mil.)	NET INCOME ($ mil.)	NET PROFIT MARGIN	EMPLOYEES
12/18	11,223	406	3.6%	24,500
12/17	10,059	377	3.8%	22,615
12/16	8,773	281	3.2%	20,075
12/15	6,672	764	11.5%	18,730
12/14	5,763	398	6.9%	18,210
Annual Growth	18.1%	0.5%	—	7.7%

2018 Year-End Financials

Debt ratio: 20.61%
Return on equity: 9.41%
Cash ($ mil.): 2,443
Current ratio: 0.64
Long-term debt ($ mil.): 3,717
No. of shares (mil.): 147
Dividends
Yield: 1.1%
Payout: 46.7%
Market value ($ mil.): 16,575

	STOCK PRICE ($) FY Close	P/E High/Low	PER SHARE ($) Earnings	Dividends	Book Value
12/18	112.65	51 37	2.65	1.24	27.89
12/17	119.77	64 45	2.42	1.16	29.80
12/16	113.28	70 49	1.82	1.00	27.54
12/15	124.30	23 13	5.70	0.84	32.37
12/14	85.36	30 20	2.99	0.66	14.04
Annual Growth	7.2%	— —	(3.0%)	17.1%	18.7%

Expeditors International of Washington, Inc.

As a freight forwarder Expeditors International of Washington keeps cargo moving. The company purchases air and ocean cargo space on a volume basis and resells that space to its customers at lower rates than they could obtain directly from the carriers. The company also acts as a customs broker for air and ocean freight shipped by its customers and offers supply chain management services. Customers include global businesses engaged in retailing and wholesaling electronics and manufacturing. How much does Expeditors ship? The company annually moves about 800 million kilograms of freight by air 900 million kilograms by ground and one million standard measurement shipping containers by sea.

Operations
Expeditors operates in three segments none of which supplies an outsized percentage of the company's revenue.

Expeditors' airfreight services segment more than 40% of revenue represents airlines as an agent in addition to providing freight consolidation for shippers. Besides shipping on scheduled flights the company sometimes charters aircraft for the delivery of backlogs. By not purchasing its own aircraft the company avoids the costs of large capital expenditures and operating costs.

Ocean freight and ocean services about 30% of revenue operates as a non-vessel operating common carrier which is a contractor with ocean shipping lines for a set amount of containers. Expeditors also obtains less-than container load freight to fill containers. The segment additionally provides such order management services as document management and SKU visibility.

Customs brokerage and other services almost 30% of revenue aids in the movement of shipments across borders by providing such services as adding up duties and taxes and arranging inspections. Beyond the border entry the segment provides additional services including warehousing product distribution and time-definite transportation. Expeditors provides these services not only for its own shipping customers but also for businesses that have not hired the company as a forwarder a class of client that accounts for a significant portion of the segment's revenue.

Geographic Reach
Expeditors is headquartered in Seattle Washington and has regional headquarters in London Dubai Singapore and Shanghai. It operates from more than 300 facilities in more than 100 countries.

North Asia is its largest market generating about 35% of revenue followed by the US with more than a quarter of revenue and Europe about 15% of revenue.

Sales and Marketing
Expeditors caters to its customers' supply chains. Therefore its marketing efforts target people in their company's logistics international and domestic transportation customs compliance and purchasing departments. It employs district managers who are responsible for marketing sales coordination and implementation in their area. The company primarily targets the aviation and aerospace health care oil and energy and retail sectors.

Financial Performance
Expeditors' revenue marched higher for several years before dropping in 2016. At the same time net income remained robust even if it didn't rise each year.

The company's revenue rebounded in 2017 rising 13% to $6.9 billion. Airfreight services turned in a 17% revenue increase because of higher tonnage and sell rates. Ocean freight and ocean services revenue rose 10% in 2017 from 2016 on higher container volume and sell rates. Higher shipping volumes drove revenue from customs brokerage and other services 12% higher.

The higher revenue helped Expeditors post a $59 million gain in net income to $490 million in 2017 from 2016.

The company's cash crested $1 billion in 2017 compared to $974 million in 2016. Cash generated by operating activities was $489 million in 2017 while cash used by investing and financing activities was $12 million and $425 million respectively.

Strategy

In its rapid development Expeditors has favored internal growth over expansion by acquisition (though it has also selectively made some strategic acquisitions) and the company continues to open new offices and to invest in its information technology infrastructure. By eschewing acquisitions as its main form of growth the company has been able to develop a common hardware platform that lets the entire company use the same accounting and transportation software.

The company is focused on diversifying its product mix through focused investments in its distribution services transcon and ocean export products. It also aims to diversify its market verticals by investing further in the pharmaceutical and automotive markets.

Expeditors wants to leverage its long presence in China to build a stronger import presence in the country. It is making investments to build its import infrastructure and its local delivery and support capabilities in China an effort that could be slowe by trade disputes between the US and China remains to be seen. The company said it believes it can weather the current dispute and can adjust if manufacturers seek alternative sources for good and products.

EXECUTIVES

Evp Europe, Timothy C. Barber, age 59, $100,000 total compensation

President Global Services, Eugene K. Alger, age 58, $100,000 total compensation

Svp And Cfo, Bradley S. (Brad) Powell, age 59, $100,000 total compensation

President Global Products, Daniel R. Wall, age 50, $100,000 total compensation

President And Ceo, Jeffrey S. Musser, age 53, $100,000 total compensation

President Global Geographies And Operations, Richard H. Rostan

Svp And Cio, Christopher J. McClincy, age 44

Svp Global Sales And Marketing, J. Jonathan Song

Senior Vice President Global Business Operations, Craig Wilwerding

Svp Global Sales And Marketing, Jonathan Song

Svp General Counsel And Corporate Secretary, Benjamin Clark

Senior Vice President Corporate Controller Expeditors Int'l Of Washington, Charles Lynch

Senior Vice President Global Order Management, Michelle Weaver

Svp Account Management, Steven Grimmer

Director, Robert R. Wright, age 59

Auditors: KPMG LLP

LOCATIONS

HQ: Expeditors International of Washington, Inc.
1015 Third Avenue, 12th Floor, Seattle, WA 98104
Phone: 206 674-3400 **Fax:** 206 674-3459
Web: www.expeditors.com

2016 Sales

	$ mil.	% of total
Asia		
North Asia	2,598	36
South Asia	684	9
North America		
US	1,962	27
Other North America	268	4
Europe	1,115	16
Middle East Africa and India	426	6
Latin America	111	2
Eliminations	(2463)	-
Total	**6,920**	**100**

PRODUCTS/OPERATIONS

2017 Sales

	$ mil.	% of total
Airfreight services	2,877	42
Ocean freight & ocean services	2,107	30
Customs brokerage & other services	1,936	28
Total	**6,920**	**100**

Selected Products and Services

Air freight consolidation
Air freight forwarding
Customs brokerage services
Warehousing and Distribution Services
Direct Ocean Forwarding
Order Management
Transcom

COMPETITORS

APL Logistics	NYK Line
C.H. Robinson	Nippon Express
Worldwide	Panalpina
CEVA Logistics	Schenker
DHL	Sino-Global
FedEx Trade Networks	Sinotrans
Kintetsu World Express	UPS Supply Chain
Kuehne + Nagel	Solutions
International	Yamato Holdings
Mitsui-Soko	

HISTORICAL FINANCIALS

Company Type: Public

Income Statement

FYE: December 31

	REVENUE ($ mil.)	NET INCOME ($ mil.)	NET PROFIT MARGIN	EMPLOYEES
12/18	8,138	618	7.6%	17,400
12/17	6,920	489	7.1%	16,500
12/16	6,098	430	7.1%	16,000
12/15	6,616	457	6.9%	15,397
12/14	6,564	376	5.7%	14,670
Annual Growth	**5.5%**	**13.2%**	**—**	**4.4%**

2018 Year-End Financials

Debt ratio: —
Return on equity: 31.08%
Cash ($ mil.): 923
Current ratio: 2.06
Long-term debt ($ mil.): —

No. of shares (mil.): 171
Dividends
 Yield: 1.3%
 Payout: 26.5%
Market value ($ mil.): 11,683

	STOCK PRICE ($) FY Close	P/E High/Low	PER SHARE ($) Earnings	Dividends	Book Value
12/18	68.09	22 17	3.48	0.90	11.58
12/17	64.69	24 19	2.69	0.84	11.29
12/16	52.96	24 18	2.36	0.80	10.26
12/15	45.10	21 18	2.40	0.72	9.29
12/14	44.61	24 20	1.92	0.64	9.75
Annual Growth	**11.2%**	**— —**	**16.0%**	**8.9%**	**4.4%**

Exxon Mobil Corp

Exxon Mobil Corporation is the world's #1 publicly traded oil company rivaled only by giants like Shell BP and Total. Its vast portfolio holds about 24 billion barrels of oil equivalent of proved reserves spread across some 25 countries on six continents. The company has a huge daily average output: 1.6 million barrels of crude oil 250000 barrels of NGLs and 9.4 billion cubic feet of natural gas. Its biggest business is selling refined products through approximately 19000 gas stations around the world. Exxon Mobil is also a leader in the chemicals industry manufacturing olefins polyolefins and aromatics that form the base for many plastic products. The company's brands?ExxonMobil Exxon Esso Mobil and XTO? enjoy global recognition.

HISTORY

Exxon's 1999 acquisition of Mobil reunited two descendants of John D. Rockefeller's Standard Oil Company. Rockefeller a commodity trader started his first oil refinery in 1863 in Cleveland. Realizing that the price of oil at the well would shrink with each new strike Rockefeller chose to monopolize oil refining and transportation. In 1870 he formed Standard Oil and in 1882 he created the Standard Oil Trust which allowed him to set up new ostensibly independent companies including the Standard Oil Company of New Jersey (Jersey Standard); Rochester New York-based Vacuum Oil; and Standard Oil of New York (nicknamed Socony).

Initially capitalized at $70 million the Standard Oil Trust controlled 90% of the petroleum industry. In 1911 after two decades of political and legal wrangling the Supreme Court broke up the trust into 34 companies the largest of which was Jersey Standard.

Walter Teagle who became president of Jersey Standard in 1917 secretly bought half of Humble Oil of Texas (1919) and expanded operations into South America. In 1928 Jersey Standard joined in the Red Line Agreement which reserved most Middle East oil for a few companies. Teagle resigned in 1942 after the company was criticized for a prewar research pact with German chemical giant I.G. Farben.

The 1948 purchase of a 40% stake in Arabian American Oil Company combined with a 7% share of Iranian production bought in 1954 made Jersey Standard the world's #1 oil company at that time.

Meanwhile Vacuum Oil and Socony reunited in 1931 as Socony-Vacuum and the company adopted the Flying Red Horse (Pegasus — representing speed and power) as a trademark. The fast-growing diversifying company changed its name to Socony Mobil Oil in 1955 and became Mobil in 1976.

Other US companies still using the Standard Oil name objected to Jersey Standard's marketing in their territories as Esso (derived from the initials for Standard Oil). To end the confusion in 1972 Jersey Standard became Exxon a name change that cost $100 million.

Nationalization of oil assets by producing countries reduced Exxon's access to oil during the 1970s. Though it increased exploration that decade and the next Exxon's reserves shrank.

Oil tanker Exxon Valdez spilled some 11 million gallons of oil into Alaska's Prince William Sound in 1989. Exxon spent billions on the cleanup and in 1994 a federal jury in Alaska ordered the company to pay $5.3 billion in punitive damages to fishermen and others affected by the spill. (Exxon appealed and in 2001 the jury award was reduced to $2.5 billion and in 2008 to $507.5 million).

With the oil industry consolidating Exxon merged its worldwide oil and fuel additives business with that of Royal Dutch/Shell in 1996. The next year under FTC pressure Exxon agreed to run ads refuting claims that its premium gas enabled car engines to run more efficiently. Another PR disaster followed in 1998 when CEO Lee Raymond upset environmentalists by publicly questioning the global warming theory.

Still Exxon was unstoppable. It acquired Mobil for $81 billion in 1999; the new company had Raymond at the helm and Mobil's Lucio Noto as vice chairman. (Noto retired in 2001.) To get the deal done Exxon Mobil had to divest $4 billion in assets.

It agreed to end its European gasoline and lubricants joint venture with BP and to sell more than 2400 gas stations in the US.

In 2000 Exxon Mobil sold 1740 East Coast gas stations to Tosco for $860 million. It sold a California refinery and 340 gas stations to Valero Energy for about $1 billion.

More than a decade after the Exxon Valdez wreaked environmental havoc off the shores of Alaska Exxon Mobil attempted to atone in 2001 by joining the California Fuel Cell Partnership a group studying possible alternatives to and supplements for gasoline in fuel-burning engines. That year Exxon Mobil also announced that it was proceeding with a $12 billion project (with Japanese Indian and Russian partners) to develop oil fields in the Russian Far East.

In 2002 Exxon Mobil sold its 50% stake in a Colombian coal mine as part of its strategy to divest coal assets in order to focus on its core businesses. That year the company sold its Chilean copper mining subsidiary (Disputada de Las Condes) to mineral giant Anglo American for $1.3 billion. Exxon Mobil sold its 3.7% stake in China Petroleum & Chemical Corp. (Sinopec) in early 2005. Later that year the company was ordered to pay $1.3 billion to about 10000 gas station owners for overcharges dating back to 1983; the average amount for each station owner was about $130000.

Shortages caused by Hurricane Katrina prompted Exxon Mobil to receive a 6 million barrel of crude oil loan primarily from the US Strategic Petroleum Reserve and increase gasoline production at its Baton Rouge facility.

Exiting the low-margin retail gasoline business in order to focus on its other operations in 2008 the company began to sell to distributors its remaining 820 company-owned US gas stations and another 1400 outlets operated by dealers.

In 2009 the company signed up to partner with TransCanada to jointly develop the $26 billion Alaska Pipeline Project. A long-term project if and when built the pipeline will deliver natural gas from Alaska's North Slope to US markets.

Also in 2009 it made its first major investment in developing biofuels agreeing to spend $600 million in an algae-to-fuel project with biotech firm Synthetic Genomics.

In a move to replace the decline of oil reserves from its mature fields in 2010 Exxon Mobil acquired XTO Energy. The $41 billion all-stock deal sharply boosted Exxon shale properties in the continental US including the Haynesville shale. Exxon followed up by acquiring Ellora Energy that same year for $695 million which further solidified Exxon's Haynesville position in Texas and Louisiana.

In 2010 in response to the BP oil rig disaster in the Gulf of Mexico Exxon Mobil joined forces with other US oil companies to create a $1 billion rapid-response joint venture capable of capturing and containing some 100000 barrels of oil in water depths of 10000 feet.

In 2011 the company reported a major oil find in the Gulf with potentially 700 million barrels of recoverable oil equivalent.

That year Exxon Mobil acquired two Pittsburgh-area natural gas producers (Phillips Resources and TWP) for $1.7 billion giving the company access to hundreds of thousands of leased acres of the Marcellus Shale in southwestern Pennsylvania.

In 2012 Saudi Basic Industries Corporation and Exxon Mobil agreed to build a world-scale specialty elastomers facility (to be completed in 2015) at the Al-Jubail Petrochemical Company manufacturing joint venture in Saudi Arabia.

To raise cash to pay down debt in 2012 the company sold its North Sea assets to Apache for $1.25 billion.

In 2013 Rosneft and Exxon Mobil agreed to expand their cooperation under their 2011 Strategic Cooperation Agreement to include an additional 150 million acres of exploration acreage in the Russian Arctic and potential participation by Rosneft in the Point Thomson project in Alaska. They also agreed to conduct a joint study on a potential LNG project in the Russian Far East. (In 2011 Exxon Mobil agreed to spend $1 billion in a joint venture with Rosneft to jointly explore oil and gas fields in the Black Sea.). However US economic sanctions on Russia in 2014 forced the company to suspend its operations in the Arctic with Rosneft.

In 2013 Exxon Mobil acquired Canada's Celtic Exploration for about about $2.5 billion Exxon Mobil's largest transaction since it bought Texas' XTO Energy for a whopping $41 billion in 2010. The Celtic deal gives Exxon 545000 net acres in the liquids-rich Montney shale 104000 net acres in the Duvernay shale and other acreage in Alberta.

EXECUTIVES

Svp And Principal Financial Officer, Andrew P. (Andy) Swiger, age 63, $1,287,500 total compensation
President Exxonmobil Chemical Company, John R. Verity
President Exxonmobil Refining & Supply Company, Darren W. Woods, age 54, $1,000,000 total compensation
Vp And President Exxonmobil Upstream Ventures, B. W. Corson
Vp And General Counsel, R. M. Ebner
Vp Human Resources, M. A. Farrant
President Exxonmobil Production Company, N. W. Duffin
President Exxonmobil Fuels Lubricants And Specialties Marketing Company, B. W. Milton
President Exxonmobil Refining And Supply Company, D. G. Wascom
President Exxonmobil Research And Engineering Company, T. J. Wojnar
President Exxonmobil Global Services Company, L. D. DuCharme
Vice President, Hugh Comer
Vice President Information Technology, Nigel Searle
Vp Human Resources, Malcolm Farrant
Vice President Business Development, John Ardill
National Accounts Manager, Juan Rodriguez
Vice President Engineering Exxonmobil Upstream Research Company, Jayme K Meier
Vice President, Lloyd Guillory
Vice President Global Procurement, Robert Noel
Senior Vice President Finance And Administration And Controller, Daniel Lyons
Vice President Synthetics, Damon Davis
Vice President Americas, Steve Kirchhoff
Vice President, Pat Doolan
Vice President, Elijah White
Senior Vice President Permian Integrated Development Xto Energy, Staale Gjervik
National Account Manager, Richard Bowen
Department Head, Michael Hotaling
Vice President, Pam Darwin
Vice President Upstream Engineering, Gerry Gabriel
Vice President Engineering, Erika Anzaldua
Vice President; President Exxonmobil Production Company, Neil Duffin
Vice President Coordinator, Jim Mchugh
Government Relations Advisor, Robert Nolan
Vice President Geoscience, Don Bagley
Vice President Facilities, John Trautchild
Vice President, Jim Parsons
Government Relations Advisor, Riva Magaru

Senior Vice President Commercial And Corporate Development, Theresa Redburn
Vice President, M Jay Wood
Vp And President Exxonmobil Upstream Ventures, Brad Corson
Vice President, Jon Gibbs
Vice President Engineering, Kenneth Warren
Vice President, Evelyn Miller
Vice President, Tina Fitts
Vice President Strategy And Planning, Ian Carr
Vice President Research And Development Exxonmobil Research And Engineering, Vijay Swarup
Government Relations, Alfredo Balena
Vice President Americas, John Dashwood
Vice President And President Exxonmobil Gas And Power Marketing Upstream, Peter Clarke
Vice President Of Engineering, Roman Perez
Vp Global It Exxonmobil Global Services Company, Michael Brown
Vice President, Christopher Vandewater
Vp And General Tax Counsel, James Spellings Jr
Treasurer???s ??? Benefits Finance And Investments, Cindy Kessel
Secretary, Suzanne Manahan-smith
L And S Downstream Treasurers Credit Analyst, Patricia Beckwith
Financial Advisor Upstream Treasurers, Todd Norman
Assistant Treasurer, Kate Shae
Assistant Treasurer, Namisa Taylor
Board Of Directors, Henrietta Fore
Secretary, Marie Clouthier
Auditors: PricewaterhouseCoopers LLP

LOCATIONS

HQ: Exxon Mobil Corp
5959 Las Colinas Boulevard, Irving, TX 75039-2298
Phone: 972 940-6000   **Fax:** 972 444-1505
Web: www.exxonmobil.com

2018 Sales

	% of total
US	35
International	65
Total	**100**

PRODUCTS/OPERATIONS

2018 Sales

	$ mil.	% of total
Downstream	221,331	79
Chemical	32,443	12
Upstream	25,517	9
Corporate and Financing	38	-
Total	**279,332**	**100**

COMPETITORS

BP	Royal Dutch Shell
Chevron	Saudi Aramco
Gazprom	Sinopec Corp.
PetroChina	Statoil
Reliance Industries	TOTAL
Rosneft	

HISTORICAL FINANCIALS

Company Type: Public

Income Statement				FYE: December 31
	REVENUE ($ mil.)	NET INCOME ($ mil.)	NET PROFIT MARGIN	EMPLOYEES
12/18	290,212	20,840	7.2%	71,000
12/17	244,363	19,710	8.1%	69,600
12/16	226,094	7,840	3.5%	71,100
12/15	268,882	16,150	6.0%	73,500
12/14	411,939	32,520	7.9%	75,300
Annual Growth	(8.4%)	(10.5%)	—	(1.5%)

2018 Year-End Financials
Debt ratio: 10.92%—
Return on equity: 10.98%
Cash ($ mil.): 3,042
Current ratio: 0.84
Long-term debt ($ mil.): 20,538

Dividends
Yield: 4.7%
Payout: 66.1%
Market value ($ mil.): —

	STOCK PRICE ($) FY Close	P/E High/Low		PER SHARE ($) Earnings	Dividends	Book Value
12/18	68.19	18	13	4.88	3.23	45.27
12/17	83.64	20	16	4.63	3.06	44.28
12/16	90.26	51	39	1.88	2.98	40.34
12/15	77.95	24	18	3.85	2.88	41.10
12/14	92.45	14	11	7.60	2.70	41.51
Annual Growth	(7.3%)	—	—	(10.5%)	4.6%	2.2%

Facebook Inc

Facebook is the face of social media for good and bad. The social networking juggernaut which continues to grow even as it struggles with public relations issues related to privacy security and fake news lets users share information post photos and videos play games and otherwise connect with one another online. The site which allows outside developers to build apps that integrate with Facebook boasts more than two billion monthly active users. In addition to its namesake platform Facebook owns photo and video sharing site Instagram messaging applications Messenger and WhatsApp and virtual reality platform Oculus. The company generates revenue through advertising; the US accounts for about 45% of total sales.

Operations
Facebook boasts more than 2.3 billion monthly Facebook users and serves a total of 7 million advertisers.

In a move that emphasizes the growing importance of the products and services it offers beyond its core platform the company has said it will stop sharing user numbers for each individual service (Facebook Instagram WhatsApp and Facebook Messenger) and instead provide one combined figure for all of its apps.

Beyond its core offerings the company has investments in longer-term technology initiatives such as artificial intelligence augmented and virtual reality and connectivity efforts.

Geographic Reach
Global in its reach the Menlo Park California-based Facebook generates about 55% of its revenue from outside of the US. The majority of its international business comes from customers located in Western Europe Australia Brazil Canada and China.

The company has offices and data center facilities located all over the world.

Sales and Marketing
Advertising accounts for nearly all of Facebook's revenue. The company uses a global sales force in more than 60 offices worldwide to attract and retain advertisers. It also serves advertising customers through a self-service ad platform.

Users have generally found the site through word-of-mouth as well as internal marketing efforts. Facebook spent $1.10 billion on advertising and promotion in 2018 compared to $324 million in both 2017 and 2016.

Financial Performance
Facebook has experienced exponential growth over the past few years enabling it to dominate the social networking world as the most trafficked site of its kind in the US. Its revenue grew from nearly $12.5 billion in 2014 to more than $55.8 billion in 2018 while its net income grew from $2.9 billion to $22.1 billion. Despite record-breaking business the company cannot rest on its laurels. Ad revenue may decelerate as Facebook begins to feel the affects of data privacy regulation such as the EU's GDPR and the California Consumer Privacy Bill (CCPA). Meanwhile founder Mark Zuckerberg has admitted the core service may be close to saturated in developed countries.

While still in growth mode Facebook's annual growth rate slowed some in 2018 when revenue increased 37% from the prior year (versus 50% in 2017). Monthly active users grew nearly 10% (versus 15% in 2017) and the average price per ad increased by 13% (versus 30% in 2017).

Net income grew 39% from $15.9 billion in 2017 to $22.1 billion in 2018 on the jump in revenue. (The prior year profits rose 55%.) Operating expenses include hiring more people to fight disinformation and moderate content.

Cash at the end of 2018 was $10.1 billion. Cash from operations contributed $29.3 billion to the coffers while investing activities used $11.6 billion. Financing activities used another $15.6 billion.

Strategy
Facebook continues to invest in and expand its service offerings in an effort to keep growth strong as it grapples with questions about data privacy security and reliability. The company in 2018 faced customer outrage and negative press related to massive security breaches as well as charges that it improperly handled people's data distributed false content and enabled the foreign influence of political campaigns across its network.

Following a sweeping investigation by several government agencies the Federal Trade Commission (FTC) in 2019 issued a $5 billion fine against the company for privacy violations. The penalty represents the largest fine in FTC history. In response founder and face of the company Mark Zuckerberg stated Facebook is focused on making major structural changes on how it builds products and runs the company.

On the product front the company is focused on selling ads across Facebook's Stories one of its newer offerings as well as enhancing its e-commerce and payment systems. It is also working to integrate the technical infrastructure of WhatsApp Instagram and Facebook Messenger so that people can communicate across the services. The company expects growth to come from global regions outside developed markets of the US and Europe.

Company Background
Facebook was launched in 2004 by Harvard student Mark Zuckerberg as an online version of the Harvard Facebook. The name comes from books of freshmen's faces majors and hometowns that are distributed to students.

In 2012 Facebook began publicly trading after filing one of the largest IPOs in US history.

EXECUTIVES

Coo, Sheryl K. Sandberg, age 50, $738,077 total compensation
Chairman And Ceo, Mark Zuckerberg, age 35, $1 total compensation
Cto, Michael (Mike) Schroepfer, age 44, $658,846 total compensation
Cio, Atish Banerjea, age 53
Cfo, David M. (Dave) Wehner, age 50, $662,692 total compensation
Chief Product Officer, Christopher K. (Chris) Cox, age 36, $658,846 total compensation
Vice President Global Public Policy, Joel Kaplan
Vice President Partnerships, Dan Rose

Vice President Global Marketing Solutions, Carolyn Everson
Vice President Growth And Analytics, Javier Olivan
Senior Vice President Production Services, Ellis Collins
Vice President Product Marketing, Ty Ahmad-Taylor
Vp And Virtual Reality Chief, Hugo Barra
Vice President Data Center Design Engineering, Jay Park
Senior Vice President Business Development Sales And Marketing, Cree Crawford
Vice President Small Business, Dan Levy
Vp. Mobile And Global Access Policy, Kevin Martin
Vice President Social Good, Naomi Gleit
Vice President Ads And Business Platform, Mark Rabkin
Vice President Global Operations, Justin Osofsky
Vp Ai, Jerome Presenti
Vp And Deputy General Counsel, Paul Grewal
Vp Deputy General Counsel And Secretary, David Kling
Vp Of Hr, Janelle Gale
Board Member, Susan Desmond-hellmann
Auditors: Ernst & Young LLP

LOCATIONS
HQ: Facebook Inc
  1601 Willow Road, Menlo Park, CA 94025
Phone: 650 543-4800
Web: www.facebook.com

2017 Sales

	$ mil.	% of total
US	17,734	44
International	22,919	56
Total	**40,653**	**100**

PRODUCTS/OPERATIONS

2017 Sales

	$ mil.	% of total
Advertising	39,942	98
Payments & other fees	711	2
Total	**40,653**	**100**

Selected Products and Features
Products for Users
  Timeline
  News feed
  Photos & videos
  Messages
  Groups
  Lists
  Events
  Places
  Notifications
  Facebook Pages
Products for Developers
  Open Graph
  Social plugins
  Like button
  Recommendations
  Comments
  Facebook Payments
  Apps on Facebook
Products for Advertisers & Marketers
  Facebook Ads
  Sponsored Stories
  Ad analytics

COMPETITORS

Bebo	Pinterest
Friendster	Snapchat
Google	Tencent Holdings
IAC	Tumblr
LiveJournal	Twitter
Meetup	Yelp
Memory Lane	craigslist
Microsoft	

HISTORICAL FINANCIALS

Company Type: Public

Income Statement
FYE: December 31

	REVENUE ($ mil.)	NET INCOME ($ mil.)	NET PROFIT MARGIN	EMPLOYEES
12/19	70,697	18,485	26.1%	49,942
12/18	55,838	22,112	39.6%	35,587
12/17	40,653	15,934	39.2%	25,105
12/16	27,638	10,217	37.0%	17,048
12/15	17,928	3,688	20.6%	12,691
Annual Growth	40.9%	49.6%	—	40.8%

2019 Year-End Financials

Debt ratio: ——
Return on equity: 19.96%
Cash ($ mil.): 19,079
Current ratio: 4.40
Long-term debt ($ mil.): —

Dividends
Yield: —
Payout: —
Market value ($ mil.): —

	STOCK PRICE ($) FY Close	P/E High/Low	PER SHARE ($) Earnings	Dividends	Book Value
12/19	205.25	32 20	6.43	0.00	35.43
12/18	131.09	28 16	7.57	0.00	29.48
12/17	176.46	33 21	5.39	0.00	25.58
12/16	115.05	37 26	3.49	0.00	20.47
12/15	104.66	83 57	1.29	0.00	15.54
Annual Growth	18.3%	— —	49.4%	—	22.9%

FAIRVIEW HEALTH SERVICES

It's fair to say that when it comes to health care Fairview Health Services takes the long view. The not-for-profit system serves Minnesota's Twin Cities and nearby communities. Fairview Health is affiliated with the medical school of the University of Minnesota and counts among its 10 hospitals the University of Minnesota Medical Center. The hospitals house more than 2500 beds and provide comprehensive medical and surgical services. The system also operates primary and specialty care clinics that provide preventive and wellness care. Additionally it operates retail pharmacies and nursing homes and provides home health care and rehabilitation. Merger talks with University of Minnesota Physicians have stalled.

EXECUTIVES

Vice President Chief Information Security Officer, Barry Caplin
Nursing Director, Debbie Tharp
Vice President Business Development, Jerry Plourde
Vice President, John Swanholm
Vp It Systems And Ciso, Judy Hatchett
Auditors: ERNST & YOUNG LLP MINNEAPOLI

LOCATIONS

HQ: FAIRVIEW HEALTH SERVICES
2450 RIVERSIDE AVE, MINNEAPOLIS, MN 554541450
Phone: 612 672-6300
Web: WWW.FAIRVIEW.ORG

COMPETITORS

Abbott Northwestern Hospital
Allina Hospitals
Bethesda Hospital
Catholic Health Initiatives
CentraCare Health
HealthEast Care System

Mayo Clinic
North Memorial Health Care
Park Nicollet Health Services
Regions Hospital
St. John's Hospital (Minnesota)

HISTORICAL FINANCIALS

Company Type: Private

Income Statement
FYE: December 31

	REVENUE ($ mil.)	NET INCOME ($ mil.)	NET PROFIT MARGIN	EMPLOYEES
12/18	5,709	5	0.1%	18,000
12/17	5,275	511	9.7%	—
Annual Growth	8.2%	(98.9%)	—	—

Fannie Mae

The Federal National Mortgage Association or Fannie Mae helps families realize the American Dream of owning a home. Like its brother Freddie Mac the government-sponsored enterprise (GSE) provides liquidity in the US mortgage market by buying mortgages from lenders and packaging them for resale transferring risk from lenders and allowing them to offer mortgages to those who may not otherwise qualify. It owns or guarantees more than $2.9 trillion in single-family home loans and about $295 billion in multifamily mortgages. Its largest customers are Wells Fargo Walker & Dunlop and Berkadia. Due to losses caused largely by the subprime mortgage crisis the government seized both Fannie and Freddie in 2008. Government plans to divest the firms into private ownership have proven difficult; they remain GSEs.

HISTORY

In 1938 President Franklin Roosevelt created Fannie Mae as part of the government-owned Reconstruction Finance Corporation; its mandate was to buy FHA (Federal Housing Administration) loans. Fannie Mae began buying VA (Veterans Administration) mortgages in 1948. It was rechartered as a public-private mixed-ownership corporation in 1954.

The Housing Act of 1968 divided the corporation into the Government National Mortgage Association (Ginnie Mae which retained explicit government backing) and Fannie Mae which went public (with only an implicit US guarantee). Fannie Mae retained its treasury backstop authority whereby the secretary of the treasury can purchase up to $2.24 billion of the company's obligations.

The company introduced uniform conventional loan mortgage documents in 1970 began to buy conventional mortgages in 1972 and started buying condo and planned-unit development mortgages in 1974. By 1976 it was buying more conventional loans than FHA and VA loans.

As interest rates rose in the 1970s Fannie Mae's profits declined and by 1981 it was losing more than $1 million a day. Then it began offering mortgage-backed securities (MBSs) — popular as an investment product because of their implicit guarantee from the government. By 1982 the company funded 14% of US home mortgages.

Fannie Mae began borrowing money overseas and buying conventional multifamily and co-op housing loans in 1984. The next year it tightened credit rules and began issuing securities aimed at foreign investors such as yen-denominated securities. Fannie Mae issued its first real estate mortgage investment conduit (REMIC) securities (shares in mortgage pools of specific maturities and risk classes) and introduced a program to allow small lenders to pool loans with other lenders to create MBSs in 1987.

After CEO David Maxwell's 1991 retirement with a reported $29 million pension package Fannie Mae's powerful Washington lobby squelched calls to limit executive salaries. Other attempts to make the company more competitive with private concerns were more successful. In 1992 Fannie Mae's capital requirements were raised; a new mandate also required the organization to lend greater support to inner-city buyers. A new client/server computer system helped the company handle the deluge of new and refinanced loans that came in 1993 (Fannie Mae had struggled to improve its information systems in the 1980s pouring more than $100 million into a mainframe system that was obsolete before it went online).

In 1997 Fannie Mae officially adopted its longtime nickname. The next year Fannie Mae named White House budget chief Franklin Raines to succeed CEO James Johnson.

Fannie Mae is no stranger to bad news or bad press. In 1999 the Department of Housing and Urban Development began investigating charges that the company's automated underwriting systems were racially biased. The next year the agency released a study that found it to be negligent in promoting homeownership in low-income neighborhoods. In response Fannie Mae eased credit requirements in an effort to boost minority homeownership (1999) and announced plans to loan some $2 trillion to minority and low-income homebuyers (2000). This move however invoked criticism that the company was exposing itself to increased risk from buyers more likely to default.

Following the lead of rival Freddie Mac in 2000 Fannie Mae offered securities for sale over the Internet. In 2002 it tightened standards for mortgage refinance cash-out loans it would buy as mortgage defaults rose (even as home sales and mortgage refinancings were helping prop up the sagging US economy).

In response to those who thought it was in bed with the federal government Fannie Mae kicked off the covers and put one foot on the floor. In 2003 it fulfilled a voluntary commitment to register its common stock with the SEC and came permanently under that organization's disclosure and oversight requirements.

But the move did not stop controversy from swirling around the lender. Chairman and CEO Franklin Raines CFO Timothy Howard and auditor KPMG were ousted in December 2004 after the SEC determined Fannie Mae had violated accounting rules. The inquiry was prompted by accusations Fannie Mae had manipulated earnings; earnings from 2001 through 2003 were restated and those from 2004 and 2005 were each released more than a year late.

In 2006 federal regulators hit the firm with a whopping $400 million fine. Investigators claimed that its former executives willfully overstated earnings by more than $10 billion — and then tried to impede an investigation into the discrepancies — in order to reap performance bonuses. Chairman Stephen Ashley and CEO Daniel Mudd who'd been brought in to replace Franklin Raines in late 2004 were brought to task by the Senate Banking Committee in regard to accounting misdeeds.

Though the Justice Department eventually dropped criminal charges against the firm Fannie Mae agreed to major changes in its accounting internal controls and management practices. It additionally agreed to appoint an independent chief risk officer as well as an organizational review overseen by a compliance committee. Meanwhile the lender suspended its home construction loan program — worth about $10 billion — while it got its financial house in order.

Fannie suffered huge losses in 2007 and 2008 as a result of the subprime mortgage crisis which saw a tremendouse increase in loan defaults. The government stepped in loans and in 2008 seized both Fannie and Freddie. It also shuffled their management teams: Fannie CEO Mudd was replaced by Herbert Allison former TIAA-CREF. Allison was later tapped by the Obama administration to run the Treasury Department's financial recovery program. Former COO Michael Williams was named CEO in 2009.

The Federal Housing Finance Agency (FHFA) was created in 2008 to oversee both Fannie and Freddie as well as the 12 Federal Home Loan Banks. The FHFA was granted more authority than its predecessor agencies the Federal Housing Finance Board and the Office of Federal Housing Enterprise Oversight.

In an historic move the government in 2008 placed the two GSEs in conservatorship which is a legal status similar to bankruptcy rather than risk the possibility that the companies might fail. The government assumed a nearly 80% stake in the troubled companies in a $111 billion bailout (with a commitment of up to $400 billion). In 2011 the Obama administration proposed to restructure the housing market in a plan that will reduce the government's role and eventually eliminate the GSEs.

In 2009 the Making Home Affordable Program was introduced to provide assistance to borrowers in default through refinancings and other loan modifications.

EXECUTIVES

President Ceo And Director, Timothy J. (Tim) Mayopoulos, age 60, $600,000 total compensation
Evp And Head Multifamily, Jeffery R. Hayward, age 63, $475,000 total compensation
Evp And Cfo, David C. Benson, age 60, $600,000 total compensation
Svp Capital Markets - Lender Channel, Andrew Bon Salle, $500,000 total compensation
Evp General Counsel And Corporate Secretary, Brian P. Brooks, $500,000 total compensation
Evp And Chief Risk Officer, Kimberly H. Johnson
Svp Operations And Technology, Bruce Lee
Vice President, Stephanie Bahr
Vice President Operations Eastern Business Center, Cheryl Croxton
Vice President, Karen Jez
Vice President Information Technology, Beth Applegate
Vice President Of Internal Audit Technology, Don Farineau
Vice President Internal Audit, John Lengel
Vice President Investigations, Leslie Arrington
Vice President Single Family Mortgage Business, Katrina Jones
Vice President Single Family Business, Greg Awad
Senior Vice President And Chief Human Resources Officer, Elcio Barcelos
Chairman, Egbert L. J. Perry, age 63
Board Member, Kenneth Duberstein
Board Member, Ryan Zanin
Auditors: DELOITTE & TOUCHE LLP

LOCATIONS

HQ: Fannie Mae
  1100 15th Street, NW, Washington, DC 20005
Phone: 800 232-6643
Web: www.fanniemae.com

Selected Locations
Atlanta
Chicago
Dallas
Pasadena
Philadelphia
Washington DC

PRODUCTS/OPERATIONS

2018 Sales

	$ mil.	% of total
Interest income		
Mortgage loans	114,605	95
Trading securities	1,336	1
Federal funds	742	1
Available-for-sale securities	230	1
Others	136	
Interest expense	(96098)	
Non-interest income		
Fair value gains (losses) net	1,121	1
Fee and other income	979	1
Investment gains net	952	1
Total	**24,003**	**100**

2018 Sales

	% of total
Single-Family	85
Multifamily	15
Total	**100**

Selected Business Segments
Single-Family Credit Guaranty
Multifamily

COMPETITORS

Freddie Mac	VBA
Ginnie Mae	Wells Fargo

HISTORICAL FINANCIALS
Company Type: Public

Income Statement
FYE: December 31

	ASSETS ($ mil.)	NET INCOME ($ mil.)	INCOME AS % OF ASSETS	EMPLOYEES
12/18	3,418,318	15,959	0.5%	7,400
12/17	3,345,529	2,463	0.1%	7,200
12/16	3,287,968	12,313	0.4%	7,000
12/15	3,221,917	10,954	0.3%	7,300
12/14	3,248,176	14,208	0.4%	7,600
Annual Growth	1.3%	2.9%	—	(0.7%)

2018 Year-End Financials

Debt ratio: 99.23%
Return on equity: ***,***.**%
Cash ($ mil.): 25,557
Current ratio: —
Long-term debt ($ mil.): —

No. of shares (mil.): 1,158
Dividends
  Yield: —
  Payout: —
Market value ($ mil.): 1,228

	STOCK PRICE ($) FY Close	P/E High/Low	PER SHARE ($) Earnings	Dividends	Book Value
12/18	1.06	4 2	0.57	0.00	5.39
12/17	2.65	— —	(1.12)	0.00	(3.18)
12/16	3.90	449110	0.01	0.00	5.24
12/15	1.64	— —	(0.05)	0.00	3.48
12/14	2.06	— —	(0.19)	0.00	3.18
Annual Growth	(15.3%)	— —	—	—	14.1%

FARM CREDIT BANK OF TEXAS

The largest member of the federal Farm Credit System the Farm Credit Bank of Texas provides loans and financial services to about 20 lending cooperatives and financial institutions in Alabama Louisiana Mississippi New Mexico and Texas. These include agricultural credit associations which provide agricultural production loans agribusiness financing and rural mortgage financing; and federal land credit associations which offer real estate loans on farms ranches and other rural property. Farm Credit Bank of Texas is owned by the lending cooperatives it serves.

EXECUTIVES

Senior Vice President, Rusty Lampman
Vice President, Steve Donnell
Vice President And Controller, Vicki Rodriguez
Vice President Business Development, Jeremy Lightfoot
Vice President, Paul Rudd
Vice President Business Systems Unit Manager, Ed Benson
Vice President, Darren Cannon
Senior Vice President And Cco, John Logsdon
Vice President Regional Manager, Chris Amend
Vice President Lending, Boyd J Chambers
Vice President Collateral Risk Management, Brad Swinney
Vice President, Amy Pala
Vice President, Ronnie Sellers
Vp Of Compliance, Thomas Ringler
Vice President, Jason Gandy
Vice President, Mike Tippit
Board Of Directors, Buddy Cortese
Board Member, Larry Fairchild
Auditors: PRICEWATERHOUSECOOPERS LLP AU

LOCATIONS

HQ: FARM CREDIT BANK OF TEXAS
  4801 PLAZA ON THE LK # 1200, AUSTIN, TX 787461081
Phone: 512 465-0400
Web: WWW.FARMCREDITBANK.COM

HISTORICAL FINANCIALS
Company Type: Private

Income Statement
FYE: December 31

	ASSETS ($ mil.)	NET INCOME ($ mil.)	INCOME AS % OF ASSETS	EMPLOYEES
12/16	21,222	192	0.9%	200
12/13	16,212	179	1.1%	—
/ 0	0	—	—	
Annual Growth	—	—	—	—

FARM CREDIT SERVICES OF AMERICA

EXECUTIVES

Pres-Ceo, Doug Stark
Exec V Pres*, Neil Olsen
Sr V Pres-Cfo*, Eugene College
Sr V Pres*, Michelle Mapes
Sr V Pres*, David Martin
Turner Youth Initiative Direct, Twila Phillips
Engineer, Dave Cook
Senior Vice President Agribusi, Marshall Hansen
Auditors: PRICEWATERHOUSECOOPERS LLP M

LOCATIONS

HQ: FARM CREDIT SERVICES OF AMERICA
5015 S 118TH ST, OMAHA, NE 681372210
Phone: 800 884-3276
Web: WWW.FCSAMERICA.COM

HISTORICAL FINANCIALS

Company Type: Private

Income Statement

FYE: December 31

	ASSETS ($ mil.)	NET INCOME ($ mil.)	INCOME AS % OF ASSETS	EMPLOYEES
12/15	24,772	514	2.1%	10,000
12/04	8,475	294	3.5%	—
12/03	7,633	114	1.5%	—
12/02	0	132	—	—
Annual Growth	—	11.0%	—	—

FARM CREDIT WEST

EXECUTIVES

Ceo-Pres, Mark D Littlefield
Sr V Pres, Chris N Brumfield
Exec V Pres, John C Boyes
Exe V Pres, William M Noland
Cfo, Chris Doherty
Exec V Pres-Fiscal ADM, Ernest M Hodges
Prin, K E Graff
Vice-President, Michael Moore
Loan Officer, Danielle Vietti
Information Technology Special, David Dynes
Senior Vice President Chief, Denise Warkomski
Auditors: PRICEWATERHOUSECOOPERS LLP SA

LOCATIONS

HQ: FARM CREDIT WEST
3755 ATHERTON RD, ROCKLIN, CA 957653701
Phone: 916 724-4800
Web: WWW.FARMCREDITWEST.COM

Farmers & Merchants Bancorp (Lodi, CA)

EXECUTIVES

Chb-pres-ceo, Kent A Steinwert
Vice President, Chris Winek
Vice President And Chief Appraiser, Jon Schrader
Vice President, Pam Mcglynn
Vice President Retail Credit Sales Manager, Gary Spears
Assistant Vice President Retail Administration, Jackie Phillips
Vice President Commercial Loan Officer, Claire Forsythe
Vice President Relationship Manager, Corinne Santos
Vice President Treasury Relationship Manager, Mike Caselli
Vice President Director Of Treasury Operations, Patty Ducato
Vice President Treasury Management Specialist LI, Patricia Preston
Senior Vice President, Carol Murray
Assistant Vice President Operations Supervisor, Carrie Henshaw
Vice President Commercial Account Officer, Jesse Pataria
Auditors: Moss Adams LLP

LOCATIONS

HQ: Farmers & Merchants Bancorp (Lodi, CA)
111 W. Pine Street, Lodi, CA 95240
Phone: 209 367-2300
Web: www.fmbonline.com

HISTORICAL FINANCIALS

Company Type: Public

Income Statement

FYE: December 31

	ASSETS ($ mil.)	NET INCOME ($ mil.)	INCOME AS % OF ASSETS	EMPLOYEES
12/18	3,434	45	1.3%	376
12/17	3,075	28	0.9%	330
12/16	2,922	29	1.0%	339
12/15	2,615	27	1.0%	316
12/14	2,360	25	1.1%	310
Annual Growth	9.8%	15.7%	—	4.9%

2018 Year-End Financials

Debt ratio: 0.30%
Return on equity: 14.91%
Cash ($ mil.): 145
Current ratio: —
Long-term debt ($ mil.): —

No. of shares (mil.): 0
Dividends
  Yield: 1.9%
  Payout: 30.9%
Market value ($ mil.): 549

Farmers & Merchants Bank of Long Beach (CA)

Auditors: KPMG LLP

LOCATIONS

HQ: Farmers & Merchants Bank of Long Beach (CA)
302 Pine Avenue, Long Beach, CA 90802
Phone: 562 437-0011
Web: www.fmb.com

HISTORICAL FINANCIALS

Company Type: Public

Income Statement

FYE: December 31

	ASSETS ($ mil.)	NET INCOME ($ mil.)	INCOME AS % OF ASSETS	EMPLOYEES
12/18	7,308	85	1.2%	—
12/17	6,991	64	0.9%	747
12/16	6,729	71	1.1%	—
12/15	6,153	64	1.1%	—
12/14	5,581	62	1.1%	—
Annual Growth	7.0%	8.2%	—	—

2018 Year-End Financials

Debt ratio: —
Return on equity: 8.62%
Cash ($ mil.): 87
Current ratio: —
Long-term debt ($ mil.): —

No. of shares (mil.): 0
Dividends
  Yield: 1.5%
  Payout: 18.5%
Market value ($ mil.): 1,008

	STOCK PRICE ($) FY Close	P/E High/Low	PER SHARE ($) Earnings	Dividends	Book Value
12/18	7,700.00 7,850.67	14 12	654.07	121.00	
12/17	7,860.00 7,325.55	16 14	494.65	119.00	
12/16	6,800.00 6,952.78	13 11	546.16	119.00	
12/15	6,240.00 6,532.83	13 12	496.06	119.00	
12/14	6,060.00 6,160.34	13 11	476.67	114.00	
Annual Growth	6.2%	—	8.2%	1.5%	6.2%

The following blocks belong to FARM CREDIT SERVICES OF AMERICA (top center and top right):

HISTORICAL FINANCIALS

Company Type: Private

Income Statement

FYE: December 31

	ASSETS ($ mil.)	NET INCOME ($ mil.)	INCOME AS % OF ASSETS	EMPLOYEES
12/12	6,668	151	2.3%	165
12/11	6,282	176	2.8%	—
12/10	6,129	0		—
Annual Growth	4.3%	—	—	—

	STOCK PRICE ($) FY Close	P/E High/Low	PER SHARE ($) Earnings	Dividends	Book Value
12/18	700.00	13 11	56.82	13.90	397.10
12/17	676.00	20 17	35.03	13.55	368.90
12/16	640.00	17 13	37.44	13.10	346.80
12/15	540.00	17 13	34.82	12.90	318.46
12/14	463.00	14 13	32.64	12.70	297.39
Annual Growth	10.9%	—	14.9%	2.3%	7.5%

Farmers National Banc Corp. (Canfield,OH)

Farmers National Banc is willing to help even nonfarmers grow their seed income into thriving bounties of wealth. The bank provides commercial and personal banking from nearly 20 branches in Ohio. Founded in 1887 Farmers National Banc offers checking and savings accounts credit cards and loans and mortgages. Farmers' lending portfolio is composed of real estate mortgages consumer loans and commercial loans. The company also includes Farmers National Insurance and Farmers Trust Company a non-depository trust bank that offers wealth management and trust services.

Geographic Reach
Farmers National Banc operates 19 branches located throughout Mahoning Trumbull Columbiana Stark and Cuyahoga Counties. Farmers Trust Company operates two offices located in Boardman and Howland Ohio.

Financial Performance
The company's revenues have ranged from $40 million to $60 million in the past decade. In 2013 overall sales fell 1% to $54 million; the slight dip was due to lessened interest income on loans and taxable securities. (Financial institutions make their money on interest income from loans and non-interest income from fees.) Its non-interest income experienced growth from service charges insurance agency commissions and consulting fees for retirement planning.

Profits decreased by 22% to $8 million in 2013 due to increase in a provision for loan losses and non-interest expenses such as salary and employee benefits.

Mergers and Acquisitions
In 2013 the bank added retirement planning services to their portfolio with the acquisition of Cleveland-based National Associates Inc. for $4.4 million. The acquisition was part of its plan to boost noninterest income and complement its existing retirement services.

EXECUTIVES

Vice President, Jon Schmied
Vice President Retail Operations Manager, Jim Swift
Vice President, David Simko
Assistant Vice President, Anita Jarvis
Vice President Commercial Lending Relationship Manager, Darrell Smucker
Senior Vice President Commercial Lending Team Leader, Thomas Stocksdale
Vp Commercial Lending Relationship Manager, David Benavides
Assistant Vice President Branch Manager Downtown Massillon, Katherine Shultz
Senior Vice President, Michael Oberhaus
Board Member, Anne Crawford
Board Member, Ralph Macali
Board Member, David Paull
Board Member, Gregory Bestic
Vice Chairman Of The Board, James Smail
Board Member, Terry Moore
Board Member, Edward Muransky
Auditors: CliftonLarsonAllen, LLP

LOCATIONS

HQ: Farmers National Banc Corp. (Canfield,OH)
20 South Broad Street, Canfield, OH 44406
Phone: 330 533-3341
Web: www.farmersbankgroup.com

PRODUCTS/OPERATIONS

Selected Products

Personal
Certificate of DepositChecking AccountsChildren's AccountsConsumer LoansHome Equity Loans & LinesMortgage LoansOnline BankingPersonal Credit CardPersonal Debit CardPhone BankingRetirementSavings Accounts
Business
Business Credit CardBusiness Debit CardBusiness DepositsBusiness LoansCash ManagementRemote Deposit Capture
Wealth Management and Insurance
Farmers Trust CompanyFarmers National InvestmentsFarmers National Insurance
On-line banking

COMPETITORS

CSB Bancorp	JPMorgan Chase
Central Federal	Killbuck Bancshares
Consumers Bancorp	National Bancshares
Cortland Bancorp	Ohio Legacy
FFD Financial	Tri-State 1st Banc
Fifth Third	United Community
First Financial	Financial
Bancorp	Wayne Savings
First Niles Financial	Bancshares
Home Loan Financial	

HISTORICAL FINANCIALS

Company Type: Public

Income Statement   FYE: December 31

	ASSETS ($ mil.)	NET INCOME ($ mil.)	INCOME AS % OF ASSETS	EMPLOYEES
12/18	2,328	32	1.4%	453
12/17	2,159	22	1.1%	445
12/16	1,966	20	1.0%	441
12/15	1,869	8	0.4%	432
12/14	1,136	8	0.8%	327
Annual Growth	19.6%	38.1%	—	8.5%

2018 Year-End Financials

Debt ratio: 0.26%	No. of shares (mil.): 27
Return on equity: 12.91%	Dividends
Cash ($ mil.): 57	Yield: 2.3%
Current ratio: —	Payout: 28.8%
Long-term debt ($ mil.): —	Market value ($ mil.): 354

	STOCK PRICE ($) FY Close	P/E High/Low		PER SHARE ($) Earnings	Dividends	Book Value
12/18	12.74	14	10	1.16	0.30	9.44
12/17	14.75	19	15	0.82	0.22	8.79
12/16	14.20	20	11	0.76	0.16	7.88
12/15	8.60	24	20	0.36	0.12	7.35
12/14	8.35	18	14	0.48	0.12	6.71
Annual Growth	11.1%	—	—	24.7%	25.7%	8.9%

Fastenal Co.

Fastenal makes for a snug fit. The industrial and fastener distributor sells products in more than nine major product lines including threaded fasteners (such as screws nuts and bolts) which represent about 30% of overall sales. Other sales come from fluid-transfer parts for hydraulic and pneumatic power; janitorial electrical and welding supplies; material handling items; metal-cutting tool blades; and safety supplies. Founded in 1967 as a

---

fastener shop Fastenal now operates more than 3200 branches and on-site locations in all 50 US states and in Canada Mexico Asia Africa and Europe. Its customers include construction manufacturing and other industrial professionals

Operations
Fastenal's fasteners product line primarily sold under the Fastenal product name accounts for about 35% of the company?s net sales. Of this threaded fasteners represent approximately 85% of total fastener sales. The rest of its revenue comes from non-fastener product lines. Most significantly safety supplies and tools account for more than 15% and 10% respectively of total net sales. Other product lines include janitorial supplies hydraulics and pneumatics material handling cutting tools electrical supplies and welding supplies. Products manufactured by other companies account for more than 95% of Fastenal's total sales. The remainder of sales come from items custommade or modified by Fastenal. The company's FAST Solutions vending machines consists of about two dozen different vending devices with over 96000 of vending devices in the field.

Geographic Reach
Fastenal is headquartered in Winona Minnesota. While it sells products in more than 25 countries the company rings more than 85% of its sales in the US. Canada and Mexico combined are its second-largest market collectively accounting for more than 10% of sales. Fastenal has about 15 distribution centers roughly a dozen of which are in the US. It also has two distribution centers in Canada and one in Mexico.

Sales and Marketing
Fastenal promotes its products using in-store signage catalogs events email radio and online marketing and direct mailing (including promotional flyers). Sponsorship activities include NASCAR Fastenal Racing through its partnership with Roush Fenway Racing.Most of Fastenal's customers operate in the manufacturing and non-residential construction markets. Other major customers include farmers truckers railroads oil exploration production and refinement companies mining companies federal state and local governmental entities schools and select retail trades. The company boasts about 256000 active customer accounts.

Financial Performance
Fastenal has enjoyed robust results in recent years resulting from growth initiatives and strength in the industrial economy. Its annual revenues have risen more than 33% since 2014.

Revenue increased to $4.9 billion in 2018 an approximately 13% increase from the year prior. The increase was driven by higher product prices and higher unit sales resulting from stronger demand and growth of the company's industrial vending devices.

Net income was $751.9 million in fiscal year 2018 an increase from $578.6 million in fiscal year 2017. Selling general and administrative expenses grew 9% in fiscal 2018 to $1.4 billion.

Cash provided by operating activities was $674.2 million in fiscal 2018 while investing activities used $173.9 million. Financing activities used another $446.5 million.

Strategy
Fastenal's growth initiatives have involved getting closer in proximity to its customers to better understand their needs and provide high quality service.

To achieve this end the company has grown its number of onsite locations industrial vending locations managed inventory restocking programs and digital solutions. Sales through vending devices have been especially strong in recent years growing by more than 20% in 2018 over the previous year. Fastenal is also investing in end market initiatives such as its Customer Service Project which expands inventory placement at branches to enhance same-day capabilities.

Another growth spot for the company is its international operations. Fastenal is focused on expanding its foreign customer base much of which is the foreign operations of US-based companies.

While branch openings used to be a growth driver the company has been slowing down store openings in recent years in favor of adding more sales personnel to boost revenues. As part of the strategy Fastenal saw a net decline in its total branch count in the past three years.

HISTORY

Peace Corps veteran Robert Kierlin led four friends and Winona Cotter High School classmates in founding Fastenal in 1967 as a distributor of threaded fasteners. (Kierlin's inspiration was customers' inquiries at his father's auto parts store.) The company and its lone store lost money its first two years but it was able to open another store by 1970. Fastenal then changed its retail focus from regular consumers to contractors and professionals.

The company expanded locating stores on the outskirts of small and medium-sized cities where real estate and operating costs are lower. By 1987 it had 58 stores. Fastenal went public that year using some 40% of the IPO proceeds to establish the Hiawatha Education Foundation to support private high school education especially the founders' financially troubled alma mater.

EXECUTIVES

Vp Manufacturing, Tim Borkowski
Sevp Human Resources, Reyne K. Wisecup, age 57, $327,500 total compensation
President And Ceo, Daniel L. (Dan) Florness, age 56, $577,500 total compensation
Sevp Operations, Nicholas J. (Nick) Lundquist, age 62, $322,917 total compensation
Sevp Sales, Leland J. (Lee) Hein, age 59, $439,167 total compensation
Evp Manufacturing, James C. (Cory) Jansen, age 49, $220,829 total compensation
Evp Fast Solutions, Gary A. Polipnick, age 57, $300,000 total compensation
Evp Information Technology, John L. Soderberg, age 49
Evp E-business, Terry M. Owen, $430,000 total compensation
Evp Sales, Charles S. Miller
Controller Chief Accounting Officer And Treasurer, Sheryl A. Lisowski, age 53, $250,000 total compensation
Evp National Accounts Sales, William J. Drazkowski, age 48
Evp And Cfo, Holden Lewis, age 50, $120,002 total compensation
Evp Information Technology, John L. Soderburg, age 48
Evp International Sales, Jeffery M. Watts, age 47, $207,596 total compensation
Vice President Director Purchasing, Mike Thompson
Vice President Of Technical Services, Christine Halvorson
Vice President Human Resources, Bonnie Zeinert
Vice President Product Development, Mike Rusk
Vice President Of Se Region, Steve Roembke
Vice President Information Technology Infrastructure And Security, Craig Weatherhead
Vice President Global Accounts, David Donahue
Vice President Marketing, Brooke Mlsna
Executive Vice President Internal Operations, Corey Jansen
National Accounts Manager, Chad Frederick

National Accounts Manager, Greg Turner
Senior Vice President Human Re, John Barrera
Vice President Finance, Tony Banks
Assistant Vice President Vendor Relations, Cody Webb
Vice President Sales, Amanda Tan
Vice President, Rodney Hill
Regional Vice President Western Canada, Greg Mees
National Accounts Manager, Patrick Logan
National Accounts Manager, Jim Besack
National Account Manager, Nicole Danner
National Accounts Manager, Devin Stephens
National Accounts Manager, Carl Bruhn
Regional Vice President, Tim Rooney
Regional Vice President, Bill Reichenbacher
Regional Vice President, Mark Wellman
Regional Vice President, Ron Kitcher
Executive Vice President National Accounts Sales, Bill Drazkowski
Vice President Of Transportation And Safety, Chris Duffenbach
Fastco Vice President, Huang Zhi
Chairman, Willard D. (Will) Oberton, age 61
Board Member, Daniel Johnson
Auditors: KPMG LLP

LOCATIONS

HQ: Fastenal Co.
2001 Theurer Boulevard, Winona, MN 55987-1500
Phone: 507 454-5374 **Fax:** 507 453-8049
Web: www.fastenal.com

2016 stores

	No.of stores
United States	2,194
Canada	198
Mexico	52
Puerto Rico and Dominican Republic	8
Central and south America	8
Asia	10
Southeast Asia	7
Europe	24
Africa	2
Total	**2,503**

2016 sales

	$ mil.	% of total
United States	3,493	88
Canada	228	6
Other foreign countries	239	6
Total	**3,962**	**100**

PRODUCTS/OPERATIONS

Selected Brands Products and Services

Blackstone (welding supplies and cutting tools)
Clean Choice (janitorial supplies)
Dynaflo (hydraulics and pneumatics)
EquipRite (material handling janitorial supplies tools and cutting tools)
Fastenal (fasteners tools hydraulics and pneumatics safety supplies and metals)
FMT (tools and cutting tools)
FNL G9 (fasteners)
Holo-Krome (fasteners)
PowerPhase (electrical supplies and fasteners)
Profitter (hydraulics and pneumatics)
Rock River (fasteners and tools)
Tritan (cutting tools)
Threaded FastenersBoltsNutsScrewsStudsRelated washers Miscellaneous supplies and hardwarePins and machinery keysConcrete anchorsMetal framing systemsWire ropeStrut RivetsRelated accessories

COMPETITORS

Ace Hardware
Align Aerospace
Applied Industrial Technologies
Do it Best
HD Supply
Menard
Noland
Park-Ohio Holdings
PennEngineering
Production Tool Supply
Snap-on
Home Depot
Lawson Products
Lowe's
MSC Industrial Direct
True Value
W.W. Grainger
WinWholesale

HISTORICAL FINANCIALS
Company Type: Public

Income Statement				FYE: December 31
	REVENUE ($ mil.)	NET INCOME ($ mil.)	NET PROFIT MARGIN	EMPLOYEES
12/19	5,333	790	14.8%	21,948
12/18	4,965	751	15.1%	21,644
12/17	4,390	578	13.2%	20,565
12/16	3,962	499	12.6%	19,624
12/15	3,869	516	13.3%	20,746
Annual Growth	8.4%	11.2%	—	1.4%

2019 Year-End Financials

Debt ratio: 9.08%
Return on equity: 31.84%
Cash ($ mil.): 174
Current ratio: 4.51
Long-term debt ($ mil.): 342
No. of shares (mil.): 574
Dividends
  Yield: 2.3%
  Payout: 63.7%
Market value ($ mil.): 21,214

	STOCK PRICE ($) FY Close	P/E High/Low	PER SHARE ($) Earnings	Dividends	Book Value
12/19	36.95	52 21	1.38	0.87	4.64
12/18	52.29	46 36	1.31	1.54	4.03
12/17	54.69	55 40	1.01	0.64	3.65
12/16	46.98	58 42	0.87	0.60	3.34
12/15	40.82	54 40	0.89	1.12	3.11
Annual Growth	(2.5%)	— —	11.7%	(6.1%)	10.5%

FB Financial Corp

Auditors: Crowe LLP

LOCATIONS

HQ: FB Financial Corp
211 Commerce Street, Suite 300, Nashville, TN 37201
Phone: 615 564-1212
Web: www.firstbankonline.com

HISTORICAL FINANCIALS
Company Type: Public

Income Statement				FYE: December 31
	ASSETS ($ mil.)	NET INCOME ($ mil.)	INCOME AS % OF ASSETS	EMPLOYEES
12/18	5,136	80	1.6%	1,356
12/17	4,727	52	1.1%	1,386
12/16	3,276	40	1.2%	1,108
12/15	2,899	47	1.7%	1,038
12/14	2,428	32	1.3%	—
Annual Growth	20.6%	25.4%	—	—

2018 Year-End Financials

Debt ratio: 4.43%
Return on equity: 12.65%
Cash ($ mil.): 93
Current ratio: —
Long-term debt ($ mil.): —
No. of shares (mil.): 30
Dividends
  Yield: 0.5%
  Payout: 7.8%
Market value ($ mil.): 1,076

	STOCK PRICE ($)	P/E	PER SHARE ($)		
	FY Close	High/Low	Earnings	Dividends	Book Value
12/18	35.02	17 13	2.55	0.20	21.87
12/17	41.99	23 13	1.86	0.00	19.54
12/16	25.95	12 9	2.10	4.03	13.71
Annual Growth	7.8%	— —	5.0%	(52.8%)	12.4%

FBL Financial Group Inc

Insurance holding company FBL Financial Group (FBL) is the parent of Farm Bureau Life Insurance Company. Through its subsidiary the firm sells life insurance annuities and investment products to farmers ranchers and agricultural businesses. Farm Bureau Life sells insurance and annuities through an exclusive network of about 2000 agents across some 15 states in the Midwest and West. (In Colorado it operates as Greenfields Life Insurance.) The company markets its products through an affiliation with the American Farm Bureau Federation. FBL also manages for a fee two Farm Bureau-affiliated property/casualty insurance companies. The Iowa Farm Bureau Federation owns close to 60% of the company.

Operations

FBL divides its business into two segments annuity and life insurance. Traditional and universal life insurance products sold primarily in Iowa Kansas and Oklahoma account for about 60% of sales. Annuities including fixed rate and index are also big in Iowa and Kansas and account for about 30% of revenue.

The two Farm Bureau-affiliated property/casualty insurers that FBL manages are Farm Bureau Property & Casualty and Western Agricultural Insurance. The two affiliates underwrite auto crop and other property/casualty policies for individuals and groups under FBL's corporate and other segment which accounts for about 10% of revenue.

Geographic Reach

FBL offers its services in 15 western and midwestern states. Iowa Kansas Oklahoma and Wyoming are key markets.

Financial Performance

After a few rocky years FBL has been back on track the last two years. In 2013 it reported a 5% increase in revenue from $656 million to $691 million as both annuity and life segments reported increases in the volume of business. Net income has been on a steady rise and increased 36% in 2013 from $80 million to $109 million due to the improved revenue and increased equity income. Cash from operations however has been declining for years and continued its trend with a $24 million drop to $182 million due to cash used for paying out and administering claims.

Strategy

Strategically FBL expands its penetration in both the life and property/casualty markets by encouraging existing policyholders to purchase other insurance products through the agents they already know. Its cross-selling technique has led the industry as a whole. Additionally FBL depends on the talent of the agents it engages and its overall ability to provide products that meet changing needs as well as superior customer service and market knowledge. It continually invests in training and supporting existing agents and recruiting new ones. FBL also launches new products like index annuities in 2012 and takes steps like decreasing commissions for some products that aren't profitable during this time of low interest rates.

EXECUTIVES

Ceo, James P. (Jim) Brannen, age 57, $700,000 total compensation
Cfo And Treasurer, Donald J. (Don) Seibel, age 55, $360,706 total compensation
Chief Investment Officer, Charles T. Happel, age 57, $353,496 total compensation
Coo Life Companies, Raymond W. Wasilewski, age 60
Cio, Casey Decker
Coo Property Casualty Companies, Daniel D. Pitcher, age 57, $383,778 total compensation
Vice President Human Resources, Lori K Strottman
Vice President Audit Services, Tricia Erb
Vice President Sales, Christopher Shryack
Vice President Commercial Lines, Steve Wittmuss
Vice Chairman, Jerry L. Chicoine, age 76
Chairman, Craig D. Hill, age 63
Board Member, James Holte
Auditors: Ernst & Young LLP

LOCATIONS

HQ: FBL Financial Group Inc
5400 University Avenue, West Des Moines, IA 50266-5997
Phone: 515 225-5400
Web: www.fblfinancial.com

Selected Areas of Operation
Farm Bureau Life Insurance Company
  Multi-line (life and property/casualty)
  Arizona
  Iowa
  Kansas
  Minnesota
  Nebraska
  New Mexico
  South Dakota
  Utah
  Life only
  Idaho
  Montana
  North Dakota
  Oklahoma
  Wisconsin
  Wyoming
Farm Bureau Property & Casualty Insurance Company
and Western Agricultural Insurance Company
  Arizona
  Iowa
  Kansas
  Minnesota
  Nebraska
  New Mexico
  South Dakota
  Utah

PRODUCTS/OPERATIONS

2015 Sales

	$ mil.	% of total
Life Insurance	409	57
Annuity	212	29
Gains on derivatives	10	1
Losses on investments	(2.7)	-
Corporate & other	93	13
Total	**722**	**100**

Selected Subsidiaries
Insurance
  Farm Bureau Life Insurance Company
Noninsurance
  5400 Holdings L.L.C.
  FBL Assigned Benefit Company
  FBL Financial Group Capital Trust
  FBL Financial Group Capital Trust II
  FBL Financial Services Inc.
  FBL Investment Management Services Inc.
  FBL Leasing Services Inc.
  FBL Marketing Services L.L.C.

COMPETITORS

AIG
Allstate
American Equity Investment Life Holding Company
American Farmers & Ranchers Mutual Insurance Co.
COUNTRY Financial
Farm Family Holdings
Farmers & Merchants Investment
Great American Financial Resources
MetLife
Midland National Life
Nationwide
Prudential
State Farm
Thrivent Investment Management

HISTORICAL FINANCIALS
Company Type: Public

Income Statement
FYE: December 31

	ASSETS ($ mil.)	NET INCOME ($ mil.)	INCOME AS % OF ASSETS	EMPLOYEES
12/18	9,833	93	1.0%	1,647
12/17	10,066	194	1.9%	1,692
12/16	9,566	107	1.1%	1,644
12/15	9,132	113	1.2%	1,637
12/14	9,064	109	1.2%	1,628
Annual Growth	2.1%	(3.9%)	—	0.3%

2018 Year-End Financials

Debt ratio: 0.99%	No. of shares (mil.): 24
Return on equity: 7.29%	Dividends
Cash ($ mil.): 19	Yield: 5.0%
Current ratio: —	Payout: 89.0%
Long-term debt ($ mil.): —	Market value ($ mil.): 1,623

	STOCK PRICE ($)	P/E	PER SHARE ($)		
	FY Close	High/Low	Earnings	Dividends	Book Value
12/18	65.65	23 17	3.75	3.34	47.90
12/17	69.65	10 8	7.75	3.26	55.71
12/16	78.15	19 13	4.28	3.68	47.73
12/15	63.64	15 11	4.53	3.60	45.73
12/14	58.03	13 8	4.39	1.40	50.69
Annual Growth	3.1%	— —	(3.9%)	24.3%	(1.4%)

Federal Agricultural Mortgage Corp

Farmer Mac (Federal Agricultural Mortgage Corporation) is Fannie Mae and Freddie Mac's country cousin. Like its city-slicker kin it provides liquidity in its markets (agricultural real estate and rural housing mortgages) by buying loans from lenders and then securitizing the loans into Farmer Mac Guaranteed Securities. Farmer Mac buys both conventional loans and those guaranteed by the US Department of Agriculture. Farmer Mac was created by Congress in 1987 to establish a secondary market for agricultural mortgage and rural utilities loans. It is a stockholder-owned publicly-traded corporation based in Washington DC with an underwriting office in Iowa.

Operations

Farmer Mac operates four segments: Farm & Ranch which accounted for 39% of revenue during 2015 purchases mortgage loans secured by first liens on agricultural real estate including part-time farms and rural housing; Institutional Credit (28% of revenue) which buys or guarantees general lender obligations secured by eligible pools of loans; the USDA Guarantees segment (18%) which buys USDA-backed agricultural rural development business and industry and community facilities loans; and Rural Utilities (10%) which buys mortgages tied to eligible rural utilities loans. The organization generates more than 90% of its revenue from interest income stemming from a roughly even mix of loans and backed loan securities. About 47% of its revenue came from interest on Farmer Mac Guaranteed or USDA securities during 2015 while another 41% came from interest on loans. The rest came from interest on other investments (5% of revenue) guarantee and commitment fees (5%) and gains on financial derivatives and hedging activities (1%).

Geographic Reach
The Washington DC-based group serves the US from satellite operations in Ames Iowa; Boise Idaho; Canton Michigan; Fresno California; Johnston Iowa; and Scottsdale Arizona.

Sales and Marketing
Farmer Mac markets its services personally and directly to agricultural lenders by participating regularly in events such as state and national banking conferences. It also has alliances with the American Bankers Association and the Independent Community Bankers of Alliances and has a business relationship with the members of the Farm Credit System.

Financial Performance
Farmer Mac's annual revenues have risen more than 25% since 2011 thanks to a stronger agricultural economy as well as product developments which have driven customer and overall loan asset growth over the years. Its annual profits have also trended higher but have fluctuated more due to the volatility of the gains it's made from financial derivatives hedging activities and other trading securities.

The group's revenue climbed 4% to $284 million during 2015 mostly thanks to double-digit interest income growth as its loan assets grew 12% to $3.96 billion and as its Farm & Ranch loans USDA Securities and AgVantage securities balances grew as well. Farmer Mac's non-interest income shrank 39% as it collected $37.4 million less in trading securities gains as it did in 2014.

Revenue growth and a decline in interest expenses in 2015 drove Farmer Mac's net income up 43% to $68.7 million. The lender's operating cash levels jumped 19% to $184 million as its cash-based earnings rose and as working capital increased with changes in other assets.

Strategy
Farmer Mac seeks to improve the availability of long-term credit at stable interest rates to rural communities. To this end its primary strategy for managing interest rate risk is to fund asset purchases with liabilities that have similar duration and cash flow characteristics so that they will perform similarly as interest rates change.

EXECUTIVES

President And Ceo, Timothy L. (Tim) Buzby, age 50, $643,750 total compensation
Evp Cfo And Treasurer, R. Dale Lynch, age 52, $375,950 total compensation
Svp Agricultural Finance, J. Curtis Covington, age 63
Svp General Counsel And Secretary, Stephen P. Mullery, age 52, $340,930 total compensation
Vice President Corporate Affairs, Chris Bohanon
Senior Vice President Business Strategy And Financial Research, Brian Brinch
Chairman, Lowell L. Junkins, age 75
Vice Chairman, Myles J. Watts, age 68
Auditors: PricewaterhouseCoopers LLP

LOCATIONS

HQ: Federal Agricultural Mortgage Corp
1999 K Street, N.W., 4th Floor, Washington, DC 20006
Phone: 202 872-7700

PRODUCTS/OPERATIONS

2015 Sales

	$ mil.	% of total
Interest income		
Farmer Mac Guaranteed Securities and USDA Securities	134	47
Loans	117	41
Investments and cash equivalents	13	5
Noninterest income		
Guarantee and commitment fees	14	5
Gains on financial derivatives and hedging activities	2	1
Other	3	1
Total	**285**	**100**

2015 Sales

	% of total
Farm & Ranch	39
USDA Guarantees	28
Rural Utilities	18
Institutional Credit	10
Corporate	4
Reconciling Adjustments	1
Total	**100**

Selected Operations
Farm & Ranch (Farmer Mac I)
USDA Guarantees (Farmer Mac II)
Rural Utilities

COMPETITORS

AgFirst	Fannie Mae
AgStar	Farm Credit Services
AgriBank	of Mid-America
Bank of America	Freddie Mac
Citigroup	

HISTORICAL FINANCIALS
Company Type: Public

Income Statement
FYE: December 31

	ASSETS ($ mil.)	NET INCOME ($ mil.)	INCOME AS % OF ASSETS	EMPLOYEES
12/18	18,694	108	0.6%	103
12/17	17,792	84	0.5%	88
12/16	15,606	77	0.5%	81
12/15	15,540	68	0.4%	71
12/14	14,287	48	0.3%	71
Annual Growth	7.0%	22.4%	—	9.7%

2018 Year-End Financials
Debt ratio: 86.89%
Return on equity: 14.80%
Cash ($ mil.): 425
Current ratio: —
Long-term debt ($ mil.): —
No. of shares (mil.): 10
Dividends
Yield: 3.8%
Payout: 26.2%
Market value ($ mil.): 645

	STOCK PRICE ($) FY Close	P/E High/Low		PER SHARE ($) Earnings	Dividends	Book Value
12/18	60.44	11	6	8.83	2.32	70.54
12/17	78.24	12	8	6.60	1.44	66.69
12/16	57.27	10	4	5.97	1.04	61.05
12/15	31.57	8	5	4.19	0.64	51.79
12/14	30.34	10	8	3.37	0.56	49.90
Annual Growth	18.8%	—	—	27.2%	42.7%	9.0%

Federal Home Loan Bank New York

Federal Home Loan Bank of New York (FHLBNY) provides funds for residential mortgages and community development to more than 330 member banks savings and loans credit unions and life insurance companies in New York New Jersey Puerto Rico and the US Virgin Islands. One of a dozen Federal Home Loan Banks in the US it is cooperatively owned by its member institutions and supervised by the Federal Housing Finance Agency. FHLBNY like others in the system is privately capitalized; it receives no taxpayer funding. The bank instead raises funds mainly by issuing debt instruments in the capital markets.

Operations
FHLBNY is a secured lender that requires collateral for its advances which are typically used by members to underwrite residential mortgages or to invest in US Treasury and agency securities mortgage-backed securities and other real estate-related assets.

A large part of FHLBNY's business is in making collateralized loans or advances to members. It serves the public through its mortgage programs. Three members — Citibank (25%) Met Life (14%) and New York Community Bank (11%) — accounted for half of total advances.

Geographic Reach
Based in New York FHLBNY serves not only New York but New Jersey Puerto Rico and the US Virgin Islands.

Sales and Marketing
FHLBNY caters to more than 330 member banks credit unions life insurance companies and savings and loans.

Financial Performance
Revenue dropped by 14% to $801 million in fiscal 2013 from 2012's $934.9 million. FHLBNY attributes the decline to a decrease in interest income and other income. Net income also dropped some 16% in 2013 to $304.6 million vs. $360.7 million in 2012. It attributes net income decreases to declining revenue and rising other expenses. Operating cash flow decreased in fiscal 2013 to $525.6 million compared to 2012's $678.9 million.

Strategy
Credit unions are a possible area of growth for FHLBNY. The bank has identified more than 50 credit unions and banks that are not members but are eligible. To be under consideration an institution must have more than $50 million in assets ($100 million for banks) be an established wholesale lender maintain a high deposit-to-loan ratio and have management that has done business with an FHLB in the past.

Beginning in 2014 it's also funding — with the help of $35.5 million in subsidies — 48 affordable housing initiatives throughout New Jersey New York Puerto Rico the US Virgin Islands Florida Maryland and Pennsylvania. The effort involves the creation or rehabilitation of more than 3000 affordable housing units.

EXECUTIVES

Vice President Director Of Human Resources, Mildred Tse-Gonzalez
Senior Vice President Acting Chief Risk Officer, Melody Feinberg
Assistant Vice President, Claudia Kim
Vice President, Edward Samson
Vice President Director Of Trading, Philip Scott
Vice President Calling Office, Alfred O'connell
Vice President Director Of Sales, Tom Settino

Senior Vice President, Phil Scott
Vice President, Eugene Khesin
Senior Vice President, Jonathan West
Vp, Brian Finnegan
Vp Director Of, Muriel Brunken
Auditors: PricewaterhouseCoopers LLP

LOCATIONS

HQ: Federal Home Loan Bank New York
 101 Park Avenue, New York, NY 10178
Phone: 212 681-6000
Web: www.fhlbny.com

PRODUCTS/OPERATIONS

2013 Sales

	$ mil.	% of total
Interest		
Advances	444	55
Long-term securities	244	30
Mortgage loans held for portfolio	68	9
Available-for-sale securities	16	2
Other	14	2
Non-interest	13	2
Total	**801**	**100**

HISTORICAL FINANCIALS

Company Type: Public

Income Statement				FYE: December 31
	ASSETS ($ mil.)	NET INCOME ($ mil.)	INCOME AS % OF ASSETS	EMPLOYEES
12/18	144,381	560	0.4%	314
12/17	158,918	479	0.3%	308
12/16	143,606	401	0.3%	280
12/15	123,248	414	0.3%	273
12/14	132,825	314	0.2%	258
Annual Growth	2.1%	15.5%	—	5.0%

2018 Year-End Financials

Debt ratio: 58.29%	No. of shares (mil.): 60
Return on equity: 7.01%	Dividends
Cash ($ mil.): 85	Yield: —
Current ratio: —	Payout: 73.2%
Long-term debt ($ mil.): —	Market value ($ mil.): —

Federal Home Loan Bank Of Cincinnati

Auditors: PricewaterhouseCoopers LLP (PwC)

LOCATIONS

HQ: Federal Home Loan Bank Of Cincinnati
 600 Atrium Two, P.O Box 598, Cincinnati, OH 45201-0598
Phone: 513 852-7500
Web: www.fhlbcin.com

HISTORICAL FINANCIALS

Company Type: Public

Income Statement				FYE: December 31
	ASSETS ($ mil.)	NET INCOME ($ mil.)	INCOME AS % OF ASSETS	EMPLOYEES
12/18	99,202	339	0.3%	229
12/17	106,895	313	0.3%	226
12/16	104,635	268	0.3%	211
12/15	118,796	248	0.2%	203
12/14	106,640	244	0.2%	204
Annual Growth	(1.8%)	8.6%	—	2.9%

2018 Year-End Financials

Debt ratio: 93.35%	No. of shares (mil.): 43
Return on equity: 6.46%	Dividends
Cash ($ mil.): 10	Yield: —
Current ratio: —	Payout: 75.6%
Long-term debt ($ mil.): —	Market value ($ mil.): —

Federal Home Loan Bank Of Dallas

Auditors: PricewaterhouseCoopers LLP

LOCATIONS

HQ: Federal Home Loan Bank Of Dallas
 8500 Freeport Parkway South, Suite 600, Irving, TX 75063-2547
Phone: 214 441-8500
Web: www.fhlb.com

HISTORICAL FINANCIALS

Company Type: Public

Income Statement				FYE: December 31
	ASSETS ($ mil.)	NET INCOME ($ mil.)	INCOME AS % OF ASSETS	EMPLOYEES
12/18	72,773	198	0.3%	197
12/17	68,524	150	0.2%	205
12/16	58,212	79	0.1%	218
12/15	42,083	67	0.2%	207
12/14	38,045	48	0.1%	192
Annual Growth	17.6%	42.3%	—	0.6%

2018 Year-End Financials

Debt ratio: 43.88%	No. of shares (mil.): 25
Return on equity: 5.49%	Dividends
Cash ($ mil.): 2,535	Yield: —
Current ratio: —	Payout: 29.7%
Long-term debt ($ mil.): —	Market value ($ mil.): —

Federal Home Loan Bank Of Des Moines

Auditors: PricewaterhouseCoopers LLP

LOCATIONS

HQ: Federal Home Loan Bank Of Des Moines
 909 Locust Street, Des Moines, IA 50309
Phone: 515 412-2100
Web: www.fhlbdm.com

HISTORICAL FINANCIALS

Company Type: Public

Income Statement				FYE: December 31
	ASSETS ($ mil.)	NET INCOME ($ mil.)	INCOME AS % OF ASSETS	EMPLOYEES
12/18	146,515	460	0.3%	372
12/17	145,099	518	0.4%	351
12/16	180,605	649	0.4%	307
12/15	137,381	131	0.1%	279
12/14	95,523	121	0.1%	228
Annual Growth	11.3%	39.6%	—	13.0%

2018 Year-End Financials

Debt ratio: 93.27%	No. of shares (mil.): 54
Return on equity: 6.31%	Dividends
Cash ($ mil.): 120	Yield: —
Current ratio: —	Payout: 54.1%
Long-term debt ($ mil.): —	Market value ($ mil.): —

Federal Home Loan Bank Of San Francisco

The city by the bay is the home to the Federal Home Loan Bank of San Francisco one of Å a dozenÅ regional banks in the Federal Home Loan Bank System chartered by Congress inÅ 1932 to provide credit to residential mortgage lenders. TheÅ government-sponsored enterpriseÅ is privately owned by its members which include some 400 commercial banks credit unions industrial loan companies savings and loans insurance companies and housing associatesÅ headquartered in Arizona California and Nevada. The bank links members to worldwide capital markets which provide them with low-cost funding. Members then pass these advances along to their customers in the form of affordable home mortgage and economic development loans.

EXECUTIVES

Senior Vice President Chief Banking Officer, Stephen P Traynor
Vice President Model Validation, Michael Roginsky
Assistant Vice President Strategic Solutions And Architecture, Gary Wells
Assistant Vice President Portfolio And Derivatives Operations, Gwen Hill
Assistant Vice President Compliance, Jamie Leong
Vice President Solution Delivery, Michael Rich
Vice President Secondary Marketing, Michael Roth
Assistant Vice President Collateral Risk Management, Douglas Aguilar
Vice President Business Continuity Management And Corporate Services, Sarah Salk
Assistant Vice President, Aashish Khatri
Vice President And Treasurer, Tony Ruscitti
Auditors: PricewaterhouseCoopers LLP

LOCATIONS

HQ: Federal Home Loan Bank Of San Francisco
 333 Bush Street, Suite 2700, San Francisco, CA 94104
Phone: 415 616-1000
Web: www.fhlbsf.com

PRODUCTS/OPERATIONS

2013

	$ mil.	% of total
Interest income	1,086	97
Other income	5	3
Total	**1,091**	**100**

HISTORICAL FINANCIALS

Company Type: Public

Income Statement				FYE: December 31
	ASSETS ($ mil.)	NET INCOME ($ mil.)	INCOME AS % OF ASSETS	EMPLOYEES
12/18	109,326	360	0.3%	282
12/17	123,385	376	0.3%	287
12/16	91,941	712	0.8%	274
12/15	85,707	638	0.7%	263
12/14	75,807	205	0.3%	255
Annual Growth	9.6%	15.1%	—	2.5%

Federal Reserve Bank of Atlanta, Dist. No. 6

One of 12 regional banks in the Federal Reserve System the Federal Reserve Bank of Atlanta oversees Fed member banks and thrifts and their holding companies throughout the Southeast including Alabama Florida Georgia and parts of Louisiana Mississippi and Tennessee. It conducts examinations and investigations of member institutions distributes cash issues savings bonds and Treasury securities and assists the Fed in setting monetary policy such as interest rates. The bank also processes checks and acts as a clearinghouse for payments between banks. Fed Reserve Banks are independent arms within the government and return earnings (gleaned mostly from investments in government bonds) to the US Treasury.

Operations

Of the 12 regional banks in the Federal Reserve System only the Atlanta bank processes both paper and electronic checks for the system.

Financial Performance

In 2012 FRB Atlanta reported about $5.5 billion in total current income about 7% of the $81.6 billion in total income for the Federal Reserve System.

Company Background

The Federal Reserve Bank of Atlanta was established in 1914.

EXECUTIVES

Senior Vice President Supervision And Regulation, William B Estes
Assistant Vp System Retail Payments Office, Marie C. Gooding
Evp, Cheryl L. Venable
Evp, David E. Altig
President And Ceo, Raphael W. Bostic
Evp, Michael Johnson
Assistant Vice President Miami, Paul Graham
Vice President Marketing, Anita Brown
Vice President, Michael Chriszt
Assistant Vice President, Nancy Montoya
Vice President Information Technology, Vicki Kosydor
Assistant Vice President Corporate Information Technology Services, Torion Kent
Assistant Vice President Systems, Brad Joiner
Assistant Vp Macropolicy And Research Economist And Policy Adviser, Tao Zha
Vice President And General Auditor, Brian Bowling
Vice President Marketing, Rob Lilly
Vice President Of Technology Solution Services Organization, David Mcdermitt
Assistant Vice President, Gregory Fuller
Vice President, Brian Egan
Vice President Sales And Marketing, Ken Willis
Vice President Marketing, Hanh Dong
Assistant Vp Check Function Office, Charles Weems
Vice President Marketing, Lane Smith
Vice President Human Resources, Blake Lyons

Vice President In Charge, Daron Peschel
Senior Vice President System Retail Payments Office, Frederick M Herr
Vice President, Nell Campbell
Vice President Of Regional Research, John Robertson
Vice President, Suzanna Costello
Assistant Vice President, Allen Stanley
Assistant Vice President, Stephen Levy
Vice President Marketing, Christopher Oakley
Assistant Vice President, Jeffrey Schiele
Vice President Human Resources, Tammy Cummings
Vice President, John Kolb
Manufacturing Vice President, John Branigin
Vice President, Doug Tillett
Svp Cio Ciso, Russell Eubanks
Vice President, Kevin Jansen
Vice President, Sheryl Britsch
Assistant Vice President And Information Security Officer, Allen Sautter
Vice President Information Technology, Gregory Johnston
Assistant Vice President Information Technology, Shilpa Dutt
Senior Vice President And Chief Audit Executive, Azher Abbasi
Executive Vice President And Chief Information Security Officer, Devon Bryan
Assistant Vice President, Paula Armstrong
Assistant Vice President, Jim Fuchs
Cota L, Desiree Hatcher
Vice President Of Service Management Operations, Lina Gladstein
Vice President And Regional Economist, Rae Rosen
Assistant Vice President, Christine Johnson
Senior Vice President, Chris Haley
Assistant Vice President, Michael Coldwell
Assistant Vice President, Maria Massei-rosato
Assistant Vice President, Jonathan Atkinson
Vice President Financial Management, Yolanda Daniel
Deputy Chairman, Michael J. (Mike) Jackson
Chairman, Thomas A. (Tom) Fanning
Board Member, Lee Thomas
Auditors: KPMG LLP

LOCATIONS

HQ: Federal Reserve Bank of Atlanta, Dist. No. 6
  1000 Peachtree Street, N.E., Atlanta, GA 30309-4470
Phone: 404 498-8500
Web: www.frbatlanta.org

HISTORICAL FINANCIALS

Company Type: Public

Income Statement				FYE: December 31
	REVENUE ($ mil.)	NET INCOME ($ mil.)	NET PROFIT MARGIN	EMPLOYEES
12/17	6,971	48	0.7%	—
12/16	6,502	66	1.0%	—
12/15	6,562	(992)	—	—
12/14	6,861	156	2.3%	—
12/13	6,105	89	1.5%	—
Annual Growth	3.4%	(14.3%)	—	—

Federal Reserve Bank of New York, Dist. No. 2

The Federal Reserve Bank of New York is the largest in the Federal Reserve System to oversee US bank activities. It issues currency clears money transfers and lends to banks in its district. In addition to the duties it shares with 11 other regional Federal Reserve Banks the New York Fed trades US government securities to regulate the money supply intervenes on foreign exchange markets and stores monetary gold for foreign central banks and governments. The New York Fed's district is relatively small (made up of New York Puerto Rico the US Virgin Islands northern New Jersey and Fairfield County Connecticut) but the bank is the largest in the Federal Reserve System in assets and volume of transactions.

Operations

Secured in a vault 80 feet below street level in the New York Fed's Manhattan headquarters is billions of dollars worth of gold — some 25% to 30% of the world's official monetary gold reserves. The vault rests on Manhattan Island's bedrock considered to be one of the few foundations adequate enough to support the weight of the vault and its contents.

Financial Performance

The New York Fed's total revenue for 2015 surged by 37% compared to 2014. The growth was mainly due to increased investment returns from treasury securities.

EXECUTIVES

Vice President Central Bank And International Account Services, Betty Lau
Evp; Head Emerging Markets And International Affairs Group, Terrence J. Checki
First Vice President, Christine M. Cumming
Svp Building Support Real Estate And General Services And Service, Roseann Stichnoth
Executive Vice President Risk Group, Sandra C. (Sandy) Krieger
Evp And Head Research And Statistics Group, James J. McAndrews
Evp Markets Group, Brian P. Sack
Evp And General Auditor, Edward C. Smith
Evp Corporate, Edward F. Murphy
President And Ceo, William C. Dudley
Executive Vice President, William T. Christie
Executive Vice President, Susan W. Mink
Evp And Head Communications, Krishna Guha
Executive Vice President Markets Group, Simon M. Potter
Chief Of Staff And Vice President, James P. Bergin
Executive Vice President And Chief Risk Officer, Joshua Rosenberg
Senior Vp, Stephanie Heller
Senior Vice President Financial Institution Supervision Group, Caroline Frawley
Assistant Vice President Accounting, Robert Pofsky
Assistant Vice President Of Financial Services Gro, Christopher Armstrong
Senior Vp, Michael Recupero
Assistant Vice President, Rona Stein
Assistant Vice President Of Legal Group, Sean Omalley
Assistant Vice President, Sarah Adelson
Assistant Vice President Of Financial Institution Supervision Group, Brian Hefferle
Vice President, Dina Maher
Assistant Vice President, Louis Scenti
Assistant Vice President, Keith Pulsifer

Senior Executive Specialist Executive Vice
President, Marlene Williams
Vice President And Counsel In The Legal Group,
Michele Kalstein
Assistant Vice President, Thomas Reilly
Assistant Vice President Of Financial Institution
Supervision Group, Glen Reppy
Senior Vice President, Nancy Bercovici
Assistant Vice President, Patrick Coyne
Vice President Information Technology, Jeffrey C
Blye
Senior Vice President Human Resources, Elaine
Mauriello
Vice President, Jack Gutt
Assistant Vice President Of Legal Group, Brett
Phillips
Vice President, Beverly Hirtle
First Vice President, Jamie B Stewart
Assistant Vice President Macroeconomic,
Domenico Giannone
Senior Vice President, Chris McCurdy
Assistant Vice President, Matt Nemeth
Assistant Vice President, GERALD MCCRINK
Assistant Vice President, Suzanne Elio
Senior Vice President And Chief Information
Security Officer, Joeseph Leonard
Executive Vice President And Chief Technology
And Strategy Officer, James Lammers
Avp Technology Group Richmond, Nicholas
Baronian
Assistant Vice President Director Of Community
Development Analysis, Claire Kramer Mills
Chairman, Lee C. Bollinger
Chairman, Emily K. Rafferty
Auditors: KPMG LLP

LOCATIONS

HQ: Federal Reserve Bank of New York, Dist. No. 2
 33 Liberty Street, New York, NY 10045-0001
Phone: 212 720-5000
Web: www.newyorkfed.org

Selected Offices
Buffalo New York
East Rutherford New Jersey
New York City
Utica New York

HISTORICAL FINANCIALS

Company Type: Public

Income Statement

	REVENUE ($ mil.)	NET INCOME ($ mil.)	NET PROFIT MARGIN	EMPLOYEES
			FYE: December 31	
12/17	65,090	(503)	—	—
12/16	64,509	328	0.5%	—
12/15	68,534	(5,604)	—	—
12/14	68,824	2,398	3.5%	—
12/13	50,355	(1,397)	—	—
Annual Growth	6.6%	—	—	—

2017 Year-End Financials
Debt ratio: 21.21%
Return on equity: (-3.87%)
Cash ($ mil.): 2,459,689
Current ratio: 1.69
Long-term debt ($ mil.): 528,663
No. of shares (mil.): 197
Dividends
 Yield: —
 Payout: —
Market value ($ mil.): —

Federal Reserve Bank of Richmond, Dist. No. 5

One of 12 regional banks in the Federal Reserve System the Federal Reserve Bank of Richmond oversees the Fifth District's system member banks and bank holding companies in Virginia; Maryland; the Carolinas; Washington DC; and most of West Virginia from branches in Maryland North Carolina and Virginia. It conducts examinations and investigations of member institutions distributes money issues savings bonds and Treasury securities and assists the Federal Reserve System in setting monetary policy. The bank also processes checks and acts as a clearinghouse for payments between banks. Federal Reserve Banks return earnings (mostly from investments in government bonds) to the US Treasury.

Operations
The Richmond Fed employs economists scholars and research associates to conduct economic study regarding the Fifth District economy and also to support the Federal Reserve System's policymakers. It was organized in 1914 subsequent to the enactment of the Federal Reserve Act in 1913.

Geographic Reach
The organization has its headquarters in Virginia. It serves the Fifth Federal Reserve District which includes Maryland North Carolina South Carolina Virginia District of Columbia and portions of West Virginia.

Financial Performance
Revenues increased 9% from 2013 to 2014. The growth was do to increased interest income and additional government-sponsored enterprise mortgage-backed securities partially offset by non-interest losses.

EXECUTIVES

Assistant Vice President Public Affairs, Steve
Malone
Assistant Vice President, Daniel Elder
Interim President And Ceo, Mark L. Mullinix
Svp And Cto Currency Technology Office And
Cash Product Office, Roland Costa
Svp And Regional Executive Baltimore, David E.
(Dave) Beck
Svp Supervision Regulation And Credit, Jennifer J.
Burns
Svp And Cio, Janice E. Clatterbuck
Svp And Regional Executive Charlotte, Matthew A.
Martin
Evp And Director Of Research, Kartik Athreya
Vice President, James Hayes
Vice President Communications, Barbara Moss
Assistant Vice President, Hattie Barley
Vice President, Steven Bareford
Assistant Vp, James Lucas
Vice President, Stephen L Scott
Vice President Currency Technology Office,
Rebecca Goldberg
Vice President Of Corporate Support Services,
Bruce Grinnell
Assistant Vice President Of Information
Technology, Johnnie Moore
Assistant Vice President, Joyce Romito
Manager Vice President, Marsha Shuler
Vice President, Terry Wright
Assistant Vice President, Jason Schemmel
Vice President, Christopher Cook

Assistant Vice President, Cathy Howdyshell
Vice President Head Of Risk Specialist Division,
Carl Tannenbaum
Vice President, Sherri Thorne
Vice President Sales And Marketing, Kevin Beyer
Assistant Vice President Information Technology,
Keith Malatesta
Vice President Operations, Jack Mccolgan
Assistant Vice President, John Carter
Senior Vice President Procurement, Jeff Crow
Vice President, R Ahern
Vice President, Mattison W Harris
Vice President, Andreas L Hornstein
Vice President, Raymond E Owens
Senior Vice President And General Auditor, Mike
Stough
Vice President Credit Risk Management, Christy
Cleare
Assistant Vice President Information Security,
Bary Dalton
Assistant Vice President, Markus Summers
Vice President And General Manager, Michael
Serrato
Assistant Vice President Application Development
Services, Gina Linkenhoker
Assistant Vice President, Phil Watts
Vice President Senior Payments Advisor, Chad
Harper
Senior Vice President Enterprise Information
Security, Chris Tignor
Vice President Information Technology Change
Management, Steve Silverman
Assistant Vice President Talent Acquisition And
Contingent Workforce And Benefits And
Compensation, Jackie Draper
Vice President Business Banker, Ott Dennis
Vice President And Assistant General Auditor Frit
Core Audit Programs Projects, Johnson Gregory
Senior Vice President, Marchetti Page
Vice President Of Telecommunications,
Westerkamp Richard
Vice President And Assistant General Auditor Frit
Core Audit Programs Projects, Johnson Steven
Vice President Corporate Banking Group, Hamilton
Mark
Vice President Sales Support Product
Development, Reichert Megan
Chairman, Margaret G. Lewis
Deputy Chair, Kathy J. Warden
Auditors: KPMG LLP

LOCATIONS

HQ: Federal Reserve Bank of Richmond, Dist. No. 5
 Post Office Box 27622, Richmond, VA 23261
Phone: 804 697-8000
Web: www.richmondfed.org

PRODUCTS/OPERATIONS

2014 sales

	$ mil.	% of total
Interest Income		
Treasury securities net	3,622	53
Government-sponsored enterprise debt securities net	92	2
Federal agency and government-sponsored enterprise mortgage-backed securities net	2,950	44
Foreign currency denominated investments net	16	0
Central bank liquidity swaps	0	0
Non-interest loss		
System Open Market Account	(600)	0
Compensation received for service costs provided	15	0
Reimbursable services to government agencies	50	1
Other	3	0
Total	6,148	100

HISTORICAL FINANCIALS

Company Type: Public

Income Statement   FYE: December 31

	REVENUE ($ mil.)	NET INCOME ($ mil.)	NET PROFIT MARGIN	EMPLOYEES
12/17	7,217	165	2.3%	—
12/16	6,604	67	1.0%	—
12/15	5,989	(3,955)	—	—
12/14	6,148	1,202	19.6%	—
12/13	5,666	284	5.0%	—
Annual Growth	6.2%	(12.7%)	—	—

2017 Year-End Financials

Debt ratio: 36.12%
Return on equity: 1.87%
Cash ($ mil.): 255,934
Current ratio: 1.62
Long-term debt ($ mil.): 105,982

No. of shares (mil.): 135
Dividends
Yield: —
Payout: —
Market value ($ mil.): —

Federal Reserve Bank of San Francisco, Dist. No. 12

One of 12 regional banks in the Federal Reserve System the Federal Reserve Bank of San Francisco through four branch offices oversees hundreds of banks and thrifts in nine western states and American Samoa Guam and the Northern Mariana Islands - the largest of the 12 districts. It conducts examinations and investigations of member institutions distributes money issues savings bonds and Treasury securities and assists the Federal Reserve in setting monetary policy. The bank also processes checks and acts as a clearinghouse for payments between banks. Federal Reserve Banks are not-for-profit and return earnings (mostly from investments in government bonds) to the US Treasury.

Geographic Reach

The bank oversees the Twelfth Federal Reserve District which includes the nine western states of Alaska Arizona California Hawaii Idaho Nevada Oregon Utah and Washington and also the American Samoa Guam and the Commonwealth of the Northern Mariana Islands.

Branch offices reside in Los Angeles; Portland Oregon; Salt Lake City; and Seattle. It also has a cash processing center in Phoenix.

EXECUTIVES

Vice President, John Fernald
First Vp And Coo, Mark A. Gould
President And Ceo, John C. Williams
Svp, Teresa M. Curran
Svp Information And Technology And Cio, Gopa Kumar
Vice President Microeconomic And Macroeconomic Research, Sylvain Leduc
Group Vice President, Stanley Crisp
Group Vice President, Fred Furlong
Group Vice President, Reuven Glick
Group Vice President, Clifford Croxall
Vice President Examinations Group, Tracy Basinger
Group Vice President, Patrick Loncar
Vice President, Thomas Cunningham

Group Vice President, Mongkha Pavlick
Group Vice President, Frederick T Furlong
Vice President Microeconomic And Macroeconomic Research, Scar Jord
Vice President Research, Robert Valletta
Vice President, Dan Wilson
Executive Vice President, Elaine S Couture
Group Vice President, David Bohm
Chairman, Roy A. Vallee
Deputy Chairman, Alexander R. (Alex) Mehran
Auditors: KPMG LLP

LOCATIONS

HQ: Federal Reserve Bank of San Francisco, Dist. No. 12
101 Market Street, San Francisco, CA 94105
Phone: 415 974-2000
Web: www.frbsf.org

HISTORICAL FINANCIALS

Company Type: Public

Income Statement   FYE: December 31

	REVENUE ($ mil.)	NET INCOME ($ mil.)	NET PROFIT MARGIN	EMPLOYEES
12/17	14,660	116	0.8%	—
12/16	13,437	51	0.4%	—
12/15	12,696	(2,426)	—	—
12/14	11,704	470	4.0%	—
12/13	8,507	323	3.8%	—
Annual Growth	14.6%	(22.6%)	—	—

2017 Year-End Financials

Debt ratio: 34.32%
Return on equity: 1.93%
Cash ($ mil.): 558,019
Current ratio: 1.57
Long-term debt ($ mil.): 195,221

No. of shares (mil.): 92
Dividends
Yield: —
Payout: —
Market value ($ mil.): —

Federal Reserve System

Where do banks go when they need a loan? To the Federal Reserve System which sets the discount interest rate the base rate at which its member banks may borrow. Known as the Fed the system oversees a network of 12 Federal Reserve Banks located in major US cities; these in turn regulate banks in their districts and ensure they maintain adequate reserves. The Fed also clears money transfers issues currency and buys or sells government securities to regulate the money supply. Through its powerful New York bank the Fed conducts foreign currency transactions trades on the world market to support the US dollar's value and stores gold for foreign governments and international agencies.

Operations

By setting the discount rate and the federal funds rate (the rate at which banks borrow from each other) the Board influences the pace of lending and many believe the pace of the economy itself. In response to the economic downturn in 2008 the Fed aggressively cut the discount interest rate in an effort to jump-start the US economy.

Fed board members are appointed by the US president and confirmed by the Senate for one-time 14-year terms staggered at two-year intervals to prevent political stacking. Seven governors comprise the majority of the 12-person Federal Open

Market Committee which determines monetary policy. The five remaining members are reserve bank presidents who rotate in one-year terms with New York always holding a place. National member banks must own stock in their Federal Reserve Bank though it is optional for state-chartered banks.

A seven-member Board of Governors oversees the Fed's activities. The board was chaired by Alan Greenspan from the Reagan administration until 2006. As chairman under four different presidents Greenspan wielded more power than perhaps any Fed chief in history and securities markets rose and fell on his every word. Greenspan was replaced by former chairman of President George W. Bush's Council of Economic Advisers and Fed board member Ben Bernanke who himself was replaced by former Vice Chair of the Board of Governors Jenet L. Yellen on February 3 2014.

Geographic Reach

The company's banks are located in Boston New York Philadelphia Cleveland Richmond Atlanta Chicago St. Louis Minneapolis Kansas City Dallas and San Francisco.

Financial Performance

The Reserve Banks' income in 2015 was $114 billion. The total expenses for the entire Federal Reserve System for 2015 were $13 billion.

HISTORY

When New York's Knickerbocker Trust Company failed in 1907 it brought on a panic that was stemmed by J. P. Morgan who strong-armed his fellow bankers into supporting shaky New York banks. The incident showed the need for a central bank.

Morgan's actions sparked fears of his economic power and spurred congressional efforts to establish a central bank. After a six-year struggle between Eastern money interests and populist monetary reformers the 1913 Federal Reserve Act was passed. Twelve Federal Reserve districts were created but New York's economic might ensured it would be the most powerful.

New York bank head Benjamin Strong dominated the Fed in the 1920s countering the glut of European gold flooding the US in 1923 by selling securities from the Fed's portfolio. After he died in 1928 the Fed couldn't stabilize prices. Such difficulty along with low rates encouraging members to use Fed loans for stock speculation helped set the stage for 1929's crash.

During the Depression and WWII the Fed yielded to the demands of the Treasury to buy bonds. But after WWII it sought independence using Congress to help free it from Treasury demands. This effort was led by chairman William McChesney Martin with the assistance of New York bank president Alan Sproul (also a rival for the chairmanship). Martin diluted Sproul's influence by governing by consensus with the other bank leaders.

The Fed managed the economy successfully in the postwar boom but it was stymied by inflation in the late 1960s. In the early 1970s the New York bank also faced the collapse of the fixed currency exchange-rate system and the growth of currency trading. Its role as foreign currency trader became even more crucial as the dollar's value eroded amid rising oil prices and a slowing economy.

The US suffered from double-digit inflation in 1979 as President Jimmy Carter appointed New York Fed president Paul Volcker as chairman. Volcker believing that raising interest rates a few points would not suffice allowed the banks to raise their discount rates and increased bank reserve requirements to reduce the money supply. By the time inflation eased Ronald Reagan was president.

During the 1980s and 1990s US budget fights limited options for controlling the economy through spending decisions so the Fed's actions became more important. Its higher profile brought calls for more access to its decision-making processes. Alan Greenspan took over as chairman in 1987 after being designated by Reagan (and reappointed by presidents George H. W. Bush Bill Clinton and George W. Bush). He stepped down during the second Bush administration and was replaced by Ben Bernanke.

While the US economy seemed immune to the Asian currency crisis of 1997 and 1998 the Federal Reserve remained relatively quiescent. But when Russia defaulted on some of its bonds in 1998 leading to the near-collapse of hedge fund Long-Term Capital Management the New York Federal Reserve Bank brokered a bailout by the fund's lenders and investors.

This led in 1999 to new guidelines for banks' risk management. The next year the Fed faced up to the Internet age taking a look at e-banking supervision. After raising interest rates to stave off inflation during the go-go late 1990s the Fed cut rates an unprecedented 11 times in 2001 (to a 40-year low of 1.75%) to help spur the flagging postboom economy.

Rate changes and subsequent economic changes continued with a low of 1% in 2003. In all rates were adjusted a total of 18 times between 2002 and 2006.

In 2008 the US faced an economic crisis as severe as any seen since the Great Depression that claimed numerous victims including Bear Stearns (the Fed brokered and assisted its purchase by JP-Morgan Chase) and Lehman Brothers. Together with former Secretary of the Treasury Henry Paulson chairman Ben Bernanke pushed for the passage of a $700 billion rescue plan — the largest in history. Through the plan the government purchased toxic assets including troubled mortgages and distressed properties. As his predecessor did during the economic downturn earlier this decade Bernanke also aggressively cut the discount interest rate in an effort to jump-start the economy.

EXECUTIVES

President Federal Reserve Bank Of Dallas, Robert S. (Rob) Kaplan
President Federal Reserve Bank Of Atlanta, Dennis P. Lockhart
President Federal Reserve Bank Of Chicago, Charles L. (Charlie) Evans
President Federal Reserve Bank Of Richmond, Jeffrey M. (Jeff) Lacker
Chairman, Janet L. Yellen
President Federal Reserve Bank Of Boston, Eric S. Rosengren
President And Ceo Federal Reserve Bank Of St. Louis, James B. Bullard
President Federal Reserve Bank Of New York, William C. Dudley
President Federal Reserve Bank Of Minneapolis, Neel T. Kashkari
President Federal Reserve Bank Of Philadelphia, Patrick T. Harker
President Federal Reserve Bank Of Kansas City, Ester L. George
President Federal Reserve Bank Of San Francisco, John C. Williams
President Federal Reserve Bank Of Cleveland, Loretta J. Mester
Vice President, Paul Rimmereid
Vice President Treasury Services, Harvey Mitchell
Vice President, Patrick Defontnouvelle
Vice Chairman, Stanley Fischer
Secretary, Ann Misback
Auditors: KPMG LLP

LOCATIONS

HQ: Federal Reserve System
20th Street and Constitution Avenue N.W.,
Washington, DC 20551
Phone: 202 452-3245   **Fax:** 202 728-5886
Web: www.federalreserve.gov

Federal Reserve Banks
Atlanta
Boston
Chicago
Cleveland
Dallas
Kansas City Missouri
Minneapolis
New York
Philadelphia
Richmond Virginia
St. Louis
San Francisco

HISTORICAL FINANCIALS
Company Type: Public

Income Statement   FYE: December 31

	REVENUE ($ mil.)	NET INCOME ($ mil.)	NET PROFIT MARGIN	EMPLOYEES
12/17	116,764	133	0.1%	—
12/16	112,207	894	0.8%	—
12/15	113,468	(17,195)	—	—
12/14	114,299	4,363	3.8%	—
12/13	90,540	(492)	—	—
Annual Growth	6.6%	—	—	—

2017 Year-End Financials

Debt ratio: 35.30%	No. of shares (mil.): 627
Return on equity: 0.33%	Dividends
Cash ($ mil.): 4,368,266	Yield: —
Current ratio: 1.95	Payout: —
Long-term debt ($ mil.): 1,570,727	Market value ($ mil.): —

FEDERAL-MOGUL HOLDINGS LLC

Auditors: GRANT THORNTON LLP SOUTHFIELD

LOCATIONS

HQ: FEDERAL-MOGUL HOLDINGS LLC
27300 W 11 MILE RD # 101, SOUTHFIELD, MI 480346193
Phone: 248 354-7700
Web: WWW.FEDERALMOGUL.COM

HISTORICAL FINANCIALS
Company Type: Private

Income Statement   FYE: December 31

	REVENUE ($ mil.)	NET INCOME ($ mil.)	NET PROFIT MARGIN	EMPLOYEES
12/16	7,434	90	1.2%	53,700
12/15	7,419	(104)	—	—
12/14	7,317	(161)	—	—
Annual Growth	0.8%	—	—	—

FedEx Corp

Holding company FedEx Corporation operates through subsidiaries FedEx Express FedEx Ground and FedEx Freight among others. Its FedEx Express unit is the world's largest express transportation provider to more than 220 countries and territories from about 2100 FedEx Office shops. It maintains a fleet of 680-plus aircraft and over 180000 motor vehicles. To complement the express delivery business FedEx Ground provides small-package ground delivery in North America and less-than-truckload (LTL) carrier FedEx Freight hauls larger shipments. FedEx Office stores offer a variety of document-related and other business services and serve as retail hubs for other FedEx units. In addition its TNT Express subsidiary is an international express transportation and small-package ground delivery company. About 70% of revenue is generated in the US.

Operations
FedEx offers a broad portfolio of transportation e-commerce and business services through its subsidiaries which operate independently and are managed collaboratively under the FedEx brand.

FedEx Express generating about 55% of revenue is the world's largest express transportation company. Its business operations provide fast time-definite delivery of packages and freight to more than 220 countries and territories through an integrated global network.

FedEx Ground generates about 30% of revenue and provides small-package ground delivery services primarily in North America. This segment includes FedEx SmartPost a business-to-consumer package delivery business that uses the US Postal Service for final mile delivery.

FedEx Freight (more than 10%) offers LTL freight services throughout North America as well as Puerto Rico and the US Virgin Islands. (LTL carriers consolidate freight from multiple shippers into a single truckload.) This unit's offerings include FedEx Freight Priority and FedEx Freight Economy.

FedEx Services (2%) provides sales and marketing technology support and other back-office functions such as billing and collection and customer service for other FedEx divisions. This unit includes FedEx Office and Print Services (document and business services for FedEx Express and FedEx Ground shipping services). The remainder of sales comprises other operations including logistics and supply chain services brokerage and freight forwarding.

Geographic Reach
FedEx operates in or delivers goods to more than 220 countries and territories. Its primary sorting facility is located in Memphis TN and it has a second national hub in Indianapolis IN. FedEx Express operates additional US hubs in Texas New Jersey California North Carolina Illinois and Alaska. It also has major hubs in Canada France Germany China and Japan. The US accounts for roughly 70% of net sales annually.

Sales and Marketing
FedEx promotes its brands through television print digital advertising sponsorships and special events. It also serves customers in airports worldwide. The company's advertising and promotional expenses were $468 million in fiscal 2019 and $442 million in 2018.

Financial Performance
FedEx has achieved several consecutive years of unprecedented growth with revenue increasing 47% since fiscal 2015 (ended May 31).

Revenue in fiscal 2019 increased 6% to a record $69.7 billion compared with $65.5 billion in 2018.

The growth for 2019 was a result of increased volumes in all its transportation segments as well as higher fuel surcharges.

After a profit of $4.6 billion in 2018 net income in 2019 plummeted to $540 million. This is attributed primarily to significantly higher retirement plan expenses due to lower discount rates changes in actuarial estimates for rates of retirement disability and salary increases.

Cash at the end of 2019 was $2.3 billion a decrease of $946 million from the prior year. Cash from operations contributed $5.6 billion to the coffers while investing activities used $5.5 billion mainly for capital expenditures. Financing activities used another $1.0 billion for dividends to stockholders and the company's stock repurchase program.

Strategy

FedEx has several initiatives in place to grow its business and meet the booming demand for package deliveries via e-commerce channels. It is increasing ground capacity and modernizing its express hubs and is continuing to integrate its FedEx Express and European TNT Express operations.

To meet the growth of e-commerce FedEx continues to open new facilities and invest in automation technologies to further increase ground delivery capacity and is expanding specialized facilities to accommodate the fast-growing oversized package delivery business. In 2019 the company built two major hubs in Pennsylvania and Connecticut to handle some of the busiest transportation lanes in the US. It is also extending its ground residential delivery schedule to seven days a week year-round starting in 2020.

At its FedEx Express hubs the company is investing in new sort systems and automation at its large Memphis World Hub and expanding its Indianapolis hub with technology enhancements. Modernization efforts at these two hubs will continue for the next several years. FedEx is also exploring same day bot deliveries using the iBOT technology developed by DEKA Development & Research.

Since the 2016 acquisition of Europe's TNT Express FedEx has been working to integrate TNT's European network with FedEx Express. The two entities are now using the same sales force and operating on the same European surface linehaul network. FedEx has replaced TNT's legacy technology infrastructure and will retire the TNT brand by the end of fiscal 2020.

FedEx's main competitor is UPS but it faces increasing competition from Amazon.com which is developing more in-house delivery capabilities and investing in expanding its network of hubs aircraft and vehicles. FedEx Express' international competitors are often government-owned or subsidized; they could have lower operating costs and profit sensitivity than FedEx Express.

Mergers and Acquisitions

In mid-2019 FedEx Express acquired Israel's FC Express the international express division of Flying Cargo Group. FC Express (previously a FedEx licensee) provides logistics warehousing fulfillment and distribution service in Israel. FedEx plans to incorporate FC Express into its international operations along with TNT.

Also in 2019 FedEx subsidiary FedEx Logistics acquired Manton Air-Sea Pty Ltd an Australian freight forwarding and 3PL company and renamed it FedEx Logistics (Australia) Pty Ltd. FedEx Logistics Australia is headquartered in Sydney and has locations in Melbourne and Brisbane. The acquisition gives FedEx Logistics greater access to this high-growth area and greater connections across the entire Asia Pacific region.

HISTORY

From his undergraduate classes at Yale and his experience as a charter airplane pilot Fred Smith got the idea that increased automation of business processes would create the need for a reliable overnight delivery service and he presented his case in a term paper in 1965. After serving in the Marine Corps in Vietnam Smith began raising money to develop the overnight delivery idea. He founded Federal Express in 1971 with $4 million inherited from his father and $80 million from investors. Overnight and second-day delivery to two dozen US cities began in 1973.

Several factors contributed to FedEx's early success: Airlines turned their focus from parcels to passengers; United Parcel Service (UPS) union workers went on strike in 1974; and competitor REA Express went bankrupt. FedEx went public in 1978.

EXECUTIVES

Evp Market Development And Corporate Communications, T. Michael Glenn, age 63, $850,028 total compensation

Evp And Cfo, Alan B. Graf, age 63, $920,840 total compensation

Chairman And Ceo, Frederick W. (Fred) Smith, age 75, $1,279,632 total compensation

President And Coo, David J. Bronczek, age 65, $960,936 total compensation

Vp Human Resources, Beth Casteel

Senior Vice President Strategic Marketing Planning And Analysis, James Webb

Evp Information Services And Cio, Robert B. (Rob) Carter, age 59, $778,216 total compensation

Coo Fedex Express; President International, Michael L. Ducker, age 66

Corporate Vp Customer And Business Transactions, Christine P. Richards, age 64, $617,640 total compensation

President And Ceo Fedex Express, David L. Cunningham

President And Ceo Fedex Ground, Henry J. Maier

Vice President Customer Services, Casey Zettler

Svp Chief Hr And Diversity Officer Fedex Express, Shannon Brown

Vice President Wro, Betty Hale

Vice President Products Services And Network Planning, Jeff Euler

Vp Finance And Administration Fedex Smartpost, Gopal Krishnamurthi

Svp Operations Fedex Ground, Scott Ray

Svp Sales Fedex Office, Aimee Dicicco

Vice President Planning And Engineering, Basil Khalil

Vice President Global Sales Operations, Chris Suhoza

Vice President Internal Audit, Karl Stingily

Vp Global Operations Fedex Office, David Sutter

Senior Vice President Senior Executive Assistant Ii, Paula Baker

Vice President Quality Operations, Cindi Henson

Senior Vice President, Mark Allen

Vice President Strategic Planning And Support, Dale Chrystie

Vp Customer Engagement Marketing, Becky Huling

Vice President Admin, Julie Hill

Vice President Senior Assistant Ii, Melissa Drum

Vice President Senior Assistant Ii, Peggy Carlisle

Vice President Admin, Caroline Clarkson

Vice President And Ww Controller, Jerry Bateman

Executive Vice President Global Sales And Solutions, Don Colleran

Vice President Operations Americas For Fedex Trade Networks, John Gazitua

Vice President Finance Fedex Services, Jane Amaba

Vice President Administration Ec Marketing, Shana Hyman

Vice President Corporate Sales, Michael Moriarty

Svp And General Counsel Fedex Supply Chain, Bradley R Peacock

Vice President Executive Creative Direct, Kelly Liu

Corporate Vice President And Chief Information Security Officer, Denise Wood

Vice President Digital Access Marketing, Tom Wicinski

Vice President Litigation, Joseph Milcoff

Vice President Marketing, Lawrence Lanier

Vice President, Dottie Berry

Vice President Strategic Planning, Stephanie Cohen

Vice President Sourcing, Susan Spence

Vice President, Don Gibson

Vice President Field Sales, Dave Russell

Svp Sales, Dan Mullally

Vice President Customer Engagement Marketing, Rebecca Huling

Senior Marketing Vice President, Kim Winstead

Executive Vice President Market Dev Corp Comm Presi Fedex Service, Michael Glenn

Vice President Marketing, Randy Scarborough

Vice President Finance, Tom Holland

Vice President, Tony Cuccia

Senior Vice President Central Support, Leonard Feiler

Vice President Inside Sales, Elizabeth Finch

Vice President Quality Assurance And F, Margaret Pelech

Senior Vice President Executive Assistant, Debbie Cain

Vice President Senior Assistant Ii, Patti Hofer

Vice President Air Express, Mark Turner

Vice President Investor Relations, A Mickey Foster

Vice President Operations Planning And Engineering Fedex Freight, Gary Bouch

Vice President Admin, Debby Davis

Executive Vice President And Chief Operating Officer Fedex Ground, Ward Strang

Vice President Of Environmental Affairs And Sustainabiltiy, Mitchell Jackson

Vice President Sales Fedex Office, John Knazur

Vice President Global Operations Planning Fedex Office, Jerod Littlefield

Vice President It Security Federal Express, Gene Sun

Vice President Of Fedex Cross Border, Charles F Hull

Vice President, Tim Leonard

Vice President Healthcare, William Ciminello

Vice President, Susan Sweat

Cvp Human Resources, Judy Edge

Vice President Information Technology Fedex Services, Jeff Roemer

Vice President Information Systems, Fred Klemashevich

Vice President Of Human Resources, Sean McNamee

Vice President, Cheryl O'brien

Senior Vice President Global Product Marketing, Jill Brown

Vp Utility Operations, Dawn Snider

Senior Vice President Admin, Mary Macon

Vice President Legal, Sean S Mcnamee

Vice President Healthcare, Kevin J Mcpherson

Senior Vice President Sales, Aimee L Dicicco

Vice President Regulatory Affairs And Compliance, Cynthia D Allen

Executive Vice President Teammate Services, Dale Dudik

Vice President Senior Assistant, Demetra Walton

Executive Vice President Global Sales And Solutions, Donald F Colleran

Vice President Of Marketing, Donald J Miller

Vice President Human Resources, Tom Tannehill

Vice President, Paul Cassel

Vice President Executive Assistant Staff, Felicia Williams

Vice President Air Network Operations Planning And Engin, Patrick Donlon
Vice President Senior Assistant, Vallerie M Bledsoe
Vp Assistant, Lillian Ventura
Svp Integrated Marketing And Communications, Patrick Fitzgerald
Senior Vice President Finance International Fedex Express, Helena Jansson
Vice President Of Worldwide Services, Dave Kevern
Vp Int'l Sales Administrative Assistant, Rhonda Edmondson
Corporate Vice President Customer And Business Transactions Legal, Jim Ferguson
Application Application Development Advisor, Rebecca Holden-williams
Vice President, Paul Melander
Senior Vice President, Michael Mitchell
Corporate Vp Operations And Service Support, Gloria Boyland
Vice President, Frank Lerose
Vice President Senior Assistant Ii, Elaine Garvey
Vice President Healthcare, Kevin Mcpherson
Vice President Admin, Susan Carey
Senior Vice President Admin, Holly Ulizzi
Vice President Information Technology Tower Group International, Carol Smith
Vice President Finance, Mark Cox
Secretary, Rona Foye
Board Member, Amber Inglis
Secretary, Toni Kooistra
Board Member, Bob Griffith
Auditors: Ernst & Young LLP

LOCATIONS

HQ: FedEx Corp
942 South Shady Grove Road, Memphis, TN 38120
Phone: 901 818-7500
Web: www.fedex.com

2018 Sales

	$ mil.	% of total
US	47,584	69
Other countries	22,109	31
Total	**69,693**	**100**

PRODUCTS/OPERATIONS

2018 Sales

	$ mil.	% of total
FedEx Express	37,331	54
FedEx Ground	20,522	29
FedEx Freight	7,582	11
FedEx Services	1,691	2
Corporate eliminations and other	2,567	4
Total	**69,693**	**100**

Services
FedEx Trade Networks
FedEx Supply Chain Systems
FedEx SmartPost
GENCO

COMPETITORS

ABF Freight System	Royal Mail
Amazon.com	Ryder System
Canada Post	The UPS Store
DHL	UPS
Japan Post	US Postal Service
La Poste	Xerox
Nippon Express	YRC Worldwide
Old Dominion Freight	

HISTORICAL FINANCIALS

Company Type: Public

Income Statement · FYE: May 31

	REVENUE ($ mil.)	NET INCOME ($ mil.)	NET PROFIT MARGIN	EMPLOYEES
05/19	69,693	540	0.8%	239,000
05/18	65,450	4,572	7.0%	227,000
05/17	60,319	2,997	5.0%	169,000
05/16	50,365	1,820	3.6%	168,000
05/15	47,453	1,050	2.2%	166,000
Annual Growth	**10.1%**	**(15.3%)**	**—**	**9.5%**

2019 Year-End Financials

Debt ratio: 32.00%	No. of shares (mil.): 261
Return on equity: 3.00%	Dividends
Cash ($ mil.): 2,319	Yield: 2.0%
Current ratio: 1.00	Payout: 19.0%
Long-term debt ($ mil.): 16,617	Market value ($ mil.): 40,238

	STOCK PRICE ($) FY Close	P/E High/Low	PER SHARE ($) Earnings	Dividends	Book Value
05/19	154.00	129 74	2.00	3.00	68.00
05/18	249.00	16 12	17.00	2.00	73.00
05/17	194.00	18 13	11.00	2.00	60.00
05/16	165.00	28 19	7.00	1.00	52.00
05/15	173.00	49 38	4.00	1.00	53.00
Annual Growth	**(2.9%)**	**— —**	**(13.6%)**	**34.3%**	**6.4%**

Fidelity National Financial Inc

To make sure that buying a dream home doesn't become a nightmare Fidelity National Financial (also known as FNF) provides title insurance escrow home warranties and other services related to real estate transactions. It is now the top dog in the residential and commercial title insurance sectors (the second-largest is First American) and issues more title insurance policies than any other title company in the US. The company operates through underwriters including Fidelity National Title Insurance Commonwealth Land Title Alamo Title and National Title of New York. It sells its products both directly and through independent agents. In 2018 FNF agreed to buy Stewart Information Services another Big Four title insurance firm.

Operations

FNF is organized into two segments: Title and Corporate and Other. The Title segment brings in most of the group's revenues; it includes title insurance and related closing services. Through subsidiary ServiceLink FNF provides mortgage transaction services such as facilitating the production and management of mortgage loans.

In late 2017 the company split off Cannae Holdings part of its former Fidelity National Finance Ventures (FNFV) segment. Now a publicly traded entity Cannae owns stakes in numerous firms including payroll and HR services firm Ceridian Holding restaurant owner American Blue Ribbon Holdings and medical software company T-System Holding.

Geographic Reach

FNF's insurance businesses operate exclusively within the US. Naturally the biggest markets are in states with the greatest populations: California Texas Florida New York and Illinois combined account for more than 45% of its title insurance premiums.

The company leases offices in more than 40 states and Washington DC as well as in Canada and India.

Sales and Marketing

FNF uses direct sales representatives and independent agents to market its title and escrow products to residential and commercial real estate customers. The company maintains some 1400 retail offices to provide residential title insurance. It markets its commercial title insurance through a network of 5200 agents in major urban real estate markets.

Financial Performance

While the company is basically sound FNF's revenues can be hampered by stiffness in the residential mortgage lending market. With the exception of 2015 revenue has been on the rise. Even more steadily net income has been rising for the past few years.

Revenue rose 6% to $7.7 billion in 2017 as title insurance premiums and escrow title-related and other fees all increased. Existing home sales increased that year but mortgage interest rates inched upward leading refinance transactions to fall.

Thanks largely to the higher revenue net income rose 19% to $771 million in 2017. However higher agent commissions expenses and personnel costs did cut into profits that year.

FNF ended 2017 with $635 million in cash and cash equivalents which was $357 million less than it had at the beginning of the year. Operating activities provided $737 million in cash financing activities (primarily long-term debt reduction) used $999 million and investing activities used another $95 million.

Strategy

Title insurance is typically one of the most stable types of insurance written. It is folded into the piles of paperwork home buyers sign during closings with little or no fuss. Even when US home sales become sluggish FNF stays active from refinancing of existing mortgages. However when interest rates rise refinancing activities tend to slow down. In the current economic cycle FNF expects that mortgage originations will slow down through 2019 but lower unemployment rates and rising consumer confidence should help offset the impact of higher interest rates. Additionally commercial real estate transactions tend to be less reliant on interest rates which should help boost the company's sales.

To stay at the top of the title insurance game FNF's core strategies include building on its various well-known brand names including Fidelity National Title Commonwealth Land Title and Alamo Title. It is also focused on delivering superior customer service and maintaining operations that can withstand the cyclical title insurance industry. For the latter it monitors its corporate organization and office network (consolidating operations as necessary) and strikes a balance between residential and commercial transactions. The company also introduces new products and technologies to remain competitive.

In a similar vein transaction services unit ServiceLink entered the auction business when FNF acquired Hudson & Marshall in mid-2017. The new ServiceLink Auction offering provides foreclosure and real estate-owned auction services.

Historically FNF and its operating subsidiaries have grown through numerous acquisitions in the title insurance space as well as by adding new offerings to attract more customers. While keeping its eye on strengthening its existing title insurance operations the company has made some moves to diversify by buying up non-insurance related businesses. In 2017 for example it acquired health care technology firm T-System for $200 million.

However in a major turnaround the company divested most of its non-insurance holdings in 2017. It separated from its Black Knight technology services arm and holding company Cannae (both of which are now public companies). The transactions helped streamline FNF's corporate structure allowing it to focus on the title insurance sector.

Mergers and Acquisitions

FNF plans to buy another Big Four title insurance firm Stewart Information Services. The $1.2 billion deal will make the nation's largest title company even bigger with some 44% of the market share.

The company made a number of acquisitions during 2017. It bought Hudson & Marshall a leading property and real estate auction firm. FNF subsidiary ServiceLink entered the auction business through that transaction; Hudson & Marshall now powers the new ServiceLink Auction offering. Also that year FNF acquired Real Geeks which provides a customer relationship management (CRM) platform and other internet tools to the real estate industry. The company then acquired control of Title Guaranty of Hawaii the state's oldest title insurance company which was previously an unaffiliated agent of Chicago Title. FNF also acquired a majority stake in SkySlope which provides digital transaction management technology to the real estate sector.

Further boosting its technology capabilities in 2016 FNF acquired Georgia-based Commissions (which provides web-based real estate marketing and CRM software) for $229 million.

Company Background

Like all title insurers Fidelity National Financial shivered when the big chill hit the real estate market in 2008. But while the company slowed it remained quick enough to take advantage of opportunities. When its ailing rival LandAmerica Financial Group filed Chapter 11 in 2008 the company bought up the choice bits for $235 million. This purchase helped make it into the largest title insurer in the US and caught the attention of the FTC prompting the company to divest a few holdings to soothe the agency's nerves. The 2009 sale of Fidelity National Capital only brought in $50 million but took $214 million of debt off company ledgers. The 2010 sale of its 32% stake in Sedgwick Claims Management brought in some $225 million.

The current company arose in 2006 when a previous company also named Fidelity National Financial split apart its title insurance operations from its information services business. What had been Fidelity National Title Group took on its former parent's name while Fidelity National Information Services took on the former parent's remaining operations. The two companies share a history and some stray holdings but are otherwise separate.

EXECUTIVES

Evp And Chief Legal Officer, Peter T. Sadowski, age 65, $431,671 total compensation
Ceo, Raymond R. (Randy) Quirk, age 73, $831,692 total compensation
Evp General Counsel And Corporate Secretary, Michael L. (Mike) Gravelle, age 58, $550,500 total compensation
Evp Corporate Strategy, Brent B. Bickett, age 55, $550,500 total compensation
Coo, Roger S. Jewkes, age 61, $630,000 total compensation
President Fidelity National Title Group National Agency Operations, Erika Meinhardt, age 61

Evp And Cfo, Anthony J. (Tony) Park, age 53, $483,000 total compensation
President, Michael J. (Mike) Nolan, age 60, $557,308 total compensation
Vp; Director It, Matt Casner
Senior Vice President, Colleen Haley
Vice President, James Sindoni
Vice President Regional Controller, Sylvia Freyling
Assistant Vice President Legal Administrator, Madeline Lovejoy
Assistant Vice President And Administrative Assistant, Jennifer Edwards
Assistant Vice President And Underwriting Counsel, Shira Burns
Assistant Vice President And Branch Manager, Tiffanie Hobgood
Assistant Vice President And Branch Manager, Sam Saravia
Assistant Vice President And Senior Counsel, Michael Behrens
Assistant Vice President Business Development, Scott Nordell
Vice President, Holly Stapley
Vice President Of Account, Kimberly Abkin
Vice President Inbound Sales, Terri Adamo
Vice President And Associate Counsel, Ian Rothenberg
Assistant Vice President, Cathy Kennedy
Vice President Agency Support Services, Lisa Beville
Vice President And Counsel, Nathaniel Yingling
Asistant Vice President, Jose Flores
Vice President, Matt Semple
Vice President And Area Counsel, Kevin Campbell
Vice President, Ann Wilbanks
Senior Vice President, Paul Mcdonald
Assistant Vice President And Agency Account Manager, Melodye Marvin
Vice President Sales Executive, April Palmer
Assistant Vice President, Yvonne Nelson
Vice President Commercial Underwriting Counsel, Walter Wilson
Assistant Vice President, Sandy Dow
Assistant Vice President Agency Auditor, Mary Rooney
Vice President, Tamara Strickland
Assistant Vice President, Erik Deppe
Assistant Vice President Asset Accounting Manager, Melissa Mannion
Vice President State Pa Agency Manager Commonwealth Land And Chicago Title, Adrienne Verdone
Vice President Kitsap Operations, Mary Schofield
Vice President, Chris Martin
Vice President Information Technology, Dan Leisle
Vice President, George Tellez
Assistant Vice President, Judith Lanahan
Vp National Operations, Karen Robertson
Assistant Vice President, Kelli Moquin
Vice President, Jason Somers
Assistant Vice President And Nw Indiana Escrow Manager, Susan Miedema
Vice President And Area Manager And Stat, Mark Schittina
Assistant Vice President And Sales Executive, Len Hyde
Senior Claims Counsel Vice President, Cheri Taylor
Avp It Strategy Manager, Janine Dapaah
Vice President Agency Counsel, Thomas Bartlett
Assistant Vice President And Director 401k Plan, Eva Chavis
Certified Escrow Officer Assistant Vice President, Kathy Nelsen
Vice President, Amy Tueckes
Assistant Vice President, David Scott
Senior Claims Counsel And Vice President, Scott Aronowitz
Vice President, Melissa Mccarty
Assistant Vice President And Analyst, Gina Stanley

Assistant Vice President, Todd Niemczyk
Vice President, Chris Jaramillo
Vp Enterprise Risk Management, Landie Brooks
Assistant Vice President, Holly Odonnell
Senior Vice President, Rick Ransom
Vice President Of Business Development, Ryan Pulliam
Vice President, Tabitha Campbell
Vice President Senior Counsel, Vanessa Elliott
Assistant Vice President Sales Representative, Christine Rifkin
Assistant Vice President, Kristin Wyckoff
Assistant Vice President, Susan Sever
Executive Vice President, Phil Shea
Senior Vice President, Kevin Gallagher
Assistant Vice President, Pati Walter
Vice President, Keith Weller
Vice President Sales, Ron Nyeholt
Assistant Vice President, Deborah Bayha
Senior Vice President And Manager New York National Commercial Services, Joanna Patilis
Assistant Vice President, Ginger Heintz
Vice President Sales, John Ravita
Assistant Vice President Associate Branch Counsel, Francis Hoffman
Assistant Vice President, Brandie Cho
Vice President Business Development, Janis Okerlund
Vice President, Brett Larocque
Vice President Business Development, Eileen Saul
Escrow Officer And Assistant Vice President, Kristin Bailey
Legal Assistant Assistant Vice President, Patricia Jandrue
Vice President, Dorry Bragg
Vice President, Gerry Grady
Assistant Vice President, Lois Watson
Assistant Vice President And Agency Account Manager, John Stilla
Vice President Business Development, Paul Jackson
Vice President, Sam Kitamura
Senior Vice President, Morris Evans
Assistant Vice President, Chris Rouly
Vice President System Admin, Tommy Bach
Managing Counsel Vice President, Elizabeth Skinner
Vice President Commercial Services Manager, Celeste Heuberger
Vice President And Georgia Underwriting Counsel, David Swan
Vice President, Mary Garcia
Senior Vice President, Kelly Feese
Vp Manager Web Based Leveraged Solutions, John Berry
Vice President, John Hlivka
Vice President National Business Development, Mark Gronke
Vice President Manager, Traci Watson
Executive Vice President, Ray Marine
Vice President Managing Director, Scott Morgano
Underwriting Counsel And Vice President, Bobbye Harris
Vice President, Jill Evans
Executive Vice President National Agency Operations, John Obzud
V.p., Edward Hamann
Vice President And Senior Escrow Officer, Lisa Wikert
Vice President And Litigation Counsel, Scott Lascari
Vice President Sales, Toni Mccarty
Vice President, Emi Tsuji
Vice President And Executive Director, Grant Miller
Agency Representative Assistant Vice President, Kristen Costello
Assistant Vice President Associate Counsel, Paul Mcgeough
Assistant Vice President, Brenda Melroy-tucson
Vice President Financial Officer, Shawn Cassidy

Managing Counsel Vice President, Todd Moody
Vice President Escrow Officer, Darla Wagner
Assistant Vice President And Chief Title Officer,
Dan Cowgill
Vice President, Sam Smith
Vice President And Area Manager, Rob Cohen
Vice President And Senior Claims Counsel,
Andrea Baird
Assistant Vice President And Associate Trial
Counsel, Austin James
Claims Counsel And Assistant Vice President,
Kelly Pritchard
Claims Counsel And Assistant Vice President,
Stacy Young
Senior Managing Major Claims Counsel Senior
Vice President, John Klein
Senior Recoupment Counsel Assistant Vice
President, Anthony Medina
Senior Vice President, Rich Cannan
Assistant Vice President And Senior Escrow
Officer, Linda Tyrrell
Vice President Business Development, Thomas
Kane
Senior Vice President, Andy Giddings
Assistant Vice President And Escrow Officer,
Nancy Wilcoxon
Vice President Commercial Escrow Officer,
Samantha Maestas
Vice President, Mark Rizzo
Senior Vice President Credit Card Services,
Barbara Hunter
Claims Counsel Assistant Vice President, Derek
Eilander
Senior Vice President, Marci Wyland
Vice President And Major Transactions Counsel,
Sarah Webb
Claims Counsel Assistant Vice President, Jodi
Hansen
Vice President Major Accounts, Valerie Lewis
Vice President Agency Counsel, Tom Bartlett
Vice President Trial Counsel, Angie Shin
Vice President, Montha Guatero
Vice President, Cindy Heidel
Vice President Associate Counsel, Michael
Tompkins
Auditors: Ernst & Young LLP

LOCATIONS

HQ: Fidelity National Financial Inc
  601 Riverside Avenue, Jacksonville, FL 32204
Phone: 904 854-8100
Web: www.fnf.com

PRODUCTS/OPERATIONS

2017 Sales

	$ mil.	% of total
Agency title insurance premiums	2,723	36
Escrow title-related & other fees	2,637	34
Direct title insurance premiums	2,170	28
Interest & investment income	131	2
Net realized gains	2	-
Total	**7,663**	**100**

COMPETITORS

American Coast Title
Equity Title Company
First American
Investors Title
North American Title
Old Republic
Old Republic National
  Title

Stewart Information
  Services
Title Resource Group
United General Title
  Insurance

HISTORICAL FINANCIALS

Company Type: Public

Income Statement

FYE: December 31

	ASSETS ($ mil.)	NET INCOME ($ mil.)	INCOME AS % OF ASSETS	EMPLOYEES
12/18	9,301	628	6.8%	23,436
12/17	9,151	771	8.4%	24,367
12/16	14,463	650	4.5%	55,219
12/15	13,931	527	3.8%	54,091
12/14	13,868	583	4.2%	56,883
Annual Growth	(9.5%)	1.9%	—	(19.9%)

2018 Year-End Financials

Debt ratio: 9.00%
Return on equity: 14.00%
Cash ($ mil.): 1,257
Current ratio: —
Long-term debt ($ mil.): —

No. of shares (mil.): 275
Dividends
  Yield: 4.0%
  Payout: 53.0%
Market value ($ mil.): 8,658

	STOCK PRICE ($) FY Close	P/E High/Low		PER SHARE ($) Earnings	Dividends	Book Value
12/18	31.00	18	13	2.00	1.00	17.00
12/17	39.00	20	14	2.00	1.00	16.00
12/16	34.00	16	12	2.00	1.00	18.00
12/15	35.00	21	17	2.00	1.00	17.00
12/14	34.00	47	34	1.00	0.00	16.00
Annual Growth	(2.3%)	—	—	31.8%	34.2%	1.1%

Fidelity National Information Services Inc

At Fidelity National Information Services (FIS) the check will never get lost in the mail. The company helps financial institutions and their clients conduct transactions through its range of software and services. It also offers outsourcing and IT consulting for the financial services industry. For banks and other financing entities the company's offerings address financial functions such as core processing decision and risk management and retail channel operations. FIS also provides payment services such as electronic funds transfer check and ticket processing and credit card production and activation. In 2019 FIS acquired Worldpay a payment processor to expand its capabilities.

Operations

The Integrated Financial Solutions (IFS) segment supplies more than half of FIS's revenue. The unit provides services to regional and community banks and savings institutions in North America. Services include transaction and account processing payment tools lending and wealth management services mobile and digital banking technologies credit and debit card technologies and fraud risk management and compliance tools and services.

The Global Financial Solutions (GFS) segment provides about 45% of the company's revenue. It provides securities processing and finance technologies and services asset management and insurance retail banking and payments services and strategic consulting to large global financial institutions.

The Corporate and Other segment 5% of revenue includes corporate overhead expense other functions and some non-strategic businesses.

Geographic Reach

FIS based in Jacksonville Florida operates through some 175 owned or leased locations in Brazil India Africa Southeast Asia and the Middle East. The company develops products and services in San Francisco London and Bangalore India.

FIS relies on its North American operations for 75% of its revenue. The company does business in more than 130 countries but most of its international revenue comes from customers in Brazil the UK Australia India and Germany.

Sales and Marketing

FIS markets its products and services through direct and indirect field sales as well as inbound and outbound lead generation and telesales. It claims about 20000 clients around the world some of whom are Ultimus Citizens Bank Kitsap Bank BNP Paribas CIBC MassMutual Slavic Integrated Administration and Stanley Black & Decker.

Financial Performance

FIS has reported lower revenue two years in a row after sales hit a high of $8.8 billion in 2016.

In 2018 revenue slipped about 3% to $8.4 billion from $8.6 billion in 2017 due to divestitures made over the past two years. The company recorded higher volumes in banking and wealth increased sales for GFS banking and payments and growth in corporate and digital services retail payments and payments in Latin America.

Net income fell to $846 million in 2018 from $1.2 billion in 2017. FIS reduced its cost of revenue and selling general and administrative expenses in 2018 which produced higher operating income for the year compared to 2017. But the company paid taxes in 2018 after receiving a tax benefit in 2017 (related to Hurricane Irma) which resulted in the lower profit.

FIS's coffers held $703 billion in cash and equivalents in 2018 compared to $665 million in 2017. Operations produced $1.9 billion in 2018 while investing activities used $668 million and financing activities used $1.2 billion.

Strategy

FIS is working to run its businesses more efficiently as well as to obtain new customers and sell additional products to current customers.

On the efficiency side FIS is moving from a legacy server-based technology to cloud technologies to gain the benefits of speed efficiency and scale. The company had 50% of its servers on its secure private cloud in 2018 and expected the percentage to increase to 65% in 2019 and 80% in 2021.

FIS has pared away operations that were outside its focus on financial services. In 2017 FIS sold majority ownership in Capco to Clayton Dubilier & Rice. FIS also sold the SunGard Public Sector and Education in 2017 and in 2018 its China-based business Kingstar.

On the other hand FIS offered $35 billion to buy Worldpay a payment processor. The deal would add additional payment capabilities to FIS's portfolio amid a consolidation wave in financial services firms. Worldpay processes about 40 billion transactions a year and supports more than 300 payment types in more than 120 currencies. The transaction is expected to close in the second half of 2019.

The $8.7 billion in debt that FIS carries could limit its ability to borrow and restrict its flexibility to allocate capital in pursuing opportunities.

Mergers and Acquisitions

In 2019 FIS bolstered the services it provides with the $35 billion acquisition of Worldpay a payment processor. The deal brought significant payment resources to FIS as other companies in the industry have consolidated.

EXECUTIVES

Corporate Evp And Coo Institutional And Wholesale, Marianne C. Brown, age 60, $700,000 total compensation
Cio, Ido Gileadi
President And Ceo, Gary A. Norcross, age 54, $1,000,000 total compensation
Corporate Evp And Coo Banking And Payments, Anthony M. Jabbour, age 51, $700,000 total compensation
Corporate Evp Chief Administrative Officer And Corporate Secretary, Michael P. Oates, age 60, $475,000 total compensation
Evp And Cfo, James W. (Woody) Woodall, age 49, $605,000 total compensation
Corporate Evp And Chief Risk Officer, Gregory G. (Greg) Montana, age 50, $365,000 total compensation
Evp International Markets, Raja Gopalakrishnan
Ceo Capco, Lance Levy
Evp And Chief Legal Officer, Marc Mayo
Coo Integrated Financial Solutions, Bruce Lowthers
Senior Vice President Global Commercial Services Supply Chain And Real Estate, Kevin Gouin
Vp Global Events, Tania Compton
Vice President Implementation Services, Chris Wichman
Senior Vice President Eft Services, Serena Smith
Vice President, Brian Paulson
Senior Vice President And Legal Executive, Duncan Mitchell
Vice President, John Kopriva
Vice President Marketing And Strategy, Linda Netherton
Assistant Vice President Chargeback Services, Christine Sterling
Vice President Consulting Operations Director, Paul Mason
Vice President, Pete Foy
Assistant Vice President, Marie Storey
Vice President, Gina Gitter
Vice President, Sean Oliver
Vice President Product Management, Dominique Stevens
Vp Product Development, Floyd Berus
Vice President Sales And Marketing, Robert Boitano
Senior Vice President Loyalty Services, Robert Legters
Vice President Operations, John Oleon
Assistant Vice President Finance, Dawn Frye
Assistant Vice President Treasury, Alex Alley
Assistant Vice President, Kimberly Sadler
Vice President Advanced Technology Solutions, Hank Godwin
Vice President Business Recovery Services Advanced Technology Solutions, Ovid Babb
Assistant Vice President Global Midrange Applications, Alex Pisieczko
Senior Vice President Channel Architecture And Strategy, Bernie Schramm
Vice President New Solutions Architecture, Will Starnes
Vice President Acbs Global Sales, Gregg Cerniglia
Senior Vice President Operations, Mike Amble
Svp Fis Global Marketing And Communications, Kim Snider
Vice President Channels Delivery, Sethu Thottikamath
Vice President North America Key Accounts, Mike Donahue
Vice President Enterprise Architecture, Roy Jutze
Senior Vice President And General Manager, Michelle Bowen
Vice President And Managing Director, Jim Gorski
Sales Senior Vice President, Michael Whitacre
Vice President Sales, Michael Daugherty
Vice President Customer Service, Christopher Hermann

Vice President Fidelity Information Services Testing, Laura Belliot
Vp Finance And Accounting, Phil Klink
Vice President Infrastructure Services, David Plante
Vice President And Managing Director, Cathy David
Vice President Fraud Management, Eric Kraus
Svp And Deputy Ciso, Ivana Cojbasic
Vice President Engineering Delivery And Nextgen Information Technology Services, Robert Collins
Vice President Strategic Account Sales, Lucy Mills
Vice President Application Services India, Vishad Gupta
Vice President Of Data Center Operations, Anna Crone
Vice President International Treasury, Andres Shuyama
Vice President Sales, Ryan Fetzer
Vice President Human Resources, Kristen Cimock
Vice President Recruiting, Praveen Tomar
Senior Vice President And Deputy General Counsel Corporate, Charles Curley
Vice President Product Management, Paul Zur Nieden
Chief People Officer, Denise Williams
Senior Vice President Development, Aaron Gerdeman
Vice President Brokerage Solutions And Strategy, David Hoffman
Senior Vice President Business Development, Chad Davis
Vice President Global Networks And Security Engineering, Chris Young
Vice President Payment Solutions Sales, Amy Hammon
Vice President And General Manager Merchant Services, Dawn Murray
Vice President, John Francis
Vp Global Voice And Network Services, Tim Ferguson
National Account Manager, Steven Romeo
Vice President Product Strategy, Dan Peacock
Vice President Sales And Relationship Management, Darryl Wims
Vice President Corporate And Executive Communications, Jen Becker
Senior Vice President Information Securi, Hamish Craig
Vp Of Prepaid Product Development, Tracy Kirkland
Chief People Officer, Dee Williams
Senior Vice President, Erik Hoag
Vice President Client Services And Application Delivery, Jon Hamilton
Vice President, Patrick Hogan
Vice President Corporate Controller, Thomas Warren
Vice President Information Technology, Leslie Harlow
Vice President Product Strategy, Ernie Buday
Vp Product Management, Kevin Mossop
Vice President, Todd Trzcinski
Assistant Vice President And Division Counsel, Stephen Teplin
Senior Vice President Professional Services, Sherry Baker
Vice President Product Manager, Lee Detlaff
Vice President Sales, Dan Buttolph
Senior Vice President Risk Management, Rick Floress
Chairman, Frank R. Martire, age 71
Auditors: KPMG LLP

LOCATIONS

HQ: Fidelity National Information Services Inc
601 Riverside Avenue, Jacksonville, FL 32204
Phone: 904 438-6000
Web: www.fisglobal.com

2018 Sales

	$ mil.	% of total
North America	6,283	75
All others	2,140	25
Total	**8,423**	**100**

PRODUCTS/OPERATIONS

2018 Sales

	$ mil.	% of total
IFS	4,401	52
GFS	3,718	44
Corporate & Other	304	4
Total	**8,423**	**100**

SOLUTIONS

SOLUTIONS
Banking and Wealth
Institutional and Wholesale
Management Consulting
Payments

COMPETITORS

ACI Worldwide	IBM
Accenture	Infosys
Alliance Data Systems	Jack Henry
First Data	MasterCard
Fiserv	Oracle Financial
Global Payments	Services Software
HP Enterprise Services	SEI Investments
Heartland Payment	Total System Services
Systems	Visa Inc

HISTORICAL FINANCIALS

Company Type: Public

Income Statement

FYE: December 31

	REVENUE ($ mil.)	NET INCOME ($ mil.)	NET PROFIT MARGIN	EMPLOYEES
12/18	8,423	846	10.0%	47,000
12/17	9,123	1,319	14.5%	53,000
12/16	9,241	568	6.1%	55,000
12/15	6,595	632	9.6%	55,000
12/14	6,414	679	10.6%	40,000
Annual Growth	7.1%	5.6%	—	4.1%

2018 Year-End Financials

Debt ratio: 38.00%
Return on equity: 8.00%
Cash ($ mil.): 703
Current ratio: 1.00
Long-term debt ($ mil.): 8,670
No. of shares (mil.): 327
Dividends
Yield: 1.0%
Payout: 50.0%
Market value ($ mil.): 33,534

	STOCK PRICE ($) FY Close	P/E High/Low		PER SHARE ($) Earnings	Dividends	Book Value
12/18	103.00	43	36	3.00	1.00	31.00
12/17	94.00	24	19	4.00	1.00	33.00
12/16	76.00	46	32	2.00	1.00	30.00
12/15	61.00	33	26	2.00	1.00	29.00
12/14	62.00	27	21	2.00	1.00	23.00
Annual Growth	13.3%	—	—	2.1%	7.5%	7.9%

Fifth Third Bancorp (Cincinnati, OH)

Fifth Third Bancorp is the holding company of Fifth Third Bank which boasts assets of more than $140 billion and more than 1100 branches in about 10 states in the Midwest and Southeast. Fifth Third offers branch banking (deposit accounts and loans for consumers and small businesses) commercial banking (lending leasing and syndicated and trade finance for corporations) consumer lending (residential mortgages home equity loans and credit cards) and wealth and asset management (private banking brokerage and asset management). Fifth Third owns part of Worldpay one of the country's largest payment processing firms. In 2019 it acquired MB Financial making the combined company the fourth largest bank in Chicago by deposits.

Operations

Fifth Third Bancorp operates four business segments: Commercial Banking Branch Banking Wealth and Asset Management and Consumer Lending. Branch Banking and Commercial Banking each generate roughly 40% of total revenue. Wealth and Asset Management contributes about 10%; Consumer Lending provides around 5%.

Commercial Banking provides financial services?like credit intermediation and cash management?to middle-market businesses and government and professional clients. Its additional services include international trade finance and derivatives and asset-based lending. Net interest income generates more than 60% of the segment's revenue.

Branch Banking offers a standard range of deposit loan and lease products to individuals and businesses. Some 70% of its revenue comes from net interest income.

Wealth and Asset Management is divided into four primary businesses: retail broker FTS risk management company Fifth Third Insurance Agency high-net worth client wealth management firm Fifth Third Private Bank and institutional advisory services provider Fifth Third Institutional Services. About 70% of its revenue derives from service fees.

Fifth Third's Consumer Lending division derives all its noninterest income from home loan and credit origination and servicing. Net interest income and mortgage banking each account for about half of the segment's revenue.

Geographic Reach

Cincinatti Ohio-based Fifth Third Bancorp has around 1100 full-service branches and about 2400 ATMs in Ohio Kentucky Indiana Michigan Illinois Florida Tennessee West Virginia Georgia and North Carolina.

Sales and Marketing

In addition to retail customers and affluent individuals Fifth Third Bancorp targets agribusinesses dealers government agencies healthcare-related companies US financial institutions and businesses seeking energy financing.

Commercial Banking offers services to large and middle-market businesses and government and professional customers. Wealth & Asset Management targets individuals companies and not-for-profit organizations. Branch Banking and Consumer Lending largely tend to the needs of retail consumers and small businesses.

Financial Performance

Fifth Third Bancorp's revenue has floundered somewhat in recent years alternately showing modest gains of about 10% or ticking down slightly for five-year growth of only 15%. Its net income has fared better over that period showing an expansion of about 50% between 2014 and 2018 thanks mostly to an increase of about 40% in 2017 when the company sold of some of its shares in former subsidiary Vantiv.

Despite increased net interest income and greater revenue from its corporate banking wealth and asset management and card and processing activities the boost in 2017 led revenue to slip by 1% to $6.9 billion in 2018. The company's net income grew by 7% to $2.2 billion thanks to those revenue gains and a lower income tax expense caused by a retroactive accounting policy change for its investments in affordable housing projects that qualified low-income housing tax credits.

Fifth Third added $167 million to its cash in 2018 to end the year with $2.7 billion. Operations contributed $2.9 billion and financing activities?mostly net changes in deposits?provided $1.5 billion. Purchase of available-for-sale debt and other securities drove investment spend which totaled $4.1 billion.

Strategy

In a move to strengthen its position in the Chicago deposit market Fifth Third Bancorp acquired MB Financial in 2019. MB Financial had about $20 billion in assets. The combination created the fourth largest Chicago bank by deposits second in estimated retail deposits and second in middle market relationships (with a 20% share).

Fifth Third is also investing in digital banking channels to move in front of the fast forming FinTech (Financial Technology) changes that are enveloping the industry. As a result Fifth Third has cut back its branch network and is seeing reduced operating costs all while giving customers faster access to banking services. To ensure it is keeping pace with the change the bank is partnering with and investing in several FinTech companies such as Current and CommonBond.

Fifth Third kicked off a 3-year growth plan in late 2016 termed NorthStar with the intention of strengthening its brand value growing tighter long-term relationships with its customers and leveraging data analytics to drive better operational efficiencies. To those ends it upgraded its mortgage and teller systems expanded its suite of credit card and treasury management products and invested in its commercial verticals (such as Healthcare with the Coker Capital acquisition).

Mergers and Acquisitions

In early 2019 Fifth Third Bancorp acquired Chicago-based bank holding company MB Financial for $4.7 billion. With about $20 billion the integration of MB's MB Financial Bank into Fifth Third created the fourth largest Chicago bank by deposits second in estimated retail deposits and second in middle market relationships (with a 20% share).

The year prior Fifth Third acquired Coker Capital Advisors an M&A advisory services firm focused on middle-market healthcare companies. The acquisition expands the bank's M&A and investment banking capabilities and strengthens its healthcare vertical one of its largest areas of industry expertise.

In 2017 the company bought Epic Insurance Solutions and Integrity HR which serve commercial and personal property insurance and casualty and employee benefits services. Fifth Third anticipates the action will help it enter the employee benefits and human resources consulting business where its sees growth opportunities.

Company Background

William W. Scarborough and 11 other entrepreneurs opened Fifth Third Bancorp's precursor The Bank of the Ohio Valley in Cincinatti Ohio in 1858. In 1927 Fifth-Third National and The Union Trust Company merged to form The Fifth Third Union Trust Company.

HISTORY

In 1863 a group of Cincinnati businessmen opened the Third National Bank inside a Masonic temple to serve the Ohio River trade. Acquiring the Bank of the Ohio Valley (founded 1858) in 1871 the firm progressed until the panic of 1907. Third National survived and in 1908 consolidated with Fifth National forming the Fifth Third National Bank of Cincinnati. The newly organized bank acquired two local banks in 1910.

A second bank consolidation in 1919 resulted in Fifth Third's affiliation with Union Savings Bank and Trust Company permitting the bank to establish branches theretofore forbidden by regulators. The company acquired the assets and offices of five more banks and thrifts that year operating them as branches.

In 1927 the bank merged its operations with the Union Trust Company forming the Fifth Third Union Trust. With its combined strength it weathered the Great Depression and acquired three more banks between 1930 and 1933. However the Depression also brought massive banking regulations to the industry limiting Fifth Third's acquisitions.

In the postwar years and during the 1950s and 1960s the bank expanded its consumer banking services offering traveler's checks. Under CEO Bill Rowe son of former CEO John Rowe the firm emphasized the convenience of its locations and increased hours of operations.

In the 1970s Fifth Third shifted its lending program's emphasis from commercial loans to consumer credit and launched its ATM and telephone banking services. Aware that the bank was technologically unprepared for the onslaught of electronic information Fifth Third expanded its data processing and information services resources forming the basis for its Midwest Payment Systems division.

The company formed Fifth Third Bancorp a holding company and began to branch within Ohio (branching had previously been limited to the home county) in 1975. Ten years later more deregulation allowed the bank to move into contiguous states. Focused on consumer banking and with cautious underwriting policies Fifth Third weathered the real estate bust and leveraged-buyout problems of the 1980s and acquired new outlets cheaply by buying several small banks as well as branches from larger banks. It acquired the American National Bank in Kentucky and moved further afield with its purchase of the Sovereign Savings Bank in Palm Harbor Florida in 1991.

The company continued to expand buying several banks and thrifts in Ohio in 1997 and 1998. In 1999 Fifth Third moved into Indiana in a big way with its purchase of CNB Bancshares then solidified its position in the state with the acquisition of Peoples Bank of Indianapolis. Fifth Third also moved into new business areas buying mortgage banker W. Lyman Case broker-dealer The Ohio Company (1998) and Cincinnati-based commercial mortgage banker Vanguard Financial (1999). The company began to offer online foreign exchange via its FX Internet Trading Web in 2000.

In 2001 Fifth Third bought money manager Maxus Investments and added some 300 bank branches with its purchase of Capital Holdings (Ohio and Michigan) and Old Kent Financial (Michigan Indiana and Illinois) its largest-ever acquisition.

Fifth Third exited the property/casualty insurance brokerage business in 2002 selling its operations to Hub International. Also that year Fifth Third arranged to enter Tennessee via its planned purchase of Franklin Financial. But the deal was stalled as industry regulators investigated Fifth Third's risk management procedures and internal controls. A moratorium on acquisitions was placed on the bank during the investigation. It was lifted in 2004 and the purchase of Franklin was completed not long afterwards. That opened the door for Fifth Third's acquisition of First National Bankshares of Florida in 2005. Two years later it continued growing with its purchase of R-G Crown Bank from R&G Financial which added some 30 branches in Florida in addition to locations in Georgia.

EXECUTIVES

President Ceo And Director, Greg D. Carmichael, age 57, $994,287 total compensation

Evp And Coo, Lars C. Anderson, age 58, $675,002 total compensation

Evp And Chief Risk Officer, Frank R. Forrest, age 64, $519,713 total compensation

Evp, Philip R. McHugh, age 54

Evp And Chief Corporate Responsibility And Reputation Officer, Brian Lamb

Evp And Chief Administrative Officer, Teresa J. Tanner, age 50

Evp And Cfo, Tayfun Tuzun, age 54, $519,342 total compensation

Evp, Chad M. Borton, age 48, $491,260 total compensation

Evp And Treasurer, James C. Leonard, age 49

Evp And Chief Strategy Officer, Timothy N. Spence, age 40, $450,008 total compensation

Evp And Chief Operations And Technology Officer, Aravind Immaneni

Evp Chief Legal Officer And Corporate Secretary, Jelena McWilliams

Evp, Richard Stein

Assistant Vice President It, Wes Debord

Vice President Finance, Dan Flanigan

Vice President Information Technology, Ken Valentine

Assistant Vice President Principal Application Developer, Aaron Stockmeister

Vice President Edm Database Administration, Tracey Tebelman

Vice President Recruiting, Nancy Pinckney

Vice President Middle Market Relationship Manager, Adam Herr

Avp And Senior Manager Applications, Terry Grooms

Senior Vice President, Jeffrey Leithauser

Vice President Of Facilities, Al Druckenmiller

Vice President Acquisitions, Jim Rose

Vice President, Kevin Zgonc

Vice President Mortgage, Alisa Hunter

Vice President Legal Counsel, Shannon Barrow

Vice President, Eric Braun

Vice President, Thomas Merkle

Vice President Senior Relationship Man, Brian Knutson

Senior Vice President And C10 Commercial Bank, Sidney Deloatch

Vice President Commercial Lending, Jerry Hartley

Assistant Vice President Manager Information Security Operations, Christopher Fant

Vice President Chief Operational Risk Officer, John Wallace

Vice President, Michael Agricola

Assistant Vice President, Mark Zink

Assistant Vice President Senior Compliance Officer, Janis Scharenberg

Vice President And Trust Officer, David Garber

Vice President Manager Project Manager, Colleen Foster

Vice President Of Enterprise Architecture, Gary Schnettler

Vice President, Greg Vollmer

Vice President, Tab Demita

Vice President And Director Commercial Analytics, Stephen Boras

Vice President Portfolio Manager, Keith McFarland

Vice President And Chief Financial Officer Of Eastern Michigan, John Worthington

Vice President Manager Financial Services, Terrence Lyons

Vice President Information Technology Compliance, Jeffrey A Jones

Vice President, Alfred Mancuso

Vice President, Douglas Schuchter

Vice President Treasury Management Officer, Alicia Mattice

Senior Vice President And Director Operations, Paul Moore

Vice President, Brian Gardner

Vice President, Tim Tierney

Vice President, William Hummel

Vice President Institutional Real Estate, Brad Boersma

Assistant Vice President, Brad Pinson

Vice President, Keith Goodpaster

Assistant Vice President, Maher Kaddoura

Vice President, Libby Chapin

Vice President Area Investment Manager, Crystal Kolcz

Vice President, Mark Telles

Vice President, Karen Mundy

Assistant Vice President, Anoopa McKim

Senior Vice President And Director Business Controls Chief Administrative Office, Peg Jula

Assistant Vice President Information Technology Projects, Michele Mcdonel

Vice President Indirect Originations, Edward Mcelveen

Vice President, Dean Haberkamp

Vice President And Sales Manager Global Cash Solutions, Megan Anderson

Vice President, Valena Allen

Vice President Global Payments, Jason Dement

Assistant Vice President Senior Market Intelligence Analyst, Ashley Wyant

Assistant Vice President, Gregory Hahn

Vice President Legal Counsel, Peter Jurs

Vice President, Jennifer Dunigan-wernke

Vice President Business Banking, Tracey Siarkowski

Vice President Commercial Banking, Tim Egloff

Relationship Manager Vice President, Andrew C Glenn

Vice President Commercial Banking, Mary Weldon

Vice President Private Client Group, Joe Wasik

Vice President Commercial Portfolio Manager, Jonathan Roe

Vice President, Meriem Blevins

Vice President Product And Risk Manager, April Cothran

Equipment Management Vice President, Donald Mcgill

Vice President, Mark Ransom

Vice President, Joe Acito

Vice President Sales, Russ Schnurr

Vice President, Herbert Kidd

Vice President Professional Services, John Huber

Vice President, Rod Brown

Vice President, Joy Byrwa

Vice President Strategic Program Manager, Michelle Evans

Vice President, Robert Hagan

Vice President Commercial Loan Operations, Margie Johnson

Vice President, Warren Berlin

Vice President Private Bank, David W Herrenbruck

Vice President, Joanne Hindel

Structured Finance Group Assistant Vice President, Paul Bahra

Vice President, Sonia Sonecha

Vice President Treasury Management, Kate Nagy

Vice President Of Marketing, Richard Steimer

Senior Vice President, Jeanne Reynolds

Assistant Vice President Institutional Investments Client Services Specialist, Rachel Trent

Vice President, Patrick Farnan

Financial Center Manager Assistant Vice President, Archard Mathis

Vice President Enterprise Qa, William Nearhood

Vice President, John Sharp

Vice President, Michael Olinsky

Senior Vice President, Tom Plodzeen

Vice President Officer, George Hunter

Vice President, Michael Hossack

Vice President Portfolio Manager, Neil Vajda

Finance Manager Vp, Janet Wolffis

Vice President Treasury Management Officer, Douglas Henderson

Vice President, Tammy Schaefer

Vice President Sba Alternative Lending, Chris Intemann

Vice President, Terry Feucht

Vice President, Jason Fronheiser

Fcm Vice President, Rubia Marins

Vice President And Director Of Accounting, Glen Napolitano

Financial Center Manager Avp, Rick Bugaj

Vice President Of Capital Markets Accounting Group, Bryan Preston

Vice President Portfolio Manager, Christopher Staples

Vice President Consumer Risk Management, Warren Butterworth

Vice President, Thomas Begam

Vice President Online Strategy, Shannon Paul

Vice President Recovery Manager, Jeremy Hejl

Senior Vice President Commercial Lending, Tom Witt

Vice President Senior Wealth Management Advisor, Craig Vaness

Vice President, Jon Powell

Vice President Healthcare Treasury Management, Lynne Pearson

Assistant Vice President Senior Group Manager Global Sourcing, Melissa Stegman

Assistant Vice President Special Assets Group, Monique Suranye

Assistant Vice President, Kerstin Rubinstein

Senior Vice President, Edward Christian

Financial Center Manager And Vice President, Adrian Mendieta

Senior Vice President Liquidity Management, Hal Coffey

Senior Vice President Audit Director, Ryan Dirks

Vice President Of Business Banking, Lisa Sammons

Vice President Sag Core, Chris C Cagle

Investment Executive Vice President, Jason Tosh

Assistant Vice President And Counsel, Gregory Sova

Senior Vice President Charitable Management Services, Deborah Moses

Vice President, John Burlowski

Vice President Commercial Equipment Finance, Charles Bonano

Vice President Area Sales Manager, Greg Elmore

Vice President Global Payments, Jim McNamara

Senior Vice President Commercial Banking, John Fittro

Vice President Team Lead, David Fuller

Vice President Product Management, Wade Edwards

Vice President Investor Reporting Loan Servicing Manager, Mark Fairchild

Vice President Senior Manager Of Treasury Analytics, Todd Okeson

Auditors: DELOITTE & TOUCHE LLP

LOCATIONS

HQ: Fifth Third Bancorp (Cincinnati, OH)
Fifth Third Center, Cincinnati, OH 45263
Phone: 800 972-3030
Web: www.53.com

Selected Markets
Florida
Georgia
Indiana
Illinois
Kentucky
Michigan
North Carolina
Ohio
Tennessee
West Virginia

PRODUCTS/OPERATIONS

2018 Sales

Interest

	$ mil.	% of total
Loans & leases including fees	4,078	51
Securities & other	1,080	13
Interest on other short-term investments	25	-
Interest Expense	(1043.0)	-
Non-Interest		
Service charges on deposits	549	7
Wealth and asset management revenue	444	6
Corporate banking revenue	438	5
Mortgage banking net revenue	212	3
Card & processing revenue	329	4
Securities gains net	(54.0)	-
Other	887	11
Total	**6,945**	**100**

2018 Sales

	% of total
Commercial Banking	37
Branch Banking	40
Consumer Lending	6
Wealth and Asset Management	9
Corporate and Other	8
Total	**100**

Selected Subsidiaries

Fifth Third Financial Corporation
  Fifth Third Bank
  GNB Management LLC
  GNB Realty LLC
  ClearArc Capital Inc.
  Fifth Third Holdings LLC
  Fifth Third Insurance Agency Inc.
  Fifth Third International Company
  The Fifth Third Auto Leasing Trust
  Fifth Third Mortgage Company — Michigan LLC
  Old Kent Mortgage Services Inc.
  Fifth Third Community Development Corporation
  Fifth Third New Markets Development Co. LLC
  Fifth Third Investment Company
  Fountain Square Life Reinsurance Company Ltd. (Turks and Caicos Islands)
  Vista Settlement Services LLC

COMPETITORS

Bank of America	KeyCorp
Citigroup	Northern Trust
Comerica	PNC Financial
Harris	U.S. Bancorp
Huntington Bancshares	Wells Fargo
JPMorgan Chase	

HISTORICAL FINANCIALS

Company Type: Public

Income Statement

FYE: December 31

	ASSETS ($ mil.)	NET INCOME ($ mil.)	INCOME AS % OF ASSETS	EMPLOYEES
12/18	146,069	2,193	1.5%	17,437
12/17	142,193	2,194	1.5%	18,125
12/16	142,177	1,564	1.1%	17,844
12/15	141,082	1,712	1.2%	18,261
12/14	138,706	1,481	1.1%	18,351
Annual Growth	**1.3%**	**10.3%**	**—**	**(1.3%)**

2018 Year-End Financials

Debt ratio: 10.00%
Return on equity: 13.00%
Cash ($ mil.): 2,968
Current ratio: —
Long-term debt ($ mil.): —
No. of shares (mil.): 647
Dividends
 Yield: 3.0%
 Payout: 24.0%
Market value ($ mil.): 15,215

	STOCK PRICE ($) FY Close	P/E High/Low	Earnings	Dividends	Book Value
12/18	24.00	11 7	3.00	1.00	25.00
12/17	30.00	11 8	3.00	1.00	24.00
12/16	27.00	14 7	2.00	1.00	22.00
12/15	20.00	11 8	2.00	1.00	20.00
12/14	20.00	14 11	2.00	1.00	19.00
Annual Growth	**3.7%**	**— —**	**16.5%**	**9.8%**	**7.3%**

Financial Institutions Inc.

Financial Institutions may not have a luxurious name but they specialize in five star service. The holding company owns Five Star Bank which provides standard deposit products such as checking and savings accounts CDs and IRAs to retail and business customers through some 50 branches across western and central New York. Indirect consumer loans originated through agreements with area franchised car dealers account for the largest percentage of the company's loan portfolio (35%) followed by commercial mortgages. The company also sells insurance while its Five Star Investment Services subsidiary offers brokerage and financial planning services.

Operations

Financial Institutions operates through two business segments: banking which includes the bank's retail and commercial banking operations; and insurance which sells insurance to both personal and business clients through its Scott Danahy Naylon Co (SDN) subsidiary.

About 65% of the company's total revenue came from loan interest (including fees) in 2014 while another 15% came from interest on its investment securities. The rest of its revenue came from deposit account service charges (7%) ATM and debit card fees (4%) insurance income (2%) investment advisory (2%) and other miscellaneous income sources.

Geographic Reach

Five Star Bank boasts 50 branches and an ATM network across Western and Central New York in the counties of Allegany Cattaraugus Cayuga Chautauqua Chemung Erie Genesee Livingston Monroe Ontario Orleans Schuyler Seneca Steuben Wyoming and Yates.

Sales and Marketing

The company offers financial and banking services to individuals municipalities and businesses in Western and Central New York.

Financial Performance

Financial Institution's revenues and profits have been rising over the past few years thanks to growing loan business (organically and from 2012 acquisitions) lower interest expenses and rising fee-based revenue.

The company's revenue rose by 2% to $126.4 million in 2014 mostly thanks to the addition of insurance income from stemming from the bank's acquisition of SDN. Financial's loan interest grew by 1% on organic loan business growth while interest on investment securities grew by 7% as it purchased more interest-earning assets.

Higher revenue and a decline in loan loss provisions from a more credit-worthy loan portfolio in 2014 drove Financial Institution's net income higher by 15% to a record $29.4 million. The com-

pany's operating cash levels dipped by 5% to $35.2 million during the year due to unfavorable changes in working capital related to its contributions to its defined benefit pension plan.

Strategy

Financial Institutions' long-term strategy reiterated in 2015 has been to "maintain a community bank philosophy which consists of focusing on and understanding the individualized banking needs of individuals municipalities and businesses of the local communities surrounding their primary service area." The firm believes this focus will enable it to better respond to customer needs and provide a higher level of personalized services giving it a competitive advantage over larger competitors.

The company has also pursued acquisitions to bolster its service lines to grow its non-interest business. Its 2014 acquisition of a New-York based full-service insurance agency for example launched it beyond banking into the insurance business.

Mergers and Acquisitions

In January 2015 Financial Institutions bolstered its investment service business after acquiring Courier Capital which offers customized investment management investment consulting and retirement plan services to some 1100 individuals businesses and institutions.

In 2014 Financial Institutions expanded its services into the insurance business after acquiring Buffalo-based Scott Danahy Naylon Co. (SDN) a full-service insurance agency for a total of $16.9 million plus a promise of $3.4 million in future payments contingent on SDN meeting revenue performance goal targets through 2017.

Company Background

In 2012 Five Star Bank acquired four retail branches owned by HSBC Bank and four owned by First Niagara Bank in upstate New York.

Five Star Bank was formed in 2005 when the company consolidated its four banking subsidiaries (First Tier Bank & Trust National Bank of Geneva Wyoming County Bank and Bath National Bank) into a single entity. First Tier Bank & Trust absorbed the other three banks and changed its name to Five Star Bank.

EXECUTIVES

Vice President Customer Service, David Macintyre
Evp Cfo And Treasurer, Kevin B. Klotzbach, age 66, $230,000 total compensation
President And Ceo, Martin K. Birmingham, $420,000 total compensation
Evp Commercial Executive And Regional President, Jeffrey P. Kenefick, $209,100 total compensation
Svp And Director Of Human Resources And Enterprise Planning, Paula D. Dolan, $140,000 total compensation
Evp And Chief Risk Officer, Kenneth V. Winn
Executive Vice President, Basar Ordukaya
Vice President Of Commercial Lending, Robert McFadden
Senior Vice President And Treasurer, Marc Swanson
Vice President, Richard Simpson
Senior Vice President And Manager Work, Steven Ambrose
Vice President Information Technology Operations, Chip Shepard
Senior Vice President, Darren Haugen
Vice Presidenti Information Technology, R McLaughlin
Senior Vice President Chief Commercial Credit Officer Of The Bank, David Case
Senior Vice President Candi Lending Executive And Buffalo Regional President Of The Bank, Edward Oexle

Senior Vice President Consumer Lending Manager, Jonathan Chase
Senior Vice President And Administrator Loan Revie, David Squire
Senior Vice President Business Banking Executive, Vito Caraccio
Senior Vice President Commercial Real Estate Executive Of The Bank, Craig Burton
Board Member, Samuel M Gullo
Chairman, Robert N. Latella, age 76
Treasurer, Kevin Kotzbach
Board Member, Susan Holliday
Auditors: RSM US LLP

LOCATIONS

HQ: Financial Institutions Inc.
   220 Liberty Street, Warsaw, NY 14569
Phone: 585 786-1100
Web: www.fiiwarsaw.com

PRODUCTS/OPERATIONS

2013 Sales

	$ mil.	% of total
Interest income		
Loans including fees	82	66
Investment securities	18	14
Noninterest income		
Service charges on deposits	10	9
ATM & debit card	5	4
Investment advisory	2	2
Other	7	5
Total	**124**	**100**

COMPETITORS

Astoria Financial	HSBC USA
Citibank	KeyCorp
Community Bank System	M&T Bank
ESL Federal Credit Union	

HISTORICAL FINANCIALS

Company Type: Public

Income Statement				FYE: December 31
	ASSETS ($ mil.)	NET INCOME ($ mil.)	INCOME AS % OF ASSETS	EMPLOYEES
12/18	4,312	40	0.9%	725
12/17	4,105	34	0.8%	656
12/16	3,710	32	0.9%	654
12/15	3,381	28	0.8%	691
12/14	3,090	29	1.0%	645
Annual Growth	8.7%	7.7%	—	3.0%

2018 Year-End Financials

Debt ratio: 1.00%	No. of shares (mil.): 16
Return on equity: 10.00%	Dividends
Cash ($ mil.): 103	Yield: 4.0%
Current ratio: —	Payout: 40.0%
Long-term debt ($ mil.): —	Market value ($ mil.): 409

	STOCK PRICE ($) FY Close	P/E High/Low	PER SHARE ($) Earnings	Dividends	Book Value
12/18	26.00	14 10	2.00	1.00	25.00
12/17	31.00	17 12	2.00	1.00	24.00
12/16	34.00	16 12	2.00	1.00	22.00
12/15	28.00	15 12	2.00	1.00	21.00
12/14	25.00	13 10	2.00	1.00	20.00
Annual Growth	0.5%	— —	4.6%	5.7%	5.9%

FINCANTIERI MARINE SYSTEMS NORTH AMERICA, INC.

EXECUTIVES

Ceo, Dario Deste
Pres*, Domenico Sorvillo
V Pres-Gen Mgr*, Richard Dinsmore
Treas, Paolo Pezzulo
Contrl, Martha Rosbrough
Manager, Pamela Thomas
Human Resources Coordinator, Ashley Morningstar

LOCATIONS

HQ: FINCANTIERI MARINE SYSTEMS NORTH
   AMERICA, INC.
   800 PRINCIPAL CT STE C, CHESAPEAKE, VA
   233203681
Phone: 757 548-6000
Web: WWW.FINCANTIERIMARINESYSTEMS.COM

HISTORICAL FINANCIALS

Company Type: Private

Income Statement				FYE: December 31
	REVENUE ($ mil.)	NET INCOME ($ mil.)	NET PROFIT MARGIN	EMPLOYEES
12/17	35,834	6,671	18.6%	56
12/16	37,568	6,366	16.9%	—
12/14	34,754	2,899	8.3%	—
12/13	0	1,230	—	—
Annual Growth	—	52.6%	—	—

First American Financial Corp

First American Financial knows that when you're buying real estate you'll probably want some insurance to go along with it. In addition to title insurance closing and escrow services from its First American Title Insurance subsidiary the company's specialty insurance arm provides residential property and casualty insurance and home warranties. Its First American Trust unit offers banking and trust services to the escrow and real estate industries. Other offerings include settlement title plant management valuation and real estate data.

Operations

First American Financial is one of the largest title insurers in the US. Its title insurance and services segment accounts for more than 90% of revenue. The unit is focused on issuing title insurance for commercial and residential real estate transactions in the US and abroad; it also provides escrow closing exchange documentation banking and other title insurance-related services. The company also provides real property-related data services to mitigate risk and facilitate transactions.

The remainder of revenue comes from the specialty insurance segment which offers property and casualty policies including homeowners renters and property hazard coverage. It also markets home warranties.

Direct premiums and escrow fees account for about 45% of total revenue while agent premiums represent about 40%. Information and other revenue provides some 15%.

Geographic Reach

With headquarters in Santa Ana California First American Financial issues policies in 49 states and Washington DC. The US market accounts about 95% of title insurance and services revenue. The company has international title insurance and closing services operations in Canada the UK South Korea Australia and Hong Kong.

First American's specialty insurance division is licensed to issue policies in 50 states and actively issues them in 47 states. Its policy liability is concentrated in the western US; California accounts for the majority. The company's home warranty business reaches 36 states and Washington DC.

Sales and Marketing

First American Financial distributes its title insurance and related products through independent issuing agents and a direct sales force. For residential products it markets to real estate agents brokers and attorneys; mortgage brokers and originators; homebuilders; and escrow service providers. For its refinance and default-related services the company targets mortgage originators servicers and government-backed entities. Commercial lines are primarily marketed to real estate investors (e.g. real estate investment trusts (REITs) insurance brokers insurance companies and asset managers). Other clients include law firms commercial and investment banks mortgage brokers and commercial real estate owners.

First American's casualty insurance is marketed through direct distribution channels (including cross-selling to existing customers) and through a network of independent brokers. The company promotes its home warranty business through real estate brokers and agents and direct consumer outreach.

Financial Performance

Amid a declining US residential purchase market First American Financial's revenue has grown modestly each year since 2014 (save 2018 when sales were stagnant) for five-year growth of about 25%. The company's net income doubled in that time as it reduced its provision for policy losses and other claims controlled direct operating expenses. First American added more than 20% to its cash stores and maintained its level of long-term debt over the last five years.

The firm's revenue ticked down less than half a percent to $5.7 billion in 2018 compared with 2017 driven by lower agent premiums in its title insurance and services segment and higher net realized investment losses due to decreased fair values of equity securities and debt securities sales losses.

Net income gained 12% to $474.5 million in 2018 as the company reduced its discretionary spending and increased earnings credits.

First American expanded its cash by $79.9 million in 2018 ending the year with $1.5 billion. Operations provided $793.2 million and financing activities contributed $514.7 million (due to net change in deposits). The company used $1.2 billion for investments mostly on debt and equity securities purchases.

Strategy

First American Financial operates through three primary strategic lenses: growing its core title and settlement businesses improving its data systems and investing in businesses that complement its core.

To grow its core First American acquires companies that widen its geographic presence. The company bought leading southern Nevada title and escrow firm Nevada Title in 2017.

First American seeks out acquisitions that complement its core by expanding its offerings and enhancing its existing products. In 2018 the company acquired First Funding (a residential warehouse funding and management service provider) and PCN (which offers residential mortgage closing services via its Safe Escrow secure cash disbursement software). That year the company built on its mortgage services business by purchasing Bank of America's lien release division. First American's mortgage services include post-closing document management loan quality control and lien release preparation.

As part of its data systems strategic focus the company is investing to expand the data coverage of its property data licensing business and Datatree.com its online real estate data and analytics platform. The company's data covers real estate assessor/property ownership deeds mortgages foreclosures assignments releases homeowners associations and map and parcel boundaries for nearly every county in the US. It also covers document images and active real estate listings in more than 80% of counties and proprietary title plants in 60% of counties. First American also bought out joint venture SIS a title information provider in 2017.

Mergers and Acquisitions

First American Financial spent more than $80 million on acquisitions in 2018. In February that year the company acquired the lien release business of Bank of America. The purchase strengthens the company's mortgage services lineup which including post-closing document management loan quality control and lien release preparation and recording. First American is providing lien release services to Bank of America under the terms of the deal.

That year the company also purchased First Funding and PCN. The former is a residential warehouse funding and management service provider; the latter is a residential mortgage closing company that markets a secure cash disbursement software called Safe Escrow. The buyouts further First American's strategy to grow its core title and settlement business through acquisitions that broaden its product base or improve its existing offerings.

Company Background

First American Financial was birthed out of the 1889 split of Orange County California from Los Angeles when two companies formed to perform title services in the new county. The two companies merged in 1994 to form First American's predecessor Orange County Title Company.

HISTORY

In 1889 when Los Angeles was on its way to becoming a real city the more countrified residents to the south (including The Irvine Company's founding family) formed Orange County a peaceful realm of citrus groves where land transactions were assisted by title companies Orange County Abstract and Santa Ana Abstract. In 1894 the firms merged under the leadership of local businessman C. E. Parker. For three decades the resulting Orange County Title limited its business to title searches.

In 1924 as real estate transactions became more complex (in part because of mineral-rights issues related to Southern California's oil boom) Orange County Title began offering title insurance and escrow services. The company remained under Parker family management until 1930 when H. A. Gardner took over and guided it through the Depression. In 1943 the company returned to Parker family control.

In 1957 the company began a major expansion beyond Orange County. The new First American Title Insurance and Trust name acknowledged the firm's expansion into trust and custody operations. Donald Kennedy (C. E. Parker's grandson) took over in 1963 and took the company public the next year.

In 1968 First American Corporation was formed as a holding company for subsidiaries First American Title Insurance and First American Trust. This structure facilitated growth as the firm began opening new offices and buying all or parts of other title companies including Title Guaranty Co. of Wyoming Security Title & Trust (San Antonio) and Ticore Inc. (Portland Oregon) all purchased in 1968.

The 1970s were a quiet time for the company but it began growing again in the 1980s as savings and loan deregulation jump-started the commercial real estate market in Southern California. First American diversified into home warranty and real estate tax services. In 1988 on the brink of the California meltdown the company bought an industrial loan corporation to make commercial real estate loans.

EXECUTIVES

Evp, Kenneth D. DeGiorgio, age 47, $749,615 total compensation

Ceo And Director, Dennis J. Gilmore, age 60, $949,231 total compensation

Coo First American Title Insurance Company, Christopher M. Leavell, age 56, $699,615 total compensation

Evp And Cfo, Mark E. Seaton, age 43, $574,231 total compensation

Vice President Of Operations, Shawna Mixon

Vp And Chief Accounting Officer, Matthew F. Wajner, age 43, $274,769 total compensation

Vice President Southern California Area Operations Director, Chris Clemens

Vice President And Manager, Jordan Dunn

Vp Real Estate First American Trust, Robert Krick

Svp And Business Development Officer First American Trust, Kenneth Petersen

Svp And General Counsel First American Trust, Stephen Minana

Vice President Corporate Information Technology, Desai Priti

Svp And Managing Director Northeast Region National Commercial Services, Michael Hillman

Vice President, Michael Kennedy

Vice President, Amanda Pomerantz

Senior Vice President, George Gauger

Vice President National Accounts, Valerie Kolytiris

Senior Vice President Sales, Caitlin Stearns

Vice President, Trish Brown

Vice President Business Development Manager, Lisa Jackson

Assistant Vice President Trust Services, Kathy Vian

Vice President, Jack Hanrahan

Executive Vice President, Scott Callender

Vice President And Wealth Management Advisor First American Trust, Nicholas Henry

Vice President And Relationship Manager First American Trust, Jamie Kim

Vp And Senior Relationship Manager First American Trust, Jody Hudson

Vp And Senior Relationship Manager First American Trust, Denise Mehus

Assistant Vice President Information Security And Continuity Officer, David Nasta

Vp And State Manager West Virginia First American Title Insurance Company, Laura Wareheim

Vp And Portfolio Manager First American Trust, Michael Serrano

Svp And Senior Portfolio Manager First American Trust, Kevin Wilcox

Svp And Relationship Manager First American Trust, Neil Schoenblum

Vice President And Wealth Management Advisor First American Trust, Kris Lanzer

Vice President Of Sales, Tori Robinson

Vice President And Operations Manager, Hess Laura

Senior Vice President Director Of Originations Operations, Mcgowan Michael

Vice President Of Marketing, Sandeep Narayan

Vice President Business Development, Richard Shackelford

Vice President Sales, Omar Kubba

Vp Division Operations, George Opelka

Chairman, Parker S. Kennedy

Board Member, Mark Oman

Auditors: PricewaterhouseCoopers LLP

LOCATIONS

HQ: First American Financial Corp
1 First American Way, Santa Ana, CA 92707-5913
Phone: 714 250-3000 **Fax:** 714 250-3151
Web: www.firstam.com

2016 Sales

	% of total
US	94
International	6
Total	**100**

PRODUCTS/OPERATIONS

2018 Sales

	$ mil.	% of total
Direct premiums and escrow fees	2,508	43
Agent premiums	2,285	39
Information and other	781	14
Net investment income	230	4
Net realized investment losses	(56.5)	-
Total	**5,748**	**100**

2018 Sales

	$ mil.	% of total
Title Insurance and Services	5,283	92
Specialty Insurance	469	8
Corporate	(3.1)	-
Eliminations	(1.2)	-
Total	**5,748**	**100**

2018 Sales (title insurance and services segment

	% of total
US	94
International	6
Total	**100**

Selected Products and Services

Title and Settlement Services
  Title Insurance - Residential
  Title Insurance - Commercial
  Title Insurance - Homebuilders
  Escrow Settlement Services
  Escrow Settlement Services - Commercial
Asset Disposition Services
  Auction Services
  Asset Closing Services
  REO Title Services
  REO Direct Production Services
Equity Services
  Title Insurance Services
  Settlement Services
  Signature Services-Origination
  National Recording Services
Due Diligence
  ALTA Land Title Survey and Coordination Services
  ExpressMap
  Flood Elevation Certificates and Determination
  Zoning Reports
Disclosure Reports
  Natural Hazard Disclosure Report
1031 Exchange Services
  Delayed Exchanges
  Improvement - Build-to-Suit Exchanges

Personal Property Exchanges
Reverse Exchanges
UCC Services
EAGLE 9 UCC Insurance Policy for Buyers
EAGLE 9 UCC Lenders Insurance Policy
EAGLE 9 UCC Foreclosure Notice Policy
EAGLE 9 UCC Vacation Interest Policy
Trustee Services
Direct Source Entry and Review
Foreclosure Processing
Senior Lien Monitoring
Loss Mitigation - Borrower Assistance
Loss Mitigation Title Services
Property Reports - Residential
Document Retrieval Services
Property Reports - Commercial
Lien Priority Insurance
Foreclosure Title Services
National Foreclosure Title Services
Mortgage Priority Reporting
Trustee Sale Guarantee
Trustee Servicing Solutions
Non-National Foreclosure Title Services
Commercial Foreclosure Services — Southwest
Software Solutions
Custom Software Solutions

COMPETITORS

American Coast Title	Old Republic National
American Home Shield	Title
Equity Title Company	Stewart Information
Fidelity National	Services
Financial	Ticor Title Co.
Home Buyers Warranty	Title Resource Group
Investors Title	United General Title
North American Title	Insurance
Old Republic	

HISTORICAL FINANCIALS

Company Type: Public

Income Statement				FYE: December 31
	ASSETS ($ mil.)	NET INCOME ($ mil.)	INCOME AS % OF ASSETS	EMPLOYEES
12/18	10,631	474	4.5%	18,251
12/17	9,573	423	4.4%	18,705
12/16	8,832	343	3.9%	19,531
12/15	8,254	288	3.5%	17,955
12/14	7,666	234	3.0%	17,103
Annual Growth	8.5%	19.4%	—	1.6%

2018 Year-End Financials

Debt ratio: 8.00%	No. of shares (mil.): 111
Return on equity: 13.00%	Dividends
Cash ($ mil.): 1,467	Yield: 4.0%
Current ratio: —	Payout: 38.0%
Long-term debt ($ mil.): —	Market value ($ mil.): 4,977

	STOCK PRICE ($) FY Close	P/E High/Low		PER SHARE ($)		
				Earnings	Dividends	Book Value
12/18	45.00	15	10	4.00	2.00	34.00
12/17	56.00	15	10	4.00	1.00	31.00
12/16	37.00	14	10	3.00	1.00	27.00
12/15	36.00	16	12	3.00	1.00	25.00
12/14	34.00	16	11	2.00	1.00	24.00
Annual Growth	7.1%	—	—	18.2%	17.5%	8.8%

First Bancorp

Not to be confused with North Carolina's First Bancorp this First BanCorp is the holding company for FirstBank Puerto Rico which provides business and retail banking services through more than 50 branches in Puerto Rico and about two dozen more in Florida and the Virgin Islands. Puerto Rico's second-largest bank gets more than one-third of its business from its Commercial and Corporate Banking loans and services. Residential mortgages make up nearly one-third of FirstBank's $9 billion loan portfolio while commercial mortgages make up another one-fifth. First BanCorp also owns FirstBank Insurance Agency Firstbank Puerto Rico Securities and the consumer loan company Money Express La Financiera.

Operations

Generating more than 80% of its revenue from loan interest First BanCorp operates through six business segments: Commercial and Corporate Banking; Consumer (Retail) Banking; Mortgage Banking; Treasury and Investments; United States Operations; and Virgin Islands Operations.

Commercial and Corporate Banking which made up roughly 35% of the company's total revenue in 2014 provides lending and other services for organizations in the public sector as well as for large and specialized middle-market businesses operating in a variety of industries.

The Consumer (Retail) Banking segment (22% of revenue) provides consumer lending and deposit services mainly through FirstBank's branch network and loan centers in Puerto Rico. FirstBank's loans include auto boat and personal loans credit cards and lines of credit.

The Mortgage Banking (18% of revenue) business buys and sells home loans through FirstBank and the company's mortgage origination subsidiary First Mortgage.

Treasury and Investments (1% of revenue) manages securities and lends funds to the company's three banking segments to finance their respective lending activities. It also borrows from those segments and from the United States Operations segment.

United States Operations (20% of revenue) consists of FirstBank's 10 retail and corporate banking businesses in the US mainland mostly in southern Florida.

Virgin Islands Operations (3% of revenue) counts FirstBank's banking business (mostly consumer commercial lending and deposit account activities) in the US Virgin Islands (USVI) and British Virgin Islands (BVI) through 12 branches in the USVI (St. Thomas St. Croix and St. John and the islands) and the BVI (Tortola and Virgin Gorda).

Geographic Reach

San Juan-based FirstBank boasts more than 50 branches across Puerto Rico around a dozen branches in the USVI and BVI and 10 US branches in southern Florida. The bank also has 27 First First Federal Finance Corp (dba Money Express La Financiera) offices in Puerto Rico.

Financial Performance

First BanCorp ended its multi-year revenue decline in 2014 with revenue rebounding by 10% to $695.3 million for the year. This is mostly because the bank in 2013 had suffered more than $200 million from a combination of losses on sales from non-performing assets and losses from a write-off of assets pledged as collateral to Lehman Brothers Inc. Despite earning lower interest income during 2014 the bank's net interest income managed to climb slightly thanks to lower interest expenses on deposits amidst the continued low-interest environment.

The company's profit jumped sharply to $392.29 million in 2014 (compared to a net loss of $164.49 million in 2013) mostly thanks to a drop in loan loss provisions as its loan portfolio's credit quality improved as the economy strengthened but also thanks to a combination of higher revenue and lower interest and non-interest expenses.

Despite higher earnings in 2014 First BanCorp's operating cash declined as the company generated less cash from proceeds on its loans held for sale.

Strategy

First BanCorp has followed an acquisition strategy to grow its loan business and bank clientele in recent years. In early 2015 for example flagship subsidiary FirstBank purchased 10 bank branches in Puerto Rico from its rival Doral Bank which added some $600 million in new deposits $300 million in new mortgage loan business and 140000 new clients. The acquisition also grew FirstBanCorp's total branch network by 20% while expanding its market presence in geographic areas with room for deposit and mortgage loan business growth. The year before in 2014 FirstBank expanded its loan business through the purchase of a $242-million portfolio of mortgage loans from Doral for some $232.9 million.

Company Background

Scotiabank a Canadian bank with operations throughout the Caribbean acquired a 10% stake in First BanCorp in 2007.

EXECUTIVES

Evp Business Group Executive, Cassan Pancham, age 59, $399,815 total compensation

Evp And Chief Risk Officer, Nayda Rivera-Batista, age 45

President And Ceo, Aurelio Aleman-Bermudez, $850,102 total compensation

Evp And Cfo, Orlando Berges-Gonzalez, $600,101 total compensation

Evp And Florida Region Executive, Calixto Garcia-Velez, $486,115 total compensation

Evp And Coo, Donald L. Kafka

Evp Retail And Business Banking Executive, Ginoris Lopez-Lay

Evp And Chief Lending Officer, Emilio Martino-Valdes

Evp And Business Group Director, Michael McDonald

Evp; General Counsel And Secretary, Lawrence Odell, $550,110 total compensation

Evp And Consumer Lending Business Executive, Carlos Power Pietrantoni

Assistant Vice President, Hiram Rivas

Vice President Of Commercial Department, Francisco Pascual

Senior Vice President Commercial Lending, Alfred Massheder

Executive Vice President General Counsel Secretary, Peck Odell

Executive Vice President Business Group Executive, Thomas Michael Mcdonald

Chairman, Roberto R. Herencia, age 59

Auditors: Crowe Horwath LLP

LOCATIONS

HQ: First Bancorp
1519 Ponce de Leon Avenue, Stop 23, Santurce 00908
Phone: 787 729-8200
Web: www.firstbankpr.com

PRODUCTS/OPERATIONS

2014 Sales

	$ mil.	% of total
Interest		
Loans	579	82
Investment securities	53	8
Money market investments	2	-
Noninterest		
Service charges on deposit accounts	17	2
Mortgage banking activities	15	2
Insurance income	7	1
Others	31	5
Adjustments	(7.7)	-
Total	695	100

2014 Sales by Segments

	% of total
Commercial and corporate banking	35
Consumer(Retail) banking	22
United State Operations	21
Mortgage Banking	18
Virgin Island Operations	3
Treasury and Investments	1
Total	**100**

Selected Subsidiaries

FirstBank Puerto Rico
  FirstBank Overseas Corporation
  FirstBank Puerto Rico Securities Corp.
  First Federal Finance Corp. (d/b/a Money Express La Financiera)
  First Insurance Agency Inc.
  First Mortgage Inc.
FirstBank Insurance Agency Inc.
Grupo Empresas de Servicios Financieros (d/b/a PR Finance)

COMPETITORS

Citigroup	Popular Inc.
OFG Bancorp	Santander BanCorp

HISTORICAL FINANCIALS

Company Type: Public

Income Statement

FYE: December 31

	ASSETS ($ mil.)	NET INCOME ($ mil.)	INCOME AS % OF ASSETS	EMPLOYEES
12/18	12,244	202	1.6%	2,643
12/17	12,261	67	0.5%	2,553
12/16	11,922	93	0.8%	2,701
12/15	12,573	21	0.2%	2,758
12/14	12,728	392	3.1%	2,617
Annual Growth	(1.0%)	(15.3%)	—	0.2%

2018 Year-End Financials

Debt ratio: 2.00%
Return on equity: 10.00%
Cash ($ mil.): 586
Current ratio: —
Long-term debt ($ mil.): —
No. of shares (mil.): 217
Dividends
  Yield: 0.0%
  Payout: 3.0%
Market value ($ mil.): 1,868

	STOCK PRICE ($) FY Close	P/E High/Low		PER SHARE ($) Earnings	Dividends	Book Value
12/18	9.00	10	6	1.00	0.00	9.00
12/17	5.00	23	16	0.00	0.00	9.00
12/16	7.00	16	5	0.00	0.00	8.00
12/15	3.00	67	31	0.00	0.00	8.00
12/14	6.00	3	2	2.00	0.00	8.00
Annual Growth	10.0%	—	—	(16.2%)	—	4.6%

First Bancorp (NC)

Don't confuse this First Bancorp with Virginia's First Bancorp or First BanCorp in Puerto Rico. This one is the holding company for First Bank which operates about 100 branch locations in east-central North Carolina east South Carolina and western Virginia (where it operates under the name First Bank of Virginia). In addition to offering standard commercial banking services such as deposit accounts and lending the bank offers investment products and discount brokerage services. Another subsidiary First Bank Insurance Services offers property/casualty products. First Bank focuses its lending on mortgages which account for more than half of its loan portfolio.

EXECUTIVES

Evp And Cfo First Bancorp And First Bank, Eric P. Credle, age 50, $325,000 total compensation
President And Director First Bancorp And President And Ceo First Bank, Michael G. Mayer, age 59, $425,000 total compensation
President Ceo And Director, Richard H. Moore, age 58, $525,000 total compensation
Senior Vice President Retail Market Manager, Carol Clagett
Senior Vice President Legal Division, Kirsten Foyles
Vice President, Jason Williams
Assistant Vice President, Laurie Byrd
Mortgage Loan Originator Assistant Vice President, Patrick Blackburn
Vice President Branch Manager, Sheldon Moser
Chairman First Bancorp And First Bank, James C. Crawford, age 62
Board Member, Dennis Wicker
Board Member, John Gould
Auditors: BDO USA, LLP

LOCATIONS

HQ: First Bancorp (NC)
  300 S.W. Broad St., Southern Pines, NC 28387
Phone: 910 246-2500
Web: www.localFirstbank.com

PRODUCTS/OPERATIONS

2016 Sales

	$ mil.	% of total
Interest Income	131	84
Non-interest Income	26	16
Total	**157**	**100**

COMPETITORS

BB&T	NewBridge Bancorp
BNC Bancorp	PNC Financial
Bank of America	South Street Financial
CommunityOne Bancorp	SunTrust
First Citizens BancShares	Wells Fargo

HISTORICAL FINANCIALS

Company Type: Public

Income Statement

FYE: December 31

	ASSETS ($ mil.)	NET INCOME ($ mil.)	INCOME AS % OF ASSETS	EMPLOYEES
12/18	5,864	89	1.5%	1,098
12/17	5,547	46	0.8%	1,166
12/16	3,615	28	0.8%	861
12/15	3,362	27	0.8%	840
12/14	3,218	25	0.8%	825
Annual Growth	16.2%	37.5%	—	7.4%

2018 Year-End Financials

Debt ratio: 1.00%
Return on equity: 12.00%
Cash ($ mil.): 463
Current ratio: —
Long-term debt ($ mil.): —
No. of shares (mil.): 30
Dividends
  Yield: 1.0%
  Payout: 15.0%
Market value ($ mil.): 971

	STOCK PRICE ($) FY Close	P/E High/Low		PER SHARE ($) Earnings	Dividends	Book Value
12/18	33.00	14	10	3.00	0.00	26.00
12/17	35.00	21	15	2.00	0.00	23.00
12/16	27.00	21	13	1.00	0.00	18.00
12/15	19.00	15	12	1.00	0.00	17.00
12/14	18.00	16	13	1.00	0.00	20.00
Annual Growth	15.3%	—	—	26.1%	5.7%	6.9%

First Bancshares Inc (MS)

Hoping to be first in the hearts of its customers The First Bancshares is the holding company for The First a community bank with some two dozen branch locations in southern Mississippi's Hattiesburg Alabama and Louisiana. The company provides such standard deposit products as checking and savings accounts NOW and money market accounts and IRAs. Real estate loans account for about 80% of the bank's lending portfolio including about equal portions of residential mortgages commercial mortgages and construction loans. The bank also writes business loans and consumer loans. The bank which has expanded beyond Mississippi through several acquisitions has approximately $970 million in assets.

EXECUTIVES

Vice President, Kevin Miller
Vp Appraisal Analyst, Lindsey Smith
Board Member, David Bomboy
Board Member, Fred Mcmurry
Board Member, Ted Parker
Auditors: Crowe LLP

LOCATIONS

HQ: First Bancshares Inc (MS)
  6480 U.S. Highway 98 West, Suite A, Hattiesburg, MS 39402
Phone: 601 268-8998
Web: www.thefirstbank.com

COMPETITORS

BancorpSouth	Peoples Financial
Community Bancshares of Mississippi	Renasant
Hancock Holding	Trustmark

HISTORICAL FINANCIALS

Company Type: Public

Income Statement

FYE: December 31

	ASSETS ($ mil.)	NET INCOME ($ mil.)	INCOME AS % OF ASSETS	EMPLOYEES
12/18	3,004	21	0.7%	641
12/17	1,813	11	0.6%	487
12/16	1,277	10	0.8%	315
12/15	1,145	9	0.8%	305
12/14	1,094	7	0.6%	278
Annual Growth	28.7%	33.8%	—	23.2%

2018 Year-End Financials

Debt ratio: 3.00%
Return on equity: 7.00%
Cash ($ mil.): 159
Current ratio: —
Long-term debt ($ mil.): —
No. of shares (mil.): 15
Dividends
  Yield: 1.0%
  Payout: 15.0%
Market value ($ mil.): 449

	STOCK PRICE ($) FY Close	P/E High/Low		PER SHARE ($) Earnings	Dividends	Book Value
12/18	30.00	25	17	2.00	0.00	24.00
12/17	34.00	31	24	1.00	0.00	20.00
12/16	28.00	15	8	2.00	0.00	17.00
12/15	18.00	11	8	2.00	0.00	19.00
12/14	15.00	12	11	1.00	0.00	18.00
Annual Growth	20.2%	—	—	6.7%	7.5%	7.9%

First Busey Corp

First Busey Corporation keeps itself busy taking care of deposits and making loans. It's the holding company for Busey Bank which boasts $4 billion in assets and 40 branches across Illinois Florida and Indiana. The bank offers standard deposit products and services using funds from deposits to originate primarily real estate loans and mortgages. Subsidiary Busey Wealth Management which manages $5 billion in assets provides asset management trust brokerage and related services to individuals businesses and foundations while FirsTech provides retail payment processing services. Most of Busey Bank's branches are located in downstate Illinois.

Operations

First Busey Corporation operates three business segments Busey Bank which generated more than 99% of its total revenue in 2014 and serves retail and corporate customers; FirsTech which provides remittance processing for online bill payments lock box and walk-in payments; and Busey Wealth Management which provides asset management tax preparation philanthropic advisory services and investment and fiduciary services to individuals businesses and foundations.

Real estate loans including commercial and residential mortgages accounted for 70% of the bank's loan portfolio in 2014 while commercial loans (25%) construction loans (4%) and consumer installments and other loans (0.5%) comprised the rest.

About 55% of First Busey's total revenue came from loan interest (including fees) while another 10% came from interest income on taxable and non-taxable investment securities. The rest of its revenue came from trust fees (11%) deposit account service charges (7%) remittance processing fees (6%) commissions and brokers' fees (2%) and various types of gains on securities and loan sales.

Geographic Reach

Busey Bank has nearly 30 branches in Illinois seven locations in southwest Florida and another office in Indianapolis. Its FirsTech subsidiary accepts payments from its 3000 agent locations across 36 US states.

Sales and Marketing

The bank which staffed 801 employees at the end of 2014 serves individuals businesses and foundations.

Financial Performance

First Busey's revenues have declined in recent years due to shrinking interest margins on loans amidst the low-interest environment. Its profits however have been rising thanks to lower interest expenses on deposits and declining loan loss provisions as its loan portfolio's credit quality has improved with higher property valuations in the strengthened economy.

The bank's revenue dipped by 2% to $167 million mostly as it collected smaller gains from loan sales due to lower refinancing volumes as interest rates began to rise. The bank's loan interest income also continued to decline with lower yields on loan and security assets in the low-interest environment.

Despite generating less revenue in 2014 First Busey's net income jumped by 14% to $32.8 million thanks to continued declines in interest expenses on deposits and lower loan loss provisions. The company's operating cash levels fell by 31% to $68.1 million after adjusting its earnings for non-cash items related to its net proceeds from its loans held-for-sale.

Strategy

First Busey sometimes strategically acquires smaller banks in its target markets to boost its market share broaden its service offerings and boost its loan and deposit business.

Mergers and Acquisitions

In 2019 First Busey agreed to acquire Fort Myers Florida-based wealth advisory firm Investors' Security Trust which will be integrated into the wealth management division of Busey Bank. The combined entity will have assets under management of more than $9.2 billion.

EXECUTIVES

Evp And Chief Risk Officer, Barbara J. Harrington, age 59
President Ceo And Director, Van A. Dukeman, age 60, $537,308 total compensation
Evp; President And Ceo Busey Bank N.a., Robert F. (Bob) Plecki, age 58, $268,654 total compensation
Cio And President And Ceo Firstech Inc., Howard F. Mooney, age 54, $240,216 total compensation
Evp And Regional President Busey Bank, Christopher M. (Chris) Shroyer, age 53, $268,654 total compensation
Evp And General Counsel, John J. Powers
Coo And Cfo, Robin N. Elliott, $256,731 total compensation
Vice President Senior Retirement Plan Services Advisor, Charlee Seaton
Senior Vice President Commercial Real Estate, Kent Poli
Senior Vice President Loan Operations, Michael Stevenson
Vice President, Kelly Dennemann
Senior Vice President Managing Director Fixed Income, Zach Hillard
Assistant Vice President Special Assets, Shana Reed-harper
Executive Vice President, Robert Ballsrud
Assistant Vice President, Emerson Schoonover
Vice President Retail Market Manager, Tami Crouch
Vice President, Brenda Carlson
Senior Vice President, Janice Wolters
Assistant Vice President Risk Management Analyst, Annie Feleccia
Vice President Senior Loan Officer, Brian Church
Assistant Vice President Wealth Advisor Assistant, Monya Russell
Vice President Retail Market Manager, Linda Smith
Vice President Commercial Credit Manager, Thomas Richlak
Vice President Mortgage Operations Manager, Kevin Hoogeveen
Vice President; Senior Mortgage Loan Originator, Erin Trescott
Assistant Vice President Wire Services Manager, Karen Aulph
Assistant Vice President, Anthony Baima
Assistant Vice President, Valerie Garrett
Senior Vice President, Harry Mcsteen
Senior Vice President, Ed Paine
Chairman, Gregory B. (Greg) Lykins, age 71
Vice Chairman, Ed Scharlau
Auditors: RSM US LLP

LOCATIONS

HQ: First Busey Corp
100 W. University Ave., Champaign, IL 61820
Phone: 217 365-4544

PRODUCTS/OPERATIONS

2014 Sales

	$ mil.	% of total
Interest		
Loans including fees	92	55
Interest & dividends on securities	16	10
Noninterest		
Trust fees	20	11
Service charges on deposit accounts	12	7
Remittance processing	9	6
Gain on sales of loans	5	3
Commissions and broker's fees net	3	2
Other	11	6
Total	**167**	**100**

COMPETITORS

Bank of America	First Midwest Bancorp
CIB Marine Bancshares	JPMorgan Chase
Fifth Third	Mercantile Bancorp
First Mid-Illinois	PNC Financial
Bancshares	Wintrust Financial

HISTORICAL FINANCIALS

Company Type: Public

Income Statement

FYE: December 31

	ASSETS ($ mil.)	NET INCOME ($ mil.)	INCOME AS % OF ASSETS	EMPLOYEES
12/18	7,702	99	1.3%	1,270
12/17	7,861	63	0.8%	1,347
12/16	5,425	50	0.9%	1,295
12/15	3,999	39	1.0%	795
12/14	3,666	33	0.9%	801
Annual Growth	**20.4%**	**31.8%**	**—**	**12.2%**

2018 Year-End Financials

Debt ratio: 2.00%
Return on equity: 10.00%
Cash ($ mil.): 240
Current ratio: —
Long-term debt ($ mil.): —
No. of shares (mil.): 49
Dividends
Yield: 3.0%
Payout: 46.0%
Market value ($ mil.): 1,199

	STOCK PRICE ($) FY Close	P/E High/Low	PER SHARE ($) Earnings	Dividends	Book Value
12/18	25.00	16 12	2.00	1.00	20.00
12/17	30.00	22 19	1.00	1.00	19.00
12/16	31.00	22 13	1.00	1.00	16.00
12/15	21.00	17 5	1.00	0.00	13.00
12/14	7.00	6 5	1.00	1.00	15.00
Annual Growth	**39.3%**	**—**	**16.0%**	**8.8%**	**8.0%**

First Citizens BancShares Inc (NC)

First Citizens BancShares owns First-Citizens Bank which operates more than 550 branches in 20 states mainly in the southeastern and western US and urban areas scattered nationwide. The $32 billion-asset bank provides standard services such as deposits loans mortgages and trust services in addition to processing and operational support to other banks. Real estate loans including commercial residential and revolving mortgages and construction and land development loans comprise most of its loan portfolio. Subsidiaries First Citizens Investor Services First Citizens Securities Corporation and First Citizens Asset Management offers investment and discount brokerage services to bank clients.

Operations

The company provides consumer business and commercial banking wealth investments and insurance through a network of branch offices internet banking mobile banking telephone banking and ATMs.

More than 60% of the bank's total revenue came from loan and lease interest during 2015 while another 6% came from interest income on investment securities. The rest of its revenue came from merchant services (6% of revenue) service charges on deposit accounts (6%) wealth management services (6%) cardholder services (4%) mortgage income (1%) insurance commissions (1%) and other miscellaneous income sources.

Geographic Reach

First Citizens BancShares has nearly 560 branches in almost 20 states (Arizona California Colorado Florida Georgia Kansas Maryland Missouri New Mexico North Carolina Oklahoma Oregon South Carolina Tennessee Texas Virginia Washington and West Virginia) and Washington DC.

Sales and Marketing

First Citizens BancShares serves both individuals and commercial entities operating in the healthcare dental practices legal services property management agribusiness nonprofit and trade association markets.

The bank has been ramping up its advertising spend in recent years. It spent $12.4 million in 2015 up from $11.4 million and $8.2 million in 2014 and 2013 respectively.

Financial Performance

First Citizens BancShares' annual revenues have risen more than 35% since 2013 thanks to growth in its variety of non-banking business. Its profits have also been trending higher thanks to declining loan loss provisions as its loan portfolio's credit quality has improved with higher property valuations in the strengthened economy.

The bank's revenue jumped 30% to $1.44 billion during 2015 mostly thanks to higher loan and lease interest income stemming from added loan business from the acquisition of First Citizens Bancorporation. Its non-interest income sources grew 36% during the year as well.

Strong revenue growth in 2015 drove First Citizen's net income up 52% to $210.3 million. The bank's operating cash levels rose 28% to $233 million with the rise in cash-based earnings.

Strategy

FCB has expanded its branch network into new markets while bolstering its loan and deposit business by acquiring small community banks in new territory.

Mergers and Acquisitions

In 2019 First Citizens Bancshares acquired Spartanburg South Carolina-based First South Bancorp the holding company for First South Bank. First South had $236 million in assets $206 million in deposits and $183 million in gross loans. The deal expanded First Citizens' geographic reach in South Carolina.

Company Background

First Citizens BancShares has been fortifying its presence along the West Coast by snapping up failed financial institutions. Since 2009 it has acquired most of the banking operations of Temecula Valley Bank Washington-based Venture Bank and First Regional Bank in Southern California. It also acquired the failed Florida-based bank Sun American and entered Colorado through the acquisitions of United Western Bank and Colorado Capital Bank. All were FDIC-assisted transactions and each acquired institution became branches of First-Citizens Bank. The deals added about 50 branches to the bank's network. First Citizens BancShares

continues to seek out acquisitions of other seized institutions.

Though the company has been able to grow geographically thanks to the economic downturn its IronStone Bank division which focused on business customers suffered from weakened markets in Florida and Georgia. (First Citizens Bancshares merged IronStone into First-Citizens Bank in 2011 to increase efficiency and unify the company's brand.) It has remained profitable thanks in part to its acquisitions which include loss-sharing agreements with the FDIC but has had to increase its provisions for loan losses each of the last five years.

The Holding family which occupies several positions in the company's board room and executive suite controls First Citizens BancShares.

EXECUTIVES

Coo Bancshares And First-citizens Bank & Trust Company, Edward L. (Ed) Willingham, age 64, $585,125 total compensation

President And Corporate Sales Executive Of Bancshares And First-citizens Bank & Trust Company, Peter M. Bristow, age 53

Chairman And Ceo First Citizens Bancshares First-citizens Bank & Trust And Ironstone Bank, Frank B. Holding, age 58, $902,875 total compensation

Evp Finance And Cfo, Craig L. Nix, age 47

Vice Chairman And Vice Chairman Evp And Business Banking Segment Manager First-citizens Bank And Trust And President Ironstone Bank, Hope Holding Connell, age 56, $563,750 total compensation

Evp And Chief Human Resources Officer First-citizens Bank & Trust, Lou J. Davis, age 66

Evp And Chief Credit Officer First-citizens Bank & Trust; Group Vp And Chief Credit Officer Ironstone, Ricky T. Holland, age 65

Executive Vice President And General Auditor Of Fcb, Donald Preskenis

Senior Vice President Commercial Banking, Stephanie Logan

Vice President, Rhonda Chapman

Vice President Marketing, Christine Thompson

Vice President, Scott German

Vice President Business Banking, Jessica Chisholm

Vice President Sba Loan Officer, Alan Black

Vice President Commercial Banking, Drew Schiavone

Senior Vice President, Virginia Lee

Svp Branch Development And Project Management, Peter Watson

Vice President Senior Business Analyst Loan Officer, Joanna Warrick

Senior Vice President Commercial Banking, Tiffani Tedder

Vp Of Sba Lending Central Region, Brett Stacey

Vice President Business Banker, Laura Mccombs

Auditors: Dixon Hughes Goodman LLP

LOCATIONS

HQ: First Citizens BancShares Inc (NC)
4300 Six Forks Road, Raleigh, NC 27609
Phone: 919 716-7000
Web: www.firstcitizens.com

2013 Branches

	No.
North Carolina	253
Virginia	48
California	21
Florida	18
Georgia	14
Washington	7
Texas	7
Colorado	6
Tennessee	6
West Virginia	5
Arizona	2
New Mexico	2
Oklahoma	2
Oregon	2
District of Columbia	1
Kanas	1
Maryland	1
Missouri	1
Total	**397**

PRODUCTS/OPERATIONS

2013 Sales

	$ mil.	% of total
Interest		
Loans & leases	757	72
Investment securities including dividends	37	3
Overnight investments	3	-
Noninterest		
Service charges on deposit accounts	61	5
Wealth management services	60	5
Merchant services	56	4
Cardholder services	48	4
Fees from processing services	23	1
Other service charges and fees	16	1
Adjustments	(72.3)	
Other	73	5
Total	**1,060**	**100**

COMPETITORS

BB&T	JPMorgan Chase
BBVA Compass Bancshares	PNC Financial
	Regions Financial
Bank of America	SunTrust
Capital One	Synovus
Citibank	Wachovia Corp
First Horizon	Wells Fargo

HISTORICAL FINANCIALS

Company Type: Public

Income Statement

FYE: December 31

	ASSETS ($ mil.)	NET INCOME ($ mil.)	INCOME AS % OF ASSETS	EMPLOYEES
12/18	35,409	400	1.1%	6,683
12/17	34,528	324	0.9%	6,799
12/16	32,991	225	0.7%	6,296
12/15	31,476	210	0.7%	6,232
12/14	30,075	139	0.5%	6,440
Annual Growth	**4.2%**	**30.4%**	**—**	**0.9%**

2018 Year-End Financials

Debt ratio: 1.00%
Return on equity: 12.00%
Cash ($ mil.): 1,125
Current ratio: —
Long-term debt ($ mil.): —

No. of shares (mil.): 12
Dividends
  Yield: 0.0%
  Payout: 4.0%
Market value ($ mil.): 4,384

	STOCK PRICE ($) FY Close	P/E High/Low		PER SHARE ($) Earnings	Dividends	Book Value
12/18	377.00	14	11	34.00	1.00	300.00
12/17	403.00	16	12	27.00	1.00	278.00
12/16	355.00	19	12	19.00	1.00	251.00
12/15	258.00	15	12	18.00	1.00	239.00
12/14	253.00	20	16	14.00	1.00	224.00
Annual Growth	**10.5%**	**—**		**25.4%**	**4.8%**	**7.6%**

First Commonwealth Financial Corp (Indiana, PA)

First Commonwealth Financial is the holding company for First Commonwealth Bank which provides consumer and commercial banking services from nearly 115 branches across 15 central and western Pennsylvania counties as well as in Columbus Ohio. The bank's loan portfolio mostly consists of commercial and industrial loans including real estate operating agricultural and construction loans. It also issues consumer loans such as education automobile and home equity loans and offers wealth management insurance financial planning retail brokerage and trust services. The company has total assets of some $6.7 billion with deposits of roughly $4.5 billion.

Operations

The bank made 65% of its total revenue from interest and fees on loans in 2014 while another 12% came from interest and dividends on its investments. Another 6% of First Commonwealth's revenue came from service charges on deposit accounts while trust income and insurance and retail brokerage commissions each made up 2% of the bank's total revenue.

Geographic Reach

The bank boasts nearly 115 branch offices in western and central Pennsylvania and Columbus Ohio. It also has loan production offices in downtown Pittsburgh Pennsylvania and Cleveland Ohio.

Sales and Marketing

First Commonwealth Financial spent $2.95 million on advertising in 2014 compared to $3.13 million and $4.16 million in 2013 and 2012 respectively.

Financial Performance

First Commonwealth's revenues have been slowly decline over the past few years due to shrinking interest margins on loans amidst the low-interest environment. The firm's profits however have been rising thanks to declining loan loss provisions as its loan portfolio's credit quality has been improving in the strengthening economy.

The bank's revenue dipped by more than 1% to $263.04 million in 2014 mostly as interest margins on loans continued to decline as it issued new loans with lower rates in the low-interest environment.

Despite lower revenue in 2014 the bank's net income jumped by 7% to $44.45 million for the year mostly thanks to further decreases in loan loss provisions with a strengthening credit portfolio and lower interest expenses on deposits. First Commonwealth's operating cash fell by 4% to $82.14 million despite higher earnings mostly as the bank collected less in cash proceeds from the sales of its mortgage loans held for sale.

Strategy

First Commonwealth Financial has historically expanded its branch reach through the acquisition smaller banks and thrifts in its market area. However in recent years the company has also been adding non-banking businesses such as insurance firms to bolster its existing non-banking service lines.

Mergers and Acquisitions

First Commonwealth Bank acquired 13 branches in Canton and Ashtabula Ohio from FirstMerit Bank in 2016. The acquisition related to FirstMerit's acquisition by Huntington Bancshares added some $735 million in deposits and some 34000 customers. It is also buying Ohio's DCB Financial parent company of Delaware County Bank & Trust for some $106 million. That deal will add nine full-service branches in central Ohio.

In 2014 First Commonwealth Bank entered the Columbus Ohio market for the first time with its purchase of the Ohio-based First Community Bank for $14.75 million cash.

Also in 2014 the bank bolstered its insurance business through its acquisition of Thompson/McLay Insurance Associates which boasted long-term client relationships in the home auto commercial and specialty insurance lines. The deal added the insurance firm's experienced sales and account management personnel as well as the popular Thompson/McLay Insurance Associates brand which it would keep as a division of its own insurance agency.

EXECUTIVES

Evp And Chief Revenue Officer, Jane Grebenc, $355,833 total compensation
Evp And Chief Credit Officer, I. Robert (Bob) Emmerich, $274,500 total compensation
President And Ceo, Thomas Michael (Mike) Price, age 56, $435,567 total compensation
Evp Cfo And Treasurer, James R. Reske, $237,372 total compensation
Evp Business Integration, Norman J. Montgomery, $261,792 total compensation
Evp Chief Risk Officer General Counsel And Secretary, Matthew C. (Matt) Tomb
Evp Human Resources, Carrie Riggle
Vice President Administration, Wendy Reynolds
Vice President Of Networking Security, Sheila Hoover
Vice President, Terry Lingenfelter
Vice President, Kevin Cribbs
Assistant Vice President And Hris Manager, Karen Livermore
Vice President, Stephen Orban
Vice President And Office Manager Of Murrysville And Export Offices, John Mango
Vice President And Commercial Real Estate, Brian Pukylo
Assistant Vice President Operations, Mona Straw
Vice President And Staffing Manager, Vicki Fox
Vice President Office Manager Ii, David Louis
Vice President Bank Secrecy Act Officer First Commonwealth Bank, David Mcgreevy
Executive Vice President First Commonwealth Advisors, David Buckiso
Senior Vice President Relationship Manager, David McGowan
Assistant Vice President Benefits Administration, Natalie Felix
Investment Commercial Real Estate Vp, Megan Dellapina
Senior Vice President Relationship Manager, Douglas Sako
Vice President Business Banker, Dan Poirier
Assistant Vice President Corporate Loan Officer, Ronald DiBiase
Senior Vice President Internal Audit, Steven Melletz
Business Banker Vice President, Susan Henigin
Vice President Sec And Regulatory Reporting, Morgan Cypher
Vice President Secured Credit, Joe Innocenti
Senior Vice President Financial Solutions Market Leader, Scott Vidovich
Executive Vice President And Chief Credit Officer Of First Commonwealth Bank, Brian Karrip
Assistant Vice President, Bradley Wojnar
Vice President Special Assets Administration, Brenda Wainwright
Vice President Senior Corporate Banker First Commonwealth Bank, Matthew Zuro
Assistant Vice President Financial Solutions Center Manager, Melissa Bartolomeo
Vice President Senior Treasury Officer, Tricia Baker
Senior Vice President Commercial Banking, Mary Patton
Assistant Vice President And Foreclosure Oreo Officer, Mark Oresick
Assistant Vice President Assistant Business Continuity Manager, Hann Candi Beltowsk
Senior Vice President, Regis Scanlon
Assistant Vice President Financial Solutions Center Manager, Mikey Boyer
Vice President Finance, Kristin Robertucci
Assistant Vice President Community Engagement Manager, Elizabeth Saraceno
Vice President Treasury Management Sales Officer, Amy Holbrook
Senior Vice President Private Banking, Walters Barbara
Vice President, Charles Bennett
Senior Vice President Corporate Banking, Huey Bartolini
Vice President Senior Analyst Business Development Officer, Richard Robinson
Senior Vice President Managing Director, Antonio Benton
Assistant Vice President Mortgage Loan Originator, Nancy Garrabrant
Evp Chief Audit Executive, Len Lombardi
Executive Vice President, Joe Culos
Chairman, David S. (Dave) Dahlmann, age 69
Auditors: KPMG LLP

LOCATIONS

HQ: First Commonwealth Financial Corp (Indiana, PA)
601 Philadelphia Street, Indiana, PA 15701
Phone: 724 349-7220
Web: www.fcbanking.com

PRODUCTS/OPERATIONS

2014 Sales

	$ mil.	% of total
Interest		
Loans including fees	171	65
Taxable investments	31	12
Noninterest		
Service charges on deposit accounts	16	7
Insurance & retail brokerage commissions	7	2
Trust income	6	2
Others	33	12
Total	**263**	**100**

Selected Subsidiaries

First Commonwealth Bank
First Commonwealth Insurance Agency
First Commonwealth Home Mortgage LLC (49.9%)
First Commonwealth Financial Advisors Incorporated

COMPETITORS

Allegheny Valley Bancorp	F.N.B. (PA)
AmeriServ Financial	Fidelity Bancorp (PA)
Citizens Financial Group	Northwest Bancshares
Dollar Bank	PNC Financial
	S&T Bancorp

Income Statement				FYE: December 31
	ASSETS ($ mil.)	NET INCOME ($ mil.)	INCOME AS % OF ASSETS	EMPLOYEES
12/18	7,828	107	1.4%	1,512
12/17	7,309	55	0.8%	1,476
12/16	6,684	60	0.9%	1,376
12/15	6,567	50	0.8%	1,311
12/14	6,360	44	0.7%	1,363
Annual Growth	5.3%	24.7%	—	2.6%

2018 Year-End Financials

Debt ratio: 2.00%
Return on equity: 12.00%
Cash ($ mil.): 99
Current ratio: —
Long-term debt ($ mil.): —
No. of shares (mil.): 99
Dividends
Yield: 3.0%
Payout: 32.0%
Market value ($ mil.): 1,190

	STOCK PRICE ($) FY Close	P/E High/Low		PER SHARE ($) Earnings	Dividends	Book Value
12/18	12.00	16	10	1.00	0.00	10.00
12/17	14.00	26	21	1.00	0.00	9.00
12/16	14.00	21	12	1.00	0.00	8.00
12/15	9.00	18	14	1.00	0.00	8.00
12/14	9.00	20	16	0.00	0.00	8.00
Annual Growth	7.0%		—	22.5%	5.7%	6.1%

First Community Bankshares Inc (VA)

First Community Bancshares doesn't play second fiddle to other area banks. The firm is the holding company for First Community Bank which provides traditional services like checking and savings accounts CDs and credit cards and serves communities through some 55 branches across Virginia West Virginia North Carolina and Tennessee. Commercial real estate loans make up 45% of its loan portfolio while commercial business loans make up another 5%. First Community Bancshares offers insurance through subsidiary Greenpoint Insurance and wealth management and investment advisory services through Trust Services and First Community Wealth Management.

Operations

First Community Bancshares operates through four main business activities: commercial and consumer banking lending activities wealth management and insurance services. Its Trust Services and First Community Wealth Management subsidiary had managed assets with a market value of nearly $700 million in 2014.

The bank which had a staff of 678 employees at the end of 2014 generated 70% of its total revenue from loan interest (including fees and loans held for investment) in 2014 and another 8% from interest on taxable and non-taxable securities. The rest of its revenue came from deposit account service charges (9%) insurance commissions (4%) wealth management (1%) and other miscellaneous sources of income.

Sales and Marketing

The bank serves individuals and businesses across several industries including: manufacturing mining services construction retail healthcare military and transportation.

Financial Performance

The company has struggled to grow its revenues in recent years due to shrinking interest margins on loans amidst the low-interest environment. Its profits however have been rising thanks to falling interest expenses and declining loan loss provisions as its loan portfolio's credit quality has improved with higher property valuations in the strengthened economy.

First Community Bancshares's revenue dipped by 2% to $136.1 million in 2014 as its interest income on loans and securities declined with fewer assets and because it took on a $1.39 million loss from the sale of its investment securities during the year.

Despite revenue declines in 2014 the bank's net income jumped 9% to $25.5 million thanks to continued declines in interest expenses on deposits and loan loss provisions. First Community's operating cash levels fell by 6% to $41.7 million for the year after adjusting its earnings for non-cash items related to its loan loss provisions and the proceeds of its mortgage loan sales.

Strategy

Faced with shrinking revenues in recent years First Community has been strategically changing its geographic positioning selling off some of its branches in certain areas and acquiring new branches in others. In late 2014 it acquired seven branches from Bank of America in Southwestern Virginia and Central North Carolina and sold 13 of its branches to Charleston-based CresCom Bank including 10 of its branches in Southeastern North Carolina and three in South Carolina.

Mergers and Acquisitions

In 2014 First Community purchased seven branches from Bank of America including six branches in Southwestern Virginia and one in Central North Carolina. The deal also added $318.9 million in new deposits as well as real estate and assumed leases associated with the branches.

Company Background

After slowing its acquisition activity during the economic downturn First Community resumed in 2012 buying Peoples Bank of Virginia which added four branches in the Richmond area. The company also acquired the failed Waccamaw Bank in a FDIC-facilitated transaction. That deal brought in 16 branches in North Carolina.

EXECUTIVES

Evp And Coo, E. Stephen (Steve) Lilly, age 60, $252,000 total compensation
Chairman And Ceo, William P. Stafford, age 55, $200,013 total compensation
Cfo, David D. Brown, age 44, $225,000 total compensation
President; Ceo First Community Bank, Gary R. Mills, $300,000 total compensation
President First Community Bank, Martyn A. Pell, $255,000 total compensation
Vice President Director Of Operations, Garry Stutts
Assistant Vice President Credit Administration, Jeff Noble
Senior Vice President On The Corporate Staff, John Spracher
Vice President And Sales And Service Leader, Brad Ferguson
Vice President Financial Center Manager, Kevin Ford
Vp Commercial Lending And Administration, Todd Brown
Vice President, Adam Jante
Vice President. Regulatory Compliance Officer, Jean Prazecky Crcm
Board Member, Samuel Elmore
Board Member, C William Davis
Board Member, M Adam Sarver
Auditors: Dixon Hughes Goodman LLP

LOCATIONS

HQ: First Community Bankshares Inc (VA)
P.O. Box 989, Bluefield, VA 24605-0989
Phone: 276 326-9000
Web: www.firstcommunitybank.com

PRODUCTS/OPERATIONS

2011 Sales

	$ mil.	% of total
Interest		
Loans including fees	81	61
Securities	13	10
Deposits in banks	0	-
Noninterest		
Service charges on deposit accounts	13	10
Insurance commissions	6	5
Net gains on sales of securities	5	4
Wealth management	4	3
Other service charges commissions & fees	6	4
Other	4	3
Adjustments	(2.3)	-
Total	130	100

COMPETITORS

BB&T
Bank of America
City Holding
First Citizens BancShares
Highlands Bankshares Inc.
Huntington Bancshares
SunTrust
United Bankshares
WesBanco

HISTORICAL FINANCIALS

Company Type: Public

Income Statement				FYE: December 31
	ASSETS ($ mil.)	NET INCOME ($ mil.)	INCOME AS % OF ASSETS	EMPLOYEES
12/18	2,244	36	1.6%	519
12/17	2,388	21	0.9%	562
12/16	2,386	25	1.1%	580
12/15	2,462	25	1.0%	673
12/14	2,608	25	1.0%	678
Annual Growth	(3.7%)	9.3%	—	(6.5%)

2018 Year-End Financials

Debt ratio: —
Return on equity: 11.00%
Cash ($ mil.): 41
Current ratio: —
Long-term debt ($ mil.): —
No. of shares (mil.): 16
Dividends
Yield: 1.0%
Payout: 10.0%
Market value ($ mil.): 504

	STOCK PRICE ($) FY Close	P/E High/Low		PER SHARE ($) Earnings	Dividends	Book Value
12/18	31.00	16	12	2.00	0.00	21.00
12/17	29.00	24	19	1.00	1.00	21.00
12/16	30.00	22	12	1.00	1.00	20.00
12/15	19.00	16	11	1.00	1.00	19.00
12/14	16.00	13	10	1.00	1.00	19.00
Annual Growth	17.6%		—	13.6%	(19.5%)	2.2%

First Defiance Financial Corp

Named for its hometown not its attitude First Defiance Financial is the holding company for First Federal Bank of the Midwest which operates more than 30 branches serving northwestern Ohio western Indiana and southern Michigan. The thrift offers standard deposit products including checking savings and money market accounts and CDs. Commercial real estate loans account for more than half of the bank's loan portfolio; commercial loans make up another quarter of all loans. The company's insurance agency subsidiary First Insurance Group of the Midwest which accounts for some 7% of the company's revenues provides life insurance property/casualty coverage and investments. In 2019 First Defiance Financial agreed to merge with Ohio-based United Community Financial (the holding company for Home Savings Bank and HSB Insurance) in a deal valued at $473 million.

Strategy
First Defiance Financial has boosted its non-banking product lines via acquisitions. It bought the employee benefits insurance business of another local agency Andres O'Neil & Lowe in 2010; and property/casualty agency Payak-Dubbs Insurance Agency in 2011. Both additions became part of First Insurance Group of the Midwest (formerly named First Insurance & Investments).

In 2016 the company agreed to buy another bank serving northwest Ohio Commercial Bancshares. The deal is valued at some $63 million and adds seven branches and $342 million in assets.

Mergers and Acquisitions
In 2019 First Defiance Financial agreed to merge with Ohio-based United Community Financial (the holding company for Home Savings Bank and HSB Insurance) in a deal valued at $473 million. United Community's Home Savings Bank subsidiary will merge into First Federal to create a bank with more than $6 billion in assets. First Defiance shareholders will have a 52.5% stake in the new company.

EXECUTIVES

Evp Business Banking First Federal Bank, Dennis E. Rose, age 50, $144,077 total compensation
President And Ceo First Defiance Financial And First Federal Bank, Donald P. Hileman, age 66, $400,000 total compensation
Evp General Counsel And Chief Risk Officer First Defiance Financial Corp And First Federal Bank, John R. Reisner, age 63, $180,147 total compensation
Evp And Community Banking President Â– First Federal Bank, Gregory R. Allen, age 55, $200,000 total compensation
Evp And President Western Market Area First Federal Bank, James R. Williams, age 51
Evp And President Eastern Market Area First Federal Bank, Timothy K. (Tim) Harris, age 60
Evp And Chief Credit Officer First Federal Bank, Michael D. Mulford, age 54, $149,387 total compensation
Evp And President Northern Market Area First Federal Bank, Marybeth Shunck, age 49
Evp And Cfo First Defiance Financial Corp. And First Federal Bank, Kent T. Thompson, age 65, $218,360 total compensation
Evp And Director Human Resources First Defiance Financial Corp. And First Federal Bank, Sharon L. Davis, age 37

Evp And President Southern Market Area First Federal Bank, Amy L. Hackenberg, age 48
Vice President, Gary Verhoff
Assistant Vice President Human Resources, Diane Beam
Assistant Vice President, Julie Harris
Senior Vice President, Lisa R Christy
Avp Information Security Analyst, Chad Kaup
Senior Vice President Information Technology, Kathy Miller
Vice President Senior Accountant, Steve Giesige
Chairman, William J. (Bill) Small, age 68
Vice Chairman, Stephen L. Boomer, age 68
Board Member, Barbara Mitzel
Auditors: Crowe LLP

LOCATIONS

HQ: First Defiance Financial Corp
601 Clinton Street, Defiance, OH 43512
Phone: 419 782-5015
Web: www.fdef.com

PRODUCTS/OPERATIONS

2016 Sales

	$ mil.	% of total
Interest		
Loans	80	66
Investment securities		
Taxable	3	3
Tax-exempt	3	2
Interest-bearing deposits	0	-
FHLB stock dividends	1	1
Non-interest		
Service fees & other charges	11	9
Insurance commissions	10	9
Mortgage banking income	7	6
Trust income	2	1
Gain on sale of non-mortgage loans	1	1
Income from bank owned life insurance	1	1
Gain on sale or call of securities	1	-
Other	2	1
Total	**121**	**100**

COMPETITORS

Farmers National
Fifth Third
First Citizens Banc Corp
First Financial Bancorp
Huntington Bancshares
KeyCorp
PNC Financial
SB Financial Group

HISTORICAL FINANCIALS

Company Type: Public

Income Statement   FYE: December 31

	ASSETS ($ mil.)	NET INCOME ($ mil.)	INCOME AS % OF ASSETS	EMPLOYEES
12/18	3,182	46	1.5%	696
12/17	2,993	32	1.1%	674
12/16	2,478	29	1.2%	581
12/15	2,298	26	1.2%	586
12/14	2,179	24	1.1%	555
Annual Growth	9.9%	17.5%	—	5.8%

2018 Year-End Financials

Debt ratio: 1.00%	No. of shares (mil.): 20
Return on equity: 12.00%	Dividends
Cash ($ mil.): 56	Yield: 3.0%
Current ratio: —	Payout: 28.0%
Long-term debt ($ mil.): —	Market value ($ mil.): 494

	STOCK PRICE ($) FY Close	P/E High/Low	PER SHARE ($) Earnings	Dividends	Book Value
12/18	25.00	30 10	2.00	1.00	20.00
12/17	52.00	35 29	2.00	1.00	18.00
12/16	51.00	32 22	2.00	0.00	16.00
12/15	38.00	29 21	1.00	0.00	15.00
12/14	34.00	27 19	1.00	0.00	15.00
Annual Growth	(7.9%)	— —	16.7%	19.6%	7.0%

First Financial Bancorp (OH)

First Financial Bancorp spreads itself thick. The holding company's flagship subsidiary First Financial Bank operates nearly 110 branches in Ohio Indiana and Kentucky. Founded in 1863 the bank offers checking and savings accounts money market accounts CDs credit cards private banking and wealth management services through its First Financial Wealth Management subsidiary. Commercial loans including real estate and construction loans make up more than 50% of First Financial's total loan portfolio; the bank also offers residential mortgage and consumer loans. First Financial Bancorp boasts more than $7 billion in assets including nearly $5 billion in loans.

Operations
The company's private banking business First Financial Wealth Management had $2.4 billion in assets under management in early 2015.

Sales and Marketing
First Financial spent $3.60 million on marketing in 2014 compared to $4.27 million and $5.55 million in 2013 and 2012 respectively.

Financial Performance
First Financial's revenue has been in decline in recent years due to shrinking interest margins on loans amidst the low-interest environment. The company has also struggled to grow its profits much past the $65 million-mark though profit levels are more than twice as high as they were prior to 2009.

The company's revenue dipped by 2% to $311.82 million in 2014 mostly as its loan interest income declined by nearly 4% as interest margins continued to shrink in the low-interest environment. First Financial's non-interest income fell by double-digits mostly due to lower FDIC loss sharing income lower income from the accelerated discount on prepaid covered loans and smaller gains on investment securities sales.

Despite lower revenue in 2014 First Financial's net income rebounded by 34% to $65 million for the year mostly thanks to an 80% reduction in loan and lease loss provisions as the bank's loan portfolio's credit quality improved with the strengthening economy. The company's non-interest expenses also declined by double-digits mostly because the bank in 2013 incurred a nonrecurring $22.4 million FDIC indemnification valuation adjustment.

First Financial's operating cash declined by 66% to $56.65 million after adjusting its earnings for non-cash items related to the indemnification asset decrease and net sales proceeds on its loans held for sale.

Strategy
First Financial has been focusing on branch expansion (on its own or through acquisitions) in

three core metropolitan markets: Cincinnati Dayton and Indianapolis. In 2014 for example First Financial acquired three Ohio-based banks and their branches in 2014 expanding its branch network in Central Ohio while adding new loan and deposit business at the same time.

Mergers and Acquisitions

In 2017 First Financial agreed to acquire Main-Source Financial Group with an expected deal completion in 2Q 2018. The purchase extends its reach in Indiana (80 branches) Ohio Illinois and Kentucky.

In 2014 to expand further into key markets in Columbus and Central Ohio First Financial purchased The First Bexley Bank which served commercial and consumer bank clients from its one branch location in Bexley Ohio. Similarly that year it purchased Insight Bank operated a branch in Worthington Ohio and a mortgage origination office in Newark Ohio; and bought Worthington-based Guernsey Bancorp and its three branches in Central Ohio.

Company Background

In the past the bank acquired 16 branches in western Ohio from Liberty Savings Bank and bought 22 Indianapolis-area branches from Flagstar Bank in 2011. Together the two acquisitions furthered the bank's growth strategy for the key markets of Dayton and Indianapolis.

EXECUTIVES

President Western Markets Commercial Banking And Wealth Management, C. Douglas (Doug) Lefferson
President And Ceo, Claude E. Davis
President And Coo, Anthony M. (Tony) Stollings
Chief Credit Officer, Richard S. Barbercheck
Svp And Cfo, John Gavigan
President Mortgage Banking, Jill A. Stanton
Evp And Chief Compliance Officer, Holly M. Foster
President Corporate Banking, Brad Ringwald
Vice President Commercial Underwriter, Brian Englert
Assistant Vice President Sales Center Manager Iii, Cooley Andrew
Vice President Of Mortgage Lending, Wade Spain
Senior Vice President, Robert Mason
Vice President Network, Brad Stroeh
Vice President, Stephen Vegh
First Vice President Director Of Corporate Facilities, Jeffrey Weingartner
Vice President Commercial Real Estate, Steve Tanner
First Financial Center Banking Center Manager Assistant Vice President, Julie Estep
Vice President Digital Sales Channel Manager, Brano Tomic
Assistant Vice President Business Banking Branch Manager, Kimberly Stitt
Assistant Vice President, Mark Gregg
Senior Vice President Chief Talent Officer, Mary Findley
Vice President And Fiduciary Manager, Paul Schwarz
Vice President, Jim Osmon
Vice President, Josh Riley
Assistant Vice President Mortgage Sales Manager, Mark Spangler
Vice President Commercial Banking First Financial Bank, Jason King
Vice President And Senior Trust Officer, Linda Glass
Assistant Vice President, Teresa Peyton
Vice President Business Development Officer, Kevin Stewart
Vice President Credit Risk Review, Mike Hurley
Vice President, Jimmy Chandler
Chairman, Murph Knapke
Vice Chairman, J. Wickliffe Ach

Board Member, J Ach
Auditors: Crowe LLP

LOCATIONS

HQ: First Financial Bancorp (OH)
  255 East Fifth Street, Suite 800, Cincinnati, OH 45202
Phone: 877 322-9530
Web: www.bankatfirst.com

PRODUCTS/OPERATIONS

2014 Sales

	$ mil.	% of total
Interest		
Loans including fees	209	66
Investment securities	45	14
(Adjustment)	(5.5)	-
Noninterest		
Service charges on deposit accounts	20	7
Trust and wealth management fees	14	5
Bankcard income	11	3
Net gains from sales on loans	4	1
Accelerated discount on covered/formerly covered loans	4	1
Others	11	3
Total	**312**	**100**

COMPETITORS

AMB Financial	Logansport Financial
Commercial Bancshares	MutualFirst Financial
Farmers National	PNC Financial
Fifth Third	Peoples Community
First Defiance	Bancorp
Financial	Peoples-Sidney
First Franklin	SB Financial Group
LCNB	U.S. Bancorp
Liberty Capital	

HISTORICAL FINANCIALS

Company Type: Public

Income Statement   FYE: December 31

	ASSETS ($ mil.)	NET INCOME ($ mil.)	INCOME AS % OF ASSETS	EMPLOYEES
12/18	13,987	173	1.2%	2,131
12/17	8,897	97	1.1%	1,366
12/16	8,438	89	1.0%	1,521
12/15	8,147	75	0.9%	1,471
12/14	7,218	65	0.9%	1,442
Annual Growth	18.0%	27.7%	—	10.3%

2018 Year-End Financials

Debt ratio: 1.00%
Return on equity: 11.00%
Cash ($ mil.): 274
Current ratio: —
Long-term debt ($ mil.): —

No. of shares (mil.): 98
Dividends
  Yield: 3.0%
  Payout: 44.0%
Market value ($ mil.): 2,322

	STOCK PRICE ($) FY Close	P/E High/Low		Earnings	PER SHARE ($) Dividends	Book Value
12/18	24.00	17	11	2.00	1.00	21.00
12/17	26.00	19	15	2.00	1.00	15.00
12/16	28.00	20	10	1.00	1.00	14.00
12/15	18.00	17	13	1.00	1.00	13.00
12/14	19.00	17	14	1.00	1.00	13.00
Annual Growth	6.3%	—	—	15.4%	6.3%	13.6%

First Financial Bankshares, Inc.

Texas hold 'em? Well sort of. First Financial Bankshares is the holding company for eleven banks consolidated under the First Financial brand all of which are located in small and midsized markets in Texas. Together they have about 50 locations. The company maintains a decentralized management structure with each of the subsidiary banks having their own local leadership and decision-making authority. Its First Financial Trust & Asset Management subsidiary administers retirement and employee benefit plans in addition to providing trust services. First Financial Bankshares also owns an insurance agency.

EXECUTIVES

Chairman President And Ceo; Chairman First Financial Bank N.a., F. Scott Dueser, age 66, $754,167 total compensation
Evp And Cfo, J. Bruce Hildebrand, age 64, $445,000 total compensation
Evp And Chief Administrative Officer, Ronald D. (Ron) Butler, age 58, $405,000 total compensation
Evp Lending, Marna Yerigan
Evp Lending, T. Luke Longhofer
Evp And Cio, Thomas S. (Stan) Limerick
Evp And Lending Officer, Gary S.Gragg, age 59, $325,000 total compensation
Evp Retail And Training, Monica Houston
Evp Chief Risk Officer, Randy Roewe
Executive Vice President, Rodney Foster
Senior Vice President, Kay Berry
Vice President, Wade Spain
Vice President Branch Manager N.a, Shay Minor
Vice President, Isabel Montoya
Senior Vice President Mortgage Lending, Janet O'Dell
Vice President Of Human Resources, Jennifer Harper
Vice President Of Information Technology, Kim Tatom
Senior Vice President, Joe Love
Vice President, Sara Burnside
Vice President Fair Lending And Responsible Banking, Jane Parsons
Senior Vice President Mortgage Lending, Wes Masters
Vice President Mortgage Lending, Jayden Slentz
Senior Vice President, Will Christoferson
Vice President Information Technology, Reid Sharp
Vice President, Robert Charles
Board Member, Kade Matthews
Board Member, Ron Giddiens
Board Member, Tim Lancaster
Auditors: Ernst & Young LLP

LOCATIONS

HQ: First Financial Bankshares, Inc.
  400 Pine Street, Abilene, TX 79601
Phone: 325 627-7155
Web: www.ffin.com

PRODUCTS/OPERATIONS

2015 sales

	$ mil.	% of total
Interest Income		
Interest and fees on loans	152	51
Interest on investment securities	70	24
Interest on federal funds sold and interest-bearing deposits in banks	0	-
Non-Interest Income		
ATM interchange and credit card fees	22	7
Trust fees	19	6
Service charges on deposit accounts	17	6
Real estate mortgage operations	10	4
Net gain on sale of available-for-sale securities	1	-
Net gain on sale of foreclosed assets	1	-
Net loss on sale of assets	(0.8)	-
Other	5	2
Total	**295**	**100**

Products/ServicesPersonal

Learn
Online Banking
Mobile Banking
Consumer Education
FAQS
Privacy & Security Information
Resources
Testimonials
Tools
Bank
Checking
Savings
Invest
CDS & IRAS
Broker Services
Borrow
Mortgage Loans
Mortgage Lenders
Auto Loans
Recreational Loans
Home Equity Loans
Personal Line of Credit
CD Secured Loans
Banking with First Financial
Mobile Banking
Online Banking
Pay Bills
Get Cash
Make Deposit
Move Money
Keep Track
Business
Learn
Online Banking
Mobile Banking
Business Education
Starting your Business
Growing your Business
Tools
Business Banking Services
Manage Cash
Send Payments
Receive Payments
Manage Fraud and Risk
Other Services
Trust & Wealth Management
Investment Management
Trust Management
Estate Management
Oil & Gas Management
Real Estate and Property Management
Company Retirement Plans

Selected Subsidiaries

First Financial Bank National Association Abilene Texas.
First Technology Services Inc. Abilene Texas (wholly owned subsidiary of First Financial Bank National Association Abilene Texas).
First Financial Trust & Asset Management Company National Association Abilene Texas.
First Financial Insurance Agency Inc. Abilene Texas.
First Financial Investments Inc. Abilene Texas.

COMPETITORS

BBVA Compass Bancshares	JPMorgan Chase
Bank of America	Wells Fargo
Cullen/Frost Bankers	Woodforest Financial

HISTORICAL FINANCIALS

Company Type: Public

Income Statement

FYE: December 31

	ASSETS ($ mil.)	NET INCOME ($ mil.)	INCOME AS % OF ASSETS	EMPLOYEES
12/18	7,732	151	1.9%	1,350
12/17	7,255	120	1.7%	1,300
12/16	6,810	105	1.5%	1,300
12/15	6,665	100	1.5%	1,270
12/14	5,848	90	1.5%	1,140
Annual Growth	**7.2%**	**13.9%**	**—**	**4.3%**

2018 Year-End Financials

Debt ratio: —	No. of shares (mil.): 135
Return on equity: 15.00%	Dividends
Cash ($ mil.): 250	Yield: 3.0%
Current ratio: —	Payout: 74.0%
Long-term debt ($ mil.): —	Market value ($ mil.): 7,763

	STOCK PRICE ($) FY Close	P/E High/Low		PER SHARE ($) Earnings	Dividends	Book Value
12/18	58.00	60	40	1.00	1.00	8.00
12/17	45.00	53	41	1.00	0.00	7.00
12/16	45.00	58	31	1.00	0.00	6.00
12/15	30.00	47	32	1.00	1.00	6.00
12/14	30.00	95	39	1.00	1.00	5.00
Annual Growth	**17.9%**	**—**	**—**	**12.4%**	**10.5%**	**9.9%**

First Financial Corp. (IN)

Which came first the First Financial in Indiana Ohio South Carolina or Texas? Regardless this particular First Financial Corporation is the holding company for First Financial Bank which offers traditional banking deposit accounts and loans as well as trust private banking wealth management and investment services through more than 70 branches in west-central Indiana and east-central Illinois. About 60% of its loan portfolio is tied to commercial loans while the rest is split between residential and consumer loans. Subsidiary Forrest Sherer sells personal and commercial insurance while subsidiary Morris Plan originates indirect auto loans through dealerships in the bank's market area.

Operations

About 59% of the bank's $1.76 billion loan portfolio was tied to commercial business loans to finance business asset purchases and expansion at the end of 2015 while the remainder of the portfolio was tied to 1-4 family residential real estate mortgages (25% of loan assets) and consumer loans (16%).

Nearly 75% of First Financial's revenue comes from interest income. About 57% of its total revenue came from loan interest (including fees) during 2015 while another 16% came from interest income on taxable and tax-exempt investment securities. The rest of its revenue came from deposit account service charges (7% of revenue) insurance commissions (5%) trust and financial services (4%) gains on mortgage loan sales (2%) and other miscellaneous income sources.

Geographic Reach

The Terre Haute Indiana-based bank operated 71 branches in west-central Indiana and east-central Illinois at the end of 2015.

Financial Performance

First Financial Corporation's annual revenues and profits have been trending lower over the past several years due to shrinking margins in the low-interest environment and as its loan assets have declined more than 5% since 2011.

The bank's revenue fell 4% to $147.86 million during 2015 mostly as its interest-earning loan and investment assets and the interest margins they command continued to decline. Its non-interest income tumbled at a similar rate due to reduced investment service and insurance agency income.

Revenue declines in 2015 caused First Financial's net income to dive nearly 11% to $30.2 million. The bank's operating cash levels plunged almost 30% to $41.26 million for the year as cash earnings shrank.

Strategy

First Financial Corporation continued in 2016 to expand its branch network in hopes to build its loan and deposit business. Indeed its branch network has steadily grown from 65 branches at the end of 2011 to 71 branches at the end of 2015.

Mergers and Acquisitions

In January 2019 First Financial agreed to purchase HopFed Bancorp in a deal valued at nearly $130 million. The Hopkinsville Kentucky-based company has 18 branches and three loan production offices in Kentucky and Tennessee new markets for First Financial.

Company Background

In 2011 First Financial bought Freestar Bank adding more than a dozen branches in central Illinois. It was the largest acquisition in the company's history.

With roots dating back to 1834 First Financial Bank is not only one of the oldest banks in Indiana but also the entire country. It is also one of the oldest continually operating businesses in its hometown of Terre Haute. Another local business Princeton Mining Company owns nearly 10% of First Financial Corporation.

EXECUTIVES

Vice Chairman And Ceo, Norman D. Lowery, age 51, $630,297 total compensation
Vice President, Jim Nichols
Personal Trust Department Assistant Vice Presiden, Carol Myers
Vice President, Brad Williams
Assistant Vice President Of Marketing And First Gold Club Coordinator, Sally Whitehurst
Vice President, Patrick R Ralston
Vice President Collections, Jeff Nickels
Vice President, Thom Frantz
Avp Consumer Lender, Thea Serrano
Vice President Human Resources, Racheal Carter
Executive Vice President, Devon Cury
Vice President Director Of Consumer Lending, Carl Britton
Vice President, Eric Feathers
Vice President, Brenda Voll
Board Member, Gregory L Gibson
Chairman, B. Guille Cox
Board Member, Ronald Rich
Board Member, William Krieble
Auditors: Crowe LLP

LOCATIONS

HQ: First Financial Corp. (IN)
One First Financial Plaza, Terre Haute, IN 47807
Phone: 812 238-6000
Web: www.first-online.com

PRODUCTS/OPERATIONS

2011 Sales

	$ mil.	% of total
Interest		
Loans including related fees	91	61
Securities	23	15
Other	2	1
Noninterest		
Service charges & fees on deposit accounts	9	6
Other service charges & fees	8	6
Insurance commissions	7	5
Trust & financial services	5	3
Other	4	3
Total	**150**	**100**

COMPETITORS

FFW	Huntington Bancshares
Fifth Third	JPMorgan Chase
First Midwest Bancorp	Old National Bancorp
First Robinson	PNC Financial
Financial	

HISTORICAL FINANCIALS

Company Type: Public

Income Statement   FYE: December 31

	ASSETS ($ mil.)	NET INCOME ($ mil.)	INCOME AS % OF ASSETS	EMPLOYEES
12/18	3,009	47	1.5%	816
12/17	3,001	29	1.0%	847
12/16	2,989	38	1.3%	846
12/15	2,980	30	1.0%	896
12/14	3,002	34	1.1%	952
Annual Growth	0.1%	8.4%	—	(3.8%)

2018 Year-End Financials

Debt ratio: —
Return on equity: 11.00%
Cash ($ mil.): 74
Current ratio: —
Long-term debt ($ mil.): —

No. of shares (mil.): 12
Dividends
  Yield: 6.0%
  Payout: 66.0%
Market value ($ mil.): 493

	STOCK PRICE ($) FY Close	P/E High/Low	Earnings	Dividends	Book Value
12/18	40.00	14 10	4.00	3.00	36.00
12/17	45.00	22 18	2.00	3.00	34.00
12/16	53.00	17 10	3.00	1.00	34.00
12/15	34.00	16 14	2.00	1.00	32.00
12/14	36.00	14 12	3.00	1.00	30.00
Annual Growth	3.0%	— —	10.5%	27.0%	4.3%

First Foundation Inc

Auditors: Eide Bailly LLP

LOCATIONS

HQ: First Foundation Inc
18101 Von Karman Avenue, Suite 700, Irvine, CA 92612
Phone: 949 202-4160
Web: www.ff-inc.com

HISTORICAL FINANCIALS

Company Type: Public

Income Statement   FYE: December 31

	ASSETS ($ mil.)	NET INCOME ($ mil.)	INCOME AS % OF ASSETS	EMPLOYEES
12/18	5,840	43	0.7%	482
12/17	4,541	28	0.6%	394
12/16	3,975	23	0.6%	335
12/15	2,593	13	0.5%	295
12/14	1,355	8	0.6%	208
Annual Growth	44.1%	50.4%		23.5%

2018 Year-End Financials

Debt ratio: 12.00%
Return on equity: 9.00%
Cash ($ mil.): 67
Current ratio: —
Long-term debt ($ mil.): —

No. of shares (mil.): 44
Dividends
  Yield: —
  Payout: —
Market value ($ mil.): 572

	STOCK PRICE ($) FY Close	P/E High/Low	Earnings	Dividends	Book Value
12/18	13.00	20 12	1.00	0.00	13.00
12/17	19.00	36 17	1.00	0.00	10.00
12/16	29.00	41 28	1.00	0.00	9.00
12/15	24.00	41 29	1.00	0.00	8.00
12/14	18.00	37 33	1.00	0.00	6.00
Annual Growth	(8.2%)	— —	18.3%	—	18.6%

First Hawaiian Inc

Auditors: DELOITTE & TOUCHE LLP

LOCATIONS

HQ: First Hawaiian Inc
999 Bishop Street, 29th Floor, Honolulu, HI 96813
Phone: 808 525-7000
Web: www.fhb.com

HISTORICAL FINANCIALS

Company Type: Public

Income Statement   FYE: December 31

	ASSETS ($ mil.)	NET INCOME ($ mil.)	INCOME AS % OF ASSETS	EMPLOYEES
12/18	20,696	264	1.3%	2,200
12/17	20,549	184	0.9%	2,300
12/16	19,662	230	1.2%	2,200
12/15	19,353	214	1.1%	2,250
12/14	18,134	217	1.2%	
Annual Growth	3.4%	5.1%		

2018 Year-End Financials

Debt ratio: —
Return on equity: 10.00%
Cash ($ mil.): 1,004
Current ratio: —
Long-term debt ($ mil.): —

No. of shares (mil.): 135
Dividends
  Yield: 4.0%
  Payout: 50.0%
Market value ($ mil.): 3,036

	STOCK PRICE ($) FY Close	P/E High/Low	Earnings	Dividends	Book Value
12/18	23.00	17 11	2.00	1.00	19.00
12/17	29.00	26 20	1.00	1.00	18.00
12/16	35.00	21 15	2.00	0.00	18.00
Annual Growth	(10.3%)	— —	4.5%	48.0%	1.3%

First Horizon National Corp

First Horizon National would like to be on banking consumers' horizons in the Volunteer State and beyond. The bank holding company operates more than 170 First Tennessee Bank branches in its home state and neighboring markets. Boasting roughly $26 billion in total assets it offers traditional banking services like loans deposit accounts and credit cards as well as trust asset management financial advisory and investment services. Subsidiary FTN Financial performs securities sales and trading fixed-income underwriting and other investment banking services through more than 25 offices in more than 15 states as well as in Hong Kong.

Operations

First Horizon operates two core business segments: Regional Banking and Capital Markets.

Regional Banking is the company's largest division (it generated 73% of the bank's total revenue in 2014) and provides traditional banking products and services to retail and commercial customers mostly in Tennessee but also in neighboring markets. The division also provides investments financial panning trust services and asset management as well as correspondent banking services such as credit depository and other banking related services for financial institutions.

The Capital Markets segment which contributed 18% to total revenues in 2014 serves mainly institutional clients in the US and overseas. Its services consist of fixed-income sales trading loan sales portfolio advisory and derivative sales.

First Horizon's two non-core segments include a Corporate division which collects gains and losses related to the bank's debt and investment activities; and the non-strategic segment (11% of total revenues in 2014) which consists of the wind down of the company's national consumer lending activities its legacy mortgage banking elements including service fees its trust preferred loan portfolio and exited businesses.

The company has diversified revenue streams generating about 56% of its total revenue from interest income (mostly from loans) in 2014 16% from capital markets-related fees nearly 10% from deposit transactions and cash management fees about 6% from its Mortgage Banking business and 6% from a combination of brokerage fees and trust services and management fees.

Geographic Reach

First Horizon National boasts more than 180 branch locations across seven US states. More than 90% of the branches are in Tennessee while just over a dozen are in the states of Georgia (northwestern) Mississippi (northwestern) North Carolina Virginia South Carolina and Florida. It also has more than 25 financial offices in 16 states across the US plus a financial office in Hong Kong.

Sales and Marketing

The company spent $18.68 million on advertising and public relations in 2014 up from $18.24 million and $17.44 million in 2013 and 2012 respectively.

Financial Performance

First Horizon's revenue has been in decline in recent years due to shrinking interest margins on loans amidst the low-interest environment. The firm's profits however have been rising thanks to declining loan loss provisions as its loan portfolio's credit quality has been improving in the strengthening economy.

The company's revenue fell by 4% to $1.26 billion in 2014 mostly as the Capital Markets business shrank by 26% as fixed-income markets suffered from low rates low market volatility and uncertainty around the Federal Reserve's monetary policy. The bank's interest income also fell by 3% despite rising commercial loan business mostly due to a combination of continued run-off of non-strategic loan portfolios lower-yielding commercial loans and lower strategic loan balances. Offsetting some of the top-line decline First Horizon's mortgage banking revenue more than doubled for the year mostly thanks to a nearly $40 million gain on the sale of its mortgage loans held-for-sale.

Despite revenue declines in 2014 First Horizon's net income skyrocket nearly seven-fold to $219.52 million thanks to a combination of lower interest and non-interest expenses and a significant decline in loan loss provisions as its loan portfolio's credit condition improved.

The company's operating cash also jumped by 63% to $704.7 million during the year as cash earnings rose and as net cash proceeds from the bank's mortgage loans held-for-sale increased.

Strategy

First Horizon National's flagship First Tennessee Bank has been expanding its geographic reach in recent years through both branch openings and strategic acquisitions of smaller banks and branches in target markets. In 2014 the bank opened its first office in Florida (in Jacksonville) as it continued its plans for growth in the Mid-Atlantic region which includes North Carolina South Carolina Virginia and northern parts of Florida. Also that year the bank agreed to purchase 13 bank branches located in the Middle and East Tennessee for a total of nearly $438 million which would add some $437 million worth of new deposits and expand its reach in its home state.

Mergers and Acquisitions

In 2014 First Horizon agreed to purchase TrustAtlantic Financial Corporation along with its five TrustAtlantic Bank branches in North Carolina (mostly in the Raleigh-Cary metro area). The deal matched First Horizon's objectives to expand in North Carolina's fast-growing Research Triangle region of the state.

In mid-2013 First Tennessee bank acquired Mountain National Bank from the FDIC adding 12 new branch locations in Sevier and Blount counties in Eastern Tennessee as well as $249 million in loan assets and $362 million in deposits.

In 2012 the company added to FTN Financial with the purchase of Las Vegas-based Main Street Capital Advisors which provides investment management and consulting services mainly to state and local municipalities.

Company Background

At the start of the recession First Horizon began selling non-core assets and refocused growth closer to home. First Horizon exited the Baltimore-Washington DC and Atlanta markets. The company also sold some 230 First Horizon Home Loan offices as well as the unit's loan origination and servicing operations outside of Tennessee to MetLife. After the sale First Horizon Financial outsourced some its mortgage origination processing and servicing operations within Tennessee to PHH Mortgage.

In 2008 the bank discontinued its specialty construction and consumer lending activities beyond Tennessee. It exited the institutional equity research business in 2010 and sold its First Horizon Insurance unit to Brown & Brown the following year. Also in 2011 First Horizon sold a subsidiary that provided administrative services for health savings accounts.

EXECUTIVES

Evp And Chief Human Resources Officer, John M. Daniel, age 64

Evp Regional Banking; Coo First Tennessee Bank, David T. Popwell, age 58, $450,000 total compensation

Chairman President And Ceo, D. Bryan Jordan, age 57, $815,000 total compensation

Evp And General Counsel, Charles T. Tuggle, age 70, $475,000 total compensation

Evp Corporate Communications, Kimberley C. (Kim) Cherry

Evp Technology And Operations And Cio, Bruce A. Livesay

Evp And Cfo, William C. (BJ) Losch, age 48, $425,000 total compensation

Evp And Chief Risk Officer, Yousef A. Valine, age 59, $362,692 total compensation

President Ftn Financial, Michael E. Kisber, age 59, $600,000 total compensation

Evp And Chief Credit Officer, Susan L. Springfield, age 54

Evp And Chief Operating And Financial Officer Ftn Financial, Michael K. Waddell

Evp Consumer Banking First Tennessee Bank, David W. Miller

Evp Corporate Banking, Steve J. Hawkins

President First Tennessee Bank Mid-atlantic Region, Billy Frank, age 48

President First Tennessee Bank Mid-atlantic Region, John Fox, age 66

Regional President First Tennessee Bank Tennessee Banking Group, Richard Shaffer, age 54

Evp And Chief Audit Executive, Vernon H. Stafford

Senior Vice President Facilities Management, Stephen Bieber

Vice President Risk Management, Kathleen Mooney

Vice President Business Process Services, Nancy Bradley

Senior Vice President And Chief Investment.., Karen Kruse

Senior Vice President And Counsel (2004), John Arthur Niemoeller

Senior Vice President, Christine Bland

Vice President, David Ward

Svp Small Business Administration, Adrienne Sipe

Svp And Credit Risk Manager, Darin Johnson

Vice President, Jack Yokley

Board Member, Luke Yancy

Board Member, Scott Niswonger

Board Member, Colin Reed

Board Member, Rajesh Subramaniam

Auditors: KPMG LLP

LOCATIONS

HQ: First Horizon National Corp
165 Madison Avenue, Memphis, TN 38103
Phone: 901 523-4444
Web: www.firsthorizon.com

PRODUCTS/OPERATIONS

2014 Sales

	$ mil.	% of total
Interest		
Loans including fees	572	45
Investment securities	93	7
Trading securities	32	3
Loans held for sale	11	1
Other	1	-
Noninterest		
Capital markets	201	16
Deposit transactions & cash management	112	9
Mortgage banking	71	6
Brokerage management fees & commissions	49	4
Trust services and investment management	28	2
Bankcard income	24	2
Bank owned life insurance	16	1
Other	49	4
Total	**1,259**	**100**

COMPETITORS

Athens Federal Community Bank	JPMorgan Chase
BB&T	Regions Financial
Bank of America	SunTrust
Citigroup	Trustmark
	Wells Fargo

HISTORICAL FINANCIALS

Company Type: Public

Income Statement				FYE: December 31
	ASSETS ($ mil.)	NET INCOME ($ mil.)	INCOME AS % OF ASSETS	EMPLOYEES
12/18	40,832	545	1.3%	5,577
12/17	41,423	166	0.4%	5,984
12/16	28,555	227	0.8%	4,288
12/15	26,195	86	0.3%	4,293
12/14	25,673	220	0.9%	4,310
Annual Growth	12.3%	25.5%	—	6.7%

2018 Year-End Financials

Debt ratio: 3.00%	No. of shares (mil.): 319
Return on equity: 12.00%	Dividends
Cash ($ mil.): 2,059	Yield: 4.0%
Current ratio: —	Payout: 29.0%
Long-term debt ($ mil.): —	Market value ($ mil.): 4,192

	STOCK PRICE ($) FY Close	P/E High/Low		PER SHARE ($) Earnings	Dividends	Book Value
12/18	13.00	12	7	2.00	0.00	14.00
12/17	20.00	31	24	1.00	0.00	13.00
12/16	20.00	22	12	1.00	0.00	10.00
12/15	15.00	48	36	0.00	0.00	10.00
12/14	14.00	15	12	1.00	0.00	10.00
Annual Growth	(0.8%)	—	—	16.0%	24.5%	9.5%

First Internet Bancorp

First Internet Bancorp was formed in 2006 to be the holding company for First Internet Bank of Indiana (First IB). Launched in 1999Â the bankÂ was the first state-chartered FDIC-insured institution to operate solely via the Internet.Â It now operates two locationsÂ in Indianapolis after adding one via its 2007 purchase of Landmark Financial (the parent of Landmark Savings Bank) a deal that also brought aboard residential mortgage brokerage Landmark Mortgage.Â First IB offers traditional checking and savings accounts in addition to CDs IRAs credit and check cards consumer installment and residential mortgage loans and lines of credit. It serves customers in all 50 states.

EXECUTIVES

Vice President, Tom Natale

Vice President Asset Quality, Gregg Feigh

Vice President Of Commercial Loan Servicing, David Sewell

Vice President Commercial Lender, Carl Osberg

Vice President Commercial Lending, Jim Laine

Vice President Commercial Lending, Kevin Lynch

Vice President Of Commercial Banking Group, Christy Smith

Vice President Commercial Banking, Suzy Sottong

Vp Human Resources, Angie Redmon

Auditors: BKD, LLP

LOCATIONS

HQ: First Internet Bancorp
11201 USA Parkway, Fishers, IN 46037
Phone: 317 532-7900
Web: www.firstinternetbancorp.com

COMPETITORS

Bank of America   Citibank
BofI   E*TRADE Bank

HISTORICAL FINANCIALS

Company Type: Public

Income Statement   FYE: December 31

	ASSETS ($ mil.)	NET INCOME ($ mil.)	INCOME AS % OF ASSETS	EMPLOYEES
12/18	3,542	22	0.6%	201
12/17	2,768	15	0.6%	206
12/16	1,854	12	0.7%	192
12/15	1,270	9	0.7%	152
12/14	971	4	0.4%	143
Annual Growth	38.2%	50.0%	—	8.9%

2018 Year-End Financials

Debt ratio: 1.00%
Return on equity: 9.00%
Cash ($ mil.): 189
Current ratio: —
Long-term debt ($ mil.): —

No. of shares (mil.): 10
Dividends
Yield: 1.0%
Payout: 10.0%
Market value ($ mil.): 208

	STOCK PRICE ($) FY Close	P/E High/Low	PER SHARE ($) Earnings	Dividends	Book Value
12/18	20.00	18 8	2.00	0.00	28.00
12/17	38.00	19 12	2.00	0.00	27.00
12/16	32.00	14 10	2.00	0.00	24.00
12/15	29.00	18 7	2.00	0.00	23.00
12/14	17.00	26 16	1.00	0.00	22.00
Annual Growth	5.1%	— —	24.4%	(0.0%)	6.8%

First Interstate BancSystem Inc

This Treasure State bank wants to be your treasury. First Interstate BancSystem is the holding company for First Interstate Bank which has about 80 branches in Montana western South Dakota and Wyoming. Serving area consumers businesses and municipalities the bank provides traditional services including deposit accounts wealth management and loans. Commercial loans including mortgages make up more than half of the bank's loan portfolio; residential real estate agricultural and construction loans round out its lending activities. On the wealth management side the bank has more than $8 billion in trust assets held in a fiduciary or agent capacity.

Financial Performance

The company's revenue decreased in fiscal 2013 compared to the previous period. It reported $369.3 million in revenue for fiscal 2013 down from $388.8 million in fiscal 2012. However despite the decreased annual revenue the company's net income increased in fiscal 2013 to $86 million up from a net income of $58 million the prior fiscal year. Cash flow increased by about $15 million in fiscal 2013 compared to 2012 levels.

Strategy

The company is always looking for opportunities for expansion including organic growth as well as growth through acquisitions. It expanded into the northwest growth market with the acquisition of Cascade Bancorp for around $589 million.

EXECUTIVES

Svp And Cio, Kevin J. Guenthner, age 55, $205,385 total compensation
President And Ceo, Kevin P. Riley, age 59, $307,270 total compensation
Evp And Chief Banking Officer, Bill Gottwals
Evp And Cfo, Marcy D. Mutch, age 59
Executive Vice President And Chief Banking Officer, Michael Huston
Assistant Vice President And Personal Banking Officer, Julie Mazza
Vice Chairman, James R. Scott, age 69
Secretary, Jana Garza
Auditors: RSM US LLP

LOCATIONS

HQ: First Interstate BancSystem Inc
401 North 31st Street, Billings, MT 59116-0918
Phone: 406 255-5390
Web: www.fibk.com

PRODUCTS/OPERATIONS

Selected ServicesBanking
Checking Accounts
Credit Cards
Debit Cards
Escrow Services
Foreign Currency
Overdraft Protection
Personal Resources
Prepaid Cards
Savings Accounts
Borrowing
AdvanceLine
Auto & Recreation
Debt Consolidation
Home Equity
Home Mortgage
Personal Loans
Create & Build Wealth
Long-Term Planning
Planning for the Unexpected
Saving for College
Saving for Retirement
Wealth Resources
Protect & Preserve Wealth
Asset Management
Employee Exit Strategies
Health Concerns
Investment Services
Retirement Plan Services
Sales 2015

Interest income	282	70
Non-interest income	121	30
Total	403	100

COMPETITORS

Bank of the West   Great Western Bancorp
Crazy Woman Creek   U.S. Bancorp
Eagle Bancorp   Wells Fargo
Glacier Bancorp

HISTORICAL FINANCIALS

Company Type: Public

Income Statement   FYE: December 31

	ASSETS ($ mil.)	NET INCOME ($ mil.)	INCOME AS % OF ASSETS	EMPLOYEES
12/18	13,300	160	1.2%	2,330
12/17	12,213	107	0.9%	2,207
12/16	9,064	96	1.1%	1,721
12/15	8,728	87	1.0%	1,742
12/14	8,610	84	1.0%	1,705
Annual Growth	11.5%	17.4%	—	8.1%

2018 Year-End Financials

Debt ratio: 1.00%
Return on equity: 10.00%
Cash ($ mil.): 822
Current ratio: —
Long-term debt ($ mil.): —

No. of shares (mil.): 61
Dividends
Yield: 3.0%
Payout: 41.0%
Market value ($ mil.): 2,216

	STOCK PRICE ($) FY Close	P/E High/Low	PER SHARE ($) Earnings	Dividends	Book Value
12/18	37.00	17 13	3.00	1.00	28.00
12/17	40.00	22 16	2.00	1.00	25.00
12/16	43.00	20 12	2.00	1.00	22.00
12/15	29.00	16 12	2.00	1.00	21.00
12/14	28.00	16 13	2.00	1.00	20.00
Annual Growth	7.1%	— —	10.1%	15.0%	8.9%

First Merchants Corp

First Merchants is the holding company that owns First Merchants Bank which operates some 120 branches in Indiana Illinois and western Ohio. Through its Lafayette Bank & Trust and First Merchants Private Wealth Advisors divisions the bank provides standard consumer and commercial banking services including checking and savings accounts CDs check cards and consumer commercial agricultural and real estate mortgage loans. First Merchants also provides trust and asset management services. Founded in 1982 First Merchants has nearly $9.4 billion worth of consolidated assets.

Operations

Real estate loans made up about 70% of First Merchants's loan portfolio while commercial and industrial agricultural and consumer loans account for the remainder of the bank's lending activity.

Geographic Reach

Muncie Indiana-based First Merchants's 120-plus bank branches are located across Indiana and in two counties each in Illinois and Ohio.

Sales and Marketing

First Merchants's marketing expense was $3.73 million in 2017 $3 million (2016) and $3.5 million (2015).

Financial Performance

Revenue jumped by 19% to $348.2 million in 2017 driven by higher interest income from more organic and inorganic loan business and more investment security income following the bank's recent acquisitions. The bank also collected significantly more non-interest income from deposit account service charges electronic card fees and insurance-related gains as it grew its customer base through acquisitions. Higher revenue drove the bank's net income up 18% to $96 million.

Total cash on hand at the end of fiscal 2017 stood at $154.9 million which was $27 million higher than cash at the start of the year. Cash from operations contributed $126 million and cash generated through financing activities added $535.8 while investments in securities and other uses used $635.3 million.

Strategy

A key part of the First Merchants's growth strategy is to expand geographically through acquisitions of small community banks operating in its key Indiana Illinois and western Ohio markets.

In 2017 and 2018 First Merchants added more nearly 3 dozen branches to its banking network after acquiring Michigan-based Monroe Bank & Trust Ohio-based Arlington Bank and Independent Alliance Banks located in Indiana. The bank has in recent years acquired 1-2 community banks operating in these states each year often adding a handful of branches as well as loans and other assets through each transaction.

Mergers and Acquisitions

In 2018 First Merchants acquired MBT Financial Corporation the holding company for Monroe Bank & Trust and its 20 branches serving Monroe Michigan and the southeastern Michigan area.

In 2017 First Merchants bought Columbus Ohio-based Arlington Bank. for $82.6 million. The same year it spent $238.8 million to acquire a majority stake in Independent Alliance Banks and IAB's 16 banking centers located in and around Fort Wayne Indiana.

EXECUTIVES

First Vice President Corporate Controller, Jeff Lorentson
Evp And Cfo, Mark K. Hardwick, age 48, $317,347 total compensation
Cto, Stephan H. Fluhler, $205,268 total compensation
President And Ceo, Michael C. (Mike) Rechin, age 60, $502,181 total compensation
Evp And Chief Banking Officer, Michael J. (Mike) Stewart, age 53, $310,077 total compensation
Evp And Chief Credit Officer, John J. Martin, age 52, $249,193 total compensation
Svp And Chief Risk Officer, Jeffery B. Lorentson
Vice President Of Marketing, Deanne Beard
Vice President, Tom Dunson
Vice President Of Loans, Christopher Allen
Vice President Marketing Manager, Dana Talaga
Vice President Cash Management, Jennifer Wehrly
Vice President Commercial Lending, Greg Lanter
Vice President, Lentz Gregory
Executive Vice President Mortgage Operations, Debra Rynearson
Senior Vice President Human Re, Leslie Holland
Vice President And Purchasing Director, Lisa Brothers
Vice President, Joseph Keyler
Vice President, Alex Jones
Assistant Vice President Relationship Manager, Michael Kahne
Vice President, Margaret Hoke
Senior Vice President, John Ditmars
Vice President Manager Small Business Credit, Robert Spencer
Assistant Vice President Banking Center Manager, Veronica Avila
Senior Vice President Chief Sales Officer Lakeshore Region, Dale Clapp
Senior Vice President And Director Of Human Resources, Kim A Ellington
Vice President Retail Market L, Roberta Salway
Vice President Structured Finance, Dave Decraene
Vice President, Daniel J Gick
Vice President Retail Lending Leader, Jill Engerer
Vice President, Candy Shumard
Vice President, James F Zimmerman
Assistant Vice President, Tammy Hall
First Vice President, Mark Stevenson
Vice President, Jeffrey Lorentson

Vice President, Josh McKenney
Vice President, Adam Treibic
Assistant Vice President Merchant Services, Brad Garrison
Vice President Manager Mortgage Sales, Elizabeth Chenore
Vice President Senior Product Manager, LuAnne Whewell
Vice President Relationship Manager Iii, Kevin Wagner
Assistant Vice President Business Banking Officer, Duane Kamminga
Senior Vice President And Director Of Finance, Michele Kawiecki
Assistant Vice President, Rob Garrett
Vice President Information Systems Director, Kevin Scharnowske
Assistant Vice President, Derek Rogers
Assistant Vice President Banking Center Manager, Sally Conyers
Vice President And Client Advisor, Rita K Smith
Vice President, Benjamin J Hartings
Assistant Vice President Manager Facilities Projects And Planning, Lindsay S Sweet
Vice President Relationship Manager Iii, Kevin M Orourke
Vice President Retirement Plan Advisor, Kristopher Feldmeyer
Vice President, Bill Robertson
Vice President Manager Commercial Lending, Scott Casbon
Senior Vice President, Brian Emmons
Vp Mortgage Operations Merchant Bank, Toni Nisbit
Assistant Vice President Executive Assistant To The Chief Operating Officer Chief Financial Officer, Nicole Weaver
Vice President, Paul Orner
Vice President Manager Commercial Banking, John Novosel
Senior Vice President, Joseph Peterson
Vice President Relationship Manager Iii, Kevin Orourke
Vice President Commercial Lending, Clark Scott
Vice President Account Executive, Lehman Gary
First Vice President Director Talent Development, Sharissa Ulrey
Svp Cash Management, Patty Hudson
Senior Vice President Director Of Human Resources, Steven Harris
Board Member, Terry Walker
Chairman, Charles E. Schalliol, age 72
Board Member, Jean Wojtowicz
Board Member, Patrick Sherman
Board Member, Robert R Halderman
Auditors: BKD, LLP

LOCATIONS

HQ: First Merchants Corp
200 East Jackson Street, Muncie, IN 47305-2814
Phone: 765 747-1500
Web: www.firstmerchants.com

PRODUCTS/OPERATIONS

2017 Sales

	$ mil.	% of total
Interest		
Loans	274	71
Investment Securities	39	10
Federal Reserve and Federal Home Loan Bank stock	.9	-
Interest Expense/Other	(36.9)	-
Non-interest		
Service charges on deposits	19	5
Fiduciary activities	12	3
Other customer fees	21	5
Earnings on cash surrender value of life insurance	4	1
Net gains and fees on sales of loans	8	2
Net realized gains on sales of available for sale securities	3	1
Others	6	2
Total	**348**	**100**

COMPETITORS

Ameriana Bancorp	NorthWest Indiana
Bank of America	Bancorp
Citigroup	Old National Bancorp
Harris	STAR Financial Group
JPMorgan Chase	U.S. Bancorp
MutualFirst Financial	

HISTORICAL FINANCIALS

Company Type: Public

Income Statement

	ASSETS ($ mil.)	NET INCOME ($ mil.)	INCOME AS % OF ASSETS	EMPLOYEES	FYE: December 31
12/18	9,885	159	1.6%	1,702	
12/17	9,367	96	1.0%	1,684	
12/16	7,212	81	1.1%	1,449	
12/15	6,761	65	1.0%	1,529	
12/14	5,824	60	1.0%	1,415	
Annual Growth	**14.1%**	**27.5%**	**—**	**4.7%**	

2018 Year-End Financials

Debt ratio: 1.00%	No. of shares (mil.): 49
Return on equity: 12.00%	Dividends
Cash ($ mil.): 176	Yield: 2.0%
Current ratio: —	Payout: 26.0%
Long-term debt ($ mil.): —	Market value ($ mil.): 1,691

	STOCK PRICE ($) FY Close	P/E High/Low		PER SHARE ($) Earnings	Dividends	Book Value
12/18	34.00	15	10	3.00	1.00	29.00
12/17	42.00	21	17	2.00	1.00	27.00
12/16	38.00	19	11	2.00	1.00	22.00
12/15	25.00	16	13	2.00	0.00	21.00
12/14	23.00	14	12	2.00	0.00	19.00
Annual Growth	**10.8%**	**—**	**—**	**18.2%**	**30.5%**	**10.3%**

First Mid Bancshares Inc

Money doesn't grow on trees so when farmers inÂ Illinois need a little cash they turn to First Mid-Illinois Bank & Trust. The primary subsidiary of First Mid-Illinois Bancshares isÂ a major supplier of farm credit (including real estate machinery and production loans; inventory financing; and lines of credit) in its market area. In addition to agricultural loans the bank offers commercial consumer and real estate lending. ItÂ also provides deposit products such as savings and checking accounts plus trust and investment services through a partnership with Raymond James.Â First Mid-Illinois Bank & Trust has about 40 branches.Other subsidiaries provideÂ data processing servicesÂ and insurance products and services.

EXECUTIVES

Vice President Branch Operations And Cashier, Rhonda Rawlings
Vice President Marketing, Rodney Morris
Executive Vice President, Clay Dean
Assistant Vice President, Jaci Manzella
Vice President, Darlene Johnson
Assistant Vice President, Dena Clifton
Senior Management (senior Vice President General Manager Director), Jason Tucker

Assistant Vice President Mortgage Lending, Mary White
Senior Vice President, Robert Weber
Senior Vice President Risk Management, Christopher Slabach
Vice President, Theresa Mangieri
Senior Vice President, Andrew Zavarella
Assistant Vice President Mortgage Loan Administration, Sue Radloff
Vice Presidents, Nancy Zike
Vice President Regional Lending Manager, Dave Garrett
Vice President Director Of Marketing, Laura Zuhone
Sr V Pres, Rhonda Gatons
Vice President, Jack Franklin
Board Member, Holly Bailey
Board Member, Gary Melvin
Board Member, Mary Westerhold
Board Member, Robert Cook
Board Member, James Zimmer
Auditors: BKD, LLP

LOCATIONS

HQ: First Mid Bancshares Inc
1421 Charleston Avenue, Mattoon, IL 61938
Phone: 217 234-7454   **Fax:** 217 258-0485
Web: www.firstmid.com

PRODUCTS/OPERATIONS

Selected Subsidiaries

The Checkley Agency Inc. (dba First Mid Insurance Group)
First Mid-Illinois Bank & Trust N.A.
First Mid-Illinois Statutory Trust I II
Mid-Illinois Data Services Inc.

COMPETITORS

Bank of America	Northern Trust
Fifth Third	PNC Financial
First BancTrust	U.S. Bancorp
First Busey	

HISTORICAL FINANCIALS

Company Type: Public

Income Statement

FYE: December 31

	ASSETS ($ mil.)	NET INCOME ($ mil.)	INCOME AS % OF ASSETS	EMPLOYEES
12/18	3,840	37	1.0%	818
12/17	2,842	27	0.9%	592
12/16	2,885	22	0.8%	598
12/15	2,114	17	0.8%	513
12/14	1,607	15	1.0%	400
Annual Growth	24.3%	24.0%	—	19.6%

2018 Year-End Financials

Debt ratio: 1.00%	No. of shares (mil.): 17
Return on equity: 9.00%	Dividends
Cash ($ mil.): 141	Yield: 3.0%
Current ratio: —	Payout: 45.0%
Long-term debt ($ mil.): —	Market value ($ mil.): 531

	STOCK PRICE ($) FY Close	P/E High/Low		PER SHARE ($) Earnings	Dividends	Book Value
12/18	32.00	17	12	3.00	1.00	29.00
12/17	39.00	20	14	2.00	1.00	24.00
12/16	34.00	17	11	2.00	1.00	23.00
12/15	26.00	14	10	2.00	1.00	24.00
12/14	19.00	13	9	2.00	1.00	23.00
Annual Growth	14.5%	—	—	8.0%	17.3%	5.1%

First Midwest Bancorp, Inc. (Naperville, IL)

There's a lot of cabbage in corn country. Just ask First Midwest Bancorp the holding company for First Midwest Bank. Through nearly 110 branches the bank mainly serves suburban Chicago though its market extends into central and western Illinois and neighboring portions of Iowa and Indiana. Focusing on area small to mid-sized businesses it offers deposit products loans trust services wealth management insurance and retirement plan services; it has $7.2 billion of client trust and investment assets under management. Commercial real estate loans account for more than half of the company's portfolio.

Operations

More than 85% of the company's loan portfolio consists of corporate loans (the majority of which are secured by commercial real estate) while the remainder of the portfolio consists of consumer loans (which include home equity loans lines of credit and 1-4 family mortgages). Illustrative of its commitment to business lending First Midwest does not originate sub-prime lending or investment banking activities.

The bank's subsidiaries include: equipment leasing and commercial financier First Midwest Equipment Finance Co.; investment security managers First Midwest Securities Management LLC and First Midwest Holdings Inc.; Section 8 housing venture investor LIH Holdings; and Synergy Property Holdings LLC which manages the bank's OREO properties.

Geographic Reach

The company operates 109 banking offices largely located in various communities throughout the suburban metropolitan Chicago market as well as central and western Illinois and eastern Iowa. It owns 145 automated teller machines most of which are housed at banking locations. First Midwest and Allpoint together provide access to more than 50000 free ATMs worldwide.

Sales and Marketing

The company serves different industry segments including manufacturing health care pharmaceutical higher education wholesale and retail trade service and agricultural. First Midwest spent about $8.2 million on advertising and promotions in 2014 up from $7.8 million in 2013 and $5.1 million in 2012.

Financial Performance

Following a modest rebound in 2013 First Midwest's revenue in 2014 dipped by less than 1% to $426.48 million mostly because of a 76% drop in net securities gains as the bank in 2013 was able to collect a non-recurring equity investment sale gain of $34 million. Lower mortgage banking income resulting from lower market pricing also contributed to the modest dip in revenue. The bank did however report higher interest income as its loan business grew higher wealth management fees with growth in assets under management and higher service charge fees as deposit accounts grew.

After healthy profit growth in 2013 net income fell by nearly 13% to $69.31 million in 2014 mostly as the bank incurred higher costs associated with the acquisition and integration of Popular and Great Lakes and because the bank had higher loan loss provision expenses. In 2013 First Midwest had posted a large jump in net income thanks to higher revenue a decrease in the provision for loan and covered loan losses and lower interest and non-interest expenses.

Continuing its annual cash declines the bank's operations provided $122.93 million (or 10% less cash than in 2013) mostly due to lower earnings.

Mergers and Acquisitions

First Midwest Bancorp acquired Bridgeview Bank in 2019. Bridgeview has about $1.1 billion in assets $755 million in loans and $1 billion in deposits.

In early 2017 the company completed the acquisition of another Chicago-area bank Standard Bancshares. The deal will add 35 branches $2.3 billion in assets $2.1 billion in deposits and $1.9 million in loans.

Company Background

First Midwest capitalized on the rash of bank failures that have occurred in the Chicago area amid the recessionary economy. Its relative financial soundness put it in a position to acquire three failed Illinois banks through separate FDIC-facilitated transactions in 2009 and 2010: First DuPage Bank Peotone Bank and Trust and Palos Bank and Trust. The deals which included loss-sharing agreements with the regulator added a total of nearly 10 branches. In 2012 the company acquired the deposits and loans of Waukegan Savings Bank in another FDIC-assisted deal that added two more branches to its network. First Midwest will continue to consider acquisitions of failed banks in the Chicago area.

EXECUTIVES

President Ceo And Director; Chairman And Ceo First Midwest Bank, Michael L. Scudder, age 58, $750,000 total compensation
Evp Cio And Coo First Midwest Bank, Kent S. Belasco, age 68, $224,000 total compensation
Evp And Cfo First Midwest Bancorp Inc. & First Midwest Bank, Paul F. Clemens, age 67, $376,000 total compensation
Sevp And Coo; Vice Chairman And President First Midwest Bank, Mark G. Sander, age 60, $545,000 total compensation
Evp And Treasurer First Midwest Bancorp Inc. & First Midwest Bank, James P. Hotchkiss, age 62
Evp And Chief Risk Officer First Midwest Bancorp Inc. & First Midwest Bank, Kevin L. Moffitt
Evp Corporate Secretary And General Counsel, Nicholas J. Chulos
Senior Vice President, Heidi Smithson
Avp Loan Operations System Administrator, Kwicha Nettles
Vice President Field, Phillip Tan
Vice President, Juan Cortez
Executive Vice President And Director Commercial Banking First Midwest Bank, Victor Carapella
Senior Vice President, Jim Schramm
Vice President Compliance Review Manager, Beth Uhlir
First Vice President, Ed Garner
Vice President, Marianne Coneset
Senior Vice President, Rob Schultz
Vice President Administration, Cheri Rubocki
Vice President Administration, Connie Steinke
Executive Vice President Chief Administrative Officer, Dean Glassberg
Vice President, Mike Trunck
Vice President, Martha Sandoval
Vice President, Sue Barreto
Vice President, Jodie Speers
Senior Vice President Director Applic, John Hudak
Assistant Vice President, Justin Luppino
Senior Vice President Financial Planning, Rich Padula
Assistant Vice President Regional Recruitment Manager, Michael Gossen
Vice President Area Sales Manager, Evan Klee
Senior Vice President, Matthew Burns

Vice President Public Funds, Susan Wade
Vice President And Assistant General Counsel, Steve Babinski
Senior Vice President Businessbanking Group Manager, Chris Esposito
Vice President Treasury Management, Ala Swais
Senior Vice President Wealth Management, Chris Ksoll
Senior Vice President, John Gaughan
Assistant Vice President, Megan Miller
Business Banking Relationship Manager Iii And Assistant Vice President, Michelle Payla
Vice President, Nick Yerkes
Vice President Business Banking, Dave Kurow
Vice President, Chad Lyons
Vice President, Gia Ormond
Vice President Commercial Banking, Abdullah Tadros
Vice President, Angela Hart
Senior Vice President Total Rewards, Steven Kull
Svp Head Structured Finance, Joseph Angel
Senior Vice President Commercial Banking, James Schramm
Executive Vice President And Chief Risk Officer, Jeff Newcom
Vice President Commercial Banking Officer, Sheela Prahlad
Assistant Vice President, Andrew Trasatt
Vice President Business Banking, Tony Martino
Senior Vice President, Steve Clingen
Vice President Sales Regional Sales Manager, Joe Creamons
Vice President Middle Market Banking, Chris Hannon
Vice President Commercial Banking Officer, Tim Meyer
Vice President Abl Relationship Manager Business Credit, Thomas Brennan
Vice President Trust Relationship Manager, Michael Lambert
Vice President Senior Talent Acquisition Manager, Jeff Boulos
Senior Vice President Structured Finance, Aaron Markos
Vice President Cra Manager, Mary Morstadt
Vice President Franchise Banking Group, Kara Symeonides
Vice President, Robert Rodie
Senior Vice President Manager Business Banking, Brian Burke
Senior Vice President, Matthew Brennan
Vice President, Rick Lang
Vice President Group Sales Manager, Joseph Palazzolo
Senior Vice President, Jim Ringer
Vice President Senior Human Resources Consultant, Anita Dwyer
Vice President, Dana Pike
Vice President Centralized Credit Underwriting, Jesse Newkirk
Senior Vice President Audit Services Director, Ted Roknich
Vice President Colleague Communications, Bridget Glavaz
Vice President First Midwest Bank, Nancy Henningfield
Vice President Regional Recruitment Manager, Linda Cleveland
Senior Vice President, Neil Prendergast
Vice President Mortgage Underwriting Manager, Erin Wehman
Avp Hr Consultant (business Partner), Amy Crabbe
Senior Vice President Healthcare Banking Coverage Group, James Goody
Vice President, Terrence Duffy
Svp And Director Corporate Communications, Maurissa Kanter
Executive Vice President And Chief Human Resources Officer, Doug Rose

Executive Vice President And Chief Credit Officer, Kevin Geoghegan
Vice President, Constance Simms
Senior Vice President, William Almond
Senior Vice President Healthcare Finance, Michael Mason
Chairman, Robert P. (Bob) O'Meara, age 81
Board Member, Barbara Boigegrain
Auditors: Ernst & Young LLP

LOCATIONS

HQ: First Midwest Bancorp, Inc. (Naperville, IL)
8750 West Bryn Mawr Avenue, Suite 1300, Chicago, IL 60631-3655
Phone: 703 831-7483
Web: www.firstmidwest.com

PRODUCTS/OPERATIONS

2016

	$ mil.	% of total
Interest Income		
Loans	338	63
Investment securities - taxable	29	5
Investment securities - tax-exempt	9	2
Other short-term investments	3	0
Noninterest Income		
Service charges on deposit accounts	41	8
Wealth management fees	33	6
Card-based fees	29	5
Merchant servicing fees	13	2
Mortgage banking income	10	2
Capital market products income	10	2
Other service charges commissions and fees	10	2
Net gain on sale-leaseback transaction	6	1
BOLI income	4	1
Net securities gains	1	0
Other income	4	1
Total	**538**	**100**

COMPETITORS

Bank of America	Meta Financial Group
BankFinancial	Northern Trust
Cummins-Allison	PrivateBank
Fifth Third	QCR Holdings
First Busey	West Suburban Bancorp
Harris	Wintrust Financial
JPMorgan Chase	

HISTORICAL FINANCIALS

Company Type: Public

Income Statement				FYE: December 31
	ASSETS ($ mil.)	NET INCOME ($ mil.)	INCOME AS % OF ASSETS	EMPLOYEES
12/18	15,506	158	1.0%	2,046
12/17	14,077	98	0.7%	2,152
12/16	11,423	92	0.8%	1,882
12/15	9,733	82	0.8%	1,790
12/14	9,445	69	0.7%	1,788
Annual Growth	13.2%	22.9%	—	3.4%

2018 Year-End Financials

Debt ratio: 1.00%
Return on equity: 8.00%
Cash ($ mil.): 289
Current ratio: —
Long-term debt ($ mil.): —

No. of shares (mil.): 106
Dividends
Yield: 2.0%
Payout: 39.0%
Market value ($ mil.): 2,107

	STOCK PRICE ($) FY Close	P/E High/Low	PER SHARE ($) Earnings	Dividends	Book Value
12/18	20.00	18 12	2.00	0.00	19.00
12/17	24.00	27 22	1.00	0.00	18.00
12/16	25.00	22 14	1.00	0.00	15.00
12/15	18.00	19 15	1.00	0.00	15.00
12/14	17.00	19 17	1.00	0.00	14.00
Annual Growth	3.7%	— —	13.4%	9.8%	8.1%

First National Bank Alaska

First National Bank Alaska is a financial anchor in Anchorage. Founded in 1922 the bank is one of the state's oldest and largest financial institutions. With about 30 branches throughout The Last Frontier (and about 20 ATMs in rural communities) the bank offers traditional deposit products such as checking and savings accounts CDs and IRAs as well as loans and mortgages credit and debit cards and trust and investment management services. The family of longtime president Daniel Cuddy owns a majority of First National Bank Alaska; he took the helm of the bank in 1951.

Geographic Reach

In order to help serve clients in remote locales First National Bank Alaska opened its first branch with a full-service customer kiosk at a joint air force/army base outside of Anchorage where customers can make routine banking transactions without teller assistance. The bank may add such kiosks at other branches.

Financial Performance

The company's total annul revenue has slowly declining across recent fiscal years. However it has managed to stay profitable.

EXECUTIVES

Senior Vice President Commercial Lending, Bill Inscho
Senior Vice President, Brent Kimball
Executive Vice President And Chief Financial Officer, Michele Schuh
Executive Vice President, Charles Weimer
Assistant Vice President, Darcy Steger
Vice President, Jennifer Mahlen
Assistant Vice President, Allen Jackson
Assistant Vice President, Sheila Lomboy
Assistant Vice President Escrow Manager, Michelle Frain
Senior Vice President, Rick Flake
Senior Vice President, Pamela Keeler
Senior Vice President, Elaine Kroll
Executive Vice President, Bill Renfrew
Senior Vice President, Karl Heinz
Board Secretary, Cheri Gillian
Loan Secretary, Kellye Linder
Auditors: Crowe LLP

LOCATIONS

HQ: First National Bank Alaska
101 West 36th Avenue, P.O. Box 100720, Anchorage, AK 99510-0720
Phone: 907 777-4362   Fax: 907 265-3528
Web: www.FNBAlaska.com

COMPETITORS

Alaska Pacific Bancshares	KeyCorp
Alaska USA	Northrim BanCorp
	Wells Fargo

HISTORICAL FINANCIALS

Company Type: Public

Income Statement				FYE: December 31
	ASSETS ($ mil.)	NET INCOME ($ mil.)	INCOME AS % OF ASSETS	EMPLOYEES
12/18	3,753	54	1.4%	—
12/17	3,653	36	1.0%	—
12/16	3,610	41	1.1%	—
12/15	3,569	36	1.0%	—
12/14	3,312	33	1.0%	—
Annual Growth	3.2%	13.5%	—	—

2018 Year-End Financials

Debt ratio: —	No. of shares (mil.): 3
Return on equity: 11.00%	Dividends
Cash ($ mil.): 109	Yield: 5.0%
Current ratio: —	Payout: 67.0%
Long-term debt ($ mil.): —	Market value ($ mil.): 798

	STOCK PRICE ($) FY Close	P/E High/Low	PER SHARE ($) Earnings	Dividends	Book Value
12/18	252.00	162 15	17.00	11.00	160.00
12/17	2,065.00	210 144	11.00	10.00	157.00
12/16	1,750.00	134 97	13.00	9.00	155.00
12/15	1,403.00	142 124	11.00	50.00	153.00
12/14	1,588.00	174 157	10.00	50.00	147.00
Annual Growth	(36.9%)	— —	13.9%	(30.9%)	2.1%

First of Long Island Corp

When it comes to banking The First of Long Island wants to be the first thing on Long Islanders' minds. The company owns The First National Bank of Long Island which offers a variety of lending investment and deposit services through around 45 commercial and retail branches on New York's Long Island and the boroughs of Manhattan and Queens. Residential and Commercial Mortgages (particularly tied to multifamily properties) make up more than 90% of the bank's loan portfolio though the bank also writes revolving home equity business and consumer loans. Its two bank subsidiaries include insurance agency The First of Long Island Agency and investment firm FNY Service.

Operations

The First National Bank of Long Island also operates an investment management division that offers trust and investment management estate and custody services.

The bank makes more than 90% of its revenue from interest income. About 70% of its total revenue came from loan interest during 2015 while another 21% came from interest income on taxable and non-taxable investment securities. The rest of its revenue came from deposit account service charges (3% of revenue) investment management division income (2%) gains on securities sales (1%) and other income sources.

Geographic Reach

The New York City-based bank operated 45 branches at the end of 2015 including 41 in Long Island and two each in Manhattan and Queens.

Sales and Marketing

First serves individuals professionals corporations institutions and governmental clients through its branches.

The bank markets its services through customer service personnel tele-sales lending relationships referral sources and advertisements. It spent $877000 on marketing during 2015 compared to $927000 and $670000 in 2014 and 2013 respectively.

Financial Performance

The First of Long Island's annual revenues have risen more than 20% since 2011 as its loan assets have more than doubled to $2.25 billion. Meanwhile the bank's profits have swelled more than 30% thanks to revenue growth and low interest expenses.

First's revenue jumped 13% to $101 million during 2015 mostly thanks to higher interest income as its average loan balances grew 26% and as its non-taxable security assets rose by 6%. The bulk of the loan asset growth was tied to residential mortgages while most of the rest came from multi-family commercial mortgage growth.

Double-digit revenue growth drove the bank's net income up 12% to $25.9 million. First's operating cash levels dipped 1% to $35 million despite the rise in earnings due to unfavorable working capital changes mostly related to a decrease in accrued expenses and other liabilities.

Strategy

The bank has been opening new branches utilizing "effective relationship management" using targeted solicitation efforts and expanding its product and service offerings to boost its loan and deposit business in recent years.

In early 2016 the company planned to open between eight and 12 more The First National Bank of Long Island branches in Queens after opening two branches there in Howard Beach and Whitestone in 2015. It also planned to open branches in Brooklyn. Expanding its branch network on Long Island the bank in 2015 launched new branches in Patchogue and Melville.

EXECUTIVES

Svp And Evp And Senior Lending Officer Commercial Lending The First National Bank Long Island, Donald L. Manfredonia, age 67, $222,500 total compensation

Svp, Richard Kick, age 61, $230,100 total compensation

Svp And Treasurer; Evp Cfo And Cashier The First National Bank Of Long Island, Mark D. Curtis, age 64, $242,700 total compensation

President And Ceo The First Of Long Island Corporation And The First National Bank Of Long Island, Michael N. Vittorio, age 66, $468,000 total compensation

Svp And Secretary; Sevp The First National Bank Of Long Island, Sallyanne K. Ballweg, age 63, $264,000 total compensation

Evp And Chief Risk Officer First National Bank Of Long Island, Christopher Becker

Vice President, Jane Reed

Assistant Vice President, Giuseppe Sparacino

Vice President, Robert Eisen

Vice President And Trust Officer, Sharon Pazienza

Vice President Director Of Human Resources, Sue Hempton

Vice President Director Of Marketing, Laura Ierulli

Avp Branch Administration, Kalpa Ved

Senior Vice President And Chief Investment Officer, Jay Mcconie

Executive Vice President, Christopher Hilton

Chairman The First Of Long Island Corporation And The First National Bank Of Long Island, Walter C. Teagle, age 69

Auditors: Crowe LLP

LOCATIONS

HQ: First of Long Island Corp
10 Glen Head Road, Glen Head, NY 11545
Phone: 516 671-4900
Web: www.fnbli.com

PRODUCTS/OPERATIONS

2015 Sales

	$ mil.	% of total
Interest and dividend income:		
Loans	71	70
Investment securities		
Taxable	8	8
Nontaxable	14	13
Noninterest income		
Investment Management Division income	2	2
Service charges on deposit accounts	3	3
Net gains on sales of securities	1	1
Other	3	3
Total	101	100

Selected Services:CheckingSavingsSaving for Retirement & EducationOnline Banking & Bill PayFirstLink Online BankingQuicken/QuickbooksFirstPay Bill PayPopMoneyAccount to Account Transfers

COMPETITORS

Astoria Financial	JPMorgan Chase
Bank of America	New York Community
Citibank	Bancorp
Dime Community	Ridgewood Savings Bank
Bancshares	Suffolk Bancorp
Flushing Financial	

HISTORICAL FINANCIALS

Company Type: Public

Income Statement				FYE: December 31
	ASSETS ($ mil.)	NET INCOME ($ mil.)	INCOME AS % OF ASSETS	EMPLOYEES
12/18	4,241	42	1.0%	344
12/17	3,895	35	0.9%	333
12/16	3,510	31	0.9%	314
12/15	3,130	26	0.8%	302
12/14	2,721	23	0.8%	284
Annual Growth	11.7%	15.9%	—	4.9%

2018 Year-End Financials

Debt ratio: —	No. of shares (mil.): 25
Return on equity: 11.00%	Dividends
Cash ($ mil.): 47	Yield: 3.0%
Current ratio: —	Payout: 41.0%
Long-term debt ($ mil.): —	Market value ($ mil.): 507

	STOCK PRICE ($) FY Close	P/E High/Low	PER SHARE ($) Earnings	Dividends	Book Value
12/18	20.00	18 12	2.00	1.00	15.00
12/17	29.00	22 18	1.00	1.00	14.00
12/16	29.00	30 19	1.00	1.00	13.00
12/15	30.00	26 19	1.00	1.00	12.00
12/14	28.00	39 21	1.00	0.00	11.00
Annual Growth	(8.4%)	— —	10.3%	7.1%	8.1%

First Republic Bank (San Francisco, CA)

No not the original Roman Republic but rather a modern-day haven for the elite. Founded in 1985 First Republic Bank offers private banking wealth management trust and brokerage services for businesses and high-net-worth clients though about 75 branches. Its main geographic focus is on urban markets including San Francisco Los Angeles New York Boston Portland and San Diego. The bank's lending focuses on commercial and residential real estate and personal loans including vacation home mortgages and aircraft and yacht financing. Trust services are offered through the bank's First Republic Trust Company division. First Republic Bank has some $83.6 billion of assets under management.

Operations

First Republic's wealth management services consists of various investment strategies and products trust and custody services online brokerage financial and estate planning access to alternative investments (private equity venture capital hedge and real estate funds) socially responsible investing insurance and foreign exchange. First Republic has a number of operating subsidiaries: it operates its wealth management through First Republic Investment Management; brokerage through First Republic Securities; trust services through First Republic Trust (a division of the bank) and First Republic Trust Company.

Geographic Reach

First Republic operates some 75 offices around 70 of which are Preferred Banking locations in Boston; Los Angeles; New York; Palm Beach Florida; Palo Alto Newport Beach San Diego San Francisco and Santa Barbara California; and Portland Oregon. The other five locations offer lending wealth management or trust services.

California accounts for around 60% of First Republic's outstanding loans.

Sales and Marketing

First Republic Bank advertises via digital media and newspaper and radio ads; its primary marketing goal is to attract deposits in its Preferred Banking offices. The vast majority of new clients are referred by word of mouth from existing clients.

Financial Performance

First Republic has recorded steady interest and non-interest revenue growth since 2010. In fiscal 2016 revenue increased 19% to $2.4 billion due to higher loan origination (particularly in single and multifamily loans) and increases in investment income relating to purchases of new investments. Offsetting factors include lower interest rates and lower investment yields.

Net income rose 29% to $673.4 million on the back of strong performances in Commercial Banking and Wealth Management. Cash from operations increased 36% to $852.5 million thanks to higher net income and adjustments to other assets.

Strategy

First Republic takes a conservative approach to banking issuing loans to high-net-worth individuals that it can work with in the long term. To support this the company ensures a low employee turnover to create deep and long-lasting relationships with its clients. Top class service is essential to the growth of the business: the majority of First Republic's new clients are sourced by word-of-mouth from within high-net-worth networks.

Mergers and Acquisitions

In 2016 First Republic acquired Gradifi a Boston-based company that helps employers offer student-loan repayment as an employee perk.

EXECUTIVES

Evp Secretary And General Counsel, Edward J. Dobranski, age 68
Chairman And Ceo, James H. Herbert
Evp And Chief Credit Officer, David B. Lichtman
President First Republic Securities, David Tateosian
Sevp And Chief Banking Officer, Michael D. (Mike) Selfridge, age 51
Chairman First Republic Trust Company, Michael J. Harrington
Evp And President Private Wealth Management, Bob Thornton
Evp And Chief Marketing Officer, Dianne Snedaker
Svp Chief Deposit Officer And Chief Investment Officer, Hafize Gaye (Gaye) Erkan
Evp And Cfo, Michael J. (Mike) Roffler
Evp; Chief Bsa And Aml And Security Officer, Bill Ward
Evp And Cio, Dale A. Smith
Evp And Coo, Jason C. Bender
President First Republic Trust Company, Kelly Johnston
Senior Vice President Foreign Exchange, Kate Kent-Sheehan
Vice President Investment Consultant, Maureen Mcnally
Vice President Portfolio Manager, Stephen Marotto
Vice President Business Analysis, Greg Boudreaux
Vice President Compliance Risk Manager, Steven Sears
Vice President Residential Lending, Lionel Antunes
Vice President, Michael Curley
Senior Vice President Chief Auditor Internal Audit, Justin Gibson
Vice President, Todd Brantley
Vice President, Margaret AE Zywicz
Vice President And Assistant General Counsel, Janisha Sabnani
Vice President First Republic Investment Management, Reynolds Ospina
Vice President Strategic Planning And Special Projects, Tim Maguire
Vice President Of Retail Marketing, Gwenn Murphy
Vice President Credit Risk Officer, Sean Callum
Vice President Director Single Family Lending, Paula Lazar
Vice President Lending Services, Pj Pamulo
Senior Vice President Chief Accounting Officer, Olga Tsokova
Vice President, David Weitgenant
Vice President Finance, Erwin Hom
Vice President Of Operations, Seth Bermel
Vice President Corporate Tax, May Chan
Vice President, Andrew Gibson
Vice President Director Deposit Technology, Dave McLelland
Vice President Digital Technologies, Yvonne Yang
Vice President, Justin Launer
Senior Vice President, Helene Jepson
Vice President Compensation, Mea Kwon
Vice President Trading, Ann Northrop
Vice President, Tim Ross
Vice President Governance And Compliance, Teresa Joyce
Vp Trading, Lynn Rueb
Senior Vice President, Christian Nelson
Vice President Head Analytics, Submanian Iyer
Cfa Vice President, Garret Giglia
Vice President Credit Risk Manager, Earl Crawford
Vice President, Roger Duke
Vice President And Associate General Counsel, Hilary Gevondyan
Vice President And Investment Consultant, Aaron Nichols
Vice President Corporate Security And Investigations Bsa Aml, Eric Breshears
Vice President Compliance Officer, Lalesh Muni
Vice President And Head Of Digital Channels (business Operations), Jonathan Kropf
Vice President And Assistant General Counsel Private Wealth Management, Debra Achkire
Senior Vice President, Jeff Cougoule
Senior Vice President, David Breslin
Vice President Info Security Programs Information Security, David Estabrook
Vice President Facilities And Admin. Services, Shannon Flynn
Vice President, Adam Rose
Vice President Lending Services, Leslie Gibin
Vice President, Jean Burns
Vp Finance Transformation, Matthew Mullen
Vice President Senior Attorney, Benjamin Spohn
Vp Head Of Technology Preferred Banking And Deposit Services, Churni Bhattacharya
Vice President Core Transformation, Mercedes Broening
Vice President Deputy Chief Auditor, Robert Pearce
Vice President And Wealth Manager First Republic Private Wealth Management, Rick Will
Vice President And Wealth Manager New York, Gregory Carafello
Vice President And Wealth Manager New York, Chad Cohen
Vice President Vendor Management, Helen Lee
Senior Vice President Financial Planning, Justin Mesko
Vp, Bob Owens
Vice Chair, Katherine August-deWilde, age 68
Assistant Treasurer, Aaron Frank
Auditors: KPMG LLP

LOCATIONS

HQ: First Republic Bank (San Francisco, CA)
111 Pine Street, 2nd Floor, San Francisco, CA 94111
Phone: 415 392-1400
Web: www.firstrepublic.com

PRODUCTS/OPERATIONS

2016 Sales

	$ mil.	% of total
Interest income other	1,981	83
Noninterest income	395	17
Total	2,376	100

Selected Affiliates

First Republic Investment Management Inc.
First Republic Securities Company LLC
First Republic Trust Company

COMPETITORS

Bank of Marin	City National
Bank of New York Mellon	JPMorgan Private Bank
Boston Private	MUFG Americas Holdings
Citigroup Private Bank	Morgan Stanley
	TriState Capital

HISTORICAL FINANCIALS

Company Type: Public

Income Statement				FYE: December 31
	ASSETS ($ mil.)	NET INCOME ($ mil.)	INCOME AS % OF ASSETS	EMPLOYEES
12/18	99,205	854	0.9%	4,480
12/17	87,781	758	0.9%	4,025
12/16	73,278	673	0.9%	3,566
12/15	58,981	522	0.9%	—
12/14	48,353	487	1.0%	2,506
Annual Growth	19.7%	15.1%	—	15.6%

Debt ratio: 2.00%		No. of shares (mil.): 165		
Return on equity: 10.00%		Dividends		
Cash ($ mil.): 2,811		Yield: 1.0%		
Current ratio: —		Payout: 15.0%		
Long-term debt ($ mil.): —		Market value ($ mil.): 14,330		

	STOCK PRICE ($) FY Close	P/E High/Low	PER SHARE ($) Earnings	Dividends	Book Value
12/18	87.00	22 16	5.00	1.00	53.00
12/17	87.00	24 20	4.00	1.00	48.00
12/16	92.00	23 14	4.00	1.00	45.00
12/15	66.00	21 15	3.00	1.00	39.00
12/14	52.00	18 14	3.00	1.00	35.00
Annual Growth	13.6%	— —	11.9%	7.1%	11.1%

FirstEnergy Corp

FirstEnergy's first goal is to generate and deliver power but its second goal is to stay profitable in a market undergoing deregulation. Its ten utilities provide electricity to 6 million customers in the Midwest and the Mid-Atlantic. The company's domestic power plants have a total generating capacity of more than 16000 MW an amount expected to diminish as the company winds down its deregulated business. Subsidiary FirstEnergy Solutions trades energy commodities in deregulated US markets. FirstEnergy's other nonregulated operations include electrical and mechanical contracting and energy planning and procurement.

Operations

FirstEnergy has three primary operating segments: Regulated Distribution Regulated Transmission and Competitive Energy Services (CES). About 65% of total revenue comes from Regulated Distribution roughly 25% from Competitive Energy Services and the rest from Regulated Transmission.

The Regulated Distribution segment distributes electricity through FirstEnergy's ten utilities which serve 6 million customers in a service area with a total population of 13.3 million. It has a controlling interest in 3800 MWs of generation capacity in West Virginia Virginia and New Jersey. It fulfills the additional electricity needs of its customers through power purchase agreements.

The Competitive Energy Services segment through its subsidiaries FES and AE Supply supplies electricity through retail and wholesale arrangements including competitive retail sale to customers primarily in Ohio Pennsylvania Illinois Michigan New Jersey and Maryland. It controls some 12300 MW of capacity.

The Regulated Transmission segment transmits electricity through transmission facilities owned and operated by American Transmission Systems Trans-Allegheny Interstate Line Company and a number of FirstEnergy's utilities. Transmission operations include approximately 24500 miles of lines and two regional transmission operation centers.

Geographic Reach

FirstEnergy operates and serves customers in a service area of 65000 square miles in Maryland New Jersey New York Ohio Pennsylvania and West Virginia.

Its power generating assets are located in Pennsylvania Ohio West Virginia New Jersey and Maryland.

Sales and Marketing

The Regulated Distribution segment sells roughly equal amounts of electricity to its residential and industrial customers and slightly less to its commercial customers. Generally there is no competition for electric distribution service in its service territories in Ohio Pennsylvania West Virginia Maryland New Jersey and New York.

FirstEnergy's CES segment participates in deregulated energy markets in Ohio Pennsylvania Maryland Michigan New Jersey and Illinois through FES and AE Supply. CES competes to provide retail generation service directly to end users to provide wholesale generation service to utilities municipalities and co-operatives which in turn resell to end users and in the electricity wholesale market.

Financial Performance

Until 2016 the company's financial performance was steady through trending slightly downward. Revenue peaked at $16.1 billion in 2011 and since slid to below $15 billion in 2016. Net income slipped from $885 million in 2011 to below $300 million in 2014 before an upward tick in 2015 which preceded a massive fall in 2016.

In 2017 revenue decreased 4% to $14 billion mostly coming from CES ($1 billion less) which saw a 10 million MWH decline in contract sales at lower prices as well as lower capacity auction prices offset by better performance from Transmission and Distribution segments.

The company posted a loss of $1.7 billion for 2017 a marked improvement from some $6.2 billion in losses the year before due to $8.3 billion reduction in impairment charges related to its exit from commodity-exposed generation at CES. In 2017 $2 billion in impairments came from nuclear generating assets.

It has $590 million in cash holdings. Operations generated $3.8 billion offset by $2.7 billion in investing cash outflow and a further $700 million going towards financing activities.

Strategy

The overriding long-term objective for FirstEnergy is to transition its business model from being a holding company of competitive energy wholesaler subsidiaries into one that holds solely regulated utilities. As an energy wholesaler the CES subsidiary is tossed about by the volatile pricing of energy products (oil coal etc.) and therefore carries a high risk with volatile financial results. The move to wind down CES and focus on regulated utilities brings with it a much lower risk profile and predictable steady cash flows.

Part of its plan includes divestitures. In 2017 FirstEnergy's CES agreed to sell four natural gas generating plants in Pennsylvania its ownership interests in a Virginia hydroelectric power station and gas/oil-fired facility to a subsidiary of LS Power Equity Partners III LP for $925 million. In total it is selling off more than 1600 MW of generation capacity. Additionally it plans to retire by 2020 720 MW of capacity at its Sammis Plant and 136 MW at its Bay Shore plant both in Ohio.

Meanwhile First Energy continues to invest in its regulated companies. To date it's installed 550000 smart meters across its Pennsylvania market and plans to replace them for all 2 million of the state's customers by 2019. It is working with Ohio regulator agencies to pursue a similar grid modernization effort in that state. In total it plans to spend roughly $1 billion/year on its utilities companies between 2017 and 2020.

HISTORY

FirstEnergy came to light in 1893 as the Akron Electric Light and Power Company. After several mergers the business went bankrupt and was sold in 1899 to Akron Traction and Electric Company which became Northern Ohio Power and Light (NOP&L).

In 1930 Commonwealth and Southern (C&S) bought NOP&L and merged it with four other Ohio utility holding companies to form Ohio Edison. The new firm increased sales during the Depression by selling electric appliances.

The Public Utility Holding Company Act of 1935 (passed to rein in uncontrolled utilities) caught up with C&S in 1949 forcing it to divest Ohio Edison. Rival Ohio Public Service was also divested from its holding company and in 1950 Ohio Edison bought it.

In 1967 after two decades of expansion Ohio Edison and three other Ohio and Pennsylvania utilities formed the Central Area Power Coordination Group (CAPCO) to share new power-plant costs including the construction of the Beaver Valley nuclear plant (1970-76). Although the CAPCO partners agreed in 1980 to cancel four planned nukes in 1985 Ohio Edison took part in building the Perry Unit 1 and Beaver Valley Unit 2 nuclear plants.

The federal Energy Policy Act of 1992 allowed wholesale power competition and to satisfy new federal requirements Ohio Edison formed a six-state transmission alliance in 1996 with fellow utilities Centerior Energy Allegheny Power System and Dominion Resources' Virginia Power to coordinate their grids.

Ohio Edison paid about $1.5 billion in 1997 for Centerior Energy formed in 1986 as a holding company for Toledo Edison and Cleveland Electric. Ohio Edison and Centerior both burdened by high-cost generating plants merged to cut costs and the expanded energy concern was renamed FirstEnergy Corp.

Looking toward deregulation FirstEnergy began buying mechanical construction contracting and energy management companies in 1997 including Roth Bros. and RPC Mechanical. In 1998 it added nine more. FirstEnergy then ventured into natural gas operations by purchasing MARBEL Energy. The company also created separate subsidiaries for its nuclear and transmission assets.

In 2000 FirstEnergy agreed to acquire New Jersey-based electric utility GPU in an $11.9 billion deal; it became one of the largest US utilities in 2001 when it completed the acquisition which added three utilities (Jersey Central Power & Light Metropolitan Edison and Pennsylvania Electric) serving 2.1 million electricity customers.

Beefing up its generation assets in 2011 the company acquired Allegheny Energy in a $8.5 billion deal. The acquisition increased FirstEnergy's power generation capacity by 70% and its customer base by 35% dramatically boosting its position as a leading regional energy provider focused on both regulated utility operations and a competitive generation business.

EXECUTIVES

President Maryland Operations, James A. Sears

Evp Corporate Strategy Regulatory Affairs And Chief Legal Officer, Leila L. Vespoli, age 60, $758,606 total compensation

President Firstenergy Solutions (fes), Donald R. (Donny) Schneider, age 58, $552,404 total compensation

Svp Corporate Services And Cio, Bennett L. Gaines, age 65

Svp Marketing And Branding, Dennis M. Chack, age 68

Svp And President Utilities Business, Steven E. (Steve) Strah, age 55, $553,286 total compensation

President Ceo And Director, Charles E. (Chuck) Jones, age 64, $1,133,840 total compensation

Evp And Cfo, James F. (Jim) Pearson, age 65, $659,884 total compensation

Evp And President Firstenergy Generation, James H. (Jim) Lash, age 68, $583,187 total compensation
Regional President The Cleveland Electric Illuminating Company, John E. Skory
Regional President Metropolitan Edison Company, Edward L. Shuttleworth
Regional President Ohio Edison Company, Randall A. Frame
Regional President West Penn Power Company, David W. McDonald
President Jersey Central Power And Light, James V. Fakult
Regional President Pennsylvania Electric Company, Scott R Wyman
President West Virginia Operations, Holly C Kauffman
President Pennsylvania Operations, Linda L. Moss, age 54
President And Chief Nuclear Officer Firstenergy Nuclear Operating Company (fenoc), Samuel L. Belcher
Regional President Toledo Edison Company, Richard S. Sweeney
Vp Investor Relations, Irene Prezelj
Executive Vice President, Charles Lasky
Vice President Energy Efficiency, John Dargie
Senior Vice President Strategic Planning And Opera, Mark Clark
Vice President Customer Service, Melanie Grant
Vice President East Fleet Operations, Peter Kotsenas
Vice President Controller And Chief Accounting Officer, Jason Lisowski
Vp And Treasurer, Steve Staub
Vice President, Ernie Maley
Vp Sales Firstenergy Solutions, Brian Farley
Vice President Transmission, Carl Bridenbaugh
Vp East Fleet Operations, Daniel Rossero
Vice President And General Counsel, Robert Reffner
Vp Fe Products, Dennis Reynolds
Medical Director, Tim Newman
Chairman, George M. Smart, age 73
Assistant Treasurer, Bill Wang
Board Member, Michael Anderson
Board Member, James O'neil
Auditors: PricewaterhouseCoopers LLP

LOCATIONS

HQ: FirstEnergy Corp
76 South Main Street, Akron, OH 44308
Phone: 800 736-3402
Web: www.firstenergycorp.com

PRODUCTS/OPERATIONS

2016 Sales

	$ mil.	% of total
Regulated Distribution	9,629	63
Competitive Energy Services	4,549	30
Regulated Transmission	1,151	7
Corporate/Other and Reconciling Adjustments	(767)	-
Total	**14,562**	**100**

COMPETITORS

AEP	Exelon
Avista	National Fuel Gas
CMS Energy	NiSource
Constellation Energy Group	PPL Corporation
	PSEG Energy Holdings
DPL	Peoples Natural Gas
Delmarva Power	Pepco Holdings
Dominion Energy	Public Service Enterprise Group
Duquesne Light	TVA
Duquesne Light Holdings	Vectren
EnergySolve	WGL Holdings

HISTORICAL FINANCIALS

Company Type: Public

Income Statement

	REVENUE ($ mil.)	NET INCOME ($ mil.)	NET PROFIT MARGIN	FYE: December 31 EMPLOYEES
12/19	11,035	912	8.3%	12,316
12/18	11,261	1,348	12.0%	12,494
12/17	14,017	(1,724)	—	15,617
12/16	14,562	(6,177)	—	15,707
12/15	15,026	578	3.8%	15,781
Annual Growth	**(7.4%)**	**12.1%**	**—**	**(6.0%)**

2019 Year-End Financials

Debt ratio: 50.00%
Return on equity: 13.00%
Cash ($ mil.): 627
Current ratio: 1.00
Long-term debt ($ mil.): 19,618

No. of shares (mil.): 541
Dividends
 Yield: 3.0%
 Payout: 71.0%
Market value ($ mil.): 26,276

	STOCK PRICE ($) FY Close	P/E High/Low	PER SHARE ($) Earnings	Dividends	Book Value
12/19	49.00	29 22	2.00	2.00	13.00
12/18	38.00	20 15	2.00	1.00	13.00
12/17	31.00	— —	(4.00)	1.00	9.00
12/16	31.00	— —	(14.00)	1.00	14.00
12/15	32.00	30 21	1.00	1.00	29.00
Annual Growth	**11.2%**	**— —**	**—**	**5.2%**	**1.4%(18.6%)**

Fiserv Inc

Fiserv Inc. provides financial companies with the technology services they need to operate. The company provides core processing systems electronic billing and payment systems ATM management and loan processing services to banks thrifts credit unions and other financial institutions. It also provides licensed software consulting and other support services. Fiserv serves customers of all sizes but its bread and butter has traditionally been small to midsized banks without in-house processing units. Other clients include insurance companies merchants leasing firms and government agencies. Fiserv agreed to buy First Data a payments processor for $22 billion.

HISTORY

When First Bank System of Minneapolis bought Milwaukee-based Midland Bank in 1984 the head of Midland's data processing operation George Dalton bought the unit and then merged that operation with Sunshine State Systems a newly independent Florida processing company headed by Leslie Muma. Christened Fiserv the company went public in 1986. It grew by providing outsourcing services to small banks and thrifts.

In the 1990s Fiserv began targeting larger clients. But industry consolidation sometimes hurt the company as when the 12-year term of a 1995 contract with Chase Manhattan was reduced to three after Chase and Chemical Bank merged in 1996.

As banks moved into new areas Fiserv went along. In the late 1990s it acquired BHC Financial and Hanifen Imhoff Holdings (securities transaction processing). Other purchases that broadened its service list included Automated Financial Technology (credit union software) and Network Data Processing (administrative software for insurance companies). The push into software continued with

1999 purchases in the field of workers' compensation systems.

Also in 1999 Fiserv bolstered its client list by buying QuestPoint's check servicing business. It moved into retirement plan administration with the purchase of a unit from what is now SunAmerica Financial Group. In 2000 a deal to provide back-office services for American Express' online Membership Banking unit fell apart but Fiserv recovered its momentum with enhanced mortgage servicing offerings and an agreement to provide technology services to cahoot the online banking unit of the UK's Abbey National (which was acquired by Spanish group Banco Santander in 2004).

Fiserv continued its acquisitive activities in 2001 buying Benefit Planners (a leading employee benefit program administrator with operations in Europe the Middle East South America and the US) Facilities and Services Corporation (a California-based insurance software maker) NCSI (information and services targeting the flood insurance industry) and the bank processing operations of NCR Corporation. The company that year also sold its Human Resources Information Services unit to buyout firm Gores Group.

Fiserv boosted its ATM and electronic funds transfer (ETF) business with the 2002 purchase of the Consumer Network Services unit of Electronic Data Systems (now HP Enterprise Services).

The company embarked on a series of sales in the next few years. It sold its securities clearing operations to a unit of FMR in 2005. Three years later it sold most of its health business to United-Health for some $480 million. The sale included Fiserv Health Plan Administration Fiserv Health Plan Management Innoviant Pharmacy Avidyn Health and other units but not WorkingRx (workers' compensation) and CareGain (technology) which remained with Fiserv.

The company also sold the bulk of its Fiserv Trust Company (also known as Fiserv Investment Support Services or Fiserv ISS) business including advisor services and institutional retirement services to TD AMERITRADE. In a separate transaction the newly formed Trust Institution Bank (headed by former Fiserv ISS management) acquired most of the company's investment administration services business.

Fiserv acquired one of the largest electronic payments firms CheckFree in 2007 boosting its capabilities in the payments landscape. In a smaller deal Fibought payment processor i_Tech from First Interstate BancSystem in 2008.

All of the acquisition activity led the company to higher debt levels which it began paying down through a combination of cost-cutting measures and divesting noncore operations. In 2008 it sold most of its health business to UnitedHealth and the bulk of Fiserv Trust Company to TD AMERITRADE. The following year it sold 51% of Fiserv Insurance Services (now StoneRiver) to investment firm Stone Point Capital for some $540 million. It also sold Loan Fulfillment Solutions a provider of mortgage-related services including settlement and title certification. As it added new operations and jettisoned others the company introduced a new marketing strategy in 2009 to unify its brands under the Fiserv banner.

In 2010 Fiserv acquired AdviceAmerica which provides desktop technology for financial advisers. It also introduced ZashPay a peer-to-peer platform available to consumers.

EXECUTIVES

Evp And Coo, Mark A. Ernst, $600,000 total compensation

Chief Sales Officer; Group President International, Steven (Steve) Tait

President Ceo And Director, Jeffery W. Yabuki, $840,000 total compensation

Chief Human Resources Officer, Kevin P. Pennington

Group President Depository Institution Services, Byron C. Vielehr, $470,000 total compensation

Evp Corporate Development, James W. Cox, $450,000 total compensation

Group President Digital Banking, Kevin J. Schultz

Cfo, Robert W. (Bob) Hau, $499,599 total compensation

Evp General Counsel And Secretary, Lynn S. McCreary

Group President Financial Institutions, Kevin P. Gregoire, $450,000 total compensation

President Billing And Payments Group, Devin B. McGranahan, $86,961 total compensation

Cio, Jim Grech

Vice President Planning And Communications India, Vikram Talwar

Vice President Institutional Retirement Plan Services, John Newman

Vice President, Rebekkah Wilson

Senior Vice President, Jed Delker

Senior Vice President Of Technology And Business Development, Oscar Mireles

Vice President Information Technology Operations, Ed Jolly

Vice President Global Sales, Vicki O'Connor

Vp It Operations, Chris Barnash

Vice President Information Technology Infrastructure, John Albor

Vice President Market Development, Kathy Herziger-Snider

Vice President And Assistant General Counsel Regulatory Compliance, Lisa Liban

Vice President Platform, Steve Hodgins

Vice President Human Resources Wisconsin, Heidi Swartz

Vp Investor Relations, Paul Seamon

Senior Vice President Enterprise Operations, Mark Prout

Vp Application Development, Sharon Dehli

Senior Vice President, Allan MacKinnon

Senior Vice President, Craig Ponsonby

Senior Vice President, Alan Eugley

Vice President And Head Of Internal Systems, Phil Demuth

Vice President Sales And Business Development Latin America, Rodrigo Silva

Senior Vice President Sales And Account Management, Dan Galway

Svp Sales North America, Andres Pasantes

Senior Vice President Product Management Card Services, David Keenan

Svp Finkit Digital Banking, Lee Cameron

Vp Application Support, Kelley Scheet

Chairman, Daniel P. Kearney

Board Member, Glenn Renwick

Board Member, Doyle Simons

Board Member, Matthew Sherman

Auditors: DELOITTE & TOUCHE LLP

LOCATIONS

HQ: Fiserv Inc
255 Fiserv Drive, Brookfield, WI 53045
Phone: 262 879-5000   **Fax:** 262 879-5013
Web: www.fiserv.com

PRODUCTS/OPERATIONS

2017 Sales

	$ mil.	% of total
Payments		
Processing & services	2,476	43
Products	758	13
Financial		
Processing & services	2,347	41
Product	183	3
Adjustments	(68)	-
Total	**5,696**	**100**

Selected Subsidiaries

BillMatrix Corporation
CheckFree Corporation
CheckFreePay Corporation
Corillian Corporation
Fiserv Global Services Inc.
Fiserv Automotive Solutions Inc.
Fiserv CIR Inc.
Fiserv (Europe) Limited (UK)
Information Technology Inc.
ITI of Nebraska Inc.
XP Systems Corp.

COMPETITORS

ACI Worldwide
Accenture
Banc of America
  Merchant Services
CGI Group
D+H USA
Fidelity National
  Information Services
First Data
Intuit
Intuit Financial
  Services

Jack Henry
MasterCard
PayPal
Q2 Holdings
SunGard
Total System Services
Vantiv
Visa Inc
Western Union

HISTORICAL FINANCIALS

Company Type: Public

Income Statement

FYE: December 31

	REVENUE ($ mil.)	NET INCOME ($ mil.)	NET PROFIT MARGIN	EMPLOYEES
12/18	5,823	1,187	20.4%	24,000
12/17	5,696	1,246	21.9%	24,000
12/16	5,505	930	16.9%	23,000
12/15	5,254	712	13.6%	22,000
12/14	5,066	754	14.9%	21,000
Annual Growth	3.5%	12.0%	—	3.4%

2018 Year-End Financials

Debt ratio: 53.00%
Return on equity: 47.00%
Cash ($ mil.): 415
Current ratio: 1.00
Long-term debt ($ mil.): 5,955

No. of shares (mil.): 393
Dividends
  Yield: —
  Payout: —
Market value ($ mil.): 28,845

	STOCK PRICE ($) FY Close	P/E High/Low	PER SHARE ($) Earnings	Dividends	Book Value
12/18	73.00	51 24	3.00	0.00	6.00
12/17	131.00	45 36	3.00	0.00	7.00
12/16	106.00	53 41	2.00	0.00	6.00
12/15	91.00	64 46	1.00	0.00	6.00
12/14	71.00	48 36	1.00	0.00	7.00
Annual Growth	0.9%	— —	17.8%	—	(3.9%)

Flagstar Bancorp, Inc.

Flagstar Bancorp is the holding company for Flagstar Bank which operates around 110 branches (including 10 in retail stores) mostly in Michigan. Beyond offering traditional deposit and loan products Michigan's largest bank specializes in originating purchasing and servicing one-to-four family residential mortgage loans across all 50 states through a network of brokers and correspondents. Around 70% of the Flagstar's revenue is linked to mortgage origination and servicing while another 25% comes from its community banking business. Boasting $14 billion in assets Flagstar is one of the nation's 10 largest savings banks.

Operations

Flagstar Bancorp operates four business segments: Mortgage Originations which made up 58% of its total revenue during 2015 and acquires and sells one-to-four family residential mortgage loans; Mortgage Servicing (12% of revenue) which charges a fee to service and sub-service mortgage loans for its own community bank and other parties; and Community Banking (24%) which provides deposit and loan products (including warehouse lending) to businesses individuals government entities and held-for-investment portfolio groups.

Unlike traditional banks which focus on interest income Flagstar makes most of its revenue from its mortgage banking business. Only about 43% of its revenue came from interest during 2015 (mostly from loans) while most of the rest came from gains on mortgage loan sales (36% of revenue) loan fees and charges (8%) and other mortgage-banking related fees (10%).

Geographic Reach

The Troy Michigan-based company had 99 branches in Michigan and another 10 locations in retail locations in nine highly-populous states. Its mortgage banking business does business in all 50 states.

Sales and Marketing

Flagstar spent $9 million on advertising in 2015 compared to $10 million and $9 million in 2014 and 2013 respectively.

Financial Performance

As with other mortgage bankers Flagstar has struggled to grow its revenues over the past few years as many borrowers have already refinanced their loans to take advantage of low interest rates. The lender has also been in and out of the red in recent years suffering losses in 2014 and 2011.

Flagstar Bancorp's revenue rebounded 28% to $825 million during 2015 however thanks to a combination of higher interest income and mortgage sales. On the mortgage side a 40% jump in loan sale gains were driven by higher fallout-adjusted lock volumes improved margins and lower representation and warranty provisions. The company's interest income grew 24% as it continued to build its average loans held-for-sale loans held-for-investment and investment security assets.

Strong revenue growth in 2015 and a sharp decline in loan loss provisions on an improving quality credit portfolio drove the company's net income up 28% to $158 million (compared to a $70 million loss in 2014). Despite earnings growth Flagstar's operations used $9.55 billion in cash or about 17% more than in 2014 mostly as it used more cash to originate mortgage loans.

Strategy

While home mortgage lending remains key to Flagstar the company hopes to diversify its revenue streams so the business eventually accounts for about a third of sales. Over the past few years the company has been transforming its branches into full-service community banks and moving toward cross-selling an expanded suite of retail commercial and government banking services.

In February 2016 the company expanded and diversified more into commercial lending after launching its national homebuilder lending platform designed to offer financing to residential developers and homebuilders across the US. In past years it introduced a line of consumer loans such as credit cards and home equity lines of credit and added services for small and midsized businesses like treasury management and specialty lending.

Company Background

In 2011 to raise capital after suffering the effects of the housing bust the company sold 27 bank branches in the suburbs north of Atlanta along with their deposits to PNC. The company also sold its 22 Indiana branches to First Financial Bancorp later that year. In addition to bringing in some cash the divestitures help Flagstar focus on its Michigan operations.

MP Thrift an affiliate of private equity firm MatlinPatterson Global Advisors assumed a controlling stake of Flagstar in 2009. Today it owns 64% of the company.

EXECUTIVES

Evp And Director Performing Servicing, Mark Landschulz, age 54
President Mortgage Banking, Leonard (Len) Israel
President Ceo And Director, Alessandro P. DiNello, age 64
Evp And Senior Deputy General Counsel, Paul D. Borja, age 58, $749,982 total compensation
Evp And Treasurer, Brian D.J. Boike, age 42
Evp And Coo, Lee M. Smith
Evp And Cfo, James K. Ciroli
Evp And Chief Risk Officer, Steve Figliuolo
Evp And Director Mis And Analytics, William D. Belekewicz
Evp And Cio, Tony Buttrick
Evp Secondary Marketing, Palmer T. Heenan
Evp And Director Mortgage Fulfillment, Donna M. Krall
Evp And Chief Lending Officer Commercial Banking, Thomas R. Kuslits
Evp And Chief Human Resources Officer, Cynthia M. Myers
Evp And Chief Credit Officer, Joseph M. Redoutey
Evp And Chief Compliance Officer, Karen A. Sabatowski
Chairman, John D. Lewis
Auditors: PricewaterhouseCoopers LLP

LOCATIONS

HQ: Flagstar Bancorp, Inc.
5151 Corporate Drive, Troy, MI 48098-2639
Phone: 248 312-2000
Web: www.flagstar.com

PRODUCTS/OPERATIONS

2015 Sales

	$ mil.	% of total
Interest income		
Loans	295	36
Investment securities	59	7
Interest-earning deposits and other	1	-
Non interest income		
Net gain on loan sales	288	36
Loan fees & charges	67	8
Deposit fees and charges	25	3
Loan administration income	26	3
Net return on mortgage serving assets	28	3
Net (loss) gain on sale of assets	(1)	-
Representation and warranty benefit (provision)	19	2
Other non-interest income	18	2
Total	**825**	**100**

2015 Sales

	% of total
Mortgage origination	58
Community Banking	24
Mortgage Servicing	12
Others	6
Total	**100**

Selected Products/Services

Personal Banking
Banking
Checking Accounts
Checking
Savings Accounts
Savings Accounts: Personal
Banking Goals
View All Rates
Online Banking Login: Personal Accounts
Mobile Banking
Detroit Red Wings Partnership
Foreign Currency
Loans
Home Loans
Refinance
Home Equity Solutions
Credit Cards
Money Market
Investment Accounts: Personal

COMPETITORS

Bank of America	JPMorgan Chase
Comerica	KeyCorp
Fifth Third	Northern Trust
Harris	PNC Financial
Huntington Bancshares	

HISTORICAL FINANCIALS

Company Type: Public

Income Statement

FYE: December 31

	ASSETS ($ mil.)	NET INCOME ($ mil.)	INCOME AS % OF ASSETS	EMPLOYEES
12/18	18,531	187	1.0%	3,938
12/17	16,912	63	0.4%	3,525
12/16	14,053	171	1.2%	2,886
12/15	13,715	158	1.2%	2,713
12/14	9,840	(69)	—	2,739
Annual Growth	17.1%	—		9.5%

2018 Year-End Financials

Debt ratio: 3.00%
Return on equity: 13.00%
Cash ($ mil.) 408
Current ratio: —
Long-term debt ($ mil.): —

No. of shares (mil.): 58
Dividends
Yield: —
Payout: —
Market value ($ mil.): 1,525

	STOCK PRICE ($) FY Close	P/E High/Low		Earnings	Dividends	Book Value
12/18	26.00	12	8	3.00	0.00	27.00
12/17	37.00	35	23	1.00	0.00	24.00
12/16	27.00	11	6	3.00	0.00	24.00
12/15	23.00	11	6	2.00	0.00	27.00
12/14	16.00	—	—	(2.00)	0.00	24.00
Annual Growth	13.8%	—	—	—	—	2.8%

FLORIDA HOUSING FINANCE CORP

Owning a home in Florida is just a bit easier thanks to Florida Housing Finance Corporation. Established in 1997 by the Florida Legislature as a public corporation Florida Housing's mission is to help Floridians obtain safe decent housing that might otherwise be unavailable to them. Florida Housing pursues its mission through a number of programs that provide financial assistance for first time homebuyers and for developers of multifamily dwellings that serve elderly and low income Floridians. Florida Housing partners with various local state and federal agencies as well as developers and not-for-profit organizations to achieve its goals.

EXECUTIVES

Exec Dir, Stephen Auger
Exec Dir*, Harold Price
Executive Officer, Vicki Robinson
Director of Asset Management, Laura J Cox
Controller, Angie Sellers
Senior Financial Administrator, Melanie Weathers
Bond Accounting Manager, Angela Scott
Homeownership Programs Adminis, Charles White
CIO, David Hearn
Director of Homeownerhip Progr, David Westcott
Federal Loan Program Manager, David Woodward
Auditors: ERNST & YOUNG LLP ORLANDO F

LOCATIONS

HQ: FLORIDA HOUSING FINANCE CORP
227 N BRONOUGH ST # 5000, TALLAHASSEE, FL 323011367
Phone: 850 488-4197
Web: WWW.FLORIDAHOUSING.ORG

PRODUCTS/OPERATIONS

Selected Programs

First Time Homebuyer Program
Down Payment Assistance
Homeownership Loan Program
Mortgage Credit Certificate
Multifamily Development Programs
Multifamily Mortgage Revenue Bonds
Florida Affordable Housing Guarantee Program
HOME Investment Partnerships
Elderly Housing Community Loan Program
Low Income Housing Tax Credits
State Apartment Incentive Loan
Predevelopment Loan Program
State Housing Initiative Partnerships
Demonstration Loans
Affordable Housing Catalyst Program

HISTORICAL FINANCIALS

Company Type: Private

Income Statement

FYE: December 31

	ASSETS ($ mil.)	NET INCOME ($ mil.)	INCOME AS % OF ASSETS	EMPLOYEES
12/17	4,765	207	4.3%	130
12/16	4,568	142	3.1%	—
12/14	5,079	24	0.5%	—
12/12	5,722	0	—	—
Annual Growth	(3.6%)	—	—	—

Florida Power & Light Co.

Florida Power & Light (FPL) sheds extra light onto the Sunshine State. The company a subsidiary of utility holding company NextEra Energy serves some 5 million electricity customers in eastern and southern Florida. FPL has more than

74800 miles of transmission and distribution lines as well as interests in fossil-fueled nuclear and solar power plants that give it a generating capacity of about 26000 MW. FPL also purchases and sells energy commodities to wholesale customers. FPL's has one of the cleanest power plant fleets across the US.

Operations

FPL's power generations relies on a mix of fuel sources which includes Fossil Operations (primarily uses fossil fuels natural gas and a joint ownership interest in 3 coal units) Nuclear Operations (supply of uranium and the conversion enrichment and fabrication of nuclear fuel) and Solar Operations (utility-owned and customer-owned or leased). In Solar Operations the energy generated goes directly to the location it is serving. In addition FPL also purchases a small amount of power and capacity from non-utility generators and other utilities.

It generates about 70% of its energy with oil/gas-sourced power plants an additional roughly 20% from four nuclear plants and the rest from coal oil and solar.

Geographic Reach

Juno Beach FL-headquartered FPL serves retail customers along Florida's Atlantic and southern Gulf Coasts.

Sales and Marketing

FPL provides service to its customers through an integrated transmission and distribution system that links its generation facilities to its customers. As a state-regulated utility its market is largely restricted to other entrants although niche project such as rooftop solar provide negligible competition.

Financial Performance

FPL produced $10.9 billion in 2016 operating revenues down 6% from the prior year due to lower fuel cost recoveries.

Despite lower revenue the utility generated $1.7 billion in net income up 5% from 2015. Lower interest expense and tighter control over operating expenses boosted the year's earnings.

Strategy

Florida Power and Light has a 2017-2020 budget of some $18 billion to pursue its strategic endeavors. About half of the capital expenditures are targeted for improvements and expansion of its transmission and distribution segment. It plans to invest heavily into solar farms envisioning nearly $3.0 billion to construct new facilities the first of which is expected to open in early 2018. Capacity expansion and modernization of generation facilities will receive the remaining funds.

In 2016 FPL and the Daytona International Speedway completed FPL Solar Circuit a system of more than 7000 solar panels with capacity of 2.1 MW to generate power for the Speedway's operations. It is one of the largest solar panel installed for US professional sports. The company also intends to build three new solar photovoltaic power plants.

Mergers and Acquisitions

In 2015 FPL and Office of Public Counsel acquired the coal-fired Cedar Bay plant and phased out 90% of its operations to will eventually phase the plant out of service. This saved FPL about a $70 million in operating costs and avoids nearly 1 million tons of carbon dioxide emissions annually.

Company Background

In 2013 FPL began installing solar panels at about 100 schools in 23 counties. It also agreed to a plan whereby more than 400 homes being built or refurbished by Habitat for Humanity and other non-profits would be fitted with solar-powered water heaters.

Between 2011 to 2013 FPL invested $9 billion to strengthen and improve its electric generation and delivery system. The company has revived a $2 billion plan to convert a plant in Port St. John and a plant in Riviera Beach from heavy fuel to natural gas. It also got a further 510 MW of capacity from its Turkey Point and St. Lucie nuclear power plants in 2012 and 2013.

In 2010 the Florida Public Service Commission turned down the company's proposed 30% retail rate hike or $1.3 billion. FPL adjusted its expansion programs accordingly.

Moving further to meet federal requirements for green energy production in 2010 the company commissioned the Space Coast Next Generation Solar Energy Center at the Kennedy Space Center three solar farms built in tandem with NASA to produce 10 MW of clean energy enough to serve 1100 homes. It also brought into service the 75-MW Martin Next Generation Solar Energy Center designed to power about 11000 homes. The hybrid facility connects more than 190000 solar thermal mirrors to an existing combined-cycle natural gas power plant.

EXECUTIVES

Evp Engineering Construction And Corporate Services, Robert L. (Bob) McGrath, age 66
Evp Finance And Cfo, Moray P. Dewhurst, age 64
Evp, Charles E. Sieving, age 46
President And Ceo, Eric E. Silagy
Evp Human Resources, Shaun J. Francis
Vice President And Agc, Robert Sendler
Vice President Smart Grid Solutions And Meter Operations, Bryan Olnick
Senior Vice President Power Delivery Florida Power And Light Company, Manny Miranda
Vice President And Chief Communications Officer Nextera Energy Inc., Rob Gould
Executive Vice President, Wanda Cantres
Gen Counsel And Vp, R Litchfield
Vice President Corporate Real Estate, Timothy Oliver
National Account Manager, Ellis Adger
Chairman, Lewis (Lew) Hay, age 63
Auditors: DELOITTE & TOUCHE LLP

LOCATIONS

HQ: Florida Power & Light Co.
700 Universe Boulevard, Juno Beach, FL 33408
Phone: 561 694-4000
Web: www.nexteraenergy.com

PRODUCTS/OPERATIONS

2016 Operating Revenues

	% of total
Residential	89
Commercial	11
Total	**100**

2016 Sales

	$ mil.	% of total
Retail base	5,807	53
Fuel cost recovery	3,120	29
Other	1,962	18
Total	**10,114**	**100**

COMPETITORS

Clay Electric	Progress Energy
Florida Public	Florida
Utilities	Seminole Electric
Gulf Power	Southern Company Gas
JEA	Sumter Electric
Orlando Utilities	Tampa Electric
Commission	

Company Type: Public

Income Statement

	REVENUE ($ mil.)	NET INCOME ($ mil.)	NET PROFIT MARGIN	EMPLOYEES
12/18	11,862	2,171	18.3%	9,100
12/17	11,972	1,880	15.7%	8,700
12/16	10,895	1,727	15.9%	8,900
12/15	11,651	1,648	14.1%	8,800
12/14	11,421	1,517	13.3%	8,700
Annual Growth	**1.0%**	**9.4%**	**—**	**1.1%**

2018 Year-End Financials

Debt ratio: 24.00%
Return on equity: 11.00%
Cash ($ mil.): 112
Current ratio: 1.00
Long-term debt ($ mil.): 11,688

No. of shares (mil.): 0
Dividends
  Yield: —
  Payout: —
Market value ($ mil.): —

Fluor Corp.

Fluor is one of the world's largest international design engineering and contracting firms. Through subsidiaries it provides engineering procurement construction and maintenance (EPCM) as well as project management services for a variety of industrial sectors around the world. Its construction portfolio includes manufacturing plants refineries pharmaceutical facilities health care buildings power plants and telecommunications and transportation infrastructure. Energy chemicals and mining sector projects account for more than 50% of its revenue. The group also provides operations and maintenance services for its projects as well as administrative and support services to the US government.

HISTORY

Fluor's history began in 1890 when three Fluor brothers immigrants from Switzerland opened a Wisconsin lumber mill under the name Rudolph Fluor & Brothers. In 1912 John Simon Fluor formed a construction firm in Santa Ana California. Fluor's company soon began a relationship with Southern California Gas which led it to specialize in oil and gas construction. The company incorporated as Fluor Construction in 1924 later began making engine mufflers. In 1930 it expanded outside of California with a contract to build Texas pipelines.

After WWII Middle East oil reserves were aggressively developed by Western companies. Fluor cashed in on the stampede winning major contracts in Saudi Arabia. During the early 1960s it continued to emphasize oil and gas work establishing a contract drilling unit and in the 1970s it began work on giant energy projects.

In 1977 Fluor made its biggest purchase: Daniel International a South Carolina engineering and construction firm with more than $1 billion in annual revenues. The contracting firm founded by Charles Daniel in 1934 initially did construction work for the textile industry then later worked for the chemical pharmaceutical metal and power industries.

Flush with cash Fluor bought St. Joe Minerals in 1981. A drop in oil prices in the 1980s killed demand for the big projects that were its bread and butter. As metal prices fell St. Joe didn't help the bottom line either. John Robert Fluor the last of the founding family to head the firm died in 1984.

When David Tappan stepped in as CEO he faced a $573 million loss the first year. The white-haired son of missionaries to China Tappan — known as the Ice Man — dumped subsidiaries and halved the payroll. In 1986 he merged Daniel into Fluor's engineering unit forming Fluor Daniel.

Leslie McCraw succeeded Tappan as CEO in 1991. McCraw saw Fluor as overly conservative and three years later he began setting up offices around the world while decentralizing Fluor's structure and adding new business such as temporary staffing and equipment leasing. Fluor also shed some of its commodity companies including its lead business in 1994. In 1996 Fluor's environmental services unit merged with Groundwater Technology and was spun off as a public company Fluor Daniel GTI.

Fluor saw mixed results from its expansion. Amid fierce competition and pricing pressure Fluor Daniel began cutting its overhead in early 1997 by reorganizing and selling noncore businesses.

Ill with cancer McCraw stepped down in 1998 and Philip Carroll who had overhauled Shell Oil took over as CEO. Carroll reorganized Fluor into four business units and tagged $90 million to rebuild its internal information management systems. Fluor also unloaded its 52% stake in Fluor Daniel GTI to The IT Group for $36 million.

Fluor in 1999 cut 5000 jobs further streamlined operations and focused on growth industries such as biotechnology and telecommunications. The next year the company split its construction and coal mining operations into two separate publicly traded companies one to concentrate on engineering and construction and one on coal mining. Former Fluor subsidiary A. T. Massey Coal was spun off as Massey Energy.

Carroll his restructuring job complete announced in December 2001 that he would retire the following February. That year the company also made plans to dispose of noncore operations of the company's construction equipment and temporary staffing businesses. Alan Boeckmann who had been president and COO succeeded Carroll in 2002.

The next year Fluor acquired Del-Jen a provider of outsourced services to US military bases and to the US Department of Labor. It also picked up five specialty operations and maintenance business groups from Philip Services. And in 2003 the company decided to dissolve its Duke/Fluor Daniel joint venture.

Fluor moved its headquarters from California to Dallas in 2006. The move resulted in the elimination of about 100 jobs. That year the company also entered the health care construction market.

In 2007 the company saw growth in all of its business segments with the exception of its government contracts in part because of the conclusion of projects for FEMA and in Iraq. The following year Fluor formed Fluor Offshore Solutions which is dedicated to global oil and gas clients in the offshore market. The company's construction segment acquired two private engineering companies in Europe — Belgium's UNEC Engineering N.V. and Spain's Europea de Ingenieria y Asesoramiento — increasing Fluor's ability to support its clients from a local level.

In early 2011 Alan Boeckmann retired as CEO after nearly a decade at the helm. He was succeeded by longtime company executive David Seaton who previously led Fluor's energy and chemicals global sales and China operations among others.

EXECUTIVES

Evp Chief Legal Officer And Secretary, Carlos M. Hernandez, $630,032 total compensation
President Power, Chris Tye
Evp And Cfo, Biggs C. Porter, $841,318 total compensation
President Government, Bruce A. Stanski, $600,018 total compensation
Evp Systems And Supply Chain, Ray F. Barnard, $564,689 total compensation
President Ameco, Tracey Cook
Evp Project Support Services, Garry W. Flowers
Chairman And Ceo, David T. Seaton, $1,295,029 total compensation
President Energy And Chemicals Americas, Jim Brittain
President Energy And Chemicals Asia/pacific, Ken R. Choudhary
President Energy And Chemicals Europe Africa And Middle East, Taco de Haan
President Life Sciences And Advanced Manufacturing, Juan G. Hern¯ndez
President Mining And Metals, Rick Koumouris
Svp Information Technology And Cio, Robert C. Taylor
Evp Business Development And Strategy, Jose L. M. Bustamante
President Infrastructure, Hans Dekker
President Construction And Fabrication, Jack Penley
Vice President Health Safety And Environmen, Jeffrey Ruebesam
Senior Vice President Government Relations, David Marventano
Sr Vp Global Projects, Joe Mcaneny
Vice President, Stewart Cameron
Vice President, Jose Herrero
Senior Vice President Investor Relations And Financial Planning, Geoff Telfer
Vice President Sales And Marketing, Larry Bolander Larry Bolander
Senior Vice President Supply Chain And C, Wheeler Mike
Vice President E And C Construction Modularization, William Meyer
Senior Vice President Procurement And Chief Procurement Officer, Mike Wheeler
Vp Quality And Cpi, Angus Murray
Vice President Construction Integrated Services, Rocky Plemons
Vice President Law And Chief Compliance Officer, Dawn Stout
Senior Vice President Chief Human Resources Officer, Mark Landry
Construction Vice President, David Gates
Vice President Sales, David Eppinger
Vice President And Project Director, Dennis Carr
Senior Vice President, Lou Del Tufo
Vice President Process Engineering And Technology, Claus-Peter Haelsig
Vp Engineering, Peter Moore
Vice President Business Services, Dave Fraley
Vice President Construction, Ian Swanbeck
Vice President Nuclear Power Projects, Michael Lackey
Vice President, Richard C Meserole
Vice President And Vc Summer Consortium Project Director, Frederick P Hughes
Senior Vice President Energy, Larry Burns
Executive Vice President Business Development And Strategy, Jose Luis Bustamante
Vice President, Richard Wolfe
Board Member, Nader Sultan
Board Member, Armando Olivera
Member Board Of Directors, Deborah McWhinney
Board Member, Mike Criss
Board Member, Lynn Swann
Board Member, Samuel Locklear
Auditors: Ernst & Young LLP

LOCATIONS

HQ: Fluor Corp.
6700 Las Colinas Boulevard, Irving, TX 75039
Phone: 469 398-7000
Web: www.fluor.com

2017 Sales

	$ mil.	% of total
United States	10,071	52
Europe	4,358	22
Canada	1,448	7
Middle East and Africa	1,690	9
Asia Pacific (includes Australia)	986	5
Central and South America	986	5
Total	**19,521**	**100**

PRODUCTS/OPERATIONS

2017 Sales

	$ mil.	% of total
Energy Chemicals & Mining	9,377	48
Industrial Infrastructure & Power	4,368	22
Government	3,233	17
Maintenance Modification & Asset Integrity	2,544	13
Total	**19,521**	**100**

Selected Services

Construction management
Design
Engineering procurement and construction (EPC)
Operations and maintenance
Program management
Project development and finance
Project management
Staffing

Selected Industries Served

Biotechnology
Chemicals and petrochemicals
Commercial and institutional
Equipment
Gas processing
Government
Manufacturing
Mining
Oil and gas production
Petroleum refining
Pharmaceuticals
Power generation
Telecommunications
Transportation

Selected Subsidiaries

American Equipment Company Inc.
  American Construction Equipment Company Inc.
Fluor Constructors International Inc.
Fluor Enterprises Inc.
  Daniel International Corporation
  Del-Jen Inc.
  Fluor Daniel Mexico S.A.
  ICA-Fluor Daniel S. de R.L. de C.V. (49% Mexico)
Fluor Holding Company LLC
TRS Staffing Solutions Inc.

COMPETITORS

ACS	JGC
AECOM	Jacobs Engineering
Amec Foster Wheeler	KBR
Balfour Beatty	Kiewit Power
Construction	Constructors
Balfour Beatty Inc	Parsons Corporation
Bechtel	Petrofac
Chicago Bridge & Iron	Quanta Services
Chiyoda Corp.	SNC-Lavalin
EMCOR	WorleyParsons Corp.
Granite Construction	
Hyundai Engineering	
and Construction	

HISTORICAL FINANCIALS

Company Type: Public

Income Statement

FYE: December 31

	REVENUE ($ mil.)	NET INCOME ($ mil.)	NET PROFIT MARGIN	EMPLOYEES
12/18	19,167	225	1.2%	53,349
12/17	19,521	191	1.0%	56,706
12/16	19,037	281	1.5%	61,551
12/15	18,114	413	2.3%	38,758
12/14	21,532	511	2.4%	37,508
Annual Growth	(2.9%)	(18.6%)	—	9.2%

2018 Year-End Financials

Debt ratio: 19.00%	No. of shares (mil.): 140
Return on equity: 7.00%	Dividends
Cash ($ mil.): 1,765	Yield: 3.0%
Current ratio: 2.00	Payout: 53.0%
Long-term debt ($ mil.): 1,662	Market value ($ mil.): 4,497

	STOCK PRICE ($) FY Close	P/E High/Low		PER SHARE ($) Earnings	Dividends	Book Value
12/18	32.00	39	19	2.00	1.00	21.00
12/17	52.00	42	27	1.00	1.00	24.00
12/16	53.00	28	20	2.00	1.00	22.00
12/15	47.00	21	14	3.00	1.00	22.00
12/14	61.00	26	17	3.00	1.00	21.00
Annual Growth	(14.6%)			(16.0%)	(0.0%)	0.3%

Flushing Financial Corp.

Flushing Financial Corp. (FFC) is the holding company for Flushing Bank which operates more than 15 branches in the New York City metropolitan area. The bank offers services catering to the sizable populations of Asians and other ethnic groups in Queens where it has the most full-service offices. Deposit products include CDs and checking savings money market and negotiable order of withdrawal (NOW) accounts. Mortgages secured by multifamily residential commercial and mixed-use real estate account for most of the company's $5.2 billion loan portfolio.

Operations

Flushing Financial generates some 85% of revenue from fees and interest on loans. About 85% of the company's lending is for mortgages including more than 40% for multifamily residences followed by commercial real estate (around 25%) and one-to-four family mixed-use properties (around 10%). Business loans account for the remainder of its lending activity.

Its deposits are equally dominated by negotiable order of withdrawal (NOW) accounts and CDs which comprise about 60% of its $4.4 billion total.

Geographic Reach

Flushing Bank operates solely in the New York City metropolitan area including Nassau County. The company's NYC branches are in Brooklyn Manhattan and Queens. Around half of its banking offices are in Queens where the company is focused on fostering its links to Asian communities.

Sales and Marketing

Flushing's marketing activities revolve primarily around promoting its online banking services which attracted nearly 10% of deposits in 2017

and outreach to Asian communities at its branches in the Queens borough of New York City.

The company has two online banking brands: iGObanking.com (offering savings and checking accounts among other traditional products) and BankPurely (positioned as an environmental sustainable philanthropic banking solution).

Flushing also has an advisory board to promote awareness of the bank's role in the Asian communities of Queens which account for more than $500 million in deposits and $450 million in loans and lines of credit outstanding. The company's employees also speak Cantonese and Mandarin in its locations that serve primarily Chinese customers.

Financial Performance

Although Flushing's revenue and net income fell by double-digits in 2017 both metrics have trended positively over the last five years as the economic environment strengthened in the New York City region and the bank expanded its asset base.

In 2017 the company reported revenue of $183.5 million down 18% from the previous year despite an increase in interest from assets. Net income was also down falling 37% to $41.1 million. Both declines resulted from an uncharacteristic $48 million bump earned in 2016 from the sale of three branch buildings.

The company's cash increased by $15.7 in 2017 to $51.5 million. Cash from operations added $83.5 million to the coffers while investing activities used $254.1 million for purchases of securities available for sale loan purchases and net originations of loans. Financing activities provided $186.3 million as a result of a net increase in interest-bearing deposits and proceeds from borrowings.

Strategy

Flushing's business strategy is centered on improving net interest income and automating bank services. The company is also working to further its presence in New York City-area Asian communities which make up a large portion of its customer base.

In its efforts increase net interest income the company is continuing a strategy which seeks higher loan prices instead of greater volume. The company is focused on growing multifamily residence mortgage loans non-owner occupied commercial mortgages and commercial business loans while pulling back on loans for one-to-four family mixed-use properties and construction. Results in 2017 showed evidence of this strategy with two of Flushing's three focus areas ticking up a point or two and both of the deemphasized areas declining.

As part of its automation push Flushing expects a 20% expense savings following the rollout of its Universal Banker model which is designed to improve efficiency at its physical branches. The technology — which Flushing has deployed at about 60% of its locations — utilizes automated bank telling from assisted service kiosks that include an option to video chat with a banker for assistance.

The bank also continues to invest in services for NYC's Asian populations. In 2018 Flushing announced plans to open a Universal Banker branch in the city's Chinatown area.

Company Background

Flushing Bank was founded as a mutual savings bank in 1929 and converted to a holding company structure in 1994.

EXECUTIVES

Sevp And Chief Of Real Estate Lending Flushing Financial And Flushing Savings Bank, Francis W. (Frank) Korzekwinski, age 56, $418,111 total compensation

President Ceo And Director Flushing Financial And Flushing Savings Bank, John R. Buran, age 69, $899,176 total compensation

Sevp Coo And Corporate Secretary Flushing Financial And Flushing Savings Bank, Maria A. Grasso, age 54, $481,222 total compensation

Evp Residential Mixed-use And Small Multi-family Real Estate Lending, Jeoung (A. J.) Jin, age 52

Evp And Cio, Allen M. Brewer, age 66

Evp And Chief Audit Officer, Robert G. (Bob) Kiraly, age 63

Evp And Director Of Government Banking, Patricia Mezeul, age 59

Evp Commercial Real Estate Lending, Ronald Hartmann, age 63

Evp Business Banking Flushing Financial And Flushing Savings Bank, Theresa Kelly, age 57, $285,704 total compensation

Evp And Chief Risk Officer, Gary P. Liotta, age 59

Evp Cfo And Treasurer, Susan Cullen

Evp And Director Of Distribution And Client Development, Michael Bingold, age 56

Evp And Chief Of Staff, John F. Stewart

Svp And Chief Investment Officer, Frank J. Akalski, age 64

Vice President Cash Management Team Leader, Anthony Campisi

Assistant Vice President Commercial Real Estate Loan Officer, Albert Bozzolo

Senior Vice President Director Strategic Development And Delivery, Caterina dePasquale

Vice President Business Development, Steven Glass

Vice President Information Security, Joe Rinaldi

Senior Vice President And Director Of Operations, Barbara Beckmann

Vice President, Rhonda Delorenzo

Assistant Vice President Loan Servicing, Marcia Witter

Vice President Business Banking, Louis Matti

Senior Vice President, Michael Nedder

Vice President Business Banking, Denis Healy

Vice President Business Banking, Jonathan Stern

Assistant Vice President Bsa Department, Karen Williams

Senior Vice President Team Leader Business Banking, Gus Buitrago

Senior Vice President, Joseph Baldasare

Senior Vice President And Accounting, Timothy Aletrakis

Vice President And Loan Review Officer, James Kumpas

Vice President And Audit Manager, Josephine Amoroso

Vice President Of Vendor Management, Alana Domill-maltese

Vice President, Jin Kim

Vice President And Budget And Financial Foreca, Edward Zekraus

Vice President And Credit Relationship Manager, Elizabeth Carroll

Assistant Vice President And Training Specialist Ii, Marva Webb

Assistant Vice President And Bsa Sar Case Manager, Nicole Santos

Executive Vice President And Chief Audit Officer, Rosina Manzi

Chairman Flushing Financial And Flushing Savings Bank, John E. Roe, age 85

Board Member, Michael Russo

Board Member, Sang Han

Auditors: BDO USA, LLP

LOCATIONS

HQ: Flushing Financial Corp.
220 RXR Plaza, Uniondale, NY 11556
Phone: 718 961-5400
Web: www.flushingbank.com

PRODUCTS/OPERATIONS

2017 Sales

	$ mil.	% of total
Interest and dividend income		
Interest and fees on loans	209	84
Interest and dividends on securities		
Interest	25	10
Dividends	0	-
Other interest income	1	-
Total interest expense	(61.5)	-
Non-interest income		
Banking services fee income	4	2
Net gain on sale of loans	1	-
Net loss on sale of securities	(0.2)	-
Net loss from fair value adjustments	(3.5)	-
Federal Home Loan Bank of New York stock dividends	3	1
Gains from life insurance proceeds	1	1
Bank owned life insurance	3	1
Other income	2	1
Total	**184**	**100**

COMPETITORS

Apple Bank for Savings	First of Long Island
Astoria Financial	HSBC USA
Bank of America	JPMorgan Chase
Bank of New York	Korea Exchange Bank
Mellon	New York Community
Citigroup	Bancorp
Dime Community	
Bancshares	

HISTORICAL FINANCIALS

Company Type: Public

Income Statement				FYE: December 31
	ASSETS ($ mil.)	NET INCOME ($ mil.)	INCOME AS % OF ASSETS	EMPLOYEES
12/18	6,834	55	0.8%	480
12/17	6,299	41	0.7%	467
12/16	6,058	65	1.1%	470
12/15	5,705	46	0.8%	442
12/14	5,077	44	0.9%	424
Annual Growth	**7.7%**	**5.6%**	**—**	**3.1%**

2018 Year-End Financials

Debt ratio: 2.00%	No. of shares (mil.): 28
Return on equity: 10.00%	Dividends
Cash ($ mil.): 119	Yield: 4.0%
Current ratio: —	Payout: 48.0%
Long-term debt ($ mil.): —	Market value ($ mil.): 602

	STOCK PRICE ($) FY Close	P/E High/Low	PER SHARE ($) Earnings	Dividends	Book Value
12/18	22.00	15 11	2.00	1.00	20.00
12/17	28.00	22 18	1.00	1.00	19.00
12/16	29.00	13 8	2.00	1.00	18.00
12/15	22.00	14 11	2.00	1.00	16.00
12/14	20.00	14 12	1.00	1.00	16.00
Annual Growth	**1.5%**	**— —**	**6.7%**	**7.5%**	**6.1%**

FNB Corp

F.N.B. Corporation is the holding company for First National Bank of Pennsylvania which serves consumers and small to midsized businesses though almost 290 bank branches in Pennsylvania northeastern Ohio and Maryland. The company also has more than 70 consumer finance offices operating as Regency Finance in those states as well as Tennessee and Kentucky. In addition to community banking and consumer finance F.N.B. also has segments devoted to insurance and wealth management. It also offers leasing and merchant banking services. F.N.B. has extended its reach in its target states through acquisitions of banks including Metro Bancorp Annapolis Bancorp and PVF Capital Corp.

Operations

F.N.B operates four segments. The Community Banking segment which made up almost 90% of the company's total revenue during 2015 provides commercial and consumer banking services including corporate banking small business banking investment real estate financing asset-based lending capital markets services and lease financing as well as traditional consumer banking products.

The company's Wealth Management segment (5% of revenue) offers trust and other fiduciary services while the Insurance segment (2% of revenue) offers commercial and personal insurance through major carriers. F.N.B.'s Consumer Finance segment (6% of revenue) which operates through subsidiary Regency Finance Company provides installment loans to individuals and buys installment loans from retail merchants.

Like other retail banks F.N.B. makes the bulk of its money from interest income. Nearly 70% of the bank's total revenue came from loan and lease interest (including fees) during 2015 while 9% came from interest on taxable and non-taxable securities. The rest of money came from service charges (10% of revenue) trust income (3%) insurance commissions and fees (2%) securities commissions and fees (2%) mortgage banking (1%) and other non-interest income sources.

Geographic Reach

Most of the Pittsburgh-based company's branches are concentrated in Pennsylvania with the next largest markets being in Ohio Maryland and West Virginia. Its consumer finance offices are mostly in Pennsylvania and Tennessee with others in Kentucky and Ohio.

Sales and Marketing

F.N.B. boosted its advertising and promotional spend by 7% to $8.4 million during 2015 mostly because of higher expenses associated with the bank's recent acquisitions as it worked to get the name out in new territories such as in Cleveland Ohio and Baltimore.

Financial Performance

F.N.B. Corporation's annual revenues have risen nearly 40% since 2011 as its loan assets have nearly doubled with new branch openings and acquisitions. Its profits have doubled as well over the period as the company has kept a lid on growing costs.

The bank's revenue climbed 6% to $709.21 million during 2015 thanks to continued loan business growth stemming from recent bank acquisitions.

Revenue growth in 2015 drove F.N.B.'s net income up 11% to $159.65 million. The company's operating cash levels plunged 50% to $223.48 million for the year due to unfavorable changes in working capital related to securities classified as trading in business combination and sold.

Strategy

F.N.B. Corporation grows its loan and deposit business while expanding into new markets by acquiring smaller banks and select bank branches. In 2016 it agreed to buy North Carolina-based Yadkin Financial for $1.4 billion. That deal will add around 100 banking locations in the Carolinas and some $7.5 billion in assets. The combined bank will have some 400 branches across the Mid-Atlantic and Southeast US.

Mergers and Acquisitions

In April 2016 the company bought 17 branch locations in the Pittsburgh area from Fifth Third Bank as well as $100000 in loans and over $300000 in deposits.

In February 2016 F.N.B. Corporation purchased Metro Bancorp along with its $3 billion in assets and more than 30 Metro Bank branches in south-central Pennsylvania. The deal effectively merged Metro Bank into F.N.B.'s First National Bank of Pennsylvania subsidiary.

In September 2015 the bank purchased five branches in southeastern Pennsylvania from Bank of America along with almost $155000 in associated deposits.

In October 2013 F.N.B. moved to expand its presence in the greater Cleveland area by purchasing PVF Capital Corp. which owned Park View Federal Savings Bank with some 20 offices in Cleveland and northeastern Ohio.

In April 2013 F.N.B. purchased Annapolis Bancorp the parent company of BankAnnapolis in an all-stock transaction valued at about $51 million. The deal expanded F.N.B.'s reach into Maryland.

Company Background

F.N.B. which moved its headquarters from Pennsylvania to Florida in 2001 spun off First National Bankshares of Florida at the start of 2004 and returned to the Pittsburgh area. F.N.B. still operates two loan offices in Florida but these primarily manage the company's legacy loan portfolio there.

The bank is again rooted firmly in the Keystone State and bordering markets. After returning it expanded via several acquisitions prior to the Parkvale deal including bank holding companies NSD Bancorp Slippery Rock Financial North East Bancshares Omega Financial and Iron and Glass Bancorp. In 2011 F.N.B. expanded in northeastern Pennsylvania through the acquisition of Comm Bancorp. The deal valued at some $70 million brought in 15 branches.

EXECUTIVES

Svp And Corporate Controller, Timothy G. Rubritz, age 66, $215,016 total compensation

Chief Legal Officer, James G. Orie, age 60, $165,000 total compensation

Cfo, Vincent J. Calabrese, age 56, $385,008 total compensation

Chief Credit Officer, Gary Guerrieri, age 58, $350,016 total compensation

President And Ceo; Ceo First National Bank, Vincent J. (Vince) Delie, age 54, $770,016 total compensation

President First National Bank, John C. Williams, $385,008 total compensation

President Charlotte Region, Gregory L. (Greg) Heaton

Vice President Of It Network Services, Brian Diegan

Vice President Business Development Officer, Leslie Harrison

Senior Vice President, Paul Puleo

Vice President, Mark Renzini

Vice President Commercial Banking First National Bank Maryland Region, Joseph Zajdel

Assistant Vice President Business Development Officer, Donnie Rhodes

Credit Support Senior Vice President Credit Officer First National Bank, Ron Scarton

Senior Vice President, Craig Muthler

Vice President, Michael Griffo

Vice President Private Banking, Donna Logan

Vice President, Colleen Ensinger

Vice President Commercial Loan Officer, Shane Moser

Vice President, Mike DeRosa

Vice President Financial Advisor, Daniel Richardson

Assistant Vice President Germantown Branch Merchant Services First National Bank, Jean Carpinone

Vice President Wealth Advisor Maryland Region, Nick Ey

Public Square Assistant Vice President

Relationship Manager Investment Real Estate, Dean Razek

Vice President Business Development Officer, Sean Laurin

Senior Vice President Managing Director, Nick Bellino

Svp Regional Manager Of Commercial Banking, Douglas Brown

Svp Market Executive, Craig Caplan

Vice President And Relationship Advisor, Keith Nazak

Vp Business Banking, Philip Persons

Senior Vice President, Mike Hendricks

Evp Capital Markets And Specialty Finance Businesses, D Bryant Mitchell

Vice President Regional Underwriting Manager, Amar Grover

Assistant Vice President Branch Manager, Amanda Escobar

Vice President, Shari Furbee

Vice President, Cindy Davidson

Chairman, Stephen J. (Steve) Gurgovits, age 75

Board Member, Stephen Martz

Board Member, Sheila Stewart

Auditors: Ernst & Young LLP

LOCATIONS

HQ: FNB Corp
One North Shore Center, 12 Federal Street,
Pittsburgh, PA 15212
Phone: 800 555-5455
Web: www.fnb-online.com

PRODUCTS/OPERATIONS

2015 Sales by Segment

	$ mil.	% of total
Community banking	616	87
Consumer finance	43	6
Wealth management	35	5
Insurance	13	2
parent & other	2	
Total	**709**	**100**

2015 Sales

	$ mil.	% of total
Interest		
Loans including fees	482	68
Securities including dividends	65	9
Other	0	
Non-interest		
Service charges	71	10
Trust Services	21	3
Insurance commissions & fees	16	2
Securities commissions & fees	14	2
Other	41	6
Total	**709**	**100**

Selected Subsidiaries

F.N.B. Capital Corporation (merchant banking)
First National Bank of Pennsylvania
Bank Capital Services LLC (also dba F.N.B. Commercial Leasing)
First National Trust Company
F.N.B. Investment Advisors
First National Investment Services Company
First National Insurance Agency LLC
Regency Finance Company
Citizens Financial Services Inc.
F.N.B. Consumer Discount Company
Finance and Mortgage Acceptance Corporation

COMPETITORS

Bank of America
Citizens Financial Group
Dollar Bank
Fifth Third
First Commonwealth Financial
Fulton Financial
Glen Burnie Bancorp

Huntington Bancshares
M&T Bank
Northwest Bancshares
PNC Financial
S&T Bancorp
Sandy Spring Bancorp
Sovereign Bank
United Community Financial

HISTORICAL FINANCIALS

Company Type: Public

Income Statement

FYE: December 31

	ASSETS ($ mil.)	NET INCOME ($ mil.)	INCOME AS % OF ASSETS	EMPLOYEES
12/18	33,102	373	1.1%	4,420
12/17	31,418	199	0.6%	4,748
12/16	21,845	171	0.8%	3,821
12/15	17,558	160	0.9%	3,205
12/14	16,127	144	0.9%	3,145
Annual Growth	**19.7%**	**26.9%**	**—**	**8.9%**

2018 Year-End Financials

Debt ratio: 1.00%
Return on equity: 8.00%
Cash ($ mil.): 488
Current ratio: —
Long-term debt ($ mil.): —

No. of shares (mil.): 324
Dividends
Yield: 5.0%
Payout: 43.0%
Market value ($ mil.): 3,191

	STOCK PRICE ($) FY Close	P/E High/Low		PER SHARE ($) Earnings	Dividends	Book Value
12/18	10.00	13	8	1.00	0.00	14.00
12/17	14.00	26	19	1.00	0.00	14.00
12/16	16.00	21	14	1.00	0.00	12.00
12/15	13.00	17	14	1.00	0.00	12.00
12/14	13.00	17	14	1.00	0.00	12.00
Annual Growth	**(7.3%)**	**—**	**—**	**8.8%**	**(0.0%)**	**5.2%**

Foot Locker, Inc.

Foot Locker is a leading retailer of athletic footwear with chains in the US and more than 25 other countries. It has about 2200 Foot Locker Kids Foot Locker and Lady Foot Locker stores in the US as well as in Canada Europe and the Asia-Pacific region. The company's other chains — totaling more than 1000 stores — include Champs Sports Footaction and SIX:02 (mostly located in the US) and Runners Point and Sidestep (mostly located in Europe). The primarily mall-based stores offer footwear apparel and accessories from leading global brands such as NIKE and adidas as well as emerging brands. Foot Locker also sells via ecommerce sites mobile devices and catalogs. The US market accounts for some 70% of total revenue.

HISTORY

With the idea of selling merchandise priced at no more than five cents Frank Woolworth opened the Great Five Cent Store in Utica New York in 1879; it failed. That year he moved to Lancaster Pennsylvania and created the first five-and-dime. Woolworth moved his headquarters to New York City (1886) and spent the rest of the century acquiring other dime-store chains. He later expanded to Canada (1897) England (1909) France (1922) and Germany (1927).

The 120-store chain with $10 million in sales incorporated as F.W. Woolworth & Company in 1905 with Woolworth as president. In 1912 the company merged with five rival chains and went public with 596 stores making $52 million in sales the first year. The next year paying $13.5 million in cash Woolworth finished construction of the Woolworth Building then the world's tallest building (792 feet). When he died in 1919 the chain had 1081 stores with sales of $119 million.

Woolworth became more competitive after WWII by advertising establishing revolving credit and self-service moving stores to suburbs and expanding merchandise selections. In 1962 it opened Woolco a US and Canadian discount chain.

From the 1960s through the 1980s the company grew by acquiring and expanding in the US and abroad. It picked up Kinney (shoes 1963) Richman Brothers (men's clothing 1969) Holtzman's Little Folk Shop (children's clothing 1983) Champs Sports (sporting goods 1987) and Mathers (shoes Australia 1988).

The company introduced Foot Locker the athletic shoe chain in 1974 later developing Lady Foot Locker (1982) and Kids Foot Locker (1987). In 1993 Woolworth launched an ambitious restructuring plan focusing on specialty stores (mostly apparel and shoes). It also closed 400 US stores and sold 122 Canadian Woolco stores to Wal-Mart that year. Former Macy's president Roger Farah became CEO in 1994. Farah eliminated 16 divisions and dozens of executives.

A year later the firm sold its Kids Mart/Little Folks children's wear chain. In 1996 Woolworth began a major remodeling program that included removing its venerable lunch counters. (Another alleged renovation at the Woolworth chain — the firing of older workers who were replaced by teenagers — led to an Equal Employment Opportunity Commission lawsuit against the company in 1999.) The changes failed and the next year the company closed its US Woolworth stores and bought athletic-products catalog company Eastbay.

In 1998 Woolworth changed its name to Venator Group and sold the Woolworth Building a national landmark (headquarters remained in the building). The company then shed itself of more than 1400 stores including Kinney shoes and Footquarters (both closed).

Internet site eVenator was launched in 1999 to sell Eastbay Champs and Foot Locker merchandise. Venator came out the champ in a proxy fight against investment group Greenway Partners in July 1999. Shortly thereafter Farah was replaced as CEO (he remained chairman) by president Dale Hilpert.

In 2000 Venator slashed 7% of its workforce in the US and Canada (a small part of the planned 30% cut) and closed 465 stores. COO Matt Serra became president and Hilpert became chairman when Farah resigned later that year.

In March 2001 Hilpert resigned replaced by Carter Bacot as chairman and Serra added CEO to his title. Venator later sold its Canadian Northern Group unit to investment firm York Management Services and closed its Northern Reflections stores in the US. Venator changed its name to Foot Locker in November. It also sold gift retailer San Francisco Music Box Co. and its hospitality division's fast-food franchises before the end of the year.

In early 2004 chairman Bacot become lead director and president and CEO Serra added chairman to his title.

In 2004 Foot Locker capitalizing on the Chapter 11 filing of Footstar Inc. purchased from the company 350 of its Footaction stores. The company also acquired 11 stores in Ireland from Champion Sports Group later in the same year.

The company's short-lived family footwear retail concept — called Footquarters — launched in early 2007 but was quickly discontinued due to poor performance. The locations were converted to Foot Lockers and Champs Sports outlet stores. Also in early 2007 Foot Locker made an unsolicited $1.2 billion bid for rival Genesco that was rejected by Genesco's board. Foot Locker closed about 275 mostly underperforming stores in 2007.

In 2008 the company reduced its store count by about 145 locations across its five chains in a bid to boost profitability by focusing on its most profitable locations and improving operations. In November Foot Locker acquired the CCS brand from dELia*s for about $103 million. The CCS brand includes skateboarding and snowboarding equipment apparel and footwear targeting primarily teenage boys.

J.C. Penney executive Kenneth Hicks was recruited to succeed Serra as president and CEO in August 2009. Serra who had held the CEO title since 2001 retained the chairman's title until his retirement in January 2010. At that time Hicks became chairman.

In July 2013 Foot Locker acquired Germany's Runners Point Group a specialty athletic store and online retailer based in Recklinghausen in a deal valued at ?72 million Euros ($94 million). The move gave Foot Locker shops in Germany that operated under the Runners Point and Sidestep banners as well as stores in the Netherlands Austria and Switzerland.

EXECUTIVES

Evp And Cfo, Lauren B. Peters, age 57, $657,500 total compensation

Chairman President And Ceo, Richard A. (Dick) Johnson, age 61, $1,087,500 total compensation

Evp And Ceo International, Lewis P. Kimble, age 60, $642,460 total compensation

Evp And Ceo North America, Stephen D. (Jake) Jacobs, age 56, $844,445 total compensation

Svp And Chief Human Resources Officer, Paulette R. Alviti, age 48, $486,250 total compensation

Svp And Cio, Pawan Verma, age 42, $216,071 total compensation

Vice President Operations, John Wompey

Vice President, Dennis Sheehan

Vp Leasing, Rita Dickerson

Vice President Brand Marketing Lady Foot Locker Six:02, Kirta Carroll

Vp And Treasurer, John Maurer

Auditors: KPMG LLP

LOCATIONS

HQ: Foot Locker, Inc.
330 West 34th Street, New York, NY 10001
Phone: 212 720-3700
Web: www.footlocker-inc.com

2018 Sales

	$ mil.	% of total
US	5,647	71
International	2,292	29
Total	**7,939**	**100**

PRODUCTS/OPERATIONS

2018 Stores

Type	No.
Foot Locker US	886
Foot Locker Europe	642
Champs Sports	535
Kids Foot Locker	428
Footaction	250
Lady Foot Locker	57
Runners Point	107
Foot Locker Canada	107
Foot Locker Asia Pacific	99
Sidestep	80
SIX:02	30
Total	**3,221**

2018 Sales

	$ mil.	% of total
Athletic Stores	6,714	85
Direct-to-Customers	1,225	15
Total	**7,939**	**100**

COMPETITORS

Academy Sports	L.L. Bean
Amazon.com	Modell's
Caleres	Shoe Carnival
DSW	Sports Authority
Dick's Sporting Goods	Target Corporation
Finish Line	Wal-Mart
Genesco	Zappos.com
Hibbett Sports	

HISTORICAL FINANCIALS

Company Type: Public

Income Statement

FYE: February 2

	REVENUE ($ mil.)	NET INCOME ($ mil.)	NET PROFIT MARGIN	EMPLOYEES
02/19	7,939	541	6.8%	49,331
02/18*	7,782	284	3.6%	49,209
01/17	7,766	664	8.6%	50,168
01/16	7,412	541	7.3%	47,025
01/15	7,151	520	7.3%	44,568
Annual Growth	**2.6%**	**1.0%**	**—**	**2.6%**

*Fiscal year change

2019 Year-End Financials

Debt ratio: 3.00%	No. of shares (mil.): 113
Return on equity: 22.00%	Dividends
Cash ($ mil.): 891	Yield: 0.0%
Current ratio: 3.00	Payout: 30.0%
Long-term debt ($ mil.): 124	Market value ($ mil.): 6,218

	STOCK PRICE ($) FY Close	P/E High/Low		PER SHARE ($) Earnings	Dividends	Book Value
02/19	55.00	13	9	5.00	1.00	22.00
02/18*	48.00	35	13	2.00	1.00	21.00
01/17	68.00	16	10	5.00	1.00	21.00
01/16	68.00	19	13	4.00	1.00	19.00
01/15	53.00	16	10	4.00	1.00	18.00
Annual Growth	**0.9%**	**—**	**—**	**7.0%**	**11.9%**	**5.8%**

*Fiscal year change

Ford Motor Co. (DE)

Ford Motor is striving to build smart vehicles for a smart world. One of the "Big Three" automakers in the US (with GM and Fiat Chrysler) the company manufactures cars trucks and SUVs under the Ford and Lincoln brands ? the F-150 the Lincoln Navigator and the Mustang among its most popular models ?- and finances sales through Ford Motor Credit. Ford which does business worldwide is making significant investments in a strategic shift to move it from solely an automaker to a leader in vehicle technology and mobility services. In 2018 Ford said it would phase out nearly all of its car offerings except for the Mustang to focus on more profitable trucks and SUVs.

HISTORY

Henry Ford started the Ford Motor Company in 1903 in Dearborn Michigan. In 1908 Ford introduced the Model T produced on a moving assembly line that revolutionized both carmaking and manufacturing. By 1920 some 60% of all vehicles on the road were Fords.

After Ford omitted its usual dividend in 1916 stockholders sued. Ford responded by buying back all of its outstanding shares in 1919 and didn't allow outside ownership again until 1956.

Ford bought Lincoln Motor Company in 1922 and discontinued the Model T in 1927. Its replacement the Model A came in 1932. With Henry Ford's health failing his son Edsel became president that year. Despite the debut of the Mercury (1938) market share slipped behind General Motors and Chrysler. After Edsel's death in 1943 his son Henry II took over and decentralized Ford following the GM model. Henry Ford died in 1947 at the age of 83. In 1950 the carmaker recaptured second place. Ford rolled out the infamous Edsel line in 1958 and launched the Mustang in 1964.

Ford acquired Hertz in 1994 and two years later bought #3 rental agency Budget Rent a Car (sold 1997). Also in 1996 it sold a 19% stake in finance unit Associates First Capital in an IPO and increased its stake in Mazda to one-third. The next year Ford sold its heavy-duty truck unit to Daimler's Freightliner subsidiary (since renamed Daimler Trucks North America) for about $200 million and spun off 19% of Hertz in an IPO. Also in 1997 it launched automotive systems supplier Visteon (formerly Ford Automotive Products Operations) at the Frankfurt Motor Show.

Decades later in order to focus on its struggling automotive operations Ford sold its Hertz car rental business in 2005 to a private equity group made up of Clayton Dubilier & Rice The Carlyle Group and Merrill Lynch Global Private Equity for $5.6 billion and the assumption of nearly $10 billion of Hertz debt.

In mid-2009 the US Department of Energy approved $5.9 billion in low-interest loans to Ford for converting its US plants to making cleaner more efficient engines transmissions and vehicles. As a result Ford reported it would spend $550 million to convert its Michigan Assembly Plant where Ford Expedition and Lincoln Navigator SUVs were produced into a modern facility for making its next-generation Focus small car. The new Focus rolled off the assembly line in 2010 with an all-electric version of the Focus to follow in 2011. Ford consolidated operations from its Wayne Assembly Plant as part of the project and worked with the UAW on more flexible work rules for the Michigan Assembly Plant. In addition Ford converted its Cuautitlan Assembly Plant in Mexico from SUV production to assembly of small cars commencing in 2011. The Mexican plant began building the new Fiesta subcompact in 2010.

With the automotive industry reeling from the Great Recession companies made decisions to streamline their operations for survival. In mid-2010 Ford sold all of Volvo Car Corporation to Geely Automotive a subsidiary of China-based Zhejiang Geely Holding Group. Volvo's headquarters and manufacturing operations remain in Sweden and Belgium with Stefan Jacoby (former CEO of Volkswagen Group of America) serving as president and CEO of Volvo Cars. At the onset of 2011 Ford's Mercury model production was discontinued.

EXECUTIVES

Vp Operations Support Finance And Strategy Ford Of Europe And Premier Automotive Group, Robert L. (Bob) Shanks, age 66, $858,000 total compensation

President Ford Motor Company Fund & Community Services, James G. (Jim) Vella

Chairman And Ceo Ford China, Jason Luo, age 53

Evp And President Global Markets, James D. (Jim) Farley, age 56, $918,750 total compensation

Evp And President Global Operations, Joseph R. (Joe) Hinrichs, age 53, $1,053,500 total compensation

Chairman And Ceo Ford China, Dave L. (Dave) Schoch, age 67

Vp And Coo Ford Europe, Steven Armstrong

Chief Marketing Officer And President Lincoln, A. Kumar Galhotra

Vp And President Global Ford Customer Service Division, Frederiek Toney, age 63

Group Vp And President Asia Pacific, Peter Fleet

Vp; President Changan Ford Automotive, Nigel Harris, age 58

Evp Product Development And Cto, Raj Nair, age 54

Evp And President Mobility, Marcy Klevorn, age 59

President Ford Middle East And Africa, Jacques Brent

President Ford South America, Lyle Watters

President And Ceo Ford Motor Company Of Canada Limited, Mark Buzzell

Group Vp; Chairman And Ceo Ford Motor Credit Company, Joy Falotico

Ceo, Jim Hackett, age 64

President And Ceo Ford Motor Company Southern Africa (fmcsa), Jeffery Nemeth

President Asean, Yukontorn (Vickie) Wisadkosin

Vp Quality And New Model Launch, Linda Cash

Interim Head Human Resources, Kiersten Robinson

Vice President Design, Moray Callum

Ric Pte Navp Portfolio Manager Vehicle Solutions, Mark Anders

Vice President Quality Ford Europe, Gunnar Herrmann

Senior Vice President And Director Of Fm, Michael Patterson

Vice President Marketing, Jim Drotman

Executive Vice President, Elizandro Martinez

Vice President Global Risk Management, Tom Schneider

Vice President Communications For Asia Pacific And Africa, Karen Hampton

National Account Manager, Vic Kachel

Senior Vice President, Jason Rau

Global Vice President Sales And Marketing, Jim Farley

National Account Manager, Bob Miller

Vp Human Resources Emea, Peter Godsell

Executive Vice President, John Frankiline

Group Vice President Communications, Ray Day

Vice President, Michael Null Parente

Vice President Marketing Sales And Service, Roelant Dewaard

Vp Vehicle Component And System Engineering, Jim Holland

Group Vp Sustainability Environment And Safety Engineering, Kimberly Pittel

Vp And Cio, Jeff Lemmer

Vice President, Curt Magleby

Vp Purchasing Europe, Verner Puetz

Manager Government Relations, Sam Scales

National Account Manager, Joel Nielsen

National Vice President, Vera Newton

Vice President Of Admissions, Allison Kozulla

Executive Vice President Marketing And Sales Executive Vice President Asia Pacific, David McClelland

Government Relations, Marilee Chlebicki

Vice President Finance Ford Of Canada, Bob Eaton

National Account Manager, Bridget Butterfield

Vice President Ford X, Sundeep Madra

Executive Chairman, William C. (Bill) Ford, age 61

Financial Sec 'y Treasurer Representative, Mike Susalla

Secretary Treasurer, Ed Hogan

Financial Strategy Treasurers Office, Mark Turner

Board Member, Christopher Thornton

Secretary, Nancy Garner

Auditors: PricewaterhouseCoopers LLP

LOCATIONS

HQ: Ford Motor Co. (DE)
One American Road, Dearborn, MI 48126
Phone: 313 322-3000
Web: www.corporate.ford.com

2017 Sales

	$ mil.	% of total
US	93,844	60
United Kingdom	9,619	6
Canada	10,580	7
Germany	7,265	5
All Others	35,468	22
Total	156,776	100

PRODUCTS/OPERATIONS

Selected Products
Automotive Products
  Automotive relays
  Camera modules
  Car navigation systems
  Car speakers
  Charging systems
  Cockpit systems
  EV relays
  Head up displays
  Instrument panel switches
  Lithium-ion batteries
  Telematics control units
Cars
  C-Max
  Fiesta
  Focus
  Fusion
  Mustang
  Taurus
Crossovers and SUVs
  EcoSport
  Escape
  Edge
  Flex
  Explorer
  Expedition
Commercial Vehicles
  Chassis Cab
  E-Series Cutaway
  F-650
  F-750
  Stripped Chassis
  Super Duty Pickup
  Transit Chassis Cab and Cutaway
  Transit Connect
Hybrids and Electric Vehicles
  C-Max Hybrid
  C-Max Energi
  Focus Electric
  Fusion Hybrid
  Fusion Energi
Performance Vehicles
  F-150 Raptor
  Fiesta ST
  Focus RS
  Focus SST
  GT
  Mustang Shelby GT350
Trucks and Vans
  F-150
  Super Duty
  Transit Connect
  Transit Passenger Wagon

2017 Sales

	$ mil.	% of total
Automotive	145,653	93
Financial services	11,113	7
Other	10	—
Total	156,776	100

COMPETITORS

BMW	Mitsubishi Motors
Daimler	Nissan
Fiat Chrysler	Peugeot
General Motors	Renault
Honda	Suzuki Motor
Hyundai Motor	Tata Motors
Isuzu	Toyota
Kia Motors	Volkswagen
Mazda	Volvo

HISTORICAL FINANCIALS
Company Type: Public

Income Statement
FYE: December 31

	REVENUE ($ mil.)	NET INCOME ($ mil.)	NET PROFIT MARGIN	EMPLOYEES
12/19	155,900	47	0.0%	190,000
12/18	160,338	3,677	2.3%	199,000
12/17	156,776	7,602	4.8%	202,000
12/16	151,800	4,596	3.0%	201,000
12/15	149,558	7,373	4.9%	199,000
Annual Growth	1.0%	(71.7%)	—	(1.2%)

2019 Year-End Financials

Debt ratio: 60.00%—
Return on equity: 0.00%
Cash ($ mil.): 17,504
Current ratio: 1.00
Long-term debt ($ mil.): 101,361
Dividends
  Yield: 6.0%
  Payout: 146.0%
Market value ($ mil.): —

	STOCK PRICE ($) FY Close	P/E High/Low		PER SHARE ($) Earnings	Dividends	Book Value
12/19	9.00	105	1778	0.00	1.00	8.00
12/18	8.00	14	8	1.00	1.00	9.00
12/17	12.00	7	6	2.00	1.00	9.00
12/16	12.00	12	10	1.00	1.00	7.00
12/15	14.00	9	7	2.00	1.00	7.00
Annual Growth	(9.9%)	—	—	(72.8%)	(0.0%)	3.8%

Fortive Corp

Auditors: Ernst & Young LLP

LOCATIONS

HQ: Fortive Corp
6920 Seaway Blvd., Everett, WA 98203
Phone: 425 446-5000
Web: www.fortive.com

HISTORICAL FINANCIALS
Company Type: Public

Income Statement
FYE: December 31

	REVENUE ($ mil.)	NET INCOME ($ mil.)	NET PROFIT MARGIN	EMPLOYEES
12/18	6,453	2,914	45.2%	24,000
12/17	6,656	1,045	15.7%	26,000
12/16	6,224	872	14.0%	24,000
12/15	6,179	864	14.0%	22,000
12/14	6,337	883	13.9%	
Annual Growth	0.5%	34.8%	—	—

2018 Year-End Financials

Debt ratio: 27.00%
Return on equity: 56.00%
Cash ($ mil.): 1,178
Current ratio: 1.00
Long-term debt ($ mil.): 2,975
No. of shares (mil.): 335
Dividends
  Yield: 0.0%
  Payout: 0.0%
Market value ($ mil.): 22,632

	STOCK PRICE ($) FY Close	P/E High/Low		PER SHARE ($) Earnings	Dividends	Book Value
12/18	68.00	10	8	8.00	0.00	20.00
12/17	72.00	25	18	3.00	0.00	11.00
12/16	54.00	22	19	3.00	0.00	8.00
Annual Growth	6.0%	—	—	34.5%	18.9%	26.2%

Fortune Brands Home & Security, Inc.

Fortune Brands Home & Security (FBHS) holds the keys to the kitchen and the garden shed. With about 45 plants worldwide the consumer products manufacturer makes and sells kitchen and bathroom cabinets faucets entry doors trim and padlocks. Its well-known brands include Moen faucets MasterBrand Cabinets SentrySafe and Therma-Tru entry doors along with Master Lock and American Lock padlocks and other security products. Most of the company's products are the top sellers in their respective markets. FBHS was formed in 2011 when its former parent company Fortune Brands spun off its alcohol and home and security brands as separate businesses.

Operations

Fortune Brands Home & Security (FBHS) operates four business segments: Cabinets Plumbing Security and Doors.

The Cabinets segment generates nearly 50% of sales and ranks as the #1 maker of such cabinetry in North America. Its brands include Aristokraft Mid-Continent Diamond Kitchen Classics among others. The Plumbing business brings in around 30% of sales and manufactures Moen Cleveland Faucet Group and Waste King brand faucets the leading brands in North America and China. Doors accounts for 10% of sales and makes doors and vinyl windows; and Security which also brings in around 10% of sales is the #1 maker of padlocks in North America and Europe.

Geographic Reach

Illinois-based Fortune Brands Home & Security (FBHS) rang up almost 85% of its sales in the US in 2015. Canada is the company's largest international market representing about 10% of sales. China and other countries account for the rest. Other major markets for FBHS include Europe Southeast Asia South America and Mexico. The company operates some 30 US manufacturing facilities in 16 states and has around 15 international plant locations in Mexico Asia Europe and Canada.

Sales and Marketing

Fortune Brands Home & Security (FBHS) two largest customers are Home Depot and Lowe's Companies together accounting for about 30% of annual sales. The company sells directly through its own sales force and indirectly through independent manufacturers' representatives. Other sales channels include kitchen and bath dealers wholesalers catering to builders or professional remodelers industrial distributors and other retail outlets including mass merchants. Sales to all US home centers in the aggregate account for approximately 25% of net sales.

Financial Performance

The improving US home products market market share gains growth overseas and acquisitions have collectively driven Fortune Brands Home & Security (FBHS)'s sales up in recent years.

In fiscal 2016 sales grew a further 9% to $5.0 billion due to continued expansion in the housing market acquisitions in the Cabinets and Plumbing segments. and higher prices.

Net income grew 31% to $413.2 million as increases in revenue outpaced the relative increase in selling costs. The company achieved productivity gains and benefited from the positive contributions from the acquired businesses.

Cash from operations grew 52% to $650.5 million due to a reduction in working capital in 2016 and higher net income.

Strategy

Fortune Brands Home Security (FBHS) is focused on expanding internationally. It is developing its relationships with its dealers and distributors and their Moen branded stores throughout China India and South America. Master Lock expanded its presence further in Europe and Asia (primarily Japan) while Therma-Tru made inroads in Canada as consumers transitioned from traditional entry door materials to more advanced and energy-efficient fiberglass doors.

FBHS is also focused on expanding its product portfolio. Its Norcraft Companies expands regional market presence and enhances frameless cabinetry. In 2016 MasterBrand Cabinets launched new cabinet door designs color palettes and features in a range of styles; exclusive laminate door & finish options. Its Moen brand introduces hand showers featuring the Magnetix magnetic docking system a new line of garbage disposals Spot Resist finish touchless Motionsense electronic faucets and pull-out and pull-down faucets with Reflex self-retraction. Its Therma-Tru released a portfolio of on-trend door and glass collections.

Signaling its intent to boost its plumbing business the company in late 2016 created Global Plumbing Group. Its goal is to increase plumbing sales to $2.5 billion by 2020 (from $1.5 billion in 2016). The division will become a multi-brand -channel and -geography business and will grow organically and through acquisitions; its first such acquisitions were Riobel a Canadian premium showroom brand; ROHL a Californian luxury brand; and TCL Manufacturing which gave it control of Perrin & Rowe a UK manufacturer of luxury kitchen and bathroom plumbing products.

Mergers and Acquisitions

In 2016 Fortune Brands Home Security made a number of acquisitions to add meat to its new Global Plumbing Group division. It bought Riobel a Canadian premium showroom brand with annual sales of $40 million which it followed up with the acquisitions of ROHL and TCL Manufacturing. ROHL is a manufacturer of high-end faucets and TCL owns Perrin & Rowe a UK luxury kitchen plumbing company.

Company Background

Formed in 1988 as a Fortune Brands subsidiary the company was spun off in 2011.

In 2013 FBHS' Kitchen & Bath Cabinetry business acquired WoodCrafters a manufacturer of bathroom vanities and tops for about $302 million. The purchase expanded the company's bathroom cabinetry products offering.

EXECUTIVES

Evp, E. Lee Wyatt, age 66, $770,333 total compensation
President The Master Lock Co., Michael P. (Mike) Bauer, age 54
Ceo, Christopher J. (Chris) Klein, age 55, $1,093,333 total compensation
President Masterbrand Cabinets, David M. Randich, age 57, $585,269 total compensation
President Therma-tru, Brett Finley, age 48
Svp Global Growth And Development, Tracey Belcourt
President Global Plumbing Group, Nicholas I. Fink, age 44, $505,833 total compensation
President U.s. Businesses Moen, Troy Shay
Svp And Cfo, Patrick D. Hallinan
Executive Vice President, Lee Wyatt
Senior Vice President Communications And Corporate Administration, Brian Lantz
Vice President Treasurer, Matt Lenz
Vice President Tax, Kathleen Weston
Vice President Controller, Dan Luburic
Vice President And Chief Internal Auditor, Gary Tobison
Vice President And Corporate Controller, Danny Luburic
Vice President Strategy, Peter Daw
Vice President And Chief Internal Auditor, Sanchez Marcela
Chairman, David M. Thomas
Board Member, Ann Hackett
Board Member, John Morikis
Assistant Treasurer, Cory Kruse
Board Member, Ad Mackay
Board Member, Susan Kilsby
Auditors: PricewaterhouseCoopers LLP

LOCATIONS

HQ: Fortune Brands Home & Security, Inc.
 520 Lake Cook Road, Deerfield, IL 60015-5611
Phone: 847 484-4400
Web: www.fbhs.com

2016 Sales

	$ mil.	% of total
US	4,259	86
Canada	406	8
China & other international	320	6
Total	**4,985**	**100**

PRODUCTS/OPERATIONS

2016 Sales

	$ mil.	% of total
Cabinets	2,398	48
Plumbing	1,534	31
Security	580	12
Doors	473	9
Total	**4,985**	**100**

Selected Brands

Aristokraft
Diamond
Homecrest
Kitchen Classics
Kitchen Craft
Master Lock
MasterBrand Cabinets
Mid-Continent
Moen
Omega
Schrock
Sentry
Safe
Star
Mark
Therma-Tru Doors
Thomasville
Ultracraft
Selected Products Cabinets
Stock cabinetry
Vanities
Plumbing Accessor

COMPETITORS

American Woodmark	Kwikset Corporation
Andersen Corporation	Masco
Armstrong World Industries	Pella
B.J. Tidwell Industries	Pfister
Conestoga	Republic National Cabinet
Delta Faucet	Stanley Black and Decker
Elkay Manufacturing	Sterilite
JELD-WEN	US Home Systems
Kohler	

HISTORICAL FINANCIALS
Company Type: Public

Income Statement   FYE: December 31

	REVENUE ($ mil.)	NET INCOME ($ mil.)	NET PROFIT MARGIN	EMPLOYEES
12/18	5,485	390	7.1%	25,300
12/17	5,283	473	8.9%	23,800
12/16	4,985	413	8.3%	22,700
12/15	4,579	315	6.9%	21,400
12/14	4,014	158	3.9%	18,000
Annual Growth	8.1%	25.3%	—	8.9%

2018 Year-End Financials

Debt ratio: 39.00%
Return on equity: 16.00%
Cash ($ mil.): 263
Current ratio: 1.00
Long-term debt ($ mil.): 1,809

No. of shares (mil.): 140
Dividends
Yield: 2.0%
Payout: 30.0%
Market value ($ mil.): 5,338

	STOCK PRICE ($) FY Close	P/E High/Low		PER SHARE ($) Earnings	Dividends	Book Value
12/18	38.00	27	13	3.00	1.00	16.00
12/17	68.00	23	17	3.00	1.00	17.00
12/16	53.00	24	17	3.00	1.00	15.00
12/15	56.00	29	22	2.00	1.00	15.00
12/14	45.00	49	38	1.00	0.00	14.00
Annual Growth	(4.3%)	—	—	29.4%	13.6%	2.1%

Fox Corp

Auditors: Ernst & Young LLP

LOCATIONS

HQ: Fox Corp
1211 Avenue of the Americas, New York, NY 10036
Phone: 212 852-7000
Web: www.FOXCorporation.com

HISTORICAL FINANCIALS
Company Type: Public

Income Statement   FYE: June 30

	REVENUE ($ mil.)	NET INCOME ($ mil.)	NET PROFIT MARGIN	EMPLOYEES
06/19	11,389	1,595	14.0%	7,700
06/18	10,153	2,187	21.5%	7,600
06/17	9,921	1,372	13.8%	—
06/16	8,894	1,072	12.1%	—
Annual Growth	8.6%	14.2%	—	—

2019 Year-End Financials

Debt ratio: 35.00%
Return on equity: 16.00%
Cash ($ mil.): 3,234
Current ratio: 4.00
Long-term debt ($ mil.): 6,751

No. of shares (mil.): 621
Dividends
Yield: 0.0%
Payout: 9.0%
Market value ($ mil.): 22,739

	STOCK PRICE ($) FY Close	P/E High/Low		PER SHARE ($) Earnings	Dividends	Book Value
06/19	37.00	16	13	3.00	0.00	16.00
06/18	0.00	—	—	(0.00)	0.00	(0.00)
Annual Growth	—			—	—	—

Franklin Financial Network Inc

EXECUTIVES

Ceo, J Myers Jones III
Exec V Pres-Cfo, Sarah L Meyerrose
Exec V Pres-Chief ADM Officer, Sally P Kimble
Evp-Cfo, Chris Black
Int Coo, Terry Howell
Evp-Gen Coun, Steve Groom
Customer Representativ, Leslie Laeng
Board Member, Henry Brockman
Senior Vice President, William Billington
Executive Assistant, Emily Kavin
Board Member, Paul Pratt
Auditors: Crowe LLP

LOCATIONS

HQ: Franklin Financial Network Inc
722 Columbia Avenue, Franklin, TN 37064
Phone: 615 236-2265
Web: www.franklinsynergybank.com

HISTORICAL FINANCIALS
Company Type: Public

Income Statement   FYE: December 31

	ASSETS ($ mil.)	NET INCOME ($ mil.)	INCOME AS % OF ASSETS	EMPLOYEES
12/18	4,249	35	0.8%	338
12/17	3,844	28	0.7%	281
12/16	2,943	28	1.0%	268
12/15	2,168	16	0.7%	226
12/14	1,356	8	0.6%	220
Annual Growth	33.1%	42.3%	—	11.3%

2018 Year-End Financials

Debt ratio: 1.00%
Return on equity: 10.00%
Cash ($ mil.): 1,432
Current ratio: —
Long-term debt ($ mil.): —

No. of shares (mil.): 15
Dividends
Yield: —
Payout: —
Market value ($ mil.): 383

	STOCK PRICE ($) FY Close	P/E High/Low		PER SHARE ($) Earnings	Dividends	Book Value
12/18	26.00	17	10	2.00	0.00	26.00
12/17	34.00	20	14	2.00	0.00	23.00
12/16	42.00	17	10	2.00	0.00	21.00
12/15	31.00	20	11	2.00	0.00	18.00
12/14	17.00	17	13	1.00	0.00	16.00
Annual Growth	11.1%	—	—	16.5%	—	13.0%

Franklin Resources Inc

Operating as Franklin Templeton Investments Franklin Resources manages mutual funds that invest in international and domestic stocks taxable and tax-exempt money market instruments and corporate municipal and US government bonds. Franklin Resources also offers separately managed accounts closed-end funds insurance product funds and retirement and college savings plans. Its open-end US funds are offered through about 1100 banks and securities and financial adviser firms; about 2700 banks and securities and finan-cial adviser firms offer shares of its cross-border non-US funds. The products are housed under the company's Franklin Templeton Franklin Mutual Series Franklin Bissett Fiduciary Trust Darby Balanced Equity Management K2 LibertyShares and Edinburgh Partners brands. The US is the company's largest market.

Operations

Most of Franklin Resources' revenue (nearly 70%) come from investment management fees which are directly tied to its assets under management. Sales and distribution fees generate about 25% of revenue and are made up of sales charges and commissions derived from sales and distribution of the company's sponsored investment products (SIPs).

In addition to its core business Franklin Resources also provides shareholder services and manages investments for high-net-worth clients and institutional investors. These services make up less than 5% of overall revenue.

Franklin Resources and its subsidiaries boast roughly $720 billion in assets under management.

Geographic Reach

Based in San Mateo California Franklin Resources boasts an extensive global presence with offices in more than 30 countries and clients reaching across 170-plus countries. The firm has operations in the Americas; Europe the Middle East and Africa (EMEA); and the Asia-Pacific region.

Of its assets under management about two-thirds are in the US; EMEA and the Asia-Pacific region each account for nearly 15%. Most of its revenue comes from the US (more than $3.7 billion) while a significant portion comes from Luxembourg (about $1.7 billion); together the two countries account for more than 85% of total company revenue.

Sales and Marketing

Franklin Resources relies on a large network of independent financial intermediaries to be the front end of the sales process. In the US approximately 1100 local regional and national banks securities firms and financial adviser firms offer shares in Franklin's US funds. Outside the US Franklin Resources leverages about 2700 banks securities firms and financial adviser firms to sell its non-US funds to the investing public.

The company sells its investment products and services under a variety of brand names such as Franklin Templeton Franklin Mutual Series Franklin Bissett Fiduciary Trust Darby Balanced Equity Management K2 LibertyShares and Edinburgh Partners.

The company generates brand awareness through advertisements in major financial publications television internet through sporting event sponsorship and social media marketing.

Financial Performance

Franklin Resources' revenue has decreased every year since fiscal 2014 ending the period down about 25% as investment management fees fell along with average assets under management and effective fee rates. Sales and distribution fees also receded due to reduced assets under management and lower commissionable sales. Net income fell more than two-thirds in that time on the poor revenue performance. The company's cash stores lost about 10% as it slashed its long-term debt by about two-thirds.

Franklin's revenue slipped 1% to $6.3 billion in 2018 compared with the prior year. Investment management fees (which account for about $4.4 billion - nearly 70% — of the company's revenue) ticked up only $8.3 million on a slight increase in average assets under management. Sales and distribution fees which provide about 25% of revenue decreased 6% on lower average US assets under management and a reduction in total commissionable sales.

The company's net income fell 55% to $764 million in 2018 owing to an income tax charge related to the enactment of the Tax Cuts and Jobs Act.

Franklin's cash dropped $1.8 billion to $6.9 billion in 2018. Operations provided $2.2 billion as net trading in securities of consolidated investment products decreased and income taxes payable increased. Investments and financings used $290.4 million and $3.8 billion respectively. Investment spend was mainly for purchase of investments and net additions of property and equipment. Major financing activities included dividend payments and common stock repurchases.

Strategy

Franklin Resources' strategy includes stemming the tide of net fund redemptions by its clientele growing its distribution network outside the US taking advantage of a global return to value investing (as opposed to growth investing which has led the charge in recent years) and acquiring companies that complement its business.

Despite its key tenet to sell more shares in its funds than it redeems Franklin has experienced net fund outflows in past years. As part of its correction efforts the firm is expanding its distribution network (particularly outside the US) to address the growing population of middle class investors in emerging markets. International institutional long-term sales increased more than 40% in Franklin's fiscal 2018 compared with the previous year.

A headwind buffeting Franklin for the last decade is a widespread investment strategy focusing on growth stocks. Franklin's equity funds typically are value oriented which have lagged the market in recent years. With the rising interest rate environment in the US and similar raises in other countries Franklin believes the headwind will turn into a tailwind as value investing returns to favor.

In early 2018 the company entered three business acquisition agreements for US alternative credit manager Benefit Street Partners data science and non-bank marketplace lending investment firm Random Forest Capital and independent value investment management firm Edinburgh Partners. The Benefit Street purchase will expand Franklin's alternative credit offerings which have seen increased demand in the last decade. Random Forest provides the company with extended data science capabilities including machine learning and statistical algorithms to solve for expected gains in financial instruments. Edinburgh brought $10 billion in global and emerging markets equities to the firm.

Mergers and Acquisitions

In 2018 Franklin Resources agreed to acquire US alternative credit manager Benefit Street Partners for $683 million in cash of which $130 million will be used to retire debt Benefit Street debt. The acquisition expected to close in Franklin's fiscal 2Q19 will bolster Franklin Templeton's alternative credit offerings which have seen increased demand in the last decade from middle market companies and investors seeking assets with higher yields and lower volatility compared with traditional fixed-income products. Based in New York with five other US offices Benefit Street had $26.2 billion in assets under management at the end of 2018.

Franklin also agreed to purchase data science and non-bank marketplace lending investment firm Random Forest Capital in 2018. Random Forest uses machine learning and statistical algorithms to solve for expected gains on financial instruments.

Furthermore Franklin acquired independent value investment management firm Edinburgh Partners in 2018. Based in Edinburgh UK with an office in London and two in the United States Edinburgh Partners managed about $10 billion in global and emerging markets equities at the end of 2017.

Company Background

Rupert Johnson Sr. founded Franklin Distributors (capitalizing on Benjamin Franklin's reputation for thrift) in New York in 1947; it launched its first fund Franklin Custodian in 1948. Custodian grew into five funds including conservatively managed equity and bond funds. In 1968 Johnson's son Charles (who had joined the firm in 1957) became president and CEO. The company went public in 1971 as Franklin Resources.

EXECUTIVES

Chairman And Ceo, Gregory E. Johnson, age 59, $783,633 total compensation
President, Jennifer M. Johnson, age 56, $527,356 total compensation
Evp And Cfo, Kenneth A. Lewis, age 59, $527,356 total compensation
Evp Alternative Strategies, William Y. Yun, age 60, $525,000 total compensation
Evp Investment Management, John M. Lusk, $527,356 total compensation
Evp And General Counsel, Craig S. Tyle, age 60
Svp And Cio, Priscilla Moyer
Vice President Alternative Investment Strategies, Brian Wachowicz
Senior Vice President Global Data Center Operations, Renee Seay
Senior Vice President Corporate Finance And Treasury, Mark Constant
Senior Vice President, Jed Plafker
Vice President Private Real Estate Franklin Templeton Real Estate Advisors, Julie Rost
Senior Vice President And Operations Director, Paul Brady
Vice President Corporate Communications And Corporate Citizenship, Holly Gibson Brady
Senior Vice President Global Brand And Advertising, Lucy Carrico
Vice President Information Technology Communications Services, Dennis Garcia
Board Member, Laura Stein
Vice President And Secretary, Maria Gray
Vice Chairman, Rupert H. Johnson, age 80
Board Member, Mariann Byerwalter
Board Member, Chutta Ratnathicam
Auditors: PricewaterhouseCoopers LLP

LOCATIONS

HQ: Franklin Resources Inc
One Franklin Parkway, San Mateo, CA 94403
Phone: 650 312-2000   **Fax:** 650 312-3655
Web: www.franklinresources.com

2018 Sales by Geography

	$ mil.	% of total
United States	3,722	59
Luxembourg	1,731	27
Canada	250	4
Asia-Pacific	297	5
The Bahamas	208	3
Europe the Middle East and Africa excluding Luxembourg	97	2
Latin America	14	-
Total	**6,319**	**100**

PRODUCTS/OPERATIONS

2018 Sales by Type

	$ mil.	% of total
Investment management fees	4,368	69
Sales & distribution fees	1,600	25
Shareholder servicing fees	222	4
Other	130	2
Total	**6,319**	**100**

2018 Average Assets Under Management by Asset Class

	% of total
Equity	43
Fixed-income	37
Hybrid	19
Cash management	1
Total	**100**

Selected Subsidiaries

Balanced Equity Management Pty. Limited
Darby - Hana Infrastructure Fund Management Co. Ltd.
Fiduciary Trust Company of Canada
Fiduciary Trust (International) Sàrl
Franklin Mutual Advisers LLC
Franklin Templeton Services LLC
ITI Capital Markets Limited
Riva Financial Systems Limited
Templeton Asset Management Ltd.

COMPETITORS

AllianceBernstein	Legg Mason
American Century	Morgan Stanley
BlackRock	Old Mutual (US)
Capital Group	PIMCO
Dodge & Cox	Principal Financial
FMR	Putnam
Invesco	T. Rowe Price
John Hancock Financial Services	The Vanguard Group

HISTORICAL FINANCIALS

Company Type: Public

Income Statement

FYE: September 30

	REVENUE ($ mil.)	NET INCOME ($ mil.)	NET PROFIT MARGIN	EMPLOYEES
09/19	5,775	1,196	20.7%	9,600
09/18	6,319	764	12.1%	9,700
09/17	6,392	1,697	26.5%	9,400
09/16	6,618	1,727	26.1%	9,100
09/15	7,949	2,035	25.6%	9,500
Annual Growth	(7.7%)	(12.5%)	—	0.3%

2019 Year-End Financials

Debt ratio: 5.00%	No. of shares (mil.): 499
Return on equity: 12.00%	Dividends
Cash ($ mil.): 5,958	Yield: 4.0%
Current ratio: 3.00	Payout: 39.0%
Long-term debt ($ mil.): 748	Market value ($ mil.): 14,410

	STOCK PRICE ($) FY Close	P/E High/Low	Earnings	PER SHARE ($) Dividends	Book Value
09/19	29.00	15 11	2.00	1.00	20.00
09/18	30.00	33 22	1.00	4.00	19.00
09/17	45.00	16 11	3.00	1.00	23.00
09/16	36.00	14 10	3.00	1.00	21.00
09/15	37.00	18 11	3.00	1.00	20.00
Annual Growth	(6.2%)	— —	(8.1%)	(1.4%)	0.3%

Freddie Mac

These siblings know there's no place like home. Government-sponsored enterprises (GSEs) Freddie Mac (officially Federal Home Loan Mortgage Corporation) and Fannie Mae were established to buy residential mortgages and boost the housing market. They do so by purchasing mortgages from lenders and packaging them for resale thereby mitigating risk and allowing lenders to provide mortgages to those who may not otherwise qualify. The agency also provides assistance for affordable rental housing. Together Fannie and Freddie guarantee some 70% of all new home loans in the US. Due to losses related to the subprime mortgage crisis the government seized Fannie and Freddie in 2008. Government plans to divest the firms into private ownership have proven difficult; they remain GSEs.

HISTORY

Ah the '60s — free love great tunes and a war nobody wanted to pay for with taxes. By the '70s inflation was rising and real income was starting to fall. To divert a construction industry recession Congress created a new entity to buy home mortgages and boost the flow of money into the housing market.

Fannie Mae had been buying mortgages since 1938 but focused on Federal Housing Administration (FHA) and Veterans Administration loans. In 1970 Congress created Freddie Mac and enlarged Fannie Mae's field of action to include conventional mortgages. Still rising interest rates in the 1970s were brutal to the US real estate market.

In the early 1980s dealers devised a way to securitize the company's loans — seen as somewhat frumpy investments — by packaging them into more alluring bond-like investments made even sexier by the implicit government guarantee. When three major government securities dealers collapsed in 1985 ownership of some Freddie Mac securities was in doubt and the Federal Reserve Bank of New York quickly automated registration of government securities.

In 1984 Freddie Mac issued shares to members of the Federal Home Loan Bank (the overseer of US savings and loans). By 1989 the shares had been converted to common stock and were traded on the NYSE. Freddie Mac's board expanded from three political appointees to 18 members.

Nationwide real estate defaults (rampant in the wake of the late 1980s crash) kindled concern about Freddie Mac's reserve levels and whether it might need to tap its US Treasury line of credit. In response Congress in 1992 created the Office of Federal Housing Enterprise Oversight to regulate Freddie Mac and Fannie Mae. Initial examinations sounded no alarms. A 1996 Congressional Budget Office report questioned whether the government should continue its implicit guarantees of the pair's debt securities.

In 1997 Freddie Mac officially adopted its longtime nickname. The next year it launched a system to cut loan approval time from weeks to minutes (it agreed to develop a similar version for the FHA). The streamlining was crucial to pacts in which mortgage lenders (including one of the US's largest Wells Fargo) promised to sell Freddie Mac their loan originations. In 1999 Freddie Mac hired former House Speaker Newt Gingrich as a consultant.

Freddie Mac made a major Internet push in 2000 with its first online taxable bond offering. A wired venture involving Freddie Mac Microsoft and such big lenders as Chase Manhattan (now part of JPMorgan Chase & Co.) Bank of America and Wells Fargo drew fire from small banks that said it would push them out of the online lending business.

In 2001 Freddie Mac bought Tuttle Decision Systems a loan-pricing software system provider. Critics responded that Freddie Mac overstepped its government charter with such a move.

In a move initiated by its auditor Freddie Mac re-audited its earnings from 2000 to 2003 uncovering accounting irregularities and employee misconduct. Further investigations executive oustings restructuring and numerous lawsuits followed. In late 2003 Freddie Mac announced the findings of

its re-audit. The company admitted to understating earnings by $4.4 billion between 2000 and 2002 and overstating profits by $989 million in 2001 all in an attempt to smooth out results and show steady profit growth.

In 2006 the company paid a record $3.8 million fine to settle allegations by the Federal Election Commission that the company made illegal campaign contributions to members of the US House Financial Services Committee. It also agreed to pay $4.65 million to settle a lawsuit related to its employee 401(k) plan. Freddie Mac did receive good news that year though when the Department of Justice dropped criminal charges against the company for misstating earnings from 2000 to 2002.

As the subprime mortgage crisis began heating up in 2007 and 2008 Freddie Mac announced plans to stop purchasing risky subprime mortgages. However the company tried to help restore stability to the teetering mortgage market by investing in billions of dollars in new jumbo mortgages raising its loan limits to more than $700000.

Although the government stepped in with loans to help Freddie the company still struggled with subprime mortgage losses. The government seized Fannie Mae and Freddie Mac in 2008 and placed them in conservatorship. Freddie Mac's leadership was also shaken up. David Moffat resigned as CEO in 2009 and chairman John Koskinen stepped in to serve as his interim replacement. Later that year Charles Haldeman Jr. the former head of Putnam Investments was selected to lead the company.

The Federal Housing Finance Administration (FHFA) was created in 2008 to oversee Fannie and Freddie as well as the 12 Federal Home Loan Banks. The FHFA was granted more authority than its predecessor agencies the Federal Housing Finance Board and the Office of Federal Housing Enterprise Oversight.

EXECUTIVES

Evp General Counsel And Corporate Secretary, William H. (Bill) McDavid, age 71, $500,000 total compensation

Ceo, Donald H. (Don) Layton, age 68, $600,000 total compensation

Vice President, James Bowden

Evp And Chief Administrative Officer, Jerry Weiss, age 58, $450,000 total compensation

Evp Multifamily Business, David M. Brickman

Chairman, Christopher S. Lynch, age 61

Evp And Cio, Stacey Goodman, age 56

Evp Single-family Business, David B. (Dave) Lowman, age 58, $500,000 total compensation

Evp And Cfo, James G. Mackey, age 52, $500,000 total compensation

Evp Investments And Capital Markets, Michael Hutchins

Evp And Chief Enterprise Risk Officer, Anil Hinduja, $500,000 total compensation

Vice President Prepayment And Portfolio Modeling, Jonathan Veum

Vice President Executive Compensation, Daniel Scheinkman

Vice President Human Resources Talent Management, Dru Fearing

Vice President And Deputy General Counsel, Melinda Reingold

Vice President Underwriting, Stephen Lansbury

Senior Vice President Division Chief Risk Officer Single Family, Donna Corley

Executive Vice President General Counsel Corporate Secretary, Robert Bostrom

Vice President Operations, Ruben Sanchez

Vice President Multifamily Capital Markets, Robert Koontz

Senior Vice President, John Cannon

Senior Vice President, Michael Lipson

Vice President Risk Process And Governance, Ken Moskowitz

Vice President Quality Control, James J Johnson

Vice President Single Family Underwriting And Quality Control, Pamela Padgett

Senior Vice President Corporate Controller And Principal Accounting Officer, Donald Kish

Vice President Servicing Operations, Ken Burke

Vice President Multiclass Issuance, Mike Dawson

Vice President Singlefamily Customer Care, Kelly Steele

Svp Enterprise Capital Liquidity And Market Risk, Jorge Reis

Vice President Loan Servicing, Carl Mclaughlin

Vice President And Chief Economist, Sean Becketti

Vice President Of Planning And Analysis, Peter Zou

Senior Vice President Sales And Relationship Mgt, Chris Boyle

Vice President Change Management, Bill Cary

Vice President Government Affairs, Barbara Fox

Vice President Sales And Relationship Management, Randy Jones

Vice President Multifamily Asset Management, Pamela Dent

Vice President Single Family Data Delivery Services, Susan Burke

Vp Targeted Affordable Sales And Investment Multifamily, David Leopold

Vice President, Buckner Bill

Assistant Vice President, Rush Brandon

Vice President Mha Complinace Program Disbursements, Thomas Lee

Vice President Chief Credit Officer Single Family, Behera Pradyot

Associate Vice President Ii Account Manager, Ates James

Vice President It Delivery, Ike Snyder

Vice President Affordable Lending And Access To Credit, Danny Gardner

Senior Vice President Human Resources Diversity And Inclusion And Chief Diversity Officer, Jacqueline Welch

Vp And Chief Economist, Sam Khater

Vice President, Beth Ryan

Vice President Sourcing, Sally W Baker

Vp Customer Technology Integration, Richard Lang

Vice President, Cheryl Wyatt

Vice Chair, Mark Friend

Auditors: PricewaterhouseCoopers LLP

LOCATIONS

HQ: Freddie Mac
8200 Jones Branch Drive, McLean, VA 22102-3110
Phone: 703 903-2000
Web: www.freddiemac.com

PRODUCTS/OPERATIONS

2017 Sales

	$ mil.	% of total
Interest		
Mortgage loans	63,735	85
Securities	3,415	5
Other	657	1
Non-interest	6,869	9
Adjustments	(53643)	-
Total	**20,692**	**100**

COMPETITORS

FHLB Atlanta

HISTORICAL FINANCIALS

Company Type: Public

Income Statement

FYE: December 31

	ASSETS ($ mil.)	NET INCOME ($ mil.)	INCOME AS % OF ASSETS	EMPLOYEES
12/18	2,063,060	9,235	0.4%	6,642
12/17	2,049,776	5,625	0.3%	6,185
12/16	2,023,376	7,815	0.4%	6,004
12/15	1,986,050	6,376	0.3%	5,462
12/14	1,945,539	7,690	0.4%	5,007
Annual Growth	1.5%	4.7%	—	7.3%

2018 Year-End Financials

Debt ratio: 97.00%	No. of shares (mil.): 650
Return on equity: 443.00%	Dividends
Cash ($ mil.): 7,273	Yield: —
Current ratio: —	Payout: —
Long-term debt ($ mil.): —	Market value ($ mil.): 4,550

	STOCK PRICE ($) FY Close	P/E High/Low		PER SHARE ($) Earnings	Dividends	Book Value
12/18	7.00	8	5	1.00	0.00	7.00
12/17	9.00	—	—	(1.00)	0.00	(0.00)
12/16	8.00	273	94	0.00	0.00	8.00
12/15	3.00	—	—	(0.00)	0.00	5.00
12/14	4.00	—	—	(1.00)	0.00	4.00
Annual Growth	15.4%	—	—	—	—	14.0%

Freeport-McMoRan Inc

Freeport McMoran (FCX) is one of the world's major mining companies with holdings in copper molybdenum and gold. It is a leading copper producer with proven or probable reserves of more than 120 billion pounds; the company also has more than 30 million ounces of gold reserves and about 3.8 billion pounds of molybdenum reserves. FCX's mines are in the Americas and Indonesia. The company consumes much of its raw output itself manufacturing copper rods and other intermediate goods. With customers across the Americas Europe and Asia the US is FCX's biggest market at more than 30% of company revenue.

HISTORY

The Freeport Sulfur Company was formed in Texas in 1912 by Francis Pemberton banker Eric Swenson and several investors to develop a sulfur field. The next year Freeport Texas was formed as a holding company for Freeport Sulfur and other enterprises.

During the 1930s the company diversified. In 1936 Freeport pioneered a process to remove hydrocarbons from sulfur. The company joined Consolidated Coal in 1955 to establish the National Potash Company. In 1956 Freeport formed an oil and gas subsidiary Freeport Oil.

Internationally Freeport formed an Australian minerals subsidiary in 1964 and a copper-mining subsidiary in Indonesia in 1967. The company changed its name to Freeport Minerals in 1971 and merged with Utah-based McMoRan Oil & Gas (formerly McMoRan Explorations) in 1982.

McMoRan Explorations had been formed in 1969 by William McWilliams Jim Bob Moffett and Byron Rankin. In 1973 McMoRan formed an exploration and drilling alliance with Dow Chemical and signed a deal with Indonesia to mine in the remote Irian Jaya region. McMoRan went public in 1978.

Moffett became chairman and CEO of Freeport-McMoRan in 1984. The company formed Freeport-McMoRan Copper in 1987 to manage its Indonesian operations. The unit assumed the Freeport-McMoRan Copper & Gold name in 1991. Two years later Freeport-McMoRan acquired Rio Tinto Minera a copper-smelting business with operations in Spain.

To support expansion in Indonesia Freeport-McMoRan spun off its copper and gold division in 1994. In 1995 Freeport-McMoRan Copper & Gold (FCX) formed an alliance with the UK's RTZ Corporation to develop its Indonesian mineral reserves. Local riots that year closed the Grasberg Mine and FCX's political risk insurance was canceled. Despite these setbacks higher metal prices and growing sales in 1995 helped the company double its operating income.

An Indonesian tribal leader filed a $6 billion lawsuit in 1996 charging FCX with environmental human rights and social and cultural violations. The company called the suit baseless but offered to set aside 1% of its annual revenues or about $15 million to help local tribes. Tribal leaders rejected the offer and in 1997 a judge dismissed the lawsuit.

In 1997 FCX pulled out of Bre-X Minerals' Busang gold mine project which independent tests later proved to be a fraud of historic proportions. Amid widespread rioting Indonesia's embattled president Suharto was forced out of office in 1998. The new government investigated charges of cronyism involving FCX.

FCX received permission from the Indonesian government in 1999 to expand the Grasberg Mine and increase ore output up to 300000 metric tons per day. However the next year an overflow accident killed four workers in Grasberg and as a result of the accident the Indonesian government ordered FCX to reduce its production at the mine by up to 30%. Normal production at the mine resumed in early 2001.

FM Services (administrative legal and financial services) was added as a subsidiary in 2002. In 2003 FCX bought an 86% stake in PT Puncakjaya Power a supplier of power to PT-FI.

The $26 billion acquisition of Phelps Dodge in 2007 brought that company's global copper gold and molybdenum business into the fold. The deal placed FCX in a position to thrive as a global competitor in the rank just below metals and mining giants such as BHP Billiton Rio Tinto and Vale. A year later FCX sold the wire and cable business it acquired in the Phelps Dodge deal to General Cable Corporation for $735 million.

Following the acquisition — and benefiting from high copper prices and a good business climate — the company began to invest in its development projects. It was also able to retire a sizable portion of its debt much of it accumulated from the Phelps Dodge acquisition.

Political and environmental controversy in Indonesia has been a problem for FCX since its major protector former President Suharto was forced to resign in 1998 after more than 30 years in power. Sectarian violence in Indonesia where FCX is one of the largest employers also makes the company vulnerable to work stoppages. Anglo-Australian mining giant Rio Tinto is jointly involved with FCX in developing mineral properties in Indonesia's politically and environmentally sensitive Papua region. The company's Tenke Fungume copper and gold mine named Too is located in the Democratic Republic of Congo which also can be an unstable environment in which to do business. Tenke Fungume is jointly owned with Lundin Mining and the Congolese government. It began production in 2009.

Beginning in 2013 FCX has also moved into the oil and gas market to broaden its portfolio as a natural resource player though acquisitions.

In 2013 the company bought Plains Exploration & Production for $16.3 billion (including $9.7 billion of debt). Assets acquired included oil production facilities in California a production base in the Eagle Ford trend in Texas and deepwater Gulf of Mexico and onshore Haynesville assets.

That year to enhance FCX's cobalt marketing position it acquired 56% of a large scale cobalt chemical refinery in Kokkola Finland. The joint venture will operate under the name Freeport Cobalt FCX will be the operator. Other JV partners include Lundin Mining (24%) and La G n rale des Carri res et des Mines (20%).

EXECUTIVES

Evp And Chief Administrative Officer, Michael J. Arnold, age 67, $550,000 total compensation
Vice Chairman President And Ceo, Richard C. Adkerson, age 72, $1,250,000 total compensation
Vice President Taxes, Hugh O Donahue
Evp Cfo And Treasurer, Kathleen L. Quirk, age 55, $650,000 total compensation
President Americas And Africa Mining, Harry M. (Red) Conger, age 87, $500,000 total compensation
Vp And Cio, Bertrand (Bert) Odinet
Vp Corporate Hr, Linda Lewis
Vice President Sales, Dennis Wright
Svp International Relations And Federal Government Affairs, W Russell King
Chairman, Gerald J. Ford, age 75
Auditors: Ernst & Young LLP

LOCATIONS

HQ: Freeport-McMoRan Inc
 333 North Central Avenue, Phoenix, AZ 85004-2189
Phone: 602 366-8100
Web: www.fcx.com

2018 Sales

	$ mil.	% of total
Indonesia Mining	5,559	25
Rod & Refining	5,134	24
North America Copper Mines	4,694	22
South America	3,655	17
Atlantic Copper Smelting & Refining	2,302	10
Molybdenum mines	410	2
Corporate other & eliminations	(3126)	-
Total	**18,628**	**100**

2018 sales

	%
US	31
Switzerland	16
Indonesia	12
Japan	10
Other	31
Total	**100**

PRODUCTS/OPERATIONS

2018 Sales

	$ mil.	% of total
Copper		
Concentrate	6,180	31
Cathode	4,366	22
Rod and other refined copper products	2,396	12
Purchased Copper	1,053	5
Gold	3,231	16
Molybdenum	1,190	6
Other	1,490	8
Adjustments to revenue	-961	-
Embedded derivatives	-317	-
Total	**18,628**	**100**

Selected subsidiaries

Atlantic Copper Holding SA (smelting and refining Spain)
Chino Mines Company
Climax Molybdenum Company
FM Service Company (administrative and financial services)
Plains Exploration & Production (oil and gas US)
PT Freeport Indonesia Co. (91% mining)
  PT Smelting (Gresik) Co. (25% smelting Indonesia)

COMPETITORS

Anglo American	Glencore
Antofagasta	KGHM Polska Miedz
BHP Billiton	Rio Tinto Limited
Codelco	Southern Copper
First Quantum Minerals	Vale Limited

HISTORICAL FINANCIALS

Company Type: Public

Income Statement — FYE: December 31

	REVENUE ($ mil.)	NET INCOME ($ mil.)	NET PROFIT MARGIN	EMPLOYEES
12/18	18,628	2,602	14.0%	50,200
12/17	16,403	1,817	11.1%	53,200
12/16	14,830	(4,315)	—	59,100
12/15	15,877	(12,195)	—	72,000
12/14	21,438	(1,268)	—	81,300
Annual Growth	(3.5%)	—	—	(11.4%)

2018 Year-End Financials

Debt ratio: 26.00%
Return on equity: 29.00%
Cash ($ mil.): 4,217
Current ratio: 3.00
Long-term debt ($ mil.): 11,124

No. of shares (mil.): 1,449
Dividends
  Yield: 1.0%
  Payout: 8.0%
Market value ($ mil.): 14,939

	STOCK PRICE ($) FY Close	P/E High/Low		Earnings	PER SHARE ($) Dividends	Book Value
12/18	10.00	11	5	2.00	0.00	7.00
12/17	19.00	15	9	1.00	0.00	6.00
12/16	13.00	—	—	(3.00)	0.00	4.00
12/15	7.00	—	—	(11.00)	1.00	6.00
12/14	23.00	—	—	(1.00)	1.00	18.00
Annual Growth (18.5%) (21.3%)	—	—		(41.1%)		

Frontier Communications Corp

Frontier Communications provides phone data and internet video and satellite TV (through a partnership with DISH Network) services to urban and rural customers in about 30 US states. The company has about 3.7 million residential and business voice subscribers about 4.3 million broadband internet customers and some 840000 video subscribers. Nearly half of its customers subscribe to at least two services and about 15% subscribe to three or more offerings. Frontier is active mostly in rural and small to mid-sized markets where it is the incumbent local-exchange carrier (ILEC).

Operations

Frontier Communications' data and internet services contribute about 45% of revenue while local and long distance services account for about a third of the company's revenue followed by video services about 15% and other services less than 5%.

The company offers a range of services including broadband video voice and other services and products to residential customers over a combination of fiber and copper-based networks. For business customers Frontier offers broadband Ethernet traditional circuit-based services service (UCaaS) and voice over Internet Protocol (VoIP). The company also sells customer premise equipment and related maintenance services.

Geographic Reach

Norwalk Connecticut-based Frontier has operations spread throughout the US in about 30 stares in the South Southwest West and Midwest. The acquisition of Verizon's wireline operations in California Texas and Florida in 2016 expanded Frontier's activities in those states.

Sales and Marketing

Frontier Communication dials in new customers through its broadband offerings and tries to sell other services such as voice and video to them.

Financial Performance

Frontier's revenue went on a three-year string of increases before falling back in 2018.

The company's revenue dropped 5% to $8.6 billion in 2018 down about $532 million from 2017. The company lost customers and therefore revenue in Voice and Video services.

Frontier trimmed its net loss to $643 million in 2018 compared to loss of $1.8 billion in 2017 when it had higher charges for impairment and taxes in 2017 than in 2018.

The company's coffers held $404 million in cash and equivalents in 2018 compared to $376 million in 2017. In 2018 Frontier's operations generated $1.8 billion while investing and financing activities used $1.2 billion and $608 million respectively.

Frontier carries significant debt some $17.4 billion and has interest expense of $1.5 billion a year which could reduce the capital available for operations.

Strategy

Although Frontier slowed the rate at which it's losing customers in 2018 the fact remains that it's losing customers ? across the board. In 2018 Frontier reported a churn rate of 1.97% compared to 2.17% in 2017. The company plans to improve operations and customer care and technical support to boost revenue.

In its field operations Frontier has initiatives to reallocate resources to improve responsiveness to customers while lowering costs.

In customer care and technical support the company is trying to reduce the need to send technicians on house calls. Part of the changes are designed to improve call center interactions with customers. So far the company had reached 20% of the targeted reductions in dispatches.

Frontier has new products on the way to keep current customers and attract new ones. In 2019 the company announced Simply Wi-Fi Secure a product aimed at small business customers. Also in 2019 Frontier plans to deploy the capability for 10GB fiber service across our FiOS footprint for commercial customers as well as for 5G backhaul capability.

Frontier agreed in 2019 to sell its operations in Washington Oregon Idaho and Montana to Wave-Division Capital and Searchlight Capital Partners for $1.3 billion. The operations serve more than 350000 residential and commercial customers and provided about $619 million in revenue in the 2019 first quarter. Frontier will use the proceeds to pay down debt. The transaction was expected to close in 2020.

Mergers and Acquisitions

The Frontier Communications acquisition of Verizon Communications' wireline operations in California Texas and Florida for $10.5 billion closed in 2016. The acquisition brought about 3.3 million voice connections 2.1 million broadband connections and 1.2 million FiOS video subscribers and the related incumbent local exchange carrier businesses to Frontier. The deal expanded Frontier's presence large but still fast-growing states and improved the revenue mix by increasing the percentage of revenue generated by segments with promising potential.

Company Background

Frontier Communications was formed in 1935 as Citizens Utilities Company to acquire Public Utilities Consolidated Corporation a Minneapolis-based company with interests in electric gas water and telephone utilities throughout the US. From 1950 to 1970 the company bought utilities in rural and suburban areas of Arizona California Hawaii Illinois Indiana Ohio and Pennsylvania. The company continued to expand by buying smaller rural phone companies.

EXECUTIVES

Evp Field Operations, John J. Lass, age 62, $436,156 total compensation
Evp Consumer Sales Marketing And Product, John Maduri
President And Ceo, Daniel J. McCarthy, age 54, $981,251 total compensation
Evp And Chief People Officer, Kathleen Weslock, age 63
Evp General Counsel And Corporate Secretary, Mark D. Nielsen, age 54, $387,500 total compensation
Evp And Cto, Steve Gable, age 45, $458,750 total compensation
Evp And Cfo, R. Perley McBride, $199,432 total compensation
Evp Commercial Sales Operations, Kenneth A. Arndt
Evp Operational Transformation, Tim Travaille
Svp And Gm Connecticut Operations, Paul Quick
Svp-gen Mgr Pennsylvania, Elena Kilpatrick
Vp It Strategy And Planning, Nick Cory
Vp Customer Insights And Reporting, Monica Braden
Vp It, Eric Del Sesto
Vice President, David Schwartz
Vp Investor Relations, Luke Szymczak
Assistant Vice President Carrier Services, Kim Czak
National Sales Manager Retail, Zabrina Mitchell
Vice President Engineering, John Hansen
Vice President National Osp Engineering, David Woods
Executive Vice President, Dan Mccarthy
Senior Vice President, Peter Chronowic
Vp Of Commercial New Products, Marcelo Oliveira
Chairman, Pamela D. A. Reeve, age 70
Auditors: KPMG LLP

LOCATIONS

HQ: Frontier Communications Corp
  401 Merritt 7, Norwalk, CT 06851
Phone: 203 614-5600
Web: www.frontier.com

PRODUCTS/OPERATIONS

2018 Sales

	$ mil.	% of total
Consumer	4,380	51
Commercial	3,848	45
Subsidy and other regulatory revenue	383	4
Total	**8,611**	**100**

2018 Sales

	$ mil.	% of total
Customer Revenue		
Data and internet services	3,878	45
Voice Services	2,721	32
Video services	1,085	13
Others	544	6
Subsidy and other regulatory revenue	383	4
Total	**8,611**	**100**

COMPETITORS

AT&T	Hulu
Altice USA	Netflix
Amazon.com	Time Warner Cable
CenturyLink	U.S. TelePacific
Charter Communications	Verizon
Comcast	Vonage
Cox Communications	XO Holdings
FairPoint	
Communications Inc.	

HISTORICAL FINANCIALS

Company Type: Public

Income Statement
FYE: December 31

	REVENUE ($ mil.)	NET INCOME ($ mil.)	NET PROFIT MARGIN	EMPLOYEES
12/18	8,611	(643)	—	21,200
12/17	9,128	(1,804)	—	22,700
12/16	8,896	(373)	—	28,300
12/15	5,576	(196)	—	19,200
12/14	4,772	133	2.8%	17,400
Annual Growth	15.9%	—	—	5.1%

2018 Year-End Financials

Debt ratio: 73.00%
Return on equity: (-33.00%)
Cash ($ mil.): 354
Current ratio: 1.00
Long-term debt ($ mil.): 16,358

No. of shares (mil.): 106
Dividends
 Yield: 50.0%
 Payout: —
Market value ($ mil.): 251

	STOCK PRICE ($) FY Close	P/E High/Low	PER SHARE ($) Earnings	PER SHARE ($) Dividends	PER SHARE ($) Book Value
12/18	2.00	— —	(8.00)	1.00	15.00
12/17	7.00	— —	(26.00)	1.00	29.00
12/16	3.00	— —	(8.00)	6.00	58.00
12/15	5.00	— —	(4.00)	6.00	72.00
12/14	7.00	4 2	2.00	6.00	55.00
Annual Growth	(22.7%)	— —	—	(33.1%)	
	(27.5%)				

Fulton Financial Corp. (PA)

Fulton Financial is a financial holding company with $20 billion in assets that owns four community banks in semi-rural and suburban areas of Pennsylvania Maryland Delaware New Jersey and Virginia. Through some 240 branches the banks offer standard products such as checking savings and credit accounts CDs retirement accounts mortgages and loans. Commercial loans — including for real estate and industrial financial and agricultural loans — account for most of the company's loan portfolio.? The company owns several non-banking units including Fulton Insurance an agency selling life insurance and related products.

Operations

More than 70% of Fulton Financial's revenue comes from net interest income particularly from loans including fees. The remainder is derived from non-interest income mostly from service charges on deposit accounts investment management and trust services and other service charges and fees. Commercial real estate loans account for about 40% of the company's nearly $16 billion loan portfolio; industrial financial and agricultural commercial loans contribute more than 25% to that lineup.

Residential mortgages and home equity each account for around 10% of the portfolio.

Fulton Financial's four subsidiary banks include Fulton Bank Fulton Bank of New Jersey The Columbia Bank and Lafayette Ambassador Bank. Fulton Bank (120-plus branches) accounts for about 60% of the holding company's total assets with Fulton Bank of New Jersey (some 65 branches) contributing about 20% and the other two banks accounting for some 10% each. In October 2018 Fulton merged subsidiary banks FNB Bank and Swineford National Bank (which each held less than 2% of its total assets) into lead bank Fulton Bank.

Geographic Reach

Fulton Financial and its subsidiary banks operate about 240 branches in suburban and semi-rural markets in the northeastern US. Lead bank Fulton Bank serves customers in Pennsylvania Delaware and Virginia. Fulton Bank of New Jersey Lafayette Ambassador Bank and The Columbia Bank serve New Jersey Pennsylvania and Maryland respectively.

Headquartered in Lancaster Pennsylvania the holding company has operations centers in East Petersburg Pennsylvania and Mantua New Jersey.

Sales and Marketing

Fulton Financial increased its marketing spend by 14% in 2017 compared with 2016 primarily for promotions to increase deposits. Commercial customers are the holding company's leading customer segment.

Financial Performance

Amid its expansion into new markets Fulton Financial saw its revenue tick up about 10% to more than $780 million between 2013 and 2017 thanks mostly to increased net interest income particularly loans including fees. Net income trended up more than 5% to about $170 million. However its cash stores were halved to less than $110 million (owing to increased use for financings and decreased proceeds from sales of mortgage loans held for sale); its debt also went up almost 20% to about $1 billion in that time.

The company's revenue gained 10% in 2017 to $783.3 million driven primarily by increased income from loans including fees in Fulton's commercial and residential mortgage commercial loan construction and leasing portfolios. Increased loan revenues also drove the company's 2017 net income up 6% to $172 million.

Fulton had cash of $108.3 million at the end of 2017 down $10.5 million from the prior year. Operations contributed $258.8 million and investments used $1.2 billion related mostly to a net increase in loans. Financings added $897.1 million due to a net increase in demand and savings deposits.

Strategy

Fulton Financial is shifting its strategy away from allowing its subsidiary banks autonomy in their regions to instead focus on consolidation of its banks expansion without geographic restriction and alignment with its customer segments. The company believes such a strategy will enable it to more efficiently manage risk through centralized risk management and compliance operations. In October 2018 Fulton merged subsidiary banks FNB Bank and Swineford National Bank into lead bank Fulton Bank. The company plans to absorb its remaining subsidiary banks into Fulton Bank by the end of 2019.

Fulton's near-term strategy is to invest in Philadelphia Pennsylvania a quickly growing urban market. The company hired a regional president and a commercial team for the area in 2016 and opened a mortgage loan production office in May 2018. The company also has regulatory approval to open two full service branches in the area which are targeted to open in early 2019. The company

also plans to grow its presence in Baltimore Maryland.

Mergers and Acquisitions

In early 2019 Fulton Financial agreed to buy the wealth management business of Altoona Pennsylvania-based Forney Financial Solutions. The deal broadens Fulton's services for clients in the central part of the state.

Company Background

Fulton Financial traces its history back to the creation of Fulton National Bank in Lancaster Pennsylvania in 1882. It began acquiring other banks in the late 1940s and launched a holding company structure in 1982.

EXECUTIVES

Sevp Community Banking, Craig A. Roda, $398,805 total compensation
Sevp Coo And Interim Cfo, Philmer H. (Phil) Rohrbaugh, age 67, $478,543 total compensation
Sevp; President And Coo Fulton Bank, Curtis J. Myers, $371,347 total compensation
Sevp And Chief Credit Officer, Meg R. Mueller
Sevp And Cio, Angela M. Sargent
Chairman President And Ceo, E. Philip (Phil) Wenger, $944,103 total compensation
Sevp And Chief Risk Officer, Beth Ann L. Chivinski
President Small Business Administration Lending, Lynn Ozer
President And Coo Fulton Mortgage Company, Jeffrey J. Scheuren
Vice President Marketing, Theresa Bachman
Executive Vice President Marketing Corporate Communications, David Hostetter
Vice President Workforce Readiness And Advancement, Tonya Aument
Vice President, Gregory Palmer
Vice President Senior Employee Relations Consultant, Vicki Bennett
Senior Vice President Loan Operations, Georgina Condran
Vice President Sales Learning And Enablement Manager, Matthew Bills
Vice President Ancillary Services Manager, Doug Tshudy
Vice President And Corporate Training Director, William Glover
Vice President Chief Appraiser, Jeffrey Gorman
Vice President, Stephanie Lavenberg
Vice President Senior Cash Management Sales Officer, Steve Schreiber Steve Schreiber
Sr Vice President, Forest Crigler
Vice President Senior Human Resources Business Partner, Lisa Whitacre
Senior Vice President Director Of Retail, Randy Metz
Vice President, Marc Ryan
Vice President Corporate Workout Manager, Chris Demko
Senior Vice President Bank Controller, Linda Schroeder
Senior Vice President Funds Management, Keith Paich
Vice President, Joe Warner
Vice President, Christopher Bigos
Vice President, Tammy Snyder
Senior Vice President, Jim Wagner
Senior Vice President, Chris Sugra
Senior Vice President, James Bush
Vice President Special Assets, Virginia Akin
Vice President Commercial Sales Performance Program Manager, Coleen Toy
V.p, Michael Thompson
Vice President Consumer Loan Review, Domenick Vitale
Senior Vice President Underwriting Manager, Bruce Spicer
Senior Vice President, Sal Marone
Vice President, Federico Manno

Vice President, Nancy Sellers
Avp Merchant Sales Officer, Diane Smith
Senior Vice President Commercial Team Leader,
  Mac Weems
Senior Vice President And Corporate Tax
  Director, Brian Demild
Senior Vice President, Travis Goode
Vice President Retirement Services, Amy White
Vice President Loan Servicing Group Manager,
  Amy Snyder
Senior Vice President And Senior Portfolio
  Manager, Walter J Banta
Senior Vice President, Willie A Maddox
Vice President And Portfolio Manager, Laurie
  Bodisch
Vice President Trust Support Services And
  Technology Manager, Loretta Gockley
Senior Relationship Manager And Vice President,
  Max Tabak
Senior Vice President, Richard J Mason
Vice President Manager Of Charities And
  Endowments, Sheri Leo
Vice President And Senior Leasing Sales Officer,
  Sharon Wingenroth
Vice President, Todd Dietrich
Senior Vice President, John D Harding
Vice President And Senior Leasing Officer, Jason
  D Ibach
Executive Vice President And Chief Investment
  Officer, Keith P Aleardi
Vice President Product Implementation And
  Process Manager, Angela Schadt
Vice President Manager, Colleen A Lukacs
Vice President, Debbie Truckermiller
Vice President Senior Regional Loan Review
  Manager, John Sawn
Vice President Deputy Bsa Director, Jamie Thomas
Vice President, Jim Pesavento
Senior Vice President Sba Portfolio Manager, Alan
  Wilson
Senior Vice President, Richard Mason
Senior Vice President, John Harding
Vice President And Senior Leasing Officer, Jason
  Ibach
Vice President Manager, Colleen Lukacs
Senior Vice President And Senior Portfolio
  Manager, Walter Banta
Senior Vice President, Willie Maddox
Vice President, Keith Silfee
Senior Vice President And Managing Director Bsa
  And Aml And Ofac, Matthew Mandrell
Senior Vice President Strategic Initiatives Group,
  Ryan Curran
Vice President, Celeste Rau
Vice President Relationship Manager Iii, Mark
  Ritter
Vice President Private Banking, Connie Beck
Vice President, Mike Weber
Senior Management (senior Vice President
  General Manager Director), Sharon Hake
Vice President Of Cash Management, Frances
  Haldeman
Senior Vice President Corporate Banking
  Division, Tim Peachey
Member Board Of Directors, Lisa Crutchfield
Board Member, Joe Ballard
Board Member, Scott Snyder
Auditors: KPMG LLP

LOCATIONS

HQ: Fulton Financial Corp. (PA)
  One Penn Square, P.O. Box 4887, Lancaster, PA 17604
Phone: 717 291-2411
Web: www.fult.com

PRODUCTS/OPERATIONS

2017 Sales

	$ mil.	% of total
Interest		
Loans including fees	604	69
Investment securities	59	7
Other	6	1
Expense	(93.5)	-
Non interest		
Service charges on deposit accounts	51	6
Other service charges & fees	53	6
Investment management & trust services	49	5
Mortgage banking income	20	2
Investment securities gains	9	1
Other	26	3
Total	783	100

COMPETITORS

First Commonwealth	Mid Penn Bancorp
Financial	PNC Financial
Investors Bancorp	Sovereign Bank
M&T Bank	TD Bank USA

HISTORICAL FINANCIALS

Company Type: Public

Income Statement   FYE: December 31

	ASSETS ($ mil.)	NET INCOME ($ mil.)	INCOME AS % OF ASSETS	EMPLOYEES
12/18	20,682	208	1.0%	3,500
12/17	20,037	172	0.9%	3,700
12/16	18,944	162	0.9%	3,500
12/15	17,915	150	0.8%	3,460
12/14	17,125	158	0.9%	3,560
Annual Growth	4.8%	7.2%	—	(0.4%)

2018 Year-End Financials

Debt ratio: 3.00%	No. of shares (mil.): 170
Return on equity: 9.00%	Dividends
Cash ($ mil.): 446	Yield: 3.0%
Current ratio: —	Payout: 50.0%
Long-term debt ($ mil.): —	Market value ($ mil.): 2,634

	STOCK PRICE ($) FY Close	P/E High/Low	Earnings	Dividends	Book Value
12/18	15.00	16 12	1.00	1.00	13.00
12/17	18.00	20 17	1.00	0.00	13.00
12/16	19.00	21 13	1.00	0.00	12.00
12/15	13.00	17 13	1.00	0.00	12.00
12/14	12.00	15 12	1.00	0.00	11.00
Annual Growth	5.8%	— —	8.9%	11.2%	4.3%

Gallagher (Arthur J.) & Co.

One of the world's largest insurance brokers Arthur J. Gallagher provides commercial insurance products and risk management services through a network of subsidiaries and agencies. It places (arranges directly with underwriters) traditional and niche property/casualty lines in addition to offering retirement solutions and managing employee benefits programs. Risk management services include claims management loss control consulting and workers' compensation investigations. Gallagher UK places insurance with the Lloyd's of London exchange. The global company operates more than 600 sales and service locations in more

than 30 nations and through correspondent brokers and consultants does business in more than 90 countries. Most of Gallagher's revenue comes from the US.

Operations

Gallagher has grown to become one of the world's top five insurance brokers based on revenue as well as a top property/casualty claims administrator. It also ranks among the top employee benefits consulting firms.

The company operates through three reportable segments: Brokerage Corporate and Risk Management.

The Brokerage segment which provides both retail and wholesale services accounts for more than 60% of annual revenue. A majority of Gallagher's brokerage income comes from commissions paid by insurance companies (upon placement of their policies). Retail insurance brokerage accounts for more than 80% of the segment's revenue.

Gallagher's Corporate segment accounts for about a quarter of total revenue; it primarily generates income from refined fuel operations. The segment's managed investments include a 46.5% stake in pollutant reduction firm Chem-Mod and a 12% stake in private carbon dioxide emissions reduction outfit C-Quest Technology.

The smaller Risk Management segment (more than 10% of sales) provides contract claim settlement and administration services for enterprises; it earns fees from insurance companies and self-insured clients. The segment primarily works with workers' compensation claims and auto liability and property claims.

Geographic Reach

Gallagher gets more than 75% of its revenue from the US but the company is working to expand its international operations. The company operates in more than 30 nations and through a brokerage and consultant network serves more than 150 nations. Its largest overseas markets include Australia Bermuda Canada the Caribbean New Zealand Singapore and the UK.

Sales and Marketing

Most of Gallagher's brokerage business comes from retail customers which include commercial industrial not-for-profit government and religious organizations. Gallagher's wholesale brokerage centers provide insurance placement assistance to affiliated and independent agents.

The company manages its brokerage operations through a network of more than 600 sales and service offices.

Financial Performance

Gallagher's growth efforts in both the brokerage segment and the risk management segment have helped the company to increase new customer volumes and has created substantial annual revenue and net income increases in recent years. Cash flow has also risen over the past few years.

In 2017 revenue rose 10% to $6.2 billion as all three segments saw growth: Brokerage earnings increased 9% Corporate earnings increased 16% and Risk Management earnings increased 7% that year. The Corporate segment primarily generates income from refined fuel operations; overall commissions fees and revenue from clean coal activities grew that year.

With the higher revenue net income rose 12% to $463.1 million in 2017.

The company ended 2017 with $2.3 billion in net cash nearly 20% more than it had at the end of 2016. Operating activities mostly from the Brokerage and Risk Management segments provided $854.2 million in cash during 2017. Investing activities — primarily business acquisitions — used $511 million and financing activities used $47.8 million.

Strategy

A key component of Gallagher's growth strategy is the ongoing acquisition of small regional insurance agencies and benefits consulting firms. The company targets strong sales organizations with a focus on middle-market clients or expertise in niche property/casualty lines (such as aviation energy hospitality and health care).

In addition to growth through acquisitions Gallagher has influenced the growth of its business by expanding and strengthening its relationships with independent brokerage partners increasing cross-selling opportunities and pursuing niche markets such as employee benefit risk management. Unfortunately the group has lagged behind its competition in introducing new types of business such as cyber protection.

Additionally the company has been successful at countering declining property/casualty insurance rates by securing new business and improving retention rates. Gallagher sees strong potential in a growing insurance market and an increasingly risky and complex world.

Gallagher was named one of the world's most ethical companies by the Ethisphere Institute for the seventh straight year in 2018; it was the only insurance brokerage named to the list. As part of the company's 90th anniversary that year the company's employees committed to perform 90000 hours of volunteer work in 2018. The firm also invests in clean energy owning some 35 commercial clean coal production facilities that emit less mercury sulfur dioxide and other chemicals. (Gallagher could lose money on it coal interests if other cleaner sources of energy increase in demand.)

Mergers and Acquisitions

A core strategy of Gallagher is to expand through acquisitions. Purchases typically cost between $1 million and $60 million.

In 2019 Gallagher acquired the aerospace retail and wholesale insurance division of Jardine Lloyd Thompson. The deal will help Gallagher offer new products and services to its clients in the aerospace industry including airlines and manufacturers.

In 2018 the company acquired more than a dozen firms including Thomas Costello Insurance Agency Pronto Insurance McGregor & Associates and Williams Insurance Agency.

Gallagher spent some $550 million on around 40 acquisitions during 2017. Companies purchased that year included Construction Risk Solutions Presidio Group GPL Assurance and Lutgert Insurance.

In 2016 Gallagher completed more than 35 acquisitions spending nearly $400 million in the process. Some of the firms acquired in that period included Kane's Insurance Management Altman & Cronin Benefit Consultants McNeary and Victory Insurance Agency.

Company Background

Gallagher is led by J. Patrick Gallagher grandson of founder Arthur Gallagher who formed the company back in 1927.

EXECUTIVES

Corporate Vice President And President U.s. Wholesale Brokerage, David McGurn
Chairman Employee Benefits Consulting And Brokerage, James W. (Jim) Durkin, age 69, $725,000 total compensation
Chairman President And Ceo, J. Patrick (Pat) Gallagher, age 66, $1,000,000 total compensation
Cfo, Douglas K. (Doug) Howell, age 57, $850,000 total compensation
President U.s. Wholesale Brokerage, Joel D. Cavaness, age 57
Chairman Brokerage Services, James S. (Jim) Gault, age 67, $800,000 total compensation

President And Ceo Risk Management Services, Scott R. Hudson, age 57
Corporate Vp And Chairman International Brokerage, Thomas J. (Tom) Gallagher, age 61, $750,000 total compensation
Global Chief Service Officer, Vishal Jain
Ceo Employee Benefits Consulting And Brokerage, William F. Ziebell, age 56
Ceo Arthur J. Gallagher Australia, Sarah Lyons
Executive Vice President, Mike Temple
Vice President, John Segredo
Senior Vice President, Diana Bertoni
Senior Area Vice President, Bill Dickenson
Area Vice President, Jerry Guy
Area Senior Vice President, Barb Galuppi
Vice President Loss Control, Jim Stover
Vice President Merger And Acquisitions, Kevin Doyle
Area Vice President, Rob Erzen
Area Senior Vice President, Maureen O'Connell
Vice President, Bruce Beardsley
Vice President Corporate Ethics And Sustainability, Tom Tropp
Area Senior Vice President, Craig Chisholm
Area Executive Vice President, Tim Gonsior
Assistant Vice President Real Estate And Hospitality, Sandy Gilder
Area Vice President Marine, Marc Dunn
Area Vice President, Jack Zogg
Aavp And Director Of Operations Tampa Bay Branch, Randi Watson
Senior Vice President, Susan Ruvolo
Division President, Teresa Koster
Area Executive Vice President, Daniel Johnson
Area Executive Vice President, Eric Olson
Area Vice President, Kelly Bonanno
Area Vice President, Cindy Caslin
Vice President Sourcing And Services, Cara Richardson
Area Vice President Of Business Insurance Sales And Risk Management Consulting, John Sence
Area Assistant Vice President Property Loss Control, Scott Quackenbush
Area Vice President And Consultant, Janet Brendis
Area Vice President Human Capital And Employee Benefits, Bobby Desai
Vp Global Cash Management, Patricia Hinton
Area Vice President, Paul Nelson
Area Vice President, Judy Worrall
Senior Vice President, Daniel R'bibo
Area Vp Insurance And Risk Management, Bob Perlman
Area Vice President, Al Lasarre
Senior Vice President Property And Casualty Insurance, Frank Cook
Senior Vice President Digital Marketing Strategy, Jen Wachtel
Vice President Marketing And Customer Insights, Felicia Stanczak
Area Vice President, Tom Deverell
Area Senior Vice President, Melissa Ginter
Assistant Vice President Property, Jason Tegan
Auditors: Ernst & Young LLP

LOCATIONS

HQ: Gallagher (Arthur J.) & Co.
2850 Golf Road, Rolling Meadows, IL 60008-4050
Phone: 630 773-3800
Web: www.ajg.com

2017 Sales

	$ mil.	% of total
U.S.	4,737	77
U.K.	718	12
Australia	271	4
Canada	155	3
New Zealand	151	2
Other foreign	128	2
Total	**6,160**	**100**

PRODUCTS/OPERATIONS

2017 Sales

	$ mil.	% of total
Brokerage		
Commissions	2,627	43
Fees	869	14
Supplemental commissions	164	3
Contingent commissions	112	2
Investment income	59	1
Risk management		
Fees	768	12
Investment income	1	-
Corporate		
Clean energy & other investment income	1,560	25
Total	**6,160**	**100**

Selected Subsidiaries

AJG Financial Services Inc.
AJG Coal Inc.
Arthur J. Gallagher & Co. (Bermuda) Limited (insurance & reinsurance placement captive risk services)
Artex Risk Solutions (Bermuda) Ltd.
Arthur J. Gallagher & Co. (Canada) Ltd.
Arthur J. Gallagher Australasia Holdings Pty Ltd (Australia)
Arthur J. Gallagher Brokerage & Risk Management Services LLC
Arthur J. Gallagher Risk Management Services Inc.
Arthur J. Gallagher Service Company
Arthur J. Gallagher (UK) Limited (Lloyd's of London brokerage)
Risk Management Partners Ltd. (customized insurance & risk management)
Gallagher Bassett Services Inc. (risk analysis)
Gallagher Bassett International Ltd. (UK)
Gallagher Bassett Services Pty Ltd. (Australia)
Gallagher Benefit Services Inc. (employee benefit program management)
Heath Lambert Limited (Gallagher Heath UK)
Protected Insurance Company
Risk Placement Services Inc.

COMPETITORS

ACE USA	Liberty Mutual
Aon	Marsh & McLennan
BroadSpire	Sedgwick Claims
Brown & Brown	Management Services
Chubb Limited	Travelers Companies
Hub International	Willis Towers Watson
Jardine Lloyd	

HISTORICAL FINANCIALS

Company Type: Public

Income Statement

	REVENUE ($ mil.)	NET INCOME ($ mil.)	NET PROFIT MARGIN	EMPLOYEES
				FYE: December 31
12/19	7,195	669	9.3%	33,300
12/18	6,934	634	9.1%	30,362
12/17	6,160	463	7.5%	26,800
12/16	5,595	414	7.4%	24,800
12/15	5,392	357	6.6%	21,500
Annual Growth	7.5%	17.0%	—	11.6%

2019 Year-End Financials

Debt ratio: 23.00%	No. of shares (mil.): 188
Return on equity: 14.00%	Dividends
Cash ($ mil.): 605	Yield: 2.0%
Current ratio: 1.00	Payout: 47.0%
Long-term debt ($ mil.): 3,816	Market value ($ mil.): 17,913

	STOCK PRICE ($) FY Close	P/E High/Low	PER SHARE ($) Earnings	Dividends	Book Value
12/19	95.00	27 20	4.00	2.00	27.00
12/18	74.00	23 18	3.00	2.00	24.00
12/17	63.00	26 20	3.00	2.00	23.00
12/16	52.00	22 16	2.00	2.00	20.00
12/15	41.00	24 19	2.00	1.00	21.00
Annual Growth	23.5%	— —	14.3%	3.8%	7.4%

GameStop Corp

GameStop holds the top score in video game retailing. The largest retailer of new and used games hardware entertainment software and accessories boasts roughly 3800 GameStop EB Games and Micromania branded stores in the US and about 2000 stores in Europe Australia and Canada. GameStop also publishes the Game Informer magazine; operates ThinkGeek a retail outlet featuring video game and pop culture products; and owns Simply Mac which sells the full line of Apple products including laptops tablets and smartphones and offers Apple certified warranty and repair services. Altogether the firm stocks more than 6000 items with about half of sales coming from new video game hardware and software.

Operations

By product GameStop generates about 30% of its total sales from new video game software while more than 20% of sales comes from pre-owned and value video game products and software. Other sales come from new video game hardware sales (about 20% of sales) and video game accessories (more than 10%). A growing source of revenue is collectable items sold through its ThinkGeek site which account for about 10% of sales. ThinkGeek is a purveyor of geek and gamer-targeted gifts like a Hans Solo refrigerator magnets Star Trek aprons and Dr. Who cookie cutters.

The company divested its Technology Brands segment when is sold its Spring Mobile smartphone retail business which included about 1200 AT&T wireless stores in 2019 to retailer Prime Communications for more than $700 million.

GameStop relies on vendors for its games. Purchases from the top ten vendors accounted for approximately 80% of its new product purchases in 2018. Nintendo Sony Microsoft Take-Two Interactive and Activision Blizzard accounted for about 25% 20% 10% more than 5% and less than 5% respectively of new video game brand purchases during fiscal 2018.

Geographic Reach

GameStop has a presence in more than a dozen countries worldwide including 10 European countries the US Canada Australia and New Zealand. About 65% of its sales come from the US while Europe generates 15%.

Sales and Marketing

GameStop develops relationships with video game enthusiasts through its PowerUp Rewards loyalty program which provides members with the opportunity to earn rewards not available through other game retailers. Vendors participate in this program to increase the sales of their individual products. Altogether the company's various loyalty programs total more than 60 million members.

GameStop uses in-store marketing efforts like window displays and signs to attract customers and promote its products. Inside stores it features selected products through the use of vendor displays or preview videos signs catalogs point-of-purchase materials and end-cap displays. These advertising efforts are designed to increase the initial sales of new titles.

Financial Performance

In recent years GameStop's revenue and net income have for the most part declined year-to-year amid intense competition. Sony Microsoft and other big publishers are directly selling new games online cutting out retail third party retailers while used games are increasingly sold via Amazon and big box discount retailers such as Best Buy Target and Walmart.

Revenues declined 3% from $8.5 billion in 2017 to $8.3 billion in 2018. GameStop attributes the decrease to fiscal 2017 including 53 weeks compared to 52 weeks in fiscal 2018 the impact of 117 store closures (net of openings) the negative impact of foreign exchange rate fluctuations and a decrease in comparable stores sales of 0.3%.

Net income swung from a profit of $34.7 million in 2017 to a loss of $673.0 million in 2018. GameStop's bottom line was affected by goodwill impairment charges totaling $970.7 million and asset impairment charges totaling $45.2 million. The impairment charges were primarily the result of a sustained decline in market capitalization and lower forecasted cash flows.

During fiscal 2018 cash provided by operations was $325.1 million compared to $434.9 million in 2017. The decrease was primarily due to lower earnings. Cash from investing activities was $635.5 million compared to $60.6 million in 2017. The increase was primarily due to $727.9 million in proceeds from the sale of Spring Mobile. Financing activities used $174.7 million consisting primarily of dividends paid of $157.4 million and repayment of acquisition-related debt of $12.2 million.

Strategy

GameStop's slumping retail sales are primarily attributed to the video game industry's transformation from physical discs to digital downloads. The industry has in recent years advanced the digitization of console games which are now sold directly via digital storefronts operated by Sony (Playstation Network) Microsoft (Xbox Live) and Nintendo (Switch). While GameStop has dabbled in digital game distribution in the past it recognizes that it needs to up its game in this category in order to avoid a fate similar to Blockbuster Video or Tower Records.

To this end the company has launched its "GameStop Reboot" turnaround plan that includes cutting costs and reducing its global base of stores. In Q3 2019 the company stated it had already closed some 200 stores in the past year and is on track to close between 180 and 200 underperforming stores by the end of fiscal year 2019.

It is also focused on improving its in-store experience expanding its PowerUp Rewards loyalty program and testing e-sports-oriented stores that encourage customers to play games together. GameStop is also working to form partnerships so that it can sell more "exclusive" digital and physical products — like games and collectibles — at its stores. Increasing sales of collectibles for tech and pop culture enthusiasts is a key component of the company's diversification strategy.

Company Background

GameStop traces its roots to the 1994 combination of software retailers Babbage's and Software Etc. which resulted in the formation of NeoStar Retail Group. (Named for 19th-century mathematician Charles Babbage considered the father of the computer Babbage's was founded by James McCurry and Gary Kusin in 1983 while Software Etc. began as a division of B. Dalton Bookseller in 1984.)

GameStop took its current name in August 2001 when NeoStar it filed to go public which it accomplished in February 2002. Though public it was still under the majority control of Barnes & Noble until 2004 when GameStop bought back its shares.

HISTORY

NeoStar Retail Group resulted from the 1994 combination of software retailers Babbage's and Software Etc. Babbage's had been founded by James McCurry and Gary Kusin in 1983. Named for 19th-century mathematician Charles Babbage

(considered the father of the computer) it went public in 1988.

Software Etc. began as a division of B. Dalton Bookseller in 1984. Bookstore chain Barnes & Noble and Dutch retailer Vendex acquired B. Dalton two years later. Software Etc. went public in 1992.

Both companies focused on mall retailing: Babbage's on game software and Software Etc. on a broader variety of PC software. Both saw growth spurred by the rising popularity of Nintendo and Sega game systems and by falling PC prices. The two merged in 1994 in an effort to stave off growing competition from big retail chains such as Best Buy and Wal-Mart. NeoStar opened 122 stores in 1995.

Amid flat sales the following year several senior executives left. Also in 1996 NeoStar lost its contract to operate software departments at 136 Barnes & Noble sites and it soon filed for Chapter 11. Late that year a group led by Barnes & Noble's head honcho Leonard Riggio purchased about 460 of NeoStar's 650 stores for $58.5 million and renamed the company Babbage's Etc. Former Software Etc. chief Dick Fontaine was named CEO.

By 1997 the company began concentrating on popular games and software and in 1999 it formed its e-commerce site GameStop.com. In late 1999 Barnes & Noble paid Riggio's group $210 million for Babbage's Etc. In June 2000 the company fortified its position and became the #1 US video game retailer with the purchase of rival game retailer Funco (about 400 stores) for $161.5 million. The company changed its name to GameStop in August 2001 and filed to go public which it accomplished in February 2002. Though public it was still under the majority control of Barnes & Noble until 2004 when GameStop bought back its shares.

GameStop bought rival Electronics Boutique in 2005 more than doubling its size from 2000 to about 4500 stores. Steven R. Morgan a former executive with Electronics Boutique became president of GameStop later that year.

A new CEO took the controls at GameStop in 2008 — its first CEO change since the company's inception in 1996. Dick Fontaine gave up the title of chief executive to Daniel DeMatteo who had served as COO since 1996 and vice chairman of the company since 2004. Also Paul Raines formerly with Home Depot joined the company as COO in September 2008. Fontaine retained the chairman's title and focused on international operations and acquisitions.

GameStop focused on international expansion in 2008 driven primarily by a pair of acquisitions. The largest of those was its $629 million purchase of video game retailer Micromania which brought with it some 330 stores in France. South of the equator GameStop acquired The Gamesman the largest independent gaming retailer in New Zealand. The deal included eight Gamesman video game stores and brought GameStop's total store count in the country to 38.

In June 2010 DeMatteo was promoted to executive chairman of the company while Raines was named CEO.

In late 2013 the company acquired the 50.1% of Simply Mac that it didn't already own boosting its Technology Brands segment. The $9.5 million deal added Apple specialty retail stores in Utah and Wyoming. Also that year GameStop bought Spring Communications for $62.6 million.

EXECUTIVES

Coo, Tony D. Bartel, age 55, $924,923 total compensation
Ceo, J. Paul Raines, age 55, $1,285,077 total compensation
Cfo, Robert A. (Rob) Lloyd, age 57, $707,385 total compensation
Evp Strategic Business And Brand Development, Michael P. (Mike) Hogan, age 60, $613,923 total compensation
Evp; President U.s. Stores, Michael T. (Mike) Buskey, age 70
President Kongregate, Emily Greer
Svp Supply Chain And Refurbishment, Michael K. (Mike) Mauler, age 58, $571,846 total compensation
Svp Information Technology And Cio, Michael Cooper
Vp Ir And Global Controller, Mike Loftus
Regional Vice President, Rory Rhodes
Vice President Stores Central Market, Matt Koch
Vice President Marketing And Sales, Art Doud
Vp Enterprise Architecture, Mark Patton
Senior Vice President Human Resources, Mike Buskey
Senior Vice President Mergers And Acquisitions Spring Mobile, Kent Forsgren
Senior Vice President Collectibles, Janet Bareis
Chairman, Daniel A. DeMatteo, age 71
Auditors: DELOITTE & TOUCHE LLP

LOCATIONS

HQ: GameStop Corp
625 Westport Parkway, Grapevine, TX 76051
Phone: 817 424-2000
Web: www.gamestop.com

2017 Sales

	% of total
US	64
Europe	15
Australia	7
Canada	4
Technology Brands	9
Total	**100**

PRODUCTS/OPERATIONS

2017 Sales

	% of total
New video game software	29
Pre-owned and value video game products	26
New video game hardware	16
Technology Brands	9
Video game accessories	8
Collectables	6
Digital	3
Other	3
Total	**100**

Selected Websites

www.ebgames.com.au
www.gamestop.ca
www.gamestop.co.uk
www.gamestop.com
www.gamestop.com/pcgames
www.gamestop.de
www.gamestop.es
www.gamestop.ie
www.gamestop.it
www.kongregate.com
www.micromania.fr

Selected Merchandise

Accessories
  PC entertainment accessories
  Video game accessories
  Other
Internet streaming technology & digital distribution
Online games
PC entertainment software & other software
Used video games
Video game hardware
Video game software

COMPETITORS

Amazon.com	GameFly
Best Buy	Kmart
Buy.com	Target Corporation
Carrefour	Wal-Mart
Costco Wholesale	Zones
Fry's Electronics	eBay

HISTORICAL FINANCIALS

Company Type: Public

Income Statement

FYE: February 2

	REVENUE ($ mil.)	NET INCOME ($ mil.)	NET PROFIT MARGIN	EMPLOYEES
02/19	8,285	(673)	—	61,000
02/18*	9,225	35	0.4%	67,000
01/17	8,608	353	4.1%	68,000
01/16	9,364	403	4.3%	82,000
01/15	9,296	393	4.2%	73,000
Annual Growth	**(2.8%)**	**—**	**—**	**(4.4%)**

*Fiscal year change

2019 Year-End Financials

Debt ratio: 20.00%
Return on equity: (-38.00%)
Cash ($ mil.): 1,624
Current ratio: 1.00
Long-term debt ($ mil.): 472

No. of shares (mil.): 102
Dividends
  Yield: 0.0%
  Payout: —
Market value ($ mil.): 1,146

	STOCK PRICE ($) FY Close	P/E High/Low		PER SHARE ($) Earnings	Dividends	Book Value
02/19	11.00	—	—	(7.00)	2.00	13.00
02/18*	16.00	78	47	0.00	2.00	22.00
01/17	24.00	10	6	3.00	1.00	22.00
01/16	26.00	12	7	4.00	1.00	20.00
01/15	35.00	13	9	3.00	1.00	19.00
Annual Growth	**(24.9%)**	**—**	**—**	**—**	**3.6%**	**(9.1%)**

*Fiscal year change

GEISINGER HEALTH

Geisinger Health System provides health care to a large portion of the Keystone State. The health care system serves more than 3 million residents of nearly 50 counties spanning central and northeastern Pennsylvania. Founded in 1915 the organization's flagship facility is Geisinger Medical Center a 400-bed medical-surgical hospital located in Danville. It includes the Janet Weis Children's Hospital. With joint venture partner HealthSouth Geisinger also runs a rehabilitation hospital in Danville. As part of its operations the health system runs the 240-bed Geisinger Wyoming Valley Medical Center as well as numerous outpatient facilities and doctors' offices located throughout the region.

Geographic Reach

Geisinger Health System extends the reach of its health care system to millions of central and northeastern Pennsylvania residents across about 50 counties.

Financial Performance

In fiscal 2014 the hospital reported net revenue of $9.8 billion a $1 billion increase over the prior year.

Strategy

Geisinger Health System has been working to standardize its procedural operations to improve the quality of care at its facilities and cut costs. Initiatives include assigning care coordinators and providing home visits for high-risk patients to avoid repeat hospitalizations. The health network also implemented an electronic medical records system and began using networking technology to reach into rural markets. Known as "telemedicine" the system's networking technologies are used among other things to facilitate remote two-way consultations between system physicians and rural patients. Additionally Geisinger runs the Geisinger Health Plan a not-for-profit HMO with some 230000 members.

In addition to its clinical operations Geisinger Health System also pursues industry partnerships and licensing opportunities through Geisinger Ventures its business development unit. The unit works to commercialize (and sometimes spin off) medical and technology-related innovations.

Mergers and Acquisitions

Geisinger has grown through several strategic acquisitions as of late. The health care system purchased central Pennsylvania's Cancer Care Centers in late 2014 adding four facilities to its network.

EXECUTIVES

Evp And Coo, Frank Trembulak
Evp Finance And Cfo, Kevin F. Brennan
Evp And Chief Medical Officer, Albert Bothe
Evp And Managing Partner Geisinger Consulting Services, Bruce H. Hamory
Evp And System Chief Nursing Officer, Susan M. Robel
Evp Clinical Operations, Lynn Miller
Evp And Chief Scientific Officer, David H. Ledbetter
President And Ceo, David T. Feinberg
President And Ceo Geisinger Health Plans, Steven R. Youso
Chief Medical Executive Geisinger Northeast Region, Robert J. Weil
Vice President Supply Chain Services, Deborah Templeton
Associate Vice President Surgery And Anesthesiology, Kyle Snyder
Senior Vice President Finance, Thomas Sokola
Assistant To Greg Snow Vice President Of Revenue Cycle, Denise Baylor
Vice President Human Resources, Rick Flynn
Vice President Clinical Informatics, Joan Topper
Director Of Pharmacy, David Klinger
Senior Vice President And Chief Inform, Thomas Barna
Executive Vice President, Julie Bordo
Medical Director Government Programs, Perry Meadows
Associate Medical Director, David Withers
Pharmacy Manager, Nannette Leganza
Medical Director, Carrie L Delone
Secretary, Alicia Laskowski
Auditors: KPMG LLP PHILADELPHIA PA

LOCATIONS

HQ: GEISINGER HEALTH
100 N ACADEMY AVE, DANVILLE, PA 178229800
Phone: 800 275-6401
Web: WWW.GEISINGER.ORG

PRODUCTS/OPERATIONS

Selected Services

Adolescent & Young Adult Medicine
Allergy
Anesthesia
Audiology
Bariatric Surgery
Cancer Institute
Cardiology
Colorectal Surgery
Cosmetics Program
Critical Care
Dental Medicine

Dermatology
Ear Nose & Throat
Emergency Medicine
Endocrinology & Metabolism
Fertility Center
Gastroenterology
Gynecology
Gynecologic Oncology
Heart Services
Hip & Knee Center
Imaging Services
Infectious Disease
Internal Medicine
Joint Replacement
Laboratory Medicine
LASIK Surgery
Mammography
Maternal Fetal Medicine
Mental Health
Minimally Invasive Surgery
Mohs Surgery
Neonatology
Nephrology
Neurodevelopmental Pediatrics
Neuroscience Institute
Neurology
Neurosurgery
Obstetrics
Ophthalmology
Orthopaedics
Osteoporosis
Pain Management
Palliative Medicine
Pediatrics (General)
Pediatric Allergy & Immunology
Pediatric Anesthesia & Sedation
Pediatric Cardiology
Pediatric Dental Surgery
Pediatric Dentistry
Pediatric Dermatology
Pediatric Endocrinology
Pediatric Gastroenterology
Pediatric General Surgery
Pediatric Genetics
Pediatric Hematology/Oncology
Pediatric Hospitalists
Pediatric Infectious Disease
Pediatric Intensive Care
Pediatric Interventional Radiology
Pediatric Nephrology
Pediatric Neurology
Pediatric Neuropsychology
Pediatric Neurosurgery
Pediatric Ophthalmology
Pediatric Orthopaedics
Pediatric Otolaryngology
Pediatric Plastic Surgery
Pediatric Psychology & Psychiatry
Pediatric Pulmonology
Pediatric Rehabilitation
Pediatric Rheumatology
Pediatric Transplant Surgery
Pediatric Trauma
Pediatric Urology
Pediatric Weight Management & Nutrition
Plastic & Reconstructive Surgery
Podiatry
Psychiatry
Pulmonary Medicine
Radiology
Rehabilitation
Rheumatology
Sleep Services
Spine Medicine
Sports Medicine
Surgery
Thoracic Surgery
Transplant Surgery
Trauma Center
Urogynecology
Urology
Vascular Surgery
Weight Management Clinic
Women's Health

Selected Facilities

Geisinger HealthSouth Rehabilitation Hospital
  (Danville)
Geisinger Medical Center (Danville)
  The Janet Weis Children's Hospital
Geisinger Wyoming Valley Medical Center (Wilkes-Barre)

Pearsall Heart Hospital
Geisinger South Wilkes-Barre Outpatient Center
Shamokin Area Community Hospital

COMPETITORS

Ascension Health
Blue Cross of Northeastern Pennsylvania
Capital BlueCross
Community Health Systems
HealthAmerica
Highmark
PinnacleHealth System
UPMC
Universal Health Services
Wyoming Valley Health Care System

HISTORICAL FINANCIALS

Company Type: Private

Income Statement				FYE: June 30
	REVENUE ($ mil.)	NET INCOME ($ mil.)	NET PROFIT MARGIN	EMPLOYEES
06/18	6,537	359	5.5%	13,030
06/17	6,337	553	8.7%	—
06/10	47	31	65.7%	—
06/09	0	0	—	—
Annual Growth	—	—	—	—

General Dynamics Corp

General Dynamics is a prime military contractor to the Pentagon (the US government accounts for 65% of sales). The company's Marine Systems unit builds warships commercial tankers and nuclear submarines. The Aerospace division - composed of Gulfstream Aerospace and Jet Aviation - makes and refurbishes business jets primarily for civilian customers. The company's Information Technology segment provides IT services and IT infrastructure to the US government. The Combat Services unit makes battle tanks wheeled combat/tactical vehicles munitions and rockets and gun systems. Mission Systems handles C4ISR (command control communications computers intelligence surveillance and reconnaissance) solutions for naval air ground space and cyber systems.

Operations

General Dynamic's Marine Systems group (24% of revenue) is a major shipbuilder for the US Navy and it provides MRO (maintenance/repair/overhaul) services. Through Electric Boat Marine Systems manufactures the Virginia-class nuclear-powered submarine while Bath Iron Works builds the Arleigh Burke-class guided-missile destroyer (DDG-51). NASSCO builds auxiliary and support ships for the US Navy as well as oil tankers and container ships for commercial customers.

On the civilian side of the business the company's Aerospace segment (23% of revenue) produces mid- and large-cabin business jet aircraft for which the company provides maintenance refurbishment and outfitting.

The Information Technology segment (23% of revenue) offers IT services (consulting design integration operations and maintenance cloud applications development and cyber defense). Other operations include IT infrastructure modernization (system development and engineering data center and cloud strategy migration and operations); and

professional services (logistics training and life sciences).

The Combat Systems division (17% of revenue) is composed of Armament and Technical Products; European Land Systems; Land Systems; and Ordnance and Tactical Systems.

Mission Systems division (13% of revenue) is a provider of C4ISR (command control communications computers intelligence surveillance and reconnaissance) products and systems. Its core offerings are space intelligence and cyber systems; ground systems and products; and naval air and electronic systems.

Geographic ReachGeneral Dynamics operates around the world serving government and commercial customers on five continents spanning more than 45 countries. The US represents its largest market generating around 80% of sales.

Sales and Marketing

General Dynamics' main customer is the US Department of Defense. The company conducts business with government customers around the world with operations in Australia Austria Brazil Canada China Estonia Germany Indonesia Malaysia Mexico the Netherlands the Philippines Russia Singapore Spain Switzerland Thailand the United Arab Emirates and the UK. About 65% of its revenues stem from the US government and 20% come from US commercial customers.

Financial Performance

General Dynamics' revenues ? apart from a slight dip in 2016 ? have seen steady growth over the last five years rising 17% between 2014 and 2018. With a strong backlog and recent contract awards the company is well positioned for long-term growth.

Revenue increased 17% to $36.2 billion in 2018 compared to $31.0 billion the prior year. Marine Systems' revenue improved amid higher volumes under US Navy contracts. The Aerospace division saw increased demand for maintenance work higher pre-owned aircraft sales and the 2018 acquisition of Hawker Pacific added to revenues. The acquisition of CSRA boosted the IT segment while Combat Systems' results experienced higher volumes for the Abrams tank and Piranha wheeled vehicle. The Mission Systems division saw stronger demand for communications and information systems from both the US and UK militaries.

General Dynamics' net income rose 14.9% to $3.3 billion in 2018 mainly due to reduced tax liability under the US Tax Cuts and Jobs Act.

The company's cash and equivalents stood at $963 million at the end of 2018 compared to $3.0 billion the year before. Cash from operations contributed $3.1 billion while investing activities used $10.2 billion mainly for acquisitions and capital expenditures. Financing activities provided $5.1 billion primarily received from debt and commercial paper issuances.

Strategy

In 2018 General Dynamics split its Information Systems and Technology (IS&T) business unit into two separate operating segments upon the completion of the company's acquisition of CSRA a provider of IT services to the US government. CSRA's operations were combined with General Dynamics' existing IT services business to create the new Information Technology division. The Mission Systems segment was established to house the company's C4ISR offerings. These moves are expected to improve operating efficiencies across the two new segments.

The company is also making investments in the Aerospace unit. In 2018 General Dynamics bought Hawker Pacific a provider of integrated aviation services in the Asia Pacific and Middle East regions. The deal added 19 new locations with fixed base operation (FBO); and maintenance repair and overhaul (MRO) facilities to the company's global footprint. Also in 2018 the company received FAA certification for its next-generation Gulfstream G500 aircraft and achieved the first G500 customer delivery.

The company is the lead contractor for the US Navy's next-generation ballistic missile submarine the Columbia-class. The Navy considers the Columbia-class sub a top priority offering strategic nuclear deterrent capabilities for decades. The Columbia-class submarines are scheduled to replace the Ohio-class fleet when it reaches the end of its service life in 2027.

Mergers and Acquisitions

In April 2018 General Dynamics acquired CRSA a provider of information technology services to the federal government for about $9.7 billion in cash and the assumption of debt. The acquisition was made to beef up the IT offerings of General Dynamics catapulting it to the No. 2 spot among large government IT contractors. The combined company would have close to $10 billion in revenue from government IT services. The move comes as government spending was expected to increase with a strong push from the White House and the US Congress.

Later in 2018 the company bought Hawker Pacific a provider of integrated aviation services. The deal which was valued at $250 million added 19 new locations in the Asia Pacific and Middle East regions with fixed base operation (FBO); and maintenance repair and overhaul (MRO) facilities.

HISTORY

In 1899 John Holland founded Electric Boat Company a New Jersey ship and submarine builder. The company built ships PT boats and submarines during WWII but when faced with waning postwar orders CEO John Jay Hopkins diversified with the 1947 purchase of aircraft builder Canadair. Hopkins formed General Dynamics in 1952 merging Electric Boat and Canadair and buying Consolidated Vultee Aircraft (Convair) a major producer of military and civilian aircraft in 1954.

EXECUTIVES

Evp Marine Systems, John P. Casey, age 64, $747,500 total compensation
Chairman And Ceo, Phebe N. Novakovic, age 61, $1,585,000 total compensation
Vp And President General Dynamics Mission Systems, Christopher (Chris) Marzilli, age 59
Vp And President Electric Boat, Jeffrey S. Geiger, age 57
Vp; President Bath Iron Works, Dirk Lesko
Vp And President Gulfstream Aerospace Corp., Mark L. Burns, age 59
Vp And President Jet Aviation, Robert E. (Rob) Smith
Evp Combat Systems, Mark C. Roualet, age 61, $747,500 total compensation
Vp; President Nassco, Kevin M. Graney
Evp General Dynamics Information Systems And Technology Group; President General Dynamics Information Technology, S. Daniel (Dan) Johnson, age 72, $713,750 total compensation
Vp And President European Land Systems, Alfonso J. Ramonet
Svp And Cfo, Jason W. Aiken, age 46, $701,250 total compensation
Vp And President Land Systems, Gary L. Whited, age 58
President General Dynamics Information Technology, M. Amy Gilliland
Executive Vice President, Gerard Demuro
Director Government Relations, Jen Navarro
Director Of Government Relations, Gerry Lamb
Vice President Sales, Murray Rapp
Vp Manufacturing, Howard Bruce

Director Of Government Relations, Tomas R Madson
Vice President Information Technology, Tommy Augustsson
Manager Of Public And Government Relations, Dennis DuBard
Vice President And Gm General Dynamics Ordnance And Tactical Systems, Steve Elgin
Director Of Surgery, Todd Tarby
Svp Finance And Operations, William Wylie
Vice President Tax, Ken Hayduk
Vice President And General Counsel Electric Boat, Matthew S Luxton
Vice President Financial Planning, Randy Collins
Vice President Planning And Development, Bob Helm
Svp Intelligence Solutions Division General Dynamics It, Bernie Guerry
Vp Pre Production Operations Nassco, Steve Davison
Vice President New Marketing, Chris Trella
Vice President Of Program Integration And Concept Development Eelectric Boat, Kenneth M Perry
Vice President Investor Relations, Howard A Rubel
Vice President, Vincent Shugrue
Executive Vice President Information Systems And Technoloy, S Daniel Johnson
Vice President Senior Vice President Adm, Ira Berman
Vice President Of Supply Chain Materials And Strategic Sourcing Electric Boat, T Blair Decker
Vice President, Christopher J Brady
Board Member, Lester Lyles
Board Member, Rudy deLeon
Board Member, Laura Schumacher
Board Member, Mark Malcolm
Board Member, Peter Wall
Board Member, Catherine Reynolds
Auditors: KPMG LLP

LOCATIONS

HQ: General Dynamics Corp
11011 Sunset Hills Road, Reston, VA 20190
Phone: 703 876-3000
Web: www.gd.com

2016 Sales

	$ mil.	% of total
North America	24,122	77
Europe	2,355	8
Africa/Middle East	2,668	8
Asia/Pacific	1,914	6
South America	294	1
Total	**31,353**	**100**

PRODUCTS/OPERATIONS

2016 Sales

	$ mil.	% of total
Information Systems and Technology	9,187	29
Aerospace	8,362	27
Marine Systems	8,202	26
Combat Systems	5,602	18
Total	**31,353**	**100**

2016 Sales

	$ mil.	% of total
Products	19,885	63
Services	11,468	37
Total	**31,353**	**100**

COMPETITORS

BAE SYSTEMS	Leidos
Boeing	Lockheed Martin
Bombardier	Motorola Solutions
Cisco Systems	Navistar International
DRS Technologies	Nokia
Dassault Aviation	Northrop Grumman
Day & Zimmermann	Peugeot

FLIR Systems	Raytheon
HP Enterprise Services	Renco
Harris Corp.	Rockwell Collins
ITT Corp.	Textron
L3 Technologies	United Technologies

HISTORICAL FINANCIALS

Company Type: Public

Income Statement

FYE: December 31

	REVENUE ($ mil.)	NET INCOME ($ mil.)	NET PROFIT MARGIN	EMPLOYEES
12/19	39,350	3,484	8.9%	102,900
12/18	36,193	3,345	9.2%	105,600
12/17	30,973	2,912	9.4%	98,600
12/16	31,353	2,955	9.4%	98,800
12/15	31,469	2,965	9.4%	99,900
Annual Growth	**5.7%**	**4.1%**	**—**	**0.7%**

2019 Year-End Financials

Debt ratio: 24.00%
Return on equity: 28.00%
Cash ($ mil.): 902
Current ratio: 1.00
Long-term debt ($ mil.): 9,010

No. of shares (mil.): 290
Dividends
  Yield: 2.0%
  Payout: 35.0%
Market value ($ mil.): 51,073

	STOCK PRICE ($) FY Close	P/E High/Low	PER SHARE ($) Earnings	Dividends	Book Value
12/19	176.00	16 13	12.00	4.00	43.00
12/18	157.00	20 13	11.00	4.00	41.00
12/17	203.00	22 18	10.00	3.00	39.00
12/16	173.00	18 13	10.00	3.00	36.00
12/15	137.00	17 14	9.00	3.00	34.00
Annual Growth	**6.4%**	**—**	**7.2%**	**10.4%**	**5.5%**

General Electric Co

From turbines and oilfield equipment to aircraft engines and power plants General Electric is plugged in to industrial equipment businesses that shape the modern world. The company produces aircraft engines locomotives and other transportation equipment generators and turbines lighting and oil and gas exploration and production equipment. GE also has a healthcare products business which it plans to separate into a standalone company and a financial services division the size of which it is reducing (especially its energy and industrial finance business). More than a third of GE's sales comes from its US operations.

HISTORY

General Electric was established in 1892 in New York the result of a merger between Thomson-Houston and Edison General Electric. Charles Coffin was GE's first president and Thomas Edison who left the company in 1894 was one of the directors.

GE's financial strength (backed by the Morgan banking house) and its research focus contributed to its initial success. Early products included such Edison legacies as light bulbs elevators motors toasters and other appliances under the GE and Hotpoint labels. In the 1920s GE joined AT&T and Westinghouse in a radio broadcasting venture Radio Corporation of America (RCA) but GE sold off its RCA holdings in 1930 because of an antitrust ruling.

By 1980 GE had reached $25 billion in revenues from plastics consumer electronics nuclear reactors and jet engines. But it had become rigid and bureaucratic. Jack Welch became president in 1981 and shook up the company. He decentralized operations and adopted a strategy of pursuing only high-achieving ventures and dumping those that didn't perform. GE shed air-conditioning (1982) housewares (1984) and semiconductors (1988) and with the proceeds acquired Employers Reinsurance (1984); RCA including NBC (1986 but sold RCA in 1987); CGR medical equipment (1987); and investment banker Kidder Peabody (1990).

In the early 1990s GE grew its lighting business. It bought mutual fund wholesaler GNA in 1993 and GE Investment Management (now GE Financial Network) began selling mutual funds to the public.

GE sold scandal-plagued Kidder Peabody to Paine Webber in 1994. General Electric Capital Services (GECS) expanded its lines buying Amex Life Insurance (Aon's Union Fidelity unit) and Life Insurance Co. of Virginia in 1995 and First Colony the next year. The company sold its struggling GEnie online service in 1996 and formed an NBC and Microsoft venture the MSNBC cable news channel. In 1997 GE Engine Services bought aircraft engine maintenance firms Greenwich Air Services and UNC.

GE acquired Lockheed Martin's medical imaging unit in 1997 and added to the medical systems business with the 1998 purchase of Marquette Medical Systems. In 1998 GECS became the first foreign company to enter Japan's life insurance market when it bought assets from Toho Mutual Life Insurance and set up GE Edison Life.

In 1999 GECS bought the 53% of Montgomery Ward it didn't already own along with the retailer's direct-marketing arm as Montgomery Ward emerged from bankruptcy. (Ward declared bankruptcy again in 2000.) In 2000 it reorganized GE Information Systems to form an e-commerce unit Global eXchange Services (GXS). (GE sold 90% of GXS to buyout firm Francisco Partners in 2002.)

Later in 2000 the company announced its biggest acquisition of the Welch era. Moving in at the last minute GE trumped a rival bid from United Technologies and agreed to pay $45 billion in stock for manufacturing giant Honeywell International and to assume $3.4 billion in Honeywell debt.

Welch by then viewed as one of the best corporate leaders in the US had agreed to postpone his retirement from April 2001 until the end of that year in order to oversee the completion of the Honeywell acquisition. But European regulators concerned about the potential strength of the combined GE-Honeywell aircraft-related businesses blocked the Honeywell deal that summer. Welch then stepped down and Jeff Immelt formerly president and CEO of GE Medical Systems succeeded him in September 2001.

Immelt initially set about reshaping GE by spinning off its life and mortgage insurance businesses into a new entity Genworth Financial which went public in 2004 (completely divested in 2006). GE acquired UK-based Amersham a medical diagnostics and life sciences company since renamed GE Healthcare Medical Diagnostics.

In 2006 GE sold off most of its remaining insurance businesses including GE Insurance Solutions and Employers Reinsurance in a sale to Swiss Re. The company kept its US life reinsurance business.

Citing rising commodities costs GE sold its advanced materials unit which produced silicone quartz and ceramics products to Apollo Management and sold its GE Plastics unit (now SABIC Innovative Plastics) to SABIC for more than $11 bil-

lion in 2007. Also that year GE shut down the operations of wholesale subprime lender WMC Mortgage.

At the same time GE built some of its traditional businesses through acquisitions. In early 2007 the company's aviation division acquired aircraft systems manufacturer Smiths Aerospace from Smiths Group. GE Energy bought oil and gas production equipment supplier Vetco Gray and the US retail natural gas distribution network of Knight (then named Kinder Morgan).

In 2011 GE sold a controlling stake in NBCUniversal to Comcast. GE retained a 49% stake in the media venture.

In 2013 GE sold its 49% stake in NBCUniversal for nearly $17 billion to Comcast as part of its strategy to focus on its industrial operations. There was already a structure in place for Comcast to eventually take full ownership of NBCUniversal but stronger than expected growth from the joint venture accelerated those plans.

GE in 2013 acquired Texas-based Lufkin Industries which specializes in providing artificial lift technologies for the oil and gas industry as well as making industrial gears. The $3.3 billion deal broadened the GE Oil & Gas unit and supports the company's plans to tighten its focus on industrial customers by providing services and equipment. In 2014 GE launched Predictivity a portfolio of web-based products to help oil and gas customers in the Asia/Pacific region improve operational and fiscal productivity.

To further boost its industrial operations the partnered with XD Electric Group in 2013 to combine GE's grid automation capabilities with XD's high-voltage power equipment. GE Energy Financial Services has also recently invested in Japan's largest solar power project to be built in Okayama Prefecture; it holds a 60% stake in the project.

In 2013 to boost its global reach GE's financial arm bought a $2.3 billion portfolio of commercial real estate loans from Deutsche Postbank that comprised 90% British as well as German and French properties. GE Capital also acquired MetLife's banking unit in 2013 adding some $6.4 billion in deposits and an established online banking platform.

That year the company also bought Italy-based industrial manufacturer Avio's aviation business which it renamed Avio Aero for $4.3 billion. The move expanded GE's activities in the appealing jet propulsion segment and strengthens its global supply chain.

In 2014 GE sold GE Money Bank AB business in Sweden Denmark and Norway to Santander for $2.3 billion. That year the company also announced plans to exit its North American Retail Finance operations.

EXECUTIVES

Svp Business Transformation, Daniel Janki
Chairman And Ceo, John L. Flannery, age 57
Svp; Chairman And Ceo Ge Capital, Richard A. (Rich) Laxer
President And Ceo Current Powered By Ge, Maryrose T. Sylvester
Svp And President And Ceo Ge Aviation, David L. Joyce, age 62, $1,333,333 total compensation
Svp And Cto, Victor (Vic) Abate, age 50
Svp And President And Ceo Ge Power, Steve Bolze, age 56
Cfo, Jamie S. Miller, age 50
President And Ceo Ge Africa, Jay W. Ireland
President And Ceo Ge Europe And Alstom Integration Leader, Mark Hutchinson, age 59
Svp And Chairman President And Ceo Ge Asset Management, Dmitri L. Stockton, age 55
President And Ceo Ge Korea, Chris Khang

Svp And President And Ceo Power Services, Paul A. McElhinney
President And Ceo Baker Hughes A Ge Company, Lorenzo Simonelli, age 46
Svp And President And Ceo Ge Power, Russell Stokes, age 48
Svp And Chief Digital Officer Ge And Ceo Ge Digital, William (Bill) Ruh, age 58
President And Ceo Ge Renewable Energy, Jér ˆme Pécresse
Vp Global Services Organization (gso), Pete McCabe
Ceo Ge Malaysia, Datuk Mark Rozario
Ceo Ge Australia, Max York
Ceo Ge New Zealand And Ge Papua New Guinea, Kevin Hart
President And Ceo Ge Apac, Wouter Van Wersch
Government Affairs And Policy Director Ge Japan, Eriko Asai
Vice President, Kevin Czarnecki
Assistant Vice President, Valerie Bouchereau
Vice President Of Sales, Michael Sylstra
Regional Vice President Sales, Bjorn Gidner
Vice President Strategic Initiatives, Allison Garrigan
Senior Vice President Vice Public Relations, Rene Buhay
Senior Vice President, Kathleen Chomienne
Legal Secretary, Marlene Gerardi
Senior Vice President, Matthew Pauley
Vice President Risk Analyst, Debra Bresnan
Senior Vice President, Thomas Costello
Vice President Engineering, Luciano Cerone
Vice President, John Laws
Vice President National Direct Sales, David Robinson
Vice President Risk, Dennis Duffany
Vice President Speciality Solutions Sales Southeast, Randy Goins
Assistant Vice President: Franchiefinance, Vince Malizia
Vice President Retail Finance, Stephen Motta
National Account Manager Sears, Gary Howard
Assistant Vice President, Dennis Leonard
Senior Vice President, Bob Vail
Senior Vice President, David Richman
National Account Manager, Jack Hodes
Vice President Labor And Employment, Amber Kagan
Vice President Middle East Ge Energy, Joseph Anis
Vice President Business Operations Ge Power And Water China, Yang Dan
Vice President Global Services Ge Transportation, Pascal Schweitzer
Vice President Global Services Turbomachinery Solutions Ge Oil And Gas, Maria Sferruzza
Vp Global Simplification Controllership And Risk Management Ge Healthcare, Thomas Westrick
Chief Accounting Officer Vice President Controller, Thomas Timko
Government Relations, Pamela Farrell
Vp Investor Communications, Steven Winoker
Vice President Senior Account Executive, Eric Busch
Vice President Regional Sales, Adam Berman
Vice President General Manager Civil Programs, Stefanie Darlington
Board Member, Shannon Winlove-smith
Board Member, Heather Bunyard
Advisory Board Member, Jill Johnson
Board Member, Elisa Morales
Board Member, Linda Reynolds
Board Member, Michael Tengelin
Vice Chairman, Jesse Rock
Board Member, Michele Zizzi
Board Member, Eric Denoyel
Treasurer Ge Aviation, David Martin
Treasurer, Craig Stevens
Board Member, Richard J Hawkins
Auditors: KPMG LLP

LOCATIONS

HQ: General Electric Co
41 Farnsworth Street, Boston, MA 02210
Phone: 617 443-3000
Web: www.ge.com

Sales 2016

	% of total
US	43
Europe	17
Asia	17
Americas	9
Middle East & Africa	14
Total	**100**

PRODUCTS/OPERATIONS

2018 Sales

	$ mil.	% of total
Power	27,300	22
Aviation	30,566	24
Healthcare	19,784	16
Oil & Gas	22,859	18
Lighting	1,723	1
Capital	9,551	8
Renewable Energy	9,533	8
Transportation	3,898	3
Corporate items & eliminations	(3600.0)	-
Total	**121,615**	**100**

2018 Sales

	$ mil.	% of total
US	46,754	38
Outside US	74,861	62
Total	**121,615**	**100**

COMPETITORS

ABB	Rockwell Automation
ALSTOM	Rolls-Royce
Agilent Technologies	Schneider Electric
Atlas Copco	Siemens AG
Caterpillar	Textron
Emerson Electric	ThyssenKrupp
FANUC	Toshiba
ITT Corp.	United Technologies
Raytheon	

HISTORICAL FINANCIALS

Company Type: Public

Income Statement
FYE: December 31

	REVENUE ($ mil.)	NET INCOME ($ mil.)	NET PROFIT MARGIN	EMPLOYEES
12/18	121,615	(22,355)	—	283,000
12/17	122,092	(5,786)	—	313,000
12/16	123,693	8,831	7.1%	295,000
12/15	117,386	(6,126)	—	333,000
12/14	148,589	15,233	10.3%	305,000
Annual Growth	(4.9%)	—	—	(1.9%)

2018 Year-End Financials

Debt ratio: 35.00%—
Return on equity: (-47.00%)
Cash ($ mil.): 35,020
Current ratio: 2.00
Long-term debt ($ mil.): 95,234

Dividends
Yield: 5.0%
Payout: —
Market value ($ mil.): —

	STOCK PRICE ($) FY Close	P/E High/Low	PER SHARE ($) Earnings	Dividends	Book Value
12/18	8.00	— —	(3.00)	0.00	4.00
12/17	17.00	— —	(1.00)	1.00	7.00
12/16	32.00	37 31	1.00	1.00	9.00
12/15	31.00	— —	(1.00)	1.00	10.00
12/14	25.00	19 16	2.00	1.00	13.00
Annual Growth	(26.0%) (27.3%)	— —	—	—	(19.7%)

GENERAL ELECTRIC INTERNATIONAL, INC.

EXECUTIVES

Pres, Giuseppe Recchi
V Pres*, Candace F Carson
V Pres*, Daniel Janki
SEC*, Pierrot Christophe
SEC*, Kristen Urso-Rio
Treas*, Michael J Geary
Senior Specialist, A Carbone
Power Performance Mana, Jerry King
Fbw Integrator, Joseph Desormeaux
Leader, Tyler Zimmer
Auditors: KPMG LLP CINCINNATI OHIO

LOCATIONS

HQ: GENERAL ELECTRIC INTERNATIONAL, INC.
191 ROSA PARKS ST, CINCINNATI, OH 452022573
Phone: 617 443-3000
Web: WWW.GE.COM

HISTORICAL FINANCIALS

Company Type: Private

Income Statement
FYE: December 31

	REVENUE ($ mil.)	NET INCOME ($ mil.)	NET PROFIT MARGIN	EMPLOYEES
12/17	14,100	686	4.9%	125
12/16	13,364	1,340	10.0%	—
12/15	13,288	83	0.6%	—
12/14	12,884	(304)	—	—
Annual Growth	3.1%	—	—	—

General Mills Inc

General Mills is high in the ranks of consumer packaged goods companies. Some of its #1 and #2 market-leading brands include Betty Crocker dessert mixes Gold Medal flour Pillsbury cookie dough and Yoplait yogurt. It competes with Kellogg to be the top cereal maker with a brand arsenal that includes Kix Chex Cheerios Lucky Charms and Wheaties. While most of the firm's sales come from the US General Mills is working to extend the reach and position of its brands globally and has facilities across five major continents. General Mills also owns the Haagen-Dazs ice cream brand in the US. The acquisition of Blue Buffalo in 2018 took General Mills into the pet food category.

HISTORY

Cadwallader Washburn built his first flour mill in 1866 in Minneapolis which eventually became the Washburn Crosby Company. After winning a gold medal for flour at an 1880 exposition the company changed the name of its best flour to Gold Medal Flour.

In 1921 advertising manager Sam Gale created fictional spokeswoman Betty Crocker so that correspondence to housewives could go out with her signature. The firm introduced Wheaties cereal in 1924. James Bell named president in 1925 con-

solidated the company with other US mills in 1928 to form General Mills the world's largest miller. The companies operated independently of one another with corporate headquarters coordinating advertising and merchandising.

General Mills began introducing convenience foods such as Bisquick (1931) and Cheerios (1941). During WWII it produced war goods such as ordnance equipment and developed chemical and electronics divisions.

When Edwin Rawlings became CEO in 1961 he closed half of the flour mills and divested such unprofitable lines as electronics. This cost $200 million in annual sales but freed resources for such acquisitions as Kenner Products (toys 1967) and Parker Brothers (board games 1968) which made General Mills the world's largest toy company.

During the next 20 years the company made many acquisitions including Gorton's (frozen seafood 1968) Monet (jewelry 1968) Eddie Bauer (outerwear 1971) and The Talbots (women's clothing 1973). It bought Red Lobster in 1970 and acquired the US rights to Yoplait yogurt in 1977. When the toy and fashion divisions' profits fell in 1984 they were spun off as Kenner Parker Toys and Crystal Brands (1985). Reemphasizing food in 1989 the firm sold many businesses including Eddie Bauer and Talbots.

To expand into Europe General Mills struck two important joint ventures: Cereal Partners Worldwide (with Nestlé in 1989) and Snack Ventures Europe (with PepsiCo in 1992).

As part of a cereal price war in 1994 the company cut coupon promotion costs by $175 million and lowered prices on many cereals. But some retailers did not pass on the price cuts to consumers due to shortages that developed after the FDA found an unauthorized pesticide in some cereals. General Mills destroyed 55 million boxes of cereal at a cost of $140 million. Stephen Sanger became CEO in 1995. That year the company sold Gortons to Unilever and spun off its restaurant businesses as Darden Restaurants.

Focused on a food-only future in the late 1990s General Mills picked up several smaller businesses including Ralcorp Holdings' Chex snack and cereal lines and Gardetto's Bakery snack mixes as well as the North American rights to Olibra an appetite suppressant food additive made by Scotia Holdings. Entering the natural foods market in 2000 General Mills launched Sunrise organic cereal and bought organic foods producer Small Planet Foods.

Big changes came in 2001 when General Mills became the #1 cereal maker in the US overtaking Kellogg for the first time since 1906. The company then completed its $10.5 billion purchase of Pillsbury from Diageo in October 2001. A month later General Mills sold competing product lines to International Multifoods. Also that year the company launched a 50-50 joint venture with DuPont to develop soy beverages marketed under the 8th Continent brand name. While busily integrating Pillsbury in 2002 General Mills saw its income fall and watched as Kellogg regained the lead in the cereal market. In 2003 the SEC began an investigation into the company's sales and accounting practices (which it terminated in 2005 taking no action against General Mills).

In 2004 General Mills filed a universal shelf registration with the SEC the result of which is that Diageo had to register the common shares of General Mills that it owns before it could sell those shares in a public offering. Also as a result of the shelf registration two Diageo-designated members of General Mills' board (including Diageo CEO Paul Walsh) resigned as a result of a change in the two companies' stockholders agreement that terminated Diageo's right to designate two General Mills' board members. Diageo sold part of its approximate 20% stake in General Mills. General Mills in turn sold an $835 million stake to an affiliate of Lehman Brothers Holding and used $750 million to buy back the Diageo shares and $85 million to pay down debt.

Also in 2004 the company sold its US Häagen-Dazs ice cream shop franchise business to Dreyer's Grand Ice Cream. In 2005 it sold its stake in Snack Ventures Europe joint venture to PepsiCo for $750 million. That year the company introduced Yoplait Healthy Heart which contains cholesterol-lowering plant sterols.

Diageo sold two-thirds of its 20% stake in General Mills in 2005. Later that year General Mills announced the sale of Lloyd's barbecue business to Hormel Foods. In 2006 Cereal Partners Worldwide (its joint venture with Nestlé) acquired the Australian breakfast cereal operations of Uncle Tobys from Burns Philp.

After more than 10 years of being ignored the Jolly Green Giant came out of retirement in 2005 as part of a multi-million dollar marketing campaign by General Mills to up its veggie sales. The next year General Mills declined to renew its licensing agreement with Archer Daniels Midland regarding the sale and marketing of Pillsbury Bakery Flour to the industrial and foodservice sectors. General Mills integrated the brand which consists of mixes and frozen bakery products into its bakery ingredients segment.

In order to develop healthier products in 2006 the company entered a supply agreement for DHA (an omega-3 fatty acid said to play a role in mental and cardiovascular health) with Martek Biosciences maker of DHA (which is already widely used in infant formula).

General Mills pulled its reduced-sugar children's cereal from the market in 2007 due to poor sales. Sweetened with SPLENDA the cereals never took off with consumers perhaps due to resistance to the sugar replacement. (Kellogg and Kraft use sugar in their reduced-sugar cereal offerings.) That year the company acquired UK chilled pastry company Saxby Bros.

Also in 2007 CEO Sanger stepped down. President and COO Ken Powell replaced him. The following year General Mills and DuPont sold their soy-milk joint venture 8th Continent to Stremicks Heritage Foods.

To better focus on its core brands and foodservice offerings the company in mid-2010 sold its Delicity chain of bakeries in Argentina to Tentissimo Group which also operates restaurants under the Tentissimo banner in the country. The deal included the Delicity brand five company-owned bakeries and franchiser rights which apply to the roughly 55 bakery locations operated by franchisees. General Mills also agreed to continue supplying dough products to the chain. It had owned Delicity since acquiring Pillsbury in 2001.

In 2008 the company sold its PopÂ·Secret operations to Diamond Foods for some $190 million in cash. PopÂ·Secret is the second-largest-selling branded popcorn in the US after Orville Redenbacher which is made by ConAgra. (ConAgra also makes Act II microwaveable popcorn.) While General Mills said it is concentrating its efforts on increasing the sales of its more lucrative core brands the high price of corn most probably also figured into the decision to jettison PopÂ·Secret.

General Mills made no divestures in 2009 but in 2010 the company ceased making Perfect Portions refrigerated biscuits and exited the kids' refrigerated yogurt beverage and microwave soup segments in its US retail operations; internationally it also stopped the manufacture of foodservice breadcrumbs with the sale of its Brazilian bread and pasta plant for $6 million. These product cessations were made in response to its declining financial results particularly in its international segment.

To better focus on its retail sales channels in late 2010 General Mills sold its Croissant King (acquired in 2005) and van den Bergh's (acquired in 1999) frozen bakery business in Australia to Ireland's Kerry Group. The sale includes frozen dough and pastry products sold to professional bakers.

Following that divestiture General Mills in 2011 acquired Australia's Pasta Master a maker of chilled Italian meals pasta and sauces. The purchase valued at nearly $40 million broadened General Mills' ready-to-cook pasta offerings.

To help offset weakness in its core cereal business General Mills is beefing up its yogurt empire through acquisitions such as its $1.2 billion purchase of a controlling stake in Yoplait in 2011 a brand that it had licensed for several decades. The company acquired the 50% stake in Yoplait owned by French investment firm PAI Partners plus 1% from dairy cooperative Social. Additionally General Mills acquired a 50% share of a related firm that owns Yoplait's global branding rights. General Mills aims to expand Yoplait's operations in France Europe and the rest of the world. Also in 2011 General Mills acquired Dean Foods' Mountain High all-natural yogurt business for about $85 million. The brand became part of General Mills' Yoplait USA division.

In line with its strategy to grow its business in global markets General Mills acquired Parampara's ready-to-cook spice and sauce mixes made and marketed in India and also exported to the US Canada and Japan. In 2012 it bought Brazilian food maker Yoki Alimentos which makes and markets more than 600 items under nine brands including Yoki and Kitano. The deal doubles General Mills' annual sales in Latin America.

EXECUTIVES

Vp; President Baking Products, David P. (Dave) Homer

Evp And Coo International, Christopher D. (Chris) O'Leary, age 60, $730,133 total compensation

Vp; President Annieâ's Foods, John M. Foraker, age 56

Svp External Relations; President General Mills Foundation, Kimberly A. (Kim) Nelson, age 56

Svp; President Greater China, Gary Chu

Evp And Cfo, Donal L. (Don) Mulligan, age 59, $736,050 total compensation

Svp; President Big G Cereals, James H. (Jim) Murphy

Evp Supply Chain, John R. Church, age 53, $577,767 total compensation

Svp; President Meals, Michele S. Meyer

Svp; President Sales And Channel Development, Shawn P. O'Grady, age 55

Ceo, Jeffrey L. Harmening, age 52, $775,000 total compensation

Evp Innovation Technology And Quality, Peter C. Erickson, age 58

Svp; President Latin America, Sean N. Walker

Svp; President Europe Australia And New Zealand, Jonathon J. (Jon) Nudi

Vp; President Snacks, Anton Vincent

Vp; President Yoplait International, Olivier Faujour

Vp; President Asia Middle East And Africa, Christina Law

Vp; President Yoplait Usa, David Clark

Vp; President Convenience And Foodservice, Bethany C. Quam

Vp; President Baking, Elizabeth M. Nordlie

Vice President Finance North American Retail, Brett White

Vice President Executive Director, Vijay K Sood

Vice President Corporate Services, Mike Nordstrom

Vice President Marketing Big G, John Haugen

Vice President Information Technology, Samuel Gale

Vice President It, Jodi Benson

Vice President Consumer Insight, Gayle Fuguitt

Vp Mergers And Acquisitions, Doug Power

Vice President And Chief Tax Officer, Gerald Morris

Vice President Corporate Strategy, Peter McDonald

Senior Vice President Chief Human Resources Officer, Jacqueline Williams-Roll

Vice President And Deputy General Counsel, Eric Wedepohl

Vice President Marketing Yoplait Division, Steve Young

Vice President Benefits, Ann Carlson

National Account Manager, Kurt Schuitema

Senior Vice President; President Bakeries And Foodservice, David E Dudick

Executive Vice President, Roderick Palmore

National Account Manager, Jim Behrle

Vp Marketing Canada, Dale Storey

Senior Vice President, Peter J Capell

Vice President, James Cooper

Vice President Sales Walmart, David Wurm

Assistant Vice President Of Network, Bill — Witz

Vp Sales, David Nagel

Vice President Of Human Resources, Victor Huang

Vice President Engineering, Gregg Stedronsky

Vice President Sales Admin, Ruth Welter

Senior Vice President Marketing, Jeff Rotsch

Vice President Information Technology, Zachariah Watne

National Account Manager, Dudley Whiteley

Senior Business Intelligence Developer, Steve Schober

Vice President Innovation Technology And Quality Global Cereal Platform, Mayank Patel

Vice President, Putnam Mcmillan

Vice President Media, Rick Hosfield

Vp Finance, Tito Wouda

Vice President Managing Director Yoplait Canada, Patrick Simmons

Vp Research And Development, John Mendesh

Vp Talent And Organization Capabilities, Mike Benson

Vpglobal Packaging And Designyoplait, Christopher Keith

Vice President Trade And Marketing, Steve Mayle

Vice President And Chief Tax Officer, Jerry Morris

National Sales Manager, Breanne Tindale

National Sales Manager Foodservice, Esme Plessis

Vice President Legal And External Affairs, Alice Lee

Senior Vice President; President Consumer Foods Sales, Shawn P Ogrady

Vice President Human Resources Corporate Functi, Kris Cotrone

Vice President Global Ecommerce, Gregory Pulsifer

National Sales Manager Vend Nfr, Richard Anastasio

Chairman, Kendall J. (Ken) Powell, age 66

Board Member, Heidi Miller

Secretary, Christopher Rauschl

Board Member, Juliana Chugg

Assistant Treasurer, Craig Shafer

Board Member, David Cordani

Board Member, Michael Rause

Auditors: KPMG LLP

LOCATIONS

HQ: General Mills Inc
Number One General Mills Boulevard, Minneapolis, MN 55426
Phone: 763 764-7600   **Fax:** 763 764-8330
Web: www.generalmills.com

2019 sales

	%
US	74
Non-US	26
Total	**100**

PRODUCTS/OPERATIONS

2019 sales

	$ mil.	% of total
Snacks	3,359	20
Cereal	2,672	16
Convenient meals	2,242	15
Yogurt	2,194	13
Baking mixes & integrates	1,704	10
Dough	1,693	10
Pet	1,431	8
Super-premium ice cream	813	5
Other	453	3
Total	**16,865**	**100**

2019 sales

	$ mil.	% of total
North America Retail	9,925	59
Convenience Stores & Foodservice	1,969	12
Europe & Australia	1,887	11
Asia & Latin America	1,653	10
Pet	1,431	8
Total	**16,563**	**100**

Selected Brands

Dessert and baking mixes
  Betty Crocker
  Bisquick
  Gold Medal
  SuperMoist
  Warm Delights
Dry dinners and shelf stable and frozen vegetable products
  Annie's
  Bac*O's
  Betty Crocker
  Chicken Helper
  Diablitos
  Green Giant
  Hamburger Helper
  Old El Paso
  Potato Buds
  Simply Steam
  Suddenly Salad
  Valley Selections
  Tuna Helper
  Wanchai Ferry
Frozen pizza and pizza snacks
  Jeno's
  Party Pizza
  Pillsbury Pizza Minis
  Pillsbury Pizza Pops
  Pizza Rolls
  Totino's
Grain fruit and savory snacks
  Annie's
  Bugles
  Chex Mix
  Fiber One
  Fruit By The Foot
  Fruit Roll-Ups
  Gardetto's
  Gushers
  Lärabar
  Nature Valley
  Stickerz
Ice cream and frozen desserts
  Häagen-Dazs
Organic products
  Annie's
  Cascadian Farm
  Muir Glen
Ready-to-eat cereals
  Basic 4
  Cheerios
  Chex
  Cinnamon Toast Crunch
  Clusters
  Cocoa Puffs
  Cookie Crisp
  Fiber One
  Golden Grahams
  Kix
  Lucky Charms
  Oatmeal Crisp
  Reese's Puffs
  Total
  Trix
  Wheaties

Ready-to-serve soup
  Progresso
Refrigerated and frozen dough products
  Big Deluxe
  Golden Layers
  Grands!
  Jus-Rol
  La Salte?a
  Latina
  Pasta Master
  Pillsbury
  Savorings
  Toaster Scrambles
  Toaster Strudel
  V.Pearl
  Wanchai Ferry
Refrigerated yogurt
  Go-GURT
  Fiber One
  Mountain High
  Trix
  Yoplait
  Yoplait Kids
  Yoplait Whips!
  YoPlus

COMPETITORS

B&G Foods	Hain Celestial
Barbara's Bakery	Hanover Foods
Bay State Milling	Heinz
Ben & Jerry's	Kellogg
Big Heart Pet Brands	King Arthur Flour
Birds Eye	Lakeside Foods
Blue Bell	MOM Brands
Bob's Red Mill Natural Foods	Manischewitz Company
Campbell Soup	McKee Foods
Carvel	Mondelez International
Chelsea Milling	Mrs. Fields
Cold Stone Creamery	Nature's Path
ConAgra	Nestlé
Dairy Queen	Pinnacle Foods
Danone	Pro-Fac
Dole Food	Procter & Gamble
Dreyer's	Ralston Food
Fresh «ns	Seneca Foods
Friendly's Ice Cream	Stonyfield Farm
Frito-Lay	Victoria Packing
Gilster-Mary Lee	YoCream

HISTORICAL FINANCIALS

Company Type: Public

Income Statement

FYE: May 26

	REVENUE ($ mil.)	NET INCOME ($ mil.)	NET PROFIT MARGIN	EMPLOYEES
05/19	16,865	1,753	10.4%	40,000
05/18	15,740	2,131	13.5%	40,000
05/17	15,620	1,658	10.6%	38,000
05/16	16,563	1,697	10.2%	39,000
05/15	17,630	1,221	6.9%	42,000
Annual Growth	(1.1%)	9.5%	—	(1.2%)

2019 Year-End Financials

Debt ratio: 48.00%
Return on equity: 27.00%
Cash ($ mil.): 450
Current ratio: 1.00
Long-term debt ($ mil.): 11,625

No. of shares (mil.): 602
Dividends
  Yield: 0.0%
  Payout: 68.0%
Market value ($ mil.): 31,786

	STOCK PRICE ($) FY Close	P/E High/Low	PER SHARE ($) Earnings	Dividends	Book Value
05/19	53.00	18 13	3.00	2.00	12.00
05/18	43.00	16 11	4.00	2.00	10.00
05/17	57.00	26 20	3.00	2.00	8.00
05/16	63.00	23 19	3.00	2.00	8.00
05/15	56.00	28 24	2.00	2.00	8.00
Annual Growth	(1.5%)	—	10.1%	4.1%	8.9%

General Motors Co

General Motors (GM) one of the world's largest auto manufacturers makes and sells cars and trucks worldwide under well-known brands such as Buick Cadillac Chevrolet GMC and Holden. Business divisions GM North America and GM International handle the automotive end of the business while General Motors Financial Co. provides financing services. Looking toward the future of transportation the company is investing in developing electric vehicles and autonomous vehicles and it has established a ride-sharing service dubbed Maven. GM's biggest single market is the US which accounts for about 80% of sales.

Operations

General Motors operates through three segments: GM North America (GMNA) GM International (GMI) and GM Financial.

GMNA generates more than 75% of revenue and manufactures vehicles marketed under the Buick Cadillac Chevrolet and GMC brands. GMI (15% of sales) sells these same brands to customers outside North America with the addition of the Holden lineup of vehicles. The company also has ownership stakes in companies in China where vehicles are also made and sold under the local Baojun Jiefang and Wuling brands.

GM Financial contributes about 10% of the company's total revenue. It provides automotive financing and retail loan and lease lending products and services. It also offers commercial products to dealers such as new and used vehicle inventory financing inventory insurance working capital capital improvement loans and storage center financing.

The company's GM Cruise unit includes the business operations of its autonomous vehicle technology development although this segment hasn't yet generated revenue.

Geographic Reach

Headquartered in Detroit GM has more than 100 locations in the US engaged in manufacturing assembly distribution warehousing engineering and testing. It has locations with similar functions in nearly 35 other countries. Its major facilities outside the US are in Brazil Canada China and Mexico.

GM Financial operates at about 40 locations globally. Some 25 are in the US. The US generates about 80% of GM's overall revenue.

Sales and Marketing

GM's cars and trucks are marketed and sold through a network of more than 12500 independent distributors dealers and authorized sales service and parts outlets all over the world. Vehicles are also sold directly to fleet customers including rental car companies commercial fleet customers leasing companies and governments.

GM is a constant presence on television and other media spending more than $4 billion a year on advertising.

Financial Performance

Since hitting a post-recession high of nearly $156 billion in revenue in 2014 GM's sales have fluctuated at lower levels.

In 2018 the company inched up slightly with a 1% increase to $147.0 billion compared with $145.6 billion in 2017. In North America increased sales of crossover and fleet vehicles in 2018 were offset by a decrease in sales of passenger cars and mid-size trucks. Sales in GM's international unit were also down due to a facility closure in Korea and the withdrawal from the Indian and South African markets. The decrease was slightly offset by higher sales in Brazil of the Chevrolet Onix Tracker and Equinox. GM posted higher revenue in its GM Financial division with increased lease vehicle income and increased income from finance charges.

After a $3.8 billion net loss in 2017 due to charges related to the US Tax Cuts and Jobs Act and the sale of the Opel/Vauxhaul business in Europe profit rebounded to $8.0 billion in 2018 more in line with GM's typical profit levels.

Cash at the end of fiscal 2018 was $23.5 billion an increase of $5.6 billion from the prior year. Cash from operations contributed $15.3 billion to the coffers while investing activities used $20.8 billion mainly for purchases of property and leased vehicles and investments in securities. Financing activities used another $11.5 billion for dividends to stockholders and the company's stock repurchase program.

Strategy

GM aims to stay ahead of changing market conditions that have seen sales of compact and mid-sized cars decline as consumers prefer trucks and crossover vehicles. As a result in late 2018 GM signaled a significant shift in its operations announcing a massive layoff that included idling five factories in North America and cutting roughly 14000 jobs?about 10% of its workforce there. The company has faced severe backlash from labor unions communities and even the president over the restructuring efforts. The company believes proceeding with restructuring while the economy is recovering and the company is profitable better positions GM for future growth.

The changes were intended to reduce the production of its smaller vehicles and provide the financial flexibility to double its investment in developing electric and autonomous vehicles. GM is committed to an all-electric future. Its next-generation vehicle technology will be launched in the new Cadillac EV scheduled to debut in 2022. It's also exploring lightweighting its new transmission systems and engines.

Geographically GM exited the unprofitable European Indian and South Africa markets in 2017 and is focused on investing in China and the Americas. In China it aims to increase the number of nameplates under the Buick Chevrolet and Cadillac brands and continues to grow its business under the local Baojun Jiefang and Wuling brands. In 2019 the company invested $2.6 billion in two of its Brazilian plants to build vehicles that will be sold in South America.

Company Background

In the early years of the auto industry hundreds of carmakers each produced a few models. William Durant who bought a failing Buick Motors in 1904 reasoned that manufacturers could benefit from banding together and formed the General Motors Company in Flint MI in 1908. In 1909 GM purchases Cadillac AC Spark Plug and Rapid Motor Vehicle Company. It later developed the General Motors Truck Company (which later became GMC) Chevrolet Motor Company of Michigan General Motors Export Company and general Motors of Canada.

After the stock market crash of 1929 GM bought out the Fokker Aircraft Company and the General Motors Aviation Company was launched. During WWII the company began making military vehicles including trucks guns airplane engines airplanes and parts tanks and shells among other products. It also provided the mobility system for the Lunar Roving Vehicle during the 1971 Apollo 15 space mission to the moon.

General Motors has manufactured some of the most popular vehicles ever made including the Cadillac Corvette El Camino Malibu and Camaro. The auto giant went through a six-week period of bankruptcy protection in 2009. GM was split into two companies when it emerged from Chapter 11 ? General Motors and Motors Liquidation (the name for leftover assets). In 2011 Motors Liquidation sold the majority of its assets which encompassed almost 90 industrial sites in 14 states which cleared the way for GM bondholders to receive stock in the new company.

EXECUTIVES

Svp; President And Ceo Gm Financial, Daniel E. (Dan) Berce, age 66

Evp Legal And Public Policy And General Counsel, Craig B. Glidden, age 61, $583,333 total compensation

Evp; President Europe; Chairman Management Board Opel Group, Karl-Thomas Neumann, age 58, $822,133 total compensation

Evp; President Cadillac, Carel Johannes de Nysschen, age 58

Evp Global Product Development Purchasing And Supply Chain, Mark L. Reuss, age 55, $1,100,000 total compensation

Chairman And Ceo, Mary T. Barra, age 58, $1,750,000 total compensation

Executive Director Global Technology Engineering, Matthew (Matt) Tsien, age 58

Evp And President Gm International, Barry Engle, age 56

Evp Global Manufacturing, Alicia Boler Davis

Evp; President North America, Alan S. Batey, age 55

President, Daniel (Dan) Ammann, age 47, $1,200,000 total compensation

Svp Global Information Technology And Cio, Randall D. (Randy) Mott

Evp And Cfo, Charles K. (Chuck) Stevens, age 59, $1,000,000 total compensation

President And Managing Director General Motors India, Sanjiv Gupta

Vp Global Purchasing And Supply Chain, Robert E Socia, age 67

U.s. Vice President Sales And Service, Kurt Mcneil

Vice President Gm Public Policy, Catherine Clegg

Senior Medical Director, Patrick Stover

Vice President Engineering Technical Center India, Lavern Sula

Vice President, Paras Dholakia

Vice President, Carlos Diaz

Medical Director, Donna Smith

Vice President And Treasurer, Rick Westenberg

Vice President Legal Affairs S, Elizabeth Shaffer

Vice President Of Industry Dealer Affairs, Bill Powell

General Motors Senior Vice President International Operations, Julian Blissett

Vice President Supply Chain, John Robertson

Senior Vice President Global Human Resources, Kim Brycz

Vice President, Jina Hwang

Senior Business Intelligence Developer, Rob Persons

Svp Global Human Resources, Kimberly kim Brycz

Senior Vice President Global Communications, Antonio Cervone

Treasurer And Vice President Of Investor Relations, Rocky Gupta

Senior Vice President Global Public Policy General Motors Company, Everett Eissenstat

Treasurer's Office, Nick Coupe

Treasurer, Niyant Shah

Board Of Directors, Joseph Ashton

Auditors: Ernst & Young LLP

LOCATIONS

HQ: General Motors Co
300 Renaissance Center, Detroit, MI 48265-3000
Phone: 313 667-1500
Web: www.gm.com

PRODUCTS/OPERATIONS

2018 Sales

	$ mil.	% of total
GM North America	113,792	77
GM International	19,148	13
GM Financial	14,016	10
Corporate	203	-
Eliminations	(110)	-
Total	**147,049**	**100**

2018 Sales

	$ mil.	% of total
Automotive		
U.S.	104,413	71
Non-U.S.	28,632	20
GM Financial		
U.S.	12,169	8
Non-U.S.	1,835	1
Total	**147,049**	**100**

Selected Brands

Buick
Cadillac
Chevrolet
GMC
Holden
Isuzu
Baojun
Jiefang
Wuling

COMPETITORS

BMW	Mitsubishi Motors
Chery Automobile	Nissan
Daimler	Peugeot
FCA US	Renault
Fiat Chrysler	Subaru
Ford Motor	Toyota
Honda	Volkswagen

HISTORICAL FINANCIALS

Company Type: Public

Income Statement

FYE: December 31

	REVENUE ($ mil.)	NET INCOME ($ mil.)	NET PROFIT MARGIN	EMPLOYEES
12/19	137,237	6,732	4.9%	164,000
12/18	147,049	8,014	5.4%	173,000
12/17	145,588	(3,864)	—	180,000
12/16	166,380	9,427	5.7%	225,000
12/15	152,356	9,687	6.4%	215,000
Annual Growth	**(2.6%)**	**(8.7%)**	**—**	**(6.5%)**

2019 Year-End Financials

Debt ratio: 45.00%	No. of shares (mil.): 1,429
Return on equity: 17.00%	Dividends
Cash ($ mil.): 23,243	Yield: 4.0%
Current ratio: 1.00	Payout: 25.0%
Long-term debt ($ mil.): 65,924	Market value ($ mil.): 52,301

	STOCK PRICE ($) FY Close	P/E High/Low		PER SHARE ($) Earnings	Dividends	Book Value
12/19	37.00	9	7	5.00	2.00	29.00
12/18	33.00	8	5	6.00	2.00	28.00
12/17	41.00	—	—	(3.00)	2.00	25.00
12/16	35.00	6	4	6.00	2.00	29.00
12/15	34.00	6	4	6.00	1.00	26.00
Annual Growth	**1.9%**	—	—	**(6.2%)**	**2.4%**	**3.2%**

Genuine Parts Co.

What do spark plugs hydraulic hoses paper clips and magnet wire have in common? They're all Genuine Parts. The diversified company is the sole member and majority owner of National Automotive Parts Association (NAPA) a voluntary trade association that distributes auto parts nationwide. Genuine Parts Company (GPC) operates about 1100 NAPA Auto Parts stores in more than 45 US states. It also distributes parts through chains in Canada Mexico and across Europe. Other subsidiaries include auto parts distributor Balkamp industrial parts supplier Motion Industries and office products distributor S.P. Richards.

HISTORY

Genuine Parts Company (GPC) got its start in Atlanta in 1928 when Carlyle Fraser bought a small auto parts store. That year GPC had the only loss in its history. Three years earlier a group that included Fraser had founded the National Automotive Parts Association (NAPA) an organization of automotive manufacturers remanufacturers distributors and retailers.

The Depression was a boon for GPC because fewer new-car sales meant more sales of replacement parts. During the 1930s GPC's sales rose from less than $350000 to more than $3 million. One tool it developed to spur sales during the Depression was its monthly magazine Parts Pups which featured pretty girls and corny jokes (discontinued in the 1990s). GPC acquired auto parts rebuilder Rayloc in 1931 and established parts distributor Balkamp in 1936.

WWII boosted sales at GPC because carmakers were producing for the war effort but scarce resources limited auto parts companies to producing functional parts. GPC went public in 1948.

The postwar boom in car sales boosted GPC's sales in the 1950s and 1960s. It expanded during this period with new distribution centers across the country. GPC bought Colyear Motor Sales (NAPA's West Coast distributor) in 1965 and introduced a line of filters and batteries in 1966 that were the first parts to carry the NAPA name.

GPC moved into Canada in 1972 when it bought Corbetts a Calgary-based parts distributor. That acquisition included Oliver Industrial Supply. During the mid-1970s GPC began to broaden its distribution businesses adding S.P. Richards (office products 1975) and Motion Industries (industrial replacement parts 1976). In the late 1970s GPC acquired Bearing Specialty and Michigan Bearing as part of Motion Industries.

In 1982 the company introduced its now familiar blue-and-yellow NAPA logo. Canadian parts distributor UAP (formerly United Auto Parts) and GPC formed a joint venture UAP/NAPA in 1988 with GPC acquiring a 20% stake in UAP.

During the 1990s GPC diversified its product lines and its geographic reach. Its 1993 acquisition of Berry Bearing made the company a leading distributor of industrial parts. The next year GPC formed a joint venture with Grupo Auto Todo of Mexico.

NAPA formed an agreement in 1995 with Penske Corporation to be the exclusive supplier of auto parts to nearly 900 Penske Auto Centers. GPC purchased Horizon USA Data Supplies that year adding computer supplies to S.P. Richards' product mix.

A string of acquisitions in the late 1990s increased GPC's industrial distribution business (including Midcap Bearing Power Drives & Bearings and Amarillo Bearing).

GPC paid $200 million in 1998 for EIS a leading wholesale distributor of materials and supplies to the electrical and electronics industries. Late in 1998 after a 10-year joint venture it bought the remaining 80% of UAP it didn't already own. GPC continued to expand its auto parts distribution network in 1999 acquiring Johnson Industries an independent distributor of auto supplies for large fleets and car dealers. GPC also acquired Oklahoma City-based Brittain Brothers a NAPA distributor that serves about 190 auto supply stores in Arkansas Missouri Oklahoma and Texas.

In 2000 the company bought a 15% interest in Mitchell Repair Information (MRIC) a subsidiary of Snap-on Incorporated that provides diagnostic and repair information services. The next year Johnson Industries acquired Coach and Motors a distribution center in Detroit.

GPC acquired NAPA Hawaii which serves more than 30 independently owned NAPA stores and four company-owned ones in Hawaii and Samoa in 2003. Also that year the company sold its interest in the partnership that distributes industrial parts in Mexico Refacciones Industriales de México.

President Thomas Gallagher became the company's fourth CEO in more than 75 years when he was named to the position in August 2004. Former CEO Larry Prince remained as chairman until early in 2005 when Gallagher was elected chairman; Prince remains on the board. Also during 2005 the company acquired a 25% interest in Altrom Canada Corp.

GPC subsidiary Motion Industries in mid-2006 acquired Lewis Supply Co. a provider of casters cutting tools machinery accessories and other general mill supplies. In October the company merged HorizonUSA Data Supplies previously a wholly owned subsidiary of S.P. Richards into S.P. Richards.

In early 2008 the company sold its Johnson Industries subsidiary which provided automotive supplies to fleets and new car dealers. In October GPC's S.P. Richards unit acquired ActionEmco's business assets in the midwestern US including its Grand Rapids Michigan distribution center. Also that year Motion Industries acquired Texas-based Drago Supply Company Mill Supply Corp. and Monroe Rubber and Plastic Supply.

In 2009 GPC added eight companies to its industrial and automotive operations for about $70 million and snapped up the remaining 11% interest in Balkamp that it did not already control for some $60 million making it a wholly owned subsidiary. These deals compare to a broader acquisition strategy in 2008 which added a dozen companies to all four of GPC's business segments (automotive industrial office products and electrical and electronic) for nearly $135 million.

Also in 2010 it acquired Canada's BC Bearing a distributor of bearing and power transmission components.

In late 2013 Motion acquired AST Bearings an industrial distributor specializing in high-precision miniature and specialty bearing with locations in New Jersey and California as well as Paragon Service & Supply (PS&S) of Lima Ohio. PS&S distributes industrial cutting tools abrasives and metalworking equipment.

In 2013 GPC acquired the remaining 70% of Melbourne-based Exego Group for approximately $800 million. (In January 2012 it purchased a 30% share in the company for around $150 million in cash). Exego an aftermarket distributor of automotive replacement parts and accessories has about 430 stores across Australia and New Zealand. The Exego stake allows GPC an entry point into Asia.

In 2012 GPC bought rival auto parts distributor Quaker City Motor Parts Co. for $343 million and thus became the only member of NAPA. Delaware-based Quaker was a long-standing NAPA distributor with annual sales of about $300 million and some 270 auto parts stores.

EXECUTIVES

Svp Finance And Corporate Secretary, Carol B. Yancey, age 56, $507,500 total compensation
Svp Human Resources, James R. (Jim) Neill, age 57, $319,000 total compensation
President And Ceo, Paul D. Donahue, age 63, $840,000 total compensation
President And Coo U.s. Automotive Parts Group, Lee A. Maher, $489,670 total compensation
President And Ceo Motion Industries, Timothy P. (Tim) Breen, age 58, $456,000 total compensation
Vp And Corporate Controller, David Haskett
Executive Vice President Global Procurement S.p. Richards Company, Steven Lynn
Vice President Southeast Division S.p. Richards Company, Lester Christian
Vice President Sales S.p. Richards Company, John Burgess
Vice President Organizational Development U.s. Automotive Parts Group, J Michael Phillips
Vice President Real Estate And Construction, Karl Koenig
Group Svp, Kevin Herron
Vp Sales And Marketing Rayloc, Scott Rolf
Vice President Retail, Cameron Richardson
Assistant Vp And Assistant Treasurer, Matthew P Brigham
Vice President Employee Relations, Vickie Smith
Vice President Western Division, Thomas Skov
Vice President Customer Relations And Sales, Stephen Yancey
Senior Vice President Human Resources S.p. Richards Company, G Henry Martin
Senior Vice President Logistics And Operations Eis, William Knight
Senior Vice President Finance And Supply Chain Rayloc, Michael Gaffney
Evp And Coo Eis, Matthew C Tyser
Senior Vice President Planning And Acquisition, Treg Brown
Executive Vice President Auto Parts Division Napa Canada Uap Inc., John Buckley
Vice President Product Development Napa Canada Uac Inc., Thomas Hunt
Vice President Distribution And Logistics Napa Canada Uap Inc., Mark Miron
Senior Vice President Marketing Distribution And Purchasing Motion Industries, Randall Breaux
Senior Vice President Hose And Rubber Shops And Service Centers Motion Industries, Anthony Cefalu
Vice President Of Safety And Industrial Of Motion Industries, Frederick Cowie
Vice President Business Systems Motion Industries, M Keith Knight
Vice President Operations Motion Industries, N Joe Limbaugh
Vice President Government Sales And Export Motion Industries, C Jeff Rouse
Vice President Of Supply Chain Of S.p. Richards Company, Dennis Flynn
Senior Vice President Of Merchandising Of S.p. Richards Company, John Reagan
Vice President Sales Emerging Markets S.p. Richards Company, Jason Smith
Vice President Sales S.p. Richards Company, Thomas Testa
Vice President Cleaning And Breakroom Supply S.p. Richards Company, Chris Whiting
Senior Vice President Sales And Marketing S.p. Richards Company, Bryan Wight
Vice President Northeast Division S.p. Richards Company, Ray Sreca

Vice President Midwest Division U.s. Automotive Parts Group, Dennis Gibbs

Executive Vice President Finance And Administration Napa Canada Uap, Frank Pipito

Vice President Sales And Marketing Napa Canada Uap, Simon Weller

Senior Vice President Marketing Eis, David Brower

Senior Vice President And Group Executive Central Motion Industries, James Randazzo

Vice President Ecommerce And Marketing Services S.p. Richards Company, Paul Gatens

Vice President Sales S.p. Richards Company, A Gaius Gough

Vice President Emerging Products And Services S.p. Richards Company, Manning Lomax

Vice President Human Resources U.s. Automotive Parts Group, Thu-Quyen Clifton

Vice President Marketing And Category Management, Matthew LeTexier

Vp Operations Rayloc, Timothy Davis

Vice President Traction Heavy Vehicle Parts, Charles Stille

Executive Vice President Heavy Vehicle Parts Division Napa Canada Uap, Pierre Rachiele

Vice President Heavy Vehicle Operations, Simon Bourque

Vice President Accounting Napa Canada Uap Inc, Martin Brisebois

Vice President Corporate Planning And Strategic Development Napa Canada Uap, Francois Cadoret

Vice President Paint Body And Equipment, Eric Levielle

Vice President Napa Store Operations Napa Canada Uap, Michel Pomerleau

Senior Vice President Marketing And Distribution Eis, Ronald Harris

Vice President Human Resources S.p. Richards Company, James Starr

Vice President Operational Excellence S.p. Richards Company, Richard Weeks

Assistant Vice President Financial Analysis, Christine Powell

Vice President Major Accounts U.s. Automotive Parts Group, Dennis Tolivar

Executive Vice President Global Procurement, Scott LeProhon

Group Senior Vice President U.s. Automotive Parts Group, M Todd McMurtrie

Vice President Benefits And Communication, Lisa Hamilton

Vice President Wholesale Product Management U.s. Automotive Parts Group, Byron Frantz

Senior Vice President Operations And Logistics S.p. Richards Company, E Chadwick Lee

Vice President Supply Chain, J Scott Mosteller

Vp Supply Chain And Logistics U.s. Automotive Parts Group, J Richard Borman

Vice President Finance Motion Industries, J Marvin Walker

Senior Vice President Of Finance And Chief Financial Officer Of S.p. Richards Company, J Phillip Welch

Senior Vice President Human Resources Napa Canada Uap Inc, Marie Claire Dupuis

Vice President Product Management Heavy Vehicle Parts Division, Marc Phillipe Beaudoin

Senior Vice President Digital, Rob Milstead

Vice President Southern Division U.s. Automotive Parts Group, Patrick Wolfe

Vice President Compensation, Phillip Johnson

Senior Vice President Sales U.s. Automotive Parts Group, Daniel Askey

Vice President Information Services Rayloc, Joseph Lashley

Vice President Finance And Treasurer Balkamp Inc., Mary Knudsen

Vice President Napa Tools And Equipment Sales U.s. Automotive Parts Group, David Nicki

Vice President Retail Product Management And Merchandising U.s. Automotive Parts Group, Michael Briggs

Vp It Eis, Andrew Hartley

Senior Vice President Human Resources And Communications Uap Inc., Caroline Tremblay

Vice President Supply Chain Management, Rick Spong

Chairman, Thomas C. (Tom) Gallagher, age 72

Board Member, Elizabeth Camp

Board Member, Gary Fayard

Board Member, John Johns

Board Member, Robert Loudermilk

Board Member, Wendy Needham

Board Member, John Holder

Board Member, Donna Hyland

Board Member, P Russell Hardin

Auditors: Ernst & Young LLP

LOCATIONS

HQ: Genuine Parts Co.
2999 Wildwood Parkway, Atlanta, GA 30339
Phone: 678 934-5000
Web: www.genpt.com

2018 Sales

	$ mil.	% of total
US	13,927	74
Europe	1,625	10
Canada	1,625	9
Australasia	1,193	6
Mexico	129	1
Total	18,735	100

PRODUCTS/OPERATIONS

2018 Sales

	$ mil.	% of total
Automotive	10,527	56
Industrial	6,299	34
Office products	1,910	10
Total	18,735	100

Selected Operations

Automotive Parts Group
  Altrom Canada Corp. (distribution of import automotive parts Canada)
  Balkamp (majority-owned subsidiary; distribution of replacement parts and accessories for cars heavy-duty vehicles motorcycles and farm equipment)
  Grupo Auto Todo S.A. de C.V. (Mexico)
  UAP Inc. (auto parts distribution Canada)
Electrical/Electronic Materials Group
  EIS Inc. (products for electrical and electronic equipment including adhesives copper foil and thermal management materials)
Industrial Parts Group
  Motion Industries (Canada) Inc.
  Motion Industries Inc.
Office Products Group
  S.P. Richards Company

COMPETITORS

Advance Auto Parts	General Parts
Applied Industrial Technologies	Gould Paper
Arrow Electronics	Graybar Electric
AutoZone	Hahn Automotive
Avnet	Ingersoll-Rand
CARQUEST	Kaman Industrial Technologies
Coast Distribution	MSC Industrial Direct
Cole Office Products	O'Reilly Automotive
Complete Office	Office Depot
D & H Distributing	Pep Boys
Essendant	Staples
Ford Motor	W.W. Grainger
General Motors	

HISTORICAL FINANCIALS
Company Type: Public

Income Statement   FYE: December 31

	REVENUE ($ mil.)	NET INCOME ($ mil.)	NET PROFIT MARGIN	EMPLOYEES
12/18	18,735	810	4.3%	50,000
12/17	16,309	617	3.8%	48,000
12/16	15,340	687	4.5%	40,000
12/15	15,280	706	4.6%	39,600
12/14	15,342	711	4.6%	39,000
Annual Growth	5.1%	3.3%	—	6.4%

2018 Year-End Financials

Debt ratio: 25.00%
Return on equity: 24.00%
Cash ($ mil.): 334
Current ratio: 1.00
Long-term debt ($ mil.): 2,432

No. of shares (mil.): 146
Dividends
  Yield: 3.0%
  Payout: 52.0%
Market value ($ mil.): 14,013

	STOCK PRICE ($) FY Close	P/E High/Low	PER SHARE ($) Earnings	Dividends	Book Value
12/18	96.00	19 16	6.00	3.00	24.00
12/17	95.00	24 19	4.00	3.00	23.00
12/16	96.00	23 17	5.00	3.00	22.00
12/15	86.00	23 17	5.00	2.00	21.00
12/14	107.00	23 17	5.00	2.00	22.00
Annual Growth	(2.6%)	— —	4.5%	5.8%	2.3%

Genworth Financial, Inc. (Holding Co)

Insurance and investment specialist Genworth Financial specializes in life insurance long-term care and retirement investments in the US market. Internationally Genworth offers mortgage insurance and other payment protection products. The firm also provides private residential mortgage insurance in the US. Traditionally Genworth has focused its retirement investment products including fixed annuities and mutual funds on affluent individuals. However facing declines in its core lines of business the company has suspended most sales of its long-term care life insurance and fixed annuity products. Chinese conglomerate China Oceanwide Holdings is buying Genworth for $2.7 billion.

Change in Company Type

In October 2016 Genworth agreed to be acquired by China Oceanwide Holdings a family-owned holding company based in Beijing. China Oceanwide plans to contribute an additional $1.1 billion to support Genworth as it restructures its life insurance operations including divesting certain annuity businesses and meeting maturing debt obligations.

However the deal has been delayed due to regulatory concerns of several bodies including governments of the US China Hong Kong Australia Canada and other jurisdictions.

Operations

Genworth operates in five segments: US Life Insurance US Mortgage Insurance Canada Mortgage Insurance Australia Mortgage Insurance and Runoff.

The US Life Insurance segment is Genworth's largest unit bringing in some 75% of total revenue. It provides long-term coverage products and services traditional life insurance policies and fixed annuity products in the US. However the company has suspended sales of all three types of products.

The three mortgage insurance segments primarily offer prime mortgage insurance coverage for individually underwritten loans; they also offer selective bulk mortgage insurance. The runoff segment managed products that are no longer actively marketed including variable annuity variable life and corporate-owned life policies.

Geographic Reach

While US operations account for around 90% of revenues Genworth's international operations include significant mortgage insurance businesses in Australia Canada and Mexico. The firm is looking to expand its mortgage insurance operations into emerging markets. For example it has a minority stake in a joint venture in India.

Sales and Marketing

Genworth's products are sold through direct sales brokerage general agencies and independent marketing organizations as well as by banks and financial advisors.

The company markets its mortgage products to financial groups and mortgage lenders that require mortgage insurance for customer financing. It has a field sales force throughout the US and a telephone sales force that primarily works with smaller lenders. Genworth also has a call center to support all customer segments.

Financial Performance

Genworth's revenue was on a downward trend until 2018 when the company had a slight recovery. And after three years in the black the company became profitable again in 2017. It has struggled with its core life insurance and fixed annuity operations the sales of which it suspended in 2016.

In 2018 revenue increased 2% to $8.4 billion. Premium income rose 13% that year but net investment income and fee income had minor decreases. The US Mortgage segment had a strong year with an increase in mortgage insurance inforce higher investment income and lower taxes. It also had lower losses which drove the segment to a 58% operating income increase. The Canada and Australia Mortgage segments had increased operating income as well. However the US Life Insurance segment had a $376 million operating loss primarily related to its long-term care and life insurance businesses.

Net income fell 85% to $119 million in 2018 due to a steep decline in income from continuing operations.

The company ended 2018 with $2.2 billion in net cash about $700 million less than it had at the end of 2017. Operating activities provided $1.6 billion in cash while financing activities used $1.6 billion and investing activities used another $622 million.

Strategy

Genworth is streamlining its operations through asset sales which allow the company to improve its cash position and focus on its core offerings. Additionally it is working to improve returns in the international mortgage units by reducing exposure in certain markets through divestitures and dissolutions.

Key to the company's survival is a restructuring of its US Life Insurance segment. It has suspended sales of its traditional life and fixed annuity products to cut expenses and is pursuing premium rate increases and associated benefit reductions to minimize losses. And in 2019 it temporarily stopped selling individual stand-alone long-term care policies. (It was formerly the largest provider of those products in the US.)

To boost its core operations the company has realigned and expanded its sales team dedicated to serving mortgage originators. Genworth is also focused on increasing the value of new and exist-

ing policies through pricing initiatives and changes in product distribution and design practices across all of its business units.

In October 2016 the company agreed to be acquired by China Oceanwide Holdings for $2.7 billion. China Oceanwide has committed another $1.1 billion to help Genworth as it restructures its operations. The acquisition will assist Genworth as it tackles another strategic initiative – reducing debt. If the deal doesn't close the company will continue to seek strategic alternatives and financing options. It may end up selling its Australia and/or Canada mortgage operations for instance.

Company Background

Genworth Financial traces its roots back to 1871 when it was founded as The Life Insurance Company of Virginia. The company was acquired by General Electric in 1996. GE combined a number of insurance businesses under the Genworth name and spun the unit off in a 2004 IPO.

HISTORY

The company was formed in 2004 to acquire certain insurance and financial services business from General Electric (GE). GE retained a controlling stake in Genworth Financial after its stock offering but sold its remaining stake in 2006.

During the downturn in the US housing market (starting in 2008) the company faced losses in its US mortgage insurance segment. After considering divestitures Genworth instead simply yanked hard on those operations making its underwriting criteria more stringent and restricting new business. The company also conducted extensive restructuring programs including a 15% workforce reduction in 2009 and a de-risking of its investment portfolio to recover from the economic downturn. Nonetheless the company saw income and cash flow losses during those years as a result of poor returns on investments.

In 2009 the company launched an IPO of its Canadian mortgage insurance business.

In late 2010 Genworth expanded its asset management operations with the purchase of hedge fund and managed futures producer Altegris Capital. The purchase brought in alternative investments and $2.2 billion in assets under management.

Despite steady growth in the sales of its Medicare supplemental products in 2011 the company sold the block of products (held by the former Continental Life Insurance Company unit) to Aetna for $290 million. In addition in 2011 the company stopped offering mortgage insurance policies in New Zealand.

EXECUTIVES

Svp And Cfo Genworth Mi Canada, Philip Mayers
President And Ceo, Thomas J. (Tom) McInerney, age 63, $996,804 total compensation
President And Ceo Us Mortgage Insurance, Rohit Gupta
Evp Human Resources, Michael S. Laming, age 68, $491,692 total compensation
Evp And Cio, Scott J. McKay, age 58
Evp And Coo, Kevin D. Schneider, age 57, $722,683 total compensation
President And Ceo Genworth Mortgage Insurance Canada, Stuart Levings
President And Ceo U.s. Life Insurance, David O'Leary
Evp And Chief Investment Officer, Daniel J. (Dan) Sheehan, age 53, $598,083 total compensation
Evp And Chief Risk Officer, Lori M. Evangel, age 56, $455,271 total compensation
Evp And General Counsel, Ward E. Bobitz, age 54, $423,642 total compensation

Evp And Cfo, Kelly L. Groh, age 50, $538,657 total compensation
President And Ceo Genworth Mortgage Insurance Australia, Georgette C. Nicholas
Senior Vice President, Roger Levy
Svp Hr Global Mortage Insurance And U.s. Life Insurance, Simon Bartle
National Account Manager, Lea Fosz
Senior Vice President Audit, Derek Venable
Vice President Talent Acquisition And Global Staffing Services, Chris Jordan
Senior Vice President Corporate Development, Charles Taben
Senior Vice President Of Finance, Matt Farnay
Regional Vice President, Erin Kirkeeng
Vice President International Government Relations, Scott Quesenberry
Vp Technical Services And Cto Genworth Mortgage, Bob Mckeown
Vice President Accounting Policy, Mitch Rosen
Regional Vice President, Maureen Doherty
Senior Vice President Of Sales, Matthew Young
Senior Vice President, Peter Hurst
Vice President National Account Manager, Carmen Richardson
Associate Vice President And Actuary, Vanesa Barbera
Regional Sales Vice President, Chuck Breen
Vice President And Associate General Counsel, David Dodd
Vice President Of Asset And Liability Management, Robert Causey
Svp And Chief Risk Officer Investments, Benjamin Perlman
Svp And Chief Commercial Officer U.s. Life Insurance, Larry Nisenson
Vice President Marketing And Communications, Susan Carter
Divisional Vice President, Stan J Mensing
Vice President Products And Services Marketing, Miller Tammy
Assistant Vice President And Actuary Life Insurance Experience Studies, Mike Krugel
Medical Director, James Wright
Vice President, Mon Szeto
Vice President Reinsurance Operations, Mark Holbrook
Vp Of Operations, Duncan Hall
Svp Chief Risk Officer For Us Mortgage Insurance, Mike Derstine
Vice President Regional Sales, Tracie Michaud
Vice President, Saul Goodman
Vice President U S Benefits, Matthew Turner
Pharmacy Manager, Eto Joshua
Vice President Long Term Care Claims, Leo Savino
Senior Vice President Product Management, Vincent Bodnar
Vice President Corporate Systems, Jp Raffenot
Chairman, James S. (Jim) Riepe, age 76
Board Member, Susan Conrad
Board Member, Greg Moloney
Board Member, Robert Restrepo
Auditors: KPMG LLP

LOCATIONS

HQ: Genworth Financial, Inc. (Holding Co)
6620 West Broad Street, Richmond, VA 23230
Phone: 804 281-6000
Web: www.genworth.com

2018 Sales

	$ mil.	% of total
US	7,466	89
Canada	526	6
Australia	526	5
Other countries	9	5
Total	**8,430**	**100**

PRODUCTS/OPERATIONS

2018 Sales by Segment

	$ mil.	% of total
US Life	6,318	75
US Mortgage Insurance	841	10
Canada Mortgage Insurance	526	8
Australia Mortgage Insurance	440	5
Run-off	294	4
Corporate & other	24	-
Total	**8,430**	**100**

2018 Sales

	$ mil.	% of total
Premiums	4,519	53
Net investment income	3,262	38
Net investment losses	(146)	-
Policy fees & and other income	795	9
Total	**8,430**	**100**

Selected Products and Services

Fixed annuities
Life insurance
Long-term care insurance
Mortgage
Retirement solutions
Wealth management solutions

COMPETITORS

AEGON USA
AIG
MGIC Investment
MassMutual
New York Life
PMI Group
Radian Group
US Department of
  Veterans Affairs

HISTORICAL FINANCIALS

Company Type: Public

Income Statement

FYE: December 31

	ASSETS ($ mil.)	NET INCOME ($ mil.)	INCOME AS % OF ASSETS	EMPLOYEES
12/18	100,923	119	0.1%	3,500
12/17	105,297	817	0.8%	3,500
12/16	104,658	(277)	—	3,400
12/15	106,431	(615)	—	4,100
12/14	111,358	(1,244)	—	5,300
Annual Growth	**(2.4%)**	**—**	**—**	**(9.9%)**

2018 Year-End Financials

Debt ratio: 4.00%
Return on equity: 1.00%
Cash ($ mil.): 2,177
Current ratio: —
Long-term debt ($ mil.): —
No. of shares (mil.): 501
Dividends
  Yield: —
  Payout: —
Market value ($ mil.): 2,335

	STOCK PRICE ($) FY Close	P/E High/Low		PER SHARE ($) Earnings	Dividends	Book Value
12/18	5.00	20	11	0.00	0.00	25.00
12/17	3.00	3	2	2.00	0.00	27.00
12/16	4.00	—	—	(1.00)	0.00	25.00
12/15	4.00	—	—	(1.00)	0.00	26.00
12/14	9.00	—	—	(3.00)	0.00	30.00
Annual Growth	**(14.0%)**	—	—	—	—	**(4.6%)**

Georgia Power Co

Georgia Power is the largest subsidiary of US utility holding company Southern Company. The regulated utility provides electricity to about 2.4 million residential commercial and industrial customers throughout most of Georgia. It has interests in about 20 fossil-fueled 2 nuclear and 20 hydro-electric power plants that give it about 22000 MW of generating capacity. When necessary the company purchases excess power from nine small power producers. Georgia Power sells wholesale electricity to several cooperatives and municipalities in the region. The utility also offers energy efficiency surge protection and outdoor lighting products and services.

Operations

Georgia Power generates purchases transmits distributes and sells electricity in Georgia. It generates power from coal and natural gas as well as from renewable sources such as solar hydroelectric and wind.

In 2012 the company purchased about 440 kilowatt hours of power from other providers.

On the financing front the company invests in domestic equity international equity fixed income trust-owned life insurance special situations real estate investments and private equity.

Geographic Reach

The company serves retail customers in Georgia. It also sells power to wholesale customers across the US Southeast.

Financial Performance

Georgia Power's revenues grew by 3% in 2013 due to increase in retail base revenues as the result of higher rates (to help pay for placing new generating units at Plant McDonough-Atkinson in service and collecting financing costs related to the construction of Plant Vogtle Units 3 and 4 as well as higher market-driven contributions from commercial and industrial customers.

Net income was flat in 2013 at stayed at $1.2 million as an increase in operating expenses (the result of a 9.9% increase in the volume of KWHs generated as a result of higher prices for purchased power and an 8.1% increase in the average cost of fuel per KWH generated for all types of fuel generation) was offset by a decrease in other expenses due to the decline in interest expenses as a result of refinancing activity.

Strategy

As part of the company's integrated resource plan in addition to a renewables push it is looking to building two additional nuclear power units at its power plant in Vogtle near Waynesboro Georgia (the country's first nuclear power plants in more than 30 years). In 2012 it secured US Nuclear Regulatory Commission approval to go ahead and build these units.

To upgrade its coal plants between 1990 and 2015 Georgia Power plans to invest $7 billion on environmental control technologies.

The company is committed to diversifying its portfolio to include more green energy. To that end in 2013 it signed a contract with EDP Renewables North America for 250 MW of wind energy which it will begin receiving in 2016. That year Georgia Power opened its Water Research Center that will look for ways to reduce its power plant water use and improve the quality of water it releases from plants.

In 2012 it opened the Piedmont Green Power Plant in Barnesville Georgia and signed a 20-year agreement with Rollcast Energy to purchase about 54 MW of biomass energy.

Company Background

The company was founded in 1927.

EXECUTIVES

Evp Cfo Treasurer And Comptroller, W. Ron Hinson, age 62
Evp And Chief Production Officer Southern Company Generation, Theodore J. (Ted) McCullough, age 56
Chairman President And Ceo, Paul Bowers
Svp Marketing, Kenny Coleman
Evp External Affairs, Chris Cummiskey
Evp Customer Service And Operations, Pedro Cherry
Chief Accounting Officer Vice President And Comptroller, Ann Daiss
Region Vice President, Terri Lupo
Vice President And Senior Production Officer Gulf Power, Michael Burroughs
Region Vice President, Cathy Hill
Vice President Of Corporate Communi, Jason Cuevas
Executive Vice President Of Finance, Larry Westbrook
Senior Vice President Human Resources, Leonard Owens
Executive Vice President External Affairs, Craig Barrs
Vice President Administrative Services, Brian Ivey
Vice President Customer Services, Louise Scott
Executive Vice President; President External Affairs, Chris Womack
Executive Vice President Nuclear Development, Joe Miller
Vice President Customer Services, Kevin Kastner
Vice Chairman, Dan Burer
Board Member, Allan Bense
Secretary, Rick Perry
Auditors: DELOITTE & TOUCHE LLP

LOCATIONS

HQ: Georgia Power Co
241 Ralph McGill Boulevard, N.E., Atlanta, GA 30308
Phone: 404 506-6526
Web: www.georgiapower.com

PRODUCTS/OPERATIONS

Selected Services

Residential Customers
My Account
Pay My Bill
Turn On/Off Power
Payment Arrangements
Paperless Billing
Budget Billing
Prices/Rate
Save Money and Energy
Energy Audits
Money-Saving Tips
Rebates & Incentives
Electric Vehicles
Products & Programs
Water Heaters
Heat Pumps
Lighting
Power Credit
Green Energy
Smart Meter
Multifamily
Business Customers
My Account
Pay My Bill
Turn On/Off Power
Budget Billing
Prices/Rates
Save Money and Energy
Energy Audits
Money-Saving Tips
Rebates & Incentives
Electric Vehicles
Programs & Services
Water Heaters
Heat Pumps
Outdoor Lighting
Electric Cooking
Forklifts
Green Energy
Smart Meter
Energydirect

2016 Sales

	$ mil.	% of total
Retail		
Residential	3,318	40
Commercial	3,077	37
Industrial	1,291	15
Other retail	86	1
Wholesale	217	2
Other	394	5
Total	**8,383**	**100**

COMPETITORS

Atmos Energy	Progress Energy
Duke Energy Progress	SCANA
Inc.	Sawnee EMC
Energen	South Carolina
Entergy	Electric & Gas
Flint Energies	Southern Company Gas
MEAG Power	TECO Energy
Oglethorpe Power	Walton EMC

HISTORICAL FINANCIALS
Company Type: Public

Income Statement				FYE: December 31
	REVENUE ($ mil.)	**NET INCOME** ($ mil.)	**NET PROFIT MARGIN**	**EMPLOYEES**
12/18	8,420	793	9.4%	6,967
12/17	8,310	1,428	17.2%	6,986
12/16	8,383	1,347	16.1%	7,527
12/15	8,326	1,277	15.3%	7,989
12/14	8,988	1,242	13.8%	7,909
Annual Growth	(1.6%)	(10.6%)	—	(3.1%)

2018 Year-End Financials

Debt ratio: 25.00%	No. of shares (mil.): 9
Return on equity: 6.00%	Dividends
Cash ($ mil.): 4	Yield: —
Current ratio: 1.00	Payout: 176.0%
Long-term debt ($ mil.): 9,364	Market value ($ mil.): —

German American Bancorp Inc

German American Bancorp is the holding company for German American Bank which operates some 65 branches in southern Indiana and Kentucky. Founded in 1910 the bank offers such standard retail products as checking and savings accounts certificates of deposit and IRAs. It also provides trust services while sister company German American Investment Services provides trust investment advisory and brokerage services. German American Bancorp also owns German American Insurance which offers corporate and personal insurance products. The group's core banking operations provide more than 90% of its total sales.

Geographic Reach
German American is headquartered in Jasper Indiana. Its subsidiaries operate from more than 60 locations in southern Indiana and Kentucky.

Sales and Marketing
German American Bancorp spent $3.5 million on advertising in 2017. Advertising expenses totaled $2.7 million in 2016 and $3.7 million in 2015.

Financial Performance
German American's revenue has been climbing steadily for the past five years thanks to the company's acquisitions of other area banks. Similarly net income has also been on the rise. In 2017 the company marked its eighth consecutive year of record earnings.

In 2017 revenue increased 4% to $131.8 million. That increase was partially due to the addition of River Valley Financial Bank which German American acquired in 2016. Growth in the company's loan portfolio also boosted net interest income. This was slightly offset by a 1% decline in non-interest income. Although trust and insurance operations rose other operating income declined $1.1 million (29%).

Net income rose 16% to $35.2 million in 2017; in addition to having higher revenue the company recognized a benefit related to the reduced corporate tax rate that year.

German American ended 2017 with $70.4 million in net cash $5.5 million more than it had at the end of 2016. Operating activities provided $54.9 million in cash and financing activities provided $139.9 million. Investing activities used $189.3 million.

Strategy
German American Bancorp has grown recently through a number of acquisitions including bank branches an insurance office and other bank holding companies. These acquisitions have also helped the company grow into new geographic markets including locations in Kentucky.

Growth by acquisition can be somewhat risky though. The company could unknowingly acquire problem assets or have difficulties integrating other banks it purchases. These issues could bring down its financial performance.

German American operates in a relatively small region which leaves it vulnerable to economic downturns in that area. If economic conditions in its market decline German American faces the risk of increased delinquencies and charge-offs. The company's larger more widespread competitors would be less impacted in such a case.

Mergers and Acquisitions
German American Bancorp agreed to acquire Citizens First in early 2019 in a cash-and-stock transaction valued at about $70 million. German American will gain Citizens' branch offices in the Barren Hart Simpson and Warren counties of Kentucky. Citizens has about $475 million in assets loans of some $375 million and deposits of around $390 million.

In October 2018 German American Bancorp acquired Kentucky's First Security Bank for $101 million. With that deal the company expanded into Kentucky's Owensboro Bowling Green and Lexington markets.

EXECUTIVES

Vice President, Lisa Matheis
General Technical; Senior Vice President, Floyd Alsman
Chairman And Ceo, Mark A. Schroeder, age 66, $342,500 total compensation
President, Clay W. Ewing, age 64, $250,000 total compensation
Evp Cfo And Senior Administrative Officer, Bradley M. Rust, age 53, $210,000 total compensation
Svp And Chief Credit Officer, Keith A. Leinenbach, age 60, $180,000 total compensation
Svp And Head Of Retail Banking, Randall L. Braun, age 59, $180,000 total compensation
Vice President Deposit Services Security, Dale Altstadt
Senior Vice President Of Technology And Operations, Clay Barrett
Vice President Commercial Banking, Dan Collignon
Senior Vice President Commercial Banking, Joe Hauersperger
Regional Senior Vice President, Jim Thomas
Vice President, Christina Lebeau
Vice President Private Banking, Sherri Alley
Vice President, Ashley McCreary
Regional Vice President Commercial Lending, Doug Bell
Region Senior Vice President, Tony Loudermilk
Svp Senior Retail Officer, Jenny Darnold
Vice President Commercial Banking, Rob Bingham
Vice President Commercial Banking, John Newcomer
Vice President, Eric Kehl
Senior Vice President Retail Banking, Brock Goggins
Senior Vice President Senior Wealth Advisor, Alan VanCleef
Regional Vice President Treasury Management, Alicia Berry
Board Member, Chris Ramsey
Auditors: Crowe LLP

LOCATIONS

HQ: German American Bancorp Inc
711 Main Street, Jasper, IN 47546
Phone: 812 482-1314
Web: www.germanamerican.com

PRODUCTS/OPERATIONS

2017 Sales

	$ mil.	% of total
Interest		
Loans including fees	92	64
Securities including dividends	19	13
Short-term investments	0	-
Non-interest		
Insurance	8	6
Service charges on deposit accounts	6	4
Trust & investment product fees	5	4
Other	12	9
Adjustments	(11.1)	-
Total	**132**	**100**

COMPETITORS

Fidelity Federal	Home Financial Bancorp
Fifth Third	Old National Bancorp
First Bancorp of	Porter Bancorp
Indiana	SVB&T
First Capital	

HISTORICAL FINANCIALS
Company Type: Public

Income Statement				FYE: December 31
	ASSETS ($ mil.)	**NET INCOME** ($ mil.)	**INCOME AS % OF ASSETS**	**EMPLOYEES**
12/18	3,929	47	1.2%	738
12/17	3,144	41	1.3%	614
12/16	2,956	35	1.2%	597
12/15	2,374	30	1.3%	596
12/14	2,237	28	1.3%	484
Annual Growth	15.1%	13.2%	—	11.1%

2018 Year-End Financials

Debt ratio: 1.00%	No. of shares (mil.): 25
Return on equity: 11.00%	Dividends
Cash ($ mil.): 97	Yield: 2.0%
Current ratio: —	Payout: 30.0%
Long-term debt ($ mil.): —	Market value ($ mil.): 693

	STOCK PRICE ($) FY Close	P/E High/Low		PER SHARE ($) Earnings	Dividends	Book Value
12/18	28.00	19 13		2.00	1.00	18.00
12/17	35.00	30 17		2.00	1.00	16.00
12/16	53.00	34 19		2.00	0.00	14.00
12/15	33.00	23 18		2.00	0.00	13.00
12/14	31.00	22 17		1.00	0.00	12.00
Annual Growth	(2.3%)	— —		8.7%	8.9%	12.3%

GGP, INC.

Auditors: DELOITTE & TOUCHE
LLP CHICAGO

LOCATIONS

HQ: GGP, INC.
350 N ORLEANS ST STE 300, CHICAGO, IL
606541607
Phone: 312 960-5000
Web: WWW.GGP.COM

COMPETITORS

CBL & Associates	Prime Retail
Properties	Simon Property Group
DDR	Tanger Factory Outlet
Glimcher Realty	Taubman Centers
JMB Realty	Trade Street
Kimco Realty	Residential
Lincoln Property	Vornado Realty
Macerich	Weingarten Realty

HISTORICAL FINANCIALS

Company Type: Private

Income Statement				FYE: December 31
	ASSETS ($ mil.)	NET INCOME ($ mil.)	INCOME AS % OF ASSETS	EMPLOYEES
12/12	27,282	(472)	—	1,500
12/11	29,518	(307)	—	—
12/10	32,367	(256)	—	—
12/09	28,150	(1,305)	—	—
Annual Growth	(1.0%)	—	—	—

GILBANE BUILDING COMPANY

Gilbane Building Company has built a big business constructing for equally large customers. The firm provides construction services consulting subcontracting and facilities management to commercial institutional and governmental markets. Operating as the construction arm of Gilbane the company builds schools hospitals laboratories and prisons serving both the public and private sectors. Its completed projects include the Stroh Center at Bowling Green State University and the National WWII Memorial in Washington DC. Founded in 1873 as a carpentry and general contracting shop the family-owned Gilbane Building Company operates from more than 50 offices around the world.

Operations

The company has worked on a wide range of projects including: the Worcester Recovery Center & Hospital El Paso Corporation Building Renovation New York State Capital Restoration Georgia Tech Carbon Neutral Energy Solutions Laboratory University of North Florida Student Wellness and Sports Albert Einstein Health Network Elmhurst Memorial Healthcare and the University of Puerto Rico Molecular Sciences Building.

As part of its business Gilbane Building Company operates ITSI Gilbane a major provider of engineering and construction services to the US federal government including the Department of

Defense Environmental Protection Agency and Department of Energy.

Geographic Reach

With more than 50 offices and 1000 projects underway around the world Gilbane Building Company enjoys a geographic footprint that extends from the US to Japan the United Arab Emirates Ireland South Korea and Afghanistan.

Sales and Marketing

Gilbane Building Company serves several sectors such as healthcare higher education K-12 schools federal and public entities mission critical corporate and sports and recreation. In 2014 the company boasted a 98.4% client satisfaction rate and reported that 65% of its work comes from repeat clients.

Some of its clients have included: Einstein Healthcare Network Google Inc. Operations Mane Inc Wilmington Public School Uihlein Wilson Architects City of Phoenix Crime Lab and the Operating Forces D&C Division.

Strategy

Gilbane Building Company has been busy working on projects in all parts of the country. In 2014 Gilbane secured a $43 million contract for historical renovation work on Pomerene and Oxley Halls on the Ohio State University campus. The firm's 2013 projects included the 131000-sq.-ft. Bergen County Justice Center in Hackensack New Jersey; the Columbus Regional Airport Authority's modernization of concourses B and C at Port Columbus international airports; and Miami University's Kreger Hall Rehabilitation & Addition Project which included the reorganization of 33372 sq. ft. of interior spaces and upgrades to the building's infrastructure as well as a major rehabilitation.

The company also continues to be recognized for its environment-conscious building designs particularly with schools. In early 2015 the company's completed Dunbar High School project — equipped with an advanced geothermal system a 482 kW array of photovoltaic panels and 20000-gallon cisterns — was awarded the LEED for Schools v2009 Platinum certification taking home the highest LEED score on record worldwide. Also in early 2015 the company was awarded the #1 ranking for Education K-12 Building Design and Construction and ranked within the top 5 of green contractor engineers.

It has also extended its reach in Europe in recent years. In 2012 the company formed a joint venture with Ed. Z blinAG known as Z blin Gilbane to pursue and execute projects in Europe.

EXECUTIVES

President And Ceo, Michael C. (Mike) McKelvy, age 59
Vice President Business Development, Randy Lowrance
Senior Vice President Director Human Resources, Pierre La Perriere
Vice President District Manager, Douglas Lim
Vice President Human Resources, Mary A Farrell
Vice President Of Construction Operations For The New England Region, Thomas Comella
Vice President And Regional Operations Manager, Stephen Oaconnor
Vice President, Jay Prybylski
Vice President, James Busam
Vice Chairman, William J. (Bill) Gilbane, age 72
Chairman, Thomas F. (Tom) Gilbane, age 71
Auditors: RSM US LLP BOSTON MASSACHUSE

LOCATIONS

HQ: GILBANE BUILDING COMPANY
7 JACKSON WALKWAY STE 2, PROVIDENCE, RI
029033694
Phone: 401 456-5800
Web: WWW.GILBANECO.COM

PRODUCTS/OPERATIONS

Selected Markets

Convention/cultural

Corporate
Criminal justice
Federal/public
Health care
　Children's hospitals
　Women's centers
　Cardiac-care centers
　Cancer centers
　Clinical and research facilities
Higher education
　Research laboratories
　Academic facilities
　Admissions buildings
　Residence halls
　Performing arts centers
　Sports and recreational centers
　Libraries and technology centers
　Student unions
K-12 schools
Life sciences
Mission critical
Sports/recreation
Transportation
Water/wastewater

Selected Services
Pre-construction
　Transition planning and management
　Building information modeling
　Conceptual cost modeling
　High-performance building & energy modeling
　Interdisciplinary document coordination
Consulting
　CAT-response
　Facilities management services
　Schedule & risk analysis
　Transition planning & management
Construction
　Construction management at risk
　Construction management as agent
　Lump sum general contracting
　Integrated project delivery

COMPETITORS

Barton Malow	McCarthy Building
Batson-Cook	Peter Kiewit Sons'
Bechtel	Skanska USA Building
Bernards Brothers	Swinerton
Clark Construction	The Pike Company
Group	Thos. S. Byrne
Dimeo Construction	Turner Construction
Fluor	Turner Corporation
KBR	Tutor Perini
L.F. Driscoll	Walbridge Aldinger
MEDCO Construction	Whiting-Turner

HISTORICAL FINANCIALS

Company Type: Private

Income Statement				FYE: December 31
	REVENUE ($ mil.)	NET INCOME ($ mil.)	NET PROFIT MARGIN	EMPLOYEES
12/18	5,453	82	1.5%	2,500
12/17	4,899	63	1.3%	—
12/14	3,841	0	—	—
12/13	4,101	0	—	—
Annual Growth	5.9%	—	—	—

Gilead Sciences Inc

Gilead Sciences has biotech balms for infectious diseases including hepatitis HIV and infections related to AIDS. The company's drug franchise includes Truvada a leading pre-exposure treatment for HIV. The company co-promotes another HIV treatment called Atripla in the US and Europe with Bristol-Myers Squibb (BMS). Other products on the market include AmBisome used to treat systemic fungal infections such as those that accompany AIDS or kidney disease and hepatitis B antiviral Hepsera. Beyond HIV/AIDS Gilead also markets cardiovascular drugs as well as respiratory and ophthalmic medicines and the Yescarta CAR-T cell therapy for cancer. About three-quarters of its sales are in the US.

Operations

Gilead primarily focuses on producing treatments for HIV liver diseases including hepatitis B and hepatitis C cancer and inflammation and cardiovascular and respiratory conditions. Its main source of revenue continues to be its antiviral franchise which accounts for about two-thirds of product sales and primarily consists of HIV medications. Genvoya has been Gilead's top-selling drug accounting for about 20% of sales.

Aside from the Atripla partnership with BMS Gilead has collaborations with other companies including Japan Tobacco which promotes HIV drugs Truvada Viread and Emtriva in Japan and GlaxoSmithKline which markets Hepsera Viread and Volbris in select international markets. Additionally Gilead receives royalties on influenza treatment Tamiflu which it developed with Roche and on Macugen an ophthalmologic drug developed by Eyetech using Gilead's technology. In addition to distributing AmBisome in Canada and the US Astellas Pharma pays royalties on US sales of Lexiscan which is used in stress tests for coronary artery disease.

Gilead continues to advance its R&D pipeline; the company had about 120 active clinical studies at the end of 2018. It had more than 40 trials in Phase III.

The company's portfolio of more than 20 marketed products contains a number of firsts such as the first complete treatment regimens for HIV and chronic hepatitis C available in a once-daily single pill.

Geographic Reach

Gilead relies on the US market for a significant portion of its revenue about 75%. Europe accounts for more than 20% of revenue while other international markets provide about 5%.

Gilead is based in Foster City California and it has R&D facilities in Oceanside and Fremont California Alberta Canada and Seattle. It has manufacturing sites in California Canada and Ireland. Commercial operations are in 20 offices throughout Europe 10 in North America seven in Asia two in South America and one each in the Middle East Australia and Africa.

Sales and Marketing

Three wholesale distributors — McKesson Cardinal Health and AmerisourceBergen — account for nearly all of Gilead's US sales. Reliance on these firms could leave Gilead vulnerable to distribution issues should any of them face financial difficulties or switch to alternative products.

Gilead also promotes its antiviral drugs through its own commercial infrastructure in North America some European and Asian countries and in Australia and New Zealand.

Financial Performance

After peaking at $32.6 billion in 2015 Gilead's revenue dropped about a third to $21.1 billion in 2018 as competitors have taken market share and forced price reductions.

In 2018 sales fell about 15% from $26.1 billion in 2017 mainly because of a 60% drop in hepatitis C virus (HCV) products due to lower volumes and prices. HIV product sales rose 12% on the launch of Biktarvy in 2018 and continuing sales of Descovy Genvoya and Odefsey. Sales of Yescarta generated $264 million in sales in 2018 compared to $7 million in sales in 2017.

Gilead posted net income of $5.4 billion in 2018 compared to $4.6 billion in 2017. The 2018 result included an impairment charge and a non-cash tax charge related to the acquisition of KITE.

The company had $17.9 billion in cash and equivalents in 2018 compared to $7.6 billion in 2017. Operations generated $8.4 billion in 2018 while investing activities provided $14.3 billion and financing activities used $12.3 billion.

Strategy

One of the pitfalls of the pharma manufacturing business is patent expirations where sales of older medications decline when they face generic competition. Gilead began to offer its own line of authorized generic versions of its HCV drugs in 2019 instead of ceding those sales go to other drugmakers. The generic versions of its Epclusa and Harvoni drugs captured 20% and 2% of the HCV market respectively in the year of their release.

Gilead has stepped up partnerships with other drug companies through licensing agreements. In 2019 the company entered into an agreement with Galapagos to get access to a portfolio of compounds more than 20 preclinical programs and a proven drug discovery platform. Gilead also gained rights to US biotech start-up Lyndra Therapeutics? platform for ultra-long-acting formulations related to HIV. In a third agreement Gilead licensed three pre-clinical antiviral programs including investigational agents with the potential to treat human rhinovirus influenza and herpes viruses from Novartis.

Gilead's Yescarta treatment was the second CAR-T cell therapy to be given FDA approval. It has since won approval for use in Europe. The drug has shown strong acceptance in the US where it has about 70 treatment centers and Europe where it has about a dozen centers.

Mergers and Acquisitions

As a way of fending off losses from patent expirations Gilead has diversified its product line through acquisitions.

In 2017 the company bought Kite Pharma a leader in the development of cell therapy treatments for cancer for $11.9 billion. That purchase provided Gilead with a pipeline of CAR-T therapy products including Yescarta which was shortly thereafter approved by the FDA. It was the second CAR-T cell therapy to receive approval in the US.

Company Background

Dr. Michael Riordan started Gilead Sciences in 1987 backed by venture capital firm Menlo Ventures. The name was derived from the Biblical phrase "Is there no balm in Gilead?" In 1990 Glaxo Wellcome (now GlaxoSmithKline) agreed to fund Gilead's research into code-blocking treatments for cancer. Gilead went public in 1992.

HISTORY

Dr. Michael Riordan started Gilead Sciences in 1987 backed by venture capital firm Menlo Ventures. The name was derived from the Biblical phrase "Is there no balm in Gilead?" In 1990 Glaxo Wellcome (now GlaxoSmithKline) agreed to fund Gilead's research into code-blocking treatments for cancer. Gilead went public in 1992.

In 1994 the company formed an alliance with American Home Products' Storz Instruments (now part of Bausch & Lomb) to develop and market a topical treatment for an ophthalmic virus. Two years later Gilead joined forces with Roche to develop treatments for influenza.

Vistide was approved in the US in 1996 and in Europe in 1997. But more-effective HIV therapies brought declining demand for Vistide.

The company bounced back with Tamiflu (the fruit of its Roche partnership) which was approved in 1999. Sales were brisk during that flu season. Also that year Gilead expanded its pipeline and geographic reach with the $550 million all-stock acquisition of NeXstar Pharmaceuticals which focused on antifungals antibiotics and cancer treatments.

In 2000 Gilead sought approval for Tamiflu in Japan and Europe (it withdrew the European application after regulators there asked for more information) and also sought approval for pediatric uses for the drug which was granted. The following year it resubmitted Tamiflu for approval in Europe.

Chairman Donald Rumsfeld resigned in 2001 to become US secretary of defense and was replaced by retired Sears Roebuck executive James Denny. Perhaps the Defense connection helped: Vistide became one of the many drugs that researchers began studying as possible alternatives to vaccines should a smallpox bio-attack occur in the US.

EXECUTIVES

Evp Pharmaceutical Development And Manufacturing, Taiyin Yang, age 65

Evp Research, William A. Lee, age 63, $363,333 total compensation

Evp Research And Development And Chief Scientific Officer, Norbert W. Bischofberger, age 63, $1,044,231 total compensation

President And Ceo, John F. Milligan, age 58, $1,465,385 total compensation

Coo, Kevin Young, $787,645 total compensation

Evp And Cfo, Robin L. Washington, age 56, $900,385 total compensation

Evp Commercial And Access Operations (asia Latin America And Africa) And Corporate And Medical Affairs, Gregg H. Alton, age 53, $925,385 total compensation

Evp Clinical Research And Development Operations, Andrew Cheng

Evp Clinical Research, John G. McHutchison

Evp Strategy, Martin B. Silverstein, age 64

Evp And General Counsel, Brett Pletcher

Evp Human Resources, Katie L. Watson

Senior Medical Director, Belinda Jump

Vice President Of U S Marketing And Sales, Jean Kress

V P Risk Management, Marti Dodson

Vice President Information Technology, Mark Hill

Senior Vice President Public Affairs, Amy Flood

Vice President Public Affairs, Sonia Choi

Vp Corp Legal, Jason Okazaki

Vp Intellectual Property, Lorie Ann Morgan

National Sales Manager Oncology, Boyd Marianna

Executive Vice President Corporate Development And Strategy, Andrew Dickinson

Vice President Human Resources, Matt Hostetler

Evp Of Worldwide Commercial Operations, Laura Hamill

Vice President Intellectual Property, J Bosse

Vice President Corporate Development, Jeremy Bender

Vice President Of Regional Sales, Ashwin Mathur

Vice President Human Resources, Jyoti Mehra

Vice President Tax, Terilea Wielenga

Vice President Government Affairs And Policy, Michael Boyd

Chairman, John C. Martin, age 67

Board Member, Nicholas G Moore

Auditors: Ernst & Young LLP

LOCATIONS

HQ: Gilead Sciences Inc
333 Lakeside Drive, Foster City, CA 94404
Phone: 650 574-3000
Web: www.gilead.com

2018 Sales

	$ mil.	% of total
US	16,269	74
Europe	4,006	18
Other International	1,852	8
Total	**30,390**	**100**

PRODUCTS/OPERATIONS

2018 Sales

	$ mil.	% of total
Genvoya	4,624	21
Truvada	2,997	14
Epclusa	1,966	9
Odefsey	1,598	7
Descovy	1,581	7
Harvoni	1,222	6
Atripla	1,206	5
Biktarvy	1,457	5
Other	5,299	24
Royalty contract and other revenue	450	2
Total	**22,127**	**100**

Selected Products

Antiviral
Atripla (HIV with Bristol-Myers Squibb)
Complera/Eviplera (HIV)
Emtriva (HIV)
Harvoni (HCV infection)
Hepsera (hepatitis B)
Sovaldi (HCV infection)
Stribild (HIV)
Tamiflu (flu treatment royalties from Roche)
Truvada (fixed-dose combination of Viread and Emtriva for HIV)
Viread (HIV chronic hepatitis B with liver disease)
Vistide (AIDS-related cytomegalovirus retinitis)
Other products
AmBisome (antifungal with Astellas)
Cayston (cystic fibrosis)
Flolan (pulmonary hypertension)
Letairis (pulmonary arterial hypertension)
Lexiscan/Rapiscan (cardiovascular with Astellas)
Macugen (age-related macular degeneration royalties from Eyetech)
Ranexa (chronic angina)
Products in development
Aztreonam (cystic fibrosis)
Cobicistat (HIV/AIDS)
Elvitegravir (HIV/AIDS)
GS-1101 (leukemia and lymphoma)
GS-7977 (hepatitis C)
Intesgrase (HIV)
Ranolazine (cardiovascular diabetes)

COMPETITORS

AbbVie	Merck
Abbott Labs	Novartis
Actelion	Pfizer
Bristol-Myers Squibb	Shire
GlaxoSmithKline	United Therapeutics

HISTORICAL FINANCIALS

Company Type: Public

Income Statement

FYE: December 31

	REVENUE ($ mil.)	NET INCOME ($ mil.)	NET PROFIT MARGIN	EMPLOYEES
12/18	22,127	5,455	24.7%	11,000
12/17	26,107	4,628	17.7%	10,000
12/16	30,390	13,501	44.4%	9,000
12/15	32,639	18,108	55.5%	8,000
12/14	24,890	12,101	48.6%	7,000
Annual Growth	**(2.9%)**	**(18.1%)**	**—**	**12.0%**

2018 Year-End Financials

Debt ratio: 43.00%
Return on equity: 26.00%
Cash ($ mil.): 17,940
Current ratio: 3.00
Long-term debt ($ mil.): 24,574
No. of shares (mil.): 1,282
Dividends
Yield: 4.0%
Payout: 185.0%
Market value ($ mil.): 80,189

	STOCK PRICE ($) FY Close	P/E High/Low		PER SHARE ($) Earnings	Dividends	Book Value
12/18	63.00	21	14	4.00	2.00	17.00
12/17	72.00	24	18	4.00	2.00	16.00
12/16	72.00	10	7	10.00	2.00	14.00
12/15	101.00	10	8	12.00	1.00	13.00
12/14	94.00	14	8	7.00	0.00	10.00
Annual Growth	**(9.7%)**	**—**	**—**	**(13.2%)**	**—**	**12.8%**

Glacier Bancorp, Inc.

Glacier Bancorp is on a Rocky Mountain high. The holding company owns about a dozen community bank divisions with about 100 locations in Montana Idaho Utah Washington Arizona Colorado and Wyoming. Serving individuals small to midsized businesses not-for-profits and public entities the banks offer traditional deposit products and credit cards in addition to retail brokerage and investment services through agreements with third-party providers. Its lending activities consist of commercial real estate loans (about half of the company's loan portfolio) as well as residential mortgages business loans and consumer loans.

Financial Performance

Glacier's financial results are on a steady upward swing since 2012 with yearly increases in interest income and near-annual improvement in non-interest income and net income.

In 2017 the company generated $375 million in interest income and $112 million in non-interest income for total revenue of $487 million. Its loan portfolio grew by $601 million or 11% in the year bringing the size of its loan portfolio to just less than $6.5 billion.

Net income for the year was $116 million 4% more than 2016 due to the higher revenue partially offset by an increase in loan loss provisions employee compensation and income tax expense.

Glacier Bancorp ended 2017 with $200 million in cash an increase of nearly $50 million over the previous year. Financing activities used $230 million for loan repayments stock dividends and a decrease in deposits. Investing activities added $24 million to the coffers and operating activities contributed $255 million mostly from net income a deferred tax expense and proceeds from selling some of its loan portfolio.

Strategy

Glacier Bancorp hopes to capitalize on additional acquisition opportunities that it expects to arise as small banks deal with new industry regulations. To this end it has been on a buying spree in recent years. In early 2018 it acquired Inter-Mountain Bancorp (Montana) Columbine Capital Corporation (Colorado); in 2017 it purchased TFB Bancorp (Arizona); in 2016 it bought Treasure State Bank (Montana) and in 2015 Glacier acquired Canon Bank Corporation (Colorado) and Montana Community Banks (Montana). In total these purchases cost $377 million.

The company is also banking on organic growth with the populations of the states in its market area growing faster than the national average thanks to an influx of retiring Baby Boomers and an increase in energy- and natural resource-related jobs.

EXECUTIVES

Evp And Cfo, Ron J. Copher, $352,651 total compensation
Evp And Chief Administrative Officer, Don J. Cherry, $299,950 total compensation
President And Ceo, Randall M. (Randy) Chesler, age 61, $153,846 total compensation
Vice President And Cra And Compliance Officer, Lanette Marcum
Senior Vice President, Robert Taylor
Vice President Internal Auditor, Judy Overcast
Vice President Compliance, April Kelso
Vice President, Ryan T Screnar
Senior Vice President Business Developme, Steve Lloyd
Senior Vice President Consumer Lending, Greg Wilcox
Vice President Finance, Mike Romm
Vice President Internal Auditor, Jessica Rice
Vice President Of Human Resources, Roger Bamford
Vice President Of Human Resources, Christopher Murphy
Vp, Preston Romm
Vice President, Melody Pieri
Senior Vice President Corporate Re Manager, Paul Peterson
Vice President Corporate Bsa Officer, Mary Strozzi
Senior Vice President Enterprise Wide Risk Manager, T Frickle
Vice President, Don McCarthy
Vice President Risk Management, T J Frickle
Senior Vice President, Lynn Riley
Board Member, Craig A Langel
Chairman, Dallas I. Herron, age 74
Board Member, Annie Goodwin
Board Member, Douglas Mcbride
Board Member, James English
Board Member, Mark Semmens
Auditors: BKD, LLP

LOCATIONS

HQ: Glacier Bancorp, Inc.
49 Commons Loop, Kalispell, MT 59901
Phone: 406 756-4200
Web: www.glacierbank.com

PRODUCTS/OPERATIONS

2016 Sales

	$ mil.	% of total
Interest income		
Commercial loans	227	47
Investment securities	82	17
Residential real estate loans	33	7
Consumer and other loans	33	7
Non-interest income		
Service charges and other fees	68	14
Gain on sale of loans	30	6
Miscellaneous loan fees and charges	4	1
(Loss) gain on sale of investments	(0.6)	-
Other income	10	2
Total	**487**	**100**

Selected Services

Commercial loan
Consumer loan
Deposits
Mortgage origination services
Real estate loan
Retail brokerage services
Transaction and savings

Selected Bank Divisions

1st Bank (Wyoming)
Bank of the San Juans (Colorado)
Big Sky Western Bank (Montana)
Citizens Community Bank (Idaho)

Collegiate Peaks Bank
First Bank of Montana
First Bank of Wyoming
First Security Bank (Montana)
First State Bank (Wyoming)
Foothills Bank
Glacier Bank (Montana)
Mountain West Bank (Idaho)
North Cascades Bank (Washington)
Valley Bank of Helena (Montana)
Western Security Bank (Montana)

COMPETITORS

Eagle Bancorp
First Citizens Banc
Corp
First Interstate

U.S. Bancorp
Wells Fargo
Zions Bancorporation

HISTORICAL FINANCIALS

Company Type: Public

Income Statement				FYE: December 31
	ASSETS ($ mil.)	NET INCOME ($ mil.)	INCOME AS % OF ASSETS	EMPLOYEES
12/18	12,115	182	1.5%	2,723
12/17	9,706	116	1.2%	2,354
12/16	9,451	121	1.3%	2,291
12/15	9,089	116	1.3%	2,245
12/14	8,307	113	1.4%	2,030
Annual Growth	9.9%	12.7%	—	7.6%

2018 Year-End Financials

Debt ratio: 1.00%
Return on equity: 13.00%
Cash ($ mil.): 204
Current ratio: —
Long-term debt ($ mil.): —

No. of shares (mil.): 85
Dividends
Yield: 3.0%
Payout: 57.0%
Market value ($ mil.): 3,349

	STOCK PRICE ($) FY Close	P/E High/Low	PER SHARE ($) Earnings	Dividends	Book Value
12/18	40.00	22 17	2.00	1.00	18.00
12/17	39.00	27 21	2.00	1.00	15.00
12/16	36.00	24 14	2.00	1.00	15.00
12/15	27.00	20 14	2.00	1.00	14.00
12/14	28.00	20 16	2.00	1.00	14.00
Annual Growth	9.3%	— —	9.5%	10.4%	7.0%

Global Partners LP

Global Partners imports petroleum products from global sources but its marketing is largely regional. The company wholesales heating oil residual fuel oil diesel oil kerosene distillates and gasoline to commercial retail and wholesale customers in New England and New York. A major player in the regional home heating oil market Global Partners operates storage facilities at 25 bulk terminals each with a storage capacity of more than 50000 barrels and with a collective storage capacity of 12.2 million barrels. It also owns and supplies a network of gasoline stations. Wholesale revenues accounts for the bulk of the company's sales.

Operations

Global Partners consists of three operating segments: Wholesale Gasoline Distribution and Station Operations (GDSO) and Commercial.

Wholesale accounts for around 50% of total sales and sells unbranded gasoline and diesel to unbranded gasoline customers and other resellers of transportation fuels. It also sells home heating oil diesel kerosene and residual oil to home heating

oil retailers and wholesale distributors; as well as crude oil to refiners.

GDSO generates more than 40% of total sales and sells branded and unbranded gasoline to gasoline stations and other sub-jobbers such as gasoline convenience store car wash and other ancillary services at company operated stores and leased gas stations.

Commercial brings in the remaining nearly 10% of sales and sells unbranded gasoline custom blended fuels home heating oil diesel kerosene residual oil renewable fuels and natural gas. Its customers are public sector and large commercial and industrial end users. The segment also includes the sale of custom blended distillates and residual oil delivered by barge or from a terminal dock to ships through its bunkering activity.

The company owns storage facilities at 25 petroleum product bulk terminals each with the capacity of more than 50000 barrels including 22 refined product terminals located throughout the Northeast.

Through gas station company Global Montello Group the company sells food beverages snacks grocery and non-food merchandise at its convenience store locations.

Geographic Reach

Global Partners has a network of refined petroleum products and renewable fuels terminals throughout the Northeast region and into the Mid-Atlantic States (Connecticut Florida Georgia Indiana Louisiana Maine Maryland Massachusetts Michigan New Hampshire New Jersey New York North Dakota Ohio Oregon Pennsylvania Rhode Island Tennessee Texas Vermont and Virginia).

It has some 1460 owned leased and/or supplied gas stations including 248 convenience stores in the Northeast Maryland and Virginia. It also owns transload and storage terminals in North Dakota and Oregon.

Sales and Marketing

Global Partners gets its revenue primarily from convenience store sales at its directly operated stores and rental income from dealer leased or commission agent leased gasoline stations. Global Partners also is one of the largest distributors of gasoline distillates residual oil and renewable fuels to wholesalers retailers and commercial customers in New England and New York

In the Commercial segment it serves customers in the public sector and large commercial and industrial end users of unbranded gasoline home heating oil diesel kerosene residual oil bunker fuel and natural gas. In the case of public sector commercial and industrial end user customers Global Partners sell products through a competitive bidding process or through contracts of various terms. It generally arranges for the delivery of the product to the customer's designated location and responds to publicly-issued requests for product proposals and quotes. The Commercial segment also includes sales of custom blended fuels delivered by barges or from a terminal dock to ships through bunkering activity.

Nearly 10% of the volume of home heating oil Global Partners sold to wholesale distributors is Heating Oil Plus. It sells home heating oil including Heating Oil Plus to about 790 wholesale distributors and retailers. About 35% of the home heating oil volume was sold using forward fixed price contracts.

Global Partners has a long term relationship with Exxon Mobil which accounts for about 15% of total sales.

Strategy

Global Partner's management's primary concern is navigating the low oil price environment that has battered revenue and profits since 2014. To support profitability and better position for future growth the company has sold off a number of its

less profitable assets. These include 31 gas stations and convenience stores its natural gas and electricity brokerage business and the termination of a sublease for more than 1600 rail cars. It is also seeking a buyer for six refined petroleum terminals.

Mergers and Acquisitions

In July 2018 the company acquired Champlain Oil of Vermont for $135 million approximately. It includes about 40 gas stations with Jiffy Mart-branded convenience stores approximately 25 fuel sites as well as term fuel supply agreements to about 65 gas stations primarily in Vermont and New Hampshire.

The acquisition increases retail portfolio and geographic footprint of Global Partners in New England and provides additional volume to strategically located terminals in New York and Vermont.

Company Background

Through AE Holdings the Slifka family controls about 21% of Global Partners; Kayne Anderson Capital Advisors L.P 12%.

Global Partners was founded in 1933 as a one-truck heating oil retailer by current CEO Eric Slifka's grandfather Abraham Slifka.

In 2010 in order to expand its wholesale supply business the company acquired about 190 retail gas stations in three states in the Northeast from Exxon Mobil and some of its dealers for $202.3 million. Pursuing a strategy of growing its storage capacity in 2010 Global Partners also acquired three terminals in Newburgh New York from Warex Terminals for $47.5 million.

In 2012 the company signed a long-term lease agreement with Getty Realty to supply gasoline to and operate about 90 of Getty's gas station in Queens Manhattan and the Bronx as well as in Long Island and Westchester County.

Boosting its gas station network in 2012 Global Partners acquired Alliance Energy a gasoline distributor and gas stations/convenience store operator controlled by the Slifka family for $180 million.

Growing its portfolio in 2013 Global Partners acquired Cascade Kelly Holdings LLC (a crude oil and ethanol facility near Portland Oregon) for $95 million. That year it also acquired 60% of Basin Transload LLC (which operates two crude oil transloading facilities in Columbus and Beulah North Dakota with a combined rail loading capacity of 160000 barrels per day) for $85 million. The transaction complements its purchase of West Coast crude oil transload and ethanol facility near Portland.

EXECUTIVES

Coo, Mark A. Romaine, age 50, $500,000 total compensation

Evp Chief Accounting Officer And Co-director Mergers And Acquisitions, Charles A. (Chuck) Rudinsky, age 71, $273,000 total compensation

Vp Marketing Manager Distillates And Gasoline Wholesale, Joseph (Joe) DeStefano

President Ceo And Director, Eric Slifka, age 53, $800,000 total compensation

Evp General Counsel And Secretary, Edward J. Faneuil, age 66, $450,000 total compensation

Cfo, Daphne H. Foster, age 61, $400,000 total compensation

Evp Director And President Alliance Gasoline, Andrew Slifka, age 50, $425,000 total compensation

Svp Information Technology, Bill Gifford

Vice President Of Marketing Information Technology, Mary McCarty

Vice President Of Business Development, Bruce Atkins

Vice President Project Management And Development, Jack Frost

Vice President Of Rail Products Division, Matt Snyder

Vice President Information Security And Compliance, Carl Stolfi

Executive Vice President Of Information Technology, Gregory Rudoy

Vp National Business Group, Ken Whalley

Vice President Heavy Oil Marketing, Dennis Bowersox

Vice President Credit, Robert J Fraczkiewicz

Vice President Health And Safety Operations, Tom Keefe

Vice President, Stephen Wyman

Senior Vice President, Mark Cosenza Mark Cosenza

Vice President Marketing, Ray Gincavage

Vice President, Jane Michalek

Vice President, Eileen Sweeney

Vice President Gdso North, Kevin Jackson

Vice President Wholesale New England, Joe Moceri

Chairman, Richard Slifka, age 78

Board Member, David Mckown

Treasurer, Greg Hanson

Board Member, Kenneth Watchmaker

Senior Executive Assistant To Edward J. Faneuil Vice President Group Chief Officer And Secretary, Lillian Santangelo

Auditors: Ernst & Young LLP

LOCATIONS

HQ: Global Partners LP
P.O. Box 9161, 800 South Street, Waltham, MA 02454-9161
Phone: 781 894-8800
Web: www.globalp.com

PRODUCTS/OPERATIONS

2016 Sales

	$ mil.	% of total
Wholesale	4,107	50
Gasoline distribution & station operations	3,443	42
Commercial	689	8
Total	**8,240**	**100**

Selected Products

Biofuels
Bunker oil
Diesel oil
Distillates
Gasoline
Home heating oil
Kerosene
Residual fuel oil

COMPETITORS

Bayside Fuel	Koch Industries Inc.
Exxon Mobil	Sprague Resources
George Warren	Tauber Oil
Gulf Oil	Warren Equities
Highlands Fuel	
Delivery	

HISTORICAL FINANCIALS

Company Type: Public

Income Statement

FYE: December 31

	REVENUE ($ mil.)	NET INCOME ($ mil.)	NET PROFIT MARGIN	EMPLOYEES
12/18	12,673	104	0.8%	2,500
12/17	8,921	59	0.7%	2,000
12/16	8,240	(199)	—	1,770
12/15	10,315	44	0.4%	1,890
12/14	17,270	115	0.7%	1,154
Annual Growth	**(7.4%)**	**(2.4%)**	**—**	**21.3%**

2018 Year-End Financials

Debt ratio: 47.00%
Return on equity: —
Cash ($ mil.): 23
Current ratio: 2.00
Long-term debt ($ mil.): 1,034

No. of shares (mil.): 34
Dividends
Yield: 12.0%
Payout: 64.0%
Market value ($ mil.): 554

	STOCK PRICE ($) FY Close	P/E High/Low		PER SHARE ($) Earnings	Dividends	Book Value
12/18	16.00	7	5	3.00	2.00	15.00
12/17	17.00	12	9	2.00	2.00	12.00
12/16	19.00	—	—	(6.00)	2.00	12.00
12/15	18.00	37	14	1.00	3.00	19.00
12/14	33.00	11	8	4.00	3.00	19.00
Annual Growth	**(16.2%)**	**—**	**—**	**(7.0%)**	**(7.2%)**	**(6.4%)**

Globe Life Inc

Torchmark Corporation a holding company for a family of financial firms specializes in individual life insurance and supplemental health insurance to middle-income families. Torchmark subsidiaries which include flagship American Income Life offer whole and term life insurance supplemental health insurance accidental death insurance Medicare Supplements and long-term care health policies for the elderly. Torchmark sells its products through direct marketing as well as through a network of exclusive and independent agents. Substantially all of Torchmark's business is conducted in the US.

Operations

Torchmark operates in four segments ? life insurance supplemental health insurance annuity and investments. The life insurance segment (about 55% of revenue) offers products including traditional and interest-sensitive whole life coverage as well as term life insurance. The supplemental health segment (about 25%) offers Medicare Supplement critical illness accident and limited-benefit supplemental hospital and surgical coverages. The annuity segment (less than 1% of sales) once provided fixed-benefit contracts although the company is no longer marketing these products ? it's focusing more on protection-oriented life and health products. Finally the investments segment (more than 20%) manages the group's capital resources.

Torchmark's American Income Life subsidiary markets and sells individual life and supplemental health insurance to working families. Targeting middle-income families Liberty National Life also provides life and supplemental health policies in this market. Torchmark's Family Heritage Life provides limited-benefit health products in non-urban areas to middle-income families. A smaller subsidiary Globe Life and Accident reaches middle-income customers with life and health insurance products including juvenile and senior life coverage and Medicare Supplement products. United American sells Medicare Supplement insurance primarily to Medicare beneficiaries.

Geographic Reach

Substantially all of Torchmark's business is in the US with headquarters in McKinney TX. United American also does business out of McKinney and leases space in Omaha NE and Syracuse NY. Liberty National operates from a facility in Hoover AL in addition to its offices in McKinney. Globe Life has offices in Oklahoma City OK and American Income life has its main offices in Waco TX with minor agent distribution in Canada and New

Zealand. Family Heritage operates out of Broadview Heights OH.

Sales and Marketing

Torchmark markets and distributes its products through a variety of channels including independent agents direct mail electronic and insert media and inbound call centers. Through Family Heritage Life the group even has agents that go door-to-door in non-urban markets.

The company's main Liberty National Life subsidiary uses a direct sales force to sell its products. The subsidiary has about 1750 producing agents and about 65 branch offices across the US. It also utilizes captive and independent agents.

Financial Performance

Torchmark's revenue and net income have seen small but steady growth over the past several years. In 2017 revenue rose more than 5% to $4.2 billion thanks to a more than $100 million increase in life insurance premiums as well as a near $30 million bump in health insurance premiums.

Net income more than tripled to $1.5 billion in 2017 compared with $550 million in 2016. The sharp increase was due to an $874 million increase related to deferred income tax liabilities resulting from favorable tax legislation (Tax Cuts and Jobs Act of 2017). After two years of cash flow increases of some 25% 2017 cash flow increased only 2% — the small percentage also related to deferred income tax charges.

Strategy

Torchmark's insurance strategy is centered on selling life and health products to middle-income households which it sees as an underserved market. In recent years the company has especially been focused on young families with children. It has also been focused on expanding its distribution channels. For example American Income Life has expanded its reach beyond unions (which have declined in membership) to offer products and services to new customers through referrals and other sources; it hopes to expand its team of agents (currently at some 7000) to 10000 within five years.

Additionally the firm continues to invest in technology to facilitate a digital experience for its customers boost its underwriting capabilities with data analytics and modernizing its back-office infrastructure.

Torchmark's investment segment invests almost exclusively in long-range fixed maturities that meet certain quality and yield objectives. Unlike many other life insurers Torchmark makes the bulk of its revenues from its premiums and relatively little (about 20%) from its investments. This allows it to ride out the economic downturns more smoothly while other life insurers take significant revenue hits when their investments falter.

HISTORY

It began as a scam plain and simple. In 1900 the Heralds of Liberty was founded as a fraternal organization — but its real reason for existence was to funnel money to its founders according to Frank Samford Torchmark's CEO from 1967 to 1985; Samford was also the great-grandson of the governor who signed the group's charter and the son of the state insurance commissioner who oversaw the Heralds of Liberty's rehabilitation into a real insurance company.

The Heralds offered a joint life distribution plan under which policyholders were divided by age; when a person died his or her beneficiary was paid along with the holder of the lowest-numbered insurance certificate in the class (if they were paid at all; the Heralds were not scrupulous about that). Postal authorities called this plan a lottery and it was illegal in many states. But the Heralds' fraternal order status allowed it to circumvent Alabama insurance laws until 1921 when its infractions could no longer be ignored.

The organization operated under state supervision until 1929 when it was recapitalized as stock company Liberty National. By 1934 despite the Depression the company was financially sound.

In 1944 Liberty National merged with funeral insurance company Brown-Service whose large sales force began selling Liberty National's policies. The added sales helped the company grow and make acquisitions from the 1950s through the 1970s. Even after it discontinued funeral insurance the company still paid out benefits. (As late as 1985 half of all Alabamans who died had the policies.)

Liberty National reorganized itself as a holding company in 1980 to accommodate the purchase of Globe Life And Accident. In 1981 it acquired Continental Investment Corp. which owned United Investors Life Insurance Waddell & Reed (financial services) and United American Insurance. In 1982 the holding company became Torchmark. Throughout its growth spurt it refrained from offering high-yield financial products and thus escaped the worst effects of the economic disruptions of the late 1980s. Its 1990 acquisition of Family Service Life Insurance put it back in the funeral insurance business (it exited again in 1995 and sold the unit in 1998).

Sales in the 1990s were affected by a decline in cash-value life insurance and Medicare supplements. Slack sales forced the company to stop having agents collect premiums personally and by 1996 all accounts were handled by mail.

In 1998 the company sought to sell its 28% stake in property insurer Vesta Insurance Group after that company became the target of numerous lawsuits. Torchmark was only able to reduce its stake to 24% on the open market but in 2000 Vesta bought out Torchmark's holdings.

Torchmark was haunted in 2000 by its own version of the undead — burial policies. An investigation by Alabama regulators was sparked by a Florida court order forcing the company to stop collecting premiums on old burial policies for which African-Americans had been charged higher premiums. In 2001 and 2002 Torchmark was hit by another dozen lawsuits including allegations of overcharging.

EXECUTIVES

Co-chairman And Co-ceo, Larry M. Hutchison, age 65, $870,865 total compensation
Co-chairman And Co-ceo, Gary L. Coleman, age 66, $870,865 total compensation
Ceo American Income Life And Liberty National Life, Roger C. Smith, age 66, $594,846 total compensation
Evp And Chief Administrative Officer, Vern D. Herbel, age 61, $519,846 total compensation
Evp And Cfo, Frank M. Svoboda, age 57, $499,692 total compensation
Evp And Chief Investment Officer, W. Michael Pressley, age 67, $499,692 total compensation
Evp And Chief Actuary, Ben W. Lutek, age 60
President Lnl Agency Division, Steven J. (Steve) DiChiaro, age 52
Evp And General Counsel, R. Brian Mitchell, age 55
President And Ceo Globe Life Direct Response, Bill E. Leavell, age 56
President Family Heritage Life Insurance, Kenneth J. (Ken) Matson, age 52
President United American Insurance And First United American Insurance, Michael C. Majors, age 57
Evp And Cio, James E. (Bo) McPartland, age 52
Evp And Chief Strategy Officer, J. Matthew Darden, age 48

President Ail Agency Division American Income, Steven K. Greer, age 46
Senior Vice President Facilities, Douglas Gockel
Avp Agent Recruiting And Leads, Kimberley Smith
Executive Vice President And Chief Strategy Officer, James Darden
Executive Vice President Chief Strategy Officer, Gregory Smith
Assistant Secretary, Christopher Moore
Board Member, Steven Johnson
Board Member, Charles Adair
Board Member, Robert Ingram
Board Member, Linda Addison
Auditors: DELOITTE & TOUCHE LLP

LOCATIONS

HQ: Globe Life Inc
3700 South Stonebridge Drive, McKinney, TX 75070
Phone: 972 569-4000
Web: www.torchmarkcorp.com

PRODUCTS/OPERATIONS

2017 Revenues

	$ mil.	% of total
Insurance		
Life	2,306,547	56
Health	976,373	23
Annuity	15	-
Investment income	847,885	20
Realized investment gain	23,611	1
Other income	1,142	-
Total	**4,155,573**	**100**

Selected Subsidiaries

American Income Life Insurance Company
Family Heritage Life Insurance Company of America
Globe Life and Accident Insurance Company
Liberty National Life Insurance Company
United American Insurance Company

COMPETITORS

Aflac	Monumental Life
Allstate	Northwestern Mutual
Amalgamated Life	Penn Treaty
Gerber Life	Prudential
Guardian Life	State Farm
Lincoln Financial Group	Texas Life
	USAA
MassMutual	Unum Group
MetLife	

HISTORICAL FINANCIALS

Company Type: Public

Income Statement
FYE: December 31

	ASSETS ($ mil.)	NET INCOME ($ mil.)	INCOME AS % OF ASSETS	EMPLOYEES
12/18	23,096	701	3.0%	3,102
12/17	23,475	1,454	6.2%	3,102
12/16	21,436	550	2.6%	3,128
12/15	19,853	527	2.7%	3,115
12/14	20,215	543	2.7%	2,980
Annual Growth	3.4%	6.6%	—	1.0%

2018 Year-End Financials

Debt ratio: 6.00%
Return on equity: 12.00%
Cash ($ mil.): 121
Current ratio: —
Long-term debt ($ mil.): —

No. of shares (mil.): 111
Dividends
 Yield: 1.0%
 Payout: 10.0%
Market value ($ mil.): 8,250

	STOCK PRICE ($) FY Close	P/E High/Low		PER SHARE ($) Earnings	Dividends	Book Value
12/18	75.00	15	11	6.00	1.00	49.00
12/17	91.00	7	6	12.00	1.00	54.00
12/16	74.00	16	11	4.00	1.00	39.00
12/15	57.00	15	12	4.00	1.00	33.00
12/14	54.00	20	12	4.00	1.00	37.00
Annual Growth	8.3%	—	—	10.5%	5.6%	7.4%

Goldman Sachs Group Inc

Goldman Sachs has long possessed the Midas touch in the investment banking world. One of the world's most powerful investment banks Goldman Sachs offers a gamut of investment banking and asset management services to corporate and government clients worldwide as well as institutional and wealth individual investors. It is a world leader in merger and acquisitions advice and equities and debt underwriting. Through its Institution Client Services division Goldman Sachs is a major market maker offering fixed income equities currency and commodity products. The bank boasts some $1.5 trillion in assets under supervision covering all major asset classes. Goldman Sachs was founded in 1869.

HISTORY

German immigrant-cum-Philadelphia retailer Marcus Goldman moved to New York in 1869 and began buying customers' promissory notes from jewelers to resell to banks. Goldman's son-in-law came aboard in 1882 and the firm became Goldman Sachs & Co. in 1885.

Two years later Goldman Sachs began offering US-UK foreign exchange and currency services. To serve such clients as Sears Roebuck it expanded to Chicago and St. Louis. In 1896 it joined the NYSE.

While the firm increased its European contracts Goldman's son Henry made it a major source of financing for US industry. In 1906 it co-managed its first public offering United Cigar Manufacturers (later General Cigar). By 1920 it had underwritten IPOs for Sears B.F. Goodrich and Merck.

Sidney Weinberg made partner in 1927 and stayed until his death in 1969. In the 1930s Goldman Sachs entered securities dealing and sales. After WWII it became a leader in investment banking co-managing Ford's 1956 IPO. In the 1970s it pioneered buying blocks of stock for resale.

Under Weinberg's son John Goldman Sachs became a leader in mergers and acquisitions. The 1981 purchase of J. Aron gave the firm a significant commodities presence and helped it grow in South America.

Seeking capital after 1987's market crash Goldman Sachs raised more than $500 million from Sumitomo for a 12% nonvoting interest in the firm (since reduced to 3%). The Kamehameha Schools/Bishop Estate of Hawaii an educational trust also invested.

The 1994 bond crash and a decline in new debt issues led Goldman Sachs to cut staffing for the first time since the 1980s. But problems went deeper. Partners began leaving and taking their equity. Cost cuts a stronger bond market and the long bull market helped the firm rebound; firm members sought protection through limited liability partnership status. The firm also extended the period during which partners can cash out (slowing the cash drain) and limited the number of people entitled to a share of profits. Overseas growth in 1996 and 1997 focused on the UK and Asia.

After three decades of resistance the partners in 1998 voted to sell the public a minority stake in the firm but market volatility led to postponement. Goldman Sachs also suffered from involvement with Long-Term Capital Management ultimately contributing $300 million to its bailout.

In 1999 Jon Corzine then co-chairman and co-CEO announced that he would leave the group after seeing it through its IPO and Goldman Sachs finally went public that year in an offering valued at close to $4 billion. In 2000 Corzine was elected to a US Senate seat. The New Jersey Democrat spent more than $64 million on his campaign (a record) nearly $61 million of it from his own personal wealth (also a record). Corzine went on to win New Jersey's gubernatorial race in 2005.

In early 2004 Goldman president and COO John Thain left the firm to assume the helm of the New York Stock Exchange. Lloyd Blankfein was named his successor and became chairman and CEO in 2006 when his predecessor Henry "Hank" Paulson was named secretary of the US Treasury.

At the height of the economic crisis Goldman Sachs converted to a bank holding company. It formed subsidiary Goldman Sachs Bank USA (GS Bank USA) to manage bank loan trading mortgage originations and other activities. The Federal Reserve mandated the change for Goldman Sachs and fellow investment bank Morgan Stanley. The shift marked a monumental change on Wall Street as it put an end to the independent brokerage firm model that had been a mainstay in the US since reform measures were implemented during the Great Depression. Rivals Merrill Lynch Lehman Brothers and Bear Stearns had already merged with larger banks or filed for bankruptcy. The bank holding company structure brought increased regulation but allowed Goldman Sachs to acquire commercial banks — all in an effort to shore up the company's balance sheet.

In the days following the Federal Reserve announcement Warren Buffett's Berkshire Hathaway invested $5 billion in Goldman Sachs and acquired an option to assume $5 billion more of the company's common shares. Goldman Sachs made an additional $5 billion worth of stock available in a public offering. Additionally the US government stepped in with funding for Goldman Sachs in late 2008 when it announced an economic stimulus plan to buy some $250 billion worth of preferred shares of the nation's top banks; approximately $10 billion went to Goldman Sachs.

The capital infusions helped but didn't completely shield Goldman Sachs from the financial crisis the effects of which were felt worldwide. To cut costs the company trimmed some 10% of its workforce. It eventually returned to profitability in 2009 and paid back the money it received from the government but still drew ire from politicians over what have been perceived to be extravagant pay packages for its top employees. (The firm's extravagant year-end bonuses had become the stuff of legend.)

Goldman Sachs opened a new $1.8-billion headquarters building in New York City's lower Manhattan in 2009.

In 2012 Goldman spent some $5.65 billion to buy back preferred shares that Warren Buffet's Berkshire Hathaway acquired in 2008. The repurchase would save the firm money as it had been paying some 10% interest on the shares (or some $500 million annually).

Also in 2012 Goldman acquired the Bermuda-based insurance and reinsurance operations of Ariel Reinsurance; an addition that should bring in a steady stream of fees. Additionally that year the company arranged to sell hedge fund administrator Goldman Sachs Administration Services to State Street for some $550 million.

In 2013 Goldman Sachs Asset Management acquired the Global Treasury Funds assets which consists of a variety of money market funds from RBS Asset Management to strengthen its strong fixed income and liquidity management businesses in Europe and around the world.

Goldman bought the remaining 20% stake it didn't already own in Endesa Gas T&D in 2013. It purchased the natural gas transport firm from Spanish power utility Endesa for about $174 million.

In January 2013 Goldman sold approximately 45% of its ordinary shares of ICBC.

EXECUTIVES

Head Merchant Banking Division, Richard A. Friedman, age 61

Evp General Counsel And Secretary, Gregory K. Palm, age 70

Chairman Goldman Sachs Bank Usa And Goldman Sachs International Bank, Esta E. Stecher, age 62

Evp And Cfo, R. Martin Chavez, age 55

Chairman And Ceo, Lloyd C. Blankfein, age 64, $2,000,000 total compensation

Evp And Head Of Global Compliance, Sarah E. Smith

Vice Chairman Ceo Goldman Sachs International And Co-head Investment Banking Division, Richard J. Gnodde, age 59

President And Co-coo, David M. Solomon, age 57

President Goldman Sachs Japan, Masanori Mochida

President Asia/pacific Outside Japan, Kenneth W. Hitchner

Evp Chief Of Staff And Secretary, John F.W. Rogers, age 62

Global Co-head Investment Management Division, Timothy J. O'Neill

Evp And Global Head Human Capital Management, Edith W. Cooper, age 57

Global Co-coo Equities Franchise, Michael D. Daffey

Head Conflicts Resolution Group, Gwen R. Libstag

President And Co-coo, Harvey M. Schwartz, age 54, $1,850,000 total compensation

Global Co-head Securities Division, Isabelle Ealet

Vice Chairman And Global Co-head Securities Division, Pablo J. Salame, age 53

Head Global Investment Research, Steven H. Strongin

Global Co-head Investment Management Division, Eric S. Lane

Chief Strategy Officer And Ceo Goldman Sachs Bank Usa, Stephen M. Scherr

Global Co-head Securities Division, Ashok Varadhan

Chief Risk Officer, Craig W. Broderick

Co-head Investment Banking Division, John Waldron

Global Head Credit Trading, Justin G. Gmelich

Co-head Of Global Mergers And Acquisitions, Gregg R. Lemkau

Head Of The Global Financing Group And Head Of Latin America, Marc Nachmann

Co-head Global Financial Institutions Group (fig), Mike Esposito

Coo Goldman Investment Banking Division, Luke Sarsfield

Co-head Global Financial Institutions Group, Todd Leland

Global Co-coo Equities Franchise, Paul M. Russo

Head Of The Global Special Situations Group (gssg), Julian Salisbury

Ceo Goldman Sachs Singapore Pte., Jason Moo

Vice President Technology, Ted Najjar

West Coast Technology Vice President, Brandon Johnson

Vice President In Technology, David Olivares

Vice President, Lorraine Sperling

Vice President Gsam Insurance Asset Management Relationship Manager, Brian Rapino

Vice President, Jill Toporek

Vice President, Jeff Boyd

Vice President, Cameron Birdwell

Vice President, Tom Healy

Vice President Global Securities Services, Megan Chastain

Vice President, Anuraag Verma

Vp And Executive Director Network Architect, James Morris

Vice President, Charu Govil

Vice President Technology, Krishnamurthy Vaidyanathan

Vice President, Curtis L Ambrose

Vice President, Neil Kaufman

Vice President, Ovadiah Jacob

Vice President Global Securities Services, Caitlin Walsh

Vice President Investment Banking, Siddharth Shrivastava

Vice President, Jim Shea

Vice President Fx Ecommerce Product Management, Soomin Hu

Vice President Private Wealth Management Investment Management Division, Cristin Dalecki

Vice President Leveraged Finance Investment Banking, Jamie Tam

Vice President, Karen Ho

Vice President, Nancy Benchoff

Vice President, Doreen Fattore

Vice President, Subhek Garg

Vice President, Gitika Gumbar

Vice President In Asset Management Operations, Maureen Hill

Vice President Information Technology Manager, Greg Killeen

Vice President Asset Management, Jordan Kaufman

Vice President Client Portfolio Manager, Ann Casser

Vice President, Jessie Sinden

Vice President Corporate Communications, Jane Kim

Vice President, Gary Godshaw

Vice President, Christopher Higgins

Vice President, Kevin Carmody

Vice President Private Wealth Management Compliance, Diana Ryan

Technology Fellow And Vice President, Michael Ahern

Vice President, Linda Avery

Vice President, Emma Taylor

Vice President, Hugh Chisholm

Vice President, Nikhil Reddy

Vice President Global Data Centre Operations, George Jurrjens

Vice President, Eric Altier

Vice President, Eric Riley

Vice President, Peter Linehan

Vice President, Arpita Mazumdar

Vice President, Douglas Wu

Vice President Technology, Eugene Gauthier

Vice President Private Wealth Management Investment Management Division, Neil Stone

Vice President, Matthew Korenberg

Vice President, Richard Lerner

Vice President Assistant General Counsel, Michael Huber

Vice President Technology, Stephen Chan

Vice President, Allison Marsh

Vice President, Sean Butkus

Vice President Systems Management, Jeff Levine

Vice President, Christopher Wright
Vice President Investment Banking Division, Thomas Lynch
Vice President Tax Department, Nicolle Lewis
Vice President, Frank Drury
Vice President, Naomi Leslie
Vice President, Robert Leggett
Vice President, Andre Benjamin
Vice President, Michael Darling
Vice President, Kathryn Boyles
Vice President, Richard Jiang
Vice President, Jia Shan
Vp Gsam Tax, Peter Lao
Vice President Prime Brokerage, John Chiesa
Vice President, Nikhil Khanna
Vice President Of Information Technology, Prasert Chirachanakul
Vice President, Farley Friedman
Vice President, Joseph Pozzi
Vice President, WILLIAM CARINCI
Vice President Information Security, Anita Nandakumar
Vice President, Erica Olsen
Vice President Infrastructure Technology Audit, Manfred Elezovski
Vice President, Joe Mella
Vice President Investment Banking Division, Dave Park
Vice President, David Bao
Vice President And Tax Counsel, James Nolan
Vice President, Farzana Morbi
Vice President, Philip Pallone
Vice President Technology Finance, David Beneventano
Vice President, Gail Reid
Vice President, SYLVIE TRUDEL
Vice President, Joseph Selvidio
Vice President, Ruben Salinas
Vice President Technology, Mayank Sharma
Vice President Technology Engineering Campus Recruiting, Mallory Leib
Vice President, Caitlin DeSantis
Vice President Software Engineer, Javier Vazquez
Vice President Legal Department Technology Intellectual Property And Contracts Group, Marie Willemsen
Vice President, Nita Birla
Vice President, Ivan Kriakov
Vice President Of Fxpb, Michael Mccreesh
Vice President Information Systems, Reto Frei
Vice President, Greg Larson
Vice President, Michael Watts
Vice President, Stephen Blumenfeld
Vice President Information Technology, David Goldman
Vice President Information Security, Donald Callahan
Vice President, Jennifer Baumgarten
Vice President, Ira Powell
Vice President, Scott Albert
Vice President Credit Risk Information Technology, Ofer Imanuel
Vice President Information Technology Infrastructure, Leonid Tsvayberg
Vice President, Sabrina Khan
Vice President Tax, Joyce Hsu
Tax Vice President Transfer Pricing, Benjamin Sun
Vice President, Greg York
Vice President Information Technology, Jayish Jivrajani
Vice President, Rich Mason
Vice President, Jonathan Rousse
Vice President In The Finance Division, Thomas Morin
Vice President Wealth Management, Charles Michaels
Auditors: PricewaterhouseCoopers LLP

LOCATIONS

HQ: Goldman Sachs Group Inc
200 West Street, New York, NY 10282
Phone: 212 902-1000   **Fax:** 212 902-3000
Web: www.gs.com

2017 Sales

	% of total
Americas	61
Europe the Middle East & Africa	24
Asia	15
Total	**100**

PRODUCTS/OPERATIONS

2017 Sales

	$ mil.	% of total
Interest income	13,113	31
Non Interest income		
Market making	7,660	18
Investment banking	7,371	18
Investment management	5,803	14
Commissions & fees	3,051	7
Other	5,256	12
Total	**42,254**	**100**

2017 Sales

	% of total
Institutional Client Services	37
Investment Banking	23
Investment Management	19
Investing & Lending	21
Total	**100**

Selected Subsidiaries

Goldman Sachs & Co.
Goldman Sachs Bank USA
Goldman Sachs Credit Partners L.P. (Bermuda)
Goldman Sachs Financial Markets L.P.
Goldman Sachs International (UK)
Goldman Sachs Japan Co. Ltd.
Goldman Sachs Mortgage Company
GSTM LLC
  Goldman Sachs Execution & Clearing L.P.
J. Aron & Company

COMPETITORS

BMO Capital Markets	FMR
Barclays	JPMorgan Chase
CIBC World Markets	Lazard
Citigroup Global	Merrill Lynch
Markets	Morgan Stanley
Credit Suisse	Nomura Securities
Credit Suisse (USA)	RBC Capital Markets
Deutsche Bank	UBS

HISTORICAL FINANCIALS

Company Type: Public

Income Statement

FYE: December 31

	ASSETS ($ mil.)	NET INCOME ($ mil.)	INCOME AS % OF ASSETS	EMPLOYEES
12/18	931,796	10,459	1.1%	36,600
12/17	916,776	4,286	0.5%	36,600
12/16	860,165	7,398	0.9%	34,400
12/15	861,395	6,083	0.7%	36,800
12/14	856,240	8,477	1.0%	34,000
Annual Growth	**2.1%**	**5.4%**	**—**	**1.9%**

2018 Year-End Financials

Debt ratio: 29.00%
Return on equity: 12.00%
Cash ($ mil.): 130,547
Current ratio: —
Long-term debt ($ mil.): —

No. of shares (mil.): 368
Dividends
  Yield: 2.0%
  Payout: 12.0%
Market value ($ mil.): 61,431

	STOCK PRICE ($) FY Close	P/E High/Low		PER SHARE ($) Earnings	Dividends	Book Value
12/18	167.00	11	6	25.00	3.00	245.00
12/17	255.00	29	23	9.00	3.00	219.00
12/16	239.00	15	8	16.00	3.00	221.00
12/15	180.00	18	14	12.00	3.00	207.00
12/14	194.00	11	9	17.00	2.00	192.00
Annual Growth	**(3.6%)**	**—**	**—**	**10.3%**	**8.8%**	**6.2%**

Goodyear Tire & Rubber Co.

Goodyear Tire & Rubber sells mainly new tires under the Goodyear Dunlop Kelly Fulda Debica and Sava brand names. The company manufactures and sells its tires across the Americas Europe Middle East & Africa (EMEA) and the Asia Pacific region including Australia and New Zealand. Goodyear also makes and markets rubber-related chemicals for various applications. It operates approximately 1100 tire and auto service centers where it offers its products for retail sale and provides automotive repair and other services. Goodyear has marketing operations in almost every country in the world although the US generates about 45% of its revenue.

HISTORY

In 1898 Frank and Charles Seiberling founded a tire and rubber company in Akron Ohio and named it after Charles Goodyear (inventor of the vulcanization process 1839). The debut of the Quick Detachable tire and the Universal Rim (1903) made Goodyear the world's largest tire maker by 1916.

Goodyear began manufacturing in Canada in 1910 and over the next two decades it expanded into Argentina Australia and the Dutch East Indies. The company established its own rubber plantations in Sumatra (now part of Indonesia) in 1916.

Financial woes led to reorganization in 1921 and investment bankers forced the Seiberlings out. Succeeding caretaker management Paul Litchfield began three decades as CEO in 1926 a time in which Goodyear emerged to become the world's largest rubber company.

Goodyear blimps served as floating billboards nationwide by the 1930s. During that decade Goodyear opened company stores acquired tire maker Kelly-Springfield (1935) and began producing tires made from synthetic rubber (1937). After WWII Goodyear was an innovative leader in technologies such as polyester tire cord (1962) and the bias-belted tire (1967).

By 1980 Goodyear had introduced radial tire brands such as the all-weather Tiempo the Eagle and the Arriva as it led the US market.

Thwarting British financier Sir James Goldsmith's takeover attempt in 1986 CEO Robert Mercer raised $1.7 billion by selling the company's non-tire businesses (Motor Wheel Goodyear Aerospace) and by borrowing heavily.

Recession overcapacity and price-cutting in 1990 led to hard times for tire makers. After suffering through 1990 its first money-losing year since the Depression Goodyear lured Stanley Gault out of retirement. He ceased marketing tires exclusively through Goodyear's dealer network by selling tires through Wal-Mart Kmart and Sears. Gault also cut costs through layoffs plant closures and spending reductions and returned Goodyear to profitability in 1991.

The company increased its presence in the US retail market in 1995 when it began selling tires through 860 Penske Auto Centers and 300 Montgomery Ward auto centers. President Samir Gibara succeeded chairman Gault as CEO in 1996. That year Goodyear bought Poland's leading tire maker T C Debica and a 60% stake in South African tire maker Contred (acquiring the rest in 1998).

In 1997 Goodyear formed an alliance with Sumitomo Rubber Industries under which the companies agreed to make and market tires for one another in Asia and North America. The next year Goodyear sold its Celeron Oil subsidiary which operated the All American Pipeline and acquired the remaining 26% stake in tire distributor Brad Ragan (commercial and retail outlets in the US) for $20.7 million.

The company acquired Sumitomo Rubber Industries' North American and European Dunlop tire businesses in 1999. The acquisition returned Goodyear to its #1 position in the tire-making industry. However the company recorded drastically low profits that year because it had cut tire production and was unable to meet supplier demands.

To improve profitability Goodyear increased tire prices in 2000 and began consolidating its manufacturing operations. Goodyear also announced plans to combine its commercial tire service centers with those of Treadco through a joint venture named Wingfoot Commercial Tire Systems. Despite record sales in 2000 the company's profits hit some hard road prompting Goodyear to lay off 10% of its workforce and implement other cost-cutting efforts.

Early in 2001 the company announced that it would close its Mexican tire plant. The same year the company agreed to replace Firestone Wilderness AT tires with Goodyear tires for Ford owners as part of Ford's big Firestone tire recall.

Early in 2002 Goodyear announced that its recent job cuts and manufacturing consolidation resulted in an $85 million decrease in annual operating costs. Later in the year the tire maker became embroiled in an age discrimination lawsuit claiming unfair job evaluations for the company's older employees. Blaming a slow US economy Goodyear announced plans to cut 450 jobs at its Union City Tennessee manufacturing plant. The job cuts were just the beginning of what would be a series of operational adjustments made as part of a Capital Structure Improvement Plan formally launched in 2003.

Although Goodyear once owned about 10% of its Sumitomo Rubber Industries it sold more than 20 million shares of its Japanese counterpart stock back to the tire maker in 2003. Later in the year as the company was embroiled in a lengthy debate with the United Steelworkers union it was announced that the Huntsville Alabama tire manufacturing plant would be closed. Goodyear also announced that it would cut 500 non-union salaried employees in North America. Later that same year it was announced that Goodyear was chosen by Volvo to be the truck manufacturer's primary tire supplier in North America; Goodyear had a similar contract with Mack Trucks.

Qantas Airways announced in early 2004 that it chose Goodyear to provide tires for the Australia-based company's Jetstar Airways. Later in the year Goodyear acquired the shares of Slovenia-based Sava Tires it did not already own and the company's Goodyear Dunlop Tires Europe unit purchased the Sweden-based Dackia retail tire stores. The company announced more job cuts in the non-tire sector in 2004 affecting Goodyear's engineered products and chemical units.

In 2005 Goodyear sold its stake in Goodyear Sumatra Plantations (rubber plantations in Indonesia) to rival Bridgestone for $62 million. Later that year the company sold its Wingtack adhesive resin business to Sartomer Company Inc. (a subsidiary of France's TOTAL S.A.) for about $65 million. As 2005 wound to a close the company sold its farm tire business to Titan International for $100 million.

Goodyear called off plans to sell its Chemical Products division. Instead the company integrated its chemical operations with those of its North American Tire division to take greater advantage of operational synergies. The company did however move forward with plans to jettison its Engineered Products division. In 2005 Goodyear secured the services of J.P. Morgan Securities and Goldman Sachs to help it explore opportunities for the sale of Engineered Products. The company struck a deal for The Carlyle Group in 2007 to buy its Engineered Products division for about $1.5 billion.

In 2011 Goodyear sold its tire reinforcement wire business (located in Luxembourg and North Carolina) to South Korea-based Hyosung for $50 million. The same year it sold its farm tire business in Latin America to a Titan International unit for $99 million. In 2010 Goodyear had agreed to sell its farm tire business in Europe as well as Latin America to Titan but the European part of the deal fell through and Goodyear does not have a time frame for making that sale. (In 2005 Titan had purchased Goodyear's North American farm tire business.) Also in 2011 Goodyear closed a facility in Union City Tennessee.

Intent on making more tires at lower-cost facilities Goodyear relocated its tire-making operations from Dalian China to Pulandian China in 2012. Additionally Goodyear is expanding or modernizing plants in Brazil Chile Germany and the US.

EXECUTIVES

Chairman President And Ceo, Richard J. (Rich) Kramer, age 55, $1,233,333 total compensation
Svp General Counsel And Secretary, David L. (Dave) Bialosky, age 62, $565,000 total compensation
Evp And Cfo, Laura K. Thompson, age 54, $621,667 total compensation
Vp Consumer Tires North American Tire, Stephen R. (Steve) McClellan, age 53, $610,000 total compensation
Svp Global Operations And Technology, Joseph (Joe) Zekoski, age 67
President North America Consumer, R. Scott Rogers, age 50
President Europe Middle East And Africa (emea), Chris Delaney, age 58
Svp Global Human Resources And Chief Human Resources Officer, John T. Lucas, age 59, $547,333 total compensation
Svp Global Sales And Marketing, Richard Kellam, age 58
Vp And Cto, Christopher Helsel, age 54
President Asia Pacific, Ryan Patterson, age 45
Vp Corporate Financial And Strategic Planning, Marc Voorhees
Vp Global It; Cio Emea, Horst Ebert
Vp Tax, Scott Scheiferstein
Vice President Human Resources North American Tire, Gary Vanderlind
Vice President Global Labor Relations, Jim Allen
Vp Compliance And Ethics, Michael Rickman
Vp Of Consumer Experience Of Americas, Andy Traicoff
Vice President Total Rewards At The Goodyear Tire And Rubber Company, Annie Granchi
Vice President Sales And Marketing, Mark Totten
Vice President Of It, John Flounders

Vice President Product Quality And Plant Technology, Donald Stanley
Vice President Public Relations Americas, Laura Duda
Senior Secretary, Monica Hill
Board Member, James Firestone
Secretary Marketing Department, Marilyn Chapanar
Senior Secretary, Melissa Gould
Emea Treasurer, Christopher Collins
Auditors: PricewaterhouseCoopers LLP

LOCATIONS

HQ: Goodyear Tire & Rubber Co.
200 Innovation Way, Akron, OH 44316-0001
Phone: 330 796-2121   **Fax:** 330 796-4099
Web: www.goodyear.com

2018 Sales

	$ mil.	% of total
Americas	8,168	53
Europe Middle East and Africa	5,090	33
Asia Pacific	2,217	14
Total	**15,475**	**100**

2018 Sales

	$ mil.	% of total
United States	6,692	43
Germany	1,883	12
Other international	6,900	45
Total	**15,475**	**100**

PRODUCTS/OPERATIONS

Selected Products
Automotive repair services
Chemical products
Natural rubber
Tires
  Automotive
  Aviation
  Buses
  Construction
  Farm
  Mining
  Motorcycles
  Trucks
Tread rubber
Wholesale tires

Selected Subsidiaries
Celeron Corporation
Dunlop Grund und Service Verwaltungs GmbH (Germany)
Dunlop Tyres Limited (UK)
Goodyear Canada Inc.
Goodyear Dalian Tire Company Ltd. (China)
Goodyear de Chile S.A.I.C.
Goodyear de Colombia S.A.
Goodyear do Brasil Produtos de Borracha Ltda (Brazil)
Goodyear Dunlop Tires Austria GmbH
Goodyear Dunlop Tires Belgium N.V.
Goodyear Dunlop Tires Czech s.r.o.
Goodyear Dunlop Tires Danmark A/S
Goodyear Dunlop Tires Espana S.A. (Spain)
Goodyear Dunlop Tires Finland OY
Goodyear Dunlop Tires Hellas S.A.I.C. (Greece)
Goodyear Dunlop Tires Hungary Ltd.
Goodyear Dunlop Tires Ireland Ltd
Goodyear Dunlop Tires Italia SpA (Italy)
Goodyear Dunlop Tires Polska Sp z.o.o. (Poland)
Goodyear Dunlop Tires Portugal Unipessoal Lda
Goodyear Dunlop Tires Slovakia s.r.o.
Goodyear Dunlop Tires Suisse S.A. (Switzerland)
The Kelly-Springfield Tyre Company Ltd (UK)
Wingfoot Corporation

COMPETITORS

Bridgestone	Pep Boys
Continental AG	Pirelli
Cooper Tire & Rubber	Sime Darby
Hankook Tire	Titan International
Kumho Tire	Toyo Tire & Rubber
Marangoni	Yokohama Rubber
Michelin	Zeon
Midas	

HISTORICAL FINANCIALS

Company Type: Public

Income Statement | | | | FYE: December 31

	REVENUE ($ mil.)	NET INCOME ($ mil.)	NET PROFIT MARGIN	EMPLOYEES
12/18	15,475	693	4.5%	64,000
12/17	15,377	346	2.3%	64,000
12/16	15,158	1,264	8.3%	66,000
12/15	16,443	307	1.9%	66,000
12/14	18,138	2,452	13.5%	67,000
Annual Growth	(3.9%)	(27.1%)	—	(1.1%)

2018 Year-End Financials

Debt ratio: 34.00%
Return on equity: 15.00%
Cash ($ mil.): 801
Current ratio: 1.00
Long-term debt ($ mil.): 5,110

No. of shares (mil.): 232
Dividends
Yield: 3.0%
Payout: 53.0%
Market value ($ mil.): 4,739

	STOCK PRICE ($) FY Close	P/E High/Low		PER SHARE ($) Earnings	Dividends	Book Value
12/18	20.00	12	7	3.00	1.00	21.00
12/17	32.00	27	21	1.00	0.00	19.00
12/16	31.00	7	5	5.00	0.00	18.00
12/15	33.00	31	21	1.00	0.00	15.00
12/14	29.00	3	2	9.00	0.00	13.00
Annual Growth	(8.1%)	—	—	(24.3%)	27.4%	11.8%

Grainger (W.W.) Inc.

W.W. Grainger distributes more than 2.9 million industrial products from supplies to equipment and tools. The company offers material-handling equipment safety and security supplies lighting and electrical products power and hand tools pumps and plumbing supplies cleaning and maintenance supplies and metalworking tools. Its more than 3.5 million customers are government manufacturing transportation commercial and contractors. Grainger sells through a network of branches distribution centers catalogs sales and service representatives and websites. More than three quarters of its revenue are generated from customers in the US.

Operations

Grainger's US business is its largest operating segment representing around 75% of net sales. The segment's product lines include lighting and electrical equipment power and hand tools pumps and plumbing and cleaning and maintenance supplies. The US business purchases products from more than 3000 key suppliers most of which are manufacturers.

The majority of products sold by the US business are nationally branded products. In addition about 20% of its sales were private label MRO (maintenance repair and operations) items bearing Grainger's trademarks including DAYTON SPEEDAIRE AIR HANDLER TOUGH GUY WESTWARD CONDOR and LUMAPRO.

Acklands-Grainger the company's core Canadian business focuses on distributing industrial and safety products via about 100 domestic branches and distribution centers. The business represents about 5% of the company's sales.

Through a global sourcing operation Grainger procures competitively priced high-quality products produced outside the US from some 5000 suppliers.

Besides a wide range of products Grainger also provides services that include inventory management and energy efficiency assistance for lower maintenance costs. The company's KeepStock program offers vendor-managed inventory customer-managed inventory and onsite vending machines. Other offerings include its endless assortment businesses US-based Zoro (online MRO distributor) and MonotaRO which operates in Japan and other Asian countries primarily through websites and catalogs.

Geographic Reach

More than 75% of Grainger's sales stem from the US 10% in Canada and the rest in Europe Asia and Latin America. With locations in all 50 states the US business has about 280 branches and more than 15 distribution centers. The company also has over 90 branches and five distribution centers in Canada.

Sales and Marketing

Grainger offers its services to a range of industries such as government manufacturing transportation commercial and contractors. It markets its products through sales and service representatives distribution centers e-commerce platforms branches and contact centers.

Financial Performance

Grainger has seen solid revenue growth in recent years. Its annual revenues have risen 12% since 2014 driven in part by an uptick in the economy and mid-sized customer growth.

Revenue grew to $11.2 billion in 2018 an approximately 8% increase from the year prior. The increase was driven by volume increases in US business due to market share gain an improved demand environment and double-digit growth in its online MRO distribution business.

Net income was $782 million in fiscal year 2018 an increase over the $586 million net income in fiscal year 2017. Selling general and administrative expenses grew 4% in fiscal 2018 to $3.1 billion.

Cash provided by operating activities was $1 billion in fiscal 2018 while investing activities used $166 million. Financing activities used another $670 million.

Strategy

Facing a competitive market with signs of a possible industrial slowdown ahead Grainger is looking for growth opportunities and streamlining the company. The company sees growth potential in Zoro an online MRO distributor. Grainger plans to increase the number of SKUs offered at Zoro from 2.5 million to 5 million by 2020 with a future goal of 15 million. The company is looking to duplicate the success it's seen with its similar endless assortment online company in Japan. MonotaRO offers 25 million SKUs has more than $1 billion in sales and has a growth rate of some 20%. Grainger has implemented a price-cutting strategy (lowering prices on products by about 4% overall) to attract more customers align with market conditions and better compete with online sellers such as Amazon.com. The lower prices have served to attract middle tier companies to the customer base and drive higher sales volume. The company also is working to cut overhead and plans to remove $200 million in costs from the business. The company has been reducing its footprint in Canada amid a challenging market in recent years. Grainger has reduced the number of Canadian branches from 181 in 2014 to approximately 50 branches in 2018.

HISTORY

In 1919 William W. Grainger a motor designer and salesman saw the opportunity to develop a wholesale electric-motor sales and distribution company. He set up an office in Chicago in 1927 and incorporated the business a year later. With sales generated primarily through postcard mailers and an eight-page catalog called MotorBook Grainger started shipping motors to mail-order customers.

Utilities and factories began to shift from direct-current to alternating-current power systems in the late 1920s. Uniform DC-powered assembly lines gave way to individual workstations each powered by a separate AC motor. This burgeoning market opened the way for distributors such as W.W. Grainger to tap into segments that high-volume manufacturers found difficult to reach. In the early 1930s W.W. Grainger opened offices in Atlanta Dallas Philadelphia and San Francisco; by 1936 it had 15 sales branches.

W.W. Grainger entered a boom period after WWII and by 1949 it had branches in 30 states. The company continued to expand in the 1950s and 1960s then went public in 1967.

William Grainger retired in 1968 and his son David succeeded him as CEO. The company expanded into electric motor manufacturing with the purchase of the Doerr Companies in 1969. Ten years later it opened its 150th branch.

Grainger's distribution became decentralized with the 1983 opening of its 1.4-million-sq.-ft. automated regional distribution center in Kansas City. The next year Grainger surpassed $1 billion in sales. The company sold its Doerr Electric subsidiary to Emerson Electric in 1986. It added 91 branches in 1987 and 1988.

After a 17-year hiatus the company started making acquisitions again buying Vonnegut Industrial Products in 1989; Bossert Industrial Supply and Allied Safety in 1990; Ball Industries a distributor of sanitary and janitorial supplies in 1991; and Lab Safety Supply in 1992. Grainger began integrating its sanitary supply business with its core activities in 1993.

For the first time in company history no Grainger held the CEO position when president Richard Keyser was appointed in 1995 replacing David Grainger. That year the company moved its headquarters to Lake Forest Illinois.

EXECUTIVES

Svp And General Counsel, John L. Howard, age 62, $673,828 total compensation
Svp And Chief People Officer, Joseph C. High, age 66, $495,250 total compensation
Svp And Cfo, Ronald L. Jadin, age 59, $721,885 total compensation
Chairman And Ceo, Donald G. (D.G.) Macpherson, age 52, $875,000 total compensation
Svp Global Supply Chain Branch Network Contact Centers And Corporate Strategy, Paige K. Robbins, age 50, $441,769 total compensation
Vice President Digital Engineering And Information Management, Scot Gillespie
Vp Global Talent Acquisition Inclusion And Diversity, Marty Belle
National Account Manager, James Bullock
Vp Compensation And Benefits, Scott Witz
Vice President Of Information Technology, Renee Lynch
Vice President Customer Information And Business Insights, Shailesh Sood
National Account Manager, Bonnie Ryckman
Regional Sales Vice President, Daniel Moscaritolo
Vice President Marketing, Jim Penvillo
Regional Sales Vice President, Lloyd Peterson
Vice President International Market Development, Bonnie McIntyre
Vice President Of Information Technology, Linda Mclaughlin
National Account Manager, Jim Chier
Regional Sales Vice President, Rick McKirahan
Vice President Federal Government Sales, Mark Snead

Vice President Corporate Strategy And Continuous Improvement, Elizabeth Ubell
Vice President User Services. Mergers And Acquisitions And Specialty Brands, Bill Koenig
Vp; President Grainger International, Fred Costello
Vice President Eps Support Services, Mike Smuda
Vice President Controller, Eric Tapia
National Account Manager, Ryan Bucher
Senior Vice President Human Resources, Lawrence Pilon
Vice President Information Technology, Nathan Goarcke
Vp Chief M And A Counsel And Corporate Secretary, Hugo Dubovoy
Vp And Cio, Gregory Harman
Vp And President Acklands Grainger Inc., John Kaul
Vp Business Development, Ronald Paulson
Svp And Cfo, Thomas B Okray
Board Member, Michael Roberts
Board Member, James Slavik
Board Member, Neil Novich
Board Member, Stuart Levenick
Auditors: Ernst & Young LLP

LOCATIONS

HQ: Grainger (W.W.) Inc.
100 Grainger Parkway, Lake Forest, IL 60045-5201
Phone: 847 535-1000   **Fax:** 847 535-0878
Web: www.grainger.com

2016 Sales

	$ mil.	% of total
US	7,834	77
Canada	740	7
Other countries	1,563	16
Total	**10,137**	**100**

PRODUCTS/OPERATIONS

2016 Sales

	$ mil.	% of total
US-based businesses	7,523	74
Canada-based businesses	734	7
Other businesses	1,881	19
Total	**10,137**	**100**

Selected Products

Adhesives
Air compressors
Air-filtration equipment
Electric motors
Electrical products
Fasteners
Fleet and vehicle maintenance products
Hand tools
Heating and ventilation equipment
Janitorial and plumbing supplies
Lab supplies
Library equipment
Lighting equipment
Material handling
Pneumatics and hydraulics
Power tools
Pumps
Safety products
Security products
Spray paints
Test Instruments

COMPETITORS

Ace Hardware
Applied Industrial Technologies
Fastenal
Genuine Parts
Gexpro
Graybar Electric
Industrial Distribution Group
International Library Furniture
Kaman Industrial Technologies
Lowe's
MSC Industrial Direct
McMaster-Carr
WESCO International
Wilson

HISTORICAL FINANCIALS

Company Type: Public

Income Statement

FYE: December 31

	REVENUE ($ mil.)	NET INCOME ($ mil.)	NET PROFIT MARGIN	EMPLOYEES
12/18	11,221	782	7.0%	24,600
12/17	10,425	586	5.6%	25,700
12/16	10,137	606	6.0%	25,600
12/15	9,973	769	7.7%	25,800
12/14	9,965	802	8.0%	23,600
Annual Growth	**3.0%**	**(0.6%)**	**—**	**1.0%**

2018 Year-End Financials

Debt ratio: 38.00%
Return on equity: 43.00%
Cash ($ mil.): 538
Current ratio: 2.00
Long-term debt ($ mil.): 2,090
No. of shares (mil.): 56
Dividends
Yield: 2.0%
Payout: 39.0%
Market value ($ mil.): 15,773

	STOCK PRICE ($) FY Close	P/E High/Low	PER SHARE ($) Earnings	Dividends	Book Value
12/18	282.00	27 16	14.00	5.00	34.00
12/17	236.00	26 16	10.00	5.00	30.00
12/16	232.00	24 18	10.00	5.00	31.00
12/15	203.00	22 16	12.00	5.00	37.00
12/14	255.00	23 20	11.00	4.00	48.00
Annual Growth	**2.6%**	**— —**	**4.6%**	**6.5%**	**(7.8%)**

Graphic Packaging Holding Co

Graphic Packaging Holding Company (GPHC) is one of the largest producers of folding cartons and paper-based foodservice products in the US. Through its operating subsidiary Graphic Packaging International (GPI) the company makes laminated coated and printed packaging such as beverage carriers cereal boxes microwavable food packaging and detergent cartons. The company operates eight paperboard mills across North America. It generates about 85% of its sales through its Americas segment. Customers have included such big names as Kraft Foods Miller-Coors Anheuser-Busch General Mills and various Coca-Cola and Pepsi bottlers.

Operations

Graphic Packaging reports its operations in three reportable segments: Americas Paperboard Packaging (roughly 70% of total sales) Paperboard Mills (nearly 20%) and Europe Paperboard Packaging (about 10%).

GPHC provides a wide range of paperboard packaging solutions for the food and beverage markets and fast food restaurant chains. Beverage products include packaging for beer soft drinks energy drinks water and juices. Food packaging comprises cereal boxes and paperboard packaging for desserts frozen refrigerated and microwavable foods and pet foods. The company also makes packaging for prepared foods including snacks quick-serve foods for restaurants and food service items. Its household products include dishwasher and laundry detergent boxes and boxes for health care beauty aids and tissues and papers.

Geographic Reach

GPHC's products are sold in North America Central and South America Europe and the Asia/Pacific region. The Americas collectively account for about 85% of its total sales. Headquartered in Atlanta GA GPHC has sales offices in the US Mexico Brazil Australia China and several European countries.

Sales and Marketing

Most of the GPHC's sales are conducted through third-party brokerage arrangements. Marketing efforts are geared towards multinational food beverage and consumer product companies with no one customer accounting for 10% or more of annual revenues. The company also makes open-market sales to integrated and independent paperboard converters.

Its beverage company customers include Anheuser-Busch MillerCoors PepsiCo and The Coca-Cola Company. Consumer product customers include Kraft Heinz General Mills Nestlé USA Kellogg's HAVI Global Solutions and Kimberly-Clark. Its quick-service restaurants (QSR) customers include McDonald's Wendy's Panda Express Dairy Queen Chipotle Panera and KFC.

Financial Performance

Revenue for GPHC has hovered around $4 billion annually since 2014 until a spike in sales in 2018.

Net Sales in 2018 were $6.0 billion versus $4.4 billion the prior year an increase of 40% due to the North America Consumer Products (NACP) Combination (its acquisition from International Paper) higher selling prices and favorable foreign currency translation.

Net Income was $221 million versus $300 million in the prior year mainly due to a $136 million tax benefit in 2017 as a result of the Tax Cuts and Jobs act.

Cash at the end of fiscal 2018 was $70.5 million an increase of $3.1 million from the prior year. Cash from operations used $373.8 million while investing activities provided $689.1 million. Financing activities used $310.7 million for dividends to stockholders and the company's stock repurchase program.

Strategy

To drive growth Graphic Packaging focuses on the main strategic points of investing it its core business and making strategic acquisitions.

The company continually invests in research and development to create innovative wood-fiber-based packaging materials that are more sustainable and recyclable than existing alternatives. Key products recently developed or enhanced include GPHC's Integraflex material which acts as a replacement for thermoformed cups and plastic pouches; paper-based bowls as a substitute for CPET plastic trays; and double-walled paper cups that can replace styrofoam cups.

Starting with the integration of International Paper's North America Consumer Packaging business Graphic Packaging significantly increased its mill and converting footprint in 2018. GPHC also aims to increase capacity and expand its customer base with its acquisition of PFP (paperboard-based air filter frames) along with its two converting plants in Tennessee and Texas and the foodservice business of Letica with its facilities in Pennsylvania and Tennessee. In addition the company started up a new converting and distribution facility in Monroe LA. As consumers shift away from polystyrene foam products new facilities and acquisitions are enabling Graphic Packaging to meet the growing demand for more sustainable paper containers and packaging.

Mergers and Acquisitions

GPHC is focused on acquisitions to support growing its packaging business. In 2018 its Graphic Packaging International subsidiary acquired the foodservice business of Letica Corporation another packaging firm based in Mississippi for $95 million. The transaction expands its customer base and increases its capacity to meet the demand for paper cups as the result of the shift from styrofoam cups to paper.

In mid?2018 the company acquired all the assets of PFP and its subsidiary PFP Dallas Converting a converter focused on the production of paperboard air filter frames. The acquisition included two facilities in Lebanon TN and Lancaster TX. PFP is included in the Americas Paperboard Packaging segment.

Also in 2018 GPHC completed the integration of 79.5% of International Paper's (IP's) North America Consumer Packaging business and assumed $660 million of IP's debt (International Paper retained 20.5% of the entity). The transaction expands GPHC's existing manufacturing and converting platforms and allows for future growth with new platforms specifically for the specialty beverage solutions (SBS) market and folding carton converting.

HISTORY

The company traces its roots to the formation of Brown Paper Company in 1923. That entity made sheet kraft paper and linerboard and changed names numerous times over the years and eventually became Riverwood International. Another predecessor Coors Paper Packaging was formed in the early 1970s eventually becoming Graphic Packaging.

In 2003 privately held Riverwood Holding owner of paperboard maker Riverwood International bought rival Graphic Packaging International Corporation. Parent company Riverwood Holding changed its name to Graphic Packaging Corporation (GPC) and combined its operating units to form subsidiary Graphic Packaging International Inc.

The company took its latest form as Graphic Packaging Holding Company (GPHC) after the businesses of GPC and Altivity Packaging were merged in 2008 with GPHC emerging as the publicly-traded parent company. With this transaction the company which had been averaging about $2.5 billion in revenues suddenly saw that number increase to more than $4 billion in 2008. The merger diversified Graphic Packaging's product lines as well through Altivity's coated-recycled boxboard operations folding carton converting operations and ink manufacturing labeling and flexible packaging facilities.

EXECUTIVES

Svp And Cfo, Stephen R. Scherger, age 54, $552,240 total compensation
President And Ceo, Michael P. Doss, age 53, $900,000 total compensation
Svp Mills Division, Alan R. Nichols, age 56, $474,900 total compensation
Svp And President Americas, Joseph P. Yost, age 51, $432,600 total compensation
Vp And Cio, Vish M. Narenda, age 50
President Graphic Packaging International Japan Ltd., Takashi Sugiyama, age 68
National Sales Manager, Doug Murray
National Account Manager, Mike Maruna
National Account Manager, Todd Taylor
Chairman, Philip R. (Phil) Martens, age 59
Secretary, Wimberl Sandra
Auditors: PricewaterhouseCoopers LLP

LOCATIONS

HQ: Graphic Packaging Holding Co
 1500 Riveredge Parkway, Suite 100, Atlanta, GA 30328
Phone: 770 240-7200
Web: www.graphicpkg.com

2018 Sales

	$ mil.	% of total
Americas	5,170	85
Europe	696	11
Asia Pacific	218	4
Corporate and Other	(60.7)	-
Total	**6,023**	**100**

PRODUCTS/OPERATIONS

2018 Sales

	$ mil.	% of total
Americas Paperboard Packaging	4,094	68
Paperboard Mills	1,077	18
Europe Paperboard Packaging	696	11
Corporate/Other/Eliminations	157	3
Total	**6,023**	**100**

Selected Products and Services

Beverage machinery
Contract packaging
Laminations and coatings
  Aqueous release coatings
  Decorative metalized laminations
  Extrusion and adhesive laminations
  Extrusion coatings
  Specialty coatings
Packaging
  Bags
  Barrier
  Beverage
  Consumer packaging
  Candy & confections
  Cereal & dry food
  Facial tissue
  Gift boxes
  Health and beauty care
  Pet foods
  Refrigerated and frozen foods
Paperboard
  Containerboard
  PaceSetter brand coated recycled paperboard
  SUS brand coated unbleached kraft paperboard
  Uncoated recycled paperboard
  Consumer Packaging
Folding Cartons
Cooking Solutions
Away from Home
Strength Solutions
Fully Enclosed Cartons
Wrap Style
Basket and Clip Style
Service and Support
Pick and Place
Hang Tag Applicators
Clamshell Labeling
Sleeve Wrapping
Consumer Specialty Machinery
Specialty Service and Support
Paperboard
Coating & Lamination
Barrier Solutions

COMPETITORS

Amcor	International Paper
Atlas Container	Klabin
Barry-Wehmiller	Mid-America Packaging
Bemis	Mondi
Caraustar	Packaging Corp. of
Cascades Inc.	America
Exopack	Sonoco Products
Hood Packaging	Stora Enso

HISTORICAL FINANCIALS

Company Type: Public

Income Statement				FYE: December 31
	REVENUE ($ mil.)	NET INCOME ($ mil.)	NET PROFIT MARGIN	EMPLOYEES
12/18	6,023	221	3.7%	18,000
12/17	4,404	300	6.8%	13,000
12/16	4,298	228	5.3%	13,000
12/15	4,160	230	5.5%	12,000
12/14	4,241	90	2.1%	11,500
Annual Growth	**9.2%**	**25.3%**	**—**	**11.9%**

2018 Year-End Financials

Debt ratio: 42.00%
Return on equity: 14.00%
Cash ($ mil.): 71
Current ratio: 2.00
Long-term debt ($ mil.): 2,905
No. of shares (mil.): 300
Dividends
 Yield: 3.0%
 Payout: 42.0%
Market value ($ mil.): 3,191

	STOCK PRICE ($) FY Close	P/E High/Low	PER SHARE ($) Earnings	Dividends	Book Value
12/18	11.00	23 14	1.00	0.00	6.00
12/17	15.00	16 13	1.00	0.00	4.00
12/16	12.00	21 15	1.00	0.00	3.00
12/15	13.00	23 17	1.00	0.00	3.00
12/14	14.00	52 34	0.00	0.00	3.00
Annual Growth	**(6.0%)**	**—** **—**	**27.3%**	**—**	**18.9%**

Graybar Electric Co., Inc.

Graybar Electric is one of the largest distributors of electrical products in the US. The employee-owned company distributes more than 1 million electrical communications and data networking products through a network of around 260 distribution facilities. Its diversified lineup includes a myriad of wire cable and lighting products from thousands of manufacturers and suppliers. It also offers supply chain management and logistics services. Affiliate Graybar Financial Services provides equipment leasing and financing. Graybar Electric sells to construction contractors industrial plants power utilities and telecommunications providers primarily in the US.

Operations

Graybar Elecetric mainly operates through its subsidiaries of Graybar Canada Advantage Industrial Automation Cape Electrical Supply and Commonwealth Controls.

Geographic Reach

Graybar's business is primarily based in the US as its headquarters are located in St. Louis Missouri. Other operations include distribution facilities in Canada and Puerto Rico. The company serves its customers through a network of nearly 300 locations across the US and Canada.

It also operates in roughly 15 geographical districts in the US each of which maintains multiple distribution facilities that consist primarily of warehouse space. Most of the districts have around 20 sales and distribution facilities.

Sales and Marketing

Among the company's strengths is a diverse and large customer base with more than 145000 clients. Graybar gets some 60% of its sales from the construction sector. Other customers come from the institutional commercial and government (more than 20%) and industrial and utility (20%) sectors.

Graybar distributes one million products purchased from more than 4500 manufacturers and suppliers. The company sells approximately 50% of the products from its top 25 suppliers.

Financial Performance

Graybar Electric's sales have been rising steadily over the last five years while profits although low have been following a broadly upward track.

In 2018 the company's sales rose 9% to $7.2 billion thanks to uplift in sales to the construction; commercial institutional and government; and industrial and utility sectors.

Net income doubled to $143.3 million — a company record — thanks mainly to a lower income tax expense following changes to the US tax code.

Graybar is weakly cash generative. Its cash on hand grew $16.1 million during 2018 ending the year at $58.9 million. The company's operations generated $42.1 million and its financing generated $16.3 million offset by $42.3 million used in its investing activities. Graybar's main cash uses in 2018 were capital expenditures ($43.0 million) dividends ($46.9 million) and share repurchases ($15.7 million).

HISTORY

After serving as a telegrapher during the Civil War Enos Barton borrowed $400 from his widowed mother in 1869 and started an electrical equipment shop in Cleveland with George Shawk. Later that year Elisha Gray a professor of physics at Oberlin College who had several inventions (including a printing telegraph) to his credit bought Shawk's interest in the shop and the firm of Gray & Barton moved to Chicago where a third partner joined.

The company incorporated as the Western Electric Manufacturing Co. in 1872 with two-thirds of the company's stock held by two Western Union executives. As the telegraph industry took off the enterprise grew rapidly providing equipment to towns and railroads in the western US.

Western Electric then formed a new distribution business in 1926 Graybar Electric Co. (from "Gray" and "Barton") the world's largest electrical supply merchandiser. In 1929 employees bought the company from Western Electric for $3 million in cash and $6 million in preferred stock. During the 1930s it marketed a line of appliances and sewing machines under the Graybar name.

EXECUTIVES

Regional Vp Western Region, Dennis E. DeSousa, age 61, $276,571 total compensation

Svp North American Business, Robert C. Lyons, age 63, $268,435 total compensation

Svp Marketing, William P. Mansfield, age 57, $256,288 total compensation

Svp And Cfo, Randall R. Harwood, age 63, $280,000 total compensation

Svp Sales And Director, David G. Maxwell

Chairman President And Ceo, Kathleen M. Mazzarella, age 58, $854,921 total compensation

Svp Secretary And General Counsel, Matthew W. Geekie, age 57, $313,119 total compensation

Svp Human Resources And Director, Beverly L. Propst, age 49, $284,632 total compensation

Vp And Cio, David Meyer

Svp Supply Chain Management, Scott S. Clifford, age 48

Vice President Education Graybar Electric, Chris Althauser

Vice President Of Marketing, Rob Bezjak

District Vice President, Joseph Lamotte

Auditors: Ernst & Young LLP

LOCATIONS

HQ: Graybar Electric Co., Inc.
34 North Meramec Avenue, St. Louis, MO 63105
Phone: 314 573-9200
Web: www.graybar.com

2018 Sales

	% of total
US	95
Other countries	5
Total	**100**

PRODUCTS/OPERATIONS

2018 Sales

	% of total
Construction	60
Commercial Institutional and Government	19
Utility & Industrial	21
Total	**100**

Selected Products

Ballasts
Batteries
Cable
Conduit
Connectors
Emergency lighting
Enclosures
Fiber-optic cable
Fittings
Fluorescent lighting
Fuses
Hand tools
Hangers/fasteners
Heating and ventilating equipment
Industrial fans
Lighting
Lubricants
Paints
Patch cords
Smoke detectors
Testing and measuring instruments
Timers
Transfer switches
Transformers
Utility products
Wire

Selected Subsidiaries

Commonwealth Controls Corporation
Distribution Associates Inc.
Graybar Business Services Inc.
Graybar Canada Limited
Graybar Commerce Corporation
Graybar Electric Canada Limited
Graybar Financial Services Inc.
Graybar International Inc.
Graybar Services Inc.

COMPETITORS

Anixter International	Rexel Canada
Border States Electric	Rexel Inc.
Communications Supply	Richardson Electronics
Consolidated Electrical	SUMMIT Electric Supply
Gexpro	Sonepar USA
HD Supply	United Electric Supply
HWC	W.W. Grainger
Premier Farnell	WESCO International

HISTORICAL FINANCIALS

Company Type: Public

Income Statement

FYE: December 31

	REVENUE ($ mil.)	NET INCOME ($ mil.)	NET PROFIT MARGIN	EMPLOYEES
12/18	7,203	143	2.0%	8,700
12/17	6,631	72	1.1%	8,500
12/16	6,385	93	1.5%	8,500
12/15	6,110	91	1.5%	8,300
12/14	5,979	87	1.5%	8,250
Annual Growth	4.8%	13.1%	—	1.3%

2018 Year-End Financials

Debt ratio: 10.00%	No. of shares (mil.): 21
Return on equity: 18.00%	Dividends
Cash ($ mil.): 59	Yield: —
Current ratio: 1.00	Payout: 36.0%
Long-term debt ($ mil.): 10	Market value ($ mil.): —

Great Southern Bancorp, Inc.

Despite its name Great Southern Bancorp is firmly entrenched in the heartland. It is the holding company for nearly 200-year-old Great Southern Bank which offers loans deposit accounts CDs IRAs and credit cards through more than 75 branches in Missouri plus more than two dozen locations in Iowa Kansas Nebraska Minnesota and Arkansas. The firm's Great Southern Travel division is one of the largest travel agencies in Missouri. It serves both leisure and corporate travelers through about a dozen offices. Great Southern Insurance offers property/casualty and life insurance while Great Southern Financial provides investment products and services through an agreement with Ameriprise.

Operations

Great Southern loan portfolio is mostly made up of real estate loans. Commercial real estate mortgages and construction and land development loans accounted for around half of its loan portfolio at the end of 2015 while single-family residential mortgages made up another roughly 15%. The bank also writes consumer (including home equity) construction and business loans.

The bank made 82% of its total revenue from loan interest during 2015 while the rest of its revenue came from service charges and fees (9% of revenue) and other non-interest income sources.

Sales and Marketing

The bank served more than 169000 households mostly in Missouri but also in Arkansas Iowa Kansas Minnesota and Nebraska. It spent $2.3 million on advertising during 2015 compared to $2.4 million and $2.17 million in 2014 and 2013 respectively.

Financial Performance

Great Southern has struggled to consistently grow its revenues in recent years despite a 30% rise in loan assets since 2011 mostly as it's been selling off more of its interest-earning mortgage-backed securities assets. Its profits have been rising thanks to declining loan loss provisions as its loan portfolio's credit quality has improved with higher property valuations in the strengthened economy.

The bank's revenue dipped less than 1% to $197.93 million during 2015 as the bank continued to sell more of its mortgage-backed securities which led to lower interest income. It also earned $2.14 million less in gains from security sales than it did in 2014.

Despite modest revenue declines in 2015 Great Southern's net income climbed 7% to $46.5 million mostly as in 2014 it incurred prepayment penalties when it repaid $130 million of its FHLB advances. The bank's operating cash levels rose 6% to $71.42 million thanks to the increase in cash-denominated earnings.

Strategy

Great Southern Bancorp continues to expand its bank network to grow its loan and deposit business either through new branch openings or by acquiring branches in new geographic markets. Its branch network has grown from 104 branches in 2011 to 110 at the end of 2015.

Mergers and Acquisitions

In 2015 the bank purchased 12 branches and related deposit and loan business in the St. Louis area from Cincinnati-based Fifth Third Bank more than doubling its branch presence in the St. Louis area.

EXECUTIVES

Vp Operations And Secretary Great Southern Bank, Douglas W. (Doug) Marrs, age 61, $122,602 total compensation
Vice President Human Resources, Matt Snyder
Vice President, Bob Ogden
Svp And Chief Lending Officer Of The Bank, Steven G. Mitchem, age 67, $227,429 total compensation
President Ceo And Director Great Southern Bancorp And Great Southern Bank, Joseph W. (Joe) Turner, age 54, $299,237 total compensation
Svp And Cfo Great Southern Bank, Rex A. Copeland, age 54, $235,201 total compensation
Vp Information Systems, Linton J. (Lin) Thomason, age 62
Vice President, Jennifer Cook
Vice President, Cal Glasco
Assistant Vice President, Denit Patrick
Vice President Commercial Lending, Kent Lammers
Vice President Operations, Tonia Tillman
Chairman Great Southern Bancorp And Great Southern Bank, William V. Turner, age 86
Board Member, Douglas Pitt
Auditors: BKD, LLP

LOCATIONS

HQ: Great Southern Bancorp, Inc.
 1451 E. Battlefield, Springfield, MO 65804
Phone: 417 887-4400
Web: www.greatsouthernbank.com

COMPETITORS

Arvest Bank	Hawthorn Bancshares
BancorpSouth	NASB Financial
Bank of America	Scottrade
Commerce Bancshares	U.S. Bancorp
First Bancshares (MO)	UMB Financial
Guaranty Federal	Wells Fargo

HISTORICAL FINANCIALS

Company Type: Public

Income Statement				FYE: December 31
	ASSETS ($ mil.)	NET INCOME ($ mil.)	INCOME AS % OF ASSETS	EMPLOYEES
12/18	4,676	67	1.4%	1,182
12/17	4,415	52	1.2%	1,225
12/16	4,551	45	1.0%	1,263
12/15	4,104	47	1.1%	1,270
12/14	3,951	44	1.1%	1,252
Annual Growth	4.3%	11.4%	—	(1.4%)

2018 Year-End Financials

Debt ratio: 2.00%
Return on equity: 13.00%
Cash ($ mil.): 203
Current ratio: —
Long-term debt ($ mil.): —

No. of shares (mil.): 14
Dividends
 Yield: 3.0%
 Payout: 28.0%
Market value ($ mil.): 651

	STOCK PRICE ($) FY Close	P/E High/Low		PER SHARE ($) Earnings	Dividends	Book Value
12/18	46.00	13	9	5.00	1.00	38.00
12/17	52.00	16	9	4.00	2.00	33.00
12/16	55.00	17	11	3.00	1.00	31.00
12/15	45.00	16	11	3.00	1.00	29.00
12/14	40.00	13	9	3.00	1.00	31.00
Annual Growth	3.8%	—	—	11.0%	10.7%	5.4%

Great West Life & Annuity Insurance Co - Insurance Products

Great-West Life & Annuity Insurance a subsidiary of Canada's Great-West Lifeco and a member of the Power Financial family represents the Great-West group's primary US operations. Through its Empower Retirement and Great-West Investments divisions GWL&A provides retirement and investment management services. Parent Great-West Lifeco sold substantially all of GWL&A's individual life insurance and annuity operations to Protective Life Insurance for $1.2 billion in 2019. The divested business operated under the Great-West Financial brand.

EXECUTIVES

Evp Individual Markets, Robert K. Shaw, age 64, $458,100 total compensation
Svp Investments, Ernie Friesen
Svp And Chief Investment Officer Separate Accounts, Catherine S. Tocher
President And Ceo, Robert L. Reynolds
President Empower Retirement, Edmund F. Murphy
Evp Great West Lifeco U.s. Inc., Charles B. McDevitt
Svp And Cio, Jeffrey W. Knight
Svp And Cfo, Louis J. Mannello
Svp Product Management, David G. McLeod
Vice President, Eve Hampton
Regional Vice President, Brian Morris
Vice President Investment Operations, Mary C Maiers
Assistant Vice President, Terry Homenuik
Senior Vice President, Brett Ford
Auditors: DELOITTE & TOUCHE LLP

LOCATIONS

HQ: Great West Life & Annuity Insurance Co - Insurance Products
 8515 East Orchard Road, Greenwood Village, CO 80111
Phone: 303 737-3000
Web: www.greatwest.com

PRODUCTS/OPERATIONS

Annuities
Life insurance
Retirement services
 Retirement plans for government corporate and not-for-profit employers
 Communication and education services
 Enrollment services
 Investment options
 Third-party administrative and record-keeping services (FASCore)

COMPETITORS

AXA Financial
Allstate
Industrial Alliance Insurance and Financial Servic
John Hancock Financial Services
Liberty Mutual
Lincoln Financial Group
Manulife Financial
MetLife
Mutual of Omaha
Nationwide Financial
Pacific Mutual
Prudential
State Farm
Sun Life
The Hartford

HISTORICAL FINANCIALS

Company Type: Public

Income Statement				FYE: December 31
	ASSETS ($ mil.)	NET INCOME ($ mil.)	INCOME AS % OF ASSETS	EMPLOYEES
12/17	62,461	369	0.6%	5,800
12/16	60,309	231	0.4%	5,800
12/15	57,900	190	0.3%	5,400
12/14	58,348	317	0.5%	4,500
12/13	55,324	129	0.2%	3,300
Annual Growth	3.1%	30.1%	—	15.1%

2017 Year-End Financials

Debt ratio: 1.00%
Return on equity: 17.00%
Cash ($ mil.): 17
Current ratio: —
Long-term debt ($ mil.): —

No. of shares (mil.): 7
Dividends
 Yield: —
 Payout: 39.0%
Market value ($ mil.): —

Great Western Bancorp Inc

Auditors: Ernst & Young LLP

LOCATIONS

HQ: Great Western Bancorp Inc
 225 South Main Avenue, Sioux Falls, SD 57104
Phone: 605 334-2548
Web: www.greatwesternbank.com

HISTORICAL FINANCIALS

Company Type: Public

Income Statement				FYE: September 30
	ASSETS ($ mil.)	NET INCOME ($ mil.)	INCOME AS % OF ASSETS	EMPLOYEES
09/19	12,788	167	1.3%	1,666
09/18	12,117	158	1.3%	1,664
09/17	11,690	145	1.2%	1,689
09/16	11,531	121	1.1%	1,649
09/15	9,799	109	1.1%	1,475
Annual Growth	6.9%	11.3%	—	3.1%

2019 Year-End Financials

Debt ratio: 4.00%
Return on equity: 9.00%
Cash ($ mil.): 243
Current ratio: —
Long-term debt ($ mil.): —

No. of shares (mil.): 56
Dividends
Yield: 3.0%
Payout: 40.0%
Market value ($ mil.): 1,857

	STOCK PRICE ($) FY Close	P/E High/Low	PER SHARE ($) Earnings	Dividends	Book Value
09/19	33.00	15 10	3.00	1.00	34.00
09/18	42.00	17 14	3.00	1.00	31.00
09/17	41.00	18 13	2.00	1.00	30.00
09/16	33.00	16 11	2.00	1.00	28.00
09/15	25.00	14 9	2.00	0.00	26.00
Annual Growth	6.8%	— —	11.3%	32.2%	6.3%

GREENSTONE FARM CREDIT SERVICES ACA

One of the largest associations in the Farm Credit System GreenStone offers FARM CREDIT SERVICES (FCS) providesÂ short intermediate and long-term loans; equipment and building leases; appraisal services; and life and crop insurance to farmers in Michigan and Wisconsin. ItÂ serves about 15000 members and has nearlyÂ 40 locations. Through an alliance with AgriSolutions a farm software and consulting company Greenstone provides income tax planning and preparation services farm business consulting and educational seminars. FCS Mortgage provides residential loans for rural properties as well as loans for home improvement construction and refinancing.

EXECUTIVES

Executive Vice President Chief Sales And Marketing Officer, Randy Stec
Senior Vice President Chief Information Officer, Steve Junglas
Regional Vice President, Erin Dubois
Regional Vice President, Cindy Birchmeier
Assistant Vice President Credit, Sarah J Morack
Vice President Credit, Kevin Emison
Vice President Commercial Lending, Daniel Gitter
Vice President Credit, Steve Kluemper
Vice President Commercial Lending, Larry Urban
Vice President Credit, Thomas Urban
Regional Vice President Sales And Customer Relations, Ben Mahlich
Regional Vice President Sales And Customer Relations, Melissa Humphrey
Second Vice President, Shane Kenner
Vice President Commercial Lending, Thomas Wilson
Vice President Commercial Lending, Kyle Hurley
Avp Credit And Syndicated Lending, Bonnie Coponen
Vice President Capital Markets, Brad Hibbert
Auditors: PRICEWATERHOUSECOOPERS LLP MI

LOCATIONS

HQ: GREENSTONE FARM CREDIT SERVICES ACA
3515 WEST RD, EAST LANSING, MI 488237312
Phone: 517 324-0213
Web: WWW.GREENSTONEFCS.COM

Group 1 Automotive, Inc.

Group 1 Automotive is the third largest of a group of new and used car retailers (behind #1 AutoNation and #2 Penske Automotive Group) striving to consolidate US auto sales. The company owns more than 155 dealerships around 210 franchises and about 35 collision service centers operating under their own branding in the US UK and Brazil. The US is the biggest market and the company is present in 14 US states. Group 1 sells more than 30 car and light truck brands of which Toyota BMW and Ford are the biggest sellers. It also offers financing provides maintenance and repair services and sells replacement parts.

Operations

Group 1 Automotive's operations include five core business segments: New Vehicles (around 55% of sales) Used Vehicles (25%) Parts & Service (10%) Used Vehicles wholesale (5%) and Finance & Insurance (5%). In the UK the auto dealer operates through its subsidiary Group 1 Automotive UK Ltd.

Geographic Reach

The auto dealer rings up about 80% of its sales in the US; the remainder comes from the UK (15%) and Brazil (5%). More than half of Group 1's dealerships are located in Texas Oklahoma and California. In the UK Group 1 Automotive has about 40 franchises 30 dealerships and nearly 10 collision centers; and in Brazil nearly 25 franchises 20 dealerships and one collision center.

The company's US operations are located primarily major metropolitan areas. It is present 20 towns and cities in the UK and has a presence in Brazil in key metropolitan areas in the states of Sao Paulo Parana and Mato Grosso do Sul.

Financial Performance

Group 1's recent strong revenue growth continued in fiscal 2016 albeit at a slower pace than previously increasing 2% to $10.9 billion. Growth in the UK new car market relating to acquisitions and overall market strength was partially offset by new car declines in the US and Brazil. Weakness in the US was concentrated in Group 1's significant Houston market as the oil city's workers have reduced their spending as the industry-wide squeeze continued. Used car sales rose 5% due to good performance in the US and UK. The Parts & Services business also grew.

Net income ticked up 56% to $147 million due mostly to higher net sales.

Cash from operations climbed 172% to $384.9 million due to higher net income and an increase in accounts payable and inventories.

Strategy

Group 1 is looking to capitalize on growth opportunities in the UK (where it already has an established presence) and in Brazil a relatively new market for the company. It acquired 12 dealerships and opened two additional dealerships in the UK in fiscal 2016. The company's strategy also includes growing its higher margin parts and services business growing its share of the new and used vehicle market taking advantage of its size to boost efficiency and continuing to make strategic acquisitions. In recent years Group 1 has seen import and luxury brands account for an increased share of its business.

Mergers and Acquisitions

In 2019 Group 1 expanded its presence in the New Mexico market with the acquisition of two BMW/MINI dealerships in Albuquerque and Santa Fe. The deal also includes BMW Motorrad franchises in Albuquerque and Santa Fe making Group 1 the exclusive seller of BMW Motorcycles in New Mexico.

In 2016 Group 1 acquired London-based Spire Automotive Group's twelve dealerships including four Audi dealerships and three BMW/MINI dealerships which will continue to use the Spire brand name. The acquired dealerships are expected to bring in approximately $575 million per year. The acquisition could also further Group 1's relationships with BMW and the Volkswagen Group in the UK.

EXECUTIVES

President Ceo And Director, Earl J. Hesterberg, age 66, $1,100,000 total compensation
Vp Manufacturer Relations, Peter C. DeLongchamps, age 58, $456,300 total compensation
Svp Human Resources Training And Operations Support, Frank Grese, age 67, $540,000 total compensation
Svp And Cfo, John C. Rickel, age 58, $583,500 total compensation
Vp And General Counsel, Darryl M. Burman, age 61, $440,300 total compensation
Vp Information Systems, James R. Druzbik
Vice President Public Affairs, Marvin Marcell
Vice President Human Resources, Brooks O'hara
Vp Operations, David Fesmire
Vice President Human Resources, Brooks OHara
Vice President, Larry Caudill
Chairman, Stephen D. Quinn, age 64
Corporate Treasurer, Kim Craig
Auditors: Ernst & Young LLP

LOCATIONS

HQ: Group 1 Automotive, Inc.
800 Gessner, Suite 500, Houston, TX 77024
Phone: 713 647-5700   **Fax:** 713 647-5858
Web: www.group1auto.com

2016 Sales

	$ mil.	% of total
U.S.	8,735	80
U.K.	1,723	16
Brazil	430	4
Total	**10,888**	**100**

Dealership presence

Dealership presence
United States
Alabama
California
Florida
Georgia
Kansas
Louisiana
Maryland

COMPETITORS

COUNTRY Financial   Rabobank Group
FB BanCorp

HISTORICAL FINANCIALS

Company Type: Private

Income Statement   FYE: December 31

	ASSETS ($ mil.)	NET INCOME ($ mil.)	INCOME AS % OF ASSETS	EMPLOYEES
12/07	4,317	70	1.6%	380
12/06	3,691	64	1.7%	—
Annual Growth	17.0%	8.9%	—	—

Massachusetts
Mississippi
New Hampshire
New Jersey
Oklahoma
South Carolina
Texas
United Kingdom
  Brighton
  Chelmsford
  Chingford
  Farnborough
  Hailsham
  Harold Wood
  Hindhead
  Southend
  Stansted
  Worthington
Brazil
  Sao Paolo
  Parana
  Mato Grosso do Sul

PRODUCTS/OPERATIONS

2016 Sales

	$ mil.	% of total
New vehicle retail	6,046	55
Used vehicle retail	2,758	25
Used vehicle wholesale	402	4
Parts & service	1,261	12
Finance insurance & other	421	4
Total	**10,888**	**100**

Selected Brands

Domestic
  Ford
  Chevrolet
  Dodge
  Jeep
  GMC
  Chrysler
  Buick
  RAM
Import
  Toyota
  Nissan
  Honda
  Volkswagen
  Hyundai
  Mazda
  Subaru
  Scion
  Kia
  Peugeot
  Renault
Luxury
  BMW
  Acura
  MINI
  Land Rover
  Lexus
  Mercedes
  Audi
  Volvo
  Cadillac
  Lincoln
  Porsche
  Sprinter
  smart
  Jaguar

COMPETITORS

Ancira	Lookers
Asbury Automotive	Pendragon
AutoNation	Penske Automotive
CarMax	Group
David McDavid Auto	Phil Long Dealerships
Group	Sonic Automotive
Herb Chambers	Sytner
Lithia Motors	

HISTORICAL FINANCIALS

Company Type: Public

Income Statement
FYE: December 31

	REVENUE ($ mil.)	NET INCOME ($ mil.)	NET PROFIT MARGIN	EMPLOYEES
12/18	11,601	158	1.4%	14,570
12/17	11,124	213	1.9%	14,108
12/16	10,888	147	1.4%	13,500
12/15	10,633	94	0.9%	12,886
12/14	9,938	93	0.9%	11,978
Annual Growth	3.9%	14.1%	—	5.0%

2018 Year-End Financials

Debt ratio: 61.00%
Return on equity: 14.00%
Cash ($ mil.): 16
Current ratio: 1.00
Long-term debt ($ mil.): 1,281

No. of shares (mil.): 18
Dividends
  Yield: 2.0%
  Payout: 13.0%
Market value ($ mil.): 966

	STOCK PRICE ($) FY Close	P/E High/Low		PER SHARE ($) Earnings	Dividends	Book Value
12/18	53.00	11	6	8.00	1.00	60.00
12/17	71.00	8	5	10.00	1.00	54.00
12/16	78.00	12	7	7.00	1.00	43.00
12/15	76.00	25	19	4.00	1.00	39.00
12/14	90.00	24	16	4.00	1.00	40.00
Annual Growth	(12.4%)	—	—	21.4%	10.4%	10.5%

GROWMARK, INC.

Agricultural and energy cooperative GROWMARK serves more than 250000 farm commercial and residential customers across the US and in parts of Canada. Under the Growmark FS name it offers a host of plant food and crop protection products as well as biotechnology services and training and agricultural marketing and consulting. The company also operates a full-line seed company Seedway and provides grain facility planning and grain marketing services. Lastly GROWMARK's energy business includes the marketing and distribution of fuels lubricants and greases and propane and the Fast Stop convenience stores and gas station chain with 230-plus locations across the Midwest.

Operations

GROWMARK's operations are divided into five major divisions: agronomy energy grain facility planning and logistics.

The agronomy division includes products and services in the areas of seeds plant food crop protection and biotechnology while the energy business includes marketing and distribution services and the Fast Stop convenience store/fuel station chain. GROWMARK provides grain handling and marketing services through its grain division and grain facility planning and consulting through its facility planning division. The company's logistics operations provide for the delivery of more than 150000 truckloads of products annually to local cooperatives.

Geographic Reach

GROWMARK is headquartered in Bloomington Illinois and serves customers in more than 40 US states and Ontario Canada.

Its Seedway business has eight office and warehouse locations in Vermont New York Pennsylvania and Florida.

Financial Performance

Although not required to publicly release full financials GROWMARK reported fiscal 2017 revenue of more than $7 billion.

Strategy

A key element of GROWMARK's strategy is the improvement of its supply chain which has been called out as one of the four major tenets for growth. In 2018 the company added a new executive position focused on supply chain optimization.

Company Background

GROWMARK traces its history back to 1920 and the establishment of local cooperatives by Farm Bureau members. One of those cooperatives Farm Bureau Service Company of Iowa in the early 1960s merged with Illinois Farm Supply Company (founded in 1927) to form the foundation of what is today GROWMARK. The GROWMARK name started being used in 1980.

EXECUTIVES

Chairman And President, John Reifsteck
Ceo, Jeff Solberg
Vice President General Counsel, Brent Bostrom
Vp Eastern Retail Operations, Steve Buckalew
Vp And Cfo, Marshall Bohbrink
Vp Energy, Kevin Carroll
Vp Midwest Retail And Acquisitions, Shelly Kruse
Vp Grain, Brent Ericson
Vice President Human Resources & Compliance, Gary Swango
Vp Agronomy, Mark Orr
Vp Financial And Risk Management, Mike Woods
Vp Member Services, Denny Worth
Vice President Of Human Resources, Ann Kafer
Vice President Systems, George Key
Region Vice President, Barry Schmidt
Vice President Of Information Technology, Rick Norton
Vice President Member Services, Dennis Farmer
Senior Vice President, Jeffrey M Solberg
National Account Manager, Norm Frank
Vice Chairman, Rick Nelson
Vice Chairman, Chet Esther
Assistant Treasurer, Karmy Kays
Treasurer, Jeffrey Lynch
Auditors: ERNST & YOUNG LLP CHICAGO IL

LOCATIONS

HQ: GROWMARK, INC.
  1701 TOWANDA AVE, BLOOMINGTON, IL 617012057
Phone: 309 557-6000
Web: WWW.GROWMARK.COM

COMPETITORS

ADM	Marathon Oil
AGRI Industries	NC Hybrids
Ag Processing Inc.	Orscheln Farm and Home
BP	Pfister Hybrid Corn
Barkley Seed	Pioneer Hi-Bred
Bayer CropScience	Rabo AgriFinance
CHS	Sakata Seed
Cargill	Seed Enterprises
Chevron	Southern States
Costco Wholesale	Terra Nitrogen
DeBruce Grain	Wal-Mart
Exxon Mobil	Wilbur-Ellis

	REVENUE ($ mil.)	NET INCOME ($ mil.)	NET PROFIT MARGIN	EMPLOYEES
08/18	8,522	66	0.8%	7,000
08/17	7,291	115	1.6%	—
08/16	7,031	102	1.4%	—
08/15	8,727	113	1.3%	—
Annual Growth	(0.8%)	(16.6%)	—	—

Income Statement   FYE: August 31

Guaranty Bancshares Inc

Guaranty Bancshares is the holding company for Guaranty Bond Bank which operates about a dozen branches in northeast Texas and another in West Texas. Guaranty Bond Bank's deposit products and services include CDs and savings checking NOW and money market accounts.Â Its lending activities include one- to four-family residential mortgages (more than a third of the company's loan portfolio) in addition to commercial mortgage construction business agriculture and personal loans. The company's GB Financial division provides wealth management retirement planning and trust services.

EXECUTIVES

Senior Vice President, Terry Todd
Senior Vice President, Steve Bledsoe
Executive Vice President General Counsel, Randall Kucera
Auditors: Whitley Penn LLP

LOCATIONS

HQ: Guaranty Bancshares Inc
  16475 Dallas Parkway, Suite 600, Addison, TX 75001
Phone: 888 572-9881
Web: www.gnty.com

PRODUCTS/OPERATIONS

2008 Sales

	$ mil.	% of total
Interest		
Loans including fees	31	70
Securities	6	13
Other	1	2
Noninterest		
Service charges	4	8
Other	3	7
Total	46	100

COMPETITORS

BancorpSouth	Southside Bancshares
Bank of America	Wells Fargo
Capital One	Woodforest Financial
Cullen/Frost Bankers	

Income Statement   FYE: December 31

	ASSETS ($ mil.)	NET INCOME ($ mil.)	INCOME AS % OF ASSETS	EMPLOYEES
12/18	2,267	21	0.9%	454
12/17	1,963	14	0.7%	407
12/16	1,828	12	0.7%	397
12/15	1,683	10	0.6%	—
12/14	1,334	10	0.7%	—
Annual Growth	14.2%	20.7%	—	—

2018 Year-End Financials

Debt ratio: 1.00%	No. of shares (mil.): 12
Return on equity: 9.00%	Dividends
Cash ($ mil.): 51	Yield: 2.0%
Current ratio: —	Payout: 41.0%
Long-term debt ($ mil.): —	Market value ($ mil.): 353

	STOCK PRICE ($) FY Close	P/E High/Low		PER SHARE ($) Earnings	Dividends	Book Value
12/18	30.00	20	16	2.00	1.00	21.00
12/17	31.00	25	20	1.00	0.00	19.00
12/16	27.00	—	—	1.00	1.00	16.00
12/15	27.00	—	—	1.00	1.00	15.00
12/14	27.00	—	—	1.00	2.00	14.00
Annual Growth	3.0%	—	—	9.1%	(20.5%)	10.2%

Halliburton Company

One of the largest oilfield services companies in the world Halliburton serves the global upstream oil and gas industry with a broad array of products and services. It manufactures drill bits and other downhole and completion tools provides pressure pumping services locates hydrocarbons and manages geological data drills new wells and optimizes production once the well is operational. The company maintains advantages in the highly competitive market by combining tried-and-true well drilling and optimization techniques with high-tech analysis and modeling software. North America accounts for about 60% of company sales.

Operations

Halliburton operates two business segments: Completion & Production and Drilling & Evaluation.

The Completion and Production segment the core business of the company accounting for 65% of annual sales provides well hole cementing stimulation intervention pressure control specialty chemicals artificial lift and completion services. This segment comprises several product service lines such as Production Enhancement Pipeline & Process Services Production Solutions Artificial Life and Multi-chem.

The Drilling and Evaluation segment (35% of revenue) offers field and reservoir modeling drilling evaluation and wellbore placement services and technology that enable clients to model measure drill and optimize their well construction activities. Product service lines in this segment include Drill Bits and Services Wireline and Perforating Testing and Subsea Baroid (drilling fluid solutions) Sperry Drilling (well bore services) Landmark Software and Services and Consulting and Project Management.

Geographic Reach

Houston TX-headquartered Halliburton has operations stretching from the North Sea to Southeast Asia spanning some 80 countries. Its Completion and Production segment has operations in Arbroath UK; Johor Bahru Malaysia; and Louisiana US. Drilling and Evaluation segment has offices in Alvarado and The Woodlands Texas; and Nisku Canada.

North America (mostly US) accounts for some 60% of Halliburton's revenues. Middle East and Asia bring in an additional 20% of revenue.

Sales and Marketing

Halliburton serves national international and independent upstream energy companies engaged in the exploration and production of oil & gas commodities. Most of its services and products are marketed through its own servicing and sales organizations.

Financial Performance

Like most companies in the oil and gas industry Halliburton's revenue fell in the aftermath of the oil price downturn of 2014. From a high of $33 billion in 2014 revenue halved to under $16 billion in 2016 before recovering in the following three years.

In 2018 the company generated $23.9 billion in revenue a 16% increase from the $20.6 billion generated in 2017 primarily coming from better results in the pressure pumping services drilling activity and artificial lift in North America as well as drilling activity in Southeast Asia. Completion and Production saw sales rise by 22%.

Net income emerged from the red as Halliburton posted $1.6 billion in profits in 2018 compared to $463 million in losses for 2017. Three factors led to this year-over-year climb: $2.3 billion reduction in cost of services $974 million reduction in income tax provisions and $382 million reduction in impairment charges.

The company's cash and cash equivalents fell by $329 million ending 2018 with $2.0 billion on hand. Cash from operations generated $3.1 billion while cash from investing used $1.9 billion. Financing activities used a further $1.4 billion.

Strategy

Halliburton is shrinking its operations to match reduced growth projections for 2019. It is focused on improving drilling margins and reducing start-up costs of new contracts by increasing equipment utilization and expanding surface efficiency model.

Facing customer budget constraints and offtake capacity limitations in the market (an agreement by buyers to purchase portions of the producer's future production) Halliburton has focused on driving down operating costs of its most efficient customers while helping them boost production. The company is also converting its hydraulic fracturing fleet to newer pumps to support increased efficiencies once deployed at customer sites.

However bottlenecks at the Permian Basin affected the company's performance in 2018 (a bottleneck is created when oil production runs ahead of pipeline capacity). The barrels sold of oil sold were sold at deep discounts. For Halliburton this means slower drilling and completion rates by producers creating a lack of demand.

Even if newer pipelines (scheduled for late-2019) fix the capacity problem a bigger concern is the slowing productivity gains in Permian wells casting a long-term doubt of the basin's growth potential. To overcome such challenges Halliburton may need to develop even more advanced fracking techniques rather than just relying on longer lateral wells and pumping in sand.

Mergers and Acquisitions

In 2018 Halliburton purchased Texas-based Athlon Solutions a leading provider of specialty water and process treatment chemicals customized engineering solutions and services. The acquisition added to Halliburton's Multi-Chem business line. It also gave Halliburton access to its first chemical manufacturing plant with full reaction and blending capabilities.

A year earlier Halliburton acquired Tulsa OK-based Summit ESP a leading provider of electric submersible pump technology and services. The acquisition added to Halliburton's Artificial Lift product suite.

Company Background

Halliburton got its start in 1919 as the Better Method Oil Well Cementing Company. The company's first assignment was to use cement to hold a steel pipe in a well which kept oil out of the water table strengthen well walls and reduce the risk of explosions. This method was patented in 1924 as the company incorporated in Oklahoma as the Halliburton Oil Well Cementing Company.

The company grew through acquisitions since the 1940s. After the 1973 Arab oil embargo Halliburton benefited from the surge in global oil exploration and later as drilling costs surged it became a leader in well stimulation.

Halliburton served the US military in Iraq and Afghanistan.

HISTORY

Halliburton got its start in 1919 as the Better Method Oil Well Cementing Company. The company's first assignment was to use cement to hold a steel pipe in a well which kept oil out of the water table strengthen well walls and reduce the risk of explosions. This method was patented in 1924 as the company incorporated in Oklahoma as the Halliburton Oil Well Cementing Company.

The company grew through acquisitions between the 1950s and the 1970s. In 1962 it bought Houston construction giant Brown & Root an expert in offshore platforms. After the 1973 Arab oil embargo Halliburton benefited from the surge in global oil exploration and later as drilling costs surged it became a leader in well stimulation.

In the 1990s Halliburton expanded abroad entering Russia in 1991 China in 1993 and Germany in 1995. The company is known to have won many US military contracts through the former US Vice President Dick Cheney especially in Iraq and Afghanistan.

The company realigned its work into Eastern and Western Hemisphere operations in 2006 and in 2007 divided its service offerings into two divisions: Completion and Production and Drilling and Evaluation.

EXECUTIVES

Evp Administration And Chief Human Resources Officer, Lawrence J. Pope, age 50, $535,000 total compensation
Evp And General Counsel, Robb L. Voyles, age 61
President Eastern Hemisphere, Joseph D. (Joe) Rainey, age 62, $809,950 total compensation
President Western Hemisphere, James S. (Jim) Brown, age 64, $873,000 total compensation
President And Ceo, Jeffrey A. (Jeff) Miller, age 55, $970,000 total compensation
Evp And Cfo, Christopher T. (Chris) Weber, age 46
Evp Global Business Lines, Eric Carre
Vp Technology, Greg Powers
Svp And Cio, Ken Braud
Regional Vice President Apac, Rao Abdullah
Vice President Mergers And Acquisitions, Michael Cheeseman
Global Account Vice President, Edmond Durre
Vp And Treasurer, Timothy Mckeon
Vp Production Enhancement, Richard Gonzalez
Account Vice President, Carl Shaw
Vice President Of Artificial Lift, Chuck Ervin
Vp Global Business Development, Bill Sanstrom

Vice President Of Manufacturing, James Shevchek
Vice President Australasia, Michael Segura
Vice President Director Of Information Technology Risk Management, Ronald Higginbotham
Vice President And Chief Ethics And Compliance Officer, Jeffrey Spalding
Chairman, David J. (Dave) Lesar, age 66
Auditors: KPMG LLP

LOCATIONS

HQ: Halliburton Company
3000 North Sam Houston Parkway East, Houston, TX 77032
Phone: 281 871-2699
Web: www.halliburton.com

2018 Sales

	$ mil.	% of total
North America	14,431	60
Middle East/Asia	4,554	19
Europe/Africa/CIS	2,945	12
Latin America	2,065	9
Total	**23,995**	**100**

PRODUCTS/OPERATIONS

2018 Sales

	$ mil.	% of total
Completion and Production	15,973	67
Drilling and Evaluation	8,022	33
Total	**23,995**	**100**

2018 Sales

	$ mil.	% of total
Services	18,444	77
Product sales	5,551	23
Total	**23,995**	**100**

Areas of Expertise

Areas of Expertise
Clean Energy
Deepwater
Heavy Oil
High Pressure/Temperature
Mature Fields
Unconventional Resources

Selected Products and Services

Artificial Lift
Cementing
Consulting
Coring
Drill Bits
Drilling
Fluid Services
Formation Evaluation
Hole Enlargement
Pipeline & Process Services
Project Management
Real Time Services
Reservoir Testing / Analysis
Sand Control
Wellbore Service Tools
Software and Services
Stimulation
Subsea
Well Completions
Well Intervention
Wireline and Perforating

Selected Brands

Baroid
Landmark
Multi-Chem
Pinnacle
Sperry Drilling

COMPETITORS

Baker Hughes	RPC
McDermott	Schlumberger
National Oilwell Varco	TechnipFMC

HISTORICAL FINANCIALS

Company Type: Public

Income Statement				FYE: December 31
	REVENUE ($ mil.)	NET INCOME ($ mil.)	NET PROFIT MARGIN	EMPLOYEES
12/18	23,995	1,656	6.9%	60,000
12/17	20,620	(463)	—	55,000
12/16	15,887	(5,763)	—	50,000
12/15	23,633	(671)	—	65,000
12/14	32,870	3,500	10.6%	80,000
Annual Growth	**(7.6%)**	**(17.1%)**		**(6.9%)**

2018 Year-End Financials

Debt ratio: 40.00%
Return on equity: 19.00%
Cash ($ mil.): 2,008
Current ratio: 2.00
Long-term debt ($ mil.): 10,421
No. of shares (mil.): 871
Dividends
Yield: 3.0%
Payout: 38.0%
Market value ($ mil.): 23,151

	STOCK PRICE ($) FY Close	P/E High/Low		PER SHARE ($)		
				Earnings	Dividends	Book Value
12/18	27.00	30	13	2.00	1.00	11.00
12/17	49.00	—	—	(1.00)	1.00	10.00
12/16	54.00	—	—	(7.00)	1.00	11.00
12/15	34.00	—	—	(1.00)	1.00	18.00
12/14	39.00	18	9	4.00	1.00	19.00
Annual Growth	**(9.3%)**		**—**	**(17.7%)**	**3.4%**	**(13.1%)**

Hancock Whitney Corp

Hancock Whitney is the holding company of Hancock Whitney Bank which has nearly 200 branches and more than 260 ATMs throughout the Gulf South from Florida to Texas. The community-oriented bank offers traditional and online products and services such as deposit accounts treasury management and investment brokerage services and loans to commercial small business and retail customers. The company also provides trust and investment management services to retirement plans corporations and individuals as well as discount investment brokerage services annuity and life insurance products and consumer financing services. Formerly Hancock Holding Company Hancock Whitney consolidated its two brands (Whitney Bank and Hancock Bank) in 2018 and changed its name.

EXECUTIVES

President Ceo And Director, John M. Hairston, age 56, $707,000 total compensation
Coo, D. Shane Loper, age 53, $400,000 total compensation
Cfo, Michael M. Achary, age 58, $400,000 total compensation
President Whitney Bank, Joseph S. Exnicios, age 63, $375,000 total compensation
Chief Credit Officer Whitney Bank, Suzanne C. Thomas, age 64
Chief Credit Risk Officer, Samuel B. Kendricks, age 59
Chief Investment Officer, David J. Lundgren
Executive Vice President General Counsel Corporate Secretary, Joy Phillips
Vice President And Private Banker, Larry Cuervo
Senior Vice President Financial And Estate Planner, Emile Koury
Assistant Vice President, Kim Gibson

Assistant Vice President, Jimmy Campbell

Assistant Vice President Technology, Roland Pittman

Vice President Project Manager Enterprise Project Office, Heather Argent

Vice President Senior Business Banker, Kai Sonnenschein

Assistant Vice President Merchant Services Sales Specialist, Lisa Parks

Assistant Vice President And Trust Officer, Kevin Peyton

Vice President, Rachel Nunez

Vice President Retirement Plan Services, Amy Grace

Assistant Vice President, Katie Widdows

Vice President Social Media And Public Relations, Janel Evans

Vice President And Business Banker, Mike Cadden

Vice President Relationship Manager, Mark Menard

Chairman, James B. Estabrook, age 75

Auditors: PricewaterhouseCoopers LLP

LOCATIONS

HQ: Hancock Whitney Corp
Hancock Whitney Plaza,, 2510 14th Street, Gulfport, MS 39501
Phone: 228 868-4000
Web: www.hancockbank.com

PRODUCTS/OPERATIONS

2017 Sales

	$ mil.	% of total
Interest income		
Loans including fees	772	66
Securities	124	11
Other	4	-
Interest expense	(108.3)	-
Non interest income		
Service charges on deposit accounts	83	7
Bank card and ATM fees	54	5
Trust fees	45	4
Investment and annuity fees	21	2
Secondary mortgage market operations	15	1
Insurance commissions and fees	3	-
Other	50	4
Total	**1,063**	**100**

Selected Services

Banking
Checking
Credit Cards
Currency Exchange
Home Equity Loans and Lines
Investment Services
Investments
Loans & Credit
Mobile Banking
Mortgage
Online & Mobile Banking
Online Banking
Personal Loans and Lines
Savings

COMPETITORS

BancorpSouth
Capital One
First Horizon
IBERIABANK
Investar

MidSouth Bancorp
Regions Financial
Renasant
Trustmark

HISTORICAL FINANCIALS
Company Type: Public

Income Statement — FYE: December 31

	ASSETS ($ mil.)	NET INCOME ($ mil.)	INCOME AS % OF ASSETS	EMPLOYEES
12/18	28,236	324	1.1%	3,933
12/17	27,336	216	0.8%	3,887
12/16	23,975	149	0.6%	3,724
12/15	22,839	131	0.6%	3,921
12/14	20,747	176	0.8%	3,794
Annual Growth	**8.0%**	**16.5%**	**—**	**0.9%**

2018 Year-End Financials

Debt ratio: 1.00%
Return on equity: 11.00%
Cash ($ mil.): 494
Current ratio: —
Long-term debt ($ mil.): —

No. of shares (mil.): 86
Dividends
Yield: 3.0%
Payout: 31.0%
Market value ($ mil.): 2,968

	STOCK PRICE ($) FY Close	P/E High/Low		PER SHARE ($) Earnings	Dividends	Book Value
12/18	35.00	15	9	4.00	1.00	36.00
12/17	50.00	21	17	2.00	1.00	34.00
12/16	43.00	24	11	2.00	1.00	32.00
12/15	25.00	20	15	2.00	1.00	31.00
12/14	31.00	18	14	2.00	1.00	31.00
Annual Growth	**3.1%**	**—**	**—**	**15.4%**	**1.5%**	**4.0%**

HanesBrands Inc

Hanesbrands Inc. is the world's largest marketer of basic apparel. It designs manufactures and sells bras hosiery men's underwear socks and other intimate apparel under brand names such as Hanes Champion Bali Just My Size L'eggs Playtex and Wonderbra. In the US Hanesbrands sells more units of intimate apparel than any other company and is the leading brand in several basic apparel markets in Europe and Australia. Hanesbrands also makes basic outerwear such as T-shirts and licensed logo apparel for college bookstores under the Champion and Gear for Sports labels and has license agreements with Donna Karan and Polo Ralph Lauren. The lineup is sold to wholesalers major retail chains (Walmart and Target) and through Hanesbrands' own outlet stores and Internet sites. Operations in the US account for more than two-thirds of the company's total sales.

Operations

Hanesbrands divides its operations into three segments: Innerwear Activewear and International.

Innerwear accounts for about 35% of revenue and includes core apparel products including men's underwear women's panties children's underwear and socks and intimate apparel such as bras and shapewear. Major brands in the Innerwear segment include Hanes Champion Maidenform Bali Just My Size Playtex and products sold under license agreements with Polo Ralph Lauren Donna Karan and DKNY.

The International segment includes innerwear activewear hosiery and home goods products sold outside the US. This segment represents about 35% of the company's total sales. Major brands in this segment that are not marketed in the US are Bonds DIM Sheridan Bras N Things Nur Die/Nur Der Lovable Berlei Abanderado Shock Absorber Zorba Explorer Sol y Oro and Bellinda.

Activewear (about 25%) makes and sells shirts fleece items sports bras thermals and teamwear under the brands Champion Hanes Alternative Gear for Sports Just My Size and Hanes Beefy-T.

Geographic Reach

Based in Winston?Salem NC Hanesbrands sells its products globally ringing up almost 70% of its sales in the Americas region followed by Asia Pacific and Europe each generating about 15% of total sales. The company operates some 45 distribution centers and about 50 manufacturing facilities in 40 countries. It also operates close to 240 retail and direct outlet stores in the US and Puerto Rico and nearly 700 internationally (outside the US).

Sales and Marketing

Hanesbrands is highly dependent on its two largest customers Walmart and Target each accounting for about 15% of total sales. Mass merchandise stores are vital to the company's performance accounting for about a third of Hanesbrands' revenue. Hanesbrands also allies with mid-tier stores including Kohl's J. C. Penney Macy's and Belk which focus on higher-income consumers and the sale of apparel rather than other consumer goods. Its L'eggs and Hanes brand underwear are also sold in food drug and variety stores. Hanesbrands also sells apparel to the US military for sale to soldiers and through discount chains such as Dollar General. About 65% of the company's revenue are wholesale sales to retailers and 35% comes from consumer-direct sales through the company's own stores and e-commerce sites.

Advertising expenses average about $150 million annually.

Financial Performance

Hanesbrands' annual sales and profits have been growing over the past few years as new brand acquisitions have spurred higher sales in more geographic markets. Net sales for fiscal 2018 amounted to $6.8 billion a more than 5% increase from $6.5 billion the previous year. The acquisition of Bras N Things in 2018 and Alternative Apparel in 2017 added $177 million to the company's top line in 2018. Other growth factors were higher global sales of its Champion brand and favorable currency exchange rates in the International business.

Net income was $553.1 million in 2018 comparable with past years excluding 2017. In 2017 net income dipped to $61.9 million due to a large provisional charge of $435 million for income tax expense that year (due to the Tax Cuts and Jobs Act).

Cash at the end of fiscal 2018 was $433.0 million an increase of $11.5 million from the prior year. Cash from operations contributed $643.4 million to the coffers while investing activities used $418.7 million mainly for business acquisitions and purchases of property and equipment. Financing activities used another $200.5 million for loan payments and dividends to stockholders.

Strategy

Hanesbrands continues to follow its Innovate-to-Elevate strategy that involves leveraging its brand power manufacturing platforms and low-cost global supply chain. The company has also been expanding its global business by acquiring top brands in its less-tapped markets. Going forward the company will focus on fast-growing key geographies outside the US including Europe Australasia Japan Canada Mexico China and Brazil.

Key to Hanesbrands' success is the ability to react to changing customer needs and industry trends. Using insights in consumer demand in the basic apparel industry the company develops new products within its existing lines and modifies core products to make them more appealing. The company focuses on identifying 5- to 10-year long-term megatrends and incorporating those trends in its manufacturing platforms. The company targets platform innovations such as tagless apparel temperature-control fabrics and odor protection technology that can be leveraged across brands product categories business segments and geographies.

To drive sales growth the company is focusing on promoting its Champion brand apparel especially in Europe and Asia and its business through consumer-direct channels such as its own stores and online channels.

Hanesbrands' large scale of operations gives it a competitive advantage. The company's global supply chain spans both the Western and Eastern hemispheres and includes a combination of owned contracted and sourced manufacturing operations that provide a reliable source of supply and reduces product cost. Plans are in place for further optimization in the size scale and production capabilities of its supply chain.

Mergers and Acquisitions

In early 2018 Hanesbrands acquired BNT Holdco Pty Limited (Bras N Things) a leading specialty retailer and online seller of intimate apparel in Australia New Zealand and South Africa for $389.2 million. The acquisition complements Hanesbrands' consumer-directed sales strategy and allows for greater expansion in the Australasia region.

EXECUTIVES

Ceo, Gerald W. Evans, age 59, $912,500 total compensation

Group President Innerwear Americas, W. Howard Upchurch, age 55, $525,000 total compensation

Cfo, Barry A. Hytinen, age 44

President Chief Supply Chain And Information Technology Officer, Michael E. Faircloth, age 53, $510,000 total compensation

President Activewear, John T. Marsh, age 53

Vice President Marketing, Richard Heller

Vice President Government And Trade Relations, Jerry Cook

National Sales Manager, Ian Ritchie

Vice President Commodity Risk Management, Vern Tyson

Vice President And Deputy General Counsel Commercial, Lynne Fuller-Andrews

Vice President, John Whitaker

Vice President Of Logistics, James Francis

Vice President Sales, Sonya Hemingway-Marion

Vice President Operations, Marilyn Hanes

Vice President Textiles E Hilos, Keith Huskins

Vice President Of Global Sc Finance, Craig Swecker

Vice President Of It, Cindy Miller

Vice President Investor Relations, Tc Robillard

Vice President Brand Management, Donna Hansen

Vice President Corporate Social Responsibility, Christopher Fox

Chairman, Richard A. (Rich) Noll, age 62

Board Of Directors, David Singer

Board Member, Robert Moran

Auditors: PricewaterhouseCoopers LLP

LOCATIONS

HQ: HanesBrands Inc
1000 East Hanes Mill Road, Winston-Salem, NC 27105
Phone: 336 519-8080
Web: www.Hanes.com

2018 Sales

	$ mil.	% of total
Americas	4,658	68
Asia Pacific	1,130	17
Europe	987	15
Other	29	-
Total	**6,804**	**100**

PRODUCTS/OPERATIONS

2018 Sales

	$ mil.	% of total
Innerwear	2,380	35
Activewear	1,792	26
International	2,344	35
Other	288	4
Total	**6,804**	**100**

Selected Brands

Bali
C9 by Champion
Champion
Gear for Sports
Just My Size
Hanes
L'eggs
Maidenform
Playtex
Sol y Oro
Wonderbra
Zorba

COMPETITORS

Converse	The Gap
Fruit of the Loom	Triumph Apparel
Gildan Activewear	Under Armour
Jockey International	Victoria's Secret
L Brands	Stores
NIKE	adidas
PUMA SE	

HISTORICAL FINANCIALS

Company Type: Public

Income Statement   FYE: December 29

	REVENUE ($ mil.)	NET INCOME ($ mil.)	NET PROFIT MARGIN	EMPLOYEES
12/18	6,804	553	8.1%	68,000
12/17	6,471	62	1.0%	67,200
12/16*	6,028	539	8.9%	67,800
01/16	5,732	429	7.5%	65,300
01/15	5,325	405	7.6%	59,500
Annual Growth	**6.3%**	**8.1%**	**—**	**3.4%**

*Fiscal year change

2018 Year-End Financials

Debt ratio: 55.00%
Return on equity: 67.00%
Cash ($ mil.): 433
Current ratio: 2.00
Long-term debt ($ mil.): 3,534

No. of shares (mil.): 361
Dividends
  Yield: 0.0%
  Payout: 39.0%
Market value ($ mil.): 4,405

	STOCK PRICE ($) FY Close	P/E High/Low		PER SHARE ($) Earnings	Dividends	Book Value
12/18	12.00	15	8	2.00	1.00	3.00
12/17	21.00	151	112	0.00	1.00	2.00
12/16*	22.00	22	15	1.00	0.00	3.00
01/16	29.00	120	25	1.00	1.00	3.00
01/15	111.00	86	48	1.00	0.00	5.00
Annual Growth	**(42.4%)**			**—**	**3.5%**	**18.9%(12.7%)**

*Fiscal year change

Hanmi Financial Corp.

Hanmi Financial owns Hanmi Bank which serves Korean-American and other ethnic communities in California Colorado Georgia Illinois New Jersey New York Texas Virginia and Washington. The company which holds $5.5 billion in assets offers traditional banking services to small and midsized businesses from about 40 branches and eight loan offices. Real estate loans — including for retail hospitality mixed-use apartment office industrial gas station faith-based facility and warehouse properties — account for about 80% of its loan portfolio; commercial and industrial loans and leases receivable make up most of the rest.

Operations

Hanmi Financial originates real estate loans (including commercial construction and residential property) commercial and industrial loans (including commercial term commercial lines of credit and international) equipment lease financing consumer loans and Small Business Administration (SBA) loans. The bank also offers traditional deposit products including checking savings negotiable order of withdrawal (NOW) and money market accounts and CDs.

Hanmi's $4.6 billion loan portfolio is made up mostly of real estate loans — particularly commercial property loans including retail (about 20% of total portfolio) hospitality (20%) and other loans (30%). Other loans include loans for mixed-use apartment office industrial gas station faith-based facility and warehouse properties. Residential property loans comprise around 10%.

Commercial and industrial loans and leases receivable together make up about 15% of the bank's portfolio.

Geographic Reach

Headquartered in a penthouse suite on Los Angeles' Wilshire Boulevard Hanmi Financial has one bank branch in each of New Jersey New York and Virginia; some five branches in Illinois; about 10 branches in Texas; and around 25 branches in California. The majority of its loan and deposit concentration is in Southern California.

Sales and Marketing

Hanmi Financial's lending is concentrated in real estate loans commercial loans and leases and Small Business Administration (SBA) loans for small and middle market businesses in California Texas Illinois and New York — primarily among Korean-American and other multi-ethnic communities.

Financial Performance

Since 2013 Hanmi Financial has grown its revenue and net income by about 60% and 40% respectively thanks to increasing net interest income. But the company also depleted its cash stores by about 15% and more than doubled its long-term debt in that time mostly due to Federal Home Loan Bank advances in 2016.

The bank's revenue increased 9% in 2017 compared with 2016 reaching $210.2 million. Higher interest and fees on loans and leases drove the improvement which was partially offset by higher expense for interest on deposits. Average loans and leases and the percentage of loans and leases in Hanmi's mix of interest-earning assets both increased in 2017.

Net income slipped 3% to $54.7 million owing mostly to an increase in the bank's income tax provision which included a $3.9 million charge for a one-time revaluation adjustment connected with the Tax Cuts and Jobs Act (TCJA).

Hanmi added $6.6 million to its cash stores in 2017 for a total of $153.8 million. Operations and financings provided $79.9 million and $445.1 million respectively. Investment activity used $518.4 million.

Strategy

Hanmi Financial is working to diversify its loan portfolio to reduce its reliance on commercial real estate and increase its composition of leases and commercial industrial and residential real estate loans. Since 2014 the company has increased the proportion of its portfolio made up of leases and residential real estate while maintaining the proportion of commercial and industrial loans.

After a review of its cost structure and operating efficiency in 2018 the company is moderating its growth expectations lowering its non-interest expenses and consolidating about 10% of its branches.

Hanmi also hired a Chief Technology officer in 2018 to implement a strategy to improve the company's use of technology including using it to increase efficiency of regulatory compliance activities (for which the company heavily relies on human capital).

Mergers and Acquisitions

In its first foray outside of California in late 2013 Hanmi agreed to acquire Central Bancorp Inc. the parent of Texas-based United Central Bank. United Central Bank serves multi-ethnic communities in Texas Illinois Virginia California New York and New Jersey through some two dozen branches. Once the acquisition is complete Hanmi will have about 50 branches and two loan production offices serving a broad range of ethnic communities in California Texas Illinois New York New Jersey Virginia and Georgia.

Company Background

Hanmi Financial was founded in 1982.

EXECUTIVES

Sevp And Coo, Bonita I. (Bonnie) Lee, age 56
Chief Compliance And Bsa Officer, Jean Lim
Evp And Cfo, Michael W. McCall
President Ceo And Director, Chong Guk (C. G.) Kum
Evp And Chief Credit Officer, Randall G. Ewig
Evp And Chief Administrative Officer, Greg D. Kim
Evp And Chief Banking Officer, Peter Yang
Evp And Chief Lending Officer, Anthony Kim
Assistant Vice President, Sue Kim
Assistant Vice President Compliance Officer, Michael Santiago
Assistant Vice President Treasury Management, Debby Sassoon
Vice President, Maheboob Kurani
Assistant Vice President Andamp; Credit Analyst, Daniel Park
First Vice President And Branch Manager, Annie Chung
Vice President Human Resources Officer, Ashley Sowa
Avp And Sba Closing Officer, Liz Choe
Senior Vice President And Operations Administrator, Nancy Lee
Vp Hr Business Partner, Kathy Kim
Vice President Human Resources Officer, Lan Nguyen
Vice President And Business Development Officer, Yusin Lee
Chairman, Joseph K. Rho, age 78
Board Member, Anna Chung
Board Member, David Yang
Auditors: Crowe LLP

LOCATIONS

HQ: Hanmi Financial Corp.
3660 Wilshire Boulevard, Penthouse Suite A, Los Angeles, CA 90010
Phone: 213 382-2200
Web: www.hanmi.com

PRODUCTS/OPERATIONS

2017 Sales

	$ mil.	% of total
Net interest income	177	84
Non-interest income	33	16
Total	**210**	**100**

COMPETITORS

Bank of America	Far East National Bank
Broadway Financial	Hope Bancorp
Cathay General Bancorp	JPMorgan Chase
East West Bancorp	Woori

HISTORICAL FINANCIALS

Company Type: Public

Income Statement   FYE: December 31

	ASSETS ($ mil.)	NET INCOME ($ mil.)	INCOME AS % OF ASSETS	EMPLOYEES
12/18	5,502	58	1.1%	635
12/17	5,210	55	1.0%	642
12/16	4,701	56	1.2%	638
12/15	4,235	54	1.3%	622
12/14	4,232	50	1.2%	699
Annual Growth	6.8%	3.8%	—	(2.4%)

2018 Year-End Financials

Debt ratio: 3.00%	No. of shares (mil.): 31
Return on equity: 10.00%	Dividends
Cash ($ mil.): 155	Yield: 5.0%
Current ratio: —	Payout: 53.0%
Long-term debt ($ mil.): —	Market value ($ mil.): 609

	STOCK PRICE ($) FY Close	P/E High/Low	PER SHARE ($) Earnings	Dividends	Book Value
12/18	20.00	18 10	2.00	1.00	18.00
12/17	30.00	21 15	2.00	1.00	17.00
12/16	35.00	20 11	2.00	1.00	16.00
12/15	24.00	16 12	2.00	0.00	15.00
12/14	22.00	16 12	2.00	0.00	14.00
Annual Growth	(2.5%)	— —	3.5%	36.1%	5.9%

Hanover Insurance Group Inc

Founded in 1852 The Hanover Insurance Group is one of the oldest property/casualty insurance holding companies around. Through Hanover Insurance Company the group provides personal and commercial automobile homeowners and workers' compensation coverage as well as commercial multi-peril insurance and professional liability coverage. The group sells its products through a network of independent agents throughout the US; Michigan Massachusetts and New York account for about 40% of its business. In Michigan it operates as Citizens Insurance Company. Hanover's Opus Investment Management subsidiary provides institutional investment management services.

Operations

Hanover's primary domestic segments are Commercial Lines Personal Lines and Other while its international segment is Chaucer.

Primarily through the Hanover Insurance Company unit Hanover writes more than $5 billion in gross premiums each year. Commercial policies account for nearly half of annual revenues while personal lines account for 30%. Former subsidiary Chaucer operated two Lloyd's of London syndicates which manage and underwrite global property/casualty policies; the subsidiary also offered specialty insurance and reinsurance coverage. In late 2018 Hanover sold Chaucer which generated about 20% of the group's revenues.

Hanover's Other segment comprises Opus Investment Management which provides investment advisory services to affiliates; it also manages assets for unaffiliated clients including insurance companies retirement plans and foundations.

Geographic Reach

Hanover is licensed to sell property/casualty insurance in all 50 US states and the District of Columbia. It actively markets commercial policies in 37 states and personal lines policies in 18 states. The group is highly dependent on three states: Michigan is the company's largest market accounting for some 20% of all commercial and personal lines. Massachusetts and New York account for about 10% each. Altogether US operations account for some 85% of annual premiums.

In addition to its headquarters in Worcester Massachusetts the company has more than 40 regional offices in cities across the US and about 10 overseas locations. It has an office in London and other global offices for sales underwriting and claims processing activities as well as offices of acquired companies in select nations.

Sales and Marketing

Hanover sells through a network of agents and brokers including about 2100 agent partners. The company's customers include individuals families and businesses.

Financial Performance

Hanover's revenues have been slightly erratic over the past five years. In 2017 revenue increased 5% to $5.2 billion as premiums and net investment income rose. Commercial lines net premiums grew by 4% that year while personal lines net premiums written grew by 8%. Chaucer net premiums written increased 4% as well.

Net income rose 20% to $186.2 million that year thanks primarily to the higher revenue and an increase in operating income. However Hanover's bottom line was impacted by catastrophe losses totaling some $382.6 million (versus $125.1 million in 2016). Hurricanes Harvey Irma and Maria wildfires in California and a heavy windstorm in the Midwest all contributed to the company's catastrophe losses.

Operating cash flow declined 5% to $704.6 million in 2017.

Strategy

One of Hanover's strategies is to build partnerships with other insurers and agents while expanding its product offerings and geographic presence beyond its three historical core markets of Massachusetts New York and Michigan. The company pursues growth in a conservative manner to preserve long-term financial and operational stability. It also intends to build on its agent-centered distribution strategy by expanding its agency network into new geographic markets. In terms of personal lines the firm is making a push to convert more of its customers into multi-policy consumers; more than 80% of its personal lines customers already fall into that bucket. In addition Hanover is working to increase efficiencies through technology upgrades.

Written premiums are balanced between personal and commercial products but competition is fierce in personal insurance so the company has placed more emphasis on expanding its commercial offerings. It does this by deepening its relationships with agents through diverse product offerings.

Wriggling into a niche is one method of expanding and Hanover has moved into several areas of specialty insurance in recent years such as health care and engineering. The company has launched several niche insurance programs such as coverage for not-for-profit youth organizations community services organizations and religious institutions. In 2017 the company launched Hanover Fusion a life sciences product that includes coverage for errors and omissions information security media and content and operations liability. Also that year Chaucer established Chaucer Dublin to write international specialty insurance. And in 2016 Chaucer partnered with another leading insurer AXA to develop specialty business in Africa.

However Hanover sold Chaucer to China Reinsurance in late 2018. It had been exploring strategic alternatives related to the UK unit. Selling Chaucer diminished its geographic diversity though which limits its growth potential.

Mergers and Acquisitions

In 2017 Hanover's international subsidiary Chaucer acquired SLE Holdings a Lloyd's managing general underwriting agency operating in Australia. SLE focuses on the sports entertainment and leisure sectors. The purchase broadened Chaucer's Australian operations as well as widening its specialty product lines. (Hanover sold Chaucer in late 2018.)

HISTORY

In 1842 a group of Worcester Massachusetts businessmen tried to form a mutual life insurance company. After a failed first attempt they succeeded with the help of lobbyist Benjamin Balch. In 1844 the State Mutual Life Assurance Co. of Worcester set up business in the back room of secretary Clarendon Harris' bookstore. The first president was John Davis a US senator. The company issued its first policy in 1845.

In the early years State Mutual reduced risk by issuing policies only for residents of such "civilized" areas as New England New Jersey New York Pennsylvania and Ohio. It also restricted movement requiring policyholders to get permission for travel outside those areas. By the 1850s the company had begun issuing policies in the Midwest (with a 25% premium surcharge) the South (for 30% extra) and California (for a pricey extra $25 per $1000) with a maximum coverage of $5000.

The Civil War was a problem for many insurers who had to decide what to do about Southern policyholders and payment on war-related claims. State Mutual chose to pay out its Northern policyholders' benefits despite the extra cost. In 1896 the firm began offering installment pay-out plans for policyholders concerned that their beneficiaries would fritter away the whole payment.

The first 30 years of the 20th century were for the company a time of growth that was stopped short by the Depression. But despite a great increase in the number of policy loans and surrenders for cash value State Mutual's financial footing remained solid.

After WWII the company entered group insurance and began offering individual sickness and accident coverage. In 1957 it was renamed State Mutual Life Assurance Co. of America. The firm added property/casualty insurance in the late 1950s through alliances with such firms as Worcester Mutual Fire Insurance. During the 1960s State Mutual continued to develop property/casualty buying interests in Hanover Insurance and Citizens Corp.

The firm followed the industrywide shift into financial services in the 1970s adding mutual funds a real estate investment trust and an investment management firm. This trend accelerated in the 1980s and State Mutual began offering financial planning services as well as administrative and other services for the insurance and mutual fund industries (the mutual fund administration operations were sold in 1995). Managing this growth was another story: Its acquisitions left it bloated and disorganized. Technical systems were in disarray by the early 1990s and the agency force had grown to more than 1400. In response the com-

pany began a five-year effort to upgrade systems cut fat and reduce sales positions.

In view of its shifting focus State Mutual became Allmerica Financial in 1992. Three years later it demutualized. In 1997 it bought the 40% of Allmerica Property & Casualty it didn't already own.

EXECUTIVES

Evp General Counsel And Assistant Secretary, J. Kendall Huber, age 64, $498,077 total compensation
Evp And Cfo, Jeffrey M. (Jeff) Farber, age 54, $150,000 total compensation
Svp And Chief Claims Officer, Mark Welzenbach, age 59
President And Ceo, John C. (Jack) Roche, age 55, $470,385 total compensation
Chief Growth Innovation Officer, Richard W. (Dick) Lavey
Chief Investment Officer; President Opus Investment Management, Ann K. Tripp, age 60
Ceo And Chief Underwriting Officer Chaucer, John Fowle, age 49
Chief Technology Innovation Officer, Mark L. Berthiaume, age 62
Evp And Chief Human Resources Officer, Christine Bilotti-Peterson, age 48
Evp Corporate Development And Strategy, Mark L. Keim, age 53
Evp; President Specialty, Bryan J. Salvatore
Vice President Management Liability Of Commercial Lines Business, Helen Savaiano
Vice President And General Auditor, Don Gilbert
Vice President, Charles Kingsbury
Vice President Investor Relations, Oksana Lukasheva
Assistant Vice President Program Director, Dennis Warren
Rvp, George Agyen
Vice President Technology Niche, Anthony Levy
Vice President, Roger Pare
Vice President Corporate Real Estate, James Johnson
Regional Vice President, Scott Betlesky
Assistant Vice President Investment Operations, Michael Pastore
Vice President And Corporate Counsel, Harris Berenson
Vice President Risk Management, Cheryl Nesta
Vice President And Chief Product Officer Personal Lines, Gavin Blair
Vice President Distribution, Michael Lewis
Regional Vice President, Paul Alan Anderson
Avp Network Telecommunications Pc Services Collabo, Steve White
Assistant Vice President Marine Uw Development, Mary Corcoran
Assistant Vice President Allied Healthcare, Eric Paynter
Assistant Vice President Technology, James Marengo
Assistant Vice President Sales Effectiveness Sales Training Field Operations, Larry Kaczmarek
Director Media Relations, Emily Trevallion
Commercial Lines Regional Vice President Michigan, Ryan Vaughn
Assistant Vice President Product Management, Joseph Brophy
Vice President Marketing And Comm., Jennifer F Luisa
Assistant Vice President Property Large Loss, Joe Green
Vice President Of Information Technology, Patty Kularski
Regional Vice President, Gregory L Parr
Regional Vice President, Steve Schaeberle
Assistant Vice President And Financial Officer, Randy Dinjian
Assistant Vice President, Lisa Binnie

Vice President Corporate Communications, Michael Buckley
Assistant Vice President Industry Solutions, Diana Obrian
Assistant Vice President Cl Operations, Julee Gianoulis
Vice President, William Cahill
Assistant Vice President Human Resources, Liz Berry
Assistant Vice President Learning And Development, Jim Gulinello
Vice President Chief Information Security Officer, Brian Haugli
Regional Vice President, Scott Couger
Assistant Vice President, Richard Drake
Assistant Regional Vice President For Nys, Steve Cibelli
Zonal Vice President Pl, Kendra Schenkel
Avp Risk Solutions Field Operations, Wayne Grudzien
Assistant Vice President Human Resources Strategic Business Partner, Kelly Villanueva
Branch Vice President, Michael Sharr
Avp Liability Strategist, Doug Kratzer
Assistant Vice President Enterprise Architecture, Brian Kane
Vice President Product Management, Jeff Berridge
Avp Claims, Matthew Hays
Regional Vice President Nh Vt, Mike Lee
Assistant Vice President Commercial Umbrella, John Lyons
Regional Vice President Cl, Angela Roman-Grimaldi
Vice President Casualty Underwriting Commercial Lines, Coleman Johnson
Vice President Quality And Learning Middle Market, Kim Callanan
Vice President Excess And Surplus Lines, Daniel Kearney
Avp Financial Officer Of Middle Market, Benjamin Selchan
Avp Industry Solutions Construction, Bill Meyer
Regional Vice President, John Scott
Assistant Vice President Head Of Medical Strategy, Helen Weber
Vice President Risk Solutions, Christina Villena
Vice President Small Commercial Renewal Organization, Matt Hudnall
Regional Assistant Vice President Claims, Kevin Pendergast
Vp Corporate Development, Kevin Coyle
Vice President State Management, Matt Hardin
Vice President Operations, Michele Streton
Vice President Distribution Management Professional Lines, Jon Martin
Rvp, Dina Amato
Chairman, Michael P. Angelini, age 76
Auditors: PricewaterhouseCoopers LLP

LOCATIONS

HQ: Hanover Insurance Group Inc
440 Lincoln Street, Worcester, MA 01653
Phone: 508 855-1000   **Fax:** 508 855-6332
Web: www.hanover.com

PRODUCTS/OPERATIONS

2017 Sales

	$ mil.	% of total
Net premiums earned		
Commercial lines	2,400	46
Personal lines	1,581	31
Chaucer	853	16
Net investment income	298	6
Net realized investment gains	24	-
Fees & other	29	1
Total	**5,184**	**100**

Selected Products

Personal Lines
  Auto Insurance
  Companion Products
  Dwelling Fire
  Home Care Services
  Homeowners Insurance
  Identity Integrity
  Umbrella
  Valuable Items
  Watercraft
Small Commercial and Middle Market Core Products
  Business Owner's Policy
  Commercial Automobile
  Commercial Package
  General Liability
  Property
  Umbrella
  Workers' Compensation
Specialized Products
  AIX Specialty Programs
  Commercial Umbrella and Excess
  Healthcare
  Industrial Property Risk
  Management Liability
  Marine (inland and ocean)
  Professional Liability
  Surety (commercial and contract)

COMPETITORS

Alleghany Corporation	Liberty Mutual
Allstate	Markel Insurance
American Automobile	Nationwide
Association (AAA)	Progressive
American Financial	Corporation
Group	State Farm
Auto-Owners Insurance	Travelers Companies
GEICO	USAA

HISTORICAL FINANCIALS

Company Type: Public

Income Statement

FYE: December 31

	ASSETS ($ mil.)	NET INCOME ($ mil.)	INCOME AS % OF ASSETS	EMPLOYEES
12/18	12,400	391	3.2%	4,200
12/17	15,470	186	1.2%	4,600
12/16	14,220	155	1.1%	4,900
12/15	13,791	332	2.4%	4,800
12/14	13,760	282	2.0%	5,100
Annual Growth	(2.6%)	8.5%	—	(4.7%)

2018 Year-End Financials

Debt ratio: 6.00%	No. of shares (mil.): 42
Return on equity: 13.00%	Dividends
Cash ($ mil.): 1,021	Yield: 2.0%
Current ratio: —	Payout: 24.0%
Long-term debt ($ mil.): —	Market value ($ mil.): 4,939

	STOCK PRICE ($) FY Close	P/E High/Low	PER SHARE ($) Earnings	Dividends	Book Value
12/18	117.00	14 11	9.00	2.00	70.00
12/17	108.00	25 18	4.00	2.00	71.00
12/16	91.00	25 20	4.00	2.00	67.00
12/15	81.00	11 9	7.00	2.00	66.00
12/14	71.00	11 8	6.00	2.00	65.00
Annual Growth	13.1%	— —	9.7%	9.9%	1.9%

HarborOne Bancorp Inc (New)

Auditors: Wolf & Company, P.C.

LOCATIONS

HQ: HarborOne Bancorp Inc (New)
  770 Oak Street, Brockton, MA 02301
Phone: 508 895-1000
Web: www.harborone.com

HISTORICAL FINANCIALS

Company Type: Public

Income Statement

FYE: December 31

	ASSETS ($ mil.)	NET INCOME ($ mil.)	INCOME AS % OF ASSETS	EMPLOYEES
12/18	3,653	11	0.3%	658
12/17	2,685	10	0.4%	581
12/16	2,448	6	0.2%	614
12/15	2,163	6	0.3%	387
12/14	2,042	3	0.1%	—
Annual Growth	15.7%	45.1%	—	—

2018 Year-End Financials

Debt ratio: 7.00%	No. of shares (mil.): 33
Return on equity: 3.00%	Dividends
Cash ($ mil.): 106	Yield: —
Current ratio: —	Payout: —
Long-term debt ($ mil.): —	Market value ($ mil.): 517

	STOCK PRICE ($) FY Close	P/E High/Low	PER SHARE ($) Earnings	Dividends	Book Value
12/18	16.00	56 42	0.00	0.00	11.00
12/17	19.00	67 49	0.00	0.00	11.00
12/16	19.00	— —	(0.00)	0.00	10.00
Annual Growth	(4.8%)	— —	—	—	1.7%

Harley-Davidson Inc

Harley-Davidson is a major US motorcycle manufacturer that sells its bikes worldwide through a network of more than 1400 dealers. The company offers heavyweight cruiser and touring models sportbikes and dual models that can be used on-and off-road. Its six families of motorcycles include Touring Trike Softail H-D Street Sportster and its Customer Vehicle Operations (CVO) models. Harley-Davidson also sells attitude with its brand-name products which include a line of riding gear and apparel (MotorClothes). Harley-Davidson Financial Services (HDFS) offers financing to dealers and consumers in the US and Canada. The US generates almost 70% of Harley's revenue.

Operations

Harley operates through two segments. Its core motorcycle manufacturing operations (HDMC) generates more than 85% of revenue each year and Harley-Davidson Financial Services (HDFS) contributes the remainder.

HDMC includes motorcycles parts and accessories general merchandising and licensing. Motorcycles include the cruiser models which focus on styling and owner customization and touring models which feature rider comfort and load ca-

pacity. It makes standard motorcycles; sportbikes which incorporate racing technology aerodynamic styling and low handlebars; and dual models designed for use on public roads as well as for off-highway riding. HDMC's parts and accessories division offers replacement parts and mechanical and cosmetic accessories. The general merchandising division comprises Harley's MotorClothes apparel and riding gear and the licensing division promotes the Harley-Davidson name by allowing its use on a wide range of products.

HDFS offers consumer loans and wholesale financing to dealers for the purchase of Harley-Davidson motorcycles. It also works with certain insurance companies to provide motorcycle insurance and protection products including extended service contracts.

Geographic Reach

Harley-Davidson is based in Milwaukee WI where it houses its corporate offices. Its manufacturing facilities are located in other cities in Wisconsin as well as in Pennsylvania and Missouri. Outside the US Harley's manufacturing plants are in Thailand Brazil India and Australia with regional offices in England and Singapore. Harley also operates a product development center in Wauwatosa WI.

The company generates about 70% of sales in the US.

Sales and Marketing

Harley-Davidson's products are marketed to retail customers worldwide through digital channels traditional promotions and advertising and by experiential activities with independent distributors. To attract customers the company participates in motorcycle rallies special motorcycle events races music festivals and sporting events. It also sponsors events and rides through Harley Owners Group (H.O.G.) where it promotes Harley-Davidson products.

The company spends about $145 million on advertising annually.

Financial Performance

Harley-Davidson's revenue has remained static for the last several years hovering around the $6 billion mark. The company's profits have tumbled 37% over the last five years although the company saw a slight uptick in 2018.

Revenue in 2018 was $5.7 billion a modest 1% increase compared with $5.6 billion in 2017 but still well below previous years' figures. However operating income for the Motorcycles segment was down $184.4 million in 2018 due to lower wholesale motorcycle shipments and higher tariffs on European and Chinese exports. Dealer sales were also down more than 6% worldwide and US retail sales decreased by more than 10% as well. This was partially offset by higher operating income in the Financial Services segment?up by $15.9 million.

Net income increased 2% to $531.5 million in 2018 from $521.8 million in 2017. The provision for income taxes was lower by $186.9 million in 2018 but this was offset by $93.4 million in restructuring expenses.

Cash at the end of fiscal 2018 was $1.3 billion an increase of $513.5 million from the prior year. Cash from operations contributed $1.2 billion to the coffers while investing activities used $622.3 million mainly for capital expenditures. Financing activities used another $14.8 million for loan payments and the company's stock repurchase program.

Strategy

Some key points in Harley's long-term strategy include launching 100 new motorcycles by 2027 developing a broader customer base and improving dealer performance. The company has also introduced a multi-year manufacturing optimization plan to reduce costs which includes consolidating its assembly plant in Kansas City MO to its York PA plant and closing its wheel operations in Australia.

In 2019 Harley introduced LiveWire its first electric motorcycle which it plans to begin selling during the second half of the year. The company is also developing a new middle-weight platform for adventure touring bikes custom motorcycles and streetfighter models.

To reach more customers in international markets the company in 2018 opened more than 20 Harley-Davidson apparel stores throughout Asia and 55 new international dealerships worldwide. The company increased e-commerce sales by more than 30 percent in 2018 with its product debut on Amazon in the US and T-Mall in China.

Harley is also working with its dealers to improve the customer experience and increase conversion to sales. It's establishing performance-oriented incentives and training for general managers and sales staff. It is also implementing more advanced analytics to generate targeted leads. With more consumers shopping online the company aims to deliver an integrated in-store and online experience.

Mergers and Acquisitions

In early 2019 Harley-Davidson acquired StaCyc maker of the EDRIVE electric-powered two-wheelers specifically designed for kids. The acquisition falls in line with Harley's plan to continue developing electric motorcycles. Harley already sells the StaCyc EDRIVE at about 30 of its dealerships. The company believes the StaCyc provides an introduction to motorcycling to the youngest riders.

Company Background

In 1903 William Harley and the Davidson brothers (Walter William and Arthur) of Milwaukee sold their first Harley-Davidson motorcycle which essentially was a motor-assisted bicycle that required pedaling uphill. Demand was high and most sold before leaving the factory. Six years later the company debuted its trademark two-cylinder V-twin engine. By 1913 it had 150 competitors; however Harley-Davidson was only one of two motorcycle companies to survive the Great Depression (the other being Indian).

During WW II Harley manufactured more than 90000 motorcycles for the US military and its allies. The company first went public in 1965 but was purchased by members of its senior management team in 1981. The group took the company public again in 1986.

HISTORY

In 1903 William Harley and the Davidson brothers (Walter William and Arthur) of Milwaukee sold their first Harley-Davidson motorcycle which essentially was motor-assisted bicycle that required pedaling uphill. Demand was high and most sold before leaving the factory. Six years later the company debuted its trademark two-cylinder V-twin engine. By 1913 it had 150 competitors.

EXECUTIVES

Vp Marketing Motor Company, Joanne M. Bischmann, age 57

President And Coo Harley-davidson Financial Services, Lawrence G. Hund, age 62, $596,668 total compensation

Vp General Counsel And Secretary, Paul J. Jones, age 49, $546,667 total compensation

President And Ceo, Matthew S. (Matt) Levatich, age 54, $1,041,667 total compensation

Svp And Cfo, John A. Olin, age 58, $651,500 total compensation

Coo Harley-davidson Motor Company, Michelle A. Kumbier, $560,000 total compensation

Svp Global Demand, Sean J. Cummings, age 56

Vice President Engineering, Jim Federico
Vice President And Chief Human Resources Officer, Julie Anding
Vice President And Treasurer, Darrell Thomas
Vice President Marketing Harley Davidson Financial Services, Eduardo Bravo
Chief Human Resource Officer Vice President, Tchernavia Rocker
Vice President Operations Management, Don Gogan
Chairman, Michael J. (Mike) Cave, age 59
Board Member, Sara Levinson
Board Member, Jochen Zeitz
Board Member, Troy Alstead
Board Member, Allan Golston
Auditors: Ernst & Young LLP

LOCATIONS

HQ: Harley-Davidson Inc
3700 West Juneau Avenue, Milwaukee, WI 53208
Phone: 414 342-4680
Web: www.harley-davidson.com

2018 Sales

	$ mil.	% of total
Revenue from motorcycles		
United States	3,159	55
EMEA	894	16
Canada	230	4
Japan	161	3
Australia and New Zealand	148	3
Other foreign countries	377	7
Financial Services		
United States	713	12
Canada	23	-
Europe	8	-
Other foreign countries	4	-
Total	**5,717**	**100**

PRODUCTS/OPERATIONS

2018 Sales

	$ mil.	% of total
Motorcycle and Related Products	4,981	87
Financial Services	747	13
	(12.00)	-
Total	**5,717**	**100**

Selected Motorcycles

Harley-Davidson
 CVO (custom vehicle operations)
 Road Gllide Ultra
 Softail Convertible
 Street Glide
 Ultra Classic Electroglide
 Dyna
 Fat BOB
 Street BOB
 Super Glide Custom
 Wide Glide
 Softail
 Black Line
 Cross Bones
 Fat Boy
 Heritage Softail Classic
 Night Train
 Rocker C
 Softail Deluxe
 Sportster
 883 (Low and Custom)
 1200 (Custom and Low)
 Forty Eight
 Iron 883
 Nightster
 SuperLow
 XR1200X
 Touring
 Electra Glide (Standard Classic and Ultra Classic)
 Road Glide Ultra
 Road King (and Classic)
 Street Glide
 Tri Glide Ultra Classic
 Trike
 Street Glide Trike
 Tri Glide Ultra Classic

VRSC
 Night Rod Special
 V-Rod (and V-Rod Muscle)

Selected Operations

Motorcycles
 Harley-Davidson Motor Company
Financial services
 Harley-Davidson Financial Services Inc.
 Harley-Davidson Credit
 Harley-Davidson Insurance

COMPETITORS

BMW	Polaris Industries
Ducati	Triumph Motorcycles
Honda	Ultra Motorcycle
Indian Motorcycle	Viper Motorcycle

HISTORICAL FINANCIALS

Company Type: Public

Income Statement

FYE: December 31

	REVENUE ($ mil.)	NET INCOME ($ mil.)	NET PROFIT MARGIN	EMPLOYEES
12/18	5,717	531	9.3%	5,300
12/17	5,647	522	9.2%	5,800
12/16	5,996	692	11.5%	6,000
12/15	5,995	752	12.5%	6,300
12/14	6,229	845	13.6%	6,500
Annual Growth	(2.1%)	(10.9%)	—	(5.0%)

2018 Year-End Financials

Debt ratio: 71.00%
Return on equity: 29.00%
Cash ($ mil.): 1,204
Current ratio: 1.00
Long-term debt ($ mil.): 4,888
No. of shares (mil.): 160
Dividends
 Yield: 4.0%
 Payout: 46.0%
Market value ($ mil.): 5,448

	STOCK PRICE ($) FY Close	P/E High/Low		PER SHARE ($)		
			Earnings	Dividends	Book Value
12/18	34.00	17 10	3.00	1.00	11.00
12/17	51.00	21 15	3.00	1.00	11.00
12/16	58.00	16 10	4.00	1.00	11.00
12/15	45.00	18 12	4.00	1.00	10.00
12/14	66.00	19 14	4.00	1.00	14.00
Annual Growth	(15.2%)	— —	(4.8%)	7.7%	(5.2%)

Hartford Financial Services Group Inc.

The Hartford Financial Services Group is an insurer offering a range of commercial and personal property/casualty insurance and financial products. Its commercial operations include auto liability and workers' compensation policies as well as group benefits and specialty commercial coverage for large companies. The Hartford also offers consumer homeowners and auto coverage. The group has been the direct auto and home insurance writer for AARP's members for more than 30 years. Through its mutual fund division the company offers wealth management products and services. The Hartford has been in business since 1810.

HISTORY

In 1810 a group of Hartford Connecticut businessmen led by Walter Mitchell and Henry Terry founded the Hartford Fire Insurance Co. Frequent fires in America's wooden cities and executive ignorance of risk assessment and premium-setting often left the firm on the edge of insolvency. (In 1835 stockholders staged a coup and threw management out.) Still each urban conflagration — including the Great Chicago Fire of 1871 — gave The Hartford an opportunity to seek out and pay all its policyholders thus teaching the company to underwrite under fire as it were and to use such disasters to refine its rates.

The company's stag logo was initially a little deer as shown on a policy sold to Abraham Lincoln in 1861. A few years later however Hartford began using the majestic creature (from a Landseer painting) now familiar to customers. By the 1880s Hartford operated nationwide as well as in Canada and Hawaii.

The company survived both world wars and the Depression but emerged in the 1950s in need of organization. It set up new regional offices and added life insurance buying Columbian National Life (founded 1902) which became Hartford Life Insurance Co.

In 1969 Hartford was bought by ITT (formerly International Telephone and Telegraph) whose CEO Harold Geneen was an avid conglomerateur. Consumer advocate Ralph Nader strongly opposed the acquisition — he fought the merger in court for years and felt vindicated when ITT spun off Hartford in 1995. Others opposed it too because ITT had engineered the merger based on an IRS ruling (later revoked) that Hartford stockholders wouldn't have to pay capital gains taxes on the purchase price of their stock.

Insurance operations consolidated under the Hartford Life Insurance banner in 1978. Through the 1980s Hartford Life remained one of ITT's strongest operations. A conservative investment policy kept Hartford safe from the junk bond and real estate manias of the 1980s.

Hartford reorganized its property/casualty operations along three lines in 1986 and in 1992 it organized its reinsurance business into one unit. The company faced some liability in relation to Dow Corning's breast-implant litigation but underwriting standards after 1985 reduced long-term risk. In 1994 the company began selling insurance products to AARP members under an exclusive agreement. In 1996 the company finished its spin-off from ITT which was acquired by Starwood Hotels & Resorts two years later.

To grow its reinsurance operation Hartford acquired the reinsurance business of Orion Capital (now Royal & SunAlliance USA) in 1996. It posted a loss of $99 million due in large part to asbestos and pollution liabilities. Late that year the firm changed its name to The Hartford Financial Services Group.

To shore up reserves and fund growth in 1997 the company spun off 19% of Hartford Life. The Hartford expanded into nonstandard auto insurance in 1998 by buying Omni Insurance Group (since sold in 2006). The company also sold its London & Edinburgh Insurance Group in 1998 to Norwich Union (now part of Aviva formerly CGNU). In 1999 The Hartford acquired the reinsurance business of Vesta Fire Insurance a subsidiary of Vesta Insurance Group.

In 2000 Hartford bought back the part of Hartford Life it had spun off. The Hartford also bought the financial products and excess and surplus specialty insurance lines of Reliance Group Holdings. Assurances G n rales de France bought the company's Dutch subsidiary Zwolsche Algemeene. In 2001 the company bought Fortis Financial a US subsidiary of Belgian insurer Fortis and sold Hartford Seguros its Spanish subsidiary to Liberty Mutual.

Before the financial crisis hit Hartford Life invested in its data management with the acquisition

of a defined contribution recordkeeping business (Princeton Retirement Group 2007) and a web-based technology company (TopNoggin 2008). Following the same strategy The Hartford acquired Sun Life's US 401K plan administration business.

Like so many others in the insurance and financial services industry The Hartford had its share of losses during the 2008 financial crisis due to its investment holdings in Fannie Mae Freddie Mac and Lehman Brothers. In mid-2009 the US Treasury stepped in and offered The Hartford and other major life insurers access to its Troubled Asset Relief Program (TARP). The Hartford borrowed $3.4 billion to shore up its capital reserves. As the company and the economy stabilized the loan was repaid by early 2010 including an additional $21.7 million dividend payment.

Prior to the creation of TARP funds the Treasury first made money available to banks through its Capital Purchase Program (CPP). To make itself more eligible The Hartford worked quickly to transform itself into a bank — at least on paper. In 2009 The Hartford acquired Federal Trust Corporation a regional bank holding company for $10 million. However shortly thereafter TARP funds became available and The Hartford readily accepted them and the strings attached. Two years later the company recognized that banking was not among its core competencies or passions and made arrangements to sell Federal Trust Corporation to CenterState Banks.

Chairman and CEO Ramani Ayer had planned on retiring at the end of 2008 but agreed to stay at the helm through 2009. His final year was marked by efforts to stem the company's losses stemming from the global economic and financial crisis that began in 2008. Former head of consumer banking at Bank of America Liam McGee was appointed as the company's new CEO in late 2009.

The Hartford then conducted restructuring measures including exiting international markets and disposing of non-core assets. It ended sales of variable annuities in Japan and the UK in 2009 and sold its Canadian mutual funds business and its Brazilian joint venture in 2010. In early 2011 The Hartford also sold off its third-party claims administration business Specialty Risk Services (SRS) unit to Sedgwick Claims Management Services for $278 million. In addition in late 2011 the company formed an agreement with Wellington Management which took over management of several of Hartford's mutual funds.

During 2010 the company reshaped its reporting segments into the commercial markets consumer markets and wealth management categories. In 2011 it also also placed a number of operations into a separate runoff segment including its exited international operations and its discontinued institutional annuities and private placement life insurance operations.

Despite all of its efforts to recover from the financial crisis of 2008-2009 (which caused heavy investment losses for The Hartford) via cost-cutting and restructuring measures in early 2012 the company began facing investor pressure to separate its life and property/casualty operations through spinoff or asset sale transactions. After reviewing its options The Hartford soon gave in to the demands. While it retained its mutual funds business the firm exited its annuity business and sold the bulk of its life insurance operations (including individual life retirement plans and Woodbury Financial Services units) in 2012 and 2013. It also sold Hartford Life Insurance KK in 2014.

Assistant Vice President Industry Practices, Melissa Zaparanick

Vice President Of Communications, Donna Gendreau

National Account Manager Group Benefits, Sarah Berard

Assistant Vice President Group Benefits Relationship Management, Alison Colli

Vice President Enterprise Process Improvement, Troy Nagel

Assistant Vice President Underwriting Officer, Matthew Giuffre

Assistant Vice President Financial Analysis And Reporting, Gail Carollo

Vice President Loss Control Commercial Markets, Carl Carano

Senior Vice President And General Auditor, Michael Hession

Assistant Vp And Senior Counsel, Leslie Soler

Vice President Human Resources, Gary West

Vp Programs And Partnerships, Kenneth Zygiel

Assistant Vice President, Jeanne Fenster

Assistant Vice President And Actuary, Ken Kasner

Senior Vice President Procurement, Jahn Surette

Vice President Houston, Jeffrey Lange

Mbr 1st Vice President, Mayer Goldberger

Evp-chief Underwriting Officer, A Morris Tooker

Vpres Strategy & Business Deve, Ray Sprague

Legal Secretary, Sandra Branz

Assistant Vice President And Senior Counsel, Jason Kuselias

Assistant Vice President Assistant General Counsel, Liz Steigman

Assistant Vice President Enterprise Risk Management, Dan OConnell

Vice President And Assistant General Counsel, Laura Santirocco

Senior Vice President, Michael Hotaling

Senior Vice President Sales And Distribution Commercial Markets Division, Mathew Kirk

Assistant Vice President Commercial Markets Technology, Ann Nemphos

Vice President Sales And Distribution Operations, Matthew Montminy

Assistant Vice President Project Management Office, Bill Lombardi

Senior Tax Counsel Assistant Vice President, William Elwell

Vice President Assistant General Counsel, Andrew Diaz-Matos

Assistant Vice President, Susan D Bencher

Vice President And General Cou, Danielle Woolsey

Assistant Vice President Senior Counsel, Cedric Delacruz

Assistant Vice President Finance Business Lead, Steven Paccioretti

Assistant Vice President Property Line Lead, Eric Cannon

Assistant Vice President Human Resources, Daniel Oshea

Vice President And Actuary, Elizabeth Horvath

Assistant Vice President And Assistant Treasurer, Mike Fixer

Assistant Vice President Program Management, Jennifer Paul

Assistant Vice President Counsel, Catherine Gregory

Vice President Internal Audit, Robin Generous

Assistant Vice President Financial Planning And Analysis, Stephen Logan

Regional Vice President Hartford Mutual Funds, Curtis Ranta

Avp Operations, Eric Myers

Senior Vice President Investor Relations, Richard Costello

Assistant Vice President Information Security, Timothy Carling

Avp, Gurunatham Pellakuru

Assistant Vice President Product Management, Chad Mirock

Vice President Government Affairs, Cliff Leach

Vice President Research, Isaac Adams

Vice President And Assistant General Counsel, Kevin LaFreniere

Regional Vice President, Tracy Charbonneau

Assistant Vice President And Counsel, Andrew Daly

Vice President, Alice Pellegrino

Vice President Small Commercial Operations, Colleen Batman

Regional Vice President, Jim Reeves

Assistant Vice President, James Plante

Assistant Vice President Claims, Barbara Agulnek

Assistant Vice President, Perry Roschelle

Avp Application Development And Corporate It And Enterprise Risk Management It, Tom Mika

Assistant Vice President Information Technology Quality, Dianne Bertolet-Duff

Assistant Vice President Internal Communication, Kristin Tetreault

Vice President Project Management Office, Ellen Below

Vice President Strategy And Business Performance Management, Robert Wentling

Assistant Vice President Project Management And Planning, Bob Leyden

Assistant Vice President And Counsel, Michael Petropoulos

Senior Vice President And Controller, Scott Lewis

Avp And Actuary, Ethan Triplett

Vice President Large Loss, Charlene Ridgeway

Avp Claims Data Science, Kari Palmer

Assistant Vice President External Communications, Michelle Loxton

Vp Digital Customer Experience, Ryan Denning

Assistant Vice President, Steve Thompson

Assistant Vice President Operational Risk Management, Lori Gattinella

Senior Vice President Small Commercial Sales, Lisa Morgan

Vice President Finance, Thomas Peloquin

Vice President Liquidity And Market Risk Management, Nancy O'Connor

Avp Underwriting, Aishwarya Kothakota

Assistant Vice President, Tracey Kamenash

Assistant Vice President, Deb Szaraburak

Avp Marine Field Sales, Harold Fowlkes

Assistant Vice President Information Technology, Carolyn Small

Vice President Of Operations, Marc Mailloux

Assistant Vice President Prod Development, Bryan R Smith

Assistant Vice President Small Commercial Information Technology, Brian Pierz

Assistant Vice President, Thomas Mika

Vice President Product Management, Brent Radeloff

Assistant Vice President Infrastructure Solutions, Kathy Kmietek

Vp Of Director Of Hr Of Hartford Life, Peg Lesiak

Assistant Vice President Strategic Marketing Small Business, Daniel Campany

Senior Vice President Specialty Commercial, M Ross Fisher

Assistant Vice President Distribution Technology Strategy, Jim Rogers

Avp Small Commercial Sales, Kim Stuhr

Assistant Vice President Agency Compensation, Keith Lawler

Vice President, Lorl Allen

Vice President Claims Operations, Matthew Scott

Vice President E Business Delivery, Thomas Nogles

Vice President Of Information Delivery Services, Rich Filthaut

Vice President Digital Strategy, Kevin Keller

Vice President Internal Communications And Corporate Sustainability, Paula Angelo

Assistant Vice President Security, Daniel J Lewis

Vice President Liability Field Claims, Richard Bowman

Rvp Claims Group Benefits Minn, Christopher Lancaster

Auditors: DELOITTE & TOUCHE LLP

LOCATIONS

HQ: Hartford Financial Services Group Inc.
One Hartford Plaza, Hartford, CT 06155
Phone: 860 547-5000
Web: www.thehartford.com

PRODUCTS/OPERATIONS

2017 Sales by Segment

	$ mil.	% of total
Commercial Lines	7,954	47
Group Benefits	4,092	24
Personal Lines	3,975	23
Mutual Funds	807	5
Property & Casualty Other Operations	120	1
Corporate	26	-
Total	**16,974**	**100**

COMPETITORS

AIG	Nationwide
Allstate	State Farm
Berkshire Hathaway	Travelers Companies
CNA Financial	Unum Group
Liberty Mutual	Zurich Insurance Group
MetLife	

HISTORICAL FINANCIALS

Company Type: Public

Income Statement — FYE: December 31

	ASSETS ($ mil.)	NET INCOME ($ mil.)	INCOME AS % OF ASSETS	EMPLOYEES
12/18	62,307	1,807	2.9%	18,500
12/17	225,260	(3,131)	—	16,400
12/16	223,432	896	0.4%	16,900
12/15	228,348	1,682	0.7%	17,400
12/14	245,013	798	0.3%	17,500
Annual Growth	(29.0%)	22.7%	—	1.4%

2018 Year-End Financials

Debt ratio: 7.00%
Return on equity: 14.00%
Cash ($ mil.): 121
Current ratio: —
Long-term debt ($ mil.): —

No. of shares (mil.): 359
Dividends
  Yield: 2.0%
  Payout: 22.0%
Market value ($ mil.): 15,964

	STOCK PRICE ($) FY Close	P/E High/Low	PER SHARE ($) Earnings	Dividends	Book Value
12/18	44.00	12 8	5.00	1.00	36.00
12/17	56.00	— —	(9.00)	1.00	38.00
12/16	48.00	21 16	2.00	1.00	45.00
12/15	43.00	12 10	4.00	1.00	44.00
12/14	42.00	23 18	2.00	1.00	44.00
Annual Growth	1.6%	— —	30.1%	13.6%	(4.6%)

HBT Financial Inc

Auditors: RSM US LLP

LOCATIONS

HQ: HBT Financial Inc
401 North Hershey Rd., Bloomington, IL 61704
Phone: 888 897-2276
Web: www.hbtbank.com

HISTORICAL FINANCIALS

Company Type: Public

Income Statement

FYE: December 31

	ASSETS ($ mil.)	NET INCOME ($ mil.)	INCOME AS % OF ASSETS	EMPLOYEES
12/18	3,250	64	2.0%	742
12/17	3,313	56	1.7%	—
12/16	0	59	—	—
Annual Growth	—	4.4%	—	—

2018 Year-End Financials

Debt ratio: 1.00%
Return on equity: 19.00%
Cash ($ mil.): 187
Current ratio: —
Long-term debt ($ mil.): —

No. of shares (mil.): 18
Dividends
Yield: —
Payout: 67.0%
Market value ($ mil.): —

	STOCK PRICE ($) FY Close	P/E High/Low	PER SHARE ($) Earnings	Dividends	Book Value
12/18	0.00	— —	4.00	2.00	19.00
12/17	0.00	— —	3.00	3.00	18.00
Annual Growth	—		6.9%	(13.6%)	2.6%

HCA Healthcare Inc

HCA dispenses TLC for a profit. HCA Healthcare (formerly HCA Holdings) through its HCA Inc. (Hospital Corporation of America) unit operates 180 hospitals — mostly acute care centers as well as three psychiatric facilities and one rehabilitation hospital — located in the US and UK. It also runs about 120 ambulatory surgery centers — as well as urgent care rehab and other outpatient centers — that form health care networks in many of the communities it serves. In total its hospitals are home to some 46700 beds. HCA's facilities are located in about 20 states; roughly half of its hospitals are in Florida and Texas. The HCA International unit operates the company's hospitals and clinics in the UK.

HISTORY

In 1987 Dallas lawyer Rick Scott and Fort Worth Texas financier Richard Rainwater founded Columbia Hospital Corp. to buy two hospitals in El Paso Texas. The partners eventually sold 40% of the hospitals to local doctors hoping that ownership would motivate physicians to increase productivity and efficiency.

The company entered the Miami market the next year and by 1990 had four hospitals. After merging with Smith Laboratories that year Columbia went public and then acquired Sutter Laboratories (orthopedic products). By the end of 1990 it had 11 hospitals.

Columbia moved into Florida in 1992 with the purchase of several hospitals and facilities. The next year it acquired Galen Health Care which operated 73 hospitals and had been spun off from health plan operator Humana earlier in the year. The merger thrust the hospital chain into about 15 new markets.

Columbia bought Hospital Corporation of America (HCA) in 1994. Thomas Frist his son Thomas Frist Jr. and Jack Massey (former owner of Kentucky Fried Chicken now part of TRICON) founded HCA in Nashville Tennessee in 1968. By 1973 the company had grown to 50 hospitals.

Meanwhile the medical industry was changing — insurers Medicare and Medicaid began scrutinizing payment procedures while the growth of HMOs (which aimed to restrict hospital admissions) cut hospital occupancy rates. HCA began paring operations in the late 1980s selling more than 100 hospitals. In 1989 the younger Frist led a $5.1 billion leveraged buyout of the company. He sold more assets and in 1992 took HCA public again but losses and a tumbling stock price made it a takeover target.

Later in 1994 the newly christened Columbia/HCA acquired the US's largest operator of outpatient surgery centers Dallas-based Medical Care America. A year later it bought 117-hospital HealthTrust a 1987 offshoot of HCA. Columbia/HCA was unstoppable in 1996 with some 150 acquisitions.

In 1997 the government began investigating the company's business practices. After executive indictments the company fired Scott and several other top officers. Frist Jr. became chairman and CEO pledging to shrink the company and tone down its aggressive approach. Columbia/HCA sold its home care business more than 100 of its less-desirable hospitals and almost all the operations of Value Health a pharmacy benefits and behavioral health care management firm it had recently bought.

The trimming continued in 1998: The company sold nearly three dozen outpatient surgery centers and more than a dozen hospitals. That year Columbia/HCA sued former financial executive Samuel Greco and several vendors accusing them of defrauding the company of several million dollars. In 1999 it spun off regional operators LifePoint Health (23 facilities) and Triad Hospitals (34) to trim its holdings. The next year it sold some 120 medical buildings to MedCap Properties a joint venture formed with First Union Capital Partners.

During 2000 the company bought out partner Sun Life and Provincial Holdings' (now AXA UK) interest in several London hospitals and bought three hospitals there from St. Martins Healthcare. It also renamed itself HCA - The Healthcare Company. While continuing a strategy of consolidating and streamlining operations (and resolving remaining legal matters) in 2001 the company streamlined its name even further to simply HCA Inc.

By 2002 HCA began shaking off its shaky past. Profits stabilized allowing it to reinvest millions into modernizing facilities and equipment at its hospitals and surgery centers. It entered the Kansas City market in 2003 by acquiring a local hospital chain.

The company finally closed the books during 2003 on the numerous government investigations launched in 1997 into its business practices. In the five years leading up to 2003 HCA paid out some $2 billion in settlements for Medicare fraud and other claims. These settlements took their toll on the firm's bottom line.

To expand its outpatient services HCA beginning in 2004 began purchasing imaging centers. In early 2005 the firm acquired Tampa Florida's Total I Imaging and its five centers that offer diagnostic services. In 2005 HCA's iMage1 Network part of HCA's outpatient services group bought more than a handful of imaging centers located in the Tampa Florida area from Ultra Open MRI Corp.

The devastating hurricane season of 2005 hit HCA's operations hard as they are concentrated in the southern US. When Hurricane Katrina hit HCA evacuated its Tulane University Hospital and Clinic (it reopened in early 2006). Hurricane Rita spurred HCA to evacuate three Houston-area hospitals (Mainland Medical Center in Texas City East Houston Regional Medical Center in Houston and Clear Lake Regional Medical Center in Webster) and partially evacuate two others.

In 2006 a group of investors — including Thomas Frist Jr. as well as Bain Capital Kohlberg Kravis Roberts and the private equity arm of Merrill Lynch — took HCA private in a $30 billion leveraged buyout. In 2009 Richard Bracken became CEO of the company.

The hospital operator maintained its private status for several years until it once again went public in 2011 as a way to pay off some debt.

EXECUTIVES

Chairman And Ceo, R. Milton Johnson, age 62, $1,391,667 total compensation
President And Coo, Samuel N. (Sam) Hazen, age 59, $995,834 total compensation
President Service Line And Operations Integration, A. Bruce Moore, age 59, $574,989 total compensation
Evp And Cfo, William B. (Bill) Rutherford, age 55, $793,750 total compensation
President American Group, Jon M. Foster, age 57, $762,781 total compensation
President Clinical Services And Chief Medical Officer, Jonathan B. (Jon) Perlin, age 58, $795,833 total compensation
President National Group, Charles J. (Chuck) Hall, age 66, $797,088 total compensation
Svp Marketing And Corporate Affairs, Jana J. Davis, age 60
Svp And Cio, P. Martin (Marty) Paslick, age 59
President Physician Services Group, Michael S. Cuffe, age 53
Svp And Chief Nursing Officer, Jane D. Englebright, age 60
Director Of Physical Therapy Physical Therapy Director, Angie Brown
Physical Therapy Director, Mary B Peterson
Assistant Vice President Risk, Joseph Haase
Vice President, Michael Marotta
Director Of Radiology Services, Phyllis Barker
Vice President Field Operations, Jay Levy
Assistant Vice President Technical Services, Bill Fitzgerald
Assistant Vice President Development, Bobby Stokes
Assistant Vice President Owned Hospitals, Ron Redding
Vice President Managed Care, James Koss
Director Of Pharmacy, Ron Nagata
Assistant Vice President Information Technology Strategy And Planning, David Catino
Vice President Human Resources Operations Support, Yonnie Chesley
Vice President Human Resources Midwest Division, Rich Lowe
Vice President Information Technology, Cyndi Talley
Regional Vice President Of Operations, John Lowe
Board Member, Thomas Frist
Auditors: Ernst & Young LLP

LOCATIONS

HQ: HCA Healthcare Inc
One Park Plaza, Nashville, TN 37203
Phone: 615 344-9551
Web: www.hcahealthcare.com

2018 Locations

US	No.
Texas	47
Florida	45
Tennessee	13
Virginia	11
Georgia	9
Utah	8
Colorado	7
Missouri	5
California	5
Kansas	4
Louisiana	4
Nevada	3
South Carolina	3
Idaho	2
Kentucky	2
New Hampshire	2
Oklahoma	2
Alaska	1
Indiana	1
Mississippi	1
UK	6
Total	**179**

Selected Segments

American Group
 Colorado
 Southern Georgia
 Kansas
 Southern Kentucky
 Louisiana
 Mississippi
 Missouri
 Oklahoma
 Tennessee
 Texas
National Group
 Alaska
 California
 Florida
 Southern Georgia
 Idaho
 Indiana
 Northern Kentucky
 Nevada
 New Hampshire
 North Carolina
 South Carolina
 Utah
 Virginia

Selected US Facilities

Alaska
 Alaska Regional Hospital (Anchorage)
California
 Good Samaritan Hospital (San Jose)
 Los Robles Medical Center (Thousand Oaks)
 Regional Medical Center of San Jose
 Riverside Community Hospital
 West Hills Hospital & Medical Center
Colorado
 Centrum Surgical Center (Greenwood Village)
 Medical Center of Aurora
 North Suburban Medical Center (Thornton)
 Presbyterian/St. Luke's Medical Center (Denver)
 Rose Medical Center (Denver)
 Sky Ridge Medical Center (Lone Tree)
 Spalding Rehabilitation Hospital (Aurora)
 Swedish Medical Center (Englewood)
Florida
 Aventura Hospital and Medical Center
 Blake Medical Center (Bradenton)
 Brandon Regional Hospital
 Capital Regional Medical Center (Tallahassee)
 Central Florida Regional Hospital (Sanford)
 Columbia Hospital (West Palm Beach)
 Doctors Hospital of Sarasota
 Edward White Hospital (St. Petersburg)
 Fawcett Memorial Hospital (Port Charlotte)
 Gulf Coast Medical Center (Panama City)
 JFK Medical Center (Atlantis)
 Kendall Regional Medical Center (Miami)
 Lake City Medical Center
 Largo Medical Center
 Memorial Hospital Jacksonville
 Memorial Hospital of Tampa
 North Florida Regional Medical Center (Gainesville)
 Northwest Medical Center (Margate)
 Ocala Regional Medical Center

Osceola Regional Medical Center (Kissimmee)
 Palms of Pasadena Hospital (St. Petersburg)
 Palms West Hospital (Loxahatchee)
 South Bay Hospital (Sun City Center)
 St. Lucie Medical Center (Port St. Lucie)
 Town and Country Hospital (Tampa)
 Twin Cities Hospital (Niceville)
 University Hospital and Medical Center (Tamarac)
 West Florida Hospital (Pensacola)
 Westside Regional Medical Center (Plantation)
Georgia
 Atlanta Outpatient Surgery Center (Atlanta)
 Cartersville Medical Center
 Coliseum Medical Centers (Macon)
 Doctors Hospital (Augusta)
 Eastside Medical Center (Snellville)
 Fairview Park Hospital (Dublin)
 Northlake Surgical Center (Tucker)
 Polk Medical Center (Cedartown)
 Redmond Regional Medical Center (Rome)
Idaho
 Eastern Idaho Regional Medical Center (Idaho Falls)
 West Valley Medical Center (Caldwell)
Indiana
 Terre Haute Regional Hospital
Kansas
 Allen County Hospital (Iola)
 Galichia Heart Hospital (Wichita)
 Menorah Medical Center (Overland Park)
 Overland Park Regional Medical Center
 Wesley Medical Center (Wichita)
Kentucky
 Frankfort Regional Medical Center
 Greenview Regional Hospital (Bowling Green)
Louisiana
 Dauterive Hospital (New Iberia)
 Lafeyette Surgicare
 Lakeview Regional Medical Center (Covington)
 Rapides Regional Medical Center (Alexandria)
 Tulane Medical Center (Metarie)
 Tulane University Hospital & Clinic (New Orleans)
 Women's & Children's Hospital (Lafayette)
Mississippi
 Garden Park Medical Center (Gulfport)
Missouri
 Centerpoint Medical Center (Independence)
 Lafayette Regional Health Center (Lexington)
 Lee's Summit Hospital
 Research Medical Center (Kansas City)
 Research Psychiatric Center (Kansas City)
Nevada
 Flamingo Surgery Center (Las Vegas)
 MountainView Hospital (Las Vegas)
 Southern Hills Hospital and Medical Center (Las Vegas)
 Sunrise Hospital and Medical Center (Las Vegas)
New Hampshire
 Parkland Medical Center (Derry)
 Portsmouth Regional Hospital
 Salem Surgery Center
Oklahoma
 Edmond Medical Center
 Oklahoma Surgicare (Oklahoma City)
 Oklahoma University Medical Center (Oklahoma City)
South Carolina
 Colleton Medical Cemter (Walterboro)
 Grand Dunes Surgery Center (Myrtle Beach)
 Grand Strand Regional Medical Center (Myrtle Beach)
 Summerville Medical Center
 Trident Regional Medical Center (Charleston)
Tennessee
 Centennial Medical Center (Nashville)
 Hendersonville Medical Center
 Horizon Medical Center (Dickson)
 Parkridge East Hospital (Chattanooga)
 Parkridge Valley Hospital (Chattanooga)
 Skyline Medical Center (Nashville)
 StoneCrest Medical Center (Smyrna)
 Summit Medical Center (Hermitage)
Texas
 Bailey Square Surgery Center (Austin)
 Bayshore Medical Center (Pasadena)
 Clear Lake Regional Medical Center (Webster)
 Conroe Regional Medical Center
 Corpus Christi Medical Center
 Del Sol Medical Center (El Paso)
 Denton Regional Medical Center
 Green Oaks Hospital (Dallas)
 Kingwood Medical Center
 Las Colinas Medical Center (Irving)
 Mainland Medical Center (Texas City)

Medical Center of Arlington
 Medical Center of Lewisville
 Medical Center of McKinney
 Medical Center of Plano
 Medical City Dallas Hospital
 Methodist Hospital (San Antonio)
 Metropolitan Methodist Hospital (San Antonio)
 North Austin Medical Center
 North Hills Hospital (North Richland Hills)
 Plaza Medical Center of Fort Worth
 Rio Grande Regional Hospital (McAllen)
 Round Rock Medical Center
 South Austin Hospital
 St. David's Medical Center (Austin)
 Valley Regional Medical Center (Brownsville)
 West Houston Medical Center
 Woman's Hospital of Texas (Houston)
Utah
 Brigham City Community Hospital
 Lakeview Hospital (Bountiful)
 Ogden Regional Medical Center
 St. Mark's Hospital (Salt Lake City)
 Timpanogos Regional Hospital (Orem)
Virginia
 CJW Medical Center (Richmond)
 Dominion Hospital (Falls Church)
 Henrico Doctors' Hospital (Richmond)
 John Randolph Medical Center
 LewisGale Medical Center (Salem)
 Pulaski Community Hospital
 Reston Hospital Center
 Spotsylvania Regional Medical Center (Fredericksburg)

Selected International Facilities

UK
 Harley Street Clinic (London)
 Lister Hospital (London)
 London Bridge Hospital (London)
 The Portland Hospital for Women and Children (London)
 Princess Grace Hospital (London)
 The Wellington Hospital (London)

PRODUCTS/OPERATIONS

2018 Sales

	$ mil.	% of total
Payer sources		
Managed care & other insurers	24,467	52
Medicare	9,831	21
Managed Medicare	5,497	12
Managed Medicaid	2,403	5
Medicaid	1,358	3
International	1,156	3
Other	1,965	4
Total	**46,677**	**100**

COMPETITORS

Ascension Health	Tenet Healthcare
CHRISTUS Health	Texas Health Resources
Catholic Health	Trinity Health (Novi)
Initiatives	United Surgical
Community Health	Partners
Systems	Universal Health
Encompass Health	Services

HISTORICAL FINANCIALS

Company Type: Public

Income Statement

FYE: December 31

	REVENUE ($ mil.)	NET INCOME ($ mil.)	NET PROFIT MARGIN	EMPLOYEES
12/18	46,677	3,787	8.1%	262,000
12/17	43,614	2,216	5.1%	253,000
12/16	41,490	2,890	7.0%	241,000
12/15	39,678	2,129	5.4%	233,000
12/14	36,918	1,875	5.1%	225,000
Annual Growth	6.0%	19.2%	—	3.9%

2018 Year-End Financials

Debt ratio: 84.00%	No. of shares (mil.): 343
Return on equity: ***,***.**%	Dividends
Cash ($ mil.): 502	Yield: 1.0%
Current ratio: 1.00	Payout: 13.0%
Long-term debt ($ mil.): 32,033	Market value ($ mil.): 42,673

	STOCK PRICE ($) FY Close	P/E High/Low		PER SHARE ($) Earnings	Dividends	Book Value
12/18	124.00	13	8	11.00	1.00	(14.00)
12/17	88.00	15	12	6.00	0.00	(19.00)
12/16	74.00	11	8	7.00	0.00	(20.00)
12/15	68.00	18	13	5.00	0.00	(19.00)
12/14	73.00	17	11	4.00	0.00	(19.00)
Annual Growth	14.1%	—		26.5%	—	

HD Supply Holdings Inc

EXECUTIVES

Pres-Ceo, Joseph J Deangelo
Cfo*, Evan Levitt
Sr V Pres*, Ronald J Domanico
Sr V Pres-Hr Mktg & Communicat*, Margaret Newman
Exec V Pres*, John Stegeman
Sr V Pres-Gen Counsel-Corp SEC*, Ricardo J Nunez
Chb*, James G Berges
Inside Sales, Marty May
Manager, Alexander Bednar
Account Manager, Brian West
Account Manager, David Velez
Auditors: PricewaterhouseCoopers LLP

LOCATIONS

HQ: HD Supply Holdings Inc
3400 Cumberland Boulevard SE, Atlanta, GA 30339
Phone: 770 852-9000
Web: www.hdsupply.com

HISTORICAL FINANCIALS
Company Type: Public

Income Statement   FYE: February 3

	REVENUE ($ mil.)	NET INCOME ($ mil.)	NET PROFIT MARGIN	EMPLOYEES
02/19*	6,047	394	6.5%	11,500
01/18	5,121	970	18.9%	11,000
01/17	7,439	196	2.6%	14,000
01/16	7,388	1,472	19.9%	14,000
02/15	8,882	3	0.0%	15,000
Annual Growth	(9.2%)	238.5%	—	(6.4%)

*Fiscal year change

2019 Year-End Financials

Debt ratio: 51.00%
Return on equity: 28.00%
Cash ($ mil.): 38
Current ratio: 2.00
Long-term debt ($ mil.): 2,129
No. of shares (mil.): 171
Dividends
  Yield: —
  Payout: —
Market value ($ mil.): 7,161

	STOCK PRICE ($) FY Close	P/E High/Low		PER SHARE ($) Earnings	Dividends	Book Value
02/19*	42.00	21	16	2.00	0.00	8.00
01/18	40.00	9	6	5.00	0.00	8.00
01/17	43.00	45	23	1.00	0.00	5.00
01/16	26.00	5	3	7.00	0.00	4.00
02/15	29.00	15091045		0.00	0.00	(4.00)
Annual Growth	9.8%	—		—222.7%	—	

*Fiscal year change

HEALTHPARTNERS, INC.

EXECUTIVES

Pres-Ceo, Mary Brainerd
Exec V Pres-Chief Mktg Offcr*, Andrea Walsh
Cfo*, David A Dziuk
Cfo*, Todd Hofheins
Analyst, Kathy Rhode
Coordinator, Renee Hannan
Team Leader Appl, Chao Nguyen
Admin Asst, Kristi Brandt
Senior Director, Frank Muller
Senior Vice-President, Scott Schnuckle
Agent, Tim M Haley
Auditors: KPMG LLP MINNEAPOLIS MINNES

LOCATIONS

HQ: HEALTHPARTNERS, INC.
8170 33RD AVE S, BLOOMINGTON, MN 554254516
Phone: 952 883-6000

HISTORICAL FINANCIALS
Company Type: Private

Income Statement   FYE: December 31

	REVENUE ($ mil.)	NET INCOME ($ mil.)	NET PROFIT MARGIN	EMPLOYEES
12/18	7,062	143	2.0%	22,000
12/97	1,248	(2)	—	—
12/96	1,178	9	0.8%	—
12/95	0	0	—	—
Annual Growth	—	—		—

Heartland Financial USA, Inc. (Dubuque, IA)

Heartland Financial USA is an $11.3 billion multi-bank holding company that owns flagship subsidiary Dubuque Bank and Trust (Iowa) and ten other banks that together operate more than 120 branches in about a dozen states primarily in the West and Midwest. In addition to standard deposit loan and mortgage services the banks also offer retirement wealth management trust insurance and investment services. Heartland also owns consumer lender Citizens Finance which has about a dozen offices in Illinois Iowa and Wisconsin.

Operations

Heartland Financial USA operates two main segments: community and other banking and retail mortgage banking services which account for about 90% and 10% of revenue respectively. The community banking business generates revenue from interest earned on loans and investment securities and fees from deposit services. Its retail mortgage banking services division collects revenue from interest from mortgage loans held for sale gains on sales of loans on the secondary market the servicing of mortgage loans for investors and loan origination fee income.

About three-quarters of Heartland's loan portfolio comes from commercial and commercial real estate loans but — in keeping with the bank's Midwestern identity — it also makes agricultural residential mortgage and consumer loans.

Heartland's subsidiaries include: Citywide Banks (approximately $1.9 billion total deposits) New Mexico Bank & Trust ($1.2 billion) Dubuque Bank and Trust Company ($1.1 billion) Wisconsin Bank & Trust ($890 million) First Bank & Trust ($820 million) Premier Valley Bank ($710 million) Illinois Bank & Trust ($690 million) Morrill & Janes Bank and Trust ($560 million) Arizona Bank & Trust ($520 million) Rocky Mountain Bank ($420 million) and Minnesota Bank & Trust ($180 million).

Geographic Reach

Dubuque Iowa-based Heartland Financial USA operates through about 145 locations (including branches and loan production offices) in local communities in Iowa Illinois Wisconsin New Mexico Arizona Montana Colorado Minnesota Kansas Missouri Texas and California. The company's three largest bank subsidiaries by number of locations are Colorado's Citywide Banks with about 25 and Wisconsin Bank & Trust and New Mexico Bank & Trust with about 20 each.

Sales and Marketing

Heartland Financial USA offers its banking services to businesses public sector and non-profit entities and individuals.

The company's Commercial Card team works with its commercial clients to help cut manual processes and costs from employee travel entertainment spending and vendor payments.

Financial Performance

As it grows its assets and loan portfolio via acquisitions Heartland Financial USA had positive overall performance in the last five years increasing revenue by some 70% and net income by more than 100% — all while expanding its cash by about 55% and reducing long-term debt by nearly 20%.

Revenue ticked up 6% to $432.3 million in 2017 on increased interest income mostly from interest and fees on a larger loan portfolio following the company's acquisitions of Citywide Banks and Founders Bancorp.

Net income trended down 6% to $75.3 million owing to higher income taxes salaries employee benefits and professional fees.

Heartland added $37.3 million to its cash stores in 2017 to end the year with $196 million. Operations and investments brought in $155.9 million and $27.3 million respectively. Financing activities used up $145.9 million due to a net decrease from savings accounts and repayments of short term Federal Home Loan Bank advances.

Strategy

Heartland Financial USA's strategy for the past two decades is centered on expanding through acquisitions in its existing and adjacent markets while balancing growth in newer western markets with the stability of its established midwestern markets. The company's goal is to have at least $1 billion in assets in each state where it operates.

Mergers and Acquisitions

In 2019 Heartland Financial USA acquired Overland Park Kansas-based Blue Valley Ban the holding company for Bank of Blue Valley. Blue Valley has $712 million in assets $564 million in gross loans outstanding and $587 million in deposits. The acquisition expands Heartland's presence in the Kansas City and Johnson County markets.

Heartland added its eleventh subsidiary in May 2018 through its acquisition of Lubbock Texas-based First Bank Lubbock Bancshares for $189.9 million. Operating under the name First Bank & Trust (which Heartland retained) the bank held $681.1 million in gross loans held to maturity and deposits of $893.8 million. First Bank & Trust has eight branches in West Texas and eight mortgage lending services offices throughout Texas.

In February 2018 the company acquired Minnetonka Minnesota-based Signature Bancshares for $61.4 million and incorporated it into its Minnesota Bank & Trust subsidiary. Signature had two branches in the Twin Cities metropolitan area with $324.5 million in gross loans held to maturity and deposits of $357.3 million.

Heartland acquired Citywide Banks (headquartered in Aurora Colorado) in July 2017 for $211.2 million. At the time of purchase Citywide had $985.4 million in net loans outstanding and $1.2 billion in deposits. Following incorporation of Citywide into its Centennial Bank and Trust subsidiary (which then adopted Citywide's name) Heartland had more than 25 branches in Colorado.

In February 2017 Heartland Financial USA acquired San Luis Obispo California-based Founders Bancorp which it incorporated into its Premier Valley Bank subsidiary for $31 million. The company's Founders Community Bank held loans totaling $96.4 million and the purchase increased Heartland's total number of branches in California from five to nine.

Company Background

Heartland Financial USA was founded in 1981 although it traces its roots back to the 1935 establishment of Dubuque Bank and Trust. It made its first bank acquisition in in 1989 - Key City Bank - and has continued acquiring community banks since.

EXECUTIVES

Vice President Marketing, Dawn Oelke

President And Ceo Minnesota Bank & Trust, Catherine T. (Kate) Kelly

Chairman President And Ceo Heartland Financial Usa Inc.; Vice Chairman Dubuque Bank & Trust Wisconsin Bank & Trust New Mexico Bank & Trust Arizona Bank & Trust Rocky Mountain Bank Centennial Bank And Trust(1) Minnesota Bank & Trust And Premier Valley Bank, Lynn B. Fuller, age 69, $486,388 total compensation

Evp Lending, Douglas J. Horstmann, age 65, $275,156 total compensation

President And Ceo New Mexico Bank & Trust, R. Greg Leyendecker

President And Ceo Wisconsin Bank & Trust, Kevin S. Tenpas

President Of Heartland Director Rocky Mountain Bank And President Heartland Financial Usa Inc. Insurance Services, Bruce K. Lee, age 58, $383,519 total compensation

Evp Human Resources And Organizational Development, Mark G. Murtha, age 57

Svp Chief Accounting Officer, Janet M. Quick

President And Ceo Riverside Community Bank, Steven E. Ward

Evp Wealth Management, Bruce C. Rehmke

Evp Commercial Sales, Frank E. Walter, age 72

Evp Senior General Counsel And Corporate Secretary, Michael J. Coyle, age 73

Evp Operations, Brian J. Fox, age 70, $190,000 total compensation

Evp And Chief Risk Officer, Rodney L. Sloan, age 59

Evp And Cfo Heartland Financial Usa Treasurer Citizens Finance Parent Co.. And Director Heartland Financial Usa Inc. Insurance Services, Bryan R. McKeag, age 58, $305,625 total compensation

Evp Finance And Corporate Strategy, David L. Horstmann, age 69

President And Ceo Arizona Bank & Trust, Jerry L. Schwallier

President And Ceo Rocky Mountain Bank, Curtis Chrystal

President And Ceo Morrill & Janes Bank And Trust Co., Kurt M. Saylor

Evp Private Client Services, Kelly J. Johnson, age 57

President And Ceo Illinois Bank And Trust, Jeff Hultman

Chief Investment Officer, Nancy Tengler

Evp And Chief Credit Officer, Drew Townsend

Evp And Private Wealth Management Director, Rick O. Terry

President And Ceo Heartland Mortgage, Paul Johnstun

Ceo Centennial Bank And Trust, Jim Basey

President Heartland Mortgage, Jack Lloyd

Vice President Finance, Sandra Wild

Vice President, Kate Barth

Vice President, Jean Harkey

Vice President Of Retirement Plan Services, Lisan Adams

Vice President Electronic Banking And Fraud, Linda Maas

Vice President Corporate Training Director, Bonnie Bollin

Assistant Vice President Commercial Services, Lynn Stoffregen

Vice President, Rachel Steiner

Vice President Information Technology, Les Oelke

Vice President Credit Administration, Ted Kraft

Senior Vice President Teller Operations Officer, Julie Shanahan

Senior Vice President Special Assets Reo, John Hawkins

Vice President, Troy Steger

Vice President, Craig Sciara

Vice President Credit Administration, Tom Steinhaus

Senior Vice President Credit Administration Officer, Joe Davis

Assistant Vice President, Michelle Schoen

Assistant Vice President Information Services, Brent Wilke

Tm Wire Transfer Manager Avp, Cori Freihoefer

Vp Engineering, Mary Burns

Vice President Director Financial Planning And Performance Management, Michael G Flood

Credit Admin Officer Iv Senior Vice President, Ralph Atkinson

Credit Admin Officer Iv Senior Vice President, Jeffery Viviano

Pcs Director Of Financial Planning Vice President, Chrisanna Elser

Executive Vice President And Chief Human Resources Officer, Deborah Deters

Vice President Director Financial Planning And Performance Management, Michael Flood

Vice Chairman Of The Board Of Heartland Financial Usa Inc.; Chairman And Director Of Dubuque Bank And Trust, Mark C. Falb, age 71

Vice Chairman Of The Board Of Heartland Financial Usa Inc.; Director And Vice Chairman Of The Board Of Dubuque Bank And Trust, Thomas L. Flynn, age 63

Auditors: KPMG LLP

LOCATIONS

HQ: Heartland Financial USA, Inc. (Dubuque, IA) 1398 Central Avenue, Dubuque, IA 52001
Phone: 563 589-2100   **Fax:** 563 589-2011
Web: www.htlf.com

PRODUCTS/OPERATIONS

2017 Sales

	$ mil.	% of total
Interest		
Loans & leases including fees	304	65
Securities	58	13
Other	2	—
Interest expense	(33.3)	-
Noninterest		
Gains on sales of loans	22	5
Service charges and fees	39	8
Trust fees	16	3
Loan serving income	6	1
Brokerage & insurance commissions	4	1
Security gains	7	2
Other	8	2
Total	**432**	**100**

Selected Subsidiaries

Arizona Bank & Trust
Citywide Banks (Colorado)
Dubuque Bank and Trust Company (Iowa)
  DB&T Community Development Corp.
  DB&T Insurance
Illinois Bank & Trust
Minnesota Bank & Trust
Morrill & Janes Bank and Trust Company (Kansas)
New Mexico Bank & Trust
Premier Valley Bank (California)
Rocky Mountain Bank (Montana)
Wisconsin Bank & Trust

COMPETITORS

Associated Banc-Corp	First Banks
BBVA Compass Bancshares	U.S. Bancorp
Bank of America	Wells Fargo
Bank of the West	Zions Bancorporation

HISTORICAL FINANCIALS

Company Type: Public

Income Statement

FYE: December 31

	ASSETS ($ mil.)	NET INCOME ($ mil.)	INCOME AS % OF ASSETS	EMPLOYEES
12/18	11,408	117	1.0%	2,045
12/17	9,811	75	0.8%	2,008
12/16	8,247	80	1.0%	1,864
12/15	7,695	60	0.8%	1,799
12/14	6,052	42	0.7%	1,631
Annual Growth	17.2%	29.3%	—	5.8%

2018 Year-End Financials

Debt ratio: 2.00%	No. of shares (mil.): 34
Return on equity: 10.00%	Dividends
Cash ($ mil.): 278	Yield: 1.0%
Current ratio: —	Payout: 17.0%
Long-term debt ($ mil.): —	Market value ($ mil.): 1,515

	STOCK PRICE ($) FY Close	P/E High/Low	Earnings	PER SHARE ($) Dividends	Book Value
12/18	44.00	17 12	4.00	1.00	38.00
12/17	54.00	20 16	3.00	1.00	33.00
12/16	48.00	15 8	3.00	1.00	28.00
12/15	31.00	14 9	3.00	0.00	30.00
12/14	27.00	13 10	2.00	0.00	27.00
Annual Growth	12.8%	— —	12.6%	10.2%	9.4%

HENRY FORD HEALTH SYSTEM

Not-for-profit Henry Ford Health System (HFHS) operates a network of medical facilities in Detroit and nearby communities. The system's half-dozen hospitals — including the flagship Henry Ford Hospital the Henry Ford Wyandotte Hospital and mental health facility Kingswood Hospital — are home to roughly 2400 beds. HFHS also operates a 1300-physician medical group (with more than 40 specialties) as well as nursing homes a hospice provider a home health care network and research and education centers. The system's Health Alliance Plan of Michigan provides managed care and health insurance to more than half a million members.

Strategy

HFHS is working to make health care more affordable for patients by improving efficiencies in both its care model and its business operations. Recent efforts to improve patient services include enacting new safety protocols and promoting virtual (telehealth) patient visits.

The company regularly upgrades or expands its facilities to provide state-of-the-art care and attract new patients and skilled health professionals. It invested $55 million to add a 66-bed patient tower and a medical education center to the Henry Ford Allegiance Health hospital campus in 2018. HFHS also partnered with the Detroit Pistons to construct a sports medicine facility (completed in 2019) and it is constructing a new Detroit cancer center the Brigitte Harris Cancer Pavilion (scheduled to open in 2020).

HFHS seeks to advance the medical profession by providing medical research and training programs. The Henry Ford Innovation Institute allows the network's specialists to engage in clinical research projects. The Henry Ford Hospital serves as an academic training center for the Wayne State University School of Medicine.

The company relies on payments from third parties for the majority of its income with reimbursements from Medicaid Medicare and commercial insurers making up the bulk of revenue. This can result in delayed payments if claims are denied. The company may also be vulnerable to reimbursement reduction decisions or non-payments from self-pay customers.

Company Background

Automaker Henry Ford founded Henry Ford Hospital in 1915.

The Health Alliance Plan became part of the Henry Ford Health System in 1986.

In 2016 Allegiance Health which operated a hospital and other health facilities in Jackson joined the Henry Ford Health System and began operating as Henry Ford Allegiance Health.

EXECUTIVES

Evp; President And Ceo Health Alliance Plan, James M. Connelly

Ceo, Nancy M. Schlichting

Svp And Coo Henry Ford Hospital And Health Network, Robert G. (Bob) Riney

President, Wright L. Lassiter, age 56

Evp And Chief Medical Officer; President And Ceo Henry Ford Hospital, John Popovich

President And Ceo Community Care Services, John J. Polanski

Evp And Cfo, Edward G. (Ed) Chadwick

Evp; Ceo Henry Ford Medical Group, William A. Conway

President And Ceo Henry Ford West Bloomfield Hospital, Lynn M. Torossian

President And Ceo Henry Ford Wyandotte Hospital, Denise Brooks-Williams

Chief Nursing Officer; Coo Henry Ford Hospital, Veronica M. Hall

President And Ceo Henry Ford Macomb Hospitals, Barbara W. Rossmann

Svp Community Health And Equity; Chief Wellness Officer, Kimberlydawn Wisdom

Svp And Cio, Mary Alice Annecharico

Director Of Radiology, Mark C Diamond

Vice President Information Technology Business And Service Integration, Geoff Patterson

Director Of Radiology, Xia Wang

Medical Director, Nabil Khoury

Senior Vice President Is Clinical Integration And Transformation, Michelle Schreiber

Senior Vice President Strategic Business Development, William Schramm

Director Of Radiology, Joseph M Silva

Director Of Radiology, Scott G Sturza

Director Of Radiology, John W Bonnett

Director Of Radiology, Paul A Suiter

Director Of Radiology, Derrick Harper

Director Of Radiology, Pranav S Doshi

Pharmacy Manager Process Improvement, Nadia Haque

Director Of Radiology, Michael J Flynn

Vice President, James O'connor

Senior Vice President And Chief Human Resources Officer, Kathy Oswald

Vice President Corporate Strategic Planning, Joel Keiper

Vice President Clinical Transformation And Information Technology Integration, Matt Walsh

Director Of Radiology, Jay Pearlberg

Director Of Radiology, Mark I Burnstein

Director Of Radiology, Peter J Feczko

Director Of Radiology, Randall R Walter

Director Of Radiology, Riffat K Ahmed

Director Of Radiology, Sabala R Mandava

Director Of Radiology, Sampath Ramachandran

Director Of Radiology, Suresh C Patel

Director Of Radiology, Todd R Aho

Director Of Radiology, Todd R Williams

Director Of Radiology, Syed Arbab Ali

Medical Director, Panayiotis Varelas

Vice President Information Technology, Veeresh Nama

Senior Vice President And Chief Development Officer, Mary Vogt

System Vice President Risk Finance And Insurance Services, John Mucha

Medical Director Of Perioperative Services, Gaylord Alexander

Vice President Of Finance, Asad Malik

Vp Of It Applications, Josephine Molle

Vice President For Research, Margot Lapointe

Director Of Radiology, David Mcvinnie

Director Of Radiology, Daniel Croteau

Medical Records Director, SUSAN GLEASON

Vp And Corporate Controller, Paul Kolpasky

Vice President And Medical Director, Usamah Mossallam

Vice President, Linda Gifford

Executive Vice President And Chief Strategy Officer, Seth Frazier

Medical Director, William O'neill

Svp And Cio, Paul Browne

Regional Vice President, Paul Szilagyi

Vice President Heart And Vascular Services, Ruth Fisher

Medical Director, Gwendolyn Graddy

Director Of Radiology, Zachary Delpropoto

Medical Director, Christopher Lewandowski

Vice President Associate General Counsel, Alice Macdermott

Secretary, Jasmine Parks

Secretary Iii, Alicia Bias

Vice Chairman Department Of Surgery, Arthur Carlin

Secretary, Mary Cantu

Secretary, Barbara Paul

Secretary Ii, Paulette Wojcik

Secretary Iii, Jacqueline Underwood

Secretary Iii, Marcia Hendrick

Medical Secretary, Diana Popp

Auditors: DELOITTE & TOUCHE LLP DETROI

LOCATIONS

HQ: HENRY FORD HEALTH SYSTEM
1 FORD PL, DETROIT, MI 482023450
Phone: 313 916-2600

HOSPITAL LOCATIONS

Henry Ford Allegiance Health
Henry Ford Hospital
Henry Ford Kingswood Hospital
Henry Ford Macomb Hospital - Clinton Township
Henry Ford West Bloomfield Hospital
Henry Ford Wyandotte Hospital

PRODUCTS/OPERATIONS

SELECTED SERVICES

Bariatric Surgery
Cancer
Heart & Vascular
Neurology & Neurosurgery
OptimEyes
Orthopedic Surgery
Primary Care
Transplant Services

COMPETITORS

Ascension Health
Beaumont Health System
Crittenton Hospital
Detroit Medical Center
Garden City Hospital
Harper-Hutzel Hospital
McLaren Health Care
Mount Clemens Regional Medical Center

OmniCare Health Plan
St. John Health
Total Health Care
Trinity Health (Novi)
University of Michigan Health System

HISTORICAL FINANCIALS

Company Type: Private

Income Statement				FYE: December 31
	REVENUE ($ mil.)	NET INCOME ($ mil.)	NET PROFIT MARGIN	EMPLOYEES
12/17	5,977	203	3.4%	23,000
12/14	1,514	(14)	—	—
12/13	4,517	135	3.0%	—
12/09	2,118	27	1.3%	—
Annual Growth	13.8%	28.8%	—	—

Heritage Commerce Corp

Heritage Commerce is the holding company for Heritage Bank of Commerce which operates about 15 branches in the southern and eastern regions of the San Francisco Bay area. Serving consumers and small to midsized businesses and their owners and managers the bank offers savings and checking accounts money market accounts and CDs as well as cash management services and loans. Commercial and commercial real estate loans make up most of the company's loan portfolio which is rounded out by land construction and home equity loans.

EXECUTIVES

Evp And Cfo, Lawrence D. McGovern, age 64, $260,753 total compensation

President And Ceo, Walter T. (Walt) Kaczmarek, age 67, $368,509 total compensation

Evp And Director Business Development, Robert P. (Bob) Gionfriddo, age 73

Evp Banking Division, Michael E. Benito, $244,826 total compensation

Coo, Keith A. Wilton, $243,025 total compensation

Evp And Chief Credit Officer, David E. Porter, $260,738 total compensation

Evp And Corporate Secretary, Deborah K. (Debbie) Reuter

Evp Hoa And Deposit Services, Teresa Powell

Vice President, Nancy Landy

Vice President Business Development Officer, David Beronio
Senior Vice President, Mike Hansen
Vice President And Financial Planning And Analysis, Minny Sue
Vice President Account Manager, Greg Ketell
Vice President Audit, Michael Egbujor
Chairman, Jack W. Conner, age 79
Auditors: Crowe LLP

LOCATIONS

HQ: Heritage Commerce Corp
150 Almaden Boulevard, San Jose, CA 95113
Phone: 408 947-6900
Web: www.heritagecommercecorp.com

PRODUCTS/OPERATIONS

2017 Sales

	$ mil.	% of total
Interest		
Loans including fees	86	74
Taxable securities	14	12
Other	7	6
Interest expense	(5.4)	-
Noninterest		
Service charges & fees on deposit accounts	3	3
Increase in cash surrender value of life insurance	2	1
Gain on sales of SBA loans	1	1
Servicing income	1	1
Other	3	2
Total	**111**	**100**

COMPETITORS

Bank of America	JPMorgan Chase
Bank of the West	MUFG Americas Holdings
Citibank	SVB Financial
Comerica	U.S. Bancorp
First Republic (CA)	Wells Fargo

HISTORICAL FINANCIALS

Company Type: Public

Income Statement				FYE: December 31
	ASSETS ($ mil.)	NET INCOME ($ mil.)	INCOME AS % OF ASSETS	EMPLOYEES
12/18	3,097	35	1.1%	302
12/17	2,843	24	0.8%	278
12/16	2,571	27	1.1%	263
12/15	2,362	16	0.7%	260
12/14	1,617	13	0.8%	242
Annual Growth	**17.6%**	**27.4%**	—	**5.7%**

2018 Year-End Financials

Debt ratio: 1.00%	No. of shares (mil.): 43
Return on equity: 11.00%	Dividends
Cash ($ mil.): 165	Yield: 4.0%
Current ratio: —	Payout: 79.0%
Long-term debt ($ mil.): —	Market value ($ mil.): 491

	STOCK PRICE ($) FY Close	P/E High/Low	PER SHARE ($) Earnings	Dividends	Book Value
12/18	11.00	21 13	1.00	0.00	8.00
12/17	15.00	26 21	1.00	0.00	7.00
12/16	14.00	20 13	1.00	0.00	7.00
12/15	12.00	26 17	0.00	0.00	8.00
12/14	9.00	21 19	0.00	0.00	7.00
Annual Growth	**6.5%**	— —	**18.9%**	**25.0%**	**5.1%**

Heritage Financial Corp (WA)

Heritage Financial is ready to answer the call of Pacific Northwesterners seeking to preserve their heritage. Heritage Financial is the holding company for Heritage Bank which operates more than 65 branches throughout Washington and Oregon. Boasting nearly $4 billion in assets the bank offers a range of deposit products to consumers and businesses such as CDs IRAs and checking savings NOW and money market accounts. Commercial and industrial loans account for over 50% of Heritage Financial's loan portfolio while mortgages secured by multi-family real estate comprise about 5%. The bank also originates single-family mortgages land development construction loans and consumer loans.

Operations

The bank also does business under the Central Valley Bank name in the Yakima and Kittitas counties of Washington and under the Whidbey Island Bank name on Whidbey Island.

About 79% of Heritage Financial's total revenue came from loan interest (including fees) in 2014 while another 7% came from interest on its investment securities. The rest of its revenue came from service charges and other fees (8%) Merchant Visa income (1%) and other miscellaneous fees. The company had a staff of 748 employees at the end of that year.

Geographic Reach

The Olympia-based bank operates more than 65 branches across Washington and the greater Portland area. It has additional offices in eastern Washington mostly in Yakima county.

Sales and Marketing

Heritage targets small and medium-sized businesses along with their owners as well as individuals.

Financial Performance

Fueled by loan and deposit growth from a series of bank acquisitions Heritage Financial's revenues and profits have been on the rise in recent years.

The company's revenue jumped 70% to a record $137.6 million in 2014 mostly thanks to new loan business stemming from its acquisition of Washington Banking Company. Deposit service charge income also increased thanks to new deposit business from the acquisition.

Higher revenue in 2014 allowed Heritage Financial's net income to more than double to a record $21 million while its operating cash levels rose 66% to $51.3 million on higher cash earnings and net proceeds from the sale of its loans.

Strategy

The bank reiterated in 2015 that it would continue to pursue strategic acquisitions of community banks to grow market share across the Pacific Northwest (its region of expertise) expand its business lines and grow its loan and deposit business.

With its focus on business and commercial lending the bank also in 2015 emphasized the importance of seeking high asset quality loans lending to familiar markets that have a historical record of success. Recruiting and retaining "highly competent personnel" to execute its strategies was also key to its long-term agenda.

Mergers and Acquisitions

In May 2014 Heritage acquired Washington Banking Company and its Whidbey Island Bank subsidiary for $265 million which "significantly expanded and enhanced" its product offerings across its core geographic market.

In July 2013 the bank acquired Puyallup Washington-based Valley Community Bancshares and its eight Valley Bank branches for $44 million. In January 2013 the company purchased Lakewood Washington-based Northwest Commercial Bank along with its two branch locations in Washington state for $5 million.

EXECUTIVES

President Ceo And Director Heritage Financial And Ceo Heritage Bank, Brian L. Vance, age 64, $494,316 total compensation
Evp And Cfo Heritage Financial And Heritage Bank, Donald J. Hinson, age 58, $255,084 total compensation
Evp And Chief Credit Officer Heritage Bank, David A. Spurling, age 66, $237,342 total compensation
Evp Heritage Financial And President And Coo Heritage Bank, Jeffrey J. (Jeff) Deuel, $291,516 total compensation
Evp And Chief Lending Officer Heritage Bank, Bryan D. McDonald, age 47, $261,374 total compensation
Vp Marketing Manager, Shaun Carson
Vice President And Financial Reporting Manager, Patrice Hernandez
Chairman, Brian S. Charneski, age 57
Board Member, Stephen Dennis
Auditors: Crowe LLP

LOCATIONS

HQ: Heritage Financial Corp (WA)
201 Fifth Avenue S.W., Olympia, WA 98501
Phone: 360 943-1500
Web: www.HF-WA.com

PRODUCTS/OPERATIONS

2014 Sales

	$ mil.	% of total
Interest income		
Interest and fees on loans	110	79
Investment securities	10	7
Others	1	-
Non-interest income		
Service charges and others	11	8
Merchant Visa income	1	1
Others	4	5
Total	**138**	**100**

COMPETITORS

Bank of America	U.S. Bancorp
Columbia Banking	Washington Federal
FS Bancorp	Wells Fargo
KeyCorp	

HISTORICAL FINANCIALS

Company Type: Public

Income Statement				FYE: December 31
	ASSETS ($ mil.)	NET INCOME ($ mil.)	INCOME AS % OF ASSETS	EMPLOYEES
12/18	5,317	53	1.0%	859
12/17	4,113	42	1.0%	735
12/16	3,879	39	1.0%	760
12/15	3,651	37	1.0%	717
12/14	3,458	21	0.6%	748
Annual Growth	**11.4%**	**26.1%**	—	**3.5%**

2018 Year-End Financials

Debt ratio: 0.00%	No. of shares (mil.): 37
Return on equity: 8.00%	Dividends
Cash ($ mil.): 162	Yield: 2.0%
Current ratio: —	Payout: 53.0%
Long-term debt ($ mil.): —	Market value ($ mil.): 1,096

	STOCK PRICE ($) FY Close	P/E High/Low	PER SHARE ($) Earnings	Dividends	Book Value
12/18	30.00	25 19	1.00	1.00	21.00
12/17	31.00	23 16	1.00	1.00	17.00
12/16	26.00	20 13	1.00	1.00	16.00
12/15	19.00	16 12	1.00	1.00	16.00
12/14	18.00	23 19	1.00	1.00	15.00
Annual Growth	14.1%	— —	16.1%	9.5%	8.3%

Hershey Company (The)

The Hershey Company works to spread Almond Joy and lots of Kisses. With its portfolio of more than 80 global brands the #1 chocolate producer in North America has built a big business manufacturing such well-known chocolate and candy brands as Hershey's Kisses Reese's peanut butter cups Twizzlers Mounds and Almond Joy candy bars (under a license) York peppermint patties and Kit Kat wafer bars. Hershey also makes grocery goods including baking chocolate chocolate syrup cocoa mix cookies snack nuts breath mints and bubble gum. Beyond candy Hershey's has expanded into the snacks category. Products from the chocolate king are sold to a variety of wholesale distributors and retailers throughout North America and exported overseas.

Operations

Hershey's operations consist of two business segments North America 90% of revenue and International and Other 10% of revenue. The company makes and sells more than 80 name brands led by Hershey's and Reese's as well as Krackle Kit Kat and York. Other popular brand franchises are Twizzlers Mounds York Ice Breakers and Bubble Yum which fall within the company's sweets and refreshment business unit. Through acquisitions Hershey has added snack brands such as Skinny Pop popcorn and other "better-for-you" snacks and Krave meat snacks (jerky).

Geographic Reach

Hershey's North America segment accounts for 90% of revenue and it caters to the traditional chocolate and non-chocolate confectionery market as well as grocery and growing snacks markets in the US and Canada.

International and Other (10% of revenue) has operations in China Mexico Brazil India and Malaysia primarily for consumers in these regions. The segment also distributes and sells confectionery products in export markets within Asia Latin America Middle East Europe Africa and other regions. It also includes global retail operations including Hershey's Chocolate World stores in Hershey Pennsylvania; New York; Las Vegas; Niagara Falls (Ontario); Dubai; and Singapore as well as operations associated with licensing the use of certain of Hershey's trademarks and products to third parties around the world.

Sales and Marketing

Two customers account for 40% of Hershey's sales. The biggest is McLane Co. 30% of revenue the primary distributor of Hershey products to Walmart while Target supplies another 10% of Hershey's sales.

Hershey leverages a staff of full-time sales representatives and food brokers to peddle its products to customers. In general the confectionery company counts wholesale distributors chain grocery stores mass merchandiser chain drug stores vending companies wholesale clubs convenience stores dollar stores concessionaires and department stores among its vast customer set. Hershey's distribution network ships its products from its manufacturing plants to strategically located distribution centers using common carriers to deliver products from there to customers.

The company makes a point to launch new versions of old favorites such as Jolly Rancher lollipops and bite-sized chocolate bars. Although chocolate bars take center stage it offers sugar-free chocolate to tempt the growing number of diabetic and overweight consumers. Moving into the snack aisle Hershey has rolled out cookies 100-calorie treats and granola bars.

Financial Performance

Hershey's revenue has trended steadily higher over the past 10 years except for a slip in sales in 2015. Sales rose about 5% a year over the decade.

The rate slowed to 1% 2017 when sales totaled $7.5 billion from 2016 sales. The company benefited from favorable currency exchange rates and from new products such as Hershey's Cookie Layer Crunch Hershey's Gold and Hershey's and Reese's Popped Snack Mix and Chocolate Dipped Pretzels.

Net income reached $783 million in 2017 a 9% increase from 2016 due to lower costs in 2017.

Hershey added about $83 million to its cash holdings to reach $380 million in 2017. Its operations generated $1.2 billion while investing and financing activities used $328.6 million and $843 million respectively.

Strategy

Hershey's growth strategy includes expanding its snack foods business while continuing to invest in its core confectionery business. The chocolate maker is bolstering its snack food line up to capitalize on US consumers' growing appetite for healthier snacks. With consumers in the US snacking more than in years past Hershey has begun offering more mixed snack options including nut pretzel and chocolate mixes. The company plans to introduce additional snack categories and might pursue acquisitions of companies that produce protein-based and other types of snacks it hasn't traditionally offered. Hershey also continues to invest in its iconic brands including Hershey's Reese's and Hershey's Kisses.

To compete with online sweets and snacks purveyors Hershey in 2017 announced plans to significantly ramp up its e-commerce operations through potential collaborations with brick-and-mortar retailers and invest more money in its technology infrastructure.

In addition to its growth initiatives the company is also cutting costs to improve profitably particularly in international markets. In 2017 Hershey announced it would lay off about 15% of its global workforce. The employee reduction intended to improve operating margins between 2017 and 2019 affected about 2700 mostly hourly workers outside of the US.

Mergers and Acquisitions

Hershey's strategic focus is on expanding its global presence as it jockeys to capture market share from rivals Mars and Kraft which owns Cadbury.

In early 2018 Hershey acquired Amplify Snack Brands a high-growth snack food company that makes SkinnyPop its market leading healthy popcorn brand. The transaction was valued at $1.6 billion and helped Hershey develop a broader portfolio of consumer snacking brands especially as they pertain to "better-for-you" products that feature clean simple and transparent ingredients. Later that year it announced plans to buy Pirate Brands from B&G Foods for $420 million. Pirate Brands includes Pirate's Booty cheese puffs along with the Smart Puffs and Original Tings brands.

In 2016 the company acquired Ripple Brand Collective LLC a privately held company based in Congers New York that owns the barkTHINS mass premium chocolate snacking brand for approximately $285 million. The acquisition was made to broaden the company's product offerings in the premium and portable snacking categories.

Company Background

The Hershey Company is the legacy of Milton Hershey of Pennsylvania Dutch origin. Apprenticed in 1872 at age 15 to a candy maker Hershey started Lancaster Caramel Company at age 30. In 1893 at the Chicago Exposition he saw a new chocolate-making machine and in 1900 he sold the caramel operations for $1 million to start a chocolate factory. Chocolate proved to be a wise decision as the company made the name Hershey synonymous with American chocolate over the century.

HISTORY

The Hershey Company is the legacy of Milton Hershey of Pennsylvania Dutch origin. Apprenticed in 1872 at age 15 to a candy maker Hershey started Lancaster Caramel Company at age 30. In 1893 at the Chicago Exposition he saw a new chocolate-making machine and in 1900 he sold the caramel operations for $1 million to start a chocolate factory.

The factory was completed in 1905 in Derry Church Pennsylvania and renamed Hershey Foods the next year. Chocolate Kisses individually hand-wrapped in silver foil were introduced in 1907. Two years later the candy man founded the Milton Hershey School an orphanage; the company was donated to a trust in 1918 and for years existed solely to fund the school. Hershey went public in 1927.

EXECUTIVES

Senior Vice President, Thomas Hernquist
President And Ceo, Michele G. Buck, age 58
Svp And Chief Product Supply And Technology Officer, Terence L. O'Day, age 69, $590,061 total compensation
Svp And Cfo, Patricia A. Little, age 59, $629,412 total compensation
Regional President Aemea, Steven C. Schiller
President U.s., Todd W. Tillemans
Vice President Us Finance, Todd Cunfer
Vice President, Joe Beck
National Account Manager, Mike Jauch
Vice President Chief Talent Officer, Chris Scalia
Vice President Finance, Gayla Molinelli
Vice President Technology And, Simon Viltz
Vice President Corporate Communications And Corporate Social Responsibility, Leigh E Horner
Senior Vice President General Counsel Secretary, Damien Atkins
Chairman, John P. (J.P.) Bilbrey, age 62
Vp Treasurer, Rosa Stroh
Vice Chairman For Finance And Informatics, Doug Eggli
Assistant Secretary, Kathleen Purcell
Board Member, Pamela Arway
Board Member, Anthony Palmer
Board Member, Anyee Davis
Auditors: Ernst & Young LLP

LOCATIONS

HQ: Hershey Company (The)
19 East Chocolate Avenue, Hershey, PA 17033
Phone: 717 534 4200   **Fax:** 717 531-6161
Web: www.hersheys.com

2017 Sales

	$ mil.	% of total
North America	6,621	88
International and Other	894	12
Total	**7,515**	**100**

2017 Sales

	$ mil.	% of total
United States	6,264	83
Other	1,252	17
Total	**7,515**	**100**

COMPETITORS

Ferrero	Mars Incorporated
Flowers Foods	Mondelez International
Ghirardelli Chocolate	Nestlé
Godiva Chocolatier	Otis Spunkmeyer
Guittard	Russell Stover
Kellogg	Smucker
Lindt & Spr ngli	Tootsie Roll

HISTORICAL FINANCIALS

Company Type: Public

Income Statement				FYE: December 31
	REVENUE ($ mil.)	NET INCOME ($ mil.)	NET PROFIT MARGIN	EMPLOYEES
12/18	7,791	1,178	15.1%	16,420
12/17	7,515	783	10.4%	16,910
12/16	7,440	720	9.7%	17,980
12/15	7,387	513	6.9%	20,710
12/14	7,422	847	11.4%	22,450
Annual Growth	1.2%	8.6%	—	(7.5%)

2018 Year-End Financials

Debt ratio: 58.00%
Return on equity: 102.00%
Cash ($ mil.): 588
Current ratio: 1.00
Long-term debt ($ mil.): 3,254

No. of shares (mil.): 210
Dividends
Yield: 3.0%
Payout: 49.0%
Market value ($ mil.): 22,479

	STOCK PRICE ($) FY Close	P/E High/Low	PER SHARE ($) Earnings	Dividends	Book Value
12/18	107.00	20 16	6.00	3.00	7.00
12/17	114.00	31 27	4.00	3.00	4.00
12/16	103.00	33 24	3.00	2.00	4.00
12/15	89.00	46 35	2.00	2.00	5.00
12/14	104.00	28 23	4.00	2.00	7.00
Annual Growth	0.8%	— —	10.3%	7.8%	0.3%

Hertz Global Holdings Inc (New)

Hertz Global Holdings is a world leader in car rental. On its own and through agents and licensees Hertz operates about 10200 rental locations in about 150 countries under the Hertz Dollar and Thrifty brands. About two-thirds of its US revenue comes from airport locations. Its fleet includes approximately 740000 cars from General Motors Nissan Toyota and other manufacturers. In addition to its signature car rental services its Donlen subsidiary offers fleet leasing and management services. The newest iteration of Hertz was formed in 2016 when it was spun off from Herc Holdings.

Change in Company Type
In the summer of 2016 the original Hertz Global Holdings spun off its car rental business and changed its name to Herc Holdings and is now focused solely on its Herc Rental equipment operations.

Operations
Hertz's three core operating segments include: US Car Rental which consists of company-owned and franchisee car rental locations in the US; International Car Rental; and All Other Operations which includes Donlen the firm's fleet leasing and management subsidiary. The US Car Rental business accounts for some 70% of sales.

Geographic Reach
Florida-based Hertz operates throughout North America Europe Latin America Asia Australia New Zealand Africa and the Middle East. It has a reservation and financial center near Dublin Ireland and European headquarters outside London.

Hertz operates 1600 US and 1500 non-US airport rental locations. Its has 2600 US and 4500 off-airport locations which primarily serve courtesy car customers and travelers going to or from airports.

Sales and Marketing
Hertz advertises its car rental services through television newspapers direct mail and the internet. Its other forms of marketing and promotion include travel industry business partnerships and press and public relations activities.

Financial Performance
Over the last five years Hertz Global Holdings' sales fell for two years before rebounding. Depreciation of its car inventory has kept the company in the red in recent years and high debts mean the company is struggling to service its interest payments.

In 2018 the company's sales grew 8% to $9.5 billion thanks to higher revenue per transaction day revenue per unit per month and total transaction days as well as currency tailwinds.

Hertz reported a net loss of $220 million due to a $2.7 billion write-down in the value of its car inventory compared to $2.8 billion and $2.6 billion write-downs in the two preceding years.

Despite continued net losses Hertz is still decently cash generative. In 2018 the company's cash on hand fell $94 million ending the year at $1.4 billion. Hertz' operations generated $2.6 billion and its financing yielded $1.6 billion partially offset by the $4.2 billion used in investing activities. Vehicle purchases and debt repayments were Hertz' main cash uses in 2018.

Strategy
Beset by heavy depreciation on its stock of unpopular cars weak used-vehicle values slumping car rental rates and the rise of smart taxi firms such as Uber Hertz booked stinging losses in 2016 2017 and 2018. CEO Kathryn Marinello implemented a turnaround plan the following year. The company is increasing spending on higher value cars after its previous decision to shrink fleet sizes hit profits.

Company Background
In 1918 22-year-old John Jacobs opened a Chicago car rental business with 12 Model T Fords that he had repaired. By 1923 when Yellow Cab entrepreneur John Hertz bought Jacobs' business it had revenues of about $1 million. Jacobs continued as top executive of the company renamed Hertz Drive-Ur-Self System. Three years later General Motors acquired the company when it bought Yellow Truck from John Hertz. Hertz introduced the first car rental charge card in 1926 opened its first airport location at Chicago's Midway Airport in 1932 and initiated the first one-way (rent-it-here/leave-it-there) plan in 1933. The company expanded into Canada in 1938 and Europe in 1950.

EXECUTIVES

President And Chief Executive Officer Director, Kathryn V. (Kathy) Marinello
Executive Vice President Of Pricing Revenue Management And Fleet Operations, Frederic (Fred) Deschamps
President Donlen Corporation, Tom Callahan
Executive Vice President Global Sales, Robert J. (Bob) Stuart
Executive Vice President And Chief Retail Operations Officer North America, Paul Stone
Executive Vice President And Chief Financial Officer, Jamere Jackson
Executive Vice President And Chief Human Resources Officer, Murali Kuppuswamy
Executive Vice President And Chief Marketing Officer, Jodi Allen
Executive Vice President General Counsel And Secretary, Richard Frecker
Executive Vice President And Chief Information Officer, Opal G. Perry
Vice President Ecommerce, Raymond Kunik
Vice President Infrastructure Services, Craig Bonza
Vice President Marketing International, Vincent Gillet
Svp And Cto, Robert Moore
Svp And Treasurer, Scott Massengill
Vice President Business Applications, Barry Lewis
Executive Vice President Global Sales, Bob Stuart
Senior Vice President Operations Services, Rob Solomon
Vp Corporate And Ip Law And Associate General Counsel, Brian Waldbaum
Senior Vice President And Chief Accounting Officer, Eric Esper
Vice President Information Technology, William Ruppel
Division Vice President, Jeff Pitz
Chairman, Henry R. Keizer
Member Board Of Directors, Dave Barnes
Auditors: Ernst & Young LLP

LOCATIONS

HQ: Hertz Global Holdings Inc (New)
8501 Williams Road, Estero, FL 33928
Phone: 239 301-7000
Web: www.hertz.com

2018 sales

	$ mil.	% of total
US	7,211	76
International	2,293	24
Total	**9,504**	**100**

PRODUCTS/OPERATIONS

2018 sales

	$ mil.	% of total
Worldwide Vehicle Rental		
US Rental Car	6,480	68
International Rental Car	2,276	24
All other operations	748	8
Total	**9,504**	**100**

COMPETITORS

Avis Budget	Ryder System
Enterprise Rent-A-Car	Uber
Europcar	

HISTORICAL FINANCIALS

Company Type: Public

Income Statement

FYE: December 31

	REVENUE ($ mil.)	NET INCOME ($ mil.)	NET PROFIT MARGIN	EMPLOYEES
12/18	9,504	(225)	—	38,000
12/17	8,803	327	3.7%	37,000
12/16	8,803	(491)	—	36,000
12/15	9,017	273	3.0%	—
12/14	9,475	(82)	—	—
Annual Growth	0.1%	—	—	—

2018 Year-End Financials

Debt ratio: 76.00%
Return on equity: (-17.00%)
Cash ($ mil.): 1,127
Current ratio: 1.00
Long-term debt ($ mil.): 16,324

No. of shares (mil.): 84
Dividends
Yield: —
Payout: —
Market value ($ mil.): 1,147

	STOCK PRICE ($) FY Close	P/E High/Low		PER SHARE ($) Earnings	Dividends	Book Value
12/18	14.00	—	—	(3.00)	0.00	13.00
12/17	22.00	7	2	4.00	0.00	18.00
12/16	22.00	—	—	(6.00)	0.00	13.00
Annual Growth	(10.8%)	—	—	—	—	(0.6%)

Hess Corp

Oil and gas company Hess can profess to owning no less than 1.1 billion barrels of oil equivalent worldwide. Crude oil is the company's primary output resource but it also produces natural gas and NGLs (natural gas liquids). Its primary operations are in the US but it also has producing interests in Denmark Malaysia and Thailand. It also offers midstream services including gathering compressing and transporting hydrocarbons as well as propane storage. Hess has been prospecting for oil since the 1920s.

HISTORY

In 1919 British oil entrepreneur Lord Cowdray formed Amerada Corporation to explore for oil in North America. Cowdray soon hired geophysicist Everette DeGolyer a pioneer in oil geology research. DeGolyer's systematic methods helped Amerada not only find oil deposits faster but also pick up fields missed by competitors. DeGolyer became president of Amerada in 1929 but left in 1932 to work independently.

After WWII Amerada began exploring overseas and during the 1950s entered pipelining and refining. It continued its overseas exploration through Oasis a consortium formed in 1964 with Marathon Shell and Continental to explore in Libya.

Leon Hess began to buy stock in Amerada in 1966. The son of immigrants he had entered the oil business during the Depression selling "resid" — thick refining leftovers that refineries discarded — from a 1929 Dodge truck in New Jersey. He bought the resid cheap and sold it as heating fuel to hotels. Hess also speculated buying oil at low prices in the summer and selling it for a profit in the winter. He later bought more trucks a transportation network refineries and gas stations and went into oil exploration. Expansion pushed up debt so in 1962 Leon's company went public as Hess Oil and Chemical after merging with Cletrac Corporation.

Hess acquired Amerada in 1969 after an ownership battle with Phillips Petroleum. During the Arab oil embargo of the 1970s Amerada Hess began drilling on Alaska's North Slope. Oilman T. Boone Pickens bought up a chunk of Amerada Hess stock during the 1980s spurring takeover rumors. They proved premature.

Amerada Hess completed a pipeline in 1993 to carry natural gas from the North Sea to the UK. In 1995 Leon Hess stepped down as CEO (he died in 1999) and his son John took the position. Amerada Hess sold its 81% interest in the Northstar oil field in Alaska to BP and the next year Petro-Canada bought the company's Canadian operations. In 1996 the company acquired a 25% stake (sold in 2002) in UK-based Premier Oil.

The company teamed with Dixons Stores Group in 1997 to market gas in the UK. It also purchased 66 Pick Wick convenience store/service stations.

In 1998 Amerada Hess signed production-sharing contracts with a Malaysian oil firm as part of its strategy to move into Southeast Asia and began to sell natural gas to retail customers in the UK.

To offset losses brought on by depressed oil prices Amerada Hess sold assets worth more than $300 million in 1999 including its southeastern pipeline network gas stations in Georgia and South Carolina and Gulf Coast terminals. It also moved into Latin America acquiring stakes in fields in offshore Brazil.

In 2000 Amerada Hess acquired Statoil Energy Services which markets natural gas and electricity to industrial and commercial customers in the northeastern US. It also announced its intention to buy LASMO a UK-based exploration and production company before Italy's Eni topped the Amerada Hess offer.

Undeterred in 2001 the company bought Dallas-based exploration and production company Triton Energy for $2.7 billion in cash and $500 million in assumed debt. Amerada Hess also acquired the Gulf of Mexico assets of LLOG Exploration Company for $750 million. That year however stiff competition prompted Amerada Hess to put its UK gas and electricity supply business on the auction block. The unit was sold to TXU (now Energy Future Holdings) in 2002.

In 2003 Amerada Hess sold 26 oil and gas fields in the Gulf of Mexico to Anadarko Petroleum. Amerada Hess was granted permission by the Equatorial Guinea government in 2004 to develop 29 new wells in that country. That year Amerada Hess acquired a 65% stake in Trabant Holdings International a Russia-based production and exploration company.

The company re-entered its former oil and gas production operations in the Waha concessions in Libya in 2006. Also that year it changed its name to Hess Corporation.

Looking to grow its position in the lucrative Bakken oil shale play in North Dakota in 2010 the company acquired American Oil and Gas in a $450 million stock deal that added 85000 net acres to Hess' holdings. It also bought 167000 acres in the Bakken play from TRZ Energy LLC for $1 billion.

Hess' former refinery in the US Virgin Islands was operated as a joint venture with Venezuela's state oil company Petr leos de Venezuela S.A (PDVSA). However the loss-making HOVENSA refinery was shut down in 2012 and converted to an oil storage terminal. In 2013 Hess announced that it completed its exit from the refining business by closing its Port Reading New Jersey refinery.

As part of its strategy of unwinding its refining and marketing assets in 2013 Hess sold Russian subsidiary Samara-Nafta to LUKOIL for $2.05 billion. It also sold its energy marketing business to Direct Energy for a $1.2 billion.

To raise cash it also sold its 2.7% interest in in India's Azeri Chirag and Guneshli Fields and its 2.4% stake in the associated BTC pipeline to ONGC Videsh for $1 billion. It also sold its Indonesian oil and gas assets for $1.3 billion.

That year it also sold 20 liquid petroleum products terminals along the US East Coast with total storage capacity of 39 million barrels to Buckeye Partners for $850 million.

The Utica Shale in Ohio was a growth area. However in 2014 low gas prices prompted Hess agreed to sell 74000 acres of dry gas acreage in the Utica Shale for $924 million in order to focus on more lucrative oil plays.

That year it also sold its oil and gas assets in Thailand to PTT Exploration and Production for $1 billion.

EXECUTIVES

Svp Hr, Brian Bohling
Chairman And Ceo, John B. Hess, age 65, $1,500,000 total compensation
Svp And Cfo, John P. Rielly, age 56, $775,000 total compensation
President And Coo, Gregory P. (Greg) Hill, age 57, $1,100,000 total compensation
Svp Global Production, Michael R. (Mike) Turner, age 59, $575,000 total compensation
Svp Offshore, Brian D. Truelove, age 60
Svp Developments Drilling And Completions, Richard Lynch
Svp Exploration, Barbara Lowery-Yilmaz, age 62
Vice President, Paul Fejer
Vice President Distribution, Chip Small
Executive Vice President, David Chaimengyew
Executive Vice President, Henrik Lund
Vp Controller Hetco, Dan Devine
Vice President Corporate Planning And Strategy, Colin Davies
Vice President Natural Gas Sales, Todd Porter
Senior Vice President Of Finance, John Scelfo
Executive Vice President, Doris Moore
Vice President Of Sales And Marketing, Patrick A Dunn
Vice President Projects Asia Pacific, Brock Hajdik
Vice President Land Global Exploration, John Y Christopher
Vice President, Jay Wilson
Vice President Human Resources Operations, Helena Deal
Executive Vice President Exploration And Productio, Eloise Castillo
Vice President Retail Field Operations, David Klavsons
Senior Vice President Development And Technical Su, Janice Flaherty
Vice President Specialist Information Security Engineer, Hamish Brown
Vice President International Exploration, Grant Gilchrist
Executive Vice President, Abhay Shah
Senior Vice President Operations And Marketing, Joseph Serafino
Vice President Bakken Wf Execution, David Mckay
Executive Vice President, Greg Hill
Vice President Of Information Technology, Debbie Mcmaster
Vice President Government And External Affairs, Drew Maloney
Vice President, Michael Fennessy
Vp Controller Hetco, Daniel Devine
Vice President, Robert Vaio
Vice President Exploration, Bob Spinieo
Vice President, Martin Edwards
Vice President, Barclay Collins
Vice President Corporate Tax, Martin Dunagin
Vice President Secretary, Joyce Crawley
Vice President Controller, Kevin Wilcox
Svp Hr And Officer Management, Andrew Slentz

Assistant Vice President, Benjamin Yau
Senior Vice President Strategy Commercial And
  New Business Development, Scott Sloan
Vice President Asia Pacific, Kakok Sauu
Vice President Corporate Communicati, Will Rea
Vice President, Stuart Lake
Senior Vice President E And P, Brent Cheshire
Vice President Government And External Affairs,
  Alex Mistri
Vice President, Bill Hanna
Vp Global Offshore Production, Gerbert Schoonman
Svp Global Exploration And New Ventures, Bill
  Drennen
Vp Exploration Global Strategy And Portfolio, Neil
  Piggott
Senior Vice President, Hess Tower
Vice President Human Resources, Zane Zumbahlen
Vice President Cognitive Solutions Us Financial
  Services Marketibm Global Markets Executive
  Staff, Nicholas Rogers
Vice President, Walter Merrill
Vice President Human Resources, Robbin Suess
Vice President Marketing, Deon Newman
Director, James H. (Jim) Quigley, age 67
Corporate Treasurer, Eric Fishman
Assistant Treasurer, Christopher Molinaro
Board Member, Kevin Meyers
Board Member, Risa Lavizzo-mourey
Board Member, Leonard Coleman
Auditors: Ernst & Young LLP

LOCATIONS

HQ: Hess Corp
  1185 Avenue of the Americas, New York, NY 10036
Phone: 212 997-8500
Web: www.hess.com

2016 sales

	% of total
US	65
Europe	13
Africa	12
Asia & other regions	10
Total	100

PRODUCTS/OPERATIONS

2016 sales

	% of total
Exploration and Production	90
Bakken Midstream	10
Total	100

2016 Sales

	% of total
Crude oil	76
Natural gas	16
Natural gas liquids	6
Other	2
Total	100

COMPETITORS

Abraxas Petroleum	Gastar Exploration
BP	Koch Industries Inc.
CMA CGM	Marathon Oil
Chevron	Norsk Hydro ASA
ConocoPhillips	Occidental Petroleum
Continental Energy	PEMEX
Devon Energy	PETROBRAS
Dominion Energy	Petr leos de
Double Eagle Petroleum	Venezuela
ERHC	Pioneer Oil and Gas
Encana Oil & Gas (USA)	Royal Dutch Shell
Inc.	Serica Energy
Eni	TOTAL
Exxon Mobil	

HISTORICAL FINANCIALS

Company Type: Public

Income Statement — FYE: December 31

	REVENUE ($ mil.)	NET INCOME ($ mil.)	NET PROFIT MARGIN	EMPLOYEES
12/18	6,466	(282)	—	1,708
12/17	5,405	(4,074)	—	2,075
12/16	4,844	(6,132)	—	2,304
12/15	6,561	(3,056)	—	2,770
12/14	11,439	2,317	20.3%	3,045
Annual Growth	(13.3%)	—	—	(13.5%)

2018 Year-End Financials

Debt ratio: 31.00%
Return on equity: (-3.00%)
Cash ($ mil.): 2,694
Current ratio: 2.00
Long-term debt ($ mil.): 6,605

No. of shares (mil.): 291
Dividends
  Yield: 2.0%
  Payout: —
Market value ($ mil.): 11,803

	STOCK PRICE ($) FY Close	P/E High/Low		PER SHARE ($) Earnings	Dividends	Book Value
12/18	41.00	—	—	(1.00)	1.00	33.00
12/17	47.00	—	—	(13.00)	1.00	35.00
12/16	62.00	—	—	(20.00)	1.00	46.00
12/15	48.00	—	—	(11.00)	1.00	68.00
12/14	74.00	13	9	8.00	1.00	78.00
Annual Growth (13.9%) (19.2%)		—	—	—	(0.0%)	

Hewlett Packard Enterprise Co

Hewlett Packard Enterprise (HPE) once part of the storied Hewlett-Packard Corp. designs and sells servers storage and networking equipment and provides technology services to help its large enterprise customers put together and deploy IT systems. HPE focuses its efforts on software-defined IT offerings for private public and hybrid cloud environments as well as technologies for industrial Internet of Things (IoT) applications. HPE is a global company and about two-thirds of its revenue comes from outside the US. It has a rich technology history and maintains a cache of about 16000 patents.

Operations

HPE has four operating segments: Hybrid IT Intelligent Edge Financial Services and corporate investments.

The Hybrid IT segment 80% of revenue provides software-defined servers storage data center networking and HPE Pointnext services. The traditional server and storage systems within the Hybrid IT segment face pricing and unit volume challenges as customers migrate to cloud-based systems.

The Intelligent Edge business 10% of revenue is composed of enterprise networking and security products and services for campus and branch environments. The segment includes the Aruba brand.

The Financial Services segment 10% of revenue provides leasing financing IT consumption and utility programs and asset management services.

Corporate Investments focuses on research and development projects. From its efforts come new technologies and ideas that HPE eventually turns into products and services. Its revenue is negligible and it typically posts small losses.

HPE uses third party contractors to make its hardware.

Geographic Reach

Palo Alto California-based HPE has operations and customers around the world. It has nearly 20 locations in the US and Puerto Rico and about 10 outside the US including sites in the UK India Brazil China Singapore and Taiwan.

The company's international customers provide about two-thirds of revenue and overseas sales have outpaced domestic sales in recent years.

Sales and Marketing

HPE customers are mostly large companies and government agencies organizations that usually are willing to spend on IT. The company reaches them through its own sales staff resellers distribution partners OEMs independent software vendors system integrators and consulting services companies. HPE account managers maintain relationships between the company's businesses and large enterprise customers.

HPE not only sells its own products and services but partners with a plethora of technologies companies to supplement its own offerings when designing and deploying customer systems.

Financial Performance

HPE's revenue slumped since the breakup of Hewlett-Packard Co. in 2015 and following the divestiture of two large segments HP Software and HP Enterprise Services.

In 2018 (ended November) the company's revenue rose about 7% to $30.1 billion from 2017 fueled by nearly 10% growth in overseas sales; US sales were about 2% higher. Stronger market demand boosted Hybrid IT sales along with a contribution from the Nimble acquisition toward storage sales. Intelligent Edge and Financial Services sales also rose year-to-year.

HPE posted net income of $1.9 billion in 2018 compared to $344 million the year before driven by lower costs and a bigger tax benefit than the company recorded in 2017.

The company closed 2018 with $4.8 billion in cash and equivalents half of what it had in 2017. The decrease came as the company spent on share repurchases and dividends debt payments and capital expenditures. In 2018 operations generated $2.9 billion while investing activities used $2.1 billion and financing activities used $5.6 billion.

Strategy

HPE is betting on what it calls the Intelligent Edge of computing which is the practice of putting more processing power in smart devices ? sensors autos oil rigs communications devices ? that collect information. The information has been processed before it gets to cloud computing environments. The company says that 75% of data is created by edge devices.

The company is investing$4 billion in the intelligent edge business over four years. So far revenue from the business has increased at a double-digit percentage annual rate and each category within the business campus and branch edge compute and Aruba services has contributed with higher sales.

The other significant area for HPE is its Hybrid IT business which allows customers to use a variety of cloud environments. The company's flagship offering in Hybrid IT HPE GreenLake has more than 400 customers on a pay-as-you-go model.

While the company is optimistic about it HPE might be late to the hybrid cloud party. Competitors such as NetApp and Nutanix have developed their own hybrid cloud products and are well-positioned in the market.

HPE doesn't lack for competitors in the overall enterprise IT market. Rivals include Dell Technologies Cisco Systems Lenovo Group Ltd. Oracle Fujitsu Ltd. Inspur Co. Huawei Technologies Hitachi Ltd. Juniper Networks and Arista Networks. With the wave of cloud services changing the way customers implement their computing system HPE also competes against Amazon Microsoft and Google.

The company continues its HPE Next initiative a program to streamline its offerings and business processes to support investments in higher growth and higher margin products and services. It includes consolidating manufacturing and support services locations streamlining business systems and reducing the number of countries in which it has a direct sales presence.

Mergers and Acquisitions

In 2019 HPE agreed to buy Cray Inc. a maker of high-performance computers for $1.3 billion net of cash. The deal would combine HPE's data gathering and analytics capabilities with Cray's supercomputing power to help customers make sense of massive amounts of data. The combined company would have a broader set of markets including enterprise academic and government customers. The deal HPE's biggest since it became a separate company in 2015 is expected to close by the first quarter of HPE's 2020 fiscal year (ended January 2020).

In 2018 HPE agreed to buy BlueData a developer of visualization software for artificial intelligence and analytics applications. HPE intends to combine BlueData's technology with its software-defined infrastructure to provide customers with faster visualizations of data. The deal is expected to close in early 2019.

Also in 2018 HPE acquired Cape Networks which develops tools for monitoring and measuring networks. HPE slotted Cape Networks in its Aruba subsidiary where the acquired technologies expanded Aruba's artificial intelligence-powered networking capabilities. Cape Networks brings tools for testing availability and performance of services and applications and issuing alerts when something is wrong. Terms were not disclosed.

HPE acquired Nimble Storage Inc. a provider of predictive all-flash and hybrid-flash storage systems for $1 billion. The acquisition was made to strengthen HPE's position in the hybrid cloud market as well as expand its flash storage offerings.

HPE acquired three companies in 2017: Cloud Technology Partners a cloud consulting design and advisory services company; Nimble Storage a provider of all-flash and hybrid storage solutions for a little more than $1 billion; SimpliVity a provider of software-defined computing infrastructure solutions for $650 million.

In 2016 HPE bought SGI (formerly Silicon Graphics) for $275 million. SGI's high performance computing products are used for data analytics and data management. The plan is to combine SGI's supercomputing capabilities to beef up HPE's enterprise offerings to provide faster and higher capacity analytics to customers. The deal is expected to close in early 2017. SGI reported a loss of $39 million on revenue of $529 million in 2015.

EXECUTIVES

President And Ceo, Margaret C. (Meg) Whitman, age 63, $1,500,058 total compensation
Evp And Chief Marketing And Communications Officer, Henry Gomez, age 56
Evp General Counsel And Secretary, John F. Schultz, age 55
Evp And Coo, Christopher P. (Chris) Hsu, age 48, $675,026 total compensation
Evp Human Resources, Alan May, age 61
Evp And General Manager Enterprise Group, Antonio Neri, age 52, $725,028 total compensation

Evp And Cfo, Timothy C. (Tim) Stonesifer, age 52, $675,026 total compensation
Vice President Human Resources, Seema Iyer
Vice President And General Manager Nokia Account, David Stone
Vice President Global Healthcare Services, Mary Mirabelli
Vice President Executive Assistant, Jeff Dolce
Vice President Product Management, Stephen Spellicy
Vice President Sales (global Accounts West Region), Lee Wilkerson
Ww Vice President Sales Big Data, Bruce Jones
Chairman, Patricia F. (Pat) Russo, age 66
Senior Vice President Finance Treasurer, Kirt Karros
Auditors: Ernst & Young LLP

LOCATIONS

HQ: Hewlett Packard Enterprise Co
6280 America Center Drive, San Jose, CA 95002
Phone: 650 687-5817
Web: www.hpe.com

2018 Sales

	$ mil.	% of total
US	10,192	33
Other Countries	20,660	67
Total	**30,852**	**100**

PRODUCTS/OPERATIONS

2018 Sales

	$ mil.	% of total
Products	19,504	63
Services	10,901	35
Financing Income	447	2
Total	**30,852**	**100**

2018 Sales

	$ mil.	% of total
Hybrid IT		
Compute	13,823	43
Storage	3,706	12
DC Networking	225	1
HPE Pointnext	7,279	23
Intelligent Edge		
HPE Aruba Product	2,619	8
HPE Aruba Services	310	1
Financial Services	3,671	12
Eliminations	(781)	-
Total	**30,852**	**100**

COMPETITORS

Amazon.com	Juniper Networks
Arista Networks	Lenovo
Cisco Systems	Microsoft
Dell	NetApp
Fujitsu	Oracle
Hitachi	salesforce.com
IBM	

HISTORICAL FINANCIALS

Company Type: Public

Income Statement				FYE: October 31
	REVENUE ($ mil.)	NET INCOME ($ mil.)	NET PROFIT MARGIN	EMPLOYEES
10/19	29,135	1,049	3.6%	61,600
10/18	30,852	1,908	6.2%	60,000
10/17	28,871	344	1.2%	66,000
10/16	50,123	3,161	6.3%	195,000
10/15	52,107	2,461	4.7%	240,000
Annual Growth	**(13.5%)**	**(19.2%)**	**—**	**(28.8%)**

2019 Year-End Financials

Debt ratio: 27.00%	No. of shares (mil.): 1,294
Return on equity: 5.00%	Dividends
Cash ($ mil.): 3,753	Yield: 3.0%
Current ratio: 1.00	Payout: 58.0%
Long-term debt ($ mil.): 9,395	Market value ($ mil.): 21,241

	STOCK PRICE ($) FY Close	P/E High/Low	PER SHARE ($) Earnings	Dividends	Book Value
10/19	16.00	22 16	1.00	0.00	13.00
10/18	15.00	16 10	1.00	0.00	15.00
10/17	14.00	118 62	0.00	0.00	15.00
10/16	22.00	13 7	2.00	0.00	19.00
10/15	15.00	13 11	1.00	0.00	19.00
Annual Growth	**2.8%**	**— —**	**(12.9%)**	**—**	**(9.0%)**

HILL/AHERN FIRE PROTECTION, LLC

EXECUTIVES

MBR, Michelle Colyar
Vice President Building Operat, Harold Hacker
Design Manager, Joe Fabis

LOCATIONS

HQ: HILL/AHERN FIRE PROTECTION, LLC
11045 GAGE AVE, FRANKLIN PARK, IL 601311437
Phone: 847 288-5100
Web: WWW.HILLGRP.COM

HISTORICAL FINANCIALS

Company Type: Private

Income Statement				FYE: December 31
	REVENUE ($ mil.)	NET INCOME ($ mil.)	NET PROFIT MARGIN	EMPLOYEES
12/11	5,669	186	3.3%	100
12/10	2,569	81	3.1%	—
Annual Growth	**120.7%**	**130.7%**	**—**	**—**

Hills Bancorporation

There's gold in them thar hills! Hills Bancorporation is the holding company for Hills Bank and Trust which has about a dozen branches located in the eastern Iowa counties of Johnson Linn and Washington. The bank provides standard commercial services to area individuals businesses government entities and institutional customers. Offerings include deposit accounts loans and debit and credit cards. Hills Bank and Trust also administers estates personal trusts and pension plans and provides farm management and investment advisory and custodial services. The bank traces its roots to 1904.

EXECUTIVES

Senior Vice President Director Of Retail, Tracy Stotler

Vice President Of Investments Trust And Wealth Management, Aaron Schaefer
Auditors: BKD, LLP

LOCATIONS

HQ: Hills Bancorporation
131 Main Street, Hills, IA 52235
Phone: 319 679-2291
Web: www.hillsbank.com

COMPETITORS

Ames National	MidWestOne
Bank of America	Regions Financial
Citigroup	U.S. Bancorp
Iowa First	Wells Fargo
Meta Financial Group	West Bancorporation

HISTORICAL FINANCIALS

Company Type: Public

Income Statement

FYE: December 31

	ASSETS ($ mil.)	NET INCOME ($ mil.)	INCOME AS % OF ASSETS	EMPLOYEES
12/18	3,042	37	1.2%	481
12/17	2,963	28	0.9%	499
12/16	2,656	32	1.2%	503
12/15	2,494	28	1.1%	464
12/14	2,334	27	1.2%	428
Annual Growth	6.8%	8.1%	—	3.0%

2018 Year-End Financials

Debt ratio: —
Return on equity: 10.00%
Cash ($ mil.): 43
Current ratio: —
Long-term debt ($ mil.): —
No. of shares (mil.): 9
Dividends
Yield: 0.0%
Payout: 19.0%
Market value ($ mil.): 567

	STOCK PRICE ($) FY Close	P/E High/Low	PER SHARE ($) Earnings	Dividends	Book Value
12/18	61.00	16 14	4.00	1.00	41.00
12/17	54.00	18 16	3.00	1.00	38.00
12/16	48.00	17 13	3.00	1.00	36.00
12/15	45.00	27 14	3.00	1.00	33.00
12/14	83.00	29 25	3.00	1.00	31.00
Annual Growth	(7.4%)	— —	8.1%	6.9%	7.4%

Hilltop Holdings, Inc.

With more than $14 billion in assets diversified financial holding company Hilltop Holdings' provides banking mortgage origination insurance and financial advisory services through its PlainsCapital Bank PrimeLending HilltopSecurities subsidiaries and National Lloyds. PlainsCapital offers community commercial and private banking through about 60 branches throughout Texas and holds more than $8 billion in deposits. PrimeLending generates mortgages in all 50 states and Washington DC through greater than 1500 loan offices. Hilltop Securities is an investment bank and is among the US' top financial advisors to municipalities based on transaction volume. Niche property and casualty insurance underwriter National Lloyds targets low-value dwellings in Texas.

Financial Performance

Despite posting decreases or middling gains in revenue the last three years a nearly 40% jump in 2015 following its acquisition of broker-dealer SWS Group and struggling First National Bank (which had been shut down by federal regulators) pushed Hilltop Holdings' revenue up 30% over the last five years. Losses in net income the last three years also mostly offset a 2015 jump in net income of about 90% which has increased about 10% since 2014.

Hilltop's revenue fell 10% to $1.4 billion in 2018. The reduction was driven by lower income from mortgage origination by the company's PrimeLending subsidiary (which underwent a cost reduction plan that included underperforming branch closures) and a drop in trading gains from derivative and trading portfolio activities caused by market volatility and competitive pricing pressures.

Declining revenue led to an 8% loss in net income which ended 2018 at $121 million.

In 2018 Hilltop added $104.5 million to its cash which totaled $778.5 million at year end. Operations provided $389.5 million and financing activities generated $4.6 million. Net changes in loans held for investment and purchases of securities available for sale drove investment spend of $289.7 million.

Strategy

As Hilltop Holdings works to reduce costs by closing underperforming mortgage origination offices the company is broadening its operations by introducing a new unit and beefing up its more successful businesses like financial advisory.

In 2019 the company launched Hilltop Opportunity Partners a merchant banking arm tasked with making long- and short-term non-control investments in middle-market companies external to the banking industry. The bank aims generally to invest between $5 million and $25 million. Notable transactions by the division include a preferred equity investment in Stan's Heating & Air Conditioning?which serves the Austin and Georgetown Texas region?and the sale of Illinois freight broker AFN to GlobalTranz. The company had invested $10 million in AFN.

That year the company also hired nine new financial advisors to its Private Client Group. The hires brought about $760 million in assets under management to Hilltop.

2018 saw the company deepened the presence of its PlainsCapital Bank subsidiary in Houston Texas with its $85 million acquisition of The Bank of River Oaks which specialized in commercial and healthcare lending and private banking. That buyout brought PlainsCapital three new branches approximately $340 million in loans and roughly $370 million in deposits.

Mergers and Acquisitions

Through its PlainsCapital subsidiary Hilltop in 2018 agreed to acquire The River Oaks Bank located in a posh region of Houston TX for $85 million.

Company Background

The company began life as Affordable Residential Communities (ARC) and spent its early days as a real estate investment trust (REIT). It went public in 2004 dropped its REIT status in 2006 and built up its collection of manufactured housing communities through acquisitions.

After several years of losses in the housing business the company chose to transition into another industry. It acquired NLASCO a niche provider of fire and homeowners insurance for manufactured homes and other low-value properties at the start of 2007. The company then renamed itself Hilltop Holdings.

EXECUTIVES

President And Co-ceo, Jeremy B. Ford, age 44, $700,000 total compensation
Vice Chairman And Co-ceo; Chairman Plainscapital Bank, Alan B. White, age 70, $1,350,000 total compensation
Coo Subsidiaries, James R. Huffines, age 68, $690,000 total compensation
Chief Administrative Officer, Darren E. Parmenter, age 56, $335,000 total compensation
Chairman And Ceo Hilltop Securities, Hill A. Feinberg, age 72, $500,000 total compensation
President And Ceo Plainscapital Bank, Jerry L. Schaffner, age 61
Cfo, William B. Furr, age 41, $143,438 total compensation
Ceo Primelending, Todd L. Salmans, age 70, $750,000 total compensation
Cio, Toby Pennycuff
Assistant Vice President, Scott Wade
Senior Vice President Corporate Development, Erik Yohe
Vice President It Audit Manager, Bo Yan
Assistant Vice President Internal Audit, Jessica Moore
Vice President, Taylor Pool
Assistant Vice President Internal Auditor Ii, Meshack Mulupi
Senior Vice President Senior Marketing Manager, Suzie Coghlan
Senior Vice President Operations, Donald Karas
Senior Vice President, Robert Flanagan
Assistant Vice President And Branch Manager, Corey Mark
Vice President Network Infrastructure, Gary Johnson
Vice President, Kayla Macewen
Senior Vice President, Perry Tipton
Senior Vice President, Nick Bulaich
Assistant Vice President, John Barganski
Assistant Vice President, Ashley Allen
Senior Vice President, Ed Stull
Vice President, William Skelton
Vice President, Erick Macha
Vice President Financial Advisor, Diane Lacina
Senior Vice President, David Quintanilla
Vice President Credit Analyst Supervisor, Joey Couch
Vice President Operations, Lee Braun
Senior Vice President, Kenny Kenvin
First Vice President, Mark Katz
Senior Vice President Financial Advisor, Wayne Daugherty
Assistant Vice President, Megan Slattery
Vice President Portfolio Manager, Dan Grant
Chairman, Gerald J. Ford, age 75
Board Of Directors, Markham Green
Board Member, Andrew Littlefair
Board Member, Charlotte Anderson
Board Member, Arthur Sherman
Auditors: PricewaterhouseCoopers LLP

LOCATIONS

HQ: Hilltop Holdings, Inc.
2323 Victory Avenue, Suite 1400, Dallas, TX 75219
Phone: 214 855-2177
Web: www.hilltop-holdings.com

PRODUCTS/OPERATIONS

2018 Revenue

	$ mil.	% of total
Interest income		
Loans including fees	437	27
Securities borrowed	67	4
Taxable Securities	51	3
Tax-exempt securities	7	1
Other	18	1
Non-interest income		
Net gains from sale of loans and other mortgage production income	445	28
Net insurance premiums earned	137	9
Securities commissions and fees	151	9
Investment and securities advisory fees and commissions	90	6
Mortgage loan origination fees	104	6
Other	96	6
Total	**1,602**	**100**

Selected Services
Financial Advisory
Clearing
Retail Brokerage
Investment Banking Services
Internet Banking
Business Check Cards

Selected Subsidiaries
PlainsCapital Bank
PrimeLending
HilltopSecurities
National Lloyds Corporation

COMPETITORS

American Modern Insurance	International Bancshares
BBVA Compass Bancshares	JPMorgan Chase
Bank of America	Morgan Keegan
Comerica	Raymond James Financial
Costco Wholesale	Republic Group
Cullen/Frost Bankers	Texas Capital Bancshares
Fannie Mae	Travelers Companies
Foremost Insurance	Wells Fargo
Freddie Mac	
ING	

HISTORICAL FINANCIALS
Company Type: Public

Income Statement				FYE: December 31
	ASSETS ($ mil.)	NET INCOME ($ mil.)	INCOME AS % OF ASSETS	EMPLOYEES
12/18	13,684	121	0.9%	5,200
12/17	13,366	133	1.0%	5,500
12/16	12,738	146	1.1%	5,400
12/15	11,867	211	1.8%	5,300
12/14	9,242	112	1.2%	4,400
Annual Growth	10.3%	2.1%	—	4.3%

2018 Year-End Financials

Debt ratio: 2.00%
Return on equity: 6.00%
Cash ($ mil.): 644
Current ratio: —
Long-term debt ($ mil.): —

No. of shares (mil.): 94
Dividends
  Yield: 2.0%
  Payout: 22.0%
Market value ($ mil.): 1,669

	STOCK PRICE ($) FY Close	P/E High/Low	PER SHARE ($) Earnings	Dividends	Book Value
12/18	18.00	21 13	1.00	0.00	21.00
12/17	25.00	22 16	1.00	0.00	20.00
12/16	30.00	20 10	1.00	0.00	19.00
12/15	19.00	12 8	2.00	0.00	18.00
12/14	20.00	22 16	1.00	0.00	16.00
Annual Growth	(2.8%)	— —	2.3%	—	6.5%

Hilton Worldwide Holdings Inc

If you need a bed for the night Hilton has a few hundred thousand of them. Hilton Worldwide is one of the world's largest hoteliers with a lodging empire that includes about 5700 hotels and resorts in more than 110 countries operating under such names as Doubletree Embassy Suites and Hampton Inn as well as its flagship Hilton brand. Many of its hotels serve the mid-market segment though its Hilton and Conrad hotels offer full-service up-scale lodging. In addition its Homewood Suites and Home2 Suites chains offers extended-stay services. The company franchises nearly all its hotels with just 70 being directly operated. Hilton became a public company again in 2013.

Operations

Hilton's management and franchise segment which accounts for nearly 85% of revenue includes about 690 managed hotels more than 4800 franchised hotels and the licensing of Hilton's brands. The segment derives revenue from a host of franchising management and licensing fees.

The ownership segment (more than 15% of sales) consists of more than 70 hotels and derives revenue from providing hotel room rentals food and beverage and other services at the company's owned and leased hotels.

Hilton controls an extensive portfolio of brands. The company's largest chains Hampton Inn and Hampton Inn & Suites include more than 2400 locations and target mid-market travelers with moderately priced rooms and limited amenities. At the other end of the scale the company's Conrad chain offers luxury services and distinctive locations while its Waldorf-Astoria Collection is a prestigious collection of hotels inspired by the New York landmark.

Hilton's "focused service" (i.e. cheaper) hotel brands include Hilton Garden Inn Hampton by Hilton Tru by Hilton Homewood Suites by Hilton Motto by Hilton Hilton Grand Vacations and Home2 Suites by Hilton. The company's Hilton Grand Vacations subsidiary operates more than 50 time-share vacation resorts.

Geographic Reach

Headquartered in Mclean Virginia the company has regional corporate offices in Watford UK; Dubai UAE; Singapore; Tokyo Japan; and Shanghai China. Additional Hilton support offices include its Hilton Honors and other commercial services office in Addison Texas; centralized operations centers in Memphis Tennessee and Glasgow UK; and our Hilton Reservations and Customer Care office in Carrollton Texas.

Hilton's holdings comprise more than 900000 rooms in more than 110 countries. The company divides its business into three geographic regions Americas; Europe Middle East and Africa ("EMEA"); and Asia Pacific. The Americas region includes North America South America and Central America including all Caribbean nations.

Properties in the US represent almost 75% of the company's system-wide hotel rooms and generate a similar portion of revenue. The UK is its second-largest market at more than 5%; all other countries account for the remainder.

Sales and Marketing

Hilton relies on traditional advertising and promotions along with a variety of direct marketing techniques such as email social media marketing and postal mailings to drum up business. When the company's hotel rooms are booked through internet travel intermediaries Hilton pays commissions and transaction fees for sales of rooms through such services.

The company also has a robust customer loyalty program Hilton Honors it uses to try to generate return business. As part of the company's hotel management business hotel owners pay for participation in the Hilton Honors guest loyalty program. The owners also pay Hilton usage fees which cover the costs of advertising and marketing programs internet technology and reservation systems and quality assurance program expenses.

Financial Performance

Aside from a blip in 2016 when it sold off operations and hotels Hilton has enjoyed strong and steady revenue in recent years.

In 2018 the company's sales grew 10% to $8.9 billion thanks to growth in system-wide revenue per available room (RevPAR) particularly in Turkey which is recovering from political turmoil and China where its new hotels are entering a new phase of maturity.

Net income fell 29% to $769 million due to an increase in income taxes. A windfall arising from the 2017 US Tax Cuts and Jobs Act inflated Hilton's net income in prior year; in 2018 it returned to more normal levels.

Hilton's cash position weakened in 2018 ending the year $186 million lower at $484 million. The company generated $1.3 billion from its operations while investing activities used $131 million and financing activities used $1.3 billion. The company's main cash uses were debt repayments stock repurchases dividend payouts and capital expenditures.

Strategy

Hilton's strategic objectives include the continued expansion of its global footprint and fee-based business. However staffing shortages in various parts of the world could slow Hilton's ability to grow and expand its businesses. Payroll costs are always a major component of the company's operating expenses at its hotels and franchised hotels.

At the end of 2018 Hilton had a total of 2400 hotels in its development pipeline representing more than 364000 rooms in upwards of 100 countries (35 being new territories). Hilton's continued growth is funded by cash generated by its operations and the occasional spin off such as the sale of its timeshare and real estate investment trust business in 2017.

HISTORY

Conrad Hilton got his start in hotel management by renting out rooms in his family's New Mexico home. He served as a state legislator and started a bank before leaving for Texas in 1919 hoping to make his fortune in banking. Hilton was unable to shoulder the cost of purchasing a bank however but recognized a high demand for hotel rooms and made a quick change in strategy buying his first hotel in Cisco Texas. Over the next decade he bought seven more Texas hotels.

Hilton lost several properties during the Depression but began rebuilding his empire soon thereafter through the purchase of hotels in California (1938) New Mexico (1939) and Mexico (1942). He even married starlet Zsa Zsa Gabor in 1942 (they later divorced of course). Hilton Hotels Corporation was formed in 1946 and went public. The company bought New York's Waldorf-Astoria in 1949 (a hotel Hilton called "the greatest of them all") and opened its first European hotel in Madrid in 1953. Hilton paid $111 million for the 10-hotel Statler chain the following year.

Hilton took his company out of the overseas hotel business in 1964 by spinning off Hilton International and began franchising the following year to capitalize on the well-known Hilton name. Barron Hilton Conrad's son was appointed president in 1966 (he became chairman upon Conrad Hilton's death in 1979). Hilton bought two Las Vegas hotels (the Las Vegas Hilton and the Flamingo Hilton) in 1970 and launched its gaming division. The company returned to the international hotel business with Conrad International Hotels in 1982 and opened its first suite-only Hilton Suites hotel in 1989.

In the 1990s Hilton expanded its gaming operations buying Bally's Casino Resort in Reno in 1992 and launching its first riverboat casino the Hilton Queen of New Orleans in 1994. Two years later it acquired all of Bally Entertainment making it the largest gaming company in the world. Also that year Stephen Bollenbach the former Walt Disney CFO who had negotiated the $19 billion acquisition of Capital Cities/ABC was named CEO — becoming the first nonfamily-member to run the company.

Hilton formed an alliance with Ladbroke Group in 1997 (later Hilton Group owner of Hilton International and the rights to the Hilton name outside the US) to promote the Hilton brand worldwide. Hilton also put in a bid that year to acquire ITT owner of Sheraton hotels and Caesars World but was thwarted when ITT accepted a higher offer from Starwood Hotels & Resorts. Hilton was foiled once again in 1998 when a deal with casino operator Circus Circus (now part of MGM Resorts International) that would have separated Hilton's hotel and casino operations fell through. With a downturn in the gambling industry translating into sluggish results in Hilton's gaming segment the company spun off its gaming interests as Park Place Entertainment later that year.

In 1999 Hilton made a massive acquisition with the $3.7 billion purchase of Promus Hotel Corp. The following year Hilton sold its Flamingo Casino-Kansas City a remaining casino property left over from the Park Place spinoff to Isle of Capri Casinos for $33.5 million. In 2001 it sold 56 of its leases and management contracts to RFS Hotel Investors for about $60 million.

Hilton continued selling properties in 2002 with the sales of two Doubletree hotels and all 41 Red Lion locations to WestCoast Hospitality (now Red Lion Hotels) for about $51 million. It also sold its Harrison Conference Center portfolio (14 conference centers and university hotels) to ARAMARK for $55 million. At the end of that same year the company formed a $400 million venture with CNL Hospitality (now CNL Hotels & Resorts) to buy and refurbish hotel properties.

Following an extended downturn in the hospitality business brought on by recession and post-9/11 fears about terrorism Hilton began to invest in refurbishments for many of its properties and added about 150 locations in 2004.

Hilton Hotels acquired Hilton International from Hilton Group (now Ladbrokes) for about $5.7 billion in 2006. The deal re-unified the Hilton brand globally and added about 400 new locations to the company's portfolio. The year after the acquisition Hilton Hotels sold its Scandic Hotels business to private equity firm EQT for $1.1 billion and later sold LivingWell Health Clubs to Bannatyne Fitness; both brands had been included in the Hilton International transaction.

Also in 2007 the company was taken private by The Blackstone Group through a $26 billion buyout. The acquisition included about $6 billion in debt. Christopher Nassetta later replaced Bollenbach as CEO. Hilton Hotels was renamed Hilton Worldwide in 2009. Through a financial restructuring in 2010 Hilton was able to cut about $4 billion of its $20 billion debt. In early 2011 its newest brand Home2 Suites by Hilton opened its first property.

Hilton sold its Waldorf Astoria New York hotel for $1.95 billion in 2015.

EXECUTIVES

Evp And President Development Architecture And Construction, Ian R. Carter, age 57, $739,302 total compensation

President Ceo And Director, Christopher J. (Chris) Nassetta, age 57, $1,200,000 total compensation

Evp And Chief Human Resources Officer, Matthew W. (Matt) Schuyler, age 53

Evp And General Counsel, Kristin A. Campbell, age 57, $638,308 total compensation

Evp Global Brands, James E. (Jim) Holthouser, age 60, $600,000 total compensation

Evp And Cfo, Kevin J. Jacobs, age 46, $743,404 total compensation

Evp And President Americas, Joe Berger

President Europe Middle East & Africa, Simon Vincent

Evp And Chief Commercial Officer, Chris Silcock

Head Architecture Design And Construction, Matt Richardson

Evp And President Asia Pacific (apac), Alan Watts

Svp Team Member And Executive Communications, Katrina Jones

Vp Global Corporate Communications, Aaron Radelet

Svp Hr Systems And Services, Doug Krey

Executive Vice President Chief Commercial Officer, Christopher Silcock

Vp System Engineering, Hector Dominguez

Vp Brand Marketing All Suites Brands, Christian Kuhn

Senior Vice President Strategy And Research, Nathalie Corredor

Vp Global Marketing Luxury And Lifestyle Brands, Sumindi Peiris

Senior Vice President Luxury Lifestyle Resort And Corporate Development, Greg Hartmann

Vice President Management Contract Services And Owner Relations, Lisa Zemke

Svp Architecture And Construction Americas, Phil Keipper

Vp Infrastructure Operations And Security, Michael Leidinger

Senior Vice President Customer Journeyman Delivery, Virginia Suliman

Svp And Global Head Doubletree By Hilton And Curio Brand, Dianna Vaughan

Vp Operations Luxury Hotels Americas, Ronen Nissenbaum

Executive Vice President Corporate Affairs, Katie Fallon

Vp Brand Communications, Craig Dezern

Vp Corporate Communications, Nigel Glennie

Vp Operations Australia, Heidi Kunkel

Vp Brand Management Asia Pacific, Sean Wooden

Vp Communications Emea, Ulrike Birner

Senior Vice President Hotel Operations, Keith Harrison

Vice President Customer Engagement Loyalty And Partnerships Emea, Heather Laverne

Chairman, Jonathan D. Gray, age 49

Board Member, Elizabeth Smith

Board Member, John Schreiber

Board Member, Melanie Healey

Auditors: Ernst & Young LLP

LOCATIONS

HQ: Hilton Worldwide Holdings Inc
7930 Jones Branch Drive, Suite 1100, McLean, VA 22102
Phone: 703 883-1000
Web: www.hiltonworldwide.com

2018 sales

	$ mil.	% of total
U.S.	6,848	77
UK	545	6
All other	1,513	17
Total	**9**	**100**

PRODUCTS/OPERATIONS

2018 sales

	$ mil.	% of total
Other revenues from managed and franchised properties	5,238	59
Franchise and licensing fees	1,530	17
Owned and leased hotels	1,484	17
Base and other management fees	235	3
Other fees and revenues	98	1
Total	**8,906**	**100**

Selected Brands

Conrad Hotels & Resorts
Doubletree
Embassy Suites Hotels
Hampton Inn
Hampton Inn & Suites
Hilton
Hilton Garden Inn
Hilton Grand Vacations Club
Homewood Suites by Hilton
Waldorf Astoria Hotels & Resorts

Selected Hotels

Chicago's Palmer House Hilton
Hilton Barcelona
Hilton Bora Bora Nui Resort & Spa
The Hilton Hawaiian Village on Waikiki Beach
Hilton Manchester Deansgate
Hilton Orlando
Hilton San Francisco on Union Square
Hilton Sedona
The New York Hilton

COMPETITORS

Accor	Interstate Hotels
Best Western	Loews
Carlson Hotels	Marriott
Choice Hotels	Omni Hotels
FRHI Hotels and Resorts	Red Lion Hotels
Four Seasons Hotels	Ritz-Carlton
Hyatt	Starwood Hotels & Resorts
InterContinental Hotels	Wyndham Destinations

HISTORICAL FINANCIALS

Company Type: Public

Income Statement

FYE: December 31

	REVENUE ($ mil.)	NET INCOME ($ mil.)	NET PROFIT MARGIN	EMPLOYEES
12/18	8,906	764	8.6%	169,000
12/17	9,140	1,259	13.8%	163,000
12/16	11,663	348	3.0%	169,000
12/15	11,272	1,404	12.5%	164,000
12/14	10,502	673	6.4%	157,000
Annual Growth	**(4.0%)**	**3.2%**	**—**	**1.9%**

2018 Year-End Financials

Debt ratio: 52.00%	No. of shares (mil.): 295
Return on equity: 58.00%	Dividends
Cash ($ mil.): 403	Yield: 1.0%
Current ratio: 1.00	Payout: 24.0%
Long-term debt ($ mil.): 7,266	Market value ($ mil.): 21,168

	STOCK PRICE ($) FY Close	P/E High/Low		PER SHARE ($) Earnings	Dividends	Book Value
12/18	72.00	35	25	3.00	1.00	2.00
12/17	80.00	21	7	4.00	1.00	7.00
12/16	27.00	26	16	1.00	1.00	18.00
12/15	21.00	7	5	4.00	0.00	18.00
12/14	26.00	13	10	2.00	0.00	14.00
Annual Growth	**28.8%**	**—**	**—**	**5.2%**	**—**	**(40.1%)**

Hingham Institution for Savings

The Hingham Institution for Savings serves businesses and retail customers in Boston's south shore communities operating more than 10 branches in Massachusetts in Boston Cohasset Hingham Hull Norwell Scituate South Hingham and South Weymouth. Founded in 1834 the bank offers traditional deposit products such as checking and savings accounts IRAs and certificates of deposit. More than 90% of its loan portfolio is split between commercial mortgages and residential mortgages (including home equity loans) though the bank also originates construction business and consumer loans. More than 95% of the company's revenue comes from loan interest.

Operations

The Hingham Institution for Savings made 96% of its total revenue from loan interest during 2015 while about 2% came from interest in equities CODs and other investments. The rest of its revenue mostly came from service fees on deposit accounts.

Of its $1.4 billion loan portfolio (at the end of 2015) about 48% was made up of commercial real estate mortgages (including multi-family housing) while 45% was tied to residential mortgages (including home equity). The remainder of the portfolio was made up of residential and commercial construction loans (7% of loan assets) and commercial business loans and consumer loans (1%).

Subsidiary Hingham Unpledged Securities Corporation holds title to certain securities available for sale.

Geographic Reach

The company mostly serves clients in Boston the South Shore and the island of Nantucket. Its branches are in Boston Cohasset Hingham Hull Nantucket Norwell Scituate South Hingham and South Weymouth Massachusetts.

Sales and Marketing

The Hingham Institution for Savings serves both individuals and small businesses in its three target markets in Massachusetts. Some of its clients (as of mid-2016) include Lyons Associates The Hub TCR Development SYA+FH Steven Young Architect + Fine Home Builder and Park Drive Inc.

The bank spent $489000 on marketing expenses during 2015 down from $557000 in each of 2014 and 2013.

Financial Performance

The bank's annual revenues have slowly trended higher over the past several years as the promising Boston real estate market has fueled its commercial real estate and residential loan business growth.

Hingham's revenue dipped 1% to $64.34 million during 2015 despite 13% mortgage loan growth mostly because in 2014 it earned a gains on life insurance distributions. The bank also continued to lose fee income as it has eliminated many fees on its deposit products to simplify offerings and attract customer deposits.

Revenue declines and higher income tax provisions in 2015 (in 2014 it earned non-taxed death benefit proceeds) caused the bank's net income to fall 13% to $19.34 million. Hingham's operating cash levels rose 11% to $20.2 million for the year thanks to a jump in cash-based earnings.

Strategy

The Hingham Institution for Savings continued in 2016 to focus on originating commercial multi-family and single-family mortgage loans in its target markets of Boston the South Shore and the island of Nantucket in Massachusetts especially as the healthy real estate market in and around Boston has provided a tailwind for its lending business.

EXECUTIVES

Chief Executive Officer; President; Director, Robert H. Gaughen, $319,615 total compensation
Vice President Of Retail Banking, Andrew Vebber
Assistant Vice President Retail Lending, Patricia Talbot
Auditors: Wolf & Company, P.C.

LOCATIONS

HQ: Hingham Institution for Savings
   55 Main Street, Hingham, MA 02043
Phone: 781 749-2200   **Fax:** 781 740-4889
Web: www.hinghamsavings.com

COMPETITORS

Bank of America	Independent Bank (MA)
Citizens Financial	Peoples Federal
Group	Bancshares Inc.
Eastern Bank	Sovereign Bank

HISTORICAL FINANCIALS

Company Type: Public

Income Statement   FYE: December 31

	ASSETS ($ mil.)	NET INCOME ($ mil.)	INCOME AS % OF ASSETS	EMPLOYEES
12/18	2,409	30	1.3%	96
12/17	2,285	26	1.1%	101
12/16	2,015	23	1.2%	103
12/15	1,769	19	1.1%	111
12/14	1,552	22	1.4%	121
Annual Growth	11.6%	8.1%	—	(5.6%)

2018 Year-End Financials

Debt ratio: 0.00%
Return on equity: 15.00%
Cash ($ mil.): 8
Current ratio: —
Long-term debt ($ mil.): —

No. of shares (mil.): 2
Dividends
   Yield: 1.0%
   Payout: 12.0%
Market value ($ mil.): 422

	STOCK PRICE ($) FY Close	P/E High/Low		Earnings	PER SHARE ($) Dividends	Book Value
12/18	198.00	16	14	14.00	2.00	100.00
12/17	207.00	19	14	12.00	2.00	87.00
12/16	197.00	18	11	11.00	2.00	76.00
12/15	120.00	15	9	9.00	2.00	65.00
12/14	87.00	9	7	10.00	1.00	57.00
Annual Growth	22.8%	—	—	7.4%	6.0%	15.0%

HollyFrontier Corp

HollyFrontier refines crude oil to produce gasoline diesel and jet fuel and sells it in erstwhile American frontier territories: the Southwest northern Mexico Kansas and the Rockies. Its major assets are a 52000 barrels-per-day (bpd) refinery in Wyoming; the 135000 bpd El Dorado Kansas refinery; a 45000 bpd Utah refinery; a 125000 bpd Tulsa refinery; and subsidiary Navajo Refining (New Mexico) which has a capacity of 100000 bpd. The company also has a 36% stake in Holly Energy Partners (HEP) which operates crude oil and petroleum product pipelines. .

Operations

HollyFrontier operates two businesses: the refining business which accounts for the vast majority of total revenue and HollyFrontier Energy Partners (HEP).

The refining segment produces products such as gasoline diesel fuel jet fuel specialty lubricant products and specialty and modified asphalt. It turns out around 46000 barrels per day of product from its El Dorado Tulsa Navajo Cheyenne and Woods Cross refineries. It also produces asphalt via the HFC Asphalt business that makes asphalt in Arizona New Mexico and Oklahoma.

By product gasoline accounts for half its HollyFrontier's sales volume; diesel fuel accounts for around 35%; and jet fuel and specialty lubricants less than 5% each.

The HEP segment generates revenues by charging tariffs for transporting petroleum products and crude oil through its pipelines.

Geographic Reach

Dallas-based HollyFrontier's refinery operations (Cheyenne Wyoming; El Dorado Kansas; Navajo New Mexico; Tulsa Oklahoma; and Woods Cross Utah) serve customers in the US Mid-Continent Rocky Mountain and Southwest regions of the US.

Sales and Marketing

HollyFrontier's principal customers for gasoline include other refiners convenience store chains independent marketers and retailers. Diesel fuel is sold to other refiners truck stop chains wholesalers and railroads. Jet fuel is sold for commercial airline use. Specialty lubricant products are sold in both commercial and specialty markets. LPG's are sold to LPG wholesalers and LPG retailers. They produce and purchase asphalt products that are sold to governmental entities paving contractors or manufacturers. Asphalt is also blended into fuel oil and is either sold locally or is shipped to the Gulf Coast.

Sales to Shell Oil represented 10% of HollyFrontier's sales as did sales to Sinclair Oil.

The primary markets for the El Dorado Refinery's refined products are Colorado and the Plains States. The Woods Cross Refinery's primary market is Utah. The Cheyenne Refinery primarily markets its products in eastern Colorado including metropolitan Denver eastern Wyoming and western Nebraska. It also sells a significant portion of its diesel directly from the truck rack at the refinery eliminating transportation costs.

Asphalt products are marketed in Arizona New Mexico Oklahoma Kansas Missouri Texas and northern Mexico. Products are shipped via third-party trucking companies to commercial customers that provide asphalt based materials for commercial and government projects.

Financial Performance

The collapse in the global oil price since 2014 has reduced net revenue by nearly half and pushed HollyFrontier into the red.

In fiscal 2016 revenue fell a further 20% to $10.5 billion relating to lower average prices across the year while a curtailing of activity at its Woods Cross refinery due to insufficient crude supply from the Plains Rocky Mountain Pipeline was also a factor.

The company lost $260.5 million mostly as a result of non-cash good will and asset impairment charges totaling $654.1 million. Additionally margins were eroded 48% as selling prices fell further than raw material costs.

Cash from operations fell 29% to $602.3 million on the back of lower net income and revenue.

Strategy

With the refining business suffering under the low oil price HollyFrontier is diversifying its operations and seeking higher margins. In 2017 it closed the acquisition of Canadian lubricants business Suncor Energy increasing its lubricants position — particularly in high-margin Group III base oils of which Suncor is the only North American producer. It is now the fourth-larges lubricants producers on the continent.

To raise cash the company on occasion carries out "drop-down" asset sales to subsidiary HollyFrontier Energy Partners. In 2016 it sold Woods Cross Refinery Units — including crude fluid catalytic cracking and polymerization units — constructed as part of the Woods Cross expansion for $275 million.

Mergers and Acquisitions

In 2017 HollyFrontier completed the $1.1 billion acquisition of Canadian lubricants company Petro-Canada Lubricants a subsidiary of Suncor. The company produces 15600 barrels per day of lubricants including specialty lubricants and white oils.

HISTORY

HollyFrontier was founded in 1947 as General Appliance Corp. to process other companies' crude oil; the current name was adopted in 1952. As Holly the company grew with the number of gas-guzzling cars in the 1950s and 1960s and in the 1970s it developed its Navajo refinery in New Mexico. In 1981 Holly began producing higher-grade gasoline and started an asphalt company at Navajo.

In 1984 Holly became a partner in Montana Refining and later bought the entire business. It upgraded the Navajo refinery in the early 1990s to meet the demand for unleaded gasoline. In 1995 Amoco Mapco and Holly formed a joint venture the 265-mile Rio Grande Pipeline (completed in 1997) to transport natural gas liquids to Mexico.

Also in 1997 FINA and Holly allied to expand and use Holly's pipelines in the southwestern US. A proposed merger with another southwestern refiner Giant Industries died in 1998 because of federal antitrust concerns and a billion-dollar lawsuit filed against Holly by Longhorn Partners Pipeline. Court papers revealed in 2000 that Holly had paid $4 million to fight Longhorn's request for a permit to transport gasoline in its Houston-to-El Paso pipeline. The permit if approved would compete with Holly's own interests in western Texas.

Later in 2000 Holly cut its workforce by about 10% mostly at Navajo Refining. The next year Navajo Refining secured a $122 million contract to provide JP-8 jet fuel to the Defense Department.

In a move to expand its production capacity in 2003 Holly acquired ConocoPhillips' Woods Cross refinery and related assets for $25 million. Holly agreed to be acquired by Frontier Oil for about $450 million that year but the companies terminated the agreement and litigation between the parties resulted.

In 2004 the company spun off its Navajo refinery-related refined petroleum pipeline and other distribution assets as Holly Energy Partners L.P.; it retains a 45% interest in the company.

In 2005 the Delaware Chancery Court ruled that Frontier Oil had not proved that Holly had repudiated the merger agreement and awarded Frontier Oil only $1 in damages. Also that year Holly acquired the remaining 51% of NK Asphalt Producers that it did not already own. The company sold its intermediate feedstock pipelines connecting two refining facilities in Lovington and Artesia New Mexico to Holly Energy Partners for $81.5 million.

To free up cash in 2008 it sold 136 miles of crude oil trunk lines and some tankage assets to Holly Energy Partners for $180 million.

To expand market share in 2011 the company acquired regional rival Frontier Oil and Holly changed its corporate name to HollyFrontier.

The all-stock deal created an enterprise valued at $7 billion and added Frontier's Kansas and Wyoming refineries to the company's portfolio. The acquisition which boosted HollyFrontier's refining capacity to 443000 barrels a day is expected to create cost savings of at least $30 million per year.

The purchase was part of a multi-year strategy of expanding refinery capacity through selective acquisitions of complementary assets. (Earlier the company bought Sunoco's 85000-barrels-per-day Tulsa refinery. Building the largest refinery complex in the Midcontinent the company also acquired Sinclair Oil's 75000-barrels-per-day Tulsa refinery for $128.5 million).

Responding to increased demand in 2012 HollyFrontier announced planned to expand the capacity of its Woods Cross Utah refinery from 31000 barrel per day to 45000 barrel per day.

Building up its infrastructure to create greater efficiencies in 2013 HollyFrontier and Holly Energy Partners agreed to build a rail facility to enable crude oil loading and unloading near HollyFrontier's Artesia and/or Lovington New Mexico refining facilities. The rail project which will be connected to Holly Energy's crude oil pipeline transportation system in southeastern New Mexico will have a capacity of up to 70000 barrels per day and will enable access to a variety of crude oil types.

EXECUTIVES

Senior Vice President, David G Blair
Senior Vice President Refinery Operations, Gary Fuller
Vice President Corporate Ehands Holly Corporation, David Jelmini
Svp Refining Operations, James M. Stump, age 52, $510,000 total compensation
President And Ceo, George J. Damiris, age 59, $1,100,000 total compensation
Svp Commercial And President Hollyfrontier Refining & Marketing Llc, Thomas G. Creery, age 60
Svp General Counsel And Secretary, Denise C. McWatters, age 59, $470,000 total compensation
Vp Information Technology, Nellson D. Burns
Evp And Cfo, Richard L. Voliva, age 41
Assistant Vice President, Margaret Schieffer
Vp Supply, Tom Creery
Assistant Vice President Senior Economist, Jeffery Gunther
Vice President Engineering And Process Development Holly Refining And Marketing, Janusz Siwek
Vice President Accounting, Kathryn Walker
Vice President, Scott Surplus
Vice President Investor Relations, Marcus Hickerson
Vice President And Controller, John W Gann
Vice President Internal Audit, Joseph Fronzaglio
Vice President Information Technology, Nelson Nelso
Vice President And Refinery Manager, Tony Conetta
Vice President, Ajay Seth
Vice President, Patrick Gray
Chairman, Michael C. Jennings, age 54
Board Member, Michael Rose
Board Member, Jerry Pinkerton
Treasurer, Steve Wise
Board Member, Douglas Bech
Board Member, Anna Catalano
Auditors: Ernst & Young LLP

LOCATIONS

HQ: HollyFrontier Corp
2828 N. Harwood, Suite 1300, Dallas, TX 75201
Phone: 214 871-3555
Web: www.hollyfrontier.com

PRODUCTS/OPERATIONS

2016 Sales

	$ mil.	% of total
Refining	10,467	96
HEP	402	4
Corporate & other	0	-
Elimination	(333.7)	-
Total	**10,536**	**100**

COMPETITORS

BP	Sunoco
Crown Central	Tesoro
Exxon Mobil	Valero Energy
George Warren	Williams Companies
Marathon Petroleum	

HISTORICAL FINANCIALS

Company Type: Public

Income Statement

FYE: December 31

	REVENUE ($ mil.)	NET INCOME ($ mil.)	NET PROFIT MARGIN	EMPLOYEES
12/18	17,715	1,098	6.2%	3,622
12/17	14,251	805	5.7%	3,522
12/16	10,536	(260)	—	2,676
12/15	13,238	740	5.6%	2,704
12/14	19,764	281	1.4%	2,686
Annual Growth	(2.7%)	40.6%	—	7.8%

2018 Year-End Financials

Debt ratio: 22.00%
Return on equity: 19.00%
Cash ($ mil.): 1,155
Current ratio: 3.00
Long-term debt ($ mil.): 2,412

No. of shares (mil.): 172
Dividends
  Yield: 3.0%
  Payout: 21.0%
Market value ($ mil.): 8,799

	STOCK PRICE ($) FY Close	P/E High/Low		PER SHARE ($) Earnings	Dividends	Book Value
12/18	51.00	13	7	6.00	1.00	34.00
12/17	51.00	11	5	5.00	1.00	30.00
12/16	33.00	—		(1.00)	1.00	26.00
12/15	40.00	14	8	4.00	1.00	29.00
12/14	37.00	37	25	1.00	3.00	28.00
Annual Growth	8.1%	—		44.5%	(20.2%)	5.1%

Home Bancorp Inc

Making its home in Cajun Country Home Bancorp is the holding company for Home Bank a community bank which offers deposit and loan services to consumers and small to midsized businesses in southern Louisiana. Through about two dozen branches the bank offers standard savings and checking accounts as well as lending services such as mortgages consumer loans and credit cards. Its loan portfolio includes commercial real estate commercial and industrial loans as well as construction and land loans. Home Bancorp also operates about half a dozen bank branches in west Mississippi which were formerly part of Britton & Koontz Bank.

Geographic Reach

Home Bancorp serves the Louisiana areas of Greater Lafayette Baton Rouge Greater New Orleans and Northshore (of Lake Pontchartrain). Its markets in Mississippi include Vicksburg and Natchez.

Financial Performance

Although the company saw assets and loans grow in 2013 net income fell 20% that year to $7.3 million on lower operating income.

Mergers and Acquisitions

In early 2014 Home Bancorp spent about $35 million on Britton & Koontz Capital Corporation the holding company of Britton & Koontz Bank; the deal added five branches in west Mississippi to Home Bancorp's operations.

EXECUTIVES

Pres-Ceo, John W Bordelon
Chb, Michael P Maraist
Exec V Pres-Coo, Jason P Freyou
Exec V Pres-Cfo, Joseph B Zanco
Corp SEC, Richard J Bourgeois
Auditors: Wipfli LLP

LOCATIONS

HQ: Home Bancorp Inc
503 Kaliste Saloom Road, Lafayette, LA 70508
Phone: 337 237-1960   **Fax:** 337 264-9280
Web: www.home24bank.com

COMPETITORS

Capital One
IBERIABANK
JPMorgan Chase
Louisiana Bancorp

MidSouth Bancorp
Regions Financial
Teche Holding

HISTORICAL FINANCIALS

Company Type: Public

Income Statement   FYE: December 31

	ASSETS ($ mil.)	NET INCOME ($ mil.)	INCOME AS % OF ASSETS	EMPLOYEES
12/18	2,154	32	1.5%	—
12/17	2,228	17	0.8%	—
12/16	1,557	16	1.0%	—
12/15	1,552	13	0.8%	—
12/14	1,221	10	0.8%	—
Annual Growth	15.2%	33.7%	—	—

2018 Year-End Financials

Debt ratio: 0.00%	No. of shares (mil.): 9
Return on equity: 11.00%	Dividends
Cash ($ mil.): 61	Yield: 2.0%
Current ratio: —	Payout: 24.0%
Long-term debt ($ mil.): —	Market value ($ mil.): 335

	STOCK PRICE ($) FY Close	P/E High/Low	PER SHARE ($) Earnings	Dividends	Book Value
12/18	35.00	14 10	3.00	1.00	32.00
12/17	43.00	19 14	2.00	1.00	30.00
12/16	39.00	17 10	2.00	0.00	24.00
12/15	26.00	14 11	2.00	0.00	23.00
12/14	23.00	15 12	1.00	0.00	22.00
Annual Growth	11.5%		24.4%	78.5%	10.4%

Home BancShares Inc

Home BancShares is the holding company for Centennial Bank which operates some 160 branches in Arkansas Florida and Alabama with an additional branch in each of New York City and Los Angeles (through which the company is building out a national lending platform). With $14.9 billion in assets the bank offers traditional services such as checking savings and money market accounts and CDs. About 60% of its lending portfolio is focused on commercial real estate loans — including non-farm and non-residential and construction and land development. The bank also writes residential mortgages and business and consumer loans. Through a subsidiary Home Banc-Shares offers insurance services.

Operations

About 80% of Home Bancshares' $10.8 billion loan portfolio comprises real estate loans including non-farm and non-residential commercial loans which make up more than 40% of the total. Residential one-to-four-family loans and commercial construction and land development loans contribute about 20% and 15% respectively. Commercial and industrial loans make up around 10%.

The holding company has built a $6.3 billion portfolio of non-farm and non-residential commercial real estate loans primarily secured by commercial real estate. Around 50% 30% and 15% of the company's commercial real estate loan portfolio is in Florida Arkansas and with its Centennial Finance Group (CFG). Home Bancshares established the group in 2015 to manage loans acquired in the company's acquisition of the Florida Panhandle business of Banco Popular and to originate new loans (with a focus on commercial real estate and commercial and industrial loans) via a national lending platform.

About 30% and 60% of the company's $2.6 billion residential real estate loan portfolio are for one-to-four-family properties and non-owner occupied one-to-four family properties respectively.

The company's commercial and industrial loans account for about $1.3 billion of the portfolio; Arkansas Florida and Centennial CFG house about 40% 35% and 25% of that segment respectively.

Geographic Reach

Conway Arkansas-based Home Bancshares' holding company's Centennial Bank operates about 90 branches in Florida more than 75 in Arkansas around five in Southern Alabama and one in each of New York City and Los Angeles.

Sales and Marketing

Home Bancshares' non-farm and non-residential lending (comprising about 40% of the total) is made up of loans for shopping and retail centers hotels and motels offices industrial warehouses churches marinas and nursing homes.

Residential one-to-four-family residential mortgages for individuals make up some 20% of the company's portfolio. About 30% and 60% of its residential mortgage loans are for one-to-four-family owner-occupied and non-owner-occupied properties respectively.

The holding company also lends heavily to residential and commercial developers to construct commercial properties and develop land. Construction and land development loans make up about 15% of its portfolio.

Around 10% of the value of Home Bancshares' loans go to commercial and industrial clients.

Financial Performance

Home Bancshares reported revenue of $555.5 million in 2017 up 174% from 2013 and net income of $135.1 million up 103% over the same period. The company's cash stores and long-term debt both about tripled during that time to $635.9 million and $1.7 billion respectively.

The holding company's revenue increased 13% in 2017 compared with 2016 owing to increased interest income from loans.

Home Bancshares' net income fell 24% due mostly to an increase in income tax expense related to the passage of the Tax Cuts and Jobs Act.

The company's $419.3 million to its cash in 2017. Operating activities provided $176.9 million down from the previous year based on decreased net income and increased charges from indemnification and other assets and accrued interest payable on other liabilities. Investments used $355.5 million while financings added $597.8 million driven mostly by proceeds from issuance of subordinated debentures.

Strategy

Home Bancshares' strategy is focused on expanding in its core Florida market through the purchase of local managed community banks including four in 2017 and 2018.

In addition to growing its geographic footprint Home Bancshares is also diversifying its product offerings through acquisitions. In 2018 the company bought the Shore Premier Finance division of Union Bankshares. Shore originated direct consumer loans for high-end sail and power boats in southeast Florida.

Mergers and Acquisitions

Home Bancshares acquired Giant Holdings The Bank of Commerce and Stonegate Bank in 2017 as well as former Union Bankshares subsidiary Shore Premier Finance in 2018.

The holding company purchased Giant Holdings for $96 million. Giant operated six branches in the Ft. Lauderdale Florida area and had $398.1 million in total assets $327.8 million in loans and $304 million in deposits.

Home Bancshares acquired The Bank of Commerce from Bank of Commerce Holdings as part of that company's bankruptcy for $4.2 million. Bank of Commerce - which had $182.5 million in assets $127.5 million in loans and $141.7 million in deposits - operated three branches in the Sarasota Florida area.

Home Bancshares bought Stonegate Bank for $820 million adding the company's $3.1 billion in total assets $2.4 billion in loans and $2.6 billion in deposits to its books. Stonegate had 24 offices in Florida markets including Broward and Sarasota counties.

In 2018 the company acquired the Shore Premier Finance division of Union Bankshares for $374.5 million in cash and 1.3 million shares. Shore originates direct consumer loans for high-end sail and power boats at 16 locations in southeast Florida. At the deal's close Shore had $384.2 million in assets including $383.4 million in total loans.

Company Background

Home Bancshares formed in 1998 as First State Bank.

EXECUTIVES

Cfo And Treasurer And Director, Randy E. Mayor, age 54, $300,000 total compensation
President And Ceo, C. Randall (Randy) Sims, age 64, $390,000 total compensation
Regional President Centennial Bank, Robert F. Birch, age 69, $290,000 total compensation
President And Ceo Centennial Bank, Tracy M. French, age 57, $290,000 total compensation
Chief Lending Officer, Kevin D. Hester, age 55
Coo Home Bancshares Inc. And Centennial Bank, John (Stephen) Tipton
Vice President Security, Jenni Holbrook
Vice President, Brian Jackson
Chairman, John W. Allison, age 72
Vice Chairman, Robert H. Adcock, age 70
Board Member, James Hinkle
Board Member, Thomas Longe
Board Member, Mike Beebe
Auditors: BKD, LLP

LOCATIONS

HQ: Home BancShares Inc
719 Harkrider, Suite 100, Conway, AR 72032
Phone: 501 339-2929
Web: www.homebancshares.com

COMPETITORS

Arvest Bank
BB&T
BBX Capital
Bank of America
Bank of the Ozarks

Bear State Financial
Regions Financial
Simmons First
Woodforest Financial

426

HISTORICAL FINANCIALS

Company Type: Public

Income Statement

FYE: December 31

	ASSETS ($ mil.)	NET INCOME ($ mil.)	INCOME AS % OF ASSETS	EMPLOYEES
12/18	15,302	300	2.0%	1,815
12/17	14,450	135	0.9%	1,744
12/16	9,808	177	1.8%	1,503
12/15	9,289	138	1.5%	1,424
12/14	7,403	113	1.5%	1,376
Annual Growth	19.9%	27.7%	—	7.2%

2018 Year-End Financials

Debt ratio: 12.00%	No. of shares (mil.): 171
Return on equity: 13.00%	Dividends
Cash ($ mil.): 658	Yield: 3.0%
Current ratio: —	Payout: 32.0%
Long-term debt ($ mil.): —	Market value ($ mil.): 2,790

	STOCK PRICE ($) FY Close	P/E High/Low		PER SHARE ($) Earnings	Dividends	Book Value
12/18	16.00	15	9	2.00	0.00	14.00
12/17	23.00	33	24	1.00	0.00	13.00
12/16	28.00	35	15	1.00	0.00	9.00
12/15	41.00	46	28	1.00	0.00	9.00
12/14	32.00	44	33	1.00	0.00	8.00
Annual Growth	(15.6%)	—		19.4%	27.3%	16.3%

Home Depot Inc

When embarking on household projects many start their journey at The Home Depot. As the world's largest home improvement chain and one of the largest retailers in the US the company operates nearly 2300 stores in North America. It targets the do-it-yourself (DIY) and professional markets with its selection of up to 40000 items including lumber flooring plumbing supplies garden products tools paint and appliances. Home Depot also offers installation services for carpeting cabinetry and other products for its do-it-for-me (DIFM) customers. It conducts e-commerce operations through its websites (including thecompanystore.com) and mobile apps.

HISTORY

Bernard Marcus and Arthur Blank founded The Home Depot in 1978 after they were fired (under disputed circumstances) from Handy Dan Home Improvement Centers. They joined Handy Dan coworker Ronald Brill to launch a "new and improved" home center for the do-it-yourselfer (DIY). In 1979 they opened three stores in the fast-growing Atlanta area and expanded to four stores in 1980.

Home Depot went public opened four stores in South Florida and posted sales of $50 million in 1981. The chain entered Louisiana and Arizona next. By 1983 sales were more than $250 million.

In 1984 Home Depot's stock was listed on the NYSE and the company acquired nine Bowater Home Centers in the South. Through subsequent stock and debenture offerings Home Depot continued to grow entering California (Handy Dan's home turf) with six new stores in 1985.

Back on track in 1986 sales exceeded $1 billion in the firm's 60 stores. Home Depot began the current policy of "low day-in day-out pricing" the following year achieving Marcus' dream of elimi-

nating sales events. The company entered the competitive northeastern market with stores in Long Island New York in 1988 and opened its first EXPO Design Center in San Diego.

Home Depot's sales continued to rise during the 1990-92 recession and the retailer kept opening stores. It entered Canada in 1994 when it acquired a 75% interest in Aikenhead's a DIY chain that it converted to the Home Depot name (it bought the remaining 25% in 1998).

A series of gender-bias lawsuits plagued the company in 1994 as female workers claimed they were not treated on an equal basis with male employees. Home Depot reached a $65 million out-of-court settlement in 1997 but not before the company was ordered to pay another female employee $1.7 million in a case in California.

Troubles aside Home Depot roared past the 500-store mark in 1997. That year Blank succeeded Marcus as the company's CEO; Marcus remained chairman. Home Depot bought National Blind & Wallpaper Factory (a mail-order firm) and Maintenance Warehouse (a direct-mail marketer) that year.

The company introduced its 40000-sq.-ft. Villager's Hardware stores designed to compete with smaller hardware shops in 1999 in New Jersey. It also bought Georgia Lighting an Atlanta lighting designer distributor and retailer. Home Depot later began adding large appliances to some stores following competitor Lowe's (most stores had them by 2000).

In 2000 Home Depot bought Apex Supply (a 20-plus-location plumbing distributor in Georgia South Carolina and Tennessee) and opened a flooring-only test store in Texas. Later that year the company named General Electric executive Robert Nardelli as its president and CEO. Marcus and Blank were named co-chairmen.

The company opened 200 new stores in 2001 and bought Total HOME a home improvement chain with four stores in Mexico. Additionally Marcus was named chairman after Blank stepped down. Later in the year Marcus retired and Nardelli became chairman. Also that year the company said it was scrapping its Villager's Hardware experiment to test a small-store concept in urban areas.

In 2002 Home Depot opened its first small store a 61000-sq.-ft. outlet in New York City. Further increasing its presence in Mexico the company acquired the four-store Del Norte chain in Ciudad Ju rez that year.

Also in 2002 Home Depot created a new subsidiary HD Builder Solutions through the acquisition of Floors Inc. Arvada Hardwood Floor Company and FloorWorks Inc. The next year the company acquired roofing installer IPUSA and replacement windows and siding installer RMA Home Services.

Home Depot expanded its business in the homebuilder market in January 2004 by purchasing Creative Touch Interiors a floor and counter installer in California and Nevada. Additionally early that year Home Depot opened its largest store ever — 205000 sq. ft. — in wealthy Anaheim Hills California. It also announced in February 2004 that it had partnered with AARP to hire people older than 50.

In addition that month Home Depot became the exclusive retailer of Maytag's SkyBox a home beverage dispenser. It acquired Home Mart a 20-unit Mexican chain in that June giving it a total of more than 40 stores in Mexico. Also in 2004 the company acquired White Cap Construction Supply; agreed to settle discrimination claims of some Colorado employees for $5.5 million; opened two trend-setting urban-oriented stores in Manhattan; and bought 18 stores from Kmart.

In mid-2005 Home Depot acquired National Waterworks Holdings (now National Waterworks Inc.)

and Williams Bros. Lumber of Georgia and folded them both into its The Home Depot Supply business (called HD Supply until it was sold). In September Home Depot Direct launched 10 Crescent Lane a high-end home decorating catalog and Web site offering furniture lighting and decorative accessories housewares and more. While some Home Depot locations in Louisiana and Texas were temporarily shut down by hurricanes Katrina and Rita its stores (and those of rival Lowe's and other building suppliers) are among the first places people visited in the wake of the disaster. In the immediate aftermath of the storms Home Depot stocked nontraditional items such as food and diapers in affected areas. Also in 2005 the company shuttered 15 EXPO Design Center stores which cater to affluent homeowners and converted five others to The Home Depot format. In all in 2005 Home Depot spent about $2.5 billion to acquire 21 companies.

The company's direct-to-consumer division launched a pair of high-end catalogs in 2005: 10 Crescent Lane and Paces Trading Company. However the catalogs which featured home furnishings and lighting products were discontinued in 2006 and selected products were folded back into the main Home Depot store catalog and website.

In January 2006 Home Depot acquired carpet and upholstery cleaning franchisor Chem-Dry and folded it into its At-Home Services division. (Chem-Dry has some 4000 franchises worldwide including 2500 in the US). In March the company completed its largest acquisition to date: the construction repair and maintenance products distributor Hughes Supply Inc. for $3.2 billion. That purchase was followed in May by the acquisition of Cox Lumber Co. a Tampa-based provider of trusses doors and lumber-related products. Also Home Depot acquired Home Decorators Collection a company specializing in catalog and online sales of home decor merchandise in 2006. Lured by the growth potential of the vast Chinese market the retailer purchased a majority stake in Taiwan-based Home-Way for about $100 million in late 2006. Home-Way operates DIY warehouse stores in northern China.

Joining the trend of big-box retailers adding gasoline and convenience store services to fuel sales Home Depot opened its first Home Depot Fuel locations in Tennessee and Georgia in 2006.

In early 2007 Nardelli left the company and vice chairman and EVP Frank Blake took the top spot. Home Depot decided to close its handful of flooring-only stores that year. The apparent nail in Nardelli's coffin was his autocratic management style and hefty compensation package (strategically based on options rather than shareholder returns and estimated at $245 million over five years). Nardelli left Home Depot with a $210 million severance package.

The company sold its HD Supply business in 2007 to Bain Capital Carlyle Group and Clayton Dubilier & Rice. The retailer used the proceeds to help it make a $10 billion stock repurchase of more than 15% of its market capitalization.

The Home Depot closed two stores in China in fiscal 2011. In fiscal 2013 it closed the last of its big-box stores there.

EXECUTIVES

President Southern Division, Tim Hourigan
Evp Corporate Services And Cfo, Carol B. Tomé, age 62, $1,079,231 total compensation
President The Home Depot Mexico, Ricardo E. Saldivar, age 66
Chairman President And Ceo, Craig A. Menear, age 61, $1,300,000 total compensation

Evp Supply Chain And Product Development, Mark Q. Holifield, age 62, $775,385 total compensation

Evp And Cio, Matthew A. (Matt) Carey, age 54, $730,385 total compensation

Svp Talent Organization And Performance Systems, Timothy M. (Tim) Crow, age 63, $586,308 total compensation

Evp U.s. Stores, Ann-Marie Campbell, age 53, $665,385 total compensation

President The Home Depot Canada, Jeff Kinnaird

Evp Outside Sales And Service, William G. (Bill) Lennie, age 63

Evp General Counsel And Corporate Secretary, Teresa W. Roseborough, age 60

President Western Division, Aaron Flowe

President Online; Chief Marketing Officer, Kevin Hofmann

Evp Merchandising, Edward P. (Ted) Decker, age 56

President Northern Division, Crystal Hanlon

Vp And Associate General Counsel, Jocelyn Hunter

Vice President Of Finance, Scott Bohrer

Vp Investor Relations, Diane Dayhoff

Vice President Human Resources, Michael Hagan

Vice President Employment Practices And Associate Relations, Derek W Bottoms

Vice President Information Technology, Daniel Grider

Vice President, Renee Murray

Vice President Internal Communications, Dennis Depot

Regional Vice President, Quonta Vance

Vice President Of Tax, Karen Dewalt

Executive Vice President Business Development And Corporate Operations, Frank Blake

Vice President, Katie Brubaker

Vice President Merchandising Operations, Mark Healy

Vice President Service Operations And Home Renovation Services, Chuyu Xi

Merchandising Vice President, Mike Hogenmiller

Vice President Supply Chain, Paul Larkin

Senior Vice President Supply Chain, Thomas Shortt

Vice President Real Estate, Michael Laferle

Senior Vice President Store Operations, Hector Padilla

Vice President Of Pro Business, Jt Rieves

Vice President Corporate Communications And External Affairs, Stacey Tank

Svp Merchandising Building Materials, Giles Bowman

Vice President And Deputy General Counsel, Peter Muniz

Senior Vice President Of Operations, Tim Applebee

National Sales Manager, Jeff Capone

Vice President Marketing, Lisa DeStefano

Executive Vice President Cio, Matt Carey

Vice President Learning And Development, Tom Spahr

Department Head, Chip Mccuiston

Department Head, William Morgan

Vice President Customer Service, Sherri Allen

Vice President And General Manager, Marconi Beth

Vice President Operations, Paul Deveno

Executive Board Member, ERIC PETERSON

Board Member, Albert Carey

Auditors: KPMG LLP

LOCATIONS

HQ: Home Depot Inc
2455 Paces Ferry Road, Atlanta, GA 30339
Phone: 770 433-8211   **Fax:** 770 431-2707
Web: www.homedepot.com

2018 Sales

	$ mil.	% of total
US	99,386	92
Other	8,817	8
Total	**108,203**	**100**

2018 Stores

	No.
US	1,981
Canada	182
Mexico	124
Total	**2,287**

PRODUCTS/OPERATIONS

2018 Sales

	$ mil.	% of total
Indoor garden	10,438	10
Appliances	9,001	8
Paint	8,461	8
Lumber	8,388	8
Tools	8,109	8
Plumbing	8,052	7
Building materials	7,772	7
Kitchen and bath	7,721	7
Flooring	7,475	7
Outdoor garden	7,257	7
Hardware	6,194	6
Millwork	5,743	5
Electrical	5,576	5
Other	8,016	7
Total	**108,203**	**100**

Selected Private Labels and Proprietary Brands

EcoSmart (lighting)
Everbilt (plumbing parts and pumps)
Glacier Bay (fixtures)
Hampton Bay (lighting)
Husky (hand tools)
LifeProof (flooring)
RIDGID (power tools)
Stanley (hand tools)
Vigoro (lawn care products)

COMPETITORS

84 Lumber	Menard
Ace Hardware	Sears Holdings
Amazon.com	Sherwin-Williams
BMC Stock	Target Corporation
Best Buy	Tractor Supply
Do it Best	True Value
Lowe's	Wal-Mart
Lumber Liquidators	

HISTORICAL FINANCIALS

Company Type: Public

Income Statement
FYE: February 3

	REVENUE ($ mil.)	NET INCOME ($ mil.)	NET PROFIT MARGIN	EMPLOYEES
02/19*	108,203	11,121	10.3%	413,000
01/18	100,904	8,630	8.6%	413,000
01/17	94,595	7,957	8.4%	406,000
01/16	88,519	7,009	7.9%	385,000
02/15	83,176	6,345	7.6%	371,000
Annual Growth	**6.8%**	**15.1%**		**2.7%**

*Fiscal year change

2019 Year-End Financials

Debt ratio: 66.00%
Return on equity: ***,***.**%
Cash ($ mil.): 1,778
Current ratio: 1.00
Long-term debt ($ mil.): 26,807

No. of shares (mil.): 1,105
Dividends
  Yield: 0.0%
  Payout: 42.0%
Market value ($ mil.): 203,729

	STOCK PRICE ($) FY Close	P/E High/Low	PER SHARE ($) Earnings	Dividends	Book Value
02/19*	184.00	22 16	10.00	4.00	(2.00)
01/18	207.00	28 19	7.00	4.00	1.00
01/17	138.00	21 17	6.00	3.00	4.00
01/16	126.00	25 19	5.00	2.00	5.00
02/15	104.00	23 16	5.00	2.00	7.00
Annual Growth	**15.3%**	— —	19.9%	21.7%	—

*Fiscal year change

HOME PROPERTIES, LIMITED PARTNERSHIP

LOCATIONS

HQ: HOME PROPERTIES, LIMITED PARTNERSHIP
850 CLINTON SQ, ROCHESTER, NY 146041730
Phone: 585 546-4900
Web: WWW.HOMEPROPERTIES.COM

HISTORICAL FINANCIALS

Company Type: Private

Income Statement
FYE: December 31

	ASSETS ($ mil.)	NET INCOME ($ mil.)	INCOME AS % OF ASSETS	EMPLOYEES
12/07	3,216	62	1.9%	1,000
12/06	3,240	110	3.4%	—
12/05	2,978	27	0.9%	—
12/01	1,347	2	0.2%	—
Annual Growth	**15.6%**	**75.1%**	—	—

HomeStreet Inc

HomeStreet aims to offer home and business mortgages to all in the Pacific Northwest and Hawaii. Its subsidiary HomeStreet Bank offers traditional consumer banking accounts as well as commercial and private banking investment and insurance products and services through 45 branches and 65 loan offices in the Pacific Northwest California and Hawaii. Specializing in residential and commercial mortgages the bank and fellow subsidiary Homestreet Capital Corp originate home loans both directly and through a joint venture Windermere Real Estate which operates about 40 offices in Washington and Oregon. HomeStreet also provides specialty financing for income-producing properties.

Operations

HomeStreet operates two lines of business: Commercial and Consumer Banking and Mortgage Banking which originates residential mortgage loans for wale in the secondary markets to be securitized by GSAs. Its primary subsidiaries are HomeStreet Bank and HomeStreet Capital Corp. (HCC). HCC sells and services multifamily mortgage loans in conjunction with HomeStreet Bank.

HomeStreet gets most of its business from mortgage originations and sales. About 53% of the company's revenue came from its mortgage banking business (origination and sales) during 2015 while another 6% came from mortgage servicing income. Another 34% of its revenue came from loan interest.

Geographic Reach

Seattle-based HomeStreet operates bank branches in Arizona California Colorado Hawaii Idaho Oregon Utah and Washington.

Sales and Marketing

HomeStreet provides financial services for small-and middle-market businesses as well as consumers.

Financial Performance

HomeStreet's annual revenues and profits have more than doubled since 2011 thanks to strong mortgage banking and loan business growth driven by a strengthening housing market.

The company's revenue spiked 50% to $446.35 million during 2015 mostly thanks to a 64% increase in gains on mortgage loan origination sales resulting from a rise in single family mortgage interest rate lock commitments.

Strong revenue growth in 2015 caused HomeStreet's net income to nearly double to $41.32 million. The company's operating cash levels spiked to $8.31 million for the year (operations had used $348.6 million in 2014) mostly because it collected more in cash-denominated proceeds from its mortgage loan sales than it did in 2014.

Strategy

HomeStreet has been moving more toward commercial mortgage and SBA originations in recent years launching its HomeStreet commercial capital business in Orange County California in 2015. It also continues to acquire other small community banks in its region to grow its loan and deposit business and expand into new geographic markets.

Additionally it's been expanding its retail operations its own opening two new branches in San Diego's Mission Gorge and Kearny Mesa markets in March 2016. To boost profitability HomeStreet looked in 2016 to enhance productivity and cut costs by streamlining operations.

Mergers and Acquisitions

The company plans to buy two Southern California banks from Boston Private Bank & Trust. Through that acquisition HomeStreet will gain some $110 million in deposit accounts. It will then have a dozen retail branches in Southern California.

In February 2016 the company purchased Orange County Business Bank for $55 million extending its reach into "one of the premier commercial and consumer banking markets in the country" according to HomeStreet CEO and chairman Mark Mason.

In March 2015 HomeStreet expanded into Southern California's retail banking market after acquiring Simplicity Bancorp and its seven Simply Bank retail deposit branches in the greater Los Angeles area. Beyond geographic expansion the deal added valuable retail deposit and loan assets.

In November 2013 HomeStreet acquired Fortune Bank a community bank with two branches in Seattle and Bellevue for about $27 million. Concurrently it purchased YNB Financial Services Corp. the parent company of Yakima National Bank which operates four branches in Yakima Selah Sunnyside and Kennewick for about $10.3 million. The twin purchases along with the acquisition of two branches from AmericanWest Bank increased the number of retail deposit branches operates by HomeStreet to 29.

Company Background

HomeStreet went public in February 2012 with an offering worth $55 million. The company sold 1.6 million shares priced at $44 each. HomeStreet had postponed two previous attempts to go public in 2011 that had planned to sell many more shares. Proceeds from the 2012 IPO were used to meet capital-ratio requirements required by regulators in the wake of allegations that the bank engaged in unsafe practices.

HomeStreet was hit hard by the economic downturn and slowdown in the housing market. Trouble in its core mortgage lending business led to losses in 2009 and 2010 and the bank entered into agreements with regulators to improve its capital position earnings and management. It brought in a new management team and launched a turnaround plan to stabilize the business which included tightening its lending standards restructuring troubled loans when necessary and the sale of real estate backed by nonperforming loans. The

measures helped HomeStreet return to profitability in 2011 and remain in the black for several years thereafter.

EXECUTIVES

Chairman President And Ceo Homestreet Inc. And Homestreet Bank, Mark K. Mason, age 59, $537,500 total compensation

Evp Chief Administrative Officer General Counsel And Corporate Secretary Homestreet Inc. And Homestreet Bank, Godfrey B. Evans, age 65, $247,200 total compensation

Sevp Commercial Banking Homestreet Bank, David H. Straus, age 72

Evp Homestreet Inc. And Evp Residential Construction And Affiliated Businesses Homestreet Bank, Richard W. H. (Rich) Bennion, age 69, $203,000 total compensation

Evp And Retail Banking Director Homestreet Bank, Paulette Lemon, age 62

Evp And Human Resources Director Homestreet Bank, Pamela J. (Pam) Taylor, age 67

Evp Chief Risk Officer And Chief Credit Officer Homestreet Inc. And Homestreet Bank, Jay C. Iseman, age 59, $200,000 total compensation

Sevp Mortgage Lending Director, Rose Marie David, age 55, $200,000 total compensation

Evp Commercial Real Estate And Commercial Capital President Homestreet Bank, William D. Endresen, age 64

Evp And Residential Construction Lending Director Homestreet Bank, Jeff Todhunter

Evp Chief Investment Officer And Treasurer Homestreet Inc. And Homestreet Bank, Darrell S. van Amen, age 53

Vice President Commercial Lending Manager, George Brace

Vice President Loan Officer, Carmen Esteban

Auditors: DELOITTE & TOUCHE LLP

LOCATIONS

HQ: HomeStreet Inc
601 Union Street, Suite 2000, Seattle, WA 98101
Phone: 206 623-3050
Web: www.homestreet.com

PRODUCTS/OPERATIONS

2015 Sales

	$ mil.	% of total
Interest		
Loans	153	34
Investment securities available for sale	12	3
Other	1	-
Non-interest		
Net gains on mortgage origination & sales activities	236	53
Mortgage servicing	24	6
Depositor & other retail banking fees	6	1
Gain on sale of investment securities available for sale	2	1
Bargain purchase gain	8	2
Insurance agency commission Income from WMS Series LLC and other		4
Total	**446**	**100**

Selected Services

Personal Banking
Home LoansInvestmentInsurancePrivate Bank
Commercial Banking
Builder Financing/Residential ConstructionCommercial LendingCommercial Real EstatePartnership Programs

COMPETITORS

American Savings Bank	KeyCorp
Bank of America	Sound Financial
Bank of Hawaii	U.S. Bancorp
Banner Corp	Umpqua Holdings
First Hawaiian	Washington Federal
JPMorgan Chase	Wells Fargo

HISTORICAL FINANCIALS

Company Type: Public

Income Statement

FYE: December 31

	ASSETS ($ mil.)	NET INCOME ($ mil.)	INCOME AS % OF ASSETS	EMPLOYEES
12/18	7,042	40	0.6%	2,036
12/17	6,742	69	1.0%	2,419
12/16	6,244	58	0.9%	2,552
12/15	4,894	41	0.8%	2,139
12/14	3,535	22	0.6%	1,611
Annual Growth	18.8%	15.8%		6.0%

2018 Year-End Financials

Debt ratio: 2.00%
Return on equity: 6.00%
Cash ($ mil.): 58
Current ratio: —
Long-term debt ($ mil.): —

No. of shares (mil.): 27
Dividends
  Yield: —
  Payout: —
Market value ($ mil.): 573

	STOCK PRICE ($) FY Close	P/E High/Low		PER SHARE ($) Earnings	Dividends	Book Value
12/18	21.00	22	14	1.00	0.00	27.00
12/17	29.00	13	9	3.00	0.00	26.00
12/16	32.00	14	8	2.00	0.00	23.00
12/15	22.00	12	9	2.00	0.00	21.00
12/14	17.00	14	11	1.00	0.00	20.00
Annual Growth	5.1%	—	—	(0.3%)	—	7.7%

HOMETOWN AMERICA MANAGEMENT CORP.

EXECUTIVES

Ceo, Richard Cline
Cao*, Tom Curatolo
Coo*, Greg Oberry
Human Resources Director, Nicole Nixon

LOCATIONS

HQ: HOMETOWN AMERICA MANAGEMENT CORP.
150 N WACKER DR STE 2800, CHICAGO, IL 606061610
Phone: 312 604-7500
Web: WWW.HOMETOWNAMERICA.COM

HISTORICAL FINANCIALS

Company Type: Private

Income Statement

FYE: December 31

	ASSETS ($ mil.)	NET INCOME ($ mil.)	INCOME AS % OF ASSETS	EMPLOYEES
12/07	3,059	57	1.9%	1,000
12/06	2,815	56	2.0%	—
12/05	2,455	56	2.3%	—
12/04	2,289	19	0.8%	—
Annual Growth	10.2%	44.8%		

HomeTrust Bancshares Inc.

EXECUTIVES

Ceo-Pres, Dana L Stonestreet
Exec V Pres-Cfo-Treas, Tony J Vuncannon
Exec V Pres-CIO, Howard L Sellinger
Exec V Pres-Cbo, C Hunter Westbrook
Exec V Pres-Chief ADM Officer-, Teresa White
Exec V Pres-Cro, R Parrish Little
Evp-Commercial Banking Group E, Mark Demarcus
Chro, Paula C Labian
President, Market, Robert D Gray
Vp, Commercial Relationship MA, Jeffery Chad Davis
Evp and Commercial Banking Gro, W Mark Demarcus
Auditors: Dixon Hughes Goodman LLP

LOCATIONS

HQ: HomeTrust Bancshares Inc.
10 Woodfin Street, Asheville, NC 28801
Phone: 828 259-3939
Web: www.hometrustbancshares.com

HISTORICAL FINANCIALS

Company Type: Public

Income Statement				FYE: June 30
	ASSETS ($ mil.)	NET INCOME ($ mil.)	INCOME AS % OF ASSETS	EMPLOYEES
06/19	3,476	27	0.8%	582
06/18	3,304	8	0.2%	520
06/17	3,207	12	0.4%	486
06/16	2,718	11	0.4%	465
06/15	2,783	8	0.3%	505
Annual Growth	5.7%	35.6%	—	3.6%

2019 Year-End Financials

Debt ratio: 0.00%	No. of shares (mil.): 18
Return on equity: 7.00%	Dividends
Cash ($ mil.): 364	Yield: 0.0%
Current ratio: —	Payout: 12.0%
Long-term debt ($ mil.): —	Market value ($ mil.): 452

	STOCK PRICE ($) FY Close	P/E High/Low		PER SHARE ($) Earnings	Dividends	Book Value
06/19	25.00	20	16	1.00	0.00	23.00
06/18	28.00	65	50	0.00	0.00	21.00
06/17	24.00	41	27	1.00	0.00	21.00
06/16	19.00	32	26	1.00	0.00	20.00
06/15	17.00	40	35	0.00	0.00	19.00
Annual Growth	10.7%	—	—	36.5%	—	4.5%

Honeywell International Inc

Jet engines and Muck Boots seem worlds apart but they coexist at Honeywell International. More than a century old the company is a diverse industrial conglomerate its four segments making and selling products from aircraft engines flight safety and landing systems to smart controls for commercial buildings to personal safety products such as gas masks and footwear. In late 2018 Honeywell completed the spin-off of its vehicle turbo charger operations and home heating and security businesses to create two new publicly-listed companies—Garrett Motion Inc. (turbo charger technology) and Resideo for home comfort and security products (formerly its Homes and ADI Distribution business). The company does business worldwide although the US generates more than half its sales.

Operations

Honeywell is organized across four segments: Aerospace; Performance Materials and Technologies; Building Technologies; and Safety and Productivity Solutions.

The Aerospace segment accounts for more than 35% of the company's revenue. It provides products and services for aircraft and vehicles sold to OEMs and other customers in a variety of end markets—air transport; regional business and general aviation aircraft; airlines and aircraft operators; defense and space contractors; and automotive and truck manufacturers.

Performance Materials and Technologies (more than 25% of revenue) operates in three divisions. Honeywell UOP provides process technology for fuel production for the petroleum refining gas processing and petrochemical industries; Process Solutions sells automation controls and software for the oil and gas pulp and paper industrial power and several other industries; and Advanced Materials manufactures high-performance products such as fluorocarbons specialty films waxes additives and advanced fibers to name a few.

The company's former Home and Building Technologies segment—now just Building Technologies—(almost 25%) sells building automation controls for commercial customers.

The Safety and Productivity Solutions segment (15%) offers products that improve productivity workplace safety and asset performance. Safety products include personal protection equipment and footwear. Productivity solutions include gas detection technology mobile devices and software for computing and data collection supply chain and warehouse automation equipment and sensors switches and controls.

Geographic Reach

The company's principal executive offices are located in Morris Plains NJ. Honeywell has approximately 1300 locations of which some 300 are manufacturing sites. The US accounts for more than 55% of total revenue.

Sales and Marketing

Honeywell's Aerospace business sells its products and services to original equipment manufacturers (OEMs) and other end markets like regional business and general aviation aircraft; airlines and aircraft operators; defense and space contractors; and automotive and truck manufacturers. The Building Technologies segment sells to commercial building owners. Performance Materials and Technologies targets several industries including oil and gas pulp and paper industrial power generation petrochemicals life sciences and mining. The Safety and Productivity Solutions business sells its products globally to a variety of industries.

Financial Performance

Honeywell's revenues increased 3% from $39.3 billion in 2016 to $40.5 billion in 2017. This growth was led by a 22% increase in its Safety and Productivity Solutions business.

Honeywell's net income plummeted to $1.7 billion in 2017 a $3.2 billion decrease from 2016. The decrease is attributed to the impact of additional tax expense from the Tax Cuts and Jobs Act. The company is working to better align its operating structure to benefit from the new tax system.

Cash at the end of fiscal 2017 was $7.0 billion a decrease of $784 million from the prior year. Cash from operations contributed $6.0 billion to the coffers while investing activities used $3.6 billion which included a net $2 billion increase in investments (mostly in marketable securities). Financing activities used another $3.5 billion for loan payments dividends to stockholders and the company's stock repurchase program.

Strategy

For all its segments Honeywell is focused on several initiatives to spur growth including R&D activities to develop new technologies. The company aims to become an industrial software company offering products for the connected plane home building and factory. Other initiatives that target lower costs are process improvements in its manufacturing and administrative operations and cost control efforts for asbestos and environmental remediation and pension and retirement benefits.

Honeywell's strategy for growth includes both acquisitions and the divestiture of under-performing units. In order to streamline its operations Honeywell in late 2018 completed the spin-off of its turbo charger unit and home heating and security businesses to create two new publicly traded companies. The new business featuring its turbo charger technology (formerly the Transportation Systems business) is now Garrett Motion Inc. Its former Homes and ADI Global Distribution business is now Resideo a company providing home comfort and security systems. After the spin-offs Honeywell believes its remaining portfolio will consist of high-growth businesses each aligned to the global megatrends of energy efficiency infrastructure investment urbanization and safety.

Mergers and Acquisitions

In 2018 Honeywell acquired the warehouse automation business Transnorm for approximately €425 million from IK Investment Partners. The acquisition enhances Honeywell's presence in the growing e-commerce market in Europe as Transnorm does more than half its business there. With Transnorm Honeywell hopes to build on the success of its 2016 acquisition of Intelligrated a maker of material handling equipment including conveyors sorters and airport baggage handling equipment as well as order fulfillment and warehouse control software.

Mid-2017 saw the company complete the purchase of Nextnine a provider of security management solutions and technologies for industrial cybersecurity. The addition of Nextnine's security solutions and secure remote service capabilities is meant to shore up Honeywells's existing range of cybersecurity technologies and increase its Connected Plant cybersecurity customer base.

HISTORY

During WWI Germany controlled much of the world's chemical industry causing dye and drug shortages. In response Washington Post publisher Eugene Meyer and scientist William Nichols organized the Allied Chemical & Dye Corporation in 1920.

Allied opened a synthetic ammonia plant in 1928 near Hopewell Virginia and became the world's leading producer of ammonia. After WWII Allied began making nylon refrigerants and other products. The company became Allied Chemical Corporation in 1958.

Seeking a supplier of raw materials for its chemical products Allied bought Union Texas Natural Gas in 1962. In the early 1970s CEO John Connor sold many of the firm's unprofitable businesses and invested in oil and gas exploration. By 1979 when Edward Hennessy became CEO Union Texas produced 80% of Allied's income.

Hennessy led the company into the electronics and technical markets. Under a new name Allied Corporation (1981) it bought the Bendix Corporation an aerospace and automotive company in 1983. In 1985 Allied merged with Signal Companies (founded by Sam Mosher in 1922) to form AlliedSignal. The company spun off more than 40 unprofitable chemical and engineering businesses over the next two years.

Larry Bossidy hired from General Electric in 1991 as the new CEO began to cut waste and buy growth businesses. In 1998 alone the company made 13 acquisitions. Late in 1999 the company acquired Honeywell (which dated back to 1906) in a deal valued at $15 billion and changed its name to Honeywell International. Honeywell after trying to make a go of it in the computer and telecommunications industries had refocused on its core products lines – thermostats security systems and other automation equipment.

In 2016 Honeywell was engaged in talks to merge with industry powerhouse United Technologies Corp. in a merger valued at around $90 billion. The talks ended however after United Technologies refused to explore the deal further fearing that the massive transaction could not clear steep regulatory hurdles.

EXECUTIVES

President And Ceo Aerospace, Timothy O. (Tim) Mahoney, age 62, $917,019 total compensation
Ceo Honeywell China And India, Shane Tedjarati
President And Ceo Home And Building Technologies (hbt), Terrence S. Hahn, age 53
Svp Engineering Operations And Information Technology, Krishna Mikkilineni, age 59, $717,678 total compensation
President And Ceo Performance Materials And Technologies, Rajeev Gautam, age 66
President And Ceo Safety And Productivity Solutions (sps), John Waldron, age 43
Svp And Cfo, Thomas A. (Tom) Szlosek, age 55, $840,000 total compensation
President And Ceo, Darius Adamczyk, age 53, $1,120,383 total compensation
President And Ceo Honeywell Transportation Systems, Olivier Rabiller
President Honeywell Intelligrated, Pieter Krynauw
President Honeywell Thailand, Mai Trang Thanh
Svp Of Finance, Greg Lewis
Vice President General Manager Resins And Chemicals, Qamar S Bhatia
Vice President Marketing, Brian Holliday
Vice President Electrical Sourcing, Lawrence Polizzotto
Vice President Marketing, Athanasios Karras
Vice President Americas Htt, Anthony Schultz
Vice President Human Resources (performance Materials And Technologies), Shaun Zitting
National Account Manager, Steve Bowman
Vice President Human Resources, Tom Smiley
Chairman, David M. (Dave) Cote, age 66
Auditors: DELOITTE & TOUCHE LLP

LOCATIONS

HQ: Honeywell International Inc
115 Tabor Road, Morris Plains, NJ 07950
Phone: 973 455-2000 **Fax:** 973 455-4807
Web: www.honeywell.com

2017 Sales

	$ mil.	% of total
US	22,722	56
Europe	10,400	26
Other International	7,412	18
Total	**40,534**	**100**

PRODUCTS/OPERATIONS

2017 Sales

	$ mil.	% of total
Aerospace	14,779	36
Performance Materials and Technologies	10,339	26
Home and Building Technologies	9,777	24
Safety and Productivity Solutions	5,639	14
Total	**40,534**	**100**

2017 Sales

	$ mil.	% of total
Product sales	32,317	80
Service sales	8,217	20
Total	**40,534**	**100**

Selected Products and Services

Aerospace
  Aircraft engines
  Auxiliary turbine power unites
  Cockpit systems and displays
  Cabin management and entertainment
  Air and thermal management
  Biofuel for aviation
  BendixKing avionics
Buildings
  Building automation systems
  Software and controls
  Construction and maintenance
  Combustion controls
Footwear
  Oliver safety footwear
  Muck boots
  Xtratuf boots
Healthcare
  Workflow automation for hospitals
  Patient monitoring systems
  Pharmaceutical laboratory products
  Pharmaceutical packaging films
Industrial
  Facility security and maintenance
  Energy solutions
  Honeywell Smart Energy for utilities
  Instrumentation for measurement and control
  Fuels and chemicals for clean power
Manufacturing
  Sensors and switches
  Advanced fibers and composites
  Renewable energy from biomass
  Honeywell MXProLine Quality Control System
  Honeywell HydroBlock anti-graffiti barrier film
Oil and Gas
  Refining technology
  Petrochemicals
  Gas processing equipment
  Adsorbents for contaminant removal
  Honeywell Green Diesel fuel
  Industrial water treatment
  Gas tank terminal operations controls
  Personal protective equipment
  Rope and performance fibers
Performance Materials
  Catalysts
  Refrigerants
  Honeywell Electronic Materials
  Research chemicals
  Honeywell Aclar barrier film for pharmaceutical packaging
  Honeywell Spectra fiber for braided fishing line
  Honeywell Specialty Additives
Productivity
  Barcode scanners
  Mobile computer devices
  Printers and media for RFID labels tags etc.
  Wearable devices
  OEM scan engines and modules
  Workflow solutions
  Vocollect voice technology for data collection
  Global tracking and messaging
  Search and rescue technology and services
Safety
  Protective equipment
  Honeywell Instant Alert cloud-based notification and emergency messaging

COMPETITORS

3M	Kion Group
Albemarle	MSA Safety
BASF SE	Rockwell Automation
BorgWarner	Rockwell Collins
Dow Chemical	Schneider Electric
Emerson Electric	Siemens AG
GE	TE Connectivity
Garmin	Thales
Itron	United Technologies
Johnson Controls Power Solutions	Zebra Technologies

HISTORICAL FINANCIALS

Company Type: Public

Income Statement
FYE: December 31

	REVENUE ($ mil.)	NET INCOME ($ mil.)	NET PROFIT MARGIN	EMPLOYEES
12/18	41,802	6,765	16.2%	114,000
12/17	40,534	1,655	4.1%	131,000
12/16	39,302	4,809	12.2%	131,000
12/15	38,581	4,768	12.4%	129,000
12/14	40,306	4,239	10.5%	127,000
Annual Growth	**0.9%**	**12.4%**	**—**	**(2.7%)**

2018 Year-End Financials

Debt ratio: 28.00%
Return on equity: 38.00%
Cash ($ mil.): 9,287
Current ratio: 1.00
Long-term debt ($ mil.): 9,756

No. of shares (mil.): 729
Dividends
  Yield: 2.0%
  Payout: 34.0%
Market value ($ mil.): 96,327

	STOCK PRICE ($) FY Close	P/E High/Low		PER SHARE ($) Earnings	Dividends	Book Value
12/18	132.00	18	14	9.00	3.00	25.00
12/17	153.00	72	54	2.00	3.00	23.00
12/16	116.00	19	15	6.00	2.00	25.00
12/15	104.00	18	15	6.00	2.00	24.00
12/14	100.00	19	16	5.00	2.00	23.00
Annual Growth	**7.2%**	**—**		**13.9%**	**13.1%**	**2.2%**

Hope Bancorp Inc

EXECUTIVES

Senior Executive Vice President Regional President Eastern Region, Kyu Kim
Vice President And Systems Support Manager, Joshua Chu
Senior Vice President And Chief Credit Officer, Peter Koh
Senior Vice President And Manager Loan Center Iii We Are Now Bank Of Hope, Christie Yoo
Vice President Information Technology Procurement Manager, Karina Moran
Vice President And Business Development Officer Commercial Lending Center I, Brian Chung
Assistant Vice President And Loan Servicing Officer Northern California Commercial Lending Center Bank Of Hope, Aekyung Park
Assistant Vice President And Loan Officer, Hyelim Choe
Executive Vice President Managing Director Of The Corporate Banking Group Of Bank Of Hope, Steven Canup
First Vice President And Portfolio Manager Commercial Lending Center I Bank Of Hope, Kay Kim
Senior Vice President 8c Branch Manager, Cindy Chi

Senior Vice President Vendor Risk Management, Bradley Martin
Aap Senior Vice President Tms Operations Manager, Rachel Lim
Vice President And Operational Risk Management Assistant, Katelyn Kang
Vice President International Operations, Lisa Lee
Vp And Loan Officer Iii, Chris Kim
Avp Loan Officer, Gina Choi
Fvp And Branch Manager, Sang Ahn
Senior Vice President And Sba Manager, Sylvester Kim
Senior Vice President Branch Manager, Eric Lee
Senior Vice President International Operations Manager, Linda Kim
First Vice President, Alex Cho
Senior Vice President And Marketing Manager Senior Business Analyst Loan Department, Gene Pak
Assistant Vice President And Service Officer Ii, Gloria Wang
Vice President And Sba Loan Officer, Ellie Park
Svp Head Of Business Solutions, Ajay Guntupalli
Managing Director Middle Market Lending, Mark Smith
Vice President Project Manager, David Son
Senior Vice President Chief Corporate Banking Officer, Alex Kim
Auditors: Crowe LLP

LOCATIONS

HQ: Hope Bancorp Inc
3200 Wilshire Boulevard, Suite 1400, Los Angeles, CA 90010
Phone: 213 639-1700   **Fax:** 213 235-3033
Web: www.bankofhope.com

PRODUCTS/OPERATIONS

2015 Sales

	$ mil.	% of total
Interest income	314	88
Non-interest income	44	12
Total	**357**	**100**

COMPETITORS

Bank of America	Grandpoint
Broadway Financial	Hanmi Financial
Cathay General Bancorp	U.S. Bancorp
East West Bancorp	Wells Fargo
Far East National Bank	Woori

HISTORICAL FINANCIALS

Company Type: Public

Income Statement

FYE: December 31

	ASSETS ($ mil.)	NET INCOME ($ mil.)	INCOME AS % OF ASSETS	EMPLOYEES
12/18	15,306	190	1.2%	1,494
12/17	14,207	139	1.0%	1,470
12/16	13,441	114	0.8%	1,372
12/15	7,913	92	1.2%	938
12/14	7,140	89	1.2%	915
Annual Growth	**21.0%**	**20.9%**	**—**	**13.0%**

2018 Year-End Financials

Debt ratio: 2.00%	No. of shares (mil.): 127
Return on equity: 10.00%	Dividends
Cash ($ mil.): 460	Yield: 5.0%
Current ratio: —	Payout: 44.0%
Long-term debt ($ mil.): —	Market value ($ mil.): 1,502

Horace Mann Educators Corp.

Naming itself in honor of Horace Mann considered the father of public education Horace Mann Educators is an insurance holding company that primarily serves K-12 school teachers and other public school employees throughout the US. Through its operating subsidiaries the company offers homeowners auto (majority of revenue) and individual and group life insurance as well as retirement annuities. Horace Mann employs some 735 agents many of whom are former teachers themselves. Writing business in 48 states and Washington DC the company derives about a third of its direct premiums and contract deposits from five states — California Illinois Texas North Carolina and Florida.

Operations
Horace Mann maintains a long-standing relationship with the country's biggest education association the National Education Association which has around 3.2 million members. It has also established a number of advertising and sponsorship agreements with a host of smaller educator groups as a way to drum up new business leads.

The company divides it business into property/casualty insurance annuities and life insurance. Property/casualty is the largest contributor to revenue with auto being the largest component of that group. The propertycasualty annuity and life segments account for some 48% 44% and 8% respectively of the company's insurance premiums and contract deposits.

Geographic Reach
The company is based in Springfield Illinois.

Strategy
In recent years the company has moved away from single-person agency operations to an agency business model (ABM) with multiple sales agents licensed product specialists and other support personnel based together in outside offices. The company saw enough success with the ABM model that it began migrating agents over to an exclusive agent agreement through which the agents become independent contractors that only sell Horace Mann products. Nearly all its agents now operate in this manner.

Mergers and Acquisitions
In early 2019 Horace Mann acquired retirement plan coordinator Benefits Consultants Group further expanding its operations in the retirement market. Later that year the company acquired National Teachers Associates Life Insurance Company to enhance its product offerings in the supplemental insurance arena.

EXECUTIVES

Executive Vice President Senior Vice President Vice President, Jeff Jaynes
Executive Vice President Service And Technology Operations And Financial Services, George J Zock
Evp And Cfo, Dwayne D. Hallman, age 56, $444,000 total compensation
President And Ceo, Marita Zuraitis, age 58, $742,333 total compensation
Evp Annuity And Life, Matthew P. Sharpe, $394,000 total compensation
Evp Property And Casualty, William J. Caldwell, $325,000 total compensation
Vice President Human Resources, Kathi Karr
Vice President Chief Actuary, Robert Rich
Assistant Vice President Product Manager, Angel Plaza
Assistant Vice President Claims Training, Jill Kilroy
Vice President Investor Relations, Ryan Greenier
Assistant Vice President Finance, Troy Gayle
Senior Vice President Personal Lines, Bill Caldwell
Vp Talent Management, Beth Moore
Vice President Of Human Resources Finance, Rob Billingsley
Vice President Corporate Accounting And Reporting, Ladd Turner
Regional Vice President, Keith Brooks
Vice President Of Information Technology Operation, Robert E Rich
Board Member, Stephen Hasenmiller
Chairman, Gabriel L. Shaheen, age 66
Board Member, Ronald Helow
Auditors: KPMG LLP

LOCATIONS

HQ: Horace Mann Educators Corp.
1 Horace Mann Plaza, Springfield, IL 62715-0001
Phone: 217 789-2500
Web: www.horacemann.com

PRODUCTS/OPERATIONS

2016 Sales

	$ mil.	% of total
Insurance premiums & contract charges earned	759	67
Net investment income	361	32
Net realized investment gains	4	-
Other income	5	1
Total	**1,129**	**100**

COMPETITORS

AIG	Nationwide
AXA	Progressive
Allstate	Corporation
Farmers Group	Security Benefit Group
GEICO	State Farm
ING Americas	TIAA
LSW	USAA
Liberty Mutual Agency	VALIC
MetLife	

HISTORICAL FINANCIALS

Company Type: Public

Income Statement

FYE: December 31

	ASSETS ($ mil.)	NET INCOME ($ mil.)	INCOME AS % OF ASSETS	EMPLOYEES
12/18	11,032	18	0.2%	1,495
12/17	11,198	169	1.5%	1,496
12/16	10,577	84	0.8%	2,061
12/15	10,059	93	0.9%	2,034
12/14	9,769	104	1.1%	2,008
Annual Growth	**3.1%**	**(35.2%)**	**—**	**(7.1%)**

2018 Year-End Financials

Debt ratio: 3.00%
Return on equity: 1.00%
Cash ($ mil.): 12
Current ratio: —
Long-term debt ($ mil.): —

No. of shares (mil.): 41
Dividends
  Yield: 3.0%
  Payout: 29.0%
Market value ($ mil.): 1,534

	STOCK PRICE ($) FY Close	P/E High/Low		PER SHARE ($) Earnings	Dividends	Book Value
12/18	37.00	107	81	0.00	1.00	31.00
12/17	44.00	12	8	4.00	1.00	37.00
12/16	43.00	21	14	2.00	1.00	32.00
12/15	33.00	17	14	2.00	1.00	31.00
12/14	33.00	13	11	2.00	1.00	33.00
Annual Growth	3.1%	—	—	(35.0%)	5.5%	(0.9%)

Horizon Bancorp Inc

For those in Indiana and Michigan Horizon Bancorp stretches as far as the eye can see. The company is the holding company for Horizon Bank (and its Heartland Community Bank division) which provides checking and savings accounts IRAs CDs and credit cards to customers through more than 50 branches in north and central Indiana and southwest and central Michigan. Commercial financial and agricultural loans make up the largest segment of its loan portfolio which also includes mortgage warehouse loans (loans earmarked for sale into the secondary market) consumer loans and residential mortgages. Through subsidiaries the bank offers trust and investment management services; life health and property/casualty insurance; and annuities.

Operations

Horizon boasted more than $2.08 billion in total assets and $1.48 billion in deposits in 2014. Commercial loans made up 49% of the bank's total loan portfolio. The bank employed nearly 450 full and part time employees that year.

Horizon's subsidiaries include: Horizon Investments which manages the bank's investment portfolio; Horizon Properties which manages the real estate investment trust; Horizon Insurance Services which sells through the company's Wealth Management; and Horizon Grantor Trust which holds title to certain company-owned life insurance policies.

The bank generated 61% of its revenue from interest income on loans in 2014 while another 13% came from interest on its taxable and tax-exempt investments. About 8% of revenues came from gains on its mortgage sales while the remainder of revenues were mostly generated by a mix of service charges on deposit accounts interchange fees and fiduciary activities fees.

Geographic Reach

The bank's more than 30 branches serve customers in north and central Indiana and southwest and central Michigan. Its mortgage-banking services are offered across the Midwest.

Financial Performance

Horizon Bancorp's revenues and profits have been trending higher over the past few years mostly as it's continued to grow its loan business and deposit customer base through acquisitions.

The bank's revenue rose by 2% to $102.5 million in 2014 mostly as the bank increased its interest-earning assets during the year. Its non-interest income also increased thanks to higher service charges on deposits and interchange fee income resulting from the growth in transactional deposit accounts and volume.

Despite higher revenue in 2014 the company's net income fell by 9% to $18.1 million for the year on higher provisions for loan losses due to loan growth and a write off of a commercial account coupled with an increase in transaction costs related to its Summit acquisition and an increase in salaries and employee benefits due to growth. Horizon's operating cash levels fell by 62% to $17.7 million after adjusting its earnings for non-cash items related to its net proceeds on the sale of its held-for-sale loans.

Strategy

Horizon Bancorp continues to expand its geographic reach and loan business through acquisitions and new branches. It acquired several banks and opened new branches throughout 2016 and 2017.

Mergers and Acquisitions

In 2017 Horizon Bancorp agreed to buy Wolverine Bancorp for $92 million and Lafayette Community Bancorp for $32 million

In 2016 Horizon Bancorp bought LaPorte Bancorp for $98.9 million boosting its total assets by 20% to more than $3.24 billion while expanding its branch reach into the LaPorte area of Indiana. It also agreed to buy CNB Bancorp which operates Central National Bank & Trust in Attica Indiana.

In 2015 Horizon Bancorp agreed to buy Peoples Bancorp and subsidiary Peoples Federal Savings Bank of DeKalb County.

In April 2014 the company purchased SCP Bancorp including subsidiary Summit Community Bank and its two branches.

EXECUTIVES

President Ceo Chief Administrative Officer And Director; Chairman And Ceo Horizon Bank, Craig M. Dwight, age 62, $300,000 total compensation
Evp; President And Coo Horizon Bank, Thomas H. Edwards, age 66, $187,000 total compensation
Cfo, Mark E. Secor, age 53, $131,921 total compensation
President Laporte County Indiana Horizon Bank, Steven C. Kring
President Southwest Michigan Horizon Bank, Donald E. (Don) Radde, age 66, $166,000 total compensation
President Porter County Indiana Horizon Bank, David G. Rose
Executive Vice President And Senior Bank Operations Officer, Kathie A Deruiter
Svp And Sr Auditor And Chief Enterprise Risk Officer, Nancy Wrzalinski
Chairman, Robert C. Dabagia, age 80
Board Member, Larry Middleton
Board Member, Peter Pairitz
Board Member, Spero Valavanis
Board Member, Susan Aaron
Board Member, Lawrence Burnell
Board Member, James Dworkin
Board Member, Daniel Hopp
Board Member, Michele Magnuson
Board Member, Steven Reed
Board Member, Eric Blackhurst
Auditors: BKD, LLP

LOCATIONS

HQ: Horizon Bancorp Inc
  515 Franklin Street, Michigan City, IN 46360
Phone: 219 879-0211
Web: www.horizonbank.com

PRODUCTS/OPERATIONS

Selected Subsidiaries

Horizon Bank National Association
Horizon Insurance Services Inc.
Horizon Investments Inc.
Horizon Trust & Investment Management N.A.

COMPETITORS

1st Source Corporation
American United Mutual
Bank of America
Brotherhood Mutual
Farmers Mutual of NE
Fifth Third
First Merchants
Indiana Farmers Mutual

HISTORICAL FINANCIALS

Company Type: Public

Income Statement   FYE: December 31

	ASSETS ($ mil.)	NET INCOME ($ mil.)	INCOME AS % OF ASSETS	EMPLOYEES
12/18	4,247	53	1.3%	716
12/17	3,964	33	0.8%	701
12/16	3,141	24	0.8%	665
12/15	2,652	21	0.8%	558
12/14	2,077	18	0.9%	448
Annual Growth	19.6%	30.9%	—	12.4%

2018 Year-End Financials

Debt ratio: 1.00%
Return on equity: 11.00%
Cash ($ mil.): 74
Current ratio: —
Long-term debt ($ mil.): —

No. of shares (mil.): 38
Dividends
  Yield: 2.0%
  Payout: 31.0%
Market value ($ mil.): 606

	STOCK PRICE ($) FY Close	P/E High/Low		PER SHARE ($) Earnings	Dividends	Book Value
12/18	16.00	24	11	1.00	0.00	13.00
12/17	28.00	30	26	1.00	0.00	12.00
12/16	28.00	40	26	1.00	0.00	10.00
12/15	28.00	33	26	1.00	0.00	10.00
12/14	26.00	30	22	1.00	0.00	9.00
Annual Growth	(11.9%)	—	—	13.1%	14.3%	8.1%

Hormel Foods Corp.

The maker of such thrifty pantry staples as SPAM lunch meat and Dinty Moore stew Hormel Foods produces a slew of refrigerated processed meats and deli items ethnic entrees and frozen foods sold under the flagship Hormel brand as well as Don Miguel and MegaMex (Mexican) and Lloyd's (barbeque). Food service offerings include Hormel Natural Choice meats Café H Austin Blues and Bread Ready pre-sliced meats. Hormel is also a major US turkey and pork processor churning out Jennie-O turkey Cure 81 hams and Always Tender pork. More than 30 Hormel brands are ranked #1 or #2 in their respective markets.

HISTORY

George Hormel opened his Austin Minnesota slaughterhouse in an abandoned creamery in 1891. By 1900 Hormel had modernized his facilities to compete with larger meat processors. In 1903 the enterprise introduced its first brand name (Dairy Brand) and a year later began opening distribution centers nationwide. The scandal that ensued after the discovery in 1921 that an assistant controller had embezzled over $1 million almost broke the company causing Hormel to initiate tighter controls. By 1924 it was processing more than a million hogs annually. Hormel introduced canned ham two years later.

Jay Hormel George's son became president in 1929; under his guidance Hormel introduced Dinty Moore beef stew (1936) and SPAM (1937). A Hormel executive won a contest and $100 by submitting the name a contraction of "spiced ham." During WWII the US government bought over half of Hormel's output; it supplied SPAM to GIs and Allied forces.

In 1959 Hormel introduced its Little Sizzlers pork sausage and sold its billionth can of SPAM. New products rolled out in the 1960s included Hormel's Cure 81 ham (1963). By the mid-1970s the firm had more than 750 products.

The company survived a violent nationally publicized strike triggered by a pay cut in 1985. In the end only 500 of the original 1500 strikers returned to accept lower pay scales.

Sensing the consumer shift toward poultry Hormel purchased Jennie-O Foods in 1986. Later acquisitions included the House of Tsang and Oriental Deli (1992) Dubuque (processed pork 1993) and Herb-Ox (bouillon and dry soup mix 1993). After more than a century as Geo. A. Hormel & Co. the company began calling itself Hormel Foods in 1993 to reflect its expansion into non-pork foods. Former General Foods executive Joel Johnson was named president and CEO that year (and chairman two years later).

Hormel proved it could take a joke with the 1994 debut of its tongue-in-cheek SPAM catalog featuring dozens of SPAM-related products. But when a 1996 Muppets movie featured a porcine character named Spa'am Hormel sued Jim Henson Productions; a federal court gave Spa'am the go-ahead.

Also in 1996 Hormel teamed up with Mexican food processor Grupo Herdez to sell Herdez sauces and other Mexican food products in the US. It then formed a joint venture with Indian food producer Patak Spices (UK) to market its products in the US. Late that year Hormel paid $64 million for a 21% interest in Spanish food maker Campofrio Alimentacion.

Earnings fell in 1996 due in part to soaring hog prices. The company was hit hard again in 1998 when production contracts with hog growers meant it wound up paying premium rates despite a market glut. In 1998 the Smithsonian Institution accepted two cans of SPAM (one from 1937 the other an updated 1997 version) for its History of Technology collection.

SPAM sales soared in 1999 as nervous consumers stockpiled provisions for the millennium. To build its growing HealthLabs division Hormel acquired Cliffdale Farms (2000) and Diamond Crystal Brands nutritional products (a division of Imperial Sugar) in 2001 — boosting its share of the market for easy-to-swallow foods sold to hospitals and nursing homes.

In early 2001 Hormel acquired family-owned The Turkey Store for approximately $334 million and folded it into its Jennie-O division.

Hormel produced its 6 billionth can of SPAM in 2002 and traded $115 million in stock to acquire the rest of Imperial Sugar's Diamond Crystal Brands unit which packages single-serve packets of sugar sweeteners seasonings and plastic cutlery for the foodservice industry.

To further diversify in 2003 Hormel acquired food manufacturer Century Foods International (whey-based protein powders beverages and nutrition bars) and added it to its burgeoning specialty foods group. In 2004 Hormel sold off its stake in Campofrio to Smithfield Foods.

Its last act of business in 2004 was to purchase Southern California's Clougherty Packing for about $186 million. The pork processor's facilities help extend Hormel's capacity for further-processed foods in the southwestern US.

In 2005 the company purchased Mexican food manufacturer Arriba Foods for $47 million in cash. Later that year it bought Lloyd's Barbecue Company from General Mills.

Responding to the growing trend of the US population to dine out Hormel expanded its foodservice segment (which it refers to as its specialty foods business) with the 2005 purchase of foodservice food manufacturer and distributor Mark-Lynn Foods. Mark-Lynn's products include salt and pepper packets ketchup mustard sauces and salad dressings creamers and sugar packets as well as jellies desserts and drink mixes.

Adding to its grocery product offerings in 2006 the company acquired canned ready-to-eat chicken producer Valley Fresh Foods for $78 million. It also bought pepperoni and pasta maker Provena Foods and sausage and sliced meat maker Saag's Products. It added another to its list of countries in which it has joint ventures in 2006 when it formed a JV with San Miguel to raise and market hogs and animal feed in Vietnam. The JV is 49%-owned by Hormel.

Hormel acquired Burke Corporation a maker of pizza toppings and other fully cooked meat items in 2007 for $115 million in cash. The acquisition allowed Hormel to extend its pizza-topping operations into the foodservice sector. The following year it acquired Boca Grande Foods for $23.5 in cash. Boca Grande makes Poco Pac branded jams jellies and pancake syrup portion-control products for foodservice operators.

EXECUTIVES

Vice President Legislative Affairs, Joe Swedberg
Vice President Marketing For Foodservice Group, David F Weber
Evp And President Hormel Business Units, Steven G. Binder, age 62, $500,965 total compensation
Group Vp And President Hormel Foods International, Larry L. Vorpahl, age 56
Svp And Cfo, James N. Sheehan, age 64
Group Vp Refrigerated Foods, Thomas R. Day, age 61, $337,900 total compensation
Svp Supply Chain, Bryan D. Farnsworth, age 62
Group Vp And President Consumer Products Sales, Deanna T. Brady, age 54
Vp Wal-mart Sales, Donald H. (Don) Kremin, age 59
Chairman President And Ceo, James P. Snee, age 51, $509,595 total compensation
Group Vp And President Jennie-o Turkey Store, Glenn R. Leitch, age 58, $380,500 total compensation
Group Vp Foodservice, Jeffrey R. Baker, age 54
Group Vp Grocery Products, Luis G. Marconi, age 52
Vp Information Technology Services, Mark D. Vaupel
Vice President Business Planning, Mike Gyarmaty
Vice President, Alan Rasell
Vice President, Brett Asleson
Vice President Of Sales, Mark Ourada
National Sales Manager, Jeff Schultz
National Sales Manager, Mark Engelhardt
National Sales Manager, Michael Dougherty
Vice President Of Sales In The Consumer Products Sales Division, Kurt Mueller
Vice President Consumer Insights And Corporate Innovation, Scott Aakre
Vp And Controller, Jana Haynes
Vice President, Mike Mccoy
Vp And Svp Sales Consumer Product Sales, Patrick Schwab
Vice President And Senior Vice President Sales And Consumer Product Sales, Erinn Mueller
Executive Vice President, Ron Fielding
Vp Treasurer, Rollie Gentzler
Vice President Supply Chain, Bill Snyder
Senior Vice President Marketing Cytosport Inc., Karen Wiernik
Senior Vice President Retail Business Unit Jennie O Turkey Store Llc, Barry Lynch
Vp Operations Refrigerated Foods, Donald Temperley
Treasurer Controller, Eldon Quam
Board Member, Dakota Pippins
Vice President Finance And Treasurer, Gary Jamison
Board Member, Terrell Crews
Auditors: Ernst & Young LLP

LOCATIONS

HQ: Hormel Foods Corp.
  1 Hormel Place, Austin, MN 55912-3680
Phone: 507 437-5611   **Fax:** 507 437-5489
Web: www.hormel.com

2018 sales

	$ mil.	% of total
US	9	94
Foreign	588	6
Total	**9,546**	**100**

PRODUCTS/OPERATIONS

2018 sales

	$ mil.	% of total
Refrigerated Foods	4,772	50
Grocery Products	2,522	26
Jennie-O Turkey Store	1,627	17
International & Other	625	7
Total	**9,546**	**100**

Selected Products and Brands

Refrigerated
  Country Crock Side Dishes
  Hormel
  Hormel Always Tender flavored pork and beef products
  Hormel Black Label and Microwave Ready bacon
  Hormel Cure 81 ham
  Hormel Fresh Pantry meats
  Hormel Little Sizzlers pork sausage
  Hormel Natural Choice meats
  Hormel pepperoni minis and stix
  Hormel refrigerated entrees
  Hormel Wranglers franks
  Hormel Snac Cups
  Lloyd's Barbeque products
  Saag's sausages
Jennie-O Turkey Store
  Bratwursts and breakfast/dinner sausages
  Breast meat products
  Deli
  Di Lusso deli meats
  Farmer John deli meats
  Hormel 100 percent natural deli meats
  Hormel Deli beef dry sausage ham and turkey
  Hormel party trays
  Ground turkey
  Marinated turkey tenderloins
  So-Easy Entrees
  Turkey burger patties and franks
  Whole turkeys
Grocery products
  Dinty Moore stew Hearty Meals varieties microwave-ready products
  Herb-Ox bouillon
  Herdez Salsa
  Hormel
  Hormel bacon toppings
  Hormel Chili Master
  Hormel chunk meats
  Hormel Compleats microwave meals
  Hormel corned beef and roast beef with gravy
  Hormel dried beef
  Hormel Kid's Kitchen microwave cups
  Hormel Mary Kitchen hash
  Hormel microwave cups
  Not-So-Sloppy-Joe sloppy joe sauce
  Skippy peanut butter
  SPAM products (classic hickory smoke flavored hot and spicy lite low-sodium spread singles and oven-roasted turkey)
  Stagg chili
  Valley Fresh chunk meats and broths
Specialty Foods

Century Foods International (dairy and vegetable proteins nutraceuticals)

Diamond Crystal Brands (salts sugar substitutes)

Hormel Foods Ingredients (sauces powders broths oils Omega-3 additives)

Private Label products (canned meats prepared foods and desserts bouillon sweeteners salts seasonings)

Other

MegaMex Mexican brands

Bufalo hot sauces

CHI-CHI'S Mexican hot sauces taco tubs dips seasoning mixes and tortillas

Do?a María Authentic Mexican products

Don Miguel burritos appetizers empanadas taquitos tacos flautas chimichangas enchiladas

El Torito sauces dressings and corn cakes

Embasa Mexican peppers salsas

Herdez imported salsas

La Victoria Mexican salsas taco sauces enchilada sauces green chile peppers

Wholly Guacamole

World Food ethnic brands

House of Tsang entrees sauces and oils

Marrakesh Express Mediterranean products (couscous risotto)

Peloponnese Greek foods olives

Selected Foodservice Brands

Always Tender Pork

Austin Blues barbeque meats

Authentic Barbeque

Bread Ready pre-sliced meats

Café H ethnic meats

Cure 81 Ham

Dry Sausage

Fast 'N Easy Fully Cooked Meats

Hormel Chili

Masterpieces Toppings

Natural Choice meats

Old Smokehouse bacon

Old Tyme breakfast sausage

Old Tyme ham

Special Recipe Sausage

Stagg Chili

COMPETITORS

B&G Foods	H. J. Heinz Limited
Boar's Head	JBS USA
Bob Evans	Perdue Incorporated
Bridgford Foods	Pilgrim's Pride
Bush Brothers	Pinnacle Foods
Butterball	Plainville Farms
Campbell Soup	Sanderson Farms
Cargill	Seaboard
ConAgra	Smithfield Foods
Cooper Farms	The Dial Corporation
Foster Farms	Tyson Foods
General Mills	

HISTORICAL FINANCIALS

Company Type: Public

Income Statement   FYE: October 27

	REVENUE ($ mil.)	NET INCOME ($ mil.)	NET PROFIT MARGIN	EMPLOYEES
10/19	9,497	979	10.3%	18,800
10/18	9,546	1,012	10.6%	20,100
10/17	9,168	847	9.2%	20,200
10/16	9,523	890	9.3%	21,100
10/15	9,264	686	7.4%	20,700
Annual Growth	0.6%	9.3%	—	(2.4%)

2019 Year-End Financials

Debt ratio: 3.00%

Return on equity: 17.00%

Cash ($ mil.): 673

Current ratio: 2.00

Long-term debt ($ mil.): 250

No. of shares (mil.): 534

Dividends

Yield: 0.0%

Payout: 47.0%

Market value ($ mil.): 21,684

	STOCK PRICE ($) FY Close	P/E High/Low		PER SHARE ($) Earnings	Dividends	Book Value
10/19	41.00	25	21	2.00	1.00	11.00
10/18	41.00	22	16	2.00	1.00	10.00
10/17	30.00	24	19	2.00	1.00	9.00
10/16	38.00	49	20	2.00	1.00	8.00
10/15	68.00	53	39	1.00	1.00	8.00
Annual Growth	(12.2%)	—		9.1%	13.8%	10.0%

Horton (DR) Inc

The largest US homebuilder by volume D.R. Horton constructs single-family homes that range in size from 1000 sq. ft. to more than 4000 sq. ft. and sell for an average price of about $300000 under the D.R. Horton Emerald Homes Express Homes and Freedom Homes brand names. Texas-based D.R. Horton is active in about 80 markets in nearly 30 states and generates about 75% of its revenue from the Southeast South Central and Western regions of the US. Beyond single-family detached homes which account for nearly 90% of sales D.R. Horton builds duplexes townhomes and condominiums. It also provides mortgage title and closing services through its DHI Mortgage subsidiary.

HISTORY

Donald R. Horton was selling homes in Fort Worth Texas when he hit upon a strategy for increasing sales — add options to a basic floor plan. In 1978 he borrowed $33000 to build his first home added a bay window for an additional charge and sold the home for $44000. Donald soon added floor plans and options that appealed to regional preferences.

The depressed Texas market drove the company to expand beyond the Dallas/Fort Worth area in 1987 when it entered the then-hot Phoenix market. It continued to expand into the Southeast Mid-Atlantic Midwest and West in the late 1980s and early 1990s. By 1991 Horton and his family owned more than 25 companies that were combined as D.R. Horton which went public in 1992.

D.R. Horton acquired six geographically diverse construction firms in 1994 and 1995. In 1996 the company started a mortgage services joint venture expanded its title operations and added three more firms.

In 1998 the company bought four builders including Scottsdale Arizona-based Continental Homes. Continental had been expanding beyond its Arizona and Southern California base and had entered the lucrative retirement community market. After the Continental purchase Donald Horton stepped down as president remaining chairman. Richard Beckwitt took over as president and Donald Tomnitz became CEO. In 1999 the company acquired Century Title and Midwest builder Cambridge Properties.

D.R. Horton sold its St. Louis assets to McBride & Son Enterprises in 2000 after spending five years trying to break into the St. Louis homebuilding market. Tomnitz also took over the duties of president in 2000 when Beckwitt retired.

D.R. Horton gained homebuilding operations in Houston and Phoenix when it bought Emerald Builders in 2001. In February 2002 the company acquired Schuler Homes for $1.2 billion including debt.

Sales continued to climb in fiscal 2003 and 2004. D.R. Horton experienced its 27th consecu-

tive year of earnings and revenue growth in 2004 and broke records by being the first residential homebuilder to sell more than 45000 homes in the US in a fiscal year; in fiscal 2005 the company closed 51172 homes. By 2007 however it was evident that the heady days were over with a rise in cancellations and a larger value of backlog orders.

CEO Donald Tomnitz summed up the housing market crash when he said "I don't want to be too sophisticated here but '07 is going to suck all 12 months of the calendar year." Indeed the company suffered a loss that year and the next when sales orders declined and cancellation rates rose due to tightened mortgage markets and severe liquidity shortages. Adding to homebuilders' difficulties an influx of foreclosed homes on the market brought down the demand for new homes.

D.R. Horton responded to the downturn in 2008 by reducing land and housing inventory controlling construction and inventory costs and using its cash to reduce debt. Despite drops in many markets D.R. Horton saw improvements in its eastern market where home affordability and employment led to a higher demand for new homes.

EXECUTIVES

President West Region, J. Matt Farris

Evp And Cfo, William W. (Bill) Wheat, age 53, $500,000 total compensation

President Financial Services, Randall C. (Randy) Present

Vp And Cio, Rick Rawlings

President Central Region, Rick Horton

President And Ceo, David V. Auld, age 62, $700,000 total compensation

Svp Busienss Development, Michael Murray, $500,000 total compensation

President East Region, Tom Hill

President North Region, Doug Brown

President Florida Region, Paul Romanowski

Vice President And Division Counsel, Carolyn Mitchell

Vp Finance, Jeff Tebeaux

Assistant Vice President And Environmental Manager, Edward Perez

Vice President Human Resources, Paula Hunter-perkins

Vice President Of Construction, David Gude

Chairman, Donald R. Horton, age 69

Auditors: PricewaterhouseCoopers LLP

LOCATIONS

HQ: Horton (DR) Inc
1341 Horton Circle, Arlington, TX 76011

Phone: 817 390-8200

Web: www.drhorton.com

2018 Homebuilding Sales by Region

	% of total
West	24
South central	24
Southeast	33
East	12
Midwest	5
Southwest	4
Total	100

PRODUCTS/OPERATIONS

2018 Homebuilding Sales by Region

	% of total
West	24
South Central	24
Southeast	29
East	12
Midwest	6
Southwest	5
Total	100

2018 Sales by Service

	$ mil.	% of total
Home building		
Home sales	15502.0	96
Land/lot sales	122	1
Financial services	375	2
Forestar	109	1
Eliminations	(39.1)	—
Other adjustments	(1.2)	—
Total	**16,068**	**100**

COMPETITORS

Beazer Homes	Meritage Homes
David Weekley Homes	NVR
Hovnanian Enterprises	PulteGroup
KB Home	TRI Pointe
Lennar	Taylor Morrison
M.D.C.	Toll Brothers
M/I Homes	William Lyon Homes

HISTORICAL FINANCIALS

Company Type: Public

Income Statement   FYE: September 30

	REVENUE ($ mil.)	NET INCOME ($ mil.)	NET PROFIT MARGIN	EMPLOYEES
09/19	17,593	1,619	9.2%	8,916
09/18	16,068	1,460	9.1%	8,437
09/17	14,091	1,038	7.4%	7,735
09/16	12,157	886	7.3%	6,976
09/15	10,824	751	6.9%	6,230
Annual Growth	**12.9%**	**21.2%**	**—**	**9.4%**

2019 Year-End Financials

Debt ratio: 22.00%	No. of shares (mil.): 368
Return on equity: 17.00%	Dividends
Cash ($ mil.): 1,494	Yield: 1.0%
Current ratio: 9.00	Payout: 14.0%
Long-term debt ($ mil.): 3,399	Market value ($ mil.): 19,420

	STOCK PRICE ($) FY Close	P/E High/Low		PER SHARE ($) Earnings	Dividends	Book Value
09/19	53.00	12	8	4.00	1.00	27.00
09/18	42.00	14	10	4.00	1.00	24.00
09/17	40.00	14	10	3.00	0.00	21.00
09/16	30.00	14	10	2.00	0.00	18.00
09/15	29.00	16	10	2.00	0.00	16.00
Annual Growth	**15.8%**	**—**	**—**	**20.6%**	**24.5%**	**14.2%**

Host Hotels & Resorts Inc

Host Hotels & Resorts is the largest hospitality real estate investment trust (REIT) in the US and one of the top owners of luxury and upscale hotels. It owns about 95 luxury and "upper upscale" hotels mostly in the US (but also in Canada and Brazil) totaling some 52000 rooms. Properties are managed by third parties; most operate under the Marriott brand and are managed by sister firm Marriott International. Other brands include Hyatt Ritz-Carlton AccorHotels and Hilton. To maintain its status as a REIT which carries tax advantages Host operates through majority-owned Host Hotels & Resorts LP.

HISTORY

That's right — The Four Seasons started as a root beer stand.

Newlyweds John and Alice Marriott left Marriott Utah (founded by John's grandparents) in 1927 and opened a root beer stand in Washington DC. As a way to attract customers during the winter they began selling tamales and tacos — recipes came from a cook at the Mexican Embassy. Dubbed the Hot Shoppe the Marriotts built the business into a regional chain.

In 1937 the Marriotts began providing boxed lunches for airlines. Hot Shoppes entered the hospital food service business in 1955 and two years later opened its first hotel in Arlington Virginia. John and Alice's son Bill became president in 1964. The company which operated four hotels 45 Hot Shoppes and the airline catering business became Marriott-Hot Shoppes.

In the 1960s the company acquired Bob's Big Boy restaurant chain (sold 1987) started Roy Rogers fast-food restaurants (sold 1990) and changed its name to Marriott Corp. Later Marriott bought an Athenian cruise line (Oceanic; sold 1987). Bill became CEO in 1972.

Marriott diversified its hotel operations in the 1980s moving into limited-service middle-priced hotels with the launch of Courtyard by Marriott in 1983. To accelerate growth the company began building hotels for sale retaining their control through management contracts. In 1987 it acquired Residence Inn Co. which targeted extended-stay travelers. The company also expanded its airline catering business and moved into retirement facilities. To fund the expansion Marriott formed limited partnerships and issued corporate bonds; when the late 1980s recession hit the company was deeply in debt.

In 1993 Marriott Corp. divided into Marriott International (hotel management services) and Host Marriott (real estate and food service) leaving Host Marriott with most of the corporation's debt. Host Marriott began focusing on full-service hotels. It raised money to buy more hotels (many of which belonged to its old limited partnerships) by taking loans from Marriott International and selling assets (including 14 retirement properties and 30 Fairfield Inns). In late 1995 the company further refined its focus by spinning off its food service and concessions business as Host Marriott Services (later acquired by Italy-based restaurant operator Autogrill).

Host Marriott acquired three Ritz-Carlton hotels in 1995 through Marriott International which owns the Ritz-Carlton name and in 1997 acquired the Forum Group owner of 29 retirement communities. The next year it spun off Crestline Capital (now Barcelo Crestline Corp.) to own its retirement properties and to lease its hotels.

In 1999 the company expanded its hotel brands adding controlling stakes in 13 luxury Ritz-Carlton Four Seasons Swiss 'tel and Hyatt properties bought from the Blackstone Group investment firm in exchange for a stake in Host Marriott. It also restructured as a real estate investment trust or REIT.

Host Marriott and Marriott International were slapped with an investor fraud lawsuit in 2000 relating to its capital-raising efforts in the late 1980s; they reached a tentative settlement under which they would buy back the partnerships. The bulk of the settlements were awarded to about 2000 investors in two of the six limited partnerships in question. That year Marriott matriarch Alice died.

Host Marriott's New York Marriott World Trade Center hotel located at Three World Trade Center was completely devastated on September 11 2001. Two blocks south the New York Marriott Financial Center hotel sustained heavy damage.

Even before September 11 brought the hotel industry to a screeching halt the company had curtailed the buying binge that saw it add more than 100 hotels to its portfolio since 1994. It decided to sell less posh noncore hotels and focus on renovating remaining holdings. Crashing per-room revenue had the company waiting for the slow return of the health of the industry and when it had the company began a cautious acquisition spree.

After a tourism industry downturn made worse by the September 11 2001 terrorist attacks the company made a key acquisition in 2006: It purchased a portfolio of 25 domestic and 3 international hotels from Starwood Hotels & Resorts for more than $4 billion and changed its name to Host Hotels & Resorts in conjunction with that buy. The package expanded the company's reach into Europe South America and the South Pacific.

In 2009 Host sold its leasehold interest in CBM Joint Venture Partnership which owned 115 Courtyard by Marriott hotels. The deal earned Host about $13 million.

In late 2011 the company sold its 95% interest in the Toronto Airport Marriott Hotel for CAD$30.6 million ($30.7 million).

Host in 2011 bought the New York Helmsley Hotel from Helmsley Enterprises and announced plans to renovate the 775-room property and re-open it under the Westin brand. In a separate deal Host acquired the Manchester Grand Hyatt San Diego's largest hotel for $570 million.

In 2012 it bought 888-room Grand Hyatt Washington for about $400 million and its acquisition of land in Rio de Janeiro to develop two hotels with a total count of 405 rooms that opened in time for the FIFA World Cup in 2014.

In 2013 the company acquired fee-simple interest in the 426-room Hyatt Place Waikiki Beach in Honolulu Hawaii from an affiliate of Chartres Lodging Group and Morgan Stanley Real Estate Fund VII Global for $138.5 million.

EXECUTIVES

Ceo, James F. Risoleo, age 63, $576,800 total compensation

Evp And Cfo, Gregory J. (Greg) Larson, age 54, $503,950 total compensation

Evp General Counsel And Secretary, Elizabeth A. Abdoo, age 60, $488,050 total compensation

Evp Asset Management, Minaz B. Abji, age 65, $546,400 total compensation

Managing Director Investments East Coast, Nathan S. Tyrrell, age 46

Evp Human Resources, Joanne G. Hamilton, age 61

Managing Director Development, Mike E. Lentz

Vp Asset Management, Georgina Sussan

Senior Vice President, Bill Kelso

Vp Financial Reporting, Joe Ottinger

Vice President Asset Management, Jeff Gross

Senior Vice President, Craig A Mason

Vice President Asset Management, Greg Fang

Vp Capital Expenditures, Jim Marthinsen

Svp And Head Enterprise Analytics Group, Sourav Ghosh

Vice President Risk Management, Gus Napoli

Vice President Design And Procurement, Helen Jorgensen

Vice President Human Resources, Lisa Whittington

Vice President Of Tax, Doug Link

Vice President Asset Management, Christopher Ostapovicz

Senior Vice President Investments, Raj Contractor

Svp It, Sukhvinder Singh

Regional Vice President, Eric Habermann

Executive Vice President Corporate Strategy And Fund Management, Greg Larson

Senior Vice President, Douglass Henry

Chairman, Richard E. Marriott, age 80

Board Member, Ann Korologos

Board Member, John Morse

Board Member, Gordon Smith

Board Member, Sheila Bair

Auditors: KPMG LLP

LOCATIONS

HQ: Host Hotels & Resorts Inc
6903 Rockledge Drive, Suite 1500, Bethesda, MD 20817
Phone: 240 744-1000
Web: www.hosthotels.com

2018 Sales

	$ mil.	% of total
US	5,417	98
Canada	67	2
Brazil	19	—
Mexico	21	—
Total	**5,524**	**100**

2018 Hotel Locations

	Nos
Domestic	80
International	5
Total	**0**	**85**

PRODUCTS/OPERATIONS

2018 Sales

	$ mil.	% of total
Rooms	3,547	64
Food & Beverage	1,616	29
Other	361	7
Total	**5,524**	**100**

2018 Brands

	No. of hotels
Marriott:	
Marriott	37
Ritz-Carlton	5
Autograph Collection	1
JW Marriott	4
W	2
St. Regis	1
Luxury Collection	2
Westin	12
Sheraton	4
Residence Inn	1
Courtyard	1
Total Marriott	70
Hyatt:	
Andaz	1
Grand Hyatt	4
Hyatt Place	1
Hyatt Regency	6
Total Hyatt	12
Hilton:	
Curio	1
Hilton	1
Embassy Suites	1
Total Hilton	3
AccorHotels:	
Swissôtel	1
Fairmont	1
ibis	1
Novotel	1
Total AccorHotels	4
Other/Independent	4
Total	**93**

COMPETITORS

Ashford Hospitality Trust
Carlson Companies
FelCor
Hospitality Properties Trust
InterContinental Hotels
LaSalle Hotel Properties
Lodgian
Pebblebrook
Strategic Hotels
Sunstone Hotel Investors

HISTORICAL FINANCIALS

Company Type: Public

Income Statement
FYE: December 31

	REVENUE ($ mil.)	NET INCOME ($ mil.)	NET PROFIT MARGIN	EMPLOYEES
12/18	5,524	1,087	19.7%	184
12/17	5,387	564	10.5%	205
12/16	5,430	762	14.0%	220
12/15	5,387	558	10.4%	240
12/14	5,354	732	13.7%	251
Annual Growth	**0.8%**	**10.4%**	**—**	**(7.5%)**

2018 Year-End Financials

Debt ratio: 32.00%
Return on equity: 15.00%
Cash ($ mil.): 1,542
Current ratio: 5.00
Long-term debt ($ mil.): 3,837

No. of shares (mil.): 740
Dividends
 Yield: 5.0%
 Payout: 58.0%
Market value ($ mil.): 12,342

	STOCK PRICE ($) FY Close	P/E High/Low	PER SHARE ($) Earnings	Dividends	Book Value
12/18	17.00	15 11	1.00	1.00	10.00
12/17	20.00	27 23	1.00	1.00	9.00
12/16	19.00	19 12	1.00	1.00	9.00
12/15	15.00	33 21	1.00	1.00	9.00
12/14	24.00	25 19	1.00	1.00	10.00
Annual Growth	**(8.5%)**	**— —**	**11.2%**	**3.2%**	**1.1%**

Howard Bancorp Inc

EXECUTIVES

Chb-Ceo, Mary Ann Scully
Exec V Pres-Cfo-Treas, George C Coffman
Exec V Pres-SEC, Charles E Schwabe
Loan Assistant, Ariel Helm
Loan Assistant, Ariel Hewitt
Underwriter, Brandi Abel
Underwriter, Kathy Diperna
Lock Desk Analyst, Ladeana Wentzel
Vice President, Marc Czosnowski
Branch Manager, Mario Orlando
Relationship Administrator, Toni Carlson
Auditors: Dixon Hughes Goodman LLP

LOCATIONS

HQ: Howard Bancorp Inc
3301 Boston Street, Baltimore, MD 21224
Phone: 410 750-0020
Web: www.howardbank.com

HISTORICAL FINANCIALS

Company Type: Public

Income Statement
FYE: December 31

	ASSETS ($ mil.)	NET INCOME ($ mil.)	INCOME AS % OF ASSETS	EMPLOYEES
12/18	2,267	(4)	—	337
12/17	1,150	7	0.6%	306
12/16	1,027	5	0.5%	300
12/15	947	1	0.1%	257
12/14	691	10	1.5%	218
Annual Growth	**34.6%**	**—**		**11.5%**

2018 Year-End Financials

Debt ratio: 6.00%
Return on equity: (-2.00%)
Cash ($ mil.): 101
Current ratio: —
Long-term debt ($ mil.): —

No. of shares (mil.): 19
Dividends
 Yield: —
 Payout: —
Market value ($ mil.): 272

	STOCK PRICE ($) FY Close	P/E High/Low	PER SHARE ($) Earnings	Dividends	Book Value
12/18	14.00	— —	(0.00)	0.00	15.00
12/17	22.00	31 20	1.00	0.00	13.00
12/16	15.00	20 16	1.00	0.00	12.00
12/15	13.00	94 69	0.00	0.00	13.00
12/14	11.00	5 4	2.00	0.00	14.00
Annual Growth	**5.8%**	**— —**	**—**	**—**	**1.8%**

HP Inc

Just about every office — from home to big business — has two basic items: a computer and printer. That's pretty much the business of HP Inc. one of two companies created from the breakup of Hewlett-Packard Co. in 2015. HP makes a full line of computing devices from desktops and laptops for commercial and consumer use to tablets and point-of-sale systems. Its printers include large format commercial printers and inkjet and laser printers as well as 3D printers. And don't forget printer supplies such as ink cartridges. HP ranks as one of the top one or two PC makers and the No. 1 printer company in the world.

Operations

HP reports its operations through three business segments: Personal Systems Printing and Corporate Investments.

Personal Systems makes and sells commercial PCs consumer PCs workstations thin clients commercial tablets and mobility devices retail point-of-sale systems displays and accessories software and support. The segment generates about 65% of HP's revenue.

Printing produces consumer and commercial printers supplies media services as well as scanning devices. About 356% of the company's revenue rolls out of the unit.

Corporate Investments includes HP Labs and business incubation projects. As a research-oriented unit it contributes a negligible amount of revenue.

HP buys some components from other companies. That includes the laser printer engines and laser toner cartridges it obtains from Canon. Processors for the company's computers come from Intel and AMD and the machines runs on Microsoft software.

While the company operates some of its own manufacturing it outsources a significant portion of the work to third party companies.

Geographic Reach

HP based in Palo Alto California gets about two-thirds of revenue from customers outside the US. The company has operations throughout the world with significant facilities in the Singapore Malaysia and Israel as well its US operations. It has regional headquarters in Geneva Switzerland and Singapore.

Sales and Marketing

HP markets its products directly as well as through a wide range of third-party channels including retailers resellers and distributors and original equipment manufacturers and systems integrators.

Financial Performance

HP has posted three years of higher revenue on rising sales of PCs and printers after the company's split with Hewlett Packard Enterprise in 2015.

The company's sales rose about 12% to $58.5 billion in 2018 (ended November) up about $6.5 billion from 2017 on stronger performance in all its product categories. Personal Systems revenue increased 13% on higher sales of notebook and desktops computers which benefited from higher volume and prices. Printing revenue increased 11% driven by higher Supplies and Hardware revenue fueled by higher printer unit volume including the Samsung-branded printers.

Despite the jump in sales HP's gross margin sipped to 18.2% in 2018 compared to 18.4% in 2018 due to an increase in commodity and logistics costs in Personal Systems.

Net income jumped to $5.3 billion in 2018 from $2.5 billion in 2017 boosted by a $2.8 billion tax benefit from the US Tax Cuts and Jobs Act.

HP's coffers held $5.2 billion in cash and equivalents in 2018 compared to $7 billion in 2017. In 2018 operations generated $4.5 billion investing activities used $716 million and financing activities used $5.6 billion which include $1.85 billion to pay down debt and $1.1 billion to buy back shares.

Strategy

HP found life as a PC-and-printer company refreshing in 2018. PC sales rose for the year and brought printer and printer supply sales with them spurred by strong cyclical demand for PCs a wave of upgrades to the Windows 10 operating system and the acquisition of the Samsung printer business.

The company has increased production of computers that convert back and forth to notebooks and tablets and released the Spectre Folio convertible in 2019. For the home market the company started selling the HP Tango which features combined voice-activated and app-based printing. In 3D printing HP introduced the Metal Jet platform which enables 3D mass production to metals manufacturing.

HP's Device-as-a-Service program in which is helps companies manage their PC and printing needs grew 50% year-to-year. The program uses data and analytics to help lower costs and improve efficiency for users.

While the company roosts at the top rungs of PC and printer sales HP faces stiff price and product competition from established competitors like Lenovo Acer and Dell Technologies as well as newcomers offering new technologies.

Mergers and Acquisitions

In 2018 HP bought Apogee Corp. a UK-based printing company for about Å 380 million. The deal should help HP expand in managed print services leveraging Apogee's long-term contracts for providing printing and publishing services. HP leads the overall printer market with a 40% market share according to IDC.

HP in 2017 bought Samsung's printer business for about $1 billion. HP gets Samsung's laser printer portfolio and thousands of patents for printing technologies as well as an increased presence in Asia. The deal particularly strengthens HP in combination printer-copier machines which helps it compete with companies such as Xerox and Canon in the enterprise and office markets. The companies expect the deal to close in 2017.

Company Background

HP is a successor to what could be considered the first Silicon Valley company.

Encouraged by Stanford professor Frederick Terman in 1938 engineers Bill Hewlett and David Packard started Hewlett-Packard (HP) in a garage in Palo Alto California with $538. Hewlett was the idea man while Packard served as manager; the two were so low-key that the company's first official meeting ended with no decision on exactly what to manufacture. Finding good people took priority over finding something to sell. The first product ended up being an audio oscillator. Walt Disney Studios one of HP's first customers bought eight to use in the making of Fantasia.

Hewlett-Packard grew into one of the top technology companies producing personal computers workstations printers and software that led their markets. The company's fortunes were tempered with the onslaught of the dot-com boom and competition from companies like Dell. In the early 2000s Hewlett-Packard bought Compaq a major PC competitor to strengthen it across the computer markets. But by 2015 Hewlett-Packard split into HP Inc. which concentrates on PCs and printers and Hewlett Packard Enterprise which focuses on hardware software and services for bigger companies.

EXECUTIVES

Chief Supply Chain Officer, Stuart C. Pann, age 60
Coo, Jon E. Flaxman, age 62, $700,027 total compensation
Svp; General Manager Graphics And Imaging Hp Imaging And Printing Group, Stephen (Steve) Nigro
Cto, Shane D. Wall, age 54
President Personal Systems Business, Ron Coughlin
Evp And Cfo, Catherine A. (Cathie) Lesjak, age 60, $850,033 total compensation
President Imaging And Printing Business, Enrique Lores, age 54
President Americas, Christoph Schell
President Asia Pacific And Japan (apj), Richard Bailey
President And Ceo, Dion J. Weisler, $1,200,046 total compensation
President Europe Middle East And Africa (emea), Nick Lazaridis
Chief Human Resources Officer, Tracy S. Keogh, $600,023 total compensation
Managing Director And General Manager Hp India, Sumeer Chandra
Vice President Big Data, Pankaj Dugar
Vice President Americas Channels And Alliances, Archie Miller
Vice President Human Resources, Kelly Parrish
National Account Manager, Jay Khaira
Senior Vice President Global Sales Best, Kelly Ducourty
National Sales Manager, Spencer Wilson
Vp It, Rob Ficalora
Vice President Head Of Current Business Management Inkjet Printing Systems, Mark Quiroz
Vice President And Chief Information Security Officer, Jack Clark
Vice President, Todd Gustafson
Assistant Vice President Operations, Sushanto Das
Vice President Ww Commercial Pc Marketing, Carol Hess
National Account Manager, Devin Pool
Vp Inkjet Printing Americas, Emre Ozguc
Assistant Vice President Loan Administration Associate, Thomas Persons
Vice President And General Manager Commercial Pc, Alex Cho
Vp And Managing Director Hp Inc Africa, Elisabeth Moreno
Vice President Global Head Of Commercial Notebook Product Management, Bill Gorden
Vice President Marketing, Joseph Pacula
Vice President And Division Manager Data Processing, Deanna Snyder
Senior Vice President Tax, Barbara Barton Weiszhaar
Senior Vice President, Schell Christoph

Chairman, Charles V. (Chip) Bergh, age 61
Board Member, Bethany Madrid
Board Member, Aida Alvarez
Board Member, Mary Citrino
Board Member, Stacy Brown-philpot
Board Member, Subra Suresh
Auditors: Ernst & Young LLP

LOCATIONS

HQ: HP Inc
1501 Page Mill Road, Palo Alto, CA 94304
Phone: 650 857-1501
Web: www.hp.com

2018 Sales

	$ mil.	% of total
US	20,602	35
Other countries	37,870	65
Total	**58,472**	**100**

PRODUCTS/OPERATIONS

2018 Sales

	$ mil.	% of total
Notebooks	22,547	39
Desktops	11,567	20
Workstations	2,246	4
Other	1,301	2
Supplies	13,575	23
Commercial Hardware	4,674	8
Consumer Hardware	2,556	4
Corporate Investments	5	-
Other	1	-
Total	**58,472**	**100**

2018 Sales

	$ mil.	% of total
Personal Systems	37,661	64
Printing	20,805	36
Corporate Investment	5	-
Other	1	-
Total	**58,472**	**100**

Selected Products and Services

Personal Systems
  Calculators
  Desktop PCs
  Digital entertainment centers
  DVD writers
  Handheld computers
  Notebook computers
  Televisions (LCD plasma)
  Workstations
Imaging and Printing
  Commercial printing
  Digital presses
  Printers
  Digital imaging
  Projectors
  Scanners
  Personal printing
  All-in-ones (copier fax printer scanner)
  Ink jet printers
  Laser printers
  Shared printing
  Networked inkjet laser and multifunction printers
  Office all-in-ones
  Services
  Supplies

COMPETITORS

ADP	Lexmark
ASUSTeK	NEC
Acer	Océ
Apple Inc.	Oki Electric
Brother Industries	Panasonic Corp
Canon	Ricoh Company
Dell	Samsung Electronics
Epson	Sharp Corp.
Fuji Xerox	Sony
Fujitsu	Toshiba
Hitachi	Unisys
Konica Minolta	Xerox
Lenovo	

HISTORICAL FINANCIALS
Company Type: Public

Income Statement | | | | FYE: October 31

	REVENUE ($ mil.)	NET INCOME ($ mil.)	NET PROFIT MARGIN	EMPLOYEES
10/19	58,756	3,152	5.4%	56,000
10/18	58,472	5,327	9.1%	55,000
10/17	52,056	2,526	4.9%	49,000
10/16	48,238	2,496	5.2%	49,000
10/15	103,355	4,554	4.4%	287,000
Annual Growth	(13.2%)	(8.8%)	—	(33.5%)

2019 Year-End Financials

Debt ratio: 15.00%
Return on equity: ***,***.**%
Cash ($ mil.): 4,537
Current ratio: 1.00
Long-term debt ($ mil.): 4,780

No. of shares (mil.): 1,458
Dividends
 Yield: 4.0%
 Payout: 24.0%
Market value ($ mil.): 25,325

	STOCK PRICE ($) FY Close	P/E High/Low		PER SHARE ($) Earnings	Dividends	Book Value
10/19	17.00	12	8	2.00	1.00	(1.00)
10/18	24.00	8	6	3.00	1.00	(0.00)
10/17	22.00	15	10	1.00	1.00	(2.00)
10/16	14.00	11	6	1.00	0.00	(2.00)
10/15	27.00	16	10	2.00	1.00	15.00
Annual Growth	(10.4%)			—	(4.4%)	(1.2%)	—

HSBC USA, Inc.

HSBC USA a subsidiary of British banking behemoth HSBC Holdings operates HSBC Bank USA one of the largest foreign-owned banks in the country. Boasting $200 billion in assets and 230-plus branches across 10 US states (including 145 in New York making it one of the state's largest banks by branches) the bank offers personal commercial and mortgage banking services as well as wealth management investment banking private banking brokerage and trust services. Its largest markets are in New York California New Jersey and Florida. Roughly 75% of HSBC USA's loan portfolio is made up of commercial loans and around 70% of its total revenue comes from interest income.

Operations

The company operates four business segments: Retail Banking and Wealth Management (RBWM); Commercial Banking which serves small and multinational businesses in five hubs where 50% of US corporate imports and exports happen (California Florida Illinois New York and Texas); Global Banking and Markets which offers advisory services and trading services for major government corporate and institutional clients; and Private Bank which serves high net worth and ultra-high net worth individuals and their families particularly focusing on multi-generational families business owners and entrepreneurs.

About 75% of HSBC USA's $82.92 billion-loan portfolio was made up of commercial loans (including global banking business and corporate banking and construction and other real estate loans) at the end of 2015. The rest of its portfolio was made up of consumer loans especially residential mortgages with some home equity credit card and other loans.

The bank makes around 70% of its revenue from interest income. About 41% of its total revenue came from loan interest during 2015 while another 27% came from interest on securities trading securities and short-term investments. The rest of its revenue came from trust and investment management fees (3% of revenue) credit card fees (1%) trading revenue (1%) residential mortgage banking revenue (1%) other fees and commissions (15%) gains on securities at fair value (5%) and other miscellaneous sources.

Geographic Reach

HSBC USA serves customers nationwide with the highest concentration of its bank branches located in New York City Los Angeles San Francisco Chicago Atlanta Houston Seattle Miami and Washington DC. The company operates foreign branches and representative offices in the Caribbean Canada Latin America Europe and Asia.

Sales and Marketing

HSBC USA serves a variety of customers such as individuals (including high net worth individuals) small businesses corporations institutions and governments. It boasted 2.4 million customers at the end of 2015 30% of which live in New York and 29% in California.

The bank has been ramping up its advertising spend in recent years. It spent $60 million on advertising in 2015 up from $53 million and $43 million in 2014 and 2013 respectively.

Financial Performance

The US division of HSBC has been struggling to grow its revenue over the past several years as low interest rates have continued to eat away at its interest margins and as its non-interest revenues have been in decline. The bank has been recovering from losses in 2013 and 2012 caused by goodwill impairments and regulatory expenses.

HSBC USA's revenue turned a corner in 2015 jumping 11% to $5.17 billion during the year mostly thanks to higher interest income on 8% commercial loan asset growth and double-digit security asset growth.

Despite strong revenue growth in 2015 the company's net income fell 7% to $330 million mainly because its credit loss provisions increased by $173 million mostly as it made more commercial loans with exposure to the oil and gas industry. HSBC USA's operating cash levels dropped 22% to $4.65 billion for the year due to unfavorable working capital changes primarily related to changes in trading assets and liabilities.

Strategy

HSBC USA as part of the broader HSBC group aims to become the world's leading international bank and seeks to connected emerging economies with developed markets. The US division like parent HSBC also continued in 2016 to look for ways to cut operating costs to boost efficiency and overall profits.

In 2014 HSBC USA became one of the nation's first major banks to roll out a new fraud protection device which employs two-factor authentication for its personal Internet customers.

Company Background

HSBC and HSBC USA restructured their operations in 2011 which included divesting operations and cutting staff. As part of the restructuring HSBC sold 195 retail branches in New York and Connecticut to First Niagara for $1 billion. Through HSBC USA and its HSBC Finance affiliate HSBC also sold its card and retail services business to Capital One Financial. In 2010 HSBC USA exited its noncore wholesale banknotes business. The company also closed and consolidated about a dozen branches in Connecticut and New Jersey. The moves are part of the company's strategy to focus more on commercial and corporate banking in New York and other key urban markets itself part of HSBC's restructuring to create a leaner group.

EXECUTIVES

Chairman President And Ceo Hsbc North America Holdings Inc. And Hsbc Bank Usa, Patrick J. (Pat) Burke, age 57
Sevp And Cfo, Mark A. Zaeske
Sevp And Coo Usa, Vittorio M. Severino
Sevp And Head Of Global Banking And Markets Americas, Thierry Roland
Sevp And Head Of Strategy And Planning, Loren C. Klug, age 58
Evp And Head Of Private Banking Americas, Marlon Young, age 63, $389,423 total compensation
Sevp And Chief Risk Officer, Rhydian H. Cox
Sevp And Head Of Commercial Banking, Wyatt E Crowell
Evp And Head Of Human Resources Usa, Maureen A. Gillan-Myer
Evp And Head Of Regulatory Remediation, Stephen R. Nesbitt
Sevp And Chief Auditor, Richard E. O'Brien
Evp And Corporate Secretary, Karen Pisarczyk
Sevp And Head Of Retail Banking And Wealth Management, Pablo Sanchez
Sevp And General Counsel, Mark Steffensen
Evp And Chief Accounting Officer, William Tabaka
Senior Vice President Compensation, Deanna Larkin
Auditors: PricewaterhouseCoopers LLP

LOCATIONS

HQ: HSBC USA, Inc.
 452 Fifth Avenue, New York, NY 10018
Phone: 212 525-5000
Web: www.us.hsbc.com

PRODUCTS/OPERATIONS

2013 Sales

	$ mil.	% of total
Interest		
Loans	1,876	39
Securities	876	19
Other	227	4
Non-interest		
Other fees & commissions	706	14
Trading revenue	474	9
Servicing and other fees from HSBC affiliates	202	4
Other securities gains	202	4
Trust income	123	3
Other	150	4
Total	**4,836**	**100**

COMPETITORS

Astoria Financial	KeyCorp
Bank of America	M&T Bank
Capital One	New York Community
Citibank	Bancorp
Citizens Financial	PNC Financial
Group	TD Bank USA
JPMorgan Chase	Wells Fargo

HISTORICAL FINANCIALS
Company Type: Public

Income Statement | | | | FYE: December 31

	ASSETS ($ mil.)	NET INCOME ($ mil.)	INCOME AS % OF ASSETS	EMPLOYEES
12/18	172,448	320	0.2%	4,933
12/17	187,235	(179)	—	5,107
12/16	201,301	129	0.1%	6,114
12/15	188,278	330	0.2%	6,173
12/14	185,539	354	0.2%	6,400
Annual Growth	(1.8%)	(2.5%)	—	(6.3%)

2018 Year-End Financials

Debt ratio: 17.00%
Return on equity: 2.00%
Cash ($ mil.): 39,192
Current ratio: —
Long-term debt ($ mil.): —

No. of shares (mil.): 0
Dividends
Yield: —
Payout: —
Market value ($ mil.): —

	STOCK PRICE ($) FY Close	P/E High/Low	PER SHARE ($) Earnings	Dividends	Book Value
12/18	0.00 28,719,887.00	— —	(0.00)	0.00	
12/17	0.00 28,142,857.00	— —	(0.00)	0.00	
Annual Growth	—	— —	—	—	0.5%

Humana Inc.

Medicare has made Humana a big-time player in the insurance game. One of the largest Medicare providers and a top health insurer Humana provides Medicare Advantage plans and prescription drug coverage to approximately 6 million members throughout the US. It also administers managed care plans for other government programs including Medicaid plans in Florida and Texas and TRI-CARE (for military personnel) in the South. Additionally Humana offers commercial health plans and specialty (life dental and vision) coverage; it also provides health management services and operates outpatient care clinics. All told it covers more than 20 million members in the US.

HISTORY

In 1961 Louisville Kentucky lawyers David Jones and Wendell Cherry bought a nursing home as a real estate investment. Within six years their company Extendicare was the largest nursing home chain in the US (with only eight homes).

Faced with a glutted nursing home market the partners noticed that hospitals received more money per patient per day than nursing homes so they took their company public in 1968 to finance hospital purchases (one per month from 1968 to 1971). The company then sold its 40 nursing homes. Sales rose 13 times over in the next five years and in 1973 the firm changed its name to Humana.

By 1975 Humana had built 27 hospitals in the South and Southwest. It targeted young privately insured patients and kept its charity caseload and bad-debt expenses low. Three years later #3 for-profit hospital operator Humana moved up a notch when it bought #2 American Medicorp.

In 1983 the government began reimbursing Medicare payments based on fixed rates. Counting on its high hospital occupancy in 1984 the company launched Humana Health Care Plans rewarding doctors and patients who used Humana hospitals. However hospital occupancy dropped and the company closed several clinics. When its net income fell 75% in 1986 the firm responded by lowering premiums to attract employers.

In 1991 co-founder Cherry died. With hospital profits down in 1993 Jones spun off Humana's 76 hospitals as Galen Healthcare which formed the nucleus of what is now HCA - The Healthcare Company. Humana used the cash to expand its HMO membership buying Group Health Association (an HMO serving metropolitan Washington DC) and CareNetwork (a Milwaukee HMO). The next year Humana added 1.3 million members

when it bought EMPHESYS and the company's income which had stagnated since the salad days of the late 1980s and early 1990s seemed headed in the right direction.

In the mid-1990s cutthroat premiums failed to cover rising health care costs as members' hospital use soared out of control particularly in the company's new Washington DC market. Profits dropped 94% and Humana's already tense relationship with doctors and members worsened. President and COO Wayne Smith and CFO Roger Drury resigned as part of a management shake-up and newly appointed president Gregory Wolf offered to drop the company's gag clause after the Florida Physicians Association threatened to sue.

A reorganized Humana rebounded in 1997. The company pulled out of 13 unprofitable markets including Alabama (though it did not drop TRI-CARE its military health coverage program in that state) and Washington DC. Refocusing on core markets in the Midwest and Southeast Humana bought Physician Corp. of America (PCA) and ChoiceCare a Cincinnati HMO. Wolf replaced Jones as CEO in 1997.

To cut costs Humana agreed in 1998 to be bought by United HealthCare (now UnitedHealth Group). The deal was abandoned however when United HealthCare took a $900 million charge in advance of the purchase. Humana found savings by pruning its Medicare HMO business.

Humana did everything but party in 1999. The company faced RICO charges for allegedly overcharging members for co-insurance; it agreed to repay $15 million in Medicare overpayments to the government; and it became the first health insurance firm to be slapped with a class-action suit over its physician incentives and other coverage policies.

Humana sold PCA in 2000 saying that it had paid too much for the company; subsidiary PCA Property & Casualty was also sold marking the company's exit from the workers' compensation business. That year Humana also sold its underperforming Florida Medicaid HMO to Well Care HMO and agreed to pay more than $14 million to the government for submitting false Medicare payment information.

In 2001 Humana bought a unit of Anthem that provides health benefits to the military. Expanding its holdings in the southeast Humana acquired Louisiana's Ochsner Health Plan in 2004.

It further grew its product line with the 2007 acquisition of Atlanta-based CompBenefits a provider of dental and vision benefits to nearly 5 million members. The acquisition gave Humana a full-service vision offering and expanded its dental benefits operations. Later that year the company bought KMG America a life and health insurer and third-party administrator for more than 1 million members. Humana combined CompBenefits KMG America and its previous dental benefits operations into a new unit in 2008 called Humana Specialty Benefits.

In 2008 Humana acquired about 25000 Medicare Advantage members in Nevada from UnitedHealth which was divesting the operations as part of its merger deal with Sierra Health Services for $225 million. And later that year it acquired smaller Florida-based Medicare Advantage provider Metcare Health Plans from Metropolitan Health Networks.

Additional acquisitions include the 2008 acquisition of OSF HealthPlans an Illinois-based managed care company belonging to OSF Healthcare. The deal worth about $90 million gave Humana another 60000 commercial members as well as some new Medicare customers in Illinois. The company had already wrapped up its acquisition of Tennessee-based PHP Companies (which does business as Cariten Healthcare) from Covenant

Health. Humana spent $250 million in late 2008 to gain Cariten's managed care operations in East Tennessee adding 70000 commercial customers and 45000 Medicare members.

One of Humana's competitive TRICARE contracts was awarded to another party in 2009; however after Humana objected and bids were re-evaluated the decision was reversed in 2011 (with no negative impact on the company's operations).

In 2010 Humana moved into an all new specialty business area with its acquisition of Concentra a provider of occupational medicine urgent care and wellness programs from Welsh Carson Anderson & Stowe for some $790 million. Humana made the purchase to bolster its consumer-focused initiatives and provide a platform for future service-offering expansion efforts.

To widen its cost-control services and advance its IT offerings Humana partnered with software firm Anvita Health in 2010. The analytics firm provided analytics capabilities to identify at-risk members and also served other insurers benefit managers health care professionals and electronic health record providers. (Humana wound up acquiring Anvita in late 2011.)

Early in 2012 Humana purchased MD Care a Medicare Advantage provider serving some 15000 members in four Southern California counties. It also acquired Arcadian Management Services a Medicare Advantage HMO with some 64000 members in 15 states including California. To complete its acquisition of Arcadian Humana was required to sell select Medicare Advantage plans serving some 12000 former Arcadian members to CIGNA (in Texas and Arkansas) and WellCare Health Plans (in Arizona).

EXECUTIVES

President And Ceo, Bruce D. Broussard, age 56, $1,235,446 total compensation
Svp And Chief Consumer Officer, Jody L. Bilney, age 57, $573,452 total compensation
Svp And Chief Medical Officer, Roy A. Beveridge, age 61
Svp And Cio, Brian P. LeClaire, age 58
Svp And Chief Human Resources Officer, Timothy S. (Tim) Huval, age 52, $573,453 total compensation
Svp And Cfo, Brian A. Kane, age 46, $636,254 total compensation
Svp And Chief Strategy Officer, Christopher H. (Chris) Hunter, age 50, $465,865 total compensation
President And Intermountain Region Market Leader Senior Products, Catherine Field
Market Vice President, Jordan Swanson
Vice President Information Technology, Michael Richmond
Medical Director, Arthur Tomases
Vice President Public Sector, Tim Snyder
Health Services Director, Yvonne Shell
Senior Vice President Marketing, Jennifer Bazante
Segment Vice President, John Delorimier
Medical Director, Earl Jackman
National Account Manager, Melissa Staton
Vice President Information Technology Transformation And Shared Services, Faheem Zuberi
Vice President, Gary Williams
Vice President National Contracting, Jason Lyvers
Vice President Marketing, Kristin Russel
Medical Director, Winston Blake
Market Vice President, Lizmary Torres
Medical Director, Bryan Carr
Srvpnr Lan Operating Systems, Wes Johnson
Medical Director, Donn Perisee
Market Vice President Dfw And Houston Senior Products, Lesli C Young
Vice President Of Clinical Compliance, Meliss A Koellner
Medical Director, Rebecc Colon

Director Of Nursing Services, Jennifer Grottkau
Segment Vice President, Thoma P Klammer
Vice President, Kristin Martin
Medical Director, Cind M Dunn
National Sales Manager, Mallor Strange
National Sales Manager, Chin Chinigo
Senior Vice President And Chief Consumer
 Officer, Jod Bilney
Medical Director, Cind Dunn
Vice President Actuarial Services, P A Hammond
Vice President And Chief Medical Officer
 Integrated Care Delivery Metcare, Yogi Hernandez
Medical Director, Ann Vaughters
Medical Director, Allan Kogan
Regional Vice President, Peggy Taylor
Vice President Network, Lisa Ferrari
Region Vice President Finance, Debbie Findlay
Vice President, Brian Witter
Chairman, Kurt J. Hilzinger, age 58
Board Member, Christopher Mitchell
Board Member, Jerry Valentine
Board Member, Adrienne F Jones
Secretary Treasurer, Jeff Fernandez
Board Member, Garry O'Brien
Board Member, Bobbi Mcdonald
Board Member, Alexis Nash
Auditors: PricewaterhouseCoopers LLP

LOCATIONS

HQ: Humana Inc.
 500 West Main Street, Louisville, KY 40202
Phone: 502 580-1000
Web: www.humana.com

PRODUCTS/OPERATIONS

2018 Sales

	$ mil.	% of total
Premiums		
Individual Medicare Advantage	35,656	63
Group Medicare Advantage	6,103	11
Fully insured	5,962	10
Medicare stand-alone PDP	3,584	6
Specialty	1,359	2
Medicaid & other	2,277	4
Services	1,457	3
Investment income	514	1
Total	**56,912**	**100**

2018 Sales by Segment

	$ mil.	% of total
Retail	48,255	60
Healthcare Services	23,811	30
Group and Specialty	7,679	10
Individual Commercial	8	-
Other Businesses	136	-
Adjustments	(22977)	
Total	**56,912**	**100**

Selected Products and Services

Government
 Medicaid managed care plans
 Medicare Advantage plans
 Medicare prescription drug plans
 TRICARE (military personnel)
Commercial
 Administrative services only (ASO)
 HMO plans
 HumanaOne (individual insurance)
 POS (point-of-service) plans
 PPO plans
 Specialty products
 Dental insurance
 Life insurance
 Short-term disability insurance

COMPETITORS

Aetna	Kaiser Foundation
Anthem	Health Plan
CIGNA	Molina Healthcare
HCSC	UnitedHealth Group
HealthSpring	WellCare Health Plans

HISTORICAL FINANCIALS

Company Type: Public

Income Statement   FYE: December 31

	ASSETS ($ mil.)	NET INCOME ($ mil.)	INCOME AS % OF ASSETS	EMPLOYEES
12/18	25,413	1,683	6.6%	43,600
12/17	27,178	2,448	9.0%	47,900
12/16	25,396	614	2.4%	54,200
12/15	24,705	1,276	5.2%	51,700
12/14	23,466	1,147	4.9%	57,000
Annual Growth	**2.0%**	**10.1%**	**—**	**(6.5%)**

2018 Year-End Financials

Debt ratio: 22.00%	No. of shares (mil.): 136
Return on equity: 17.00%	Dividends
Cash ($ mil.): 2,343	Yield: 1.0%
Current ratio: —	Payout: 16.0%
Long-term debt ($ mil.): —	Market value ($ mil.): 38,837

	STOCK PRICE ($) FY Close	P/E High/Low	Earnings	PER SHARE ($) Dividends	Book Value
12/18	286.00	29 21	12.00	2.00	75.00
12/17	248.00	15 12	17.00	2.00	71.00
12/16	204.00	53 37	4.00	1.00	72.00
12/15	179.00	25 16	8.00	1.00	70.00
12/14	144.00	20 13	7.00	1.00	64.00
Annual Growth	**18.8%**	**— —**	**13.4%**	**15.9%**	**3.8%**

Hunt (J.B.) Transport Services, Inc.

J.B. Hunt Transport Services is one of the largest transportation delivery and logistics companies in North America. Through its divisions the company transports freight including general merchandise automotive parts building materials chemicals electronics food and beverages and forest and paper products. Its Intermodal unit the company's largest maintains over 5000 tractors more than 6200 drivers and about 90000 pieces of trailing equipment and moves customers' cargo by combinations of truck and train. The company also offers dedicated contract services truckload freight transportation and transportation management and logistics services. The company traces its roots back to 1961 when it was founded by Johnnie Bryan (J.B.) Hunt.

Operations

The company divides its operations across four segments: Intermodal (JBI) Dedicated Contract Services (DCS) Integrated Capacity Solutions (ICS) and Truckload (JBT).

J.B. Hunt's Intermodal segment is the company's largest and generates around 55% of the company's net sales. JBI offers intermodal freight services (a combination of truck and rail) to customers in Canada Mexico and the US relying on its partnerships with major North American rail carriers. Pickups and deliveries (drayage services) are handled by company-owned tractors on either end of the rail component.

The Dedicated Contract Services unit (25% of total sales) provides dedicated truck fleets drivers and supply chain services for freight transport including final mile delivery. DCS uses its network of more than 100 cross-dock and delivery network locations primarily in the US. Other segments include Integrated Capacity Solutions (15% of sales)

which provides traditional freight brokerage and transportation logistics solutions using third-party carriers integrated with company-owned equipment and Truckload (5%) which offers full-load dry-van freight services using its own tractors and employee drivers.

Geographic Reach

J.B. Hunt is headquartered in Lowell AK and owns or leases more than 40 other facilities in the US for maintenance and fueling. It also operates about 100 cross-dock and other delivery system networks for its Dedicated Contract Services segment and about 45 remote sales offices or branches for its Intermodal business. In addition it owns or leases small facilities offices and parking yards throughout the US.

J.B. Hunt does business in North America (primarily in the US) with very minor operations in foreign countries.

Sales and Marketing

J.B. Hunt markets its services through a nationwide sales and marketing network. It uses a specific sales force within its Dedicated Contract Services segment due to the length and complexity of the sales cycle. In addition the Integrated Capacity Solutions segment utilizes its own local groups of salespeople.

Financial Performance

J.B. Hunt has enjoyed significant growth over the last several years with revenue increasing 40% since 2014.

Sales in 2018 jumped 20% to $8.6 billion from $7.2 billion in 2017 (a 10% increase over 2016). Higher revenue in 2018 is primarily attributed to the overall increase in load volume and higher revenue per load across all segments. The increase was also aided by higher fuel surcharge revenue which increased 40.2% to $1.1 billion in 2018 compared to $754 million in 2017.

Profits however slid to $489.6 million a 29% decrease compared with the previous year. The drop was due to a one-time tax benefit posted in 2017 due to the Tax Cuts and Jobs Act.

Cash at the end of fiscal 2018 was $7.6 billion a decrease of $7.0 billion from the prior year. Cash from operations contributed $1.1 billion to the coffers while investing activities used $886.8 million mainly for additions to property and equipment. Financing activities used another $208.1 million for dividends to stockholders and the company's stock repurchase program.

Strategy

J.B. Hunt is well-positioned to leverage opportunities in the fast-growing e-commerce market with its range of services from full load highway and intermodal and final-mile delivery. Companies are increasingly outsourcing their transportation fleet needs another benefit to the J.B. Hunt. To ensure growth the company has made recent strategic acquisitions is improving its digital services and revamping its technology infrastructure and is expanding its geographic footprint.

The company continues to build out its Final Mile Services business with the 2019 acquisition of Cory 1st Choice Home Delivery and Special Logistics Dedicated (SLD) in 2017. Both of these companies specialize in furniture delivery aligned with the growing trend in big and bulky item delivery.

In 2018 the company launched its Marketplace for J.B. Hunt 360Â° a digital platform for matching carriers and shippers and continues to make enhancements to the application. To support its digital initiatives J.B. Hunt is in the midst of an enterprise-wide information technology overhaul that includes moving all its systems from a legacy mainframe to a cloud-based infrastructure.

The company also aims to expand geographically targeting the intermodal and brokerage businesses in Canada and Mexico and developing and expanding its operations in Puerto Rico and its in-bounds programs from China.

Mergers and Acquisitions

In 2019 J.B. Hunt acquired Cory 1st Choice Home Delivery a trucking firm specializing in furniture delivery. 1st Choice will be integrated with J.B. Hunt's Final Mile Services division part of its Dedicated contract Services business unit. The acquisition increases the Final Mile business to include 100 locations and more than 3 million square feet of warehouse and facilities space.

Company Background

J.B. Hunt was founded by Johnnie Bryan Hunt in 1961. Hunt had been in business since the late 1950s in Arkansas selling rice hulls as poultry litter. In 1961 he began the J.B. Hunt Company with help from future Arkansas governor Winthrop Rockefeller who owned Winrock grass company where Hunt bought sod for one of his side businesses. Hunt developed a machine to compress the rice hulls which made their transportation profitable and within a few years the company was the world's largest producer of rice hulls for poultry litter.

Still looking for new opportunities Hunt bought some used trucks and refrigerated trailers in 1969 though the company continued to focus on its original business. In the 1980s J.B. Hunt's trucking division grew dramatically and became lucrative as the trucking industry was being deregulated. In 1981-82 the Hunt trucking business had higher margins than most trucking firms. In 1983 when J.B. Hunt Transport Services went public Hunt sold the rice hull business to concentrate on trucking.

HISTORY

Johnnie Bryan (J.B.) Hunt's life was a classic tale of rolling from rags to riches — with a little help from a Rockefeller. Hunt grew up in a family of sharecroppers during the Depression and he left school at age 12 to work for his uncle's Arkansas sawmill. In the late 1950s after driving trucks for more than nine years Hunt noticed that the rice mills along his eastern Arkansas route were burning rice hulls. Believing the hulls could be used as poultry litter Hunt got a contract to haul away the hulls and began selling them to chicken farmers.

In 1961 he began the J.B. Hunt Company with help from future Arkansas governor Winthrop Rockefeller who owned Winrock grass company where Hunt bought sod for one of his side businesses. Hunt developed a machine to compress the rice hulls which made their transportation profitable and within a few years the company was the world's largest producer of rice hulls for poultry litter.

Still looking for new opportunities Hunt bought some used trucks and refrigerated trailers in 1969 though the company continued to focus on its original business. In the 1980s J.B. Hunt's trucking division grew dramatically and became lucrative as the trucking industry was being deregulated. In 1981-82 the Hunt trucking business had higher margins than most trucking firms. In 1983 when J.B. Hunt Transport Services went public Hunt sold the rice hull business to concentrate on trucking.

EXECUTIVES

Evp Operations And Coo, Craig Harper, age 62, $375,000 total compensation

President Dedicated Contract Services; Evp Enterprise Solutions, John N. Roberts, age 54, $807,747 total compensation

Vice President Strategic Planning, Richie Henderson

Evp And Cio, Stuart L. Scott, age 53

Evp; President Intermodal, Terrence D. (Terry) Matthews, age 61, $478,819 total compensation

Evp Finance And Administration Cfo And Corporate Secretary, David G. Mee, age 59, $480,660 total compensation

Evp; President Integrated Capacity Solutions, Shelley Simpson, age 47, $476,923 total compensation

Evp; President Dedicated Contract Services, Nicholas (Nick) Hobbs, age 56, $454,808 total compensation

Vice President Sales National Accounts, Mark Calcagni

Vice President Pricing And Revenue Management, Ed Harwell

Vice President Of Transportation, Tami Allensworth

Vice President Of Transportation, Nick Gowen

Senior Vice President, Brian Webb

Vice President Pricing, Stacey Griffin

Vice President Finance, Erin Taylor

Vice President Of Operations, Jon Payne

Vice President Of Sales, Chris Sandor

National Account Manager, Chris Putnam

Vice President Pricing, Sarthak Verma

National Sales Manager, Ed Page

Vice President, Brad Dexter

National Sales Manager, Keith Brown

Vice President Strategic Accounts, Clay Cox

Vp Sales, William Carver

National Account Manager, Kevin Boortz

Senior Vice President Sales, Paul Bingham

National Sales Manager, Brandon Parker

Vice President Of Maintenance, Derek Kennemer

Svp And Treasurer Finance, Kevin Bracy

Vice President Business Development, Jason Fountain

Vice President Of Sales And Marketing, Jessica Brooks

National Account Manager, Linda Peak

Vice President Business Development, Raul Cavazos

Vice President Sales, Jason Bohannon

National Account Manager, Kim Armstrong

National Account Manager, Christopher Trout

Vice President National Accounts, Bill Copelin

Vice President Of Maintenance, Michael Ralston

Vice President Maintenance Maintenance Manager, Charles Radcliffe

National Account Manager, Todd Witt

National Sales Manager, Scott Coleman

International Vice President Marketing, John Hammond

Senior Vice President Sales, Spencer Frazier

National Sales Manager, Bill Gasaway

Vice President Of Sales, David Will

Svp And Controller Finance, John Kuhlow

National Sales Manager, John Perrine

Vice President Sales Southern Region, Shannon Foley

National Account Manager, Jack Willis

Vice President Of Operations, Brian Dieringer

Vice President Of Business Development Dedicated Contract Services, Mike Belshe

Vice President Sales Eastern Region, Bill Fedorchak

National Account Manager, Rick Thurow

Vice President Of Finance And Accounting, Stephen Guenther

Senior Vice President Human Resources, Mark Greenway

Vice President Strategic Accounts, David Keefauver

Senior Vice President Sales And Marketing, Gregory Breeden

National Account Manager, Tina Sanders

Vice President Of Strategic Accounts, Gabe Waldrop

Vice President Of Operations, Steve Rogers

National Sales Manager, Ben Mallard

Vice President Of Sales, Bill Carver

Vice President, Steve Guthrie

Vice President, Keith Stevens

National Sales Manager, Jack Page

National Sales Manager, Randall Markis

Senior Vice President Infrastructure And Operations, Vana Matte

Chairman, Kirk Thompson, age 66

Auditors: Ernst & Young LLP

LOCATIONS

HQ: Hunt (J.B.) Transport Services, Inc.
615 J.B. Hunt Corporate Drive, Lowell, AR 72745
Phone: 479 820-0000
Web: www.jbhunt.com

PRODUCTS/OPERATIONS

2018 Sales

	$ mil.	% of total
Intermodal (JBI)	4,717	55
Dedicated contract services (DCS)	2,163	25
Integrated capacity solutions (ICS)	1,335	15
Trucking (JBT)	417	5
Intersegment adjustments	(17)	-
Total	**8,615**	**100**

Selected Trucking Services

Dedicated
Expedited
Final Mile
Flatbed
Intermodal
Less Than Truckload
Refrigerated
Truckload

COMPETITORS

C.H. Robinson Worldwide
CSX
Expeditors
Hub Group
Kansas City Southern
Norfolk Southern
Old Dominion Freight

Republic Services
Ryder System
Schneider National
Swift Transportation
Waste Management
XPO logistics
YRC Worldwide

HISTORICAL FINANCIALS

Company Type: Public

Income Statement   FYE: December 31

	REVENUE ($ mil.)	NET INCOME ($ mil.)	NET PROFIT MARGIN	EMPLOYEES
12/18	8,615	490	5.7%	27,621
12/17	7,190	686	9.5%	24,681
12/16	6,555	432	6.6%	22,190
12/15	6,188	427	6.9%	21,562
12/14	6,165	375	6.1%	20,158
Annual Growth	8.7%	6.9%	—	8.2%

2018 Year-End Financials

Debt ratio: 23.00%
Return on equity: 25.00%
Cash ($ mil.): 8
Current ratio: 1.00
Long-term debt ($ mil.): 898

No. of shares (mil.): 109
Dividends
  Yield: 1.0%
  Payout: 14.0%
Market value ($ mil.): 10,114

	STOCK PRICE ($) FY Close	P/E High/Low	PER SHARE ($) Earnings	Dividends	Book Value
12/18	93.00	29 20	4.00	1.00	19.00
12/17	115.00	19 13	6.00	1.00	17.00
12/16	97.00	26 17	4.00	1.00	13.00
12/15	73.00	25 19	4.00	1.00	11.00
12/14	84.00	27 22	3.00	1.00	10.00
Annual Growth	2.5%	— —	8.8%	4.7%	17.0%

Huntington Bancshares Inc

Huntington Bancshares is the holding company for The Huntington National Bank which operates around 950 branches mostly in Ohio and Michigan. In addition to traditional retail and commercial banking services the bank offers mortgage banking capital market services equipment leasing brokerage services investment management recreational vehicle and marine financing and trust and estate services. The company's automobile finance business provides car loans to consumers and real estate and inventory finance to car dealerships throughout the Midwest and Northeast. Founded in 1866 the company boasts total assets of more than $100 billion.

Operations

Huntington Bancshares operates through four main business segments: Consumer and Business Banking Commercial Banking Vehicle Finance and the Regional Banking and The Huntington Private Client Group (RBHPCG). The company also records a Treasury/Other function.

Huntington's Consumer and Business Banking division which contributes about 55% to total revenue provides traditional banking products and services to consumer and small business customers as well as investment insurance foreign exchange hedging and treasury management services.

Its Commercial Banking division (almost 30% of revenue) is made up of six business units: Middle Market (addressing companies with annual sales of $20 million-500 million) Specialty Banking (for select industries in the Midwest) Asset Finance (a combination of its Huntington Equipment Finance Huntington Public Capital Technology and Healthcare Equipment Leasing and Lender Finance divisions) Capital Markets/Institutional Corporate Banking (offering corporate risk management services; institutional sales trading and underwriting; and institutional corporate banking) Commercial Real Estate (serving real estate developers REITs and commercial customers) and Treasury Management (which helps businesses manage working capital and reduce expenses).

Vehicle Finance (about 10% of revenue) lends to customers purchasing automobiles light-duty trucks recreational vehicles and marine craft. The company also finances new and used inventory acquisition by franchised dealerships through the segment.

Huntington's Regional Banking and The Huntington Private Client Group (RBHPCG) accounts for under 10% of sales. Through The Huntington Private Bank Huntington offers high net-worth clients deposit lending wealth management legacy planning investment and portfolio management fiduciary administration and trust services.

Treasury/Other covers technology and operations other unallocated assets liabilities revenue and expense.

Geographic Reach

Huntington Bancshares is headquartered in Columbus Ohio. The holding company operates around 10 private client offices and some 950 branches in Ohio Michigan Pennsylvania Indiana Illinois Wisconsin West Virginia and Kentucky. Ohio is home to about 450 branches; Michigan has about 300.

Sales and Marketing

In addition to traditional bank branches Huntington Banchsares distributes its products and services through convenience branches (in grocery stores and retirement centers for example) and an ATM network as well as via internet and mobile services. The bank's branches can be found in Ohio's Giant Eagle grocery stores.

Financial Performance

Amid a positive market environment Huntington Bancshares' revenue has increased modestly or moderately each year since 2014 for overall five-year growth of around 60%. Net income more than doubled in that time mostly due to gains made in 2017. Cash and debt both about doubled over that period.

The holding company's revenue added 5% to $4.5 billion in 2018 on growth in its Consumer & Business Banking Commercial Banking and Regional Banking and The Huntington Private Client Group (RBHPCG) segments. Revenue for Huntington's Vehicle Finance business fell due to a reduction in net interest margin reflecting a run off of the higher yielding portfolio acquired by the company in 2016 through its purchase of Akron Ohio-based financial services company FirstMerit.

Huntington's net income climbed 17% in 2018 compared with 2017 ending the year at $1.4 billion. Strong sales combined with lower expenses following the FirstMerit acquisition drove the improvement.

The company's cash stores expanded by $1.2 billion. Operations provided $1.7 billion and financings added $3.1 billion (mostly from an increase in deposits). Huntington used $3.7 billion on investments primarily for net loan and lease activity (excluding sales and purchases) and purchase of available-for-sale securities.

Strategy

Following its acquisition of rival bank FirstMerit in 2016 Huntington Bancshares' strategic plan has shifted focus to organic growth and reducing exposure to market volatility. The company is assuming no interest rate hikes in its revenue expectation and has adjusted its expense expectation accordingly.

In its automobile RV and marine finance portfolios Huntington is targeting borrowers with high FICO and internal custom scores. Following the financial crisis the company is taking a conservative approach to home loans; it does not originate residential mortgages allowing for negative amortization or multiple payment options.

Furthermore Huntington is investing in its digital technology to personalize clients' banking experience. In February 2019 the company launched its Huntington Heads Up platform an AI-based tool to help customers manage their finances by making spending and saving suggestions.

Mergers and Acquisitions

In August 2016 Huntington Bancshares paid $3.7 billion to buy Akron-based rival FirstMerit Corporation making it Ohio's largest bank and boosting its total assets by 41% to $100 billion. The acquisition also expanded Huntington's branch network by nearly 50% to some 1000 branches extending into the surrounding states of Michigan and Pennsylvania.

Company Background

With the economy in the Midwest wracked by the recession Huntington posted losses in 2008 and 2009 — more than $3 billion in the latter year alone — mainly attributable to credit losses due to nonperforming assets and the write down of goodwill related to past acquisitions. It returned to profitability in 2010 thanks in part to higher interest margins as a result of the company's focus on lower-cost customer checking accounts.

HISTORY

Pelatiah Webster (P. W.) Huntington descendant of both a Revolutionary War leader and a Declaration of Independence signer went to work at sea in 1850 at age 14. He returned to go into banking and in 1866 founded what would become Huntington National Bank of Columbus. As the business grew he conscripted four of his five sons. The bank took a national charter in 1905 and became The Huntington National Bank of Columbus. It survived the hard times of 1907 and 1912 through the Huntington philosophy of sitting on piles of cash.

P. W. died in 1918 and his son Francis became president. Francis expanded the company into trust services. Unlike many bankers in the 1920s he refused to make speculative loans based on the stock market. Francis died in 1928 and was succeeded by brother Theodore. By 1930 Huntington's trust assets accounted for more than half of the total. The family's conservative philosophy helped the bank sail through the 1933 bank holiday although when it reopened the amount of cash it could pay out was restricted to 10% of deposits.

P. W.'s son Gwynne chaired the bank during its post-WWII expansion. His death in 1958 ended the Huntington family reign. The bank began opening branches and adding new services such as mortgage and consumer loans. In 1966 in order to expand statewide the bank formed a holding company Huntington Bancshares. In the 1960s and 1970s the corporation added new operations including mortgage and leasing companies and an international division to help clients with foreign exchange.

In 1979 the company consolidated its 15 affiliates into The Huntington National Bank. Three years later the company bit off more than it could chew with the acquisitions of Reeves Banking and Trust Company of Dover and Union Commerce Corporation of Cleveland. The latter purchase loaded the company with debt. Nevertheless it continued to expand particularly after 1985 when banking regulations allowed interstate branch banking and it soon had operations in Florida Indiana Kentucky Michigan and West Virginia.

Huntington Bancshares was largely insulated from the real estate problems of the late 1980s and early 1990s thanks to its continuing conservative lending policies. But the company was at risk from the nationwide consolidation of the banking industry which made it a potential takeover target. It increased its service offerings and bolstered its place in the market through acquisitions. In 1996 Huntington Bancshares bought life insurance agency Tice & Associates and began cross-selling bank and insurance products. Important banking acquisitions in 1997 included First Michigan Bank and several Florida companies.

Also in 1997 the company took advantage of deregulation to consolidate its interstate operations (except for The Huntington State Bank) into a single operating company. In 1998 Huntington Bancshares continued to build its Huntington insurance services unit with the acquisition of Pollock & Pollock. In 1999 the bank launched a mortgage program aimed at wealthy clients and sold its credit card receivables portfolio to Chase Manhattan (now JPMorgan Chase & Co.). In 2000 the company bought Michigan's Empire Banc Corporation.

Former BANK ONE executive Thomas Hoaglin was named president and CEO in 2001. Later that year he became chairman when Frank Wobst retired after leading the company for 20 years.

In 2002 the company consolidated some branches in the Midwest to cut costs and exited the retail banking market in Florida selling some 140 retail branches there to SunTrust. After the mid-2007 acquisition of Sky Financial Sky's CEO Marty Adams became president and COO of Huntington Bancshares. He retired at the end of 2007 and Hoaglin resumed the president's role until his own retirement in 2009; Stephen Steinour then took the helm.

EXECUTIVES

Executive Vice President And Director Corporate Tax, Edward Kane

President Northwest Ohio Region, Sharon S. Speyer

Evp General Counsel And Secretary, Richard A. Cheap, age 67, $279,833 total compensation

Chairman President And Ceo, Stephen D. (Steve) Steinour, age 61, $1,061,538 total compensation

Sevp And Managing Director Auto Finance Commercial Real Estate And Community Development Lending And Investment, Nicholas G. (Nick) Stanutz, age 64, $465,000 total compensation

Sevp Retail And Business Banking, Mary W. Navarro, age 63, $541,154 total compensation

Sevp And Chief Risk Officer, Helga S. Houston, age 58, $542,308 total compensation

Sevp And Director Regional Banking And The Huntington Private Client Group, James E. (Jim) Dunlap, age 66, $518,333 total compensation

Region President Central Ohio/west Virginia, James E. Kunk

Sevp And Director Corporate Operations And Corporate Services, Mark E. Thompson, age 60, $315,340 total compensation

President Central Ohio Region, Sue E. Zazon

President West Virginia Region, Andrew J. Paterno

President Western Pennsylvania And Ohio Valley Region, Susan (Susie) Baker Shipley

Sevp And Cfo, Howell D. (Mac) McCullough, age 61, $596,538 total compensation

President Greater Cleveland Region, Sean P. Richardson

President Chicago Region, Peter K. Gillespie

Vp Commercial Banking Greater Akron/canton Region, William C. Shivers

Sevp And Chief Credit Officer, Daniel J. Neumeyer, age 59

Sevp Chief Technology And Operations Officer, Paul G. Heller, age 55, $590,385 total compensation

President West Michigan Region, John Irwin

President Southern Ohio And Northern Kentucky Region, Kevin Jones

Sevp And Director Commercial Banking, Richard (Rich) Remiker, age 61

Sevp And Chief Human Resources Officer, Rajeev (Raj) Syal, age 53

President Akron Region, Nicholas Browning

President Indiana Region, John Corbin

President Wisconsin Region, Kevin Leissring

President East Michigan, David Lochner

Sevp Private Bank; Regional Banking Director And Chair Michigan, Sandra E. Pierce, $222,789 total compensation

Evp And Chief Communications And Marketing Director, Julie C. Tutkovics

Senior Vice President Treasury Management Sales Manager, Robin Triplett

Vice President, Connor Chambers

Vice President, Denise Stone

Senior Business Banker Vice President, Connie Condo

Assistant Vice President Community Affairs, Steven Fields

Assistant Vice President, Jill Pazerski

Vice President, Bruce Sautter

Senior Vice President, Lee Bentley

Vice President, Couturier Jan

Assistant Vice President And Senior Product Manage, Amy Beck

Vice President International Services, Robert Storbeck

Vice President, Geoffrey Mowery

Vice President Sec Reporting Manager, Jeff Endres

Vice President Executive Recruiter, Mary Smith

Senior Vice President, Clint Sommer

Vice President, James Matousek

Assistant Vice President Section Manager, Gayla Strickler

Vice President And Community Development Director, Staci Glenn

Vice President National Sales Manager And Key Accounts, Patrick Prato

Vice President Senior Sba Lender, Paul Collinsworth

Senior Vice President And Relationship Manager, Carrie Fraser

Vice President Senior Sales Executive, Bret Haggy

Vice President I Treasury Management Industry Solutions, Brett Bailey

Vice President Risk Manager Retail And Business Banking, Heidi Sims

Senior Vice President, Peter Arendt

Senior Vice President Marketing Operations Director, Janice Tedesco

Vice President Enterprise Technology Systems, Carolyn Jones

Senior Vice President Information Technology Risk, Christine Holland

Assistant Vice President Treasury Management Sales Executive, Faith Hansen

Vice President, Nadine Liggett

Assistant Vice President, John Breitling

Senior Vice President And Director Government Relations, Todd Bailey

Vice President Segment Risk Manager Senior, Pamela Birnbrich

Assistant Vice President, Jenny Nickles

Vice President, Brad Udy

Assistant Vice President 1 Portfolio Manager, Nick Markovich

Senior Vice President, Neil S Clark, age 68

Senior Vice President Total Rewards, Craig Wilkins

Vp And Senior Product Manager, Shannon Gardner

Senior Vice President Credit Risk Management, Tim Barber

Vice President Tm Liquidity And Fraud Group Product Manager, Ashley Sanders

Vice President Business Unit Controller, Scott Dupler

Vice President Treasury Management Sales, John Tremoulis

Assistant Vice President Senior Human Resources Generalist, Susan Lelonek

Vice President Collections Management Information Systems, Willie Tackett

Vice President, Joseph Ahee

Senior Vice President Treasury Management, Steve Veach

Assistant Vice President Home Lending Compliance Section Manager, Omar Ramsay

Vice President Loan Syndications, Chad Lowe

Vice President Credit Review, Lucia West

Senior Vice President Deposit Product Pricing And Fees Director, David Schamer

Vice President, Roy Dsa

Vice President Human Resources Senior Staffing Specialist, Karis Spence

Vice President Senior Sourcing Manager, Jay Gomer

Senior Vice President Retail Marketing, Karen Maruna

Assistant Vice President, Tony Ruberg

Senior Vice President, Michael Price

Vp It Security, Julie Lucas

Assistant Vice President Regional Property Manager, Cheryl Pitzer

Vice President Of The Mortgage Group, Linda Zack

Vice President, Renee Ross

Vice President, Dan Lowrie

Assistant Vice President, Schlosser James

Vice President, Terri Whitman

Executive Vice President Marketing, Chandra Kimble

Vice President Commercial Loans, John Leuhmann

Senior Vice President, Bruce Shearer

Vice President Senior Commercial Relationship Manager, Kevin Contat

Vice President Commercial Banking, Grant Friend

Assistant Vice President And Branch Manager, Amber Babik

Assistant Vice President Third Party, Michael Adams

Vice President, Michael Williams

Vice President R Receivables Specialist, Rick Dison

Vice President And Manager Customer Information And Market Research, Joyce Smith

Vice President, Bill Crum

Vice President Senior Relationship Manager, Jason Ratkovich

Assistant Vice President Deposit Pricing And Product Lead Analyst, Dominic Monley

Vice President, Gary Bogan

Vice President, Tony Paterno

Vice President Sales, Tom Obrian

Assistant Vice President Scrum Master, Laura Elliott

Assistant Vice President Commercial Loan Closer, Marianne Kartson

Assistant Vice President Branch Manager Ii, Scott Johnson

Assistant Vice President Auto Finance Credit Rep Senior, Jeremy Menning

Vice President Relationship Manager, David Stiller

Senior Vice President Change Management Director, Lin Hillis

Vice President, Dee Giles

Vice President Lease Administration Manager, Lynn Putterbaugh

Vice President Business Banking, Julie Roth

Vice President, Thomas Hannaford

Cml Strategy Implementation Manager Senior Vice President, Michelle Friend

Vice President And Team Leader Special Assets Division, Alfred Casino

Assistant Vice President Senior Risk Man, Na Jin

Senior Vice President Segment Risk Officer, Mindy Ball

Senior Vice President, Mark Izzo

Senior Vice President Retail And Business Banking Risk Manager, David Mehrle

Vice President Segment Risk Manager, Joe Anderson

Assistant Vice President Business Banking Underwriter, John Hogue

Vice President Portfolio Risk Manager, Scott Neff

Senior Vice President Managing Director Lender Finance, Dennis Conway

Vice President Business Banking Support Manager, Roland Brooks

Senior Vice President, Robyn Griffin

Vice President Associate Counsel, Dana Farthing

Vice President Mortgage Collections, Shane Rito

Vice President, Jeff Cholley

Senior Vice President, Monique Legris

Vice President Senior Portfolio Manager, Craig Gephart

Vice President; Senior Financial Advisor Team Leader, Patrick Riepenhoff

Vice President Product Manager Commercial Deposits And Fees, Larry Matteson

Vice President Change Management, Andi Frescura

Vice President Director Currency Risk Management (foreign Exchange), Rory Kemp

Vice President, Steve Wasmer

Vice President And Senior Financial Advisor, Terresa Pratt

Vice President Senior Financial Advisor, Andrew Lukcso

Avp Treasury Management Sales Specialist, Lauren Krysiak

Executive Vice President Chief Strategy Officer, Amit Dhingra

Vice President Portfolio Risk Specialist Senior, Yianni Vitellas

Senior Vice President Public Relations, Maureen Brown
Senior Closer Assistant Vice President, Melanie Ornas
Vice President Business Banking Underwriter Iii, Brock Yates
National Account Manager, Jamie McShane
Senior Vice President Relationship Manager, Tania Deng
Auditors: PricewaterhouseCoopers LLP

LOCATIONS

HQ: Huntington Bancshares Inc
41 South High Street, Columbus, OH 43287
Phone: 614 480-2265
Web: www.huntington.com

2016 Bank Branches

	No.
Ohio	523
Michigan	353
Pennsylvania	53
Indiana	46
Illinois	39
Wisconsin	37
West Virginia	30
Kentucky	10
Total	**1,091**

2016 sales

	No.
Consumer and Business Banking	43
Commercial Banking	23
Commercial Real Estate and Vehicle Finance	24
Regional Banking and The Huntington Private Client Group	8
Home Lending	2
Total	**100**

PRODUCTS/OPERATIONS

2018 Bank Branches

	No.
Ohio	451
Michigan	300
Pennsylvania	49
Indiana	41
Illinois	37
Wisconsin	31
West Virginia	25
Kentucky	10
Total	**944**

2018 Sales

	$ mil.	% of total
Interest		
Loans & leases	3,305	63
Available-for-sale and other securities	376	7
Held-to-maturity securities	211	4
Other	57	1
Interest Expense	(760.0)	
Noninterest		
Service charges on deposit accounts	364	7
Cards and payment processing income	224	4
Mortgage banking income	108	2
Trust services	171	3
Insurance income	82	2
Capital markets fees	91	2
Bank-owned life insurance income	67	1
Gain on sales of loans	55	1
Net gains on sales of securities	(21.0)	
Other	180	3
Impairment losses recognized in earnings on available-for-sale securities	-	
Total	**4,510**	**100**

COMPETITORS

Citizens Financial Group	PNC Financial
Comerica	Park National
Fifth Third	Regions Financial
JPMorgan Chase	TFS Financial
KeyCorp	U.S. Bancorp
	Wells Fargo

HISTORICAL FINANCIALS
Company Type: Public

Income Statement   FYE: December 31

	ASSETS ($ mil.)	NET INCOME ($ mil.)	INCOME AS % OF ASSETS	EMPLOYEES
12/18	108,781	1,393	1.3%	15,693
12/17	104,185	1,186	1.1%	15,770
12/16	99,714	712	0.7%	15,993
12/15	71,045	693	1.0%	12,243
12/14	66,298	632	1.0%	11,873
Annual Growth	**13.2%**	**21.8%**	**—**	**7.2%**

2018 Year-End Financials

Debt ratio: 8.00%
Return on equity: 13.00%
Cash ($ mil.): 3,290
Current ratio: —
Long-term debt ($ mil.): —

No. of shares (mil.): 1,047
Dividends
  Yield: 4.0%
  Payout: 39.0%
Market value ($ mil.): 12,477

	STOCK PRICE ($) FY Close	P/E High/Low		PER SHARE ($) Earnings	Dividends	Book Value
12/18	12.00	14	9	1.00	1.00	11.00
12/17	15.00	15	12	1.00	0.00	10.00
12/16	13.00	19	11	1.00	0.00	9.00
12/15	11.00	14	12	1.00	0.00	8.00
12/14	11.00	15	12	1.00	0.00	8.00
Annual Growth	**3.2%**			**13.6%**	**24.2%**	**8.0%**

Huntington Ingalls Industries, Inc.

Huntington Ingalls Industries (HII) is the sole designer builder and refueler of the US Navy's nuclear aircraft carriers. Rivaling nuclear submarine builder General Dynamics HII is the largest naval shipbuilder in America; it also maintains and repairs nuclear submarines and aircraft carriers. In addition HII builds expeditionary warfare ships surface combatants submarines and Coast Guard surface ships and provides aftermarket fleet support. Almost all its offerings are sold to the US government.

Operations

The shipbuilder has three reportable segments: Newport News Ingalls and Technical Solutions.

Newport News includes the manufacture of nuclear-powered aircraft carriers and submarines and services such as overhaul repair maintenance and fleet support. It accounts for more than 55% of Huntington Ingalls Industries' net sales.

The Ingalls segment accounts for roughly 30% of net sales. It designs and constructs non-nuclear ships for the US Navy and US Coast Guard including amphibious assault ships expeditionary warfare ships surface combatants and national security cutters.

Technical Solutions (about 10%) includes information technology fleet maintenance and modernization nuclear management and operations and oil and gas engineering and support.

Geographic Reach

Headquartered in Newport News VA HII operates in 42 US states and 13 countries. It has offices in Huntsville AL; San Diego CA; Broomfield CO; Pascagoula MS; Houston TX; Fairfax Hampton Newport News Suffolk and Virginia Beach VA; and Washington DC.

Sales and Marketing

In addition to the US government HII provides services for commercial customers in the private sector specifically in the energy and oil and gas industries. The US government is its largest customer with the US Navy accounting for almost 90% of its net sales. The US Coast Guard generates about 5%. Although HII has secured contracts with the US Navy for the next several years its business is highly dependent on this single customer. Any changes affecting government spending may also adversely affect Huntington Ingalls.

Financial Performance

Huntington Ingalls' revenue has been increasing steadily over the past five years. Sales in 2018 were up 10% reaching $8.2 billion compared with $7.4 billion the previous year. Higher volumes specifically in amphibious assault ships and aircraft carriers were cited as primary factors for growth.

Net earnings amounted to $836 million a 75% increase from $479 million in 2017. The increase was primarily due to higher net sales as well as lower expenses for income tax interest and retirement benefits.

Cash at the end of fiscal 2018 was $240 million an increase of $461 million from the prior year. Cash from operations contributed $914 million to the coffers while investing activities used $476 million mainly for capital expenditures and acquisitions (G2). Financing activities used another $899 million for dividends to stockholders and the company's stock repurchase program.

Strategy

Huntington Ingalls Industries continues to benefit from strong Navy and Coast Guard expenditures for ships. To prepare for current and future programs the company has been deploying capital to reactivate its East Bank facilities for Ingalls Shipbuilding in Pascagoula MS and continues to outfit the Joint Manufacturing Assembly Facility (JMAF) at Newport News Shipbuilding in Virginia.

In 2018 the US Navy awarded a multiyear contract for six destroyers valued at $5.1 billion to Ingalls Shipbuilding and in 2019 it awarded Newport News Shipbuilding a contract for two aircraft carriers?the CVN 80 and 81?worth almost $15 billion. Ships in construction and on contract are now providing a 10-15 year backlog for HII.

Diversification in the growing non-shipbuilding sector is providing revenue growth for HII. Recent bolt-on acquisitions within its Technology Solutions division are adding threat analytics and cybersecurity capabilities to its professional services portfolio allowing the company to reach key new customers in the intelligence and special operations communities as well as additional defense and federal agencies.

Mergers and Acquisitions

In early 2019 HII acquired Virginia-based Fulcrum IT Services an information technology and government consulting company. Fulcrum joins HII's Technical Solutions division and expands its capabilities in enhanced situational awareness and predictive threat analytics through Fulcrum's advanced engineering cyber security software development big data engineering and intelligence and special operations experience.

In 2018 the company acquired G2 a nationally recognized cybersecurity solutions and services company headquartered in Annapolis Junction MD. G2's operations are also being integrated into HII's Technical Solutions division. The acquisition adds advanced cybersecurity capabilities to HII's portfolio and expands its professional services business.

EXECUTIVES

President And Ceo, C. Michael (Mike) Petters, age 59, $328,847 total compensation
Evp Communications, Jerri Fuller Dickseski
Evp; President Newport News Shipbuilding, Matthew J. (Matt) Mulherin, age 59, $515,000 total compensation
Evp And General Counsel, Kellye L. Walker, age 52, $505,096 total compensation
Evp And Chief Human Resources Officer, William R. (Bill) Ermatinger
Evp And President Technical Solutions, Andy Green
Evp; President Ingalls Shipbuilding, Brian Cuccias, $514,906 total compensation
Evp Business Management And Cfo, Christopher D. Kastner, age 55, $463,462 total compensation
Evp Government And Customer Relations, Mitchell B. (Mitch) Waldman
Evp Strategy And Development, Michael S. Smith
Vp Quality Newport News Shipbuilding, Ron Murray
Corporate Vice President, Bruce Hawthorne
Corp Vice President Benefits And Compensatio, Jim Taylor
Vp Central Planning And Process Excellence Ingalls Shipbuilding, Rick Spaulding
Vp Manufacturing And Material Distribution Newport News Shipbuilding, Rob Hogan
Corporate Vice President Benefits And Compensation, Karen Velkey
Vp Legistlative Affairs, Andrew Hicks
Vice President Legislative Affairs, Carrie Apostolou
Vp And Controller Newport News Shipbuilding, Carolyn Pittman
Vp Supply Chain Management Ingalls Shipbuilding, Lori Harper
Corporate Vice President Associate General Counsel And Secretary, Charles Chuck Monroe
Vice President Program Management Ingalls Shipbuilding, Kari Wilkinson
Vp Human Resources And Administration Newport News Shipbuilding, Susan Jacobs
Vice President Construction John F. Kennedy (cvn79) Newport News Shipbuilding, Lucas Hicks
Vice President Of Nuclear, Barry Fletcher
Vp Human Resources And Administration Ingalls Shipbuilding, Edmond E Hughes
Vp Quality Engineering And Ils Ingalls Shipbuilding, Dave Belanger
Vp Strategy Ingalls Shipbuilding, Mike Lipski
Chairman, Thomas B. Fargo, age 71
Board Member, Anastasia Kelly
Board Member, Victoria Harker
Board Member, Thomas Schievelbein
Board Member, John Welch
Auditors: DELOITTE & TOUCHE LLP

LOCATIONS

HQ: Huntington Ingalls Industries, Inc.
4101 Washington Avenue, Newport News, VA 23607
Phone: 757 380-2000
Web: www.huntingtoningalls.com

PRODUCTS/OPERATIONS

2018 Sales

	$ mil.	% of total
Newport News	4,722	57
Ingalls	2,607	31
Technical Solutions	988	12
Intersegment eliminations	(141)	-
Total	**8,176**	**100**

2018 Sales

	$ mil.	% of total
Product sales	6,023	74
Service revenues	2,153	26
Total	**8,176**	**100**

Selected Products
Aircraft carriers (nuclear-powered)
Amphibious assault ships
National Security Cutters (US Coast Guard ships)
Expeditionary warfare ships
Fleet services
Submarines (nuclear-powered)
Surface combatants

COMPETITORS

BAE SYSTEMS
Direction des Constructions Navales
Electric Boat
General Dynamics
Northrop Grumman
Todd Shipyards

HISTORICAL FINANCIALS

Company Type: Public

Income Statement — FYE: December 31

	REVENUE ($ mil.)	NET INCOME ($ mil.)	NET PROFIT MARGIN	EMPLOYEES
12/18	8,176	836	10.2%	40,000
12/17	7,441	479	6.4%	38,000
12/16	7,068	573	8.1%	37,000
12/15	7,020	404	5.8%	36,000
12/14	6,957	338	4.9%	38,000
Annual Growth	**4.1%**	**25.4%**	**—**	**1.3%**

2018 Year-End Financials

Debt ratio: 20.00%
Return on equity: 51.00%
Cash ($ mil.): 240
Current ratio: 1.00
Long-term debt ($ mil.): 1,283
No. of shares (mil.): 42
Dividends
Yield: 2.0%
Payout: 16.0%
Market value ($ mil.): 7,974

	STOCK PRICE ($) FY Close	P/E High/Low		PER SHARE ($) Earnings	Dividends	Book Value
12/18	190.00	14	9	19.00	3.00	36.00
12/17	236.00	24	18	10.00	3.00	39.00
12/16	184.00	15	10	12.00	2.00	36.00
12/15	127.00	17	12	8.00	2.00	32.00
12/14	112.00	17	13	7.00	1.00	28.00
Annual Growth	**14.1%**	**—**	**—**	**29.2%**	**31.8%**	**6.4%**

Huntsman Corp

Operating its businesses through subsidiary Huntsman International global chemical manufacturer Huntsman Corporation makes a broad range of products that include polyurethanes amines surfactants adhesives resins dyes and inks. Huntsman's chemicals are sold worldwide to a variety of customers in the adhesives construction products aerospace energy and home furnishings. Huntsman operates manufacturing and research and development facilities worldwide.

Operations

Huntsman makes differentiated organic chemical products. Its products comprise a broad range of chemicals and formulations which it markets globally to a diversified group of consumer and industrial customers.

The company operates through four business segments: Polyurethanes Performance Products Advanced Materials and Textile Effects. Polyurethanes represent more than half of revenues followed by Performance Products at about 25% of revenues. In this latter segment the company is well positioned in growing markets for chemicals needed in end uses like detergents and fuel additives.

The Polyurethanes unit makes MDI propylene oxide and propylene glycol for automotive interiors construction material and furniture cushioning. It is one of the largest producers of MDI which is used in producing rigid and other types of foams.

Other segments include: Advanced Materials (epoxy acrylic and polyurethane-based polymers) where some of its products are key to aerospace applications and Textile Effects (textile chemicals dyes and inks).

Geographic Reach

Huntsman Corporation's four segments operate in more than 75 locations in about 30 countries including North America Europe the Middle East and Asia. But among these China is key. China is considered among the largest MDI markets; thus the company has opened a MDI production plant in that country. The U.S China Mexico and Germany are the company's largest markets. U.S. and China account for about a third and some 15% of revenue. Mexico and Germany contribute just more than 10%. Operations in China could be subject to uncertainty due to ongoing debate over US-China trade relations and the need to transact in multiple foregin currencies.

Sales and Marketing

Huntsman markets polyurethane chemicals to more than 6000 customers in about 90 countries and is fond of saying its products are "all around us."

The company serves a host of multinational businesses through its four business segments including manufacturers (BMW Electrolux Louisiana-Pacific) consumer product makers (Unilever Procter & Gamble Colgate) fuel and fuel additives (Chevron Lubrizol) and paints/coatings (Akzo Sherwin Williams).

Financial Performance

The company grew revenue double digits in the past two years after declines in 2015 and 2016 primarily from lower prices in a competitive environment. Net income has ranged from $93 million to as high as $636 million in the past five years.

Huntsman Corporation revenues of $9.4 billion increased 12% in 2018 compared to 2017. Polyurethanes have powered much of this growth but all four segments of its business increased prices in 2018 while most saw sales volumes increase too.

Net income for Huntsman's controlling interests decreased 47% to $337 million in 2018 largely due to the deconsolidation of former subsidiary Venator of which it retains majority ownership. However the company's Performance Products segment grew net income by 24 percent. This was due to higher margins but also a favorable compare to 2017 when it experienced production outages due to hurricane-related weather.

The company is combining its free cash flow proceeds from the spinoff of its subsidiary Ventnor and leverage to drive shareholder value through increased dividends and stock repurchases. Cash and cash equivalents totaled $340 million down from $719 million at the beginning of the period. Cash from operations was $1.2 billion. Cash used in investing equaled $973 million an increase from the prior year of about $550 million notably including a $350-million acquisition along with $313 million in other capital expenditures. Cash used in financing activities totaled $424 million including $277 million in stock purchases and $156 million in dividends to shareholders.

Strategy

To be successful Huntsman spends a great deal of time and money on research and development to formulate proprietary products that limit competition. MDI and polyols formulated MDI and thermal plastic are notable areas of focus.

The company is focused on higher-margins from specialized products like these that separate itself from large competitors like DowDuPont. This has led to a focus on polyurethanes and to spin off Venator a manufacturer of compounds used to manufacture pigments. Much of the proceeds from the Venator IPO helped pay down Huntsman debt and free the company from a highly cyclical market.

The company anticipates spending $390 million in 2019 on capital projects including $50 million on a new MDI unit in Louisiana.

Mergers and Acquisitions

Huntsman Corporation acquired Demilec in 2018 in a $350-million transaction from Sun Capital Partners. The company made the move for the manufacturer and distributor of spray polyurethane foam to access a higher-margin segment of the polyurethane business. Acquiring new businesses will continue to play into the company's strategy but also introduces a measure of risk that is involved with financing the transactions and integrating the operations of these companies.

Company Background

Huntsman Corporation was formed in 2004 to hold businesses founded by Jon M. Huntsman in 1970. The company began with the manufacturing of plastic packaging and expanded through acquisitions.

EXECUTIVES

Evp Strategy And Investment, J. Kimo Esplin, age 57, $686,575 total compensation
President And Ceo, Peter R. Huntsman, age 56, $1,700,000 total compensation
Evp And Cfo, Sean Douglas, age 55
Division President Performance Products, Monte G. Edlund, age 64
Vp And Cio, Delaney M. Bellinger
Ceo Asia/pacific; Division President Polyurethanes, Anthony P. Hankins, age 62, $865,650 total compensation
Evp General Counsel Chief Compliance Officer And Secretary, David M. Stryker, age 61, $505,900 total compensation
Division President Pigments, Simon Turner, age 56, $544,616 total compensation
Division President Advanced Materials, Scott J. Wright
Division President Textile Effects, Rohit Aggarwal
Managing Director Indian Subcontinent, Harshad Naik
Vice President, David Hester
Vice President And General Manager, Eric Phillips
Executive Vice President Strategy And Investment, J Kimo Esplin
Vice President, Russell Healy
Vp Safety, Ron Gerrard
Vice President Performance Chemicals, Stu Monteith
Vice President Research And Development Performance Products, Ralph Diguilio
Vice President Financial Planning And Analysis, Nooshin Vaughn
Vice President Global Supply Chain Polyurethanes, Mike Fowles
National Sales Manager, Katy Zukis
Vice President Corporate Development, Luciano Reyes
Vice Chairman, Nolan D. Archibald
Executive Chairman, Jon M. Huntsman, age 82
Treasurer, Brandon Gray
Board Member, Daniele Ferrari
Auditors: DELOITTE & TOUCHE LLP

LOCATIONS

HQ: Huntsman Corp
10003 Woodloch Forest Drive, The Woodlands, TX 77380
Phone: 281 719-6000
Web: www.huntsman.com

2016 Sales

	$ mil.	% of total
US	3,005	31
China	1,021	10
Germany	676	7
Mexico	453	5
Other	4,502	47
Total	**9,657**	**100**

PRODUCTS/OPERATIONS

2016 Sales

	$ mil.	% of total
Polyurethanes	3,667	38
Performance Products	2,126	22
Pigments and Additives	2,139	22
Advanced Materials	1,020	10
Textile Effects	751	8
Corporate and eliminations	(46)	-
Total	**9,657**	**100**

Segments & Selected Products

Polyurethanes
  Aniline
  MDI (methylene diphenyl diisocyanate)
  MTBE (methyl tertiary-butyl ether)
  PG (propylene glycol)
  PO (propylene oxide)
  Polyols
  TPU (thermoplastic polyurethane)
Performance Products
  Ethylene glycol
  Ethylene oxide
  Ethanolamines
  Ethyleneamines
  Maleic anhydride
  Polyetheramines
  Surfactants
Materials & Effects
  Adhesives
  Acrylic
  Polyurethane-based
  Epoxy
  Epoxy resin compounds
Pigments
  Titanium dioxide

COMPETITORS

Akzo Nobel	Evonik Degussa
BASF SE	LyondellBasell
Bayer AG	Wanhua Chemical Group
Covestro	Co. Ltd.
Dow Chemical	

HISTORICAL FINANCIALS

Company Type: Public

Income Statement

FYE: December 31

	REVENUE ($ mil.)	NET INCOME ($ mil.)	NET PROFIT MARGIN	EMPLOYEES
12/18	9,379	337	3.6%	10,000
12/17	8,358	636	7.6%	10,000
12/16	9,657	326	3.4%	15,000
12/15	10,299	93	0.9%	15,000
12/14	11,578	323	2.8%	16,000
Annual Growth	**(5.1%)**	**1.1%**	**—**	**(11.1%)**

2018 Year-End Financials

Debt ratio: 29.00%
Return on equity: 13.00%
Cash ($ mil.): 340
Current ratio: 2.00
Long-term debt ($ mil.): 2,224
No. of shares (mil.): 233
Dividends
  Yield: 3.0%
  Payout: 46.0%
Market value ($ mil.): 4,494

	STOCK PRICE ($) FY Close	P/E High/Low		Earnings	Dividends	Book Value
12/18	19.00	25	13	1.00	1.00	11.00
12/17	33.00	13	7	3.00	1.00	11.00
12/16	19.00	15	6	1.00	1.00	5.00
12/15	11.00	64	25	0.00	1.00	6.00
12/14	23.00	22	16	1.00	1.00	7.00
Annual Growth	**(4.1%)**	**—**		**1.5%**	**6.8%**	**10.3%**

HY-VEE, INC.

Give Hy-Vee a high five for being one of the largest privately owned US supermarket chains despite serving some modestly sized towns in the Midwest. The company runs some 260 stores in eight Midwestern states. The company's brands include Hy-Vee Hy-Vee Select That's Smart! Baking Stone Bread and Full Circle among others. It distributes products to its stores through several subsidiaries including Lomar Distributing (specialty foods) Perishable Distributors of Iowa (fresh foods) and Florist Distribution (flowers). Other activities include construction and specialty pharmacies. Charles Hyde and David Vredenburg founded the employee-owned firm in 1930. It takes its name from a combination of its founders' names.

Strategy

Looking to leverage the large amount of traffic its website receives in 2018 Hy-Vee partnered with Australian advertising company to insert adverts into search results on its website. The specific nature of its website — buying food and drink — means Hy-Vee has access to a very specific customer segment providing advertisers with a high-value prospect. The move opens up a new revenue stream and monetizes unused screen real estate.

EXECUTIVES

V Pres, Dennis Ausenhus
Assistant Vp Real Estate, David Bailie
Evp And Chief Merchandising Officer, Jon S. Wendel
Chairman President And Ceo, Randy Edeker
Evp And Chief Customer Officer, Sheila Laing
Evp Cfo And Treasurer, Mike Skokan
Vice Chairman Evp And Chief Administrative Officer, Andy McCann
Evp Western Region, Brett Bremser
Evp And Coo, Jay Marshall
Evp Eastern Region, Darren Baty
Vice President Retail Information Technology, Julie Proffitt
Assistant Vice President Operations, Jim Watters
Senior Vice President And Chief Health Officer, Kristin Williams
Pharmacy Manager, Marrianne Ryno
Assistant Vice President Sec, Angie Rosenberger
Assistant Vice President Operations, Rob Eslick
Assistant Vice President Bakery Operations, Tony Byington
Group Vice President Equipment Purchasing, Mark Brauer
Assistant Vice President Engineering And Construction, Dave Kozak
Assistant Vice President Meat Operations, Kenan Judge
Assistant Vice President For Marketing Projects, Erin Bailey
Assistant Vice President Logistics, Jody Sandy
Assistant Vice President, Tony Kaska

Assistant Vice President Western Region, Pat Hensley

Vice President Special Projects, Gary Goodhall

Vice President Government Relations, Noreen Otto

Assistant Vice President Store Setup, Mark Millsap

Vice President Distribution, Tod Hockenson

Vice President Information Technology Operation, Cevin Anderson

Assisant Vice President, Chuck Seaman

Vice President, Karl Kruse

Assistant Vice President Information Technology Operations, Travis Hoover

Assistant Vice President Risk Management, Janet Crocker

Group Vice President Information Technology, Tom Settle

Assistant Vice President, Marshall Sanders

Avp Produce Operations, Mike Orf

Vice President, Aaron Wiese

Assistant Vice President Risk Management, John Brummit

Assistant Vice President Information Technology Projects, Angie Dachenbach

Pharmacy Manager, Jeff Jorgensen

Pharmacy Manager, Brad Moriarty

Pharmacy Manager, Heather Yennie

Vice President Business Development, Kevin Sherlock

Vice President Of Real Estate, Pete Hosch

Vice President Of Human Resources, Karen Boriskey

Assisant Treasurer, Jeff Pierce

Secretary To Greg Frampton, Stacey Groff

Assistant Secretary, Michael Jurgens

Senior Vice President Secretary And General Counsel, Steve Meyer

LOCATIONS

HQ: HY-VEE, INC.
5820 WESTOWN PKWY, WEST DES MOINES, IA
502668223
Phone: 515 267-2800
Web: WWW.HY-VEE.COM

PRODUCTS/OPERATIONS

Selected Subsidiaries
D & D Foods Inc. (salads dips and meats)
Florist Distributing Inc. (flowers plants and florist supplies)
Hy-Vee Construction L.C. (construction)
Hy-Vee Pharmacy Solutions (specialty pharmacy services)
Hy-Vee Weitz Construction L.C. (construction)
Lomar Distributing Inc. (specialty foods)
Midwest Heritage Bank FSB (banking)
Perishable Distributors of Iowa Ltd. (meat fish seafood and ice cream)

COMPETITORS

ALDI	Niemann Foods
Associated Wholesale Grocers	Rite Aid
	Roundy's
Ball's Food	SUPERVALU
CVS	Save-A-Lot Food Stores
Casey's General Stores	Target Corporation
Fareway Stores	Wal-Mart
Kmart	Walgreen
Kroger	

HISTORICAL FINANCIALS
Company Type: Private

Income Statement   FYE: September 30

	REVENUE ($ mil.)	NET INCOME ($ mil.)	NET PROFIT MARGIN	EMPLOYEES
09/18*	10,291	0	—	83,000
12/16	9,842	0	—	
09/13	8,014	0	—	
Annual Growth	**5.1%**	**—**	**—**	**—**

*Fiscal year change

IBERIABANK Corp

Holding company IBERIABANK Corporation through its flagship bank subsidiary IBERIABANK operates some 230 branches in Louisiana and about 10 other states. It also has about 30 title insurance offices in Louisiana Arkansas and Tennessee in addition to some 90 mortgage loan offices in a dozen states and about 20 wealth management offices in four states. Offering deposit products such as checking and savings accounts CDs and IRAs the bank uses funds gathered mainly to make loans. Commercial loans and leases make up around two-thirds of the company's $22.3 billion loan portfolio which also includes consumer loans and residential mortgages. IBERIABANK Corp. has $30.1 billion in assets.

Operations

IBERIABANK operates through its IBERIABANK mortgage and LTC segments.

The IBERIABANK segment — which includes commercial and retail banking wealth management capital markets and other corporate functions — accounts for about 90% of revenue. Net interest income comprises about 85% of the segment's revenue. Commercial loans provide about 70% of the holding company's loan interest income; consumer and other loans generate about 20% of its loan interest income.

The mortgage segment accounts for nearly 10% of revenue. Through that business IBERIABANK originates funds and sells one-to-four family residential mortgages. Such loans account for about 10% of the company's loan interest income.

IBERIABANK offers title insurance and loan closing services through its LTC segment.

Geographic Reach

IBERIABANK operates about 330 combined offices including around 230 bank branch offices and two loan production offices in Louisiana Arkansas Tennessee Alabama Texas Florida Georgia South Carolina New York and North Carolina; about 30 title insurance offices in Arkansas Tennessee and Louisiana; and mortgage representatives at some 90 locations in 12 US states.

Some 40% 20% and 10% of the company's loans are in Florida Louisiana and Texas respectively.

Financial Performance

IBERIABANK has seen strong revenue and net income growth from 2013 to 2017 adding 82% and 119% respectively. Cash stores increased 60% to $625.7 million while long-term debt ballooned by 433% to $1.5 billion.

The holding company's revenue trended up 15% to $1 billion in 2017 compared with 2016 thanks to increased interest and fees from loans caused by improvements in loan yields and average earning assets. The growth was offset slightly by a decline in non-interest income primarily from the residential mortgage business.

Net income however fell 24% to $142.4 million in that time owing to non-interest expenses related to IBERIABANK's acquisition of southeastern Florida bank chain Sabadell United Bank and a $51 million increase in income tax expense caused by the 2017 Tax Cuts and Jobs Act.

The bank's cash stores were depleted by $736.4 million in 2017. Operations added $263.6 million and investments used $1.9 billion including $490.4 million for acquisitions. Financings added another $908.5 million from proceeds from long-term debt and common stock issuances.

Strategy

IBERIABANK announced its 2020 strategic goals in April 2018 which include improving operating efficiency using a “branch-lite” approach that involves digitalization of client services and back-office processes. Since 2012 the company has increased the proportion of its alternative transactions — including via online digital and smart device delivery systems — by 10 percentage points. The bank opened 28 offices and closed 11 branches in 2017 and scheduled more than 20 branch closures or consolidations for 2018.

In 2018 IBERIABANK also launched a mobile banking app introduced robotic process automation back offices created a mortgage self-fulfillment application and announced plans to update its internet banking website.

IBERIABANK is working to increase its presence in Miami Florida which holds $226 billion in total market deposits. IBERIABANK acquired Southeast Florida-based Sabadell United Bank in July 2017. The deal gave IBERIABANK 25 offices serving the Miami metropolitan area and three offices in Naples Sarasota and Tampa. In March 2018 the bank acquired Gibraltar Private Bank & Trust another Florida bank with seven offices in the Miami Key West and Naples metropolitan areas and one in New York City.

The bank owns around 90 branches in Florida with about $9 billion total deposits. The company has significantly increased its presence in Florida; since 2014 it has grown the share of its portfolio comprising loans and deposits in that state by 13 and 22 percentage points respectively. Other growth markets for the company include Dallas and Houston as well as Atlanta Orlando and Tampa.

Mergers and Acquisitions

Since 2008 IBERIABANK has made more than 20 acquisitions of live and failing banks branches and wealth management and title insurance companies.

IBERIABANK acquired Gibraltar Private Bank & Trust another Florida bank in March 2018 for about $214.7 million. Gibraltar had seven offices in the Miami Key West and Naples metropolitan areas and one in New York City prior to the acquisition. The agreement conferred $1.5 billion in loans and $1.1 billion in deposits to IBERIABANK's portfolio.

The bank acquired SolomonParks Title & Escrow in January 2018 for $3.3 million thereby gaining eight title offices in the Nashville Tennessee area.

In July 2017 IBERIABANK acquired Southeast Florida-based Sabadell United Bank for $809.2 million in cash and 2.6 million IBERIABANK shares. The deal gave IBERIABANK $4 billion in loans and $4.4 billion in deposits as well as 25 offices serving the Miami metropolitan area and three offices in Naples Sarasota and Tampa.

Company Background

IBERIABANK was founded in 1887 in New Iberia Louisiana. It operated in just two states -

Louisiana and Arkansas - until 2008 when it began spreading across the Southeast.

EXECUTIVES

President And Ceo, Daryl G. Byrd, age 64, $1,015,000 total compensation

Sevp Mergers And Acquisitions Finance And Investor Relations; Director Financial Strategy And Mortgage, John R. Davis, age 58, $456,154 total compensation

Vice Chairman And Managing Director Of Brokerage Trust And Wealth Management, Jefferson G. (Jeff) Parker, age 66, $480,192 total compensation

Sevp And Director Communications Facilities And Human Resources, Elizabeth A. (Beth) Ardoin, age 50

Sevp And Cfo, Anthony J. Restel, age 49, $480,385 total compensation

Vice Chairman; Sevp And Coo, Michael J. (Mike) Brown, age 55, $598,269 total compensation

President And Ceo Iberiabank Mortgage, Bill Edwards

Evp And Director Retail Small Business And Mortgage, Robert M. (Bob) Kottler, age 60

Evp And Executive Credit Officer, H. Spurgeon Mackie, age 68

Evp And Chief Risk Officer, J. Randolph Bryan, age 51

Evp Corporate Secretary And General Counsel, Robert B. Worley, age 59

President And Ceo Lender's Title Company, David B. Erb

Senior Vice President Training Manager, Tracey Hirsch

Assistant Vice President Retail Support Specialist, Sheila Montgomery

Vice President And Business Banking Relationship Manager, Daniel Maurin

Senior Vice President Director Of Compliance Bsa Officer, Donna Davidek

Senior Vice President, Steve Krueger

Assistant Vice President, Dolores Hernandez

Vice President, Tom Chelewski

Vice President Bcs Ore Officer, Neel Stacy

Vice President Support Services, Jerry Prejean

Vice President, Debbie Pasierb

Vice President Commercial Lending, Jeremy Young

Vice President, Mary Rice

Senior Vice President Network Support Manager, Chris Berthaut

Senior Vice President Retail Market Manager, Trich Worthington

Senior Vice President Retail Market Manager, Donnie Dobbins

Senior Vice President, Greg Mendez

Senior Vice President, William Albanese

Exec Vice President, Cleland Powell

Senior Vice President, Eric Movassaghi

Vice President Ore Property Manager, Brian Buczko

Senior Vice President Corporate Banking, C Mizelle

Vice President, Michael Hallmark

Vice President, Mark Pharr

Vice President, Carrie Curet

Senior Vice President Director Of Corporate Compensati, Andrew Wilson

Vice President Branch Manager Business Development Officer, Pedro Diaz

Vice President Business Credit Services Officer, Michael Schaefer

Vice President Public Relations Director, Judi Lejeune

Vice President Of Services, Timothy Wilson

Vice President Infrastructure Engineering, Kevin Plaisance

Senior Vice President Treasury Management Sales, Ted Graphos

Assistant Vice President, Patti Oufnac

Vice President, Howard Mary

Vice President Branch Manager, Cindy Winter

Vice President Senior Loan Review Officer, Geoffrey Houlditch

Svp Private Banking And Retail Market Manager, Ginger Harper

Senior Vice President Commercial Banking, Holly Popham

Vice President Human Resources And Employee Development And Training, Mike Pelletier

Vice President Controller, Angela Robert

Assistant Vice President Branch Manager, Melissa Krackenberger

Vice President Business Banking Relationship Manager, Jason Kern

Vice President Business Credit Services, David Krage

Assistant Vice President Marketing, Jessica Porter

Vice President, Keith Dameron

Vice President, Paul Cotoni

Senior Executive Vice President And Director Of Communications Facilities And Human Resources, Beth Ardoin

Senior Vice President, Richard Perdue

Vice President Commercial Lending, Jamie Vaught

Vice President Business Banking, Eugene Castrejon

Assistant Vice President Commercial Portfolio Manager, Jennifer Bordelon

Executive Vice President, Norman Vascocu

Vice President Commercial Banking, William Biossat

Vice President, Sean Friend

Assistant Vice President, Cathleen Caldwell

Senior Vice President And Business And Retail Market Manger, Maurice Butler

Vice President, Kimberly Williams

Executive Vice President, Mark Tipton

Vice President Branch Manager, Samantha McDermott

Vice President Mortgage Executive, Mark Young

Evp Director Treasury Management Services, Donna Kasmiersky

Assistant Vice President, Felesha Finch

Assistant Vice President Treasury Management Sales Officer, Ansley Oliver Cooper

Vice President Corporate Accounting, Robert Robertson

Vice President Central Retail Administration, Donna Pye

Vice President Of Asset Based Lending, Michael Jennings

Vice President, Blake Norris

Vice President Commercial Banking, Luke Spaulding

Vice President, ToniRae Hurley

Assistant Vice President Branch Manager, Adam Golden

Vice President, Linda Rodriguez

Vice President Private Banking Relationship Manager, Carrie Standlee

Vice President Business Banking, Tim Finn

Vice President, Cody Walker

Senior Vice President, Kevin Hagan

Vice President, Matthew Rink

Vice President Deposit Operations, Felicia Weeks

Vice President Quality Control, Cheryl Terry

Senior Vice President Relationship Manager Energy Banking, Tyler Thoem

Assistant Vice President Branch Manager, Kirstin Wicker

Senior Vice President Commercial Relationship Manager Assistant Rebecca Oberg, Kelly Gegerson

Vice President, Karen Hardy

Vice President Manager Commercial Cash Vault, Anna Taylor

Business Intelligence Analyst Assistant Vice President, Kevin Cagle

Senior Vice President Manager, Jill Merkt

Assistant Vice President Business Banking Relationship Manager, Deborah Sefcik

Vice President Construction Lending Manager, Lisa Bott

Vice President Commercial Lending, Jesse Erickson

Assistant Vice President Retail Support Specialist, Heather Wade

Assistant Vice President, Christie Bell

Asst. Vice President Branch Manager, Tamela Leger

Vice President Retail Support Lead Florida, Sherri Kinsey

Vp Treasury Management Operations Manager, Kevin Northcutt

Assistant Vice President, Erica Murphy

Vice President Private Banking, Casey Lawhead

Vice President Business Analyst Iii, Ron Zimmerman

Vice President Retail Support Lead, Terri Bridges

Executive Vice President And Commercial Group Manager, John Reingardt

Senior Vice President Compliance Manager Central Florida Cra Liaison, Susan DeFreese

Vice President, Kim Leech

Vice President Treasury Management Implementations Manager, Megan Alesci

Senior Vice President Commercial Banking Relationship Manager, Amanda Smith

Assistant Vice President Construction, Carmalynn May

Vice President Consumer Lending Manager, Todd Ezell

Vice President Commercial Relationship Manager, Tanner Livingston

Senior Vice President, Bob Burnside

Vice President Manager, Bill Roche

Vice President Senior Business Analyst Development Officer, Martin Chapman

Assistant Vice President Branch Manager, Heather Ross

Assistant Vice President Lending Services Supervisor, Heidi Tyra

Vice President Private Banking Relationship Manager, Jennifer Esler

Vice President Commercial Relationship Manager, Karen Shawdee

Vice President, Bob Ferguson

Vice President Relationship Manager, Amy Moore

Senior Vice President Commercial Manager Collin County, Shannon Bettis

Executive Vice President Dallas Region, Tony Kruse

Vice President Commercial Relationship Manager, Madalyn Allen

Senior Vice President Audit Manager, Emily Sebourn

Vice President Corporate Strategy, Oliver Greening

Assistant Vice President Branch Manager, Carolanne Parks

Vice President Director Boca And Delray Branches, Shane Sweet

Vice President Senior Underwriter, Daniel Scheuermann

Vice President Real Estate Appraisal Analyst, Matthew Reid

Vice President Senior Relationship Manager, Mitch Wilson

Vice President Private Mortgage Banker, Matthew Westervelt

Vice President Private Banking Relationship Manager, Peter Mihopoulos

Senior Vice President Corporate Banking, Brian Hanley

Vp Mortgage Branch Manager, Donna Frost

Vice President Marketing, Laura Sillars

Vice President, Sheila Cooley

Vice President, Don Lucas

Assistant Vice President Mortgage Loan Officer, Ginger Holton

Chairman, William H. Fenstermaker, age 70

LOCATIONS

HQ: IBERIABANK Corp
  200 West Congress Street, Lafayette, LA 70501
Phone: 337 521-4003
Web: www.iberiabank.com

COMPETITORS

BancorpSouth	Investar
Bank of America	JPMorgan Chase
Bank of the Ozarks	Louisiana Bancorp
Capital One	MidSouth Bancorp
Hancock Holding	Regions Financial
Home Banc	Teche Holding

HISTORICAL FINANCIALS

Company Type: Public

Income Statement

FYE: December 31

	ASSETS ($ mil.)	NET INCOME ($ mil.)	INCOME AS % OF ASSETS	EMPLOYEES
12/18	30,833	370	1.2%	3,441
12/17	27,904	142	0.5%	3,604
12/16	21,659	187	0.9%	3,155
12/15	19,504	143	0.7%	3,216
12/14	15,759	105	0.7%	2,825
Annual Growth	18.3%	36.9%	—	5.1%

2018 Year-End Financials

Debt ratio: 1.00%	No. of shares (mil.): 55
Return on equity: 10.00%	Dividends
Cash ($ mil.): 690	Yield: 2.0%
Current ratio: —	Payout: 37.0%
Long-term debt ($ mil.): —	Market value ($ mil.): 3,522

	STOCK PRICE ($) FY Close	P/E High/Low		PER SHARE ($) Earnings	Dividends	Book Value
12/18	64.00	13	9	6.00	2.00	74.00
12/17	78.00	33	27	3.00	1.00	69.00
12/16	84.00	21	10	4.00	1.00	66.00
12/15	55.00	19	15	4.00	1.00	61.00
12/14	65.00	22	18	3.00	1.00	55.00
Annual Growth	(0.2%)	—	—	18.3%	3.5%	7.5%

Icahn Enterprises LP

Icahn Enterprises has a can-do attitude when it comes to making money. The holding company has stakes in firms in a diverse array of industries including metals manufacturing energy real estate gaming and home fashion. Holdings include car parts maker Federal-Mogul; energy refinery and production company CVR; PSC Metals one of the largest scrap yard operators in the US; residential developer Bayswater which is active in Florida and Massachusetts; and WestPoint Home a maker of bed bath and other home products. Billionaire corporate raider Carl Icahn and his affiliates control his namesake firm. The US is the company's largest market accounting for about 70% of the revenue.

Operations

Icahn Enterprises holds and operates companies across several industries each of which is called out as a distinct segment in its financial statements.

Automotive Energy and Railcar segments comprise more than 85% of annual company revenue. The remaining industry segments each generate between 0.5% and 4% of revenue and are: Gaming/Casinos Metals Mining Food Packaging Real Estate and Home Fashion. Icahn Enterprises also runs an Investment segment which invests money in private investment funds for the benefit of Icahn and his affiliates.

The Automotive segment generates nearly 50% of revenue and operates mainly through its Federal-Mogul holding. It also owns IEH Auto and Pep Boys: Manny Moe and Jack. The Energy segment (more than 25% of revenue) operates through the CVR Energy Inc. subsidiary and is engaged in petroleum refining and nitrogen fertilizer manufacturing. The Railcar segment (about 10%) is run through the American Railcar Industries Inc. subsidiary which designs and manufactures hopper and tank railcars and then sells or leases them to customers.

Geographic Reach

The New York-headquartered company owns stakes in a number of companies operating worldwide. Federal-Mogul operates more than 250 facilities globally including manufacturing technical sales and administration and distribution centers. Icahn Enterprises' Energy segment holdings are mainly in Kansas and Oklahoma and its Railcar operations are in Missouri Arkansas and Texas.

Sales and Marketing

Icahn Enterprises' Federal-Mogul customers include automotive and heavy-duty vehicle manufacturers agricultural off-highway marine railroad aerospace high performance and industrial application manufacturers.

Its CVR subsidiary's petroleum customers include retailers railroads and farm cooperatives while its nitrogen fertilizer customers include retailers and distributors (for UAN products) and agricultural and industrial businesses (for ammonia products). It supplies jet fuel to the U.S. Department of Defense. One customer accounted for approximately 20% of CVR Refining's sales and more than 50% of CVR Refining's sales were made to its 10 largest customers.

Financial Performance

Icahn Enterprises has resumed generating rising revenue for the past two years after a sales drop in 2015 ended a six-year string of increases.

Revenue jumped 33% to $21.7 billion in 2017 from $16.3 billion in 2016 while the company turned in a $2.6 billion profit in 2017 after posting a $2.2 billion loss the year before. Automotive provided the bulk of Icahn's revenue (48%) in 2017 but the railcar unit delivered 48% of the profit due to the sale of the American Rail Leasing unit for $1.8 billion. All other segments posted higher revenue except for Home Fashion.

Cash at the 2017 year-end was $1.7 billion a decrease of $151 million compared to 2016. Cash used by operations was $1.4 billion. Cash provided by investing activities was $41 million and cash provided by financing activities was $743 million.

Strategy

Icahn Enterprises' strategy known as The Icahn Formula and named after its lead investment strategist Carl Icahn is to seek undervalued or bankrupt assets improve their operations enhance their valuation and sell them for a profit. The firm typically purchases substantial stakes in companies with an eye toward gaining control of them often by waging proxy battles for seats on their boards of directors. Icahn — famous for his activism — is known for his ability to force underperforming management teams to maximize value for shareholders.

In recent years Icahn Enterprises increased its holdings in the Automotive and Energy businesses

and repositioned its investment in its Railcar segment.

Icahn Enterprises' diversification across multiple industries and geographies acts as a natural hedge against cyclical and general economic swings. Through its investment segment the firm has held significant positions in various companies including Dell Inc. Herbalife Chesapeake Energy Hain Celestial Group Forest laboratories and Transocean.

Mergers and Acquisitions

In 2018 Icahn Enterprises continued a push into automotive by purchasing four independently-owned service centers in Metro Detroit: Belanger Tire & Auto Service in Westland Novi Motive Goodyear in Novi and Fix N Go Auto Centers in Troy and Oxford. The locations will convert to Pep Boys Service and Tire Centers.

In 2017 the company sold for $2.8 billion its American Railcar Leasing LLC to a subsidiary of Sumitomo Mitsui Banking Corporation. Icahn still owns its American Railcar Industries subsidiary.

In 2016 Icahn Enterprises purchased the Trump Taj Mahal Atlantic City casino fresh out of bankruptcy. Citing New Jersey political gamesmanship and workers' compensation demands as the cause Icahn shuttered the casino later that year and sold the property to Hard Rock Café; in early 2017.

Also in 2016 the firm acquired The Pep Boys for some $1.03 billion which provided "excellent synergistic opportunities for Auto Plus" its automotive aftermarket company.

In June 2015 subsidiary IEH Auto bought Uni-Select USA (the US auto parts assets of auto parts distributor Uni-Select Inc.) and Beck/Arnley Worldparts Inc. for a purchase price of $340 million. The firm acquired all 39 distribution centers and satellite locations and 240 corporate-owned jobber stores in the US. The business became part of Icahn Enterprises' automotive segment with Federal-Mogul.

EXECUTIVES

Cfo And Director, SungHwan Cho, age 44, $822,616 total compensation
Chief Accounting Officer, Peter Reck, age 52, $300,000 total compensation
President Ceo And Director, Keith Cozza, age 40, $1,557,736 total compensation
Senior Vice President Commercial Strategy Americas Federal Mogul Motoparts, Phil Halberg
Vice President South America Viskase, Newton Martins
Senior Vice President Global Sales And Corporate Strategy Powertrain Federal Mogul, Richard Llope
Senior Vice President And General Manager Rings And Liners Valve Seats And Guides Powertrain Federal Mogul, Michael Hedderich
Senior Vice President Finance Federal Mogul Powertrain, Shaun Merry
Senior Vice President And General Manager Global Valvetrain Powertrain Federal Mogul, Jean-Philippe Keller-Comte
Senior Vice President And Chief People Officer Icahn Automotive, Athony Tony Papa
Senior Vice President Information Technology Icahn Automotive, Gary Desai
Senior Vice President Global Braking Federal Mogul Motorparts, Neville Rudd
Senior Vice President Globla Oe Sales And Commercial Strategy Emea Federal Mogul Motorparts, Detlev Baudach
Senior Vice President And General Manager Sealing And Gaskets Federal Mogel Powertrain, Andrea Pappagallo
Senior Vice President And General Manager Bearings Federal Mogel Powertrain, Olaf Weidlich

Vice President Engineering And Technolgoy Asia
Pacific Federal Mogul, Weibo Weng
Senior Vice President And General Manager
Global Pistons Powertrain Federal Mogul,
Bernhard Motel
Evp Refining Operations Cvr Energy, Robert
Haugen
Senior Vice President Corporate Development
And Strategy Icahn Automotive, James Healy
Vice President Corporate Technology And
Cybersecurity, Dustin Goodwin
Vice President Treasury Management, Courtney
Mather
Chairman, Carl C. Icahn, age 83
Board Member, Jack Wasserman
Treasurer, John Saldarelli
Board Member, William Leidesdorf
Auditors: Grant Thornton LLP

LOCATIONS

HQ: Icahn Enterprises LP
767 Fifth Avenue, Suite 4700, New York, NY 10153
Phone: 212 702-4300
Web: www.ielp.com

2017 Sales

	% of total
United States	69
Germany	9
Other countries	22
Total	**100**

PRODUCTS/OPERATIONS

2017 Sales

	$ mil.	% of total
Automotive	10,528	48
Energy	5,918	27
Railcar	2,306	11
Gaming	960	4
Real Estate	590	2
Metal	408	2
Home Fashion	183	1
Mining	93	-
Holding company	68	-
Investment	297	1
Total	**21,744**	**100**

Selected Subsidiaries

Ace Nevada Corp.
American Entertainment Properties Corp.
American Railcar Industries
AREP Oil & Gas Holdings LLC
AREP Real Estate Holdings LLC
Atlantic Coast Entertainment Holdings Inc.
Bayswater Development LLC
Federal-Mogul Corporation
Icahn Capital LP
Icahn Capital Management LP
Icahn Enterprises Holdings L.P.
Icahn Offshore LP
Icahn Onshore LP
New Seabury Properties L.L.C.
PEP Boys: Manny Moe and jack
PSC Metals Inc.
Tropicana Entertainment Inc.
Trump Taj Mahal
Viskase Companies Inc.
WestPoint Home LLC

COMPETITORS

Apollo Global
 Management
Berkshire Hathaway
Blackstone Group
Clark Enterprises
D. E. Shaw
KKR

Leucadia National
MSD Capital
Soros Fund Management
The Trump Organization
Vulcan
Wesco Financial

HISTORICAL FINANCIALS
Company Type: Public

Income Statement
FYE: December 31

	REVENUE ($ mil.)	NET INCOME ($ mil.)	NET PROFIT MARGIN	EMPLOYEES
12/18	11,777	1,507	12.8%	29,034
12/17	21,744	2,430	11.2%	89,034
12/16	16,348	(1,128)	—	90,960
12/15	15,272	(1,194)	—	73,786
12/14	19,157	(373)	—	66,559
Annual Growth	**(11.5%)**	—	—	**(18.7%)**

2018 Year-End Financials

Debt ratio: 31.00%	No. of shares (mil.): 191
Return on equity: —	Dividends
Cash ($ mil.): 5,338	Yield: 12.0%
Current ratio: 5.00	Payout: 61.0%
Long-term debt ($ mil.): 7,326	Market value ($ mil.): 10,923

	STOCK PRICE ($) FY Close	P/E High/Low		PER SHARE ($) Earnings	Dividends	Book Value
12/18	57.00	7	4	11.00	7.00	34.00
12/17	53.00	4	3	15.00	6.00	29.00
12/16	60.00	—	—	(8.00)	6.00	15.00
12/15	61.00	—	—	(9.00)	6.00	30.00
12/14	92.00	—	—	(3.00)	6.00	44.00
Annual Growth	**(11.4%)**	—	—	—	**3.9%**	**(6.3%)**

IHC HEALTH SERVICES, INC.

EXECUTIVES

Pres-Ceo, William Nelson
Svp-Cfo, Bert Zimmerli
V Pres-Pres, Charles Sorenson
Chief Staff, Steven Vannorman
Surgery Director, Brent Hardy
Food Manager, Brent Lamoreaux
Manager Plant Operations, George McGee
Purchasing Agent, Don Cannon
Biomedical Engineer, Bryan White
Womens Health Director, Kenzie Peterson
Family Practitioner, Michael Cascio
Auditors: KPMG LLP SALT LAKE CITY UT

LOCATIONS

HQ: IHC HEALTH SERVICES, INC.
1380 E MEDICAL CENTER DR, ST GEORGE, UT
847902123
Phone: 435 251-2992
Web: WWW.SELECTHEALTH.ORG

HISTORICAL FINANCIALS
Company Type: Private

Income Statement
FYE: December 31

	REVENUE ($ mil.)	NET INCOME ($ mil.)	NET PROFIT MARGIN	EMPLOYEES
12/18	6,037	318	5.3%	4,000
12/17	5,483	885	16.1%	—
12/16	5,275	564	10.7%	—
12/14	394	56	14.2%	—
Annual Growth	**97.8%**	**54.3%**	—	—

iHeartMedia Inc

iHeartMedia is one of the world's leading radio companies. The firm owns and operates some 850 radio stations in about 160 markets. With more than 245 million listeners a month it generates revenue by selling ads and subscriptions. The company also owns subsidiaries Premiere Networks (syndication) Katz Media Group (ad sales) and Total Traffic & Weather Network (real time reports for commuters). The company filed for Ch. 11 bankruptcy protection in March 2018 and emerged a newly reorganized company in May 2019. It returned to public markets in July 2019 after spinning off billboard subsidiary Clear Channel Outdoor. Before the restructuring about two-thirds of sales came from the US.

Change in Company Type
iHeartMedia emerged from a bankruptcy restructuring in May 2019. After a brief period of control by a group of hedge and mutual fund companies it went public in July 2019. It plans to use any cash raised by the IPO to reduce debt and fuel growth.

Bankruptcy
Saddled with some $16 billion in debt iHeartMedia and certain subsidiaries (including iHeart-Communications) filed for Chapter 11 in early 2018 and emerged from bankruptcy in May 2019. As part of the reorganization it spun off Clear Channel Outdoor Holdings which became its own independent publicly traded company. The balance-sheet restructuring allowed the firm to shed almost $10.4 billion in debt leaving about $5.75 billion debt on its books.

Operations
iHeartMedia provides radio content via broadcast and digital delivery and has a national syndication business that features personalities such as Rush Limbaugh Ryan Seacrest Steve Harvey and Glenn Beck. Formats include news talk sports and music (such as top 40 soft rock classic rock hip hop and R&B among others). It also produces live music events such as the iHeartRadio Music Festival.

The company reports 128 million registered users of its iHeartRadio service and app which is available on a range of platforms and devices including digital auto dashboards tablets wearables smartphones virtual assistants TVs and gaming consoles. It also produces podcasts that reach audiences through some 148 million monthly downloads and streams.

Geographic Reach
Headquartered in San Antonio Texas the company serves about 150 markets including the top 25 US markets. It has six stations in New York City eight in Los Angeles and six each in Chicago San Francisco and Dallas/Ft. Worth.

Prior to the spinoff of Clear Channel the company generated about two-thirds of its revenue from the Americas.

Sales and Marketing
The company's advertising expenses were $213.8 million $201.5 million and $132.7 million for 2018 2017 and 2016 respectively.

Financial Performance
Even with billions in revenue iHeartMedia has suffered net losses in recent fiscal periods caused by the company's high cost of doing business. The firm had been troubled by $20 billion in debt since a 2008 leveraged buyout. The radio business struggled with flat advertising revenues over the last decade amid competition from Google and Facebook for ad dollars. iHeartMedia's Chapter 11 restructuring resulted in a disruption to of its radio business which the company says had an adverse

impact on its 2018 financial results. Analysts say its emergence from bankruptcy gives the company a chance to use its cash flow to reinvest in the business rather than make massive interest payments. The balance-sheet restructuring allowed the firm to shed almost $10.4 billion in debt leaving about $5.75 billion debt on its books.

Strategy

iHeartMedia's growth strategy includes investing in digital platforms such as podcasting and streaming. It is developing the next generation of iHeartRadio an integrated digital radio platform that listeners can stream across a variety of devices. As smart speakers are creating an in-home audio hub that enhances radio's reach establishing a foothold in this category is key element of the company's growth strategy. iHeartMedia expects to expand its reach deeper into mobile social live events and on-demand entertainment.

Company Background

The company can trace its roots to 1972 when Texas businessman J. "Red" McCombs and his then business partner L. Lowry Mays bought an FM radio station in San Antonio to form the backbone of what eventually became Clear Channel Communications. More recently private equity funds sponsored by Bain Capital and Thomas H. Lee Partners acquired the business in a 2008 leveraged buyout. Clear Channel became iHeartRadio in 2014.

EXECUTIVES

Senior Vice President Urban Operations, Earl Jones

President Coo And Cfo, Richard J. Bressler, age 61, $1,200,000 total compensation

President Entertainment Enterprises, John Sykes, age 58

Chairman And Ceo, Robert W. (Bob) Pittman, age 65, $1,200,000 total compensation

Ceo Clear Channel International, C. William Eccleshare, age 63, $927,601 total compensation

Ceo Clear Channel Outdoor America, Scott R. Wells, age 50, $750,000 total compensation

Evp And Chief Communications Officer, Wendy Goldberg, age 55

Evp And General Counsel, Robert H. Walls, age 58, $750,000 total compensation

Evp And Chief Marketing Officer, Gayle Troberman

Global Cio, Steve Mills

Senior Vice President Real Estates, Chad Dan

Vice President Of Information Technology, Jeff Cage

Vice President Of Sales Atlanta Division, Jonathan Graviss

Vice President Sales, Adam Pullman

Vice President Human Resources Ccme, Scott Logeman

Vice President, Alyson Richards

Vice President, Elizabeth Bethea

Vice President Procurement, Dave Rokosky

Senior Vice President Sales, Craig Hahn

Vice President And Information Technology Sales, Trisha Dall

National Sales Manager, Nicolette Kelly

Senior Vice President And Chie, Michael Walsh

Vice President Business Operations, Barbara Caraballo

Vice President Corporate Reporting, Susan Krieg

Vice President Product Management, R O Catalfo

Vice President And Market Manager, Jackie Rinker

Executive Vice President Communications, Angel Aristone

Vice President Marketing Solutions, Tara Adamos

Vp Government And Public Affiars Clear Channel Outdoor, Mitchell Schwartz

Vice President Of Marketing, Eileen Woodbury

Vice President Of Sales Denver Market, Tim Hager

Vice President Assistant Treasurer, Jason Menzel

Vice President Of Marketing, Justin Tanis

Vice President Las Vegas Operations And Partnerships, Edward Sheftel

Senior Vice President Corporate Relations, Kathryn Johnson

Senior Vice President And Chief Accounting Officer, Herbert Hill

Vice President Level, Vice president sales Diane Veres

Vice President, Susan Holshouser

Executive Vice President Automotive Business Development And Partnerships, John Karpinski

Senior Vice President Chief Accounting Officer, Scott Hamilton

Vice President Sales Digital And Alternative, Dean Peterson

Vice President Sales, Caroline Earley

Vice President, Amy Roach

National Sales Manager, Guy Goldschmidt

Vice President Sales, Joe Madden

Vice President And Associate General Counsel, Lauren Wood

Vice President Test Engineering, Aj Almanzor

Vice President And Sales, Damon Gunkel

Senior Vice President Of Sales Northeast Region, Robert Schachter

Senior Vice President Director Of Sales, Bill Barker

Vice President Director Of Sales, Michael Newman

Vice President Director Of Sales, Michelle Olivera

Vice President And Regional Market Manager, Kristen Delaney

Vice President And Market Mana, George Allen

Vice President, Britt Levine

Vice President General Manager, Tom Davis

Vice President Sales, Lisa Neugarten

Vice President Director Of Sales, Dan Smith

Vice President, Bill Mcmartin

Senior Vice President Of Programming, Tony Banks

Vice President, Monica Young

Senior Vice President Of Programming, Michael Mccoy

Vice President National Sales, Lee Smith

Vice President Of Business Development, Greg Yelverton

Vice President And Director Of Sales, Paul Masse

Senior Vice President Of Sales, Scott Hogle

Vice President Of Sales, Jeff Luckoff

Vice President Director Of Sales, Brian Callahan

Vice President Sales Q104.3 Wor Mets Radio Network, Brian Rooney

Vice President Sales, Janey Nackley

National Sales Manager, Josh Brooks

Vice President Sales, Kevin O'Malley

Vice President Of Sales, Jason Mosher

Vice President Of Sales, Todd Freundlich

Vice President Of Sales, Colleen Grant

Vice President Of Sales, Melody Caldwell

Vice President Of Sales, Amy Boeka

Vice President And Director Of Sales, David Scott

Vice President Of Sales, Joel Kelly

Vice President Sales Kfi Klac Keib Radio Los Angeles, Bill Denton

Senior Vice President And General Manager Iheartradio, Owen Grover

Senior Vice President Of Sales, Marlon George

Senior Vice President Business Affairs, Keith Kauffman

Vice President Finance, Steve Trubiano

Senior Vice President Corporate Finance, Chris Skillin

Executive Vice President Programming Operations, Jon Zellner

Vice President Connections, John Lilliquist

Vice President Network Sales, Kelly Gittleman

Vice President Talent Management, Joyce Keilen

Executive Vice President Sales Total Traffic And Weather Network, Gary Larkin

Vice President Marketing And Content, Andy Kelly

Vice President Director Of Sales National Sales, Brigid Walje

Senior Vice President Of Sales, Ann Postell

Vice President Media, Tammy Dunn

Senior Vice President Of Sales, Claudia Bays

Senior Vice President Sales, Sabrena Martin

National Sales Manager, Jeff Howard

Senior Vice President Of Sales, Vicki Ward

Vice President Sales, Darren McMillan

Senior Vice President Of Sales, Tim Etes

Vice President Of Sales Business Development, Micah Goldberg

Vice President General Manager Iheartmedia Hawaii, Charles Cotton

Vice President Strategic Partnerships, Heather Baumli

Senior Vice President Engineering, Dan Mettler

Regional Vice President Market Manager, Andrew Lohman

Vice President Connections, Joe Shields

Vice President Of Digital Markets, Jonathan Faulkner

Vice President Connections, Victoria Pollard

Vice President Media Planning, Kevin Ryan

Senior Vice President Marketing Solutions, Amy Newman

Vice President Of Sales, Shari Gonzalez

Vice President West Coast Digital Sales, Melanie Gensler

Vice President Director Of Sales Connections, Erin Collier

Vice President Of Real Estate, Cody Rutschman

Vice President, Kyle Kupchak

Vice President Revenue Strategy And Analytics, James Liao

Vice President Integrated Media Sales, Darryl Miner

Executive Vice President And Gm, Brad Hardin

Executive Vice President Us Hispanic Strategy And Sales Iheartmedia, Liz Saracheck

Senior Vice President Of Sales, Judy Copier

Vice President Of Online Content And Design, Alexus Dominguez

Executive Vice President Of Operations, Tom Mcconnell

Svp Product Innovation Iheartradio Networks, Steven Radley

Senior Vice President Accounting, Jason Dilger

Vice President Of Automotive, Larry Barditch

Vice President Connections, Stephanie Stein

Vice President Business Development And Partnerships, Peter Volynsky

Vice President Of Sales Las Vegas West Division, Stacey Eisenberg

Senior Vice President I Programmatic, Ross Geier

Senior Vice President National Research, David Shiffman

Vice President, Rachel Herskovitz

Vice President Client Solutions, Lisa Kruglov

National Account Manager, Michelle Brown

Senior Vice President Programming, Gator Harrison

National Sales Manager, Sharon Moses

Vice President Connections, Cyrus Hekmaty

Executive Vice President Tech, Lasse Hamre

Vice President Corporate Accounting, Steve Brunner

Vice President Revenue Strategy Analytics, Peter Keefe

Vice President Automotive Business Development And Partnerships, Julie Beaty

Executive Vice President, Jim Donovan

Vice President Connections East, Ethan Turner

Vice President Of Financial Planning And Analysis, Brennan Gerster

Vice President Automotive Nashville Region, Kelley Mcgrath

Regional Vice President Programming, Greg Swedberg

Svp Programming, John Ivey

Vice President Landlease Div, Mary Groves
Senior Vice President Engineering, Michael Guidotti
Senior Vice President Programming, Mike Killabrew
National Account Manager, Joan Selfa
Senior Vice President Programming, Mark Murphy
Auditors: Ernst & Young LLP

LOCATIONS

HQ: iHeartMedia Inc
20880 Stone Oak Parkway, San Antonio, TX 78258
Phone: 210 822-2828
Web: www.iheartmedia.com

PRODUCTS/OPERATIONS

2016 Sales

	$ mil.	% of total
iHM	3,403	54
Americas Outdoor Advertising	1,278	20
Internationl Outdoor Advertising	1,424	23
Other	172	3
Eliminations	(3.4)	-
Total	**6,274**	**100**

Sales - 2016

Source of revenue	% of total
Billboards:	
Bulletins	59
Posters	10
Street furniture displays	7
Transit displays	16
Spectaculars/walls capes	4
Other	4
Total	**100**

COMPETITORS

CBS Corp
Cumulus Media
JCDecaux
Lamar Advertising
Live Nation Entertainment
Radio One Inc.

HISTORICAL FINANCIALS

Company Type: Public

Income Statement				FYE: December 31
	REVENUE ($ mil.)	NET INCOME ($ mil.)	NET PROFIT MARGIN	EMPLOYEES
12/18	6,326	(202)	—	18,300
12/17	6,171	(394)	—	17,900
12/16	6,274	(296)	—	18,700
12/15	6,242	(755)	—	18,700
12/14	6,319	(794)	—	19,200
Annual Growth	**0.0%**	**—**	**—**	**(1.2%)**

2018 Year-End Financials

Debt ratio: 43.00%
Return on equity: ***,***.**%
Cash ($ mil.): 406
Current ratio: 2.00
Long-term debt ($ mil.): 5,277

No. of shares (mil.): 91
Dividends
  Yield: —
  Payout: —
Market value ($ mil.): —

Illinois Tool Works, Inc.

Illinois Tool Works (ITW) hammers out more than just basic tools. With operations in about 55 countries ITW manufactures and services equipment for the automotive construction electronics food beverage power system decorative surfaces and medical components industries. The largest of its segments is Automotive OEM which provides metal and plastic fasteners components and chassis used in light vehicles automobiles and industrial applications. Other major segments include Food Equipment (cooking equipment such as ovens ranges and broilers) and Test & Measurement and Electronics (equipment and software for testing and measuring materials structures gases and fluids). Customers in the US supply about 45% of ITW's revenue.

Operations

ITW operates through seven segments each providing ample revenue. The segments are Test & Measurement and Electronics about 15% of revenue; Automotive OEM about 25% of revenue; Polymers & Fluids about 10% of revenue; Food Equipment 15% of revenue; Construction Products about 10%; Welding 10%; and Specialty Products close to 15%.

Subsidiaries include Instron Vulcan-Hart CFC International Quipp FB Johnston Graphics Miller Electric Manufacturing Hobart Corp. Wynn's Avery Weigh-Tronix RainX Vitronics Soltec and Zip Pack.

Innovation is a big selling point for ITW's products. The company holds about 11600 US and foreign patents as well as 6100 patents pending. R&D is executed cooperatively with customers seeking specific applications.

Geographic Reach

ITW operates more than 300 plants and offices in about 55 countries notably China France Germany and the UK. The US represents ITW's largest market generating 45% of net sales. Other major markets include EMEA about 30% of revenue and Asia/Pacific about 15% of revenue.

Sales and Marketing

ITW distributes its products directly to industrial manufacturers and through independent distributors. It serves customers in a range of industries including automotive manufacturers automotive aftermarket general industrial commercial food equipment and construction.

Financial Performance

ITW has posted two years of revenue gains after several years of uneven sales. Even with the gains the company has not returnd to its six-year sales high of about $14.8 billion in 2012.

In 2017 the Automotive OEM segment led the company to a 5% sales increase to $14.3 billion from $13.6 billion in 2016. The Automotive segment's sales rose 14% on organic growth in China and Europe and help from the EF&C acquisition made in 2016. The other segments reported higher sales ranging from less than 1% to about 5%. Overall organic growth was 3% in 2017.

Net income slipped to $1.7 billion in 2017 from $2 billion in 2016. ITW had an additional expense of about $658 million in 2017 from 2016 related to the US Tax Cuts and Jobs Act of 2017.

ITW's coffers held $3.1 billion in cash in 2017 compared to $2.47 billion in 2016. Operations generated cash totaling $2.4 billion in 2017 while investing and financing activities used $251 million and $1.6 billion respectively.

Strategy

ITW focuses on a five-year enterprise strategy with key initiatives that include portfolio management business structure simplification and strategic sourcing. This entails making internal investments that support organic growth to sustain its core businesses. The strategy is driven by the company's 80-20 rule that calls for focusing resources on the 80% of its biggest and most rewarding opportunities and reducing expenses for less profitable opportunities which comprise the other 20%.

ITW's portfolio management initiative includes divesting businesses that are no longer aligned with the company's long-term objectives. This strategy which reduced the company's global workforce from 59000 to 50000 over nine years which has cuts expenses and increased operating income despite slowly shrinking revenue totals.

As the US and China have engaged in trade disputes ITW maintains it has been largely unaffected with about 10%-15% of its cost inflation in 2018 was related to tariffs. The company makes most of its products in the markets in which they are used and it sources just 2% of it goods in China.

Mergers and Acquisitions

ITW has focused on organic growth and has been quiet on the acquisition side since it bought Engineered Fasteners and Components (EF&C) business from ZF TRW for approximately $450 million in 2016. EF&C is a global supplier of engineered fastening systems and interior technical components to the automotive OEM market operating about a dozen manufacturing facilities globally. The deal bolstered the ITW's Automotive OEM segment.

Company Background

In the early years of the 20th century Byron Smith founder of Chicago's Northern Trust Company recognized that rapid industrialization was outgrowing the capacity of small shops to supply machine tools. Smith encouraged two of his four sons to launch Illinois Tool Works (ITW) in 1912. Harold C. Smith became president of ITW in 1915 and expanded its product line into automotive parts.

ITW developed the Shakeproof fastener the first twisted-tooth lock washer in 1923. When Harold C. died in 1936 his son Harold B. took up the torch and he decentralized the company and exhorted salesmen to learn customers' businesses so they could develop products before customers recognized they needed them. Smith plowed profits back into research as WWII spurred demand.

EXECUTIVES

Evp Test And Measurement And Electronics, Steven L. (Steve) Martindale, age 62
Chairman And Ceo, E. Scott Santi, age 57, $1,205,313 total compensation
Evp Specialty Products, Roland M. Martel, age 65, $534,434 total compensation
Evp Polymers And Fluids, Juan Valls, age 58
Svp And Cfo, Michael M. Larsen, age 50, $702,152 total compensation
Evp Automotive Oem, Sundaram (Naga) Nagarajan, age 56, $520,456 total compensation
Evp Welding, John R. Hartnett, age 59
Vp And Cio, Mike Parisi
Evp Construction Products, Michael R. Zimmerman, age 58
Evp Food Equipment, Lei Zhang Schlitz, age 52
Executive Vice President, Jane Warner
Vice President Strategic Marketing, Hannelore Rittinger
National Account Manager, Bob Beal
Vice President And General Manager, Cary Moreth
Vice Chairman, Christopher (Chris) O'Herlihy, age 55
Auditors: Deloitte & Touche LLP

LOCATIONS

HQ: Illinois Tool Works, Inc.
155 Harlem Avenue, Glenview, IL 60025
Phone: 847 724-7500
Web: www.itw.com

2017 Sales

	$ mil.	% of total
North America		
United States	6,243	43
Canada/Mexico	996	7
Europe Middle East and Africa	4,102	29
Asia Pacific	2,577	18
South America	396	3
Total	**14,314**	**100**

PRODUCTS/OPERATIONS

2017 Sales

	$ mil.	% of total
Automotive OEM	3,271	23
Food Equipment	2,123	15
Test & Measurement and Electronics	2,069	14
Specialty Products	1,938	14
Polymers & Fluids	1,724	12
Construction Products	1,672	12
Welding	1,538	10
Intersegment revenue	(21)	-
Total	**14,314**	**100**

Selected Products

Construction products
  Anchors for concrete applications
  Anchors for retail
  Fasteners concrete applications
  Fasteners for retail
  Fasteners for wood and metal applications
  Metal plate truss components
  Packaged hardware for retail
Decorative surfaces
  Decorative high-pressure laminate for furniture office
  and retail space and countertops
  High-pressure laminate worktops
Food equipment
  Cooking equipment
  Ovens
  Ranges
  Broilers
  Food processing equipment
  Slicers
  Mixers
  Scales
  Kitchen exhaust systems
  Pollution-control systems
  Refrigeration equipment
  Refrigerators
  Freezers
  Prep tables
  Ventilation Systems
  Warewashing equipment
Industrial packaging
  Metal jacketing
  Paper products that protect goods in transit
  Plastic products that protect goods in transit
  Plastic strapping
  Plastic stretch film
  Steel strapping
Polymers and fluids
  Adhesives
  Industrial
  Construction
  Consumer
  Chemical fluids that clean or add lubrication to
  machines
  Epoxy and resin-based coating products for industrial
  applications
  Hand wipes and cleaners for industrial applications
  Pressure-sensitive adhesives and components
  Telecommunications
  Electronics
  Medical
  Transportation
  Resin-based coating products for industrial
  applications
Power systems and electronics
  Airport ground support equipment
  Arc welding equipment
  Component packaging
  Electronic components
  Equipment for microelectronics assembly
  Metal arc welding consumables
  Metal solder materials for PC board fabrication
Transportation
  Fillers for auto body repair
  Fluids for auto aftermarket maintenance and
  appearance
  Metal components for automobiles and light trucks
  Patch products for the marine industry
  Plastic components for automobiles and light trucks
  Polyester coatings for the marine industry
  Polymers for auto aftermarket maintenance and
  appearance
  Putties for auto body repair
Other
  Equipment and related software for testing and
  measuring of materials and structures

Film used to decorate consumer products
Foil used to decorate consumer products
Plastic reclosable packaging for consumer food storage
Plastic consumables that multi-pack cans and bottles
and related equipment
Plastic for appliances and industrial applications
Metal fasteners for appliances and industrial
applications

COMPETITORS

3M	Marmon Group
BASF SE	NCH
Cummins	Nordson
ESAB	Park-Ohio Holdings
Emerson Electric	PennEngineering
Federal Screw Works	Snap-on
GE	Stanley Black and
Graco	Decker
IBIDEN	Textron
Koch Enterprises	TriMas
Lincoln Electric	Victor Technologies
Manitowoc	W. R. Grace

HISTORICAL FINANCIALS

Company Type: Public

Income Statement

FYE: December 31

	REVENUE ($ mil.)	NET INCOME ($ mil.)	NET PROFIT MARGIN	EMPLOYEES
12/18	14,768	2,563	17.4%	48,000
12/17	14,314	1,687	11.8%	50,000
12/16	13,599	2,035	15.0%	50,000
12/15	13,405	1,899	14.2%	48,000
12/14	14,484	2,946	20.3%	49,000
Annual Growth	0.5%	(3.4%)	—	(0.5%)

2018 Year-End Financials

Debt ratio: 50.00%
Return on equity: 65.00%
Cash ($ mil.): 1,504
Current ratio: 2.00
Long-term debt ($ mil.): 6,029

No. of shares (mil.): 328
Dividends
  Yield: 3.0%
  Payout: 47.0%
Market value ($ mil.): 41,567

	STOCK PRICE ($) FY Close	P/E High/Low	PER SHARE ($) Earnings	Dividends	Book Value
12/18	127.00	23 16	8.00	4.00	10.00
12/17	167.00	35 25	5.00	3.00	13.00
12/16	122.00	22 14	6.00	2.00	12.00
12/15	93.00	19 16	5.00	2.00	14.00
12/14	95.00	13 10	7.00	2.00	18.00
Annual Growth	7.5%	— —	1.1%	18.4%	(13.6%)

Independent Bank Corp (MA)

Independent Bank wants to rock the northeast. Its banking subsidiary Rockland Trust operates almost 75 retail branches as well as investment and lending offices in Eastern Massachusetts and Rhode Island. Serving area individuals and small to midsized businesses the bank offers standard services such as checking and savings accounts CDs and credit cards in addition to insurance products financial planning trust services. Commercial loans including industrial construction and small business loans make up more than 70% of Rockland Trust's loan portfolio. Incorporated in 1985 the bank boasts total assets of some $7.5 billion.

Operations

About 28% of Independent Bank's loan portfolio is made up of consumer real estate loans which include residential mortgages and home equity loans and lines; while personal loans and auto loans make up around 1% of the portfolio. Through an agreement with LPL Investment Holdings Rockland Trust offers investment products such as securities and insurance.

Independent Bank generated 70% of its total revenue from interest and fee income on loans in 2014 and another 6% from interest and dividends on investment securities. Investment management fees made up 6% of total revenue for the year while deposit account fees and interchange and ATM fees combined made up 11%.

Geographic Reach

Rockland Trust boasts nearly 75 retail branches and three limited-services branches located in Eastern Massachusetts in the counties of Barnstable Bristol Middlesex Norfolk Plymouth and Worcester.

Sales and Marketing

The company's borrowers include consumers and small-to-medium sized businesses with credit needs up to $250000 and revenues of less than $2.5 million. Independent Bank spent $3.86 million on advertising in 2014 compared to $4.28 million and $3.95 million in 2013 and 2012 respectively.

Financial Performance

Independent Bank Corp's revenues and profits have trended higher in recent years thanks to continued loan business growth from both acquisitions and through organic expansion higher deposit account and ATM fee income from customer base growth and thanks to a decline in loan loss provisions as the credit quality of its loan portfolio has improved with the strengthened economy.

The bank's revenue rose by 5% to $286.40 million in 2014 mostly thanks to higher interest income as its loan business growth continued to outpace the margin-eating impacts of low interest rates. Independent's non-interest income also rose by 3% thanks to a combination of higher interchange and ATM fees and investment management fees.

Higher revenue and lower interest expenses on deposits in 2014 drove Independent Bank Corp's net income up by 19% to $59.85 million. Despite higher earnings the company's operating cash dove sharply primarily because of working capital changes related to its loans held for sale and changes in other assets.

Strategy

Independent Bank planned in 2015 to grow its loans organically between 4-6% for the year while growing its deposits between 3% and 4%. The company has also been expanding its fee-based revenue business especially in its investment management segment with expectations of growing the business by another 3% to 4% in 2015.

In addition to organic growth in other financial services areas Independent Bank has expanded via acquisitions.

Mergers and Acquisitions

In 2019 Independent Bank acquired Hyde Park Massachusetts-based Blue Hills Bancorp—the holding company for The Blue Hills Bank—for about $170 million. The acquisition furthers Independent's strategy of acquiring banks in overlapping and adjacent markets.

Company Background

In past years Independent Bank launched institutional asset managers Bright Rock Capital Management (2010) and Compass Exchange Advisors (2006) and formed a handful of mutual funds.

EXECUTIVES

Executive Vice President Director Of Retail Delivery Business Banking & Home Equity Lending, Jane L. Lundquist, age 62, $262,981 total compensation

President Ceo And Director Independent Bank Corp. And Rockland Trust, Christopher (Chris) Oddleifson, age 60, $589,616 total compensation

Cfo, Robert D. Cozzone

Executive Vice President Commercial Banking, Gerard F. Nadeau, age 61, $322,308 total compensation

Chief Information Officer, Barry Jensen

Chairman, Donna L. Abelli

Auditors: Ernst & Young LLP

LOCATIONS

HQ: Independent Bank Corp (MA)
2036 Washington Street, Hanover, MA 02339
Phone: 781 878-6100
Web: www.RocklandTrust.com

PRODUCTS/OPERATIONS

2012 Sales

	$ mil.	% of total
Interest		
Loans	178	69
Taxable securities including dividends	17	6
Other	1	-
Noninterest		
Service charges on deposit accounts	16	6
Wealth management	15	6
Interchange & ATM fees	10	4
Other	22	9
Adjustments	(0.1)	-
Total	**258**	**100**

COMPETITORS

Bank of America
Citizens Financial Group
Eastern Bank

Hingham Institution for Savings
Sovereign Bank
TD Bank USA

HISTORICAL FINANCIALS

Company Type: Public

Income Statement				FYE: December 31
	ASSETS ($ mil.)	NET INCOME ($ mil.)	INCOME AS % OF ASSETS	EMPLOYEES
12/18	8,852	122	1.4%	1,188
12/17	8,082	87	1.1%	1,108
12/16	7,709	77	1.0%	1,103
12/15	7,210	65	0.9%	1,051
12/14	6,365	60	0.9%	980
Annual Growth	8.6%	19.4%	—	4.9%

2018 Year-End Financials

Debt ratio: 1.00%
Return on equity: 12.00%
Cash ($ mil.): 250
Current ratio: —
Long-term debt ($ mil.): —

No. of shares (mil.): 28
Dividends
  Yield: 2.0%
  Payout: 35.0%
Market value ($ mil.): 1,974

	STOCK PRICE ($) FY Close	P/E High/Low		PER SHARE ($) Earnings	Dividends	Book Value
12/18	70.00	21	15	4.00	2.00	38.00
12/17	70.00	24	19	3.00	1.00	34.00
12/16	70.00	24	14	3.00	1.00	32.00
12/15	47.00	21	15	3.00	1.00	29.00
12/14	43.00	17	14	2.00	1.00	27.00
Annual Growth	13.2%	—	—	15.3%	12.2%	9.4%

Independent Bank Corporation (Ionia, MI)

Independent Bank Corporation is the holding company for Independent Bank which serves rural and suburban communities of Michigan's Lower Peninsula from more than 100 branches. The bank offers traditional deposit products including checking and savings accounts and CDs. Loans to businesses account for about 40% of the bank's portfolio; real estate mortgages are more than a third. Independent Bank also offers additional products and services like title insurance through subsidiary Independent Title Services and investments through agreement with third-party provider PrimeVest.

Operations

The company also owns Mepco Finance which acquires and services payment plans for extended automobile warranties.

Financial Performance

The company's revenue has been trending down year-over-year. However its net income and cash on hand have both been spiking up across recent fiscal years.

Strategy

As Michigan's economy has exhibited signs of stabilizing and the company's results have relatively improved as well. Independent Bank has reduced its number of high-risk loans non-performing loans and delinquency rates.

EXECUTIVES

Vice President, Patrick Dunn

Assistant Vice President Senior Business Analyst, Phil Hamlin

Vice President Team Leader Commercial Loans, Stephen Hale

Vice President Sales Manager, Sue Fulk

Assistant Vice President Bank Manager, Chelsee Warman

Senior Vice President, Hank B Risley

Executive Vice President And General Cou, Mark Collins

Auditors: Crowe LLP

LOCATIONS

HQ: Independent Bank Corporation (Ionia, MI)
4200 East Beltline, Grand Rapids, MI 49525
Phone: 616 527-5820
Web: www.independentbank.com

COMPETITORS

Bank of America
Chemical Financial
Fifth Third
Firstbank

Flagstar Bancorp
Huntington Bancshares
JPMorgan Chase
Mercantile Bank

HISTORICAL FINANCIALS

Company Type: Public

Income Statement				FYE: December 31
	ASSETS ($ mil.)	NET INCOME ($ mil.)	INCOME AS % OF ASSETS	EMPLOYEES
12/18	3,353	40	1.2%	976
12/17	2,789	20	0.7%	911
12/16	2,549	23	0.9%	885
12/15	2,409	20	0.8%	831
12/14	2,249	18	0.8%	876
Annual Growth	10.5%	21.9%	—	2.7%

2018 Year-End Financials

Debt ratio: 1.00%
Return on equity: 13.00%
Cash ($ mil.): 71
Current ratio: —
Long-term debt ($ mil.): —

No. of shares (mil.): 24
Dividends
  Yield: 3.0%
  Payout: 44.0%
Market value ($ mil.): 496

	STOCK PRICE ($) FY Close	P/E High/Low		PER SHARE ($) Earnings	Dividends	Book Value
12/18	21.00	16	12	2.00	1.00	14.00
12/17	22.00	24	20	1.00	0.00	12.00
12/16	22.00	21	13	1.00	0.00	12.00
12/15	15.00	18	14	1.00	0.00	11.00
12/14	13.00	18	15	1.00	0.00	11.00
Annual Growth	12.7%	—	—	21.5%	35.1%	7.2%

Independent Bank Group Inc.

It makes sense that a company that calls itself Independent Bank Group (IBG) would do business in a state that was once its own country. The bank holding company does business through subsidiary Independent Bank which operates about 40 banking offices and 70 branches in North and Central Texas Houston and Colorado. The banks offer standard personal and business accounts and services including some focused on small business owners. IBG has total assets of nearly $8.9 billion and loans of about $6.4 billion. The company traces its roots back 100 years but took its current shape in 2002.

Operations

In addition to its banking activities Independent Bank Group (IBG)also owns IBG Adriatica a mixed use development in the Dallas-Fort Worth area. The company does not intend to move into real estate but purchased the development where one of its branches is located to help maintain business in the area. It had also made commercial loans to several tenants of the development and saw the purchase as a way to protect its investments rather than have the entire property go into foreclosure.

Financial Performance

Independent Bank Group has shown increasing net income for several years and in fiscal 2016 grew revenue a further 20% to $210.0 million. Net income has likewise been consistently growing reaching $53.5 million up 39%. Cash from operations increased 85% to $80.3 million.

Strategy

Independent Bank Group's strategy is all about growth. It seeks organic growth in loans and deposits in existing locations by developing customer relationships while maintaining the quality of its loan portfolio. It also makes acquisitions: since 2010 it has made nine acquisitions most recently of Carlile Bancshares and its subsidiary Northstar Bank and Grand Bank in Dallas.

Mergers and Acquisitions

Independent Bank Group acquired Carlile Bancshares and its subsidiary Northstar Bank for around $434 million in 2017.

EXECUTIVES

Chairman President And Ceo, David R. Brooks, age 61, $650,000 total compensation

Evp And Coo, James C. (Jim) White, age 54

Vice Chairman And Chief Lending Officer And President Independent Bank Central Texas, Brian E. Hobart, age 54, $350,000 total compensation

Executive Vice President And Chief Financial Officer, Michelle S. Hickox, age 52, $265,000 total compensation

Evp And Secretary And Evp And Senior Operations Officer Independent Bank, Jan C. Webb, age 61

Senior Vice President, Amy Feagin

Assistant Vice President, Mallory Smith

Vice President Commercial Lending, Richard Berman

Vice President Market Manager, Tisha Reyes

Senior Vice President Director Of Financial Reporting, Leslie Beseda

Vice President Commercial Lending, Ozzie Martinez

Svp Hr Director Texas, Pam Murray

Vice President, Montgomery Brenda

Senior Vice President Director Of Human Resources, Murray Pam

Senior Vice President, Julie Crump

Senior Vice President, Noorani Feroz

Senior Vice President Commercial Relationship Manager, Charlie Cartwright

Vp. Treasury Management Operations Manager, Brian Oathout

Svp Commercial Lending, Tom Doonan

Assistant Vice President Senior Financial Analyst, Lesli Gilbert

Vice President, Lynda Dean

Vice President, Paul Langdale

Vice President Commercial Lending, Robin Thomas

Vice Chairman And Chief Risk Officer, Daniel W. Brooks, age 59

Auditors: RSM US LLP

LOCATIONS

HQ: Independent Bank Group Inc.
7777 Henneman Way, McKinney, TX 75070-1711
Phone: 972 562-9004
Web: www.ibtx.com

PRODUCTS/OPERATIONS

2012 Loan Portfolio

	% of total
Real estate	
Commercial	47
Residential	23
Construction land & land development	7
Single-family interim construction	5
Commercial	12
Agricultural	3
Consumer	3
Total	**100**

Selected Acquisition

Town Center Bank (2010 North Texas)
Farmersville Bancshares Inc. (2010 North Texas)
I Bank Holding Company Inc. (2012 Austin/Central Texas)
The Community Group Inc. (2012 Dallas/North Texas)

COMPETITORS

BBVA Compass Bancshares
Bank of America
Broadway Bancshares
Capital One
Citigroup
Comerica
Cullen/Frost Bankers
Extraco
First Financial Bankshares

HSBC International Bancshares
JPMorgan Chase
Lone Star Bank
PlainsCapital
Prosperity Bancshares
Texas Capital Bancshares
Wells Fargo
Woodforest Financial

HISTORICAL FINANCIALS

Company Type: Public

Income Statement

FYE: December 31

	ASSETS ($ mil.)	NET INCOME ($ mil.)	INCOME AS % OF ASSETS	EMPLOYEES
12/18	9,850	128	1.3%	1,087
12/17	8,684	77	0.9%	924
12/16	5,853	54	0.9%	577
12/15	5,055	39	0.8%	587
12/14	4,133	29	0.7%	511
Annual Growth	**24.3%**	**45.0%**	**—**	**20.8%**

2018 Year-End Financials

Debt ratio: 2.00%
Return on equity: 9.00%
Cash ($ mil.): 131
Current ratio: —
Long-term debt ($ mil.): —

No. of shares (mil.): 31
Dividends
Yield: 1.0%
Payout: 14.0%
Market value ($ mil.): 1,401

	STOCK PRICE ($) FY Close	P/E High/Low	PER SHARE ($) Earnings	Dividends	Book Value
12/18	46.00	18 10	4.00	1.00	52.00
12/17	68.00	24 18	3.00	0.00	47.00
12/16	62.00	22 9	3.00	0.00	36.00
12/15	32.00	21 13	2.00	0.00	34.00
12/14	39.00	33 21	2.00	0.00	32.00
Annual Growth	**4.0%**	**—**	**23.7%**	**22.5%**	**13.4%**

Ingredion Inc

Sweet sodas and diet desserts alike get their taste and feel from Ingredion's ingredients. The company makes food ingredients and industrial products from corn and other starch-based raw materials. It serves customers in more than 60 markets including food brewing and paper companies. Ingredion's largest product line is starches used in food for stabilization feel and texture and in paper packaging and other materials for quality strength and a host of other attributes. Its other product lines include sweeteners (high-fructose corn syrup dextrose) specialty ingredients (products focused on health affordability and sustainability) and co-products (refined corn oil corn gluten feed and meal). Ingredion operates worldwide but generates most of its sales in North America.

Operations

Cornstarch and other starch products account for about 45% of Ingredion's revenue and are used in processed foods as well as in paper and packaging adhesives textiles pharmaceuticals make-up and other products.

Sweeteners used in a wide range of foods — from condiments to candy — generate more than 35% of sales with specialty ingredients designed to capitalize on consumer trends bringing in about a quarter. Sweeteners include glucose syrups high maltose syrup high fructose corn syrup dextrose polyols maltrodextrin glucose syrup solids and non-GMO syrups.

The company's smallest product segment co-products includes refined corn oil sold to a variety of food producers and corn gluten feed and meal used for pet food. It also makes fruit and vegetable products such as concentrates purees and essences. The segment accounts for about 15% of revenue.

Geographic Reach

Well-covered geographically Ingredion serves customers in more than 60 countries worldwide. North America is its largest market accounting for some 60% of sales. South America represents more than 15% of sales the Asia Pacific region generates 15% and EMEA (Europe Middle East and Africa) represents 10% of sales.

Ingredion has some 45 manufacturing plants in about a dozen countries (the US is home to about a third of them).

Sales and Marketing

Ingredion exploits the versatility of corn in supplying customers across some 60 industries. Food is the company's largest industry segment generating about 55% of revenue with the next biggest being the beverage (10%) animal nutrition (10%) and brewing (5%) industries.

Ingredion sells its products through its own sales force directly to manufacturers and distributors.

Financial Performance

Ingredion has struggled to attain meaningful revenue growth over the last five years up just 3% in total. Profits have been stable.

In 2018 revenue of $5.8 billion was unchanged from 2017. Volume growth of 1% and a favorable price/mix of 2% was offset by unfavorable currency movements. By geography falls in Latin and North America were offset by increases in the Asia/Pacific region and EMEA.

Net income fell 15% to $443 million due to severance costs higher shipping and handling expenses and an increase in restructuring and impairment charges partially offset by lower income taxes.

Ingredion's cash on hand fell $268 million during 2018 ending the year at $327 million. The company's operations generated $703 million offset by $361 million used in its investing activities and $589 million used in its financing. Ingredion's main cash uses in 2018 were capital expenditures share repurchases and debt payments.

Strategy

While America's appetite for corn syrup remains as strong as it is Ingredion's strategy is mostly tinkering around the edges. It invests in its specialty business to meet new trends in the ingredients market finds cheaper ways to carry out its regular activities and seeks growth abroad. It is investing $60 million in operations in Thailand and China to expand its tapioca waxy corn and rice capabilities. Driven by demand for low-calorie sweeteners Ingredion is building a new factory in Mexico to produce Allulose a rare sugar that will allow manufacturers to reduce calories. And outside sweeteners Ingredion is investing $140 million to grow its plant-based protein businesses amid rising global demand. To free up resources Ingredion closed a corn syrup factory in Stockton California.

Ingredion is also targeting a $125 million cost reduction by 2021. The savings should come mainly from lower input costs and lower selling general and administrative expenses.

Mergers and Acquisitions

Ingredion bought the rice starch and flour business of Thailand's Sun Flour Industries in 2017 which boosts the company's specialty ingredients segment.

In late 2016 it paid nearly $400 million for Maryland-based TIC Gums which provides gums and resins to improve the texture of foods and beverages. The deal expands Ingredion's customer base and again adds to its specialty ingredients segment. Also that year the company acquired state-owned Shandong Huanong Specialty Corn Development Co. in China's Shandong Province to increase its manufacturing capacity in the country.

Ingredion in March 2015 acquired Iowa-based Penford Corp. a maker of carbohydrate-based specialty starches used by the paper packaging and food industries. The deal was valued at around $330 million and extended Ingredion's core offerings and geographical footprint; Penford has offices and plants in Colorado Idaho Iowa Pennsylvania South Carolina Washington and Wisconsin.

EXECUTIVES

Svp And Chief Innovation Officer, Anthony P. (Tony) Delio, age 63

President Ceo And Director, James P. Zallie, age 57, $600,000 total compensation

Svp Operating Excellence Sustainability Information Technology And Chief Supply Chain Officer, Robert J. (Bob) Stefansic, age 57

Svp And President Asia/pacific And Emea, Jorgen Kokke, age 50, $403,340 total compensation

Evp And Cfo, James D. (Jim) Gray, age 52

Vp Business Development South America, Jose Bertoli

Vice President U.s Canada Sweetener Solutions, Rob Ritchie

Vice President Marketing Us And Canada, Jim Low

National Account Manager, Enid Irizarry

Senior Corporate Management Vice President General Manager, Robert Markatos

Vice President Applications Research And Technical Services, Ron Deis

Vp Regional Sales, Robin Brown

Vice President Investor Relations And Corporate Communications, Heather Kos

Vice President Compensation Benefits And Hris, Robert Simitz

Vp Engineering, Randy Loewen

Vice President Global Wholesome And Texture Springboards, Luc Bertram

Vice President Talent Management, Henry Artalejo

Vice President And Managing Director Canada, Rob Kee

Senior Vice President And President Asia Pacific, Valdirene Bastos Licht

Vp And Corporate Treasurer, C Kevin Wilson

National Account Manager, Jeffrey Goldman

Chairman, Ilene S. Gordon, age 65

Board Member, Luis Aranguren-trellez

Auditors: KPMG LLP

LOCATIONS

HQ: Ingredion Inc
5 Westbrook Corporate Center, Westchester, IL 60154
Phone: 708 551-2600   **Fax:** 708 551-2700
Web: www.ingredion.com

2018 Sales

	$ mil.	% of total
North America	3,511	60
South America	943	16
Asia Pacific	803	14
EMEA	584	10
Total	**5,841**	**100**

PRODUCTS/OPERATIONS

2018 Sales

	% of total
Starch products	45
Sweetener products	36
Co-products & others	19
Total	**100**

Selected Products

Sweetener products
  Dextrose
  Glucose corn syrups
  High fructose corn syrup
  High maltose corn syrup
  Maltodextrins
  Polyols
Starch products
  Corn starch (consumer and industrial)
  Specialty Starches

Co-products and others
  Corn gluten feed
  Corn gluten meal
  Refined corn oil
Specialty Ingredients
  Delivery systems
  Green Solutions
  Nutrition
  Sweetness
  Texture
  Wholesome

COMPETITORS

ACH Food Companies
ADM
Ajinomoto
Cargill
Cumberland Packing
DSM
Global Bio-chem
Grain Processing
  Corporation
Imperial Sugar

Malt Products
  Corporation
Merisant
NutraSweet
PureCircle
Roquette Frres
Sweet Green Fields
Sdzucker
Tate & Lyle
  Ingredients

HISTORICAL FINANCIALS

Company Type: Public

Income Statement

FYE: December 31

	REVENUE ($ mil.)	NET INCOME ($ mil.)	NET PROFIT MARGIN	EMPLOYEES
12/18	5,841	443	7.6%	11,000
12/17	5,832	519	8.9%	11,000
12/16	5,704	485	8.5%	11,000
12/15	5,621	402	7.2%	11,000
12/14	5,668	355	6.3%	11,400
Annual Growth	0.8%	5.7%	—	(0.9%)

2018 Year-End Financials

Debt ratio: 37.00%
Return on equity: 17.00%
Cash ($ mil.): 327
Current ratio: 2.00
Long-term debt ($ mil.): 1,931

No. of shares (mil.): 67
Dividends
  Yield: 3.0%
  Payout: 40.0%
Market value ($ mil.): 6,080

	STOCK PRICE ($) FY Close	P/E High/Low	Earnings	PER SHARE ($) Dividends	Book Value
12/18	91.00	23 14	6.00	2.00	36.00
12/17	140.00	20 16	7.00	2.00	40.00
12/16	125.00	21 13	7.00	2.00	35.00
12/15	96.00	18 14	6.00	2.00	30.00
12/14	85.00	18 12	5.00	2.00	31.00
Annual Growth	1.9%	—	6.8%	9.9%	4.1%

Insight Enterprises Inc.

Insight Enterprises distributes computer hardware and software and provides IT services for businesses schools and government agencies and departments. The company offers thousands of devices and applications from major manufacturers (including Microsoft HP Inc. IBM and Cisco) as well as cloud services. Insight also provides integration services to knit hardware and software together for its customers. The company uses direct telesales field sales agents and an e-commerce site to reach its clients. Geographically Insight gets about 60% of sales from customers in the US and in terms of customers its large business clients provide about 70% of sales.

Operations
Insight sells technology in three areas: Hardware software and services.

In hardware about 60% of sales the company offer products from Cisco Systems Dell Technologies HP Inc. Lenovo Hewlett Packard Enterprise Co. NetApp Apple Microsoft IBM and hundreds of others.

The software segment about 30% of sales carries products from Microsoft VMware Adobe IBM Software Symantec Citrix and more.

Insight's services business about an eighth of sales combines the hardware and software aspects for its customers. Among the needs it addresses are supply chain outfitting the workforce with appropriate equipment helping companies move operations to cloud environments and implementing digital technologies.

Geographic Reach
Insight's sales are concentrated in the US which provides 70% of revenue with Canada contributing another few percentage points. The Europe the Middle East and Africa region contributes about 20% and the Asia-Pacific less than 5%. The Tempe Arizona-based company has operations in about 20 counties.

Sales and Marketing
Although the company sells software and hardware from hundreds of companies Insight relies on five major vendors Microsoft Dell Cisco System HP Inc. and Lenovo for about 55% of its sales. Microsoft alone accounts for 20% of Insight's sales.

Insight makes more than 70% of its sales to large corporate customers while government and small and medium business customers about split the other 30%.

Financial Performance
Insight has posted rising sales for the past five years (since 2015) at a 7% annual clip boosted by a 22% jump in 2017 from 2016 due to increased integration work and acquisitions.

In 2018 revenue rose about 6% to $7.1 billion up about $1.4 billion from 2017 on higher sales in all geographic regions as well as stronger hardware and services sales. Hardware revenue increased 8% driven by sales of client devices storage and networking products to large customers. Service sales jumped 23% from cloud maintenance and enterprise agreement fees as well as contributions from the Cardinal acquisition. Software sales dropped 15% as customers moved to cloud offerings which are billed over a longer period.

Insight's net income leaped 80% to $163.6 million in 2018 from 2017 boosted by a lower tax rate from the US Tax Cuts and Jobs Act. The company's effective tax rate was about 23% in 2018 compared to 43% in 2017.

The company's cash and equivalents rose to $142.7 million in 2018 an increase of about $30 million from 2017. Operations generated $292.6 million in 2018 while investing activities and financing activities used $91.7 million and $159 million respectively.

Although capital expenditures dipped 10% to $17.3 million in 2018 from 2017 Insight continued to invest in its enterprise resource planning systems and its e-commerce and digital marketing platforms.

Strategy
Insight transfers hardware and software from vendors to clients using its scale to get the best prices for the goods. But perhaps the most valuable part of its business is in integrating the hardware and software to best suit the customer. While generating just around 10% of sales service-related activities — professional services Insight-delivered services cloud component and others ? accounts for about 45% of gross profit. This reflects investment the company has made over the past five

years to become systems integrator as well as an equipment and software provider.

The company's cloud business has grown with the help of acquisitions accounting for 18% of consolidated gross profit in 2018 compared to 13% in 2017.

Insight has put resources toward workforce development and has made Fortune's list for best companies for diversity and workplaces in technology. At the same time the company has turned to automation to make customer-facing operations more efficient through process automation and optical scanning technologies. It also has devoted capital expenditures to it e-commerce and digital marketing platforms.

Insight has made acquisitions to strengthen parts of its portfolio including its digital capabilities and cloud services. The Datalink acquisition made in 2017 has produced revenue from cross-selling in data center and cloud services.

Insight's is a fiercely competitive business with rivals among other suppliers and integrators such as CDW and Accenture as well as Insight's own partners such as Microsoft Dell Technologies and HP Inc. (especially true for big customers which provide about 70% of Insight's revenue). The competition puts constant pressure on pricing and bigger companies with deep pockets can ride out low prices.

Mergers and Acquisitions

In 2018 Insight acquired Cardinal Solutions Group a provider of digital tools and services to bolster its digital innovations capabilities.

In 2017 Insight acquired Datalink a Minnesota-based IT service and enterprise data center solutions provider for $257.5 million. The acquisition addresses market opportunities in hybrid cloud and other data center categories.

In another 2017 transaction Insight bought Caase Group B.V. to boosts its cloud and data center portfolio for its clients in the EMEA region.

In 2016 it acquired Ignia an Australian digital mobile and cloud company with a foot in application design digital solutions cloud mobility and business analytics. The acquisition will also further Insight's reach into the APAC market.

Company Background

Eric Crown worked for a small computer retail chain in the mid-1980s before leaving to market PCs. In 1986 he and his brother Tim pooled $2000 from credit cards and $1300 in savings and anticipating a drop in hard drive prices placed an ad for low-cost hard drives in a computer magazine. The ad pulled in $20000 worth of sales and since costs did indeed drop the profit was enough to start a new company Hard Drives International. In 1988 they changed the name to Insight Enterprises; by 1991 the Crowns also sold Insight-branded PCs software and peripherals (discontinued in 1995). The company passed the $100 million revenue mark in 1992.

Over the years through organic growth and acquisitions Insight expanded into new markets and exited others and growing to compete with top distributors and integrators such as CDW and Accenture.

HISTORY

Eric Crown worked for a small computer retail chain in the mid-1980s before leaving to market PCs. In 1986 he and his brother Tim pooled $2000 from credit cards and $1300 in savings and anticipating a drop in hard drive prices placed an ad for low-cost hard drives in a computer magazine. The ad pulled in $20000 worth of sales and since costs did indeed drop the profit was enough to start a new company Hard Drives International. In 1988 they changed the name to Insight Enterprises; by 1991 the Crowns also sold Insight-branded PCs

software and peripherals (discontinued in 1995). The company passed the $100 million revenue mark in 1992.

Insight shifted its marketing focus to catalogs in 1993 and had a circulation of more than 7 million by 1995. The company went public that year and entered an alliance with Computer City (acquired by CompUSA in 1998) to handle its mail-order fulfillment. It also launched its website. The next year subsidiary Insight Direct began to offer on-site service warranties and in 1997 retailing subsidiary Direct Alliance was chosen to provide product fulfillment for Internet software firm Geo Publishing. That year the company began sponsoring the Copper Bowl a college football game played in Arizona which was renamed the Insight.com Bowl (and later the Insight Bowl).

Looking beyond the US in 1998 Insight established operations in Canada and acquired direct marketers Choice Peripherals (UK) and Computerprofis Computersysteme (Germany). At home it added direct marketer Treasure Chest Computers. Sales passed the billion-dollar mark that year.

The company formed an alliance with Daisytek International in 1999 that expanded its product line by more than 10000. Soon thereafter Insight walked away from a merger with UK-based computer wholesaler Action Computer Supplies when Action's profits slumped.

Insight withdrew its planned IPO and spinoff of Direct Alliance in 2001 due to poor market conditions. Also that month Eric became chairman and Tim became CEO (they had previously shared the title of co-CEO). Insight ended up buying Action Computer Supplies in 2001. It also shut down its German operations and acquired computer direct marketers in both the UK and Canada in late 2001.

In April 2002 Insight acquired Comark a leading private reseller of computers peripherals and computer supplies in the US and began integrating its operations into Insight North America's existing operational structure.

Tim stepped down as president and CEO and became chairman in late 2004 while Eric assumed the title of chairman emeritus. The company appointed IBM veteran Richard Fennessy to the position of president and CEO. That year Insight spun off its UK-based Internet service provider PlusNet.

In 2006 Insight Enterprises bought software and mobile solutions firm Software Spectrum.

EXECUTIVES

President And Ceo, Kenneth T. (Ken) Lamneck, age 64, $800,000 total compensation

Cio, Michael Guggemos, age 54, $398,989 total compensation

Cfo, Glynis A. Bryan, age 60, $466,140 total compensation

President Insight Us, Steven W. Dodenhoff, age 56, $488,625 total compensation

President Insight Emea, Wolfgang Ebermann, age 54, $578,726 total compensation

Vice President Marketing, David Locker

Vice President Sales, Rob McConnell

Svp Finance And Operations Emea, Russell Leighton

Vice President Sales, Luke Purdon

Vice President Sales, Collin Ryan

Vp Commercial And Legal Emea, Jet Golia

Vice President Sales, Christy Arnold

Vp And Gm Digital Innovation, Stan Lequin

Vice President Sales, Jason Sullivan

Vp Business Transformation, Bret Wingert

Senior Vice President Na And Apac Software, Andrea Mattea

Senior Vice President Human Resources, Jennifer Fernandez

Vice President Sales, Mark Zawacki

Vice President Inside Sales, Brenda Hudson

Vice President Of Information Technology, Joseph Flynn

Vp Services Emea, Rolf Adam

Vice President Services, Matt Jackson

Senior Vp, Gina Morckol

Regional Vice President, Heath Tow

Vice President, Mickey Bland

Chairman, Timothy A. (Tim) Crown, age 55

Auditors: KPMG LLP

LOCATIONS

HQ: Insight Enterprises Inc.
6820 South Harl Avenue, Tempe, AZ 85283
Phone: 480 333-3000
Web: www.insight.com

2018 Sales

	$ mil.	% of total
North America	5,363	75
Europe Middle East & Africa	1,530	22
Asia/Pacific	187	3
Total	**7,080**	**100**

2018 Sales

	$ mil.	% of total
United States	5,101	72
United Kingdom	843	12
Others Foreign	1,136	16
Total	**7,080**	**100**

PRODUCTS/OPERATIONS

2018 Sales

	$ mil.	% of total
Hardware	4,293	60
Software	1,957	28
Services	830	12
Total	**7,080**	**100**

Selected Products

Computer memory and processors
Desktop computers
Monitors
Networking equipment
Notebook computers
Printers and printing consumables
Servers
Software
Storage devices
Tablet computers

Selected Services

Business optimization software
  Business productivity
  Core infrastructure
  Software asset management
Collaboration
  Call/contact center
  Unified communications/messaging
  Video collaboration/conferencing
Cloud services
  Collaboration
  Infrastructure
  Messaging
  Security
Data center
  Infrastructure solutions
  Server solutions
  Storage solutions
Infrastructure and security
  Network infrastructure
  Security infrastructure
Managed services
  Business process outsourcing
  Connected real estate and sports
  Financing and leasing
  IT asset disposal
  Maintenance
  Product provisioning
  Remote network operations
  Telecom expense management
  Warehouse/integration
Mobility
Big Data
Creativity
Data protection

COMPETITORS

Accenture	HP
Amazon.com	IBM
Best Buy	Lenovo
Buy.com	Microsoft
CDW	Newegg
CompuCom	PC Mall
Convergys	PFSweb
Dell	SHI International
Digital River	Zones

HISTORICAL FINANCIALS

Company Type: Public

Income Statement

FYE: December 31

	REVENUE ($ mil.)	NET INCOME ($ mil.)	NET PROFIT MARGIN	EMPLOYEES
12/18	7,080	164	2.3%	7,420
12/17	6,704	91	1.4%	6,697
12/16	5,486	85	1.5%	5,930
12/15	5,373	76	1.4%	5,761
12/14	5,316	76	1.4%	5,406
Annual Growth	7.4%	21.3%	—	8.2%

2018 Year-End Financials

Debt ratio: 7.00%
Return on equity: 18.00%
Cash ($ mil.): 143
Current ratio: 2.00
Long-term debt ($ mil.): 196

No. of shares (mil.): 35
Dividends
Yield: —
Payout: —
Market value ($ mil.): 1,446

	STOCK PRICE ($) FY Close	P/E High/Low		PER SHARE ($) Earnings	Dividends	Book Value
12/18	41.00	12	7	5.00	0.00	28.00
12/17	38.00	19	14	3.00	0.00	24.00
12/16	40.00	18	9	2.00	0.00	20.00
12/15	25.00	16	12	2.00	0.00	18.00
12/14	26.00	17	11	2.00	0.00	18.00
Annual Growth	12.0%	—		25.6%	—	11.6%

Intel Corp

Intel Corp. is the brains of the operation. One the biggest computer chip companies Intel controls roughly 90% of the market for microprocessors that act as the brains of desktop notebook and server computers. It has dominated the PC chip market from the early x86 processors to Pentiums to today's Core technology. Intel also makes chips for smartphones and tablets as well as embedded semiconductors for the industrial medical and automotive markets. The company develops its chips and makes most of them itself in one of the industry's biggest manufacturing systems. While PC chips account for most sales Intel has shifted focus and resources to chips for the data centers that power cloud computing.

Operations

Intel Corp.'s Client Computing Group is the company's workhorse and cash generator delivering more than half of its revenue and more than 6% of operating income. The business churns out chips for notebooks 2-in-1 systems desktops tablets phones wireless and wired connectivity products and mobile communication components.

The Data Center Group generates about a third of Intel's revenue with chips for server-platforms and related products designed for the enterprise cloud government and communication infrastructure markets.

The Internet of Things Group makes chips for connected devices in retail transportation industrial video buildings smart cities and other markets. It accounts for about 5% of revenue.

Taken together the Programmable Solutions and Non-Volatile Memory Solutions groups provide about 10% of the company's revenue.

Intel makes most of its products in its own manufacturing facilities which allows the company to control the process for quality speed and flexibility. For some communications connectivity networking field programmable and memory components the company outsources manufacturing to third parties. Intel handles test and assembly in-house and through contractors.

Geographic Reach

Intel Corp. has more than 150 locations around the globe with assembly and test facilities in China Malaysia and Vietnam. Sales are well-distributed geographically with customers in China (including Hong Kong) generating about a quarter of Intel's sales followed by Singapore and US customers about 20% each and customers in Taiwan who kick in more than 15% of revenue.

Sales and Marketing

Intel sells its products primarily to original equipment manufacturers (OEMs) and original design manufacturers (ODMs). In addition Intel products are sold to makers of industrial and communications equipment.

Its customers also include those who buy PC components and other products through distributor reseller retail and OEM channels. Intel's worldwide reseller sales channel consists of thousands of indirect customers who are systems builders that purchase microprocessors and other products from distributors.

Intel's three largest customers account for nearly 40% of revenue. They are Dell Technologies more than 15% of sales and Lenovo Group and HP Inc. each with about 10%.

Financial Performance

Intel has posted company-record revenue in each of the past three year as it has maintained revenue from computer-related products and sales of its lineup of newer products for data centers and cloud computing have grown.

In 2018 sales reached $70.8 billion up $8.1 billion a 13% increase from 2017 driven by several factors notably Intel's data-related businesses. Sales of data products jumped 18% year-to-year and accounted for about half of the company's revenue in 2018. The Mobileye business acquired in 2017 added nearly $700 million in sales. The PC business contributed a 9% sales increase on demand from the commercial 2-in-1 and gaming markets as well as a higher share of the modem market.

Intel's profit jumped to $21 billion in 2018 about $10.4 billion more than in 2017. The company's operating expenses were 28% of revenue in 2018 compared to 36% in 2017 and Intel paid less in taxes in 2018 than in 2017 when the tax rate was higher due to the US Tax Cuts and Jobs Act.

Intel's coffers held $3 billion in cash and equivalents in 2018 about $400 million less than in 2017. Operations generated $29.4 billion in 2018 while investing and financing activities used $11.2 billion and $18.6 billion respectively.

Strategy

Although Intel had higher sales of PC chips in 2016 2017 and 2018 the company is investing in other areas to reduce its PC-dependence. (Intel remains the dominant chip supplier for PCs with a 90% market share.)

Intel is investing in its data-related processors and supplying them for growing markets such as data centers cloud computing 5G communications artificial intelligence and autonomous driving. The

units that address those markets are growing quickly.

Intel's acquisition of Mobileye in 2017 staked out a prominent position for providing technology for self-driving cars. Mobileye's sensor technologies combined with Intel's semiconductors should make for a formidable competitor in developing autonomous vehicles. Intel has teamed with BMW AG and Delphi Automotive for developing driverless vehicle technology.

With annual revenue north of $70 billion Intel has deep resources. It had close to $12 billion in capital investment in 2017 with most it devoted to equipment and facilities to produce advanced chips.

Intel faces challenges from other semiconductor companies that offer strong products in growing markets. Samsung Electronics' chip business has grown in recent years and the companies run neck-and-neck for the title of biggest chipmaker. Long-time rival AMD has released high-performance chips at price points that could undercut Intel's offerings. NVIDIA is growing quickly from its graphics chips that are well-suited to artificial intelligence applications.

Mergers and Acquisitions

Intel agreed to acquire Barefoot Networks in 2019 to beef up its offerings for cloud computing applications. Barefoot designs and make chips that manage communication via Ethernet which is used to connect networked computers and servers. Barefoot's products fill a gap in Intel's portfolio and could help it compete more effectively against Broadcom the foremost product of such devices. The deal was expected to close in the 2019 third quarter.

In 2019 Intel acquired Omnitek a provider of video and vision for programmable processors that enable customized vision and artificial intelligence. Terms of the deal were not disclosed

Intel acquired Ineda Systems a fabless chip company in 2019. Ineda's chips are used in autonomous driving artificial intelligence and the Internet of Things. The company is based in Hyderbad India where Intel plans to put a technology development center.

In 2018 Intel acquired Netspeed Systems which makes tools for designing system-on-chip (SoC) devices. Intel is one of several chip companies that include NVIDIA and Qualcomm increasingly making circuits that handle multiple functions. Netspeed's tools speed up the design of SoCs through automation. Netspeed becomes part of Intel's Silicon Engineering Group.

In 2017 Intel acquired Mobileye for more than $15 billion. Mobileye based in Israel develops sensors and cameras for vehicles. The acquisition broadens Intel's offerings for makers of driverless vehicles beyond the chips that are brains of such vehicles. Mobileye's technologies provide more of the critical capabilities that autonomous autos need to maneuver safely.

Company Background

The founding of Intel is one of the legendary stories of Silicon Valley. In 1968 three engineers from Fairchild Semiconductor created Intel in Mountain View California to develop technology for silicon-based chips. ("Intel" is a contraction of "integrated electronics.") The trio consisted of Robert Noyce (who co-invented the integrated circuit or IC in 1958) Gordon Moore and Andy Grove.

Intel initially provided computer memory chips such as DRAMs (1970) and EPROMs (1971). These successes funded the microprocessor designs that revolutionized the electronics industry. In 1971 Intel introduced the 4004 microprocessor promoted as "a micro-programmable computer on a chip."

EXECUTIVES

Corporate Vp And Gm Global Supply Management, Jacklyn A Sturm

Vp Software And Services Group And Gm Platforms Security Division, Ricardo J Echevarria

Vp Finance Controller, Corine Perez

Evp Corporate Strategy, Thomas M Kilroy, age 63

Interim Ceo, Robert H. (Bob) Swan, age 59, $194,800 total compensation

Evp And General Manager Product Assurance And Security, Leslie S. Culbertson

Svp, Gregory R. (Greg) Pearson, age 59, $545,000 total compensation

Vp Finance And Enterprise Services; Assistant Cfo, Stacy J. Smith, age 57, $800,000 total compensation

Svp And General Manager Automated Driving Group (adg), Douglas L. (Doug) Davis, age 58

Svp And General Manager Technology And Manufacturing Group, Sohail U. Ahmed

Svp And General Manager Non-volatile Memory (nvm) Solutions Group, Robert B. Crooke

Svp And General Manager Client Computing Group, Diane M. Bryant, age 58, $618,700 total compensation

Svp And Managing Director Intel Labs And Cto, Michael C. (Mike) Mayberry, age 62

Svp And General Manager Intel Product Assurance And Security Engineering Group, Joshua M. (Josh) Walden, age 57

Svp And General Manager Platform Engineering Group, Amir Faintuch

Svp And General Manager Software And Services Group (ssg), Douglas W. (Doug) Fisher

Evp And General Counsel, Steven R. (Steve) Rodgers

Evp And General Manager Data Center Group, Navin Shenoy

Svp And Chief Marketing Officer, Steven L. Fund

Svp And Chief Strategy Officer, Aicha S. Evans

Svp And General Manager Internet Of Things (iot) Group, Thomas P. (Tom) Lantzsch

Svp And President Intel Capital, Wendell M. Brooks

Corporate Vp And Cio, Paula C. Tolliver

Group President Technology Systems Architecture And Client Group And Chief Engineering Officer, Venkata M. (Murthy) Renduchintala, age 54, $900,000 total compensation

Corporate Vp And General Manager Technology And Manufacturing Group, Ann B. Kelleher

Corporate Vp And General Manager Programmable Solutions Group (psg), Daniel R. (Dan) McNamara

Corporate Vp And General Manager Artificial Intelligence Products Group, Naveen G. Rao

Vice President Law And Policy Group And Associate General Counsel Director Intel Standards Group, Ann K Armstrong

Vice President Tmg And General Manager Intel Ireland, Eamonn Sinnott

Intel Information Technology Vpro Amt Product Manager, Omer Livne

Vice President Platform Engineering Group And Gm Quality Advancement, John Pierron

Vp Non Volatile Memory Solutions Group And Director Non Volatile Memory Solutions Group, Thomas R Macdonald

Vice President Sales And Marketing Group Gm Global Communications Group, Paul Bergevin

Vice President Software And Services Group And Gm Developer Products Division, William Savage

Senior Vice President, Arun Chandrasekhar

Vice President Law And Policy Group And Associate General Counsel Law And Policy Group, Joseph Adams

Vp Sales And Marketing Group And Gm Global Markets And Partners Emea Territory, Maurits Tichelman

Northeast Regional Vice President, Praveen Kundurthy

Vice President Data Center Group And Gm Cloud Service Provider Group, Raejeanne Skillern

Corporate Vp Non Volatile Memory Solutions Group Worldwide Manufacturing, Keyvan Esfarjani

Vp Data Center Group And Gm Data Center Strategic Planning, Robert C Hays

Vp Software And Services Group And Gm Developer Programs And Initiatives, Roger Chandler

Vice President Platform Engineering Group And Director Manufacturing Validation Engineering Pre S, Jagannath Keshava

Vice President Client And Internet Of Things Businesses And Systems Architecture; Gm Next Generati, Asha Keddy

National Sales Manager Intel Malaysia, Simon Chan

Technical Assistant To Kim Stevenson Corporate Vice President And Cio Intel, Debbie Doran

Vice President, John Jacobs

Vice President, Lei Shao

Vice President Technology And Manufacturing Group And Director Technology Optimization Solutions, Changhong Dai

Vp Global Marketing And Communications And Gm Global Communications Group, Laura Anderson

Vice President Of Systems, Patricia A Mcdonald

Vice President Data Center Group And Director Platform Hardware Engineering Division, Viktor Tymchenko

Vice President, Sanjiv Shah

Vp Law And Policy Group And Deputy General Counsel Legal Policy Group, Lynn E Blough

Vice President Technology And Manufacturing Group And Director Lead Technology Vehicle Development, Ying Zhang

Vice President Intel Labs And Director Integrated Platform Research Lab, Vida Ilderem

National Sales Manager, Vineet Giri

Vice President Associate General Counsel, Mark Friedman

Executive Vice President And Chief Development Officer, Gadi Oren

Corporate Vp And Cfo Data Center Group, Christina Min

Technical Advisor To Intel Vp (sales Marketing Group), Iris Wu

Vice President, Paul Stacey

Vice President Director Manager, Ulf Hofemeier

Vp Sales And Marketing Group Director Emea Marketing, Bernadette Andrietti

Vice President Applications And Support, John Kreatsoulas

Vice President Tmg Plant Manager Nm Site Fab 11x, Kirby Jefferson

Vp Technology And Manufacturing Group And Director Chemical Mechanical Polish Technology, Herng Liu

Corporate Vice President And Gm Data Center Engineering And Architecture Group, Zane Ball

Vp Technology And Manufacturing Group And Plant Manager D1dr Fab, Gulsher S Grewal

Vp Law And Policy Group And Director Intel Patent Group, Jeffrey S Draeger

Corporate Vice President Deputy General Counsel Corporate Secretary, Suzan Miller

Vice President Human Resources, Michael Forrest

Vp Internet Of Things Group And Gm Operations And Group Marketing Division, Franklin B Jones

Vp And Germany Country Manager, Christin Eisenschmid

Vice President And General Manager, Gadi Singer

Vice President Software And Services Group And Director Open Source Technology Center Core Operati, Hillarie Prestopine

Vice President Events, Stephen Logan

Corporate Vp And Gm Datacenter Solutions Group, Jason Waxman

Vp New Devices Group And Gm Program Management, Yuri Tsuchitani

Vp Software And Services Group And Gm Intel Compilers And Languages, Alice Chan

Vice President Non Volatile Memory Solutions Group And Director Manufacturing And Automation Syste, Kumud Srinivasan

Vice President Core And Visual Computing Group And Gm Visual Technologies Team, Ari Rauch

Vice President Communication And Devices Group And Gm Modem And Platform Software Group, Abhay Joshi

Vice President, Armin Sarstedt

Vp Finance And Finance Controller Platform Engineering Group, Doug B Klucevek

Vice President, Shahaf Kieselstein

Vice President Consumer Product Management, Alan LeFort

Vp International Site Operations Group And Gm Intel Israel, Maxine Fassberg

Vp Sales And Marketing Group And Director Microprocessor Marketing And Business Planning, Gilberto A Vargas

Vice President Executive Assistant, Valerie Montoya

Senior Vice President General Manager, Tom Lantzsch

Vice President Global Marketing And Communications, Alyson Griffin

Corporate Vice President And Gm Global Accounts Sales And Marketing Group, Christopher J Bruno

Corporate Vice President And Gm Assembly Test Manufacturing, Robin Martin

Vp Of Automated Driving Group And Gm Of Automated Driving Solutions, Katherine Winter

Senior Vice President And General Manager Network Platforms Group, Sandra Rivera

Vice President Information Technology Group And General Manager Information Technology Client And Collaboration Solutions, Dave Aires

Vice President Platform Engineering Group, Anwar Awad

Vice President Architecture Data Center Group, Anil Rao

Vice President Engineering, Raheel Khan

Vice President Of Visual Technology Architecture Group, Martin Ashton

Vice President Platform Engineering Group And Director Product Development Itgs Devices Developme, Boyd Phelps

Vice President Sales And Marketing Group And General Manager Sales Non Volatile Memory Solutions Group, John Vossoughi

Vice President, Amir Khosrowshahi

Vice President, Rahul Goyal

Senior Vice President Intel President And Chief Executive Officer Of Mobileye An Intel Company, Amnon Shashua

Vice President Network Platforms Group And Gm Network Custom Solutions Division, Cristina Rodriguez

Corporate Vice President And Corporate Secretary, Susie Giordano

Vice President Intel Capital And Director Mergers And Acquisition, Raheel A Shah

Vice President, Doug Davis

Vice President Software And Services Group And Director Platform Application Engineering, Peter Baker

Vice President Client Computing Group And Gm Business Client Platforms Division, Thomas Garrison

Vice President Global Marketing And Communications And Gm Global Client Marketing, Robert DeLine

Vice President Technology And Manufacturing Group And Director Assembly And Test Technology Develo, Jeffrey Pettinato

Vice President Client Computing Group And Gm
Client Planning And Architecture, Adam King
Vice President Technology And Manufacturing
Group And 22nm Plant Manager Arizona Fab
Sort Manufa, Joseph McDonnell
Vice President Client Computing Group And Gm
Connected Home Division, Daniel Artusi
Vice President Client Computing Group And Gm
Mobility Client Platform, Christopher Walker
Vice President Data Center Group; President And
Gm Intel Federal Llc, O'Neil Green
Vp Information Technology And Ciso, Brent
Conran
Vp Software And Services Group And Gm
Internet Of Things Security, Lorie Wigle
Vp Technology And Manufacturing Group And
Director Advanced Transistor Development
Portland Technology Development, Christopher P
Auth
Vp Platform Engineering Group And Director
Power Performance And Firmware Architecture,
Bradley M Dendinger
Vp Platform Engineering Group And Gm High
Velocity Products Group India, Sambit Sahu
Vp Intel Labs And Director Security And Privacy
Research, Sridhar R Iyengar
Vp Platform Engineering Group And Director
Product Management Integrated Ip And
Technology Group, Bradley G Heaney
Corporate Vp And Gm Internet Of Things Group
Sales, Rosemary M Schooler
Vp Software And Services Group And Gm Client
Systems And Software, Michael C Uhl
Vp Software And Services Group And Director
Big Data Technologies, Ziya Ma
Vp Programmable Solutions Group Americas
Sales, Richard X Madormo
Vp Finance And Assistant Treasurer Cash
Investments And Capital Markets, Gary Kershaw
Vp Core And Visual Computing Group And Gm
Intel Architecture Cores Group, Ziv Hammer
Vp Data Center Group And Gm Silicon Photonics
Product Division, Philip L Gadd
Vp Technology And Manufacturing Group And Gm
Intel Kulim Assembly And Test Operations, Yu
Teong Chow
Vp Programmable Solutions Group Asia Pacific,
Hans P H Chuang
Vp Platform Engineering Group And Director
Manufacturing Validation Engineering
Manufacturing Validation Solutions, Karin
Eibschitz Segal
Corporate Vp Platform Engineering Group And
Gm Product Development Solutions, Kalyan
Thumaty
Vp Software And Services And Gm Intel Russia
Software And Services Group; Director Software
Product Services, Marina B Alekseeva
Vp Law And Policy Group And Associate General
Counsel Antitrust And Commercial Litigation,
Evangelina Almirantearena
Vp Programmable Solutions Group Marketing,
Reynette K Au
Corporate Vp And Gm Integrated Ip And
Technology Group, Daaman Hejmadi
Corporate Vp And Gm Global Data Center Group
Sales, Rupal Shah Hollenbeck
Vp Sales And Marketing Group And Gm Network
Platforms Group And Communications Service
Provider Sales, Werner G Schaefer
Vp Intel Capital And Managing Director Greater
Asia, Li-chung Lin
Vp Technology And Manufacturing Group And
Director Corporate Services Operations, Anne
Mcswiggan
Vp Platform Engineering Group And Director
Strategy And Operations Visual And Parallel
Computing Group, W Eric Mentzer

Vp Software And Services Group And Director
Android Operating Systems Products, Nirmal
Pandey
Vp Technology And Manufacturing Group And
Director Advanced Patterning Logic Technology
Development, Christopher N Kenyon
Vp Platform Engineering Group And Gm Client
Development Group, Valentin D Kaplan
Auditors: Ernst & Young LLP

LOCATIONS

HQ: Intel Corp
2200 Mission College Boulevard, Santa Clara, CA
95054-1549
Phone: 408 765-8080   Fax: 408 765-2633
Web: www.intc.com

2018 Sales

	$ mil.	% of total
China (including Hong Kong)	18,824	27
Singapore	15,409	22
US	14,303	20
Taiwan	10,646	15
Other	11,666	16
Total	**70,848**	**100**

PRODUCTS/OPERATIONS

2018 Sales

	$ mil.	% of total
Client computing Group	37,004	52
Data Center Group	22,991	33
Internet of Things Group	4,307	6
Non-Volatile Memory Solutions Group	3,455	5
Programmable Solutions Group	2,123	3
All others	968	1
Total	**70,848**	**100**

Selected Products

Systems and Devices
  Laptops
  Desktops
  Tablets
  Smartphones
  Drones
Processors
  Intel Core
  Intel Xeon
  Intel Atom
  Pentium
  Celeron
  Intel Quark
Boards and Kits
  Intel NUC Boards and Kits
  Intel IoT RFP Ready Kits
  Server Motherboards
  Intel Quark D2000 Development Kit
Chipsets
  Mobile
  Desktop
  Server
  Embedded
FPGAs and Programmable Devices
  Intel FPGAs
  Intel Agilex
  Intel Stratix
  Intel Cyclone
Memory and Storage
  Solid State Drives
  Intel Optane Memory

COMPETITORS

AMD	SK Hynix
ARM Holdings	STMicroelectronics
Apple Inc.	Samsung Electronics
Fujitsu Semiconductor	Silicon Integrated
GLOBALFOUNDRIES	Systems
Maxim Integrated	Sony
Products	TSMC
Microchip Technology	Texas Instruments
Micron Technology	Toshiba Semiconductor
NVIDIA	& Storage Products
QUALCOMM	

HISTORICAL FINANCIALS

Company Type: Public

Income Statement   FYE: December 28

	REVENUE ($ mil.)	NET INCOME ($ mil.)	NET PROFIT MARGIN	EMPLOYEES
12/19	71,965	21,048	29.2%	110,800
12/18	70,848	21,053	29.7%	107,400
12/17	62,761	9,601	15.3%	102,700
12/16	59,387	10,316	17.4%	106,000
12/15	55,355	11,420	20.6%	107,300
Annual Growth	**6.8%**	**16.5%**	**—**	**0.8%**

2019 Year-End Financials

Debt ratio: 21.00%—
Return on equity: 28.00%
Cash ($ mil.): 4,194
Current ratio: 1.00
Long-term debt ($ mil.): 25,308

Dividends
  Yield: 0.0%
  Payout: 27.0%
Market value ($ mil.): —

	STOCK PRICE ($) FY Close	P/E High/Low		PER SHARE ($) Earnings	Dividends	Book Value
12/19	60.00	13	9	5.00	1.00	18.00
12/18	47.00	12	9	4.00	1.00	17.00
12/17	46.00	23	16	2.00	1.00	15.00
12/16	36.00	17	13	2.00	1.00	14.00
12/15	35.00	16	11	2.00	1.00	13.00
Annual Growth	**14.5%**	**—**	**—**	**19.2%**	**7.0%**	**8.4%**

INTERACTIVE DATA CORPORATION

EXECUTIVES

Pres, Scott A Hill
Treasurer, Martin Hunter
Secretary, Octavia Spencer
Vice President, Chuck Adkins
Database Programmer, Harsh Nayak
Director, Michael Scotland
Assistant General Counsel, Nathan Bouley
Vice President Information TEC, Scott Caudell
Director Evaluated Op, Steve Miano
Senior Business Analyst, Tim Sweeney
Senior Director, Bob Leone

LOCATIONS

HQ: INTERACTIVE DATA CORPORATION
32 CROSBY DR STE 100, BEDFORD, MA 017301448
Phone: 781 687-8500
Web: WWW.THEICE.COM

HISTORICAL FINANCIALS

Company Type: Private

Income Statement   FYE: December 31

	ASSETS ($ mil.)	NET INCOME ($ mil.)	INCOME AS % OF ASSETS	EMPLOYEES
12/13	3,968	34	0.8%	2,600
12/12	3,962	1	0.0%	—
12/11	4,094	(29)	—	—
Annual Growth	**(1.5%)**	**—**	**—**	**—**

Intercontinental Exchange Inc

EXECUTIVES

Chb-Ceo, Jeffrey C Sprecher
V Chb, Charles A Vice
Pres, Benjamin R Jackson
Coo, Mark P Wassersug
Cfo, Scott A Hill
Cso, David S Goone
Gen Counsel, Andrew J Surdykowski
Pres-Coo Ice Data Svcs, Lynn C Martin
General Counsel, Kara Dutta
Information Security Analyst, Kyle Takeuchi
Senior Software Engineer, Slava Letov
Auditors: Ernst & Young LLP

LOCATIONS

HQ: Intercontinental Exchange Inc
5660 New Northside Drive, Atlanta, GA 30328
Phone: 770 857-4700   **Fax:** 770 937-0020
Web: www.theice.com

HISTORICAL FINANCIALS

Company Type: Public

Income Statement

FYE: December 31

	REVENUE ($ mil.)	NET INCOME ($ mil.)	NET PROFIT MARGIN	EMPLOYEES
12/19	6,547	1,933	29.5%	5,989
12/18	6,276	1,988	31.7%	5,161
12/17	5,834	2,514	43.1%	4,952
12/16	5,958	1,422	23.9%	5,631
12/15	4,682	1,274	27.2%	5,549
Annual Growth	8.7%	11.0%	—	1.9%

2019 Year-End Financials

Debt ratio: 8.00%
Return on equity: 11.00%
Cash ($ mil.): 841
Current ratio: 1.00
Long-term debt ($ mil.): 5,250

No. of shares (mil.): 554
Dividends
　Yield: 1.0%
　Payout: 30.0%
Market value ($ mil.): 51,273

	STOCK PRICE ($) FY Close	P/E High/Low		PER SHARE ($) Earnings	Dividends	Book Value
12/19	93.00	28	21	3.00	1.00	31.00
12/18	75.00	24	19	3.00	1.00	30.00
12/17	71.00	17	13	4.00	1.00	29.00
12/16	56.00	119	22	2.00	1.00	26.00
12/15	256.00	115	89	2.00	1.00	25.00
Annual Growth	(22.5%)	—	—	10.7%	17.4%	5.8%

INTERMOUNTAIN HEALTH CARE INC

If you whoosh down the side of one of Idaho's majestic mountains and take a nasty spill Intermountain Health Care (dba Intermountain Healthcare) can pick you up and put you back together. From air ambulance services to urgent care clinics and general hospitals Intermountain has all the tools to mend skiers (and non-skiers alike) in Utah and southern Idaho. With about 1600 physicians

the not-for-profit health system operates 22 hospitals and some 180 clinics as well as urgent care centers and rehabilitation centers. Intermountain also has an insurance arm named SelectHealth.

Operations

Intermountain Healthcare's hospitals range from general surgical to specialty care including orthopedic and pediatric facilities. Along with the full spectrum of physical health care services Intermountain also offers comprehensive mental health and substance abuse programs for patients of all ages. The organization's spectrum of care includes acute inpatient residential treatment day treatment chemical dependency inpatient/detoxification and intensive outpatient programs.

The system conducts cancer research through its partnership with Huntsman Cancer Institute at the University of Utah. The two share data best practices funding and co-conduct clinical trials. They also operate a number of cancer-specific treatment centers including multi-disciplinary tumor-specific clinics designed to provide one-stop service for cancer patients to meet with different cancer specialists on the same day for a more comprehensive treatment plan. Other areas of research include cardiovascular intensive medicine surgical care and behavioral health.

On the physician side the Intermountain Medical Group administers multi-specialty health care services in clinics located throughout the region. The group also operates urgent care clinics under the InstaCare and KidsCare banners.

Entering itself into the "what doesn't Intermountain do?" category the health system also provides health and dental insurance plans through its SelectHealth division.

Geographic Reach

Intermountain Healthcare serves the health care needs of Utah and Idaho residents.

Financial Performance

In 2016 Intermountain Healthcare's revenue grew 14% to $7.6 billion in fiscal 2016. This was due to increases in net patient services income non-patient activity income and investment income. Net patient services accounted for 63% of the system's total revenue that year.

The company used $7 billion of that revenue towards operating expenses including salaries and benefits medical supplies and facilities maintenance and other business services as well as towards funds dedicated to future needs.

Strategy

Intermountain Healthcare uses its dedicated supply chain organization to continuously improve system efficiency. In addition to delivering medical supplies the unit also oversees hospital vehicles.

The system partners with several leading IT companies (including Xi3 Intel Dell and NetApp) to operate its Healthcare Transformation Lab on the campus of its flagship hospital Intermountain Medical Center in Murray Utah. The lab researches develops and measures new ideas to improve patient care.

In 2016 the system launched Navican Genomics its genomics research and testing arm. Also that year it partnered with the Stanford Genome Technology Center to establish a collaborative research program.

Intermountain has a number of projects underway to add expand or replace existing facilities.

Company Background

Intermountain was formed in 1975 when the Church of Jesus Christ of Latter Day Saints donated 15 hospitals to local communities.

EXECUTIVES

Senior Vice President Community Health, Mikelle Moore
Senior Vice President, Greg Poulsen
Ceo Intermountain Medical Group And Vp Physician Division, Linda C. Leckman
President And Ceo Selecthealth, Patricia R. Richards
Evp And Cfo, Bert R. Zimmerli
Evp And Coo, Laura S. Kaiser
Regional Vp Central Region, Moody L. Chisholm
Vp And Cio, Marc Probst
President And Ceo, A. Marc Harrison, age 55
Regional Vp Soutwest Region, Terri Kane
Svp And Coo, Robert Allen
Vp Clinical Operations And Chief Nursing Officer, Kim Henrichsen
Regional Vp North Region, Timothy T. Pehrson
Chief Medical Officer, Brent E. Wallace
Ceo Primary Childrenâ's Medical Center, Katherine A. (Katy) Welkie
Regional Vp South Region, Steve Smoot
Vp Supply Chain And Support Services, Joe Walsh
Assistant Vice President Of Risk Management Services, Harlan Hammond
Assistant Vice President Investments, Stacy Jennings
Assistant Vice President Communications, Tom Vitelli
Assistant Vice President Compensation And Benefits, David Adams
Medical Director Utah County Region Intermountain Medical Group, Gordon Harkness
Vice President Healthcare Transformation, Joe Mott
Vice President, George Null Hamilton
Director Of Pharmacy, Scott Yardley
Medical Director, Dean Mayer
Assistant Vice President, Ray Morales
Medical Director, Scott Whittle
Vice President Of Pharmacy Affairs, Eric Cannon
Vice President Human Resources, Dan Zuhlke
Vice President And General Counsel, Doug Hammer
Medical Director, Tamara Lewis
Avp Pharmacy Services, Nannette Berensen
Assistant Vice President Clinical Is Operations, Tammy Madsen
Medical Director Community Health And Prevention, Tamara Sheffield
Pharmacy Manager, Robb Dengg
Pharmacy Manager, Bevan Jensen
Director Of Him, Mary Staub
Pharmacy Manager, Heather Hansen
Assistant Vice President Telehealth Services, Brian Wayling
Medical Director Clinical Genetics Institute, Steven Bleyl
Clinical Director Primary Children's Pediatric Behavioral Health Clinic, Nancy Cantor
Nursing Director, David Hurst
Vice President Of Operational Finance, Mark Runyon
Medical Director Informatics, Farukh Usmani
Pharmacy Manager, Lara Nye
Medical Director Palliative Medicine Mckay Dee Hospital, April Krutka
Pharmacy Director Vice President Of Pharmacy Services, Matt Mitchell
Vice Chairman, Bruce T. Reese
Chairman, A. Scott Anderson
Secretary, Nicole Houghton
Secretary, Jeri Lay
Secretary, Sheri Jones
Medical Secretary, Janet Staker
Medical Secretary, Renee Harston
Scheduling Secretary, Jeanine Price
Secretary, JoAnn Fountain
Medical Secretary, Sherri Longhurst
Secretary, Stephanie Stromberg
Secretary, Jodi Simmons
Auditors: KPMG LLP SALT LAKE CITY UT

LOCATIONS

HQ: INTERMOUNTAIN HEALTH CARE INC
36 S STATE ST STE 1600, SALT LAKE CITY, UT
841111633
Phone: 801 442-2000
Web: WWW.INTERMOUNTAINHEALTHCARE.ORG

PRODUCTS/OPERATIONS

2016 Sales

	$ mil.	% of total
Net patient services	4,369	57
Non-patient activities	3,011	40
Non-operating income	238	3
Total	**7,617**	**100**

Selected Hospitals

Alta View Hospital (Sandy UT)
American Fork Hospital (Utah)
Bear River Valley Hospital (Tremonton UT)
Cassia Regional Medical Center (Burley ID)
Delta Community Medical Center (Utah)
Dixie Regional Medical Center (St. George UT)
Fillmore Community Medical Center (Utah)
Garfield Memorial Hospital (Panguitch UT)
Heber Valley Medical Center (Heber City UT)
Intermountain Medical Center (Murray UT)
LDS Hospital (Salt Lake City)
Logan Regional Hospital (Orem UT)
McKay-Dee Hospital Center (Ogden Utah)
   McKay-Dee Behavioral Health Institute
Orem Community Hospital (Utah)
Park City Medical Center (Park City UT)
Primary Children's Medical Center (Salt Lake City)
Riverton Hospital (Riverton UT)
Sanpete Valley Hospital (Mt. Pleasant UT)
Sevier Valley Hospital (Richfield UT)
TOSH - The Orthopedic Specialty Hospital (Murray UT)
Utah Valley Regional Medical Center (Provo UT)
Valley View Medical Center (Cedar City UT)

COMPETITORS

CHRISTUS Health	Regence BlueCross
Encompass Health	BlueShield of Utah
HCA	St. Mark's
LifePoint Health	University of Utah
Ogden Regional Medical Center	Hospitals & Clinics

HISTORICAL FINANCIALS

Company Type: Private

Income Statement   FYE: December 31

	REVENUE ($ mil.)	NET INCOME ($ mil.)	NET PROFIT MARGIN	EMPLOYEES
12/18	7,724	421	5.4%	35,000
12/17	6,940	1,062	15.3%	—
12/16	6,717	606	9.0%	—
12/15	6,059	156	2.6%	—
Annual Growth	**8.4%**	**39.3%**	**—**	**—**

International Bancshares Corp.

International Bancshares is leading post-NAFTA banking in South Texas. One of the state's largest bank holding companies it does business through nearly 200 locations of International Bank of Commerce (IBC) IBC-Oklahoma Commerce Bank IBC Zapata and IBC Brownsville. The company facilitates trade between the US and Mexico and serves Texas' growing Hispanic population; about 30% of its deposits come from south of the border. In addition to commercial and international banking services for small and midsized businesses International Bancshares provides retail deposit services insurance and investment products mortgages and consumer loans. The bulk of the company's portfolio is made up of commercial financial and agricultural loans and real estate loans for construction.

Operations

Operating under a single segment International Bancshares garners around 70% of its revenue from interest income particularly loans including fees. Non-interest income - mostly from service charges on deposit accounts and other banking service charges commissions and fees - accounts for the rest.

Commercial financial and agricultural loans represent half of International Bancshares' $6.5 billion portfolio. Mortgages and construction real estate loans comprise roughly 20% and 30% of that total respectively.

Geographic Reach

Based in the border city of Laredo Texas International Bancshares has many customers living in Mexico especially northern Mexico. The holding company has nearly 200 branches in South Central and Southeast Texas and Oklahoma. Its primary market area in Texas is bordered on the east by the Galveston area the northwest by Dallas the southwest by Del Rio and to the southeast by Brownsville.

The branches are in the regions of Laredo San Antonio Austin Dallas Houston Zapata Eagle Pass the Rio Grande Valley of Texas the Coastal Bend area of Texas and throughout the State of Oklahoma.

Sales and Marketing

A large proportion of International Bancshares' business is with customers in Mexico; deposits from such clients comprise around 30% of its deposit base.

Financial Performance

International Bancshares has seen modest sputtering growth since 2013 adding approximately 5% to its revenue and 25% to its net income. Cash and long-term debt have fallen less than 5% and about 15% respectively in that time.

International Bancshares' revenue ticked up 4% to $526.6 million in 2017 owing to increased interest income caused by higher loan volume and overall yield. The company's interest expense also decreased following early termination of long-term repurchase agreements by its lead subsidiary bank.

The holding company's net income increased 18% to $157.4 million based on the same interest income improvement and a reduction in its provision for probable loan losses and a tax refund.

Cash stores fell $3.8 million to $265.4 million. Operations provided $196.8 million down slightly from 2016; financing provided $203.1 million mostly due to a net increase in other borrowed funds (which include Federal Home Loan Bank borrowings). Investments used $403.8 million owing primarily a large net decrease in loans.

Strategy

International Bancshares is attempting to shift its focus from commercial banking for small and midsized businesses to consumer and retail banking including mortgage lending and opening branches in retail properties and shopping malls. About 52% of the company's portfolio comprised commercial financial and agricultural loans compared with 56% in 2013. The share accounted for by mortgages increased from 16% in 2013 to 18% in 2017.

Company Background

International Bancshares was founded in 1966.

EXECUTIVES

Senior Vice President, Anselmo Castro
Executive Vice President And Senior Auditor, William Cuellar
Vp And Director; President And Ceo International Bank Of Commerce Mcallen, R. David Guerra, age 66, $245,668 total compensation
Chairman And Ceo; Ceo International Bank Of Commerce Laredo, Dennis E. Nixon, age 76, $659,632 total compensation
President Coo And Cfo International Bank Of Commerce Laredo, Imelda Navarro, age 61, $235,960 total compensation
President And Ceo Commerce Bank Laredo Texas, Ignacio Urrabazo
President And Ceo International Bank Of Commerce Eagle Pass Texas, Hector J. Cerna
Chairman And Ceo International Bank Of Commerce Houston Texas, Jay Rogers
President And Ceo International Bank Of Commerce Zapata Texas, Renato Ramirez
President And Ceo International Bank Of Commerce Austin Texas, Robert B. (Bob) Barnes
Evp And Investor Relations Officer, Eliza Gonzalez
President International Bank Of Commerce Houston Texas, Jeff Samples
President And Ceo International Bank Of Commerce San Antonio, Mike K. Sohn
President And Ceo International Bank Of Commerce Port Lavaca, Derek Schmidt
President And Ceo Corpus Christi, Harold Shockley
President And Ceo International Bank Of Commerce Brownsville, Al Villareal
Ceo San Antonio Service Center, Julie Tarvin
President Southwest Region International Bank Of Commerce, Brian Henry
President International Bank Of Commerce Tulsa, Andrew Levinson
President International Bank Of Commerce Zapata, Ricardo Ramirez
Evp Corporate International, Gerardo (Gerald) Schwebel
President And Ceo International Bank Of Commerce Oklahoma, Bill Schonacher
Evp And International Loan Officer, Natividad Lozano
Senior Vice President Of Marketing And International Banking, Dora Brown
Assistant Vice President, W S Bauer
Senior Vice President Of Commercial Lending, Craig Bunk
Assistant Vice President, Monique Jackson
Vice President Area Sales Manager, Rene Arriaga
First Vice President, Angelica Padron
Vice President, Jennifer Alvarado
Senior Vice President Of It, Hector Vasquez
Vice President Of Accounting, Alvaro Martinez
Vice President Human Resources, Rosie Ramirez
Senior Vice President Of Electronic Services, Kevin Mullins
Vice President Accounting And Operations, David Shinn
Senior Vice President, Eddie Aldrete
Assistant Vice President Support Services, Fernando Santos
Senior Vice President, Efren Pena
Executive Vice President Ibc Service Center, Rene Avila
Executive Vice President, Carlos Martinez
Vice President, Mirta Salcedo
Executive Vice President, Lee Reed
Vice President Life Sales, Markham Benn
Assistant Vice President Commercial Lending, Jose Palafox
Vice President, Anna Mercado
Assistant Vice President Commercial Lender, Bernardo De La Garza
Assistant Vice President, Trena Grob
Senior Vice President, Allen Wise

Senior Vice President Crm Practice Manager
Senior Data Analyst, Shannon Galloway
Assistant Vice President, Debra Lozano
Senior Vice President Mortgage Division Manager,
 Dustin Wells
Auditors: RSM US LLP

LOCATIONS

HQ: International Bancshares Corp.
 1200 San Bernardo Avenue, Laredo, TX 78042-1359
Phone: 956 722-7611
Web: www.ibc.com

PRODUCTS/OPERATIONS

2017 Sales

	% of total
Interest income	
Loans including fees	57
Investment securities	16
Other	
Interest expense	-
Non interest income	
Service charges on deposit accounts	13
Other service charges commissions & fees	9
Other investments net	3
Other	2
Net investment securities transactions	
Total	**100**

Selected Services

Business Investors
Business Online Banking Services
Checking Options
Commercial Insurance
Home and Personal Loans
IBC First Equity
IBC Investment Services
Individual Investors
Life And Health
Manage Your Account
Mobile Banking
Online Banking Center
Online Banking Services
Other Personal Services
Overdraft Courtesy
Personal
Personal Insurance

COMPETITORS

BancFirst	JPMorgan Chase
Bank of America	Lone Star National
Broadway Bancshares	Bancshares
Citigroup	Midland Financial
Cullen/Frost Bankers	Wells Fargo
Falcon Bancshares	
First Victoria	
National Bank	

HISTORICAL FINANCIALS

Company Type: Public

Income Statement

FYE: December 31

	ASSETS ($ mil.)	NET INCOME ($ mil.)	INCOME AS % OF ASSETS	EMPLOYEES
12/18	11,872	216	1.8%	3,390
12/17	12,185	157	1.3%	3,273
12/16	11,804	134	1.1%	3,216
12/15	11,773	137	1.2%	3,218
12/14	12,197	153	1.3%	3,256
Annual Growth	(0.7%)	9.0%	—	1.0%

2018 Year-End Financials

Debt ratio: 7.00%	No. of shares (mil.): 66
Return on equity: 11.00%	Dividends
Cash ($ mil.): 317	Yield: 2.0%
Current ratio: —	Payout: 25.0%
Long-term debt ($ mil.): —	Market value ($ mil.): 2,257

	STOCK PRICE ($) FY Close	P/E High/Low		PER SHARE ($) Earnings	Dividends	Book Value
12/18	34.00	15	10	3.00	1.00	30.00
12/17	40.00	18	14	2.00	1.00	28.00
12/16	41.00	21	11	2.00	1.00	26.00
12/15	26.00	15	11	2.00	1.00	25.00
12/14	27.00	12	9	2.00	1.00	24.00
Annual Growth	6.7%	—	—	9.2%	9.6%	5.6%

International Business Machines Corp

International Business Machines (IBM) bets that cognition is the ignition for growth. The company is investing in it what is calls cognitive computing systems led by the Watson artificial intelligence platform that help customers analyze massive amounts of data to make better decisions. Among other areas the company is betting on for growth are analytics artificial intelligence security cloud blockchain and quantum computing. IBM's information technology business services and software units are among the largest in the world. While IBM has placed less emphasis on hardware the company maintains enterprise server and data storage product lines that are among industry leaders.

Operations

IBM manages its sprawling operations in five segments.

Technology Services and Cloud Platforms which generates about 45% of revenue provides cloud outsourcing and other managed services focused on clients' enterprise IT infrastructure. Offerings include maintenance for IBM products and other technology platforms as well as support.

Cognitive Solutions which provides about a quarter of revenue includes Watson IBM's cognitive computing project. Major Watson initiatives are Watson Platform Watson Health Watson Weather & Media and Watson Internet of Things. Another part of the unit is the company's security platform which provides detection and protection against cyber threats across a customer's operations.

Global Business Services about 20% of revenue provides consulting application management services and global process services to help customers move their businesses to digital platforms.

Systems about 10% of revenue is IBM's hardware business providing technologies for hybrid cloud and cognitive workloads. The unit sells servers storage systems and operating systems software. The segment also designs semiconductor and systems technology in collaboration with IBM Research.

Global Financing provides credit for customers to buy IBM products. It also handles used equipment returned from leases as well as other used and surplus equipment. The unit accounts for about 2% of revenue.

Geographic Reach

IBM has clients in about 175 countries with sales outside the US accounting for more than 45% of revenue. Customers in Europe the Middle East and Africa (EMEA) generate about 30% of sales and those in Asia/Pacific supply about 20% of sales.

Sales and Marketing

IBM operates country-based units where consultants product specialists and other workers facilitate the adoption and fulfillment of its products and services. It serves clients across most industries; leading industry groups include financial services industrial and communications.

Financial Performance

Since IBM posted its highest revenue of nearly $107 billion in 2011 the company's revenue has tumbled nearly $31 million as its older products faded from favor or were sold off. Net income while also losing ground stayed above the $10 billion mark before sliding lower in the past two years.

In 2018 IBM halted the revenue slide reporting a less-than-1% sales increase to $79.6 billion from 2017. It was the first time in six years that sales beat the previous year's results. None of the company's business segments turned in robust growth in 2018 although cloud revenue of $19 billion was 23% higher year-to-year. Systems segment sales weakened dropping 2% which IBM blamed on comparison to a strong performance the previous year and price pressure on storage systems.

Geographically sales in the Europe the Middle East and Africa region rose about 5% while the Asia/Pacific region's sales were flat and the America's sales slipped about 2% in 2018 from 2017.

Net income jumped more than 50% to $8.7 billion in 2018 from $5.7 billion in 2017 due lower year-to-year tax charges related to the US Tax Cuts and Jobs Act of 2017.

IBM had cash and equivalents of $11.6 billion in 2018 down about $600 million from the year before. In 2018 the company's operations generated $15.2 billion in cash while investing activities and financing activities used $4.9 billion and $10.4 billion respectively.

Strategy

IBM thinks its investments in cognitive computing cloud security big data and analytics are beginning to pay off. IBM reported that its newer offerings accounted more than 50% of 2018 revenue compared to 25% four years ago.

IBM also is investing in emerging technologies such as blockchain and those in earlier stages of research such as quantum computing. As the perennial leader (26 straight years) in the number of US patents granted IBM maintains a steady pipeline of potential products.

In cloud computing the company competes with Amazon Microsoft and Google which have built up strong leads. IBM focuses on hybrid cloud the mixture of keeping data on IBM computers and the customer's own systems.

The acquisition of Red Hat (for about $34 billion) was made to turbocharge IBM's hybrid cloud business. IBM intends to offer customers a path to cloud environments in a way that's not dependent on hardware but on Red Hat's open source software which should be less costly and time-consuming. The deal closed in mid-2019.

IBM strives to move its offerings to higher margin products and services as it sells those with lower margins even if it reduces overall revenue. In 2018 the company sold collaboration marketing and commerce software assets to HCL Technologies for $1.8 billion. IBM in 2019 said it would sell the Seterus mortgage servicing platform business. In another 2019 divestment IBM agreed to sell marketing platform and commerce software products to Centerbridge Partners an investment firm. Centerbridge intends to create a standalone company from the software assets.

Mergers and Acquisitions

IBM in 2019 acquired Red Hat for $34 billion one of the biggest software acquisitions in history. The deal brings Red Hat's open source software to IBM's cloud efforts. Red Hat became a unit in IBM and reports as part of the Cloud and Cognitive

464

Software segment. The deal was proposed in 2018 and closed in 2019.

In 2018 IBM acquired Armanta a provider of aggregation and analytics software to financial services firms. The acquisition allows IBM to customers further integrate their risk management practices with other front or back office functions.

In another 2018 deal IBM bought Oniqua Holdings a provider of maintenance repair and operations (MRO) services for the mining oil and gas transportation utilities manufacturing and other asset-intensive industries. With the Oniqua products IBM can offer MRO services that connect with data to help users forecast equipment failures optimize spare parts and reduce unplanned downtime.

Company Background

In 1914 National Cash Register's star salesman Thomas Watson left to rescue the flagging Computing-Tabulating-Recording (C-T-R) Company the pioneer in US punch card processing that had been incorporated in 1911. Watson aggressively marketed C-T-R's tabulators supplying them to the US government during WWI and tripling company revenues to almost $15 million by 1920. The company became International Business Machines (IBM) in 1924 and soon dominated the global market for tabulators time clocks and electric typewriters. It was the US's largest office machine maker by 1940.

IBM perfected electromechanical calculation (the Harvard Mark I 1944) but initially dismissed the potential of computers. When Remington Rand's UNIVAC computer (1951) began replacing IBM machines IBM quickly responded. The company unveiled its first computer in 1952. With its superior research and development and marketing IBM built a market share near 80% in the 1960s and 1970s.

In 1993 CEO John Akers was replaced by Louis Gerstner the first outsider to run IBM. He began to turn the ailing antiquated company around by slashing costs and nonstrategic divisions cutting the workforce shaking up entrenched management and pushing services. In 1994 Big Blue reported its first profit in four years. It also began making computer chips that year.

Since then IBM has tried to keep ahead of its aging product lineup. It introduced the Watson artificial intelligence platform (named after Thomas Watson) in 2011 (as a contest on special episodes of Jeopardy!) as part of its renewal program that took it into cloud computing cybersecurity blockchain and it hopes someday into quantum computing.

EXECUTIVES

Vp Ww Isc Engineering, Sophie Bechu

Svp Ibm Watson And Cloud Platform, David W. Kenny, age 57

Vice President Of Legal, Martha Rendeiro

Svp Technology And Intellectual Property, John E. Kelly, age 66, $754,000 total compensation

Chairman President And Ceo, Virginia M. (Ginni) Rometty, age 61, $1,600,000 total compensation

Svp Ibm Cloud, Robert J. LeBlanc, age 60

Svp Global Business Services, Mark Foster, age 60

Svp Global Markets And Chairman Ibm Europe, Erich Clementi, age 60, $703,500 total compensation

Svp Global Markets, Martin J. Schroeter, age 54, $754,000 total compensation

Svp Ibm Watson Group, Michael D. (Mike) Rhodin, age 58, $630,000 total compensation

Svp Ibm Systems, Thomas W. (Tom) Rosamilia, age 58

Svp Global Markets, Bruno V. Di Leo, age 61

Svp Ibm Analytics, Robert J. (Bob) Picciano, age 60

Svp And Cfo, James J. Kavanaugh, age 52

Svp Ibm Industry Platforms, Bridget A. van Kralingen, age 55, $665,000 total compensation

Svp Ibm Global Technology Services, Martin Jetter, age 59, $650,000 total compensation

Cio, Fletcher Previn

Vice President, David Smith

Vice President, Mike Wing

Vice President Information Technology Services Strategy And Cloud, Ric Telford

Vice President Information Technology, Bryan Adair

Vice President Architect Global Sales Manager Software Engineering, Don Bradford

Vice President, John Kirkwood

Vice President Mergers And Acquisitions, Kareem Yusuf

Vice President Software Ibm Research, David Mcqueeney

Vice President Of Human Resources, Gary Kildare

Vice President Finance And Operations Ibm Channels, David Colistra

Vice President Finance And Director, James W Boyken

Vp Software General Business Americas, Tom Turchet

Vice President World Wide Dcm, Annie Cheung

Vice President Marketing And Communications, Brad Timothy

Vice President Systems Hardware Us Federal Team, Sandy Krawchuk

Vp Global Client Innovation Centers, Albert Schneider

Vice President And Partner, Srinivas Attili

Executive Vice President World Wide Sales Tivoli S, Baba Gold

Vp Industry Sales, Mark Easton

Vice President Of Sales For Global Telecommunications Industry, John Polly

Vice President Strategic Services, Randall Dalia

Vice President Telecommunications Industry Americas, Dave Mancl

Vice President Worldwide Sales, Robert Wong

Vice President And Partner Digital Service Line Leader, Susan Wedge

Vice President Software Business Partners And Midmarket, Mark Register

Vice President Of Human Resources Technology, Steve Rolando

Vice President Human Resources Business, Tania Mcveety

Vice President Mkt Channels Websphere, Kristen Lauria

Vice President Operations, Emilio Griman

Vice President Partner Energy And Utility Industry Leader, Jim Bales

Vice President North America Microelectronics Sales, David Faircloth

Vice President Sales, Arlene Garcia

Vice President Human Resources Sales Incentive Compensation, Richard Rabjohn

Vice President Human Resources Ibm Canada Ltd, Anne Berend

Vice President Of Marketing, Jack Brown

Vice President Global Sales, Rick Fuchs

Vice President Business Development, Mark Bytner

Vice President Operations Ibm Uk And Ireland, Joseph Sweeney

Vp Marketing Ibm Systems North America, Christine Lemyze

Vp Ips, Jason Silvia

Vice President, Don Jue

Vice President, Daniel Delena

Vice President Of Marketing And Strategy, Roland Hagan

Vice President Public Sector Americas, Marianne Cooper

Vp Global Infor Alliance, Michael Uhl

Vice President Strategic Services, Brett Flory

Vice President Semiconductor Research And Development Center, Gary Patton

Vice President Ar Bcs, Christine Kinser

Vice President, Vince Masi

Vice President Technology, Jay Cook

Vice President Marketing, Deon Newman

Vice President, David Simms

Vice President, Juhi Jotwani

Vice President Human Resources Software Group, Thomas Fleming

Vice President Demand Generation, Ed Abrams

Vice President Marketing Nonesuch, Patrick Clarke

Vice President Assistant General Counsel, Daniela Combe

Vice President Marketing And Communications, Maria Reeves Hayes

Senior Vice President Marketing Storage Technologies, Jim Kely

Vice President, James Wallis

Vice President Partner Enablement, William Bill Liebler

Senior Vice President, Bob Moffat

Vice President Iseries Marketing, Peter Bingaman

Vice President Social Business And Smarter Workforce Solutions, Katrina Troughton

Vice President Information Security Strategy, John Hsieh

Vice President Federal Systems Integration Sales, Kevin Costello

International Leader Vice President Worldwide Sales, David Valovcin

Vp Storage Transformation Systems, Cristiane Hilkner

Vice President Ibm Enterprise Storage Ds8870 And Tape, Calline Sanchez

Vice President East Coast Sales, Craig Singler

Vice President, Ben Edwards

Vice President Ibm Storage Systems, Michael Kuhn

Vice President Bcs Procurement, Brian Eck

Vice President Sales, Michele Stern

Vice President Manager Director, Christopher Goudreau

Vice President Digital Sales Marketing And Private Digital Commerce North America, Julie Ciardi

Vp Global Senior Pe, Scott Roberts

Vice President Of Global Community Initiatives, Paula Baker

Vice President Global University Programs, Naguib Attia

Vice President Information Technology, Dennis Jay

Assistant Vice President Services Overall, Jen Noble

Vice President Of Business Development, Janine Grasso

Worlwide Vice President Of Sales Systems And Tech, Bob Hoey

Worldwide Vice President Business Partners Sales Ibm Software Group, Vincent Zandvliet

Vice President Sales, Peter Andino

Vice President Product Management Watson Health, Cory Wiegert

Vice President Of Mobile Brand Marketing, Rick McGee

Vice President Marketing Systems And Technology Gr, Carla Pun

Vice President Advanced Technology, Gina Willis

Vice President Tax And Treasurer, Simon Beaumont

Vice President Security Growth Initiatives Security Services, Shelley Westman

Vice President Sales And Marketing Western Region, Scott Ferber

Vice President Technical Sales Support, Walt Ling

Vice President, Luis Fernandez

Vice President Finance, Neal Marx

Vice President Storage Systems, Brian Hamel

Vice President Human Resources, Horst Gallo

Vice President For Software Standards And Cloud Co, Angel Thompson

Vice President Information Technology, Bob Weber

Vice President Of Marketing Communication, Lisa Baird

Vice President Diversity Employee Experience, Patricia Lewis

Vice President, Sean Hogan

Vice President Of Sales Strategy Ibm Software Grou, Barry — Freimark

Vp Ww Client Centers, Doug Dreyer

Vice President Marketing, Katharyn White

Vice President Of Sales: East Smb, John Schultz

Vice President Marketing, Jennifer Bucher

Vice President Worldwide Market Development, John Holz

Vp It Service, Sam Lee

Vice President Worldwide Saas Sales Leader Software Group, Beth Vaughn

Vice President Technical Support Services, John Porter

Vice President Of Strategy For Ibm Sales, Felicia Hochheiser

Vice President And Chief Techn, Jason Wilkinson

Vice President Of Strategy Global Business Services, Ian Watson

Vice President Of Supply Chain Management, Tom Edwards

Vice President, Allen Downs

Client Unit Vice President Of Sales Distribution Sector, Curtis Cade

Vice President And Partner Sap Leader, Mark Towell

Vice President Business And Corporate Development, Morgan Crew

Vice President Federal Software Group, Dermot Murray

Vice President Software Alliances, Mark Hanny

Senior Vice President And Trust Officer, George Araujo

Senior Vice President Ibm Systems And Technology Group, Andrew Mason

Vice President North America Competitive Sales General Business Ibm, Bill Brooks

Vice President, Bob Curran

Vice President Business Development Its, Anil Philip

Vice President, Michael Karasick

Vice President Ibm Global Financing North America Client Financing, Brad Graham

Vice President World Wide Sales Data Management Division, Marc Dupaquier

Vice President Marketing Ibm Security, Lindsey Lurie

Vice President Development Websphere, Buff Jones

Vice President Life Sciences Compliance Global Regulatory And Cyber Security Management, Jim McCormack

Vice President Global Business Development, Dan Friedman

Vice President And Partner North America Delivery Leader, Gloria Samuels

Auditors: PricewaterhouseCoopers LLP

LOCATIONS

HQ: International Business Machines Corp
One New Orchard Road, Armonk, NY 10504
Phone: 914 499-1900   Fax: 914 765-4190
Web: www.ibm.com

2018 Sales

	$ mil.	% of total
Americas	36,994	46
Europe/Middle East/Africa	25,491	32
Asia Pacific	17,106	22
Total	**79,591**	**100**

PRODUCTS/OPERATIONS

2018 Sales

	$ mil.	% of total
Technology Services & Cloud Platforms	34,462	44
Cognitive Solutions	18,481	23
Global Business Services	16,817	21
Systems	8,034	10
Global Financing	1,590	2
Other	2,017	-
Total	**79,591**	**100**

Selected Services

Global Technology Services
  Cloud Services
  Mobility Services
  Networking Services
  Outsourcing and Managed Services
  Resiliency Services
  Security Services
  Site and Data Center Services
  Systems Services
  Technical Support Services
Financing
Technology services
  Application Management
  Global Process Services
  IT Infrastructure Services
  IT Outsourcing
Training
  Offerings
  Certification
  Conferences & Events
Additional Services
  System Lab Services
  Consulting Alliances
  Mobile Enterprise Services
  Project Financing
  Working Capital
Technology Services
  Business Process Outsourcing
  Infrastructure
  System Integration
  Systems Management
  Web Hosting

Selected Products

Systems
  Power Systems
  Z Systems
  LinuxOne
  Middleware
  Application Platform
  Smarter Process
Servers
Software
  Application development
  Business Analytics (Cognos SPSS)
  Cloud & Smarter Infrastructure
  Enterprise Content Management
  IBM Platform Computing
  Information Management (DB2 Informix InfoSphere)
  Rational (Software and Systems Delivery)
  IBM Security
  WebSphere (Integration a nd Optimization)
  Z Systems Software
Storage
  Software Defined Storage
  Flash Storage
  Optical Libraries
  Storage Area Networking
  Tape/Virtual Tape Storage
  Storage networking

COMPETITORS

AWS	Hewlett Packard
Accenture	Enterprise
Apple Inc.	Hitachi
Capgemini	Infosys
Cisco Systems	Microsoft
Cognizant Tech	NEC
Solutions	NTT DATA
DXC Technology	Oracle
Dell	SAP
Deloitte Consulting	Tata Consultancy
Fujitsu	Wipro Technologies
Google	

HISTORICAL FINANCIALS

Company Type: Public

Income Statement

FYE: December 31

	REVENUE ($ mil.)	NET INCOME ($ mil.)	NET PROFIT MARGIN	EMPLOYEES
12/18	79,591	8,728	11.0%	350,600
12/17	79,139	5,753	7.3%	366,600
12/16	79,919	11,872	14.9%	380,300
12/15	81,741	13,190	16.1%	377,757
12/14	92,793	12,022	13.0%	379,592
Annual Growth	(3.8%)	(7.7%)	—	(2.0%)

2018 Year-End Financials

Debt ratio: 37.00%
Return on equity: 51.00%
Cash ($ mil.): 11,604
Current ratio: 1.00
Long-term debt ($ mil.): 35,605

No. of shares (mil.): 892
Dividends
  Yield: 5.0%
  Payout: 65.0%
Market value ($ mil.): 101,448

	STOCK PRICE ($) FY Close	P/E High/Low		PER SHARE ($) Earnings	Dividends	Book Value
12/18	114.00	18	11	10.00	6.00	19.00
12/17	153.00	29	23	6.00	6.00	19.00
12/16	166.00	14	9	12.00	6.00	19.00
12/15	138.00	13	10	13.00	5.00	15.00
12/14	160.00	17	13	12.00	4.00	12.00
Annual Growth	(8.3%)	—	—	(5.4%)	9.9%	11.9%

International Paper Co

International Paper (IP) is one of the world's largest manufacturers of printing papers. Products include uncoated paper used in printers and market pulp for tissue and paper products. In the US IP is #1 in containerboard production where 80% of materials are converted to industrial corrugated boxes. IP serves more than 25000 customers in 150 countries. Most of its more than 250 mills converting and packaging plants and recycling facilities are in the US. It also runs a pulp and paper business in Russia via a 50/50 joint venture with Ilim Holding. About 75% of IP's revenue is generated in the US.

Operations

IP operates in three segments: Industrial Packaging (almost 70% of net sales) Printing Papers (about 20%) and Global Cellulose Fibers (more than 10%).

Industrial Packaging is the largest manufacturer of containerboard in the US with a production capacity of more than 13 million tons annually. Products include linerboard and recycled linerboard medium and recycled medium whitetop and saturating kraft. This business makes the company's ClimaShield moisture barrier which comprises an environmentally-friendly coating used on some of its products. About 80% of Industrial Packaging production is converted into corrugated boxes and other packaging by its 180-plus North American container plants.

The Printing Papers segment produces printing and writing papers mainly uncoated papers. These are sold under private label and International Paper brands such as Hammermill Springhill Williamsburg Postmark and several others. The Global Cellulose Fibers product portfolio includes fluff (filler in diapers and incontinence products) market pulp (used for tissue and paper products) and specialty pulps used for such things as textiles filtration and paints and coatings.

Geographic Reach

Headquartered in Memphis TN IP has manufacturing operations in Europe North and South America North Africa and Asia (India and Russia). In the US it operates more than 25 pulp paper and packaging mills about 165 converting and packaging plants more than 15 recycling plants and three bag facilities. Outside the US the company operates some 15 mills roughly 45 converting and packaging plants and two recycling plants.

The company operates its primary research and development center in Loveland Ohio as well as several other product development facilities including the Global Cellulose Fibers technology center in Federal Way WA.

The US is IP's largest market representing about 75% of sales each year. EMEA is its second-largest market generating around 15% followed by the Asia Pacific region?almost 5%.

Sales and Marketing

IP's products are used in copiers desktop and laser printers digital imaging filtration construction materials and paints and coatings. End-use applications include advertising and promotional materials such as brochures pamphlets greeting cards books annual reports and direct mail.

The company sells products directly to end users and converters as well as through agents resellers and paper distributors.

Financial Performance

IP's revenue has fluctuated over the last five years with sales in 2018 still below previous years' figures. Profits however have more than doubled in the same time period.

Revenue went from $21.7 billion in 2017 to $23.3 billion in 2018?an increase of 7% and the second consecutive year of higher sales. Higher sales volumes and higher average sales prices contributed to the increase.

The company's profits dipped to $2.0 billion in 2018 compared with $2.1 billion the previous year. Although IP's corporate costs and tax expenses were lower increases in operating costs and maintenance outage costs drove profits down.

Cash at the end of fiscal 2018 was $589 million a decrease of $429 million from the prior year. Cash from operations contributed $3.2 billion to the coffers while investing activities used $1.6 billion mainly for capital projects. Financing activities used another $2.0 billion for loan payments dividends to stockholders and the company's stock repurchase program.

Strategy

After experiencing a sharp decline in demand as more media is consumed digitally IP has gotten back on track in recent years by focusing on products that are spiking in other markets. It zeroed in on the aging baby boomers generation as the adult diaper market is predicted to explode in the years ahead. As a global maker of fluff?a primary ingredient in adult incontinence products?IP is poised to take advantage of this swiftly growing market through its Global Cellulose Fibers segment.

To focus on its industrial packaging business the company transferred its North American consumer packaging business which included its North American coated paperboard and foodservice businesses to Graphic Packaging International Partners (GPIP) a subsidiary of Graphic Packaging Holding Company in exchange for a 20.5% ownership interest in GPIP.

Capitalizing on the low-cost high-growth markets in Russia and Asia IP has partnered with Ilim Holding S.A. in Russia forming a 50/50 joint venture to produce uncoated paper and packaging products in the region.

HISTORY

In 1898 nearly 20 northeastern pulp and paper firms consolidated to lower costs. The resulting International Paper had 20 mills in Maine Massachusetts New Hampshire New York and Vermont. The mills relied on forests in New England and Canada for wood pulp. When Canada enacted legislation to stop the export of pulpwood in 1919 International Paper formed Canadian International Paper.

During the 1940s and 1950s the company bought Agar Manufacturing (shipping containers 1940) Single Service Containers (Pure-Pak milk containers 1946) and Lord Baltimore Press (folding cartons 1958). It diversified in the 1960s and 1970s buying Davol (hospital products 1968; sold to C. R. Bard 1980) American Central (land development 1968; sold to developers 1974) and General Crude Oil (gas and oil 1975; sold to Mobil Oil 1979).

Decades later International Paper picked up Shorewood Packaging for $850 million in 2000. That year it made an unsolicited $6.2 billion bid for Champion International— which had previously agreed to be acquired by UPM-Kymmene— igniting a bidding war. UPM withdrew its offer however and International Paper acquired Champion for about $9.6 billion.

After surviving the Great Recession IP made one of its most significant acquisitions to date in 2012 when it acquired Temple-Inland one of North America's top producers of corrugated packaging in a transaction valued at $4.5 billion.

EXECUTIVES

National Account Manager, Todd J Taylor

Svp Human Resources Government Relations And Global Citizenship, Thomas G. (Tom) Kadien, age 63, $629,167 total compensation

Svp Consumer Packaging, Catherine I. Slater, age 55

Svp Industrial Packaging The Americas, Timothy S. (Tim) Nicholls, age 58, $710,000 total compensation

Chairman And Ceo, Mark S. Sutton, age 58, $1,200,000 total compensation

Svp Manufacturing Technology Ehs And Global Sourcing, Tommy S. Joseph, age 59, $600,000 total compensation

Svp Pulp, Jean-Michel Ribieras, age 56, $420,000 total compensation

Svp And President Ip Latin America, Glenn R. Landau, age 50

Svp Paper The Americas, W. Michael Amick, age 55, $500,000 total compensation

Svp And President Europe The Middle East Africa And Russia, John V. Sims, age 56

Svp North American Container, Gregory T. Wanta, age 53

Svp Global Cellulose Fibers, Jean-Michel Ribiéras, age 56

Senior Vice President Online Marketing, Chris Werner

Vice President Human Resources Operations, Bathsheba Sams

National Account Manager, Jennifer Mugavero

Vice President Investments, Robert Hunkeler

Vice President Supply Chain North American Papers Pulp And Coated Paperboard, Fred Towler

Vice President Ir, Guillermo Gutierrez

Svp Corporate Development, Carleton Ealy

National Account Manager, Doug Arters

Vice President And General Manager Xpedx Illinois Division, Thomas Plath

National Account Manager, Thomas Hendricks

National Account Manager, Axel Iglesias

Vp And General Manager North American Container, Gary Gavin

Vice President Pulp, John Fisher

Carolinas Vice President Operations, John Hash

Vp Industrial Packaging Group Strategy And Finance, September Blain

Vp And General Manager Containerboard And Recycling, Thomas Cleves

Vice President, Pamela Hollingsworth

National Account Manager, Jenae Lewis

Vice President, Pat Leggett

Vice President Corporate Audit, Marc Van Lieshout

National Accounts Manager, Michael T Murphy

Senior Vice President Consumer Pkg, Catherine I Slater

Senior Vice President, Debbie Ellington

National Sales Manager, Dennis Smith

National Account Manager, Mike Nelson

National Accounts Manager, Michael Murphy

National Accounts Manager, Dan Hensley

Svp Paper The Americas, W Michael Amick Jr

Department Head, Philandria Hughes

Vp Of Information Technology, Malgorzata Szarek

National Account Manager, Lauren Sickinger

Board Member, J Steven Whisler

Board Member, Jay Johnson

Board Member, A Johnson

Board Member, Steven Whisler

Board Member, Stacey Mobley

Auditors: DELOITTE & TOUCHE LLP

LOCATIONS

HQ: International Paper Co
6400 Poplar Avenue, Memphis, TN 38197
Phone: 901 419-7000
Web: www.internationalpaper.com

2016 Sales

	$ mil.	% of total
Americas		
US	15,918	76
Other countries	1,581	7
EMEA	2,862	14
Pacific Rim & Asia	718	3
Total	**21,079**	**100**

PRODUCTS/OPERATIONS

2016 Sales

	$ mil.	% of total
Industrial packaging	14,191	67
Printing papers	4,058	19
Consumer packaging	1,954	9
Global Cellulose Fibers	1,092	5
Adjustments	(216)	-
Total	**21,079**	**100**

Selected Operations and Products

Consumer Packaging
  Cold cups and lids
  Consumer-ready packaging (Shorewood Packaging folding carton set-up box)
  Folding carton board
  Food buckets and lids
  Hot cups and lids
  Milk container and lids
  Starcote tobacco board
Distribution North America (xpedx)
  Building services and away-from-home markets with facility supplies
  Commercial printers with printing papers and graphic pre-press printing presses post press equipment
  Manufacturers with packaging supplies and equipment
  Warehousing and delivery services
Industrial Packaging
  Automotive packaging
  Corrugated pallet
  Die-cut package
  Flapless
  Kraft linerboard
  Laminated bulk bin
  Liquid bulk
  Litho lamination
  Medium paper
  Retail displays
  Saturating kraft

Slotted container
White top liner
Papers
HP (Hewlett-Packard) home and commercial papers
Office papers
Pulp
Fluff pulp
Paper and tissue pulp
Recycling products
Old corrugated containers and kraft corrugated cuttings
Old newspaper

COMPETITORS

Amcor	Nippon Paper
Cascades Inc.	Packaging Corp. of
ENCE Energia y	America
Celulosa SA	Smurfit Kappa
Georgia-Pacific	Stora Enso
Louisiana-Pacific	UPM-Kymmene
M-real	Weyerhaeuser
Mondi	

HISTORICAL FINANCIALS

Company Type: Public

Income Statement   FYE: December 31

	REVENUE ($ mil.)	NET INCOME ($ mil.)	NET PROFIT MARGIN	EMPLOYEES
12/18	23,306	2,012	8.6%	53,000
12/17	21,743	2,144	9.9%	56,000
12/16	21,079	904	4.3%	55,000
12/15	22,365	938	4.2%	56,000
12/14	23,617	555	2.4%	58,000
Annual Growth	(0.3%)	38.0%	—	(2.2%)

2018 Year-End Financials

Debt ratio: 32.00%
Return on equity: 29.00%
Cash ($ mil.): 589
Current ratio: 1.00
Long-term debt ($ mil.): 10,015

No. of shares (mil.): 401
Dividends
  Yield: 5.0%
  Payout: 40.0%
Market value ($ mil.): 16,168

	STOCK PRICE ($) FY Close	P/E High/Low		PER SHARE ($) Earnings	Dividends	Book Value
12/18	40.00	13	8	5.00	2.00	18.00
12/17	58.00	11	10	5.00	2.00	16.00
12/16	53.00	25	15	2.00	2.00	11.00
12/15	38.00	26	16	2.00	2.00	9.00
12/14	54.00	43	35	1.00	1.00	12.00
Annual Growth	(6.8%)			39.2%	7.3%	10.8%

Interpublic Group of Companies Inc.

The Interpublic Group of Companies is one of the world's largest advertising and marketing services conglomerates. Its flagship creative agencies include McCann Worldgroup and Lowe & Partners while such firms as Deutsch and Hill Holliday are leaders in the US advertising business. Interpublic also offers direct marketing media services and public relations through such agencies as Initiative and Weber Shandwick. Its largest have clients included General Motors Johnson & Johnson Microsoft Samsung and Unilever.

HISTORY

Standard Oil advertising executive Harrison McCann opened the H. K. McCann Company in 1911 and signed Standard Oil of New Jersey (later Exxon) as his first client. McCann's ad business boomed as the automobile became an integral part of American life. His firm merged with Alfred Erickson's agency (created 1902) in 1930 forming the McCann-Erickson Company. At the end of the decade the firm hired Marion Harper a top Yale graduate as a mailroom clerk. Harper became president in 1948.

Harper began acquiring other ad agencies and by 1961 controlled more than 20 companies. That year he unveiled a plan to create a holding company that would let the ad firms operate separately allowing them to work on accounts for competing products but giving them the parent firm's financial and information resources. He named the company Interpublic Inc. after a German research company owned by the former H. K. McCann Co. The conglomerate continued expanding and was renamed The Interpublic Group of Companies in 1964. Harper's management capabilities weren't up to the task however and the company soon faced bankruptcy. In 1967 the board replaced him with Robert Healy who saved Interpublic and returned it to profitability. The company went public in 1971.

The 1970s were fruitful years for Interpublic; its ad teams created memorable campaigns for Coke ("It's the Real Thing" and "Have a Coke and a Smile") and Miller Beer ("Miller Time" and Miller Lite ads). After Philip Geier became chairman in 1980 the company gained a stake in Lowe Howard-Spink (1983; it later became The Lowe Group) and bought Lintas International (1987). Interpublic bought the rest of The Lowe Group in 1990.

Interpublic bought Western International Media (now known as Initiative) and Ammirati & Puris (which was merged with Lintas to form Ammirati Puris Lintas) in 1994. As industry consolidation picked up in 1996 Interpublic kept pace with acquisitions of PR company Weber Group and Draft-Worldwide. Interpublic bought a majority stake in artist management and film production company Addis-Wechsler & Associates (now Industry Entertainment) in 1997 and later formed sports marketing and management group Octagon.

Interpublic acquired US agencies Carmichael Lynch and Hill Holliday Connors Cosmopulos in 1998. It also boosted its PR presence with its purchase of International Public Relations (UK) the parent company of public relations networks Shandwick and Golin/Harris. Interpublic strengthened its position in the online world in 1999 when it bought 20% of Stockholm-based Internet services company Icon Medialab International. That year the company merged agencies Ammirati and Lowe & Partners Worldwide to form Lowe Lintas & Partners Worldwide (in 2002 they changed the name to just Lowe & Partners Worldwide).

Interpublic bought market research firm NFO Worldwide for $580 million in 2000 and merged Weber Public Relations with Shandwick International to form Weber Shandwick Worldwide one of the world's largest PR firms. Later that year the company bought ad agency Deutsch for about $250 million. John Dooner took the position of chairman and CEO at the end of the year after Geier resigned. His first move proved a big one: Interpublic acquired True North Communications for $2.1 billion in stock in 2001.

The honeymoon was short lived; facing a recession the mounting debt from its buying spree and with the revelation of accounting discrepancies at McCann-Erickson WorldGroup (renamed McCann Worldgroup in 2004) Dooner stepped aside as chairman and CEO in 2003. Interpublic chose vice chairman David Bell (former CEO of True North) as Dooner's replacement. After almost two years of work to improve Interpublic's balance sheet Bell was replaced by former MONY Group chief Michael Roth.

In 2005 Roth was tasked with straightening out Interpublic's financial controls and improving its balance sheet. Later that year the company revealed extensive bookkeeping problems primarily in its overseas operations leading to a financial restatement going back to 2000.

In order to simplify its operating structure in 2006 Interpublic integrated direct marketer Draft Inc. with advertising agency Foote Cone & Belding (forming DraftFCB). A year later it restructured its vast network of media brands to report under a single management structure (Mediabrands).

Looking to India in mid-2007 Interpublic bought all the shares of FCB Ulka a top-five ad agency in the country that operated from six offices. Interpublic integrated the Indian agency with its Draft-FCB operations. At the same time it acquired the remaining 51% stake it didn't hold in Lintas India Private Limited at a cost of $50 million in cash and integrated it into its Lowe Worldwide network.

In 2010 Interpublic acquired Brazilian creative advertising strategy firm CUBOCC and London-based marketing agency Delaney Lund Knox Warren & Partners (DLKW). During 2011 the company acquired several marketing agencies. In early 2012 Interpublic obtained German consumer lifestyle agency Nicole Weber Communications (NWC) and UK-based digital and interactive agency FUSE.

EXECUTIVES

Svp And Managing Director, Terry D. Peigh
Chairman And Ceo, Michael I. Roth, age 73, $1,500,000 total compensation
Evp And Cfo, Frank Mergenthaler, age 58, $1,000,000 total compensation
Evp And Chief Strategy And Talent Officer, Philippe Krakowsky, age 57, $1,000,000 total compensation
Svp And Managing Director, Peter Leinroth
Svp General Counsel And Secretary, Andrew Bonzani, age 55, $800,000 total compensation
Svp Controller And Chief Accounting Officer, Christopher F. Carroll, age 52, $587,714 total compensation
Svp And Cio, John Halper
Vice President Associate General Counsel And Assistant Secretary, Robert Dobson
Vice President Business Strategy, Helene Yan
Vice President Associate General Counsel Managing Attorney Chief Of Staff And Latam Regional Coordinator, William Crosby
Svp And Chief Growth Officer, Simon Bond
Vice President Financial Planning And Analysis, Michael Delvecchio
Senior Vice President And Account Group Director Accentmarketing, Alice Rivera
Executive Vice President Creative Director And Managing Partner Accentmarketing, Diana Ocasio-Fant
Vice President Global Client Finance Director Mediabrands, Nicole Aronzon
Vice President Global Sourcing And Chief Procurement Officer, Eliseo Rojas
Vice President Real Estate And Insurance, Richard Haray
Vp Corporate Communications, Tom Cunningham
Senior Vice President External Affairs, Nancy Nichols
Senior Vice President And Deputy Managing Director T, Michelle Maggs

Executive Vice President Chief Growth Officer, Barry Wacksman

Senior Vice President Human Resources, Molly Roenna

Vice President Crrd Pm, Lori Woodcock

Executive Vice President Worldwide Director Of Employee Learning Hfd, Stewart Alter

Senior Vice President Group Mng. Director, Kevin Scher

Executive Vice President Account Director, Craig Bagno

Vice President Global Training Manager, Adeline Mahoney

Senior Vice President Art Director, Kris Kiger

Vice President Executive Creative Director Mobile And Emerging Platforms Group, Richard Ting

Vice President Director Of Client Finance, Jonathan Schechter

Senior Vice President Creative Director, Marcia J Goddard

Vice President Finance, Andy Queen

Vice President Director Of Payroll Admin, Francelia Febus

Senior Vice President Broadcast Operations, Eileen Feeney

Vice President, Patrick Reyes

Vice President Account Director Brand Century Regal 365 Golf, Michael Crone

Vice President Creative Director, Kathleen Vanhoff

Vice President Worldgroup Technology, Ed Recinto

Senior Vice President, Michael Presson

Vice President Strategic Planning, BRIAN SCRANTON

Experiential Marketing Vice President, John Sattler

Vice President Strategy Director, Barbara Hirsch

Executive Vice President Executive Creative Director, Auge Reichenberg

Senior Vice President Group Creative Director, Nadia Kamran

Senior Vice President Group Strategy Director, Julieta Smith

Vice President Account Director, Tanya Kennedy

Vice President Senior Producer, Chance Bassett

Vice President Ad Operations Analytics And Product Management, Liam Ross

Senior Vice President Talent Acquisition, Aimee Collin

Board Member, Mary Guilfoile

Board Member, Jocelyn Carter-miller

Board Member, William Kerr

Board Member, Patrick Moore

Auditors: PricewaterhouseCoopers LLP

LOCATIONS

HQ: Interpublic Group of Companies Inc.
909 Third Avenue, New York, NY 10022
Phone: 212 704-1200
Web: www.interpublic.com

COMPETITORS

Dentsu	Omnicom
Dentsu Aegis	Publicis Groupe
Hakuhodo	WPP
Havas	

HISTORICAL FINANCIALS

Company Type: Public

Income Statement — FYE: December 31

	REVENUE ($ mil.)	NET INCOME ($ mil.)	NET PROFIT MARGIN	EMPLOYEES
12/18	9,714	619	6.4%	54,000
12/17	7,882	579	7.3%	50,200
12/16	7,847	609	7.8%	49,800
12/15	7,614	455	6.0%	49,200
12/14	7,537	477	6.3%	47,400
Annual Growth	6.5%	6.7%	—	3.3%

2018 Year-End Financials

Debt ratio: 24.00%
Return on equity: 27.00%
Cash ($ mil.): 673
Current ratio: 1.00
Long-term debt ($ mil.): 3,660

No. of shares (mil.): 384
Dividends
Yield: 4.0%
Payout: 53.0%
Market value ($ mil.): 7,914

	STOCK PRICE ($) FY Close	P/E High/Low	PER SHARE ($) Earnings	Dividends	Book Value
12/18	21.00	16 12	2.00	1.00	6.00
12/17	20.00	17 12	1.00	1.00	6.00
12/16	23.00	16 13	1.00	1.00	5.00
12/15	23.00	21 16	1.00	0.00	5.00
12/14	21.00	18 14	1.00	0.00	5.00
Annual Growth	(0.2%)	— —	9.2%	21.9%	5.1%

INTL FCStone Inc.

Going global is the name of the game for commodities broker INTL FCStone. The company specializes in the physical trade of commodities such as corn gold renewable fuels and livestock though its primary activities are hedging securities trading and clearing. It offers clearing and execution services of listed futures and options on futures and serves as a market-maker for some 5000 foreign securities. It operates in international markets offering commodity risk management consulting asset management and commodity financing. Its client base includes financial institutions corporations and charitable organizations in the US and abroad.

Operations

INTL FCStone garners a diverse revenue stream across five operating segments. Its global platform provides execution market intelligence and post-trade services across all its asset classes and markets.

Although the Physical Commodities segment accounts for 99% of overall revenue it is the only segment that has significant operating costs (the costs of traded commodities) and therefore contributes only about 5% of operating revenue. It provides trading and hedging capabilities for precious metals and physical agricultural and energy commodities and commits its own capital for buying and selling on a spot and forward basis. The company's preferred performance metric is operating revenue as it removes dramatic multi-year price swings in commodities.

The CES segment matches customer trades with the relevant commodity or stock exchange collects and manages customer margin deposits and accounts for and reports on transactions for all major futures and securities exchanges globally. CES provides about 35% of INTL's operating revenue.

Commodity pricing is susceptible to a great many variables and therefore producers consumers and investors institute hedging strategies to soften the vagaries of the financial risk. The Commercial Hedging segment provides assesses risk and designs and executes hedging strategies particularly for agricultural and energy commodities and base metals. The segment produces about 30% of INTL's operating revenue.

Accounting for some 20% of operating revenue the Securities segment facilitates cross-border currency stock share and debt instrument trades.

Global Payments (which contributes around 10% to operating revenue) provides cross-border money movement services to banks businesses charities and non-government and government or-

ganizations in approximately 170 countries and 140 currencies.

Geographic Reach

New York City-headquartered INTL FCStone serves 20000 customers in more than 130 countries around the world. The company operates through a network of more than 20 offices in the US. Just as many international offices support the company's business in the rest of the world with about half of them in the commodity-active region of South America. London and Dublin house its European facilities Sydney hosts its Australian operations and Shanghai Beijing Singapore and Hong Kong are home to its Asia offices.

The US provides about 70% of INTL's operating revenue. Europe and South America account for approximately 20% and 10% of operating revenue. Despite contributing less than 5% to operating revenue Asia represents about 95% of the company's total revenue.

Sales and Marketing

With more than 20000 customers INTL FCStone utilizes a direct sales force of risk management consultants who are organized by commodity verticals such as agriculture energy metals and livestock.

Its clients include commercial customers asset managers broker-dealers insurance companies brokers institutional and professional investors commercial and investment banks and governmental and non-governmental organizations.

Financial Performance

While INTL FCStone produces eye-popping revenue numbers - almost $28 billion in its fiscal 2018 - its preferred performance metric is operating revenue as it removes dramatic multi-year price swings in commodities. Operating revenue has risen year after year since 2014 from roughly $80 million in FY2009 to about $975 million in FY2017.

For 2018 revenue was $27.6 billion; operating revenue was $975.8 million. Operating revenue grew 24% from the prior year owing to record performance in all five of the company's segments. The growth was spurred by periods of increased market volatility that bolstered client activity and widened spreads as well as higher short-term interest rates and average client balances.

INTL's net income ended 2018 at $56 million regaining ground lost in 2017 when it fell to $6 million from $55 million the previous year. The 2017 losses stemmed from charges recorded to allow for doubtful accounts related to bad debt incurred by its coal business in Singapore. Gains in 2018 were driven by operating revenue growth and bad debt reduction.

Cash at the end of the year was $342.3 million an increase of $27.4 million from the prior year. Operations used $74 million and financing activities added $120.9 million. Investing activities used $15.4 million for property and equipment purchases and net acquisitions. Currency fluctuations reduced stores another $4.1 million.

Strategy

INTL FCStone is focused on broadening its customer base in new markets by offering more services. It continues to improve platforms and tools for internal and customer-facing functions. In its fiscal 2018 INTL expanded its OTC interest rates swap trading and advisory offerings to include cap and floor options on the London Interbank Offered Rate (LIBOR). Earlier that year the company soft-launched FXePrice a web-based platform that allows its local currency liquidity providers to feed the company local currency live prices electronically. That year the company also partnered with Allfunds Bank to gain direct access to Allfunds' offshore mutual fund distribution platform. The platform provides INTL's customers with access to more than 57000 offshore funds.

INTL is also expanding its offerings and footprint through acquisitions. In November 2018 the company acquired Luxembourg-based Carl Kliem an independent interdealer broker providing foreign exchange interest rate and fixed income products to more than 400 institutional customers throughout the EU. In January 2019 the company purchased the US-based broker-dealer subsidiary of GMP Capital GMP Securities. The deal extended INTL's fixed income product offerings to include high yield convertible and emerging market debt and brought more than 2400 institutional customers in the company's fold.

Mergers and Acquisitions

In March 2019 INTL FCStone acquired online precious metal providers CoinInvest and European Precious Metal Trading. Through their websites coininvest.com and silver-to-go.com the companies provide gold silver platinum and palladium to private individuals institutional investors and financial advisors. The deal extends INTL's Precious Metals Division allowing customers to purchase the metals in multiple forms and denominations.

INTL bought the US-based broker-dealer GMP Securities a subsidiary of GMP International Holdings in January 2019. The purchase expanded INTL's fixed income product portfolio to include high yield convertible and emerging market debt gave the company more than 2400 institutional customers.

In November 2018 INTL acquired Luxembourg-based interdealer broker Carl Kliem which provides foreign exchange interest rate and fixed income products to more than 400 institutional customers throughout the EU.

Company Background

INTL FCStone which traces its roots to 1924 was created after the 2009 merger of FCStone Group and International Assets Holding.

EXECUTIVES

Vice President And Global Head Compliance, Nancey M McMurtry

President And Ceo, Sean M. O'Connor, age 57, $400,000 total compensation

Cfo, William J. (Bill) Dunaway, age 48, $275,000 total compensation

Coo, Xuong Nguyen, age 51, $325,000 total compensation

Chief Risk Officer, Tricia Harrod, age 60

Ceo Europe Middle East Africa And Asia, Philip A. Smith, age 47, $324,105 total compensation

Executive Chairman Europe Middle East Africa And Asia, Malcolm Wilde, age 68

Ceo Intl Fcstone Markets, Mark Maurer, age 43

Vice President, Thiago Vieira

Svp Global Payments, Byard Bridge

Vice President Equity Trading, Thomas Moore

Assistant Vice President Financial Operations, Marcelo Taborda

Vice President, Shaun Finnerty

Vice President Equity Trading, Al Barbella

Senior Vice President Base Metals Lead, Tom Gramlich

Vice President Energy, Jonathan Kist

Vice President Technology, David Leung

Vice President Latin America Payments Division, Fernando Mazzanti

Vice President Digital Marketing, Monica Schmidt

Senior Vice President, Emily Barnes

Vice President Content And Digital Media, Eileen Stein

Vice President Business And Legal Affairs, Ryan Mcnearney

Vice President, Robert Chesler

Senior Vice President Energy, John Best

Chairman, John Radziwill

Board Member, Bruce Krehbiel

Board Member, Eric Parthemore

Board Member, Brent Bunte

Board Member, Daryl Henze

Board Member, John M Fowler

Treasurer, Bruce Fields

Auditors: KPMG LLP

LOCATIONS

HQ: INTL FCStone Inc.
155 East 44th Street, Suite 900, New York, NY 10017
Phone: 212 485-3500
Web: www.intlfcstone.com

2018 Sales

	% of total
US	6
Asia	93
Europe	1
South America	0
Other	0
Total	**100**

PRODUCTS/OPERATIONS

2018 Total Revenue

	% of total
Commercial Hedging	1
Global Payments	0
Securities	1
Clearing & Execution Services	1
Physical Commodities	97
Corporate unallocated	0
Total	**100**

Selected Subsidiaries

FCC Futures Inc.
INTL Asia Pte. Ltd.
INTL FCStone Pte. Ltd.
FCStone do Brazil Ltda.
FCStone Financial Inc.
FCStone Group
FCStone Merchant Services LLC
FCStone Paraguay S.R.L.
FCStone LLC
Gainvest Asset Management Ltd.
Gainvest S.A.
Gainvest Uruguay Asset Management S.A.
Gletir S.A.
INTL Capital S.A. (Argentina)
INTL CIBSA Sociedad de Bolsa S.A.
INTL Commodities DMCC
INTL Custody & Clearing Solutions Inc.
INTL FCStone (Europe) Ltd.
INTL FCStone Financial
INTL FCStone (Netherlands) B.V.
INTL Netherlands B.V.
INTL Participacoes Ltda.
SA Stone Investment Advisors Inc.
Westown Commodities LLC

COMPETITORS

ADM
BGC Partners
CAPIS
Citigroup Global Markets
Credit Suisse (USA)
Glencore
Goldman Sachs
Interactive Brokers
J.P. Morgan Clearing
Morgan Stanley
NEX
R.J. O'Brien
Susquehanna International Group LLP
Wedbush Securities

HISTORICAL FINANCIALS

Company Type: Public

Income Statement

FYE: September 30

	REVENUE ($ mil.)	NET INCOME ($ mil.)	NET PROFIT MARGIN	EMPLOYEES
09/19	32,742	85	0.3%	2,012
09/18	27,542	56	0.2%	1,701
09/17	29,382	6	0.0%	1,607
09/16	14,727	55	0.4%	1,464
09/15	34,676	56	0.2%	1,231
Annual Growth	**(1.4%)**	**11.2%**	**—**	**13.1%**

2019 Year-End Financials

Debt ratio: 4.00%
Return on equity: 15.00%
Cash ($ mil.): 1,896
Current ratio: 1.00
Long-term debt ($ mil.): 168

No. of shares (mil.): 19
Dividends
  Yield: —
  Payout: —
Market value ($ mil.): 783

	STOCK PRICE ($) FY Close	P/E High/Low		PER SHARE ($) Earnings	Dividends	Book Value
09/19	41.00	11	8	4.00	0.00	31.00
09/18	48.00	19	13	3.00	0.00	27.00
09/17	38.00	138	107	0.00	0.00	24.00
09/16	39.00	13	8	3.00	0.00	24.00
09/15	25.00	13	6	3.00	0.00	21.00
Annual Growth	**13.6%**	**—**	**—**	**11.2%**	**—**	**10.2%**

Intuit Inc

Intuit's fact is: It handles other people's taxes? and their bookkeeping and other financial management tasks. The company is a leading developer of software used for small business accounting (QuickBooks) and consumer tax preparation (TurboTax). Mint the online service helps manage personal finances and budgeting. Professional accountants boot up Intuit's Lacerte ProSeries and ProConnect Tax Online products. More than 70% of revenue comes from products hosted on Intuit's servers what the company calls connected services. Intuit claims more than 50 million users for its products and services. Not surprisingly about half of annual revenue comes in the quarter that includes April 15.

Operations

Intuit operates in three segments Small Business & Self-Employed Consumer and Strategic Partner.

The Small Business & Self-Employed segment about 50% of sales offers QuickBooks financial and business management online services and desktop software payroll and payment processing products and financing for small businesses.

The Consumer segment about 40% of sales offers the TurboTax income tax preparation products and services as well as the Mint financial planning service.

The Strategic Partner segment some 10% of sales sells Intuit's professional tax products like Lacerte ProSeries ProFile and ProConnect Tax Online.

Geographic Reach

California-based Intuit has operations in some 20 locations in nine countries including US Canada India the UK Israel and Australia. International sales consistently account for less than 5% of Intuit's sales.

Sales and Marketing

Intuit relies on web marketing and targeted advertising such as search engine optimization and purchasing key words from major search engine companies; placing its mobile application in proprietary online stores (including Google's Play Store and Apple's App Store) direct-response mail and email campaigns telephone solicitations TV radio and print advertisements social media and coordinated promotional offers with major retailers. Its TurboTax tax preparation software is displayed prominently in stores such as Office Depot Best Buy and Sam's Club through April 15 each year.

As new competitors join existing rivals in the tax prep and financial planning software business Intuit has responded by advertising more. From 2017 to 2019 the company increased its ad and marketing budget by two-thirds to reach about $800 million in 2019.

Financial Performance

Intuit has reported three years of higher revenue after an off-year in 2017 and the company recorded strong net income in the past three years.

In 2019 (ended July) revenue rose 13% to about $6.8 billion up $759 million from 2018. Sales in the Small Business & Self-Employed segment jumped 15% thanks to growth in its online business while the Consumer segment's revenue increased 11% due to a shift to higher end products growth in TurboTax federal units and higher average revenue per customer.

Net income rose to $1.5 billion in 2019 from $1.3 billion in 2018 on the strength of higher revenue.

Intuit's coffers held $2.1 billion in cash in 2019 compared to $1.4 billion the year before. In 2019 operations generated $2.3 billion while investing activities used $566 million and financing activities used $1 billion.

Intuit's aggregate of $436 million of indebtedness could take money away from capital expenditures and acquisitions and limit financial flexibility.

Strategy

Intuit uses artificial intelligence to strengthen its products across its businesses adding AI capabilities to its small business and consumer offerings. In one example natural language is used to deal with all of the questions addressed to its TurboTax Live product based on their type and complexity. Using the technology to screen questions if not answer them had led Intuit to expand its live offerings and maintain a healthy operating margin.

The company adds services and capabilities to its small business products. It offers a next business day payments service that enables customers to receive payment the next business day instead of waiting three to five days. That addition helped increase the volume of QuickBooks Online about 40% in 2019.

Helping people with simple tax returns file them for no charge has been a strategic focus for the company. Free products help the company expand the do-it-yourself category and then transform customers to the assisted category and finally connecting customers to financial products.

Mergers and Acquisitions

In 2019 Intuit agreed to buy Origami Logic developer of a data integration ingestion and analytics platform for analyzing multiple data sets. Intuit intends to use the technology to help customers get more information out of their data. The transaction is expected to close in the 2019 fourth quarter.

HISTORY

After earning his MBA from Harvard founder Scott Cook spent three years in marketing at Procter & Gamble and four years with consultancy Bain & Company before establishing Intuit in 1983. Research showed that consumers wanted an easy-to-use personal finance software package. Quicken was introduced in 1984.

Intuit was near collapse in 1986 when it received its first big order from software retailer Egghead.com. Intuit released QuickBooks in 1992 and went public in 1993. The next year it acquired a number of firms including tax preparation software developer ChipSoft which brought TurboTax onboard.

In 1995 Microsoft's $2 billion bid to buy Intuit was halted by a Justice Department antitrust lawsuit. Also that year Intuit launched an online banking service and forged its first ties with the Web by bundling a browser and free Internet access with Quicken. It sold its online banking and bill presentation business to CheckFree in 1997. In 1998 the company bought Lacerte Software a provider of software and services to tax professionals.

EXECUTIVES

Evp And Chief People Officer, Sherry Whiteley
Chairman And Ceo, Brad D. Smith, age 55, $1,000,000 total compensation
Evp General Counsel And Secretary, Laura A. Fennell, age 58, $575,000 total compensation
Evp And General Manager Small Business Group, Sasan K. Goodarzi, age 51, $625,000 total compensation
Evp And General Manager Proconnect Group, CeCe Morken
Evp And Cto, H. Tayloe Stansbury, age 58, $625,000 total compensation
Evp And General Manager Consumer Tax Group, Daniel A. (Dan) Wernikoff, age 47, $725,000 total compensation
Svp And General Manager Consumer Ecosystem Group, Al Ko
Evp And Chief Marketing And Sales Officer, Lucas Watson
Evp And Cfo, Michelle Clatterbuck, age 51
Vice President Global Communications Small Business Division, Heather McLellan
Vice President Corporate Finance And Treasurer, Jerry Natoli
Senior Vice President And Chief Communications Officer, Rob Lanesey
Vice President Communications, Sandra Corradetti
Vice President Of Design, Kurt Walecki
Vice President Of Product Management, Barry Saik
Svp Technology Accounting Professionals Division, Mamie Jones
Vp Of Platform And Core Services Chief Architect, Brian Ellison
Vice President Corporate Development, Erika Swanson
Senior Vice President Investment Services, Rajneesh Gupta
Vice President Marketing, Patti Newcomer
Vice President Engineering Financial Data Platform, Bhushan Heda
Vp Sales, Barry Pennett
Vice President Tax Regulatory Affairs, David Sullivan
Vice President Of Design, Leslie Witt
Vice President Sales Care And Marketing Technology, Olga Braylovskiy
Vp And Fellow Marketing Technologies, Aditi Dhagat
Auditors: Ernst & Young LLP

LOCATIONS

HQ: Intuit Inc
2700 Coast Avenue, Mountain View, CA 94043
Phone: 650 944-6000
Web: www.intuit.com

PRODUCTS/OPERATIONS

2019 Sales

	$ mil.	% of total
Small Business	3,533	52
Consumer Tax	2,775	41
ProConnect	476	7
Total	**6,784**	**100**

2019 Sales

	$ mil.	% of total
Product	1,623	24
Service and other	5,161	76
Total	**6,784**	**100**

Products and services
Individuals
Manage budgeting and taxes with confidence
Mint Budgeting
Quicken Personal Finance
QuickBooks Self-Employed
TurboTax Tax Preparation
Small Businesses
The tools you need to run your company
Checks & Supplies
Demandforce Marketing
Intuit Payroll Services
QuickBooks Business Finance
QuickBooks Payments
Accountants
Pro software for the range of client needs
Intuit Tax Online
Lacerte Pro Tax Software
ProSeries Pro Tax Software
QuickBooks for Accountants

COMPETITORS

ADP	H&R Block
Bank of America	JPMorgan Chase
CCH Incorporated	Jackson Hewitt
Elavon	PayPal
Fidelity National	Paychex
Information Services	Square
First Data	Thomson Reuters
Fiserv	Universal Tax
Global Payments	Wells Fargo

HISTORICAL FINANCIALS

Company Type: Public

Income Statement FYE: July 31

	REVENUE ($ mil.)	NET INCOME ($ mil.)	NET PROFIT MARGIN	EMPLOYEES
07/19	6,784	1,557	23.0%	9,400
07/18	5,964	1,211	20.3%	8,900
07/17	5,177	971	18.8%	8,200
07/16	4,694	979	20.9%	7,900
07/15	4,192	365	8.7%	7,700
Annual Growth	12.8%	43.7%	—	5.1%

2019 Year-End Financials

Debt ratio: 7.00%
Return on equity: 51.00%
Cash ($ mil.): 2,116
Current ratio: 2.00
Long-term debt ($ mil.): 386
No. of shares (mil.): 260
Dividends
  Yield: 1.0%
  Payout: 30.0%
Market value ($ mil.): 72,151

	STOCK PRICE ($) FY Close	P/E High/Low		PER SHARE ($) Earnings	Dividends	Book Value
07/19	277.00	47	31	6.00	2.00	14.00
07/18	204.00	46	28	5.00	2.00	9.00
07/17	137.00	38	28	4.00	1.00	5.00
07/16	111.00	31	21	4.00	1.00	5.00
07/15	106.00	83	60	1.00	1.00	8.00
Annual Growth 27.2%		—	—	46.5%	17.1%	14.5%

Invesco DB Commodity Index Tracking Fund

EXECUTIVES

Prin, Sonja Olsen
Auditors: PricewaterhouseCoopers LLP

LOCATIONS

HQ: Invesco DB Commodity Index Tracking Fund
c/o Invesco Capital Management LLC, 3500 Lacey Road, Suite 700, Downers Grove, IL 60515
Phone: 800 983-0903
Web: www.invescopowershares.com

HISTORICAL FINANCIALS

Company Type: Public

Income Statement   FYE: December 31

	ASSETS ($ mil.)	NET INCOME ($ mil.)	INCOME AS % OF ASSETS	EMPLOYEES
12/18	2,010	25	1.2%	—
12/17	2,264	(1)	—	—
12/16	2,559	(14)	—	—
12/15	2,011	(26)	—	—
12/14	4,948	(45)	—	—
Annual Growth (20.2%)		—	—	—

2018 Year-End Financials

Debt ratio: —
Return on equity: 1.00%
Cash ($ mil.): —
Current ratio: —
Long-term debt ($ mil.): —

No. of shares (mil.): 134
Dividends
  Yield: 1.0%
  Payout: 118.0%
Market value ($ mil.): 1,939

	STOCK PRICE ($) FY Close	P/E High/Low		PER SHARE ($) Earnings	Dividends	Book Value
12/18	14.00	116	90	0.00	0.00	14.00
12/17	17.00	—	—	(0.00)	0.00	17.00
12/16	16.00	—	—	(0.00)	0.00	16.00
12/15	13.00	—	—	(0.00)	0.00	13.00
12/14	18.00	—	—	(0.00)	0.00	18.00
Annual Growth (5.9%)		—	—	—	—	(5.9%)

Invesco Mortgage Capital Inc

Invesco Mortgage Capital is ready to roll now that the mortgage industry has finally reversed its course. Invesco Mortgage is a real estate investment trust (REIT) that finances and manages residential and commercial mortgage-backed securities and mortgage loans. It purchases agency-backed mortgages secured by the likes of Fannie Mae and Freddie Mac and is managed and advised by sibling Invesco Institutional a subsidiary of Invesco Ltd. The firm's mortgage-backed securities portfolio is concentrated within the four populous states of California Florida Texas and New York. Invesco Mortgage Capital began operations and went public in 2009.

Geographic Reach

Invesco Mortgage's mortgage-backed securities portfolio is primarily centered around the states of California Florida Texas and New York. Its residential mortgage-backed securities (RMBS) portfolio is centered around California (43% of total) Florida (7%) and New York (7%). Its commercial mortgage-backed securities (CMBS) portfolio is concentrated in California (16%) New York (13%) Texas (9%) and Florida (6%).

Strategy

Invesco Mortgage's strategy for expansion involves organic growth through its investing in financing and managing residential and commercial mortgage-backed securities (RMBS and CMBS) non-agency RMBS credit risk transfer securities issued by government-sponsored enterprises residential and commercial mortgage loans and other real estate-related financing.

EXECUTIVES

Chief Investment Officer, John M. Anzalone, age 54
Managing Director And Head Portfolio Management, Jason Marshall, age 44
President, Robson J. (Rob) Kuster, age 46
Cfo, Richard L. Phegley
Evp Residential Credit, David Lyle
Evp Commercial Credit, Kevin Collins
Vice President Client Services, Betsy Warrick
Chairman, James S. Balloun, age 81
Auditors: PricewaterhouseCoopers LLP

LOCATIONS

HQ: Invesco Mortgage Capital Inc
1555 Peachtree Street N.E., Suite 1800, Atlanta, GA 30309
Phone: 404 892-0896
Web: www.invescomortgagecapital.com

PRODUCTS/OPERATIONS

2014 Sales

	$ mil.	% of total
Interest income		
Mortgage-backed and credit risk transfer securities	579	86
Residential loans	88	13
Commercial loans	10	1
Total interest income	677	100
Other income	-572.8 -	
Total	**104**	**100**

COMPETITORS

Annaly Capital Management
Anworth Mortgage Asset Management
Capstead Mortgage
Impac Mortgage Holdings
Redwood Trust
Walter Investment Management
iStar Financial Inc

HISTORICAL FINANCIALS

Company Type: Public

Income Statement   FYE: December 31

	ASSETS ($ mil.)	NET INCOME ($ mil.)	INCOME AS % OF ASSETS	EMPLOYEES
12/18	17,814	(71)	—	—
12/17	18,657	349	1.9%	—
12/16	15,706	254	1.6%	—
12/15	16,773	104	0.6%	—
12/14	21,231	(199)	—	—
Annual Growth (4.3%)		—	—	—

2018 Year-End Financials

Debt ratio: 9.00%
Return on equity: (-3.00%)
Cash ($ mil.): 136
Current ratio: —
Long-term debt ($ mil.): —

No. of shares (mil.): 112
Dividends
  Yield: 12.0%
  Payout: —
Market value ($ mil.): 1,616

	STOCK PRICE ($) FY Close	P/E High/Low		PER SHARE ($) Earnings	Dividends	Book Value
12/18	14.00	—	—	(1.00)	2.00	20.00
12/17	18.00	6	5	3.00	2.00	24.00
12/16	15.00	8	5	2.00	2.00	20.00
12/15	12.00	24	18	1.00	2.00	20.00
12/14	15.00	—	—	(2.00)	2.00	21.00
Annual Growth (1.6%)		—	—	—	(3.7%)	(0.8%)

Investors Bancorp Inc (New)

Investors Bancorp is the holding company for Investors Savings Bank which serves New Jersey and New York from more than 130 branch offices. Founded in 1926 the bank offers such standard deposit products as savings and checking accounts CDs money market accounts and IRAs. Nearly 40% of the bank's loan portfolio is made up of residential mortgages while multi-family loans and commercial real estate loans make up more than 50% combined. The bank also originates business industrial and consumer loans. Founded in 1926 Investors Bancorp's assets now exceed $20 billion.

Operations

About 86% of Investors Bancorp's revenue came from interest income from loans and loans held-for sale in 2014 while another 8% came from interest income on the bank's mortgage-backed securities municipal bonds and other debt. The remainder of its revenue came from fees and service charges (3%) and other miscellaneous income sources. Investors Bancorp boasted a staff of more than 1700 at the end of 2014.

Geographic Reach

Based in Short Hills New Jersey Investors Bancorp has more than 130 branches across New Jersey and New York. It also has lending offices in New York City Short Hills Spring Lake Newark Astoria and Brooklyn. Its operation center is in Iselin New Jersey.

Sales and Marketing

The company offers retail and commercial banking services to individuals professional service firms municipalities small and middle-market companies commercial and industrial firms and other businesses.

Financial Performance

Investors Bancorp's revenues and profits have been rising thanks to strong loan growth from bank acquisitions falling interest expenses on deposits and declining loan loss provisions as its loan portfolio's credit quality has improved with higher property valuations in the strengthened economy.

The bank's revenue jumped by 21% to a record $702.7 million in 2014 mostly thanks to loan asset growth stemming from the bank's 2014 acquisition of Gateway Community Financial.

Higher revenue and a continued decline in loan loss provisions in 2014 drove the bank's net income higher by 18% to a record $131.7 million. Investor Bancorp's operating cash levels spiked by 58% to $277.4 million for the year on higher cash earnings and favorable changes in its working capital.

Strategy

Investors Bancorp continues to expand its geographic reach in its core New Jersey and New York markets and boost its loan and deposit business mainly through select bank and branch acquisitions. Indeed the bank noted in 2015 that it had made eight bank or branch acquisitions since 2008 adding that they have counted for "a significant portion" of the bank's historic growth.

The company's 2014 and 2013 bank acquisitions bolstered its expansion in New Jersey into the suburbs of Philadelphia the boroughs of New York City the Nassau and Suffolk Counties on Long Island and historic markets throughout New Jersey.

Mergers and Acquisitions

In May 2016 Investors Bancorp agreed to purchase the $1 billion-asset The Bank of Princeton along with its 13 branches in the greater Princeton New Jersey and Philadelphia Pennsylvania areas. The added locations would grow Investors Bancorp's branch network by almost 10% to 156 branches in the Philadelphia to New York City corridor.

In January 2014 Investors Bancorp purchased Gateway Community Financial Corp along with its four branches in Gloucester County New Jersey. The deal added nearly $255 million in customer deposits and $195 million in new loan business to its books.

In December 2013 the company bought Roma Financial Corporation and its 26 branches in Burlington Ocean Mercer Camden and Middlesex counties in New Jersey. The deal added $1.34 billion in deposits and $991 million in loan assets while expanding the company's reach into the Philadelphia suburbs of New Jersey.

Company Background

In late 2012 the company acquired Marathon Banking Corporation (a subsidiary of Greece-based Piraeus Bank) for $135 million adding 13 branches in the New York metro area and more than doubling its branches in New York. The deal also would mark Investors Bancorp's entry into Manhattan and Staten Island.

EXECUTIVES

Sevp And Coo, Domenick A. Cama, age 63, $621,000 total compensation

President And Ceo, Kevin Cummings, age 64, $935,000 total compensation

Evp And Chief Lending Officer, Richard S. Spengler, age 57, $400,000 total compensation

Evp And Chief Retail Banking Officer, Paul Kalamaras, $375,000 total compensation

Svp And Cfo, Sean Burke

Senior Vice President, Jawad Chaudhry

Vice President Information Security Officer

Director Of Information Security, David Van

Vice President Systems, Charles Little

Chairman, Robert M. Cashill, age 76

Auditors: KPMG LLP

LOCATIONS

HQ: Investors Bancorp Inc (New)
101 JFK Parkway, Short Hills, NJ 07078
Phone: 973 924-5100
Web: www.myinvestorsbank.com

PRODUCTS/OPERATIONS

2014 Sales

	$ mil.	% of total
Interest		
Loans receivable and held-for-sale	603	86
Mortgage-backed securities	44	6
Federal Home Loan Bank stock	7	1
Municipal bonds & other debt	6	1
Other	1	-
Non-interest		
Fees & service charges	19	3
Gain on loan transaction	5	2
Others	17	1
Total	**703**	**100**

COMPETITORS

Bank of America	M&T Bank
Bank of New York	New York Community
Mellon	Bancorp
Citigroup	OceanFirst Financial
ConnectOne Bancorp	PNC Financial
Fulton Financial	

HISTORICAL FINANCIALS

Company Type: Public

Income Statement				FYE: December 31
	ASSETS ($ mil.)	NET INCOME ($ mil.)	INCOME AS % OF ASSETS	EMPLOYEES
12/18	26,229	203	0.8%	1,962
12/17	25,129	127	0.5%	1,959
12/16	23,175	192	0.8%	1,829
12/15	20,889	182	0.9%	1,768
12/14	18,774	132	0.7%	1,708
Annual Growth	8.7%	11.4%	—	3.5%

2018 Year-End Financials

Debt ratio: 21.00%
Return on equity: 7.00%
Cash ($ mil.): 197
Current ratio: —
Long-term debt ($ mil.): —

No. of shares (mil.): 286
Dividends
  Yield: 4.0%
  Payout: 67.0%
Market value ($ mil.): 2,977

	STOCK PRICE ($) FY Close	P/E High/Low	PER SHARE ($) Earnings	Dividends	Book Value
12/18	10.00	20 14	1.00	0.00	10.00
12/17	14.00	34 29	0.00	0.00	10.00
12/16	14.00	22 16	1.00	0.00	10.00
12/15	12.00	24 19	1.00	0.00	10.00
12/14	11.00	74 26	0.00	0.00	10.00
Annual Growth	(1.9%)	— —	17.3%	47.6%	1.2%

IQVIA Holdings Inc

IQVIA Holdings has plenty to CRO about. One of the world's largest contract research organizations (CROs) it helps pharmaceutical biotechnology and medical device companies develop and sell their products. The firm provides a comprehensive range of clinical trials management services including patient recruitment data analysis laboratory testing and regulatory filing assistance. Its consulting offerings include strategic advice at each stage of drug discovery and development. The company also provides data analytics technology and expertise to medical researchers government agencies and health care payers. IQVIA gets more than 40% of its revenue in the US.

Operations

IQVIA operates through three segments: Research & Development Solutions Technology & Analytics Solutions and Contract Sales & Medical Solutions.

The Research & Development segment which accounts for about half of revenue offers project management virtual trials clinical monitoring clinical trial support and strategic planning and design services.

The Technology & Analytics Solutions segment about 40% of revenue provides technology insight workflow analytics and consulting national and sub-national information and reference information; it has access to data on the treatments and outcomes of more than 600 million unidentified patients.

The Contract Sales & Medical Solutions segment about 10% of revenue provides health care provider and patient engagement services as well as medical affairs services.

The company has a 60% stake in a joint venture with Quest Diagnostics. Named Q2 Solutions the venture provides clinical trials lab services.

Geographic Reach

IQVIA splits its headquarters between Durham North Carolina and Danbury Connecticut and it has some 300 offices in more than 85 countries in the Americas Europe Africa and the Asia/Pacific region.

The US supplies more than 40% of IQVIA's revenue while the UK provides about 10%. Regionally the Americas account for about half of the company's revenue Europe and Africa provide about a third and the Asia/Pacific region supplies about 20%.

Sales and Marketing

IQVIA has a broad base of customers which include most of the top 100 global pharmaceutical and biotechnology companies (in terms of revenue). Customers in pharmaceutical biotechnology device and diagnostic and consumer health businesses account for most of IQVIA's revenue. Other clients include payers government and regulatory agencies providers pharmaceutical distributors and pharmacies.

Financial Performance

IQVIA's revenue has risen at a robust 18%-a-year clip in the past five years driven by the merger with IMS Health in 2016.

In 2018 IQVIA's revenue advanced $710 million about 7% to $10.4 billion from 2017. The company reported higher revenue in the Technology & Analytics Solutions segment (up 12%) and Research & Development Solutions segment (up 7%) while sales contracted in the Contract Sales & Medical Solutions segment (down 11%).

Net income fell to $259 million in 2018 from $1.2 billion in 2017 when the company had a $992 million tax benefit from the US Tax Cuts and Jobs Act. Revenue before tax was $328 million in 2018 compared to $294 million in 2017.

IQVIA had $891 million in cash and equivalents in 2018 compared to $959 million the year before. In 2018 operations generated $1.2 billion while investing and financing activities used $810 million and $452 million respectively.

The company has $10.1 billion indebtedness which could limit its ability to respond to positive or negative changes in its markets or the economy. IQVIA had $406 million in interest expense in 2018 compared to $339 million in 2017.

Strategy

IQVIA benefits from its expertise in clinical trials and its information and technology capabilities. It taps into these assets to offer its clients new ways to bring their drugs to market quickly and efficiently. In late 2017 the company offered its Orchestrated Customer Engagement (OCE) platform a customer relationship management product. The product has more than 30000 users in more than 100 countries and has helped IQVIA grab business with Roche and Novo Nordisk.

IQVIA has also introduced automation into its tools for smart trials. The company's smart trial products can generate analytics in minutes instead of weeks as in the past. It has some 500 smart trials in operation about third of its total trials.

Additionally the company continues to invest in quality data and electronic health records. It has acquired data analytics products and services as well as personnel and created a proprietary data integration tool to manage data from multiple sources. Altogether the group owns more than 30 (one petabyte is equal to a million gigabytes) of unique data.

Because IQVIA serves clients that conduct clinical trials it is vulnerable to the loss of business when trials go awry. Negative results can lead the firm's customers to shut down those research activities thereby terminating their contracts with IQVIA. Even successfully getting a drug to market can mean the loss of a contract. Therefore it is important for IQVIA to maintain a strong backlog of R&D jobs.

Mergers and Acquisitions
In 2019 IQVIA acquired Linguamatics a bioinformatics company that employs natural language processing. The deal boosts IQVIA's ability to find additional information in patient data.

Company Background
The company was founded as Quntiles by Dennis Gillings a British biostatistician who had worked with Hoechst (later part of Sanofi) on data analysis in the 1970s. Gillings set up Quintiles (Quantitative Information Technology In The Life and Economic Sciences) in 1982 at the University of North Carolina where he was then teaching. The company grew as drug companies began outsourcing some of the more irksome tasks of drug development. Quintiles went public in 1994.

The company used the proceeds of the IPO to expand its health economics segment with the purchases of Benefit International (1995) and Lewin Group (1996). These purchases introduced it to such new clients as governments and HMOs. Quintiles' 1996 purchase of Innovex (unrelated to the computer hardware maker of the same name) made it the world's largest CRO.

The company changed its name to IQVIA in 2017 following the merger with IMS Health.

HISTORY

Quintiles was founded by Dennis Gillings a British biostatistician who had worked with Hoechst (later part of Sanofi) on data analysis in the 1970s. Gillings set up Quintiles (Quantitative Information Technology In The Life and Economic Sciences) in 1982 at the University of North Carolina where he was then teaching. The company grew as drug companies began outsourcing some of the more irksome tasks of drug development. Quintiles went public in 1994.

The company used the proceeds of the IPO to expand its health economics segment with the purchases of Benefit International (1995) and Lewin Group (1996). These purchases introduced it to such new clients as governments and HMOs. Quintiles' 1996 purchase of Innovex (unrelated to the computer hardware maker of the same name) made it the world's largest CRO. The buying spree continued in 1997 and 1998. Among the purchases were some intended to strengthen Quintiles' marketing services (Data Analysis Systems

Inc. Q.E.D. International and France-based Serval). The firm also formed new collaborations with such academic research organizations as Johns Hopkins Medicine.

In 1999 Quintiles expanded its marketing arm with the purchase of Pharmaceutical Marketing Services (parent of the leading pharmaceuticals industry research company Scott-Levin) and jumped headlong into data mining with its purchase of ENVOY — which processed insurance claims. Quintiles found the core business uninspiring and sold it to Healtheon (now Emdeon formerly WebMD) the next year. But it kept rights to ENVOY's stream of treatment outcome and insurance data gleaned from health care providers hospitals payers and pharmacies — a treasure house of information useful to salespeople and health providers.

The company continued in 2000 to add offices in Europe Asia and Latin America. It also opened additional offices in the US and Europe to help Japanese pharmaceutical companies market their products in those regions. Late in the year Quintiles bought the clinical development unit of Pharmacia.

In 2001 Quintiles became embroiled in a legal dispute with WebMD involving the availability of data associated with ENVOY; the company challenged WebMD's efforts to withhold such data. The two companies settled the squabble later that year and agreed to sever all ties. Also in 2001 Quintiles streamlined operations and cut about 5% of its workforce.

The future structure of the CRO came into question at the end of 2002. Gillings presented the company with a buyout offer; he planned to take the company private so he could pursue a new growth strategy Wall Street would surely find risky. The board rejected that offer in October 2002 but it opened up an auction. Some leading equity firms reportedly made offers but Gillings — with backing from Blackstone Group and BANK ONE's One Equity Partners (later part of JPMorgan Chase) — placed another offer for Quintiles and won the prize in April 2003. Some five months later Quintiles went private.

EXECUTIVES

Chairman And Ceo, Ari Bousbib, age 57, $390,137 total compensation
Cfo, Michael R. (Mike) McDonnell, age 55, $650,000 total compensation
Svp And Executive Director Quintilesims Institute, Murray L. Aitken
President Novella Clinical, W. Richard Staub, age 56, $485,923 total compensation
President Clinical Operations Research And Development Solutions, Cynthia L. Verst
Evp And Chief Customer Officer, Paul Spreen
President Information And Technology Solutions, Kevin C. Knightly, age 57, $119,399 total compensation
President Asia/pacific, Anand Tharmaratnam
President Central East And South Europe, Elisabeth Beck
President North Europe Middle East And Africa, Alistair Grenfell
President Japan, Norihiko Minato
President Latin America, Nilton Paletta
Evp And General Counsel, James H. (Jim) Erlinger, age 60, $468,333 total compensation
President Real-world Insights (rwi), Jon Resnick
President Integrated Engagement Services, W. Scott Evangelista
Svp And Cio, Karl Guenault
President United States And Canada, Hossam Sadek

President Data Sciences Safety And Regulatory Research And Development Solutions, Margaret Keegan
Ceo Qâ‚ Solutions, Costa Panagos
Vp Administration And Chief Of Staff To The Ceo Ims Health, Trudy Stein
Svp Strategy Marketing And Communications, Marla Kessler
President Global Services, José Luis Fernández
Vice President And Global Head Of Risk Management, Stella Blackburn
Vice President Commercial Sales, Jay Schwartz
Vice President Executive Strategist, David Hauser
Auditors: PricewaterhouseCoopers LLP

LOCATIONS

HQ: IQVIA Holdings Inc
  4820 Emperor Blvd., Durham, NC 27703
Phone: 919 998-2000
Web: www.quintiles.com

2018 Sales

	$ mil.	% of total
Americas	4,998	48
Europe & Africa	3,448	33
Asia/Pacific	1,966	19
Total	**10,412**	**100**

PRODUCTS/OPERATIONS

2018 Sales by Segment

	$ mil.	% of total
Research & Development Solutions	5,465	52
Technology & Analytics Solutions	4,137	40
Contract Sales & Medical Solutions	810	8
Total	**10,412**	**100**

Selected Therapeutic Specialties
Cardiovascular
Central nervous system
Gastrointestinal/NASH
Infectious diseases
Internal medicine
Oncology
Pediatrics
Rheumatology
Women's health

COMPETITORS

Accenture	PRA Health Sciences
CMIC HOLDINGS CO. LTD.	Pharmaceutical Product
Covance	Development
ICON	Publicis Groupe
Kantar Group	Veeva Systems
PAREXEL	

HISTORICAL FINANCIALS
Company Type: Public

Income Statement
FYE: December 31

	REVENUE ($ mil.)	NET INCOME ($ mil.)	NET PROFIT MARGIN	EMPLOYEES
12/18	10,412	259	2.5%	58,000
12/17	9,739	1,309	13.4%	55,000
12/16	6,878	115	1.7%	50,000
12/15	5,738	387	6.7%	36,100
12/14	5,460	356	6.5%	32,600
Annual Growth	17.5%	(7.7%)	—	15.5%

2018 Year-End Financials

Debt ratio: 49.00%	No. of shares (mil.): 198
Return on equity: 3.00%	Dividends
Cash ($ mil.): 891	Yield: —
Current ratio: 1.00	Payout: —
Long-term debt ($ mil.): 10,907	Market value ($ mil.): 22,944

	STOCK PRICE ($)	P/E	PER SHARE ($)		
	FY Close	High/Low	Earnings	Dividends	Book Value
12/18	116.00	103 75	1.00	0.00	34.00
12/17	98.00	18 13	6.00	0.00	39.00
12/16	76.00	105 73	1.00	0.00	37.00
12/15	69.00	25 18	3.00	0.00	(5.00)
12/14	59.00	22 16	3.00	0.00	(6.00)
Annual Growth	18.5%	— —	(17.8%)	—	—

Jabil Inc

Jabil Inc. makes a jabillion different kinds of electronics. The company is one of the leading providers of outsourced electronics manufacturing services (EMS) in the world. It makes electronics components and parts on a contract basis for computers smartphones printers and other consumer electronics as well as more complex specialized products for the aerospace automotive and healthcare industries. The company's services range from product design and component procurement to product testing order fulfillment and supply chain management. US-based Jabil operates more than 100 plants in about 30 countries with international customers accounting for about 90% of sales.

Operations

Jabil conducts business in two segments: Electronics Manufacturing Services (EMS) and Diversified Manufacturing Services (DMS).

The EMS segment (about 55% of revenue) focuses on IT supply chain design and engineering for all things electronic. The products Jabil makes for its customers are used in the automotive digital home industrial and energy networking and telecommunications point of sale printing and storage businesses.

The DMS segment (about 45% of revenue) focuses on manufacturing services for material sciences and technologies. It works with customers to develop and manufacture products for consumer wearable technologies defense and aerospace emerging growth healthcare mobility and packaging.

Geographic Reach

Jabil has manufacturing plants in the US Canada and Mexico as well as Europe Asia South Africa Asia and South America.

Singapore and China are its largest markets accounting for about 35% and more than 20% of sales respectively. Mexico accounts for about 15% of revenue.

Sales and Marketing

Jabil depends on a small number of customers for a significant percentage of revenue - five customers account for just less than 50% of sales. Its top customer is Apple (about 30% of sales) and other significant customers are Cisco Systems Dell Technologies HP Inc. LM Ericsson General Electric Ingenico NetApp Valeo and Zebra Technologies.

Financial Performance

Jabil's string of annual revenue increases continued for a fourth year in 2018 (ended August) with a 16% jump from 2017.

The company reported sales of $22.1 billion in 2018 up $3.1 billion from 2017 propelled by a 23% increase in the DMS segment on strong demand from mobility customers and higher sales to existing healthcare customers. The EMS segment's revenue rose 11% year-to-year boosted by customers in industrial and energy digital home and capital equipment.

The company's profit fell to $86.3 million in 2018 from $129 million in 2017 due to a $142 million tax expense related to the US Tax Cuts and Jobs Act.

Jabil had about $1.3 billion in cash and equivalents in 2018 compared to $1.2 billion in 2017. Operations generated about $933 million in cash in 2018 while investing and financing activities used $798 million and $47 million respectively.

Strategy

To compete in a rapidly consolidating industry Jabil provides production on a global scale and operates through semi-autonomous business units that are dedicated to individual customers. The company continues to add services and to expand globally through acquisitions including deals to acquire manufacturing operations from customers looking to reduce costs through outsourcing. The company tends to place manufacturing plants close to its customers.

Jabil had expanded its work in the health care device market and it has been a strong performer for the company. Operating income from production for health-related products which include drug-delivery systems continues to grow at better-than-expected levels.

Apple has been a long and profitable customer for Jabil a key supplier for Apple's iPhone. However Apple warned that sales of its phones slowed in emerging markets which would affect Jabil's revenue.

Jabil implemented a restructuring program in 2017 to realign costs and consolidate manufacturing in lower cost areas. The program included job cuts and cost the company about $160 million in 2017 and about $37 million in 2018. It plans to save up to $90 million a year with the moves.

Mergers and Acquisitions

Acquisitions have extended Jabil's product portfolio and its geographic reach.

In 2017 Jabil acquired True-Tech Corp. to expand its capital equipment division. True-Tech specialized in high-precision machining mechanical assembly and clean room assembly for semiconductor and aerospace customers.

In January 2016 Jabil acquired Inala a South African energy products provider and systems integrator. The deal acquisition expanded Jabil's presence in the market for remote location energy products and marked its first venture in Africa.

Company Background

Jabil Circuit was named for founders James Golden and Bill Morean. The duo who originally ran an excavation business started Jabil in suburban Detroit in 1966 to provide assembly and reworking services to electronics manufacturers. Jabil incorporated in 1969 and began making printed circuit boards for Control Data Corporation (later renamed Control Data Systems) that year.

William D. Morean the founder's son who had worked summers at Jabil while in high school joined the company in 1977. The next year the younger Morean took over Jabil's day-to-day operations. The company had entered the automotive electronics business in 1976 through a $12 million contract with General Motors.

During the 1980s Jabil began building computer components adding such customers as Dell NEC Sun Microsystems and Toshiba. Jabil moved its headquarters to St. Petersburg Florida in 1983. William Morean became Jabil's chairman and CEO in 1988.

EXECUTIVES

Ceo And Director, Mark T. Mondello, age 55, $1,100,000 total compensation
Evp And Coo, William D. (Bill) Muir, age 51, $700,000 total compensation
Evp Corporate Development And Chief Of Staff, Courtney J. Ryan, age 49
Cfo, Forbes I. J. Alexander, age 59, $700,000 total compensation
Evp And Ceo Healthcare, Steven D. (Steve) Borges, age 50
Evp General Counsel And Corporate Secretary, Robert L. (Bobby) Katz, age 57
Svp Materials Technology, Hwai Hai (HH) Chiang, $445,000 total compensation
Evp And Ceo Jabil Packaging Solutions, Erich Hoch, age 49
Svp High Velocity, Michael J. Loparco, age 48
Evp And Ceo Enterprise And Infrastructure, Alessandro Parimbelli, age 51, $444,392 total compensation
President, William E. (Bill) Peters, age 56, $700,000 total compensation
Svp And Cio, Gary L. Cantrell
Evp Human Resources And Human Development, Scott D Slipy, age 53
Executive Vice President National Operations, Mark Butler
Vice President Of Finance After Market Services Division, Brian Greff
Vice President Real Estate And Construction, Jacky Lau
Vice President After Market Services, Hartmut Liebel
Assistant Vice President Sales National Accounts, Dennis Maddock
Vp And Cio Jabil Digital Solutions, Bhaskar Ramachandran
Vp Global Security, David Benner
Vp Total Rewards, Daniel Lynch
Chairman, Timothy L. (Tim) Main, age 62
Vice Chairman, Thomas A. Sansone, age 70
Board Member, Steven Raymund
Auditors: Ernst & Young LLP

LOCATIONS

HQ: Jabil Inc
10560 Dr. Martin Luther King, Jr. Street North, St. Petersburg, FL 33716
Phone: 727 577-9749
Web: www.jabil.com

2018 Sales

	$ mil.	% of total
Singapore	7	33
China	4,585	21
Mexico	3,533	16
U.S.	1,845	8
Malaysia	1,390	6
Hungary	897	4
Other	2,652	12
Total	**22,095**	**100**

PRODUCTS/OPERATIONS

2018 Sales

	$ mil.	% of total
Electronics Manufacturing Services	12,269	56
Diversified Manufacturing Services	9,827	44
Total	**22,095**	**100**

Services

Component selection sourcing and procurement
Design and prototyping
Engineering
Order fulfillment
Printed circuit board and backplane assembly
Product testing
Repair and warranty
Systems assembly
Test development
Tooling design (molds and dies)

ASUSTeK
AptarGroup
BenQ
Benchmark Electronics
CATCHER TECHNOLOGY CO.
LTD.
Celestica
Compal Electronics

Flextronics
Hon Hai
Inventec
Key Tronic
Plexus
Sanmina
Venture Corp.
Wistron

HISTORICAL FINANCIALS

Company Type: Public

Income Statement

FYE: August 31

	REVENUE ($ mil.)	NET INCOME ($ mil.)	NET PROFIT MARGIN	EMPLOYEES
08/19	25,282	287	1.1%	200,000
08/18	22,095	86	0.4%	199,000
08/17	19,063	129	0.7%	170,000
08/16	18,353	254	1.4%	138,000
08/15	17,899	284	1.6%	161,000
Annual Growth	9.0%	0.3%		5.6%

2019 Year-End Financials

Debt ratio: 19.00%
Return on equity: 15.00%
Cash ($ mil.): 1,163
Current ratio: 1.00
Long-term debt ($ mil.): 2,121

No. of shares (mil.): 154
Dividends
Yield: 0.0%
Payout: 18.0%
Market value ($ mil.): 4,423

	STOCK PRICE ($) FY Close	P/E High/Low		PER SHARE ($) Earnings	Dividends	Book Value
08/19	29.00	17	12	2.00	0.00	12.00
08/18	30.00	63	49	0.00	0.00	12.00
08/17	31.00	44	29	1.00	0.00	13.00
08/16	21.00	19	13	1.00	0.00	13.00
08/15	19.00	17	12	1.00	0.00	12.00
Annual Growth	10.5%	—	—	5.7%	(0.0%)	0.5%

Jacobs Engineering Group, Inc.

Jacobs Engineering Group provides technical professional and construction services for industrial government and commercial clients throughout the world. Jacobs handles project design and engineering construction operations maintenance and scientific consultation. Typical projects include oil refineries manufacturing plants infrastructure & telecommunications and aerospace facilities. About two-thirds of revenue comes from the US while the rest originates in other countries primarily in Europe. Founded in 1947 Jacobs Engineering has more than 200 global offices. In 2018 the company agreed to sell its Energy Chemicals and Resources segment to WorleyParsons for $3.3 billion in cash and stock.

HISTORY

Joseph Jacobs graduated from the Polytechnic Institute of Brooklyn in 1942 with a doctorate in engineering. He went to work for Merck designing processes for pharmaceutical production. Later he moved to Chemurgic Corp. near San Francisco where he worked until 1947 when he founded Jacobs Engineering as a consulting firm. Jacobs also sold industrial equipment avoiding any apparent conflict of interest by simply telling his consulting clients.

When equipment sales outstripped consulting work by 1954 Jacobs hired four salesmen and engineer Stan Krugman who became his right-hand man. Two years later the company got its first big chemical design job for Kaiser Aluminum. Jacobs incorporated his sole proprietorship in 1957.

In 1960 the firm won its first construction contract to design and build a potash flotation plant and Jacobs Engineering became an integrated design and construction firm. In 1967 it opened its first regional office but kept management decentralized to replicate the small size and hard-hitting qualities of its home office. Three years later Jacobs Engineering went public.

The firm merged with Houston-based Pace Companies which specialized in petrochemical engineering design in 1974. Also that year the firm became Jacobs Engineering Group and began building its first major overseas chemical plant in Ireland.

By 1977 sales had reached $250 million. A decade of lobbying paid off that year when the firm won a contract for the Arab Potash complex in Jordan. Jacobs began to withdraw from his firm's operations in the early 1980s but the 1982-83 recession and poor management decisions pounded earnings. Jacobs returned from retirement in 1985 fired 14 VPs cut staff in half and pushed the firm to pursue smaller process-plant jobs and specialty construction.

After abandoning a 1986 attempt to take the company private Jacobs began making acquisitions to improve the firm's construction expertise. In 1992 he relinquished his role as CEO to president Noel Watson. The next year the company expanded its international holdings by acquiring the UK's H&G Process Contracting and H&G Contractors.

The firm's $38 million purchase of CRS Sirrine Engineers and CRSS Constructors in 1994 was the company's largest buy at that point and added new markets in the paper and semiconductor industries. By 1995 Jacobs Engineering was working on a record backlog.

Continuing its acquisition drive the company bought a 49% interest in European engineering specialist Serete Group in 1996; it bought the rest the next year. Also in 1997 it gained control of Indian engineering affiliate Humphreys & Glasgow (now Jacobs H&G) increasing its 40% stake to 70% and bought CPR Engineering a pulp and paper processing specialist. It also formed a joint venture with Krupp UHDE to provide design engineering and construction management services in Mexico.

In 1999 the company paid $198 million for St. Louis construction and design firm Sverdrup which had completed projects in some 65 countries. The next year Jacobs Engineering purchased half of Dutch firm Stork Engineering's business (it acquired the rest in 2001). But the company's bid to buy the assets of bankrupt power plant construction company Stone & Webster in 2000 was topped by Shaw Group.

After being accused of overcharging the US government Jacobs Engineering settled a whistle-blower lawsuit (for $35 million) in 2000 while continuing to deny the allegations. However the next year Jacobs continued to receive federal contracts including contracts for boosting security at the US Capitol complex and providing logistics to the US Special Operations Command. Jacobs completed its acquisition of the UK-based GIBB unit of engineering consulting firm LawGibb Group in 2001 as well as the purchase of McDermott Engineers and Constructors (Canada).

EXECUTIVES

Group Vice President, Walter Barber
Svp Information Technology, Cora L. Carmody, age 62
Chairman President And Ceo, Steven J. Demetriou, age 60, $125,000 total compensation
Evp And Cfo, Kevin C. Berryman, age 60, $544,832 total compensation
President Industrial, Robert V. (Bob) Pragada, age 51
President Petroleum And Chemicals, Joseph G. Mandel, age 59, $699,996 total compensation
Evp Operations, Phillip J. Stassi, age 64, $639,423 total compensation
President Aerospace And Technology, Terence D. Hagen, age 54
Gvp Consulting Operations, Robert McWhinney
Vice President Information Technology, Pete Young
Division Vice President Director Construction Services, Joseph Franco
Vice President, Albert Pozotrigo
Gvp Federal Operations, James Thiesing
Vice President, David Lewia
Vice President Global Information Technology Security, George Hull
Vice President, Jonathan Doros
Svp And Gm Global Environmental Solutions Aerospace Technology Environmental And Nuclear, Jan Walstrom
Vice President, Edward Motley
Auditors: Ernst & Young LLP

LOCATIONS

HQ: Jacobs Engineering Group, Inc.
1999 Bryan Street, Suite 1200, Dallas, TX 75201
Phone: 214 583-8500
Web: www.jacobs.com

2018 Sales

	$ mil.	% of total
US	9,519	64
Europe	2,769	18
Canada	864	6
Asia	316	2
India	212	1
Australia and New Zealand	720	5
South America and Mexico	160	1
Middle East and Africa	426	3
Total	**14,985**	**100**

PRODUCTS/OPERATIONS

2018 Sales by Segment

	$ mil.	% of total
Aerospace Technology Environmental and Nuclear	4,372	29
Buildings Infrastructure and Advanced Facilities	6,185	41
Energy Chemicals and Resources	4,428	30
Total	**14,985**	**100**

COMPETITORS

AECOM
Aker Solutions
Amec Foster Wheeler
BWX Technologies
Bechtel
Fluor
HDR
HNTB Companies

HOK
KBR
Leidos
Lockheed Martin
Tetra Tech
Turner Construction
WS Atkins

Company Type: Public

Income Statement   FYE: September 27

	REVENUE ($ mil.)	NET INCOME ($ mil.)	NET PROFIT MARGIN	EMPLOYEES
09/19	12,738	848	6.7%	52,000
09/18	14,985	163	1.1%	80,800
09/17	10,023	294	2.9%	54,700
09/16*	10,964	210	1.9%	54,900
10/15	12,115	303	2.5%	64,000
Annual Growth	1.3%	29.3%	—	(5.1%)

*Fiscal year change

2019 Year-End Financials

Debt ratio: 12.00%	No. of shares (mil.): 133
Return on equity: 15.00%	Dividends
Cash ($ mil.): 631	Yield: 1.0%
Current ratio: 1.00	Payout: 14.0%
Long-term debt ($ mil.): 1,201	Market value ($ mil.): 12,051

	STOCK PRICE ($) FY Close	P/E High/Low	PER SHARE ($) Earnings	Dividends	Book Value
09/19	91.00	15 9	6.00	1.00	43.00
09/18	77.00	66 47	1.00	1.00	41.00
09/17	58.00	26 20	2.00	0.00	37.00
09/16*	52.00	32 20	2.00	0.00	35.00
10/15	37.00	20 15	2.00	0.00	35.00
Annual Growth	24.8%	—	26.2%	—	5.4%

*Fiscal year change

EBSCO
Easton-Bell Sports
Elmer's Products
Energizer Holdings
Evenflo
Female Health
Gaming Partners
 International
Gerber Products
Habasit America
Hamilton Beach
Hanesbrands
Head N.V.
Hillerich &
 Bradsby
HoMedics
Home Depot
Honeywell ACS
Igloo Products
Intex DIY
Invensys
Johnson & Johnson

Russell Hobbs
SEB
Sealy
Simmons
Spectrum Brands
Suncast
Target Corporation
Tecnica
Tegrant
UTC Climate Controls
 & Security
Universal Security
 Instruments
VF Corporation
W.C. Bradley Co.
Wahl Clipper
West Pharmaceutical
 Services
Whirlpool
Worthington Industries
adidas

Company Type: Private

Income Statement   FYE: December 31

	REVENUE ($ mil.)	NET INCOME ($ mil.)	NET PROFIT MARGIN	EMPLOYEES
12/15	8,604	147	1.7%	17,000
12/14	8,287	243	2.9%	—
12/13	7,356	204	2.8%	—
12/12	6,696	244	3.6%	—
Annual Growth	8.7%	(15.6%)	—	—

JARDEN LLC

EXECUTIVES

Chair, Patrick D Campbell
Ceo, Debra A Crew
Pres, Ravi Saligram
National Account Sales Manager, Joe Cunningham
Auditors: PRICEWATERHOUSECOOPERS LLP NE

LOCATIONS

HQ: JARDEN LLC
 221 RIVER ST, HOBOKEN, NJ 070305989
Phone: 201 610-6600
Web: WWW.NEWELLBRANDS.COM

COMPETITORS

AZZ
Academy Sports
Amazon.com
Amer Sports
Andis
BWAY
Bass Pro Shops
Bauer Hockey
Bed Bath & Beyond
Burton
Cabela's
CalCedar
Canadian Tire
Carrefour
Church & Dwight
Conair Consumer
 Products
Costco Wholesale
Crayola
Daiwa
De'Longhi
Deswell
Dick's Sporting Goods

Johnson Outdoors
Kaz
Kellwood
Lasko Products
Lifetime Brands
Lowe's
MEGA Brands
Mattel
Mayborn Group
Mizuno
NACCO Industries
NIKE
New Balance
Newell Rubbermaid
Owens-Illinois
Patch Products
Philips Avent
Procter & Gamble
Quiksilver
REI
Richco
Rollerblade
Rossignol

JetBlue Airways Corp

Airline JetBlue Airways offers one-class service?with leather seats satellite radio and TV and movies?to over 42 million passengers a year and takes them to more than 100 cities. It has 1000 daily flights in about 30 US states Washington DC Puerto Rico and 21 countries in the Caribbean and Latin America. Domestic flights represent its largest market accounting for about 70% of total company sales. Most of its flights arrive or depart from Boston New York Orlando Fort Lauderdale Los Angeles and San Juan Puerto Rico. JetBlue's fleet of more than 250 aircraft consists mainly of Airbus A320s and A321s but also includes Embraer E190s. Dubbed "New York's Hometown Airline" about half of JetBlue's flights are to and from the New York metropolitan area.

HISTORY

JetBlue took to the skies in 2000 as the third airline start-up for founder and CEO David Neeleman. The first airline Neeleman helped create Morris Air was formed in 1984. Named after his business partner June Morris the discount airline was operating 22 planes out of Salt Lake City by 1993. While with Morris Air Neeleman pioneered ticketless travel which a decade later would become an industry standard.

Impressed with Morris Air's efficient and strategic network its e-ticket system and Neeleman Southwest Airlines acquired its smaller rival in 1993. Neeleman left Southwest after just six months but not without signing a non-compete clause that prevented him from attempting to repeat his Morris Air success in the US for five years.

Not willing to sit still for long (a characteristic he attributes to attention deficit disorder) Neeleman partnered with David Evans to create Open Skies an integrated e-ticket Internet booking and sales management tool that they began to market to smaller airlines.

Meanwhile Neeleman had skirted the terms of his non-compete agreement to help the founders of Canadian low-fare carrier WestJet get their project off of the ground serving as a consultant and a board member.

In 1999 a year after his non-compete agreement expired Neeleman sold Open Skies to Hewlett-Packard and set to work creating a new airline. In a matter of weeks he had managed to gather $130 million the most ever raised for a start-up airline from investors that included Chase Capital and financier George Soros. Neeleman immediately began acquiring new Airbus A320 jets and fitting them with satellite TV.

JetBlue's first flight was from New York to Fort Lauderdale in 2000. During the year the airline added nine more destinations in California Florida New York Utah and Vermont. By 2001 the airline was operating 20 new A320s with an ambitious 131 on order.

On September 11 of that year terrorists commandeered four passenger aircrafts and turned them into instruments of destruction killing some 3000 people. The events shocked the world and crippled the airline industry. Despite the climate however JetBlue continued to expand its network and it went public in 2002.

The industry star took some heat in 2003 for violating its own privacy policy when it gave the personal information of 1.1 million customers to the Department of Defense as part of anti-terrorism project.

JetBlue added nine new destinations in 2004 including Boston — a major market not dominated by a single carrier and lacking what the company deemed to be sufficient low-fare domestic service.

Consecutive losses in the fourth quarter of 2005 and the first quarter of 2006 — caused in part by rising fuel costs— led the carrier to raise fares on some routes redouble its efforts to keep expenses down and slow some of its expansion plans.

As part of the effort to improve the company's operations JetBlue's board in May 2007 asked David Neeleman to step down as CEO in favor of former president Dave Barger. Neeleman remained with the company as nonexecutive chairman until May 2008.

To grow JetBlue increased capacity at its base at New York's JFK airport with the opening of a new terminal in October 2008. The 630000 sq. ft. Terminal 5 has 26 gates solely used by JetBlue and can accommodate 250 daily departures. The $875 million renovation took three years; it has the largest single security checkpoint in the US and an adjacent 1500-space parking lot.

JetBlue expanded service in 2009 to Bogota Colombia and the Caribbean islands of St. Maarten and Jamaica.

In 2010 JetBlue ink a limited partnership with AMR Corp.'s legacy airline American; the two are sharing activities in New York and Boston including customer "interline" service one-stop booking and check-in and bag transfers for connecting flights. The partnership gives the younger low-cost carrier eight pairs of the Texas-based carrier's take-off and landing slots at Ronald Reagan Washington National Airport and swells American Airlines' New York market with 12 pairs of JetBlue's slots at John F. Kennedy International Airport.

In early 2011 the airline signed an interline agreement with Virgin Atlantic that allows passengers to make connecting flights on transatlantic routes using a single itinerary and baggage check.

EXECUTIVES

Vice President, Jim Hnat
Vice President Sales And Revenue Management, Dennis Corrigan
Evp Corporate Affairs General Counsel And Secretary, James G. (Jim) Hnat, age 48, $425,000 total compensation
President And Ceo, Robin Hayes, age 52, $550,000 total compensation
Evp Customer Experience, Joanna Geraghty
Evp Operations, Jeff Martin
Cio, Eash Sundaram
Evp People, Mike Elliott
Evp Commercial And Planning, Martin (Marty) St. George, $400,000 total compensation
Evp And Cfo, Stephen J. (Steve) Priest, age 49
Vice President Government And Airport Affairs, Jeffrey Goodell
Vice President Flight Operations, Andres Sandoval
Vice President Tax, Chris Lippi
Vice President Associate General Counsel, Michael P Carbone
Vp Inflight Experience, John Culp
Vice President Flight Operations, Bart Roberts
Senior Vice President Airline Planning, Scott Laurence
Senior Vice President System Operations, Alex Battaglia
Vice President For Security, Ken Maxwell
Vice President Compensation Benefits And Corporate Social Responsibility, Harry Spencer
Vice President Network Planning, John Checketts
Vice President Customer Support, Frankie Littleford
Vice President Marketing, Elizabeth Windram
Vice President Information Technology Technology And Integration, Ramki Ramaswamy
Vice President Airports Focus Cities, Mike Parkinson
Vice President Operational Planning And Analysis, David Jehn
Vice Chairman, Frank V. Sica, age 68
Chairman, Joel C. Peterson, age 72
Auditors: Ernst & Young LLP

LOCATIONS

HQ: JetBlue Airways Corp
27-01 Queens Plaza North, Long Island City, NY 11101
Phone: 718 286-7900
Web: www.jetblue.com

2018 Sales

	$ mil.	% of total
Domestic	5,386	70
Caribbean & Latin America	2,272	30
Total	**7,658**	**100**

PRODUCTS/OPERATIONS

2018 Sales

	$ mil.	% of total
Passenger	7,381	96
Other	277	4
Total	**7,658**	**100**

COMPETITORS

AirTran Airways	Frontier Airlines
Alaska Air	Southwest Airlines
American Airlines Group	United Continental
	Virgin America
Delta Air Lines	WestJet

HISTORICAL FINANCIALS

Company Type: Public

Income Statement

FYE: December 31

	REVENUE ($ mil.)	NET INCOME ($ mil.)	NET PROFIT MARGIN	EMPLOYEES
12/18	7,658	188	2.5%	20,892
12/17	7,015	1,147	16.4%	19,978
12/16	6,632	759	11.4%	18,406
12/15	6,416	677	10.6%	16,862
12/14	5,817	401	6.9%	15,334
Annual Growth	**7.1%**	**(17.3%)**	**—**	**8.0%**

2018 Year-End Financials

Debt ratio: 16.00%
Return on equity: 4.00%
Cash ($ mil.): 474
Current ratio: 1.00
Long-term debt ($ mil.): 1,361

No. of shares (mil.): 306
Dividends
  Yield: —
  Payout: —
Market value ($ mil.): 4,914

	STOCK PRICE ($) FY Close	P/E High/Low		PER SHARE ($) Earnings	Dividends	Book Value
12/18	16.00	38	25	1.00	0.00	15.00
12/17	22.00	7	5	3.00	0.00	15.00
12/16	22.00	10	7	2.00	0.00	12.00
12/15	23.00	13	7	2.00	0.00	10.00
12/14	16.00	12	6	1.00	0.00	8.00
Annual Growth	**0.3%**		**—**	**—(15.7%)**	**—**	**16.6%**

JOHNS HOPKINS UNIVERSITY

Founded in 1876 with a $7 million bequest from its namesake The Johns Hopkins University has established its reputation by molding itself in the image of a European research institution. While renowned for its School of Medicine the private university offers 260 academic programs spanning fields of study including arts and sciences business and international studies. The university enrolls more than 24000 full- and part-time students. Johns Hopkins has about a half-dozen campuses in Maryland and Washington DC as well as facilities in China and Italy. The student-teacher ratio is 13:1. The affiliated Johns Hopkins Health System provides health care from its three Baltimore-area hospitals.

Operations

Johns Hopkins University a private and non-profit institution with 1700 non-medical and 2800 medical faculty members offers education research and professional medical services. Its research and related services are offered through about 1800 government and private sponsors.

Keenly focused on research Johns Hopkins is engaged in a range of disciplines including health and medicine social sciences humanities the arts natural sciences engineering and technology. Projects include researching alternatives to animal testing disease treatments and chemical and biomolecular engineering topics among others.

The Johns Hopkins University offers graduate programs in business finance and real estate through its relatively new Carey Business School. Trustee emeritus William Polk Carey chairman of W. P. Carey & Co. partially funded the $100 million development of the school with $50 million which was completed in 2007.

Notable alumni of the school include 28th US president Woodrow Wilson Michael Bloomberg and horror film director Wesley Craven.

Geographic Reach

The university boasts three major campuses in Baltimore as well as single campus locations in (Montgomery County) Maryland and Washington DC. Johns Hopkins also operates facilities in the Baltimore-Washington area and abroad in China and Italy.

Strategy

Johns Hopkins is mid-way through its Ten By Twenty program — comprising 10 goals to achieve by 2020 — launched in 2013. The 10 goals are divided into four categories: One University (forging collaboration across disciplines); Individual Excellence (supporting faculty students and staff); Commitment to Our Communities (enriching ties to Baltimore the US and the world); and Institution Building (building a stronger university). In its 2017 progress report some of the achievements listed are more robust mental health resources; smaller class sizes; around 25 (out of a goal of 50) hires of interdisciplinary scholars; improved diversity and inclusion; and raised $4.6 billion in donations.

EXECUTIVES

Cio And Vice Provost Information Technology, Stephanie L. Reel
President, Ronald J. (Ron) Daniels
Svp Finance And Administration, Daniel G. Ennis
Svp Academic Affairs And Provost, Sunil Kumar
Vice President, Joseph Zolenas
Medical Director, Haig Kazazian
Senior Vice President Patient Care Services, Laura Wood
Vice President, Ben Myers
Medical Director Wilmer Eye Instructor At Columbia, Dean Glaros
Medical Director, Jeanette Nazarian
Pharmacy Manager, Michael Brown
Clinical Director, Peter Hill
Pharmacy Manager, Charles Wells
Vice President, Keith Hill
Medical Director Of Care Coordination, Joseph Perno
Vice President For Quality, Renee Demski
Senior Vice President Human Resources (john Hopkins Health System), Inez Stewart
Vice President And Chief Administrator, Sowell Ashlyn
Vice President Human Resources, Marcos Deleon
Director Of Nursing, Laurie Saletnik
Director Of Nursing, Deborah Baker
Senior Vice President Health Care Transformation And Strategic Planning, John Colmers
Vice President For Finance, Sidd Patel
Secretary Iii, Kristy Stewart
Medchi Vice Chair, Pranjal Gupta

LOCATIONS

HQ: JOHNS HOPKINS UNIVERSITY
3400 N CHARLES ST, BALTIMORE, MD 212182680
Phone: 410 516-8000

PRODUCTS/OPERATIONS

Selected Schools and Colleges

Bloomberg School of Public Health
Carey Business School
Krieger School of Arts and Sciences
Peabody Institute
School of Advanced International Studies
School of Education
School of Medicine
School of Nursing
Whiting School of Engineering

Selected Centers and Institutes

American Institute for Contemporary German Studies
Bloomberg School of Public Health Department of Health Policy and Management Fall Institute in Barcelona Spain
Bloomberg School of Public Health Research Centers
Center for Africana Studies
Center for Communication Programs
Center for Constitutional Studies and Democratic Development
Center for Clinical Global Health Education
Center for Global Health
Center for International Business and Public Policy
Center for Language Education
Center for Talented Youth
Center for Transatlantic Relations
Central Asia Caucasus Institute
Foreign Policy Institute
Hopkins Nanjing Center
Institute for Global Studies in Culture Power and History
Institute for Policy Studies
Johns Hopkins SAIS Bologna Center
Office of Global Nursing
SAIS Research Centers
Summer Language Institute
The Institute for Johns Hopkins Nursing
Yeung Center for Collaborative China Studies

Selected Campuses

Columbia Center - Columbia Maryland
East Baltimore Campus - Baltimore
Harbor East - Downtown Baltimore
Homewood Campus - Baltimore
Hopkins-Nanjing Center - Nanjing Jiangsu Province People's Republic of China
Johns Hopkins University Applied Physics Laboratory - Laurel MD; Baltimore and Washington
Johns Hopkins University Zanvyl Krieger School of Arts & Sciences Advanced Academic Programs - Washington DC
Montgomery County Center - Rockville Maryland
Nitze School of Advanced International Studies (SAIS) - Washington D.C
Peabody Campus - Baltimore
School of Advanced International Studies - Bologna Italy

HISTORICAL FINANCIALS

Company Type: Private

Income Statement   FYE: June 30

	REVENUE ($ mil.)	NET INCOME ($ mil.)	NET PROFIT MARGIN	EMPLOYEES
06/18	6,021	705	11.7%	37,600
06/13	4,794	526	11.0%	—
06/11	4,370	826	18.9%	—
06/05	788	0	—	—
Annual Growth	16.9%	—	—	—

Johnson & Johnson

It's difficult to get well without Johnson & Johnson (J&J). The diversified health care giant operates in three segments through more than 260 operating companies located in more than 60 countries. Its Medical Devices division offers surgical equipment monitoring devices orthopedic products and contact lenses among other items. J&J's Pharmaceuticals division makes drugs for an array of ailments such as neurological conditions blood disorders autoimmune diseases and pain. Top sellers are psoriasis and arthritis drugs Remicade and Stelara. Finally J&J's Consumer business makes over-the-counter (OTC) drugs and products for baby skin and oral care as well as first-aid and nutritional uses. The company operates worldwide but makes more than half of its revenues in the US.

HISTORY

Brothers James and Edward Mead Johnson founded their medical products company in 1885 in New Brunswick New Jersey. In 1886 Robert joined his brothers to make the antiseptic surgical dressings he developed. The company bought gauze maker Chicopee Manufacturing in 1916. In 1921 it introduced two of its classic products the Band-Aid and Johnson's Baby Cream.

Robert Jr. became chairman in 1932 and served until 1963. A WWII Army general he believed in decentralization; managers were given substantial freedom a principle still used today. Product lines in the 1940s included Ortho (birth control products) and Ethicon (sutures). In 1959 Johnson & Johnson bought McNeil Labs which launched Tylenol (acetaminophen) as an OTC drug the next year. Foreign acquisitions included Switzerland's Cilag-Chemie (1959) and Belgium's Janssen (1961). The company focused on consumer products in the 1970s gaining half the feminine protection market and making Tylenol the top-selling painkiller.

Trouble struck in 1982 when someone laced Tylenol capsules with cyanide killing eight people. The company's response is now a damage-control classic: It immediately recalled 31 million bottles and totally redesigned its packaging to prevent future tampering. The move cost $240 million but saved the Tylenol brand. The next year prescription painkiller Zomax was linked to five deaths and was pulled.

New products in the 1980s included ACUVUE disposable contact lenses and Retin-A. The company bought LifeScan (blood-monitoring products for diabetics) in 1986. In 1989 it began a joint venture with Merck to sell Mylanta and other drugs bought from ICI Americas.

The firm continued its acquisition and diversification strategy in the 1990s. After introducing the first daily-wear disposable contact lenses in 1993 it bought skin-care product maker Neutrogena (1994) to enhance its consumer lines. To diversify its medical products and better compete for hospital business it bought Mitek Surgical Products (1995) and heart disease product maker Cordis (1996). The FDA cleared J&J's Renova wrinkle and fade cream in 1996. The company also began selling at-home HIV test Confide but pulled it the next year after low sales and other problems.

EXECUTIVES

Vp Of Investor Relations, Louise Mehrotra
Evp And Cfo, Dominic J. Caruso, age 62, $909,500 total compensation
Evp And Worldwide Chairman Consumer Group, Jorge S. Mesquita, age 57
Evp And Group Worldwide Chairman, Sandra E. Peterson, age 61, $963,462 total compensation
Chairman And Ceo, Alex Gorsky, age 58, $1,600,000 total compensation
Company Group Chairman Consumer Medical Devices, Ashley A. McEvoy
Evp And Chief Scientist Officer, Paulus (Paul) Stoffels, age 57, $1,144,000 total compensation
Evp And Worldwide Chairman Pharmaceuticals, Joaquin Duato, age 56, $875,000 total compensation
Evp And Chief Human Resources Officer, Peter M. Fasolo, age 56
Evp And General Counsel, Michael H. Ullmann, age 60, $645,385 total compensation
Evp And World Chairman Medical Devices, Gary Pruden, age 57
Company Group Chairman Pharmaceuticals The Americas, Jennifer Taubert

Vice President Innovation Global Health And Policy Communication, Seema Kumar
Vp Hr, Martha Liano
Vice President Worldwide Engineering, Gary Warren
Vp Emerging Technologies, Joseph Smith
Vice President Human Resources, Danielle Devine
Corporate Vice President Worldwide Government Affairs And Policy, Clifford Holland
Vice President Global Consumer Insights, Jim Norgren
Vp Worldwide Compensaiton, Donna Ng
Vice President North America For Global Marketing Group, Darryl Nicholson
Vice President Human Resources, Marc Schorpion
Vp Sales, Rob Case
Vice President World Wide Consumer Supply Chain, Robert Wuesthoff
Vice President Oncology Sci Innovation, Pamela Carroll
Vice President Research And Development Healthcare Compliance, Frank Konings
Vice President Human Resources, Brenda Bass
Vice President, Brenda Squaire
Vice President Of Medical Affairs, Diego Miralles
Vice President Global Medical Affairs, Craig Tendler
Vice President Comm And Public Affairs Med Dev, Tom Sanford
Vice President Clinical Development Regulatory Affairs, Jessica Shen
Vice President Global Engineering, Michael Maggio
Vice President Business Transformation, Angie Caswell
Area Vice President Northeast, Travis Williams
Vice President Of Global Health, Scott Ratzan
Vice President Prod Stewardship, Susan Nettesheim
Vice President Quality Assurance J And J Consumer Group Of Companies, Teresa Gorecki
Vice President Global Account Management, Jack Gelman
Vice President Global Pharmaceutical Communications, Craig Rothenberg
Vice President Sterile Process Technolog, Rainer Newman
Vice President Global Strategic Marketing, Aldo Denti
Vice President Business Development, Robert Havard
Vice President Marketing Mcneil Consumer Healthcare, Catherine Devine
Executive Vice President, Edgardo Fabregas
Vice President Human Resources At Jandj, Hilde Claes
Vice President Marketing, Joe Marrone
Vp Marketing, David Sampson
Vice President Planning Global Surgery Supply Chain, Matt Perry
Vice President Marketing Policy And Advocacy, John Hoffman
Vice President Global Tox And Path, Peggy Guzzie-peck
Vice President Us Medical Affairs Virology, Richard Nettles
Vp Preclinical, Alfred Tonelli
Vice President State Govt Affairs, Don Bohn
Vice President Business Development Neuroscience, Cindy Warren
Vice President Research Analytics, Elizabeth Blackwood
Vice President Immunology Research And Development, Dan Baker
Regional Vice President, Mark Sienkiewicz
Vpcx Infrastructure Services, Nick Fisher
Vice President, Li Mao
Vp Cfo Global Consumer Supply Chain, Jill Freedman
Senior Vice President, Instructor Sunywcc
Vice President Quality Systems, Cherian George

Vice President Supply Chain North America Otc, Gaspar Zuniga

Vp Health System Innovation, Brad Moore

Vice President Quality Systems And Services, Jackie Maestri

Vice President, Jane Wood

Vice President Scientific Fellow, Vladimir Dragalin

Vice President Worldwide Business Development Consumer Healthcare, Randy Goodreau

Vice President Global Distribution Operations, Eduardo Baez-Toro

Vice President Global Brand Protection, Richard Kaeser

Vice President North America Revenue Growth Management And Sales Activation, Mark Pettiford

Vice President Franchise Medical Leader Metabolism, Gary Meininger

Executive Vice President Information Management, Bob Daretta

Vice President R And D, Erin Johnson

Vice President Esp Technology Programs, Salvatore Trovato

Ww Vp And Head Of Supply Chain, Craig Russell

Worldwide Vice President Global Ecommerce And Digital, Manuel Suro

Vice President Law, Conde Kathryn

Vice President Idar Gcdo, Weston Darren

Senior Medical Director, Jeysen Yogaratnam

Vice President Consumer Medical Device Communications, Donna Lorenson

Vice President Compensation And Benefits Tax Counsel, Liza Leandre

Vice President Of Immunology Scientific Innovation, Jackie Papkoff

Vice Chair Of The Executive Committee And Chief Scientific Officer, Paul Stoffels

Board Member, Dirk Collier

Auditors: PricewaterhouseCoopers LLP

LOCATIONS

HQ: Johnson & Johnson
One Johnson & Johnson Plaza, New Brunswick, NJ 08933
Phone: 732 524-0400   **Fax:** 732 214-0332
Web: www.jnj.com

2017 Sales

	$ mil.	% of total
US	39,863	52
Europe	17,126	22
Asia/Pacific & Africa	13,420	18
Western hemisphere excluding US	6,041	8
Total	**76,450**	**100**

PRODUCTS/OPERATIONS

2017 Sales by Segment

	$ mil.	% of total
Pharmaceutical	36,356	47
Medical Devices	26,592	35
Consumer	13,602	18
Total	**76,450**	**100**

COMPETITORS

3M Health Care	Genzyme
Abbott Labs	GlaxoSmithKline
Alcon	Kimberly-Clark Health
Allergan plc	L'Oréal USA
Amgen	Medtronic
ArthroCare	Mentholatum Company
AstraZeneca	Merck
B. Braun Melsungen	Mylan
Bard	Novartis
Bausch & Lomb	NutraSweet
Baxter International	Perrigo
Bayer AG	Pfizer
Beckman Coulter	Procter & Gamble
Becton Dickinson	Roche Holding
Biogen	Sanofi
Boehringer Ingelheim	Shire

Boston Scientific	Smith & Nephew
Bristol-Myers Squibb	St. Jude Medical
Chattem	Stryker
Colgate-Palmolive	Terumo
Cook Incorporated	Teva
Dr. Reddy's	The Dial Corporation
Edwards Lifesciences	UCB
Eli Lilly	Zimmer Biomet

HISTORICAL FINANCIALS

Company Type: Public

Income Statement

FYE: December 30

	REVENUE ($ mil.)	NET INCOME ($ mil.)	NET PROFIT MARGIN	EMPLOYEES
12/18	81,581	15,297	18.8%	135,100
12/17*	76,450	1,300	1.7%	134,000
01/17	71,890	16,540	23.0%	126,400
01/16	70,074	15,409	22.0%	127,100
12/14	74,331	16,323	22.0%	126,500
Annual Growth	**2.4%**	**(1.6%)**	**—**	**1.7%**

*Fiscal year change

2018 Year-End Financials

Debt ratio: 20.00%—
Return on equity: 26.00%
Cash ($ mil.): 18,107
Current ratio: 1.00
Long-term debt ($ mil.): 27,684

Dividends
Yield: 0.0%
Payout: 63.0%
Market value ($ mil.): —

	STOCK PRICE ($) FY Close	P/E High/Low	PER SHARE ($) Earnings	Dividends	Book Value
12/18	127.00	26 21	6.00	4.00	22.00
12/17*	140.00	299 233	0.00	3.00	22.00
01/17	115.00	21 16	6.00	3.00	26.00
01/16	103.00	19 16	5.00	3.00	26.00
12/14	105.00	19 15	6.00	3.00	25.00
Annual Growth	**4.9%**	**— —**	**(0.4%)**	**6.4%**	**(2.7%)**

*Fiscal year change

JOHNSON CONTROLS, INC.

EXECUTIVES

Ceo, Alberto Ventura
Pres-Coo*, George R Oliver
Exec V Pres-Cfo*, Brian Stief
V Pres-Gen Counsel-Sec*, Brian J Cadwallader
V Pres-Corp Contrl*, Suzanne M Vincent
Cpo-V Pres of Controls Operati*, Michael Bartschat
Coordinator, Bob Anders
Designer, Ed Stevens
Coordinator, Debra Morley
Coordinator, Mary Moore
Compliance Staff, Melissa Goetz-Krummel
Auditors: PRICEWATERHOUSECOOPERS LLP MI

LOCATIONS

HQ: JOHNSON CONTROLS, INC.
5757 N GREEN BAY AVE, MILWAUKEE, WI 532094408
Phone: 414 524-1200
Web: WWW.JOHNSONCONTROLS.COM

COMPETITORS

3M	Honeywell
A123 Systems	International
Addison	Illinois Tool Works

Alcoa	Inci Aku
Building Technologies	International Paper
Caterpillar	Invensys
Comfort Systems USA	Lear Corp
DENSO	Lennox
Deere	Lockheed Martin
Delphi Automotive Systems	Magna International
Dow Chemical	Northrop Grumman
DuPont	Paloma Group
Eagle-Picher	Raytheon
East Penn Manufacturing	Rieter Automotive North America
Eaton	Robert Bosch
Emerson Electric	SPX
Exide	Trane Inc.
Faurecia	United Technologies
GS Yuasa	Valeo
General Dynamics	Visteon
General Motors	Whirlpool
Goodman Global	Yazaki North America
Goodyear Tire & Rubber	

HISTORICAL FINANCIALS

Company Type: Private

Income Statement

FYE: September 30

	REVENUE ($ mil.)	NET INCOME ($ mil.)	NET PROFIT MARGIN	EMPLOYEES
09/15	37,179	1,679	4.5%	139,000
09/14	42,828	1,335	3.1%	—
09/13	42,730	1,297	3.0%	—
Annual Growth	**(6.7%)**	**13.8%**	**—**	**—**

Jones Financial Companies LLLP

Auditors: PricewaterhouseCoopers, LLP

LOCATIONS

HQ: Jones Financial Companies LLLP
12555 Manchester Road, Des Peres, MO 63131
Phone: 314 515-2000

HISTORICAL FINANCIALS

Company Type: Public

Income Statement

FYE: December 31

	REVENUE ($ mil.)	NET INCOME ($ mil.)	NET PROFIT MARGIN	EMPLOYEES
12/18	8,469	990	11.7%	47,000
12/17	7,506	872	11.6%	45,000
12/16	6,557	746	11.4%	43,000
12/15	6,619	838	12.7%	41,000
12/14	6,278	770	12.3%	40,000
Annual Growth	**7.8%**	**6.5%**	**—**	**4.1%**

2018 Year-End Financials

Debt ratio: —
Return on equity: —
Cash ($ mil.): 2,409
Current ratio: 1.00
Long-term debt ($ mil.): —

No. of shares (mil.): 1
Dividends
Yield: —
Payout: —
Market value ($ mil.): —

Jones Lang LaSalle Inc

Jones Lang LaSalle (JLL) provides real estate without borders. Its services include commercial leasing real estate brokerage management advisory and financing through some 300 corporate offices in more than 80 countries around the world. The company's LaSalle Investment Management arm is a diversified real estate management firm with about $60 billion in assets under management. JLL has commercial real estate expertise across office retail hotel health care industrial cultural and multifamily residential properties. It manages more than 4.5 billion sq. ft. worldwide. JLL was formed through the 1999 merger of Jones Lang Wootton (founded in England in 1783) and LaSalle Partners (founded in the US in 1968).

HISTORY

Jones Lang Wootton had roots in London's Paternoster Row auction houses in 1783. LaSalle Partners originally known as IDC Real Estate was founded in El Paso Texas in 1968. The two companies could not have started out in a more disparate fashion yet their combined force is now one of the largest real estate services firms in the world.

Richard Winstanley opened an auction house in 1783 and his son James joined him in that business in 1806. In 1840 the Joneses entered the picture – the Winstanleys created a partnership with one James Jones. The business moved to King Street (in the Guildhall section of London) in 1860 and remained in that location for some 100 years in various incarnations – James' son Frederick took over the business renaming it Frederick Jones and Co. When James retired in 1872 the firm was again renamed to Jones Lang and Co. and was controlled by C. A. Lang. Jones Lang merged with Wootton and Son in 1939 becoming Jones Lang Wootton and Sons.

Jones Lang Wootton was active in redrawing the property lines in London after the Blitz. In 1945 the firm began contacting small landowners and by combining small parcels of land secured development leasing and/or purchase contracts. When the rebuilding of London began in 1954 Jones Lang Wootton was in a secure place to be right at the forefront of that new development. The firm began engaging in speculative development in the West End and in the City of London.

The year 1958 saw the expansion of Jones Lang Wootton into Australia; the firm had offices throughout the Asia/Pacific region by 1968. Further expansion took place closer to home in Scotland (1962) and Ireland (1965) and the first continental European office in Brussels (also 1965). The firm moved into the Manhattan market in 1975.

On the other side of the story IDC Real Estate (the name change to LaSalle Partners came in 1977) was a group of partnerships initially focused on investment banking investment management and land. The firm began offering development management services in 1975; it moved into property management leasing and tenant representation in 1978 and facility management operations in 1980.

It built market share by buying other firms including Kleinwort Benson Realty Advisors Corp. (1994) and UK-based investment adviser CIN Property Management (1996).

The firm leveraged its experience and long-term client base to pursue an acquisition strategy taking advantage of trends shaping commercial real estate – globalization consolidation and merchant banking. LaSalle went public in 1997 amalgamating the Galbreath Company (a property and development management firm with which it merged that year) with its other partnerships and becoming a corporation.

In 1998 it acquired the project management business of Satulah Group and two retail management business units from Lend Lease and took real estate investment trust LaSalle Hotel Properties public. In 1999 the firm strengthened its world position by merging with Jones Lang Wootton; the company was renamed Jones Lang LaSalle.

The merger with Jones Lang Wootton combined Wootton's strength in Asia and Europe with LaSalle Partners' large presence in North America to create a worldwide real estate services firm. In 2006 the company acquired Spaulding & Slye strengthening operations in the Mid-Atlantic and New England. Also that year it opened an office in Dubai and acquired RSP Group which operates in North Africa and the Middle East. In 2007 Jones Lang LaSalle bought German property advisory firm Kemper's Holding and took a stake in the former Trammell Crow Meghraj one of the largest private real estate companies in India.

The company broadened its presence in key North American markets when it acquired The Staubach Company in 2008. Jones Lang LaSalle paid $613 million for the rival real estate services firm which was founded by football legend and former Dallas Cowboys quarterback Roger Staubach.

Jones Lang LaSalle slowed its acquisition pace during the economic recession. But managed to cut a few deals. In 2009 Jones Lang LaSalle teamed up with Real Estate Disposition to begin offering online auction sales a product to help customers quickly sell commercial property and other distressed assets.

In another deal Jones Lang LaSalle acquired the third-party leasing and management duties of General Growth Properties in 2010 as part of the mall owner's restructuring efforts. The deal added about 20 shopping centers to Jones Lang LaSalle's management portfolio.

EXECUTIVES

Vp It, Susan Nuccio
Ceo Americas, Gregory P. (Greg) O'Brien, age 56, $400,000 total compensation
Regional Ceo European Operations, Jeff A. Jacobson, age 57, $400,000 total compensation
President Ceo And Director, Christian Ulbrich, age 53, $481,619 total compensation
Ceo Europe Middle East And Africa, Guy Grainger
Managing Director Shanghai And East China, Anthony Couse, $420,902 total compensation
Global Ceo Corporate Solutions, John Forrest
Chief Administrative Officer, Patricia (Trish) Maxson, age 60
Global Chief Executive Officer Capital Markets, Richard Bloxam
Ceo Jll Netherlands, Pieter Hendrikse
Global Chief Financial Officer, Stephanie Plaines
Vice President Finance, Bill Grice
Senior Vice President, David Roberts
Vice President, Mia Eglinton
Vice President, Bob Gross
Senior Vice President Information Technology, David Laduke
Vice President Corporate Solutions Energy And Sustainability Clean Tech, Michael Bosco
Vice President Facility Management, Quentin Graves
Senior Vice President, Kevin Brant
Senior Vice President Of Engineering, Miles Anderson
Vice President, Michael Billing
Executive Vice President Strategic Advisory, Clay Dickinson
Vice President, Truitt Alday
Vice President Of Sponsorship Marketing, Sally Hertz
Senior Vice President, Alex Lassar
Vice President, Laurie Christian
Senior Vice President, Louis Molinini
Vice President, William Schuch
Assistant Vice President, Clayton Kline
Avp New York Brokerage Operations, Jason Roberts
Vice President, James Ezell
Assistant Vice President, Jim Woodard
Senior Vice President, Peter Richardson
Vice President, Jeremiah Riordan
Executive Vice President, Wade Clark
Senior Vice President International Desk, Julie Steffen
Executive Vice President, Jim Plummer
Senior Vice President, Brad Shokes
Senior Vice President Hotels And Hospitality, Nick Baer
Senior Vice President Strategic Consulting, James Rice
Executive Vice President, Darcy Miramontes
Executive Vice President, Daryl Mullin
Vice President Prosite Director Operations, George O'donnell
Vice President, Barry Josowitz
Senior Vice President, Brendan Callahan
Senior Vice President Finance Client Manager And Compliance, Greg Sheehan
Vice President, Ryan Matthews
Vice President Strategic Sourcing West Region, Tim Hamill
Vice President And General Manager, Jennifer Christakes
Vice President Corp. Property Services, Kevin Griffin
Vice President Project And Development Services, Pam Heckman
Vice President, Alex Holton
Vice President, Cliff West
Senior Vice President, Melvin Chu
Vice President, Ben Casper
Vice President Retail, Mike Horner
Senior Vice President Hotels, John L Strauss
Vice President, Michele Barkinge
Executive Vice President, Jorg Mast
Vice President, Tony Haning
Senior Vice President, Tom Fox
Svp, Bruce Gordon
Vice President, Bret Felberg
Senior Vice President, Zach Anderson
Vice President, Steve Borup
Vp And Director Geographic Information Systems, Michael Startin
Vice President, Teri Bell
Senior Vice President Regional Finance Director, Cliff Marnick
Vice President, Tom Doupe
Senior Vice President, Chuck Straw
Executive Vice President Supply Chain Management, Gerald Donovan
Senior Vice President Of Development And Asset Strategy, Jeffrey Adkison
Senior Vice President, Cameron Driscoll
Senior Vice President Tenant R, Patrick Bolick
Executive Vice President, Michael Diaz
Vice President, Michael Streit
Executive Vice President Of Human Resources, Renee Cassella
Vice President, Dan Reynolds
Executive Vice President Tenant Reperesentation, Rob Nielsen
Senior Vice President, Andrea Sylvester
Senior Vice President, Jim Cahlin
Executive Vice President, Gregg Raus
Senior Vice President Business Consulting, Shannon Curley
Vice President Corporate Properties Group, Allen Merrill

Executive Vice President, Jason Volpe
Vice President, Scott Harrison
Senior Vice President, Steve Ostrowski
Senior Vice President Retail, Kirk Horiuchi
Vice President Strategic Consulting Workplace
 And Occupancy Planning, Laura Delafuente
Assistant Vice President, Yorke Allen
Vice President, Koley X MacKay
Vice President, Michelle Monhaut
Senior Vice President, Bradley McGill
Vice President, Heather Filkins
Senior Vice President, Tim Glenn
Senior Vice President, Evamarie Smith
Senior Vice President National Director, Gary
 Gersten
Senior Vice President, Steve Trapp
Senior Vice President, Leo O'loughlin
Vice President, Matthew Ruffing
Senior Vice President Retail, Mike Longmore
Senior Vice President, Arthur Frye
Senior Vice President, William M Korchak
Senior Vice President, David Oh
Senior Vice President Transition Manager, Cathy
 Frampton
Vice President, Stephen Chastain
Vice President Engineering And Operati, Bruce
 Sirota
Senior Vice President Group Property
 Management, Steve Mace
Vp Retail Development Strategy Services, Cynthia
 Pearl
Vice President, Jeff Bellitti
Senior Vice President, Robert Tomsovic
Senior Vice President, Seth Heikkila
Vice President Pmp, Chris Ferreira
Senior Vice President, Arthur Turowski
Vice President Associate Director, Julie Bane
Senior Vice President Lease Administration,
 Michael Mavilla
Senior Vice President, Luanne Atkinson
Senior Vice President, Chris Hile
Vice President, Judy Caruthers
Executive Vice President, George Nicholas
Senior Vice President Project, Don Bucci
Vice President, Paul Kelsey
Senior Vice President, Joshua Sloan
Vice President, Lori Horvath
Executive Vice President Managing Director,
 Walter Wahlfeldt
Vice President, Charlie Floberg
Senior Vice President, Brian Walsh
Senior Vice President, Brendan Mcarthur
Senior Vice President, Sam Durkin
Vice President, Coleen Cecil
Senior Vice President, Brian Ackerman
Executive Vice President, Glenn Aspinwall
Vice President, Jon Packee
Senior Vice President, Sherri Lusk
Senior Vice President, Andrew Whipple
Executive Vice President, Bill Suits
Senior Vice President, Griffin Guthneck
Vice President, Chris Chornohos
Executive Vice President, Nate Demetsky
Vice President, Jamie Vari
Vice President, Ryan Lawrence
Senior Vice President, Joe Greco
Vice President, Lesa French
Executive Vice President, Bruno Fiorvento
Vice President Associate Director, Jesse Mangum
Senior Vice President, David Chapin
Vice President, Michael Paul
Senior Vice President, Mark Newman
Senior Vice President, Nick Francic
Senior Vice President, Marlon Wenstrom
Senior Vice President, Xavier Wasiak
Auditors: KPMG LLP

LOCATIONS

HQ: Jones Lang LaSalle Inc
 200 East Randolph Drive, Chicago, IL 60601
Phone: 312 782-5800   Fax: 312 782-4339
Web: www.jll.com

2017 Sales by Business Segment

	$ mil.	% of total
Americas	3,355	42
Europe Middle East Africa	2,586	33
Asia Pacific	1,637	21
Investment management	355	4
Total	**7,932**	**100**

PRODUCTS/OPERATIONS

2017 Sales

	$ mil.	% of total
Real Estate Services		
Property and facility management	2,382	30
Leasing	2,023	26
Project and development services	1,349	17
Capital Markets & Hotels	1,139	14
Advisory Consulting and Other	685	9
LaSalle Investment Management	355	4
Total	**8**	**100**

Selected Services

Investor services
 Agency leasing
 Property management
 Valuations and consulting
Occupier services
 Facilities management
 Project and development services
 Tenant representation
Construction management
Capital markets
Hotel advisory
Strategic consulting

COMPETITORS

BGC Partners
CBRE Group
Colliers International
Colliers International
 Group
Cushman & Wakefield

Hines
Lend Lease
Newmark Knight Frank
Prologis
Savills

HISTORICAL FINANCIALS

Company Type: Public

Income Statement

FYE: December 31

	REVENUE ($ mil.)	NET INCOME ($ mil.)	NET PROFIT MARGIN	EMPLOYEES
12/18	16,318	485	3.0%	90,000
12/17	7,932	254	3.2%	81,900
12/16	6,804	318	4.7%	77,300
12/15	5,966	439	7.4%	61,500
12/14	5,430	386	7.1%	58,100
Annual Growth	**31.7%**	**5.8%**	—	**11.6%**

2018 Year-End Financials

Debt ratio: 10.00%
Return on equity: 14.00%
Cash ($ mil.): 481
Current ratio: 1.00
Long-term debt ($ mil.): 656

No. of shares (mil.): 46
Dividends
 Yield: 1.0%
 Payout: 8.0%
Market value ($ mil.): 5,773

	STOCK PRICE ($) FY Close	P/E High/Low		PER SHARE ($) Earnings	Dividends	Book Value
12/18	127.00	17	12	11.00	1.00	81.00
12/17	149.00	27	18	6.00	1.00	71.00
12/16	101.00	23	13	7.00	1.00	62.00
12/15	160.00	18	15	10.00	1.00	60.00
12/14	150.00	18	12	9.00	0.00	53.00
Annual Growth	**(4.1%)**	—	—	**5.5%**	**14.3%**	**11.0%**

JPMorgan Chase & Co

Boasting some $2.5 trillion in assets JPMorgan Chase is the largest bank holding company in the US and among the largest half-dozen in the world. With some 5250 branches in about two dozen states it is among the nation's top mortgage lenders and credit card issuers (it holds some $141 billion in credit card loans). Active in 60 countries the bank also boasts formidable investment banking and asset management operations through its subsidiaries JPMorgan Private Bank and institutional investment manager JPMorgan Asset Management which has $2.5 trillion in assets under supervision. The company can trace its history back to the Bank of Manhattan Company founded in 1799.

HISTORY

JPMorgan Chase & Co.'s roots are in The Manhattan Company created in 1799 to bring water to New York City. A provision buried in its incorporation documents let the company provide banking services; investor and future US Vice President Aaron Burr brought the company (eventually the Bank of Manhattan) into competition with The Bank of New York founded by Burr's political rival Alexander Hamilton. JPMorgan Chase still owns the pistols from the notorious 1804 duel in which Burr mortally wounded Hamilton.

In 1877 John Thompson formed Chase National naming it for Salmon Chase Abraham Lincoln's secretary of the treasury and the architect of the national bank system. Chase National merged with John D. Rockefeller's Equitable Trust in 1930 becoming the world's largest bank and beginning a long relationship with the Rockefellers. Chase National continued growing after WWII and in 1955 it merged with the Bank of Manhattan. Christened Chase Manhattan the bank remained the US's largest into the 1960s.

When soaring 1970s oil prices made energy loans attractive Chase invested in Penn Square an obscure oil-patch bank in Oklahoma and the first notable bank failure of the 1980s. (The legal aftereffects of Penn Square's 1982 failure dragged on until 1993.) Losses following the 1987 foreign loan crisis hit Chase hard as did the real estate crash. In 1995 the bank went looking for a partner. After talks with Bank of America it settled on Chemical Bank.

Chemical Bank opened in 1824 and was one of the US's largest banks by 1900. As with Chase Chemical began as an unrelated business (New York Chemical Manufacturing) in 1823 largely in order to open a bank (it dropped its chemical operations in 1844). Chemical would merge with Manufacturers Hanover in 1991.

After its 1996 merger with Chase Chemical Bank was the surviving entity but assumed Chase's more prestigious name. Initial cost savings from the merger were substantial as jobs and branch offices were eliminated. In 1997 Chase acquired the credit business of The Bank of New York and the corporate trustee business of Mellon Financial but underwent another round of belt-tightening the next year when it took a $320 million charge and cut 4500 jobs. The bank also suffered losses related to its involvement with the ill-starred Long-Term Capital Management hedge fund.

In 1999 Chase focused on lending buying two mortgage originators and forming a marketing alliance with subprime auto lender AmeriCredit (now General Motors Financial Company). Chase also bought Mellon Financial's residential mortgage unit and Huntington Bancshares' credit card portfolio. It bought UK investment bank Robert Fleming Holdings in 2000.

In 2001 it closed its $30 billion buy of J.P. Morgan and renamed itself JPMorgan Chase & Co. The new firm eliminated some 10% of its combined workforce as a result of the merger. Chairman Sandy Warner (who ran J.P. Morgan) retired at year-end and was replaced by former Chase Manhattan leader CEO William Harrison.

JPMorgan Chase had more than $1 billion in exposure to Enron but in 2003 recovered some $600 million after a court battle with the failed energy trader's insurers which claimed the losses stemmed from loans by JPMorgan Chase disguised as oil and gas transactions. Nonetheless JPMorgan Chase ended up paying some $135 million to settle actions relating to the questionable loans.

In 2004 JPMorgan Chase joined forces with venerable investment bank Cazenove; the joint venture called JPMorgan Cazenove handles corporate finance and capital markets activities in the UK.

The next year JPMorgan Chase and its investment banking arm J.P. Morgan Securities avoided a trial by paying some $2 billion to settle claims from investors who lost money on bonds that the firm underwrote in 2000 and 2001 for scandal-ridden WorldCom which eventually declared bankruptcy (WorldCom became MCI and later was acquired by Verizon Communications).

On the heels of the its massive BANK ONE buy in 2004 JPMorgan Chase made several smaller purchases including global trade management and logistics software maker Vastera (renamed JPMorgan Chase Vastera) trading technology firm Neovest and the credit card business of Sears Canada. JPMorgan Chase also sold online brokerage subsidiary J.P. Morgan Invest and its BrownCo unit to E*TRADE. The following year the company acquired student lender Collegiate Funding Services which JPMorgan Chase combined with its existing Chase Education Finance division. The company also got the go-ahead from the FTC and bought Kohl's$1.6 billion credit card portfolio.

Enron continued to haunt the company: in 2005 it forked over $2.2 billion to settle part of an investor class-action suit over fraud charges related to the Enron debacle and paid another $350 million to the infamous energy trading firm which asserted that JPMorgan Chase and about 10 other banks aided and abetted the company's collapse. However the next year the company got some good news regarding its alleged involvement with the collapse of Enron when the class action suit against it was dismissed.

Also in 2006 the company cut ties with private equity investment arm J.P. Morgan Partners which divided into two companies CCMP Capital and Panorama Capital. JPMorgan Chase retained the former private equity operations of BANK ONE One Equity Partners.

In keeping with the lesson learned regarding its $2 billion fine to settle claims in the WorldCom debacle in 2006 the bank was quick to settle its part of another class-action lawsuit this time brought by investors claiming they were cheated in the dot-com IPO boom. JPMorgan Chase paid $425 million to settle that case. It paid a much smaller settlement of $3.8 million for its part in the demise of the ill-fated telecom Global Crossing.

All was not lawsuits and settlements in 2006 however: that year it swapped its corporate trust business for Bank of New York's nearly 340-branch network in the New York metropolitan area. Both units were valued at about $2 billion with JPMorgan Chase paying Bank of New York around $150 million more to make up the difference.

William Harrison retired as chairman at the end of 2006; he was succeeded by president and CEO (and the CEO of BANK ONE when it was acquired) Jamie Dimon.

As one of the largest mortgage and home equity providers in the country JPMorgan Chase was hurt by the subprime mortgage crisis and subsequent fall in home values in 2007. About a third of its loans were home equity loans and it had to write off more than $500 million in home equity loans that year.

In 2008 the bank assumed full ownership of payments processor Chase Paymentech Solutions which had been a joint venture with First Data. First Data assumed 49% of Chase Paymentech's assets and clients in the deal.

Also that year as part of a plan to stimulate the economy the US government invested in JPMorgan Chase and other banks. The bank got $25 billion of the $700 billion taxpayer-funded bailout package that was approved in late 2008 with the stipulation that the banks use the money and not hoard it. The investment came with restrictions on executive pay and other rules and JPMorgan returned the money the following year saying it was doing just fine without it.

Led by CEO Jamie Dimon JPMorgan Chase closed a couple of very high profile deals as the economic crisis claimed numerous victims. It acquired Bear Stearns one of Wall Street's top investment banks and the operations of Washington Mutual (WaMu) the largest bank to fail in US history. Both deals closed in 2008.

Initially JPMorgan Chase made a bargain-basement offer of $270 million (around $2 a share) for the struggling Bear Stearns which was drowning in subprime mortgage investment debt. It ultimately raised its offer to around $10 a share or some $1.2 billion. The deal came after the Fed extended a $30 billion lifeline to Bear Stearns to keep the firm afloat; JPMorgan Chase was one of the lenders.

The company also stepped in to buy WaMu when that bank failed and was seized by regulators. It paid $1.9 billion for the bank's operations and assumed some $31 billion in losses. JPMorgan began integrating WaMu's branches with its own retail network phasing out the WaMu brand and closing about 10% of the combined branches (especially in markets where there was overlap). Shortly after the acquisition JPMorgan cut 9200 WaMu jobs — about 20% of its workforce.

In 2009 JPMorgan Chase sold specialist firm Bear Wagner acquired in the Bear Stearns deal to Barclays Capital.

JPMorgan Chase agreed to pay more than $153 million to the Securities and Exchange Commission in order to settle a claim that it misled investors during the 2007 housing market crash. The company was among others that were investigated for improper sales practices.

In 2010 JPMorgan acquired the European and Asian segments of RBS Sempra Commodities the energy trading joint venture between Royal Bank of Scotland and Sempra Energy. The $1.6 billion deal did not include RBS Sempra's more valuable North American segment. JPMorgan integrated the business into the bank's existing global commodities business doubling its corporate client numbers.

Also in 2010 the company bought the private equity administration services of Schroders. That deal added more than $6 billion in committed capital. J.P. Morgan Worldwide Securities Services already had some $15.3 trillion in assets under custody. In 2011 the company sold its 41% stake in mutual fund company American Century to CIBC for some $848 million.

EXECUTIVES

Vice President, Brian Coats
Vice President, John Bradley
Chairman And Ceo, James (Jamie) Dimon, age 62, $1,500,000 total compensation
Ceo Card Services, Gordon A. Smith, age 60, $500,000 total compensation
Executive Committee Member Investment Bank, Daniel E. Pinto, age 56, $8,303,234 total compensation
Cio, Lori A. Beer, age 51
Ceo Commercial Banking And Executive Committee Member, Douglas B. (Doug) Petno, age 53
Ceo Asset And Wealth Management, Mary Callahan Erdoes, age 51, $750,000 total compensation
Cfo, Marianne Lake, age 49, $750,000 total compensation
Chief Risk Officer, Ashley Bacon, age 49
Ceo Jpmorgan Emea And Jp Morgan Securities Plc, Vis Raghavan
Vice President, Josephine Norris
First Vice President District Manager, Sean Cummings
Vice President, Jeanne Garcia
1st Vice President, Patti Shultz
Vice President Technology Program Director, Mark Koban
Vice President Information Technology, Jay Barret
Vice President Information Security Officer, Todd Bailey
Vice President Human Resources, Jim Odonnell
Vice President, Madhu Tumma
Vice President Information Technology, Dennis Ramawy
Vice President, Edwin Tate
Vice President, Michael Green
Desktop Support Vice President, Jeff Morgan
Vice President Of Technology, Tracey Ball
Vice President Market Risk Technology, Kevin Ford
Vice President, David Elmquist
Vice President Trading Technologies, Ann Billak
Vice President Talent And Development Operations, Ning Ham
Senior Vice President Middle Market Banking, Jim Nicholas
Senior Vice President Client Care, Terry Hansen
Vice President Of International Comp And B, Patricia Hasse
Vice President Of It, Jose Sousa
Vice President Strategic Event Marketing, Lisl Stanton
Svp Shared Services Consumer Bank, John Samenuk
Vice President, Richard Hixson
Vice President Technology Director, Ed White
Vice President Of Fxpb, Anne Pfeiffer
Assistannt Vice President, Jason Silbaugh
Vice President, Diane Genovesi
Vice President Finance, Matthew Gallino
Vice President, Jose Poblete
Vice President Client Service J.p. Morgan Securities Llc, Barbara Fuqua
Vice President Global Investment Banking, Michael Shaw
Vice President, Chet Zhang
Vice President Risk Modeling Manager Mortgage Banking Modeling And Analytics, Tracy Wu
Global Vice President Information Technology Investment Banking Division, Brian Zitterkopf
Vice President, Douglas Savage
Vice President Corporate And Investment Bank Strategy And New Business Development, John Curry
Senior Vice President, Dan Howat
Vice President, Anatoly Morosov
Vice President, Joe Pedone
Vice President, Jeff Wright
Vice President, Jennifer Acosta

Vice President Balance Data Mart Ib Si, Robert Depowski

Vice President Information Technology Operations Support, Sekou H Kaalund

Vice President Of Information Technology, Lonnie Goldman

Vice President, Gene Huang

Vice President Of Project Management, David Bell

Vice President, Harvey Klyce

Vice President, Kenneth Coons

Vice President Investment Bank Technology, Farhan Jaffery

Vice President Information Technology Risk And Security Management, John Finizio

Senior Vice President, Nancy McDonnell

Vice President, Ryan P Griswold

Vice President Architecture, Prasad Chaubal

Vice President, Laura Cussen

Vice President Executive Recruiter Ii, Tom Suhm

Vice President Global Market Tech, Robert Stepanski

Vice President Accounting Manager, Jeanne Higgins

Vice President, Lewis Rieck

Vice President Business Relationship Manager, Jaime Garcia

First Vice President, Michael V McCann

Vice President Human Resources And Employee Development And Training, Sophia Chu

Vice President, Curt Barrentine

Vice President Client Advisor, Dan Brown

Vice President, Sahil Agarwal

Vice President And Sales Manager, Chris Redvers

Vice President Information Risk And Business Continuity Management, Dennis McFadden

Assistant Vice President Banker, Javier Varela

Vice President, Sue Kay

Vice President Of Architecture, Adam Goldin

Vice President Of Application Infrastructure Arc, Alan Higgins

Vice President Corporate Derivatives Marketing Interest Rate Risk Management, Munsamy Govender

Vice President, Vinay Somashekar

Vice President, Bruce Goldberg

Vice President, Donna Kopelman

Vice President Equity Prime Brokerage, Andrew Hannigan

Vice President, Claudia Castillo

Vice President Senior P And A Manager, Charles Chiappone

Vice President Finance, Laurie Goodman

Vice President, Ryan Mccauley

Senior Vice President, Gerry Murphy

Vice President Customer Experience, Kelly Ballas

Executive Vice President, Emmett Vollenweider

Vice President, Michelle Erny

Assistant Vice President And Fixed Income Trading Operations, Joy Hayes

Vice President Of Desktop Computing And Application Integration, Leonard Friedman

Tulsa Middle Market Senior Vice President, Jennifer Kalvaitis

Vice President Global Infrastructure, Ken Defilippo

Vice President, Jason Hand

Vice President, Nazli Beirne

Vice President Commercial Banking Multinational Corporations, Naomi Sanghavee

First Vice President, David Shaw

Vice President Of Central Technology Operations Retail Financial Services, Kevin Kirkpatrick

Vice President, John Mathai

Vice President, Bob Cummings

Vice President Marketing And Communicati, Monica Mack

Vice President, Robert Grigg

Vice President, Laura Bosma

Vice President Of Infrastructure, Michael Knight

Vice President, Liliya Simkhayeva

Vice President Regulatory And Compliance Project Management, Himani Ranjan

Vice President Crm Retention Management, Gail Timmerman

Vice President, Kelly Devlin

Vice President Of Business Development, Kyle Smith

Vice President Senior Lead Architect, Mark Cates

Vice President Business Development, Dionisia Coffman

Vice President, Molly Morgan

Vice President Application Development Manager, Kiran Mudichintala

Assistant Vice President Credit Risk Officer, Kelly Shrader

Vp Critical Systems And Engineering Support, John Groenewold

Vice President, John Tabback

Vice President Client Satisfaction, Giovanna Pape

Vice President, Muhammad Hasan

Senior Vice President Special Credits Group, Phil Martin

Vice President, David Salaverry

Vice President Commercial Banking, Bill Cook

Vice President, Chris Collins

Vice President, Keith Jia

Vice President Customer Analytics, Stella Ng

Vice President, Matthew Green

Vice President, Rosanne Moeslein

Vice President Of Technology, Miguel Choto

Vice President, Lisamarie Devilbiss

Vice President, Matthew Gildard

Vice President, Mark Chilewitz

Vice President, Alice Lo

Vice President, Luis Oganes

Vice President Digital And Interactive Marketing Manager, Tanya Morris

Global Technology Vice President, Tom Pryor

Vice President, Denise Connors

Senior Vice President, Mary Reilly

Vice President, Kevin Connor

Vice President, Michael Tsang

Vice President Enterprise Technology Services, Josiah Lam

Vice President Area Manager, Sherry Minda

Senior Vice President, Bill W Handley

Senior Vice President, Craig Reese

Vice President Treasury Services Manager, Jenny Chan

Vice President, Jennifer Stewart

Auditors: PricewaterhouseCoopers LLP

LOCATIONS

HQ: JPMorgan Chase & Co
383 Madison Avenue, New York, NY 10179
Phone: 212 270-6000
Web: www.jpmorganchase.com

PRODUCTS/OPERATIONS

2016 Sales

	$ mil.	% of total
Interest		
Loans	36,634	35
securities	7,304	7
Trading assets	7,292	7
Federal funds sold & securities purchased under resale agreements	2,265	2
Deposits with banks	1,863	2
Securities borrowed	(332)	-
Other	875	1
Non-interest		
Asset management administration & commissions	14,591	14
Principal transactions	11,566	11
Investment banking fees	6,448	6
Lending- and deposit-related fees	5,774	5
Credit card income	4,779	4
Mortgage fees and related income	2,491	2
Securities gains	141	-
Other	3,795	4
Total	**101,006**	**100**

COMPETITORS

American Express	Goldman Sachs
Bank of America	HSBC
Bank of New York Mellon	Morgan Stanley
Barclays	PNC Financial
CIBC	RBC Financial Group
Capital One	State Bank Financial Corporation
Citigroup	SunTrust
Citigroup Global Markets	TD Bank USA
Credit Suisse (USA)	UBS
Deutsche Bank	Wells Fargo

HISTORICAL FINANCIALS

Company Type: Public

Income Statement

FYE: December 31

	ASSETS ($ mil.)	NET INCOME ($ mil.)	INCOME AS % OF ASSETS	EMPLOYEES
12/18	2,622,532	32,474	1.2%	256,105
12/17	2,533,600	24,441	1.0%	252,539
12/16	2,490,972	24,733	1.0%	243,355
12/15	2,351,698	24,442	1.0%	234,598
12/14	2,573,126	21,762	0.8%	241,359
Annual Growth	0.5%	10.5%	—	1.5%

2018 Year-End Financials

Debt ratio: 10.00%—
Return on equity: 13.00%
Cash ($ mil.): 278,793
Current ratio: —
Long-term debt ($ mil.): —

Dividends
Yield: 3.0%
Payout: 28.0%
Market value ($ mil.): —

	STOCK PRICE ($) FY Close	P/E High/Low	Earnings	Dividends	Book Value
12/18	98.00	13 10	9.00	2.00	78.00
12/17	107.00	17 13	6.00	2.00	75.00
12/16	86.00	14 9	6.00	2.00	71.00
12/15	66.00	12 9	6.00	2.00	68.00
12/14	63.00	12 10	5.00	2.00	62.00
Annual Growth	11.8%	— —	14.2%	12.3%	5.8%

KAISER FOUNDATION HOSPITALS INC

Kaiser Foundation Hospitals is on a roll. The hospital group operates nearly 40 acute care hospitals and 680 medical offices in eight states (California Colorado Georgia Hawaii Maryland Oregon Virginia and Washington) and Washington D.C. The company's largest presence is in California where the majority of its hospitals are located. Kaiser Foundation Hospitals employs more than 21000 physicians representing all medical specialties. Kaiser Foundation Hospital's doctors group is controlled by Permanente Medical Groups and its HMO is offered through Kaiser Foundation Health Plan. Altogether the group provides care for about 11.7 million members.

Operations

Kaiser Foundation Hospitals works with other organizations to tackle such issues as obesity access to care and violence. It also works to promote health in the communities it serves through wellness programs.

In 2016 Kaiser Foundation Hospitals logged 44 million office visits. It facilitated 106000 births performed 129000 surgeries and filled 90 million prescriptions.

Company Background

Kaiser Foundation Hospitals was founded in 1945.

EXECUTIVES

Evp Kaiser Foundation Hospitals And Health Plan; Group President Kaiser Permanente Northern California And Mid-atlantic States; President Kaiser Permanente Northern California, Gregory A. Adams

Evp Kaiser Foundation Hospitals And Health Plan; Group President Kaiser Permanente Southern California And Hawaii; President Kaiser Permanente Southern California, Benjamin K. Chu

Chairman Southern California Permanente Medical Group And Executive Medical Director, Edward Ellison

Senior Management Senior Vice President General Manager Director, Anne Mcnealis

Managing Director Special Projects, Ann Cahill

LOCATIONS

HQ: KAISER FOUNDATION HOSPITALS INC
1 KAISER PLZ, OAKLAND, CA 946123610
Phone: 510 271-6611
Web: WWW.HEALTHY.KAISERPERMANENTE.ORG

PRODUCTS/OPERATIONS

Selected Hospitals

Antioch Medical Center
Fremont Medical Center
Fresno Medical Center
Hayward Medical Center
Manteca Medical Center
Modesto Medical Center
Oakland Medical Center
Redwood City Medical Center
Richmond Medical Center
Roseville Women and Children's Center
San Jose Medical Center
Santa Clara Medical Center
Sacramento Medical Center
South San Francisco Medical Center
South Sacramento Trauma Center
Santa Rosa Medical Center
San Francisco Medical Center
San Rafael Medical Center
Vacaville Medical Center
Vallejo Medical Center
Walnut Creek Medical Center
Baldwin Park Medical Center
Downey Medical Center
Fontana Medical Center
Los Angeles Medical Center
Moreno Valley Community Hospital
Orange County - Anaheim Medical Center
Orange County - Irvine Medical Center
Panorama City Medical Center
Riverside Medical Center
San Diego Medical Center
Harbor City (South Bay Medical Center)
Woodlands Hills Medical Center
West Los Angeles Medical Center
Sunnyside Medical Center (Portland Oregon area)
Moanalua Medical Center (Hawaii)

COMPETITORS

Adventist Health System West	Dignity Health
Ascension Health	HCA
Banner Health	LifePoint Health
CHRISTUS Health	Sutter Health
Catholic Health Initiatives	Tenet Healthcare
Community Health Systems	The Cleveland Clinic
	Universal Health Services

HISTORICAL FINANCIALS

Company Type: Private

Income Statement				FYE: December 31
	REVENUE ($ mil.)	NET INCOME ($ mil.)	NET PROFIT MARGIN	EMPLOYEES
12/09	14,795	429	2.9%	175,668
12/08	0	0	99.0%	—
12/05	9,852	774	7.9%	—
Annual Growth	10.7%	(13.7%)	—	—

Kansas City Life Insurance Co (Kansas City, MO)

Kansas City Life Insurance and subsidiary Sunset Life provide insurance products throughout the US to individuals (life and disability coverage and annuities) and to groups (life dental vision and disability insurance). Subsidiary Old American Insurance focuses on burial and related insurance. The insurance companies sell through more than 2500 independent agents brokers and third-party marketers. Kansas City Life also operates its own insurance and investment brokerage network through its Sunset Financial Services unit. Chairman and CEO R. Philip Bixby and his family control the company.

Operations

Kansas City Life operates in three business segments: Individual Insurance Group Insurance and Old American.

The Individual Insurance segment (which brings in about half of the company's revenue) consists of individual insurance products for both Kansas City Life and Sunset Life as well as reinsurance. Sunset Life maintains its existing policies but doesn't market new sales.

The Group Insurance segment (some 30% of the company's revenue) consists of group life dental vision disability products.

Old American (around 20% of revenue) sells final expense life insurance products.

Geographic Reach

Kansas City Life operates across the US. Some of its largest state markets include Texas California Minnesota Ohio and New Jersey.

Sales and Marketing

Kansas City Life markets its products through independent agents and agencies.

Financial Performance

After seeing dropping revenue for a couple of years Kansas City Life has seen revenue recovery for the past two years thanks primarily to rising premiums earned. Similarly net income declined in 2015 and 2016 but jumped back up in 2017.

Revenue increased 1% to $450.7 million in fiscal 2017. Net premiums and contract charges both increased that year but those gains were partially offset by a drop in net investment income. Renewal premium revenue rose 5% to $174.6 million while total new premiums earned remained flat.

Net income more than doubled in 2017 rising 131% to $51.5 million. That increase was primarily due to a decrease in income tax expenses related to changes in the federal tax code.

The company ended 2017 with $9.5 million in net cash essentially the same amount it had at the end of 2016. Operating activities provided $14.5 million in net cash and financing activities provided another $13.8 million while investing activities used $28.4 million.

Strategy

Kansas City Life has grown by acquiring other life insurance companies expanding its product portfolio moving into new markets and by enhancing technology.

Mergers and Acquisitions

In 2018 Kansas City Life acquired Ohio-based Grange Life Insurance Company for $77.2 million. The deal expanded the group's operations particularly in Ohio.

Company Background

The Bixby family owns about 60% of Kansas City Life through trusts and investment partnerships.

Founded in 1895 the company built up its operations through a number of historical acquisitions including GuideOne Life (2003) Old American (1991) and Sunset Life (1974). The company exited its banking operations (Generations Bank) in 2007.

EXECUTIVES

Svp And Actuary Kansas City Life And Vp And Actuary Sunset Life Insurance Company Of America, Mark A. Milton, age 60, $325,812 total compensation

Chairman President And Ceo, R. Philip Bixby, age 65, $779,160 total compensation

Vice Chairman And Evp And President Old American Insurance Company, Walter E. (Web) Bixby, age 60, $347,088 total compensation

Svp Finance Cfo And Director, Tracy W. Knapp, age 56, $322,344 total compensation

Vp Agency Marketing, Donald E. (Don) Krebs, age 61, $300,060 total compensation

Svp Operations, Stephen E (Steve) Ropp, age 59

Assistant Vice President Systems And Computer Operations, Rick Komer

Vice President Taxes, John Nogalski

Regional Vice President West, Chris Bor

Medical Director, Charlotte Lee

Regional Vice President, Bill Browning

Assistant Vice President, Dawn Roy

Vice President, Timothy Knott

Senior Vice President General Counsel, Craig Mason

Regional Vice President Special Markets, Robert Petzold

Assistant Vice President, Stephen Mack

Vice President, Kathryn Church

Assistant Vice President Corporate Communications, Holly Ropp

Vice President Operations, Steve Ropp

Assistant Vice President Marketing Services, Jim Wilcox

Senior Vice President Finance, Philip A Williams

Senior Vice President Sales And Marketing, Don Krebs

Auditors: BKD, LLP

LOCATIONS

HQ: Kansas City Life Insurance Co (Kansas City, MO)
3520 Broadway, Kansas City, MO 64111
Phone: 816 753-7000   **Fax:** 816 753-4902
Web: www.kclife.com

PRODUCTS/OPERATIONS

2017 Sales

	$ mil.	% of total
Insurance		
Individual insurance	146	32
Group insurance	60	13
Old American	89	20
Net investment income	146	33
Net realized investment gains	5	1
Other	6	1
Total	**451**	**100**

Selected Subsidiaries

Old American Insurance Company
Sunset Financial Services
Sunset Life Insurance Company of America

COMPETITORS

AEGON USA	MassMutual
Advance Insurance of Kansas	MetLife
	National Western
American Equity Life	Nationwide
American Heritage Life Insurance	New York Life
	Northwestern Mutual
American National Insurance	Phoenix Companies
	Primerica
Americo	Protective Life
Citizens Inc.	Prudential
Delphi Financial Group	Security Benefit Group
FBL Financial	The Hartford
Homesteaders Life	Torchmark
Kemper Corp	Universal American

HISTORICAL FINANCIALS

Company Type: Public

Income Statement
FYE: December 31

	ASSETS ($ mil.)	NET INCOME ($ mil.)	INCOME AS % OF ASSETS	EMPLOYEES
12/18	4,971	16	0.3%	—
12/17	4,531	52	1.1%	—
12/16	4,449	22	0.5%	—
12/15	4,422	29	0.7%	441
12/14	4,572	30	0.7%	436
Annual Growth	**2.1%**	**(15.0%)**	**—**	**—**

2018 Year-End Financials

Debt ratio: —	No. of shares (mil.): 10
Return on equity: 2.00%	Dividends
Cash ($ mil.): 32	Yield: 3.0%
Current ratio: —	Payout: 23.0%
Long-term debt ($ mil.): —	Market value ($ mil.): 358

	STOCK PRICE ($) FY Close	P/E High/Low	Earnings	PER SHARE ($) Dividends	Book Value
12/18	37.00	28 21	2.00	1.00	71.00
12/17	45.00	9 8	5.00	1.00	76.00
12/16	48.00	21 15	2.00	1.00	71.00
12/15	38.00	18 15	3.00	1.00	69.00
12/14	48.00	18 15	3.00	1.00	69.00
Annual Growth	**(6.3%)**	**— —**	**(12.4%)**	**0.1%**	**1.0%**

Kearny Financial Corp (MD)

Auditors: Crowe LLP

LOCATIONS

HQ: Kearny Financial Corp (MD)
120 Passaic Avenue, Fairfield, NJ 07004
Phone: 973 244-4500
Web: www.kearnybank.com

HISTORICAL FINANCIALS

Company Type: Public

Income Statement
FYE: June 30

	ASSETS ($ mil.)	NET INCOME ($ mil.)	INCOME AS % OF ASSETS	EMPLOYEES
06/19	6,635	42	0.6%	565
06/18	6,580	20	0.3%	565
06/17	4,818	19	0.4%	466
06/16	4,500	16	0.4%	459
06/15	4,237	6	0.1%	491
Annual Growth	**11.9%**	**65.4%**	**—**	**3.6%**

2019 Year-End Financials

Debt ratio: 20.00%	No. of shares (mil.): 89
Return on equity: 4.00%	Dividends
Cash ($ mil.): 39	Yield: 0.0%
Current ratio: —	Payout: 80.0%
Long-term debt ($ mil.): —	Market value ($ mil.): 1,184

	STOCK PRICE ($) FY Close	P/E High/Low	Earnings	PER SHARE ($) Dividends	Book Value
06/19	13.00	31 26	0.00	0.00	13.00
06/18	13.00	65 54	0.00	0.00	13.00
06/17	15.00	73 57	0.00	0.00	13.00
06/16	13.00	74 62	0.00	0.00	12.00
06/15	11.00	191 179	0.00	0.00	12.00
Annual Growth	**4.5%**	**— —**	**66.4%**	**—**	**0.3%**

Kellogg Co

This Special K is a cereal winner. From the company's home base in Battle Creek Michigan Kellogg Company battles with rival General Mills for the #1 spot in the US cereal market. Kellogg founded in 1906 boasts many familiar cereal brands including Kellogg's Corn Flakes Frosted Flakes Froot Loops Special K and Rice Krispies. While the company works to fill the world's cereal bowls it actually makes more money these days from its snacks and convenience brands such as Kashi Pringles Keebler Cheez-It and Famous Amos (snacks) and Eggo waffles and Nutri-Grain and Bear Naked cereal bars (convenience). Its products are sold worldwide.

Operations

Kellogg operates through several segments based on product category and geographic location. They include US Snacks (around 25% of sales) US Morning Foods (another 25% of sales) and US Specialty (around 10%). Kellogg rings up nearly 20% of sales in its Europe segment 12% in other North America (Canada) and around 5% each in Asia and Latin America.

US Snacks includes cookies crackers cereal bars savory snacks and fruit-flavored snacks. The US Morning Foods segment includes cereal toaster pastries health and wellness bars and beverages. US Specialty primarily represents non-residential food operations including food service convenience vending Girl Scouts (Kellogg produces Girl Scout Cookies for the Girl Scouts of the USA who sell them as a fundraiser) and food manufacturing.

Geographic Reach

The food company manufactures its products in over 20 countries and markets them in more than 180. It generates around 65% of its revenue in the US.

The company's manufacturing facilities in the US include four cereal plants and warehouses in Battle Creek Michigan; Lancaster Pennsylvania; Memphis Tennessee; and Omaha Nebraska. Its other facilities are mostly in Georgia Kentucky Michigan and Ohio.

Outside the US Kellogg has additional manufacturing locations (some with warehousing facilities) in about 20 countries in Europe Asia Africa and South America. The company has joint ventures in China Nigeria and Turkey.

Sales and Marketing

Kellogg's top five customers generate some 35% of Kellogg's total sales and over 45% of US sales.

The company markets its cereal products in general under the recognizable Kellogg's name as well as its "healthy" brand Kashi. Products are sold to supermarkets through a direct sales force model for resale to consumers. Kellogg uses broker and distributor arrangements for certain products in retail stores restaurants and other food service establishments. These particular arrangements are leveraged to market its products in less-developed areas or in markets outside its focus.

Financial Performance

Kellogg continued a four-year slide in revenue in fiscal 2016 (ended December).

Revenue fell a further 4% to $13 billion. By comparison it made not far off $15 billion in 2013. Kellogg's North America Other segment declined due to weakness in Kashi and Morningstar Farms a poor first half of 2016 pushed US Snacks revenue down and US Morning Foods' non-core categories fell sharply.

Net income climbed for the first time in a few years climbing 13% to $694 million. The increase came from the success of Kellogg's "Project K" cost cutting program.

Cash from operating activities was down 4% to $1.6 billion due to $97 million of after-tax costs relating to redeemed debentures.

Strategy

Kellogg is working at cutting costs and expanding revenue as consumers are turning away from its old reliable cereal lines as awareness of the health risks of sugar increases.

Its ongoing "Project K" efficiency and effectiveness program began in 2013 and will continue through to 2018. This program is designed to help the company focus on core products with increased level of value-added innovation.

On the product side Kellogg is extending and repositioning several brands. It reformulated Special K to create Special K Nourish with probiotic qualities. The company believes probiotics have greater appeal than low calories. Other product extensions include Mini-Wheats Harvest Delights Smorz and Dory-themed cereal (in line with the Disney Pixar movie "Finding Dory.") The company also is putting attention and muscle behind the Kashi brand. It intends to promote Kashi Go-Lean products which have been Non-GMO Project Verified and Kashi Heart-to-Heart products which have been fashioned to meet the USDA's organic standard.

On the flip side Kellogg in mid-2019 agreed to sell its cookie fruit snack pie crust and ice cream cone businesses to Luxembourg-based Ferrero Group for about $1.3 billion as it reshapes its portfolio. The list of brands includes Keebler Famous Amos Mother's Murray and Stretch Island as well as Little Brownie Bakers which supplies cookies to the Girl Scouts.

Mergers and Acquisitions

In 2016 Kellogg acquired Ritmo Investments a Brazilian food group that owns the Parati Zoo Cartoon Hot Cracker and Padua brands. The acquisition strengthens its snacking and emerging market businesses.

HISTORY

Will Keith (W. K.) Kellogg first made wheat flakes in 1894 while working for his brother Dr. John Kellogg at Battle Creek Michigan's famed homeopathic sanitarium. While doing an experiment with grains (for patients' diets) the two men were interrupted; by the time they returned to the dough it had absorbed water. They rolled it anyway toasted the result and accidentally created the first flaked cereal. John sold the flakes via mail order (1899) in a partnership that W. K. managed. In 1906 W. K. started his own firm to produce corn flakes.

As head of the Battle Creek Toasted Corn Flake Company W. K. competed against 42 cereal companies in Battle Creek (one run by former patient C. W. Post) and roared to the head of the pack with his innovative marketing ideas. A 1906 Ladies' Home Journal ad helped increase demand from 33 cases a day earlier that year to 2900 a day by year-end. W. K. soon introduced Bran Flakes (1915) All-Bran (1916) and Rice Krispies (1928). International expansion began in Canada (1914) and followed in Australia (1924) and England (1938).

EXECUTIVES

Ceo And Director, Steven A. (Steve) Cahillane, age 54
Vice Chairman Corporate Development And Chief Legal Officer, Gary H. Pilnick, age 55, $719,092 total compensation
Svp; President Kellogg North America, Paul T. Norman, age 55, $783,319 total compensation
Chief Growth Officer, Clive Sirkin
President U.s. Specialty Channels, Wendy Davidson, age 48
Svp And Cfo, Fareed A. Khan, age 54
President U.s. Morning Foods, Craig Bahner, age 54
Svp Global Snacks Category, Jim Cali, age 58
President Asia/pacific, Amit Banati, age 50
Svp And Cio, Brian S. Rice, age 56
President Us Snacks Division, Deanie Elsner
President Kellogg Canada, Carol Stewart
Ceo Kashi Company, David J. Denholm
Svp Global Supply Chain, Alistair D. Hirst, age 59, $552,770 total compensation
Svp; President Kellogg Latin America, Maria F. Mejia
President Kellogg Europe, Chris Hood, $540,896 total compensation
President U.s. Frozen Foods, Andrew Loucks
Svp Global Breakfast Category, Doug VanDeVelde
Vp Shared Services, David Pelyhes
Vp Global Revenue Management, Amjad Malik
Vice President Global Procurement Cpo, Michele Tyler
Vice President Nutrition, Guy Johnson
Vice President And Treasurer, Joel Vanderkooi
Vice President Marketing, Brad Goist
Vice President Treasury And Investor Relations, Joel R Wittenberg
Vice President, Margaret Bath
Senior Vice President Morning Foods Supply Chain, George Chumakov
Vice President Sales, Kristina Geier
Svp Hr, Cydney Kilduff
Division Vice President, Cecile Mutch
Vp Of Strategy Corporate Development In Transition, Steve Hyde
Vice President Industry Initiatives, Dave Jones

Vice President Human Resources, Shawn Zimmerman
Svp Global Hr, Melissa Howell
Vp Finance And Corporate Development, Jan Perkins
Vice President Human Resources Emea, Samantha Thomas Berry
National Account Manager, Laura Scherer
Vice President Human Resources Global Supply Chain And Global Functions, Jim Stockman
Vp Supply Chain, Jeffrey Arnold
Vice President And Chief Sustainability Officer, Diane Holdorf
Vice President Global Nutrition Scientific Affairs And Technology Scouting, Nelson Almeida
Vice President Corporate Controller, Kurt Forche
Board Member, Donald Knauss
Chairman, John A. Bryant, age 54
Board Member, Cynthia Milligan
Board Member, Carolyn Tastad
Abm, Eric Hines
Board Member, Mary Laschinger
Board Member, Stephanie Burns
Board Member, Richard Dreiling
Board Member, Carter Cast
Auditors: PricewaterhouseCoopers LLP

LOCATIONS

HQ: Kellogg Co
One Kellogg Square, P.O. Box 3599, Battle Creek, MI 49016-3599
Phone: 269 961-2000
Web: www.kelloggcompany.com

2016 Sales

	$ mil.	% of total
United States	8,560	63
International	4,965	37
Total	**13,525**	**100**

2016 Sales

	$ mil.	% of total
United States	8,438	65
International	4,576	35
Total	**13,014**	**100**

PRODUCTS/OPERATIONS

2016 Sales

	$ mil.	% of total
U.S. Snacks	3,198	25
U.S. Morning Foods	2,931	23
Europe	2,377	18
North America Other	1,598	12
U.S. Specialty	1,214	9
Asia Pacific	916	7
Latin America	780	6
Total	**13,014**	**100**

2016 Sales

	$ mil.	% of total
Cereal	5,440	42
Snacks	6,660	51
Frozen	914	7
Total	**13,014**	**100**

Selected Cereal Brands

Asia and Australia
  BeBig
  Cerola
  Chex
  Frosties
  Goldies
  Kellogg's Iron Man Food
  Nutri-Grain
  Rice Bubbles
  Sultana Bran
Canada
  Vector
  Vive
Europe
  Choco Pops
  Chocos

  Country Store
  Frosties
  Fruit ‘n' Fibre
  Honey Loops
  Kellogg's Crunchy Nut Corn Flakes
  Kellogg's Crunchy Nut Red Corn Flakes
  Kellogg's Extra
  Muslix
  Optima
  Pops
  Ricicles
  Smacks
  Start
  Sustain
Latin America
  Choco Krispis
  Choco Zucaritas
  Crusli Sucrilhos
  Musli
  NutriDia
  Sucrilhos Chocolate
  Vector
  Zucaritas
US
  All-Bran
  Apple Jacks
  Bran Buds
  Cinnamon Crunch
  Cocoa Krispies
  Complete Bran Flakes
  Complete Wheat Flakes
  Corn Pops
  Cracklin' Oat Bran
  Crispix
  Crunch
  Cruncheroos
  Froot Loops
  Frosted Krispies
  Frosted Mini-Wheats
  Just Right
  Kellogg's Corn Flakes
  Kellogg's Frosted Flakes
  Kellogg's Low-Fat Granola
  Kellogg's Raisin Bran
  Mueslix
  Pops
  Product 19
  Raisin Bran
  Rice Krispies
  Smacks/Honey Smacks
  Smart Start
  Special K
  Special K Red Berries

Selected Other Brands

Cereal Bars and Granola
  All-Bran
  Bear Naked
  Choco Krispies
  Froot Loops
  GoLean
  Kashi
Convenience Foods
  Austin
  Cheez-It
  Chips Deluxe
  Club
  Croutettes Croutons
  E. L. Fudge
  Famous Amos
  Fudge Shoppe
  Hi-Ho
  Keebler
  Kellogg's Corn Flake Crumbs
  Krispy Munch'Ems
  Murray
  Pop-Tarts
  Pop-Tarts Pastry Swirls
  Pop-Tarts Snak-Stix
  Pringles
  Ready Crust
  Rice Krispies Squares
  Rice Krispies Treats
  Right Bites
  Sandies
  Soft Batch
  Stretch Island
  Sunshine
  Toasteds
  Town House
Frozen Waffles and Pancakes

Eggo
Froot Loops
Nutri-Grain
Special K
Water and Water Mixes
Special K
Special K2O
Meat and Egg Alternatives
Gardenburger
Loma Linda
Morningstar Farms
Natural Touch
Worthington

COMPETITORS

Amy's Kitchen	McKee Foods
Barbara's Bakery	Mondelez International
Bob's Red Mill Natural	Nestlé
Foods	Patty King
Boca Foods	PepsiCo
Campbell Soup	Pinnacle Foods
ConAgra	PowerBar
Frito-Lay	Ralston Food
General Mills	Schulze and Burch
Gilster-Mary Lee	Snyder's-Lance
Goodman Fielder	Weetabix
Hain Celestial	Wellness Foods
J & J Snack Foods	Wessanen
Jordans & Ryvita	granoVita
MOM Brands	

HISTORICAL FINANCIALS
Company Type: Public

Income Statement   FYE: December 29

	REVENUE ($ mil.)	NET INCOME ($ mil.)	NET PROFIT MARGIN	EMPLOYEES
12/18	13,547	1,336	9.9%	34,000
12/17	12,923	1,269	9.8%	33,000
12/16*	13,014	694	5.3%	37,369
01/16	13,525	614	4.5%	33,577
01/15	14,580	632	4.3%	29,790
Annual Growth	(1.8%)	20.6%	—	3.4%

*Fiscal year change

2018 Year-End Financials

Debt ratio: 50.00%	No. of shares (mil.): 344
Return on equity: 56.00%	Dividends
Cash ($ mil.): 321	Yield: 0.0%
Current ratio: 1.00	Payout: 57.0%
Long-term debt ($ mil.): 8,207	Market value ($ mil.): 19,686

	STOCK PRICE ($) FY Close	P/E High/Low	Earnings	Dividends	Book Value
12/18	57.00	19 14	4.00	2.00	8.00
12/17	68.00	21 16	4.00	2.00	6.00
12/16*	74.00	44 35	2.00	2.00	5.00
01/16	72.00	42 35	2.00	2.00	6.00
01/15	65.00	39 32	2.00	2.00	8.00
Annual Growth	(3.3%)	— —	21.6%	3.7%	(0.9%)

*Fiscal year change

Kelly Services, Inc.

EXECUTIVES

Pres-Ceo, George S Corona
Chb, Donald R Parfet
Sr V Pres-Cfo, Olivier G Thirot
Clo, Hannah S Lim-Johnson
V Pres-Corp Contrl-Cao, Laura S Lockhart
Field Facilities Project Manag, Dionne Zaratzian

Director, Hope Bradford
Director, Jane Stehney
Vice President, Judy Snyder
Manager, Kim Dorman
Software Engineer, Michael Morris
Auditors: PricewaterhouseCoopers LLP

LOCATIONS

HQ: Kelly Services, Inc.
999 West Big Beaver Road, Troy, MI 48084
Phone: 248 362-4444
Web: www.kellyservices.com

COMPETITORS

ATC Healthcare	Randstad Holding
Adecco	Robert Half
Allegis Group	Technical Aid
Insperity	Corporation
ManpowerGroup	TrueBlue
On Assignment	Volt Information

HISTORICAL FINANCIALS
Company Type: Public

Income Statement   FYE: December 30

	REVENUE ($ mil.)	NET INCOME ($ mil.)	NET PROFIT MARGIN	EMPLOYEES
12/18	5,514	23	0.4%	506,800
12/17*	5,374	72	1.3%	507,800
01/17	5,277	121	2.3%	507,500
01/16	5,518	54	1.0%	558,100
12/14	5,563	24	0.4%	563,300
Annual Growth	(0.2%)	(0.9%)	—	(2.6%)

*Fiscal year change

2018 Year-End Financials

Debt ratio: 0.00%	No. of shares (mil.): 39
Return on equity: 2.00%	Dividends
Cash ($ mil.): 35	Yield: 0.0%
Current ratio: 2.00	Payout: 52.0%
Long-term debt ($ mil.): —	Market value ($ mil.): 788

	STOCK PRICE ($) FY Close	P/E High/Low	Earnings	Dividends	Book Value
12/18	20.00	54 33	1.00	0.00	30.00
12/17*	27.00	17 11	2.00	0.00	30.00
01/17	23.00	8 5	3.00	0.00	26.00
01/16	16.00	13 10	1.00	0.00	24.00
12/14	17.00	42 25	1.00	0.00	22.00
Annual Growth	4.5%	— —	(1.3%)	10.7%	7.8%

*Fiscal year change

Kemper Corp (DE)

Kemper is among the largest nonstandard auto insurers in the US and holds a strong position in the overall personal vehicle coverage market. The Kemper family of companies specializes in property/casualty insurance and life and health insurance products for individuals families and businesses. Policies include auto homeowners property life accident and health coverage. Kemper serves more than 6.4 million policyholders and has some $12 billion in assets. The company's policies are sold through independent and direct agents across the US.

Operations

The company operates through three operating segments: Specialty Property and Casualty Insur-

ance Preferred Property and Casualty Insurance and Life and Health Insurance.

The Specialty Property and Casualty Insurance segment (about 60% of earned premiums) provides nonstandard personal and commercial automobile insurance to low-income customers or those with poor driving or payment records. Underwriting subsidiaries include Alpha Property and Casualty Charter Indemnity Unitrin County Mutual Financial Indemnity and Alliance United. The division was expanded significantly through the acquisition of Infinity Property and Casualty in 2018.

The Preferred Property and Casualty Insurance segment (more than 20%) offers preferred automobile (both standard and nonstandard risk) homeowners fire renters umbrella and other personal insurance. Underwriting subsidiaries include Kemper Independence Unitrin Advantage and Unitrin Auto and Home.

The Life and Health Insurance segment (roughly 20%) provides individual life accident and health insurance. It primarily does business through the Kemper Home Service Companies group of businesses (including United Insurance Reliable Life and Union National Life) which provide individual life and supplemental accident and health insurance products to customers with limited incomes. The smaller Reserve National unit sells specialty individual accident life and health insurance policies including illness and hospitalization plans.

The company is reorganizing its operating divisions under four sub-brands: Kemper Auto Kemper Personal Insurance Kemper Life and Kemper Health.

Geographic Reach

Headquartered in Chicago Illinois Kemper sells its policies in 50 US states and Washington DC.

The Specialty Property and Casualty unit earns most of its revenue in California Texas and Florida while the Preferred Property and Casualty Insurance segment gets two-thirds of sales from California New York Texas North Carolina and Illinois.

The Life and Health Insurance segment earns nearly half of sales in Texas Louisiana Alabama Mississippi and Florida.

Sales and Marketing

Kemper offers its services through independent and direct agents and brokers. The Specialty Property and Casualty segment's products are offered by 21000 independent insurance agents and brokers while the Preferred Property and Casualty Insurance segment sells via 4800 independent agents. Kemper Home Services uses a network of some 2200 career agents while Reserve National uses about 4800 independent agents.

The company's Specialty Property and Casualty Insurance segment targets value-seeking consumers who may have difficulty obtaining preferred or standard auto insurance policies due to driving or payment histories. Meanwhile the Preferred Property and Casualty Insurance segment targets individuals who have favorable loss histories and risk characteristics. The Life and Health segment serves low-income customers seniors and other demographic segments.

Financial Performance

Kemper's revenue has climbed steadily over the past five years including a sizable bump from acquisition activities in 2018 for total growth of 82% between 2014 and 2018. Net income fluctuated rising in 2018 and 2017 but declining in 2015 and 2016. Overall earnings grew 63% over the five-year period.

The company reported a 44% sales increase in 2018 to some $3.7 billion largely due to higher earned premiums related to its acquisition of Infinity Property and Casualty. Kemper also reported growth in sales of its legacy personal specialty auto products and higher investment income that year.

Net income increased 57% in 2018 to $190.1 million due to higher revenue volumes and lower income tax expenses (due to the US Tax Act) despite an increase in operating expenses.

The company ended 2018 with $75.1 million in cash up $29.4 million from 2017. Operating activities contributed $539.2 million while investing activities used $497.6 million (mostly acquisition costs) and financing activities used $12.2 million via dividend payments.

Strategy

Kemper is making some changes to rejuvenate the company and focus strongly on niche and underserved markets. Its 2018 acquisition of Infinity Property and Casualty served to increase the scale of its specialty auto offerings grow its distribution network and expand its share in key geographic markets. The company hopes the purchase will accelerate growth and enhance product offerings for policyholders.

Following the acquisition Kemper announced a rebranding effort through which it is regrouping its operating divisions under four sub-brands over time to better reflect its core offerings: Kemper Auto Kemper Personal Insurance Kemper Life and Kemper Health. The brand refresh includes a new slogan: Affordable protection in an ever-changing world. In 2019 the company announced plans to move its collector vehicle book of business to fellow insurer Hagerty to increase its focus on core specialty and preferred auto lines.

Other strategic initiatives include investing in new technologies to support and improve operations. The company launched a new sales and service technology platform for its personal lines businesses in 2017 and had released the capability in 35 states as of the end of 2018. It is also improving IT systems in its life and health business to modernize processes. The company also launches new products to improve sales and customer retention rates.

Like other property/casualty insurers the company is struggling with an increase in catastrophe losses in recent years from wildfires hurricanes and other weather or man-made events. The company is working to reduce catastrophe exposure through reinsurance (risk-sharing) agreements and selective underwriting practices.

Mergers and Acquisitions

In 2018 Kemper acquired nonstandard auto insurer Infinity Property and Casualty for $1.4 billion. Infinity does most of its business in California Florida and Texas and one of its key target markets is Hispanic consumers. Through the purchase Kemper diversified its offerings and strengthened its position in the nonstandard auto insurance realm while improving operational efficiencies.

Company Background

James Kemper founded National Underwriters insurance exchange in 1913 to provide supplementary fire insurance for lumbermen.

The insurance holding company was formed in 1990. It changed its name from Unitrin to Kemper in August 2011; it also rebranded several of its business units under the Kemper name.

The name change followed a downsizing where the company shed or shuttered several operations. Its Fireside Bank subsidiary which purchased subprime loan contracts from used automobile dealers halted lending activities in 2009 and ceased banking operations in 2012. Kemper also narrowed its Reserve National subsidiary's focus on specialized life and health policies.

Kemper's disposal-heavy strategy followed a period of expansion in its consumer insurance options via acquisitions of smaller companies. It returned to growth through the 2015 purchase of nonstandard auto insurer Alliance United Group for $70 million.

EXECUTIVES

Executive Vice President Chief Financial Officer A, Eric Draut

Vp And Chief Accounting Officer, Richard Roeske, age 59, $371,000 total compensation

Evp Kemper Preferred, Naimish Patel

Svp And Chief Investment Officer, John M. Boschelli, age 51, $400,000 total compensation

President And Ceo, Joseph P. (Joe) Lacher, age 50, $750,000 total compensation

President Property And Casualty, George D. (Chip) Dufala, age 47, $214,519 total compensation

Evp; General Manager Kemper Specialty California, Timothy D. Bruns

President Kemper Home Service, Thomas D. Myers

Chief Risk Officer, Shekar G. Jannah

Svp Operations And Systems, Charles T. Brooks, age 53

Svp; President Life And Health, Mark A. Green, age 52, $240,692 total compensation

Svp And Cfo, James J. McKinney, age 40

Vice President Human Resources, Lisa M King

Vice President, Brad Andrekus

Vp It, Greg Olds

Vp And Treasurer, Christopher Moses

National Accounts Manager, Douglas Clayton

Vice President Of Actuarial Services, Bradley Andrekus

Assistant Vice President Planning And Analysis, Justin Westcott

Vp Kemper Benefits, Tracy Berwick

Vice President, Jack Broughton

Vice President National Product Management Strategy, David Pearlmutter

Vp Financial Planning And Analysis, Maxwell Mindak

Senior Vice President Product Underwriting And Pricing, Eric Neely

Associate Vice President Financial Analysis And Planning, Edward Aguirre

Svp Secretary And General Counsel, C Thomas Evans Jr

Vice President Human Resources, Robin Buendia

Vice President Sales, Steve Bell

Vice President Is, Bhaskar Bulusu

Chairman, Robert J. (Bob) Joyce

Board Member, George Cochran

Board Member, Lacy Johnson

Auditors: DELOITTE & TOUCHE LLP

LOCATIONS

HQ: Kemper Corp (DE)
200 E. Randolph Street, Suite 3300, Chicago, IL 60601
Phone: 312 661-4600
Web: www.kemper.com

PRODUCTS/OPERATIONS

2016 sales

	$ mil.	% of total
Property/casualty insurance	1,688	66
Life & health insurance	821	32
Net realized gains on the sales of investments	33	1
Net impairment losses recognized in earning	(33)	
Other	13	1
Total	**2,522**	**100**

Selected Insurance Options

Auto
Boat
Collectibles
Commercial Auto
Condo
Home
Identity Fraud
Life and Health
Package
Personal Catastrophe Liability
Personal Valuables
Renters

COMPETITORS

Allstate	Penn-America
Citizens Financial	Security National
Citizens Inc.	Financial
GEICO	State Farm
Liberty Mutual Agency	USAA
Nationwide	

HISTORICAL FINANCIALS

Company Type: Public

Income Statement

FYE: December 31

	ASSETS ($ mil.)	NET INCOME ($ mil.)	INCOME AS % OF ASSETS	EMPLOYEES
12/18	11,545	190	1.6%	8,100
12/17	8,376	121	1.4%	5,550
12/16	8,211	17	0.2%	5,750
12/15	8,036	86	1.1%	5,600
12/14	7,833	115	1.5%	5,350
Annual Growth	**10.2%**	**13.5%**	**—**	**10.9%**

2018 Year-End Financials

Debt ratio: 8.00%	No. of shares (mil.): 65
Return on equity: 7.00%	Dividends
Cash ($ mil.): 75	Yield: 1.0%
Current ratio: —	Payout: 30.0%
Long-term debt ($ mil.): —	Market value ($ mil.): 4,299

	STOCK PRICE ($) FY Close	P/E High/Low		PER SHARE ($)	
			Earnings	Dividends	Book Value
12/18	66.00	26 16	3.00	1.00	47.00
12/17	69.00	30 16	2.00	1.00	41.00
12/16	44.00	138 72	0.00	1.00	39.00
12/15	37.00	25 21	2.00	1.00	39.00
12/14	36.00	19 16	2.00	1.00	40.00
Annual Growth	**16.4%**	**— —**	**11.0%**	**(0.0%)**	**4.2%**

Keurig Dr Pepper Inc

EXECUTIVES

Exec Chb-Pres, Robert Gamgort
Cfo, Ozan Dokmecioglu
Clo-General Counsel-Sec, James L Baldwin
Cco, Herbert Hopkins
Chief Hr Officer, Margaret Newman
Contrl, Angela Stephens
Pres, Direct Store Delivery, Rodger L Collins
Chief Supply Chain Officer, Fernando Cortes
Pres, Keurig Appliances, Brian Loucks
Chief Corp Affairs Officer, Maria Sceppaguercio
Chief Cncntrte & Int'l Officer, James R Trebilcock
Auditors: DELOITTE & TOUCHE LLP

LOCATIONS

HQ: Keurig Dr Pepper Inc
53 South Avenue, Burlington, MA 01803
Phone: 802 244-5621
Web: www.keurig.com

COMPETITORS

American Beverage
Austin Coca-Cola
Campbell Soup
Coca-Cola
Coca-Cola Bottling Consolidated
Coca-Cola Bottling company of southern california
Coca-Cola Bottling of Northern New England
Coca-Cola FEMSA
Coca-Cola North America

Coca-Cola Refreshments
Coca-Cola Tennessee
Coke United
Cott
Country Pure Foods
Del Monte Foods
Dole Food
Faygo
Florida's Natural
G & J Pepsi-Cola Bottlers
Gatorade
Great Plains Coca-Cola
Great Western Juice
Hornell Brewing
IZZE
Jones Soda
Jugos del Valle
Lane Affiliated
Mondelez International
Monster Beverage
National Beverage
Nestle
Ocean Spray
Odwalla
Old Orchard
Pepsi Bottling Ventures
Pepsi-Cola Bottling Company of NY
Pepsi-Cola Bottling of Central Virginia
Pepsi-Cola of Ft. Lauderdale
PepsiCo
Philadelphia Coca-Cola
Red Bull
Reed's
Roll Global
South Beach Beverage
Sunny Delight
Swire Coca-Cola
Tree Top
Tropicana
Wet Planet Beverages

HISTORICAL FINANCIALS

Company Type: Public

Income Statement

FYE: December 31

	REVENUE ($ mil.)	NET INCOME ($ mil.)	NET PROFIT MARGIN	EMPLOYEES
12/18	7,442	586	7.9%	25,500
12/17	6,690	1,076	16.1%	21,000
12/16	6,440	847	13.2%	20,000
12/15	6,282	764	12.2%	19,000
12/14	6,121	703	11.5%	19,000
Annual Growth	5.0%	(4.4%)	—	7.6%

2018 Year-End Financials

Debt ratio: 33.00%	No. of shares (mil.): 1,406
Return on equity: 5.00%	Dividends
Cash ($ mil.): 129	Yield: 410.0%
Current ratio: 0.00	Payout: 19,823.0%
Long-term debt ($ mil.): 14,506	Market value ($ mil.): 36,048

	STOCK PRICE ($) FY Close	P/E High/Low		PER SHARE ($) Earnings	Dividends	Book Value
12/18	26.00	229	41	1.00	105.00	16.00
12/17	97.00	17	14	6.00	2.00	14.00
12/16	91.00	22	18	5.00	2.00	12.00
12/15	93.00	24	18	4.00	2.00	12.00
12/14	72.00	21	13	4.00	2.00	12.00
Annual Growth	(22.7%)	—	—	(37.9%)	182.9%	7.8%

KeyCorp

With a focus on retail operations KeyCorp sbusidiary bank KeyBank operates about 1160 branches and 1500 ATMs in some 15 states across the US. Its operations are divided into two groups: Key Community Bank offers traditional services such as deposits loans credit cards and financial planning; Key Corporate Bank provides investment banking services real estate capital equipment financing and capital markets services primarily to middle-market companies in industries including energy healthcare and real estate. KeyCorp is also one of the largest servicers of commercial and multifamily loans in the US.

Operations

KeyCorp have two major business segments: Key Community Bank and Key Corporate Bank.

Key Community Bank offers traditional products and services including deposits loans mortgages credit cards and financial planning to retail customers and small and mid-sized businesses. It also buys retail car sales contracts through a dealer network. The segment generates about 60% of the company's revenue.

Key Corporate Bank provides investment banking services real estate capital equipment financing and capital markets services primarily to middle-market companies. It addresses seven client markets: consumer energy healthcare industrial public sector real estate and technology. The segment houses KeyCorp's commercial mortgage loan servicing operations; the company is one of the largest commercial mortgage servicers in the US. Key Corporate Bank produces around 35% of KeyCorp's revenue.

The company also reports an Other Segments division which comprises its corporate treasury principal investing and exit portfolios. It represents less than 5% of revenue.

KeyCorp derives around 60% of its revenue from loan interest. Approximately half of the holding company's portfolio consists of commercial and industrial loans. Some 25% of its lending is for commercial real estate. Consumer loans?mostly prime residential loans?make up the remainder.

The company garners roughly 10% of its revenue from investment banking and debt placement fees. Trust and investment services generate more than 5% as do deposit service charges.

Geographic Reach

Cleveland Ohio-based KeyCorp has about 1160 US branches in Ohio Alaska Indiana Michigan New York Oregon Washington and throughout New England. The company has around 1500 ATMs in 15 states.

Sales and Marketing

KeyCorp's Key Community Bank provides traditional banking services to individuals and small and mid-sized businesses while Key Corporate Bank provides its investment banking services to middle-market clients in seven client markets: consumer energy healthcare industrial public sector real estate and technology. Less than 5% of its noninterest expense is used on marketing.

Financial Performance

KeyCorp's revenue has grown some 60% since 2014 thanks mostly to strong gains in 2016 and 2017 after it acquired First Niagara Financial Group which boosted both its interest and non-interest income. Despite a dip in 2016 caused by the acquisition the company's net income has more than doubled in the last five years.

KeyCorp's revenue growth normalized substantially in 2018 following banner performance associated with the First Niagara buy. It ticked up 3% to $6.2 billion.

Net income posted a gain of 44% to end the year at $1.9 billion. The company experienced a large reduction in income tax expense following US tax reform and managed to reduce its interest expense compared with the previous year.

KeyCorp added $7 million to its cash in 2018 for total stores of $678 million. Operations provided slightly over $2.5 billion and investments (particularly purchases of securities available for sale and a net increase in loans) used just below $2.5 billion. Financing activities used $17 million.

Strategy

In 2018 KeyCorp hit its cash efficiency ratio target of 60% through a multiyear initiative to control costs and reduce expenses from the front to the back office embracing digital banking platforms and cutting costly branch operations.

In furtherance of its online banking push KeyCorp purchased the digital lending business of student loan originator Laurel Road Bank in 2019. The company's student loan refinancing and online mortgage platforms expanded KeyCorp's reach among millennials a growing wealth demographic with which Laurel Road has seen success. The company launched an instant payment product the previous year in collaboration with Ingo Money. The Ingo Push platform allows KeyCorp's business banking customers to disburse funds instantly.

In 2012 the company had 1088 branches; in 2015 it had 966. The holding company's acquisition of First Niagara pushed the network up to 1322 but then the cull continued: by the end of 2016 closures and consolidations reduced that number to 1217. At the end of 1Q19 the company had 1158.

KeyCorp has also reduced inefficiency through select divestments. In 2018 the company sold its Key Insurance & Benefits Services subsidiary?a group it acquired through its acquisition of First Niagara Financial Group in 2016.

Mergers and Acquisitions

In 2019 KeyCorp acquired the digital lending business of New York City-based Laurel Road Bank; the company's technology enhances KeyCorp's ability to serve professional millennial clients. Launched in 2013 Laurel Road's student loan refinancing platform has originated $4 billion in loans and was expanded in 2018 to include a platform for mortgage lending.

Company Background

KeyCorp predecessor Commercial Bank of Albany was chartered in 1825. In 1865 it joined the new national banking system and became National Commercial Bank of Albany. After WWI National Commercial consolidated with Union National Bank & Trust as National Commercial Bank and Trust which then merged with First Trust and Deposit in 1971. In 1973 Victor Riley became president and CEO. Under Riley National Commercial grew during the 1970s and 1980s through acquisitions. Riley sought to make the company a regional powerhouse but was thwarted when several New England states passed legislation barring New York banks from buying banks in the region.

As a result the company renamed Key Bank in 1979 turned west targeting small towns with less competition. Thus situated it prospered despite entering Alaska just in time for the 1986 oil price collapse. Its folksy image and small-town success earned it a reputation as the "Wal-Mart of banking."

HISTORY

KeyCorp predecessor Commercial Bank of Albany was chartered in 1825. In 1865 it joined the new national banking system and became National Commercial Bank of Albany. After WWI National Commercial consolidated with Union National Bank & Trust as National Commercial Bank and

Trust which then merged with First Trust and Deposit in 1971.

In 1973 Victor Riley became president and CEO. Under Riley National Commercial grew during the 1970s and 1980s through acquisitions. Riley sought to make the company a regional powerhouse but was thwarted when several New England states passed legislation barring New York banks from buying banks in the region.

As a result the company renamed Key Bank in 1979 turned west targeting small towns with less competition. Thus situated it prospered despite entering Alaska just in time for the 1986 oil price collapse. Its folksy image and small-town success earned it a reputation as the "Wal-Mart of banking."

Meanwhile in Cleveland Society for Savings followed a different path. Founded as a mutual savings bank in 1849 the institution succeeded from the start. It survived the Civil War and postwar economic turmoil and built Cleveland's first skyscraper in 1890. It continued to grow even during the Depression and became the largest savings bank outside the Northeast in 1949.

In 1955 the bank formed a holding company Society National. Society grew through the acquisitions of smaller banks in Ohio until 1979 when Ohio allowed branch banking in contiguous counties. Thereafter Society National opened branches as well. In the mid-1980s and the early 1990s the renamed Society Corporation began consolidating its operations and continued growing.

A 1994 merger of National Commercial with Society more than doubled assets for the surviving KeyCorp; compatibility of the two companies' systems and software simplified consolidation. KeyCorp sold its mortgage-servicing unit to NationsBank (now Bank of America) in 1995 and over the next year bought investment management finance and investment banking firms.

In 1997 KeyCorp began trimming its branch network divesting 200 offices including its 28-branch KeyBank Wyoming subsidiary. It expanded its consumer lending business that year by buying Champion Mortgage. In cooperation with USF&G (now part of The St. Paul Travelers Companies) and three HMOs KeyCorp began offering health insurance to the underserved small-business market.

In 1998 the company bought Leasetec which leases computer storage systems globally through its StorageTek subsidiary; it also bought McDonald & Company Investments (now McDonald Investments; sold in 2007) with an eye toward reaching its goal of earning half of its revenues from fees. Also in 1998 KeyCorp began offering business lines of credit to customers of Costco Wholesale the nation's largest wholesale club.

As part of a restructuring effort KeyCorp sold 28 Long Island New York branches to Dime Bancorp in 1999. The next year the company sold its credit card portfolio to Associates First Capital (now part of Citigroup) and bought National Realty Funding a securitizer of commercial mortgages. In 2001 it acquired Denver-based investment bank The Wallach Company.

The company expanded further in the Denver area with its 2002 purchase of Union Bankshares. Two years later KeyCorp bought Seattle-area bank EverTrust Financial Group.

In 2007 the company bought Tuition Management Systems which provides outsourced tuition billing accounting and counseling services for schools and colleges; the unit was later merged into its Key Education Resources operations. Also that year KeyCorp sold investment bank and brokerage McDonald Investments to UBS Financial Services.

The company bought New York-based U.S.B. Holding Co. and its Union State Bank subsidiary

for some $550 million in early 2008. The deal added more than 30 branches nearly doubling KeyCorp's presence in the Hudson River Valley region.

EXECUTIVES

Vice Chairman And President Banking, Christopher M. (Chris) Gorman, age 58, $638,462 total compensation

Secretary And General Counsel, Paul N. Harris, age 60

Vice Chairman And Cfo, Donald R. Kimble, age 59, $638,462 total compensation

Co-president Key Community Bank, Edward J. (E.J.) Burke, $550,000 total compensation

Sevp And Chief Risk Officer, William L. (Bill) Hartmann, $500,000 total compensation

Chairman And Ceo, Beth E. Mooney, age 63, $1,000,000 total compensation

Co-president Key Community Bank, Dennis A. Devine, $571,154 total compensation

Cio, Amy G. Brady

Evp And Director Corporate Center, Katrina M. (Trina) Evans

Chief Human Resources Officer, Craig A. Buffie

Evp; Head Real Estate Capital, Angela G. Mago

Evp; President Keybank Capital Markets, Andrew J. (Randy) Paine, $500,000 total compensation

Executive Vice President Marketing, Bonnie Squadere

Vice President Database Marketing, Jonathan Boyer

Vice President, Alison Sammon

Assistant Vice President, Paul Pace

Assistant Vice President Senior Financial Analyst Planning And Forecasting, Danny Pho

Vice President International Marketing, Robert Kurek

Senior Vice President, Mark Kleinhaut

Vice President, Colleen Daly

Senior Vice President, Kim Monson

Senior Vice President Risk Policy Manager, JoAnn Schaeublin

Vice President Financial Risk Governance Manager, Anna Norcross

Vice President Information Technology Project Management, Lari Greenleaf

Vice President National Ach Edi Operat, Eric Foust

Vice President Business Development, Carol Schafer

Vice President Of Information Technology, Roy Woodbury

Vice President And Manager Regional Reporting, Melissa Werner

Vice President Information Technology Delivery Manager Wealth And Commercial Segments, Mark Melaragno

Senior Vice President Central Ohio District, Thomas Spilman

Vice President, Marcella Pardo

Senior Vice President Payment Deposit, Dominic Cugini

Vice President Credit Risk Management, Bob Fisco

Senior Vice President Capital Planning, Jay Luzar

Assistant Vice President Auditor, Dominic Fabiilli

Vice President And Compliance Officer, Tamara Darnow

Senior Treasury Services Sales Officer Vice President, Anwar Smiley

Vice President Meeting Marketing Manager, Laurie Masters

Executive Vice President, George Emmons

Co Chief Operating Officer, Douglas Preiser

Vice President Originations Specialty Finance And Syndications, Ric Andersen

Senior Vice President, Patrick Fish

Senior Vice President And Chief Underwriter Cmbs, Alan Williams

Vice President Consumer Finance, Dan Sukys

Vice President Corporate Communications, Alison Altre-Kerber

Vice President And Trust Team Lead Real Estate, Emily Mogen

Vice President Senior Business Banker, John Marriott

Vice President Credit Officer, Kellie Whelan

Senior Vice President Manager, Robert Likes

Assistant Vice President Retail Banking, Michael Emerson

Senior Vice President And Finance Director, William Shaw

Vice President Credit Risk Reviewer, Greg Newhouse

Senior Vice President Commercial Banking, Stephen Markley

Vice President Private Banking, Andrew Bowen

Vice President Team Leader, Pete Dunbar

Senior Vice President, James Harnett

Vice President Manager, Larissa Tadiello

Vice President Product Manager, Natalie Treibatch

Vice President Credit Officer, Jay Coleman

Vice President Senior Portfolio Manager, Jeff Stegeman

Senior Vice President Enterprise Architecture, Mike Onders

Vice President Business Development, Alice Karn

Vice President Senior Treasury Advisor Institutional Banking, Michael Thomas

Vice President Client Services Consumer Segment, Cheryl Towns

Vice President District Operations Manager, Monica Cichon

Senior Cash Management Advisor And Assistant Vice President Treasury Services, Kristina Simpson

Vice President And Senior Trust Officer, Daryl Hembry

Vice President Compliance And Security Operations, Anthony Rini

Senior Vice President Real Estate Finance, Craig Younggren

Vice President And District Operations Manager, Laurie Dickinson

Senior Vice President Corporate Bank Technology And Sales Tool Team Manager, Brian Utrup

Senior Vice President District Retail Leader, Curtis Hollis

Senior Vice President And Manager Instit, Flavio Giust

E C Manager Assistant Vice President System Administrator, Margaret Mason

Vice President And Senior Associate Counsel, Mark Freeman

Vice President Network Solutions Engineering, Daniel Godlewski

Assistant Vice President Portfolio Manager, Sara Smith

Assistant Vice President Team Lead, Lashawn Dalton

Executive Vice President And Director Call Center Sales And Service, Dean Kontul

Senior Vice President Senior Relationship Manager, David Brown

Senior Vice President Asset Management, Amy Paine

Vice President Consumer Credit Risk Management, Kevin Takac

Executive Vice President Human Resources, Beth Yates

Executive Vice President Marketing, David Odell

Vice President And Senior Lit Counsel, Michelle Deshon

Senior Vice President, Jeff Link

Vice President, Aaron Klein

Senior Vice President, John Nolting

Vice President, Joyce Weiler

Relationship Manager Vice President Commercial Banking, Hanna Piechocka

Vice President Leveraged Loans, David Opatrny

Senior Vice President, Alyce Juby

Vice President, James Gelle
Senior Vice President, Carey Spencer
Vice President, Jennie Bacon
Assistant Vice President, Erik Vohs
Vice President Senior Relationship Manager, Brian Flewelling
Vice President Commercial Banking Relationship Manager, Adam Clinton
Vice President, Dan Schock
Vice President, Gordon Ostler
Assistant Vice President Business Banking Relationship Manager, Jennifer Regelski
Assistant Vice President And Relationship Manager, Brian Herrick
Vice President, Eric Hafertepen
Vice President Business Banking, John Fidler
Assistant Vice President, Max Rebello
Vice President, Seth Reimer
Vice President And Senior Portfolio Manager, Lynn Wilson
Vice President Credit Officer Business Banking, Peg Misencik
Vice President Senior Bus. Relationship Manager, Rachel Galusha
Assistant Vice President Business Banking Relationship Manager, Nicholas Emmett
Senior Commercial Relationship Manager Vice President, Sabrina Webster
Senior Vice President, Sanya Valeva
Assistant Vice President, Teena Heasley
Vice President, Sally Barton
Vice President, Selina Moriarty
Senior Vice President, Jerold Myler
Vice President, Michael Keach
Vice President, Suzan Jones
Vice President Regional Facilities Manager, Michael Leonardo
Senior Vice President, Sharon Lochocki
Senior Vice President, Denise Povolny
Senior Vice President And Senior Relationship Manager, Jun Chea
Vice President Relationship Manager, Todd Remy
Vice President Commercial Relationship Manager, Thomas Gunter
Vice President, Paul Taubeneck
Assistant Vice President Key Center Manager, Nicole Bier
Senior Vice President Loan Servicing And Asset Management, Clark Rogers
Vice President, Charles Arenas
Vice President Rocky Mountain And Agri Business Service Team Manager, Chantel West
Senior Vice President Senior Investment Portfolio Manager, Cheryl Ennis
Vice President Senior Business Banking Relationship Manager, Ed Korsok
Credit Executive Senior Vice Presidfent, Gary Knapp
Senior Vice President Director Of National Facilities, Brian Lawhead
Vice President Corporate Treasury Service Manager Enterprise Commercial Payments, Tami Riley
Senior Vice President Eastern Regional Manager, John Manginelli
Assistant Vice President; Senior Treasury Client Manager, Lynn Barclay
Vice President, William Schlag
Vice President Of Technology, Dani Madi
Vice President Global Information Technology Asset Management, Warren Edris
Vice President Federal Sales, Gina Ringgenberg
Vice President, Christine Anderson
Assistant Vice President Asset Based Lending, Andrew Ashley
Vice President, Dale Williams
Vice President And Senior Relationship Manager, Bart Gebers
Vice President Institutional Equity Sale, Christopher Brady

Assistant Vice President Branch Manager, David Butler
Vice President, George Mohan
Senior Vice President, Kenneth Lynch
Senior Vice President, Nick Edwards
Assistant Vice President Ap Accounting And Audit Manager, Dore Wawrzyniak
Vice President Regional Facilities Manager, Chris Headrick
Auditors: Ernst & Young LLP

LOCATIONS

HQ: KeyCorp
127 Public Square, Cleveland, OH 44114-1306
Phone: 216 689-3000
Web: www.key.com

PRODUCTS/OPERATIONS

2018 Sales

	$ mil.	% of total
Interest		
Loans	4,023	54
Securities available for sale	409	6
Held-to-maturity securities	284	4
Loans held for sale	66	1
Trading account assets	46	-
Short-term investments	29	-
Other investments	21	-
Interest Expense	969	-
Less: TE adjustment	31	-
Noninterest		
Trust & investment services	499	7
Investment banking and debt placement fees	650	9
Service charges on deposits	349	5
Corporate Service income	233	3
Cards and payments income	270	4
Corporate owned life insurance income	137	2
Operating lease income and other leasing gains	89	1
Mortgage servicing fees	82	1
Consumer mortgage income	30	-
Other income	176	2
Total	**6,455**	**100**

2018 Sales

	$ mil.	% of total
Key Community Bank	3,971	62
Key Corporate Bank	2,255	35
Other Segment	151	2
Reconciling Items	78	1
Total		**100**

2018 Loan Portfolio

	% of total
Commercial Loans	
Commercial and Industrial	51
Commercial Real Estate	
Commercial Mortgage	16
Construction	2
Commercial Lease Financing	5
Consumer Loans	
Real estate-residential mortgage	6
Home equity loans	13
Consumer direct loans	2
Credit cards	1
Consumer indirect loans	4
Total	**100**

COMPETITORS

Bank of America	Huntington Bancshares
Citigroup	JPMorgan Chase
Citizens Financial Group	M&T Bank
	Northern Trust
Comerica	PNC Financial
Fifth Third	Sovereign Bank
Flagstar Bancorp	U.S. Bancorp
HSBC USA	Wells Fargo

HISTORICAL FINANCIALS

Company Type: Public

Income Statement

				FYE: December 31
	ASSETS ($ mil.)	NET INCOME ($ mil.)	INCOME AS % OF ASSETS	EMPLOYEES
12/18	139,613	1,866	1.3%	18,180
12/17	137,698	1,296	0.9%	18,415
12/16	136,453	791	0.6%	15,700
12/15	95,133	916	1.0%	13,359
12/14	93,821	900	1.0%	13,853
Annual Growth	10.4%	20.0%	—	7.0%

2018 Year-End Financials

Debt ratio: 9.00%
Return on equity: 12.00%
Cash ($ mil.): 1,527
Current ratio: —
Long-term debt ($ mil.): —

No. of shares (mil.): 1,020
Dividends
  Yield: 4.0%
  Payout: 39.0%
Market value ($ mil.): 15,068

	STOCK PRICE ($) FY Close	P/E High/Low		PER SHARE ($)		
				Earnings	Dividends	Book Value
12/18	15.00	13	8	2.00	1.00	15.00
12/17	20.00	18	14	1.00	0.00	14.00
12/16	18.00	23	12	1.00	0.00	14.00
12/15	13.00	15	11	1.00	0.00	13.00
12/14	14.00	14	12	1.00	0.00	12.00
Annual Growth	1.5%	—	—	14.6%	22.6%	5.7%

KIEWIT CORPORATION

EXECUTIVES

Ceo, Bruce E Grewcock
Exec V Pres, Richard W Colf
Exec V Pres, Douglas E Patterson
Exec V Pres, Scott L Cassels
Sr V Pres, Steven Hansen
Treas, Stephen S Thomas
SEC, Michael F Norton
Major Project Mana, Joe Wingerter
Career, Heather Semple
Vice-President, Larry Cochran
Senior Manager, Michael Ramsey
Auditors: KPMG LLP OMAHA NE

LOCATIONS

HQ: KIEWIT CORPORATION
3555 FARNAM ST STE 1000, OMAHA, NE 681313302
Phone: 402 342-2052
Web: WWW.KIEWIT.COM

HISTORICAL FINANCIALS

Company Type: Private

Income Statement

				FYE: December 28
	REVENUE ($ mil.)	NET INCOME ($ mil.)	NET PROFIT MARGIN	EMPLOYEES
12/13	11,826	796	6.7%	10,441
12/12	11,220	512	4.6%	—
12/11	10,381	796	7.7%	—
Annual Growth	6.7%	(0.0%)	—	—

Kimberly-Clark Corp.

One of the world's largest makers of personal paper products Kimberly-Clark operates through three business segments: Personal Care Consumer Tissue and K-C Professional. Kimberly-Clark's largest unit Personal Care makes products such as diapers (Huggies Pull-Ups) feminine care items (Kotex) and incontinence care products (Poise Depend). Through its Consumer Tissue segment the manufacturer offers facial and bathroom tissues paper towels and other household items under the names Cottonelle Kleenex Viva and Scott (plus the Scott Naturals line). Kimberly-Clark's K-C Professional unit makes WypAll commercial wipes among other items. The US accounts for around half of Kimberly-Clarke's sales.

Operations

Kimberly-Clark has three reportable segments: Personal Care (50%) Consumer Tissue (a third) and K-C Professional (nearly 20%).

Personal Care offers products such as disposable diapers training and youth pants swimpants baby wipes feminine and incontinence care products and other related products. Its products are sold under the Huggies Pull-Ups Little Swimmers GoodNites DryNites Kotex U by Kotex Intimus Depend Plenitud Poise and other brands.

Consumer Tissue's products include facial and bathroom tissue paper towels napkins and related products and are sold under the Kleenex Scott Cottonelle Viva Andrex Scottex Neve and other brand names.

K-C Professional (KCP) partners with businesses and provides supporting products such as wipers tissue towels apparel soaps and sanitizers sold under the Kleenex Scott WypAll Kimtech and KleenGuard brands.

Consumer tissue and KCP products are produced in 55 facilities and personal care products are produced in 49 facilities.

Geographic Reach

Dallas Texas-based Kimberly-Clark maintains a broad global presence as part of its growth strategy. It boasts nearly 90 manufacturing facilities in about 35 countries across the US Canada Europe Asia and Latin America and records sales in more than 175 countries. Kimberly-Clarke records an even split of sales within North America and outside it.

Sales and Marketing

Kimberly-Clark sells its household items directly to supermarkets mass merchandisers drugstores warehouse clubs variety and department stores and other retail outlets as well as through distributors and e-commerce. For the away-from-home market it serves the company sells through distributors and directly to high-volume public facilities and to manufacturing lodging office building food service and health care establishments.

Its largest customer worldwide retailer Wal-Mart represents about 15% of net sales.

Financial Performance

Kimberly-Clark has struggled to attain meaningful revenue growth in recent years while profits have fluctuated. In fiscal 2018 the company's sales grew a limp 1% to $18.5 billion thanks to growth in the US; non-US sales were materially flat. By segment K-C Professional was the strongest performer and Personal Care the weakest.

Kimberly-Clark's net income fell 38% to $1.4 billion due to a a restructuring program undertaken in 2018. The company incurred layoff expenses asset write-offs and impairments and depreciation. It hopes the restructuring will generate $500 million in pre-tax savings by 2021.

Kimberly-Clarke's cash on hand fell slightly during 2018 ending the year $77 million lower at $539 million. The company's operations generated $3.0 billion while its investing activities used $902 million and its financing used $2.1 billion. Kimberly-Clark's main cash uses in 2018 were capital expenditures share repurchases debt repayments and dividends.

Strategy

With business performance lower than desired Kimberly-Clark undertook a global restructuring program in 2018 that will see 10 factories close and certain low-margin businesses divested (mainly in the consumer tissue segment) as well as potentially saving some $500-550 million in annual costs. The restructuring which resulted in 5000-5500 job cuts should leave Kimberly-Clark on surer footing to invest in its brands and growth initiatives. The company has earmarked $1.1-1.3 billion in capex for 2019 an increase on the $0.9 and $0.8 billion in the two preceding years.

HISTORY

John Kimberly Charles Clark Havilah Babcock and Frank Shattuck founded Kimberly Clark & Company in Neenah Wisconsin in 1872 to manufacture newsprint from rags. The company incorporated as Kimberly & Clark Company in 1880 and built a pulp and paper plant on the Fox River in 1889.

In 1914 the company developed cellu-cotton a cotton substitute used by the US Army as surgical cotton during WWI. Army nurses used cellu-cotton pads as disposable sanitary napkins and six years later the company introduced Kotex the first disposable feminine hygiene product. Kleenex the first throwaway handkerchief followed in 1924. Kimberly & Clark joined with The New York Times Company in 1926 to build a newsprint mill (Spruce Falls Power and Paper) in Ontario Canada. Two years later the company went public as Kimberly-Clark.

EXECUTIVES

Chairman And Ceo, Thomas J. (Tom) Falk, age 61, $1,318,750 total compensation
Svp And Cfo, Maria G. Henry, age 52, $772,500 total compensation
President Latin America, Sergio Cruz
President Global Brands And Innovation, Anthony J. (Tony) Palmer, age 59, $655,000 total compensation
President Coo And Director, Michael D. Hsu, age 55, $833,750 total compensation
Svp And Chief Supply Chain Officer, Sandra J. MacQuillan, age 52, $392,424 total compensation
President Asia-pacific Region, Achal Agarwal
President Europe Middle East And Africa, Gustavo Calvo Paz
President Kimberly-clark Professional, Kim Underhill
Vice President Investor Relations, Paul Alexander
Vice President Kimberly Clark Professional Asia Pacific, Richard Thorne
Vice President Its Infrastructure, Ryan Ramirez
Vp Government Relations, Susan Phillips
Vice President Internal Audit, Stephen Frimpong
Vice President Walmart International Development, John Scholes
Vice President Transportation, Scott Degroot
Vice President Human Resources, Rick Purdy
Vice President Global Communications, Christopher Wyse
Vice President Of Human Resources, Tina Busch
Vice President Industry And Customer Development, Dennis Delcastro
Vice President And Global Sector Leader Adult And Feminine Care, Fiona Tomlin

Global Vp Logistics, Shane Azzi
Auditors: DELOITTE & TOUCHE LLP

LOCATIONS

HQ: Kimberly-Clark Corp.
P.O. Box 619100, Dallas, TX 75261-9100
Phone: 972 281-1200
Web: www.kimberly-clark.com

2018 Sales

	$ mil.	% of total
North America	9,532	51
Outside North America	9,256	49
Total	**18,486**	**100**

PRODUCTS/OPERATIONS

2018 Sales

	$ mil.	% of total
Personal Care	9,037	49
Consumer Tissue	6,015	33
K-C Professional	3,382	18
Corporate & other	52	-
Total	**18,486**	**100**

Selected Products and Brands

Baby & Child Care
  Huggies
  Pull-Ups
  GoodNites
  DryNites
  Little Swimmers
  Kleen Bebe
  Green Finger
Family Care
  Kleenex
  Andrex
  Hakle
  Cottonelle
  Scottes
  Page
  Neve
  Petalo
  Wondersoft
  Tela
  Scott
  Viva
Feminine Care
  U by Kotex
  Kotex
  Intimus
  CAmelia
K-C Professional
  KleenGuard
  Kimtech
  WypAll
  Scott
  Kleenex

COMPETITORS

3M	Johnson & Johnson
Ansell	Medline Industries
Becton Dickinson	Nice-Pak Products
Bristol-Myers Squibb	Potlatch
CCA Industries	Procter & Gamble
DSG International Ltd	SSI Surgical Services
Edgewell Personal Care	Suominen
Georgia-Pacific	

HISTORICAL FINANCIALS

Company Type: Public

Income Statement   FYE: December 31

	REVENUE ($ mil.)	NET INCOME ($ mil.)	NET PROFIT MARGIN	EMPLOYEES
12/18	18,486	1,410	7.6%	41,000
12/17	18,259	2,278	12.5%	42,000
12/16	18,202	2,166	11.9%	42,000
12/15	18,591	1,013	5.4%	43,000
12/14	19,724	1,526	7.7%	43,000
Annual Growth	(1.6%)	(2.0%)	—	(1.2%)

2018 Year-End Financials

Debt ratio: 51.00%
Return on equity: 604.00%
Cash ($ mil.): 539
Current ratio: 1.00
Long-term debt ($ mil.): 6,247

No. of shares (mil.): 345
Dividends
  Yield: 4.0%
  Payout: 99.0%
Market value ($ mil.): 39,305

	STOCK PRICE ($) FY Close	P/E High/Low		PER SHARE ($) Earnings	Dividends	Book Value
12/18	114.00	30	24	4.00	4.00	(1.00)
12/17	121.00	21	17	6.00	4.00	2.00
12/16	114.00	23	19	6.00	4.00	(0.00)
12/15	127.00	47	37	3.00	4.00	(0.00)
12/14	116.00	29	25	4.00	3.00	2.00
Annual Growth	(0.3%)	—	—	(0.1%)	4.5%	—

Kinder Morgan Inc.

Kinder Morgan Inc. (KMI) is one of the largest energy infrastructure companies in North America. It operates approximately 85000 miles of pipelines and more than 150 terminals that transport natural gas refined petroleum products crude oil condensate CO2 and other products to its customers across America. The company is also a leading producer of CO2 used in oilfield operations. Most of KMI's customers are major oil companies energy producers and shippers as well as local distribution companies. It generates most of its sales in the US. In 2019 KMI agreed to sell its 70% stake in Kinder Morgan Canada Limited to Pembina Pipeline Corporation.

Operations

KMI reports via five segments: Natural Gas Pipelines Terminals Products Pipelines CO2 and Kinder Morgan Canada.

Natural Gas Pipelines is KMI's most significant business segment accounting for more than 60% of total revenue. This line of business operates approximately 72000 miles of pipelines and storage facilities which supply roughly 40% of all consumed natural gas in the US.

Terminals is the transportation arm of KMI and brings in roughly 15% of annual sales. With more than 50 liquid terminals about 35 bulk terminals and over 15 Jones Act approved tankers KMI is the largest independent terminal operator in North America. (Jones Act restricts US point-to-point maritime shipping to vessels that are 75% US-owned.) The terminals transload store or blend refined petroleum products crude oil chemicals ethanol and bulk products to US and parts of Canada.

The Products Pipelines segment includes more than 9700 miles of pipelines and over 70 terminals making this sector the largest independent transporter of petroleum products (more than 2 million barrels per day). Moving gasoline jet fuel diesel crude and NGL products this sector brings in just more than 10% of annual sales.

Although KMI is the largest CO2 transporter in North America (2.0 billion cubic feet/ day) this segment only accounts for less than 10% of the company's total sales.

Kinder Morgan Canada (2%) includes the Trans Mountain pipeline system (now sold-off) and a 25-mile Jet Fuel pipeline system.

Geographic Reach

KMI has operations in the US Canada and Mexico. KMI buys and sells significant volumes of natural gas in Texas. US customers account for some 95% of the company's revenue.

Sales and Marketing

KMI customers include major oil companies energy producers and shippers as well as local distributors. The company does business under extended transport and sales contracts. KMI conducts its Midstream assets on a fee-based arrangement and its CO2 business has third-party contracts with minimum volume requirements.

Financial Performance

Revenue at KMI grew from $7.8 billion in 2010 to a decade-peak of $16.2 billion before declining to $13 billion in 2017. Though mostly profitable in the last decade KMI has drastically cut its profit from around $1 billion in the 2013-14 years to below $200 million in 2017.

In 2017 annual sales increased 5% to $13.7 billion primarily due to a $600 million YOY increase in natural gas pipeline revenue thanks to volume growth.

Net income reduced from $708 million in 2016 to $183 million in 2017 primarily due to a $1 billion increase in income tax expenses.

Cash holdings declined to $264 million at the end of 2017. Operations provided $4.6 billion offset by $3.3 billion used in investments and a further $1.6 billion used by financing activities. The company paid $11 billion in debt while CAPEX stood at $3.1 billion.

Strategy

KMI is moving away from its over-leveraged years thanks to strong earnings promising new projects and a successful debt reduction strategy.

The sale of TMX to the Canadian government for C$4.5 billion helped KMI conclude its successful debt reduction strategy on a high going from $42.5 billion in the third quarter 2015 to $34.5 billion three years later. The company anticipates $7.5 billion of adjusted EBITDA for 2018.

With the leverage target reached sooner than expected the company now plans to invest its proceeds into attractive growth projects and share repurchases.

The TMX expansion project stalled with political stalemate between Alberta and British Columbia. However KMI made a successful exit thanks to the terms of its deals with lenders and oil producers which shielded it from massive write-downs suffered by rivals TransCanada Corp and Enbridge.

Emboldened by this success KMI wants its GCX and Permian Highway projects to be fully operational by 2020. For the GCX Project KMI along with DCP Midstream and Targa Resources will target moving natural gas from the prolific Permian Basin to the Gulf Coast (430 miles 1.92 Bcf/d) with additional access to the Midland Basin and export opportunities to Mexico. The other project Permian Highway Pipeline in a partnership with EagleClaw Midstream and Apache will develop another new gas pipeline (430 miles 2bcf/day) out of the same Basin.

Company Background

Kinder Morgan Energy Partners (KMP) was founded in February 1997 when a group of investors led by Executive Chairman Richard D. Kinder and Vice Chairman William V. Morgan decided to build an energy company by utilizing the master limited partnership (MLP) financial structure as a growth vehicle—something that had never been done before.

Their innovative approach proved so successful that in two decades KMP has becomes the largest publicly traded pipeline limited partnership in America based on enterprise value. Initially the company grew mostly through acquisitions of existing operations but eventually took on the construction of projects.

Separately in 1999 Mr. Kinder took over the reins of KN Energy from Lakewood Colorado a natural gas pipeline company serving small communities and rural areas in Kansas and Nebraska and turned it to Kinder Morgan Inc. Kinder Morgan's second publicly traded company.

EXECUTIVES

President And Ceo, Steven J. (Steve) Kean, age 58, $1 total compensation
Vp And Cfo, Kimberly A. (Kim) Dang, age 50, $375,000 total compensation
President Kinder Morgan Canada, Ian D. Anderson, age 62
Vp; President Natural Gas Pipelines, Thomas A. (Tom) Martin, $375,000 total compensation
Vp Corporate Development, Dax Sanders, $375,000 total compensation
President Products Pipelines, Ronald G. (Ron) McClain
President Terminals, John W. Schlosser
Vp And Cio, Mark Huse
President Co2, Jesse Arenivas, $325,000 total compensation
Vice President Information Technology, Dan Henningsen
Vice President Project Management (jurisdictional Assets), Tom Otjen
Vice President Procurement, Kim Richardson
Vice President Pipeline Scheduling, Holly Breaux
Vp And Controller, Gary Bohnsack
Executive Vice President And Chief Operating Officer, Scott Stoness
Vice President, Douglas Lawing
Vice President Employee Benefits, Mark Smith
Vice President Marketing, Don Lindley
Vice President Logistic, James Holland
Vice President Marketing, Jim Kehlet
Vice President, Dirk Cockrum
Vice President, David Michels
Vice President Of Engineering, Lanny Shoeling
Vice President Of Business Development, David Grisko
Vice President Technology, Dan Rizzo
Vp Government Relations And Communications, David Conover
Vice President Pacific Business Development And Marketing, Mary Morgan
Vice President Operations (central Region), Michael Catt
Vice President Of Retail Operations, Stve Kean
Assistant Vice President, Guadalupe L Rivera
Executive Chairman, Richard D. (Rich) Kinder, age 75
Board Of Directors, Ron Mcclain
Board Member, Robert Vagt
Vice President And Treasurer, Anthony Ashley
Auditors: PricewaterhouseCoopers LLP

LOCATIONS

HQ: Kinder Morgan Inc.
1001 Louisiana Street, Suite 1000, Houston, TX 77002
Phone: 713 369-9000
Web: www.kindermorgan.com

2017 Sales

	$ mil.	% of total
US	13,073	95
Canada	503	4
Mexico	129	1
Total	**13,705**	**100**

PRODUCTS/OPERATIONS

2017 Sales

	$ mil.	% of total
Natural Gas Pipelines	8,618	63
Terminals	1,966	14
Products Pipelines	1,661	12
CO2	1,196	9
Kinder Morgan Canada	256	2
Corporate and intersegment eliminations	8	-
Total	**13,705**	**100**

2017 Sales

	$ mil.	% of total
Services	7,901	58
Natural gas sales	3,053	22
Product sales and other	2,751	20
Total	**13,705**	**100**

COMPETITORS

Denbury Resources	Energy Transfer Equity
Devon Energy	Enterprise Products
EnLink Midstream	ONEOK
Partners	TRII
Enbridge	Williams Companies

HISTORICAL FINANCIALS

Company Type: Public

Income Statement   FYE: December 31

	REVENUE ($ mil.)	NET INCOME ($ mil.)	NET PROFIT MARGIN	EMPLOYEES
12/18	14,144	1,609	11.4%	11,012
12/17	13,705	183	1.3%	10,897
12/16	13,058	708	5.4%	11,121
12/15	14,403	253	1.8%	11,290
12/14	16,226	1,026	6.3%	11,535
Annual Growth	(3.4%)	11.9%	—	(1.2%)

2018 Year-End Financials

Debt ratio: 47.00%—
Return on equity: 5.00%
Cash ($ mil.): 3,280
Current ratio: 1.00
Long-term debt ($ mil.): 33,936

Dividends
  Yield: 5.0%
  Payout: 110.0%
Market value ($ mil.): —

	STOCK PRICE ($) FY Close	P/E High/Low	PER SHARE ($) Earnings	Dividends	Book Value
12/18	15.00	30 22	1.00	1.00	15.00
12/17	18.00	22941676	0.00	1.00	15.00
12/16	21.00	93 48	0.00	1.00	15.00
12/15	15.00	446145	0.00	2.00	16.00
12/14	42.00	48 35	1.00	2.00	16.00
Annual Growth	(22.4%)	—	—	(7.2%)(19.2%)(1.8%)

Knight-Swift Transportation Holdings Inc

Auditors: Grant Thornton LLP

LOCATIONS

HQ: Knight-Swift Transportation Holdings Inc
  20002 North 19th Avenue, Phoenix, AZ 85027
Phone: 602 269-2000
Web: www.investor.knight-swift.com

HISTORICAL FINANCIALS

Company Type: Public

Income Statement   FYE: December 31

	REVENUE ($ mil.)	NET INCOME ($ mil.)	NET PROFIT MARGIN	EMPLOYEES
12/18	5,344	419	7.8%	22,800
12/17	2,425	484	20.0%	25,400
12/16	1,118	94	8.4%	5,971
12/15	1,183	117	9.9%	6,196
12/14	1,102	103	9.3%	5,485
Annual Growth	48.4%	42.1%	—	42.8%

2018 Year-End Financials

Debt ratio: 9.00%
Return on equity: 8.00%
Cash ($ mil.): 129
Current ratio: 1.00
Long-term debt ($ mil.): 631

No. of shares (mil.): 173
Dividends
  Yield: 1.0%
  Payout: 10.0%
Market value ($ mil.): 4,333

	STOCK PRICE ($) FY Close	P/E High/Low	PER SHARE ($) Earnings	Dividends	Book Value
12/18	25.00	21 10	2.00	0.00	32.00
12/17	44.00	10 4	4.00	0.00	29.00
12/16	24.00	23 11	1.00	0.00	10.00
12/15	14.00	20 9	1.00	0.00	9.00
12/14	29.00	23 15	1.00	0.00	8.00
Annual Growth	(3.3%)	—	17.2%	—	39.8%

KNIGHTS OF COLUMBUS

Good Knight! The Knights of Columbus is a formidable volunteer group boasting more than 15300 councils made up of 1.9 million Roman Catholic male members in the US Canada Mexico Cuba the Philippines Poland and several other countries. The fraternal organization is also a force to be reckoned with in the insurance world providing life insurance annuities and long-term care insurance to its members and their families. More than 1500 full-time insurance agents work across the United States and Canada. In addition the group manages the Knights of Columbus Museum in New Haven Connecticut featuring exhibits of religious art and history. The group was founded in 1882 by Father Michael J. McGivney.

Operations

The Knights of Columbus (KoC) was formed to render financial aid to members and their families. Mutual aid and assistance are offered to sick disabled and needy members and their families. Social and intellectual fellowship is promoted among members and their families through educational charitable religious social welfare war relief and public relief works. KoC is also engaged in religious education the support of public policy issues and charitable activities such as disaster relief.

The entity is a Catholic family fraternal service organization. This theme permeates the entire Service Program: all Church community council family culture of life and youth activities. The Service Program is designed to establish each council as an influential and important force within the community elevate the status of the programming personnel provide more meaningful and relevant programs of action establish direct areas of responsibility build leadership and ensure the success of council programs.

The group's supreme council has more than 75 state council organizations.

Geographic Reach

The Knights of Columbus is made up of local councils throughout the US Canada Mexico Puerto Rico Guam Saipan and the US Virgin Islands. It also has councils in the Bahamas Cuba the Dominican Republic Guatemala Lithuania Panama the Philippines Poland South Korea and Ukraine. The United States Canada and the Philippines have the largest membership numbers.

Financial Performance

In 2019 its Knights of Columbus Insurance reported $8.6 billion in annual sales and more than $26?billion in assets under management. The organization gave $185.7 million to charity and donated 76.7 million hours of hands-on service in 2018.

Strategy

Known for its charitable giving the Knights of Columbus is also an insurance company providing insurance to its membership.

The organization has 1500 agents who are also members of the Knights. In 2018 Knights of Columbus Insurance issued $8.6 billion of new life insurance provided $1 billion in benefits including $441 million in death benefits and $262 million in refunds to members. Once the company?s revenue covers operational costs and refunds (dividends) to its membership the remaining profits are directed to charity.

The Knights of Columbus wants to attract younger members to the organization and has made some adjustments such as offering streamlined online memberships and eliminating some of its longstanding uniform requirements.

Company Background

The Knights of Columbus was founded in New Haven by Father Michael J. McGivney in 1882 and has been selling insurance since its founding.

EXECUTIVES

Supreme Knight, Carl A. Anderson
Supreme Secretary, Michael J. (Mike) O'Connor
Supreme Chaplain, William E. Lori
Deputy Supreme Knight, Patrick E. Kelly
Supreme Treasurer, Ronald F. Schwarz
Vice President Communications And Strategic Planning, Andrew Walther
Assistant Vice President Of Application Development, Niki Kratzert
Vice President, Gary Nolan
Vice President Actuary, Marc Andre-Brunet
Senior Vice President Chief Communications Officer, Kevin Shinkle
Vice President Portfolio Manager, Gil Marchand
Treasurer, Logan Ludwig
Treasurer, Keith Ryan
Treasurer, Ron Schwarz

LOCATIONS

HQ: KNIGHTS OF COLUMBUS
1 COLUMBUS PLZ STE 1700, NEW HAVEN, CT 065103326
Phone: 203 752-4000
Web: WWW.KOFC.ORG

HISTORICAL FINANCIALS

Company Type: Private

Income Statement   FYE: December 31

	ASSETS ($ mil.)	NET INCOME ($ mil.)	INCOME AS % OF ASSETS	EMPLOYEES
12/13	20,534	114	0.6%	2,300
12/12	19,402	128	0.7%	—
12/11	18,027	81	0.4%	—
12/10	16,862	87	0.5%	—
Annual Growth	6.8%	9.5%	—	—

Kohl's Corp.

HISTORICAL FINANCIALS

Company Type: Public

Income Statement				FYE: February 2
	REVENUE ($ mil.)	**NET INCOME** ($ mil.)	**NET PROFIT MARGIN**	**EMPLOYEES**
02/19	20,229	801	4.0%	129,000
02/18*	19,095	859	4.5%	137,000
01/17	18,686	556	3.0%	138,000
01/16	19,204	673	3.5%	140,000
01/15	19,023	867	4.6%	137,000
Annual Growth	1.5%	(2.0%)	—	(1.5%)

*Fiscal year change

2019 Year-End Financials

Debt ratio: 28.00%	No. of shares (mil.): 163
Return on equity: 15.00%	Dividends
Cash ($ mil.): 934	Yield: 0.0%
Current ratio: 2.00	Payout: 50.0%
Long-term debt ($ mil.): 3,384	Market value ($ mil.): 10,870

	STOCK PRICE ($) FY Close	P/E High/Low		PER SHARE ($) Earnings	Dividends	Book Value
02/19	67.00	17	12	5.00	2.00	34.00
02/18*	63.00	13	7	5.00	2.00	32.00
01/17	39.00	19	11	3.00	2.00	30.00
01/16	50.00	23	12	3.00	2.00	30.00
01/15	60.00	15	11	4.00	2.00	30.00
Annual Growth	2.8%	—	—	3.4%	11.8%	3.3%

*Fiscal year change

Kraft Heinz Co (The)

Bringing together packaged food giants Kraft Foods and H.J. Heinz The Kraft Heinz Company is one of the largest food and beverage companies in the world. In addition to its two namesakes the company's portfolio of iconic brands (eight of them billion-dollar brands) include such names as Oscar Meyer Capri Sun Ore-Ida Kool-Aid Jell-O Planters Philadelphia Lunchables Maxwell House and Velveeta. Kraft Heinz which generates nearly half a sales from condiments and sauces and cheese and dairy products offers its goods through retailers and foodservice distributors in some 190 countries across the globe.

Operations

Kraft Heinz's operations are organized across some half a dozen specific product categories. Its largest categories are condiments and sauces (about a quarter of sales) and cheese and dairy (about 20%). Others include frozen and chilled foods; meats and seafood; and ambient or shelf-stable meals (at about 10% each); as well as refreshment beverages coffee infant and nutrition nuts and salted snacks and desserts toppings and baking.

The company's leading brands include Kraft and Heinz of course as well as Oscar Mayer Planters Maxwell House and Velveeta. It also licenses brands from third parties such as Capri-Sun TGI Fridays and McCafe.

Geographic Reach

Unlike many of its major competitors Kraft Heinz counts the US as its largest market by far accounting for about 70% of total revenue. Canada and the EMEA (Europe Middle East and Africa) region together contribute nearly 20% with the remaining revenue coming from Latin America and the Asia-Pacific region.

The company has co-headquarters in Pittsburgh Pennsylvania and Chicago Illinois. It also owns other facilities across the world including about 85 manufacturing and processing plants.

Sales and Marketing

Kraft Heinz's products are sold through its sales organizations and through independent brokers agents and distributors. This network sells to chain wholesale cooperative and independent grocery accounts as well as drug stores and pharmacies value and club stores and foodservice distributors. It also caters to hotels restaurants hospitals health care facilities and certain government agencies.

Kraft Heinz is heavily reliant on its largest customer Wal-Mart Stores which represents more than 20% of sales.

Financial Performance

Kraft Heinz enjoyed a spike in revenues from $18.3 billion in 2015 to $26.3 billion in 2016 primarily due to the results of its 2015 merger. Since then however sales have been stagnant. Net income had been on an upward trajectory until plummeting in 2018.

The company reported revenue of $26.3 billion in 2018 up less than a percent from the prior year. The condiments and sauces category saw solid growth that year but was offset by declines in the other categories especially cheese and dairy. Geographically sales were up in the EMEA region Latin America and the Asia-Pacific region but down in the US and Canada.

Substantial impairment losses in 2018 resulted in a net loss of $10.2 billion compared to a profit of $10.9 billion the year before. Struggles in the fourth quarter of the year including a sustained decrease in share price disappointing quarterly results and pending asset divestitures led Kraft Heinz

to perform an impairment test which resulted in more than $15 billion in losses.

Cash at the end of 2018 was $1.1 billion a decrease of $633 million from the prior year. Cash from operations contributed $2.6 billion to the coffers while investing activities added $288 million mainly from sold recievables. Financing activities used $3.4 billion primarily for dividends to stockholders.

Strategy

Like many of its competitors in the packaged foods space Kraft Heinz is struggling as consumer tastes move toward fresher healthier items. In addition it was notified in late 2018 that the Securities and Exchange Commission (SEC) was investigating the company's accounting practices related to its goodwill and intangible asset impairments. These issues among others culminated in a more than $15 billion charge in the fourth quarter of 2018 to write down the value of some of its assets including the Kraft and Oscar Mayer trademarks.

With a new CEO taking the reins in mid-2019 the company is seeking to move past its problems with a renewed focus on brand building and organic growth powered by a better understanding of customers. Kraft Heinz sees initial opportunities in the Philadelphia Heinz and Planter's brands.

This could signify a real change in strategy away from extreme cost-cutting which has been a philosophy of Brazilian private equity firm and Kraft Heinz stakeholder 3G Capital. Since the 2015 merger of Kraft Foods and H.J. Heinz 3G has implemented multiyear cost-cutting measures across the business to reduce overhead by streamlining operations. It has closed plants reduced headcount and slashed advertising expenses among other initiatives.

In line with 3G's approach to growth (centered on buying and consolidating large companies) Kraft Heinz had been expected by some industry experts to leverage acquisitions of other major players in the food and beverage industry. In early 2017 the company did make an unsolicited bid for consumer goods manufacturing giant Unilever for $143 billion; however Unilever quickly rebuffed the bid.

Mergers and Acquisitions

In late 2018 Kraft Heinz agreed to buy condiment company Primal Kitchen for some $200 million. Primal Kitchen makes paleo-friendly mayonnaise and other condiments oils and dressings. The deal helps bolster Kraft in the competitive space as more companies both new and established look to produce healthier alternatives of kitchen staples.

Company Background

Kraft Heinz was formed from the 2015 merger of Kraft Foods and H.J. Heinz. Ultimately however it traces its history back some 150 years

Svp Marketing Innovation Research And Development, Nina Barton
President Kraft Heinz Canada, Carlos Piani, $169,481 total compensation
Svp Global People Performance And Information Technology, Melissa Werneck
Zone President Europe, Rafael Oliveira
Head U.s. Commercial Finance, Andre Maciel
Vp And Category Head Planters, David Knopf, age 31
Vice President, Bill Durbin
National Account Manager, Angie Carpenter
Global Performance Vice President, Simone Hirakuri
Senior Vice President Of Sales, Michael Crouse
National Account Manager, Travis Ulrich
Svp Corporate And Government Affairs, Michael Mullen
Sr V Pres Global General Couns, James Savina
Vice President Sales And Foodservice Canada, Dan Lafrance
Vice President Investor Relations, Chris Jakubik
Vp Of It, Gustavo De Souza
Vice President Of It, Julia Ritchie
Vice President Director Of Information Technology Risk Management, Martina Del Raso Davis
Vice Chairman, John T. Cahill, age 62
Chairman, Alexandre (Alex) Behring, age 52
Board Member, Jorge Lemann
Auditors: PricewaterhouseCoopers LLP

LOCATIONS

HQ: Kraft Heinz Co (The)
One PPG Place, Pittsburgh, PA 15222
Phone: 412 456-5700
Web: www.kraftheinzcompany.com

2018 Sales

	$ mil.	% of total
US	18,122	69
Canada	2,173	8
EMEA	2,718	10
Rest of world	3,255	13
Total	**26,268**	**100**

PRODUCTS/OPERATIONS

2018 Sales

	$ mil.	% of total
Condiments and sauces	6,752	26
Cheese and dairy	5,287	20
Meats and seafood	2,505	9
Ambient meals	2,576	10
Frozen and chilled meals	2,548	10
Refreshment beverages	1,507	6
Coffee	1,438	5
Desserts toppings and baking	1,038	4
Nuts and salted snacks	967	4
Infant and nutrition	756	3
Other	894	3
Total	**26,268**	**100**

COMPETITORS

B&G Foods	Hormel
Campbell Soup	Kellogg
ConAgra	McCormick & Company
Frito-Lay	Mondelez International
General Mills	Nestlé USA
Hershey	Unilever PLC
Hillshire Brands	

HISTORICAL FINANCIALS

Company Type: Public

Income Statement

FYE: December 29

	REVENUE ($ mil.)	NET INCOME ($ mil.)	NET PROFIT MARGIN	EMPLOYEES
12/18	26,268	(10,192)	—	38,000
12/17	26,232	10,999	41.9%	39,000
12/16*	26,487	3,632	13.7%	41,000
01/16	18,338	634	3.5%	42,000
12/14	10,922	657	6.0%	
Annual Growth	**24.5%**	—	—	—

*Fiscal year change

2018 Year-End Financials

Debt ratio: 30.00%
Return on equity: (-17.00%)
Cash ($ mil.): 1,130
Current ratio: 1.00
Long-term debt ($ mil.): 30,770

No. of shares (mil.): 1,220
Dividends
Yield: 0.0%
Payout: —
Market value ($ mil.): 53,155

	STOCK PRICE ($) FY Close	P/E High/Low		PER SHARE ($) Earnings	Dividends	Book Value
12/18	44.00	—	—	(8.00)	3.00	42.00
12/17	78.00	11	8	9.00	2.00	54.00
12/16*	87.00	32	24	3.00	2.00	47.00
01/16	73.00	—	—	(0.00)	2.00	54.00
Annual Growth	**(12.0%)**	—	—	—	10.1%	(6.1%)

*Fiscal year change

Kroger Co (The)

Kroger is the world's largest traditional grocer despite Wal-Mart overtaking the chain as the world's largest seller of groceries years ago. It operates some 2750 supermarkets in 35 states under two dozen banners; more than 2250 locations have pharmacies and nearly 1550 have fuel centers. The company offers Pickup and Harris Teeter ExpressLane ? personalized order online pick up at the store services ? at about 1580 of its supermarkets and provide home delivery service to over 90% of Kroger households. It also has over 35 food processing plants in the US mostly bakeries and dairies. Kroger also operates about 250 fine jewelry stores under the Fred Meyer Jewelers and Littman Jewelers brands.

Operations

Kroger's supermarkets are generally operated under one of the following formats: combination food and drug stores multi-department stores marketplace stores or price impact warehouses. Its supermarkets on average stock over 15000 private label items. Private label products are primarily produced and sold in three "tiers": Private Selection one of its premium quality brands; Kroger which represents the majority of its private label items; and Big K Check This Out and Heritage Farm which are some of its value brands. In addition the company continues to grow its natural and organic brand offerings with Simple Truth and Simple Truth Organic.

About a third of its brands and nearly 45% of its grocery brands sold in its supermarkets are produced in production plants while the remaining brand items are produced by outside manufacturers. The company operates more than 35 food production plants consisting of primarily dairies (17) and deli or bakery (10) plants. Other plants include grocery product plants (5) beverage plants

(2) cheese plants (2) and meat plants (1). Kroger's retail operations represent almost all of its consolidated sales and is its only reportable segment. Additionally non-perishables accounted for about half of its total revenue while fresh merchandise accounts for about a quarter. Other product categories include supermarket fuel (over 10%) Pharmacy (about 10%) Convenience (before it was discontinued and sold in 2018) and other products.

Geographic Reach

Cincinnati-based Kroger operates supermarkets in about 35 US states from coast to coast. Key markets include California (about 320 locations) Ohio (215) Texas (210) and Georgia (173).

Sales and Marketing

Kroger offers a robust loyalty card program which offer discounts and other benefits to customers. The loyalty card program reaches 60 millions households and is used in more than 95% of Kroger transactions. The company can leverage the shopping and personal data collected through the loyalty card program to develop targeted marketing strategies. Kroger also offers its customer shopping insights to product manufacturers through its Kroger Precision Marketing unit.

Financial Performance

Kroger's revenues and profits have been rising over the past several years thanks to new store openings and acquisitions and a steady increase in same-store sales revenue. Its annual revenues have grown more than 11% since 2015. Revenue fell slightly to $121.1 billion in 2018 a 1% decrease from the year prior. The decrease was due to an extra week included in fiscal year 2017 and partially offset by an increase in 2018 sales.

Net income was $3.1 billion in fiscal year 2018 an increase from $1.9 billion in fiscal year 2017. Selling general and administrative expenses fell 3% in fiscal 2018 to $20.3 million.

Cash provided by operating activities was $4.1 billion in fiscal 2018 while investing activities used $1.1 billion. Financing activities provided another $2.8 billion.

Strategy

Kroger operates amid an intensely competitive grocery market that has seen Amazon's acquisition of Whole Foods and a European invasion of discount grocery chains such as Aldi and Lidl. It is looking to both accentuate and move beyond its traditional grocery store roots.

The company's Restock Kroger plan includes some $9 billion in capital investments over a three-year period dedicated to technology (including the "Scan Bag Go" handheld scanner initiative and online ordering) as well as training and higher pay. The strategic plan also includes an increased focus on Kroger's private-label brands. Each supermarket carries about 15000 private-label products and Kroger added more than 1000 private-label item offerings in 2018. The company's house brands account for some 30% of unit sales.

The grocery giant also launched as part of Restock Kroger an everyday activewear apparel line called "Dip" in 2018 to make its stores more of a shopping destination. In addition it sold its $4 billion convenience store business to UK-based EG Group for just more than $2 billion in mid-2018.

Recognizing the growing role of convenience for shoppers Kroger acquired private meal kit leader Home Chef. The kits are available in Kroger stores and online. Convenience is also driving a new pilot program called Kroger Express between Walgreens and Kroger. Kroger's is putting more than 2000 grocery products into select Walgreens to better reach customers and compete with e-commerce retailers.

Mergers and Acquisitions

In 2018 Kroger completed the purchase of private meal kit leader Home Chef. The grocery giant paid $200 million for Home Chef with future payouts of up to $500 million if certain milestones are achieved. The deal accelerates Kroger's move into the meal kit space; the kits will be available in stores and online.

In 2017 Kroger's acquired Murray's Cheese a New York-based specialty cheesemaker. This acquisition bolsters Kroger's push into upscale and organic foods.

Company Background

In 1883 Barney Kroger invested his life savings of $372 to open a grocery store at 66 Pearl Street in downtown Cincinnati. In 1972 Kroger became the first grocery retailer in America to test an electronic scanner.Mergers have played a key role in Kroger's growth over the years. In 1983 100 years after the company's founding Kroger merged with Dillon Companies Inc. in Kansas to become a coast-to-coast operator of food drug and convenience stores. The biggest merger in Kroger's history came in 1999 when the company teamed up with Fred Meyer Inc. in a $13 billion deal that created a supermarket chain with the broadest geographic coverage and widest variety of formats in the food retailing industry. In 2014 Kroger finalized its merger with Harris Teeter a regional chain of more than 200 stores. This merger brought to Kroger a well-known brand and complementary base of stores in high-growth markets primarily in the Mid-Atlantic region and the District of Columbia. Later that year Kroger merged with Vitacost.com an e-commerce company in the nutrition and healthy living market. In 2015 Kroger merged with Roundy's in Wisconsin adding Pick 'N Save Metro Market and Mariano's stores in Wisconsin and Illinois to the Kroger family.

HISTORY

Bernard Kroger was 22 when he started the Great Western Tea Company in 1883 in Cincinnati. Kroger lowered prices by cutting out middlemen sometimes by making products such as bread. Growing to 40 stores in Cincinnati and northern Kentucky the company became Kroger Grocery and Baking Company in 1902. It expanded into St. Louis in 1912 and grew rapidly during the 1910s and 1920s by purchasing smaller cash-strapped companies. Kroger sold his holdings in the company for $28 million in 1928 the year before the stock market crash and retired.

The company acquired Piggly Wiggly stores in the late 1920s and bought most of Piggly Wiggly's corporate stock which it held until the early 1940s. The chain reached its largest number of stores — a whopping 5575 — in 1929. (The Depression later trimmed that total.) A year later Kroger manager Michael Cullen suggested opening self-service low-price supermarkets but company executives demurred. Cullen left Kroger and began King Kullen the first supermarket. If he was ahead of his time at Kroger it wasn't by much; within five years the company had 50 supermarkets.

During the 1950s Kroger acquired companies with stores in Texas Georgia and Washington DC. It added New Jersey-based Sav-on drugstores in 1960 and it opened its first SupeRx drugstore in 1961. The company began opening larger supermarkets in 1971; between 1970 and 1980 Kroger's store count grew just 5% but its selling space nearly doubled.

In 1983 the grocer bought Kansas-based Dillons Food Stores (supermarkets and convenience stores) and Kwik Shop convenience stores. Kroger sold most of its interests in the Hook and SupeRx drug chains (which became Hook-SupeRx) in 1987 and focused on its food-and-drugstores. (It sold its remaining stake to Revco in 1994.) The next year it faced two separate takeover bids from the Herbert Haft family and from Kohlberg Kravis Roberts. The company warded off the raiders by

borrowing $4.1 billion to pay a special dividend to shareholders and to buy shares for an employee stock plan.

To reduce debt Kroger sold most of its equity in Price Saver Membership Wholesale Clubs and its Fry's California stores. In 1990 the company made its first big acquisition since the 1988 restructuring by buying 29 Great Scott! supermarkets. Joseph Pichler became CEO that year.

Kroger sold its Time Saver Stores unit in 1995. In 1999 Kroger acquired Fred Meyer operator of about 800 stores mainly in the West in a $13 billion deal. Late in 1999 it announced it was buying nearly 75 stores (mostly in Texas) from Winn-Dixie Stores; the deal was called off in 2000 shortly after the FTC withheld its approval. But the company kept buying — acquisitions included 20 former Hannaford stores in Virginia in 2000 as well as 16 Nebraska food stores bought from food distributor Fleming and seven New Mexico stores bought from Furrs Supermarkets in 2001.

Kroger acquired 17 supermarkets (16 in the Houston area) from Albertson's (now Albertsons LLC) and another seven stores from Winn-Dixie in the Dallas/Fort Worth area in 2002.

In April 2003 Kroger introduced Naturally Preferred its own brand of some 140 natural and organic items including baby food pastas cereal snacks milk and soy products.

In 2012 with pharmacies in many of its stores nationwide Kroger purchased specialty pharmacy company Axium Pharmacy Holdings based in Florida. The move satisfied Kroger's long-term growth plans and allowed the grocery chain to serve customers that require complex drug therapies.

EXECUTIVES

Chairman And Ceo, W. Rodney McMullen, age 58, $1,251,781 total compensation
Evp And Cfo, J. Michael Schlotman, age 61, $850,360 total compensation
President Harris Teeter Supermarkets, Frederick J. (Fred) Morganthall, age 67, $691,487 total compensation
Sr V Pres, James Thorne
Evp And Cio, Christopher T. (Chris) Hjelm, age 57, $703,367 total compensation
Evp Merchandising, Michael J. (Mike) Donnelly, age 60, $757,036 total compensation
Vp Grocery Products Group, Katie Wolfram, age 64
President Mid-atlantic Division, Jerry L. Clontz
President Houston Division, Marlene Stewart, age 63
Vp Merchandising Fred Meyer Stores, Dan De La Rosa
Vp Manufacturing, Erin S. Sharp, age 61
President Fred Meyer Stores, Joe Grieshaber
President Nashville Division, Zane Day
President Roundy's Supermarkets Wisconsin, Michael Marx
President Mariano's, Don Rosanova
President Smith's, Kenny Kimball
President Dillons Division, Colleen Juergensen
Group Vp And Chief Digital Officer, Yael Cosset, age 45
Senior Vice President, R Williams
Vice President, Jeremy Stover
Pharmacy Manager, Eric Manchester
Vp Digital Business, Matt Thompson
Director Of Surgery, Frank Zagar
Vice President, Bruce Gack
Vice President Finance Controller Quik Stop Division, Jim Bradshaw
Senior Vice President, Mark Tuffin
Vice President Of Marketing, Barbara White
Vice President, Steve Jones
Pharmacy Manager, Peggy Gilligan
Associate Vice President Devel, Rebecca Thompson

Pharmacy Manager, Diane Chance
Vice President Information Systems And Services, Nick Kaufman
Merchandising Vice President, Chris Albi
Senior Vice President New Business Development, Alessandro Tosolini
Vice President Of Brand Management, James Jenson
Vp Branding Marketing And Corporate Brands, Gil Phipps
Pharmacy Manager, Gayle Townsend
Pharmacy Manager, Avi Bhatia
Vp Technical Strategy And Architecture, Ryan Kean
Vice President Sales And Marketing, Norm Carhill
Pharmacy Manager, Cc Hepburn
Department Head, Jeffrey Everling
Pharmacist (manager), Lauren Luken
Pharmd, Carrie Mott
Assistant Treasurer, Kathy Hanna
Auditors: PricewaterhouseCoopers LLP

LOCATIONS

HQ: Kroger Co (The)
1014 Vine Street, Cincinnati, OH 45202
Phone: 513 762-4000   **Fax:** 513 762-1400
Web: www.thekrogerco.com

PRODUCTS/OPERATIONS

2017 Sales

	$ mil.	% of total
Supermarket	96,900	84
Supermarket fuel sales	13,979	12
Other stores & manufacturing	4,458	4
Total	**115,337**	**100**

2017 Stores

	No.
Supermarkets & multidepartment stores	2,796
Convenience stores	784
Jewelry	319
Total	**3,899**

2017 Sales

	$ mil.	% of total
Non-perishable	60,220	52
Perishable	27,666	24
Fuel	13,979	12
Pharmacy	10,432	9
Other	3,040	3
Total	**115,337**	**100**

Selected Kroger Stores

Multidepartment stores
  Fred Meyer
Supermarkets
  Baker's
  City Market Food & Pharmacy
  Dillon Food Stores
  Fry's Food & Drug Stores
  Gerbes Supermarkets
  Harris Teeter Supermarkets
  Jay C Food Stores
  King Soopers
  Kroger
  Kroger Fresh Fare
  Owen's
  Pay Less Super Markets
  Quality Food Centers (QFC)
  Ralphs
  Scott's Food & Pharmacy
  Smith's Food & Drug Centers
Warehouse stores
  Food 4 Less
  FoodsCo
Jewelry stores
  Barclay Jewelers
  Fox's Jewelers
  Fred Meyer Jewelers
  Littman Jewelers
Food Production
Bread and other baked goods
Cheese

Coffee
Crackers
Cultured products (cottage cheese yogurt)
Deli products
Fruit juices and fruit drinks
Ice cream
Juice
Meat
Milk
Nuts
Oatmeal
Peanut butter
Snacks
Soft drinks
Spaghetti sauce
Water

Selected Private-Label Brands

Bath & Body Therapies (body and bath)
Banner brands (Kroger Ralphs King Soopers)
Everyday Living (kitchen gadgets)
FMV (For Maximum Value)
HD Design (upscale kitchen gadgets)
Moto Tech (automotive)
Naturally Preferred (premium quality natural and
    organic brand)
Office Works (office and school supplies)
Private Selection (premium quality brand)
Splash Spa (body and bath)
Splash Sport (body and bath)

COMPETITORS

99 Cents Only	Raley's
A&P	Randall's
Albertsons	Rite Aid
CVS	SUPERVALU
Costco Wholesale	Safeway
Dollar General	Save Mart
Family Dollar Stores	Stater Bros.
GNC	Sterling Jewelers
Giant Eagle	Target Corporation
H-E-B	Tesco
Hy-Vee	Vitamin Shoppe
IGA	Wal-Mart
Kmart	Walgreen
Marsh Supermarkets	Wegmans
Meijer	Whole Foods
NBTY	Winn-Dixie
Publix	Zale

HISTORICAL FINANCIALS

Company Type: Public

Income Statement
FYE: February 2

	REVENUE ($ mil.)	NET INCOME ($ mil.)	NET PROFIT MARGIN	EMPLOYEES
02/19	121,162	3,110	2.6%	453,000
02/18*	122,662	1,907	1.6%	449,000
01/17	115,337	1,975	1.7%	443,000
01/16	109,830	2,039	1.9%	431,000
01/15	108,465	1,728	1.6%	400,000
Annual Growth	2.8%	15.8%	—	3.2%

*Fiscal year change

2019 Year-End Financials

Debt ratio: 40.00%	No. of shares (mil.): 798
Return on equity: 42.00%	Dividends
Cash ($ mil.): 429	Yield: 0.0%
Current ratio: 1.00	Payout: 14.0%
Long-term debt ($ mil.): 12,072	Market value ($ mil.): 22,400

	STOCK PRICE ($) FY Close	P/E High/Low		PER SHARE ($) Earnings	Dividends	Book Value
02/19	28.00	9	6	4.00	1.00	10.00
02/18*	29.00	16	9	2.00	0.00	8.00
01/17	33.00	20	14	2.00	0.00	7.00
01/16	39.00	37	16	2.00	0.00	7.00
01/15	69.00	40	20	2.00	0.00	6.00
Annual Growth	(20.2%)			21.6%	11.7%	15.5%

*Fiscal year change

L Brands, Inc

L Brands (formerly Limited Brands) is as much of a shopping-mall mainstay as food courts and teenagers. The company operates over 2900 specialty stores in North America the UK and China primarily under the Victoria's Secret PINK and Bath & Body Works (BBW) banners as well as corresponding websites and catalogs. Originally focused on apparel the company turned into a segment leader focused on women?s intimate and other apparel personal care and beauty and home fragrance products. L Brands also owns apothecary C.O. Bigelow and The White Barn Candle Co. Most of the company?s revenue are generated in the US. L Brands completed the sale of its La Senza business and the closing of all its Henri Bendel stores and websites in 2019.

Operations

L Brands has realigned its reportable segments into Victoria's Secret Bath & Body Works (BBW) and Victoria's Secret and Bath and Body Works International. More than 55% of sales come from domestic Victoria's Secret stores and direct channel operations. The Victoria's Secret segment sells women's intimate and other apparel personal care and beauty products under the Victoria's Secret and PINK brand names. About 35% of sales come from the BBW segment. The Bath & Body Works segment sells personal care soaps sanitizers and home fragrance products under the Bath & Body Works White Barn Candle Company C.O. Bigelow and other brand names. The remaining revenue comes from Victoria's Secret and BBW International and other revenues which include the revenues from the company?s sourcing function as well as sales from its previous Henri Bendel and La Senza operations. Victoria's Secret and Bath & Body Works International segments include the Victoria's Secret and Bath & Body Works company-owned and partner-operated stores. Mast Global is the company's production sourcing and logistics arm. It sources and develops intimates apparel accessories and gifts home fragrances and personal care products.

Geographic Reach

In addition to its more than 2700 US stores L Brands has about 250 company-owned retail stores in Canada the UK and China. About 95% of the company?s revenue are generated in the US. In addition to its company-owned stores L Brands' products are available at more than 670 Victorió s Secret Victorió s Secret Beauty and Accessories and Bath & Body Works partner locations in more than 70 countries. Based in Ohio the company also has several distribution and product development facilities located in New York and Ohio as well as Canada Hong Kong mainland China and various other international locations.

Sales and Marketing

L Brands utilizes merchandise presentation in-store marketing music and its sales associates to reinforce the image represented by its brands. It also uses marketing advertising and promotional programs to attract customers through various media including social media websites mobile applications email print and television. The company spent $476 million on advertising and marketing expenses in 2018 up from $383 million and $323 million in 2017 and 2016 respectively.

Financial Performance

L Brands has seen limited revenue growth in recent years as it has struggled amid intense competition. Its annual revenues have risen 15% since 2014. Revenue increased to $13.2 billion in 2018 an approximately 5% increase from the year prior. The increase was driven by a comparable sales in-crease of 3%. Net income was $644 million in 2018 from $983 million in 2017. Selling general and administrative expenses grew 9% in fiscal 2018 to $3.5 billion driven by the change in presentation for income received from the Victoria's Secret private label credit card arrangement incremental wage investments higher selling expenses related to higher sales volumes at Bath & Body Works and new company-owned stores in Greater China. Cash on hand at the end of fiscal 2018 was $1.4 billion. Cash provided by operating activities was $1.3 billion in 2018 while investing activities used $609 million. Financing activities used another $872 million.

Strategy

Continuing to battle underperformance at its top brands L Brands has made significant changes to its business to refocus its resources on core categories and accelerate growth.

As part of its strategic plan the company decided to close its Henri Bendel business and sell its La Senza business as well as reduce its regular dividends to reduce debt levels. L Brands shuttered the upscale Henri Bendel business which it had acquired in 1985 to focus on its larger brands with greater growth potential. It sold its La Senza lingerie business to private-equity firm Regent in 2018. In recent years Victorió s Secret business has struggled due in part to major fashion merchandise misses and difficulty connecting with younger shoppers. The company has also seen competition increase from direct-to-consumer retailers such as ThirdLove which have actively positioned themselves against Victoria's Secret. L Brands is reorganizing its Victoria's Secret division which has included employee layoffs and change-ups at the executive level. Meanwhile its Bath & Body Works business has picked up growth as customers have continued to flock to stores to pick up seasonal scents. The company has also remodeled more than 600 Bath & Body Works stores to separate its lotions and fragrances from its candles collection into what looks like two different stores. Its Victoria's Secret and Bath & Body Works International segment has also performed well overall. The strategy at Victoria's Secret has been to capture the teen and college-age female customer with its youth-oriented PINK brand which is sold in freestanding stores as well as Victoria's Secret shops. While the retailer doesn't break out PINK sales the brand is meeting stiff competition from American Eagle's Aerie brand and Gilly Hicks by Abercrombie & Fitch. Both target the youth market.

HISTORY

After a disagreement with his father in 1963 over the operation of the family store (Leslie's) Leslie Wexner then 26 opened the first Limited store in Columbus Ohio with $5000 borrowed from his aunt. The company was named from Wexner's desire to do one product line well — moderately priced fashionable attire for teenagers and young women.

When The Limited went public in 1969 it had only five stores but the rapid development of large covered malls spurred growth to 100 stores by 1976. Two years later The Limited acquired MAST Industries an international apparel purchasing and importing company. The company opened Express in 1980 to serve the teen market.

The Limited grew with acquisitions including the 1982 purchases of Lane Bryant (large sizes) and Victoria's Secret (lingerie). That year it formed the Brylane fashion catalog division and acquired Roaman's a bricks-and-mortar and catalog merchandiser of plus sizes.

Wexner bought The Lerner Stores (budget women's apparel) and Henri Bendel (high fashion) in 1985 sportswear retailer Abercrombie & Fitch (A&F) in 1988 and London-based perfumer Penhaligon's in 1990 (sold in 1997). The Limited introduced several in-store shops including Cacique (French lingerie) in 1988 and Limited Too (girls' fashions) which were later expanded into stand-alone stores. It also launched Structure (men's sportswear) in 1989 and Bath & Body Works shops in 1990. All of these stores were in malls often strategically clustered together.

The company closed many The Limited and Lerner stores in 1993 and sold 60% of its Brylane catalog unit to Freeman Spogli (Brylane went public in 1997). It opened four Bath & Body Works stores in the UK (its first non-US stores) to compete with British rival The Body Shop.

In 1994 The Limited bought Galyan's Trading Company a chain of sporting goods superstores. The company began spinning off its businesses while keeping controlling stakes; it spun off Intimate Brands (Victoria's Secret and Bath & Body Works) in 1995 and A&F in 1996. (The Limited sold its remaining 84% in A&F in 1998.)

The Limited closed more than 100 of its women's apparel stores in 1997 and Intimate Brands shuttered the Cacique chain; the next year The Limited closed nearly 300 more stores companywide (excluding the Intimate Brands chains) and the majority of its Henri Bendel stores.

In 1998 The Limited launched White Barn Candle Co. (candle and home fragrance stores). The following year the company spun off Limited Too its most successful chain as Too Inc. and reduced its interest in Galyan's to 40%. (Galyan's management and buyout firm Freeman Spogli bought the remaining 60% of the sporting goods chain.) The Limited (as well as Intimate Brands) declared a two-for-one stock split in 2000.

To boost profits in 2001 The Limited folded the Structure brand into the Express unit and spun off its Galyan's and Alliance Data Systems subsidiaries retaining 22% and 20% respectively. The Limited sold its Lane Bryant unit to Charming Shoppes for $335 million that year.

The Limited bought back the remaining shares of Intimate Brands it did not already own in March 2002 and over the course of the year phased it into a business segment. In May 2002 the company changed its name to Limited Brands from The Limited. Later that year Limited Brands sold off its remaining stake in Lerner New York and in late 2003 sold its Structure label (which it had rebranded as Express Men's) to Sears Roebuck and Co.

In 2007 Limited Brands completed its acquisition of lingerie maker and retailer La Senza based in Montreal for about $600 million. It also sold a 75% stake in its 251-store Limited Stores business to Sun Capital Partners taking a loss on the sale. In mid-2010 it sold the rest. Three years later in 2013 it finally changed the company name from The Limited to L Brands. In 2018 the company agreed to sell its La Senza business and shuttered its Henri Bendel business as it refocused on its biggest brands.

EXECUTIVES

Evp And Cfo, Stuart B. Burgdoerfer, age 55, $890,923 total compensation
Chairman And Ceo, Leslie H. Wexner, age 81, $2,000,000 total compensation
Evp And Cio, Steven M. Stone, age 58
Coo, Charles C. (Charlie) McGuigan, age 62, $1,290,385 total compensation
President And Ceo Bath & Body Works, Nicholas P.M. (Nick) Coe, age 56, $1,080,769 total compensation

Senior Vice President And Chief Techno, Kurt Schnieders
Vice President Human Resources, Cheryl Stevens
Associate Vice President Patents, Bianca Peachey
Vice President Project Management, Beth Knuckles
Senior Vice President, Claudia Lucas
Assistant Vice President Compensation, Gina Johnson
Senior Vice President, Paul Jones
Vice President Consumer Services, Mike Underhill
Senior Vice President Human Resources Limited Brands Victorias Secret Direct, Sheena Null Foley
Vice President Application Services, Nada Aried
Vice President Retail Selling Technologies, Anne Ritchey
Vice President Human Resources, Mike Kiida
Avp Legal, Robert Stalter
Vice President Logistics, Bryan R Eccard
Executive Vice President Production Victoria Secret's Intimates Division, Margaret M Wright
Vice President Integration Global Sourcing And Logistics, Laura Warren
Avp Ecommerce, Ryan Davis
Vice President Brand Human Resources, Andre Joyner
Evp And Chief Human Resources Officer, Shelley Milano
Vice President, Polly Sinesi
Vice President Production And Operations, Marlene Manser
Vice President Production And Sourcing, Chris Kennedy
Svp Finance, Jennie Wilson
Assistant Vice President Product Quality And Manufacturing Engineering, Steve Smith
Ass Vice President Consumer Insights, Cliona Miller
Vice President Human Resources Shared Services, Joyce Stearn
Senior Vice President Marketing, Edward Wolf
Vice President Marketing, Shannon Glass
Assistant Vice President Beauty Finance, Shannon Damen
Vice President, Thomas Mc Fadden
Avp Financial Reporting, Kevin Wynk
Board Member, David Kollat
Board Member, Donna James
Board Member, Abigail S Wexner
Auditors: Ernst & Young LLP

LOCATIONS

HQ: L Brands, Inc
   Three Limited Parkway, Columbus, OH 43230
Phone: 614 415-7000
Web: www.lb.com

PRODUCTS/OPERATIONS

2017 Stores

	No.
Bath & Body Works U.S.	1,591
Victoria's Secret U.S.	1,131
La Senza Canada	122
Bath & Body Works Canada	102
Victoria's Secret Canada	46
Victoria's Secret Beauty and Accessories	31
Henri Bendel	29
Victoria's Secret U.K.	18
La Senza U.S.	4
Total	**3,074**

2017 Sales

	$ mil.	% of total
Victoria's Secret	7,781	62
Bath & Body Works	3,852	31
Victoria's Secret and Bath & Body Works International	423	3
Other	518	4
Total	**12,574**	**100**

Selected Retail Brands

Bath & Body Works
C.O. Bigelow
Henri Bendel
La Senza
Pink
The White Barn Candle Company
Victoria's Secret

COMPETITORS

Abercrombie & Fitch	Macy's
American Eagle Outfitters	Mary Kay
	Natori
Avon	Nordstrom
Body Shop	Revlon
CVS	Saks
Dillard's	Sephora USA
Estée Lauder	Shiseido Americas
Frederick's of Hollywood	Target Corporation
	The Gap
Fruit of the Loom	Ulta
Hanesbrands	VF Corporation
Jockey International	Wal-Mart
Kiehl's	Warnaco Group

HISTORICAL FINANCIALS

Company Type: Public

Income Statement

FYE: February 2

	REVENUE ($ mil.)	NET INCOME ($ mil.)	NET PROFIT MARGIN	EMPLOYEES
02/19	13,237	644	4.9%	88,900
02/18*	12,632	983	7.8%	93,200
01/17	12,574	1,158	9.2%	93,600
01/16	12,154	1,253	10.3%	87,900
01/15	11,454	1,042	9.1%	80,100
Annual Growth	**3.7%**	**(11.3%)**	**—**	**2.6%**

*Fiscal year change

2019 Year-End Financials

Debt ratio: 72.00%
Return on equity: ***.***.**%
Cash ($ mil.): 1,413
Current ratio: 2.00
Long-term debt ($ mil.): 5,739

No. of shares (mil.): 275
Dividends
 Yield: 0.0%
 Payout: 104.0%
Market value ($ mil.): 7,466

	STOCK PRICE ($) FY Close	P/E High/Low		PER SHARE ($) Earnings	Dividends	Book Value
02/19	27.00	21	11	2.00	2.00	(3.00)
02/18*	48.00	18	10	3.00	2.00	(3.00)
01/17	59.00	24	15	4.00	4.00	(3.00)
01/16	96.00	23	18	4.00	4.00	(1.00)
01/15	85.00	24	14	4.00	2.00	0.00
Annual Growth	**(24.7%)**	**—**	**—**	**(9.9%)**	**0.4%**	**—**

*Fiscal year change

L3Harris Technologies Inc

L3Harris Technologies (formerly Harris Corp. and L3 Technologies) develops communications electronics space and aviation equipment for government and commercial customers in more than 100 countries. It makes radio and satellite communications and other wireless network transmission equipment; air traffic control systems; and intelligence surveillance and reconnaissance systems. Although about three-quarters of L3Harris' revenue comes from US government agencies particularly the Department of Defense it also has customers in the commercial sector. In 2019 the former Harris Corp. and L3 Technologies combined to form L3Harris Technologies the sixth largest defense contractor in the US.

Change in Company Type

Harris Corp. in 2019 merged with L3 Technologies to form L3Harris Technologies a company with $17 billion in revenue. The combined company has complementary products and services and deeper resources that enable it to bid on large-scale Department of Defense projects. The all-stock deal resulted in Harris shareholders owning 54% of the company and L3 shareholders owning the rest. The company falls in line behind Lockheed Martin Boeing General Dynamics and Northrop Grumman as one of the biggest defense contractors in the US and in the top 10 internationally.

Operations

Harris before the merger operated in three business segments.

The Electronic Systems segment nearly 40% of revenue provides electronic warfare avionics; command control communications computers and intelligence surveillance and reconnaissance equipment for the defense industry. It also makes communication systems for civil and military aviation.

Its Communication Systems segment more than 30% of revenue develops and makes tactical communications and defense products including tactical ground and airborne radio communications equipment and night vision technology and equipment for public safety networks.

The Space and Intelligence Systems segment about 30% of revenue provides intelligence space protection geospatial complete Earth observation universe exploration positioning navigation and timing and environmental equipment for national security defense civil and commercial customers. Among its products are advanced sensors antennas and payloads as well as ground processing and information analytics.

Geographic Reach

L3Harris operates some 170 locations in Canada Europe the Middle East Central and South America Africa Asia and the US. Customers in the US account for some 95% of revenue.

Sales and Marketing

L3Harris relies on US government agencies for most of its revenue. US government-related revenue including prime contractors and supported foreign defense organizations accounts for more than 75% of sales.

Financial Performance

Financials are for Harris Corp. before the merger with L3 Technologies which became effective June 29 2019.

Revenue rose 10% to $6.8 billion in 2019 (ended June) from 2018 on higher Department of Defense tactical radio sales in the Communication Systems segment reflecting a ramp up in DoD modernization programs. It also reported higher Avionics and Electronic Warfare revenue from long-term avionics platforms including the F-35 F/A-18 and F-16 in the Electronic Systems Segment. The company saw increased sales from classified programs in the Space and Intelligence Systems segment.

Net income rose about $250 million to $949 million in 2019 from 2018 boosted by higher sales and lower income taxes due to lower tax rates that were part of the US Tax Cuts and Jobs Act of 2017.

The company's coffers held $530 million in cash in 2019 compared to $288 million the year before. In 2019 operations generated $1.2 billion while investing activities used $159 million and financing activities used $781 million.

Harris had $3.4 billion in debt and about $1.2 billion of unfunded defined benefit plans liability at the end of 2019. It also took on $3.4 billion in debt in connection with the L3Harris merger. Paying off its obligations could reduce the money that could be used for operating activities and capital expenditures.

Strategy

Bigger and more comprehensive is better and more lucrative is the thinking behind the merger that produced L3Harris Technologies. The combined company has a wider and deeper set of products and services to offer to a wider array of government and military customers. L3Harris' goal is to nab contracts for work that neither could get on its own.

The size of the company grew with the merger to some $17 billion in revenue and 50000 employees around the world.

The company has divested services businesses to narrow its focus on technology and it has reorganized to take advantage of similar functions among its businesses. The new segments are Integrated Mission Systems Space and Airborne Systems Communication Systems and Aviation Systems.

L3Harris plans to reduce costs by about $500 million eliminating duplication combining processes and other methods.

While its plans to partner with other defense contractors to get parts of contracts its scope should enable the company to move into a prime contracting role in some of its areas of expertise such as communications networking and electronics.

EXECUTIVES

Chairman President And Ceo, William M. (Bill) Brown, age 56, $1,172,913 total compensation
Svp And Chief Global Business Development Officer, Dana A. Mehnert, age 57, $527,770 total compensation
Svp Integration And Engineering, Sheldon J. Fox, age 61, $521,346 total compensation
Vp Environmental-energy Solutions Business Government Communications Systems Division, Carl D'Alessandro, age 55
Svp Human Resources And Administration, Robert L. Duffy, age 51, $459,885 total compensation
Cio, Henry Debnam
President Electronic Systems, Edward J. (Ed) Zoiss, age 53
President Space And Intelligence Systems, William H. (Bill) Gattle, age 57
President Communication Systems, Christopher D. (Chris) Young, age 58, $411,749 total compensation
Svp And Cfo, Rahul Ghai, age 47, $376,238 total compensation
Vice President Mission Critical Networks Business Government Communications Systems Division, John O'Sullivan
Senior Vice President Of Business Development, Alex Heidt
Vice President Corporate Technology, Kent Buchanon
Vice President Controller, Daniel Heneghan
Vice President Operations, Paul North
Vice President Sales, John Koening
Broker And Vice President, George Hurst
Vice President Products And Systems, Shawn Baerlocher
Vice President Large Account Sales, Kevin Lombardo
Senior Vice President, Neal Serven
Vice President Information Technology, Michele St Mary
Vice President, Brett Kleefisch
Vice President, Daniel Flugstad
Vice President General Counsel, Eugene Cavallucci

Vice President Information Technology, Mark Gawron
Vice President, Paul Eisner
Vice President Human Resources, Ken Laprade
Vice President Lean Six Sigma, Phil Burroughs
Vice President Finance Public Safety And Professional Communications, William Cullen
Vice President, Erick Sanz
Vice President And Managing Director International Business Development, Leon Shivamber
Vp And Managing Director Middle East Operations, Chris Tucker
Vice President Business Development, Jeff Smith
Board Member, Thomas Dattilo
Engineering Team Manager Treasurer, David Bruder
Treasurer, Steve Thompson
Treasurer, Harmon David
Auditors: Ernst & Young LLP

LOCATIONS

HQ: L3Harris Technologies Inc
  1025 West NASA Boulevard, Melbourne, FL 32919
Phone: 321 727-9100
Web: www.l3harris.com

2019 sales

	$ mil.	% of total
US	6,530	96
Other countries	271	4
Total	**6,817**	**100**

PRODUCTS/OPERATIONS

2019 sales

	$ mil.	% of total
Communication Systems	2,177	32
Space and Intelligence Systems	2,057	30
Electronic Systems	2,583	38
Adjustments	(16)	38
Total	**6,801**	**100**

Selected Product Groups

Government Communications Systems
  Civil programs
  Aviation
  Weather
  IT services
  Mission command-and-control
  National intelligence programs
Radio-frequency (RF) Communications
  Antennas and accessories
  Information assurance
  Internet protocol voice and data networks
  Public safety
  Tactical radio communications

COMPETITORS

BAE Systems Inc.	Motorola Solutions
Boeing	Northrop Grumman
General Dynamics	Raytheon
IBM	United Technologies
Lockheed Martin	

HISTORICAL FINANCIALS

Company Type: Public

Income Statement — FYE: June 28

	REVENUE ($ mil.)	NET INCOME ($ mil.)	NET PROFIT MARGIN	EMPLOYEES
06/19	6,801	949	14.0%	18,200
06/18	6,182	718	11.6%	17,500
06/17*	5,900	553	9.4%	17,000
07/16	7,467	324	4.3%	21,000
07/15	5,083	334	6.6%	22,300
Annual Growth	7.6%	29.8%	—	(5.0%)

*Fiscal year change

Debt ratio: 35.00%
Return on equity: 28.00%
Cash ($ mil.): 530
Current ratio: 1.00
Long-term debt ($ mil.): 2,763

No. of shares (mil.): 119
Dividends
Yield: 1.0%
Payout: 37.0%
Market value ($ mil.): 22,422

	STOCK PRICE ($) FY Close	P/E High/Low	PER SHARE ($) Earnings	Dividends	Book Value
06/19	189.00	25 16	8.00	3.00	28.00
06/18	145.00	28 18	6.00	2.00	28.00
06/17*	109.00	25 18	4.00	2.00	24.00
07/16	83.00	34 27	3.00	2.00	25.00
07/15	78.00	26 20	3.00	2.00	27.00
Annual Growth	24.9%	— —	26.1%	9.9%	0.8%

*Fiscal year change

Laboratory Corporation of America Holdings

This company pricks and prods for profit. Laboratory Corporation of America (LabCorp) is a top provider of clinical laboratory services performing blood and other tests on more than 500000 specimens daily for some 220000 clients including managed care organizations contract research organizations (CROs) hospitals doctors government agencies drug companies independent clinical labs food and nutritional companies and employers. Services range from routine urinalyses HIV tests and Pap smears to specialty testing for diagnostic genetics disease monitoring forensics identity clinical drug trials and allergies. Through Covance it provides end-to-end drug development support. LabCorp operates more than 1750 service sites that collect specimens and 40 primary labs where tests are performed.

Operations

LabCorp operates through two primary segments: LabCorp Diagnostics (LCD) and Covance Drug Development (CCD).

The LCD segment which accounts for some 70% of LabCorp's annual revenues offers more than 4800 different tests. Many of the tests it performs each year are routine tests (including blood chemistry analyses blood cell counts and HIV tests) and nutritional chemistry and safety tests. It also offers specialty testing services for women's health allergies infectious disease oncology pain management and other areas. LCD's genomic and esoteric testing operations include subsidiaries Esoterix Monogram Biosciences and Integrated Genetics while specialty testing units include Cellmark Forensics Dianon Pathology and MedTox Laboratories.

CDD (30% of revenue) provides early drug development associated laboratory testing efficacy studies and clinical trial services to biopharmaceutical clients.

Geographic Reach

Most of LabCorp's operations are conducted through its extensive network of facilities throughout the US (which accounts for more than 80% of total revenue). The company also has joint ventures in Canada where it provides diagnostic testing services in several provinces and it has established presences in China Japan Singapore the United Arab Emirates and the UK.

CDD operates a network of laboratories in the US Switzerland Belgium Singapore and China. Covance has pre-clinical laboratories in Wisconsin Virginia Michigan and Indiana. It also operates labs in the UK (3) Germany China and Singapore.

Altogether LabCorp operates in approximately 60 countries.

Sales and Marketing

LabCorp uses a direct sales force to promote its products and services to customers including doctors hospitals clinical labs drugmakers managed care companies and government agencies. As payments from managed care entities (HMOs and PPOs) make up a significant part of LabCorp's net patient revenue gaining and maintaining contracts with these clients is a main thrust of the company's strategy. For instance LabCorp has a multi-year contract with UnitedHealth that makes LabCorp the insurer's exclusive national laboratory services provider.

LabCorp's LCD segment receives about 15% of its net revenue from Medicare and Medicaid programs.

Financial Performance

All of LabCorp's efforts towards expanding its offerings and geographic presence have helped keep the company's finances healthy for several consecutive years with its revenue growing each year since 2008. In 2016 the group reported an 11% increase in sales to some $9.6 billion. Both the LCD and CDD segments saw growth that year: LCD rose 6% due to organic volume growth and CDD rose 23% thanks to the addition of revenues from the recently acquired Covance.

After years of falling net income rose 68% to $732.1 million in 2016. A decline in restructuring and other special charges as well as a relatively low increase in selling general and administrative expenses helped boost the company's bottom line.

With the higher net income cash flow from operations increased 20% to $1.2 billion that year.

Strategy

Over the past seven years LabCorp has invested some $6.3 billion in strategic acquisitions. The company is focused on expanding its advanced testing capabilities especially in the areas of genetic and cancer testing. One particular area of interest for the company's product development efforts is the field of personalized medicine. It has introduced a number of "companion" diagnostic tests that determine whether a patient will react well or poorly to certain drugs. LabCorp is developing such tests internally as well as through partnerships with life science entities such as Duke University and Johns Hopkins University. Additional areas of focus are molecular diagnostics and the introduction of new assay platforms (both developed and acquired).

LabCorp strives to capitalize on its nationwide presence to strengthen managed care partnerships. In addition LabCorp looks to keep its physician customers happy with education tools and integrated information management systems including eLabCorp a web-based tool that allows doctors to access testing services online and its electronic health record (EHR) solution.

The company is also expanding consumer-focused tools such as its LabCorp Beacon patient portal. In 2017 it partnered with Walgreens to develop and operate patient service centers within Walgreens stores. These centers will offer lab testing to provide patients with a broader range of health care services.

Meanwhile LabCorp's specialty subsidiaries such as kidney stone analysis firm Litholink work to control costs for payers by focusing on providing patient-specific tools to manage chronic conditions.

Mergers and Acquisitions

In 2015 LabCorp bought New Jersey-based Covance one of the world's largest contract research organizations and a leader in nutritional analysis for approximately $5.7 billion. The deal provided LabCorp with new revenue sources and a broader international presence which has long been a goal for the company. The company also completed the $85 million acquisition of diagnostic testing firm LipoScience; that move strengthened LabCorp's position in the cardiovascular and metabolic disorder testing market. LabCorp addtionally purchased Bode Technology Group which provides specialized forensic DNA collection analysis and relationship testing.

In 2016 LabCorp acquired Sequenom a specialist in tests for the prenatal and women's health markets. The deal was valued at $371 million. It also purchased women's health laboratory Pathology further building on its women's health offerings.

In mid-2017 the company bought UK-based CRO Chiltern International for $1.2 billion. With that deal it expanded its oncology operations as well as growing its international business.

The following year LabCorp acquired scientific process services firm Sciformix for an undisclosed amount. Sciformix became part of Covance strengthening that unit's pharmacovigilance capabilities. The newly acquired firm's operations are primarily located in Asia.

EXECUTIVES

Evp Cfo And Treasurer, Glenn A. Eisenberg, age 57, $653,438 total compensation
Ceo Covance Drug Development, John D. Ratliff, age 59
Svp Chief Legal Officer Secretary And Chief Compliance Officer, F. Samuel Eberts, age 59, $486,875 total compensation
Chairman President And Ceo, David P. (Dave) King, age 61, $1,133,333 total compensation
Svp And Cio, Lance V. Berberian, age 56, $396,112 total compensation
Vice President Information Technology Business Relations, George Meister
Vp Of It, Devin Lorsson
Senior Vice President Chief Medical Officer, Mark Brecher
Vice President Information Technology Enterprise Solutions, Mahesh Nair
Senior Vice President Of Facilities, Mark Schroeder
Vice President Information Technology, Mark Ysteboe
Vice President, Traci Butler
Associate Vp And Technical Director Dna Identification Testing Division, Uwe Heine
Medical Director Mid America Division, Kyle Eskue
Vice President Information Systems Laboratory Systems, Bobbi Croy
Vice President Strategic Planning And Corporate Development, Anil Asnani
Medical Director Northeast Division, Araceli Reyes
Vice President And Director Medical Drug Monitoring; Discipline Director Forensic Toxicology, Glynn Chaney
Assistant Vice President And Information Technology Director Atlantic Division, Ronald K Tirpak
Senior Vice President, Chris Bosler
Vice President Translational Research, Margery Connelly
Executive Vice President, Ben Miller
Evp Esoteric Business, William Haas
Assistant Vice President Information Technology (viromed Laboratories), Vickie Grawey
Vice President, Carl Epple
Assistant Vice President Pre Analytical, Edwin Johnson
Associate Vice President, Joe Palughi
Senior Vice President, Tom Kaminski
Vice President Corporate Development, Sridhar Koneru
Auditors: PricewaterhouseCoopers LLP

LOCATIONS

HQ: Laboratory Corporation of America Holdings
358 South Main Street, Burlington, NC 27215
Phone: 336 229-1127
Web: www.labcorp.com

2016 Sales

	% of total
US	81
Switzerland	5
Canada	3
United Kingdom	3
Other	8
Total	**100**

PRODUCTS/OPERATIONS

2016 Sales

	$ mil.	% of total
LCD	6,594	68
CDD	2,844	30
Reimbursable out-of-pocket expenses	205	2
Intercompany eliminations	-0.8 -	
Total	**9,642**	**100**

Selected Subsidiaries

DIANON Systems Inc. (pathology Connecticut)
Dynacare Laboratories Inc. (clinical labs; Tennessee Washington Wisconsin Canada)
Esoterix Inc. (esoteric testing Colorado)
Integrated Genetics (formerly Genzyme Genetics fertility testing labs across the US)
Integrated Oncology (formerly US Labs esoteric oncology tests US)
Litholink Corporation (kidney patient testing Illinois)
Monogram Biosciences Inc. (HIV resistance testing and personalized medicine California)
National Genetics Institute (NGI infection testing and blood screening California)
Viro-Med Laboratories Inc. (molecular microbial testing Minnesota)

Selected Acquisitions

COMPETITORS

Arup Laboratories	NeoGenomics
Bio-Reference Labs	Oncolab
Celera	Orchid Cellmark
CompuNet Clinical Laboratories	Pathology Associates Medical Laboratories
HedgePath	Pharmaceutical Product Development
IDENTIGENE	Psychemedics
Kroll Background America	Quest Diagnostics
Laboratory Sciences of Arizona	Solstas
MEDTOX Laboratories	Sonic Healthcare
Medtox Scientific	eScreen
Mid America Clinical Laboratories	

HISTORICAL FINANCIALS

Company Type: Public

Income Statement
FYE: December 31

	REVENUE ($ mil.)	NET INCOME ($ mil.)	NET PROFIT MARGIN	EMPLOYEES
12/18	11,333	884	7.8%	61,000
12/17	10,441	1,268	12.1%	60,000
12/16	9,642	732	7.6%	52,000
12/15	8,680	437	5.0%	50,000
12/14	6,012	511	8.5%	36,000
Annual Growth	**17.2%**	**14.7%**	**—**	**14.1%**

2018 Year-End Financials

Debt ratio: 37.00%
Return on equity: 13.00%
Cash ($ mil.): 427
Current ratio: 2.00
Long-term debt ($ mil.): 6,042

No. of shares (mil.): 99
Dividends
Yield: —
Payout: —
Market value ($ mil.): 12,497

STOCK PRICE / P/E / PER SHARE

	STOCK PRICE ($) FY Close	P/E High/Low	Earnings	Dividends	Book Value
12/18	126.00	22 14	9.00	0.00	70.00
12/17	160.00	13 10	12.00	0.00	67.00
12/16	128.00	20 14	7.00	0.00	54.00
12/15	124.00	29 24	4.00	0.00	49.00
12/14	108.00	18 15	6.00	0.00	33.00
Annual Growth	**4.0%**	**— —**	**9.9%**	**—**	**20.6%**

Ladder Capital Corp

This specialty finance firm is looking to climb to the top of the commercial real-estate lending business. Ladder Capital Corp. is a non-bank operating company engaged in three major lines of business: commercial mortgage lending mortgage backed securities and real-estate assets. Its loans typically range from $5 million to $100 million. More than 50% of its loans originate in the Northeast. Hotel retail and office properties account for about three-quarters of Ladder's loan portfolio. Since its founding in 2008 the commercial real estate finance firm has originated $5.4 billion in conduit loans. Ladder Capital went public in 2014 with an offering valued at $225 million.

IPO

The company's February 2014 IPO raised $225 million by offering 13.3 million shares at $17 the midpoint of the $16 to $18 range. Ladder Capital intends to use the IPO proceeds to grow its loan origination and related commercial real estate business lines and for general corporate purposes.

Geographic Reach

Ladder Capital is headquartered in New York City and has branches in Los Angeles and Boca Raton Florida.

EXECUTIVES

Cfo, Marc A. Fox, age 59
Ceo, Brian R. Harris, age 58, $1,000,000 total compensation
Head Asset Management, Robert M. Perelman, age 56
Head Merchant Banking And Capital Markets, Thomas Harney, age 57, $400,000 total compensation
President, Pamela McCormack, age 48, $600,000 total compensation
Chairman, Alan H. Fishman, age 73
Board Member, Michael Mazzei
Auditors: PricewaterhouseCoopers LLP

LOCATIONS

HQ: Ladder Capital Corp
345 Park Avenue, New York, NY 10154
Phone: 212 715-3170
Web: www.laddercapital.com

2013 Loans by Region

	% of total
Northeast	56
South	20
Southwest	10
Midwest	5
West	1
Other	8
Total	**100**

PRODUCTS/OPERATIONS

2013 Loans by Type

	% of total
Hotel	34
Retail	22
Office	20
Multifamily	15
Condo	7
Mixed use	2
Total	**100**

COMPETITORS

CIT Group	Citigroup

HISTORICAL FINANCIALS

Company Type: Public

Income Statement
FYE: December 31

	ASSETS ($ mil.)	NET INCOME ($ mil.)	INCOME AS % OF ASSETS	EMPLOYEES
12/18	6,273	180	2.9%	74
12/17	6,026	95	1.6%	72
12/16	5,578	67	1.2%	69
12/15	5,895	74	1.3%	73
12/14	5,824	44	0.8%	66
Annual Growth	**1.9%**	**42.1%**	**—**	**2.9%**

2018 Year-End Financials

Debt ratio: 40.00%
Return on equity: 13.00%
Cash ($ mil.): 68
Current ratio: —
Long-term debt ($ mil.): —

No. of shares (mil.): 117
Dividends
Yield: 8.0%
Payout: 83.0%
Market value ($ mil.): 1,811

	STOCK PRICE ($) FY Close	P/E High/Low	Earnings	Dividends	Book Value
12/18	15.00	10 7	2.00	2.00	12.00
12/17	14.00	13 11	1.00	1.00	11.00
12/16	14.00	14 9	1.00	1.00	9.00
12/15	12.00	14 8	1.00	2.00	8.00
12/14	20.00	23 18	1.00	0.00	8.00
Annual Growth	**(5.8%)**	**— —**	**20.9%**	**—**	**11.7%**

Lakeland Bancorp, Inc.

Lakeland Bancorp is the holding company for Lakeland Bank which serves northern and central New Jersey from around 50 branch offices. Targeting individuals and small to midsized businesses the bank offers standard retail products such as checking and savings accounts money market and NOW accounts and CDs. It also offers financial planning and advisory services for consumers. The bank's lending activities primarily consist of commercial loans and mortgages (around three-quarters of the company's loan portfolio) and residential mortgages. Lakeland also offers commercial lease financing for commercial equipment.

Operations

Lakeland Bancorp operates through a single business segment. Around 70% of its $4.3 billion loan portfolio is made up of commercial mortgages. Industrial commercial loans residential mortgages real estate construction loans and home equity and consumer loans each represent between 5%-10% of the company's lending activity. The company holds $5.5 billion in assets and $4.4 billion in deposits.

Geographic Reach

Headquartered in Oak Ridge New Jersey Lakeland Bancorp boasts about 50 banking offices across the New Jersey counties of Bergen Essex Morris Ocean Passaic Somerset Sussex Union and Warren. The company also has a branch in Highland Mills New York; six New Jersey regional commercial lending centers in Bernardsville Jackson Montville Newton Teaneck and Waldwick; and two commercial loan production offices serving Middlesex and Monmouth counties in New Jersey and the Hudson Valley region of New York.

Sales and Marketing

Lakeland Bancorp serves a variety of customers from individuals to businesses to municipalities.

One-fifth of Lakeland's commercial loan segment - the largest in its portfolio - is made up of owner-occupied real estate loans. Multifamily and retail loans make up about 15% each and industrial and office loans each comprise around 10%.

Financial Performance

Lakeland Bancorp has seen major five-year growth expanding revenue by 53% to $190.7 million net income by 111% to $52.6 million and cash by 39% to $142.9 million between 2013 and 2017. However the company's debt has risen 85% to $296.9 million in that time.

The holding company's revenue increased 14% in 2017 owing primarily to increased net interest income from growing average earning assets. Net income added 27% on the strength of those gains.

Lakeland's cash dipped $32.9 million in 2017. Operations and financings contributed $67.5 million and investments used $355.1 million. Financings provided $254.8 million down nearly $200 million from the previous year following an increase in net deposits federal funds purchased and securities sold under repurchase agreements.

Strategy

Lakeland Bancorp is focused on growth through acquisitions. The company has acquired at least eight community banks since its inception including Highlands Bancorp. which operates in northern New Jersey. The company also offers internet banking mobile banking and cash management services.

Mergers and Acquisitions

In January 2019 Lakeland Bancorp acquired Vernon New Jersey-based Highlands Bancorp in a deal valued at $56.7 million. The holding company - which operated branches in the New Jersey municipalities of Sparta Totowa and Denville - had consolidated total assets of $5.53 billion.

Company Background

Lakeland Bancorp was founded in 1969. It organized into a bank holding company in 1989.

EXECUTIVES

President And Ceo Lakeland Bancorp And Lakeland Bank, Thomas J. Shara, age 61, $650,000 total compensation
Sevp And Coo, Ronald E. (Ron) Schwarz, age 62, $266,769 total compensation
Sevp And Regional President, Robert A. Vandenbergh, age 67, $360,212 total compensation
Evp And Senior Government Banking And Financial Services Officer, Jeffrey J. Buonforte, age 67, $205,075 total compensation
Evp And Chief Credit Officer, James R. Noonan, age 67
Evp And Chief Risk Officer, James M. Nigro
Cfo, Thomas F. Splaine, age 54
First Svp And Chief Technology And Information Security Officer, Mary Kaye Nardone
Evp And Chief Retail Officer, Ellen Lalwani
Evp And Chief Lending Officer, David S. Yanagisawa, $220,000 total compensation

Evp Chief Administrative Officer General Counsel And Corporate Secretary, Timothy J. Matteson, age 49
Evp And Regional President, Michael A. Schutzer
Vice President Asset Based Lending, Steven Breeman
Vice President Commercial Lending, Bruce Bready
Vice President, Scott Heiman
Vice President Area Manager, Hafeza Mohammed
Executive Vice President And Chief Lending Officer Of The Company And The Bank, John Rath
Chairman Lakeland Bancorp And Lakeland Bank, Mary Ann Deacon, age 67
Board Member, Brian M Flynn
Board Member, Lawrence Inserra
Auditors: KPMG LLP

LOCATIONS

HQ: Lakeland Bancorp, Inc.
250 Oak Ridge Road, Oak Ridge, NJ 07438
Phone: 973 697-2000
Web: www.lakelandbank.com

PRODUCTS/OPERATIONS

2017 Sales

	$ mil.	% of total
Interest		
Loans & fees	172	80
Investment securities and other	18	8
Interest expense	(25.0)	-
Non-interest		
Service charges on deposit accounts	11	5
Commissions & fees	5	2
Income on bank owned life insurance	2	1
Other	8	4
Total	**191**	**100**

Selected Services

401K and IRA Rollovers
Certificates of deposit & individual retirement accounts
Checking accounts
Consumer loans
Home loans
Insurance
Investment management
Online services
Retirement income planning
Savings and money market accounts

COMPETITORS

Bank of America	PNC Financial
Bank of New York Mellon	Sovereign Bank
Capital One	Sussex Bancorp
Clifton Bancorp	TD Bank USA
Hudson City Bancorp	Valley National Bancorp
Investors Bancorp	Wells Fargo
JPMorgan Chase	
New York Community Bancorp	

HISTORICAL FINANCIALS

Company Type: Public

Income Statement

FYE: December 31

	ASSETS ($ mil.)	NET INCOME ($ mil.)	INCOME AS % OF ASSETS	EMPLOYEES
12/18	5,806	63	1.1%	652
12/17	5,406	53	1.0%	621
12/16	5,093	42	0.8%	592
12/15	3,870	32	0.8%	551
12/14	3,538	31	0.9%	566
Annual Growth	13.2%	19.5%	—	3.6%

2018 Year-End Financials

Debt ratio: 5.00%		No. of shares (mil.): 47	
Return on equity: 11.00%		Dividends	
Cash ($ mil.): 209		Yield: 3.0%	
Current ratio: —		Payout: 35.0%	
Long-term debt ($ mil.): —		Market value ($ mil.): 703	

	STOCK PRICE ($) FY Close	P/E High/Low	Earnings	PER SHARE ($) Dividends	Book Value
12/18	15.00	16 11	1.00	0.00	13.00
12/17	19.00	20 16	1.00	0.00	12.00
12/16	20.00	21 10	1.00	0.00	12.00
12/15	12.00	15 12	1.00	0.00	11.00
12/14	12.00	15 12	1.00	0.00	10.00
Annual Growth	6.1%	— —	12.6%	11.0%	7.0%

Lakeland Financial Corp

Lakeland Financial is the holding company for Lake City Bank which serves area business customers and individuals through around 50 branches scattered across about 15 northern and central Indiana counties. With $4.8 billion in assets the community bank offers such standard retail services as checking and savings accounts money market accounts and CDs. Commercial loans including agricultural loans and mortgages make up about 90% of the bank's loan portfolio. Lake City Bank also offers investment products and services such as corporate and personal trust brokerage and estate planning.

EXECUTIVES

Evp And Retail Banking Manager, Kevin L. Deardorff, age 58, $217,963 total compensation
President And Ceo Lakeland Financial And Lake City Bank, David M. Findlay, age 57, $493,360 total compensation
Svp Commercial Lake City Bank, Michael E. Gavin
Evp And Cfo, Lisa M. O'Neill, age 51, $206,286 total compensation
Svp And General Counsel, Kristin L. Pruitt, age 47
Svp Wealth Advisory, Eric H. Ottinger, $218,263 total compensation
Vice President And Trust Officer, Patricia Culp
Vice President, Mark Rensner
Vice President Commercial Banking Officer, Mike Ryan
Chairman Lakeland Financial And Lake City Bank, Michael L. Kubacki, age 67
Auditors: Crowe LLP

LOCATIONS

HQ: Lakeland Financial Corp
202 East Center Street, P.O. Box 1387, Warsaw, IN 46580
Phone: 574 267-6144
Web: www.lakecitybank.com

PRODUCTS/OPERATIONS

2017 Sales

	$ mil.	% of total
Interest		
Loans	151	75
Securities	14	7
Other	0	-
Interest expense	(29.8)	-
Noninteresst		
Service charges on deposit accounts	14	7
Loan and service fees	8	4
Wealth advisory fees	6	3
Investment brokerage fees	1	-
Other	8	4
Total	**172**	**100**

COMPETITORS

1st Source Corporation	PNC Financial
KeyCorp	Peoples Bancorp (IN)
Northeast Indiana Bancorp	

HISTORICAL FINANCIALS

Company Type: Public

Income Statement

FYE: December 31

	ASSETS ($ mil.)	NET INCOME ($ mil.)	INCOME AS % OF ASSETS	EMPLOYEES
12/18	4,875	80	1.6%	553
12/17	4,683	57	1.2%	539
12/16	4,290	52	1.2%	524
12/15	3,766	46	1.2%	518
12/14	3,443	44	1.3%	496
Annual Growth	9.1%	16.4%		2.8%

2018 Year-End Financials

Debt ratio: 1.00%
Return on equity: 16.00%
Cash ($ mil.): 217
Current ratio: —
Long-term debt ($ mil.): —

No. of shares (mil.): 25
Dividends
Yield: 2.0%
Payout: 36.0%
Market value ($ mil.): 1,009

	STOCK PRICE ($) FY Close	P/E High/Low	Earnings	PER SHARE ($) Dividends	Book Value
12/18	40.00	16 12	3.00	1.00	21.00
12/17	48.00	23 18	2.00	1.00	19.00
12/16	47.00	26 16	2.00	1.00	17.00
12/15	47.00	26 20	2.00	1.00	16.00
12/14	43.00	25 20	2.00	1.00	15.00
Annual Growth	(2.0%)	— —	15.8%	16.3%	9.1%

Lam Research Corp

Lam Research is a leading manufacturer of the equipment used to make semiconductors. Its market-leading plasma etch machines are used to create tiny circuitry patterns on silicon wafers. The company also makes cleaning equipment that keeps unwanted particles from contaminating processed wafers. Lam also provides products and services to maximize equipment performance. Lam's customers include some of the world's largest chip makers such as Micron Technology and Samsung Electronics. Customers in four Asian countries account for more than 80% of Lam's revenue. The company's products are installed in more than 45000 semiconductor processing chambers around the world.

Operations

Lam makes equipment for processes used to make semiconductors.

Its products for deposition processes include the ALTUS SABRE SOLA SPEED and Striker lines. For etch processes Lam makes the Flex Kiyo and Syndion lines as well as others. The clean processes product lines include Coronus DV-Prime Da Vinci EOS and the SP Series. The Metryx line is Lam's offering for mass metrology processes.

The company handles most of its own manufacturing but outsources some aspects to contractors.

Geographic Reach

Lam's sales are concentrated in South Korea (about 25% of revenue) China and Japan (about 20% each) and Taiwan (more than 15%). The US accounts for less than 10% of sales.

The Fremont California-based company has manufacturing facilities in the US China Europe South Korea Southeast Asia and Taiwan.

Sales and Marketing

Lam relies on four customers — Micron Technology Samsung Electronics Company SK Hynix and Toshiba — for at least 40% of its revenue.

Makers of memory chips account for 70% of revenue foundries account for 20% and logic and integrated device makers account for 10%.

Financial Performance

Lam's revenue climbed steadily from 2014 through 2018 but retreated in 2019.

In 2019 (ended June) revenue fell 13% to $9.6 billion from about $11 billion in 2018 reflecting the volatility of customers' investments in semiconductor equipment.

The company's net income slipped to $2.2 billion in 2019 down about $200 million from 2018 due to the lower revenue.

Lam had $3.6 billion in cash and equivalents in its coffers in 2019 compared to $4.5 billion in 2018. Its operating activities generated $3.1 billion in 2019 while investing and financing activities used $1.6 billion and $2.4 billion respectively.

Lam carries about $4.5 billion in debt and had annual interest expense of about $117 million in 2019 (ended June). The debt level could lead the company to shift spending from working operations to debt payment and hurt its ability to obtain additional financing.

Strategy

The semiconductor business is notoriously cyclical rising and falling according to the strength of the overall economy and the capital equipment needs of Lam's customers. The volatility struck Lam in 2019 when revenue slumped to $9.6 billion from $11 billion the year before.

The high expense of semiconductor manufacturing equipment has resulted in consolidation of manufacturers. Samsung and Intel are among the few companies left that make their own products. So far Lam has maintained a mix of sales to manufacturers such as Samsung and to contract chip makers such as Taiwan Semiconductor.

A heavy investor in innovation the company's R&D expenses increased about 15% from 2017 through 2019. In late 2019 Lam shifted higher percentage of is operating expenses to R&D than in any quarter in its history. One area of focus is 3D chip architectures which provide more room on which to place transistors.

Mergers and Acquisitions

In 2017 Lam Research acquired Coventor which develops simulation and modeling software for the semiconductor industry. Coventor's software helps manufacturers predict structures and behaviors of design before committing to production.

EXECUTIVES

Vice President Of Global Operations, Thomas Bondur
Evp Global Products Group, Richard A. (Rick) Gottscho, age 68, $545,296 total compensation
Vp New Product Development, David J. (Dave) Hemker
President And Ceo, Martin B. Anstice, age 52, $937,789 total compensation
Evp And Cfo, Douglas R. (Doug) Bettinger, age 52, $548,827 total compensation
Evp And Coo, Timothy M. (Tim) Archer, age 52, $624,061 total compensation
Svp Chief Legal Officer And Secretary, Sarah A. O'Dowd, age 69, $434,488 total compensation
Svp Strategic Development Corporate Marketing And Communications, Gary Bultman
Senior Vice President, Kevin Jennings
Vp PI, Thorsten Lill
Vice President And General Manager Surface Integrity Group (sig), Mark Merrill
Vice President Organization Development, Amir Yasseri
Corporate Vice President, Harmeet Singh
Vice President, Mohsen Salek
Vice President Regional Operations, Vince Brigman
Senior Vice President, Audrey Charles
Group Vice President Global Sales And Corporate Marketing, Steven Lindsay
Vice President And General Manager, Erik Edelberg
Vice President And General Manager, Kaihan Ashtiani
Vice President Global Operations Lam Research Corporation, Abdi Hariri
Vice President Marketing, Dinesh Kalakkad
Vice President Corporate Marketing, Gary Blutman
Corporate Vice President Global Quality, Jerry Sowers
Vice President Engineering Pilot Operations, Karsten Theess
Vice President, Joon Park
Vice President, Joseph Han
Group Vice President Asia Pacific, Daniel Liao
Group Vp Customer Support Business Group Gm, Pat Lord
Vp, Steve Lanza
Senior Vice President, Sesha Varadarajan
Vice President, Natan Solomon
Svp Global Customer Operations, Scott Meikke
Vice President Computational Products, David Fried
Senior Vice President Global Customer Operations, Scott Meikle
Chairman, Stephen G. (Steve) Newberry, age 65
Board Member, Helen Tsai
Board Member, Catherine Lego
Auditors: Ernst & Young LLP

LOCATIONS

HQ: Lam Research Corp
4650 Cushing Parkway, Fremont, CA 94538
Phone: 510 572-0200   **Fax:** 510 572-6454
Web: www.lamresearch.com

2019 Sales

	$ mil.	% of total
Korea	2,205	23
China	2,161	22
Japan	1,161	20
Taiwan	1,596	17
Southeast Asia	616	6
United States	749	8
Europe	356	4
Total	**9,654**	**100**

PRODUCTS/OPERATIONS

Selected Products

Plasma ("dry") wafer-etching equipment
Plasma-based bevel clean system

Single-wafer spin and linear clean products
Three-dimensional integrated circuit etch equipment
Transformer Coupled Plasma (TCP) silicon etch equipment

COMPETITORS

ASM International	SCREEN Holdings
Applied Materials	Tokyo Electron
Hitachi	Wonik IPS Co. Ltd.
High-Technologies	

HISTORICAL FINANCIALS

Company Type: Public

Income Statement
FYE: June 30

	REVENUE ($ mil.)	NET INCOME ($ mil.)	NET PROFIT MARGIN	EMPLOYEES
06/19	9,654	2,191	22.7%	10,700
06/18	11,077	2,381	21.5%	10,900
06/17	8,014	1,698	21.2%	9,400
06/16	5,886	914	15.5%	7,500
06/15	5,259	656	12.5%	7,300
Annual Growth	16.4%	35.2%	—	10.0%

2019 Year-End Financials

Debt ratio: 37.00%	No. of shares (mil.): 144
Return on equity: 38.00%	Dividends
Cash ($ mil.): 3,658	Yield: 0.0%
Current ratio: 4.00	Payout: 32.0%
Long-term debt ($ mil.): 3,823	Market value ($ mil.): 27,130

	STOCK PRICE ($) FY Close	P/E High/Low		PER SHARE ($) Earnings	Dividends	Book Value
06/19	188.00	14	9	14.00	4.00	33.00
06/18	175.00	16	9	13.00	3.00	42.00
06/17	152.00	16	8	9.00	2.00	43.00
06/16	82.00	15	11	5.00	1.00	38.00
06/15	83.00	21	16	4.00	1.00	34.00
Annual Growth	22.7%			38.7%	51.3%	(0.8%)

Las Vegas Sands Corp

Las Vegas Sands (Sands) brings a touch of Venice to the US and China. Replete with gondoliers and a replica of the Rialto Bridge the company's Venetian Las Vegas offers a 225000-sq.-ft. casino and a 4000-suite hotel as well as a shopping dining and entertainment complex. Through its majority-owned Sands China subsidiary the firm operates The Venetian Macao on the Cotai Strip (the Chinese equivalent of the Las Vegas Strip) as well as four other properties in Macao the only place in China where gambling is legal. Sands' portfolio also includes the Marina Bay Sands in Singapore and The Palazzo in Las Vegas. Approximately 80% of the company's revenue is generated outside the US.

Operations
Sands' collection of resorts in Asia and the US feature upscale convention accommodations and entertainment options. Dining facilities include celebrity chef restaurants while shopping malls feature upscale tenants including Cartier Chanel Dior Prada and Versace. Many of its hotels operate under the Sheraton Holiday Inn Conrad and Four Seasons banners.

More than 70% of Sands' revenue comes from its casino operations while its hotel rooms bring in nearly 15% of revenue. Food and beverage mall activities and convention retail and other make up

the remaining revenue accounting for around 5% each.

The company's properties in Macao Singapore and Las Vegas feature a total of nearly 13000 slot machines nearly 3000 table games and some 21000 mostly upscale hotel suites. By these metrics Sands's largest properties include Sands Cotai Central and Venetian Macao in Macao China and The Venetian and The Palazzo in Las Vegas.

While the company's casinos attract travelers and guests primarily on weekends its convention centers draw business and other travelers during the slower mid-week period. Its Sands Expo Center in Las Vegas is one of the largest trade show and convention center venues in the US. The facility offers 2.3 million gross square feet of meeting exhibit and conference space to parties leasing space for events like trade shows and conferences.

Geographic Reach
Outside of Las Vegas Sands operates in Macao and Singapore. Macao accounts for more than 60% of the company's revenue Singapore accounts for more than 20% and the US accounts for the remainder. The company exited the Pennsylvania market in 2019 when it closed the $1.3 billion sale of its Sands Bethlehem property.

Sales and Marketing
Sands operates The Paiza Club a key part of its gaming marketing strategy. Paiza Clubs are exclusive "invitation-only" clubs located within its properties available to premium VIP players. The clubs feature high-end services and amenities including luxury accommodations restaurants lounges and private gaming salons.

The company also offers loyalty programs that provide members with access to rewards privileges and events.

Sands spends about $130 million on advertising costs each year.

Financial Performance
Sands is highly reliant on revenues in China's gambling district. Before two years of growth from 2016 to 2017 and 2017 to 2018 the company's revenue shrank year-over-year from 2014 to 2016 as it suffered from decreased gaming activity in Macao where China's anti-corruption campaign and slow economic growth triggered a slump. Profits mostly decreased from year-to-year during this period as well. However the Parisian Macao which opened in late 2016 spurred a jump in casino revenue in 2017 as the region's economy rebounded.

The company reported $13.7 billion in revenue for fiscal 2018 an 8% increase over fiscal 2017. The increase was primarily driven by stronger operating performance in Macao.

Net income decreased nearly 10% to $2.95 billion for 2018 compared to $3.26 billion for 2017. The decrease was primarily driven by an increase in tax expense due to a nonrecurring non-cash income tax benefit of $526 million related to US tax reform.

The company ended 2018 with about $4.7 billion in cash on hand. Cash from operations contributed $4.7 billion while financing activities used $1.5 billion and investing activities used $930 million.

Strategy
Sands provides non-gaming attractions and amenities (including dining entertainment retail and convention facilities) to appeal to a diverse set of leisure-seekers and contribute to longer visits and higher levels of consumer spending. The company's convention-based business strategy allows it to attract business travelers during the slower mid-week periods while leisure travelers occupy properties on the weekends.

Regular renovation projects are focused on upgrades and adding hotel suites and other property expansion and in some instances thematic rebranding. Sands is spending some $2 billion on

renovating and enhancing its Macau properties primarily on rebranding the Sands Cotai Central into The Londoner Macau a London-themed resort. The Londoner Macao is being completed in phases throughout 2020 and 2021. In Singapore a $3.3 billion expansion of Marina Bay Sands is underway.

In the US the company is working with Madison Square Garden Company to bring a 400000-square-foot venue built specifically for music and entertainment to Las Vegas at The Venetian which is expected to open in 2021. Elsewhere in the country it is divesting assets to focus on large-scale resort developments in growth markets. To this end in 2019 it closed the $1.3 billion sale of its Sands Bethlehem property in Pennsylvania to Wind Creek Hospitality an affiliate of the Poarch Band of Creek Indians of Alabama.

Company Background
Las Vegas Sands Corp. traces its roots back to the late 1980s when Sheldon Adelson founder the computer trade show COMDEX and other partners bought the Sands Hotel in Las Vegas. Ten years after buying the historic casino Adelson demolished the Sands Hotel and opened The Venetian Las Vegas a Venice-themed casino resort inspired by a trip Adelson took with his wife to the coastal Italian city.

The company went public in 2004 and fueled by the influx of cash from public investors began establishing itself internationally in Asia in the late 2000s.

EXECUTIVES

Chairman And Ceo, Sheldon G. Adelson, age 85, $1,000,000 total compensation

President And Coo, Robert G. (Rob) Goldstein, age 63, $3,400,000 total compensation

Evp Global General Counsel And Secretary, Lawrence A. (Lon) Jacobs, age 64, $284,800 total compensation

President Sands Bethlehem, Mark Juliano, age 64

President And Ceo Marina Bay Sands, George Tanasijevich, age 58, $864,140 total compensation

President And Coo The Venetian The Palazzo And Sands Expo & Convention Center, George M. Markantonis, age 61, $863,077 total compensation

Evp And Cfo, Patrick Dumont, age 44, $1,200,000 total compensation

President And Coo Sands China, Wilfred Wong

Vice President Of Retail Division, Tina Peetris

Senior Vice President, Darcy Martinez

Svp Special Projects Sands China, Scott Messinger

Svp And Global Chief Marketing Officer, David Horton

Svp Of And Chief Casino Marketing Officer Of Marina Bay Sands, Jeremy Bach

Vice President Of Global Sustainability, Katarina Tesarova

Senior Vice President Government Relations, Andy Abboud

Vice President Financial Systems And Application Development, Travis Phillips

Vice President Global Head Of Infrastructure And Operations, Edwin Grogan

Vice President, Robert Cilento

Vp Accounting, Chad Petrozza

Vice President Of Interiors Las Vegas Sa, Mark Signorio

Vice President Information Technology, Bill Mcarthur

Vice President And General Counsel, Frederick Kraus

Global Vice President Of Marketing, Michael Volkert

Senior Vice President Corporate Information Technology, Gideon Berkowitz

Senior Vice President Chief Procurement And Sustainability Officer, Norbert Riezler

Vice President Of Gaming Operations, Mia Banks
Senior Vice President Of Operations, Pete Boyd
Svp And Chief Security Officer, Brian Nagel
Vice President Investor Relations, Alistair Scobie
Vice President Casino Marketing, Kathy Mccracken
Senior Vice President Global Controller, Joseph Erickson
Senior Vice President Global Business Development, Wilson Ning
Vice President Procurement, Mike Merlin
Vice President Brand Marketing, Angela Wise
Vice President Corporate Information Technology, Alberto Jose
National Sales Manager, Mikki Dejurnett
Vice President Of Public Relations, Alyssa Anderson
Senior Vice President Global Human Resources, Amy Lee
Senior Vice President And Global Chief Compliance Officer, Matthew Frank
Vice President Global Restaurant And Nightlife Devel01ment, Patrick Lang
National Sales Manager, Melissa Wilson
Vice President And Senior Associate General Counsel Real Estate Development, Christine Sommella
Auditors: DELOITTE & TOUCHE LLP

LOCATIONS

HQ: Las Vegas Sands Corp
3355 Las Vegas Boulevard South, Las Vegas, NV 89109
Phone: 702 414-1000
Web: www.sands.com

PRODUCTS/OPERATIONS

2017 Sales

	$ mil.	% of total
Macao		
Marina Bay Sands	3,154	24
The Venetian Macao	2,990	23
Sands Cotai Central	1,943	15
The Parisian Macao	1,429	11
Sands Macao	640	5
The Plaza Macao and Four Seasons Macao	607	5
Ferry Operations and Other	177	1
United States		
Las Vegas Operating Properties	1,618	13
Sands Bethlehem	579	5
Intersegment eliminations	(255) (2)	
Total	12,882	100

2017 Sales

	$ mil.	% of total
Casino	10,058	78
Rooms	1,619	13
Food and beverage	843	7
Mall	651	5
Convention retail and other	550	4
Promotional allowances	(839) (7)	
Total	12,882	100

Selected Properties

Sands Expo & Convention Center
THE Venetian Vegas
Sands Macao
The Venetian Macao
The Palazzo Las Vegas
The Plaza Macao
Sands Bethlehem
Marina Bay Sands
Sands Cotai Central
The Parisian Macao

COMPETITORS

Boyd Gaming
Caesars Entertainment
Galaxy Entertainment
Genting Singapore
MGM Resorts
Melco Crown Entertainment
Penn National Gaming
Tropicana Entertainment
Wynn Resorts

HISTORICAL FINANCIALS

Company Type: Public

Income Statement

FYE: December 31

	REVENUE ($ mil.)	NET INCOME ($ mil.)	NET PROFIT MARGIN	EMPLOYEES
12/19	13,739	2,698	19.6%	50,000
12/18	13,729	2,413	17.6%	51,500
12/17	12,882	2,806	21.8%	50,500
12/16	11,410	1,670	14.6%	49,000
12/15	11,688	1,966	16.8%	46,500
Annual Growth	4.1%	8.2%	—	1.8%

2019 Year-End Financials

Debt ratio: 54.00%
Return on equity: 50.00%
Cash ($ mil.): 4,226
Current ratio: 2.00
Long-term debt ($ mil.): 12,422

No. of shares (mil.): 763
Dividends
 Yield: 4.0%
 Payout: 124.0%
Market value ($ mil.): 52,711

	STOCK PRICE ($) FY Close	P/E High/Low	PER SHARE ($) Earnings	Dividends	Book Value
12/19	69.00	20 15	4.00	3.00	7.00
12/18	52.00	26 16	3.00	3.00	7.00
12/17	69.00	20 15	4.00	3.00	8.00
12/16	53.00	30 18	2.00	3.00	8.00
12/15	44.00	25 15	2.00	3.00	9.00
Annual Growth	12.0%	—	9.1%	4.3%	(5.7%)

Lauder (Estee) Cos., Inc. (The)

EXECUTIVES

Prin, Est E Lauder
President, Patrick B Chavanne
Vice-President Merchandising, Scott Blair
Svp, Glenn Evans
Vice President, Maureen Weiss
Auditors: KPMG LLP

LOCATIONS

HQ: Lauder (Estee) Cos., Inc. (The)
767 Fifth Avenue, New York, NY 10153
Phone: 212 572-4200
Web: www.elcompanies.com

HISTORICAL FINANCIALS

Company Type: Public

Income Statement

FYE: June 30

	REVENUE ($ mil.)	NET INCOME ($ mil.)	NET PROFIT MARGIN	EMPLOYEES
06/19	14,863	1,785	12.0%	48,000
06/18	13,683	1,108	8.1%	46,000
06/17	11,824	1,249	10.6%	46,000
06/16	11,262	1,115	9.9%	46,000
06/15	10,780	1,089	10.1%	44,000
Annual Growth	8.4%	13.2%	—	2.2%

2019 Year-End Financials

Debt ratio: 26.00%
Return on equity: 39.00%
Cash ($ mil.): 2,987
Current ratio: 2.00
Long-term debt ($ mil.): 2,896

No. of shares (mil.): 361
Dividends
 Yield: 0.0%
 Payout: 35.0%
Market value ($ mil.): 66,121

	STOCK PRICE ($) FY Close	P/E High/Low	PER SHARE ($) Earnings	Dividends	Book Value
06/19	183.00	37 25	5.00	2.00	12.00
06/18	143.00	53 31	3.00	1.00	13.00
06/17	96.00	29 22	3.00	1.00	12.00
06/16	91.00	32 25	3.00	1.00	10.00
06/15	87.00	31 25	3.00	1.00	10.00
Annual Growth	20.6%	—	14.3%	16.1%	5.7%

Lear Corp.

Lear Corporation is a leading manufacturer of seating and related components for automobiles. In addition to seating the company's E-Systems business produces automotive electronics and manufactures wire harnesses junction boxes terminals and connectors and body control modules. The company operates from some 260 facilities in about 40 countries. It generates more than 80% of revenue outside the US. Its largest customers are General Motors Ford and BMW. Lear traces its history back to 1917 when it was founded in Detroit as American Metal Products.

Operations
Lear's operations are split between Seating (around 75% of sales) and E-Systems (about 25%).

The Seating segment consists of the manufacture and delivery of complete seat systems and seat components including seat covers and surface materials such as leather and fabric seat structure and mechanisms. Products and brands include Eagle Ottawa leather Guilford textiles and its new sustainable SoyFoam product.

E-Systems makes complete electrical distribution systems as well as sophisticated electronic control modules electrification products and connectivity products. Some products include lighting controls smart junction boxes and a virtual car key that enables vehicle access via a smartphone.

Geographic Reach
Based in Southfield MI Lear operates from about 260 facilities in some 40 countries. The company's operations include around 85 just-in-time manufacturing facilities 125 dedicated component manufacturing facilities 35 administrative and technical support facilities and a small number of advanced technology centers.

Lear's home market the US generates approximately 20% of sales annually. Other important markets are Mexico (about 15% of revenue) China (almost 15%) and Germany (10%).

Sales and Marketing
Lear serves the worldwide automotive and light truck market. More than 40% of Lear's sales are generated by only three customers. General Motors accounts for close to 20% of revenue followed by Ford with around 15% and BMW with more than 5%.

The Seating segment's top five customers are General Motors Daimler Ford Fiat Chrysler and Volkswagen. The E-system segment's top customers are Ford General Motors Renault-Nissan Jaguar Land Rover and Volkswagen.

Financial Performance
Increasing global auto sales particularly in the advantageous crossover and sport utility vehicle segment have helped Lear enjoy unprecedented growth over the years. Sales have increased by 19% since 2014.

Revenue hit a record-setting $21.1 billion in 2018 up 3% over 2017. New business in all regions contributed to the increase in sales as well as revenue from the acquired Antolin Seating business. E-Systems increased by 12% ($533 million) and the seating business was up 1% ($149 million).

Net income decreased 12% to $1.1 billion mainly due to a higher provision for income taxes in 2018.

Cash at the end of fiscal 2018 was $1.5 billion an increase of $19.4 million from the prior year. Cash from operations contributed $1.8 billion to the coffers while investing activities used $693.5 million mainly for additions to property plant and equipment. Financing activities used another $1.0 billion for dividends to stockholders and the company's stock repurchase program.

Strategy

Lear Corporation is well-positioned to capitalize on several current trends in the automotive industry. The shift to SUVs and increasing demands for luxury and performance features and autonomy and connectivity capabilities is driving growth as Lear has the goods to supply vehicles with the latest features and technology.

The consumer shift to crossover vehicles and SUVs increases the percentage of vehicle content supplied by the company. In China utility vehicle production has increased from 16% to 41% in the past five years. Lear continually realigns its manufacturing footprint to leverage operations in low-cost countries but is focused on China which it believes is the world's largest major automotive market with above-average growth potential.

Lear has expanded component and software capabilities both through internal development efforts and through acquisitions. In 2018 the company acquired an Israeli firm specializing in GPS for cars. Its expertise in V2X communication technology allows the company to provide high-speed communication between vehicles and road infrastructure even in extreme weather conditions. It has also developed standardized seat structures and mechanisms that can be adapted across multiple segments of its manufacturing operations.

Mergers and Acquisitions

One way Lear has achieved milestone revenue growth recently is through acquisitions.

In 2019 Lear agreed to acquire Xevo an automotive software supplier that develops solutions for cloud car and mobile devices. Xevo's Journeyware application and Xevo Market platform will broaden Lear's connectivity portfolio. Also in 2019 the company through its Lear Innovation Ventures (LIV) subsidiary made an investment in Israel-based Maniv Mobility a company focused on advancing mobility technology.

In early 2018 Lear acquired Israel-based EXO Technologies a developer of GPS technology providing high-accuracy positioning systems for autonomous and connected vehicles. Its operations are in San Mateo California and Tel Aviv Israel.

Company Background

Lear dates back to 1917 when American Metal Products began supplying seats to Detroit's fledgling car industry. The seat maker incorporated in 1928 and grew during the 1950s and 1960s by buying other auto parts makers. In 1966 American Metal Products was acquired by Lear Siegler a manufacturer of aerospace auto parts and climate-control equipment. The company's aerospace unit sputtered in the 1970s but the seat business did well. By 1985 metal seat frames had become Lear Siegler's major auto parts revenue producer. Spurred by growing competition with Japanese carmakers the company built a plant near a General Motors factory in Michigan to allow for swift delivery of its car seats. In 1989 the company became Lear Seating.

Lear Seating bought a slice of Ford's North American automotive and trim operation and manufacturing factory in Ciudad Juárez Mexico in 1993. As a result of the purchase the company entered into a long-term supply agreement with Ford. The following year Lear Seating went public. In 1995 it bought Automotive Industries and inked a contract to provide seats for Brazil's top-selling car the Volkswagen Gol. To reflect the broader scope of its business the company dropped "Seating" from its name and became Lear Corporation in 1996.

The company narrowed its product focus and sold its interior product lines (instrument panels door panels flooring acoustic systems and other interior products) in 2006. In the midst of the Great Recession Lear filed for Chapter 11 bankruptcy emerging in late 2009.

EXECUTIVES

President European Customer Focused Division, Raymond E. (Ray) Scott, age 53, $855,098 total compensation

Svp; President Asia/pacific Operations, Jay K. Kunkel, age 59

Evp Business Development And General Counsel, Terrence B. (Terry) Larkin, age 64, $855,098 total compensation

Svp And Cfo, Jeffrey H. Vanneste, age 59, $787,437 total compensation

Svp; President E-systems, Frank C. Orsini, age 46, $736,375 total compensation

Vp Global Engineering E Systems, Mike Fawaz

Vice President Korea, Dean M Ackerman

Vp Global Facilities And Real Estate, Doug Daugherty

Vice President Human Resources North America, Pete Camarata

Multi Cultural Vice President, Jolito Bustamante

Vice President Talent Acquisition, Dave McNulty

Vice President Engineering, Stephen Rober

Vice President, Joe Duran

Svp Human Resources, Thomas Didonato

Vp Hse, Jack Nunes

Global Vice President Trim Cover Sales And Prgm Management, Dreta Roggenbuck

Vice President Connectivity, Doug Moeller

Vice President Of It Infrastructure, Jon Damm

Vp Finance And Investor Relations, John Trythall

Vice President Software And Systems Engineering, Michael Badalament

Vice President And Treasurer, Shari L Burgess

Chairman, Henry D. G. Wallace, age 73

Assistant Treasurer, Ed Lowenfeld

Auditors: Ernst & Young LLP

LOCATIONS

HQ: Lear Corp.
21557 Telegraph Road, Southfield, MI 48033
Phone: 248 447-1500   **Fax:** 248 447-5250
Web: www.lear.com

2018 Sales

	$ mil.	% of total
US	3,718	18
Mexico	3,237	15
China	2,782	13
Germany	2,187	10
Other countries	9,225	44
Total	**21,149**	**100**

PRODUCTS/OPERATIONS

2018 Sales

	$ mil.	% of total
Seating	16,022	76
E-Systems	5,127	24
Total	**21,149**	**100**

2018 Sales by Customer

	% of total
GM	18
Ford	16
BMW	7
Others	59
Total	**100**

Selected Products

Seating
  Adjusters
  Automotive seats
  Fabrics
  Head restraints
  Mechanisms
  Seat foam
  Structure systems
  Trim covers
Electrical power management
  Electrical distribution and power management systems
  Fuse boxes
  Junction boxes
  Terminals and connectors
  Wire harness assemblies
  High-power electrical systems
  Hybrid electrical systems
  Specialty electronics
  Audio sound systems
  In-vehicle television tuner module
  LED electronics (interior/exterior)
  Lighting control module
  Media console
  Radio amplifiers
  Wireless systems
  Keyless entry systems
  Passive entry systems
  Tire pressure monitoring systems

COMPETITORS

Continental AG	Robert Bosch
DENSO	Sumitomo
Faurecia	TE Connectivity
Honda	TS TECH CO
LEONI	Toyota Boshoku
Magna International	Valeo
Molex	Visteon
Peugeot	Yazaki

HISTORICAL FINANCIALS

Company Type: Public

Income Statement

FYE: December 31

	REVENUE ($ mil.)	NET INCOME ($ mil.)	NET PROFIT MARGIN	EMPLOYEES
12/19	19,810	754	3.8%	164,100
12/18	21,149	1,150	5.4%	169,000
12/17	20,467	1,313	6.4%	165,000
12/16	18,558	975	5.3%	148,400
12/15	18,211	746	4.1%	136,200
Annual Growth	**2.1%**	**0.3%**	**—**	**4.8%**

2019 Year-End Financials

Debt ratio: 18.00%
Return on equity: 18.00%
Cash ($ mil.): 1,488
Current ratio: 1.00
Long-term debt ($ mil.): 2,294

No. of shares (mil.): 60
Dividends
  Yield: 2.0%
  Payout: 22.0%
Market value ($ mil.): 8,292

	STOCK PRICE ($) FY Close	P/E High/Low		PER SHARE ($) Earnings	Dividends	Book Value
12/19	137.00	12	8	13.00	3.00	72.00
12/18	123.00	12	7	17.00	3.00	67.00
12/17	177.00	10	7	19.00	2.00	62.00
12/16	132.00	10	7	13.00	1.00	44.00
12/15	123.00	13	10	10.00	1.00	39.00
Annual Growth	**2.8%**	**—**	**—**	**7.4%**	**31.6%**	**16.3%**

Leidos Holdings Inc

Leidos Holdings provides cybersecurity information technology and analytics services to government agencies and companies in the defense intelligence homeland security civil and health markets. The company's areas of expertise include operations and logistics; sensors; software development; and systems engineering. It also operates one of the country's largest health system integrators. Most of the company's revenue comes from the US government. In 2016 Leidos merged with Lockheed Martin's Information Systems & Global Solutions segment to expand the scale and scope of its IT and intelligence services.

Change in Company Type

The combination with Lockheed Martin's Information Systems & Global Solutions unit created a company with a $10 billion portfolio of products and services. Leidos said the combined company serves more diverse markets with greater scale. The transaction included a special cash payment of approximately $1.8 billion to Lockheed Martin.

Operations

Leidos Holdings operates through three segments: Defense Solutions Civil and Health.

Defense Solutions which accounts for about 50% of total sales offers technology development and integration capabilities in surveillance and reconnaissance integrated systems and global services for the US intelligence community the military and other government and commercial customers.

The Civil segment which accounts for about a third of revenue provides aviation services security products enterprise IT services federal environment and infrastructure management and logistics services.

The Health segment about 20% of revenue provides complex systems integration managed health services enterprise IT services and life sciences services and support.

Geographic Reach

Leidos has some 350 offices in about 40 states across the US as well as in more than a dozen international locations where it works with US customers.

Sales and Marketing

The US government accounts for about 85% of Leidos Holdings' revenue with the US Department of Defense accounting for Other major federal customers are the Navy Air Force the Defense Advanced Research Projects Agency the Department of Homeland Security and NASA. International customers account for about 10% of revenue.

Financial Performance

The acquisition of Lockheed Martin's Information Systems and Global Solutions boosted Leidos Holdings revenue 45% to $10.2 billion in 2017 from 2016. The defense business reported higher airborne systems revenue while the health segment had growth in federal health services.

The US Tax Cuts and Jobs Act reduced Leidos' tax bill in 2017 helping the company to a $366 million profit compared to a $244 profit the year before.

Cash generated by operations increased $77 million to $526 million in 2017 from 2016 because of favorable timing of working capital changes somewhat offset by higher integration and restructuring costs and higher payments for interest and taxes.

Strategy

The acquisition of Lockheed's Information Systems and Global Solutions (IS&GS) group in 2016 provided Leidos Holdings with the resources and capabilities that enable it to go after business it would not have qualified before. In one example IS&GS brought biometrics capabilities that improve its competitive position. Leidos has worked on bidding for contracts that total more than half a billion dollars as a result of the acquisition.

Leidos is putting its capabilities on the line with the multi-company project to modernize health records for the US Department of Defense. Working with Cerner Accenture and Henry Schein Leidos is putting together a modern EHR system that helps health systems run more efficiently and provide better care while protecting the privacy of patients.

In 2016 Leidos sold its heavy construction business to Haskell an engineering procurement and construction firm. Leidos sold the unit to focus more on market opportunities in the integration of physical and digital worlds.

Mergers and Acquisitions

The 2016 acquisition of Lockheed Martin's Information Systems and Global Solutions business for about $4.6 billion added multiple capabilities to the Leidos portfolio.The increased resources enable Leidos to go after projects with bigger scope than it had in the past.

EXECUTIVES

Chairman And Ceo, Roger A. Krone, age 63, $988,462 total compensation

Evp And Cfo, James C. (Jim) Reagan, age 60, $561,538 total compensation

Evp And Chief Human Resources Officer, Ann M. Addison, age 57

President Technology Group And Cto, John J. Fratamico, age 61

Evp And Chief Of Business Development And Strategy, Gerard A. (Gerry) Fasano, age 53

President Health Group, Jonathan W. Scholl, age 57

Evp And General Counsel, Vincent A. (Vince) Maffeo, age 68, $575,000 total compensation

President Civil Group, Angela L. Heise, age 44

President Defense And Intelligence Group, Timothy J. Reardon, age 54, $162,240 total compensation

President Advanced Solutions Group, Michael L. Chagnon

Vp Strategic Accounts And Government Relations, Rob Thomas

Vice President, John Russell

Vice President, Jack Gumbert

Vice President, Steve Ventsam

Vice President Business Development, Karen Walton

Senior Vice President Corporate Controller And Chief Accounting Officer, Ken Sharp

Vice President And Senior Pricing Director, Mark Achenbach

Assistant Vice President Senior Program Manager Fo, Richard Deason

Vice President Security Solutions, Jeffrey Murter

Vice President For Cybersecurity, Robert Pate

Vice President Production, Paul Dickinson

Vice President Information Technology, Chris Russeau

Vice President Enterprise Business Systems, Kenneth Kicia

Vice President Chief Engineer, Derek Lewis

Vice President And Director Human Resources Shared Services, Gayle Connatser

Svp, Paul Greiner

Vice President, Paul Bollinger

Senior Vice President, Doug Charles

Executive Vice President, W Roper

Executive Vice President, J Warner

Vice President Information Technology Quality User Experience, Gisele Moro

Vice President Director Of Operations Contracts, Graeme Ritchie

Vice President And Division Manager, Brian Follmer

Senior Vice President Enterprise Shared Service Director, Chris Buffoni

Vice President Government Compliance, Matthew Popham

Vice President Program Risk Assessment And Execution, Daniel Wollenhaupt

Vice President Division Manager, John Lynch

Svp And Cio, Steve Hull

Svp Investor Relations, John Sweeney

Vp Public Health, Edwin Kilbourne

Vp Media Relations, Jason Kello

Svp Transportation Solutions, Fran Hill

Svp Leidos Civil Health, Doreen Cohen

Senior Vice President Of Government Affairs, Valerie Baldwin

Auditors: Deloitte & Touche LLP

LOCATIONS

HQ: Leidos Holdings Inc
11951 Freedom Drive, Reston, VA 20190
Phone: 571 526-6000
Web: www.leidos.com

PRODUCTS/OPERATIONS

2016 Sales

	$ mil.	% of total
National Security solutions	3,610	51
Information Systems & Global Solutions	1,971	28
Health and engineering	1,463	21
Adjustments	(-1) -	
Total	**7,043**	**100**

Selected Capabilites:

Civil:
Aviation
Cyber Solutions
Energy
Environment & Infrastructure
Exploration & Mission Support
Financial Solutions
Homeland & Transportation Security
Defense & Intelligence:
Airborne
Command & Control
Data Analytics
Enterprise IT
Federal Cybersecurity
Intelligence Services
Operations & Logistics
Sensors
Training
Health:
Federal Health IT
Hospitals & Health Systems
Life Sciences
Advanced Solutions:
Airborne Systems Integration
Maritime

COMPETITORS

Accenture
American Science and Engineering
BAE Systems Technology Solutions
Battelle Memorial
Boeing
Booz Allen
CACI International
Computer Sciences Corp.
Engility
Exelis
General Dynamics
HP Enterprise Services
Honeywell Technology Solutions
IBM Global Services
KBR
KEYW
Kratos Defense & Security Solutions
L3 Technologies
ManTech
OSI Systems
Raytheon Intelligence Information and Services
Serco
Unisys

HISTORICAL FINANCIALS

Company Type: Public

Income Statement — FYE: December 28

	REVENUE ($ mil.)	NET INCOME ($ mil.)	NET PROFIT MARGIN	EMPLOYEES
12/18	10,194	581	5.7%	32,000
12/17	10,170	366	3.6%	31,000
12/16*	7,043	244	3.5%	32,000
01/16	4,712	242	5.1%	18,000
01/15	5,063	(323)	—	19,000
Annual Growth	19.1%	—		13.9%

*Fiscal year change

2018 Year-End Financials

Debt ratio: 36.00%	No. of shares (mil.): 146
Return on equity: 17.00%	Dividends
Cash ($ mil.): 327	Yield: 2.0%
Current ratio: 1.00	Payout: 39.0%
Long-term debt ($ mil.): 3,052	Market value ($ mil.): 7,650

	STOCK PRICE ($) FY Close	P/E High/Low		PER SHARE ($) Earnings	Dividends	Book Value
12/18	52.00	19	13	4.00	1.00	23.00
12/17	65.00	27	20	2.00	1.00	22.00
12/16*	51.00	24	16	2.00	15.00	21.00
01/16	56.00	18	11	3.00	1.00	15.00
01/15	41.00	—	—	(4.00)	1.00	13.00
Annual Growth	6.1%	—	—	—	(0.0%)	13.8%

*Fiscal year change

LELAND STANFORD JUNIOR UNIVERSITY

Prospectors panning for gold in higher education can strike it rich at The Leland Stanford Junior University. The school known as Stanford University is one of the premier educational institutions in the US boasting respected programs in business engineering law and medicine among others. Stanford serves more than 16300 students (taught by 2180 faculty members) and a student-teacher ratio of about 4:1. A private institution Stanford is supported through an endowment of some $22.4 billion one of the largest in the US. The university was established in 1885 by Leland Stanford Sr. who made his fortune selling provisions to California gold miners; it was named after his son Leland Stanford Jr.

Operations

Stanford University is widely recognized as one of the top US research universities and sports a host of laboratories and research centers including the Stanford Institute for Economic Policy Research and the Stanford Linear Accelerator Center. Its faculty members include around 20 Nobel Prize winners a handful of Pulitzer Prize winners and more than 20 MacArthur fellows.

The university also offers 35 varsity sports and 20 club sports; it boasts more than 110 NCAA team championships.

Geographic Reach

Stanford is located in the heart of California's Silicon Valley known worldwide as an epicenter for technology and research ventures. Google (headquartered in Silicon Valley) got its start at Stanford when Sergey Brin and Larry Page developed the page-rank algorithm while they were still computer science graduate students.

The university is located on 8180 contiguous acres and has almost 700 major buildings.

Financial Performance

Stanford University reported revenues of some $9.8 billion in fiscal 2016 up from $9.1 billion in 2015 due to an increase in student income higher patient service revenues (from the Stanford Hospitals and Clinics organization) sponsored research funding and increased returns on its investment portfolio assets.

Net income fell to $490 million in 2016 (versus $700 million in 2015) as expenses including salaries and benefits rose especially within the medical school. Other expenditures that year such as facilities and infrastructure maintenance and higher depreciation also impacted net income.

The university has received sizable donations from notable alumni such as Jerry Yang (cofounder of Yahoo!) Charles Schwab Texas billionaire Robert Bass and William Hewlett (of Hewlett-Packard who has since died).

Strategy

To further widen its student resources Stanford has recently completed renovation and construction efforts on some 40 campus buildings and added a number of new faculty and fellowship positions. The university is also exploring options to establish a satellite-applied science and engineering campus in another US city. In addition Stanford is examining whether it might begin to offer courses through an online platform.

In 2017 Stanford launched a new major in aeronautics and astronautics (allowing students to work with unmanned aerial vehicles satellites autonomous systems and other flight technologies).

HISTORY

In 1885 Leland Stanford Sr. and his wife Jane established Leland Stanford Junior University in memory of their son Leland Jr. who had died of typhoid at age 15. Stanford made his fortune selling provisions to California gold miners and as a major investor in the Central Pacific Railroad one of the two companies that built the first transcontinental railway. It was Stanford who connected the tracks laid eastward by Central Pacific and westward by Union Pacific with a gold railway spike in 1869. He also served as California's governor and as a US senator.

The Stanfords donated more than 8000 acres of land from their own estate to establish an unconventional university one that was coeducational and nondenominational with a focus on preparing students for a profession. Stanford opened its doors in 1891 to a freshman class of 559 students. It awarded its first degrees four years later and among the graduates was future US president Herbert Hoover.

Leland Stanford Sr. died in 1893 and in 1903 Jane Stanford turned the university over to the board of trustees. After weathering significant damage in 1906 from the Great San Francisco Earthquake the university established a law school in 1908 and its medical school five years later.

During WWI the university mobilized half of its students into the Students' Army Training Corps. The School of Education was established in 1917 followed by the School of Engineering and Graduate School of Business eight years later. In 1933 a rule limiting the number of women admitted to Stanford was abolished.

Wallace Sterling who became president of the university after WWII initiated the transformation of Stanford into a world-class institution with a reputation for teaching and research. Under Sterling the university initiated development on the Stanford Research Park.

In 1958 Stanford opened its first overseas campus (near Stuttgart Germany) and the Stanford Medical Center was completed the following year. The university created a computer science department in 1965 and two years later opened the Stanford Linear Accelerator Center dedicated to physics research.

Donald Kennedy became president in 1980. The next year students voted to abandon the university's official mascot the "Indians" in response to concerns raised by Native American students. The nickname "Cardinal" was adopted in its place. The term refers to the school's color cardinal red.

Also during Kennedy's tenure it was revealed that Stanford had overcharged the Office of Naval Research for indirect costs associated with research. The scandal led to Kennedy's resignation in 1992 and in 1994 the Office of Naval Research and the university settled a related lawsuit for $1.2 million and a stipulation that Stanford had not committed any wrongdoing. Gerhard Casper succeeded Kennedy as president.

In 1997 Stanford and the University of California at San Francisco combined their teaching hospitals in a public/private merger. Two years after the controversial experiment had harmed both hospitals' financial pictures the merger was terminated and the two hospitals agreed to go their separate ways.

In 1999 Casper announced his intention to resign as president. The school tapped provost John Hennessy as his replacement. Soon after his appointment in 2000 Hennessey launched a campaign to raise $1 billion. Former Stanford professor and Netscape co-founder Jim Clark donated $150 million later that year to support Stanford's biomedical engineering and sciences program. The school also launched a new company SKOLAR which developed an online search engine for the medical industry.

EXECUTIVES

President, John L. Hennessy
Provost, John W. Etchemendy
Dean School Of Humanities And Science, Richard P. Saller
Vp Business Affairs And Cfo, Randall S. (Randy) Livingston
Dean School Of Earth Energy And Environmental Sciences, Pamela Matson
Associate Vp It Services, Bill Clebsch
President And Ceo Stanford Health Care, Amir Dan Rubin
Vice Provost And Dean Of Research, Ann Margaret Arvin
Dean Graduate School Of Business, Garth Saloner
Dean Graduate School Of Education, Deborah Stipek
Dean School Of Engineering, Persis S. Drell
Dean Law School, M. Elizabeth Magill
Dean School Of Medicine, Lloyd Minor
President And Ceo Stanford Children's Health, Christopher Dawes
Assistant Vice President And Chief Information Security Officer, Michael Duff
Vice President Human Resources, David Jones
Vice President, Britt Hedman
Vice President, Philip Scherrer
Associate Vice President For Government Relations, Ryan Adesnik
Vice President, Stephen Krasner
Associate Vice President, Anne Hannigan
Vice President Information Technology, Stephen Wong
Vice Provost Budget, Tim R Warner
M.s. Candidate In Computer Science Audit Intern
Vice President Of Board Games, Hana Lee
Professor And Associate Chair Department Of Psychiatry And Behavioral Sciences, Bruce Arnow

Associate Vice President Of Sponsored Research,
Russell Brewer
Medical Director, Kirsti Weng
**Assoc. Vice President Of Human Resources
Benefits,** Leslie Schlaegel
Senior Vice President Human Resources,
Rosemary Monroe
**Assistant Vice President Medical Center
Development,** Jennifer Kitt
Vice President Human Resources, Elizabeth
Zacharias
**B.s. Candidate Computer Science Vice President
Of External Affairs Co Director Spectra
Hackathon,** Cynthia Yin
Associate Vice President For The Arts, Matthew
Tiews
Medical Director Emergency Medicine, Sam Shen
**B.s. Candidate Product Design Blackstage Vice
President,** Adriana Ganem
Vice President Accountable Care, Thomas Williams
Vice President Of External Relations, Tina Jiang
Medical Director Vaden Health Center, Robyn
Tepper
Medical Director, James Lau
Clinical Director Ibd, Sarah Streett
**Vice President Communications And Marketing
Publisher,** Edie Feilce Barry
**Associate Vice President Human Resources
Communications,** Melissa Mcvicker
Vice President And Corporate Controller, James
Martin
Chairs Secretary, Debbi Barley
Secretary Of State, Condoleezza Rice
Vice Chair, Mary Goldstein
Auditors: PRICEWATERHOUSECOOPERS LLP SA

LOCATIONS

HQ: LELAND STANFORD JUNIOR UNIVERSITY
450 SERRA MALL, STANFORD, CA 943052004
Phone: 650 723-2300
Web: WWW.STANFORD.EDU

PRODUCTS/OPERATIONS

2014 Sales

	$ mil.	% of total
Healthcare services	3,943	50
Sponsored reseach support	1,266	16
Investment income	1,181	15
Student income	534	7
Special program fee and other income	642	7
Gifts	213	3
Net assets released from restrictions	146	2
Total	**7,924**	**100**

Selected Schools

Undergraduate
  School of Earth Sciences
  School of Engineering
  School of Humanities and Sciences
Graduate
  School of Business
  School of Earth Sciences
  School of Education
  School of Engineering
  School of Humanities and Sciences
  School of Law
  School of Medicine

Selected Interdisciplinary Research Centers

Alliance for Innovative Manufacturing at Stanford
Center for Computer Research in Music and Acoustics
Center for Integrated Facility Engineering
Center for Integrated Systems

Selected Laboratories Centers and Institutes

Center for Research on Information Storage Materials
Center for the Study of Language and Information
Edward L. Ginzton Laboratory
Institute for International Studies
Institute for Research on Women and Gender
John and Terry Levin Center for Public Service and
  Public Interest Law

Stanford Center for Buddhist Studies
Stanford Humanities Center
Stanford Institute for Economic Policy Research
W.W. Hansen Experimental Physics Laboratory

Selected Medical Research Facilities

Center for Biomedical Ethics
Center for Research in Disease Prevention
Human Genome Center
Richard M. Lucas Center for Magnetic Resonance
  Spectroscopy & Imaging
Sleep Disorders Center
Other Selected Research Facilities
Hoover Institution on War Revolution and Peace
Hopkins Marine Station
Martin Luther King Jr. Papers Project
Stanford Linear Accelerator Center

HISTORICAL FINANCIALS

Company Type: Private

Income Statement   FYE: August 31

	REVENUE ($ mil.)	NET INCOME ($ mil.)	NET PROFIT MARGIN	EMPLOYEES
08/18	11,311	2,653	23.5%	15,000
08/17	5,605	2,972	53.0%	—
08/06	4,511	3,008	66.7%	—
08/05	4,163	2,897	69.6%	—
Annual Growth	**8.0%**	**(0.7%)**		

LendingClub Corp

Auditors: DELOITTE & TOUCHE
LLP

LOCATIONS

HQ: LendingClub Corp
595 Market Street, Suite 200, San Francisco, CA 94105
Phone: 415 632-5600
Web: www.lendingclub.com

HISTORICAL FINANCIALS

Company Type: Public

Income Statement   FYE: December 31

	ASSETS ($ mil.)	NET INCOME ($ mil.)	INCOME AS % OF ASSETS	EMPLOYEES
12/18	3,820	(128)	—	1,768
12/17	4,641	(154)	—	1,837
12/16	5,563	(146)	—	1,530
12/15	5,794	(5)	—	1,382
12/14	3,890	(33)	—	843
Annual Growth	**(0.5%)**	**—**		**20.3%**

2018 Year-End Financials

Debt ratio: 69.00%   No. of shares (mil.): 86
Return on equity: (-14.00%)   Dividends
Cash ($ mil.): 373   Yield: —
Current ratio: —   Payout: —
Long-term debt ($ mil.): —   Market value ($ mil.): 226

	STOCK PRICE ($) FY Close	P/E High/Low	PER SHARE ($) Earnings	Dividends	Book Value
12/18	3.00	— —	(2.00)	0.00	10.00
12/17	4.00	— —	(2.00)	0.00	11.00
12/16	5.00	— —	(2.00)	0.00	12.00
12/15	11.00	— —	(0.00)	0.00	14.00
12/14	25.00	— —	(2.00)	0.00	13.00
Annual Growth	**(43.2%)**	**— —**	**—**	**—**	**(6.3%)**

Lennar Corp

Lennar is one of the largest homebuilding land-owning loan-making leviathans in the US. The company builds single-family attached and detached homes and multi-family rental properties in more than 20 states under brand names including Lennar Village Builders and CalAtlantic Group. Lennar targets first-time move-up active adult and luxury homebuyers and markets its homes as "everything included." The company delivered more than 45000 homes in 2018 at an average price of around $410000. Lennar purchased Florida homebuilder WCI Communities in 2017 and acquired rival CalAtlantic for $6 billion in 2018.

HISTORY

Lennar is the creation of Leonard Miller and Arnold Rosen and the name of the company is a combination of their given names. Rosen a Miami homebuilder formed F&R Builders in 1954. A year later Miller graduated from Harvard with no firm career plans. Having worked summers in Florida Miller decided it would be a good place to make his fortune and the 23-year-old began selling real estate there.

With $10000 earned from commissions Miller bought 42 lots and in 1956 entered a joint venture with Rosen to build homes on the lots. They worked well together and Miller soon joined F&R. The operation grew emphasizing marketing and concentrating on low- and medium-priced single-family homes for first-time buyers and retirees.

After expanding into commercial real estate in the late 1960s the duo folded F&R into a new company — Lennar Corporation — in 1971 and went public. During the 1970s and 1980s the company hawked Jacuzzi tubs and designer homes (such as the Calvin and the Liz) and promised customers "$10000 worth of extras" free at Midnight Madness shopping mall sales. Lennar also began expanding acquiring land and builders in the Phoenix area in 1973. Rosen retired in 1977.

Spurred by a recession Lennar began offering mortgage services nationwide in 1981 keeping the potentially lucrative servicing for itself and selling its mortgages to Fannie Mae Ginnie Mae and Freddie Mac among others. In 1984 it dissolved its construction operations and began subbing out its work (a practice that it continues today). Lennar was relatively unscathed by the recession of the late 1980s in part because Miller had foreseen a slump and had cut corporate debt and overhead. When other builders were overextending themselves by buying land in good times Miller had used profit to pay down debt so he would have the resources to buy land cheap when bad times arrived.

During the 1990s Lennar targeted other Sun Belt markets and began buying portfolios of distressed property in partnership with heavy hitters like Morgan Stanley. Although Miller had looked at Texas as a development site since 1987 it was not until 1991 that Lennar entered the state beginning in Dallas.

The company bought up the secured debt of Bramalea Homes in Southern California in 1995 and entered Northern California with its acquisition of Renaissance Homes. Lennar's acquisition of Village Homes and Exxon's Friendswood Development in 1996 made it Houston's top home builder and Lennar surpassed $1 billion in sales.

In 1997 Stuart Miller became president and CEO (Leonard his father remained chairman). That year Lennar also spun off its commercial real estate operations as LNR Property a separately traded public company and acquired Pacific Greystone a Los Angeles builder.

The following year the company strengthened its position in the western US acquiring three California homebuilders: Winncrest Homes (Sacramento) ColRich Communities (San Diego) and Polygon Communities (Southern California and Sacramento). Lennar also purchased North American Title an escrow and title services company operating in Arizona California and Colorado.

In 2000 Lennar bought fellow builder U.S. Home for about $1.1 billion in a deal that expanded its operations into 13 states. The company acquired the North and South Carolina operations of The Fortress Group in late 2001 giving Lennar the Don Galloway Homes and Sunstar Homes brands. Through its FG Acquisition Corporation subsidiary Lennar acquired 93% of The Fortress Group in 2002; it also added Maryland-based Patriot Homes and assets of California homebuilders Pacific Century Homes and Cambridge Homes to bring its homebuilding operations to 16 states.

In July 2002 Leonard Miller died of liver cancer. Stuart Miller continues to lead the company as its president and CEO. The company acquired nine homebuilders that year which expanded its operations into markets in Chicago (Concord Homes and Summit Homes) Baltimore the Carolinas and California's Central Valley; some of the acquisitions strengthened Lennar's position in its existing markets. Lennar subsidiary North American Title Group acquired The Sentinel Title Corporation with nine branches in Maryland Virginia and Washington DC.

Lennar continued to acquire in 2003 adding Seppala Homes and Coleman Homes (with a backlog of about 300 homes and 3000 owned or controlled homesites) expanding its positions respectively in South Carolina and the Central Valley of California. The company's North American Title Group Inc. subsidiary acquired Mid America Title Company (Waukegan Illinois) which strengthened Lennar's homebuilding operations in the Chicago market.

In mid-2003 an entity jointly owned by Lennar and LNR Property Corporation (real estate investment finance and management) agreed to acquire The Newhall Land and Farming Company (master-planned communities) for about $1 billion. The deal closed in January 2004 enabling LNR to buy existing income-producing commercial assets from the venture and Lennar to option certain current homesites. Also that year Lennar's Texas operations grew with its cash purchase of San Antonio-based Connell-Barron Homes and the company expanded into Jacksonville by acquiring Classic American Homes for an undisclosed cash price. Lennar closed out the year with increased revenues and earnings of 18% and 26% respectively over the previous year and a strong backlog of about 15550 homes valued at about $5 billion.

As the real estate market continued to thrive Lennar acquired regional builders mortgage operations and title and closing businesses. During 2005 Lennar entered the Boston New York City and Reno markets; it also expanded its Jacksonville operations by acquiring Admiral Homes. The condo and apartment buildings in New York and Boston were valued at more than $2 billion.

Along with the rest of the homebuilding industry Lennar started to see trouble in 2006 as interest rates rose and years of overbuilding began taking their toll. Fallout from the subprime mortgage crisis and global credit crunch further unraveled the market. Lennar's average price per home fell by $40000 and the number of homes delivered fell by approximately 40000 (in 2009 as compared with fiscal 2005).

In early 2007 Lennar and its spun-off investment unit LNR Properties reduced their stakes in LandSource a joint venture that invests in raw land (among the riskiest of real estate investments particularly vulnerable to market downturns). MW Housing Partners an investment vehicle of the California Public Employees' Retirement System bought 68% of LandSource for $900 million in cash and property; Lennar lowered its stake from 50% to 16%. The sale proved to be fortuitous for Lennar: Not only did it bring the company much-needed cash but it also reduced Lennar's exposure to the debt-laden LandSource which filed for Chapter 11 bankruptcy protection a year later. LandSource emerged from bankruptcy as the debt-free Newhall Land Development. In 2009 Lennar bought back a 15% stake in the reorganized company for $140.

Lennar survived the economic downturn by shifting its focus and tightening its belt. As one of the larger builders it weathered the downturn by exiting slower markets lowering prices and reducing staff. The company also bought fewer home sites and tightened its lending standards to reduce its exposure to loan defaults. Lennar also increased its focus on the first-time buyer and limited the number of home plans offered.

EXECUTIVES

Vp And Coo, Jonathan M. (Jon) Jaffe, age 59, $800,000 total compensation

Vp And Cfo, Bruce E. Gross, age 60, $650,000 total compensation

Ceo, Stuart A. Miller, age 61, $1,000,000 total compensation

President, Richard (Rick) Beckwitt, age 59, $800,000 total compensation

Ceo Rialto Capital Management, Jeffrey P. (Jeff) Krasnoff

Regional President Lennar Land And Homebuilding, Jeff Roos

Regional President Lennar Land And Homebuilding, Rob Hutton

President Strategic Holdings Inc., David J. Kaiserman

President North American Title Group, Thomas J. (Tom) Fischer

President Rialto Capital Management, Jay Mantz

Secretary And General Counsel, Mark Sustana, age 58, $450,000 total compensation

President Universal American Mortgage And Eagle Home Mortgage, James T. (Jimmy) Timmons

Regional President Lennar Land And Homebuilding, Fred Rothman

President Lennar Multifamily Communities, Todd Farrell

Regional President Lennar Multifamily Communities, Ed Easley

Cio, Laura Lete

Regional President Lennar Homebuilding And Land, Greg McGuff

President Lennar International, Chris Marlin

Vice President Of Marketing And Sales, Susan Wilke

Vice President Sales And Marketing, Carlos Gonzalez

Vice President Sales And Marketing, Courtney Jaskiewicz

Vice President Sales, Dan Koontz

Svp National Finance Group, Joy Condon

Vice President Of Sales, Joe Catanzariti

Vice President Compensation Payroll And Hrms, Manny Murias

Executive Vice President, Al Lee

Division President, Mark Torres

Division President Carolinas, Jeff Harris

Vice President Operations Atlanta South, Chris Recker

Regional Vice President Land, Matthew Wineman

Vice President Land Acquisitions And Development, Jim Bowersox

West Region Vice President Of Marketing, Janice Hinshaw

Vice President Controller, Ryan Smith

Vice President Land Division, Anthony Mignone

Vice President Purchasing, Scott Handt

Vice President Forward Planning, Geoffrey Smith

Vice President Of Sales, Lori Pennebaker

Vice President Of Land Acquisition, Jeff Minich

Vice President Of Finance, Lance Ellis

Vice President Controller, Ryan Gatchalian

Vice President Acquisition, Christina Hart

Division President, JJ Abraham

Vice President Of Construction, Al Kaufman

Vice President Of Land And Acquisitions, Greg Urech

Vp Of Construction Orlando, Mark Revell

Regional Vice President Land, Jim Bavouset

Senior Vice President Of Operations And Technology, Alex Burris

Vice President Land Acquisitions, David Stearn

Vice President Land Acquisition, John Cheney

Regional Vice President, Darin Mcmurray

Vice President Land Acquisition, Richard Maier

Division President, WORTH JENKINS

Vice President Of Land, Bruce Grundt

Vice President Government Relations, Dave Williams

Vice President Of Construction, John Bishop

Vice President Quality Assurance, Norm Greuel

Vice President Of Construction, Kevin Stream

Vice President Supply Chain Management And Strategic Initiatives, Paul Dodge

Vice President Of Sales And Marketing, Karen Morgan

Vice President Of Marketing, Stacy Sanders

Vice President Development, Ryan Hauck

Vice President Loan Servicing, Brian Westerbeke

Chief Sales Officer, Juan Gomez-sanchez

Division President, John Merlino

Vice President Of Sales And Marketing, Jeff Morin

Vice President Sales And Marketing, Garrett Chan

Vice President Quality Assurance, Norman Greuel

Vice President Of International Sales, Paulo Neto

Vice President Regional Operations Center, Brian McElwain

Senior Vice President, Jeff Mccall

Vp Sales, Tammy Hathaway

Vice President Forward Planning, Bridgit Koller

Vp Operations, Mike Gillett

Vice President Of Operations, Robert Smart

Vice President Of Land Development, Kurt Bruskotter

Vice President Of National Purchasing, Kemp Gillis

Vp Of Marketing, Christina Traver

Vice President Of Land Development, Joseph Fortino

Vice President Of Acquisitions, Michael Mashioff

Senior Vice President, Matt Sonntag

Designated Broker Vice President Sales Marketing Calatlantic Homes, Katy Spencer

Board Member, Theron I Gilliam

Vice Chairman Rialto Capital Management, Eric Feder

Assistant Treasurer, Gerry Rodriguez

Assistant Treasurer, Jacqui DeSouza

Treasurer And Vice President Fivepoint Communities, Mike White

Auditors: DELOITTE & TOUCHE LLP

LOCATIONS

HQ: Lennar Corp
700 Northwest 107th Avenue, Miami, FL 33172
Phone: 305 559-4000
Web: www.lennar.com

Selected Markets

East
Florida
New Jersey
North Carolina
South Carolina
Central
Georgia
Illinois
Indiana
Maryland
Minnesota
Tennessee
Virginia
Texas
West
Arizona
California
Colorado
Nevada
Oregon
Utah
Washington
Other: Urban divisions and other homebuilding related investments including FivePoint.

PRODUCTS/OPERATIONS

2018 Sales

	$ mil.	% of total
Homebuilding West	8,060	40
Homebuilding East	6,250	30
Homebuilding Texas	2,421	12
Homebuilding Central	2,291	11
Homebuilding Other	56	
Lennar Financial Services	868	4
Lennar Multifamily	421	2
Rialto	205	1
Total	**20,572**	**100**

Selected Subsidiaries

360 Developers LLC
Eagle Bend Commercial LLC
Eagle Home Mortgage LLC
Heritage of Auburn Hills LLC
Lennar Associates Management LLC
Lennar Homes of California Inc.
Lennar Homes of Texas Sales and Marketing Ltd.
Lennar Ventures LLC
LH-EH Layton Lakes Estate LLC
Majestic Woods LLC
North American Title Company (MD)
Raintree Village L.L.C.
Savell Gulley Development LLC
Universal American Mortgage Company LLC
U.S. Home of Arizona Construction Co.

COMPETITORS

Beazer Homes
D.R. Horton
Hovnanian Enterprises
KB Home
M.D.C.
Meritage Homes
NVR
PulteGroup
TRI Pointe
Taylor Morrison
Toll Brothers

HISTORICAL FINANCIALS

Company Type: Public

Income Statement
FYE: November 30

	REVENUE ($ mil.)	NET INCOME ($ mil.)	NET PROFIT MARGIN	EMPLOYEES
11/19	22,260	1,849	8.3%	10,106
11/18	20,572	1,696	8.2%	11,626
11/17	12,646	810	6.4%	9,111
11/16	10,950	912	8.3%	8,335
11/15	9,474	803	8.5%	7,749
Annual Growth	**23.8%**	**23.2%**	**—**	**6.9%**

2019 Year-End Financials

Debt ratio: 26.00%
Return on equity: 12.00%
Cash ($ mil.): 1,574
Current ratio: 18.00
Long-term debt ($ mil.): 7,777

No. of shares (mil.): 316
Dividends
Yield: 0.0%
Payout: 3.0%
Market value ($ mil.): 18,843

	STOCK PRICE ($) FY Close	P/E High/Low		PER SHARE ($) Earnings	Dividends	Book Value
11/19	60.00	11	7	6.00	0.00	50.00
11/18	43.00	13	7	5.00	0.00	45.00
11/17	63.00	18	12	3.00	0.00	33.00
11/16	43.00	13	9	4.00	0.00	30.00
11/15	51.00	15	11	3.00	0.00	26.00
Annual Growth	**3.9%**	**—**	**—**	**14.1%**	**(0.0%)**	**17.8%**

LETTIE PATE EVANS FOUNDATION

EXECUTIVES

President, Charles H McTier
V Pres, P Russell Harding
Treasurer, J Lee Tribble
Secretary, Erik S Johnson
Officer, Elizabeth A Smith
Vice-Chairman, James M Sibley
Executive Director, Antone Callaway
Manager, Amy Todd
Vice President, Susan Shows
Vice President Marketing, John Cooper

LOCATIONS

HQ: LETTIE PATE EVANS FOUNDATION
191 PEACHTREE ST NE # 3540, ATLANTA, GA
303031740
Phone: 404 522-6755
Web: WWW.LPEVANS.ORG

HISTORICAL FINANCIALS

Company Type: Private

Income Statement
FYE: December 31

	ASSETS ($ mil.)	NET INCOME ($ mil.)	INCOME AS % OF ASSETS	EMPLOYEES
12/16	2,695	90	3.3%	12
12/15	45	11	25.0%	—
12/14	34	0	—	—
12/12	34	0	0.3%	—
Annual Growth	**198.4%**	**444.0%**	**—**	**—**

Levi Strauss & Co.

Pioneering American apparel maker Levi Strauss & Co. has jeans in its genes. A global manufacturer of brand-name clothing Levi Strauss sells jeans and sportswear under the Levi's Dockers Signature by Levi Strauss and Denizen labels in more than 110 countries. It also markets men's and women's underwear and loungewear. The company distributes its brand products through more than 800 company-operated stores located in over 30 countries and through the third-party and first-party online stores. Levi Strauss makes some 70% of its revenue from Levi's branded men's pants. The company went public (again) in early 2019 although the Haas family (descendants of founder Levi Strauss) still controls it.

IPO

In early 2019 Levi Strauss raised some $625 million in a public offering. The company plans to use the proceeds to support store expansion and developing its online business.

Operations

Levi Strauss & Co (LS&CO). designs markets and sells jeans casual and dress pants tops shorts skirts jackets footwear and related accessories for men women and children. It has two principal brands Levi's which is known best for its jeans but makes a full wardrobe besides; and Dockers which makes business casual clothing mainly for men. Sales of the Levi's brand accounts for 85% of the total sales of menswear accounts for 70% and sales of pants represents 70% of sales as well.

LS&CO reaches customers indirectly through third-party wholesale customers such as department stores and directly through owned and operated freestanding physical stores concession stands in departments stores and e-commerce sites. The wholesale channel generates two-thirds of LS&CO's sales. Within the direct channel which accounts for the other third of sales physical retail represents nearly 25% and e-commerce nearly 15%.

Outside the US LS&CO operates a franchise model consisting of around 1200 stores.

Geographic Reach

LS&CO. sells its products in more than 110 countries. It operates manufacturing distribution and finishing facilities in the Americas Europe and Asia/Pacific regions. The company's Americas segment contributes about 55% of total revenue while its Europe and Asia (which includes the Middle East and North Africa) segments contributed about 30% and 15% respectively. Its key markets are the US France Germany Mexico and the UK.

Sales and Marketing

A multi-channel marketer LS&CO. sells its products in more than 50000 retail locations worldwide. Its brands lend themselves to a variety of retail formats including chain retailers (Wal-Mart and Target) department stores (Nordstrom and Bloomingdale's) and company-operated e-commerce sites and online stores of other retailers. Sales to its top 10 wholesale customers account for more than 25% of revenues.

The company distributes its products through a wide variety of retail formats around the world including chain and department stores franchise stores and shop-in-shops company-operated retail network multi-brand specialty stores mass channel retailers and both company-operated and retailer ecommerce sites.

Extremely successful marketing means Levi's jeans are much more expensive in Europe where they are considered a luxury brand than in the US where they have a more workmanlike image.

LS&CO. records a high marketing spend of roughly 10% of total sales. Advertising expenses were $400 million in 2018 up from $325 million in 2017.

Financial Performance

After a difficult spell Levi Strauss & Co.'s sales growth has kicked up a gear. In 2018 the company's revenue grew 14% to $5.6 billion thanks to surging sales in Europe a broader product range and new store additions. LS&CO. grew its range of women's clothes expanded its Signature label and added 21 stores in the Americas 17 in Europe and 36 in the Asia/Pacific region.

Net income was materially unchanged in 2018 at $285.3 million as higher sales were offset by a sharp increase in income taxes. LS&CO. paid $214.8 million in tax up from $64.2 million in 2017 due to a one-off charge from the US Tax Cuts and Jobs Act.

LS&CO.'s cash on hand grew $79.5 million during 2018 ending the year at $633.6 million. The company's operations generated $420.4 million partially offset by $179.4 million used in its investing activities and $148.2 million used in its financing. LS&CO.'s main cash uses were capital expenditures dividends and share repurchases.

Strategy

Levi Strauss & Co.'s strategy is two-fold: increase direct sales to offset declines in the department store sector; and expand its product lines including a greater focus on women.

The well-documented difficulties of the department store sector which is taking a hammering from e-commerce (among other things) is having a material impact on LS&CO.'s wholesale division. Wholesale has historically accounted for around two-thirds of its sales and is declining by a few percent annually. To mitigate the threat the company is growing its direct-to-consumer channel. It has accelerated its store opening program across all geographies adding around 75 stores in 2018 and improved its online business through new features and new websites such as a website serving the Indian market in 2018.

But LS&CO is also finding ways e-commerce can help slow the decline in its wholesale channel. LS&CO partnered with Amazon to establish what is essentially a Levi's shop-in-shop concession stand (albeit a digital one).

Long dependent on the men's bottoms category LS&CO. is expanding its women's and tops ranges. Logo t-shirts have been growing strongly as are fleece sweatshirts and trucker jackets. The strategy appears to be working: Pants are declining as a proportion of total sales fairly rapidly down from 77% in 2016 to 68% in 2018 while men's products are declining at a similar rate.

HISTORY

Levi Strauss arrived in New York City from Bavaria in 1847. In 1853 he joined his brother-in-law David Stern in San Francisco selling dry goods to the gold rushers. Shortly after a prospector told Strauss of miners' problems in finding sturdy pants. Strauss made a pair out of canvas for the prospector; word of the rugged pants spread quickly.

Strauss continued his dry-goods business in the 1860s. During this time he switched the pants' fabric to a durable French cloth called serge de Nimes soon known as denim. He colored the fabric with indigo dye and adopted the idea from Nevada tailor Jacob Davis of reinforcing the pants with copper rivets. In 1873 Strauss and Davis produced their first pair of waist-high overalls (later known as jeans). The pants soon became de rigueur for lumberjacks cowboys railroad workers oil drillers and farmers.

Strauss continued to build his pants and wholesaling business until he died in 1902. Levi Strauss & Co. passed to four Stern nephews who carried on their uncle's jeans business while maintaining the company's philanthropic reputation.

After WWII Walter Haas and Peter Haas (a fourth-generation Strauss family member) assumed leadership of LS&CO. In 1948 they ended the company's wholesaling business to concentrate on Levi's clothing. In the 1950s Levi's jeans ceased to be merely functional garments for workers; they became the uniform of American youth. In the 1960s LS&CO. added women's attire and expanded overseas.

The company went public in 1971. That year it added a women's career line and bought Koret sportswear (sold in 1984). By the mid-1980s profits declined. Peace Corps-veteran-turned-McKinsey-consultant Robert Haas (Walter's son) grabbed the reins of LS&CO. in 1984 and took the company private the next year (he became chairman in 1989). He also instilled a touchy-feely corporate culture often at odds with the bottom line.

In 1986 LS&CO. introduced Dockers casual pants. The company's sales began rising in 1991 as consumers forsook the designer duds of the 1980s for more practical clothes. LS&CO. says seven out of every 10 American men own a pair of Dockers. However LS&CO. missed out on the birth of another trend: the split between the fashion sense of US adolescents and their Levi's-loving baby boomer parents.

In 1996 the company introduced Slates dress slacks. That year LS&CO. bought back nearly one-third of its stock from family and employees for $4.3 billion. Grappling with slipping sales and debt from the buyout in 1997 LS&CO. closed 11 of its 37 North American plants laying off 6400 workers and 1000 salaried employees; it granted generous severance packages even to those earning minimum wage.

In 1998 citing improved labor conditions in China LS&CO. announced it would step up its use of Chinese subcontractors. Further restructuring added a third of its European plants to the closures list that year. LS&CO.'s sales fell 13% in fiscal 1998. Also that year Haas handed his CEO title to Pepsi executive Philip Marineau; Haas remained chairman.

LS&CO. closed 11 of 22 remaining North American plants in 1999. It also unleashed several new jeans brands that eschewed the company's one-style-fits-all approach of old.

In April 2002 LS&CO. announced it would close six of its last eight US plants and cut 20% of its worldwide staff (3300 workers). In September 2003 it cut another 5% of its global staff (650 workers). That month the company opened its first girls-only store located in Paris. In December LS&CO. replaced CFO Bill Chiasson with an outside turnaround specialist.

Pinpointing 2006 as the best time to step down as the company's chief executive Philip Marineau retired at the end of 2006. John Anderson president of LS&CO.'s Asia/Pacific division and head of the firm's global supply chain unit replaced Marineau as president and CEO.

Levi Strauss chairman Robert Haas retired in 2008 after 18 years in that role. His successor was Dryer's ice cream executive T. Gary Rogers who became the first leader in the company's history who was not a descendant of the founder. In August 2008 CFO Hans Ploos van Amstel left the company the and was replaced by Heidi Manes its corporate controller and principal accounting officer.

Looking to gain a more active role in its store business LS&CO. in July 2009 bought the operating rights for more than 70 Levi's and Dockers Outlet locations from store operator Anchor Blue Retail Group which had filed for bankruptcy for $72 million. Anchor Blue said the US recession and drop in consumer spending especially among teens severely affected its financial performance. LS&CO. said the acquisition will enable it to better manage its brands' positioning.

Rogers retired in late 2009 and Richard Kauffman became chairman.

EXECUTIVES

Executive Vice President And President Europe, Seth M. Ellison, age 60, $609,808 total compensation

President & Ceo Director, Charles V. (Chip) Bergh, age 61, $1,343,077 total compensation

Evp And Cfo, Harmit J. Singh, age 55, $746,538 total compensation

Executive Vice President And General Counsel, Seth R. Jaffe

Chief Human Resources Officer, Elizabeth Wood

Executive Vice President And President Of Direct-to-consumer (dtc), Marc Rosen, age 50

Executive Vice President And President Of Levi Strauss Asia Middle East And Africa, David Love, age 56, $580,387 total compensation

Senior Vice President And Chief Communications Officer, Kelly McGinnis

Executive Vice President And President Levi Strauss Americas, Roy Bagattini, age 55, $690,433 total compensation

Executive Vice President And President Product Innovation And Supply Chain, Liz O'Neill

Senior Vice President & Chief Marketing Officer, Jennifer (Jen) Sey

Vice President Global Mand D Plng And Operations, Barb Gollert

Vice President Sustainability, Michael Kobori

Vice President Human Resources, Karthik Sarma

Vice President Global Logistics, Doug Flores

Vice President Dtc Merchandising, Simon Haskell

Senior Vice President Global Distribution And Logistics, Stephen Berube

Vice President Managing Director South Europe, Diana Dimitian

Vice President Merchandising Levi's Wome, Julie Pike

Executive Vice President President, Levi Strauss Americas

Chairman, Stephen C. Neal, age 69

Auditors: PricewaterhouseCoopers LLP

LOCATIONS

HQ: Levi Strauss & Co.
1155 Battery Street, San Francisco, CA 94111
Phone: 415 501-6000
Web: www.levistrauss.com

2018 Stores

	#
Americas region	268
Europe region	300
Asia/Pacific region	256
Total	**0** 697

2018 Sales

	$ mil.	% of total
Americas	3,043	55
Europe	1,646	29
Asia/Pacific region	887	17
Total	**5,575**	**100**

PRODUCTS/OPERATIONS

2018 Sales

	% of total
Levi's brand	86
Dockers brand	7
Signature by Levi Strauss & Denizen brands	7
Total	**0** **100**

Selected Brands

Denizen
Dockers
  Dockers Alpha Khaki
  Dockers for Men
  Dockers for Women
Levi's
  Levi's 501 Original
  Levi's 505 Straight
  Levi's 511 Skinny
  Levi's 513 Slim
  Levi's 514 Slim Straight
  Levi's Curve ID
Signature by Levis Strauss & Co.
Intro
Waterless
Wellthread
Wasteless

COMPETITORS

Abercrombie & Fitch	Nine West
American Eagle	OshKosh B'Gosh
Outfitters	Oxford Industries
Benetton	PVH
Calvin Klein	Perry Ellis
Diesel SpA	International
Fast Retailing	Ralph Lauren
Fruit of the Loom	Sean John
Guess?	Sears
Haggar	Target Corporation
Hugo Boss	The Gap
Inditex	True Religion Apparel
J. Crew	Under Armour
Jockey International	VF Corporation
Joe's Jeans	Victoria's Secret
Kmart	Stores
Kohl's	Wacoal
Lands' End	Wal-Mart
Macy's	Warnaco Group
NIKE	adidas
Nautica Apparel	

HISTORICAL FINANCIALS

Company Type: Public

Income Statement   FYE: November 24

	REVENUE ($ mil.)	NET INCOME ($ mil.)	NET PROFIT MARGIN	EMPLOYEES
11/19	5,763	395	6.8%	15,800
11/18	5,575	283	5.1%	15,100
11/17	4,904	281	5.7%	13,800
11/16	4,553	291	6.4%	13,200
11/15	4,494	209	4.7%	12,500
Annual Growth	6.4%	17.2%	—	6.0%

2019 Year-End Financials

Debt ratio: 24.00%	No. of shares (mil.): 341
Return on equity: 31.00%	Dividends
Cash ($ mil.): 934	Yield: 0.0%
Current ratio: 2.00	Payout: 15.0%
Long-term debt ($ mil.): 1,007	Market value ($ mil.): 5,788

	STOCK PRICE ($) FY Close	P/E High/Low	PER SHARE ($) Earnings	Dividends	Book Value
11/19	17.00	24 16	1.00	0.00	5.00
Annual Growth	—	— —	—	—	—

LEVI STRAUSS & CO.

Pioneering American apparel maker Levi Strauss & Co. has jeans in its genes. A global manufacturer of brand-name clothing Levi Strauss sells jeans and sportswear under the Levi's Dockers Signature by Levi Strauss and Denizen labels in more than 110 countries. It also markets men's and women's underwear and loungewear. The company distributes its brand products through more than 800 company-operated stores located in over 30 countries and through the third-party and first-party online stores. Levi Strauss makes some 70% of its revenue from Levi's branded men's pants. The company went public (again) in early 2019 although the Haas family (descendants of founder Levi Strauss) still controls it.

IPO

In early 2019 Levi Strauss raised some $625 million in a public offering. The company plans to use the proceeds to support store expansion and developing its online business.

Operations

Levi Strauss & Co (LS&CO). designs markets and sells jeans casual and dress pants tops shorts skirts jackets footwear and related accessories for men women and children. It has two principal brands Levi's which is known best for its jeans but makes a full wardrobe besides; and Dockers which makes business casual clothing mainly for men. Sales of the Levi's brand accounts for 85% of the total sales of menswear accounts for 70% and sales of pants represents 70% of sales as well.

LS&CO reaches customers indirectly through third-party wholesale customers such as department stores and directly through owned and operated freestanding physical stores concession stands in departments stores and e-commerce sites. The wholesale channel generates two-thirds of LS&CO's sales. Within the direct channel which accounts for the other third of sales physical retail represents nearly 25% and e-commerce nearly 15%.

Outside the US LS&CO operates a franchise model consisting of around 1200 stores.

Geographic Reach

LS&CO. sells its products in more than 110 countries. It operates manufacturing distribution and finishing facilities in the Americas Europe and Asia/Pacific regions. The company's Americas segment contributes about 55% of total revenue while its Europe and Asia (which includes the Middle East and North Africa) segments contributed about 30% and 15% respectively. Its key markets are the US France Germany Mexico and the UK.

Sales and Marketing

A multi-channel marketer LS&CO. sells its products in more than 50000 retail locations worldwide. Its brands lend themselves to a variety of retail formats including chain retailers (Wal-Mart and Target) department stores (Nordstrom and Bloomingdale's) and company-operated e-commerce sites and online stores of other retailers. Sales to its top 10 wholesale customers account for more than 25% of revenues.

The company distributes its products through a wide variety of retail formats around the world including chain and department stores franchise stores and shop-in-shops company-operated retail network multi-brand specialty stores mass channel retailers and both company-operated and retailer ecommerce sites.

Extremely successful marketing means Levi's jeans are much more expensive in Europe where they are considered a luxury brand than in the US where they have a more workmanlike image.

LS&CO. records a high marketing spend of roughly 10% of total sales. Advertising expenses were $400 million in 2018 up from $325 million in 2017.

Financial Performance

After a difficult spell Levi Strauss & Co.'s sales growth has kicked up a gear. In 2018 the company's revenue grew 14% to $5.6 billion thanks to surging sales in Europe a broader product range and new store additions. LS&CO. grew its range of women's clothes expanded its Signature label and added 21 stores in the Americas 17 in Europe and 36 in the Asia/Pacific region.

Net income was materially unchanged in 2018 at $285.3 million as higher sales were offset by a sharp increase in income taxes. LS&CO. paid $214.8 million in tax up from $64.2 million in 2017 due to a one-off charge from the US Tax Cuts and Jobs Act.

LS&CO.'s cash on hand grew $79.5 million during 2018 ending the year at $633.6 million. The company's operations generated $420.4 million partially offset by $179.4 million used in its investing activities and $148.2 million used in its financing. LS&CO.'s main cash uses were capital expenditures dividends and share repurchases.

Strategy

Levi Strauss & Co.'s strategy is two-fold: increase direct sales to offset declines in the department store sector; and expand its product lines including a greater focus on women.

The well-documented difficulties of the department store sector which is taking a hammering from e-commerce (among other things) is having a material impact on LS&CO.'s wholesale division. Wholesale has historically accounted for around two-thirds of its sales and is declining by a few percent annually. To mitigate the threat the company is growing its direct-to-consumer channel. It has accelerated its store opening program across all geographies adding around 75 stores in 2018 and improved its online business through new features and new websites such as a website serving the Indian market in 2018.

But LS&CO is also finding ways e-commerce can help slow the decline in its wholesale channel. LS&CO partnered with Amazon to establish what is essentially a Levi's shop-in-shop concession stand (albeit a digital one).

Long dependent on the men's bottoms category LS&CO. is expanding its women's and tops ranges. Logo t-shirts have been growing strongly as are fleece sweatshirts and trucker jackets. The strategy appears to be working: Pants are declining as a proportion of total sales fairly rapidly down from 77% in 2016 to 68% in 2018 while men's products are declining at a similar rate.

HISTORY

Levi Strauss arrived in New York City from Bavaria in 1847. In 1853 he joined his brother-in-law David Stern in San Francisco selling dry goods to the gold rushers. Shortly after a prospector told Strauss of miners' problems in finding sturdy pants. Strauss made a pair out of canvas for the prospector; word of the rugged pants spread quickly.

Strauss continued his dry-goods business in the 1860s. During this time he switched the pants' fabric to a durable French cloth called serge de Nimes soon known as denim. He colored the fabric with indigo dye and adopted the idea from Nevada tailor Jacob Davis of reinforcing the pants with copper rivets. In 1873 Strauss and Davis produced their first pair of waist-high overalls (later known as jeans). The pants soon became de rigueur for lumberjacks cowboys railroad workers oil drillers and farmers.

Strauss continued to build his pants and wholesaling business until he died in 1902. Levi Strauss & Co. passed to four Stern nephews who carried on their uncle's jeans business while maintaining the company's philanthropic reputation.

After WWII Walter Haas and Peter Haas (a fourth-generation Strauss family member) assumed leadership of LS&CO. In 1948 they ended the company's wholesaling business to concentrate on Levi's clothing. In the 1950s Levi's jeans ceased to be merely functional garments for workers; they became the uniform of American youth. In the 1960s LS&CO. added women's attire and expanded overseas.

The company went public in 1971. That year it added a women's career line and bought Koret sportswear (sold in 1984). By the mid-1980s profits declined. Peace Corps-veteran-turned-McKinsey-consultant Robert Haas (Walter's son) grabbed the reins of LS&CO. in 1984 and took the company private the next year (he became chairman in 1989). He also instilled a touchy-feely corporate culture often at odds with the bottom line.

In 1986 LS&CO. introduced Dockers casual pants. The company's sales began rising in 1991 as consumers forsook the designer duds of the 1980s for more practical clothes. LS&CO. says seven out of every 10 American men own a pair of Dockers. However LS&CO. missed out on the birth of another trend: the split between the fashion sense of US adolescents and their Levi's-loving baby boomer parents.

In 1996 the company introduced Slates dress slacks. That year LS&CO. bought back nearly one-third of its stock from family and employees for $4.3 billion. Grappling with slipping sales and debt from the buyout in 1997 LS&CO. closed 11 of its 37 North American plants laying off 6400 workers and 1000 salaried employees; it granted generous severance packages even to those earning minimum wage.

In 1998 citing improved labor conditions in China LS&CO. announced it would step up its use of Chinese subcontractors. Further restructuring added a third of its European plants to the closures list that year. LS&CO.'s sales fell 13% in fiscal 1998. Also that year Haas handed his CEO title to Pepsi executive Philip Marineau; Haas remained chairman.

LS&CO. closed 11 of 22 remaining North American plants in 1999. It also unleashed several new jeans brands that eschewed the company's one-style-fits-all approach of old.

In April 2002 LS&CO. announced it would close six of its last eight US plants and cut 20% of its worldwide staff (3300 workers). In September 2003 it cut another 5% of its global staff (650 workers). That month the company opened its first girls-only store located in Paris. In December LS&CO. replaced CFO Bill Chiasson with an outside turnaround specialist.

Pinpointing 2006 as the best time to step down as the company's chief executive Philip Marineau retired at the end of 2006. John Anderson president of LS&CO.'s Asia/Pacific division and head of the firm's global supply chain unit replaced Marineau as president and CEO.

Levi Strauss chairman Robert Haas retired in 2008 after 18 years in that role. His successor was Dryer's ice cream executive T. Gary Rogers who became the first leader in the company's history who was not a descendant of the founder. In August 2008 CFO Hans Ploos van Amstel left the company the and was replaced by Heidi Manes its corporate controller and principal accounting officer.

Looking to gain a more active role in its store business LS&CO. in July 2009 bought the operating rights for more than 70 Levi's and Dockers Outlet locations from store operator Anchor Blue Retail Group which had filed for bankruptcy for $72 million. Anchor Blue said the US recession and drop in consumer spending especially among teens severely affected its financial performance. LS&CO. said the acquisition will enable it to better manage its brands' positioning.

Rogers retired in late 2009 and Richard Kauffman became chairman.

EXECUTIVES

Executive Vice President And President Europe, Seth M. Ellison, age 60, $609,808 total compensation
President & Ceo Director, Charles V. (Chip) Bergh, age 61, $1,343,077 total compensation
Evp And Cfo, Harmit J. Singh, age 55, $746,538 total compensation
Executive Vice President And General Counsel, Seth R. Jaffe
Chief Human Resources Officer, Elizabeth Wood
Executive Vice President And President Of Direct-to-consumer (dtc), Marc Rosen, age 50
Executive Vice President And President Of Levi Strauss Asia Middle East And Africa, David Love, age 56, $580,387 total compensation

Senior Vice President And Chief Communications Officer, Kelly McGinnis
Executive Vice President And President Levi Strauss Americas, Roy Bagattini, age 55, $690,433 total compensation
Executive Vice President And President Product Innovation And Supply Chain, Liz O'Neill
Senior Vice President & Chief Marketing Officer, Jennifer (Jen) Sey
Vice President Global Mand D Plng And Operations, Barb Gollert
Vice President Sustainability, Michael Kobori
Vice President Human Resources, Karthik Sarma
Vice President Sales, Donna Null Paulo
Vice President Global Logistics, Doug Flores
Vp Purchasing, Dean Edwards
Vice President Dtc Merchandising, Simon Haskell
Senior Vice President Global Distribution And Logistics, Stephen Berube
Vice President Managing Director South Europe, Diana Dimitian
Vice President Merchandising Levi's Wome, Julie Pike
Executive Vice President President, Levi Strauss Americas
Chairman, Stephen C. Neal, age 69
Auditors: PRICEWATERHOUSECOOPERS LLP SA

LOCATIONS

HQ: LEVI STRAUSS & CO.
1155 BATTERY ST, SAN FRANCISCO, CA 941111264
Phone: 415 501-6000
Web: WWW.LEVISTRAUSS.COM

2018 Stores

	#
Americas region	268
Europe region	300
Asia/Pacific region	256
Total	**697**

2018 Sales

	$ mil.	% of total
Americas	3,043	55
Europe	1,646	29
Asia/Pacific region	887	17
Total	**5,575**	**100**

PRODUCTS/OPERATIONS

2018 Sales

	% of total
Levi's brand	86
Dockers brand	7
Signature by Levi Strauss & Denizen brands	7
Total	**100**

Selected Brands

Denizen
Dockers
  Dockers Alpha Khaki
  Dockers for Men
  Dockers for Women
Levi's
  Levi's 501 Original
  Levi's 505 Straight
  Levi's 511 Skinny
  Levi's 513 Slim
  Levi's 514 Slim Straight
  Levi's Curve ID
Signature by Levis Strauss & Co.
Intro
Waterless
Wellthread
Wasteless

COMPETITORS

Abercrombie & Fitch	Nine West
American Eagle	OshKosh B'Gosh
Outfitters	Oxford Industries
Benetton	PVH
Calvin Klein	Perry Ellis
Diesel SpA	International
Fast Retailing	Ralph Lauren
Fruit of the Loom	Sean John
Guess?	Sears
Haggar	Target Corporation
Hugo Boss	The Gap
Inditex	True Religion Apparel
J. Crew	Under Armour
Jockey International	VF Corporation
Joe's Jeans	Victoria's Secret
Kmart	Stores
Kohl's	Wacoal
Lands' End	Wal-Mart
Macy's	Warnaco Group
NIKE	adidas
Nautica Apparel	

HISTORICAL FINANCIALS

Company Type: Private

Income Statement   FYE: November 25

	REVENUE ($ mil.)	NET INCOME ($ mil.)	NET PROFIT MARGIN	EMPLOYEES
11/18	5,575	285	5.1%	14,400
11/17	4,904	285	5.8%	—
11/16	4,553	291	6.4%	—
11/15	4,494	210	4.7%	—
Annual Growth	**7.4%**	**10.8%**	**—**	**—**

Liberty Media Corp (DE)

Auditors: KPMG LLP

LOCATIONS

HQ: Liberty Media Corp (DE)
12300 Liberty Boulevard, Englewood, CO 80112
Phone: 720 875-5400
Web: www.libertymedia.com

HISTORICAL FINANCIALS

Company Type: Public

Income Statement   FYE: December 31

	REVENUE ($ mil.)	NET INCOME ($ mil.)	NET PROFIT MARGIN	EMPLOYEES
12/18	8,040	531	6.6%	4,641
12/17	7,594	1,354	17.8%	4,393
12/16	5,276	680	12.9%	3,626
12/15	4,795	64	1.3%	3,503
12/14	4,450	178	4.0%	3,690
Annual Growth	**15.9%**	**31.4%**	**—**	**5.9%**

2018 Year-End Financials

Debt ratio: 33.00%	No. of shares (mil.): 608
Return on equity: 3.00%	Dividends
Cash ($ mil.): 358	Yield: —
Current ratio: 0.00	Payout: —
Long-term debt ($ mil.): 13,371	Market value ($ mil.): 22,474

	STOCK PRICE ($) FY Close	P/E High/Low		PER SHARE ($) Earnings	Dividends	Book Value
12/18	37.00	— —		(0.00)	0.00	27.00
12/17	40.00	— —		(0.00)	0.00	27.00
12/16	34.00	32 26		1.00	0.00	25.00
Annual Growth	**2.2%**			**—**	**—**	**2.1%**

Liberty Media Corp (DE)

Auditors: KPMG LLP

LOCATIONS

HQ: Liberty Media Corp (DE)
12300 Liberty Boulevard, Englewood, CO 80112
Phone: 720 875-5400
Web: www.libertymedia.com

HISTORICAL FINANCIALS

Company Type: Public

Income Statement   FYE: December 31

	REVENUE ($ mil.)	NET INCOME ($ mil.)	NET PROFIT MARGIN	EMPLOYEES
12/18	5,771	676	11.7%	4,555
12/17	5,425	1,124	20.7%	4,393
12/16	5,014	413	8.2%	3,626
12/15	4,552	259	5.7%	—
12/14	4,141	231	5.6%	—
Annual Growth	8.7%	30.8%	—	—

2018 Year-End Financials

Debt ratio: 28.00%	No. of shares (mil.): 326
Return on equity: 6.00%	Dividends
Cash ($ mil.): 91	Yield: —
Current ratio: 0.00	Payout: —
Long-term debt ($ mil.): 7,855	Market value ($ mil.): 11,988

	STOCK PRICE ($) FY Close	P/E High/Low	PER SHARE ($) Earnings	Dividends	Book Value
12/18	37.00	24 17	2.00	0.00	33.00
12/17	40.00	14 10	3.00	0.00	32.00
12/16	35.00	44 33	1.00	0.00	30.00
12/15	39.00	— —	(0.00)	0.00	(0.00)
12/14	35.00	— —	(0.00)	0.00	(0.00)
Annual Growth	1.1%		—	—	—

Lilly (Eli) & Co

Best known for its neuroscience products pharmaceutical firm Eli Lilly also makes endocrinology oncology and cardiovascular care medicines. Its top-selling drugs include Cymbalta for depression and pain Alimta for lung cancer Humalog and Humulin insulin for diabetes and Cialis for erectile dysfunction. Lilly also makes medications to treat schizophrenia and bipolar disorder (Zyprexa) osteoporosis (Evista and Forteo) heart conditions (Effient) ADHD (Strattera) gastric and lung cancer (Cyramza) and diabetes (Jardiance and Trulicity) as well as anti-infective agents.

HISTORY

Colonel Eli Lilly pharmacist and Union officer in the Civil War started Eli Lilly and Company in 1876 with $1300. His process of gelatin-coating pills led to sales of nearly $82000 in 1881. Later the company made gelatin capsules which it still sells. Lilly died in 1898 and his son and two grandsons ran the business until 1953.

Eli Lilly began extracting insulin from the pancreases of hogs and cattle in 1923; 6000 cattle glands or 24000 hog glands made one ounce of the substance. Other products created in the 1920s and 1930s included antiseptic Merthiolate sedative Seconal and treatments for pernicious anemia and heart disease. In 1947 the company began selling diethylstilbestrol (DES) a drug to prevent miscarriages. Eli Lilly researchers isolated the antibiotic erythromycin from a species of mold found in the Philippines in 1952. Lilly was also the major supplier of Salk polio vaccine.

The company enjoyed a 70% share of the DES market by 1971 when researchers noticed that a rare form of cervical cancer afflicted many of the daughters of women who had taken the drug. The FDA restricted the drug's use and Lilly found itself on the receiving (and frequently losing) end of a number of trailblazing product-liability suits that stretched into the 1990s.

The firm diversified in the 1970s buying Elizabeth Arden (cosmetics 1971; sold 1987) and IVAC (medical instruments 1977). It launched such products as analgesic Darvon and antibiotic Ceclor.

Lilly's 1982 launch of Humulin a synthetic insulin developed by Genentech made it the first company to market a genetically engineered product. In 1986 the company introduced Prozac; that year it also bought biotech firm Hybritech for $300 million (sold in 1995 for less than $10 million). In 1988 Lilly introduced anti-ulcerative Axid. It founded pesticides and herbicides maker DowElanco with Dow Chemical in 1989.

Trying to find a new product outlet the firm bought pharmacy benefit management company PCS Health Systems from what is now McKesson in 1994. But an FTC mandate to offer rival drugs and a lack of mail-order sales contributed to poor results which ultimately led Lilly to sell PCS to Rite Aid and exit this arena completely in 1998.

Eli Lilly in 1995 bought medical communications network developer Integrated Medical Systems. That year the firm and developer Centocor introduced ReoPro a blood-clot inhibitor used in angioplasties. The next year it launched antipsychotic Zyprexa Humalog and Gemzar and Prozac was approved to treat bulimia nervosa.

In 1997 the firm sold its DowElanco stake to Dow. In 1998 the Lilly Endowment passed the Ford Foundation as the US's largest charity largely due to Prozac (it has since been passed by the Bill & Melinda Gates Foundation). That year Lilly began trying to stop Chinese drugmakers from infringing on its patents for Prozac's active ingredient.

In 1999 a US federal judge found the firm illegally promoted osteoporosis drug Evista as a breast cancer preventative similar to AstraZeneca's Nolvadex. Lilly halted tests on its variation of heart drug Moxonidine after 53 patients died. Also that year Zyprexa was approved to treat bipolar disorder.

In 2000 the firm began marketing Prozac under the Sarafem name for severe premenstrual syndrome. A federal appeals court knocked more than two years off Prozac's patent reducing the expected 2003 expiration date to 2001 creating a negative impact on Lilly's annual sales (Prozac had accounted for 30% of revenues). Lilly suffered another blow when a potential successor to Prozac failed in clinical trials and became embroiled in legal maneuverings with generics maker Barr Pharmaceuticals.

While the firm fretted over Prozac and its patents it continued work to find its next blockbuster. In 2000 Lilly and partner ICOS announced favorable results from a study of erectile dysfunction treatment Cialis which was approved in Europe in 2002 and in the US in 2004. (Several years later Lilly acquired ICOS and with it full ownership of the Cialis franchise.)

In 2001 Lilly bought a minority stake in Isis Pharmaceuticals a developer of antisense drugs and licensed from it an antisense lung cancer drug.

Also that year the firm launched Lilly BioVentures a venture fund aimed at private biotech startup companies. In 2002 the company settled with eight states in an infringement-of-privacy case involving the company's accidental disclosure of e-mail addresses for more than 600 Prozac patients.

In late 2004 the druggernaut was one of several pharmas hit by bad news about drug side effects. Lilly announced its attention-deficit disorder drug Strattera had been linked to rare liver problems. The company agreed to add warning labels about the potential side effects to the drug's packaging and advertisements. The company also began facing trouble over Zyprexa as consumer lawsuits claiming diabetes and high blood pressure began pouring in. The majority of suits were settled in 2005 and 2007 for some $1.2 billion.

Generalized anxiety disorder drug Cymbalta was approved by the FDA and released in 2006 and osteoporosis drug Evista was approved for an expanded indication as a breast cancer preventative for postmenopausal women in 2007.

Also in 2007 the company acquired and absorbed development partner ICOS for $2.1 billion; the deal gave Lilly full ownership of Viagra-competitor Cialis. Lilly dropped a joint-development effort with another partner Alkermes for an inhaled insulin device in 2008.

The company gradually reduced its workforce by more than 10% between 2003 and 2008 to fight off the effects of generic competition and other challenges. Other restructuring measures included an employee attrition plan announced in 2007 a management restructuring in 2008 and a manufacturing consolidation program launched in 2008.

After a lengthy lawsuit regarding its patents for its top seller Zyprexa a federal judge ruled in Lilly's favor in 2008 against generic manufacturers IVAX Dr. Reddy's Laboratories and Teva Pharmaceutical Industries. Federal courts ruled that the drug's patents would remain valid until October 2011.

To fuel growth in the biopharmaceuticals market the firm completed a $1 billion biotech research facility in Indianapolis in 2008. It further expanded through the 2008 acquisition of biotech firm ImClone for about $6.5 billion; ImClone began operating as a research subsidiary of Lilly following the transaction. ImClone already had one approved blockbuster therapy Erbitux for colorectal and head/neck cancers and was developing numerous other cancer therapy candidates. Lilly also expanded its biotech oncology program earlier that year by purchasing development partner SGX Pharmaceuticals for $64 million. SGX was absorbed into Lilly's research operations.

EXECUTIVES

Svp And President Elanco Animal Health, Jeffrey N. (Jeff) Simmons, age 52

Svp And President Diabetes Business Unit And Lilly Usa, Enrique A. Conterno, age 52, $727,960 total compensation

President Manufacturing Operations, Maria Crowe, age 59

Svp And President Lilly International, Alfonso G. (Chito) Zulueta, age 56

Svp And President Lilly Oncology, Susan (Sue) Mahony, age 54

President And Ceo, David A. Ricks, age 51

Svp And President Lilly Bio-medicines, Christi Shaw

Svp And President Manufacturing Operations, Myles O'Neill

Svp Enterprise Risk Management And Chief Ethics And Compliance Officer, Melissa Stapleton Barnes, age 50

Svp And General Counsel, Michael J. Harrington, age 56, $827,400 total compensation

Svp And Cio, Aarti Shah
Svp And Cfo, Josh Smiley
Svp Science And Technology And President Lilly Research Labs, Daniel (Dan) Skovronsky
Senior Management (senior Vice President General Manager Director), Kent Supancik
Svp Development Center Of Excellence And Chief Medical Officer, Timothy Garnett
Department Head Space Planning, Brent Blanchard
National Account Manager Managed Healthcare Services, Ruthanna Curry
Vice President Medical Affiars, Robert Heine
Vice President Medicine Development Unit Diabetes And Clinical Transformation, Rob Metcalf
Senior Vice President Finance And Treasurer, Philip Johnson
Senior Medical Director, Thomas Hardy
Medical Director, Anurita Majumdar
Vice President And Medical Director China, Li Wang
Government Relations, Joel Worthington
National Sales Manager, Paul Huibers
Vice President Parenteral Manufacturing Operations, Ken Whitehead
Vice President, Julie Xing
Medical Director, Susan Kindig
Medical Director, Bo Chao
Vp And General Auditor, Kathy St Louis
Associate Vp It, Geri Kern
Senior Vice President Global Quality, Johna Norton
Vice President Human Resources, Giorgio Davidoni
Department Head, Lisa Little-tranter
Medical Director Diabetes, Elisa Razzoli
Vp Branchburg Technical Services Manufacturing Science, Victor Goetz
Vice President, Marie Schiller
Vice President Marketing, Daniel Lucas
National Account Manager Channel Accounts, Kristen Tinglum
Associate Vice President Organizational Learning And Development, Kristin Zemanek
Pharmd Surveillance Assoc, Russell Nichols
Senior Medical Director, Paulo Reis
National Account Manager, Nguyen Trang
Vice President, Gregory Plowman
National Sales Manager, Hostettler Danica
Medical Director Onc Platform Team, Metzka Lorraine Fonny
Chairman, John C. Lechleiter
Treasurer, Mike Wolf
Auditors: Ernst & Young LLP

LOCATIONS

HQ: Lilly (Eli) & Co
Lilly Corporate Center, Indianapolis, IN 46285
Phone: 317 276-2000
Web: www.lilly.com

2017 Sales

	$ mil.	% of total
US	12,785	56
Europe	3,943	17
Japan	2,420	11
Other	3,723	16
Total	22,871	100

PRODUCTS/OPERATIONS

2017 Sales

	$ mil.	% of total
Endocrinology	10,085	44
Oncology	3,812	17
Cardiovascular	2,871	13
Neurosciences	2,171	9
Immunology	605	3
Other human pharmaceuticals	241	1
Animal Health	3,086	13
Total	22,871	100

Selected Products and Indications

Neuroscience
Amyvid (florbetapir F 18 injection)
Cymbalta (duloxetine hydrocholoride; depression anxiety pain; also for managing fibromyalgia and chronic musculoskeletal pain in the US)
Prozac (fluoxetine hydrochloride; depression panic disorder obsessive-compulsive disorder and bulimia nervosa)
Strattera (atomoxetine hydrochloride ADHD)
Symbyax (olanzapine and fluoxetine hydrochloride bipolar and treatment-resistant depression)
Zyprexa (olanzapine schizophrenia and bipolar)
Zyprexa Relprevv (Zypadhera in the EU long-acting injectable Zyprexa)
Endocrinology (including diabetes)
Actos (pioglitazone hydrochloride type 2 diabetes)
Alimta (non-small cell lung cancer)
Axiron (testosterone topical for testosterone deficiency)
Erbitux (colorectal cancers head and neck cancers)
Evista (raloxifene hydrochloride osteoporosis and breast cancer prevention in postmenopausal women)
Forteo (osteoporosis)
Gemzar (pancreatic cancer metastatic breast cancer non-small cell lung cancer; bladder cancer in the EU)
Glucagon (injection rDNA origin)
Humalog (insulin lispro injection rDNA origin; diabetes)
Humalog Mix 75/25 (75% Insulin lispro protamine suspension 25% insulin lispro injection rDNA origin; diabetes)
Humalog Mix 50/50 (50% Insulin lispro protamine suspension 50% insulin lispro injection rDNA origin; diabetes)
Humalog Pen (insulin lispro rDNA origin; diabetes)
Humatrope (somatropin for injection rDNA origin; growth disorders)
Humulin (human insulin rDNA origin; diabetes)
Humulin Pen (human insulin rDNA origin; diabetes)
Tradjenta (type 2 diabetes)
Oncology (cancer)
Alimta (pemetrexed non-small cell lung cancer and malignant pleural mesothelioma)
Erbitux (colorectal head and neck cancers; from ImClone)
Gemzar (gemcitabine hydrochloride; pancreatic breast lung bladder and ovarian cancers)
Cardiovascular
Adcirca (pulmonary arterial hypertension)
Cialis (tadalafil erectile dysfunction; benign prostatic hyperplasia in US)
Efient/Effient (atherothrombotic events)
Livalo (statin high cholesterol)
ReoPro (percutaneous coronary intervention)
Animal Health (Elanco)
Apralan (antibiotic to control enteric infections in calves and swine)
Coban Monteban and Maxiban (anticoccidial for poultry)
Comfortis (flea infestation prevention tablets for dogs)
Micotil Pulmotil and Pulmotil AC (antibiotics for respiratory disease in cattle swine and poultry respectively)
Paylean Optaflexx (leanness and performance enhancers for swine and cattle respectively)
Posilac (protein supplement for enhanced milk productivity in cows)
Reconcile (separation anxiety for dogs)
Rumensin (feed additive)
Surmax/Maxus (performance enhancer for swine and poultry)
Trifexis (chewable tablet for dogs to prevent flea infestations and heartworm disease and control intestinal parasite infections)
Tylan (antibiotic)
Other pharmaceuticals (including anti-infectives)
Ceclor (bacterial infections)
Vancocin (staphylococcal infections)

COMPETITORS

Abbott Labs	Mylan
Amgen	Myriad Genetics
AstraZeneca	Novartis
Bayer AG	Novo Nordisk
Boehringer Ingelheim	Pfizer
Bristol-Myers Squibb	Roche Holding
Dr. Reddy's	Sanofi
GlaxoSmithKline	Shire
Johnson & Johnson	Takeda Pharmaceutical
Merck	Teva
Merck KGaA	

HISTORICAL FINANCIALS

Company Type: Public

Income Statement

FYE: December 31

	REVENUE ($ mil.)	NET INCOME ($ mil.)	NET PROFIT MARGIN	EMPLOYEES
12/18	24,556	3,232	13.2%	38,680
12/17	22,871	(204)	—	40,655
12/16	21,222	2,738	12.9%	41,975
12/15	19,959	2,408	12.1%	41,275
12/14	19,616	2,391	12.2%	39,135
Annual Growth	5.8%	7.8%	—	(0.3%)

2018 Year-End Financials

Debt ratio: 29.00%
Return on equity: 30.00%
Cash ($ mil.): 8,086
Current ratio: 2.00
Long-term debt ($ mil.): 11,640

No. of shares (mil.): 1,057
Dividends
Yield: 2.0%
Payout: 72.0%
Market value ($ mil.): 122,320

	STOCK PRICE ($) FY Close	P/E High/Low		PER SHARE ($) Earnings	Dividends	Book Value
12/18	116.00	38	24	3.00	2.00	9.00
12/17	84.00	—	—	(0.00)	2.00	11.00
12/16	74.00	33	25	3.00	2.00	13.00
12/15	84.00	40	30	2.00	2.00	13.00
12/14	69.00	33	23	2.00	2.00	14.00
Annual Growth	13.8%	—	—	8.8%	3.5%	(9.5%)

LIMETREE BAY TERMINALS LLC

HOVENSA brings together US and Latin American know-how and operations to handle oil products in the US Virgin Islands. HOVENSA is a joint venture of Hess and Venezuelan oil giant PDVSA (its major crude oil supplier). Once the largest private employer in the US Virgin Islands the company operated a 500000-barrels-per-day crude oil refinery on St. Croix along with two specialized oil processing complexes a 150000-barrels-per-day fluid catalytic cracking unit and a 58000-barrels-per-day delayed coker unit. However the St. Croix refinery had run up losses for years; it was shut down in 2012 and was put up for sale in 2013.

Strategy

Citing high operating and maintenance costs (the refinery was fueled by oil not the cheaper natural gas) and the growth of lower-cost refineries in emerging markets HOVENSA has posted $1.3 billion in losses since 2009. As a result the company decided to cut its losses by converting the refinery into an oil storage terminal which can take advantage of St. Croix's strategic location. Its 55-ft. deep harbor enables it to receive crude oil tanker deliveries from Venezuela and around the world. The storage terminal employs about 100 workers. The shutdown of the refinery resulted in more than 2000 employes being laid off.

Company Background

In 2009 the global economic downturn depressed demand for oil caused a dip in production and prompted the company to lay off 270 employees (about 21% of its total contract workers).

Crude thoughput has declined steadily at HOVENSA due to weaker refining margins and planned and unplanned maintenance from 402000 barrels per day (bpd) in 2009 to 390000 bpd in 2010 to 284000 bpd in 2011.

Auditors: ERNST & YOUNG LLP
NEW YORK N

LOCATIONS

HQ: LIMETREE BAY TERMINALS LLC
1 ESTATE HOPE, CHRISTIANSTED, VI 00820
Phone: 340 692-3000

COMPETITORS

Chevron	Royal Dutch Shell
ConocoPhillips	Sunoco
Exxon Mobil	Valero Energy
Marathon Oil	

HISTORICAL FINANCIALS

Company Type: Private

Income Statement				FYE: December 31
	REVENUE ($ mil.)	NET INCOME ($ mil.)	NET PROFIT MARGIN	EMPLOYEES
12/09	10,048	(451)	—	1,300
12/08	17,480	95	0.5%	
Annual Growth	(42.5%)	—	—	

Lincoln National Corp.

Lincoln National which operates as Lincoln Financial Group provides retirement planning and life insurance to individuals and employers through annuities 401k and savings plans and a variety of life dental and disability insurance products. The company does business through such subsidiaries as Lincoln National Life Insurance Lincoln Life & Annuity Company of New York and First Penn-Pacific Life Insurance Company. Lincoln Financial is also active in the investment management business offering individual and institutional clients such financial services as pension plans trusts and mutual funds through its subsidiaries.

Operations

Lincoln Financial operates through four segments: Life Insurance Annuities Group Protection and Retirement Plan Services.

The company's largest segment Life Insurance (more than 40% of total sales) offers term universal and variable policies; a linked benefit product; and a critical illness rider.

The Annuities segment (more than 25% of sales) offers fixed and variable annuities.

Group Protection (some 25% of sales) offers non-medical policies — primarily term life dental critical illness accident vision and disability products — to the employer market.

Retirement Plan Services (more than 5% of sales) provides employers with plans and services primarily in the defined contribution retirement plan marketplace.

Geographic Reach

Headquartered in Radnor Pennsylvania Lincoln Financial also has offices in Atlanta (Group Protection); Dover New Hampshire; Fort Wayne Indi-

ana (Annuities and Retirement Plan Services); Greensboro North Carolina (Life Insurance); Omaha Nebraska; and Philadelphia.

Sales and Marketing

Lincoln Financial Network distributes Lincoln Financial products through a network of some 1000 planners and agents. Lincoln Financial Distributors is the company's wholesale distributor serving brokers consultants planners agents third party administrators financial advisors and other intermediaries. Lincoln Financial Distributors has more than 600 internal and external wholesalers and approximately 8600 active producers.

Group Protection distributes its products through employee benefits brokers third-party administrators and other employee benefit firms.

Financial Performance

Lincoln Financial has seen overall revenue growth over the past few years especially in 2017 and 201. Net income growth has been sporadic though.

In 2018 revenue increased 15% to $16.4 billion as insurance premiums fee income and net investment income all rose. Contributing to the rise in earned premiums was the addition of Liberty Life Assurance Company of Boston acquired midway through the year.

However net income fell 21% to $1.6 billion in 2018. This drop was largely due to a one-time federal income tax benefit received in 2017 which boosted net income that year by 74%. Acquisition-related expenses and the company's digitization initiative also cut into the bottom line.

The company ended 2018 with $2.3 billion in net cash some $7 million more than it had at the end of 2017. Operating activities provided $1.9 billion in cash and financing activities provided another $4.6 billion while investing activities used $5.8 billion.

Strategy

Like any company with heavy exposure to global macroeconomic conditions Lincoln Financial is vulnerable to capital market downturns which could lead to corporate losses. Additionally a number of the company's competitors have greater access to funds offer a broader range of products and enjoy a greater market share than Lincoln does. To meet the challenges of difficult economic times in the market the company has adopted strategies to strengthen its business that include investing in high-quality corporate securities to reduce asset risk escalating share repurchases and debt repayment and repricing life and annuity products to guarantee new business that is profitable. It is investing in product innovations and distribution channels to drive up revenues. And the company targets the fastest-growing industry segments while steering away from long-term guarantee products.

Lincoln Financial is also investing in technology to increase margins. Its current enterprise-wide digitization initiative is designed to improve customer experiences and provide for ease in meeting changing marketplace shifts. It expects to see annual benefits of between $90 million and $150 million beyond 2020 through the initiative.

Lincoln Financial is exploring additional financial strategies to address the statutory reserve strain that comes with its term and universal life products that contain secondary guarantees. It will shift its business to focus on products with shorter-duration liabilities and more limited liabilities.

Mergers and Acquisitions

In 2018 Lincoln Financial acquired Liberty Life Assurance Company of Boston from Liberty Mutual Insurance for $1.5 billion. The deal included Liberty's group benefits operations. Through the purchase Lincoln expanded its distribution reach.

Company Background

Lincoln National traces its roots to the founding of the Fraternal Assurance Society of America in 1902. After a founding member absconded with funds the remaining members obtained permission from Abraham Lincoln's son Robert to use his father's name and image to clean up the organization's reputation.

The company bought up other firms in the 1950s and 1960s and in 1968 it formed holding company Lincoln National. Soon it began diversifying buying Chicago Title and Trust (1969; sold 1985) as well as more life and reinsurance companies. Lincoln National also went into the health benefits business setting up its own HMO and investing in EMPHESYS (which it took public in 1994 divesting the remainder of its stock in 1995).

With the growth of retirement savings from baby boomers hitting their 50's the company shifted gears into wealth management. Lincoln National bought CIGNA's annuity and individual life insurance business and Aetna's US individual life insurance operations in 1998.

In 1999 after nearly a century in the heartland Lincoln National moved its headquarters to Philadelphia.

EXECUTIVES

President And Ceo; President Lincoln Financial Group, Dennis R. Glass, age 69, $1,200,000 total compensation

Evp Chief Human Resources Officer And Head Brand And Enterprise Communications, Lisa M. Buckingham, age 53, $578,448 total compensation

President Annuity Solutions Lincoln Financial Distributors And Lincoln Financial Network, Wilford H. (Will) Fuller, age 48, $650,000 total compensation

Evp And Cfo, Randal J. Freitag, age 56, $669,708 total compensation

Evp And Chief Investment Officer, Ellen Cooper, age 54

Evp And General Counsel, Kirkland L. Hicks, age 48, $575,000 total compensation

Evp Cio And Head Of Administrative Services, Kenneth S. Solon, age 58

Senior Vice President, Beth O'Brien

Assistant Vice President, Gina Boulton

National Account Manager, Erica Hinz

Assistant Vice President, Richard Clay

Sales Vice President, Eric Patterson

Senior Vice President And Head Insurance Solutions Distribution, Andrew Bucklee

Assistant Vice President Senior Employee Relations, Mary Carruth

Assistant Vice President, Jennifer Flanagan

Assistant Vice President Actuary, Henry Cheng

Senior Vice President, Andrew Yorks

Executive Vice President, Scott Summerlin

Assistant Vice President And Senior Counsel, Jennifer Petruccelli

Assistant Vice President, Andy Scanlon

National Account Manager, Beth Griffith

Senior Counsel And Assistant Vice President, Michael Arnold

National Account Manager, Matt Jasa

Assistant Vice President, Amy Eby

Assistant Vice President Financial Reporting And Expense Controls, Kathy Tibke

Vice President Human Resources, Rebecca Silva

Vice President, Brian Jenkins

Assistant Vice President Human Resources Business Partner, Carol Dowling

Second Vice President Corporate Actuary, Mike Antrobus

Vice President Customer Service, Wanda Pritchett

Vice President Talent Management, Nancy Rogers

Vp And Head Consultant Relations Retirement Plan Services, Jason Key

Senior Counsel And Assistant Vice President, Wayne Mcclain

Senior Vice President And Chief Human Resources Officer, Lisa Bettinger-buckingham

Vice President Institutional Retirement Distribution Retirement Plan Services, Jayson West

Vice President Of Human Resources Administration, Stephen Dovey

Senior Vice President And Head Talent, Jen Warne

Assistant Vice President, Marc Tomlinson

Assistant Vice President Information Technology Shared Services, Michele Fedgechin

Vp National Director Of Enterprise Initiatives For Lincoln Financial Advisor, Joseph Gaeckle

Vice President Marketing, Diane Russell

Assistant Vice President Total Rewards, Amber Chandler

Assistant Vice President Internal Audit, Claude Campbell

Sales Vice President, David Duckworth

Sales Vice President, Valerie Staublin

Assistant Vice President Field Development, Angela Whitcher

Assistant Vice President Business Analysis And Digital Technology, Casey Mathews

Vice President Internal Communications, Claudia Wieber

Senior Vice President Human Resources And Employee Relations, Patricia Insley

Assistant Vice President Procurement Strategy And Performance Excellence, John Hendrick

Tax Assistant Vice President, Jan Webb

Assistant Vice President Retirement Benefits, John Arko

Assistant Vice President Finance, Chris Reed

Assistant Vice President Analytics, Michael Mocanu

Vice President Commercial Real Estate Investments, Nick Heinzelmann

Vice President Talent Acquisition, Michael Kellar

Assistant Vice President And Associate Actuary, Jeffrey Curley

Senior Vice President Head Of Fixed Income, John Morriss

Senior Vice President Product And Solutions Management Rps, Ralph Ferraro

Senior Vice President And Head Annuity Life Retirement Group Protection And Distribution Informa, Robert Klaczak

Senior Vice President Finance Group Protection, Roger Martin

Senior Vice President Funds Management And Investments Law, Ronald Holinsky

Vice President And Associate General Counsel, Andrea Fox

Svp And Chief Ethics And Compliance Officer, Steve Harris

Senior Vice President Individual Annuity Operations, Nancy Jordan

Senior Vice President And Head Enterprise Litigation And Legal Operations, Richard Spenner

National Account Manager, Tracey Lemelin

National Account Manager, Juanita Morris-gettings

Vice President Human Resources, Michael Semo

Assistant Vice President Enterprise Business Systems, Ken Weaver

Senior Vice President Life Product Management Individual Life Insurance, Stafford Thompson

Vice President Sales, Kevin Swantek

National Sales Manager, Tad Fifer

Medical Director, Mark Bell

Avp And Senior Counsel, Matt Creech

Vice President And Chief Counsel Group Protection, Tom Waldman

Assistant Vice President, Matt Pons

National Account Manager, Lori Dobbs

Vice President And Associate General Counsel, Mary Potter

Vice President Chief Architect, Matthew Daniels

Vice President Data Center Network And Storage Services, Joseph Brannan

Vice President Individual Annuity New Business, Scott Bodenhafer

Vice President Account Management, Kerry Brooks

Avp National Accounts, Eli Oake-libow

Vice President Actuarial Valuation, William Obert

Regional Vice President Claims, Jeanette Zenner

Vice President Broker Dealer Operations, Jeff Sheftic

Assistant Vice President Digital Strategy Life And Annuities, Angie Curry

Assistant Vice President Sales Training Group Protection, Karen Rice

Vice President Customer Service, Wendy Chase

Vice President National Account Sales, John Lemire

Assistant Vice President Product Risk Management, Tim Stickney

Assistant Vice President, Jeanine Phr

Board Member, Eric Johnson

Chairman, William H. Cunningham, age 75

Board Member, Isaiah Tidwell

Board Member, Marilyn Ondecker

Board Member, David McDunn

Board Member, Deirdre Connelly

Corporate Treasurer, Christopher Giovanni

Vice President And Assistant Treasurer, Shantanu Mishra

Board Director, Pat Pittard

Auditors: Ernst & Young LLP

LOCATIONS

HQ: Lincoln National Corp.
150 N. Radnor Chester Road, Suite A305, Radnor, PA 19087
Phone: 484 583-1400
Web: www.lfg.com

PRODUCTS/OPERATIONS

2018 Sales

	$ mil.	% of total
Fee income	5,986	36
Net investment income	5,085	31
Insurance premiums	4,601	28
Realized gain excluding other-than-temporary impairment losses on securities	148	1
Amortization of deferred gain on business sold through reinsurance		9
Other	602	4
Adjustments	(7)	-
Total	**16,424**	**100**

2018 Sales by Segment

	$ mil.	% of total
Life Insurance	6,922	42
Annuities	4,383	27
Group Protections	3,757	23
Retirement Plan Services	1,178	7
Other	235	1
Adjustments	(51)	-
Total	**16,424**	**100**

Selected Subsidiaries

First Penn-Pacific Life Insurance Company
Lincoln Financial Advisors
Lincoln Financial Distributors
Lincoln Financial Foundation
Lincoln Financial Securities Corporation
Lincoln Investment Management Company
The Lincoln National Life Insurance Company
Lincoln National Management Corporation

COMPETITORS

AEGON
AIG
AXA Financial
American Equity Investment Life Holding Company
Guardian Life
John Hancock Financial Services
MassMutual

Nationwide Financial
New York Life
Northwestern Mutual
Principal Financial
Prudential
TIAA
Torchmark
Unum Group

HISTORICAL FINANCIALS
Company Type: Public

Income Statement
FYE: December 31

	ASSETS ($ mil.)	NET INCOME ($ mil.)	INCOME AS % OF ASSETS	EMPLOYEES
12/18	298,147	1,641	0.6%	11,034
12/17	281,763	2,079	0.7%	10,194
12/16	261,627	1,192	0.5%	10,282
12/15	251,937	1,154	0.5%	10,535
12/14	253,377	1,515	0.6%	11,046
Annual Growth	4.2%	2.0%	—	(0.0%)

2018 Year-End Financials

Debt ratio: 2.00%
Return on equity: 10.00%
Cash ($ mil.): 2,345
Current ratio: —
Long-term debt ($ mil.): —

No. of shares (mil.): 206
Dividends
Yield: 3.0%
Payout: 18.0%
Market value ($ mil.): 10,563

	STOCK PRICE ($) FY Close	P/E High/Low		PER SHARE ($) Earnings	Dividends	Book Value
12/18	51.00	11	6	7.00	1.00	70.00
12/17	77.00	8	7	9.00	1.00	79.00
12/16	66.00	13	6	5.00	1.00	64.00
12/15	50.00	13	10	5.00	1.00	56.00
12/14	58.00	10	8	6.00	1.00	61.00
Annual Growth	(2.9%)	—	—	6.9%	19.8%	3.2%

Lithia Motors Inc

Lithia Motors has its foot on the growth pedal. The auto dealer specializes in famed US auto brands such as Chrysler General Motors and Ford through about 180 stores in select markets in nearly 20 states. The firm sells some 30 brands of new domestic and imported vehicles and all brands of used cars and trucks through its stores and on-line. It also offers financing and replacement parts as well as vehicle protection and credit insurance. Chairman Sidney DeBoer controls Lithia Motors through Lithia Holding Co.

Operations

Lithia has three segments: Import (more than 40% of sales) Domestic (around 35%) and Luxury (over 20%). The Domestic segment comprises retail automotive franchises that sell new vehicles manufactured by Chrysler General Motors and Ford. The Import segment covers retail automotive franchises that sell new vehicles made by Honda Toyota Subaru Nissan and Volkswagen. The Luxury segment sells new vehicles manufactured made by BMW Mercedes-Benz and Lexus. The franchises in each segment also sell used vehicles parts and automotive services and automotive finance and insurance products. Lithia sells about 185000 new vehicles and 150000 used vehicles each year.

Geographic Reach

Medford Oregon-based Lithia sells vehicles across nearly 30 US states. California is Lithia's biggest market accounting for about a quarter of the company's total sales (and over 20% of total stores) followed by Oregon and Texas.

Sales and Marketing

Lithia sells through its stores and online website. It also maintains mobile versions of its websites and a mobile application in anticipation of greater adoption of mobile technology. The company posts its inventory on major new and used vehicle listing services such as cars.com autotrader.com kbb.com and edmunds.com to reach online shoppers. It also employs search engine optimization search engine marketing and online display advertising (including re-targeting) to reach more online prospects.

Financial Performance

Lithia Motors has seen solid revenue growth in recent years as a growing economy has strengthened vehicle sales. Its annual revenues have risen close to 119% since 2014.

Revenue increased to $11.8 billion in 2018 an approximately 17% increase from the year prior. The increase was driven by acquisitions and continued growth in used vehicle sales.

Net income was $265.7 million in fiscal year 2018 an increase from the $245.2 million in fiscal year 2017. Selling general and administrative expenses grew nearly 20% in fiscal 2018 to $1.2 billion.

Cash provided by operating activities was $519.7 million in fiscal 2018 while investing activities used $557.1 million. Financing activities provided $11.7 million.

Strategy

Lithia Motors relies on acquisitions to increase its revenue and diversify its brand portfolio. Indeed the company has completed more than 100 acquisitions since it went public in 1996.

Recently the company has shifted its acquisition strategy towards new markets in the US and larger multi-store dealerships. Lithia Motors acquired 17 stores in 2018. Its preference for larger organizations resulted from the assessment that they take less manpower to integrate than smaller "mom and pop" dealerships due to a more established corporate culture.

Lithia is investing in an omnichannel strategy to give customers a modern shopping experience integrating its online and dealership sales and delivery methods. The company invested more than $50 million in a partnership with Shift Technologies a San Francisco-based digital retailer to explore improving the digital customer experience and data analytics.

The company has also focused on improving cost controls at corporate headquarters and dealership locations saving $25 million in 2018.

Mergers and Acquisitions

Lithia Motors has made a number of acquisitions in 2019. In August 2019 the company acquired Hazelton Honda in Pennsylvania which expands Lithia's store network into Eastern Pennsylvania. In mid-2019 Lithia acquired a Jaguar-Land Rover dealership in Mission Viejo California from Pendragon. It also added dealerships in New Jersey and West Virginia.

Company Background

Lithia Motors was founded in 1946 by Walt DeBoer as a Chrysler-Plymouth-Dodge dealership in Ashland Oregon. Walt's son Sidney is its chairman and grandson Bryan is president and CEO of the growing auto dealer.

EXECUTIVES

Svp Mergers And Acquisitions/operations, Bryan B. DeBoer, age 52, $950,000 total compensation
Evp And Chief Human Resources Officer, Christopher (Chris) Holzshu, age 45, $485,100 total compensation

Svp Operations, Scott A. Hillier, age 56, $485,100 total compensation
Svp And Cfo, John F. North, age 42, $302,500 total compensation
Vp Information Technology And Cio, Mark Smith
Svp Operations Dch Operations, George C. Liang, age 63, $378,000 total compensation
Regional Manager Vice President, Ken Wright
Vice President, TIM FREEBORN
Chairman, Sidney B. (Sid) DeBoer, age 75
Auditors: KPMG LLP

LOCATIONS

HQ: Lithia Motors Inc
150 N. Bartlett Street, Medford, OR 97501
Phone: 541 776-6401
Web: www.lithia.com

2016 Stores

	No.
California	35
Oregon	25
Texas	16
Montana	11
New Jersey	11
New York	10
Alaska	9
Washington	8
Iowa	7
Hawaii	5
Nevada	4
Idaho	4
North Dakota	3
New Mexico	2
Vermont	2
Massachusetts	1
Wyoming	1
Total	**154**

PRODUCTS/OPERATIONS

2016 Sales

	$ mil.	% of total
Import	3,764	43
Domestic	3,382	39
Luxury	1,529	18
Corporate and other	3	-
Total	**8,678**	**100**

2016 Sales

	$ mil.	% of total
New vehicles	4,939	57
Used vehicle retail	2,227	25
Service body & parts	845	10
Finance & insurance	331	4
Used vehicle wholesale	277	3
Fleet & other	61	1
Total	**8,678**	**100**

COMPETITORS

Ancira
AutoNation
Autobytel
CarMax
David McDavid Auto Group
Gillman Auto

Group 1 Automotive
Internet Brands
McCombs Enterprises
Penske Automotive Group
Sonic Automotive

HISTORICAL FINANCIALS

Company Type: Public

Income Statement · FYE: December 31

	REVENUE ($ mil.)	NET INCOME ($ mil.)	NET PROFIT MARGIN	EMPLOYEES
12/18	11,821	266	2.2%	13,643
12/17	10,087	245	2.4%	12,899
12/16	8,678	197	2.3%	11,170
12/15	7,864	183	2.3%	9,574
12/14	5,390	139	2.6%	8,827
Annual Growth	**21.7%**	**17.6%**	**—**	**11.5%**

2018 Year-End Financials

Debt ratio: 64.00%
Return on equity: 23.00%
Cash ($ mil.): 32
Current ratio: 1.00
Long-term debt ($ mil.): 1,358
No. of shares (mil.): 23
Dividends
Yield: 1.0%
Payout: 10.0%
Market value ($ mil.): 1,756

	STOCK PRICE ($) FY Close	P/E High/Low		PER SHARE ($) Earnings	Dividends	Book Value
12/18	76.00	12	6	11.00	1.00	52.00
12/17	114.00	13	8	10.00	1.00	43.00
12/16	97.00	14	9	8.00	1.00	36.00
12/15	107.00	18	12	7.00	1.00	32.00
12/14	87.00	18	10	5.00	1.00	26.00
Annual Growth	(3.1%)	—	—	19.9%	16.9%	19.3%

Live Nation Entertainment Inc

Live Nation Entertainment holds center stage as the world's largest ticket seller and promoter of live entertainment. All total the company connects nearly 93 million fans to almost 35000 events each year. Through Ticketmaster it sells more than 480 million tickets annually for events at arenas stadiums theaters festival sites clubs and other venues across the world. Live Nation owns operates has exclusive booking rights for or has an interest in some 240 venues including the House of Blues clubs. Also a leading artist management firm the company has nearly 110 managers providing services to more than 400 artists. Live Nation has offices in 40 countries and venues in 11 countries.

HISTORY

Robert Sillerman began his career teaching advertisers how to reach young consumers. He started investing in radio and TV stations and founded SFX Broadcasting (named for a scrambling of his initials) in 1992. In early 1997 the firm entered the live entertainment field with the formation of SFX Concerts and the purchase of concert promoter Delsener/Slater.

When SFX Broadcasting agreed to be bought in 1997 by Capstar Broadcasting 87% controlled by investment firm Hicks Muse Tate & Furst (now HM Capital) SFX Entertainment was formed to house the live entertainment operations (it was spun off in 1998). In 1998 the company continued its rapid acquisition rate with the purchases of sports marketing and management team FAME New England concert promoter Don Law and national concert producer PACE Entertainment.

In 1999 the company bought concert promoter The Cellar Door Companies (which almost doubled SFX's size) sports marketing firm Integrated Sports International sporting event management company The Marquee Group sports talent agency Hendricks Management 50% of urban-music producer A.H. Enterprises and troubled theatrical producer Livent. SFX also made its first foray abroad through its purchase of Apollo Leisure a UK-based live entertainment firm. The company rolled all of its sports talent and marketing businesses into a new division SFX Sports Group that year.

In 2000 SFX jumped on the other side of the acquisition train when it was bought by radio station owner Clear Channel Communications for about $4 billion. Sillerman stepped down as chairman and CEO and was replaced by Clear Channel EVP Brian Becker. Later that year SFX acquired Philadelphia-based concert promoter and venue operator Electric Factory Concerts; Core Audience Entertainment Canada's second-largest concert promoter and events marketer; and the Cotter Group a North Carolina-based motorsports marketing agency.

In 2001 SFX acquired a majority interest in the International Hot Rod Association. It also bought professional golf talent agency Signature Sports Group. Later that year the company changed its name to Clear Channel Entertainment. It also continued expansion into Europe with the acquisition of Trident Agency and Milano Concerti music promotion businesses in Italy.

While operating as Clear Channel Entertainment Live Nation spent nearly $2 billion on acquisitions (Pace Entertainment Livent) almost single-handedly consolidating the live entertainment industry.

Before being spun off in December 2005 the company changed its name to CCE Spinco then Live Nation. Also that year Randall Mays became chairman and Michael Rapino replaced Becker as CEO. As part of the Clear Channel spinoff the company relocated from Houston to headquarters in tony Beverly Hills. It trimmed the fat by shutting down operating divisions such as museum exhibitions and music publishing (and laying off about 400 employees in the process) in order to focus on its core businesses of live music concerts venue management and website brand development.

In 2006 the company acquired rival HOB Entertainment for $354 million. Live Nation used the acquisition to expand its presence in the midsized venue business and fill in geographic gaps in its existing amphitheater network. As part of the deal Live Nation gained high-profile House of Blues-branded music venues such as San Francisco's Fillmore Auditorium Jones Beach in New York and London's Apollo Theatre and Wembley Arena. The company subsequently began re-branding many of its midsize clubs "Fillmore" after the San Francisco venue.

The company had in 2005 formed Delirium Concert LP a joint venture with Cirque du Soleil. The Delirium tour began in 2006. The following year Live Nation signed a $120 million deal with pop icon Madonna. Through its North American Music segment in 2007 Live Nation promoted or produced some 10000 live music events including tours for Van Halen Dave Matthews Band and Kenny Chesney. International Music operations for the year included Cirque De Soleil's Delirium as well as UK's Reading Festival. Also in 2007 the company produced global tours for legends such as The Police The Rolling Stones Genesis and The Who and presented some 5000 theatrical performances such as the UK touring production of Chicago through its Global Theater operations.

In 2008 the company divested itself of its North American theatrical assets. Later that year the company signed pacts with U2 and Jay-Z. Michael Cohl chairman and Live Nation Artists chief who spearheaded the deals later resigned over conflicts with CEO Rapino. Also in 2008 the company sold its motor sports operations. In early 2010 the company acquired Ticketmaster Entertainment and Live Nation changed its name to Live Nation Entertainment.

EXECUTIVES

President House Of Blues Entertainment, Ronald (Ron) Bension, age 64
Evp General Counsel And Secretary, Michael G. Rowles, age 54, $750,000 total compensation
Co-president North America Concerts, Mark Campana, age 61

Ceo And Director, Michael (Mike) Rapino, age 54, $2,300,000 total compensation
President Global Touring Tna International, Arthur Fogel, age 66
President And Coo, Joe Berchtold, age 54, $1,100,000 total compensation
President European Music Clear Channel Music Group, Alan Ridgeway, age 52, $730,025 total compensation
Cfo, Kathy Willard, age 53, $850,000 total compensation
President Media And Sponsorship, Russell Wallach, age 53
President Live Nation Europe - Concerts, John Reid, age 57
Evp Mergers And Acquisitions And Strategic Finance, John Hopmans, age 60
President Ticketmaster North America, Jared Smith, age 41
Co-president North America Concerts, Bob Roux, age 61
President Ticketmaster International, Mark Yovich, age 44
Cio, David Huckabay
President Production Film And Television, Heather Parry
Vice President National Sales, Craig Hoover
Senior Vice President Of Global Information Technology Financial Systems, Tim Moran
Senior Vice President Audit And Compliance, Brad Nelson
Vice President Of Marketing, Peter Harper
Vice President Legal Business Affairs, Chris Laffoon
Senior Vice President, Jim Mallonee
Senior Vice President Marketing And Business Development, David Fortin
Svp Business Development Strategic Alliances, Frank Gutierrez
Vice President Information Technology Ap, Alysia Piccioni
Vice President Finance House Of Blues Clubs, Nathan Scott
Vice President Of Sales, Kate Walsh
Vice President Of Marketing, Julia Heiser
Vp Of Marketing, Jim Sutcliffe
Vice President Planning, George Duran
Vice President Human Resources, Shawn Imitatesdog
Regional Vice President, Danny Eaton
Svp Digital Sales, Jeremy Levine
Regional Vice President Of Finance, Frank Brayer
Senior Vice President Marketing, Joey Scoleri
Evp And President Global Talent And Artist Development, David Zedeck
Svp And Ciso, Jonathan Chow
Svp Marketing Solutions, Jeff Condon
Vice President Legal Affairs, Leslie Holland
Senior Vice President Of Legal Affairs, Sheila Small
Senior Vice President Human Resources, Laura Morton-rowe
Vice President Marketing, Brad Locker
Senior Vice President Of Production, Stacey Harper
Svp And Treasurer, Bill Lowe
Executive Vice President Operations, Robert Simeone
Vice President Information Technology, Dave Gerardi
Senior Vice President, Matt Prieshoff
Senior Vice President, Rich Levy
Executive Vice President Strategic Alliances, Kevin Chernett
Svp Sales, Andy Peikon
Senior Vice President Aoministration, Linda Gross
Vp Marketing, Kim Shiver
Senior Vice President, Django Bayless
Vice President Marketing And Publicity, Annasivia Britt

Regional Vice President, Rob Scolaro
Vice President Midwest Music, Dan Kemer
Svp Mergers And Acquisitions, Michael Wichser
Vice President Programmatic And Product Innovation, Mike Finnegan
Vice President, Michael McGaw
Vice President Account Management, Joe Ventura
Vice President Of Business Development And Strategy, Christopher Sumner
Regional Vice President, Louis Giangola
Vice President Technology Optimization, Brent Eubanks
Vice President Strategy And Insights Media And Sponsorship, Amanda Fraga
Vice President Business Development, Patti Kim
Svp Marketing And Sales, Barry Gabel
Senior Vice President Software Development, Alex Hazboun
Vp Pricing And Distribution, John Ketchum
Senior Vice President, Greg Gillin
Vice President, Harvey Cohen
Vice President Brand Strategist, Denise Quattrochi
Vice President Of Foundation Room House Of Blues, Victor Sutter
Vice President Product Management, Bob Ritter
Vice President Diversity And Inclusion, Elizabeth Morrison
Vice President Analytics And Optimization, Christine Chu
Vice President Engineering And Data Science, Wojciech Jawor
Vice President, Julie Jin
Senior Vice President Media And Sponsorship, Jon Landa
Senior Vice President Of Legal, Dan Palumbo
Vice President Touring, Omar Al-joulani
Vice President Of Branding Strategy, Bryan Burney
Chairman, Gregory B. (Greg) Maffei, age 58
Auditors: Ernst & Young LLP

LOCATIONS

HQ: Live Nation Entertainment Inc
9348 Civic Center Drive, Beverly Hills, CA 90210
Phone: 310 867-7000
Web: www.livenationentertainment.com

2017 Sales

	$ mil.	% of total
Domestic operations	6,773	65
Foreign operation:		
UK operations	785	8
Other operations	2,779	27
Total	**10,337**	**100**

PRODUCTS/OPERATIONS

2017 Sales

	$ mil.	% of total
Concerts	7,892	76
Ticketing	2,144	21
Sponsorship & advertising	445	4
Other revenue	21	-
Eliminations	(164.6)	-
Total	**10,337**	**100**

COMPETITORS

Brillstein
CAA
Dodger Properties
Feld Entertainment
IMG
International Creative Management
Jujamcyn Theaters
MSG Networks
Nederlander Producing Company
Octagon
On Stage Entertainment
Palace Sports & Entertainment
Ryman
SMG Management

Shubert Organization
TBA Global
United Talent
Universal Music Group
Warner Music
WestwoodOne
William Morris Endeavor Entertainment

HISTORICAL FINANCIALS
Company Type: Public

Income Statement
FYE: December 31

	REVENUE ($ mil.)	NET INCOME ($ mil.)	NET PROFIT MARGIN	EMPLOYEES
12/18	10,788	60	0.6%	9,500
12/17	10,337	(6)	—	8,800
12/16	8,355	3	0.0%	8,300
12/15	7,246	(33)	—	7,700
12/14	6,867	(91)	—	14,000
Annual Growth	12.0%	—	—	(9.2%)

2018 Year-End Financials
Debt ratio: 33.00%
Return on equity: 5.00%
Cash ($ mil.): 2,372
Current ratio: 1.00
Long-term debt ($ mil.): 2,733

No. of shares (mil.): 210
Dividends
  Yield: —
  Payout: —
Market value ($ mil.): 10,349

	STOCK PRICE ($) FY Close	P/E High/Low	PER SHARE ($) Earnings	Dividends	Book Value
12/18	49.00	— —	(0.00)	0.00	5.00
12/17	43.00	— —	(0.00)	0.00	6.00
12/16	27.00	— —	(0.00)	0.00	6.00
12/15	25.00	— —	(0.00)	0.00	6.00
12/14	26.00	— —	(0.00)	0.00	6.00
Annual Growth	17.2%	— —	—	—	(5.1%)

Live Oak Bancshares Inc

Auditors: Dixon Hughes Goodman LLP

LOCATIONS
HQ: Live Oak Bancshares Inc
  1741 Tiburon Drive, Wilmington, NC 28403
Phone: 910 790-5867
Web: www.liveoakbank.com

HISTORICAL FINANCIALS
Company Type: Public

Income Statement
FYE: December 31

	ASSETS ($ mil.)	NET INCOME ($ mil.)	INCOME AS % OF ASSETS	EMPLOYEES
12/18	3,670	51	1.4%	506
12/17	2,758	100	3.6%	528
12/16	1,755	14	0.8%	425
12/15	1,053	21	2.0%	366
12/14	673	10	1.5%	263
Annual Growth	52.8%	50.4%	—	17.8%

2018 Year-End Financials
Debt ratio: —
Return on equity: 11.00%
Cash ($ mil.): 324
Current ratio: —
Long-term debt ($ mil.): —

No. of shares (mil.): 40
Dividends
  Yield: 1.0%
  Payout: 4.0%
Market value ($ mil.): 595

	STOCK PRICE ($) FY Close	P/E High/Low	PER SHARE ($) Earnings	Dividends	Book Value
12/18	15.00	25 11	1.00	0.00	12.00
12/17	24.00	9 7	3.00	0.00	11.00
12/16	19.00	50 30	0.00	0.00	7.00
12/15	14.00	31 20	1.00	0.00	6.00
Annual Growth	1.1%	— —	17.5%	56.5%	20.5%

LIVE OAK BANKING COMPANY

EXECUTIVES

Ceo, Chip Mahan
Chb, James S Mahan III
Coo, Neil L Underwood
Cfo, Brett Caines
Pres, Scott Custer
Financial Controller, Amy Rogers
Loan Officer, Angus McDonald
Loan Officer, Anna Taylor
Loan Officer, Bert Smith
Treasurer, Betty Norris
Senior Loan Officer, Brian Faulk

LOCATIONS

HQ: LIVE OAK BANKING COMPANY
  1741 TIBURON DR, WILMINGTON, NC 284036244
Phone: 910 790-5867
Web: WWW.LIVEOAKBANK.COM

HISTORICAL FINANCIALS
Company Type: Private

Income Statement
FYE: December 31

	ASSETS ($ mil.)	NET INCOME ($ mil.)	INCOME AS % OF ASSETS	EMPLOYEES
12/17	2,667	114	4.3%	30
12/16	1,701	22	1.3%	—
12/15	1,009	23	2.2%	—
12/14	634	22	3.5%	—
Annual Growth	61.4%	73.3%	—	—

LKQ Corp

LKQ distributes replacement parts and components needed to repair passenger cars and trucks. It's one of the leading aftermarket parts suppliers in the US through subsidiary Keystone Automotive. LKQ also offers reconditioned remanufactured and refurbished parts including wheels bumpers mirrors and engines as well as recycled parts that are reclaimed from salvage vehicles. Customers include collision repair and mechanical repair shops.

Additionally LKQ operates self-service retail yards that allow customers to come in search through and buy recycled auto parts. LKQ which generates just more than half its sales in the US was formed in 1998.

Operations
LKQ operates through three reportable segments: North America (about 45%) Europe (about 45%) and Specialty (more than 10%).

The North America and Europe segments consist of wholesale operations (aftermarket refurbished recycled and OEM parts) and self-service retail operations (which allows consumers to come directly to the yard to pick parts off of salvage vehicles) in their respective markets. Leading products include brake pads clutches electrical products such as spark plugs and batteries filters and oil and automotive fluids.

The Specialty segment serves major markets in the US and Canada focusing on six product segments: truck and off-road; speed and performance; RV; towing; wheels tires and performance handling; and miscellaneous accessories. RV appliances & air conditioners towing hitches truck bed covers vehicle protection products and wheels tires & suspension products are among the segment's leading offerings.

Geographic Reach
Headquartered in Chicago Illinois LKQ operates about 550 facilities in the US and some 1150 facilities in two dozen other countries. It has regional headquarters in Nashville Tennessee as well as Tamworth England; Schiedam and Amsterdam the Netherlands; Milan Italy; Prague Czech Republic; and Poing Germany. Certain back-office support functions are performed in Bangalore India.

The US is its largest market accounting for more than half of total revenue. Its European operations are led by the UK (some 15% of revenue) and Germany (nearly 10%); other markets in Europe include the Benelux region (Belgium Netherlands and Luxembourg) Italy Czech Republic Poland Slovakia Austria Sweden and Norway.

Sales and Marketing
LKQ sells its products to wholesale customers such as collision and mechanical repair shops and new and used car dealerships as well as to retail customers. Customers of self-service yards are frequently do-it-yourself mechanics small independent repair shops auto rebuilders and resellers.

The company markets its products directly to customers through sales personnel e-commerce partners and distributors. It has an extensive and growing network of some 1700 facilities. LKQ's marketing activities include catalogs advertising sponsorships and promotional activities product-level marketing and online initiatives.

Financial Performance
Powered by its acquisition strategy LKQ has achieved substantial growth over the past five years. Revenue has jumped 76% since 2014 with net income up 26% during that time.

In 2018 the company reported sales of $11.9 billion up 22% from the prior year. Most the growth was the result of acquisitions particularly those that boosted European operations. The Europe segment grew nearly 45% year-over-year compared to just more than 5% for North America.

Net income however was down 10% that year to $480 million. Most expenses as a percent of total revenue rose in 2018 and LKQ reported interest and other income of just $6.5 million that year compared to nearly $20 million the previous year. In addition the company had losses of nearly $65 million from unconsolidated subsidiaries specifically its interest in Nordic car parts chain Mekonomen.

Cash at the end of 2018 was $337.3 million an increase of $57.5 million from the prior year. Cash from operations contributed $710.7 million to the coffers while investing activities used $1.5 billion mainly for acquisitions. Financing activities added another $883 million from borrowings and proceeds from issuance of Euro Notes.

Strategy

LKQ is focused on expanding both its distribution network which currently includes some 1700 locations worldwide and its product offerings. Key to both these strategies are acquisitions. Indeed the company has completed more than 270 acquisitions in the US and abroad since its founding in 1998. In just a few years LKQ's European operations have doubled as a percent of total revenue because of acquisitions.

Mergers and Acquisitions

To strengthen its business in Europe in mid-2018 LKQ purchased for some ?1.5 billion Stahlgruber GmbH a wholesale distributor of aftermarket spare parts for passenger cars tools and capital equipment. Stahlgruber has operations in Germany Eastern Europe Italy and Switzerland.

The company acquired the aftermarket business of Warn Industries a leading designer and manufacturer of high-performance vehicle equipment and accessories the prior year. Warn which was a subsidiary of Dover Corporation will enhance LKQ's Specialty segment.

Company Background

LKQ was created in 1998 through the combination of a number of wholesale recycled products businesses located in Florida Michigan Ohio and Wisconsin. It has grown through internal development and 270-plus acquisitions.

EXECUTIVES

Ceo And Managing Director European Operations, John S. Quinn, age 60, $565,000 total compensation

Svp Development, Walter P. Hanley, age 53, $400,000 total compensation

President And Ceo, Dominick P. (Nick) Zarcone, age 60, $1,000,000 total compensation

Svp And Cio, Ashley T. Brooks

Svp Operations Wholesale Parts Division, Justin L. Jude, age 42

Evp And Cfo, Varun Laroyia

Vp Finance And Controller, Michael Clark

Svp General Counsel And Corporate Secretary, Victor Casini

Vice President Investor Relations, Joseph Boutross

National Account Manager, David Bowers

National Accounts Manager North America, Steven Crutchfield

Vp It, Chad Cowan

Senior Vice President Development, Jerry Girsch

Senior Vice President, Bruce Morgan

Vice President, Dudley Smith

Senior Vice President Of Sales And Marketing, Chris Patti

Vice President, Adam Gifford

Svp Strategy And Innovation, Robert Reppa

Chairman, Joseph M. Holsten, age 66

Board Member, Guhan Subramanian

Auditors: DELOITTE & TOUCHE LLP

LOCATIONS

HQ: LKQ Corp
500 West Madison Street, Suite 2800, Chicago, IL 60661
Phone: 312 621-1950
Web: www.lkqcorp.com

2018 Sales

	$ mil.	% of total
US	6,193	52
UK	1,665	14
Germany	975	8
Other countries	3,044	26
Total	11,877	100

PRODUCTS/OPERATIONS

2018 Sales

	$ mil.	% of total
North America	5,182	44
Europe	5,222	44
Specialty	1,473	12
Total	11,877	100

Products & Services

Accessories
Fleet Service
Refinishing
Vehicle & Salvage Disposal
Warranty
Wheels

COMPETITORS

Cardone Industries	Halfords
Copart	Jasper Engines
Delphi Automotive Systems	Kirk's Automotive
	O'Reilly Automotive
Federal-Mogul	Titan International
Fred Jones Enterprises	U.S. Auto Parts
Genuine Parts	Valeo
Hahn Automotive	

HISTORICAL FINANCIALS

Company Type: Public

Income Statement — FYE: December 31

	REVENUE ($ mil.)	NET INCOME ($ mil.)	NET PROFIT MARGIN	EMPLOYEES
12/18	11,877	480	4.0%	51,000
12/17	9,737	534	5.5%	43,000
12/16	8,584	464	5.4%	42,500
12/15	7,193	423	5.9%	31,100
12/14	6,740	382	5.7%	29,500
Annual Growth	15.2%	5.9%	—	14.7%

2018 Year-End Financials

Debt ratio: 38.00%
Return on equity: 11.00%
Cash ($ mil.): 332
Current ratio: 3.00
Long-term debt ($ mil.): 4,189
No. of shares (mil.): 316
Dividends
Yield: —
Payout: —
Market value ($ mil.): 7,502

	STOCK PRICE ($) FY Close	P/E High/Low		PER SHARE ($) Earnings	Dividends	Book Value
12/18	24.00	28	15	2.00	0.00	15.00
12/17	41.00	24	16	2.00	0.00	14.00
12/16	31.00	24	16	2.00	0.00	11.00
12/15	30.00	23	17	1.00	0.00	10.00
12/14	28.00	26	20	1.00	0.00	9.00
Annual Growth	(4.2%)	—	—	5.2%	—	14.0%

Lockheed Martin Corp

EXECUTIVES

Chm, Patrick M Dewar
Pres*, Richard G Kirkland
V Pres*, Christopher J Gregoire
V Pres*, John M Ward
V Pres*, Kevin Darrenkamp
Prin*, Edward Whalen
General, Kreg Purcell
Manager of Information, Marlin Nielson
Administrator, Chad Vaughn
Manager Advanced Conce, Larry Capots
Information Technology Manager, Rod Traff
Auditors: Ernst & Young LLP

LOCATIONS

HQ: Lockheed Martin Corp
6801 Rockledge Drive, Bethesda, MD 20817
Phone: 301 897-6000
Web: www.lockheedmartin.com

HISTORICAL FINANCIALS

Company Type: Public

Income Statement — FYE: December 31

	REVENUE ($ mil.)	NET INCOME ($ mil.)	NET PROFIT MARGIN	EMPLOYEES
12/19	59,812	6,230	10.4%	110,000
12/18	53,762	5,046	9.4%	105,000
12/17	51,048	2,002	3.9%	100,000
12/16	47,248	5,302	11.2%	97,000
12/15	46,132	3,605	7.8%	126,000
Annual Growth	6.7%	14.7%	—	(3.3%)

2019 Year-End Financials

Debt ratio: 27.00%
Return on equity: 276.00%
Cash ($ mil.): 1,514
Current ratio: 1.00
Long-term debt ($ mil.): 11,404
No. of shares (mil.): 280
Dividends
Yield: 2.0%
Payout: 43.0%
Market value ($ mil.): 109,026

	STOCK PRICE ($) FY Close	P/E High/Low		PER SHARE ($) Earnings	Dividends	Book Value
12/19	389.00	18	12	22.00	9.00	11.00
12/18	262.00	20	14	18.00	8.00	5.00
12/17	321.00	46	36	7.00	7.00	(2.00)
12/16	250.00	15	12	17.00	7.00	5.00
12/15	217.00	19	16	11.00	6.00	10.00
Annual Growth	15.7%	—	—	17.6%	10.0%	2.2%

Loews Corp.

When it comes to diversification Loews definitely has the low-down. The holding company's main interest is insurance through publicly traded subsidiary CNA Financial which offers commercial property/casualty coverage. It also owns hotels in the US and Canada through its Loews Hotels subsidiary. The group's energy holdings include contract oil-drilling operator Diamond Offshore Drilling (which operates roughly 20 offshore oil rigs) and interstate natural gas transmission pipeline systems operator Boardwalk Pipeline. Loews is controlled and run by the Tisch family including co-chairmen and cousins Andrew and Jonathan.

Operations

Loews is organized into five segments: CNA Financial Diamond Offshore Drilling Boardwalk Pipeline Partners Loews Hotel Holdings and Corporate.

Flagship unit CNA Financial is the company's cash cow accounting for some 70% of its annual revenue. Its specialty offerings include professional financial and property/casualty products; the company also offers commercial property/casualty coverage. CNA's other operations primarily include its run-off long-term care business. Affiliates include The Continental Insurance Company and CNA Surety.

Diamond Offshore Drilling owns and operates rigs located offshore of five countries including the US. Boardwalk Pipeline consists of interstate natural gas pipeline systems originating in the Gulf Coast region Oklahoma and Arkansas and extending north and east; natural gas storage facilities in four states; and natural gas liquids pipelines and storage facilities in Louisiana and Texas.

Loews Hotels operates about 25 hotels and resorts — 23 in the US and one in Canada.

The newly established Consolidated Container arm which is part of the Corporate segment manufactures plastic packaging for the beverage food and household chemical industries.

Geographic Reach

Through its subsidiaries diversified Loews has operations in the US Canada and beyond. Its CNA Financial unit operates primarily in the US. Loews Hotels has 23 properties in the US and one property in Canada. Diamond Offshore has drilling rigs located off the coasts of the US Mexico Brazil Scotland and Singapore and itmarkets its products worldwide. Boardwalk Pipeline operates approximately 14000 miles of pipelines in 13 US states and serves customers in the northeastern and southeastern US.Consolidated Container has offices in Nebraska and Georgia; it operates about 60 manufacturing plants in the US and another in Canada.

Sales and Marketing

Loews' largest division CNA Financial markets its products through independent brokers agents and managing general underwriters. CNA Financial targets professionals and small to large businesses as well as insurers associations and other groups.

Diamond Offshore's main customers include oil and gas companies ranging from large corporations to independent businesses as well as government-owned entities. Major customers include Petrobras Anadarko and Exxon Mobil . Boardwalk Pipeline serves gas producers distributors transporters and marketers as well as electric and industrial plants.

Consolidated Container's largest customer is Dean Foods Company which brings in some 10% of its revenue. The unit has more than 1000 customers in all.

Financial Performance

Loews' revenues had been slipping since 2013 but they rose 5% to $13.7 billion in 2017. Insurance premiums and other revenues (largely related to plastic packaging) increased slightly but investment gains accounted for the bulk of the revenue growth.

Net income nearly doubled that year to $1.2 billion. That gain was primarily due to a $200 million tax benefit as part of the 2017 Tax Act but CNA Financial Loews Hotels and Diamond Offshore also had higher earnings during the year. Cash flow from operations held steady at $2.6 billion.

Strategy

Each Loews business pursues customer growth in their various industries; the holding company prides itself on selecting quality leaders and it helps its various divisions in decision-making related to capital allocation strategic planning and financial planning. CNA Financial for instance is working to grow its base of commercial customers in each of the small midsized and large account categories. It has been strengthening its core property/casualty operations while exiting underperforming segments. Boardwalk Pipeline has its sights set on diversification to offset slowdown in the oil and gas industry.

As a group Loews has been conservative lately with its acquisition activity. It completed its first purchase in a while when it bought Consolidated Container Company in 2017. By adding a new line of business the holding company is increasingly diversified which helps it endure different markets' cyclical downturns.

Mergers and Acquisitions

In 2017 Loews Corporation acquired Consolidated Container Company (CCC) a Georgia-based rigid plastic packaging manufacturer for $1.2 billion. With nearly 60 manufacturing facilities CCC serves the food beverage and household chemical industries in North America.

HISTORY

In 1946 Larry Tisch who earned a business degree from New York University at age 18 dropped out of Harvard Law to run his parents' New Jersey resort. Younger brother Bob joined him in creating a new entity Tisch Hotels. The company bought two Atlantic City hotels in 1952 quickly making them profitable. Later Tisch purchased such illustrious hotels as the Mark Hopkins The Drake the Belmont Plaza and the Regency.Moving beyond hotels the brothers bought money-losing companies with poor management. Discarding the management along with underperforming divisions they tightened operational control and eliminated such frills as fancy offices company planes and even memos.

In 1960 Tisch Hotels gained control of MGM's ailing Loew's Theaters to take advantage of their desirable city locations. The company then began demolishing more than 50 stately movie palaces and selling the land to developers. In 1968 the company bought Lorillard the oldest US tobacco company; it shed Lorillard's unprofitable pet food and candy operations and reversed its slipping tobacco market share.

Taking the Loews name in 1971 the company bought CNA Financial in 1974. The Tisch method turned losses of more than $200 million to profits of more than $100 million the very next year. It bought Bulova Watch in 1979 and guided by Larry's son Andrew it gradually returned to profitability.

In the early 1980s Loews entered the energy business by investing in oil supertankers. The company sold its last movie theaters in 1985. Then in 1987 Loews helped CBS fend off a takeover attempt by Ted Turner and ended up with about 25% of the company. Larry became president of the broadcaster.

In 1989 Loews acquired Diamond M Offshore a Texas drilling company and with the acquisition of Odeco Drilling in 1992 the company amassed the world's largest fleet of offshore rigs. The next year Loews grouped its drilling interests as Diamond Offshore Drilling.

In 1994 CNA expanded its insurance empire buying The Continental Corp. The next year Loews sold its interest in CBS and the following year Diamond Offshore Drilling merged with Arethusa (Off-Shore) Limited.

As deft as the Tisch brothers had been in accumulating their riches Larry's bearish investment strategy (short-selling stocks) cost Loews in the late 1990s (more than $900 million alone during 1997's bull market). Larry and Bob retired as co-CEOs at the end of 1998; Larry's son James already president and COO became CEO.

That year Lorillard signed on to the 46-state tobacco lawsuit settlement; the first payment cost the company $325 million (payments continue until 2025). Facing a softened insurance market CNA sold unprofitable lines to focus on commercial insurance; in 1999 it transferred its auto and homeowners lines to Allstate (it continues writing and renewing these policies) and put its life and life reinsurance units up for sale in 2000. Also that year Lorillard was hit with $16 billion of a record-breaking $144 billion punitive damage award in a smokers' class-action suit in Florida. CNA Financial paid out over $450 million in 2001-02 for claims related to the attacks on the World Trade Center.

In 2004 the company continued to expand its natural resource offerings when its subsidiary Boardwalk Pipelines (formerly known as TGT Pipeline) acquired Gulf South Pipeline which operates natural gas pipeline and gathering systems in Texas Louisiana Mississippi Alabama and Florida including several major supply hubs. Loews had acquired gas pipeline operator Texas Gas Transmission in 2003. Texas Gas operates natural gas pipeline systems reaching from the Louisiana Gulf Coast and East Texas north through Louisiana Arkansas Mississippi Tennessee Kentucky Indiana and into Ohio and Illinois.

Tobacco had long been a staple in Loews' portfolio until the company kicked the habit. Prior to quitting the company kept its 62% ownership of Lorillard rolled up as Carolina Group and traded it as a tracking subsidiary. Lorillard which included the Kent Newport and True cigarette brands in the US accounted for more than 20% of Loews' revenues. However after a steady stream of tobacco-related litigation the company spun Lorillard off into an independent public company in 2008 eliminating the Carolina Group and exiting the industry. Additionally while accessories make the outfit in 2008 Loews slipped its Bulova subsidiary off of its wrist and handed it to competitor Citizen Watch for $250 million.

Larry Tisch died at the age of 80 in 2003. Chairman Bob Tisch died of cancer in late 2005. Tisch also was co-owner of the New York Giants of the National Football League.

In keeping with the Loews strategy of acquiring what can be turned around letting go of what can't and the wisdom to know the difference the company spent $4 billion to acquire oil and gas exploration operator HighMount Exploration & Production and disposed of its tobacco interests and Bulova subsidiary in 2008.

EXECUTIVES

Co-chairman Loews Corporation And Chairman And Ceo Loews Hotels, Jonathan M. Tisch, age 65, $975,000 total compensation

President And Ceo, James S. Tisch, age 67, $975,000 total compensation

Svp And Cfo, David B. Edelson, age 59, $975,000 total compensation

Svp And Chief Investment Officer, Richard W. Scott, age 65

Svp, Kenneth I. Siegel, age 62, $975,000 total compensation

Vp Information Technology, Herb E. Hofmann

Senior Vice President And Chief Business Officer Loews Hotels And Resorts, Constantine Dimas

Vp Corporate Development, Jonathan Koplovitz

Regional Vice President, Felicia Marockie

Vice President Loews Cna Holdings Investments, Winifred Harrison

Senior Vice President Of Sales, David Wiener

Senior Vice President, Marc Shapiro

Vice President, Ramu Venkatachalam

Vp Tax, Susan Becker

Svp General Counsel And Corporate Secretary, Marc Alpert

Evp And Chro, Liz Aguinaga

Vp Purchasing And Materials Control Diamond Offshore, Duane Beair

Vice President Human Resources Diamond Offshore, R Lynn Charles

Vice President Operations Diamond Offshore, Steven Nelson

Svp Investments And Treasury Cna Financial, Amy Adams

Svp Sales And Distribution, John Hennessy

Senior Vice President Cna, Steve Wachtel

Vp Of Hr And Chro Of Diamond Offshore, Aaron Sobel

Vp Global Services, Laurie Munson

Vp. Product And Process Systems, Lindsay Lovvorn

Vp Corporate Development, Emma Riza

Svp Chief Diversity Officer And Head Operations, Joyce Trimuel

Vice President Operations Diamond Offshore, Jimmy Moore

Evp Technology And Operations Cna Financial Corporation, Joseph Merten

Svp Of International Of Cna Commercial, Kathleen Ellis

Svp Underwriting Services Cna Commercial, Barb Sandelands

Vp Minneapolis Branch, Joe Cranny

Vp Commercial Underwriting Eando Cyber And Media, Andy Lea

Svp Business Strategy Technology And Operations, Caroline King

Svp Special Projects And Strategic Initiatives Diamond Offshore, Lyndol Dew

Senior Vice President Administration Diamond Offshore, Mark Baudoin

Senior Vice President Tax Diamond Offshore, Stephen Elwood

Svp Technical Services Diamond Offshore, Karl Sellers

Vice President Health Safety And Environment Diamond Offshore, Neil Hall

Vice President Contracts And Marketing Diamond Offshore, Kane Liddelow

National Sales Manager, Jay Smith

National Sales Manager, Christopher McLaren

National Sales Manager, Michael Westfield

National Sales Manager, Rania Hammad

Vice President Of Sales And Marketing, Christopher Cawley

Vice President Operations Loews Hotels Universal Orlando, David Bartek

Vice President Accounting And Assistant Corporate Controller, Tracy Bress

National Sales Manager, Cristina Godwin

National Sales Manager, Megan Mcgauran

National Sales Manager, Mike Westfield

National Sales Manager, Nick Auckland

National Sales Manager, Melanie Lee

National Sales Manager, Jey Dutertre

National Sales Manager, Emily Friel

Vice President Of Operations, David Weidlich

Vp Risk Management, Audrey A Rampinelli

Evp And Cfo Of Cna Financial Corporation, D Craig Mense

Svp And Cto, Bahr Omidfar

Svp Of Underwriting Of Workers' Compensation Of Cna, Chris Thurman

Evp And General Counsel Of Cna Financial Corporation, Scott Weber

Assistant Vp Of It Services Of Cna, Tony Katrib

National Sales Manager, Jeremy Keippela

Vice President Editorial, Erin Mcknight

Vp And Publisher, Debra Dorfman

Co-chairman, Andrew H. Tisch, age 70

Board Member, Walter Harris

Board Member, Charles Diker

Board Member, Philip Laskawy

Treasurer, Andrew Stegen

Board Member, Anthony Welters

Board Member, Ann Berman

Board Member, Jacob Frenkel

Board Member, Joseph Bower

Auditors: DELOITTE & TOUCHE LLP

LOCATIONS

HQ: Loews Corp.
667 Madison Avenue, New York, NY 10065-8087
Phone: 212 521-2000
Web: www.loews.com

PRODUCTS/OPERATIONS

2017 Sales

	$ mil.	% of total
Insurance premiums	6,988	51
Net investment income	2,182	16
Contract drilling revenues	1,451	11
Investment gains	122	-
Other	2,992	22
Total	**13,735**	**100**

2017 Sales by Segment

	$ mil.	% of total
CNA Financial	9,583	70
Diamond Offshore	1,500	11
Boardwalk Pipeline	1,325	10
Loews Hotels	682	5
Corporate & Other	645	4
Total	**13,735**	**100**

Selected Subsidiaries

Boardwalk Pipeline Partners LP (51%)
CNA Financial Corporation (89%)
Diamond Offshore Drilling Inc. (53%)
Loews Hotels Holding Corporation (100%)

COMPETITORS

AIG	Noble
American Financial Group	Shaner Hotel Group
Berkshire Hathaway	Statoil
Cincinnati Financial	The Hartford
Menasha	Travelers Companies
	W. R. Berkley

HISTORICAL FINANCIALS

Company Type: Public

Income Statement

FYE: December 31

	ASSETS ($ mil.)	NET INCOME ($ mil.)	INCOME AS % OF ASSETS	EMPLOYEES
12/18	78,316	636	0.8%	17,900
12/17	79,586	1,164	1.5%	18,100
12/16	76,594	654	0.9%	15,800
12/15	76,029	260	0.3%	16,700
12/14	78,367	591	0.8%	17,510
Annual Growth	(0.0%)	1.9%	—	0.6%

2018 Year-End Financials

Debt ratio: 15.00%	No. of shares (mil.): 312
Return on equity: 3.00%	Dividends
Cash ($ mil.): 405	Yield: 1.0%
Current ratio: —	Payout: 13.0%
Long-term debt ($ mil.): —	Market value ($ mil.): 14,205

	STOCK PRICE ($) FY Close	P/E High/Low	PER SHARE ($) Earnings	Dividends	Book Value
12/18	46.00	27 21	2.00	0.00	59.00
12/17	50.00	15 13	3.00	0.00	58.00
12/16	47.00	25 18	2.00	0.00	54.00
12/15	38.00	59 49	1.00	0.00	52.00
12/14	42.00	31 25	2.00	0.00	52.00
Annual Growth	2.0%	— —	6.4%	(0.0%)	3.5%

Lowe's Companies Inc

Lowe's Companies has built a strong business out of lumber cement power tools and other merchandise. The company is the nation's #2 home improvement chain (after The Home Depot) with some 2000 mostly US-based locations. Its stores offer some 34000 products for repair and improve-ment projects (such as lumber paint plumbing and electrical supplies and tools) gardening and outdoor living and home furnishing and decorating. Lowe's is also one of the country's leading retailers of home appliances. It targets both the professional and consumer markets with national brand-name merchandise as well as its own private labels (Kobalt Blue Hawk Garden Treasures). The company only operates in North America with the vast majority of sales generated in the US.

HISTORY

Lowe's Companies was founded in 1921 as Mr. L. S. Lowe's North Wilkesboro Hardware in North Wilkesboro North Carolina. A family operation by 1945 Mr. Lowe's store (which also sold groceries snuff and harnesses) was run by his son Jim and his son-in-law H. Carl Buchan. Buchan bought Lowe's share of the company in 1956 and incorporated as Lowe's North Wilkesboro Hardware; he wanted Lowe's as part of the company name because he liked the slogan "Lowe's Low Prices." The chain expanded from North Carolina into Tennessee Virginia and West Virginia. By 1960 Buchan had 15 stores and sales of $31 million — up $4 million from a decade before.

Buchan planned to create a profit-sharing plan for Lowe's employees but in 1960 he died of a heart attack at age 44. In 1961 Lowe's management and the executors of Buchan's estate established the Lowe's Employees Profit Sharing and Trust which bought Buchan's 89% of the company (later renamed Lowe's Companies). That year they financed the transaction through a public offering which diluted the employees' stock. Lowe's was listed on the NYSE in 1979.

Robert Strickland who had joined the company in 1957 became chairman in 1978. Revenues increased from $170 million in 1971 to more than $900 million with a net income of $25 million in 1979. Traditionally the majority of Lowe's business was in sales to professional homebuilders but in 1980 housing starts fell and company profits dropped. Concurrently The Home Depot introduced its low-price warehouse concept. Instead of building warehouse stores of its own Strickland changed the stores' layouts and by 1982 had re-designed half of the 229 stores to be more oriented toward do-it-yourself (DIY) consumers. The new designs featured softer lighting and displays of entire room layouts to appeal to women who made up over half of all DIY customers. In 1982 Lowe's made more than half of its sales to consumers for the first time in its history.

Although Lowe's had more than 300 stores by 1988 its outlets were only about 20000 sq. ft. (one-fifth the size of Home Depot's warehouse stores). By 1989 Lowe's which had continued to target contractors as well as DIYers was overtaken by Home Depot as the US's #1 home retail chain.

Since 1989 the company has focused on building larger stores taking a charge of $71 million in 1991 to phase out smaller stores and build warehouse outlets. In 1993 Lowe's opened 57 large stores (half were replacements for existing stores) almost doubling its total floor space.

The retailer opened 29 new stores in 1995. During 1996 Lowe's added a net of 37 stores and in 1997 it opened 42 stores in new markets. Also that year president and CEO Leonard Herring retired and was replaced by former COO Robert Tillman who also took the post of chairman when Strickland stepped down in 1998.

Also in 1998 the company entered a joint venture to sell an exclusive line of Kobalt-brand professional mechanics' tools produced by Snap-on and to better serve commercial customers began allowing them to special order items not stocked in stores. In addition Lowe's announced it would spend $1.5 billion over the next several years on a 100-store push into the western US. Lowe's westward expansion was fueled when it purchased Washington-based 38-store Eagle Hardware & Garden in 1999 in a stock swap deal worth $1.3 billion. The company gradually converted the Eagle stores into Lowe's.

In 2001 the company earmarked $2.4 billion of its $2.7 billion capital budget for store expansions and new distribution centers.

Robert Niblock was promoted from CFO to president in March 2003. Lowe's sold its some 30 outlets operating as The Contractor Yard to The Strober Organization in February 2004. In April 2004 the company opened its first predominantly urban-oriented store suited to the needs of city dwellers and building superintendents in Brooklyn.

Chairman and CEO Robert Tillman retired in January 2005. He was succeeded by president Robert Niblock.

Lowe's entered the Canadian market in 2007.

The home improvement chain expanded its distribution footprint in 2008 opening a regional distribution center in Pittston Pennsylvania and a flatbed distribution center in Purvis Mississippi.

During 2010 Lowe's opened its first location in Mexico (in Monterrey). In 2011 the company made a rare acquisition: online home-improvement retailer ATG Stores based in Kirkland Washington.

In 2013 the company acquired a majority stake of California-based Orchard Supply Hardware (OSH) adding 70 stores to the 110 stores that Lowe's already operated in California.

EXECUTIVES

Chairman President And Ceo, Robert A. Niblock, age 56, $1,300,000 total compensation
Cfo, Marshall A. Croom, age 58
President Orchard Supply Hardware, Lara L. Lee
Chief Supply Chain Officer, Brent G. Kirby
Coo, Richard D. Maltsbarger, age 43
Chief Customer Officer, Michael P. McDermott
Cio, Paul D. Ramsay, age 54
Managing Director Loweâ's India, James A. Brandt
President And Managing Director Loweâ's Mexico, Juan L. Pier Castell
President Atgstores.com, Michelle M. Newbery
President And Ceo Loweâ's Canada, Sylvain PrudÂ'homme
Svp Corporate Finance And Treasurer, Tiffany Mason
Svp Services, Kevin Measel
Senior Vice President Pro Sales, Michael Tummillo
Regional Vice President For Eastern North Carolina, Jeff Blocker
Vice President Installed And Special Order Sales, Gary Gross
Svp Store Operations, William Edwards
Vice President Of Client Services, Marian Craig
Vice President Of Merchandisin, Daryl Tilley
Vice President Information Technology Business Management, Kathy Higgins
Vice President Global Sourcing And Quality Assurance, Zach Miller
Senior Vice President, Belinda Rumple
Regional Vice President Distribution, Calvin Adams
Vice President Of Asia Sourcing, Scott Jenkins
Vice President Vendor Service Management, Ron Lutz
Vice President Real Estate Construction And Store Design Canada, Jeff Boyd
Vice President Corporate Communication, Tracey Ahearn
Merchandising Vice President Flooring Division, Joseph Thomas
Vice President Corporate Payables, Linda Coffey

Senior Vice President Chief Accounting Officer, Matthew Hollifield
Vice President Merchandising Fashion Fixtures, Ann Haines
Vice President Transportation, Rick Gabrielson
Senior Vice President, Susan Burtt
Vice President Contact Center Operations, Donna Neale
Svp Strategy And Development, James Han
Vice President Of Operations, Jeffrey Blocker
Vice President, Beth Macdonald
Vice President Merchandising Canada, Alan Blundell
Vp Organizatioinal Effectiveness, Gregory Neill
Svp Chief Compliance Officer And Associate General Counsel, Jeff Vining
Svp And Chief Digital Officer, Vikram Singh
Vp Store Operations Support, Glenn Feazell
Merchandising Vice President, Revis Felts
Evp, William P Boltz
Vice President Store Operations, Kissel Goldman
Vice President Operations Engineering, Ram Krishnamurthy
Vice President In Home And Specialty Sales, Angela Huggins
Board Member, Bob Scott
Board Member, James Morgan
Secretary Treasurer, Arlene Holland
Board Member, Marshall Larsen
Board Member, Sandra Cochran
Board Member, Raul Alvarez
Board Member, Robert Johnson
Auditors: DELOITTE & TOUCHE LLP

LOCATIONS

HQ: Lowe's Companies Inc
  1000 Lowe's Blvd., Mooresville, NC 28117
Phone: 704 758-1000
Web: www.lowes.com

2018 Stores

	No.
US	1,723
Canada	279
Mexico	13
Total	**2,015**

2018 Sales

	% of total
US	92
Other	8
Total	**100**

PRODUCTS/OPERATIONS

2018 Sales

	$ mil.	% of total
Building & Maintenance	28,581	40
Appliances	27,987	39
Seasonal	12,786	18
Other	1,955	3
Total	**71,309**	**100**

Selected Product Categories

Appliances
Fashion Fixtures
Flooring
Home Fashions
Kitchens
Lawn & Garden
Lumber & Building Materials
Millwork
Outdoor Power Equipment
Paint
Rough Plumbing & Electrical
Seasonal Living
Tools & Hardware

Selected Proprietary Brands

allen+roth
Aquasource
Garden Treasures
Harbor Breeze

Kobalt
Portfolio
Reliabilt
Top Choice
Utilitech

COMPETITORS

84 Lumber	Lumber Liquidators
Ace Hardware	Menard
Amazon.com	Sears Holdings
Beacon Roofing	SiteOne
Best Buy	Tractor Supply
Builders FirstSource	True Value
Do it Best	Wal-Mart
Home Depot	

HISTORICAL FINANCIALS

Company Type: Public

Income Statement

				FYE: February 1
	REVENUE ($ mil.)	NET INCOME ($ mil.)	NET PROFIT MARGIN	EMPLOYEES
02/19	71,309	2,314	3.2%	300,000
02/18	68,619	3,447	5.0%	310,000
02/17*	65,017	3,093	4.8%	290,000
01/16	59,074	2,546	4.3%	270,000
01/15	56,223	2,698	4.8%	266,000
Annual Growth	6.1%	(3.8%)	—	3.1%

*Fiscal year change

2019 Year-End Financials

Debt ratio: 47.00%
Return on equity: 49.00%
Cash ($ mil.): 511
Current ratio: 1.00
Long-term debt ($ mil.): 14,391

No. of shares (mil.): 801
Dividends
  Yield: 2.0%
  Payout: 65.0%
Market value ($ mil.): 77,785

	STOCK PRICE ($) FY Close	P/E High/Low		PER SHARE ($) Earnings	Dividends	Book Value
02/19	97.00	41	29	3.00	2.00	5.00
02/18	102.00	26	18	4.00	2.00	7.00
02/17*	73.00	24	18	3.00	1.00	7.00
01/16	72.00	28	24	3.00	1.00	8.00
01/15	68.00	26	16	3.00	1.00	10.00
Annual Growth	9.4%			— —	1.2%	20.8%(18.6%)

*Fiscal year change

LPL Financial Holdings Inc.

LPL Financial is one of the largest distributors of financial products and services in the US. It provides an integrated platform of brokerage and investment advisory services to more than 14000 independent financial advisors including those at more than 700 financial institutions (such as credit unions) across the country. LPL also supports 4000 advisors affiliated with insurance companies that use LPL's clearing and advisory platforms. It does not sell direct to retail consumers but instead supports independent advisors who serve retail consumers. Total investable assets affiliated with LPL's licensed and independent advisors exceed $500 billion. LPL was formed in 1989 by the merger of Linsco and Private Ledger.

Operations

LPL Financial provides the front- middle- and back-office support that financial advisors need to offer independent investment advice to their own clients. LPL does this through a combination of an integrated technology platform comprehensive self-clearing services and open architecture access to a wide range of non-proprietary products. Working with over 750 product providers LPL offers its advisors access to a variety of annuities mutual funds retirement plan products unit investment trusts and other products. LPL also helps advisors navigate the complex and sometimes cumbersome financial regulatory environment.

In addition to its brokerage activities LPL acts as a custodian for registered investment advisers (RIAs) and is a leading consultant to retirement plans. The firm serves as custodian for more than $500 billion in brokerage and advisory assets in some 4.6 million advisory client accounts.

The primary manner in which LPL generates revenue is by taking a cut of the action undertaken by its advisors. In exchange for providing access to support services the company typically retains 10% to 20% of commissions and fees generated from advisors' activities. These commissions and fees represent roughly 75% of the LPL's revenue.

Geographic Reach

Boston-headquartered LPL Financial operates its business from three main locations Boston MA San Diego CA and Charlotte NC. The advisor network spans the US and is mainly found in suburbs of large cities and in rural communities.

Sales and Marketing

The company's direct customer are financial advisors. Its efforts to develop that network of advisors includes training offerings access to financial products and services a current and efficient trading & clearing platform and occasional acquisitions of independent brokerage houses.

The majority of LPL-served advisors are entrepreneurial financial consultants and are viewed as local providers of independent advice. Many advisors operate under their own business name and LPL may assist them with their own branding marketing and promotion and regulatory review.

Financial Performance

LPL delivered steady financial performance in recent years. Revenue grew steadily from $2.7 billion in 2009 to a recent peak of $4.4 billion in 2014 before tapering off in the last few years. Net income remained range bound between 2011 and 2016 between $150 million and $200 million.

In 2016 revenue fell 5% to $4.1 billion on reduced sales from commissions (down 12%) and advisory fees (5%) both adversely affected by the market volatility and uncertainty of 2016. Asset-based fees and transaction revenues increased modestly during the year offsetting some of the downside from LPL's primary revenue sources (commissions & advisory fees). Despite lower revenue the company was able to grow its total brokerage and advisory assets 7% ending 2016 with $509 billion.

Net income overcame the revenue fall and jumped 14% to $192 million. In general net income growth came from across-the-board expense controls. With lower commission revenue LPL incurred lower commission expenses. It's sales and marketing expenditures ticked down 5% lowering that cost by over $250 million.

Cash at the end of 2016 was $748 million up $23 million from the prior year. Cash used by investing activities (mainly capital expenditures) and by financing activities (primarily shareholder dividend payout and repurchase of common stock) totaled $250 million. Cash provided by operating activities was $275 million.

Strategy

LPL's operations are well positioned to produce organic growth. As underlying economic activity grows and as the target markets of its advisors grow so too do its commissions and advisory fees.

Demand for financial advice from independent advisors is expected grow 9% annually and LPL expects to fill its sails with the tailwind.

Growing its network of advisors scales LPL's business model. In 2016 it added more than 300 advisors organically and brought onboard another 3200 in 2017 with the acquisition of National Planning Holdings. LPL believes that its scale the fragmented market in which it serves its focus on advisor empowerment all contribute to a competitive advantage when it comes to future M&A activity.

LPL reiterated in 2016 that its focus is to remain on advisors who serve the mass-affluent customer market (those with $100000-plus to invest) where it believes there continues to be "attractive opportunities" for growth. Indeed at the end of 2016 some 20% of its total assets under custody (and $102 billion in advisory and brokerage assets) came from its advisor-supported accounts that each carried more than $1 million in assets.

The company also targets areas with high job growth to set up shop. LPL in late 2016 opened a new regional headquarters in Fort Mill South Carolina to serve the Charlotte area. The firm has designated the Charlotte area as its primary destination for job growth during the next several years and plans to invest at least $150 million in the region by the end of 2022.

Mergers and Acquisitions

In mid-2017 LPL purchased the assets and advisor network of National Planning Holdings for $325M plus a future contingent payment indexed to the performance of the acquired advisor network. The acquisition adds 3200 new advisors to LPL's core markets.

Company Background

LPL went public in 2010. The company raised some $470 million from its IPO and used some of the proceeds to repay debt. The stock offering also gave the company a source of new capital to possibly fund new acquisitions. However charges related to the IPO contributed to a net loss for the year despite an increase in revenue.

EXECUTIVES

Divisional President National Sales And Consulting, J. Andrew (Andy) Kalbaugh, age 55

Divisional President Business Development, William P. (Bill) Morrissey, age 54

Managing Director Legal And Government Relations And General Counsel, David P. Bergers, age 51, $600,000 total compensation

Cfo, Matthew J. (Matt) Audette, age 45, $600,000 total compensation

President And Ceo, Dan H. Arnold, age 54, $666,120 total compensation

Managing Director And Chief Risk Officer, Michelle Oroschakoff, age 57, $350,000 total compensation

Managing Director And Cio, Victor P. Fetter, age 50, $495,014 total compensation

Managing Director And Chief Human Capital Officer, Sallie R. Larsen, age 65

Evp And Cto, David Wright

Managing Director Service Trading And Operations, Thomas (Tom) Gooley, $500,000 total compensation

Managing Director And Deputy Chief Risk Officer, Tracy Calder, age 59, $413,016 total compensation

Managing Director Investor And Investment Solutions, George B. (Burt) White, age 49, $474,764 total compensation

Senior Vice President Sponsor Relations, Brad Cornell

Senior Vice President Associate Counsel, Keith Fine

Executive Vice President Business Technology Services, Donie Lochan

Senior Vice President Technology, Brady Green

Avp Supervision Business Risk Management, Taryn Crabb

Assistant Vice President Tax, Kathleen Rowatt

Assistant Vice President Application Development, Luis Marcelino

Senior Vice President Chief Audit Executive, Gerry Soderstrom

Executive Vice President And Chief Compliance Officer, Kathleen VanNoy-Pineda

Vice President Marketing Analytics, Craig Engelman

Vice President Finance, Garrett Beam

Vice President Institutional Services, Kathryn Busch

Vice President Governance Risk And Compliance, Michele Comarsh-Hein

Evp And Deputy General Counsel Regulatory Affairs, James Shorris

Senior Vice President Cash Management Services, Joy Goble

Executive Vice President Retirement Partners, David Reich

Executive Vice President Investments, Bryan Foster

Executive Vice President National And Managed Accounts Institution Services, Bruce Miller

Senior Vice President And Ciso, James Powell

Assistant Vice President Internal Consulting, Deanna Moss

Vice President Associate General Counsel, Thomas Barnett

Vice President Operations, Wendie Hernandez

Vice President Business Consulting, Rosanne Green

Senior Vice President Associate Counsel, Amanda Hawley

Senior Vice President Business Consulting, Matthew Barhorst

Svp Business Development Sales Operations And Enablement, Ken Hullings

Senior Vice President Division Manager, Brett Waterfield

Senior Vice President Associate General Counsel, Steve Morrison

Vice President Strategic Business Solutions, Dan Valente

Vp Regional Advisory Consultant, Mark Ramsey

Svp Service Trading And Operations, Timothy Graham

Senior Vice President Operations, Shawn White

Svp Advisor Diversity And Inclusion, Kathleen Zemaitis

Vice President Business Analysis, Lee Alcorn

Avp Compliance And Registration Service Center, Travis Otis

Assistant Vice President Product Manager, Jerremy Hisel

Vice President Internal Audit, John Reilly

Vice President And Assistant General Counsel, Andrea Ferranti

Senior Vice President Compliance, Bryon Abel

Vp Tax Reporting, Timothy Gacsy

Avp Corporate Real Estate Corporate Security, Mike Sannella

Vp Regional Advisory Consultant, John Stadtmueller

Vp Strategic Sourcing, Kate Puckett

Senior Vice President, Marc Ehlers

Vice President, Matthew Robichaud

Vice President Human Resources, Sheree Lovering

Vice President Managing Partner, J Winchek

Treasurer, Cindy Staples

Auditors: DELOITTE & TOUCHE LLP

LOCATIONS

HQ: LPL Financial Holdings Inc.
75 State Street, Boston, MA 02109
Phone: 617 423-3644
Web: www.lpl.com

PRODUCTS/OPERATIONS

2016 Sales

	$ mil.	% of total
Commissions	1,737	43
Advisory fees	1,290	32
Asset-based fees	557	14
Transaction & other fees	416	10
Interest	21	0
other	29	1
Total	**4,049**	**100**

Selected Subsidiaries

LPL Financial LLC
LPL Holdings Inc.
LPL Insurance Associates Inc.
Independent Advisers Group Corporation
Fortigent Holdings Company Inc.
The Private Trust Company N.A.
PTC Holdings Inc.
UVEST Financial Services Group

COMPETITORS

Ameriprise	Morgan Stanley Smith
Aretec Group	Barney
Charles Schwab	Pershing LLC
E*TRADE Financial	Raymond James
Edward Jones	Financial
FMR	TD Ameritrade
Merrill Lynch	UBS Financial Services
Morgan Keegan	Wells Fargo Advisors

HISTORICAL FINANCIALS

Company Type: Public

Income Statement

FYE: December 31

	REVENUE ($ mil.)	NET INCOME ($ mil.)	NET PROFIT MARGIN	EMPLOYEES
12/18	5,188	439	8.5%	4,229
12/17	4,281	239	5.6%	3,736
12/16	4,049	192	4.7%	3,288
12/15	4,275	169	3.9%	3,410
12/14	4,374	178	4.1%	3,384
Annual Growth	4.4%	25.3%	—	5.7%

2018 Year-End Financials

Debt ratio: 46.00%
Return on equity: 45.00%
Cash ($ mil.): 1,496
Current ratio: 1.00
Long-term debt ($ mil.): 2,517

No. of shares (mil.): 85
Dividends
  Yield: 2.0%
  Payout: 24.0%
Market value ($ mil.): 5,197

	STOCK PRICE ($) FY Close	P/E High/Low		PER SHARE ($) Earnings	Dividends	Book Value
12/18	61.00	14	11	5.00	1.00	11.00
12/17	57.00	22	13	3.00	1.00	11.00
12/16	35.00	20	8	2.00	1.00	9.00
12/15	43.00	27	21	2.00	1.00	8.00
12/14	45.00	31	23	2.00	1.00	10.00
Annual Growth	8.2%	—	—	29.0%	1.0%	3.4%

Luther Burbank Corp

Auditors: Crowe LLP

LOCATIONS

HQ: Luther Burbank Corp
520 Third Street, Fourth Floor, Santa Rosa, CA 95401
Phone: 844 446-8201
Web: www.lutherburbanksavings.com

HISTORICAL FINANCIALS

Company Type: Public

Income Statement

FYE: December 31

	ASSETS ($ mil.)	NET INCOME ($ mil.)	INCOME AS % OF ASSETS	EMPLOYEES
12/18	6,937	45	0.6%	278
12/17	5,704	69	1.2%	266
12/16	5,065	52	1.0%	274
12/15	4,363	35	0.8%	
Annual Growth	16.7%	8.4%	—	—

2018 Year-End Financials

Debt ratio: 2.00%
Return on equity: 8.00%
Cash ($ mil.): 92
Current ratio: —
Long-term debt ($ mil.): —

No. of shares (mil.): 56
Dividends
  Yield: 2.0%
  Payout: 18.0%
Market value ($ mil.): 509

	STOCK PRICE ($) FY Close	P/E High/Low		PER SHARE ($) Earnings	Dividends	Book Value
12/18	9.00	17	10	1.00	0.00	10.00
12/17	12.00	8	7	2.00	2.00	10.00
12/16	0.00	—	—	1.00	0.00	10.00
Annual Growth	—	—		(14.0%)	(22.3%)	2.3%

M & T Bank Corp

Bank holding company M&T Bank offers deposit loan trust investment brokerage mortgage and insurance services to individuals and small- and mid-sized businesses. With about $120 billion in total assets and $90 billion in deposits the bank operates some 750 branches and over 1800 ATMs in New York Pennsylvania other eastern states and Washington DC. Its lending is largely focused in those states but it originates its loans via offices in other states and Canada. The firm also manages a proprietary line of mutual funds through Wilmington Funds Management. M&T was founded in 1856 as Manufacturers and Traders Trust in Buffalo New York.

Operations

M&T Bank comprises three wholly-owned bank subsidiaries?M&T Bank Wilmington Funds Management and Wilmington Trust?and has a revenue stream diversified across six segments. M&T Bank represents 99% of the company's consolidated assets.

The Retail Banking segment offers standard banking services including consumer credit deposit products and generates nearly 30% of the company's total revenue. About 20% comes from its other activities not classified under its reporting segments. Those include trust income and allocation methodologies for internal transfers for funding charges and credits tied to earning assets and interest-bearing liabilities.

Commercial Banking brings in almost 20% of revenue and markets credit and banking services to middle-market and large corporate clients. Commercial Real Estate generates about 15% of revenue and offers credit and deposit products to clients seeking loans on apartments multifamily buildings offices and retail and industrial locations. Business Banking contributes around 10% of revenue and targets small businesses and professionals. Its provides loans (including Small Business Administration loans) leases credit and deposit products cash management and payroll services.

Residential Mortgage Banking originates and services consumer mortgages which it sells to investors or its Discretionary Portfolio division. It accounts for about 5% of the holding company's revenue. The company's Discretionary Portfolio segment produces less than 5% of its revenue. It houses investment and trading account securities residential real estate loans borrowed funds and brokered deposits.

Geographic Reach

Buffalo New York-based M&T Bank has operations in New York Maryland New Jersey Pennsylvania Delaware Connecticut Virginia West Virginia and Washington DC. It has commercial banking offices in Florida and Ontario Canada and an office in George Town Cayman Islands.

Sales and Marketing

M&T Bank caters to customers through multiple channels including physical branches and business banking centers telebanking the internet and ATMs. M&T markets its commercial and lending services and products to consumers small businesses middle-market and large corporations professionals governmental clients and financial institutions.

Financial Performance

Since 2014 M&T Bank has seen substantial revenue gains in each of its segments except for one; Residential Mortgage Banking revenue fell by about $80 billion due to losses in 2017 and 2018 caused by slowing loan originations and narrower margins. However revenue-producing activities not captured by any of the segments (such as internal accounting methodologies) were the holding company's prime growth driver as it more than doubled over five years. Despite stagnancy in 2014 and 2015 M&T's Retail Banking segment posted revenue gains from 2016 to 2018 that led to an overall increase of some 35%. Overall the company has expanded its revenue by about a third and its net income by about 80% since 2014.

M&T's revenue increased 5% to some $5.9 trillion in 2018. Despite a slide of more than 25% in its Discretionary Portfolio solid gains in its Retail Banking Business Banking and Commercial Real Estate segments bolstered the company's performance. Net income rose significantly by 36% to $1.9 billion boosted by increases in all segments except for the Discretionary Portfolio and Residential Mortgage Banking?which remained stagnant despite revenue losses thanks to reduced income taxes and lower depreciation and amortization.

The bank added $184.5 million to its cash in 2018 to end the year with stores of $1.6 billion. Operations provided $2.1 billion?a reduction from 2017 caused by a huge decrease in commercial real estate loans originated for sale to other investors. A net increase in interest-bearing deposits at banks mainly accounted for investment spend of $1.4 billion; financing activities depleted $495.3 million due to a net decrease in deposits dividend payments and long-term debt payments.

Strategy

A strategic shift initiated in 2015 has seen M&T Bank halt acquisitions of smaller rivals in its operating regions while maintaining a trend of reducing its reliance on physical banking offices as it turns its focus to more modern banking channels like the internet and mobile apps. Since that year (when it acquired New York-area bank holding company Hudson City Bancorp) it has reduced its number of branches from about 810 to some 750.

Despite that general strategy M&T still does make calculated branch openings in areas with growing economies. The company entered the Florida market in 2019 with the opening of a commercial banking branch in North Palm Beach. In 2018 it opened a Business Banking Center in Brooklyn an area of New York which has attracted a glut of new businesses in recent years. That center operates on the second floor of a regular banking branch it opened shortly before.

The holding company is also making moves to bolster its public image: in 2018 it announced it had provided more than $20 million in equipment lease financing to Cianbro to build the largest solar energy production facility in Maine; that year it also disclosed that it increased its employee's base wage and paid time off and that it had made $50 million in charitable contributions the year prior.

Company Background

M&T Bank traces its roots to the 1856 founding of Manufacturers and Traders Trust in Buffalo New York. M&T Bank reorganized as a bank holding company in 1969 called First Empire State. It changed its name in 1998 to M&T Bank.

EXECUTIVES

Group Vice President Commercial Equipment Finance, Mohannad Jishi

Evp Wealth And Institutional Services Division M&T Bank Corp And M&T Bank, William J. (Bill) Farrell, age 61

Evp M&t Bank Corporation And Evp And Co-head Commercial Banking M&t Bank, Brian E. Hickey, age 67, $299,231 total compensation

Evp M&t Bank Corporation And Vice Chairman And Evp M&t Bank, Kevin J. Pearson, age 58, $725,000 total compensation

Svp And Deputy Credit Officer, Robert J. Bojdak, age 64

Evp And Cio M&t Bank Corporation And M&t Bank, Michele D. Trolli, age 58

Chairman And Ceo M&t Bank Corporation And M&t Bank, René F. Jones, age 55, $725,000 total compensation

President Coo And Director M&t Bank Corporation And M&t Bank, Richard S. Gold, age 59, $725,000 total compensation

Evp And Treasurer M&t Bank Corporation And M&t Bank, D. Scott N. Warman, age 53

Evp And Cfo M&t Bank Corporation And M&t Bank, Darren J. King, age 49, $600,000 total compensation

Evp And Area Executive M&t Bank Corporation And M&t Bank, Gino A. Martocci, age 53

Evp Human Resources M&t Bank Corp And M&t Bank, Janet M. Coletti, age 55

Evp M&t Bank Corporation And Evp Wilmington Trust Wealth Management M&t Bank, Doris P. Meister, age 63

Evp Retail And Business Banking M&t Bank, Neil J. Hosty

Evp M&t Bank Corporation And Evp Mortgage And Customer Asset Management M&t Bank, Michael J. Todaro, age 57

Regional President Western New York And President M&t Charitable Foundation, Shelley Drake

Evp, Stephen Braunscheidel

Vice President Systems Manger, Sheila Brown

Vice President, Jim DiStefano

Assistant Vice President Platform Management Group, Erik Steensen

Assistant Vice President And Performance Test Team Leader, Paula Henderson

Vice President Information Technology, Krista Swann

Assistant Vice President Technology Infrastructure Operations, Zana Vernon

Vice President, Kim Phelan

Vice President Business Planning And Commercial Equipment Finance, Lisa Pawlowski

Vice President Network Telecommunications, Chris Tolomeo

Assistant Vice President Operations, Katie Schultz

Assistant Vice President Information Systems, Bob Roeder

Vice President, Maureen Stevens

Vice President Global Sourcing, Patti Haan

Senior Vice President, Ayan Das Gupta

Assistant Vice President Technology, Steven Destro

Vice President, Ron Rozanski

Group Vice President, Jim Kaiser

Assistant Vice President Senior Software Engineering, Ashish Vikram

Vice President Senior Real Estate Counsel, Donna Suchan

Vice President Marketing, Bonnie Mikolajczak

Vice President Human Resources Business Partner, Amy Walker

Vice President Trust Risk Manager, Dawn Snelling

Vice President Human Resources Business Partner Mortgage And Consumer Lending, Donna Harlacher

Assistant Vice President Talent Acquisition Senior Recruiter, Roni Thomas

Assistant Vice President Team Lead, Bemina Rohde

Assistant Vice President And Compliance Officer, Barbara Moynihan

Assistant Vice President Relationship Manager, Sam Higgins

Vice President Finance, David Zolnowski

Vice President, Beth Beshaw

Vice President, Karen Boyle

Vice President, Christa DeSpirt

Assistant Vice President Accounting Policy, Nick Ambrose

Vice President Accounting Policy, Timothy Cahlstadt

Vice President Commercial Banking, William Johnston

Assistant Vice President, Lisa Dente

Assistant Vice President Branch Manager, Lauren Perrone

Group Vp, Kelley Attig

Group Vice President For Residential Lending, Nick Buscaglia

Executive Vice President, James Beardi

Vice President, Juliet Alexander

Vice President Senior Product Manager, David Reif

Group Vp And Corporate Secretary, Marie King

Vice President And Assistant Corporate Secretary, Karl Braun-Kolbe

Vice President, Gerald Brautlacht

Vice President Solutions Delivery, Boris Roginsky

Senior Vice President Quantative Risk, Carol Bartosz

Svp And Assistant Treasurer, Douglas Sheline

Vice President End User Computing Manager, Mike Ferger

Avp Technology Infrastructure, Laurie Popielarski

Executive Vice President And Chief Risk Officer, John D'Angelo

Vice President Senior Project Manager, David Lee

Vice President Cybersecurity, Lynne Erickson

Assistant Vice President Information Technology Audit, John Gagne

Group Vp And Assistant Secretary, Randall Krolewicz

Vice President And Manager Business And Planning, John Heimback

Vice President Corporate Training Support Services, Lynne Kreiner

Group Vice President Technology Infrastructure Operations, Mark Kumro

Svp Alternative Banking, Michael Shryne

Senior Vice President And Bsa Aml Ofac Officer, Tracy Woodrow

Vice President Admin, Detra Miller

Assistant Vp And Project Manager, Fred Peckham

Vice President Business Continuity, Jeff Shaw

Vice President Consumer Risk Management, Scott Warman

Group Vice President Wealth And Institut, Myles McHale

Administrative Vice President Retail Banking, Matt Calhoun

Vice President Portfolio Manager, Courtney Herbert

Vice President, John Lewis

Group Vice President, John Federici

Assistant Vice President Team Lead End User Experience, David Cuviello

Vice President, Sarah Sember

Group Vice President, Denise Cramer

Vice President Business And Retail Web Banking Central Technology, Muhammad Akhtar

Vice President Of Healthcare Division, Sharon Obrien

Vice President Indirect Relationship Manager, Jim Eriksen

Vice President Product Management (digital Workspace), Amy LePenske

Group Vice President Enterprise Data Services, Seetharaman Kishor

Vice President Information Technology, Kalimuthu Chithambaram

Vice President Data Services, Shashi Shankar

Senior Vice President Digital And Telephone Banking, Paris Roselli

Vice President And Legal Counsel, Demario Carswell

Vice President, Jerry Laspisa

Vice President, Steven Wendelboe

Vp Senior User Experience Designer, Thomas Marks

Vice President Human Resources Business Partner, Vivek Siddhu

Vice President Commercial Credit Modeling, Vito Flitt

Assistant Vp Enterprise Data Mater Data Manager, Matt Krause

Vice President Commercial Real Estate, Paul Ciancimino

Group Vice President, Trevor Foote

Vp Mortgage Originations, Julie Deglopper

Vice President Group Sales Manager, John Vilardo

Vice President Business Relationship Manager, Ana Saraiva

Senior Vice President, Ralph W Emerson

Vice President Residential Mortgage Accounting Manager, Diane Kinton

Vice President Global Operations Risk Management Services, Neal Harrington

Vice President Cybersecurity, Jason Linton

Vice President Debt Capital Markets, Ajibola Fadahunsi

Vice President, Amy Devine

Risk Analyst Avp, Robin Grzechowiak

Vice President, Bradley Myers

Senior Relationship Manager Vice President, Lola Gazivoda

Vice President, Michele Kubik

Assistant Vice President Indirect Lending, Alan Helfgott

Vice President, Aaron Nodar

Vice President, Gaye Boyette

Vice President, Suzanne Rosaschi

Vice President Product Data Analytics Manager, Yu-hin Wong

Vice President, Alexis Agnello

Vp Group Manager, Mark Adiletta

Vp Commercial Banking Team Leader, Ramal Moreland

Vice President Cybersecurity, Lynn Decourcey

Group Vp And Head Of Technology Architecture, Steve Webb

Vice President Commercial Relationship Manager, Dayana Villanueva

Vice President And Counsel, Paul Woodard

Vice President Central Technology, Beatrice Smallets

Vice President, Kenneth Stolarick

Vice President, Rory Hertzog

Administrative Vice President Corporate Banking, William Long

Group Vice President, Richard Mueller

Vice President And Team Leader, Deborah Urtz

Vice President, Lisa Lipira

Group Vp Advertising Promotions And
Sponsorships, Betsy Locke
Vice President Team Leader Business And
Professional Banking Group, Eric Tommasi
Regional Vice President, John Dimino
Vice President Relationship Manager, Anne Roder
Avp Business Systems Analyst V, Kathleen Wilston
Vice President Business Banking, Kimberly Dewitt
Vp Middle Market Relationship Manager, Carolyn
Zazzarino
Vp Sr Relationship Manager Business Banking,
Chad Shank
Vice President Leadership Development, Kristina
Farrell
Vice Chairman, Robert T. (Bob) Brady, age 78
Board Member, Herbert Washington
Abm, Robyn Cargill
Board Member, Brent Baird
Board Member, Melinda Rich
Auditors: PricewaterhouseCoopers LLP

LOCATIONS

HQ: M & T Bank Corp
One M & T Plaza, Buffalo, NY 14203
Phone: 716 635-4000
Web: www.mtb.com

PRODUCTS/OPERATIONS

Selected Subsidiaries
M&T Life Insurance Company
M&T Insurance Agency Inc
M&T Mortgage Reinsurance Company Inc.
M&T Real Estate Trust
M&T Realty Capital Corporation
M&T Securities Inc.
Wilmington Trust Company
Wilmington Trust Investment Advisors Inc.
Wilmington Funds Management Corporation
Wilmington Trust Investment Management LLC

2018 Sales

	$ mil.	% of total
Interest income		
Loans and leasesincluding fees	4,165	62
Investment securities	325	5
Deposits at banks	108	2
Others	1	0
Interest expense	(526.4)	-
Non-interest income		
Trust income	538	9
Service charges on deposit accounts	429	7
Mortgage banking revenue	360	6
Brokerage services income	51	1
Others	478	8
Total	**5,928**	**100**

2018 Sales

	$ mil.	% of total
Retail Banking	1,675	28
Commercial Banking	1,111	19
Commercial Real Estate	849	14
Business Banking	546	9
Residential Mortgage	320	5
Discretionary Portfolio	218	4
All Others	1,209	21
Total		100

COMPETITORS

Citigroup
Citizens Financial
  Group
Fulton Financial
HSBC USA
JPMorgan Chase

KeyCorp
Northwest Bancshares
PNC Financial
Sovereign Bank
SunTrust
TriState Capital

HISTORICAL FINANCIALS
Company Type: Public

Income Statement
FYE: December 31

	ASSETS ($ mil.)	NET INCOME ($ mil.)	INCOME AS % OF ASSETS	EMPLOYEES
12/18	120,097	1,918	1.6%	17,267
12/17	118,593	1,408	1.2%	16,794
12/16	123,449	1,315	1.1%	16,973
12/15	122,788	1,080	0.9%	17,476
12/14	96,686	1,066	1.1%	15,782
Annual Growth	5.6%	15.8%	—	2.3%

2018 Year-End Financials
Debt ratio: 7.00%
Return on equity: 12.00%
Cash ($ mil.): 9,896
Current ratio: —
Long-term debt ($ mil.): —
No. of shares (mil.): 139
Dividends
  Yield: 2.0%
  Payout: 28.0%
Market value ($ mil.): 19,825

	STOCK PRICE ($) FY Close	P/E High/Low		PER SHARE ($) Earnings	Dividends	Book Value
12/18	143.00	15	11	13.00	4.00	112.00
12/17	171.00	20	16	9.00	3.00	108.00
12/16	156.00	20	13	8.00	3.00	106.00
12/15	121.00	18	16	7.00	4.00	101.00
12/14	126.00	17	15	7.00	3.00	93.00
Annual Growth	3.3%		—	14.5%	6.1%	4.6%

Macy's Inc

Auditors: KPMG LLP

LOCATIONS

HQ: Macy's Inc
7 West Seventh Street, Cincinnati, OH 45202
Phone: 513 579-7000
Web: www.macys.com

HISTORICAL FINANCIALS
Company Type: Public

Income Statement
FYE: February 2

	REVENUE ($ mil.)	NET INCOME ($ mil.)	NET PROFIT MARGIN	EMPLOYEES
02/19	25,739	1,108	4.3%	130,000
02/18*	24,837	1,547	6.2%	130,000
01/17	25,778	619	2.4%	148,300
01/16	27,079	1,072	4.0%	157,900
01/15	28,105	1,526	5.4%	166,900
Annual Growth	(2.2%)	(7.7%)	—	(6.1%)

*Fiscal year change

2019 Year-End Financials
Debt ratio: 25.00%
Return on equity: 18.00%
Cash ($ mil.): 1,162
Current ratio: 1.00
Long-term debt ($ mil.): 4,708
No. of shares (mil.): 308
Dividends
  Yield: 0.0%
  Payout: 42.0%
Market value ($ mil.): 7,912

	STOCK PRICE ($) FY Close	P/E High/Low		PER SHARE ($) Earnings	Dividends	Book Value
02/19	26.00	12	7	4.00	2.00	21.00
02/18*	25.00	7	3	5.00	2.00	19.00
01/17	29.00	22	14	2.00	1.00	14.00
01/16	40.00	22	11	3.00	1.00	14.00
01/15	64.00	16	12	4.00	1.00	16.00
Annual Growth	(20.3%)	—	—	(4.2%)	6.2%	7.3%

*Fiscal year change

Magellan Health Inc.

Magellan Health is one of the largest managed behavioral health care companies in the US. The company manages mental health plan employee assistance and work/life programs through its nationwide third-party provider network. Magellan also provides radiology benefits management specialty pharmaceutical management and Medicaid management. Overall it serves about 55 million members through contracts with federal and local government agencies insurance companies and employers. Magellan's Pharmacy Management segment's services include benefit management dispensing administration clinical programs medical pharmacy management and care coordination.

Operations
Magellan operates through two primary business segments: Healthcare (which brings in over 60% of revenue) and Pharmacy Management (some 40% of revenue).

The Healthcare segment provides managed behavioral health care services and employee assistance program (EAP) services as well as managing other specialty areas including diagnostic imaging and musculoskeletal health. It also provides the integrated management of physical behavioral and pharmaceutical health care for special populations through Magellan Complete Care (MCC).

Magellan's Pharmacy Management segment offers products and services to help its clients manage pharmacy benefit programs. It provides pharmacy benefit management (PBM) services pharmacy benefit administration (PBA) for Medicaid and other government-sponsored programs medical pharmacy management and programs to integrate management of specialty drugs across medical and pharmacy benefits in complex cases.

Geographic Reach
Magellan Health operates about 70 offices in 25 states and Washington DC.

Sales and Marketing
Magellan's customers include health plans employer groups government and military agencies labor unions third-party administrators and pharmaceutical manufacturers. It serves more than 55 million members including some 38 million from commercial entities some 15 million from pharmacy management entities and some 1.5 million from government entities. The government accounts for about 60% of total revenue though.

The company has a network of approximately 220000 health care providers as well as a third-party network of facilities including psychiatric and substance abuse hospitals partial hospitalization facilities rehab centers and community health centers.

Financial Performance
Magellan's revenues have been climbing upward over the past five years but net income has been volatile from year to year.

In 2018 the company's revenue increased 25% to $7.3 billion. In the Healthcare segment this was largely due to the 2017 acquisition of Senior Whole Health new contracts secured and higher membership but partially offset by unfavorable rate changes and terminated contracts. The Pharmacy Management segment had a 12% decrease in revenue though due to factors including decreased formulary management revenue lower government pharmacy revenue and decreased medical pharmacy revenue.

Net income fell 78% to $24.2 million that year; it posted a $28 million loss in the fourth quarter. The losses were attributed to $50 million out-of-period and non-recurring items.

The company ended 2018 with $272.3 million in net cash $127 million less than it had at the end of 2017. Operating activities provided $164.8 million while investing activities used $128.4 million and financing activities used another $162.8 million.

Strategy

Magellan's growth strategy include maximizing and expanding its key value drivers. This includes a continued focus on specialty drug management (by utilizing analytics high-touch clinical programs and comprehensive specialty drug solutions) Medicaid behavioral health and specialty health care. It aims to expand its management programs for special populations such as individuals dealing with serious mental illness. The company is also expanding Medicaid management programs for certain high-cost populations including dual-eligibility patients (those qualifying for both Medicare and Medicaid services) forming partnerships and ventures with regional health plans. According to the Centers for Medicare and Medicaid Services Medicaid enrollment is projected to increase rapidly over the next decade and Magellan intends to take advantage of that increase by marketing itself to states that need guidance navigating the public mental health system.

Magellan is also working to expand its pharmacy management business. In 2018 it launched MRx Predict an analytics product that proactively identifies patients at risk of experiencing adverse events and predicts future drug cost drivers for customers.

Other initiatives include driving new sales while retaining existing customers. Its efforts include seeking new employer contracts and upselling to its customers. It is also looking to reduce its cost of care and make operational improvements to improve margins. The last key to its core strategy is to engage its workforce through development opportunities while streamlining its corporate structure.

Mergers and Acquisitions

Magellan acquired Senior Whole Health for $400 million in 2017. The formerly privately held Senior Whole Health provides Medicare and Medicaid dual-eligible benefits in the states of Massachusetts and New York. With that purchase Magellan expanded into Massachusetts' Senior Care Options program as well as the managed long-term care market in New York City.

Company Background

William Fickling once a star basketball player at Auburn University started his career in his father's real estate office in Georgia. In 1969 Fickling founded Charter Medical as a holding company for the family's six nursing homes and one hospital. The company went public in 1971 as an owner/manager of general acute care hospitals. By the mid-1980s it had focused on psychiatric facilities and was adding addiction treatment centers to its portfolio.

The company went into Chapter 11 in 1991 emerging in 1992 with a plan to focus on behavioral health care; it also went public again. As part of its reorganization Charter in 1995 bought Magellan Health Services and took that name. It also bought 51% of Green Spring Health Services a managed care company specializing in mental health and substance abuse. (It bought the rest in 1998.)

EXECUTIVES

Chairman And Ceo, Barry M. Smith, age 65, $1,000,000 total compensation

Cfo, Jonathan N. (Jon) Rubin, age 55, $535,600 total compensation

General Counsel And Secretary, Daniel N. (Dan) Gregoire, age 64, $470,350 total compensation

Ceo Magellan Healthcare, Sam K. Srivastava, age 51, $609,000 total compensation

Cto, Srinivas (Srini) Koushik

Chief Medical Officer, Karen Amstutz

Ceo Magellan Rx Management, Mostafa M. Kamal, age 38, $412,000 total compensation

Vice President, Tom Lenhart

Senior Vice President And Chief Compliance Officer At Magellan Health Services, John DiBernardi

Vice President Human Resources Enterprise, Erin Kirchhardt

Vice President Benefits, Christine Barnard

Senior Vice President Specialty Sales, Terah Cochrane

Vice President Client Analytics, Peter Lee

Vice President Strategy And Corporate Development, Sprague Mark

Vice President Federal Affairs, Brian Coyne

Senior Vice President Business Development, Thomas O'Connor

Associate Medical Director, Lashondra Washington

Auditors: Ernst & Young LLP

LOCATIONS

HQ: Magellan Health Inc.
4800 N. Scottsdale Rd., Suite 4400, Scottsdale, AZ 85251
Phone: 602 572-6050
Web: www.magellanhealth.com

PRODUCTS/OPERATIONS

2018 Sales by Segment

	$ mil.	% of total
Healthcare	4,639	62
Pharmacy Management	2,866	38
Adjustments	(190.3)	-
Total	**7,314**	**100**

2018 Sales

	$ mil.	% of total
Managed care & other	4,879	67
Pharmacy benefit management	2,436	33
Total	**7,314**	**100**

COMPETITORS

APS Healthcare	Horizon Health
CIGNA Behavioral Health	Mental Health Network
ComPsych	OptumRx
Comprehensive Care	PharMerica
First Health Group	Schaller Anderson Inc
Health Net	UBH

HISTORICAL FINANCIALS

Company Type: Public

Income Statement   FYE: December 31

	REVENUE ($ mil.)	NET INCOME ($ mil.)	NET PROFIT MARGIN	EMPLOYEES
12/18	7,314	24	0.3%	10,500
12/17	5,839	110	1.9%	10,700
12/16	4,837	78	1.6%	9,700
12/15	4,597	31	0.7%	6,900
12/14	3,760	79	2.1%	6,600
Annual Growth	**18.1%**	**(25.7%)**	**—**	**12.3%**

2018 Year-End Financials

Debt ratio: 25.00%
Return on equity: 2.00%
Cash ($ mil.): 272
Current ratio: 2.00
Long-term debt ($ mil.): 729

No. of shares (mil.): 24
Dividends
  Yield: —
  Payout: —
Market value ($ mil.): 1,362

	STOCK PRICE ($) FY Close	P/E High/Low	PER SHARE ($) Earnings	Dividends	Book Value
12/18	57.00	112 54	1.00	0.00	54.00
12/17	97.00	21 14	5.00	0.00	53.00
12/16	75.00	23 15	3.00	0.00	47.00
12/15	62.00	57 37	1.00	0.00	43.00
12/14	60.00	21 18	3.00	0.00	42.00
Annual Growth	**(1.3%)**	**— —**	**(24.0%)**	**—**	**6.3%**

ManpowerGroup Inc

EXECUTIVES

Chb-Ceo, Jonas Prising
Exec V Pres-Cfo, John T McGinnis
Exec V Pres, Mara E Swan
Sr V Pres-Gen Counsel-Sec, Richard D Buchband
Staffing Specialist, Aimee Doyle
Information Technology, Ajay Rudara
Tax Manager, Andy Wagner
Staffing Specialist, Ann Stoffel
Director, Annette Busateri
Benefits Analyst, Carla Campbell
Lead Financial Analyst, Cesiah Kessler
Auditors: DELOITTE & TOUCHE LLP

LOCATIONS

HQ: ManpowerGroup Inc
100 Manpower Place, Milwaukee, WI 53212
Phone: 414 961-1000   **Fax:** 414 332-0796
Web: www.manpower.com

COMPETITORS

Adecco	Randstad Holding
Kelly Services	Robert Half
Korn/Ferry	TrueBlue
Michael Page	Volt Information

HISTORICAL FINANCIALS

Company Type: Public

Income Statement   FYE: December 31

	REVENUE ($ mil.)	NET INCOME ($ mil.)	NET PROFIT MARGIN	EMPLOYEES
12/18	21,991	557	2.5%	30,000
12/17	21,034	545	2.6%	29,000
12/16	19,654	444	2.3%	28,000
12/15	19,330	419	2.2%	27,000
12/14	20,763	428	2.1%	26,000
Annual Growth	**1.4%**	**6.8%**	**—**	**3.6%**

2018 Year-End Financials

Debt ratio: 13.00%
Return on equity: 21.00%
Cash ($ mil.): 592
Current ratio: 1.00
Long-term debt ($ mil.): 1,025

No. of shares (mil.): 61
Dividends
  Yield: 3.0%
  Payout: 24.0%
Market value ($ mil.): 3,937

	STOCK PRICE ($) FY Close	P/E High/Low	PER SHARE ($) Earnings	Dividends	Book Value
12/18	65.00	16 7	9.00	2.00	43.00
12/17	126.00	16 11	8.00	2.00	42.00
12/16	89.00	15 9	6.00	2.00	35.00
12/15	84.00	18 12	5.00	2.00	36.00
12/14	68.00	16 11	5.00	1.00	38.00
Annual Growth	**(1.3%)**	**— —**	**12.7%**	**19.8%**	**3.5%**

Marathon Oil Corp.

In the long-running competition for success in the oil and gas industry Marathon Oil is keeping up a steady pace. It has proved reserves of more than 2.1 billion barrels of oil equivalent including 692 million barrels of synthetic oil derived from oil sands mining. It major focus of production is the US in the Gulf of Mexico Oklahoma Texas north Delaware and North Dakota. Its areas of production outside of the US include Europe (the UK); and Africa (Equatorial Guinea Gabon and Libya).

Operations

Marathon Oil is engaged in oil and gas exploration production worldwide and LNG and methanol marketing in Equatorial Guinea.

The company operates through two reportable operating segments: North America E&P (over 70% of total revenues) which explores for produces and markets crude oil and condensate NGLs and natural gas in the US; and International E&P (roughly 30%) which explores for produces and markets crude oil and condensate NGLs and natural gas outside of the US and produces and markets products manufactured from natural gas such as LNG and methanol in Equatorial Guinea.

Geographic Reach

Marathon Oil has oil and gas assets in Equatorial Guinea Gabon Kurdistan (Iraq) Libya the UK and the US.70% of revenue comes from the US.

Sales and Marketing

Marathon Oil's marketing activities include the transportation of oil and gas to market centers the sale of commodities to third parties and the storage of hydrocarbon products.In 2017 sales to Vitol and affiliates accounted for approximately 10% of the company's total revenue.

Financial Performance

Marathon revenue has fallen from $13 billion in 2010 to just below $5 billion in 2017 mostly from asset sell-offs and divestment. Net Income also declined from a $2 billion average per year to losses from 2015 onwards. In the last three years the company has had losses of some $10 billion.

Revenue in 2017 rose some 25% to $4.8 billion from the previous year. Volumes increased due to the Delaware acquisition new wells to sales in other US assets and better sales in Libya.

Net income for Marathon got worse. From a loss of $2.1 billion in 2016 it registered losses of $5.7 billion in 2017 mostly due to a 10% increase in depreciation and amortization costs ($2.4 billion in 2017) as well as a $248 million increase in impairment charges over 2016 (totaling $638 million for 2017).

Cash holdings declined from $2.5 billion to just over $560 million. Operations generated $2 billion but financing and investment activities used $2 billion in cash each mostly in acquisition and debt reduction.

Strategy

Marathon Oil continues to focus on lower cost/higher return liquid hydrocarbon reserves and production in the US. To accelerate this push in 2017 the company agreed to sell its 20% stake in the Athabasca Oil Sands Project for $2.5 billion to pay down debt and reinvest in core projects (it sold assets in 2015-16 period totaling $1.5 billion). In 2017 Marathon also bought 70000 net acres in the lower-cost Permian Basin from BC Operating for $1.1 billion.

One of Marathon's biggest strengths is its differentiated position in the four most productive low-cost resource plays: Eagle Ford Bakken Oklahoma and north Delaware. In 2018 90% of its capital allocation budget of $ 2.3 billion will come from the US resource plays (its development budget is self-funded). Excess cash from higher commodity prices and divestiture proceeds is being strategically invested. Since 2017 saw rise in production margins (oil production was 30% higher than last quarter of 2016) the company predicts a greater percentage of production being sourced from its high quality assets. Marathon expects 410000 boed of production for 2018 excluding Libya up some 18% year-over-year as resource plays grow in the US.

With a somewhat unexpectedly good production results from its unconventional wells in the Eagle Ford and Bakken assets further aided by strong rates from the nine-well STACK infill assets Marathon is now focused on increasing corporate-level returns as the company has had massive losses in the last three years totaling more than $10 billion. In 2017 Marathon was able to achieve cash flow neutrality including working capital. It also reduced gross debt by $1.8 billion in 2017 lowering its annual interest expense by at least $115 million.

Mergers and Acquisitions

In 2016 the company acquired Payrock Energy Holdings (a portfolio company of EnCap Investments) for $888 million. The deal added to Marathon Oil's position in the STACK play in Oklahoma where the break-even crude price for commercially viable oil production is in the low $40s.

HISTORY

Marathon Oil was founded in 1887 in Lima Ohio as The Ohio Oil Company by 14 independent oil producers to compete with Standard Oil. Within two years Ohio Oil was the largest producer in the state. This success did not go unnoticed by Standard Oil which proceeded to buy Ohio Oil in 1889. In 1905 the company moved to Findlay Ohio where it remained until it relocated to Houston in 1990.

When the US Supreme Court broke up Standard Oil in 1911 Ohio Oil became independent once again and expanded its exploration activities to Kansas Louisiana Texas and Wyoming.

In a 1924 attempt to drill three wells west of the Pecos River in Texas Ohio Oil mistakenly drilled three dry holes to the east. The company was on the verge of abandoning the project until a geologist reported the error. Ohio Oil drilled in the right area and the wells flowed. That year the company bought Lincoln Oil Refining — its first venture outside crude oil production.

Ohio Oil continued its expansion into refining and marketing operations in 1927. Following WWII the company began international exploration. Through Conorada Petroleum (later Oasis) a partnership with Continental Oil (later Conoco and then ConocoPhillips) and Amerada Hess the company explored in Africa and South and Central America. Conorada's biggest overseas deal came in 1955 when it acquired concessions on more than 60 million acres in Libya.

In 1962 the company acquired Plymouth Oil and changed its name to Marathon Oil Company; it had been using the Marathon name in its marketing activities since the late 1930s.

EXECUTIVES

Vice President Emerging Technology Marathon Oil, Linda A Capuano

Evp And Cfo, Dane E. Whitehead, age 57

Vp Human Resources Communications And Administrative Services, Deanna L. Jones

Evp Operations, T. Mitchell (Mitch) Little, age 55, $529,615 total compensation

Chairman President And Ceo, Lee M. Tillman, age 57, $1,050,000 total compensation

Senior Vice President Technology & Innovation And Cio, Bruce A. McCullough

Svp General Counsel And Secretary, Reggie Hedgebeth

Regional Vice President, Mike Henderson

Evp Operations, Mitch Little

Vp And Treasurer, Morris Clark

Vice President Geophysical It, Trevor Chargois

Vice President Risk Management And Trading, Kevin Fowler

Vice President Manager Director, Ellen Norton

Vice President Information Technology, Thomas Need

Vice President, Gary Loftus

Vice President, Ross Palmiero

Vice President, Cindy Worthman

Executive Vice President Corporate Development And Strategy, Pat Wagner

Vp Conventional, Cathy Krajicek

Svp Of General Counsel And Secretary, Reginald Hedgebeth

Senior Vice President General Counsel And Secretary, Reginald D Hedgebeth

Regional Vice President Permian, Thomas Hellman

Senior Vice President Of Marketing, Thomas Kelley

Vice President Of Risk Management, Gregs Holt

Executive Vice President Advisor To The, Bj Boening

Vice President, Todd Abbott

Board Member, Gregory Boyce

Auditors: PricewaterhouseCoopers LLP

LOCATIONS

HQ: Marathon Oil Corp.
5555 San Felipe Street, Houston, TX 77056-2723
Phone: 713 629-6600
Web: www.marathonoil.com

2016 Sales

	% of total
United States	60
Canada	21
Libya	1
Other international	18
Total	**100**

PRODUCTS/OPERATIONS

2016 Sales

	% of total
North American E&P	61
International E&P	19
Oil Sands Mining (OSM)	21
Total	**100**

2016 Sales

	% of total
Crude oil and condensate	65
Synthetic crude oil	20
Natural Gas	9
Natural Gas liquids	5
Other	1
Total	**100**

COMPETITORS

BP	Occidental Petroleum
Chevron	PEMEX
ConocoPhillips	Petr leos de
Exxon Mobil	Venezuela
Hess Corporation	Royal Dutch Shell
Koch Industries Inc.	

Company Type: Public

Income Statement				FYE: December 31
	REVENUE ($ mil.)	NET INCOME ($ mil.)	NET PROFIT MARGIN	EMPLOYEES
12/18	6,582	1,096	16.7%	2,400
12/17	4,765	(5,723)	—	2,300
12/16	4,650	(2,140)	—	2,117
12/15	5,861	(2,204)	—	2,611
12/14	11,258	3,046	27.1%	3,330
Annual Growth	(12.6%)	(22.6%)	—	(7.9%)

2018 Year-End Financials

Debt ratio: 26.00%	No. of shares (mil.): 819
Return on equity: 9.00%	Dividends
Cash ($ mil.): 1,462	Yield: 1.0%
Current ratio: 2.00	Payout: 16.0%
Long-term debt ($ mil.): 5,499	Market value ($ mil.): 11,744

	STOCK PRICE ($) FY Close	P/E High/Low		PER SHARE ($) Earnings	Dividends	Book Value
12/18	14.00	18	10	1.00	0.00	15.00
12/17	17.00	—	—	(7.00)	0.00	14.00
12/16	17.00	—	—	(3.00)	0.00	21.00
12/15	13.00	—	—	(3.00)	1.00	27.00
12/14	28.00	9	6	4.00	1.00	31.00
Annual Growth	(15.6%) (17.0%)	—	—	(26.7%)	(29.3%)	

Marathon Petroleum Corp.

Marathon Petroleum the former refining and marketing unit of Marathon Oil Corporation operates more than five refineries with the capacity to process about 1.9 million barrels of crude oil a day. Marathon Petroleum sells refined products through a nationwide network of branded gas stations. It also holds stakes in pipelines and is one of the largest asphalt and light oil product terminal operators in the US. The company distributes petroleum products wholesale to private-brand marketers and to large commercial and industrial consumers as well as to the spot market.

Operations

Marathon's operations consist of three business segments. Its Refining & Marketing segment which makes up more than 70% of the company's total revenue refines crude oil and other feedstocks at more than 5 refineries in the US Gulf Coast and Midwest regions purchases ethanol and refined products for resale and distributes refined products. It sells refined products to wholesale marketing customers buyers on the spot market its Speedway business segment and to independent entrepreneurs who operate Marathon retail outlets.

The Speedway segment (more than 25%) sells transportation fuels and convenience products in the retail market in the Midwest primarily through Speedway convenience stores. The Midstream segment (less than 5% of revenue) transports crude oil and other feedstocks to Marathon Petroleum's refineries and other locations delivers refined products to wholesale and retail markets and affiliated pipeline assets and investments.

Marathon holds stakes in about 10800 miles of pipeline (MPLX LP) and is one of the largest asphalt and light oil product terminal operators in

the US (about 80 terminals). In addition the company has a large US private inland product fleet that includes roughly inland towboats and close to 250 barges.

Geographic Reach

Marathon Petroleum sells refined products at some 5600 Marathon-branded gas stations in some 20 US states.

Sales and Marketing

Marathon Petroleum sells to wholesale suppliers of gasoline and distillates to resellers and consumers. Customers include independent retailers wholesale customers their Marathon brand jobbers and Speedway brand convenience stores airlines transportation companies and utilities. It also sells gasoline distillates and asphalt for export primarily out of their Garyville and Galveston Bay refineries.

The company sells more than 50% of its gasoline sales volumes and about 90% of its distillates sales volumes on a wholesale or spot market basis. It also sells via retail outlets primarily in Florida Mississippi Tennessee and Alabama.

Financial Performance

Over the last decade (2008-17) Marathon revenue has gone up from $65 billion in 2008 to a peak of $100 billion in 2013 before declining for three years in a row to $63 billion (2016) before making up some of that ground the following year. Net income in the same period has seen a somewhat upward trajectory growing from $450 million in 2009 to a yearly average of $2.4 billion from 2011 onwards.

In 2017 marathon revenue grew 20% year-over-year to $75.4 billion primarily due to higher average prices (by $0.25 per gallon) as well as a 42 mbpd increase in product sales volume.

Net income in 2017 was $3.4 billion the highest in a decade. The 200% year-over-year increase in profits stemmed mostly from a $1.5 billion in gains from the new tax reform kicking into law in 2017 the absence of a charge of $370 million in inventory value adjustment as well as higher income from the refining and marketing segment (thanks to higher LLS crack spreads in Gulf Coast and Chicago).

Marathon's cash holdings increased from $890 million to just over $3 billion. Operating activities provided $6.6 billion in cash. $3.4 billion went towards investment activities (mostly in purchase of property plant and equipment) and a further $1.1 billion went towards the company's financing activities.

Strategy

Encouraged by signs of strong economic growth an improving exports market and boosted by favorable tax reform in the US Marathon took the bold step to acquire and merge with rival Andeavor in a $23 billion deal to create an integrated energy company that is valued at $90 billion. The deal is expected to close late 2018.

The catalyst the company underlines is $1 billion in cost synergies over the first three years with possible further gains from Andeavor's refining assets. The deal immediately increases Marathon's refining footprint from east of Mississippi to California and the Pacific Northwest regions. Midstream it increases its presence in the Permian basin and Bakken regions and adds the Andeavor Logistics limited partnership to its own MLPX. The company is also promising an enhanced integration model?from wellhead to the customer and customer loyalty programs.

Beyond the new merger in 2017 Marathon continued upgrading its Galveston Bay refinery grew its footprint in the Permian basin as well as kick-started plans to expand its Speedway segment by opening more store locations. Marathon plans to invest half a billion on Speedway sector in 2018.

In 2018 the company has capital investment plans of $1.6 billion majority of it going towards

the Refining and Marketing segment for the Galveston Bay refinery and upgrading residual fuel oils to higher-value products.

MPLX announced a budget of $2.3 billion in organic growth and maintenance costs for 2018 with a plan to add 8 processing plants (1.5 billion cubic-feet per day capacity) and crude oil and refined products infrastructure projects.

Mergers and Acquisitions

In April 2018 Marathon announced buying out its rival refiner Andeavor for a $23 billion deal in one of the largest-ever tie-ups of two US refiners. The deal which is expected to close late 2018 will make Marathon the largest US refiner surpassing Valero and increasing the company's access to US shale business concentrated in Texas and North Dakota as well as fuel market penetration in a rapidly growing Mexican market.

In March 2017 Marathon acquired the Ozark pipeline from Enbridge for $219 million.

In 2017 Enbridge and Marathon Petroleum bought a partial indirect equity interest in the Dakota Access Pipeline and Energy Transfer Crude Oil Company Pipeline projects (the Bakken Pipeline system) which transports crude from North Dakota to the eastern Gulf Coast for $2 billion. Enbridge agreed to pay $1.5 billion for its 28% share of the network while Marathon will pay $500 million for its 9% stake.

EXECUTIVES

Chairman And Ceo, Gary R. Heminger, age 65, $1,600,000 total compensation
Evp Human Resources Health And Administrative Services, Rodney P. Nichols, age 66
President Speedway, Anthony R. (Tony) Kenney, age 66, $687,500 total compensation
Svp Marketing, Thomas M. (Tom) Kelley, age 59
Svp Cfo And Treasurer, Timothy T. Griffith, age 49, $600,000 total compensation
Svp Supply Distribution And Planning, C. Michael Palmer, age 65, $637,500 total compensation
President, Donald C. (Don) Templin, age 55, $800,000 total compensation
Svp Transportation And Logistics, John S. Swearingen, age 59
Vp And Cio, Donald W. Wehrly, age 59
Svp Refining, Raymond L. Brooks, age 58
President Mplx Lp, Mike Hennigan
Corporate Medical Director, Peter Fass
Senior Vice President Marketing, Tom Kelley
Vp Finance And Treasurer, Thomas Kaczynski
Evp, C Michael Palmer
Board Member, Charles Bunch
Auditors: PricewaterhouseCoopers LLP

LOCATIONS

HQ: Marathon Petroleum Corp.
539 South Main Street, Findlay, OH 45840-3229
Phone: 419 422-2121
Web: www.marathonpetroleum.com

PRODUCTS/OPERATIONS

2016 Sales

	% of total
Refining & marketing	68
Speedway	29
Midstream	3
Total	**100**

2016 Sales

	% of total
Refined products	86
Merchandise	8
Crude oil & refinery feedstocks	3
Transportation & other	3
Total	**100**

Selected Products

Asphalt
Branded Distillates
Branded Gasoline
Branded Lubricants
Heavy Oil
Petroleum Coke
Specialty Products
Wholesale Light Products

COMPETITORS

BP	Koch Industries Inc.
CITGO	Motiva Enterprises
Chevron	Murphy Oil
ConocoPhillips	Shell Oil Products
Exxon Mobil	Sunoco
Hess Corporation	Tesoro
HollyFrontier	Valero Energy

HISTORICAL FINANCIALS

Company Type: Public

Income Statement				FYE: December 31
	REVENUE ($ mil.)	NET INCOME ($ mil.)	NET PROFIT MARGIN	EMPLOYEES
12/18	97,102	2,780	2.9%	60,350
12/17	75,369	3,432	4.6%	43,800
12/16	63,364	1,174	1.9%	44,460
12/15	72,258	2,852	3.9%	45,440
12/14	98,102	2,524	2.6%	45,340
Annual Growth	(0.3%)	2.4%	—	7.4%

2018 Year-End Financials

Debt ratio: 30.00%
Return on equity: 11.00%
Cash ($ mil.): 1,687
Current ratio: 1.00
Long-term debt ($ mil.): 26,980

No. of shares (mil.): 680
Dividends
  Yield: 3.0%
  Payout: 35.0%
Market value ($ mil.): 40,127

	STOCK PRICE ($) FY Close	P/E High/Low	PER SHARE ($) Earnings	Dividends	Book Value
12/18	59.00	16 10	5.00	2.00	52.00
12/17	66.00	10 7	7.00	2.00	29.00
12/16	50.00	23 14	2.00	1.00	26.00
12/15	52.00	20 8	5.00	1.00	25.00
12/14	90.00	22 17	4.00	1.00	20.00
Annual Growth	(10.1%)	— —	4.7%	18.9%	27.4%

Markel Corp (Holding Co)

Have you ever thought about who insures the manicurist or an antique motorcycle? Specialty insurer Markel takes on the risks other insurers won't touch from amusement parks to thoroughbred horses to summer camps. Coverage is also available for one-time events such as golf tournaments and auto races. The company provides customized direct and facultative placements in the US and abroad as well as treaty reinsurance. Markel International provides specialty insurance internationally from its base in the UK while investment management is provided by Markel CATCo and Nephila Holdings. Subsidiary Markel Ventures invests in non-insurance companies.

Operations

Markel operates through two primary segments: Insurance (more than half of all sales) and Reinsurance.

The Insurance segment writes commercial risks — primarily excess and surplus lines — which are distributed through a network of wholesale brokers. Excess insurance kicks in when a company's regular insurance fizzles out. For example a regular policy might pay up to $100000 on claims but the excess policy could then pay any amounts over $100000 and up to $10 million. Surplus insurance is coverage that no regular insurance company can offer and typically comes with a higher level of risk and higher-priced premiums. Markel Assurance writes business for commercial and Fortune 1000 accounts Markel Specialty writes program insurance and other specialty coverage London-based Markel International writes business worldwide and State National writes collateral protection insurance.

US Insurance also provides specialty insurance to clients that engage in highly specialized activities requiring niche coverage typically not offered by standard insurers. Underwriting entities include FirstComp Insurance Markel Insurance and Markel American Insurance. Excess and surplus insurance is provided by Evanston Insurance.

The Reinsurance segment provides property casualty and specialty treaty reinsurance to other insurers around the world. Key products include property professional liability credit surety general casualty auto and workers' compensation. These are underwritten by the Global Reinsurance and Market International divisions.

The remainder of revenue comes from private equity unit Markel Ventures and investment income.

Geographic Reach

Markel primarily operates in the US market which accounts for roughly 80% of premiums. Its UK unit Markel International writes policies for UK clients as well as on a global basis through the Lloyd's of London market.

Markel's Insurance segment has some 65 locations around the world mostly in North America and Europe while the Reinsurance segment has nearly 100 locations in the US and Bermuda. The group has other operations in about 15 offices.

Sales and Marketing

Markel distributes its products through independent agents and brokers. Its top three independent brokers represent nearly 25% of the group's gross premiums written.

Financial Performance

Markel's revenue has been climbing steadily for the past five years as premium and fee income has grown. However net income has been declining and the company fell into the red in 2018.

In 2018 revenue increased 15% to $6.9 billion due to higher earned insurance premiums net investment income and products and services revenues. In the Insurance segment general liability professional liability and personal lines saw the highest gains. The casualty reinsurance business also performed well but the property reinsurance business declined that year.

The company lost $128.2 million in 2018 after netting $395.3 million in 2017. Increases in operating and non-operating expenses as well as declines in the value of its investment portfolio drove that result. Although the company had higher-than-average property losses on catastrophes that figure declined when compared to the prior year.

Markel ended 2018 with $2.4 billion in net cash about $100 million less than it had at the end of 2017. Operating activities provided $892.9 million while investing activities used $797.2 million and financing activities used another $179 million.

Strategy

Markel's strategy for growth is to leverage its expertise and specialized market knowledge of niche markets to differentiate its business from competitors. It is also looking to diversify into new specialty insurance markets as well as developing innovative products to reach more clients. The firm works at improving its existing policies to provide its customers with the evolving types of coverage they need. For example in 2017 it expanded the professional liability offerings it provides for law firms. Another area Markel is heavily invested in is the insurance linked securities market bolstered by its purchase of Nephila Holdings in 2018.

The group has also been growing other operations through acquisitions. In 2017 it acquired insurance fronting services provider State National Companies for $919 million fresh on the heels of its purchase of commercial surety firm SureTec.

The company is additionally focused on expanding international operations. It plans to establish an insurance provider in Germany ahead of the UK's pending exit from the European Union. (It currently offers insurance in Germany from a branch office in Munich where the new company will eventually be located.) That should help the company as it seeks other opportunities to expand in Europe. In Asia Markel opened its first Indian office located in Mumbai in 2018.

Markel is fully cooperating with inquiries by US and Bermuda authorities into loss reserves recorded in 2017 and 2018.

Mergers and Acquisitions

In late 2018 Markel acquired Nephila Holdings an investment manager specializing in reinsurance risk for $972.6 million. It has offices in Bermuda San Francisco Nashville and London.

In 2017 Markel acquired surety firm SureTec Financial for $246.9 million. SureTec operates in all 50 states specializing in small and midsize contract bonds and commercial surety. The company joined the specialty division of Markel's US Insurance segment.

Also that year the company bought State National Companies the nation's largest provider of fronting services. With that $919 million purchase Markel entered that line of business and it will begin offering collateral protection coverage for financial institutions.

Markel Ventures' recent acquisitions have included Brahmin Leather Works (2018) and Costa Farms (2017).

Company Background

In the 1920s Sam Markel formed a mutual insurance company for "jitneys" (passenger cars refurbished as public transportation buses). In 1930 he founded Markel Service to expand nationally. To keep up with industry growth the company revamped itself as a managing general agent and independent claims service organization in the late 1950s. In 1978 Markel began covering taverns restaurants and vacant buildings. It created excess and surplus lines underwriter Essex Insurance in 1980.

Markel went public in 1986.

HISTORY

In the 1920s Sam Markel formed a mutual insurance company for "jitneys" (passenger cars refurbished as public transportation buses). In 1930 he founded Markel Service to expand nationally. To keep up with industry growth the company revamped itself as a managing general agent and independent claims service organization in the late 1950s. In 1978 Markel began covering taverns restaurants and vacant buildings. It created excess and surplus lines underwriter Essex Insurance in 1980.

Markel went public in 1986. The next year it invested in Shand Morahan and Evanston Insurance (specialty coverage including architects engineers and lawyers professional liability; officers and directors insurance; errors and omissions; and medical malpractice). It bought summer camp insurer Rhulen Agency in 1989.

In the 1990s Markel began buying insurers with their own offbeat niches. In 1990 it bought the rest of Shand Morahan and Evanston Insurance. In 1995 it bought Lincoln Insurance (excess and surplus lines) from media giant Thomson (now Thomson Reuters). The next year the company bought Investors Insurance Holding (excess and surplus lines). Markel which already owned nearly 10% of Gryphon Holdings (commercial property/casualty) bought the rest in 1999.

Expanding internationally Markel bought Bermuda-based Terra Nova Holdings a reinsurer and a Lloyd's managing agency in 2000. The company experienced heavy losses in 2001 not only related to the events of September 11 but also to its slumping international business (the company took a $100 million charge).

Unlike standard insurers (whose rates are generally regulated) specialty insurers can charge the rates they consider reasonable. To that end after taking significant losses from the 2005 hurricane season (Katrina Rita Wilma) and additional hits from the 2008 season (Gustav Ike) the company decided to raise the rates on its catastrophe-exposed businesses.

EXECUTIVES

Co-ceo, Thomas S. Gayner, age 57, $807,692 total compensation
Co-ceo, Richard R. Whitt, age 55, $807,692 total compensation
Vice Chairman, F. Michael Crowley, age 67, $793,269 total compensation
Chief Administrative Officer, Britton L. (Britt) Glisson, age 62
Evp And Chief Underwriting Officer, Gerard Albanese, age 66, $615,385 total compensation
Evp And Cfo, Anne G. Waleski, age 52, $578,846 total compensation
Evp And Chief Actuarial Officer, Bradley J. Kiscaden, age 56
Cio, Mike Scyphers
Associate Vice President Of Claims, David Ashley
Senior Vice President, Nessa Goodman
Vice President And Chief Administrative Officer, Robert Blazer
Vice President Marketing, Cara Bowen
Vice President Professional Liability, Michael Driscoll
Svp Strategic Management, Linda Schreiner
Vice Presidentclaims, Alex Sardinia
Vice President Ocean Marine, Karla Scott
Vice President Western Region Marine Underwriting, Philip B Nelson
Vice President Ocean Marine, John Grossenbacher
Vice President Professional Liability, Michael Cunney
Executive Vice President Professional Liability, Daniel Gamble
Vice President, Lyle Mccoy
Senior Vice President Financial Institutions, Bret Hilgart
Senior Vice President, Mike Mccarthy
Senior Vice President, Steven Schreiber
Senior Vice President And Marketing Director, Kip Herring
Regional Vice President, Melissa Kelly
Vice President Western Region Marine Underwriting, Philip Nelson
Assistant Vice President Medical Malpractice And Professional Liability, Amy Gimbel

Vice President North American Property Cat Reinsurance, Miles Staples
Assistant Vice President, Louis Botticelli
Vp Hr, Pam Terrott
Vice President Human Resources, Mollie Stone
Senior Vice President, Tony Markel
Vice President Central Region, Michael Buckley
Assistant Vice President Credit Surety And Political Risk, Margaux Hackett
Vice President Of Manufacturing Operations, Rick Kreppel
Vice Chairman, Anthony F. Markel, age 77
Vice Chairman, Steven A. Markel, age 70
Chairman, Alan I. Kirshner, age 83
Board Member, Stewart Kasen
Board Member, Michael Schewel
Board Member, Debora Wilson
Board Member, Lemuel Lewis
Board Member, Michael O'reilly
Board Member, Alfred Broaddus
Board Member, Bruce Connell
Auditors: KPMG LLP

LOCATIONS

HQ: Markel Corp (Holding Co)
4521 Highwoods Parkway, Glen Allen, VA 23060-6148
Phone: 804 747-0136
Web: www.markelcorp.com

2018 Gross Written Premiums

	% of total
US	79
UK	8
Canada	2
Other	11
Total	**100**

PRODUCTS/OPERATIONS

2018 Sales

	$ mil.	% of total
Earned premiums		
Insurance	3,784	51
Reinsurance	929	13
Other	(0.5)	-
Products	1,498	20
Services & other	635	9
Net investment income	434	6
Net foreign exchange gains	107	1
Adjustments	(437.6)	-
Total	**6,948**	**100**

Selected Products

Insurance
FirstComp - Workers' Comp
Global Insurance
Practice Groups
Specialty Commercial
Specialty Personal
Reinsurance
Casualty
Property
Public Entity
Specialty

COMPETITORS

Assurant
CNA Financial
Great American Insurance Company
HCC Insurance
Meadowbrook Insurance
Medical Liability Mutual Insurance
National Indemnity Company
Nationwide
Philadelphia Insurance Companies
ProSight Specialty Insurance Group
RLI
United States Liability Insurance Group
XL Group plc

HISTORICAL FINANCIALS
Company Type: Public

Income Statement   FYE: December 31

	ASSETS ($ mil.)	NET INCOME ($ mil.)	INCOME AS % OF ASSETS	EMPLOYEES
12/18	33,306	(128)	—	1,700
12/17	32,805	395	1.2%	15,600
12/16	25,875	456	1.8%	10,900
12/15	24,941	583	2.3%	10,600
12/14	25,200	321	1.3%	8,600
Annual Growth	**7.2%**	**—**	**—**	**(33.3%)**

2018 Year-End Financials

Debt ratio: 9.00%
Return on equity: (-1.00%)
Cash ($ mil.): 2,014
Current ratio: —
Long-term debt ($ mil.): —

No. of shares (mil.): 14
Dividends
Yield: —
Payout: —
Market value ($ mil.): 14,416

	STOCK PRICE ($) FY Close	P/E High/Low		PER SHARE ($) Earnings	Dividends	Book Value
12/18	1,038.00	—	—	(10.00)	0.00	654.00
12/17	1,139.00	44	34	26.00	0.00	684.00
12/16	905.00	31	26	31.00	0.00	606.00
12/15	883.00	22	16	42.00	0.00	561.00
12/14	683.00	31	24	22.00	0.00	544.00
Annual Growth	**11.0%**	**—**	**—**	**—**	**—**	**4.7%**

Marriott International, Inc.

Marriott International is one of the world's leading hoteliers. The company operates or franchises some 6900 hotel residential and timeshare properties worldwide. Its hotel portfolio which comprises some 1.3 million guest rooms includes the premium Sheraton and Renaissance Hotels brands and its flagship Marriott Hotels & Resorts as well as the Ritz-Carlton W Hotels The Luxury Collection and St. Regis luxury brands. Additionally the company operates the select-service and extended-stay brands Courtyard and Fairfield Inn. It also manages about 80 golf courses. North America accounts for about 80% of Marriott International's revenue.

Operations

Marriott International operates through three reportable business segments: North American Full-Service North American Limited-Service and Asia/Pacific segment.

The North American Full-Service generates more than 60% of Marriott International's total revenue. It includes Marriott's luxury and premium brands (JW Marriott The Ritz-Carlton W Hotels and others) located primarily in the US and Canada.

The North American Limited-Service segment accounts for more than 15% of sales and consists of Courtyard Residence Inn Fairfield Inn & Suites and other hotels in the US and Canada.

The Asia/Pacific segment which has hotels in Indonesia China India and Japan accounts for around 5% of sales. Other operations including corporate and international operations in EMEA Latin America and beyond account for about 10% of sales but are not part of Marriott International's core reportable business units.

Geographic Reach

Marriott International's presence extends to more than 130 countries in North America Latin America the Caribbean Europe the Middle East and Africa and Asia Pacific.

Operations in North America account for 80% of total company revenue.

Sales and Marketing

Marriott International's marketing activities include email online advertising and postal mailing. It encourages cross-brand loyalty via a point-based membership scheme based on money spent at hotels on timeshare intervals fractional ownership and residential products.

The company's advertising costs were $660 million in 2018 up slightly from $562 million the prior year.

Financial Performance

Over the past five years Marriott International's revenue has trended upwards. Revenue spiked in fiscal 2017 following its acquisition of Starwood Hotels & Resorts which added billions to its top line. Company profits also benefited from the acquisition nearly doubling with the acquisition.

Revenue growth slowed in 2018 with the company reporting a 1% uptick to $20.7 billion over 2017 results. Modest increases in franchise fees as well as base management and incentive management fees (percentages of revenue earned in exchange for services Marriott provides to its managed hotels) across its three operating units drove the company's mild top-line increase.

A lower income tax rate in 2018 helped push net income up 31% to $1.9 billion over 2017 results which incurred a one-off income tax expense not deducted in 2018. Excluding adjustments for income taxes Marriott International's income fell 21% during the period.

Cash on hand at the end of 2018 was $360 million down $69 million from cash at the end of the previous year. Operating activities added $2.3 billion to the coffers while investing activities used $52 million and financing activities used $2.3 billion mostly for the purchase of treasury stock.

Strategy

Building on the momentum of its of 2016 Starwood Hotels and Resorts acquisition Marriott International is pushing ahead with an aggressive growth plan to open more than 1700 hotels around the world by 2021. The Starwood acquisition boosted Marriott's international presence particularly in the Asia-Pacific region and the company is now looking to expand its geographic footprint in the region by opening hotels in China (which accounts for 50% of the company's Asia-Pacific presence) India Indonesia Australia the Philippines. The company is also planning to open 100 new properties in the Middle East by 2023.

Hotel rooms are not the only thing Marriott has to offer. To compete with HomeAway and Airbnb in 2019 the company expanded into the home rental business through its Homes & Villas unit. Homes & Villas offers guests premium and luxury home rentals in more than 100 destinations in the US Europe the Caribbean and Latin America. Its more than 2000 unique homes range from four-bedroom cottages in California wine country to an 18th century Irish Castle that sleeps more than a dozen guests. Marriott's home rentals are offered at higher price points than many of its hotel rooms and boast an average guest stay that's three times longer than the average hotel stay.

Company Background

Marriott International began in 1927 as a Washington DC root beer stand operated by John and Alice Marriott. Later they added hot food and named their business the Hot Shoppe. In 1929 the couple incorporated and began building a regional chain.

Hot Shoppes opened its first hotel the Twin Bridges Marriott Motor Hotel in Arlington Virginia in 1957. When the Marriotts' son Bill became president in 1964 (CEO in 1972 chairman in 1985) he focused on expanding the hotel business. The company changed its name to Marriott Corp. in 1967.

Marriott split its operations into two companies in 1993: Host Marriott to own hotels and Marriott International primarily to manage them. However Marriott International still owned some of the properties and in 1995 it bought 49% of the Ritz-Carlton luxury hotel group.

In 1998 after the division of its lodging and food distribution services the new Marriott International then began trading as a separate company. That year Marriott also acquired the rest of Ritz-Carlton.

HISTORY

The company began in 1927 as a Washington DC root beer stand operated by John and Alice Marriott. Later they added hot food and named their business the Hot Shoppe. In 1929 the couple incorporated and began building a regional chain.

Hot Shoppes opened its first hotel the Twin Bridges Marriott Motor Hotel in Arlington Virginia in 1957. When the Marriotts' son Bill became president in 1964 (CEO in 1972 chairman in 1985) he focused on expanding the hotel business. The company changed its name to Marriott Corp. in 1967. With the rise in airline travel Marriott built several airport hotels during the 1970s. By 1977 sales had topped $1 billion.

Marriott became the #1 operator of airport food beverage and merchandise facilities in the US with its 1982 acquisition of Host International and it introduced moderately priced Courtyard hotels in 1983. Acquisitions in the 1980s included a time-share business foodservice companies and competitor Howard Johnson. (Marriott later sold the hotels but kept the restaurants and turnpike units.)

The company entered three new market segments in 1987: Marriott Suites (full-service suites) Residence Inn (moderately priced suites) and Fairfield Inn (economy hotels). It also began developing "life-care" communities which provide apartments meals and limited nursing care to the elderly in 1988.

Marriott split its operations into two companies in 1993: Host Marriott to own hotels and Marriott International primarily to manage them. However Marriott International still owned some of the properties and in 1995 it bought 49% of the Ritz-Carlton luxury hotel group.

In 1996 Marriott purchased the Forum Group (assisted living communities and health care services) and merged it into Marriott Senior Living Services.

Marriott introduced its Marriott Executive Residences in 1997. Also that year the firm expanded overseas operations with its purchase of the 150-unit Hong Kong-based Renaissance Hotel Group a deal that included branding rights to the Ramada chain.

In 1998 after the division of its lodging and food distribution services the new Marriott International then began trading as a separate company. That year Marriott also acquired the rest of Ritz-Carlton and established SpringHill Suites by Marriott.

Marriott entered the corporate housing business in 1999 through its acquisition of ExecuStay Corporation (renamed ExecuStay by Marriott) which provided fully furnished and accessorized apartments for stays of 30 days or more. The following year it joined Italy's Bulgari the world's #3 jeweler in a $140 million venture of luxury hotels sporting the Bulgari name.

Marriott refocused its operations on the lodging market in 2003 when it exited both the senior living and distribution services businesses. It sold Marriott Distribution Services (food and beverage distribution) to Services Group of America and sold Marriott Senior Living Services to Sunrise Assisted Living (the management business) and CNL Retirement Properties (nine communities). The following year Marriott sold the international branding rights to the Ramada and Days Inn chains to Cendant (now Avis Budget Group) for about $200 million.

In 2005 Marriott acquired about 30 properties from CTF Holdings (an affiliate of Hong Kong-based New World Development) for nearly $1.5 billion. It sold 14 properties immediately to Sunstone Hotel Investors and Walton Street Capital. The deal put an end to an ongoing legal battle between Marriott and CTF Holdings which had alleged that the hotelier had pocketed kickbacks and fees from outside vendors.

Marriott invested about $200 million in 2005 to upgrade its hotel beds with higher thread-count sheets and triple-sheeted tops and it renovated and upgraded many of its Courtyard and Residence Inn locations during 2006. A difficult 2009 called for the elimination of more than 1000 jobs. Also that year the company cut costs by modifying menus and restaurant hours adjusting room amenities and relaxing some brand standards.

In 2010 Marriott introduced two new hotel brands into the market: Edtion (a boutique luxury chain) and Autograph Collection (independent luxury properties that each have their own unique identity). The firm spun off its time-share business Marriott Vacations Worldwide in 2011.

EXECUTIVES

Evp Finance, Carl Berquist

Executive Vice President, Geoffrey Garside

President And Ceo, Arne M. Sorenson, age 60, $1,236,000 total compensation

Vice President For Student Life, Marilyn Lasecki

Evp Finance And Global Treasurer, Carolyn B. Handlon

Group President, David J. Grissen, age 61, $725,000 total compensation

Evp Lodging Human Resources, David A. Rodriguez, age 60

President And Managing Director Europe, Amy C. McPherson, age 57

Global Chief Communications And Public Affairs Officer, Tricia Primrose

Evp And Global Chief Development Officer, Anthony G. (Tony) Capuano, age 53, $750,000 total compensation

President Caribbean And Latin America (cala), Tim Sheldon

Global Chief Commercial Officer, Stephanie C. Linnartz, age 50, $700,000 total compensation

Global Cio, Bruce Hoffmeister

President And Managing Director Middle East And Africa, Alex Kyriakidis, age 66

Cfo, Kathleen K. (Leeny) Oberg, age 58, $650,000 total compensation

President And Managing Director Asia Pacific, Craig S. Smith, age 56

President Marriott Hotels Of Canada, Don Cleary

Vice President Information Technology Delivery, Maureen Young

Regional Vice President Revenue Strategy Uk, Vivienne Lepage

Executive Vice President, Pamela Murray

Svp Canadian Development Ritz Carlton Hotels, Michael Beckley

Svp Middle East And Africa, Philip Bryson

Vp Design And Project Management, Robert Reinders

Assistant Vice President, Karina Barney

Vice President Human Resources Change Management, Heather Powell

Vice President, Alejandro Acevedo

Area Vice President, Robert Sanger

Vice President Talent Acquisition And Selection, Steve Bauman

Regional Vice President Central, Teresa Walrath

Vice President Human Resources, Kimberly Reed

Vice President Brand Marketing Courtyard, Gini Gladstone

Vp Digital And Social Marketing Brands And Loyalty, Lynne Deroche

Vice President, Russell Vereb

Regional Vice President Human Resources, Marisa Milton

Vice President Brand Operations Design And Development, James Addison

Senior Vice President Global Marketing Optimization, Andy Kauffman

Vice President, Julie Sieracki

Vice President Marketing, Amy Mullens

Vice President Business Process Governance, Carol Cernugel

Vice President Sales And Marketing, Chris Greenleaf

Vice President Consumer Insight And Advisory Services Marketing Digital, Cathy Hartman

Vp Human Resources, Shelly Ahrens

Vice President, Michelle Mutton

Regional Vice President Of Sales And Marketing Caribbean And Latin America Region, Alex Fiz

Vice President, Cecilia Lewis

Area Vice President, Dan Kelleher

Vice President, Jeff Spilman

Vice President, Molaine Noel

Vp Loyalty, Thom Kozik

Vice President Human Resources, Porter Shifflett

Vice President Global Property Systems, Violeta Seidell

Regional Vice President Sales And Marketing Asia Pacific, Kent Maury

Vice President And Senior Counsel, Taisha Urland

Senior Vice President Lodging Development, Christopher Rose

Senior Vice President Comp And Benefits, Tracey Ballow

Senior Vice President Finance Department, Gary Rosenthal

Vice President, Jennie Benzon

Vice President And Senior Counsel, Linda Miller

Senior Vice President Brand Strategy And Innovation, Julie Moll

Vice President Contract Management, Yvette Young

Vice President, Brandon Linton

Senior Vice President Reservations Sales And Customer Care, Kaye Dengel

Senior Vice President And General Counsel, Myron Walker

Vice President, William Holmes

Vice President Marketing, Daniel Vihn

Vice President, Jim O'Hern

Senior Vice President, Jasraj Singh

Vice President, Judy Fennimore

Vice President Of Human Resources, Debbie Wilson

Vp Application Development Brand Marketing And Global Operations Services, John Whitridge

Vice President Leisure Business Development, Warren Ruello

Vice President Jw Marriott Hotels And Resorts Marriott Hotels And Resorts, Michael Darne

Vice President Sales And Marketing Support, Beth Jones

Executive Vice President Architecture And Construction, Susan Levenson

Vice President New Business Development, Annie Brooks

V P And Sr Coun, Karin Trantallis

Senior Vice President Global Marketing, Rick Medwedeff

Senior Vice President And Chief Techno, Barry Schuler

Vice President Of Interior Design, Teri Urovsky

Vice President Assistant General Counsel And Corporate Secretary, Bancroft S Gordon

Evp, Jurgen Giesbert

Vice President, Stephen Maselko

Svp And Deputy General Counsel, Nancy Lee

Vice President International Business, Howard Leigh

Senior Vice President Owner And Franchise Services, James Fisher

Vice President Application Development, Dave Rupp

Vice President And Executive Director, Tad Asbury

Vice President Application Development Digital Platforms And Reservations, Dave Blankenship

Vice President And Senior Counsel, Brendan Ross

Vice President Hotel Development Latin America And Caribbean, Paul Adan

Vice President Marriott Rewards Partnerships And Global Card Programs, Misha Lapcevic

Vice President And Senior Counsel, Carnot Evans

Vice President Global Claims, Stephen Perroots

Vice President Brand Marketing And Communications (asia Pacific), Mike Fulkerson

Vp Brands Marketing And Digital Cala, Diana Plazas

Senior Vice President Human Resources, Carol S Anderson

Vice President Communications Asia Pacific, Alethea Lam

Senior Vice President Information Technology Business Partnership And Planning, Jenifer L Mason

Vice President Of Tax Planning, Joseph Donahue

Vice President Asset Management Europe, Laurent Pavageau

Executive Vice President And Chief Financial Officer, Leeny Oberg

Vice President Global Sales Asia Pacific, John Toomey

Vice President Global Tax Accounting And Compliance, Barbara Young

Vice President Human Resources Europe, Ben Di Benedetto

Vice President And Assistant General Counsel Practice Group Leader, Shazmah Hakim

Global Vice President Infrastructure Engineering And Operations, Lenny Guardino

Vice President Sales And Marketing, Andrew Cymrot

Vice President Interior Design, David Kepron

Vice President Luxury Brand Marketing And Brand Management Middle East And Africa, Candice D'Cruz

Vice President Luxury Brands And Brand Marketing Asia Pacific Marriott International, Bruce Ryde

Vice President Information Technology, Mary Lou Bondel

Vice President Event Production, Patricia Campbell

Vice President Community Footprints, Stewart Ron

Vp Revenue Management Operations, Nancy Bergamini

Vice President Managing Director Jw Rc, Marc Hoffman

Senior Vice President And Associate General Counsel For Dispute Resolution, Michael Martinez

Vice President Of Business Development, Chris Dabi

Vp Brand Marketing And Digital U.s. East, Dennis Skiba

Svp Global Brand Leader For Westin Le Meridien Renaissance Autograph Tribute And Design Hotels, Brian Povinelli

Vice President And Assistant General Counsel, David Manderscheid

Vice President Finance At Marriott International, Don Clendenin

Area Vice President Luxury Brands United Arab Emirates, Sandeep Walia

Vice President Brand Marketing And Sales, Pj Rivera

Vp Asset Management, Eric Czech

Vice President Design Management, Rob Reinders

Vice President Andamp; Assistant General Counsel Employment Law Gr, Patricia Cousins

Vice President Sales And Marketing, Elizabeth Green

Chairman, John W. (Bill) Marriott

Senior Secretary, Katie Widler

Board Member, Mary Bush

Board Member, Debra Lee

Board Member, Steven Reinemund

Auditors: Ernst & Young LLP

LOCATIONS

HQ: Marriott International, Inc.
10400 Fernwood Road, Bethesda, MD 20817
Phone: 301 380-3000
Web: www.marriott.com

PRODUCTS/OPERATIONS

2018 Sales

	$ mil.	% of total
North American Full-Service segment	13,072	63
North American Limited-Service segment	3,217	16
Asia Pacific	1,118	5
Other	3,351	16
Total	**20,758**	**100**

2018 Sales

	$ mil.	% of total
Cost reimbursements	15,543	75
Franchise fees	1,849	9
Owned leased and other revenue	1,635	8
Base management fees	1,140	5
Incentive management fees and other	591	3
Total	**20,758**	**100**

COMPETITORS

Accor	Four Seasons Hotels
Best Western	Hilton Worldwide
Carlson Hotels	Hyatt
Choice Hotels	InterContinental
Club Med	Hotels
Extended Stay America Inc.	LXR Luxury Resorts
FRHI Hotels and Resorts	Loews Hotels

HISTORICAL FINANCIALS

Company Type: Public

Income Statement

FYE: December 31

	REVENUE ($ mil.)	NET INCOME ($ mil.)	NET PROFIT MARGIN	EMPLOYEES
12/18	20,758	1,907	9.2%	176,000
12/17	22,894	1,372	6.0%	177,000
12/16	17,072	780	4.6%	226,500
12/15	14,486	859	5.9%	127,500
12/14	13,796	753	5.5%	123,500
Annual Growth	**10.8%**	**26.2%**	**—**	**9.3%**

2018 Year-End Financials

Debt ratio: 39.00%	No. of shares (mil.): 339
Return on equity: 64.00%	Dividends
Cash ($ mil.): 316	Yield: 1.0%
Current ratio: 0.00	Payout: 29.0%
Long-term debt ($ mil.): 8,514	Market value ($ mil.): 36,813

Marsh & McLennan Companies Inc.

One of the world's largest insurance brokers Marsh & McLennan Companies (MMC) is a heavyweight insurance middleman. Through core subsidiary Marsh the company provides a broad array of insurance-related brokerage consulting and risk management services to clients in more than 130 countries. Customers include large and small companies government entities and not-for-profit organizations. MMC's global reinsurance brokerage business is handled by subsidiary Guy Carpenter. The company also owns Mercer which provides human resources and financial consulting services to customers in about 45 nations worldwide; and Oliver Wyman which provides management consulting services.

Operations

MMC's operations are split into two groups — the Risk and Insurance Services (RIS) segment (consisting of Marsh and Guy Carpenter) and the Consulting segment (Mercer and Oliver Wyman). Both segments help clients assess risks in their businesses and ascertain whether those risks are insurable.

The RIS segment accounts for about 55% of revenue; insurance subsidiary Marsh alone accounts for about 45% of MMC's total revenues while Guy Carpenter accounts for about 10%.

The Consulting segment brings in the remaining revenue; its Mercer human resources unit (MMC's second-largest subsidiary) accounts for a third of the group's total revenues. Oliver Wyman brings in another 10%.

Geographic Reach

MMC provides services in the Americas the Asia/Pacific region and the EMEA (Europe Middle East and Africa) region.

The US contributes about half of annual revenues. The UK and Continental Europe bring in about one-third of total sales while the Asia/Pacific region and other markets each bring in about 10%.

Sales and Marketing

MMC's business customers include small mid-sized and multinational corporations. Its consulting division serves entities engaged in industries including transportation communication technology energy retail distribution and wholesale and finance.

Financial Performance

MMC has seen relatively steady revenue growth over the last few years. Net income was also rising but took a dip in 2017.

In 2018 revenue rose 7% to $15 billion. Marsh's revenue increased 7% and Guy Carpenter's revenue increased 8% resulting in an 8% rise for the RIS segment. In Consulting revenue increased 5% for Mercer and 7% for Oliver Wyman resulting in a 5% increase for the segment.

Net income rose 11% to $1.7 billion in 2018 (still less than the $1.8 billion MMC netted in 2016.) That increase was largely due to a lower income tax expense for the group that year.

The company ended 2018 with $1.1 billion in net cash $139 million less than it had at the end of 2017. Operating activities provided $2.4 billion while investing activities (mostly company acquisitions) used $1.1 billion and financing activities used another $1.3 billion.

Strategy

Citing the rise of economic difficulties natural disasters such as tsunamis and hurricanes international terrorism and other hazards for businesses MMC has been working to expand its role as a risk consultant. Subsidiary Marsh has been steadily branching out from its straight brokerage operations expanding its offerings of risk and insurance-related services including benefits management international risk placement and consumer programs for executives employees and high-net-worth individuals. The Mercer business has also been expanding through acquisitions in recent years especially in the growing field of data solutions. Furthermore Mercer is seeking to expand its investment consulting operations.

Nonetheless like its leading US competitors Marsh's most basic strategy for growth through the years has been to buy up regional brokerages large and small. It has kept up a steady pace of acquisitions of regional commercial brokerage firms especially in the mid-sized business market. The 2019 $6.4 billion acquisition of UK-based Jardine Lloyd Thompson positioned the group for further international expansion.

Because the company is so acquisitive it carries the risk of not being able to successfully integrate new businesses. Related challenges include integrating IT financial reporting human resources and other systems as well as retaining key customers and personnel.

While continuing to pursue an aggressive acquisition strategy — the firm has acquired more than 110 businesses since 2013 — MMC has also been working to de-risk its own operations by enacting some cost-cutting measures in recent years. Restructuring measures such as divesting underperforming businesses aim to overcome the impact of historical regulatory and litigation issues as well as economic and competitive conditions on its bottom line.

Mergers and Acquisitions

MMC is a very acquisitive group; its Marsh subsidiary makes numerous purchases each year. However it made a big splash in 2019 when it acquired another top 10 broker Jardine Lloyd Thompson (JLT). The deal valued at some $6.4 billion created the world's largest reinsurance broker. The company agreed to sell JLT's aerospace division to Arthur J. Gallagher to gain approval for the merger.

Most of the group's acquisitions though are of smaller regional practices. Purchases in 2018 included North Carolina-based brokerage Highsmith Insurance Agency Japan-based agency Hoken Soken UK-based consultancy 8Works and India-based investment advisor India Life Capital. In all the group completed some 20 acquisitions for a total of $1 billion that year.

Company Background

Marsh & McLennan was founded in 1905 when Henry W. Marsh and Donald R. McLennan merged their firms to form the world's largest insurance brokerage.

HISTORY

Marsh & McLennan Companies dates back to the Dan H. Bomar Company founded in 1871 after the Great Chicago Fire. In 1885 a plucky Harvard dropout named Henry Marsh joined the company then known as R.A. Waller and Company. When Robert Waller died in 1889 Marsh and fellow employee Herbert Ulmann bought a controlling stake and renamed the company Marsh Ulmann & Co. Marsh pioneered insurance brokering and in 1901 set up U.S. Steel's self-insurance program.

In 1904 different directors at Burlington Northern Railroad promised their account to Marsh Ulmann as well as Manley-McLennan of Duluth (railroad insurance) and D.W. Burrows (a small Chicago-based railroad insurance firm). Rather than fight over it the firms joined forces to form the world's largest insurance brokerage. When Burrows retired in 1906 the firm became Marsh & McLennan.

In the early 20th century Marsh won AT&T's business and McLennan landed the account of Armour Meat Packing.

In 1923 Marsh & McLennan became a closely held corporation. Marsh sold out to McLennan in 1935. The company weathered the Depression without major layoffs by cutting pay and branching into life insurance and employee-benefits consulting after passage of the Social Security Act (1935).

The firm grew through acquisitions in the 1950s went public in 1962 and in 1969 formed a holding company that became Marsh & McLennan Companies. In the 1970s it diversified into investment management employee-benefits consulting and geographically into the UK with C.T. Bowring Reinsurance. As the insurance business slowed in the 1980s the financial and consulting fields grew through acquisitions and organic growth.

With offices in the World Trade Center the company lost some 300 employees in the September 11 terrorist attacks. Following the attacks on the World Trade Center Marsh & McLennan launched a new subsidiary (AXIS Specialty) to deal with the capacity shortage in the insurance industry.

Two major Marsh & McLennan units came under legal fire in probes of the mutual fund and insurance brokerage industries respectively in the early 2000s. In 2003 Putnam agreed to settle securities fraud charges with the SEC and reimburse investors; many of Putnam's top officers were replaced and its compliance procedures were restructured.

The following year Marsh found itself at the center of a price-fixing investigation that involved several insurance companies including AIG and Chubb Limited. At least nine employees of Marsh and AIG pled guilty to criminal charges. Jeffery Greenberg the son of outspoken AIG chairman and CEO Maurice Greenberg who had served as Marsh & McLennan's chairman and CEO since 1999 resigned in 2004 as a result of the price-fixing allegations.

EXECUTIVES

President And Ceo Mercer, Julio A. Portalatin, age 59, $900,000 total compensation

Cfo, Mark C. McGivney, age 51, $750,000 total compensation

President Ceo And Director, Daniel S. (Dan) Glaser, age 58, $1,400,000 total compensation

Evp And General Counsel, Peter J. Beshar, age 58, $800,000 total compensation

Svp And Cio, E. Scott Gilbert, age 64

President Marsh, John Q. Doyle, age 55

President And Ceo Oliver Wyman Group, Scott McDonald, age 53

Ceo Marsh International, Flavio Piccolomini

Ceo Marsh, John Doyle

Chief Executive Marsh Continental Europe, Siegmund Fahrig

Vice President, Eric Ritter

Vice President Information Technology, Patty Martucci

Vice President, Bradley Morrow
Vice President Of Client Operations, William Walker
Senior Vice President, Lisa Kremer
Systems Director; Vice President It Project Manager, Michael Leyvi
Senior Vice President Regional Premium Finance, Irene Kaminski
Senior Vice President, David Abbene
Vice President Market Information Group, Yadilsa Fernandez
Assistant Vice President Security Engineering, Ashit Desai
Vice President Budgets, Carlota Vargas
Senior Vice President, Cindy L Lusignan
Vice President And Chief Counsel Global Risk And Specialties, Barry Kerschner
Senior Vice President And Placement Specialist, Mary Naughton
Senior Vice President Private Equity And M And A Services, Matson Allen
Senior Vice President, Niki Tsalikis
Assistant Vice President, Jean Aguirre
Vice President, Rob Selnes
Senior Vice President Of The National Construction Practice, Ric Glover
Vice President, Tarique Nageer
Senior Vice President, Debby Colquhoun
Vp Audit Risk Management, Michelle Viotty
Svp Strategic Solutions Group, Joseph Fusco
Assistant Vice President, Nazrin Zahani
Vice President Client Executive Practice, Julie Chu
Senior Vice President, Ronald Reinartz
Senior Vice President Global Information Technology, Scott Francis
Senior Vice President, Marla Nicholson
Cpcu Vice President And Knowledge Manager, Karen Parker
Vice President Administration, Michael Petrullo
Vice President Risk Consulting, Matthew Blair
Senior Vice President, Sean Crnkovich
Svp, Robert Welsh
Vice President Finance Director, Brent Donnelly
Senior Vice President, Anna Kohli
Senior Vice President, Eric Peabody
Senior Vice President Risk Intelligence Strategies And Resiliency Solutions, Beth Enslow
Vice President Emea Voice Manager, Edward Shanley
Senior Vice President, David Finz
Senior Vice President Information Technology And Operations, John Doran
Vice President And Chief Information Officer Middl, Nixon Thomas
Systems Director Vice President Information Techn, Michele Leyvi
Assistant Vice President Client Manager, Martin Goh
Senior Vice President, Eileen Quenell
Assistant Vice President Sales And Business Development, Pepper Periquet
Senior Vice President, Tim Brandt
Vice President, Joan Spiegel
Vice President, Florence Vasquez
Vice President, Patricia Robinson
Senior Vice President, Joseph Asmar
Vice President Finance, Michael Murphy
Senior Vice President Northeast Sales Operations Leader, David Russell
Senior Vice President, Bijesh Jacob
Vice President Clincal Consulting, Dawn Schrader
Senior Vice President, Daniel Kelley
Assistant Vice President, Matthew Theriault
Senior Vice President, Randy Dickman
Vice President Business Development, Hallie Beddes
Vice President, Romaneo Adams
Vice President In Marsh Risk Consulting's Reputational Risk And Crisis Management Practice Based, Susan Morton

Vice President, Virginia Del Lago
Assistant Vice President, Felix Chung
Vice President, Catherine Ricia
Senior Vice President, Dawn Buelow
Vice President, Jessica Hatch
Assistant Vice President, Thadd Northam
Vice President Environmental Practice, Jack Palis
Senior Vice President, Mark Alderman
Senior Vice President Global Program Manager, Lori Suske
Vice President, Raegan Buckley
Senior Vice President And Global Head Of Operational Services, Gregg Congleton
Senior Vice President, Jeralyn Sorensen
Senior Vice President, Stanley Zimmerman
Senior Vice President, Eugene Charney
Assistant Vice President, Edward Mitchell
Executive Vice President Of Information Technology, Jennifer Adams
Vice President, Louise Casazza
Senior Vice President, Marcy Waterfall
Senior Vice President U S Marine And Energy, John Pallasch
Dip Fs (gen Ins) Qpib Cipvice President Head Of Businessdevelopment Singapore, Andrew Paul
Vice President Human Resources Manager, Sarah Randall
Assistant Vice President, Kristin Will
Sr Vice President Multinational Client S, Janis Thornton
Senior Vice President, Rita Patullo
Vice President, Michael Hargis
Senior Vice President Advanced Risk Solutions, Scott Sanderson
Senior Vice President, James Helm
Vice President Information Technology, Gursharan Sant
Senior Vice President, Mary Berry
Vice President, Thomas Luty
Vice President National Brokerage Property Practice, Natalie Kenny
Senior Vice President, Chris Victorino
Senior Regional Premium Finance Vice President, Natasha Lee
Senior Vice President Strategic Development Officer At Marsh And Mclennan, Leonard Battifarano
Senior Vice President, Brett Gillmon
Assistant Vice President, Jenny Dickson
Assistant Vice President Asia Client Services, Kathleen Schimmenti
Senior Vice President, Michaela Grasshoff
Senior Vice President Global Broking North America, Jason Monteforte
Senior Vice President Global Broking Specialties, Jack Reid
Vice President, Melanie Dunne
Senior Vice President, Tracey Cole
Vice President Private Client Services, Susan Ott
Senior Vice President And Chief Financial Officer For Largest Insurance Broker, Adrian Serge
Vice President, Lynn Patino
Senior Vice President And Chief Compliance Officer, Scott E Gilbert
Vice President Global Tech Srv, Christopher Murphy
Vice President, Rich Cuff
Vice President Information Systems, Sue Denecke
Senior Vice President At Marsh, Lynda Gammons
Senior Vice President Client Executive, Allan Smith
Assistant Vice President, Aimee Vella
Senior Vice President Risk Consulting, Steve Logoyda
Avp It Project Manager, Kelly Lively
Senior Vice President And Compliance Officer, April Bohmler
Vice President Project Manager, Paul Gibaldi
Vice President, Lori Bassano
Senior Vice President Human Resources, Joseph Bongiovi

Vp, Mathew Keecheril
Senior Vice President Finpro, Jennifer Dowd
Senior Vice President, Ken Kosinski
Vice President, Tim Wright
Assistant Vice President Placement Specialist Qsg, Anna Medvinsky
Vice President Senior Client Advisor, John Nelson
Vice President, Timothy Tumulty
Vice President Business Development Vice President, Eric Fine
Vice President, Donald W Russell
Vice President Treasurer, Ferdinand Jahnel
Senior Vice President Zone Operating Officer (finance), Pinder Sekhon
Senior Vice President Internal Communication, Jodi Cohen
Vice President, Nicole Mccormack
Senior Vice President, Wayne Hoffmann
Svp Global Program Management, Nick Maniscalco
Assistant Vice President Senior Infrastructure Engineer, Kirk Shipley
Vice President Of Human Resources, Christina Harris
Auditors: DELOITTE & TOUCHE LLP

LOCATIONS

HQ: Marsh & McLennan Companies Inc.
1166 Avenue of the Americas, New York, NY 10036-2774
Phone: 212 345-5000   **Fax:** 212 345-4809
Web: www.mmc.com

2018 Sales

	$ mil.	% of total
US	7,219	48
Continental Europe	2,694	18
UK	2,243	15
Asia/Pacific	1,616	11
Other	1,235	8
Adjustments	(57)	-
Total	**14,950**	**100**

PRODUCTS/OPERATIONS

2018 Sales by Segment

	$ mil.	% of total
Risk & Insurance Services		
Marsh	6,877	46
Guy Carpenter	1,286	9
Fiduciary interest income	65	
Consulting		
Mercer	4,732	31
Oliver Wyman	2,047	14
Adjustments	(57)	-
Total	**14,950**	**100**

COMPETITORS

Accenture	Gallagher
AmWINS Group	Hub International
Aon	McKinsey & Company
Bain & Company	National Financial
Booz Allen	Partners
Brown & Brown	USI
FTI Consulting	Willis Towers Watson

HISTORICAL FINANCIALS

Company Type: Public

Income Statement   FYE: December 31

	REVENUE ($ mil.)	NET INCOME ($ mil.)	NET PROFIT MARGIN	EMPLOYEES
12/18	14,950	1,650	11.0%	65,000
12/17	14,024	1,492	10.6%	65,000
12/16	13,211	1,768	13.4%	60,000
12/15	12,893	1,599	12.4%	60,000
12/14	12,951	1,465	11.3%	57,000
Annual Growth	3.7%	3.0%	—	3.3%

Debt ratio: 27.00%
Return on equity: 22.00%
Cash ($ mil.): 1,066
Current ratio: 1.00
Long-term debt ($ mil.): 5,510

No. of shares (mil.): 504
Dividends
  Yield: 2.0%
  Payout: 49.0%
Market value ($ mil.): 40,181

| | STOCK PRICE ($) | P/E | | PER SHARE ($) | | |
	FY Close	High/Low	Earnings	Dividends	Book Value
12/18	80.00	27 23	3.00	2.00	15.00
12/17	81.00	30 23	3.00	1.00	14.00
12/16	68.00	20 15	3.00	1.00	12.00
12/15	55.00	20 17	3.00	1.00	12.00
12/14	57.00	22 17	3.00	1.00	13.00
Annual Growth	8.6%	— —	5.1%	10.5%	3.4%

Masco Corp.

Masco Corporation doesn't mask its penchant for indoor style. It is a global leader in the design manufacturing and distribution of home improvement and building products. Well-known brands include Delta and Peerless (plumbing) KraftMaid (cabinetry) Behr (paints and stains) and Milgard (windows). It boasts a vast portfolio of diversified products ranging from storage containers to patio doors but its plumbing products account for half of all sales. Although most of its sales are within the US Masco has a major presence in the UK mainland Europe and China.

HISTORY

Masco founder Alex Manoogian moved to the US at age 19 in 1920. He wound up in Detroit and with partners Harry Adjemian and Charles Saunders he started Masco (the first letters of their last names plus "co" for "company") Screw Products Company eight days before the crash of 1929. Manoogian's partners left within the year.

Largely reliant on Detroit's auto industry Masco grew slowly during the Depression making custom parts for Chrysler Ford and others. With sales of $200000 by 1937 it went public on the Detroit Stock Exchange. During WWII Masco focused on defense and in 1942 sales passed $1 million. A new plant opened in 1948 in Dearborn Michigan as Masco resumed peacetime business mainly in the auto industry.

In 1954 Masco began selling Manoogian's one-handle kitchen faucet (Delta). Sales of faucets passed $1 million by 1958 and Masco opened a new faucet factory in Indiana.

Under Manoogian's son Richard — whose dinner was often delayed while his father used the stove to test the heat tolerance of new faucet parts — Masco Corporation (so renamed in 1961) diversified. From 1964 to 1980 it bought more than 50 companies concentrating on tool and metal casting energy exploration and air compressors. In 1984 the firm split. Masco Corporation pursued the course set by its successful faucet sales expanding its interests in home improvement and furnishings. The industrial products business was spun off as Masco Industries a separate public corporation (later Metaldyne) in which Masco maintained a sizable stake.

Masco Corporation became the #1 US furniture maker in the late 1980s by buying Lexington Furniture (1987) and Universal Furniture (1989) both of North Carolina. In 1990 Masco acquired KraftMaid cabinets.

Two years later the company sold its interests in Mechanical Technology Payless Cashways and Emco Limited of Canada (Masco bought back 40% of Emco in 1997). Masco reduced its stake in Metaldyne from 47% to 35% in 1993.

Masco sought to establish itself in Europe and in 1994 it bought a German cabinetmaker and a UK producer of handheld showers. In 1996 founder Manoogian died but the company flowed on. It added a UK cabinetmaker a German shower manufacturer and a German insulation firm. That year Masco sold its troubled furniture unit to a group of investors and executives (who renamed the unit LifeStyle Furnishings International) for about $1 billion and further reduced its stake in Metaldyne to less than 20% (and later sold it all).

Acquisitions in 1997 included cabinetmakers Texwood Industries of Texas and Liberty Hardware Manufacturing of Florida. The next year it bought Vasco (heating systems and equipment Belgium) and Brugman (building and home-improvement products the Netherlands). It sold its Thermador unit (ovens and ranges) to US joint venture Bosch-Siemens Hausgerate.

Masco made 13 acquisitions from 1999 through early 2000 including Heritage Bathrooms (bathroom equipment UK) Faucet Queens (plumbing and hardware supply) GMU Group (kitchen cabinets Spain) Avocet Hardware (locks and hardware UK) BEHR Process (coatings) and Mill's Pride (cabinets). Boosting its services in 1999 it acquired The Cary Group an installer of fiberglass insulation.

To increase its geographic reach Masco bought Tvilum-Scanbirk (ready-to-assemble furniture Denmark) Masterchem Industries (specialty paint products) and Glass Idromassaggio (bathroom equipment Italy) in 2000. In late 2000 and early 2001 it acquired two US-based installation services companies Davenport Insulation Group and BSI Holdings respectively. Also in 2001 Masco acquired Milgard Manufacturing a vinyl window and patio door maker.

During 2002 Masco acquired home improvement products and service companies that included Bristan Ltd. (kitchen and bath faucets and shower and bath accessories) Brasstech Inc. (faucets plumbing specialties and bath accessories; California) Cambrian Windows Ltd. (vinyl window frames) Duraflex Ltd. (extruded vinyl frame components) Premier Manufacturing Ltd. (vinyl window and door frames) SCE Unlimited (siding shutters gutters; Illinois) IDI Group (fireplaces garage doors shower enclosures; Atlanta) Service Partners LLC (insulation and other building products Virginia) several small installation and other service companies and Diversified Cabinet Distributors (cabinets and countertops Atlanta). Masco also increased its interest in Hansgrohe AG (kitchen and bath faucets hand-held and fixed showerheads luxury shower systems and steam showers; Germany) to 64%. The company sold its StarMark Cabinetry business for about $15 million.

In 2003 Masco increased its ownership interest in Hansgrohe AG (kitchen and bath faucets handheld and fixed showerheads luxury shower systems and steam showers; Germany) to 64% from 27%. The company established Color Solutions Centers in more than 1500 Home Depot stores throughout the US. Masco sold its Baldwin Hardware and Weiser Lock businesses (builders' hardware and locksets) to Black & Decker (now Stanley Black & Decker) and The Marvel Group a provider specialty products such as office work stations and machine stands to members of Marvel's management team (led by president John Dellamore) for $289 million in total. Acquisitions in 2003 included PowerShot Tool Company Inc. (fastening products New Jersey) and several small installation service companies for a combined $63 million.

The next year Masco sold its Jung Pumpen (pumps) The Alvic Group (kitchen cabinets) Alma Kuchen (kitchen cabinets) E. Missel (acoustic insulation) and SKS Group (shutters and ventilation systems) businesses for $199 million. Masco continued its business review in 2005 selling two operating companies that made and distributed cabinets vanities medicine cabinets shower rods and bath accessories.

After reorganizing its European business operations Masco sold off several of its operating units including Gebhardt Consolidated (HVAC) The Heating Group (radiators) and GMU Group (cabinets). The company also disposed of North American businesses that were not core to its long-term growth strategy which included Computerized Security Systems (CSS) and Zenith Products (bathroom storage).

In 2008 the company merged its Mill's Price brand with KraftMaid to form the Masco Retail Cabinet Group. It also merged Merillat and Quality Cabinets to form Masco Builder Cabinet Group.

In addition to cutting costs through divestitures Masco has streamlined its operating structure to trim spending. In 2011 the company merged its wholesale and retail cabinet units to form Masco Cabinetry. It also decided to stop making ready-to-assemble cabinets a non-core offering.

Looking toward a growth market in 2012 Masco entered into the fast-growing Indian bathroom and kitchen faucet sector by launching its line of residential and commercial products in that country. The company sees India as an integral part of the global expansion plan for the Delta Faucet Company.

During 2013 Behr Process Corporation completed the rollout of its products to Home Depot stores across Mexico continued to build the foundation of its China business with dealers and expanded its retail relationships into Latin America. Hansgrohe one of the leading global bathroom specialists continued geographic expansion in its Decorative Architectural Products and Plumbing Products segments.

In 2013 Masco Cabinetry launched Arbor Creek Cabinets a stand-alone brand of ready-to-assemble cabinetry in four birch door styles and three finishes offering customers choices ranging from a sleek contemporary look to more traditional options.

EXECUTIVES

Vp General Counsel And Secretary, Kenneth G. Cole, $421,058 total compensation
Vp Cfo And Treasurer, John G. Sznewajs, age 52, $653,353 total compensation
President And Ceo, Keith J. Allman, $1,126,654 total compensation
Group President Global Plumbing, Richard O'Reagan, $481,188 total compensation
Vp Strategy And Corporate Development, Amit Bhargava, $339,231 total compensation
Vp Masco Operating System, Christopher K. Kastner, $366,962 total compensation
Chairman, J. Michael (Mike) Losh, age 73
Auditors: PricewaterhouseCoopers LLP

LOCATIONS

HQ: Masco Corp.
17450 College Parkway, Livonia, MI 48152
Phone: 313 274-7400
Web: www.masco.com

2017 Sales

	$ mil.	% of total
North America	6,069	79
Europe & other regions	1,575	21
Total	**7,644**	**100**

PRODUCTS/OPERATIONS

2017 Sales

	$ mil.	% of total
Plumbing products	3,735	49
Decorative architectural products	2,205	29
Cabinetry products	934	12
Windows and Other specialty products	770	10
Total	**7,644**	**100**

Selected Brand Names

Plumbing products
Axor
BrassCraft
Brasstech
Bristan
Brizo
Caldera
Cobra
Delta
Endless Pools
Fantasy Spas
Freeflow Spas
Ginger
Hansgrohe
Heritage
Hot Spring
Huppe
Mirolin
Newport Brass
Peerless
Plumb Shop
Waltec
Cabinets products
Cardell
KraftMaid
Merillat
Quality Cabinets
Decorative architectural products
BEHR
Kilz
Windows and Other specialty products
Duraflex
Griffin
Milgard Windows
Premier

COMPETITORS

American Woodmark
Andersen Corporation
Benjamin Moore
Elkay Manufacturing
Fortune Brands Home & Security
JELD-WEN
Jacuzzi Brands
Kohler
LIXIL Group
Master Spas
MasterBrand Cabinets
PPG Industries
Ply Gem Holdings
Sherwin-Williams

HISTORICAL FINANCIALS

Company Type: Public

Income Statement — FYE: December 31

	REVENUE ($ mil.)	NET INCOME ($ mil.)	NET PROFIT MARGIN	EMPLOYEES
12/18	8,359	734	8.8%	26,000
12/17	7,644	533	7.0%	26,000
12/16	7,357	491	6.7%	26,000
12/15	7,142	355	5.0%	25,000
12/14	8,521	856	10.0%	32,000
Annual Growth	(0.5%)	(3.8%)	—	(5.1%)

2018 Year-End Financials

Debt ratio: 55.00%
Return on equity: ***,***.**%
Cash ($ mil.): 559
Current ratio: 2.00
Long-term debt ($ mil.): 2,971

No. of shares (mil.): 294
Dividends
Yield: 1.0%
Payout: 18.0%
Market value ($ mil.): 8,594

	STOCK PRICE ($) FY Close	P/E High/Low		PER SHARE ($) Earnings	Dividends	Book Value
12/18	29.00	19	12	2.00	0.00	(0.00)
12/17	44.00	26	19	2.00	0.00	(0.00)
12/16	32.00	25	16	1.00	0.00	(1.00)
12/15	28.00	30	22	1.00	0.00	(0.00)
12/14	25.00	11	8	2.00	0.00	3.00
Annual Growth	3.8%	—	—	(0.1%)	7.2%	

MasTec Inc. (FL)

MasTec goes the last mile ? and the first mile and the miles in between ? to bring communications and energy to homes offices factories and other places. The company digs the trenches lays the cable and builds the towers that power communications and provide cell service and high-speed internet. The contractor plans and builds pipelines that transport natural gas and oil from wells to processing plants. It provides infrastructure construction to telecom vendors wireless providers cable TV operators and energy and utility companies. MasTec also builds electrical utility transmission and distribution and power generation wind and solar farms industrial infrastructure and water and sewer systems.

Operations

With more than 17000 employees and locations throughout North America MasTec has the size to tackle big projects that require large resources in equipment and people. Much of the company's equipment ? bucket trucks forklifts backhoes side-booms bulldozers excavators trenchers graders loaders directional boring machines digger derricks pile drivers and cranes ? can be used on any of its projects.

MasTec operates in five business units with most focused on a particular industry. The units are: Communications; Electrical Transmission; Oil and Gas; Power Generation and Industrial; and Other.

The Oil and Gas segment does engineering construction and maintenance on oil and natural gas pipelines and processing facilities for the energy and utilities industries. It accounts for about 55% of sales.

The Communications segment performs engineering construction and maintenance of communications infrastructure primarily related to wireless and wireline communications and install to the home and infrastructure for electrical utilities. It accounts for about 35% of sales.

The Electrical Transmission segment primarily serves energy and utility industries through the engineering construction and maintenance of electrical transmission lines and substations. It accounts for about 5% of sales.

The Power Generation and Industrial segment serves the energy and utility through the installation and construction of power plants wind farms solar farms related electrical transmission infrastructure ethanol plants and other industrial infrastructure. It accounts for less about 5% of sales.

The Other segment primarily includes small business units that perform construction services for a variety of end markets in Mexico and in other locations outside the US. It accounts for less than 1% of sales.

Geographic Reach

MasTec headquartered in Coral Gables Florida has about 400 locations in the US Canada and Mexico.

Sales and Marketing

MasTec sells directly to existing and potential customers for service agreement contracts and individual projects. MasTec's current fortunes are tied to two companies Energy Transfer and AT&T. Pipeline work for Energy Transfer accounts for about 40% of MasTec's revenue. MasTec's communications work revolves around AT&T (including DirecTV) which supplies about 25% of revenue. The company's level of business with AT&T has been consistent in recent years but business with Energy Transfer grew from just 7% of revenue in 2017.

Financial Performance

After eight years of steady gains MasTec recorded a dip in revenue and a loss in 2015 but rebounded with increasing revenue and profit in 2016 and 2017.

Sales rose about 30% to $6.6 billion in 2017 from 2016 on the strength of a big year for MasTec's Oil and Gas unit. Several long-haul pipeline projects combine to drive Oil & Gas revenue about 75% higher for 2017. The Communications business also recorded higher revenue up about 4% entirely on the contributions by acquisitions. The unit's organic revenue dipped about 10% from lower install-to-the-home work. Sales in the Electrical Transmission and the Power Generation and Industrial units decreased in 2017 from 2016.

Higher revenue enabled MasTec to absorb higher costs and post a profit of $347 million in 2017 up from $39 million in 2016. The company had a lower tax bill in 2017 because of the US Tax Cuts and Jobs Act which was signed into law at the end of the year.

Cash on hand was about the same at $40 million for 2016 and 2017 but free cash flow fell to about $33 million in 2017 from about $88 million the year before.

Strategy

MasTec is riding a wave of oil and gas activity in the US Canada and Mexico and it expects the wave to continue. The company has worked on several large projects connecting gas fields to processing facilities in the past few years and expects the trend to continue for several more years.

MasTec sees another force at work that could mean more business. The company itself benefited from the US Tax Cuts and Jobs Act of 2017 with lower taxes. Its customers with lower tax bills might be encouraged to spend more on projects that could add to MasTec's backlog.

The company sees new construction for its Communications division with industry initiatives in the offing. Construction of infrastructure to support 5G networks is on the horizon. More immediately is the build out of the FirstNet network for public safety communications by AT&T and a large fiber project from Verizon Communications.

MasTec works in industries that go through cycles but its multiple capabilities help it weather ups and downs. Currently its oil and gas work is booming while the previous big revenue producer communications has waned by comparison. But transmission work should rev up as renewable energy projects move beyond the drawing board and into construction phases.

Mergers and Acquisitions

MasTec uses acquisitions to add to its capabilities and expand its footprint into new geographic regions.

In 2017 the company made three acquisitions: a wireline/fiber deployment construction contractor a heavy civil construction services company and an oil and gas pipeline equipment company. The company spent more than $115 million on acquisitions in 2017.

HISTORY

MasTec was formed by the merger of Burnup & Sims (B&S) and Church & Tower (C&T). B&S was founded in 1929 to provide construction and maintenance services to the phone and utilities industries. C&T began in 1968 building phone networks in Miami and Puerto Rico. Jorge Mas Canosa was brought on board in 1969 and given half of the company in exchange for managing it. By 1971 he had succeeded in turning C&T around and had bought the remainder.

In 1994 C&T and B&S merged; B&S became MasTec and C&T became a subsidiary. Mas was named chairman and his son who had been at C&T since 1980 was named president and CEO. The company began a program of acquisitions and started building a presence in Latin America.

MasTec doubled its size in 1996 by acquiring Sintel a telecom infrastructure construction firm operating in South America and Spain from Telefonica. MasTec continued to grow through acquisitions buying 10 more companies the next year. Mas died in 1997 and his son Jorge Jr. succeeded him. It sold a near-bankrupt Sintel and began to refocus on domestic operations.

EXECUTIVES

Ceo And Director, José R. Mas, age 47, $980,000 total compensation
Evp And Cfo, George L. Pita, age 57, $450,000 total compensation
Evp General Counsel And Secretary, Alberto de Cardenas, age 50, $385,000 total compensation
Coo, Robert E. (Bob) Apple, age 69, $585,000 total compensation
Cio, Albert Iturrey
Vice President Business Intelligence, Ben Boyd
Vice President Partnership And Resource Management, Jay Carroll
Regional Vice President, Clint Grassmick
Vice President And General Manager, Chris Bracken
Regional Vice President South Region, Helbert Villa
Senior Vice President And President Mastec Wireless Division, Darrell Mays
Senior Vice President, Rick Gray
Vice President Field Service, Chris Gera
Vice President Southwest Region, Erik Hughes
Assistant Vice President Corporate Operations, Jose Tarafa
Vice President Business Development, Karen Roth
Vice President, Ron Martin
Vice President Of Sales, Stephen Guillot
Division Vice President, Carl Basden
Vp Operations Mastec Canada, Wayne Baron
Chairman, Jorge Mas, age 56
Board Member, Robert Dwyer
Board Member, Javier Palomarez
Auditors: BDO USA, LLP

LOCATIONS

HQ: MasTec Inc. (FL)
800 S. Douglas Road, 12th Floor, Coral Gables, FL 33134
Phone: 305 599-1800
Web: www.mastec.com

PRODUCTS/OPERATIONS

2017 Sales

	$ mil.	% of total
Oil & Gas	3,497	53
Communications	2,424	37
Electrical Transmission	378	6
Power Generation & Industrial	300	4
Other	21	-
Adjustments	(13.5)	-
Total	**6,607**	**100**

Selected Services

Broadband networks
  Aerial and underground construction
  Bonding/grounding
  Engineering and design
  FCC testing
  Modem installation
  Optical fiber splicing activation and testing
  Warehouse and inventory management
Telecommunications
  Aerial construction
  Copper/coaxial cable systems
  Directional drilling
  Engineering
  Fiber-optic cable systems
  Fiber-to-the-premises (FTTP) deployment
  Splicing and testing
  Underground construction
Utilities
  Design and engineering
  Gas distribution construction and maintenance
  Storm restoration
  Submarine cable installation
  Substation construction
  Transmission line construction
  Trench construction

COMPETITORS

Bechtel	MDU Construction Services
Black & Veatch	
Dycom	MYR Group
General Dynamics	Pike Corporation
Goldfield	Primoris
Henkels & McCoy	Quanta Services
Jacobs Engineering	Sirti
M. A. Mortenson	Willbros

HISTORICAL FINANCIALS

Company Type: Public

Income Statement

FYE: December 31

	REVENUE ($ mil.)	NET INCOME ($ mil.)	NET PROFIT MARGIN	EMPLOYEES
12/18	6,909	260	3.8%	19,000
12/17	6,607	347	5.3%	17,300
12/16	5,135	131	2.6%	15,400
12/15	4,208	(79)	—	15,900
12/14	4,612	116	2.5%	15,550
Annual Growth	**10.6%**	**22.3%**	**—**	**5.1%**

2018 Year-End Financials

Debt ratio: 32.00%
Return on equity: 18.00%
Cash ($ mil.): 27
Current ratio: 2.00
Long-term debt ($ mil.): 1,324
No. of shares (mil.): 76
Dividends
  Yield: —
  Payout: —
Market value ($ mil.): 3,082

	STOCK PRICE ($) FY Close	P/E High/Low		PER SHARE ($) Earnings	Dividends	Book Value
12/18	41.00	17	11	3.00	0.00	18.00
12/17	49.00	12	8	4.00	0.00	17.00
12/16	38.00	25	8	2.00	0.00	13.00
12/15	17.00	—	—	(1.00)	0.00	12.00
12/14	23.00	31	13	1.00	0.00	13.00
Annual Growth	**15.7%**			**24.7%**	**—**	**7.9%**

Mastercard Inc

Surpassing Visa in market share — now that would be priceless. Serving financial institutions around the world Mastercard is the second largest payment system in the US. The company does not issue credit or its namesake cards; rather it mar-

kets the Mastercard Maestro and Cirrus brands provides a transaction authorization network and collects fees from members. The company provides its services in more than 210 countries and territories more than 150 currencies and its branded cards are accepted at millions of locations globally.

HISTORY

A group of bankers formed The Interbank Card Association (ICA) in 1966 to establish authorization clearing and settlement procedures for bank credit card transactions. This was particularly important to banks left out of the rapidly growing BankAmericard (later Visa) network sponsored by Bank of America.

By 1969 ICA was issuing the Master Charge card throughout the US and had formed alliances in Europe and Japan. In the mid-1970s ICA modernized its system replacing telephone transaction authorization with a computerized magnetic strip system. ICA had members in Africa Australia and Europe by 1979. That year the organization changed its name (and the card's) to MasterCard.

In 1980 Russell Hogg became president when John Reynolds resigned after disagreeing with the board over company performance and direction. Hogg made major organizational changes and consolidated data processing in St. Louis. MasterCard began offering debit cards in 1980 and traveler's checks in 1981.

MasterCard issued the first credit cards in China in 1987. The next year it bought Cirrus then the world's largest ATM network. It also secured a pact with Belgium-based card company Eurocard (which later became Europay) to supervise MasterCard's European operations and help build the brand.

Hogg resigned in 1988 after disagreements with the board and was succeeded by Alex Hart. In 1991 the Maestro debit card was unveiled.

The 1990s were marked by trouble in Europe: The pact with Europay hadn't resulted in the boom MasterCard had hoped for customer service was below par and competition was keen. Alex Hart retired in 1994 and was succeeded by Eugene Lockhart who tackled the European woes. Lockhart considered ending the relationship but eventually worked things out with Europay. By the end of the decade Europay was locked in a vicious battle to undercut Visa's market share through lower fees.

MasterCard in 1995 invested in UK-based Mondex International maker of electronic set-value refillable smart cards. But US consumer resistance to cash cards and competition in the more advanced European market delayed growth in this area.

In October 1996 a group of merchants including Wal-Mart and Sears filed class-action lawsuits against both MasterCard and Visa challenging the "honor all cards" rule. Because usage fees are higher merchants balked at accepting consumers' MasterCard- or Visa-branded off-line or signature-based debit cards and claimed the card issuers violated antitrust laws by tying acceptance of debit to that of credit. In a dramatic twist minutes before the trial was set to begin in 2003 MasterCard announced a settlement (the card issuer was required to pay $125 million in 2003 and $100 million annually from 2004 through 2012).

Just months later armed with the lawsuit's settlement which also freed merchants to pick which credit and debit card services they use Wal-Mart (along with a handful of others) stopped accepting signature debit cards issued by MasterCard.

Lockhart resigned in 1997 and was succeeded by former head of overseas operations Robert Selander. Yet another management upheaval began in 1999 as the company moved to streamline its organizational structure and shift away from geographical divisions. It also said member banks could boost visibility by putting their logos on card fronts and moving MasterCard's logo to the back.

In 2002 MasterCard merged with Europay with which it already had close ties. As part of the transaction holding company MasterCard Incorporated was formed; MasterCard International become the company's main subsidiary and MasterCard Europe (formerly Europay) became its European subsidiary.

After some 40 years as a private entity MasterCard went public in 2006 in one of the largest IPOs of its time. Following the offering the approximately 1400 financial institutions that wholly owned MasterCard before the offering retained a stake of more than 40%. Two of the top three US banks (Citigroup and JPMorgan Chase) remained among MasterCard's largest shareholders.

Some of the proceeds from the company's IPO were used to fight antitrust lawsuits from such rivals as American Express and Discover as well as other payment processors. In 2008 the company agreed to a $1.8 billion settlement with American Express which had claimed that MasterCard and others tried to stop financial institutions from issuing its AmEx cards. Later that year MasterCard settled the Discover lawsuit agreeing to pay $862.5 million.

Also in 2008 MasterCard bought Ireland-based software provider Orbiscom. The acquired company's technology was used to create MasterCard inControl a platform for making secure Internet and telephone purchases.

MasterCard promoted president and COO Ajay Banga to CEO in 2010. He succeeded Robert Selander who stepped down after more than a dozen years at the helm.

EXECUTIVES

Evp General Manager National Accounts, Michael Fiore
Cfo, Martina Hund-Mejean, age 59, $691,667 total compensation
President And Ceo, Ajaypal S. (Ajay) Banga, age 59, $1,200,000 total compensation
Evp Global Account Management, Gary J. Flood, age 61, $650,000 total compensation
President International Markets, Ann Cairns, age 62, $609,427 total compensation
Chief Services Officer, Kevin J. Stanton
President U.s. Issuers, Raj Seshadri
President Europe, Javier Perez
General Counsel And Chief Franchise Officer, Timothy H. (Tim) Murphy, age 52
Chief Product Officer, Michael Miebach
Chief Innovation Officer, Garry Lyons
President Operations And Technology, Edward (Ed) McLaughlin
Vice Chairman And President Center For Inclusive Growth, Walt W. Macnee, age 64
President North America, Craig Vosburg, age 52
President Middle East And Africa, Raghu Malhotra
President Enterprise Security Solutions, Ajay Bhalla
Co-president Asia/pacific, Hai Ling
Co-president Asia/pacific, Ari Sarker
President Latin America And Caribbean Region, Gilberto Caldart
President Processing Services, Andrea Scerch
President Prepaid Management Services, Fabrizio Burlando
Senior Vice President And Group Head, Michael Robichaud
Senior Vice President Chief Admin Officer, Joy Thoma
Executive Vice President And Chief Data Officer, Joann Stonier

Vice President Issuer Marketing, Jon Briggs
Vice President Product Strategic Alliances, Robert Mandato
Assistant Vice President Product Marketing, Elaine Tham
Vice President Market Development, Adrienne Chambers
Vice President Customer Account Management, Jason Taylor
Vice President, Anne Valentzas
Vice President Global Digital Communications, Jennifer Stalzer
Vice President, Michael Moutenot
Vice President, Naya Larsson
Vice President Team Lead, Candace DeBarger
Senior Vice President, Patricia Preston
Vice President Co Brand Development, George Zilvetti
Executive Vice President Digital Partnerships, Sherri Haymond
Vice President Senior Business Leader Us Commercial Products, Jennifer Merli
Senior Business Leader Vice President Brand Strategy And Design, Chuck Breuel
Vice President Global Marketing And Communications Strategy And Operations, Amy Fuller
Vice President Senior Business Leader, Mathias Lilja
Vice President Merchant Marketing, Luciana Amano
Vice President Debit Development, Anna Zanghi
Vice President Caribbean, Mario Perez
Vice President Global Prepaid Solutions, Ryan Bodman
Vice President Emerging Payments Central Lac Region, Ali Aidi
Vice President Business Leader, Sharon Rosano
Vice President Global Supply Managment, Bryan Fuller
Vice President And Senior Business Leader Worldwide Communications, Jean Altz
Vice President New Product Development, Elizabeth Rensel
Vice President Account Management, Patrick Sulston
Senior Vice President Corporate Philanthropy And Citizenship, Patricia Devereux
Vice President, Theresa Craw
Svp Social Networks And Digital Payment Platforms, Raj Dhamodharan
Vice President Finance And Planning Global Prepaid, Prasad Iyer
Vice President U.s. Markets Emerging Payments, Brian Northey
Senior Vice President Employment Law, Diane Dann
Evp Market Development U.s., Michael Cyr
Vice President Operations And Infrastructure Us Market Development, John Hierholzer
Vice President And Business Leader, Regina Ng
Vice President (business Leader) Commercial Product Development Authentication Services, Laurie Nicoletti
Vice President Market Development, Tor Opedal
Vice President Country Head, Manuel Catedral
Vice President Business Leader Global Business Process Excellence, Richard Blood
Vice President Business Leader Crm Platform Management Global Digital Marketing, Shertina Gillespie
Vice President Senior Business Leader, Julie Schanzer
Vice President Corporate Philanthropy, Leslie Meek-Wohl
Vice President, Linda Paczkowski
Group Head Senior Vice President Senior Engineer, Marie Russo
Vice President Loyalty Solutions, Nick Pifani
Vice President Marketing, Arturo Saldana

Vice President Senior Business Leader Financial Analysis, Joe Cardoso
Vice President Product Sales Loyalty And Rewards, Carrie Dweck
Vice President, Gary Sofko
Vice President, Dawn Barger
Vice President Consultant, Susan Connors
Vice President New Markets, Rich Ciamillo
Vice President Global Commercial Products, Caroline Mcgrath
Vice President Global Digital Payments Strategic Alliances, Sekai Ndemanga
Vice President Fpanda Strategy International Markets, Walter Rodriguez
Vice President B2b Marketing, Bill Braine
Vice President Global Product And Partnerships Digital Payments, Mark Corritori
Vice President Financial Planning And Analysis, Tania Banens
Vice President Senior Counsel Intellectual Property, Edward Tempesta
Vice President, Wade Plummer
Vice President Incident Management, John Artman
Vice President, Carla Dodds
Vice President Product Management, Gowri Narayanan
Vice President, Karen Lindsay
Senior Vice President, Trish Preston
Senior Vice President And Group Head, Greg Boosin
Vice President Mobile Alliances, Jeffrey Allen
Vice President Global Interactive Marketing, Elena D'andrea
Svp Global Business Services Gbs Hr Systems Operations, Lois Miller
Executive Vice President B2b Marketing, Elisa Romm
Vice President Mobile Applications Emerging Payments, Subu Musti
Vice President Lac Communications, Mateo Lleras
Vice President Business Leader Financial Analysis, Sarah Jakeway
Vice President Account Management National Accounts, Deb Morrison
Vice President Healthcare Business Development, Meigan Fukushima
Executive Vice President Global Tax, Tim Berger
Business Leader Vice President Product Operations Digital Payments Masterpass, Chris Giza
Senior Vice President Group Head Emerging Verticals And Acceptance, Joel Henckel
Vice President Digital Payment Products, Gaurav Khillan
Vice President Data Strategy Lead Digital Payments, John Mwangi
Vice President Api Product Launch Andamp; Market Development, Manash Bhattacharjee
Vice President And Tax Counsel, Millie Chun
Vice President And Business Leader, Lori Singer
Vice President, Joyce Laubert
Vice President Global Consumer Marketing, Alison Giordano
Vice President Us Markets Finance, Donna Klecker
Senior Business Leader Vice President Corporate Development, Sergiu Cecoltan
Senior Vice President Integration Lead Enterprise Security Solutions, Ian Webb
Vice President Prepaid Product Management, Jason Tymms
Vice President, Rob Keenan
Vice President Mobile Money, Henry Gewirtz
Vice President, Chris Harrall
Vice President Business Leader Emerging Payments, Alex Zerio
Vice President Global Marketing Solutions, Caroline Granville
Vice President Corporate Security, Richard Gunthner

Vice President Global Digital Strategy, Sharon
 Maddaloni
Vice President, Renee Pirone
Vice President Senior Account Manager, Greg
 Pastorek
Executive Vice President Mobile Solutions, Felix
 Marx
Senior Business Leader Vice President, Stephen
 Parento
Vice President, Ellen Stibler
Vice President And Senior Business Leader, Chris
 Morris
Vice President Corporate Strategy, Gaurav Mittal
Vice President Strategic Alliances, Louann Loriggio
Senior Vice President Mobile Product
 Development, James Anderson
Senior Vice President Retail And Commerce
 Solutions Development, Curtis Villars
Vice President, Elizabeth Gorton
Vice President And Senior Counsel, Joe Halprin
Vice President Of Social Media, Greg Weiss
Vice President, Ranjita Iyer
Vice President Technical Account Manager, Sandra
 Mackert
Vice President, Michael Mcnamara
Vice President Product Development, Paulo
 Fernandes
Senior Business Leader Vice President, Jennifer
 Berry
Vice President Product Development, Jeff
 Feuerstein
Svp, Paul Musser
Executive Vice President, Jennifer Rademaker
Senior Vice President Group Head, Ben Colvin
Vice President: Global Product Development,
 Natashe Barnard
Vice President Of Information Technology,
 Thomas Cronin
Auditors: PricewaterhouseCoopers LLP

LOCATIONS

HQ: Mastercard Inc
 2000 Purchase Street, Purchase, NY 10577
Phone: 914 249-2000
Web: www.mastercard.com

2016 Revenue

	% of total
US	38
International	62
Total	100

PRODUCTS/OPERATIONS

2018 Revenue

	$ mil.	% of total
North America	5,311	36
International	9,441	63
Other	198	1
Total	14,950	100

2018 Revenue

	$ mil.	% of total
Transaction processing fees	7,391	34
Domestic assessments	6,138	28
Cross-border volume fees	4,954	23
Other	3,348	15
Adjustments	(6881)	-
Total	14,950	100

COMPETITORS

Alibaba.com	JCB International
Amazon.com	NYCE Payments Network
American Express	PULSE Network
China UnionPay	PayPal
Discover	Total System Services
Fifth Third	Visa Inc
First Data	Visa International

HISTORICAL FINANCIALS

Company Type: Public

Income Statement

FYE: December 31

	REVENUE ($ mil.)	NET INCOME ($ mil.)	NET PROFIT MARGIN	EMPLOYEES
12/18	14,950	5,859	39.2%	14,800
12/17	12,497	3,915	31.3%	13,400
12/16	10,776	4,059	37.7%	11,900
12/15	9,667	3,808	39.4%	11,300
12/14	9,473	3,617	38.2%	10,300
Annual Growth	12.1%	12.8%	—	9.5%

2018 Year-End Financials

Debt ratio: 25.00%
Return on equity: 108.00%
Cash ($ mil.): 6,682
Current ratio: 1.00
Long-term debt ($ mil.): 5,834

No. of shares (mil.): 1,031
Dividends
 Yield: 1.0%
 Payout: 18.0%
Market value ($ mil.): 194,498

	STOCK PRICE ($) FY Close	P/E High/Low	PER SHARE ($) Earnings	PER SHARE ($) Dividends	PER SHARE ($) Book Value
12/18	189.00	40 27	6.00	1.00	5.00
12/17	151.00	42 29	4.00	1.00	5.00
12/16	103.00	29 22	4.00	1.00	5.00
12/15	97.00	30 24	3.00	1.00	5.00
12/14	86.00	271 22	3.00	0.00	6.00
Annual Growth	21.6%	—	15.9%	22.8%	(2.9%)

MAYO CLINIC HOSPITAL-ROCHESTER

Multidisciplinary teamwork with coordinated care is Mayo Clinic's secret sauce. The not-for-profit Mayo Clinic provides health care most notably for complex medical conditions through its clinics in Rochester Minnesota Arizona and Florida. The clinics' multidisciplinary approach to care attracts more than a million patients a year from around the globe. For less specialized care the Mayo Clinic Health System operates a regional network of affiliated community hospitals and clinics in Minnesota Iowa and Wisconsin. Mayo Clinic also conducts research and trains physicians nurses and other health professionals. The Mayo Clinic is named for Dr. William Worrall Mayo who settled in Rochester in 1863.

Operations

Mayo Clinic Health System's regional network operates more than a dozen hospitals that combined are home to about 1000 beds and 3800 staff physicians medical scientists and clinical and research associates. The system also includes roughly 70 clinics in northern Iowa western Wisconsin and southeastern Minnesota. To manage its patient load Mayo forms referral alliances with other hospital groups HMOs and other organizations.

The clinic's education programs include the Mayo Medical School Mayo Graduate School and the Mayo School of Health Sciences; some medical training programs are conducted through partnerships with universities including the University of Minnesota. It also provides continuing education programs to medical professionals.

Financial Performance

The Mayo Clinic's revenue increased by nearly 7% in 2011 vs. 2010 while net income declined 18% over the same period. Indeed revenue gains and other support has steadily increased in recent years to nearly $8.5 billion in 2011. Sales of medical services (which account for about 85% of the Mayo Clinic's total) grew by 6% vs. the prior year. The Mayo Clinic list more than $10 billion in total assets.

Strategy

Already a giant in health care in the Midwest the Mayo Clinic continues to grow in other regions. In 2018 it announced plans to invest some $648 million in its Phoenix campus over the next five years. The project will roughly double the size of the campus allowing the system to meet growing demand for complex health care services in the Southwest. Similarly Mayo Clinic is investing some $144 million in its Jacksonville Florida campus.

Mayo Clinic strives to accommodate patients who travel to get to its facilities and will schedule multiple appointments and tests tightly together to make the most of patient's time. Rather than paying physicians based upon the quantity of patients seen the clinic's doctors are paid salaries as an incentive to quality care. These and other innovations have drawn attention to the clinic's patient-centered model of care. It has created a Center for the Science of Health Care Delivery and collaborates with other innovators including Cleveland Clinic and Intermountain Healthcare.

To reach remote areas Mayo Clinic in Arizona pioneered a telemedicine program that places robots in rural hospitals allowing local doctors and hospital staff to communicate with Mayo doctors in real time as they treat patients with such conditions as stroke or collapsed lungs.

EXECUTIVES

Regional Vice President, Annie Sadosty
Vice President, Brian Arendt
Assistant Treasurer, Paul A Gorman
Medical Secretary, Judy Jerabek
Vice Chair Dermatology, Marian Mcevoy
Medical Secretary, Deborah Stark
Medical Secretary, Mark Wojahn
Medical Secretary, Gina Robertson
Auditors: ERNST & YOUNG LLP MINNEAPOLIS

LOCATIONS

HQ: MAYO CLINIC HOSPITAL-ROCHESTER
 200 1ST ST SW, ROCHESTER, MN 559050002
Phone: 507 284-2511
Web: WWW.MAYOCLINIC.ORG

Selected Locations and Affiliates

Direct subsidiaries
 Arizona
 Mayo Clinic Hospital (Phoenix)
 Mayo Clinic Scottsdale
 Florida
 Mayo Clinic Hospital (Jacksonville)
 Mayo Clinic Jacksonville
 Minnesota
 Mayo Clinic Rochester
 Rochester Methodist Hospital
 Saint Marys Hospital (Rochester)
 Mayo Eugenio Litta Children's Hospital
Mayo Health System affiliates
 Iowa
 Armstrong Clinic
 Decorah Clinic
 Lake Mills Clinic
    Franciscan
 Swea City Clinic
 Minnesota
 Fountain Centers in Fairmont
 Fountain Centers in Waseca
    FamilyHeal
 FamilyHealth Medical Clinic - Northfield Hospital
 Franciscan Healthcare in Caledonia
 Franciscan Healthcare La Crescent Clinic

Mayo Clinic Health System - Albert Lea
    Mayo Clini
    Mayo Clini
    Mayo Clini
    Mayo Clini
Wisconsin
Chippewa Valley in Bloomer
Chippewa Valley in Chippewa Falls
Chippewa Valley in Colfax
Eau Claire Home Health & Hospice
Franciscan Healthcare Arcadia Campus
Franciscan Healthcare Holmen Clinic
Franciscan Healthcare Lake Tomah Clinic
Franciscan Healthcare Onalaska Clinic
Franciscan Healthcare Prairie du Chien Clinic
Franciscan Healthcare Sparta Campus
Northland in Barron
Red Cedar in Elmwood
Red Cedar in Glenwood
Red Cedar in Menomonie

PRODUCTS/OPERATIONS

2015 Revenues

	$ mil.	% of total
Medical services	8,620	84
Grants & contracts	386	4
Investment return	233	2
Contributions	211	2
Premiums	144	1
Other	721	6
Total	**8,476**	**100**

COMPETITORS

Allina Hospitals
Ascension Health
Beth Israel Deaconess Medical Center
CentraCare Health
Children's Hospitals and Clinics of Minnesota
Dana-Farber
Fairview Health
Fox Chase Cancer Center
Gundersen Lutheran
HCA
Henry Ford Health System
Intermountain Health Care
Johns Hopkins Medicine
MD Anderson Cancer Center
Memorial Sloan-Kettering
North Memorial Health Care
Olmsted Medical
Park Nicollet Health Services
Roswell Park Cancer Institute
Scottsdale Healthcare
Tenet Healthcare
The Cleveland Clinic
Wistar Institute

HISTORICAL FINANCIALS

Company Type: Private

Income Statement				FYE: December 31
	REVENUE ($ mil.)	NET INCOME ($ mil.)	NET PROFIT MARGIN	EMPLOYEES
12/17	11,993	856	7.1%	32,271
12/16	10,998	(480)	—	—
Annual Growth	**9.0%**	—	—	—

MBIA Inc.

MBIA does what it can to make sure that bonds get paid no matter what. The holding company's independent subsidiary National Public Finance Guarantee Corporation is a provider of insurance for municipal bonds and stable corporate bonds (such as utility bonds) in the US. Separately its MBIA Insurance Corporation provides global structured finance products and non-US public financial guarantees. Faced with a significant amount of default activity MBIA is currently not issuing new policies.

Operations

MBIA conducts most of its business through subsidiaries National Public Finance Guarantee and MBIA Insurance Corporation. Formed after the economic collapse in 2008 National provides US public finance insurance (although it hasn't written any new business since 2009;). In 2017 MBIA determined that National would no longer write new financial guarantee policies.MBIA Insurance has issued structured finance and international insurance but MBIA does not expect that unit to write any significant new policies in the foreseeable future either. Today MBIA's primary focus is to keep watch on its existing insured portfolio.

Another subsidiary MBIA Services Corporation provides fee-based support services (surveillance risk management IT etc.) to National and MBIA Insurance.

Geographic Reach

MBIA is headquartered in Purchase New York; it also has offices in New York City San Francisco and Mexico City.

Financial Performance

MBIA's revenue fell in 2015 and 2016 but it increased 40% to $405 million in 2017. That gain was largely driven by the group's sale of its UK operations. Net loss totaled $1.6 billion in 2017 versus a loss of $333 million the prior year as expenses nearly doubled. With that loss operating cash outflow also increased rising 350% to $630 million.

Strategy

MBIA spent several years working to stabilize its financial position and deal with the massive fallout from the subprime mortgage-backed security implosion that led to the housing collapse and the Great Recession. Unfortunately the company found itself in more trouble when certain investment vehicles it had guaranteed soured with one defaulting in late 2016. To help cover its losses MBIA sold its UK operations to Assured Guaranty.It also cut its workforce by some 25%.

The company operates with a high level of debt (more than $1.6 billion) which makes it difficult to dedicate funds to other operating activities. Additionally MBIA has insured exposure in Puerto Rico which has been struggling to meet its legacy debts in the aftermath of Hurricane Maria; in 2017 Puerto Rico defaulted on its scheduled debt service for insured bonds.

Company Background

That MBIA is still standing is remarkable. As one of the largest providers of insurance to asset- and mortgage-based securities MBIA was among the most vulnerable companies when the US housing market imploded in 2007. The company posted losses of $2.3 billion the last quarter of 2007 a result of its investments in subprime mortgage-backed securities.

MBIA split apart its public structured and asset management businesses to separate the stable from the unstable in early 2009: MBIA split its municipal bond insurance business off into an independent subsidiary named National Public Finance Guarantee Corporation. It receives a credit rating separate from the rest of MBIA's riskier structured-finance businesses.

Following the split some 20 banks grew prickly and sued MBIA with one hand while steadily collecting claims with the other. However by mid-2011 banks began dropping out of the lawsuit; the company settled with the final three in 2013.

EXECUTIVES

Evp Chief Legal Officer And Secretary, Ram D. Wertheim, age 65, $500,000 total compensation
Ceo, William C. (Bill) Fallon, age 59, $812,500 total compensation
Evp And Cfo, Anthony McKiernan, age 49, $500,000 total compensation
Assistant Vice President Financial Reporting, James Brown
Assistant Vice President, Emily Johnson
Vice President, Cathleen Murray
Vice President, Greg Wright
Vice President, Donna Soto
Chairman, Charles R. Rinehart, age 72
Board Member, Richard Vaughan
Board Member, Francis Chin
Auditors: PricewaterhouseCoopers LLP

LOCATIONS

HQ: MBIA Inc.
  1 Manhattanville Road, Suite 301, Purchase, NY 10577
Phone: 914 273-4545
Web: www.mbia.com

COMPETITORS

Ambac	Primus Guaranty
Assured Guaranty	Radian Group
FGIC	Syncora Holdings

HISTORICAL FINANCIALS

Company Type: Public

Income Statement				FYE: December 31
	ASSETS ($ mil.)	NET INCOME ($ mil.)	INCOME AS % OF ASSETS	EMPLOYEES
12/18	8,076	(296)	—	96
12/17	9,095	(1,605)	—	103
12/16	11,137	(338)	—	164
12/15	14,855	180	1.2%	170
12/14	16,284	569	3.5%	252
Annual Growth	**(16.1%)**	—	—	**(21.4%)**

2018 Year-End Financials

Debt ratio: 58.00%
Return on equity: (-23.00%)
Cash ($ mil.): 280
Current ratio: —
Long-term debt ($ mil.): —

No. of shares (mil.): 90
Dividends
  Yield: —
  Payout: —
Market value ($ mil.): 801

	STOCK PRICE ($) FY Close	P/E High/Low		PER SHARE ($) Earnings	Dividends	Book Value
12/18	9.00	—	—	(3.00)	0.00	12.00
12/17	7.00	—	—	(14.00)	0.00	15.00
12/16	11.00	—	—	(3.00)	0.00	24.00
12/15	6.00	9	5	1.00	0.00	25.00
12/14	10.00	5	3	3.00	0.00	20.00
Annual Growth	**(1.7%)**	—	—	—	—	**(11.7%)**

McCormick & Co Inc

McCormick & Company is more than just the flavor of the month. As one of the world's leading spice makers the company offers a broad assortment of herbs spices seasonings flavorings sauces and extracts. McCormick distributes and markets its products under brands including Lawry's Club House and McCormick as well as ethnic labels Zatarain's Thai Kitchen and Simply Asia and regional brands Ducros and Schwartz. Its products are sold to customers spanning the entire food industry from food retailers to food service businesses and industrial food manufacturers. McCormick operates in some 150 countries across North and Central America Europe the Asia/Pacific region and South Africa but generates about 60% of sales in the US.

HISTORY

McCormick & Company was founded in 1889 by 25-year-old Willoughby McCormick who crafted fruit syrups root beer and nerve and bone liniment in his Baltimore home. He employed three assistants to hawk his wares door-to-door. His company soon expanded its product line to include food coloring cream of tartar and blood purifier. By 1894 McCormick was exporting and two years later it acquired the F.G. Emmett Spice Company of Philadelphia firmly committing itself to the spice industry. By the turn of the century McCormick was trading around the world.

Willoughby's nephew Charles McCormick joined the company as a part-time shipping clerk in 1912. When Willoughby died in 1932 Charles succeeded him as CEO. He increased employee wages shortened the workweek and established the Multiple Management system (still an integral part of the company's management structure) which solicited employee input. By 1933 McCormick was on a growth track that continued unabated through the 1930s. In 1938 Charles wrote a book expounding his participative management philosophy.

The company opened its first international office in 1940 and achieved coast-to-coast distribution seven years later with the acquisition of A. Schilling & Co. producers of spices and extracts. In 1959 McCormick purchased Gorman Eckert & Co. Canada's largest spice business and the precursor to Club House Foods. It acquired Gilroy Foods in 1961 and rival Baker Extract in 1962. From 1962 until its sale in 1988 McCormick ran a real estate subsidiary Maryland Properties (renamed McCormick Properties 1979).

Charles died in 1970. Though the years following his death were characterized by acquisitions and joint venture agreements in the US and abroad profits slumped until his son Charles "Buzz" McCormick took over as CEO in 1987.

In 1989 Australia's Burns Philp began challenging McCormick by buying up spice companies in the US and Europe including the Spice Islands and Durkee French brands. Buzz — succeeded twice as CEO in the mid-1990s only to return when one successor died and the other left for health reasons — responded with a bruising battle for shelf space that led to Burns Philp's near-collapse in 1997. The company also sold garlic and onion processing subsidiary Gilroy Foods Minipack Systems (UK) and several smaller noncore operations. In 1997 Buzz yielded the CEO's post — for good — to Robert Lawless.

The company's earnings were erratic in the 1990s partly because of a price war with then-rival Burns Philp but also due to the decline of home cooking in the US. McCormick countered with increased advertising and a growing emphasis on industrial sales to flavor the foods eaten outside the home. McCormick also has been expanding internationally through its Decors spice business and operations in China.

Economic woes in Venezuela caused McCormick to cease manufacturing operations there in 1998. In 1999 Lawless succeeded Buzz as chairman. That year the company announced it would cut costs by eliminating 300 jobs (mostly overseas) and closing a British plant.

McCormick's sweet victory over Burns Philp was soured by an FTC investigation into its alleged practice of offering some grocery chains low prices in exchange for up to 90% of their shelf space for spices. The investigation brought scrutiny on a common supermarket practice known as slotting fees. McCormick settled with the FTC in 2000 agreeing not to illegally discriminate against retailers in its pricing. Also that year the company bought France-based Ducros (spices herbs dessert aid products) from B ghin-Say for about $380 million.

In 2003 McCormick's UK subsidiary acquired condiment maker Uniqsauces adding the Beswicks and Hammonds as well as the licensed Newman's Own brands to its European product line. That year the company also acquired New Orleans-style cuisine product maker Zatarain's. Saying that the packaging business was not a strategic part of the company McCormick also sold its packaging business (Setco and Tubed Products) to Kerr Group in 2003.

Acquisitions continued in 2004 with McCormick's purchase of C.M. van Sillevoldt and its Silvo brand of spices herbs and seasonings which is sold in the Netherlands and Belgium. In 2006 the company consolidated its North American operations with the closure of its manufacturing facility in California.

About 39% of McCormick's sales came from its international operations in 2005. The year was not the company's best however as a drop in vanilla prices and the effects of Hurricane Katrina both cut into sales.

Continuing its expansion via acquisitions the company purchased Dessert Products International (DPI) in 2006. DPI markets the Vahine brand dessert toppings in Europe. It also purchased Simply Asia Foods that year for $97.6 million in cash. Simply Asia manufactures products under the Thai Kitchen and Simply Asia brands; its products include noodle and soup bowls meal kits coconut milk and sauces and pastes.

Expanding its well-known roster of brands McCormick acquired Lawry's marinades and spice blends from Unilever for $605 million in 2008; the deal represented McCormick's largest acquisition in company history. To buy Lawry's however the company was required by the FTC to sell its Season-All business which it did — to Morton International. The company also purchased Canada's largest honey business Billy Bee Honey Products for $75 million.

EXECUTIVES

President Global Consumer Business And North America, Brendan M. Foley, age 55, $519,809 total compensation
Chairman President And Ceo, Lawrence E. Kurzius, age 62, $861,374 total compensation
President Global Industrial And International Business, Malcolm Swift, age 58, $407,714 total compensation
Svp Corporate Finance, Michael R. Smith, $394,943 total compensation
Vice President Of Marketing, Lori Robinson
Vice President, Todd Osterhaus
Vice President Information Technology, Jeff Malat
Vp Tax And Government Relations, Paul Nolan
Vp Hr, Martin Bazinet
Vp Global Process And Application Management, John Holmes
Svp Business Transformation, Nneka Rimmer
Vice President Global Sustainability And Packaging Innovation, Michael Okoroafor
Vice President, Mark Madonia
Vice President Marketing Us Consumer Products, Jill Pratt
Vp Sales Uscpd, Ed Landry
National Account Manager, Lisa Nivens
Auditors: Ernst & Young LLP

LOCATIONS

HQ: McCormick & Co Inc
24 Schilling Road, Suite 1, Hunt Valley, MD 21031
Phone: 410 771-7301   **Fax:** 410 771-7462
Web: www.mccormickcorporation.com

2018 Sales

	$ mil.	% of total
US	3,267	60
Europe the Middle East & Africa	1,021	19
Other countries	1,121	21
Total	**5,409**	**100**

PRODUCTS/OPERATIONS

2018 Sales

	$ mil.	% of total
Consumer Products	3,318	61
Flavor Solutions	2,091	39
Total	**5,409**	**100**

Selected Brands

Billy Bee
Club House
Ducros
Kamins
Kohinoor
Lawry's
McCormick
Old Bay
Schwartz
Silvo
Simply Asia
Thai Kitchen
Vahiné
Zatarain's

Selected Products

Consumer Products
  Dessert items
  Extracts
  Food colors
  Grill mates
  Herbs
  Seafood
  Seasoning mixes
  Seasonings
  Spices
Flavor Solutions
  Coating systems
  Compound flavors
  Herbs
  Seasoning blends
  Spices
  Wet flavors

COMPETITORS

A.A. Sayia	Goya
Adams Extract & Spice	International Flavors
Ajinomoto	Kerry Group
Associated British Foods	Kraft Heinz
	Magic Seasoning Blends
B&G Foods	Newly Weds Foods
First Spice Mixing	Olam
Givaudan	Sensient

HISTORICAL FINANCIALS

Company Type: Public

Income Statement				FYE: November 30
	REVENUE ($ mil.)	NET INCOME ($ mil.)	NET PROFIT MARGIN	EMPLOYEES
11/19	5,347	703	13.1%	12,400
11/18	5,409	933	17.3%	11,600
11/17	4,834	477	9.9%	11,700
11/16	4,412	472	10.7%	10,500
11/15	4,296	402	9.3%	10,000
Annual Growth	**5.6%**	**15.0%**	**—**	**5.5%**

Debt ratio: 42.00%	No. of shares (mil.): 133
Return on equity: 21.00%	Dividends
Cash ($ mil.): 155	Yield: 0.0%
Current ratio: 1.00	Payout: 44.0%
Long-term debt ($ mil.): 3,626	Market value ($ mil.): 22,493

	STOCK PRICE ($) FY Close	P/E High/Low	PER SHARE ($) Earnings	Dividends	Book Value
11/19	169.00	32 23	5.00	2.00	26.00
11/18	150.00	21 14	7.00	2.00	24.00
11/17	102.00	28 24	4.00	2.00	20.00
11/16	91.00	29 21	4.00	2.00	13.00
11/15	86.00	27 23	3.00	2.00	13.00
Annual Growth	18.5%	— —	13.9%	9.3%	18.6%

McDonald's Corp

Serving billions of hamburgers has put a shine on these arches. McDonald's has more than 38000 restaurants serving burgers and fries in about 100 countries. (There are roughly 14000 Golden Arches locations in the US.) The popular chain is well-known for its Big Macs Quarter Pounders and Chicken McNuggets. In addition to freestanding units with dine-in take-out and drive-through service McDonald's also has locations inside airports train stations malls and other high-traffic retail areas. More than 90% of the restaurants are run by franchisees or affiliates. More than half of revenues are generated outside the US.

HISTORY

The first McDonald's opened in 1948 in San Bernardino California. In 1954 owners Dick and Mac McDonald signed a franchise agreement with 52-year-old Ray Kroc (a malt machine salesman) and a year later Kroc opened his first restaurant in Des Plaines Illinois. By 1957 Kroc was operating 14 McDonald's restaurants in Illinois Indiana and California. In 1961 Kroc bought out the McDonald brothers for $2.7 million.

In 1962 the now-ubiquitous Golden Arches appeared for the first time and the company sold its billionth burger. Ronald McDonald made his debut the following year and the company introduced its first new menu item — the Filet-O-Fish. Two years later McDonald's went public and ran its first TV ads. The company opened its first stores outside the US (in Canada) in 1967 and the next year it added the Big Mac to the menu and opened its 1000th restaurant.

During the 1970s McDonald's grew at the rate of about 500 restaurants per year and the first Ronald McDonald House (a temporary residence for families of hospitalized children) opened in 1974. The drive-through window appeared in 1975.

McDonald's introduced Chicken McNuggets in 1983. Kroc who had become senior chairman in the 1970s died the next year. Growing competition slowed the company's US sales growth to about 5% per year at the end of the 1980s. In response McDonald's added specially priced "value menu" items.

In 1990 the company made history and headlines when it opened the first McDonald's in Moscow. Two years later the Golden Arches expanded into China. The company stumbled with the pricey Arch Deluxe hamburger in 1996 and its Campaign 55 discount promotion the next year.

However the giveaway of Teenie Beanie Babies in 1997 was its most successful promotion ever. McDonald's decentralized US operations that year to bring decision-making closer to local franchises. US division CEO Edward Rensi retired and was replaced by division chairman Jack Greenberg.

The next year Greenberg launched the Made For You food preparation system designed to reduce waste and produce a better tasting burger. He was named CEO later that year. McDonald's also made its first investment in another restaurant concept in 1998 when it bought a stake in Chipotle Mexican Grill a Denver-based chain of Mexican food restaurants. That same year saw the death of co-founder Dick McDonald who died at age 89.

During Greenberg's first year he slowed US expansion and stepped up international growth. In 1999 McDonald's added a third brand to its family when it acquired the Ohio-based Donatos Pizzeria chain. The company's biggest deal though came in 2000 when it purchased the Boston Market chain from struggling Boston Chicken for about $175 million.

Early in 2001 McDonald's unveiled its New Tastes Menu in which local markets could feature up to four regional or seasonal foods out of a 40-item national selection. The company continued its move toward diversification and international expansion purchasing a 33% stake in the UK limited-service sandwich chain Pret A Manger for $40 million. It also spun off its Japanese unit to the public retaining a 50% ownership stake.

But even with all its size and power McDonald's found out it was not immune to economic trouble and corporate blunders. The company suffered from ill-thought product changes less-than-successful marketing plans and the growing public preference for lighter fast-food options such as sub sandwiches and salads. Following three quarters of declining profits in 2001 McDonald's announced a major restructuring of its US operations. It cut about 700 corporate jobs hired five new managers and consolidated its service regions.

Business failed to improve however and in 2002 it laid off approximately 600 corporate employees and closed about 175 underperforming units. At the end of 2002 after the company posted its first quarterly loss in history vice chairman and president Jim Cantalupo a veteran of McDonald's international operation replaced Jack Greenberg as chairman and CEO.

McDonald's business began to improve during 2003 with the introduction of healthier menu fare. Late that year the company sold Donatos Pizza back to its founder Jim Grote and closed all Boston Market locations outside the US in order to focus more attention on its core chains. The company ended a joint venture with Seed Restaurant Group that would have led to the development of new Fazoli's locations. Japan however remained a particularly rough market: McDonald's Holdings (Japan) posted losses for both 2002 and 2003. It also gave up on efforts to establish the Pret A Manger sandwich shops in Japan.

Putting its advertising dollars to work McDonald's introduced a global branding campaign in 2003 to help change its image. Called "I'm Lovin' It" the campaign attempted to up the restaurant chain's hip factor and draw young customers. These efforts showed positive results: McDonald's posted steady sales increases through most of 2003 and into early 2004 and investors were encouraged by the progress.

Cantalupo died in 2004. Director Andrew McKenna was named chairman and president. Charlie Bell became CEO. Diagnosed with cancer and undergoing surgery a month later Bell curtailed his workload but returned to his job full-time later that month. He underwent a second surgery procedure later that year again cancer-related

and eventually stepped down near the end of 2004 in order to devote all his time to fighting cancer. (Bell died early the next year.) Vice chairman Jim Skinner assumed the mantle of CEO becoming the company's third chief executive in seven months. Mike Roberts the CEO of McDonald's USA assumed the additional titles of president and COO.

In a David and Goliath scenario the Venezuelan government ordered all 80 of the country's McDonald's restaurants closed for three days in 2005 as punishment for not following the country's tax laws. McDonald's sold a 35% stake in Chipotle through an IPO in 2006 and disposed of its remaining holdings later that year. It sold Boston Market to private equity firm Sun Capital Partners for $250 million the following year and in 2008 McDonald's cashed out its stake in Pret A Manger as part of a $670 million buyout by private equity firm Bridgepoint Capital.

In 2011 McDonald's sold its 50% stake in Hardcastle Restaurants one of two joint ventures operating McDonald's restaurants in India and converted it to a franchisee operation.

EXECUTIVES

Evp And Global Chief Marketing Officer, Silvia Lagnado, $615,000 total compensation
President International Lead Markets, Douglas M. (Doug) Goare, age 66, $648,750 total compensation
President Mcdonald's Usa, Chris (Chris K) Kempczinski, age 50, $111,538 total compensation
Evp And Chief People Officer, David Fairhurst, age 51
Corporate Evp And Cfo, Kevin M. Ozan, age 56, $683,333 total compensation
President Ceo And Director, Stephen J. (Steve) Easterbrook, age 51, $1,266,667 total compensation
Corporate Evp Operations And Technology Systems, Jim Sappington, age 60
Evp Corporate Relations; Chief Communications Officer, Robert Gibbs
President High Growth Markets, Joe Erlinger
Evp General Counsel And Secretary, Jerry Krulewitch
President Foundational Markets, Ian Borden
Vice President, Gerald Newman
Vice President Supply Chain Management, Bob Stewart
Vice President Of Operations, Marcy Amble
Vice President Of Strategy, Greg Watson
Senior Vice President Marketing Technology, Bob Rupczynski
Vice President Of Restaurant Development, Robert Lancaster
Senior Vice President, Piotr Jucha
Executive Vice President, Daniel Henry
Chairman, Enrique (Rick) Hernandez, age 64
Auditors: Ernst & Young LLP

LOCATIONS

HQ: McDonald's Corp
110 North Carpenter Street, Chicago, IL 60607
Phone: 630 623-3000
Web: www.mcdonalds.com

2017 Sales

	$ mil.	% of total
U.S.	8,000	35
International Lead Markets	7,340	32
High Growth Markets	5,533	24
Foundational Markets & Corporate	1,941	9
Total	**22,820**	**100**

2017 Locations

	No.
US	14,036
International Lead Markets	6,921
High Growth Markets	5,884
Foundational Markets & Corporate	10,400
Total	**37,241**

PRODUCTS/OPERATIONS

2017 Locations

	No.
Franchised	34,108
Company-owned	3
Total	**37,241**

2017 Sales

	$ mil.	% of total
Company-owned restaurants	12,719	56
Franchised restaurants	10,101	44
Total	**22,820**	**100**

Selected Products

Big Mac
Chicken McNuggets
Egg McMuffin
Filet-O-Fish
Happy Meal
Mac Snack Wrap
McCafe
McChicken
McDouble
McFlurry
McGriddle
McRib
Quarter Pounder

COMPETITORS

Burger King	Quiznos
CKE Restaurants	Sonic Corp.
Chick-fil-A	Starbucks
Church's Chicken	Subway
Dairy Queen	Tim Hortons
Jack in the Box	Wendy's
Panda Restaurant Group	YUM!
Popeyes	

HISTORICAL FINANCIALS

Company Type: Public

Income Statement   FYE: December 31

	REVENUE ($ mil.)	NET INCOME ($ mil.)	NET PROFIT MARGIN	EMPLOYEES
12/18	21,025	5,924	28.2%	210,000
12/17	22,820	5,192	22.8%	235,000
12/16	24,622	4,687	19.0%	375,000
12/15	25,413	4,529	17.8%	420,000
12/14	27,441	4,758	17.3%	420,000
Annual Growth	(6.4%)	5.6%	—	(15.9%)

2018 Year-End Financials

Debt ratio: 95.00%
Return on equity: ***,***.**%
Cash ($ mil.): 866
Current ratio: 1.00
Long-term debt ($ mil.): 31,075

No. of shares (mil.): 767
Dividends
 Yield: 2.0%
 Payout: 56.0%
Market value ($ mil.): 136,214

	STOCK PRICE ($) FY Close	P/E High/Low	PER SHARE ($) Earnings	Dividends	Book Value
12/18	178.00	25 19	8.00	4.00	(8.00)
12/17	172.00	27 19	6.00	4.00	(4.00)
12/16	122.00	24 20	5.00	4.00	(3.00)
12/15	118.00	25 18	5.00	3.00	8.00
12/14	94.00	21 18	5.00	3.00	13.00
Annual Growth	17.3%	— —	11.8%	6.3%	—

McKesson Corp

McKesson is a top global pharmaceuticals distributor. The company delivers prescription and generic drugs as well as health and beauty care products to retail and institutional pharmacies worldwide. The company is also a major medical supplies wholesaler providing medical and surgical equipment to alternate health care sites such as doctors' offices surgery centers and long-term care facilities. In addition to distribution McKesson offers management consulting and technology services that help customers navigate supply chain clinical administrative and financial operations.

HISTORY

John McKesson opened a Manhattan drugstore in 1833 and Daniel Robbins joined him as a partner in 1840. McKesson-Robbins soon expanded into chemical and drug production and the enterprise grew steadily. In 1926 after differences arose between the McKesson and Robbins heirs the company was sold to Donald Coster.

Coster was actually convicted felon Philip Musica who purchased McKesson-Robbins with fraudulently obtained bank loans. For more than a decade his real identity remained secret from all but one blackmailer. By 1930 McKesson-Robbins had wholesale drug operations in 33 states. The company appeared to be growing but a treasurer discovered a Musica-orchestrated accounting scam and a cash shortfall of $3 million. Faced with exposure Musica killed himself in 1939; company bankruptcy followed. McKesson-Robbins emerged from bankruptcy in 1941.

In a hostile takeover in 1967 San Francisco-based Foremost Dairies bought McKesson-Robbins to form Foremost-McKesson. Over the next 20 years the company bought liquor chemical and software wholesalers as well as several bottled-water companies. It sold Foremost Dairies in 1983 to focus on distribution changed its name to McKesson the next year and continued to build its drug wholesaling business through acquisitions. By 1985 it was the US's largest distributor of drugs and medical equipment wine and liquor bottled water and car waxes and polishes.

In 1986 McKesson narrowed its focus to the health industry by selling its liquor and chemical distributors. It acquired Canadian drug distributor Medis by halves in 1990 and 1991 and a 23% stake in Mexican drug distributor Nadro in 1993.

McKesson sold PCS the US's #1 prescription claims processor (acquired in 1970) to Eli Lilly in 1994. In 1996 the firm bought bankrupt distributor FoxMeyer Drug and sold its stake in Armor All (auto and home cleaning products) to Clorox.

In 1997 the company purchased General Medical the US's largest distributor of medical surgical supplies for about $775 million. McKesson began to focus on health care selling its Millbrook Distribution Services unit (health and beauty products general merchandise and specialty foods).

Under new CEO Mark Pulido it agreed to buy drug wholesaler AmeriSource Health (now AmerisourceBergen) but withdrew the offer in 1998 facing FTC opposition. Instead McKesson moved into information systems paying $14 billion for health care information top dog HBO & Company and forming McKesson HBOC. HBO a high-flyer in the high-growth health information systems segment balanced its rather dowdy drug and medical distribution operations.

But just months after the deal closed accounting inconsistencies at HBO prompted McKesson to restate fourth-quarter results for fiscal 1999 twice triggering shareholder lawsuits and a housecleaning of top brass. Five ex-HBO executives including McKesson HBOC chairman Charlie McCall (who was later indicted for securities fraud) were canned for using improper accounting methods. McKesson's veteran CEO Pulido and CFO Richard Hawkins were forced to resign for not seeing the problems coming.

The company changed its name to McKesson Corporation in 2001. The National Health Services Information Authority entered into an agreement with McKesson to develop a human resources and payroll system for use at the more than 600 NHS locations throughout the UK.

To catch then #1 pharmaceutical distributor Cardinal Health McKesson built up its core areas in 2003 and 2004 while trimming away some of the dead weight (Abaton.com Amysis Managed Care Systems and ProDental Corp.). The company bought PMO a specialty mail-order prescription business. It also acquired Canadian firm A.L.I. Technologies which provided systems for managing medical images.

In 2007 McKesson acquired Oncology Therapeutics Network a specialty pharmaceuticals distributor for $519 million. McKesson launched a new Plasma and BioLogics division in 2008 to deliver plasma and plasma-related products to hospital pharmacies and it expanded its regional drug distribution network through the purchase of Midwest pharmacy distributor McQueary Brothers for $190 million.

The company grew in the oncology physician practice management realm through the $2.2 billion acquisition of US Oncology in 2010. In 2014 it expanded into European drug distribution and retail pharmacy operations by purchasing Celesio for $8.3 billion.

In buying Vantage Oncology Holdings for $515 million McKesson got an oncology management services business that offers comprehensive cancer treatment in 50 facilities in 13 states. Biologics acquired for $692 million added another oncology-focused US specialty pharmacy.

The firm bolstered its position in Ireland and the UK with the purchase of the pharmaceutical distribution businesses of UDG for $447 million in 2016. McKesson also bought Rexall Health in Canada for C$3 billion.

McKesson bought CoverMyMeds which developed software for the pre-authorization of prescription drugs for pharma manufacturers clinicians and payers for $1.1 billion in 2017.

EXECUTIVES

Chairman President And Ceo, John H. Hammergren, age 60, $1,680,000 total compensation

Evp Human Resources, Jorge L. Figueredo, age 58, $708,167 total compensation

Evp And Cfo, James A. Beer, age 58, $840,167 total compensation

Evp And Group President Domestic And International Distribution Solutions, Paul C. Julian, age 63, $1,148,333 total compensation

Evp Cio And Cto, Kathleen D. (Kathy) McElligott, age 63

Evp General Counsel And Chief Compliance Officer, Lori A. Schechter, age 57

Evp And Group President Mckesson Technology Solutions, Patrick J. (Pat) Blake, age 55, $765,500 total compensation

Evp Corporate Strategy And Business Development, Bansi Nagji, age 54

Vice President Home Care Sales, Jeff Bowman

Assistant Vice President Product Development, Beth Kuzmak

Senior Vice President Retail National Accounts, Michael Gallagher

Senior Vice President Investor Relations, Holly Weiss

Vice President National Accounts, Mark Snodgrass

Vice President And General Manager, Andrew Moore

Vice President National Accounts, Mike Ferguson

Vice President, Mike Cesarz

Assistant Vice President Software Development Mckesson Corporation, Karen Erickson

Vice President Of Marketing, Andy Burtis
Senior Vice President Distribution Systems, Ronald Bone
Vice President Business Development, Deann Cushman
Vice President Of Sales, Deborah Smith
Vice President Of Sales And Operations, Mauricio Chavez
Vice President Office Product Sales, Kevin Boyle
Vice President Marketing And Sales Program, David Brown
Vice President Laboratory Account Sales, Jerry Morrow
Vice President Software Engineering, Jason Warner
Vice President Of Customer Operations, Kathy McGrath
Executive Vice President And Cio, Zalise Edwards
Vice President Segment Marketing, Chris Garnett
Vp Business Architecture, Dan Gray
Vice President, Victor Solomon
Svp And Gm Mckesson Rxo, Mark Eastham
Vice President Pharmacy Operations Health Mart, Charles Wilson
Vice President Corporate Strategy And Business Development, Aaron Apodaca
Vice President Research And Development, Binny John
Senior Vice President Compliance Regulatory And Ethics, Erik Sandstedt
Vice President Central Fill Operations, Mark Edwards
Vice President Strategy Rxo, Barbara Giacomelli
Vice President Of Materials Management, John Pildis
Vice President Business Strategy And Industry Relations Supplylogix, Victor Vercammen
Board Member, Lauren Coles
Auditors: DELOITTE & TOUCHE LLP

LOCATIONS

HQ: McKesson Corp
6555 State Highway 161, Irving, TX 75039
Phone: 972 446-4800
Web: www.mckesson.com

2018 Sales

	$ mil.	% of total
US	169,943	82
International	38,414	18
Total	**208,357**	**100**

PRODUCTS/OPERATIONS

2018 Sales

	$ mil.	% of total
Distribution Solutions		
North American pharmaceutical distribution & services	174,186	84
International pharmaceutical distribution & services	27,320	13
Medical-Surgical distribution & services	6,611	3
Technology Solutions — products & services	240	—
Total	**208,357**	**100**

Selected Operations and Services

COMPETITORS

Allscripts	H. D. Smith Wholesale Drug
AmerisourceBergen	Imperial Distributors
Apothecary Products	Medline Industries
BioScrip	Omnicare
Cardinal Health	Owens & Minor
CuraScript	PharMerica
Diplomat Pharmacy	QK Healthcare
FFF Enterprises	Surgical Express
Grifols	

HISTORICAL FINANCIALS

Company Type: Public

Income Statement — FYE: March 31

	REVENUE ($ mil.)	NET INCOME ($ mil.)	NET PROFIT MARGIN	EMPLOYEES
03/19	214,319	34	0.0%	80,000
03/18	208,357	67	0.0%	78,000
03/17	198,533	5,070	2.6%	78,000
03/16	190,884	2,258	1.2%	68,000
03/15	179,045	1,476	0.8%	70,400
Annual Growth	4.6%	(61.0%)	—	3.2%

2019 Year-End Financials

Debt ratio: 13.00%
Return on equity: 0.00%
Cash ($ mil.): 2,981
Current ratio: 1.00
Long-term debt ($ mil.): 7,265
No. of shares (mil.): 190
Dividends
Yield: 0.0%
Payout: 888.0%
Market value ($ mil.): 22,241

	STOCK PRICE ($) FY Close	P/E High/Low		PER SHARE ($) Earnings	Dividends	Book Value
03/19	117.00	93	06 37	0.00	2.00	43.00
03/18	141.00	55	24 22	0.00	1.00	49.00
03/17	148.00	9	5	23.00	1.00	53.00
03/16	157.00	25	15	10.00	1.00	40.00
03/15	226.00	36	26	6.00	1.00	34.00
Annual Growth	(15.2%)	—	—	(59.4%)	12.0%	5.4%

MCLANE COMPANY, INC.

McLane Company is one of the largest wholesale suppliers of grocery and food products in the US serving some 50000 retail locations and 35000 restaurants across all 50 states. It delivers more than 50000 different consumer products to customers such as convenience and discount stores mass merchandisers wholesale clubs drug stores military bases and quick-service and casual dining restaurants. The company also distributes alcoholic beverages in the southeastern US and Colorado through subsidiaries. McLane is owned by Warren Buffett's Berkshire Hathaway and accounts for about a fifth of its revenue.

Operations

McLane operates through three business units: grocery distribution foodservice distribution and beverage distribution.

Its grocery business which accounts for about two-thirds of sales serves convenience stores and other retailers nationwide. The company's foodservice business focuses on restaurants across the country while subsidiaries such as Empire Distributors and Baroness Small Estates provide spirits wine and beer to more than 25000 retail locations in the southeastern US and Colorado. Food and beverage distribution together generates about a third of sales.

Geographic Reach

McLane has an extensive distribution network of some 80 facilities across the country with reach in all 50 US states. Its headquarters and grocery operations are based in Temple Texas while its Foodservice operation is based in Carrollton Texas.

The company supplies alcoholic beverages throughout the southeastern US and in Colorado through distribution centers in Colorado Georgia North Carolina and Tennessee.

Sales and Marketing

McLane is a leading supplier to convenience stores; other customers include discount and drug stores mass merchants wholesale clubs military bases and quick-service and casual dining restaurants.

The company is heavily reliant on former parent Walmart which generates about 20% of its revenue; 7-Eleven and Yum! Brands each account for about 10% of revenue.

Financial Performance

McLane's revenue has grown slightly over the past several years up 4% since 2016 amid intense competition.

The company reported 2018 revenue of about $50 billion up less than a percent from the prior year. A slight rise in grocery sales was mostly offset by a decline in foodservice sales because of a net loss in customers.

Strategy

Although McLane is one of the leaders in grocery and food distribution the business is low-margin and intensely competitive. As the company continues to expand by opening new distribution centers it is focused on technology and automation that can improve service while reducing costs. In late 2017 it opened what was its most technologically advanced distribution center in Findlay Ohio. The facility makes use of automation robotics and artificial intelligence among other technologies. McLane has continued opening distribution centers since then including a 2018 opening in Fort Worth Texas and a 2019 opening in Ocala Florida.

In addition to distribution center technology the company has also introduced a new mobile app (Mobile Virtual Trade Show or Mobile VTS) to simplify the ordering process for convenience store retailers.

Company Background

Starting as a family-owned grocery store in 1894 McLane expanded into wholesale distribution in the early 1900s. The McLane family including former Houston Astros owner Drayton McLane sold the business to Wal-Mart Stores in the 1990s. Conglomerate Berkshire Hathaway acquired McLane Company in 2003 for about $1.5 billion.

EXECUTIVES

President Mclane Grocery, Mike Youngblood
Evp Administration, James L. (Jim) Kent
President And Ceo, W. Grady Rosier
President Southeast And Dothan Divisions, Ron Clark
President Mclane Carolina And Mid-atlantic Divisions, George Bolts
President Southwest And High Plains Divisions, Scott Braden
Svp And Chief Marketing Officer, Tom Sicola
Vice President Of Information Technology, Mona Huffman
Vice President Of Sales, Jimmy Morales
Vice President Distribution, Curtis Carpenter
Senior Vice President, Charles Freeman
Senior Vice President, Julie Norris
Vice President National Accounts, Jeff Hayes
Vice President Of Logistics, Robbie Wainwright
Vice President Of Sales Convenience And Military Executive, Vito Maurici
Division Vice President, John Havel
Region Vice President, Calvin Parker
Senior Vice President Midwest Division, Tim Donahoe
Senior Vice President Midwest Division, Matt Bowen
Vice President Information Systems, Melanie Lewis

LOCATIONS

HQ: MCLANE COMPANY, INC.
4747 MCLANE PKWY, TEMPLE, TX 765044854
Phone: 254 771-7500
Web: WWW.MCLANECO.COM

COMPETITORS

AMCON Distributing	MAINES
Associated Wholesale Grocers	Performance Food Group
	Reinhart FoodService
Ben E. Keith	SUPERVALU
C&S Wholesale	Southern Glazer's Wine
Core-Mark	and Spirits
Eby-Brown	Sysco
GSC Enterprises	US Foods
Golden State Foods	United Natural
Gordon Food Service	Wakefern Food
H. T. Hackney	

HISTORICAL FINANCIALS

Company Type: Private

Income Statement   FYE: December 30

	REVENUE ($ mil.)	NET INCOME ($ mil.)	NET PROFIT MARGIN	EMPLOYEES
12/16*	48,016	0	—	20,128
01/16	48,145	0	—	—
12/12	37,390	0	—	—
01/09	29,800	0	—	—
Annual Growth	6.1%	—	—	—

*Fiscal year change

MEDSTAR HEALTH, INC.

Whether you're seeing stars or are just plain sickly MedStar Health can cater to you. The not-for-profit organization runs 10 hospitals and about 20 other health-related businesses across Maryland and the Washington DC area including Union Memorial and Georgetown University Hospital. With more than 3000 beds and 6000 affiliated physicians MedStar has a comprehensive service offering including acute and long-term sub-acute care emergency services home health care and rehabilitation. It also operates emergency clinics and assisted living and nursing homes maintains a primary care and specialist physician network (MedStar Physician Partners) and conducts research and medical education activities.

Operations

Along with its 10 hospitals and a dizzying array of inpatient and outpatient services MedStar Health also operates a Medicaid managed care program called MedStar Family Choice.

Its Nascott Orthotics and Prosthetics division provides adult and pediatric prosthetic services and devices to patients in Washington DC and Baltimore. The company provides a continuum of care from initial measurement to fabrication of the device and maintenance through four locations scattered throughout the service areas.

MedStar Health's Visiting Nurse Association (VNA) administers home health care infusion services private duty nursing and hospice as well as immunizations. The VNA also uses telemonitoring services to keep tabs on home care patients without having to physically visit each patient's home.

In 2014 the system had 148685 inpatient admissions and nearly 4 million outpatient visits.

Financial Performance

In fiscal 2014 MedStar Health's net operating revenue totaled $4.6 billion.

Strategy

Despite its already hefty size MedStar Health is not adverse to getting bigger. It grows usually through acquisitions of existing facilities but also through alliances with other health care providers. MedStar Health has acquired several hospitals in recent years including St. Mary's Hospital with 100 beds in southern Maryland and Montgomery General Hospital a 150-bed general acute care facility located in Montgomery County Maryland.

The company also grows by establishing new facilities. In 2014 it opened an integrated multi-specialty care center in downtown Baltimore as well as four new PromptCare locations in Maryland and Virginia. That year it began work on a new ambulatory care center at the 16-acre MedStar Health Bel Air Medical Campus. MedStar is also developing a new ambulatory care center at Lafayette Centre in northwest Washington DC.

MedStar Health has also entered the growing quick-care and urgent care market by partnering with Rite Aid to establish walk-in health clinics in a number of Rite Aid pharmacies throughout the Baltimore and Washington DC markets.

In 2015 the system expanded its Medicare Choice plan into Baltimore City and Anne Arundel Baltimore Charles Prince George's and St. Mary's counties.

EXECUTIVES

Evp Insurance And Diversified Operations, Eric R. Wagner
Evp And Chief Administrative Officer, Michael J. Curran
Evp And Coo, M. Joy Drass
President Medstar Ambulatory Services, Bob Gilbert
Svp And President Medstar Good Samaritan Hospital And Medstar Union Memorial Hospital, Bradley S. Chambers
Svp And Chief Nursing Officer, Maureen P. McCausland
President Medstar Medical Group, Richard Goldberg
President Ceo And Director, Kenneth A. Samet
President Medstar Visiting Nurse Association, Traci K. Anderson
Evp Medical Affairs And Chief Medical Officer, Stephen R. T. Evans
Svp And President Medstar National Rehabilitation Network, John D. Rockwood
President Medstar Health Research Institute, Neil J. Weissman
Svp And President Medstar Southern Maryland Hospital Center And St. Mary's Hospital, Christine R. Wray
Svp And President Medstar Franklin Square Medical Center, Samuel E. Moskowitz
Evp And General Counsel, Oliver M. Johnson
Svp And President Medstar Washington Hospital Center, John Sullivan
Svp Marketing And Strategy, Kevin P. Kowalski
Evp And Cfo, Susan K. Nelson
Vp Applications And Interim Cio, Mark K. Schneider
Svp And President Medstar Georgetown University Hospital, Michael C. Sachtleben
Svp And President Medstar Montgomery Medical Center, T. J. Senker
Vice President Digital Marketing, Sameer Kasargod
Chairman, William R. Roberts
Vice Chairman, William J. Oetgen
Auditors: KMPG LLP BALTIMORE MD

LOCATIONS

HQ: MEDSTAR HEALTH, INC.
10980 GRANTCHESTER WAY WA, COLUMBIA, MD 210446097
Phone: 410 772-6500
Web: WWW.MEDSTARHEALTH.ORG

Selected Facilities

Maryland
Franklin Square Hospital Center (Baltimore)
Good Samaritan Hospital (Baltimore)
Harbor Hospital (Baltimore)
Montgomery General Hospital (Olney)
St. Mary's Hospital (Leonardtown)
Union Memorial Hospital (Baltimore)
Washington DC
Georgetown University Hospital
National Rehabilitation Hospital
Washington Hospital Center

PRODUCTS/OPERATIONS

Selected Affiliates/Operations

Clinical Research
  Georgetown University Medical Center (Washington DC)
  MedStar Research Institute (Hyattsville Maryland)
Home Health Care
  MedStar Health VNA (Washington DC)
  MedStar Health Infusion (Elkridge Maryland)
  MGH Community Health (Olney Maryland)
Managed Care
  MedStar Family Choice (Baltimore Maryland)
Nursing Homes/Senior Living
  Franklin Woods (Rosedale Maryland)
  Good Samaritan Nursing Center (Baltimore Maryland)
  Belvedere Green (Baltimore Maryland)
  Woodbourne Woods (Baltimore Maryland)
Primary Care
  MedStar Physician Partners (Washington DC)
Outpatient Surgery Centers
  MedStar Surgery Center (Washington DC)
  Harbor Hospital HealthPark (Pasadena Maryland)
  SurgiCenter at Pasadena (Pasadena Maryland)

COMPETITORS

Adventist HealthCare
Anne Arundel Medical Center
Ascension Health
Bon Secours Health
Carilion Clinic
Children's National Medical Center
Christiana Care
Civista Health
Franklin Square Hospital Center
GBMC
Harbor Hospital
Inova
Johns Hopkins Health System
Johns Hopkins Medicine
Kaiser Foundation Health Plan of the Mid-Atlantic
Levindale Hospital
LifeBridge Health
MedStar Union Memorial Hospital
Sinai Hospital of Baltimore
Suburban Hospital
Trinity Health (Novi)
University of Maryland Medical System
Valley Health
Virginia Hospital Center

HISTORICAL FINANCIALS

Company Type: Private

Income Statement   FYE: June 30

	REVENUE ($ mil.)	NET INCOME ($ mil.)	NET PROFIT MARGIN	EMPLOYEES
06/18	5,604	325	5.8%	33,000
06/13	4,217	311	7.4%	—
06/11*	4,012	271	6.8%	—
12/09	1,937	201	10.4%	—
Annual Growth	14.2%	6.2%	—	—

*Fiscal year change

MEMORIAL HERMANN HEALTH SYSTEM

EXECUTIVES

Ceo, Charles Stokes
Cfo*, Dennis Laraway
Svp-Cceo*, Alexander Greengold
Chief of Medicine, Todd M Price
Coordinator, Melissa Aing
Director of Radiology, Alla Vargo
Educator, Linda Whitson
Obstetrics, Jennifer Weber
Director, Scott Pruzan
Human Resources Manager, Shanobia Stovall
Director of Business Developme, Amanda Spielman
Auditors: ERNST & YOUNG LLP HOUSTON TX

LOCATIONS

HQ: MEMORIAL HERMANN HEALTH SYSTEM
929 GESSNER RD STE 1900, HOUSTON, TX
770242317
Phone: 713 242-3000
Web: WWW.MEMORIALHERMANN.ORG

HISTORICAL FINANCIALS

Company Type: Private

Income Statement				FYE: June 30
	REVENUE ($ mil.)	NET INCOME ($ mil.)	NET PROFIT MARGIN	EMPLOYEES
06/18	5,258	318	6.1%	14,000
06/17	5,062	313	6.2%	—
06/14	3,742	454	12.1%	—
06/13	3,285	231	7.0%	—
Annual Growth	9.9%	6.6%	—	—

Mercantile Bank Corp.

Mercantile Bank Corporation is the holding company for Mercantile Bank of Michigan (formerly Mercantile Bank of West Michigan) which boasts assets of nearly $3 billion and operates more than 50 branches in central and western Michigan around Grand Rapids Holland and Lansing. The bank targets local consumers and businesses offering standard deposit services such as checking and savings accounts CDs IRAs and health savings accounts. Commercial loans make up more than three-fourths of the bank's loan portfolio. Outside of banking subsidiary Mercantile Insurance Center sells insurance products.

Operations

Mercantile Bank Corp. generated 82% of its total revenue from loan interest (including fees) in 2014 with securities interest contributing another 8% to total revenue. Service charges on deposit and sweep accounts and credit and debit card fees made up another 5% of Mercantile's total revenue while its mortgage banking income generated another 2%.

Sales and Marketing

Mercantile provides its banking services to businesses individuals and government organizations. Its commercial banking services mostly cater to small- to medium-sized businesses.

The company spent $1.315 million on advertising in 2014 compared to $1.113 million and $1.167 million in 2013 and 2012 respectively.

Financial Performance

Mercantile Bank Corp's revenues had been declining for a number of years as its loan business withered while profits have remained mostly flat.

The company had a breakout year in 2014 however after its historic acquisition of FirstBank Corp. The bank's revenue skyrocketed by 53% to $99.15 million (the highest level since 2009) mostly as the acquisition nearly doubled its loan assets and boosted its interest income on loans and securities by significant amounts. The bank's non-interest income also grew by 46% thanks to higher fee income across the board also resulting from the recent acquisition.

Higher revenue and a $3.2 million reduction in loan loss provisions with a stronger credit portfolio in 2014 also pushed the company's net income up by 2% to $17.33 million for the year. Mercantile's operating cash declined by 50% to $14.41 million due to changes in accrued interest and other liabilities during the year.

Strategy

Mercantile Bank Corporation has been growing its loan business and branch network reach through strategic acquisitions of smaller banks and bank branches. Its mid-2014 acquisition of Firstbank Corporation was perhaps the most effective to date as the purchase doubled its assets and boosted the size of its branch network nearly seven-fold from seven branches to a whopping 53.

Mergers and Acquisitions

In June 2014 Mercantile Bank Corp. purchased Firstbank Corp of Alma Michigan for a total purchase price of $173 million adding 46 branches and $1.3 billion in assets. The deal which made Mercantile the third-largest bank based in the state also expanded the bank's service offerings diversified its loan portfolio boosted its loan origination capacity and significantly extended its geographic footprint into Michigan's lower peninsula.

EXECUTIVES

Svp Cfo And Treasurer Mercantile Bank Corporation And Svp And Cfo Mercantile Bank Of Michigan, Charles E. (Chuck) Christmas, age 53, $263,000 total compensation
President And Ceo, Robert B. Kaminski, age 57, $315,000 total compensation
Evp Corporate Finance And Strategic Planning Mercantile Bank Corporation And Mercantile Bank Of Michigan, Samuel G. Stone, age 74, $159,833 total compensation
Vice President Treasury Sales, John Byl
Vice President Electronic Banking, Shannon Tramontin
Vice President Security, Paul Wegener
Assistant Vice President Human Resources Specialist, Tina Van Valkenburg
Assistant Vice President, Amy Ervin
Senior Vice President Business Development Officer, Brian Talbot
Vice President Commercial Loan Officer, Jeff Hicks
Branch Manager Vice President, Andrea Spagnuolo
Vice President, Teresa Rupert
Assistant Vice President, Jennifer Harris
Senior Vice President, Mike Siminski
Senior Vice President Corporate Banking, Matt Zimmerman
Mortgage Operations Manager Vice President, Lori Schafer
Vice President Commercial Lender, Andrew Miedema
Assistant Vice President Human Resources Administrator, Kate Glover
Assistant Vice President Assistant Controller, Peggy Coutchie

Senior Vice President Information Systems Manager, Allen Smith
Assistant Vice President Commercial Loan Officer, Justin Horn
Vice President, Martin Smith
Vice President Corporate Banking, Bob Klimczak
Assistant Vice President Mortgage Operations Manager, Sarah Smith
Senior Vice President General Counsel Chief Operating Officer And Secretary Of The Company And Ban, Bob Worthington
Vice President Treasury Sales Officer, Tim Ladd
Vice President, Holly Williams
Vice President Commercial Loan Risk Assets, Traci Courter
Vice President, Betsy Mccue
Vice President Risk Asset Management, Danna Mathiesen
Assistant Vice President Leonard Branch Manager, Daniel Zink
Senior Vice President, Michael Erfourth
Vice President, Jim Kloostra
Vice President, Cindy Carter
Assistant Vice President Mortgage Lender, Debra Fuller
Senior Vice President Commercial Lending, Michael Stapleton
Chairman, Michael H. Price, age 62
Auditors: BDO USA, LLP

LOCATIONS

HQ: Mercantile Bank Corp.
310 Leonard Street N.W., Grand Rapids, MI 49504
Phone: 616 406-3000
Web: www.mercbank.com

PRODUCTS/OPERATIONS

2014 Sales

	$ mil.	% of total
Interest income		
Loans and leases including fees	81	82
Securities taxable	6	6
Securities tax-exempt	2	2
Other	0	-
Noninterest income		
Service charges on accounts	3	3
Credit and debit card fees	3	2
Mortgage banking activities	2	2
Other	3	3
Total	99	100

COMPETITORS

Chemical Financial	Flagstar Bancorp
ChoiceOne Financial Services	Huntington Bancshares
Comerica	Independent Bank (MI)
Fifth Third	Macatawa Bank

HISTORICAL FINANCIALS

Company Type: Public

Income Statement				FYE: December 31
	ASSETS ($ mil.)	NET INCOME ($ mil.)	INCOME AS % OF ASSETS	EMPLOYEES
12/18	3,364	42	1.2%	693
12/17	3,287	31	1.0%	701
12/16	3,083	32	1.0%	682
12/15	2,904	27	0.9%	701
12/14	2,893	17	0.6%	731
Annual Growth	3.8%	24.8%		(1.3%)

2018 Year-End Financials

Debt ratio: 1.00%	No. of shares (mil.): 17
Return on equity: 11.00%	Dividends
Cash ($ mil.): 75	Yield: 3.0%
Current ratio: —	Payout: 72.0%
Long-term debt ($ mil.): —	Market value ($ mil.): 467

	STOCK PRICE ($) FY Close	P/E High/Low	Earnings	Dividends	Book Value
12/18	28.00	15 11	3.00	2.00	23.00
12/17	35.00	20 15	2.00	1.00	22.00
12/16	38.00	19 11	2.00	1.00	21.00
12/15	25.00	16 12	2.00	1.00	20.00
12/14	21.00	19 15	1.00	2.00	19.00
Annual Growth	7.7%	— —	18.6%	(9.3%)	4.1%

Merchants Bancorp (Indiana)

Auditors: BKD, LLP

LOCATIONS

HQ: Merchants Bancorp (Indiana)
410 Monon Blvd., Carmel, IN 46032
Phone: 317 569-7420
Web: www.merchantsbankofindiana.com

HISTORICAL FINANCIALS

Company Type: Public

Income Statement — FYE: December 31

	ASSETS ($ mil.)	NET INCOME ($ mil.)	INCOME AS % OF ASSETS	EMPLOYEES
12/18	3,884	63	1.6%	259
12/17	3,393	55	1.6%	194
12/16	2,719	33	1.2%	157
12/15	2,269	28	1.3%	—
Annual Growth	19.6%	30.4%	—	—

2018 Year-End Financials

Debt ratio: 1.00%
Return on equity: 16.00%
Cash ($ mil.): 337
Current ratio: —
Long-term debt ($ mil.): —
No. of shares (mil.): 29
Dividends
  Yield: 1.0%
  Payout: 10.0%
Market value ($ mil.): 573

	STOCK PRICE ($) FY Close	P/E High/Low	Earnings	Dividends	Book Value
12/18	20.00	14 9	2.00	0.00	15.00
12/17	20.00	9 7	2.00	0.00	13.00
12/16	0.00	— —	1.00	0.00	10.00
Annual Growth	—	— —	12.1%	6.3%	14.5%

Merck & Co Inc

A top 5 global drugmaker Merck makes medicines for an array of maladies ranging from hypertension to cancer. The pharmaceutical giant's top products include cancer drug Keytruda diabetes drugs Januvia and Janumet HPV vaccine Gardasil cholesterol combatants Vytorin and Zetia and HIV therapy Isentress. In addition Merck makes childhood and adult vaccines for such diseases as measles mumps pneumonia and shingles as well as veterinary pharmaceuticals through Merck Animal Health. In addition the company provides analytics and clinical services to the health care sector. The US market accounts for about 45% of sales.

HISTORY

Merck traces its roots to the formation of Schering-Plough in 1851 and the founding of the original Merck entity in 1887. (The two companies merged in 2009.)

Schering-Plough dates back to 1851 when Berlin chemist Ernst Schering began to sell chemicals to apothecary shops. By 1880 Schering's business (which eventually became Bayer Schering Pharma) was exporting pharmaceuticals to the US where a subsidiary (the predecessor to Schering-Plough) was established in 1928.

At the outbreak of WWII the US government seized the US Schering subsidiary severing links with its German parent. The company went on to develop such new drugs as Chlor-Trimeton one of the first antihistamines and the cold medicine Coricidin. The US government sold Schering in 1952 to Merrill Lynch which took it public. Schering bought White Labs (which made Coppertone sunscreen) in 1957. In the 1960s the company introduced Garamycin (antibiotic 1964) Tinactin (antifungal 1965) and Afrin (decongestant 1967).

Schering's 1971 merger with Memphis-based Plough expanded the product line to include such cosmetics and consumer items as Coppertone and Di-Gel. Plough's founder Abe Plough had borrowed $125 from his father to found the company in 1908. Abe remained chairman at Schering-Plough until 1976. Schering-Plough introduced many products after the merger including Lotrimin AF (antifungal 1975) antibiotic Netromycin (1980) and Drixoral (a cold remedy made nonprescription in 1982).

The company was one of the first drug giants to make significant investments in biotechnology: It bought DNAX Research Institute of Palo Alto California in 1982. Acquisitions in the late 1970s and 1980s included Scholl (foot care 1979) Key Pharmaceuticals (cardiovascular drugs 1986) and Cooper Companies (eye care 1988).

In 1993 Schering-Plough began marketing its non-sedating antihistamine Claritin in the US. (Claritin became an OTC drug in 2002.) The next year it gained FDA approval to market the first colored disposable contact lenses only to sell its contact lens business later in the year. In 1996 Schering-Plough bought Canji to strengthen its gene therapy research program. It strengthened its veterinary medicine segment in 1997 when it bought Mallinckrodt's animal health operations.

The firm bought the marketing rights to Centocor's treatment for Crohn's disease in 1998. In 1999 the FDA approved the company's Temodar a chemotherapy treatment for brain tumors and it bought the US rights to Pfizer's Bain de Soleil sun care product line. In 2000 Schering-Plough formed its first collaboration with Merck. In 2002 the company paid a $500 million fine to the FDA over manufacturing concerns.

As Schering-Plough's revenues started to decline in 2003 the company brought in several executives from Pharmacia including CEO Fred Hassan (who retired following the 2009 merger with Plough) to help streamline its operations and expand its R&D programs and product offerings. The firm gave itself a major boost by acquiring Akzo Nobel's Organon unit in 2007 growing in the areas of women's health care neurology vaccines animal health (Intervet) and third-party biologics manufacturing (through Diosynth).

The original Merck was started in 1887 when German chemist Theodore Weicker came to the US to set up a branch of German firm E. Merck AG (which was founded in 1668 and later became Merck KGaA). George Merck (grandson of the German company's founder) came in 1889 and formed a partnership with Weicker and eventually bought out Weicker's shares. At first the firm imported and sold drugs and chemicals from Germany but in 1903 it began manufacturing its own products. During WWI Merck gave the US government the 80% of the US Merck unit's stock owned by the family in Germany (George kept his shares). After the war the stock was sold to the public.

The firm acquired Powers-Weightman-Rosengarten of Philadelphia (a producer of antimalarial quinine) in 1927. Merck opened its first research lab in 1933; Merck scientists there developed the first steroid cortisone in 1944. Five Merck scientists received Nobel Prizes in the 1940s and 1950s. In 1953 Merck bought drugmaker Sharp & Dohme of Philadelphia which brought with it a strong sales force.

The 1958 introduction of Diuril (antihypertensive) and several other drugs (including the first measles vaccine) in the early 1960s was followed by a dry spell. In the 1970s an accelerated R&D organization created new products including Clinoril (antiarthritic) Flexeril (muscle relaxant) and Timoptic (for glaucoma). Merck introduced 10 major new drugs in the 1980s including Mevacor (high cholesterol) and Vasotec (high blood pressure).

In 1990 the company bought the nonprescription drug segment of ICI Americas; products from the purchase were contributed to a Consumer Pharmaceuticals joint venture with Johnson & Johnson. Merck bought pharmacy benefits manager Medco Containment Services in 1993. New drug launches in 1995 and 1996 included Cozaar (for reducing hypertension) and Pepcid AC (antacid). Also in 1996 Merck expanded its pharmacy benefit management operations with the purchase of Systemed.

In 1997 Merck and Rh "ne-Poulenc (now part of Sanofi-Aventis) merged their animal health units to form Merial. Merck also sold its insecticide and fungicide business to Novartis that year. In 1998 DuPont bought out Merck's 50% stake in a drug-marketing joint venture formed by the two firms in 1991. In 1999 the FDA approved Merck's preservative-free hepatitis B vaccine Recombivax HB.

In 2001 Merck acquired biotech firm Rosetta Inpharmatics. The company spun off its highly successful Medco Health Solutions drug distribution subsidiary in 2003.

In 2004 Merck pulled its blockbuster pain medication Vioxx off the market after studies linked the drug to increased risks of strokes and heart attacks. (Merck settled thousands of class-action and personal-injury lawsuits related to Vioxx in 2007 for $4.85 billion.) The Vioxx safety scandal along with the pending loss of patent protection on some of its biggest sellers like Zocor (which began facing competition in 2006) sent the company into recovery mode. Merck announced restructuring plans to make the company's operations leaner and more cost-effective in 2005 under new CEO Richard (Dick) Clark a longtime Merck executive. Between 2005 and 2008 the company eliminated more than 10000 jobs and closed a handful of manufacturing plants.

From 2006 to 2009 Merck worked aggressively to expand its biotech operations through the acquisition of companies including GlycoFi (biologic drug molecules) Abmaxis (monoclonal antibodies) Sirna Therapeutics (RNA interference or RNAi) and NovaCardia (cardiology drugs) as well as the follow-on (generic) biologic assets of Insmed. New drug launches included HIV drug Isentress and diabetes therapy Janumet in 2007 and blockbuster HPV vaccine Gardasil the world's first anti-cancer vaccine which was approved by the FDA in 2006.

553

In 2008 Merck sold off the assets of its Rosetta Inpharmatics subsidiary to Covance (gene expression laboratory assets) and Microsoft (expression analysis software assets). It also sold another research lab to PPD and contracted out certain lab functions to the buyer. Merck launched a new product Emend for chemotherapy side-effects that year. New drug launches in 2009 included Saphris a treatment for schizophrenia and bipolar disorder and Simponi the next-generation version of top-selling drug Remicade.

Cholesterol drug Vytorin — a combination of Schering-Plough's Zetia and Merck's Zocor — began facing controversy in 2008 when study results were released questioning the drug's effectiveness compared to Merck's older medication Zocor. Controversy over Vytorin along with some other pipeline setbacks (including the FDA's rejection of a Merck/Schering-Plough combo asthma drug and Merck's Cordaptive cholesterol candidate) led both predecessors Merck and Schering-Plough to announce layoffs and restructuring measures in 2008. Each company reduced its workforce by around 10% that year with their respective US sales teams bearing the brunt of the cuts. The companies' troubles with Vytorin came to a head in 2009 when they agreed to pay about $42 million to settle class-action lawsuits filed by consumers and health plans over Vytorin's efficacy.

Later that year Merck and Schering-Plough decided to merge taking the logical step of marriage to strengthen their defenses against future troubles (especially in light of increasing competitive challenges in the market) as well as to create cost savings opportunities and expanded avenues for revenue growth. The $41 billion transaction was conducted through a reverse-merger transaction in which the legacy Schering-Plough entity acquired the legacy Merck entity and took on the Merck name.

Following the merger Merck began simplifying its global branding under the Merck and MSD names gradually phasing out the Schering-Plough moniker. The purchase expanded Merck's offerings in areas including inflammation allergy and cancer treatment as well as biotech drugs. The acquisition also greatly expanded Merck's operations in the animal health and consumer health arenas.

However to gain Schering-Plough's animal health unit Intervet (later renamed Merck Animal Health) Merck had to sell its stake in veterinary joint venture Merial to partner Sanofi-Aventis for about $4 billion later that year to avoid anti-trust issues. (Merck and Sanofi-Aventis later explored options to strike a fresh veterinary medicine joint venture by combining Merial with Intervet; however after a year of planning the two companies called off the deal in 2011 due to concerns over further anti-trust issues.)

The company experienced a sharp gain in profits in 2009 (reporting net income of $12.9 billion) due to gains on the sale of the Merial stake and on recognized equity from assets previously owned jointly with Schering-Plough.

When the Merck/Schering-Plough merger closed the existing Merck CEO Dick Clark took the helm at the new Merck. Once the dust from the merger settled however Clark retired from the CEO post at the end of 2010 while remaining as chairman. President Kenneth Frazier stepped into the CEO role.

EXECUTIVES

Evp; President Global Human Health, Kenneth C. (Ken) Frazier, age 64, $1,527,404 total compensation

Evp Strategic Communications Global Public Policy And Population Health And Chief Patient Officer, Julie L. Gerberding, age 64

Evp Global Services And Cfo, Robert M. Davis, age 52, $991,654 total compensation

Evp; President Merck Research Laboratories, Roger M. Perlmutter, age 66, $1,052,288 total compensation

Evp; President Global Human Health, Adam H. Schechter, age 55, $1,003,094 total compensation

Evp Human Resources, Mirian M. Graddick-Weir, age 65

Evp; President Merck Animal Health, Richard R. DeLuca, age 56

Evp And General Counsel, Michael J. Holston, age 56, $761,538 total compensation

Evp And Cio, Clark Golestani, age 52

Evp; President Merck Manufacturing, Sanat Chattopadhyay

Ceo Merck Foundation, Rasha Kelej, age 47

Vice President Human Resources And Global Diversity And Inclusion Center Excellence, Celeste Warren

Vice President, John Mccubbins

Vice President Biotechnology Development, Stephen Farrand

Vice President Manufacturing Division Strategy And Integration, Richard Hofmann

Vice President Global Compensation And Benefits, Jeff Geller

Vice President Global Engineering Services, Arthur Burson

Associate Medical Director, Lana Garafola

Associate Vice President, Curtis Scott

Legal Pa For Uk Director And Also Pa To The Assistant Vice President For Europe And Canada, Michele Creamer

National Sales Manager (turkey), Alper Alptekin

Senior Vice President Managing Director, Pierluigi Antonelli

Executive Vice President Process Solutions, Andrew Bulpin

Senior Vice President Strategy And Business Development, Galeota James

Associate Vice President Formulation Sciences, Nancy Agrawal

Vice President North America, Scott Bormann

Assistant Vice President Merck Consumer Care Information Technology, Fran Geatens

Vp Supply Chain, Francisco Toste

Avp Mmd Trade Compliance, Joseph Koerwer

Vice President, Susanna Webber

Vice President Commercial Operations, Hugo Nisenbom

Vice President Of Imaging, Jeffrey Evelhoch

Vice President Global Technical Operations Vaccines Biolog, Vijay Yabannavar

Senior Vice President Preclinical Development, Guy Padbury

Svp Global Regulatory Affairs And Clinical Safety, Sandra Milligan

Senior Vice President Tax, Jerome Mychalowych

Vice President, Pk Yegneswaran

Medical Director, Betty Malloy

Vice President, Patricia Hiley

Vice President Oncology, Ravinder Dhawan

National Account Manager, Carrie Westphal

Vp Corporate Communications, Jennifer Mauer

Vice President, Carmen Svillar

Executive Vice President Chief Human Resources Officer Human Resources, Steven Mizell

Medical Director Global Vaccine Medical Affairs, Chimeremma Md

National Account Manager, Brad Vines

Assistant Treasurer, Joe Promo

Assistant Treasurer, Joseph Promo

Board Member, Craig Thompson

Auditors: PricewaterhouseCoopers LLP

LOCATIONS

HQ: Merck & Co Inc
2000 Galloping Hill Road, Kenilworth, NJ 07033
Phone: 908 740-4000 **Fax:** 908 735-1500
Web: www.merck.com

2017 Sales

	$ mil.	% of total
US	17,424	43
Europe Middle East & Africa	11,478	29
Asia/Pacific	4,337	11
Japan	3,122	8
Latin America	2,339	6
Other	1,422	3
Total	**40,122**	**100**

PRODUCTS/OPERATIONS

2017 Sales by Segment

	$ mil.	% of total
Pharmaceutical		
Primary care & women's health	10,260	25
Hospital & specialty	7,546	19
Vaccines	6,159	15
Oncology	4,636	12
Diversified brands	2,494	6
Other	4,295	11
Other segments	4,272	11
Other	460	1
Total	**40,122**	**100**

COMPETITORS

Abbott Labs	Johnson & Johnson
Allergan plc	Merck KGaA
Amgen	Mylan
AstraZeneca	Novartis
Bayer AG	Perrigo
Biogen	Pfizer
Boehringer Ingelheim	Roche Holding
Bristol-Myers Squibb	Sandoz International
Eli Lilly	GmbH
Gilead Sciences	Sanofi
GlaxoSmithKline	Teva
Heska	Virbac Corporation

HISTORICAL FINANCIALS

Company Type: Public

Income Statement

FYE: December 31

	REVENUE ($ mil.)	NET INCOME ($ mil.)	NET PROFIT MARGIN	EMPLOYEES
12/18	42,294	6,220	14.7%	69,000
12/17	40,122	2,394	6.0%	69,000
12/16	39,807	3,920	9.8%	68,000
12/15	39,498	4,442	11.2%	68,000
12/14	42,237	11,920	28.2%	70,000
Annual Growth	**0.0%**	**(15.0%)**	**—**	**(0.4%)**

2018 Year-End Financials

Debt ratio: 30.00%—
Return on equity: 20.00%
Cash ($ mil.): 7,965
Current ratio: 1.00
Long-term debt ($ mil.): 19,806

Dividends
Yield: 3.0%
Payout: 86.0%
Market value ($ mil.): —

	STOCK PRICE ($) FY Close	P/E High/Low	PER SHARE ($) Earnings	Dividends	Book Value
12/18	76.00	34 23	2.00	2.00	10.00
12/17	56.00	76 61	1.00	2.00	13.00
12/16	59.00	46 34	1.00	2.00	15.00
12/15	53.00	40 31	2.00	2.00	16.00
12/14	57.00	15 12	4.00	2.00	17.00
Annual Growth	**7.7%**	**— —**	**(13.1%)**	**3.0%**	**(12.0%)**

Mercury General Corp.

Named after the Roman god of commerce and travel Mercury General hopes to combine the two and become the ultimate auto insurance provider. The company is the parent of a group of insurers including Mercury Casualty Company that write automobile insurance for all risk classifications in about a dozen states. Plain old private auto insurance accounts for a majority of premiums written. However Mercury General also sells commercial vehicle insurance and a bit of homeowners mechanical breakdown umbrella and fire insurance. The company is a leader in the California auto market and has significant operations in Florida.

Operations

Mercury General offers automobile insurance products including comprehensive collision property damage body injury personal injury protection underinsured/uninsured motorist and other coverage. It also provides homeowners' coverage including dwelling liability personal property fire and other products.

Private passenger automobile insurance accounts for some 75% of the company's premiums followed by homeowners insurance (around 15%). The rest comes from commercial auto insurance and other products.

Geographic Reach

While Mercury General has ventured out of its California comfort zone the state still accounts for about 85% of total premiums. The company operated solely in its home state until 1990; it now underwrites auto insurance in about a dozen other states including Arizona Florida Georgia Illinois Nevada New Jersey New York Oklahoma Texas and Virginia.

Sales and Marketing

Mercury General sells policies through approximately 10000 independent agents including around 2000 in California and another 1500 in Florida. It also owns insurance agencies AIS and PolicySeek and it sells coverage online.

The company uses television radio newspaper direct mail and online campaigns to market its products. Mercury General spent some $40 million on advertising in fiscal years 2018 2017 and 2016.

Financial Performance

Mercury General's revenue has been trending upward for the past few years with the exceptions of 2015 and 2018 when revenue slipped around 1%. The company's market share has declined as California's insurance sector has become saturated. Net income has been more volatile nearing $200 million in 2014 and entering the red in 2018.

In 2018 revenue fell 1% to $3.4 billion. That decline driven by net realized investment losses but partially offset by higher net premiums earned and net investment income. The company sold more policies in 2018 and it sold them at higher rates boosting overall sales.

Mercury General netted $144.9 million in 2017 but reported a loss of $5.7 million in 2018. That year the company recorded catastrophe losses of some $289 million primarily related to wildfires in Northern and Southern California. It also had weather-related losses in other states.

The company ended 2018 with $314.3 million in cash $23 million more than it had at the end of 2017. Operating activities provided $383.4 million while investing activities used $222.4 million and financing activities used another $138.1 million.

Strategy

Core to Mercury General's strategy for growth is managing rates to achieve the right balance between attracting customers through lower rates and remaining competitive. For example to counteract the overall increase in auto accidents the company has recently implemented price hikes.

The company also places value in its agent relationships and underwriting processes to achieve favorable margins. To encourage policy growth and broaden its customer base Mercury General offers multi-policy discounts to those who bundle their home and car insurance together. It also employs marketing initiatives to build brand recognition and generate leads.

Additionally Mercury General is gradually widening its operations by expanding into new states while being mindful of the risks of establishing new divisions. Mercury General also maintains a conservative investment strategy by maximizing long-term performance opportunities.

Company Background

Chairman George Joseph founded Mercury General in Los Angeles in 1962. Since it was established the company has paid out more than $20 billion in claims.

EXECUTIVES

Vp Underwriting, Kenneth G. Kitzmiller, age 72
President And Ceo, Gabriel Tirador, age 54, $948,931 total compensation
Svp And Cfo, Theodore R. Stalick, age 55, $589,445 total compensation
Vp And Chief Investment Officer, Christopher Graves, age 53, $381,679 total compensation
Vp And Chief Actuary, Charles Toney, age 57
Svp And Cio, Allan Lubitz, age 61, $449,470 total compensation
Vp And Chief Product Officer, Robert Houlihan, age 62, $404,493 total compensation
Vp Marketing, Brandt N. Minnich, age 52
Vice President Corporate Controller, David Yeager
Vp And Chief Human Capital Officer, Heidi Sullivan
Chairman, George Joseph, age 97
Auditors: KPMG LLP

LOCATIONS

HQ: Mercury General Corp.
4484 Wilshire Boulevard, Los Angeles, CA 90010
Phone: 323 937-1060
Web: www.mercuryinsurance.com

PRODUCTS/OPERATIONS

2018 Sales

	$ mil.	% of total
Net premiums earned	3,368	96
Net investment income	136	4
Other	9	-
Net realized investment losses	(133.5)	-
Total	**3,380**	**100**

Selected Products

Auto
  Commercial auto
  Mechanical breakdown (extended warranty coverage)
  Niche commercial
  Personal auto
Condo
  Contents coverage
  Guest medical protection and liability
  Personal liability protection
  Personal property
Homeowners
  Apartments
  Condominiums
  Single-family homes
Personal umbrella
Renter
  Liability protection
  Personal property

Selected Operating Brands and Divisions

AIS Management
American Mercury Insurance
American Mercury Lloyds Insurance
American Mercury MGA
Auto Insurance Specialists
California Automobile Insurance
California General Underwriters Insurance
Mercury Casualty
Mercury County Mutual Insurance
Mercury Group
Mercury Indemnity
Mercury Insurance
Mercury National Insurance
Mercury Select Management
PoliSeek AIS Insurance Solutions

COMPETITORS

21st Century Insurance	GEICO
Allstate	State Farm
Auto Club of Southern California	USAA
CSAA Inter-Insurance Bureau	

HISTORICAL FINANCIALS

Company Type: Public

Income Statement

FYE: December 31

	ASSETS ($ mil.)	NET INCOME ($ mil.)	INCOME AS % OF ASSETS	EMPLOYEES
12/18	5,434	(6)	—	4,400
12/17	5,101	145	2.8%	4,300
12/16	4,789	73	1.5%	4,200
12/15	4,629	74	1.6%	4,300
12/14	4,600	178	3.9%	4,400
Annual Growth	**4.3%**	—	—	**0.0%**

2018 Year-End Financials

Debt ratio: 7.00%	No. of shares (mil.): 55
Return on equity: (-0.00%)	Dividends
Cash ($ mil.): 314	Yield: 5.0%
Current ratio: —	Payout: —
Long-term debt ($ mil.): —	Market value ($ mil.): 2,862

	STOCK PRICE ($) FY Close	P/E High/Low	PER SHARE ($) Earnings	Dividends	Book Value
12/18	52.00	— —	(0.00)	3.00	29.00
12/17	53.00	24 20	3.00	2.00	32.00
12/16	60.00	46 33	1.00	2.00	32.00
12/15	47.00	45 34	1.00	2.00	33.00
12/14	57.00	18 13	3.00	2.00	34.00
Annual Growth	**(2.3%)**	—	—	**0.4%**	**(3.7%)**

MERCY HEALTH

Mercy Health formerly known as the Sisters of Mercy Health System provides a range of health care and social services through its network of facilities and service organizations. The organization operates some 35 acute care hospitals (including four specialty heart hospitals and two children's hospitals) with more than 4200 licensed beds as well as 700 clinics and outpatient facilities in four Midwestern states. Its hospital groups include facilities for nursing homes medical practices and outpatient centers. Mercy Health also operates Resource Optimization & Innovation (ROi) its industry-leading health care supply chain organization and health outreach organizations in Louisiana Mississippi and Texas.

Operations

Mercy Health also operates three rehabilitation hospitals and two orthopedic hospitals. The system has more than 2000 Mercy Clinic physicians.

In 2014 Mercy Health had 150696 acute inpatient discharges; 158911 inpatient and outpatient surgeries; 631444 emergency department visits; 23213 births; and nearly 8.4 million outpatient visits.

Geographic Reach

The system operates in Arkansas Kansas Missouri and Oklahoma.

Mercy Health's outreach efforts include Mercy Ministries of Laredo a group providing primary health care and social services to residents of Laredo Texas. In New Orleans Mercy Health sponsors Mercy Family Center which provides mental health services; in Mississippi it funds a health care advocacy group.

Sales and Marketing

Commercial and other third-party payments accounted for 44% of net patient service revenue while Medicare and Medicaid combined accounted for 51%.

Financial Performance

Mercy Health's operating revenue increased 14% to $4.5 billion in 2014 as net patient and other revenues grew. However the system reported a net loss of $6.5 million that year (versus net income in 2013) as a result of interest rate swap agreement losses and higher expenses as well as lower investment earnings.

Cash flow from operations fell 46% to $354 million in 2014.

Strategy

In 2013 Mercy Health opened new facilities in Missouri (St. Charles and Wentzville) as well as a new heart and vascular center that centralized its outpatient heart and vascular offerings. The following year it opened a new orthopedic hospital in Fort Smith and a 60-bed rehabilitation hospital.

The system acquired Lincoln County Medical Center (renamed Mercy Hospital Lincoln) and its eight affiliated clinics in 2015 expanding its presence in eastern Missouri.

Despite its various expansions the Mercy system experienced the same industry challenges as its health care brethren including escalating medical and pharmaceutical costs and increasing self-pay bad debts (uninsured patients who leave their medical bills unpaid). Several of the health system's facilities have seen a decline in discharges.

Company Background

The organization was founded by the Sisters of Mercy of the St. Louis Regional Community in 1986 and operated under that model until 2008 when its sponsorship was transferred from the Sisters of Mercy of the St. Louis Regional Community to a new entity Mercy Health Ministry. The shift to the new sponsorship organization was made to allow lay members to join the Sisters of Mercy in sponsoring the ministry. It also reflected the growing number of lay people holding executive positions at the system's hospitals and on the board of directors.

EXECUTIVES

Pres-Ceo, Lynn Britton
Evp-Coo*, Michael McCurry
Evp-Cfo*, Shannon Sock
Vp of Information, Mike Mc Creary
Vp of Operations, Mike Mc Curry
Health Professional, Lora Petty
Chief Information Security Off, David Westman
Chief of Medicine, Edson Carrel
Information, Jon Allen
Project Manager Information Sy, Adam Williams
Vp For Audiology, Amanda Moore
Auditors: ERNST & YOUNG LLP ST LOUIS

LOCATIONS

HQ: MERCY HEALTH
 14528 SOUTH OUTER 40 RD # 100, CHESTERFIELD, MO 630175743
Phone: 314 579-6100

Selected Locations

Arkansas
 Berryville
 Fort Smith
 Hot Springs
 Ozark
 Paris
 Rogers
 Waldron

Kansas
 Columbus
 Fort Scott
 Independence

Missouri
 Aurora
 Cassville
 Joplin
 Lebanon
 Mountain View
 St. Louis
 Springfield
 Washington

Oklahoma
 Ada
 Ardmore
 El Reno
 Guthrie
 Healdton
 Kingfisher
 Marietta
 Oklahoma City
 Tishomingo
 Watonga

PRODUCTS/OPERATIONS

2014 Sales

	$ mil.	% of total
Net patient service revenue less provision for bad debts	3,838	85
Member revenue	477	11
Other revenue	195	4
Total	**4,510**	**100**

Selected Facilities

Arkansas
 Mercy Hospital Berryville
 Mercy Hospital Fort Smith
 Mercy Hospital Hot Springs
 Mercy Hospital Northwest Arkansas
 Mercy Hospital of Scott County
 Mercy Hospital Ozark
 Mercy Hospital Paris
 Mercy Hospital Waldron
Kansas
 Mercy Health Center
 Mercy Hospital Fort Scott
 Mercy Hospital Independence
 Mercy Maude Norton Hospital Columbus
Missouri
 Mercy Hospital Aurora
 Mercy Hospital Cassville
 Mercy Hospital Joplin
 Mercy Hospital Lebanon
 Mercy Hospital St. Louis
 Mercy Children's Hospital St. Louis
 Mercy Heart and Vascular Hospital St. Louis
 Mercy Heart Hospital St. Louis
 Mercy Rehabilitation Hospital St. Louis
 Mercy Hospital Springfield
 Mercy Children's Hospital Springfield
 Mercy Hospital Washington
 Mercy McCune-Brooks Hospital
 Mercy St. Francis Hospital
Oklahoma
 Arbuckle Memorial Hospital
 Mercy Health Love County
 Mercy Hospital Ardmore
 Mercy Hospital El Reno

Mercy Hospital Healdton
Mercy Hospital Logan County
Mercy Hospital Oklahoma City
Mercy Hospital - Tishomingo
Valley View Regional Hospital
Watonga Municipal Hospital

COMPETITORS

Ascension Health
BJC HealthCare
Baptist Health
 (Arkansas)
Barnes-Jewish Hospital
CHRISTUS Health
Christian Hospital
Community Health
 Systems
CoxHealth
HCA
INTEGRIS Health
Memorial Hospital
 (Illinois)
RehabCare

SSM Health Care
Saint Luke's Health
 System
Shawnee Mission
 Medical Center
Sisters of Charity of
 Leavenworth
St. Anthony's Medical
 Center
St. Vincent Health
 System
Tenet Healthcare
Universal Health
 Services

HISTORICAL FINANCIALS

Company Type: Private

Income Statement

	REVENUE ($ mil.)	NET INCOME ($ mil.)	NET PROFIT MARGIN	FYE: June 30 EMPLOYEES
06/18	6,254	244	3.9%	8,800
06/17	5,528	558	10.1%	—
06/10*	19	7	38.4%	—
03/09	2,936	(196)		—
Annual Growth	**8.8%**	**—**	**—**	**—**

*Fiscal year change

Meridian Bancorp Inc

Meridian Bancorp is the holding company of East Boston Savings Bank which provides standard deposit and lending services to individuals and businesses in the greater Boston area. The bank writes single-family commercial and multi-family mortgages as well as construction and business loans and consumer loans. East Boston Savings operates about 30 branches in eastern Massachusetts. Mutual holding company Meridian Financial Services owns 59% of Meridian Bancorp.

EXECUTIVES

Cfo And Treasurer, Mark L. Abbate, age 64
Svp Consumer And Business Banking, Keith D. Armstrong
Chairman President And Ceo Meridian Interstate Bancorp And East Boston Savings Bank, Richard J. Gavegnano, age 71, $311,400 total compensation
Evp Corporate Banking, Frank Romano
Evp Lending, John Migliozzi
Evp And Coo, John A. Carroll
Svp Electronic Banking, Mary Hagen
Svp Retail Banking, James Morgan
Svp Residential Lending, Joseph Nash
Vice President, Michael Raftery
Auditors: Wolf & Company, P.C.

LOCATIONS

HQ: Meridian Bancorp Inc
 67 Prospect Street, Peabody, MA 01960
Phone: 617 567-1500

Selected Locations
Allpoint Locator
Allston
Belmont
Cambridge
Danvers
Dorchester
East Boston
Everett
Jamaica Plain
Lynn
Medford
Melrose
Peabody
Revere
Saugus
Somerville
South Boston
South End
Wakefield
West Roxbury
Winthrop

PRODUCTS/OPERATIONS

2015 Sales

	$ mil.	% of total
Interest & dividend income		
Interest & fees on loans	119	87
Interest on debt securities	2	1
Dividends on equity securities	2	1
Others	1	1
Non-interest income		
Customer service fees	8	6
Gain on sales of securities net	2	2
Income from bank-owned life insurance	1	1
Loan fees	1	1
Mortgage banking gains & other income	1	-
Total	**136**	**100**

Selected Products & Services

Personal
  Deposit Rates
  Investments
  Personal Checking
  Personal Lending
  Personal Online Banking
  Retirement Services
  Savings & CDs
Business
  Business Checking
  Business Lending
  Business Online Banking
  Business Retirement Services
  Business Savings
  Deposit Rates
  Institutional Banking
  Merchant Services
Commercial
  Cash Management
  Commercial Lending
  Corporate Banking
  Deposit Rates

COMPETITORS

Bank of America
Cambridge Financial
Citizens Financial
  Group
Eastern Bank

Middlesex Savings
Peoples Federal
  Bancshares Inc.
Sovereign Bank
TD Bank USA

HISTORICAL FINANCIALS
Company Type: Public

Income Statement				FYE: December 31
	ASSETS ($ mil.)	NET INCOME ($ mil.)	INCOME AS % OF ASSETS	EMPLOYEES
12/18	6,179	56	0.9%	549
12/17	5,299	43	0.8%	538
12/16	4,436	34	0.8%	500
12/15	3,525	25	0.7%	488
12/14	3,279	22	0.7%	466
Annual Growth	17.2%	25.7%	—	4.2%

2018 Year-End Financials

Debt ratio: 9.00%
Return on equity: 8.00%
Cash ($ mil.): 377
Current ratio: —
Long-term debt ($ mil.): —

No. of shares (mil.): 54
Dividends
  Yield: 2.0%
  Payout: 22.0%
Market value ($ mil.): 767

	STOCK PRICE ($) FY Close	P/E High/Low	Earnings	PER SHARE ($) Dividends	Book Value
12/18	14.00	20 13	1.00	0.00	13.00
12/17	21.00	25 19	1.00	0.00	12.00
12/16	19.00	29 19	1.00	0.00	11.00
12/15	14.00	31 24	0.00	0.00	11.00
12/14	11.00	27 24	0.00	0.00	11.00
Annual Growth	6.3%	—	26.0%	—	4.5%

Meta Financial Group Inc

Delivering financial products and services to Iowa and South Dakota is the calling of Meta Financial Group. The group's biggest component is MetaBank a 10-branch operation that offers standard banking solutions such as deposit accounts CDs home mortgages and student loans. Other subsidiaries provide prepaid card services insurance and a variety of tax related solutions. It holds a loan portfolio that exceeds $1 billion and deposits that surpass $3 billion.

Operations

Meta Financial Group operates two customer-facing business segments Banking and Payments and a supporting segment that includes corporate services and other sources of revenue. The Banking segment generates the majority of interest income and a small amount of non-interest income. The Payments unit is the opposite where non-interest income accounts for 90% of its overall revenue and interest income is less than 10% of its business.

The Banking unit doing business as MetaBank operates 10 branches in four key geographic markets: Central Iowa Storm Lake Iowa Brookings South Dakota and Sioux Falls South Dakota. It offers standard deposit products and services including checking and savings accounts. Its lending and investment activities are weighted towards real estate and real estate-related assets; commercial and multifamily residential mortgages comprise more than half of the bank's loan portfolio. It also writes single-family residential mortgages and business loans.

Meta Financial's bread and butter however is the bank's Meta Payment Systems (MPS) division which provides prepaid cards consumer credit and ATM sponsorship services nationwide under operating names of MPS Refund Advantage EPS Financial and SCS. The segment has grown primarily through acquisitions.

Geographic Reach

The MetaBank subsidiary of Sioux Falls SD-based Meta Financial Group operates mainly in Iowa and South Dakota. Its Payment segment includes subsidiaries that run business out of Dallas TX Newport Beach CA Louisville KY Easton PA and Hurst TX.

Financial Performance

Non-interest income from the Payments business grew more than 70% in the year to $166 million. Interest income from the Bank segment rose 37% to $52 million. Total revenue for 2017 was $265 million. The stellar growth is the result of acquisitions and organic growth ? the Bank unit acquired $134 million of private student loans in late 2016 and a further $73 million portfolio in late 2017. The Payment business grew its tax refund business 13-fold underwriting and originating $1.3 billion of refund advance loans for the 2017 tax season.

Net income in 2017 rose 33% to $45 million thanks to the significant upswing in Payments revenue including big growth in its tax business along with improvements in card fee income.

Strategy

Meta Financial Group is looking to boost is non-interest income business endeavors in the Payments division. It feels constrained in its banking business by the need to raise more capital before it can lend out more money from which it would generate interest income. Without the ability to raise more capital (or to raise it at an advantageous cost) the Group believes its efforts are better directed at growth that is not hindered by insufficient capital.

EXECUTIVES

Chairman And Ceo Meta Financial Group And Metabank, J. Tyler Haahr, age 56, $550,000 total compensation
Evp Sales And Operations Metabank And Director Meta Financial Group (mfg) And Metabank, Troy Moore, age 51, $252,350 total compensation
Evp Secretary Treasurer And Cfo, David W. Leedom, age 65, $215,000 total compensation
President Meta Financial Group Inc. (mfg) And Metabank And Division President Meta Payment System, Bradley C. (Brad) Hanson, age 55, $550,000 total compensation
Evp Meta Payment Systems, Scott Galit, age 49, $235,000 total compensation
Evp And Cfo Meta Financial Group (mfg) And Metabank, Glen W. Herrick, age 56, $255,000 total compensation
Vice Chairman Meta Financial Group (mfg) And Metabank, Frederick V. (Fred) Moore, age 63
Auditors: Crowe LLP

LOCATIONS

HQ: Meta Financial Group Inc
  5501 South Broadband Lane, Sioux Falls, SD 57108
Phone: 605 782-1767
Web: www.metabank.com

COMPETITORS

Blackhawk Network
Bofl
Citi Prepaid Services
First National of
  Nebraska

Great Western Bancorp
Green Dot
HF Financial
West Bancorporation

HISTORICAL FINANCIALS
Company Type: Public

Income Statement				FYE: September 30
	ASSETS ($ mil.)	NET INCOME ($ mil.)	INCOME AS % OF ASSETS	EMPLOYEES
09/19	6,183	97	1.6%	1,186
09/18	5,835	52	0.9%	1,219
09/17	5,228	45	0.9%	827
09/16	4,006	33	0.8%	672
09/15	2,530	18	0.7%	638
Annual Growth	25.0%	52.2%	—	16.8%

2019 Year-End Financials

Debt ratio: 2.00%
Return on equity: 12.00%
Cash ($ mil.): 127
Current ratio: —
Long-term debt ($ mil.): —

No. of shares (mil.): 38
Dividends
Yield: 1.0%
Payout: 9.0%
Market value ($ mil.): 1,233

	STOCK PRICE ($) FY Close	P/E High/Low		PER SHARE ($)		
			Earnings	Dividends	Book Value
09/19	33.00	33 7	2.00	0.00	22.00
09/18	83.00	70 46	2.00	0.00	19.00
09/17	78.00	66 39	2.00	0.00	15.00
09/16	61.00	47 28	1.00	0.00	13.00
09/15	42.00	59 36	1.00	0.00	11.00
Annual Growth	(6.0%)	— —	29.5%	3.6%	19.0%

MetLife Inc

While its name evolved from "metropolitan" MetLife's policies are found in villages towns and huge cities around the world. Its companies offer life accident and health insurance as well as retirement and savings products around the world. The group is a big force in Japan and growing in more than 50 other countries especially in Latin America. It distributes its products to retail corporate and government customers through agents third-party distributors including banks and brokers and direct marketing channels. About half of its revenue comes from the US but in mid-2017 MetLife split off much of its US life business.

Operations

MetLife is organized into five primary segments: US; Latin America; Asia; Europe the Middle East and Africa (EMEA); and MetLife Holdings. Certain results are also reported in the operations of the Corporate & Other segment including MetLife Home Loans. The US segment is MetLife's largest accounting for about half of total sales. Asia accounts for nearly 20% of revenue and Latin America and EMEA each account for more than 5%. MetLife Holdings brings in more than 15% of revenue.

In the US MetLife provides a range of insurance and financial services offerings including renewable term life property/casualty disability dental guaranteed interest and annuities. These are distributed through both in-house and independent retail channels and in the workplace. Internationally the company provides life accident medical dental credit and other insurance as well as annuities and other retirement and savings products to individuals and groups.

MetLife Holdings comprises businesses no longer actively promoted in the US including variable life and universal life products term and whole life products and annuities. It also includes the group's discontinued long-term care business.

Geographic Reach

MetLife operates in the Americas and Asia and in Europe the Middle East and Africa (EMEA). In Latin America it operates in Argentina Brazil Chile Colombia Ecuador Uruguay and Mexico (with the bulk of regional revenues coming from Mexico and Chile).

The company does business in about 10 countries in Asia with its largest operations in Japan. It has an innovation center in Singapore (it is testing an automated insurance solution using blockchain and electronic medical records) and a data analytics center in Malaysia. It also does business in Australia Bangladesh Hong Kong and Nepal and

through a joint venture in China Korea India Malaysia and Vietnam.

MetLife is active in more than 25 countries across EMEA. The segment's biggest operations are in the UK the Persian Gulf Poland and Turkey.

Sales and Marketing

MetLife's policies and other products are sold to some 100 million customers through a vast network of targeted marketing and sales forces financial advisors consultants agency distribution groups captive agents independent agents affiliated broker-dealers and direct marketing (including direct response television web-based lead generation telemarketing and print media). In addition MetLife sells some products through affinity groups and through employers.

Financial Performance

MetLife's revenue peaked at $73.3 billion in 2014 but has been been somewhat lower (above $60 billion) since then. Net income has been fluctuating reaching $6.3 billion in 2014 but falling to $850 million in 2016. The company's cash levels have also fluctuated recently.

In 2017 revenue increased 3% to $62.3 billion. Growth in the retirement and income solutions business and the group benefits business drove that increase. International sales also rose overall. Midway through the year MetLife spun much of its US life and annuity operations which resulted in a decline in those revenue lines.

Net income rose 371% to $4 billion in 2017. A number of factors led to that jump including favorable changes in discontinued operations and a $1.3 billion benefit related to US tax reform.

The company ended 2017 with $12.7 billion in net cash some $5 billion less than it had at the end of 2016. Operating activities provided $12.3 billion while investing activities used $16.9 billion and financing activities used $906 million.

Strategy

In 2017 MetLife spun off much of its US retail operations into a new company named Brighthouse Financial. Its MetLife Insurance Company USA Metropolitan Tower Life Insurance Company General American Life Insurance Company (which is being merged into Metropolitan Tower Life) and several other units were included in the transaction which took the form of an initial public offering. Together those units represented about 20% of MetLife's total earnings.

MetLife's move to divest part of its core operations came in the wake of the financial crisis and subsequent changes in the regulatory landscape. US regulators had designated MetLife one of four non-bank systemically important financial institutions (meaning it would pose a risk to the economy if it should collapse) but MetLife fought the designation winning its case in a federal court in 2016. Regardless the separation of its US life insurance business should calm any unrest over the group's size. The newly created company also benefits from having a lower capital and compliance burden.

In another divestiture in mid-2016 MassMutual bought MetLife's US retail captive agency distribution channel MetLife Premier Client Group and broker dealer MetLife Securities. (US retail businesses that were not sold in the deal included the closed-block life insurance property/casualty and Metropolitan Life Insurance Company's life and annuity operations.)

These moves were not the first major shufflings of MetLife's operations in recent years. It is exiting the bulk of its banking operations to avoid the increased scrutiny of banks under Dodd-Frank financial regulations. The company is working to surrender its status as a bank holding company. It has already sold its MetLife Bank depository operations and has stopped writing new residential mortgages and reverse mortgages.

Going forward MetLife plans to focus on pension and retirement products insurance sold to employers and non-US life insurance. In a shift away from market-sensitive products it will only invest in businesses that have strong rates of return require less capital and offer a higher ratio of free cash flow to operating earnings. The company has pinned much of its growth efforts on emerging markets by increasing its already-strong presence in the Asia/Pacific region and in Latin America through acquisitions and new product introductions. To support this growth the company has organized its operations along geographic lines: US; Latin America; Asia; and Europe the Middle East and Africa (EMEA).

Other strategic areas of focus include creating a high-performance operation with competitive prices transforming distribution channels (especially through digital means) and connecting customers with the most appropriate products and services.

Some of the individual and group products MetLife sells overseas include life insurance accident and health insurance credit insurance and annuities and retirement products. It has also created a global employee benefits business to reach into new markets. To focus on core international businesses Metlife has been selling off select foreign assets.

Mergers and Acquisitions

In 2017 MetLife acquired Logan Circle Partners from Fortress Investment Group for some $250 million. Logan was the traditional fixed income asset management business of Fortress; it serves institutional investors and has more than $33 billion in assets under management. The purchase helped expand MetLife's investment management business for third-party customers.

Company Background

Metropolitan Life Insurance was established as a stock company in 1868. It became a mutual company (owned by its policyholders) in 1915. Starting off serving mutual assistance societies for German immigrants the company began offering auto and homeowners insurance in 1974 and entered the life insurance and annuities business in the 1980s.

HISTORY

New York merchant Simeon Draper tried to form National Union Life and Limb Insurance to cover Union soldiers in the Civil War but investors were scared away by heavy casualties. After several reorganizations and name changes the enterprise emerged in 1868 as Metropolitan Life Insurance (MetLife) a stock company.

Sustained at first by business from mutual assistance societies for German immigrants MetLife went into industrial insurance with workers' burial policies. The firm was known for its aggressive sales methods. Agents combed working-class neighborhoods collecting small premiums. If a worker missed one payment the company could cancel the policy and keep all premiums paid a practice outlawed in 1900.

MetLife became a mutual company (owned by its policyholders) in 1915 and began offering group insurance two years later.

After a period of conservative management under the Eckers family from 1929 to 1963 MetLife began to change dropping industrial insurance in 1964. It started offering auto and homeowners insurance in 1974.

To diversify the company bought State Street Research & Management (1983) Century 21 Real Estate (1985 sold 1995) London-based Albany Life Assurance (1985) and Allstate's group life and health business (1988). In 1987 it took over the annuities segment of the failed Baldwin United Co. and expanded into Spain and Taiwan in 1988.

During the early 1990s MetLife reemphasized insurance adding such new products as long-term-care insurance.

EXECUTIVES

Evp And Global Chief Marketing Officer, Esther Lee

Chairman President And Ceo, Steven A. (Steve) Kandarian, age 67, $1,525,000 total compensation

Evp And Cfo, John C. R. Hele, age 61, $781,250 total compensation

Evp Global Employee Benefits, Maria R. Morris, age 56, $525,000 total compensation

Evp And General Counsel, Ricardo A. Anzaldua

Evp Chief Investment Officer And Interim President Metlife Asia, Steven J. Goulart, age 60, $725,000 total compensation

President Us, Michel Khalaf, $476,313 total compensation

Evp Global Technology And Operations And Metlife Holdings, Martin J. (Marty) Lippert, $756,250 total compensation

Managing Director Institutional Client Group, Thomas Metzler

Ceo Metlife Hong Kong, Lee Wood

Vice President Of Information Technology, Jeff Seltzer

Vice President Learning And Development, John Wiltshire

Vp Itg Vendor Mgmt Sourcing, Elizabeth Langone

Svp And Chief Administrative Officer Global Technology And Operations, Mona Moazzaz

Regional Vice President Northeast Region, Joe Heaney

Vice President Information Technology, Maryann Prudente

Vice President Human Resources, Doris Jackson

Vice President Information Technology, Annette Fugina

Vice President Risk Management, Richard Barquist

Senior Vice President Marketing Planning, James Valentino

Vice President Information Technology, Marcella Kelly

Assistant Vice President, George Klisures

Vice President Global Information Security Officer, Jesus L Montano

Vice President Of Technology, Linus Makhulo

Vice President, Andrew Aoyama

Vice President And Actuary, Enid Reichert

Vp, Curt Breckon

Vice President, Michele Brooks

Sec Reporting Assistant Vice President, Matt Gominiak

Assistant Vice President, Gary Glacken

Vice President Information Technology, Neil Melleky

Vice President Information Technology, Alvin Sheinheit

Vice President, Peter Pastre

Vice President Information Technology, Tom Kelly

Vice President And Chief Privacy Officer, Joseph Trovato

Distribution Vp, Pam Blalock

Vice President, Bob Broseker

Vice President, Larry Martin

Vice President Information Technology, Roderick Pasqualicchio

Assistant Vice President, Robert Lynch

Vice President Actuary, Marian Zeldin

Vice President, Jamie Granese

Regional Sales Vice President, Scott Safranek

Vice President, Guy Lawrence

Vice President, Randy Stram

Assistant Vice President And Actuary, Jonathan Trend

Assistant Vice President, John Gilmore

Medical Director, Charles Arnold

Vice President, Rose Wolf

Evp Global Corporate Services Global Technology And Operations, Joe Sprouls

Vice President Of Application Development, Jack Rooney

Vice President Human Resources, Lynne Distasio

Vice President And Actuary, James Reilly

Assistant Vice President, Gladys Rosetta

Regional Vice President, Brenda Perkins

Vice President Life And Income Funding Solutions, Tim Brown

Vice President, Michael Nardone

Vice President, Harry Xiao

Assistant Vice President, Andy Vigar

Assistant Vice President, Robert Bean

Vice President And Actuary, Douglas Kudler

Regional Vice President Broker Dealer Group, Orv Mohler

Vice President, Santhosh Aravindakshan

Assistant Vice President, Crystal Mcelroy

Vice President Information Technology Infrastructu, Gail Weimer

Regional Sales Vice President, Michael Casimiro

Assistant Vice President, Patricia Wersching

Vice President, Bob Linzey

Vice President Global Operations, Lisa Pang

Vice President Information Technology International Asia Pacific Region, Nancy Perez-Vasquez

Vice President Retirement Plans, Bill Slater

Vice President Corporate Information Technology Security D, Steve Vnuck

Svp Global Talent Processes And Organizational Effectiveness, Rachel Lee

Vice President Life Product Development, Bobby Samuelson

Vice President Of Information Technology, Ron Gillmore

Vice President Actuary, Jill Garofalo

Assistant Vice President, Betty Dubuisson

Vice President, Don Anderson Don Anderson

Assistant Vice President Cloud Engineering, Lance Roller

Executive Vice President, Todd Katz

Regional Sales Vice President, Shaun Seales

Vice President, Ignazio Greco

Vice President Global Internal Audit, Carlos Mendez

Vice President Operations Governance Strategy, Pamela Hallagan

Vice President Actuary, Laura Vazquez

Vp And Associate General Counsel, Nancy Badeer

Regional Sales Vice President, Ed Wustefeld

Assistant Vice President, Amie Donahue

Assistant Vice President Enterprise Strategy Group, Kevin Chean

Vice President, Nancy Davenport

Vice President Disability And Absence Practice Leader, Phil Bruen

Vice President, Robert Klahre

Vice President Capital Strategy Planning, Kevin Mackay

Assistant Vice President And Actuary, Barbara Stroz

Assistant Vice President, Basha Hoffman

Regional Sales Vice President, Stacey Waite

Vice President, Michael Evenzwig

Vice President Finance Principal, John Wiede

Svp And Head Mergers And Acquisitions, Adam Hodes

Regional Sales Vice President, Steve Shrout

Senior Vice President Executive And Global Compensation, Kathryn Kessel

Vice President Of Retail Marketing, Matthew Quale

Regional Sales Vice President, Derrik Bullen

Senior Vice President Investments And Br, Anthony Colyandro

Vp Head Of Health And Wellness, Leena Johns

Regional Sales Vice President, Tony Nguyen

Vice President, Emilia Kyff

Regional Sales Vice President, Chris Bunting

Vice President, George Bell

Assistant Vice President And Actuary Financial Research, William Chirolas

Regional Sales Vice President, Michelle Perez

Regional Sales Vice President, Nancy Power

Vice President Investments Controller, David Rooney

Senior Vice President And Associate General Counsel, Lawrence Wolff

Second Vice President, Mark Remington

Vice President, James Donnellan

Vice President, Chris Stern

Assistant Vice President, John Zelinske

Vice President, Lise Hasegawa

Assistant Vice President, Share Winn

Senior Vice President, Joseph Reali

Vice President Human Resources, Stuart Cook

Vice President Operations, John Abela

Assistant Vice President Individual Disability Underwriting, Rod Boggs

Regional Sales Vice President, Jan Primmer

Assistant Vice President Information Technology, Paul Mattern

Regional Sales Vice President, Sarah Kim

Senior Vice President, Debra Capolarello

Svp Global Shared Services India, Kush Kamra

Avp Global Product, Mira Shastry

Avp Global Strategy, Suresh Gunupure

Vice President Workforce Enablement Glob, Kate Day

Vice President, Arthur Bruhmuller

Assistant Vice President, Jai Maxwell

Assisttant Vice President Growth Strategies, Tina Beckwith

Vice President Information Technology, Leonard Kasendorf

Vice President, Marc Cohn

Vice President Sales And Marketing, Suzanne Andrews

Vice President Information Technology Services, Bob Levin

Vice President Global Technology, Ed Evans

Vice President, Melissa Grady

Associate Vice President Enterprise Security, Satin Montano

Vice President, Dennis Gates

Vice President, Alexander Beauchamp

Vice President Executive Learning And Development, Mara Jane

Vice President, Gary Hediger

Assistant Vice President Of Enterprise Security, Laz Montano

Vice President Director Fund Administration, Alan Otis

Regional Vice President Agency Asia Pacific, Stephen Zhang

Senior Vice President, Frank Cassandra

Assistant Vice President And Actuary Actuarial, Simone Chen

Auditors: Deloitte & Touche LLP

LOCATIONS

HQ: MetLife Inc
200 Park Avenue, New York, NY 10166-0188
Phone: 212 578-9500
Web: www.metlife.com

2017 Sales by Segment

	$ mil.	% of total
US	31,810	50
Asia	11,875	19
MetLife Holding	11,005	17
Latin America	5,118	8
EMEA	3,729	6
Adjustments	(1229)	-
Total	**62,308**	**100**

PRODUCTS/OPERATIONS

2017 Sales

	$ mil.	% of total
Premiums	38,992	62
Net investment income	17,363	27
Universal life & investment-type product policy fees	5,510	9
Other	1,341	2
Adjustments	898	–
Total	**62,308**	**100**

Selected Subsidiaries and Affiliates

American Life Insurance Co. (ALICO)
General American Life Insurance Company
Hyatt Legal Plans Inc. (prepaid legal plans)
MetLife Funding Inc.
MetLife Insurance Company USA
MetLife Investors Group Inc. (distribution)
Metropolitan Property and Casualty Insurance Company
New England Life Insurance Company

COMPETITORS

AEGON USA	Liberty Mutual
AIG	MassMutual
AXA	Meiji Yasuda Life
Aetna	Mutual of Omaha
Allianz	Nationwide
Allstate	New York Life
American General	Nippon Life Insurance
Aon	Northwestern Mutual
COUNTRY Financial	Pacific Mutual
Genworth Financial	Prudential
Guardian Life	TIAA
ING	The Hartford
John Hancock Financial Services	

HISTORICAL FINANCIALS

Company Type: Public

Income Statement
FYE: December 31

	ASSETS ($ mil.)	NET INCOME ($ mil.)	INCOME AS % OF ASSETS	EMPLOYEES
12/18	687,538	5,123	0.7%	48,000
12/17	719,892	4,010	0.6%	49,000
12/16	898,764	800	0.1%	58,000
12/15	877,933	5,310	0.6%	69,000
12/14	902,337	6,309	0.7%	68,000
Annual Growth	**(6.6%)**	**(5.1%)**	**—**	**(8.3%)**

2018 Year-End Financials

Debt ratio: 2.00%
Return on equity: 9.00%
Cash ($ mil.): 15,821
Current ratio: —
Long-term debt ($ mil.): —

No. of shares (mil.): 959
Dividends
  Yield: 4.0%
  Payout: 34.0%
Market value ($ mil.): 39,361

	STOCK PRICE ($) FY Close	P/E High/Low		PER SHARE ($) Earnings	Dividends	Book Value
12/18	41.00	11	8	5.00	2.00	55.00
12/17	51.00	15	13	4.00	2.00	56.00
12/16	54.00	91	56	1.00	2.00	61.00
12/15	48.00	13	10	5.00	1.00	62.00
12/14	54.00	10	9	5.00	1.00	64.00
Annual Growth	**(6.7%)**	**—**	**—**	**(2.4%)**	**5.8%**	**(3.6%)**

METROPOLITAN TRANSPORTATION AUTHORITY

The largest public transportation system in the US New York City's Metropolitan Transportation Authority (MTA) provides about 2.6 billion passenger trips and sees about 380 million vehicles travel its system annually. The MTA's largest agency the New York City Transit Authority operates about 8700 rail and subway cars that provide service across New York's five boroughs; it also runs a fleet of some 5900 buses. Other MTA units offer bus and rail service to Connecticut and Long Island and operate the Triborough system of toll bridges and tunnels.

Strategy
The government-owned MTA a public-benefit corporation chartered by the New York Legislature in 1965 operates with an annual budget of $12.6 billion. The system has been working to become more self-sufficient in recent years but it has battled persistent operating losses brought on by among other causes high operating costs and the struggling US economy. In an attempt to reduce its expenses the company in 2010 cut payroll by 20% at its headquarters and 15% at other agencies. The MTA has also bolstered its revenue through increased fares and tolls and freed up capital by restructuring its debt at lower interest rates.

While it is making cuts in some areas the MTA is investing in capital improvements to its system including extending the Long Island Rail Road to Grand Central Station and creating a direct link between John F. Kennedy Airport and downtown Manhattan. Other key projects have included the construction of the Second Avenue Subway and renovations at the Fulton Street Transit Center. The MTA also is looking at installing wireless Internet access on its Metro-North and Long Island rail lines' trains.

EXECUTIVES

Cfo, Robert E. (Bob) Foran
Executive Officer Corporate Communications Marketing And Branding, John McKay
Director Security, Raymond Diaz
Coo, Phil Eng
Interim Executive Director, Veronique Hakim
President Mta Bridges And Tunnels, Cedrick Fulton
Chairman, Joseph J. Lhota
Auditors: DELOITTE & TOUCHE LLP NEW YOR

LOCATIONS

HQ: METROPOLITAN TRANSPORTATION AUTHORITY
2 BROADWAY BSMT B, NEW YORK, NY 100043354
Phone: 212 878-7000

PRODUCTS/OPERATIONS

Selected Operations

Bus
  Long Island Bus
  MTA Bus Company
  New York City Transit
Commuter Rail
  Long Island Rail Road
  Metro-North Railroad
  Staten Island Railway

HISTORICAL FINANCIALS

Company Type: Private

Income Statement
FYE: December 31

	REVENUE ($ mil.)	NET INCOME ($ mil.)	NET PROFIT MARGIN	EMPLOYEES
12/18	8,736	(145)	—	67,457
12/17	9	(1)	—	—
12/16	8,527	(271)	—	—
12/15	8,408	370	4.4%	—
Annual Growth	**1.3%**	**—**	**—**	**—**

Metropolitan Bank Holding Corp

Auditors: Crowe LLP

LOCATIONS

HQ: Metropolitan Bank Holding Corp
  99 Park Avenue, New York, NY 10016
Phone: 212 659-0600
Web: www.metropolitanbankny.com

HISTORICAL FINANCIALS

Company Type: Public

Income Statement
FYE: December 31

	ASSETS ($ mil.)	NET INCOME ($ mil.)	INCOME AS % OF ASSETS	EMPLOYEES
12/18	2,183	26	1.2%	153
12/17	1,760	12	0.7%	129
12/16	1,220	5	0.4%	118
12/15	965	4	0.4%	—
Annual Growth	**31.3%**	**81.6%**	**—**	**—**

2018 Year-End Financials

Debt ratio: 1.00%
Return on equity: 10.00%
Cash ($ mil.): 233
Current ratio: —
Long-term debt ($ mil.): —

No. of shares (mil.): 8
Dividends
  Yield: —
  Payout: —
Market value ($ mil.): 254

	STOCK PRICE ($) FY Close	P/E High/Low		PER SHARE ($) Earnings	Dividends	Book Value
12/18	31.00	18	10	3.00	0.00	32.00
12/17	42.00	21	15	2.00	0.00	29.00
12/16	0.00	—	—	0.00	0.00	22.00
Annual Growth	**—**	**—**	**—**	**92.3%**	**—**	**12.8%**

MGIC Investment Corp. (WI)

Since a pinkie-promise isn't good enough for most lenders there's MGIC Investment's mortgage insurance to protect lenders from home buyers who don't hold up their end of the bargain. MGIC owns Mortgage Guaranty Insurance Corporation

(MGIC) the largest provider of private mortgage insurance in the US Puerto Rico and Guam. Such coverage allows otherwise-qualified buyers who aren't able to scrape up the standard 20% down payment to get mortgages. MGIC writes primary insurance on individual loans; its customers include banks mortgage brokers credit unions and other residential mortgage lenders. In 2017 MGIC had $194.9 billion primary insurance in force covering 1 million mortgages.

Operations

Historically MGIC has provided two primary types of private mortgage insurance — primary and pool. Primary insurance default protection on individual mortgages and covers unpaid loan principal related delinquent interest and expenses and foreclosure or sale approved by MGIC. Pool insurance is typically an additional credit enhancement for secondary market mortgage transactions. It generally covers the loss on a defaulted loan exceeding the claim payment under the primary coverage (if required) or the total loss on a defaulted loan which did not require primary coverage. Although the company hasn't written any new pool risk since 2009 it may do so in the future as it weighs the market.

Other offerings include contract underwriting services for lenders and mortgage lead generation for the finance industry.

Geographic Reach

MGIC operates in every US state the District of Columbia Puerto Rico and Guam.

Sales and Marketing

MGIC's customers include savings institutions commercial banks mortgage brokers credit unions mortgage bankers and other lenders. The company's products are sold by its employees.

Financial Performance

MGIC's revenue stayed flat at $1.1 billion in 2017. Although net premiums written and earned and net investment income increased net realized investment gains and other income decreased that year.

Like other private mortgage insurers MGIC has seen improvements to its earnings since 2014 the first year it returned to the black since the Great Recession. The stronger economy has led to a decrease in delinquencies and subsequent claims filed. In 2018 net income totaled $355.8 million a 4% increase over the prior year. This was driven by lower net losses (which decreased 78%) and the absence of significant losses on debt extinguishment. Operating cash flow rose 81% to $406.7 million in 2017 thanks largely to higher deferred tax expenses.

Strategy

MGIC's core strategies include growing the amount of insurance it has in force seeking attractive business opportunities to provide optimal returns and to broaden its presence in the private mortgage insurance sector. In 2017 it increased its insurance in force by more than 7% a rate that falls in line with its goals.

The company faces competition from alternatives to mortgage insurance such as certain capital market transactions credit risk investors and piggyback loans. And as the entire private mortgage insurance industry nervously gauges its future government-sponsored enterprises (GSEs) Freddie Mac and Fannie Mae have taken over a huge share of the business during the past few years. However the Trump administration has proposed ending Freddie's and Fannie's conservatorship and privatizing the GSEs which could boost business.

MGIC has enhanced its consumer offerings through technology. In 2018 it launched Readynest a website that breaks down the steps of buying a home. The prior year it launched the updated Buy Now Vs. Wait calculator for first-time home buyers which is now mobile-friendly and includes a version for Spanish speakers. It also improved its rate quote tools such as its mobile application Rate Finder.

Company Background

Before the mortgage mess unfolded in the US MGIC had marked its entry into the global market by opening offices in Toronto and in Sydney Australia. In less than two years however MGIC closed its Canadian office stopped issuing new policies abroad and began searching for a buyer for its Australian operations (which it records as immaterial) in order to focus on its domestic operations.

EXECUTIVES

Vice President Human Resources, Kurt Thomas
Senior Vice President Information Services And Chief Information Officer Of Mgic, Michael Meade
Senior Vice President, Carla A Gallas
President And Coo, Patrick Sinks, age 62, $524,423 total compensation
Evp General Counsel And Secretary, Jeffrey H. Lane, age 69, $415,385 total compensation
Evp Risk Management, Lawrence J. Pierzchalski, age 66, $449,654 total compensation
Chairman And Ceo, Curt S. Culver, age 66, $898,269 total compensation
Evp And Cfo, Timothy Mattke
Vice President Investments, Paul Spiroff
Vice President Marketing And Customer Experience, Margaret Crowley
Vice President National Account Manager Mortgage Guaranty Insurance Corporation And Mgic Investmen, Luis Contreras
Assistant Vice President Regulatory Relations, Chris Burns
Vice President Claims, David Schroeder
Vice President, Lisa Pendergast
Vice President, Julie Sperber
Vice President, John Schroeder
Vice President, Mike Kull
Vice President Field Operations, Jerry Murphy
Executive Vice President Business Strategy And Operations, Sal Miosi
National Accounts Manager, Rick Lewandowski
Vice President Talent Management, Stacey Murphy
Vice President National Accounts Manager, Robert Bates
Vice President, Janice Beder-yee
Vice President Product Development, Geoffrey Cooper
Svp National Sales, Jay Hughes
Auditors: PricewaterhouseCoopers LLP

LOCATIONS

HQ: MGIC Investment Corp. (WI)
250 E. Kilbourn Avenue, Milwaukee, WI 53202
Phone: 414 347-6480
Web: www.mgic.com

PRODUCTS/OPERATIONS

2017 Sales

	$ mil.	% of total
Net premiums earned	935	88
Net investment income	121	11
Net realized investment gains	0	—
Other	10	1
Total	**1,066**	**100**

COMPETITORS

Fannie Mae	Radian Group
Freddie Mac	US Department of
Genworth Mortgage	Veterans Affairs
Insurance	United Guaranty
National Mortgage	
Insurance	

HISTORICAL FINANCIALS

Company Type: Public

Income Statement

FYE: December 31

	ASSETS ($ mil.)	NET INCOME ($ mil.)	INCOME AS % OF ASSETS	EMPLOYEES
12/18	5,678	670	11.8%	793
12/17	5,619	356	6.3%	819
12/16	5,735	343	6.0%	823
12/15	5,880	1,172	19.9%	800
12/14	5,266	252	4.8%	800
Annual Growth	1.9%	27.7%	—	(0.2%)

2018 Year-End Financials

Debt ratio: 15.00%
Return on equity: 20.00%
Cash ($ mil.): 152
Current ratio: —
Long-term debt ($ mil.): —

No. of shares (mil.): 355
Dividends
  Yield: —
  Payout: —
Market value ($ mil.): 3,717

	STOCK PRICE ($) FY Close	P/E High/Low		PER SHARE ($) Earnings	Dividends	Book Value
12/18	10.00	9	5	2.00	0.00	10.00
12/17	14.00	16	10	1.00	0.00	9.00
12/16	10.00	11	5	1.00	0.00	7.00
12/15	9.00	3	2	3.00	0.00	7.00
12/14	9.00	13	10	1.00	0.00	3.00
Annual Growth	2.9%	—	—	29.1%	—	34.7%

MGM Resorts International

MGM Resorts International is one of the world's largest gaming firms. The company's properties include some of the biggest names on the Las Vegas Strip including MGM Grand The Mirage and the Monte Carlo as well as Luxor Bellagio Circus Circus New York-New York Mandalay Bay and the new T-Mobile Arena. MGM Resorts also operates regional properties in a handful of other US states including the MGM Grand Detroit and the Borgata in Atlantic City New Jersey among others. Internationally MGM Resorts operates in Macau an autonomous Chinese territory famed for gambling. Revenue comes from gambling room reservations food and drinks entertainment and retail operations.

Operations

MGM Resorts' hotels boast a combined 49000 rooms. Domestic properties on the Las Vegas strip and other regional locations include more than 41000 rooms and its CityCenter joint venture a mixed-use development in Las Vegas has another 5500. Its hotels in Macau have nearly 2000 rooms. The company's properties altogether host more than 2.5 million square feet of casino space more than 31000 slot machines and some 2000 gaming tables.

Casino operations generate nearly half the company's total revenue while hotel rooms generate about 20% and food and drink bring in approximately 15%. Other revenue-generators include entertainment and retail holdings.

The company operates and manages its hotels which are owned by MGM Growth Properties an affiliated real-estate investment trust.

Geographic Reach

MGM Resorts' reportable segments are based on the geographic regions in which it operates. Domestic Resorts including Las Vegas strip resorts and regional operations account for nearly 75% of sales while MGM China accounts for about 20%. (A corporate segment occupies the remainder.)

The company has nine properties on the Las Vegas strip. It has another six in the US in Maryland Massachusetts Michigan Mississippi and New Jersey. MGM also owns 50% of the CityCenter in Las Vegas which it manages for a fee and is expanding in Ohio with MGM Northfield Park and in New York with Empire City.

MGM Resorts' China operations consist of two sites in Macau: MGM Macau resort and casino and MGM Cotai a casino hotel and entertainment resort on the Cotai strip China's equivalent of the Las Vegas strip.

Sales and Marketing

MGM Resorts advertises on the radio television internet billboards and in newspapers and magazines in selected cities throughout the US and overseas. MGM Resorts also uses direct mail and social media to target past guests and potential customers. The company advertises through regional marketing offices located in major cities.

The firm encourages customers to keep their total gaming and entertainment spending at its casino resorts through its customer loyalty program M life Rewards. The tiered program allows customers to qualify for benefits across participating resorts in both gaming and non-gaming areas. It also offers the Golden Lion Club for gaming-focused customers in addition to M life Rewards at MGM China.

Advertising expenses exceeded $300 million in 2018 and reached nearly $225 million in 2017.

Financial Performance

MGM Resorts International has for the most part grown its revenue year-over-year in recent years. The company's net income during the most recent five-year period ending 2018 has been more sporadic ? up one year and down the next. Fiscal 2017 was something of a breakthrough for earnings with acquisitions and a major tax gain fueling record profits that year.

Overall revenue for 2018 increased 9% compared to 2017 due primarily to the openings of MGM Cotai and MGM Springfield in 2018. Specifically 2018 revenue grew to a whopping $11.8 billion on the back of full-year contributions from the Macau market where gaming revenue increased 14% compared to 2017 primarily as a result of growth on the Cotai Strip.

MGM Resorts posted profits of $467 million in 2018 down from record profits of nearly $2 billion in 2017 when the company benefited from an exceptional item recording a $1.4 billion tax benefit relating to the 2017 US Tax Cuts and Jobs Act.

At the end of 2018 MGM Resorts had $1.5 billion in cash and cash equivalents. Cash from operations was $1.7 billion. Cash used in investing activities was $2.1 billion an increase from the prior year as a result of its Northfield acquisition. Cash provided by financing activities was $389.2 billion.

Strategy

MGM Resorts International in 2019 announced the implementation of the MGM 2020 plan to reduce costs improve efficiencies and drive revenue growth. The MGM 2020 plan is a company-wide initiative aimed to create a more centralized organizational structure and lay the groundwork for a digital transformation through key investments in technology. As part of MGM 2020 the company cut more than 1000 jobs at its properties in 2019. The plan is expected to boost earnings before interest taxes depreciation and amortization by $200

million by the end of 2020 and another $100 million by the end of 2021.

In addition to increasing margins and maximizing profitability the company wants to establish new relationships with professional sports leagues and teams to expand sports wagering after a US ban on such betting in most states was lifted in 2018. MGM Resorts has also expressed interest in developing a resort in Japan where the government recently passed legislation allowing the construction of three casino resorts.

In 2018 the company expanded internationally and domestically when it opened two new major properties. It opened MGM Cotai an integrated casino hotel and entertainment resort on the Cotai Strip in Macau in February of that year and MGM Springfield in Springfield Massachusetts in August.

Mergers and Acquisitions

In 2019 MGM Resorts acquired Empire City Casino's race track and casino in Yonkers New York just 15 miles north of Manhattan's Times Square for approximately $864 million. The purchase gives MGM a fourth property in the Northeast; it previously opened its MGM Springfield resort casino in Massachusetts in 2018. Representatives from MGM say the Empire City deal is designed to tap into the underserved New York market and will complement the MGM Springfield market.

MGM is also in the final stages of buying Hard Rock Rocksino Northfield Park in Ohio for $1 billion. It plans to re-brand the property MGM Northfield Park.

Company Background

Billionaire Kirk Kerkorian purchased a stake in famed movie studio Metro-Goldwyn-Mayer (formed 1924) for just over $80 million in 1970. Around the same time he began acquiring property in Las Vegas and started construction on the city's largest hotel.

Financial difficulties led Kerkorian to sell his new hotel but he retained the rights to the MGM Grand name and logo. Kerkorian founded MGM Grand Inc. in 1986 and took the company public in 1987. In 1993 Kerkorian and company unveiled Las Vegas' MGM Grand a $1.1 billion complex featuring a theme park and at the time the largest casino on the planet. The project was a success and spawned plans for expansion.

In a landmark deal MGM Grand bought rival Mirage Resorts for $6.4 billion (including $2 billion in debt) in 2000 and became one of the top gaming companies in the world. The purchase of Mirage Resorts allowed MGM Grand to add a string of opulent casinos to its collection including Las Vegas strip properties Bellagio and The Mirage. After the deal closed MGM Grand changed its name to MGM MIRAGE.

The company opened MGM Grand Macau in China in 2007. In 2010 MGM MIRAGE changed its name to MGM Resorts International to emphasize the brand's global scope.

EXECUTIVES

Coo, Corey I. Sanders, age 55, $1,119,368 total compensation
President And Chief Marketing Officer, William J. Hornbuckle, age 61, $1,269,368 total compensation
Chairman And Ceo, James J. Murren, age 57, $2,000,000 total compensation
Chief Design And Construction Officer And Director, Robert H. Baldwin, age 68, $1,650,000 total compensation
Evp Special Counsel Litigation And Chief Diversity Officer, Phyllis A. James, age 66
Evp Cfo And Treasurer, Daniel J. D'Arrigo, age 50, $875,000 total compensation

Evp And Chief Accounting Officer, Robert C. Selwood, age 63, $439,286 total compensation
Evp General Counsel And Secretary, John M. McManus, age 51
President And Coo Borgata Hotel Casino & Spa, Marcus Glover
Representative Officer And President Mgm Resorts Japan, Jason P. Hyland
President And Coo Gold Strike Casino Resort, Melonie Johnson
Vice President Of Corporate Ticketing, Cynthia Jones
Vice President Digital Design, Christopher Hume
Vice President, Vanesa Bui
Senior Vice President And Chief Sales Officer, Michael Dominguez
Vice President Of Global Sports And Events Sales, Daniel Rush
Vice President, Jeff Eisenhart
Vice President Gaming Operations, Todd Haushalter
Vp Field Technology Services, Bill Driver
Vice President Labor Relations, Wendy Nutt
Senior Vice President Customer Development, Larry Altschul
Corporate Vice President Talent And Organizational Effec, Christopher Henry
Vice President Global Sourcing, Paul Sinowitz
Senior Vice President Of Finance, Yvette Harris
Vice President Of Hotel Sales, Jay Simpson
Vice President Marketing International, Kimie Masumoto
Executive Vice President, William Scott
Vice President Of Casino Operations, Patrick Miller
Senior Vice President Capital Markets And Strategy, Jim Freeman
Vice President Of Human Resources At Circus Circus Las Vegas, Ashley Eddy
Senior Vice President International Development, Rishi Kapoor
Svp Entertainment Operations, Mark Prows
Vice President Marketing, Jessie Yee
Assistant Vice President Taxes, Marcie Fleck
Svp Innovation Station Casinos, Thomas Mikulich
Senior Vice President And Chief Compliance Officer, Stephen Martino
Senior Vice President Hotel Strategy, Cliff Atkinson
National Sales Manager, John Montes
Vice President, Anna Romanova
Senior Vice President Far East Marketing Mgm Grand Mgm Resorts International Marketing, Tracy Tsoi
Vice President, Bruce Barclay
Svp Hr Operations And Shared Services, Tonia Horton
Vice President Of Legal Affairs, Greg Riches
Svp Global Retail Leasing And Development, Farid Matraki
Vice President Of Labor Analytics, Jason Ansuini
Senior Vice President Global Security, Steve Martinez
Vice President Construction Finance, Alan Palardy
National Sales Manager, Sarah Abbott
Vice President Client Services, Troy Jenkins
Vice President Procurement Vice President, Amanda Prochaska
Vp Entertainment Administration Operations, Nathalie Binette
Board Member, Daniel Taylor
Board Member, Mary Chris Gay
Auditors: Deloitte & Touche LLP

LOCATIONS

HQ: MGM Resorts International
3600 Las Vegas Boulevard South, Las Vegas, NV 89109
Phone: 702 693-7120
Web: www.mgmresorts.com

2017 Sales

	$ mil.	% of total
Domestic resorts	8,322	77
MGM China	1,971	18
Corporate & other	481	5
Total	**10,774**	**100**

PRODUCTS/OPERATIONS

2017 Sales

	$ mil.	% of total
Casino	5,984	51
Rooms	2,151	18
Food and beverage	1,790	15
Entertainment	543	5
Retail	214	2
Other	606	5
Reimbursed costs	402	4
Less: Promotional allowances	(917.0)	-
Total	**10,774**	**100**

Selected Properties

Nevada
  Las Vegas
  Bellagio
  Circus Circus
  CityCenter (50%)
  Excalibur
  Luxor
  Mandalay Bay Resort & Casino
  MGM Grand
  The Mirage
  T-Mobile Arena
  Monte Carlo
  New York-New York
Other US
  Beau Rivage (Biloxi MS)
  Borgata (Atlantic City New Jersey)
  Gold Strike (Tunica County MS)
  Grand Victoria (50%; Elgin New Jersey)
  MGM Grand Detroit
  MGM National Harbor (Prince George's Country Maryland)
  MG Springfield
China
  MGM Grand Macau (51%; Macau)
  MGM Cotai

COMPETITORS

Boyd Gaming	Sands China
Caesars Entertainment	Star City
Galaxy Entertainment	Station Casinos
Las Vegas Sands	Stratosphere
Rio All-Suite Hotel & Casino	Tropicana Entertainment
Riviera Holdings	Trump Resorts
SJM	Wynn Resorts

HISTORICAL FINANCIALS

Company Type: Public

Income Statement				FYE: December 31
	REVENUE ($ mil.)	NET INCOME ($ mil.)	NET PROFIT MARGIN	EMPLOYEES
12/18	11,763	467	4.0%	72,000
12/17	10,774	1,960	18.2%	68,000
12/16	9,455	1,101	11.6%	69,000
12/15	9,190	(448)	—	59,500
12/14	10,082	(150)	—	68,100
Annual Growth	**3.9%**	**—**		**1.4%**

2018 Year-End Financials

Debt ratio: 50.00%
Return on equity: 7.00%
Cash ($ mil.): 1,527
Current ratio: 1.00
Long-term debt ($ mil.): 15,088

No. of shares (mil.): 527
Dividends
  Yield: 2.0%
  Payout: 59.0%
Market value ($ mil.): 12,797

	STOCK PRICE ($) FY Close	P/E High/Low		PER SHARE ($) Earnings	Dividends	Book Value
12/18	24.00	46	27	1.00	0.00	12.00
12/17	33.00	10	8	3.00	0.00	13.00
12/16	29.00	15	9	2.00	0.00	11.00
12/15	23.00	—	—	(1.00)	0.00	9.00
12/14	21.00	—	—	(0.00)	0.00	8.00
Annual Growth	**3.2%**	**—**	**—**	**—**	**—**	**10.3%**

Michaels Companies Inc

Auditors: Ernst & Young LLP

LOCATIONS

HQ: Michaels Companies Inc
  8000 Bent Branch Drive, Irving, TX 75063
Phone: 972 409-1300
Web: www.michaels.com

HISTORICAL FINANCIALS

Company Type: Public

Income Statement				FYE: February 2
	REVENUE ($ mil.)	NET INCOME ($ mil.)	NET PROFIT MARGIN	EMPLOYEES
02/19	5,272	320	6.1%	47,000
02/18*	5,362	390	7.3%	49,000
01/17	5,197	378	7.3%	50,000
01/16	4,913	363	7.4%	50,000
01/15	4,738	217	4.6%	51,000
Annual Growth	**2.7%**	**10.2%**	**—**	**(2.0%)**

*Fiscal year change

2019 Year-End Financials

Debt ratio: 127.00%
Return on equity: ***.***.**%
Cash ($ mil.): 246
Current ratio: 2.00
Long-term debt ($ mil.): 2,681

No. of shares (mil.): 158
Dividends
  Yield: —
  Payout: —
Market value ($ mil.): 2,147

	STOCK PRICE ($) FY Close	P/E High/Low		PER SHARE ($) Earnings	Dividends	Book Value
02/19	14.00	14	7	2.00	0.00	(10.00)
02/18*	26.00	13	8	2.00	0.00	(8.00)
01/17	20.00	17	11	2.00	0.00	(9.00)
01/16	22.00	17	12	2.00	0.00	(8.00)
01/15	26.00	25	14	1.00	0.00	(10.00)
Annual Growth	**(14.8%)**	**—**	**—**	**15.4%**	**—**	**—**

*Fiscal year change

Microchip Technology Inc

Microchip Technology's products are embedded in your car your copier and even your wallet. The semiconductor maker offers a variety of embedded devices including eight- 16- and 32-bit microcontrollers (it's a leading producer worldwide). It also makes specialty memory products such as electrically erasable programmable read-only memories (EEPROMs) and field programmable gate arrays (FPGA). Microchip's KeeLoq-brand code-hopping devices are used in keyless locks garage door openers and smart cards. Its chips have customers in the automotive consumer aerospace defense computing industrial and telecommunications markets. Microchip gets about 80% of sales from customers outside the US.

Operations

Microchip's two biggest product lines are microcontrollers (about 55% of sales) a family of proprietary general purpose microcontroller products and Analog Interface and Mixed Signal Products (about 30% of sales) which consist of several families with more than 3800 power management linear mixed-signal thermal management RF Linear drivers USB Ethernet and wireless products.

Supplying another 15% of sales are its smaller lines. Memory Products consists of serial electrically erasable programmable read-only memory (referred to as Serial EEPROMs) Serial Flash memories Parallel Flash memories and Serial SRAM memories. The Technology Licensing unit includes license fees and royalties associated with technology licenses for the use of Microchip's SuperFlash embedded flash and Smartbits one time programmable NVM technologies. Then there's the multi-market products segment which consists of manufacturing services legacy application specific integrated circuits complex programmable logic devices and aerospace products.

Microchip's manufacturing operations do it all: wafer fabrication wafer probe and assembly and test. The company achieves high production yields through direct control of manufacturing. However outsourcing has increased with acquisitions of companies that farmed out manufacturing to third parties; more than 55% of its sales come from products made by third parties.

Geographic Reach

Microchip Technology based in Chandler Arizona has about 10 manufacturing plants in the US located in Arizona Oregon Colorado California Connecticut Massachusetts and Pennsylvania. It also makes chips in Germany France and Ireland. The company operates a probe assembly and test facility in Thailand and a probe and test facility in the Philippines.

Sales are spread geographically to major markets. China and the US each account for about 20% of sales while Europe accounts for close to 25% and Taiwan supplies about 15% of sales.

Sales and Marketing

Microchip uses a direct sales force and distributors to sell its products worldwide. About 50% of its business goes through distributors with Arrow accounting for about 10% of sales. Direct sales account for about 45% of revenue.

Financial Performance

Microchip's revenue has increased about 150% in the past five years fueled by acquisitions general economic conditions and rising prices for its products.

In 2019 (ended March) sales jumped 34% to $5.3 billion from $3.9 billion in 2017 driven by the acquisition of Microsemi. The Microsemi gains were somewhat offset by accounting changes and demand fluctuations. While the sales of each product line rose in 2019 from 2018 the increase if analog interface mixed signal and timing products sales outpaced the others jumping about 60% with the help of Microsemi products.

Microchip posted net income of $355 million in 2019 about $100 million higher than the 2018 profit. Although the company had higher interest expense in 2019 it also had a tax benefit that pushed the bottom line higher.

The company ended 2019 with about $428.6 million in cash and equivalents compared to $901.3 million the year before. In 2018 operations generated $1.6 billion and investing activities used $6.8 billion. Financing activities provided $4.6 billion due to heavy borrowing to pay for Microsemi.

Overall Microchip carries about $11.6 billion in debt which could curtail its spending and borrowing flexibility to respond to opportunities and threats. Interest expense was about $503 million in 2019.

Strategy

Microchip's strategic focus is on the embedded control market which includes microcontrollers high-performance analog interface and mixed-signal devices power management and thermal management devices connectivity devices interface devices Serial EEPROMs SuperFlash memory products and its KeeLoq security devices and Flash IP products. Unlike many chip makers Microchip hasn't experienced significant fluctuations in average selling prices particularly in its microcontroller and analog and interface groups where a large proportion of products are considered proprietary.

The company has joined the move to get stronger by getting bigger with several acquisitions in the past few years. The biggest was its purchase of Microsemi for more than $10 billion in 2018. Before that Microchip spent $3.6 billion to buy Atmel in 2016 after acquiring Micrel and SuperTex in previous years. The deals helped move Microchip up to No. 3 on the microcontroller leaderboard (behind Renesas and NXP).

Microchip's business in China grew to account for about 30% of revenue in 2018. But the trade war between the US and China dampened demand reducing sales to China to just more than 20% of Microchip's revenue. Additional tariffs would extend the impact to components and equipment sourced from China by increasing costs.

Mergers and Acquisitions

Microchip has made acquisitions expand its capabilities and product lines.

In 2018 Microchip bought Microsemi for more than $10 billion. The deal enables Microchip to push into Microsemi's markets that include data centers communications defense and aerospace.

Microchip in 2016 bought microcontroller competitor Atmel for $3.6 billion. The deal deepens Microchip's product portfolio and provides both companies with more resources with which to withstand the increasingly competitive semiconductor environment.

Company Background

Investment firm Sequoia Capital acquired a washed-up semiconductor subsidiary from General Instrument in 1989. Sequoia executive Steve Sanghi a veteran of Intel was tapped to head the operation Microchip Technology. Sanghi instituted a bare-bones operating budget and broadened the company's focus beyond low-cost memory products to include more profitable embedded microcontrollers. By 1992 Microchip turned a small profit.

In 1995 Microchip acquired the rights to KEELOQ secure data transmission products developed by South Africa's Nanoteq Ltd. The following year the company introduced its own line of secure data transmission products and its first flash memory microcontrollers. In 1997 Microchip unveiled the world's smallest erasable read-only memory to be used in devices such as keyless entries dimmers and thermostats.

EXECUTIVES

Vice President Mcu16 And Ung, Mitchel Obolsky

Chairman And Ceo, Steve Sanghi, age 64, $645,619 total compensation

President And Coo, Ganesh Moorthy, age 59, $326,918 total compensation

Vp And Cfo, J. Eric Bjornholt, age 48, $221,559 total compensation

Vp Global Information Services, Robert Williams

Vice President, Thomas J Grune

Vice President Of Marketing, Ron Cates

Vice President, Sudarshan Iyengar

Vice President Digital Signal Controller Division, Sumit Mitra

Vice President, Mark W Reiten

Vice President, Ian Yue

Vice President Of Advanced Microcontroller Architecture Division, Mitch Obolsky

Senior Vice President, Matthew B Bunker

Vice President, Joseph Thomsen

Vice President, Ken Pye

Vp Fab 5 Operations, Dan Malinaric

Auditors: Ernst & Young LLP

LOCATIONS

HQ: Microchip Technology Inc
 2355 W. Chandler Blvd., Chandler, AZ 85224-6199
Phone: 480 792-7200   Fax: 480 792-7790
Web: www.microchip.com

2019 Sales

	$ mil.	% of total
Asia	2,771	52
Americas	1,354	25
Europe	1,225	23
Total	**5,350**	**100**

PRODUCTS/OPERATIONS

2019 Sales

	$ mil.	% of total
Microcontrollers	2,922	55
Analog & interface mixed signal and timing products	1,531	29
Field-programmable gate array products	304	6
Memory products	184	3
Technology licensing	132	2
Multi-marker and other	277	5
Total	**5,350**	**100**

Selected Products

Analog and Interface Integrated Circuits (ICs)
 Interface devices
 Controllers
 Infrared codecs
 Linear devices
 Audio amplifiers
 Comparators
 Operational amplifiers
 Mixed-signal devices
 Analog-to-digital (A/D) and digital-to-analog (D/A) converters
 Digital potentiometers
 Power management devices
 DC-to-DC converters
 Linear regulators
 Power MOSFET drivers
 Switching regulators
 System supervisors
 Voltage detectors
 Voltage references
 Thermal management devices
 Brushless DC fan controllers
 Temperature sensors
KEELOQ Security Devices
 Decoders
 Encoders
 Transcoders
Memory Chips
 Serial and parallel erasable programmable read-only memories (EPROMs)
 Serial electrically erasable programmable read-only memories (EEPROMs)
Microcontrollers
 Eight-bit microcontrollers (PICmicro and rfPIC lines)
 Mixed-signal controllers
Radio-frequency identification (RFID) ICs

COMPETITORS

Analog Devices	NXP Semiconductors
Cypress Semiconductor	ON Semiconductor
Fujitsu Semiconductor	ROHM
Intel	Renesas Electronics
Macronix International	STMicroelectronics
Maxim Integrated	Silicon Labs
Products	Texas Instruments
Mitsubishi Electric	Winbond Electronics

HISTORICAL FINANCIALS
Company Type: Public

Income Statement

	REVENUE ($ mil.)	NET INCOME ($ mil.)	NET PROFIT MARGIN	EMPLOYEES
03/19	5,350	356	6.7%	18,286
03/18	3,981	255	6.4%	14,234
03/17	3,408	165	4.8%	12,656
03/16	2,173	324	14.9%	9,766
03/15	2,147	369	17.2%	280
Annual Growth	**25.6%**	**(0.9%)**	**—**	**184.3%**

FYE: March 31

2019 Year-End Financials

Debt ratio: 56.00%	No. of shares (mil.): 238
Return on equity: 8.00%	Dividends
Cash ($ mil.): 429	Yield: 0.0%
Current ratio: 1.00	Payout: 103.0%
Long-term debt ($ mil.): 8,946	Market value ($ mil.): 19,710

	STOCK PRICE ($) FY Close	P/E High/Low	PER SHARE ($)		
			Earnings	Dividends	Book Value
03/19	83.00	68 41	1.00	1.00	22.00
03/18	91.00	91 73	1.00	0.00	14.00
03/17	74.00	98 62	1.00	1.00	14.00
03/16	48.00	32 25	1.00	1.00	11.00
03/15	49.00	28 21	2.00	1.00	10.00
Annual Growth	**14.1%**	**— —**	**(3.7%)**	**0.6%**	**21.8%**

Micron Technology Inc.

Micron Technology is one of the largest memory chip makers in the world. It makes DRAM (Dynamic Random Access Memory) NAND Flash and NOR Flash memory and other memory technologies. The company sells to customers in networking and storage consumer electronics solid-state drives and mobile telecommunications but its largest concentration (about a quarter of sales) is the computer market. Micron's products are offered under the Micron Crucial and Ballistix brands as well as private labels. The US-based company generates about 90% of sales internationally. Besides being one of the biggest chipmakers Micron is one the most durable marking its 40th anniversary in 2018.

Operations

Micron operates through four segments centered on its markets. The largest segment accounting for 50% of sales is the Compute and Networking Business Unit which sells products for the computing networking graphics and cloud server markets. The Storage Business Unit contributes more than 15% of revenue with the Mobile Business Unit memory for smartphone tablet and other mobile-device markets generating more than 20% of sales. About 10% of revenue comes from the Embedded Business Unit which makes memory and storage products for the automotive industrial and consumer markets.

Almost 70% of revenue comes from DRAM products and NAND Flash memory products supply the rest. DRAM and flash are sold throughout each of Micron's segments.

The company makes its own products in a dozen plants throughout the world; most of its products are made on 300mm wafers.

Geographic Reach

Boise Idaho-based Micron generates about 55% of its revenue in China with 20% from Taiwan Japan and other Asia/Pacific region countries. The US and Europe contribute about 10% and 5% respectively. The company has fabrication and assembly facilities in China Japan Malaysia Singapore Taiwan and the US. With customers and manufacturing locations around the world Micron has been subject to tariffs generated in trade tensions between the US and China.

Sales and Marketing

Micron sells to equipment manufacturers and retailers via a direct sales force third-party sales representatives and distributors. The company sells its Crucial-branded products through a web-based customer direct sales channel as well as through channel and distribution partners.

Micron's gets about 10% of sales from Kingston.

Financial Performance

Micron's financial results for the past decade were typical of the cyclical semiconductor industry - up and down but trending higher. The last two years however have been straight up delivering record revenue and net income.

In 2018 (ended September) revenue jumped 50% to $30.4 billion from $20.3 billion in 2017 propelled by stronger sales in each of its segments. The CNBU segment drove the increase providing about 70% of the additional $10 billion overall revenue on strong market conditions and demand in the cloud server client enterprise server and graphics markets. The MBU segment's revenue rose about 50% year-to-year on higher sales of mobile DRAM and managed NAND products.

The higher sales combined with modest increases in expenses resulted in higher margins and a profit of $14.1 million in 2018 compared to a $5.1 million profit in 2017.

Micron's coffers held $6.6 billion in cash and equivalents at the end of 2018 compared to $5.2 billion the year before. Operations generated $17.4 billion and investing activities used $8.2 billion and financing activities used $7.7 billion in 2018.

Strategy

Micron has rolled out DRAM and NAND products based on increasing complex productions methods which has increased yield and help increase prices for some products. Sales of the company's products for the graphics market have increased as companies such as NVIDIA have tapped Micron as a partner. Micron will chip in to produce NVIDIA's GeForce RTX devices for the gaming market.

Micron's automotive business has a full pipeline of projects including a collaboration with BMW. Growth in automotive and other chips with long life-cycle led the company to a $3 billion expansion of its manufacturing plant in Manassas Virginia over the next 10 years.

The company is expanding manufacturing capacity for DRAM and NAND chips at other sites providing greater flexibility in managing operations.

Mergers and Acquisitions

In 2018 Micron said it would exercise its right to buy Intel's interest in the companies' joint venture IM Flash Technologies. The $1.5 billion deal would give Micron full control of IM Flash's 3D XPoint technology.

EXECUTIVES

President And Ceo, Sanjay Mehrotra, age 60
Vice President Operations, Jay Hawkins
Vp Finance And Cfo, Ernest E. (Ernie) Maddock, age 61, $550,000 total compensation

Vp Information Technology And Cio, Trevor Schulze
Human Resource Vice President Director Manager, Dan Spangler
Vice President Of Procurement, John Whitman
Vice President, Matt Elzie
Vice President Nsg Design Engineering, Ramin Ghodsi
Senior Vice President And Gm Computer And Networking Business Unit, Tom Eby
Vice President Advanced Storage Solutions, Robert Peglar
Vice President Of Software Engineering, Steve Moyer
Vice President Japan Process Research, Hideki Gomi
Vice President Wsg Marketing, Reynette Au
Vice President Ww Enterprise Sales, Mark Glasgow
Vp Global Hr Operations And Services, Michael Zeigler
Executive Vice President, Michael Sadler
Vice President Worldwide Oem Sales, Mike Bokan
Vice President Of Marketing, Eric Endebrock
Vice President Director Manager, Brian Kalisek
Vice President Director Manager, Michael Knapp
Vice President Business Planning And Process Management, Karen Metz
Vice President Memory Marketing, Jan duPreez
Vp Dram Development, John Schreck
Evp And Chief Business Officer, Sumit Sadana
Vice President Marketing Cnbu, Malcolm Humphrey
Executive Vice President Sales And Marketing, Brian Klene
Vice President Enigneering, Currie Munce
Corporate Vice President And Gm Embedded Business Unit, Jeffrey Bader
Executive Vice President Global Operations, Manish Bhatia
Corporate Vice President And Gm Storage Business Unit, Derek Dicker
Vice President 3dxp Systems And Solutions Engineering, Samir Mittal
Vp Package Technology Development, Mark Tuttle
Vp Technology Strategy And Operations, Linda Somerville
Chairman, Robert E. (Bob) Switz, age 72
Treasurer, Bill Stover
Board Member, Caleb Bailey
Auditors: PricewaterhouseCoopers LLP

LOCATIONS

HQ: Micron Technology Inc.
8000 S. Federal Way, Boise, ID 83716-9632
Phone: 208 368-4000
Web: www.micron.com

2018 Sales

	$ mil.	% of total
China	17,357	57
United States	3,624	12
Asia Pacific (exclusive China Taiwan and Japan)	2,559	9
Taiwan	2,798	9
Europe	2,128	7
Japan	1,254	4
Other	671	2
Total	**30,391**	**100**

PRODUCTS/OPERATIONS

2018 Sales

	$ mil.	% of total
Compute and Networking Business Unit	15,252	50
Storage Business Unit	5,022	17
Mobile Business unit	6,579	22
Embedded Business Unit	3,479	11
All Other	59	-
Total	**30,391**	**100**

2018 Sales

	$ mil.	% of total
DRAM	21,232	70
Trade NAND	7,843	26
Non-Trade	554	2
Other	578	3
Total	**30,391**	**100**

Semiconductor Products

Dynamic random-access memories (DRAMs)
  Direct Rambus DRAMs (RDRAMs)
  Synchronous DRAMs (SDRAMs)
  Double data rate synchronous DRAMs (DDR SDRAMs)
Flash memory devices
Memory modules
Photomasks

COMPETITORS

Atmel
Cypress Semiconductor
Intel
Kingston Technology
Mosel Vitelic
Nanya
PNY Technologies
SK Hynix

SMART Modular
  Technologies
Samsung Electronics
SanDisk
Toshiba Semiconductor
  & Storage Products
Western Digital

HISTORICAL FINANCIALS

Company Type: Public

Income Statement

				FYE: August 29
	REVENUE ($ mil.)	NET INCOME ($ mil.)	NET PROFIT MARGIN	EMPLOYEES
08/19	23,406	6,313	27.0%	37,000
08/18	30,391	14,135	46.5%	36,000
08/17*	20,322	5,089	25.0%	34,100
09/16	12,399	(276)	—	31,400
09/15	16,192	2,899	17.9%	31,800
Annual Growth	9.6%	21.5%	—	3.9%

*Fiscal year change

2019 Year-End Financials

Debt ratio: 12.00%
Return on equity: 19.00%
Cash ($ mil.): 7,152
Current ratio: 3.00
Long-term debt ($ mil.): 4,541

No. of shares (mil.): 1,106
Dividends
  Yield: —
  Payout: —
Market value ($ mil.): 49,405

	STOCK PRICE ($) FY Close	P/E High/Low		PER SHARE ($) Earnings	Dividends	Book Value
08/19	45.00	9	5	6.00	0.00	32.00
08/18	53.00	5	3	12.00	0.00	28.00
08/17*	32.00	7	4	4.00	0.00	17.00
09/16	17.00	—	—	(0.00)	0.00	12.00
09/15	17.00	13	5	2.00	0.00	12.00
Annual Growth	28.1%	—	—	22.2%	—	28.7%

*Fiscal year change

Microsoft Corporation

EXECUTIVES

Ceo, Satya Nadella
Chb*, John W Thompson
Pres-Clo, Bradford L Smith
Exec V Pres-Cfo, Amy E Hood
Exec V Pres-Cmo, Christopher C Capossela
Exec V Pres Hr, Kathleen T Hogan
Evp-Pres, McRsft Glbl Sls Mkt, Jean-Philippe Courtois
Evp Bus Dev't, Margaret L Johnson
Corp Vp-Technology, William Stasior
Pres-Microsoft Japan, Hitoshi Yoshida
General Manager, Brad Wilson
Auditors: DELOITTE & TOUCHE LLP

HQ: Microsoft Corporation
One Microsoft Way, Redmond, WA 98052-6399
Phone: 425 882-8080
Web: www.microsoft.com

COMPETITORS

Adobe Systems	Nintendo
Amazon.com	Nokia
Apple Inc.	Novell
CA Inc.	Opera Software
EMC	Oracle
Google	Red Hat
Hewlett-Packard	SAP
IBM	Sony
Logitech	Yahoo!
Mozilla	salesforce.com

HISTORICAL FINANCIALS

Company Type: Public

Income Statement   FYE: June 30

	REVENUE ($ mil.)	NET INCOME ($ mil.)	NET PROFIT MARGIN	EMPLOYEES
06/19	125,843	39,240	31.2%	144,000
06/18	110,360	16,571	15.0%	97,535
06/17	89,950	21,204	23.6%	124,000
06/16	85,320	16,798	19.7%	114,000
06/15	93,580	12,193	13.0%	118,000
Annual Growth	7.7%	33.9%	—	5.1%

2019 Year-End Financials

Debt ratio: 25.00%—
Return on equity: 42.00%
Cash ($ mil.): 11,356
Current ratio: 3.00
Long-term debt ($ mil.): 66,662

Dividends
Yield: 0.0%
Payout: 36.0%
Market value ($ mil.): —

	STOCK PRICE ($) FY Close	P/E High/Low		PER SHARE ($) Earnings	Dividends	Book Value
06/19	134.00	27	18	5.00	2.00	13.00
06/18	99.00	48	32	2.00	2.00	11.00
06/17	69.00	26	19	3.00	2.00	9.00
06/16	51.00	27	19	2.00	1.00	9.00
06/15	44.00	33	27	1.00	1.00	10.00
Annual Growth	32.0%	—	—	36.0%	10.4%	7.6%

Mid Penn Bancorp Inc

Mid Penn Bancorp is the holding company for Mid Penn Bank which operatesÂ more thanÂ a dozen branches in central Pennsylvania's Cumberland Dauphin Northumberland and Schuylkill counties. The bank offers full-service commercial banking insuranceÂ and trust services.Â Its deposit products include checking savings money market and NOWÂ accounts. Commercial real estate construction andÂ land developmentÂ loans account for nearly 80% of the company's loan portfolio; the bank also writes residential mortgages and business agricultural and consumer loans. Mid Penn is a descendant of Millersburg Bank founded in 1868. Trust company CEDE & Co. ownsÂ about aÂ thirdÂ of Mid Penn Bancorp.

EXECUTIVES

Pres-Ceo, Rory G Ritrievi
Non Exec Chb, Robert C Grubic
V Chb, William A Specht III

Sr Exec V Pres-Cfo, Michael D Peduzzi
Auditors: BDO USA, LLP

LOCATIONS

HQ: Mid Penn Bancorp Inc
349 Union Street, Millersburg, PA 17061
Phone: 866 642-7736
Web: www.midpennbank.com

COMPETITORS

Fulton Financial
PNC Financial
Pennsylvania State Employees Credit Union

HISTORICAL FINANCIALS

Company Type: Public

Income Statement   FYE: December 31

	ASSETS ($ mil.)	NET INCOME ($ mil.)	INCOME AS % OF ASSETS	EMPLOYEES
12/18	2,078	11	0.5%	406
12/17	1,170	7	0.6%	277
12/16	1,033	8	0.8%	257
12/15	932	7	0.7%	252
12/14	756	6	0.8%	203
Annual Growth	28.8%	16.8%	—	18.9%

2018 Year-End Financials

Debt ratio: 4.00%
Return on equity: 7.00%
Cash ($ mil.): 29
Current ratio: —
Long-term debt ($ mil.): —

No. of shares (mil.): 8
Dividends
Yield: 3.0%
Payout: 69.0%
Market value ($ mil.): 195

	STOCK PRICE ($) FY Close	P/E High/Low		PER SHARE ($) Earnings	Dividends	Book Value
12/18	23.00	25	15	1.00	1.00	26.00
12/17	33.00	21	14	2.00	1.00	18.00
12/16	24.00	13	8	2.00	1.00	17.00
12/15	16.00	12	10	1.00	1.00	17.00
12/14	16.00	11	9	2.00	0.00	17.00
Annual Growth	10.3%	—	—	(0.8%)	11.7%	11.8%

MIDFLORIDA FEDERAL CREDIT UNION

EXECUTIVES

Pres, Kevin Jones
Cao, Gail O'Brien
Coo, Dennis Pershing
Clo, Sandra Gibson
Vice-President Human Resources, Nancy Irvin
Human Resources Director, Brian Palmer
Member Officer, Amanda Jones
Associate Manager, Amber Kelly
Executive Administrative Assis, Rhonda Oliva
Loss Prevention Manager, Nicole Moore
Network Security Engineer, Bobby Hiers

LOCATIONS

HQ: MIDFLORIDA FEDERAL CREDIT UNION
129 S KENTUCKY AVE # 100, LAKELAND, FL 338015073
Phone: 866 913-3733
Web: WWW.MIDFLORIDA.COM

HISTORICAL FINANCIALS

Company Type: Private

Income Statement   FYE: December 31

	ASSETS ($ mil.)	NET INCOME ($ mil.)	INCOME AS % OF ASSETS	EMPLOYEES
12/17	3,056	36	1.2%	278
12/16	2,641	29	1.1%	—
Annual Growth	15.7%	24.5%		

Midland States Bancorp Inc

Born in rural Illinois Midland States Bancorp is now discovering banking life in new states. It is the $3 billion-asset holding company for Midland States Bank a community bank that operates more than 35 branches in central and northern Illinois and around 15 branches in the St. Louis metropolitan area. The bank offers traditional consumer and commercial banking products and services as well as merchant card services insurance and financial planning. Subsidiary Midland Wealth Management which boasts $1.2 billion-plus in assets under administration provides wealth management services while Heartland Business Credit offers commercial equipment leasing services. Midland States Bancorp went public in 2016.

IPO

The bank holding company raised $80.1 million in its initial public offering. It plans to contribute some $25 million to Midland States Bank and use the rest for general corporate purposes including possible acquisitions.

Operations

About 57% of Midland States Bancorp's total revenue came from loan interest during 2014 while another 17% came from interest income from investment securities. The rest came from wealth management fees (8% of revenue) deposit account service charges (3%) ATM and interchange revenue (3%) mortgage banking revenue (3%) merchant services revenue (1%) and nonrecurring gains on the sales of assets (around 8%).

Subsidiary Love Funding provides multifamily and healthcare facility FHA financing.

Geographic Reach

Midland has more than 80 branches and offices across the US with around 50 in Illinois and around the St. Louis metro area and the rest in California Colorado Florida Massachusetts North Carolina Ohio Tennessee and Texas.

Financial Performance

Midland States Bancorp's revenue climbed 3% to $93 million despite a decline in loan interest income during 2014 mostly thanks to profitable asset sales and other income.

Despite modest revenue growth in 2014 the bank's net income dove 67% to $3.2 billion as acquisition and integration expenses stemming from its late 2014 acquisition of Heartland ate up any revenue gains it had made. Excluding these nonrecurring items the bank's net income grew modestly.

Strategy

Midland States Bancorp has been pursuing an acquisition and branch expansion growth strategy since 2007 after it replaced its executive management and laid out a plan to expand Midland States

Bank's presence in Illinois. Midland States Bank continues to focus on moving into suburban areas and other markets in Illinois and Missouri that have growing populations. During 2015 it opened a new branches in the St. Louis region (in Jennings) downtown Joliet and downtown Effingham areas as well as a wealth management office in downtown Decatur.

The company also planned in 2016 to continue building its fast-growing wealth management business which now makes up nearly 10% of its total revenue. Thanks to Midland's efforts the business' wealth management assets under administration have skyrocketed twelve-fold since 2008 growing from $95 million then to $1.19 billion at the end of 2014.

Mergers and Acquisitions

Midland States Bancorp agreed to acquire HomeStar Financial Group in 2019 in a transaction valued at about $10 million. HomeStar's Manteno Illinois-based HomeStar Bank and Financial Services has about $375 million in assets $220 million in loans and $330 million in deposits. HomeStar has five locations in northern Illinois. The deal expands Midland's presence in the Kankakee Illinois metropolitan area.

In 2017 CEO Leon Holschbach signed a $175 million deal with rival Centrue Bank to merge. The two banks had been treading on each others' toes in Princeton Illinois.

Company Background

Between 2008 and 2010 the bank's branch locations grew from just a half-dozen in central Illinois and St. Louis to nearly 30 around the state and in the St. Louis metropolitan area. During that time the bank acquired the assets of Waterloo Bancshares and WestBridge in St. Louis AMCORE in northern Illinois and Strategic Capital in central Illinois. It also opened new locations in some of its faster-growing markets. As a result of its efforts Midland States Bancorp has watched its revenue and profits trend upward significantly from 2007 levels.

EXECUTIVES

Vice Chairman President And Ceo, Leon J. Holschbach, age 66, $529,389 total compensation
Evp Midland States Bancorp And President Midland States Bank, Jeffrey G. Ludwig, age 47, $367,500 total compensation
Evp Banking, Jeffrey S. Medford
Cfo Midland States Bancorp And Midland States Bank, Kevin L. Thompson
Vice President Commercial Banking, Jan Woodward
Senior Vice President And Corporate Counsel Of The Company And The Bank, Douglas Tucker
Vice President, Deanna Haught
Vice President Mortgage Banking, Mark Widdicombe
Senior Vice President, Sharon Schaubert
Svp, James Thompson
Chairman, John M. Schultz, age 67
Board Member, Robert Schultz
Board Member, Deborah Golden
Board Member, Jeffrey Mcdonnell
Board Member, Dwight Miller
Board Member, Richard Ramos
Auditors: Crowe LLP

LOCATIONS

HQ: Midland States Bancorp Inc
1201 Network Centre Drive, Effingham, IL 62401
Phone: 217 342-7321
Web: www.midlandsb.com

PRODUCTS/OPERATIONS

2014 Sales

	$ mil.	% of total
Interest income		
Loans	56	57
Investment Securities & others	17	17
Noninterest income		
Wealth management revenue	7	8
Service charges on deposit accounts	3	3
Mortgage banking revenue	3	3
Gain on sale of other assets	3	3
ATM and interchange revenue	3	3
Impairments	(2.6)	-
Other	4	6
Total	**94**	**100**

Selected Services

Bank By Phone
Bill Paying
Checking
Debit Card
Online Banking
Savings & CDs

COMPETITORS

Bank of America
Edward D. Jones
Fifth Third
First Mid-Illinois Bancshares
Harris
Mercantile Bancorp
PNC Financial
U.S. Bancorp

HISTORICAL FINANCIALS

Company Type: Public

Income Statement				FYE: December 31
	ASSETS ($ mil.)	NET INCOME ($ mil.)	INCOME AS % OF ASSETS	EMPLOYEES
12/18	5,638	39	0.7%	1,100
12/17	4,413	16	0.4%	840
12/16	3,234	32	1.0%	715
12/15	2,885	24	0.8%	700
12/14	2,677	11	0.4%	—
Annual Growth	20.5%	38.2%	—	—

2018 Year-End Financials

Debt ratio: 3.00%
Return on equity: 7.00%
Cash ($ mil.): 211
Current ratio: —
Long-term debt ($ mil.): —
No. of shares (mil.): 24
Dividends
  Yield: 4.0%
  Payout: 85.0%
Market value ($ mil.): 531

	STOCK PRICE ($) FY Close	P/E High/Low		PER SHARE ($) Earnings	Dividends	Book Value
12/18	22.00	21	12	2.00	1.00	26.00
12/17	32.00	40	33	1.00	1.00	24.00
12/16	36.00	17	9	2.00	0.00	21.00
Annual Growth	(11.4%)	—	—	(6.5%)	25.0%	5.4%

MidWestOne Financial Group, Inc.

MidWestOne Financial Group is the holding company for MidWestOne Bank which operates about two dozen branches throughout central and east-central Iowa. The bank offers standard deposit products such as checking and savings accounts CDs and IRAs in addition to trust services credit cards insurance and brokerage and investment services. About two-thirds of MidWestOne Financial's loan portfolio consists of real estate loans including residential and commercial mortgages and farmland and construction loans. Founded in 1983 MidWestOne has total assets of $1.8 billion.

Geographic Reach

Headquartered in Iowa City MidWestOne Financial Group's MidWestOne Bank has branches and loan production offices in 15 counties in central and east-central Iowa.

Financial Performance

MidWestOne Financial Group reported net income of $18.6 million in 2013 a 13% increase over 2012. Earnings have been rising steadily while the bank's revenue has been trending downward. Indeed 2013's $80.8 million in revenue was 10% below 2012. Assets declined slightly over the same period as did deposits. (The bank is facing stiff competition for deposits from aggressive credit unions offering above market deposit rates.) However loans increased 5% year over year and the growth in loans combined with stable net interest margins of about 3.5% resulted in a modest uptick in net interest income. Non-interest income got a boost from the bank's wealth management division which posted a 7% revenue gain in 2013 versus 2012.

EXECUTIVES

President And Ceo, Charles N. Funk, age 65, $422,000 total compensation
Evp And Chief Credit Officer, Kent L. Jehle, age 59, $271,000 total compensation
Vp And Chief Risk Officer, James M. Cantrell, $205,000 total compensation
Coo, Kevin Kramer
Svp And Cfo, Katie A. Lorenson, age 39, $206,231 total compensation
Senior Regional President, Mitchell W. Cook, age 55, $204,400 total compensation
Vice President Information Technology Managing Officer, Allen Schneider
Senior Vice President Loan Sales, Jason Swestka
Vice President Lpl Financial Advisor Located, John Evans
Vice President And Program Manager, Daniel Bailey
Senior Vice President Treasury Management, Kevin Pleasant
Vice President Mortgage Loan Operations, Linda Nelson
Vice President And Trust Officer, Lia Lovelace
Vice President Mortgage Loan Operations, Linda A Nelson
Second Vice President Mortgage Banker, Niki Gysbers
Senior Vice President Small Business Administration, John Kimball
Vice President Commercial Banking, Jeff Schebler
Vice President Commercial Lending, Andrew L Brust
Vice President Human Resource Manager, Cathi Weber
Senior Vice President Retail Banking, David Lindstrom
Vice President Commercial Banking, Nick Raffensperger
Chairman, Kevin W. Monson, age 67
Board Member, Michael Hatch
Board Member, Nate Kaeding
Auditors: RSM US LLP

LOCATIONS

HQ: MidWestOne Financial Group, Inc.
102 South Clinton Street, Iowa City, IA 52240
Phone: 319 356-5800
Web: www.midwestone.com

PRODUCTS/OPERATIONS

2015 Sales

	$ mil.	% of total
Interest Income		
Interest and fees on loans	87	71
Interest on investment securities	13	11
Other	1	1
Non-Interest Income		
Trust investment and insurance fees	6	5
Other service charges commissions and fees	6	5
Service charges and fees on deposit accounts	4	3
Mortgage origination and loan servicing fees	3	3
Other	2	2
Total	**122**	**100**

Selected Subsidiaries

MidWestOne Bank
MidWestOne Insurance Services Inc.
MidWestOne Statutory Trust II

COMPETITORS

Bank of the West
Hills Bancorporation
QCR Holdings

U.S. Bancorp
Wells Fargo
West Bancorporation

HISTORICAL FINANCIALS
Company Type: Public

Income Statement

	ASSETS ($ mil.)	NET INCOME ($ mil.)	INCOME AS % OF ASSETS	EMPLOYEES
				FYE: December 31
12/18	3,291	30	0.9%	597
12/17	3,212	19	0.6%	610
12/16	3,080	20	0.7%	587
12/15	2,980	25	0.8%	648
12/14	1,800	19	1.0%	374
Annual Growth	16.3%	13.1%	—	12.4%

2018 Year-End Financials

Debt ratio: 1.00%
Return on equity: 9.00%
Cash ($ mil.): 45
Current ratio: —
Long-term debt ($ mil.): —

No. of shares (mil.): 12
Dividends
 Yield: 3.0%
 Payout: 45.0%
Market value ($ mil.): 302

	STOCK PRICE ($) FY Close	P/E High/Low	PER SHARE ($) Earnings	Dividends	Book Value
12/18	25.00	14 10	2.00	1.00	29.00
12/17	34.00	25 21	2.00	1.00	28.00
12/16	38.00	22 14	2.00	1.00	27.00
12/15	30.00	14 12	2.00	1.00	26.00
12/14	29.00	13 10	2.00	1.00	23.00
Annual Growth	(3.6%)	— —	3.2%	7.7%	6.2%

MODERN WOODMEN OF AMERICA

No need to pitch a tent to have Modern Woodmen in your camp. One of the largest fraternal benefit societies in the US Modern Woodmen of America provides annuities life insurance and other financial savings products to more than 770000 members through some 1600 agents. The group founded in 1883 is organized into "camps" (or chapters) that provide financial social recreational and service benefits to members. Founder Joseph Cullen Root chose the society's name to compare pioneering woodmen clearing forests to

men using life insurance to remove the financial burdens their families could face upon their deaths.

Operations

The organization claims some 2400 family and summit chapters and more than 900 youth clubs nationwide. In addition to financial services the chapters also offer social activities and community service opportunities for members and their families. In addition to life insurance and annuities the company offers retirement accounts including IRAs college savings plans investment assistance and other insurance products. Modern Woodmen has more than $36 billion in life insurance in force.

Subsidiary MWA Financial Services offers securities and brokered insurance products. The MWABank (dba Modern Woodmen Bank) division provides retail banking services.

Financial Performance

All told the company has more than $13 billion in assets and roughly $36 billion of life insurance in force. Its 2013 surplus totaled $1.5 billion a 14% increase over 2012.

Strategy

The company enhances its operations by adding new products as well as through marketing efforts for existing products. For instance in 2012 Modern Woodsmen's financial representatives increased promotional efforts for life insurance products leading to a 5% increase in certificates and a 12% rise new policies that year. The increase in life insurance sales was also attributed to the Planning for Life program a system introduced in 2011 to help members understand the role of life insurance in financial planning.

Mergers and Acquisitions

In 2012 Modern Woodmen grew its membership by more than 17000 through the acquisition of Equitable Reserve Association. Through the combination Modern Woodmen assumed the assets liabilities and operations of Equitable Reserve.

Company Background

Although Modern Woodmen's roots are tangled with Woodmen of the World Life Insurance Society the two fraternal benefit societies are not related.

EXECUTIVES

Vice President Of It, Becky Hansen

LOCATIONS

HQ: MODERN WOODMEN OF AMERICA
 1701 1ST AVE, ROCK ISLAND, IL 612018779
Phone: 309 793-5537
Web: WWW.MODERNWOODMEN.ORG

PRODUCTS/OPERATIONS

Selected Products

Annuities (fixed immediate and variable; through MWA
 Financial Services)
Banking (MWABank)
 Certificates of Deposit
 Checking and savings accounts
 Credit cards and gift cards
 First mortgage and refinancing home loans
 Home equity loans
Insurance (through MWAGIA)
 Dental and vision insurance
 Disability income insurance
 Group employee benefits
 Group voluntary benefits
 Impaired risk life insurance
 International life and health insurance
 Long-term care insurance
 Major medical insurance
 Medicare supplement insurance
Investment (through MWA Financial Services)
 Brokerage services
 College savings plans
 Mutual funds

Retirement plans
Life Insurance
 Term life insurance
 Term life insurance for children
 Universal life insurance
 Whole life insurance

COMPETITORS

Allstate
MassMutual
MetLife
Nationwide Financial
New York Life
Northwestern Mutual
Prudential

Reliance Standard
Royal Neighbors Of
 America
State Farm
Thrivent Financial
Woodmen of the World
 Life Insurance

HISTORICAL FINANCIALS
Company Type: Private

Income Statement

	ASSETS ($ mil.)	NET INCOME ($ mil.)	INCOME AS % OF ASSETS	EMPLOYEES
				FYE: December 31
12/07	8,318	97	1.2%	480
12/06	7,929	99	1.3%	—
Annual Growth	4.9%	(2.6%)	—	—

Mohawk Industries, Inc.

Mohawk Industries is the world's largest maker of commercial and residential flooring products. The company manufactures carpets and rugs ceramic and stone tile and laminate wood and vinyl flooring. It produces a range of broadloom carpets and rugs under such names as Mohawk Aladdin Durkan Karastan and Leoline. Mohawk's ceramic tile and stone flooring products are marketed under the popular Daltile brand and Unilin and Pergo laminate and wood flooring and other wood products round out Mohawk's operations. The company sells its products worldwide. Most of its revenue is generated in the US and it has a strong market position in Brazil.

Operations

Mohawk works through three business segments: Flooring North America (NA) Global Ceramic and Flooring Rest of World (ROW).

The Flooring NA segment generates about 40% of total sales and makes several floor covering products for residential and commercial markets for both remodeling and new construction. This segment includes products such as broadloom carpet carpet tile rugs and mats wood laminate luxury vinyl tile (LVT) and sheet vinyl. In addition to its own Mohawk brands it markets and distributes brands such as Aladdin Commercial Durkan IVC Karastan Pergo Portico and Quick-Step.

The Global Ceramic segment (more than 35%) comprises ceramic porcelain and natural stone tile products used for floors and walls in both residential and commercial applications. It also provides natural stone quartz and porcelain slab countertops and installation materials. Some Global Ceramic segment brands are American Olean Daltile KAI and Marazzi.

The Flooring ROW segment (almost 25%) manufactures and distributes most of the company's products as well as roofing panels insulation boards and chipboards. In addition Flooring ROW licenses certain manufacturers' patents which it sells through retailers and distributors. Flooring

ROW has significant operations in Europe Russia Malaysia Australia and New Zealand.

On a product level Mohawk generates nearly 40% of revenue from its carpet and resilient product group about 35% from ceramic and stone and about 10% from laminate and wood. Other products represent the remaining 10%.

Geographic Reach

Georgia-based Mohawk Industries sells its products to more than 170 countries around the world. It generates around 60% of its revenue in the US. Other significant markets include Europe (about 25%) and Russia (about 5%).

The company has more than 90 manufacturing and distribution facilities in about 20 countries. It has more than 25 manufacturing and nearly 20 distribution facilities in North America and nearly 30 manufacturing and roughly 10 distribution facilities in Europe and Russia.

Sales and Marketing

Mohawk exports its products worldwide and is a market leader in North America Brazil Europe Russia and Australasia. For distribution it uses regional distribution centers as well as direct shipping and customer pick-up from manufacturing facilities. Mohawk's truck fleet operates from warehouses and cross-docks that receive products from the company's manufacturing plants.

Through its sales force the company sells its products to more than 25000 customers which include independent floor covering retailers and distributors ceramic specialists home centers wholesalers and mass merchandisers. Mohawk's top 10 customers account for nearly 20% of its total sales.

Financial Performance

Mohawk Industries has seen a significant upward trend in revenue increasing 28% since 2014 and has posted five consecutive years of record profits.

Sales in 2018 amounted to $9.9 billion up by 5% compared with $9.5 billion in 2017. The increase was primarily due to higher sales volume in all its divisions with the highest growth (15.7%) in the Flooring ROW segment.

Net income however dropped by 11% to $864.9 million in 2018 down from $974.7 the previous year. The company cites dramatically higher material costs as the primary factor partially offset by favorable price and product mix in the Flooring ROW segment.

Cash at the end of fiscal 2018 was $119.0 million an increase of $34.2 million from the prior year. Cash from operations contributed $1.2 billion to the coffers while investing activities used $1.3 billion mainly for additions to property plant and equipment and acquisitions. Financing activities provided $198.0 million from increased borrowings offset by stock repurchases.

Strategy

Mohawk's 2018 acquisitions served to strengthen the company's geographic reach with the purchase of Godfrey Hirst in Australia and New Zealand and with the Eliane ceramic tile company in Brazil. In Australasia Mohawk plans to expand Godfrey Hirst's commercial carpet position and capitalize on New Zealand's wool collections adding those to the US luxury carpet portfolio.

Product innovations such as Mohawk's Reveal Imaging printing technology (replicates the appearance of natural wood and stone) are driving increases in sales and Mohawk's SmartStrand fiber technology was introduced to create softer yet stain-resistant carpets and rugs. In laminates the company has increased the water resistance properties of its products which allow for more kitchen and bath installations. Mohawk has also started making quartz countertops in addition to its existing stone and porcelain countertop slabs.

As luxury vinyl tile (LTV) is becoming more popular it's taking market share from other products and Mohawk is scrambling to catch up with demand. Pressured to increase supply the company will expand its LTV operations specifically in the US and Europe.

Mergers and Acquisitions

Mohawk is extending its international reach and augmenting its product portfolio through acquisitions. In mid-2018 the company acquired Godfrey Hirst Group the leading flooring company in Australia and New Zealand leveraging its global flooring resources and further extending Mohawk's global position. Godfrey Hirst provides broadloom modular carpet and hard surface products for both residential and commercial applications.

The same year the company purchased Eliane Brazil's largest ceramic tile exporter for approximately $250 million. It also acquired Berghoef a European mezzanine flooring manufacturer.

Company Background

The company was founded in 1902 in Amsterdam New York as the Shuttleworth Brothers Company later becoming Mohawk Carpet Mills in 1920. As Mohawk's carpet business grew it merged with other carpet manufacturers and was eventually bought by MHS Holdings in 1988. MHS spun off the carpet business as Mowhawk Industries.

From 1992 (when Mohawk Industries went public) to 2000 the company made twelve soft surface acquisitions and grew to ten times its size. With the acquisition of Dal-Tile in 2002 the company became the largest ceramic provider in North America and added international manufacturing to its operations. It entered the European market in 2005 with the acquisition of Belgium-based laminate manufacturer Unilin and in 2007 the purchase of Columbia Wood Flooring added engineered and solid wood flooring to its product lineup and expanded its presence in Asia with a manufacturing facility in Malaysia.

Mohawk began doing business in Brazil through a joint venture in 2012 that included the company's laminate flooring. A year later it added laminate producer Pergo to its fold and also became the world's largest ceramic tile supplier with the acquisition of Marazzi which added operations in Italy Spain Russia and the US.

To continue to add revenue to its bottom line Mohawk gobbled up several more flooring product companies including IVC Group (sheet vinyl and LVT) Kai Group in Eastern Europe Xtratherm (insulation board) in Europe European ceramic tile maker EmilGroup Godfrey Hirst (carpeting) in Australia and New Zealand and Brazilian tile manufacturer Eliane.

HISTORY

Mohawk traces its origins to the Shuttleworth family who founded the company in Amsterdam New York in 1878 setting up their business with 14 second-hand looms imported from England. The company was incorporated as Shuttleworth Brothers in 1902. It introduced the popular Karnak carpet design in 1908.

EXECUTIVES

Svp Marketing, Karen R. Mendelsohn
Chairman And Ceo, Jeffrey S. Lorberbaum, age 64, $1,142,473 total compensation
President And Coo, W. Christopher (Chris) Wellborn, age 63, $987,186 total compensation
President Ceramic North America, John C. Turner, age 50
President Flooring North America, Brian M. Carson, age 54, $618,000 total compensation

Vp Finance And Cfo, Frank H. Boykin, age 63, $615,605 total compensation
President Flooring Rest Of World, Bernard P. Thiers, age 63, $609,312 total compensation
Vice President Sales Bigelow And Mohawk Commercial Brands, Jeff Davis
Regional Vice President Strategic And Global Customers Pacific Northwest, Lori Edwards
Vp Internal Audit, Carley Ferguson
Vice President Of Flooring Production, Willy Chandler
Vice President Sales, Craig Trimble
Vice President Sourcing, Jim Mason
Regional Vice President, Russell Ence
Vice President Sales, Tom Merriman
Vice President Research And Development, David Earl
Vice President Of Residential Carpet Product Development, Jamie Welborn
National Sales Manager Multi Family, Doug Davis
Mohawk Commercial Sales Flooring Commercial Rvp Mountain West, Ralph Holland
Vice President Of Design And Product Development, Neil Hegwood
National Accounts Manager, Farris Cagle
Vice President Se Region, Brian Ellis
Regional Vice President, Mike Stinnette
Vice President, Carl Holdridge
Vice President Marketing, Tom Donoghue
Vice President Business Development And International Sales, Nick Sterghos
Vice President Logistics, Scot Bernstein
Senior Vice President Learning Development, Ashley Brown
Regional Vice President, Frank Abraham
Mvp, Michelle Rhodes
Regional Vice President Sales Southeast, Tracy Lambeth
Regional Vice President, O'hara Jerry
Regional Vice President, Jim Waters
Regional Vice President Mid Atlantic, Jeff Weaver
Vice President Commercial Marketing, Kevin Wildes
Regional Vice President Of Sales Midsouth Region, Todd Lomas
Regional Vice President, Cheryl Peale
Regional Vice President Builder Multi Family Division, Dan Hill
Auditors: KPMG LLP

LOCATIONS

HQ: Mohawk Industries, Inc.
160 S. Industrial Blvd., Calhoun, GA 30701
Phone: 706 629-7721
Web: www.mohawkind.com

2018 Sales

	$ mil.	% of total
US	6,104	61
Europe	2,583	26
Russia	349	4
All other countries	948	9
Total	**9,984**	**100**

PRODUCTS/OPERATIONS

2018 Sales

	$ mil.	% of total
Carpet and Resilient	3,904	39
Ceramic and Stone	3,621	36
Laminate and wood	1,553	16
Other	906	9
Total	**9,984**	**100**

2018 Sales

	$ mil.	% of total
Flooring NA	4,029	40
Global Ceramic	3,553	36
Flooring ROW	2,402	24
Total	**9,984**	**100**

Products Selected

Residential Carpet
Commercial Carpet
Bath Rugs Area Rugs and Mats
Ceramic Tile & Stone
Laminate Flooring
Hardwood Flooring
Luxury Vinyl Tile (LVT)

Selected Operations

Glazed wall tile
Hardwood flooring
Hardwood flooring
Insulation panels
Laminate flooring
Laminate flooring
Porcelain tile
Quarry tile
Resilient flooring
Roofing systems
Rugs
Stone products

Selected Brand NamesAladdinAmerican OleanBigelow CommercialCentury FlooringColumbia FlooringDal-TileDurkanHorizonKarastanLeesMeritMohawkMohawk HomeQuick-Step

COMPETITORS

Armstrong World Industries	Interface Inc.
Beaulieu of America	International Textile Group
Couristan	JJJ Floor Covering
Dixie Group	Mannington Mills
Formica	MasterTile
Guilford Performance Textiles	Perstorp
Hollander Home Fashions	Shaw Industries
Interceramic Inc.	Tarkett Inc.
	Wilsonart International

HISTORICAL FINANCIALS

Company Type: Public

Income Statement

FYE: December 31

	REVENUE ($ mil.)	NET INCOME ($ mil.)	NET PROFIT MARGIN	EMPLOYEES
12/18	9,984	862	8.6%	42,100
12/17	9,491	972	10.2%	38,800
12/16	8,959	930	10.4%	37,800
12/15	8,072	615	7.6%	34,100
12/14	7,803	532	6.8%	32,300
Annual Growth	6.4%	12.8%	—	6.8%

2018 Year-End Financials

Debt ratio: 25.00%
Return on equity: 12.00%
Cash ($ mil.): 119
Current ratio: 1.00
Long-term debt ($ mil.): 1,516

No. of shares (mil.): 72
Dividends
Yield: —
Payout: —
Market value ($ mil.): 8,457

	STOCK PRICE ($) FY Close	P/E High/Low		PER SHARE ($) Earnings	Dividends	Book Value
12/18	117.00	24	10	11.00	0.00	103.00
12/17	276.00	22	15	13.00	0.00	95.00
12/16	200.00	17	12	12.00	0.00	78.00
12/15	189.00	25	18	8.00	0.00	66.00
12/14	155.00	22	17	7.00	0.00	61.00
Annual Growth	(6.9%)	—	—	12.2%	—	14.1%

Molina Healthcare Inc

Molina Healthcare is dedicated to helping low-income Americans receive health and behavioral health coverage as well as primary care services. The company's Health Plan segment arranges for the delivery of health services to some 4.5 million people who receive their care through Medicaid Medicare and other government-funded programs in about a dozen states and Puerto Rico. Its Medicaid Solutions segment provides business process outsourcing (BPO) solutions to Medicaid agencies in six states for their Medicaid Management Information Systems (MMIS) the tool used to support administration of state health care entitlement programs. The family of founder C. David Molina controls the company through holdings and trusts.

Operations

Until 2018 Molina operated through two primary segments: Health Plan and Molina Medicaid Solutions. Altogether the company's operations provide plans or services to 4.5 million individuals in a dozen states. Molina's Health Plans segment accounts for more than 95% of revenues. The company's health plans provide medical services through state networks of contracted hospitals and physicians that accept Molina health plan coverage. The health plans are each licensed as health maintenance organizations (HMOs).

The Medicaid segment helped state agencies administer their Medicaid programs with such offerings as IT development and business processing. Molina sold that business to DXC Technology in 2018.

Geographic Reach

Molina's health plans primarily operate in Washington California South Carolina Texas Ohio and Michigan as well as in New Mexico and Florida.

Molina's Health Plans segment leases around 70 facilities while the Medicaid solutions segment leases a dozen facilities.

Sales and Marketing

Molina's primary customers include state Medicaid agencies and the federal government.

Financial Performance

Molina has seen steady revenue increases over the last few years. In 2017 revenue rose 25% to $19.8 billion as premium revenue increased (largely as a result of a 10% increase in membership) and investment income saw growth. Premium revenue growth was led by California Florida Texas and Washington. However a decline in service revenue and the absence of reimbursed health insurer fees partially offset those gains.

As a participant in the Affordable Care Act marketplace the company has been struggling to be profitable. It has initiated a restructuring effort that included a management shakeup in 2017. That year it fell into the black in 2017 with a net loss of $512 million. One factor contributing to that loss was the federal government's move to stop funding cost-sharing reduction (CRS) payments. As such medical care costs increased and the company had $470 million in impairment losses. It also had $234 million in restructuring and separation costs.

Operating cash flow totaled $804 million that year a 19% increase from that of 2016.

Strategy

One of Molina's immediate initiatives is advocating for the improvement of the insurance marketplace under regulatory guidelines. The company says that it is owed $128 million in risk corridor payments from the federal government and it has yet to recognize revenue from these payments. (The risk corridor program established as part of the Affordable Care Act aimed to protect insurers participating in exchanges from higher-than-expected claims through 2016.) In a mid-2017 win a federal claims court ruled that the government owes Molina $52 million in risk corridor payments. That ruling followed a string of upsets from quarterly losses and company layoffs to the withdrawal from Utah's and Wisconsin's exchanges and the firing of the company's CEO and CFO (both sons of Molina's founder). Restructuring expenses led the company to incur $234 million in related losses in 2017.

A key Molina strategy for growth is to expand membership especially in its existing markets by acquiring the Medicaid contracts of other businesses. It made several of these purchases in 2016 adding more than 220000 Medicaid members to its books. It has also secured a number of state contracts including deals made in 2017 to provide Medicaid coverage in Illinois and Mississippi and a deal in 2018 to provide Children's Health Insurance Program (CHIP) services in Texas. In addition Molina enters new markets through both organic measures and through acquisitions targeting large markets with competitive provider communities.But in 2017 the company lost certain Medicaid contracts in New Mexico Florida and Illinois which ultimately contributed to a $470 million impairment loss. Molina is working to regain contracts lost in New Mexico and Florida.

The company is also working on cutting costs to improve efficiency. In addition to its restructuring efforts mentioned above it has also improved its care management systems and processes. It is increasingly utilizing hospitalists (dedicated physicians working in hospitals) and coordinating care efforts among teams of providers to both save money and improve health outcomes.

Molina's former Pathways subsidiary (acquired in late 2016) provided home- and community-based behavioral health services which the company believed would see a growth in demand over the next few years. However after reporting $173 million impairment loss primarily related to the Pathways business the company sold the unit to investment firm Atar Capital in 2018.

In the past Molina's growth strategy also consisted of opening additional primary care clinics in existing and new territories. The addition of more clinics helped Molina diversify its operations by expanding its involvement in the direct delivery of primary care. Recently though the company has been quietly exiting the primary care business. It has closed down several clinics and sold several others.

With these exits and divestitures Molina is increasingly focused on its core health plan operations.

Mergers and Acquisitions

In 2016 Molina Healthcare bought Total Care Medicaid a plan serving some 39000 members in upstate New York from Universal American for $41.3 million. Other deals that year included the purchases of Loyola Physician Partners ($15 million adding 21000 Medicaid members in Illinois) and HAP Midwest Health Plan (adding some 81000 Medicaid and MIChild members).

EXECUTIVES

Cfo And Treasurer, Joseph W. White, age 60, $538,000 total compensation

Evp Research And Development, Martha Molina Bernadett, $357,000 total compensation

President Ceo And Director, Joseph M. Zubretsky, age 63

Coo, Terry P. Bayer, age 68, $644,000 total compensation

Svp General Counsel And Secretary, Jeff D. Barlow, age 56, $525,000 total compensation

Cio, Rick Hopfer

Associate Vp State Affairs Policy And Government Advocacy, David Pingree
Associate Vice President And Assistant General Counsel, Erin Hiley
Associate Vice President, Chang Liu
Mhi Associate Vice President Program Management, Kristine MacRae
Associate Vice President Care Management, Kelly Giardina
Medical Director, Lawrence O'Brien
Vice President Enterprise Pmo, Sanjay Bhat
Regional Vice President, Del Bell
Corporate Assistant Vice President Of Risk Adjustment, Kimberly Reid
Avp Accounting, Fay Adams
Assistant Vice President Rating, Ben Lynam
Vice President Of Accounting, Derek Danley
Vice President Of Clinic Operations, Anya Sage
Associate Vice President Enterprise Infrastructure Services, Bharani Krish
Vice President Healthcare Services, Jeffrey King
Mhu Associate Vice President Government Contracts, Douglas Springmeyer
Vice President, Mohit Ghose
Director Of Pharmacy, John Vu
Vice President Sales, Ryan Boe
Medical Director, Delores Baker
Vice President, Anne Lee
Vice President Of Call Centre, Randall Fillmore
Associate Vice President Of State Affairs, Cameron Smyth
Senior Vice President Provider And Member Engagement And Operations, Mary Syiek
Medical Director, Raymond Zastrow
Avp Medicare Pharmacy Services, Erin Gordon
Assistant Vice President Of Health Plan Operations, Betty Thomas
Vice President Tax, George Figueroa
Associate Vice President Of Government Contracts, David Vinkler
Vice President Business Innovation, Tom Giedlin
Associate Vice President Of Molina Healthcare Inc., Brian Monsen
Vice President Business Services, Bryce Berg
Vice President Network Development And Operations, Nancy Wohlhart
Vice President Network Strategy And Services, Kim Sweers
Vice President Finance And Analytics, Steve Whiting
Vice President Enterprise Infrastructure, Ben Gordon
Vice President Of Finance And Analytics, Dennis Akotia
Vice President Financial Planning And Analysis, Eduardo Silva
Medical Director, James Bowerman
Medical Director, Richard Sharon
Vice President Healthcare Services, Jessie Sanchez
Associate Vice President, Anita Carter
Vice President, Carolyn Ingram
Vice President Government Contracts, Karen Zeiler
Assistant Vice President, Cheryl Faroughi
Medical Director, David Eibling
Pharmacy Manager, Sima Firouzdehghan
Vice President Corporate Development, Eric De Garceau
Medical Director, Terry Fowler
Avp Government Contracts, Barbara Maxwell
Vice President Of Operations, Elizabeth Richardson
Avp Healthplan Operations, Jaime Perikly
National Medical Director, Douglas Allen
Director Of Pharmacy, Jennifer Strohecker
Vice President Of Government Contracts, Jeremy Greenfield
Vice President Medical Affairs And Chief Medical Officer, Gaspere Geraci
Vp And Medical Director, Michael Siegel
Avp Of Healthcare Services, Lorena Moore
Medical Director, Mary Engrav

Medical Director Of Behavioral Health, Ayo Gathing
Assistant Vice President Government Contracts, Nichole Mitchell
Assistant Vice President Of Community Engagement, Cynthia Young
Medical Director, Freda Gardner
Medical Director, Felix Nunez
Vice President, Dave Boim
Associate Vice President, Suma Simcoe
Vice President Finance And Analytics, Ivonne Garrote-torra
Executive Assistant To Sudhakar Gummadi Vice President, Chandara Toler
Assistant Vice President Of Long Term Care Operations, Robert Kalin
Medical Director, Shyama Gandhi
Associate Vice President Sales, Rick Knickerbocker
Associate Vice President Medicare Sales, Brian Shasha
Medical Director, Latha R Shankar
Associate Vice President, Mario J Garza
Senior Vice President Deputy General Counsel, Ronald D Kurtz
Director Of Pharmacy, Jacqueline Jacobi
Assistant Vice President Health Plan Operations, Kathy Lyall
Medical Director, Arik Olson
Vice President Of Clinical Operations And New Initiatives, Rebecca Wozniak
Avp, Elizabeth Lau
Exec Vp Research And Innovation, Mary Bernadett
Associate Vice President Community Engagement, Babette Honore
Avp Of Community Outreach And Appointment Center For The Mmg Clinics, Oscar Narro
Vice President, Debra Enigl
Vice President Of Network And Operations, Matt Wolf
Vice President Behavioral Health Plans, Taft Parsons
Assistant Vice President Community Engagement Enrollment Growth, Ruth Villalonga
Executive Vice President Strategic Planning Corporate Development And Transformation, Mark L Keim
Exec V Pres Health Plan Oprs, Pamela S Sedmak
Associate Vice President Internal Communications, David Sommers
Associate Vice President Healthcare Services, Deborah Mccormick
Vice President Business Innovation, Thomas Giedlin
Vice President Senior Assistant General Counsel And Assistant Secretary, Burt Park
Assistant Vice President Siu, Mary Alice Garcia
Associate Vice President Business Development, Chris Heldman
Avp, Ana Rivera
Vice President Of Manufacturing, Quiros Alice
Medical Director, Ilyse Lifton
Vice President Sandm, Svitek David
Associate Vice President Finance And Analytics, Rossi Gabriel De
Vice President, Lekan Lawal
Senior Vice President Investor Relations, Julie Trudell
Vice President Provider Network Management And Operations, Bryon Grizzard
Chairman, Dale B. Wolf, age 64
Auditors: Ernst & Young LLP

LOCATIONS

HQ: Molina Healthcare Inc
200 Oceangate, Suite 100, Long Beach, CA 90802
Phone: 562 435-3666   Fax: 562 437-1335
Web: www.molinahealthcare.com

2017 Membership by Health Plan

	$ mil.	% of total
Washington	777,000	17
California	746,000	17
Florida	625,000	14
Texas	430,000	9
Michigan	398,000	9
Ohio	327,000	7
Puerto Rico	314,000	7
New Mexico	253,000	6
Illinois	165,000	4
Utah	152,000	3
Wisconsin	118,000	3
South Carolina	116,000	3
New York	32,000	1
Total	**4,453,000**	**100**

PRODUCTS/OPERATIONS

2017 Sales

	$ mil.	% of total
Health plans	19,352	97
Medicaid solutions	187	1
Other	344	2
Total	**19,883**	**100**

2017 Sales

	$ mil.	% of total
Premiums	18,884	95
Services	521	3
Premium tax revenue	438	2
Investment income	70	—
Total	**19,883**	**100**

COMPETITORS

AMERIGROUP	Humana
Aetna	Kaiser Foundation
Anthem	Health Plan
CIGNA	L. A. Care Health Plan
Cambia Health Solutions	Premera Blue Cross
	Priority Health
Centene	Total Health Care
Community Health Group	UnitedHealth Group
HCSC	WellCare Health Plans

HISTORICAL FINANCIALS

Company Type: Public

Income Statement   FYE: December 31

	REVENUE ($ mil.)	NET INCOME ($ mil.)	NET PROFIT MARGIN	EMPLOYEES
12/18	18,890	707	3.7%	11,000
12/17	19,883	(512)	—	20,000
12/16	17,782	52	0.3%	21,000
12/15	14,178	143	1.0%	21,000
12/14	9,667	62	0.6%	10,500
Annual Growth	18.2%	83.6%	—	1.2%

2018 Year-End Financials

Debt ratio: 20.00%
Return on equity: 47.00%
Cash ($ mil.): 2,826
Current ratio: 2.00
Long-term debt ($ mil.): 1,217
No. of shares (mil.): 62
Dividends
  Yield: —
  Payout: —
Market value ($ mil.): 7,206

	STOCK PRICE ($) FY Close	P/E High/Low		Earnings	PER SHARE ($) Dividends	Book Value
12/18	116.00	13	6	11.00	0.00	27.00
12/17	77.00	—	—	(9.00)	0.00	22.00
12/16	54.00	73	49	1.00	0.00	29.00
12/15	60.00	30	18	3.00	0.00	28.00
12/14	54.00	41	25	1.00	0.00	20.00
Annual Growth	21.4%	—	—	69.3%	—	6.9%

Molson Coors Beverage Co

Auditors: PricewaterhouseCoopers LLP

LOCATIONS

HQ: Molson Coors Beverage Co
1555 Notre Dame Street East, Montreal, Quebec H2L 2R5
Phone: 514 521-1786
Web: www.molsoncoors.com

HISTORICAL FINANCIALS

Company Type: Public

Income Statement

FYE: December 31

	REVENUE ($ mil.)	NET INCOME ($ mil.)	NET PROFIT MARGIN	EMPLOYEES
12/18	10,770	1,117	10.4%	17,750
12/17	11,003	1,414	12.9%	17,200
12/16	4,885	1,976	40.4%	17,400
12/15	3,568	360	10.1%	17,500
12/14	4,146	514	12.4%	17,400
Annual Growth	**27.0%**	**21.4%**	**—**	**0.5%**

2018 Year-End Financials

Debt ratio: 35.00%
Return on equity: 8.00%
Cash ($ mil.): 1,058
Current ratio: 1.00
Long-term debt ($ mil.): 8,894

No. of shares (mil.): 216
Dividends
  Yield: 3.0%
  Payout: 32.0%
Market value ($ mil.): 12,136

	STOCK PRICE ($) FY Close	P/E High/Low		PER SHARE ($) Earnings	Dividends	Book Value
12/18	56.00	16	11	5.00	2.00	63.00
12/17	82.00	15	12	7.00	2.00	61.00
12/16	97.00	12	9	9.00	2.00	53.00
12/15	94.00	49	34	2.00	2.00	38.00
12/14	75.00	28	18	3.00	1.00	42.00
Annual Growth	**(6.8%)**	**—**	**—**	**16.9%**	**2.6%**	**10.2%**

Mondelez International Inc

One of the world's largest snack companies Mondelez International owns a pantry of billion-dollar brands such as Cadbury and Milka chocolates; LU BelVita and Oreo biscuits; Trident gum; and Tang powdered beverages. The company's portfolio includes global national and regional brands many of which are more than 100 years old. Biscuits (cookies crackers and salted snacks) and chocolate account for most of the company's sales. Mondelez which operates in more than 80 countries and sells its products in some 150 generates most of its revenue outside the US.

HISTORY

The Kraft tale began in 1903 when James L. Kraft began delivering cheese to Chicago grocers. His four brothers joined in forming the J.L. Kraft & Bros. Company in 1909. By 1914 the company had opened a cheese factory and was selling cheese across the US. Kraft developed its first blended pasteurized cheese the following year.

Kraft went public in 1924; four years later it merged with Philadelphia cream-cheese maker Phoenix and also created Velveeta cheese spread. In 1930 Kraft was bought by National Dairy but its operations were kept separate. New and notable products included Miracle Whip salad dressing (1933) macaroni and cheese dinners (1937) and Parkay margarine (1940). In the decades that followed Kraft expanded into foreign markets.

National Dairy became Kraftco in 1969 and Kraft in 1976 hoping to benefit from its internationally known trademark. To diversify Kraft merged with Dart Industries in 1980; Dart's subsidiaries (including Duracell batteries) and Kraft kept separate operations. With non-food sales sagging Dart & Kraft split up in 1986. Kraft kept its original lines and added Duracell (sold 1988); the rest became Premark International. Tobacco giant Philip Morris Companies bought Kraft in 1988 for $12.9 billion. The next year Philip Morris joined Kraft with another unit General Foods.

General Foods began when Charles Post who marketed a wheat/bran health beverage established the Postum Cereal Co. in 1896; he expanded the firm with such cereals as Grape-Nuts and Post Toasties. The company went public in 1922. Postum bought the makers of Jell-O (1925) Baker's chocolate (1927) Log Cabin syrup (1927) and Maxwell House coffee (1928) and in 1929 it acquired control of General Foods (owned by frozen vegetable pioneer Clarence Birdseye) and changed its own name to General Foods.

Its later purchases included Perkins Products (Kool-Aid 1953) and Kohner Brothers (toys 1970). Most of its non-food lines proved unsuccessful and were sold throughout the years. General Foods bought Oscar Mayer the US's #1 hot dog maker in 1981. Philip Morris bought General Foods for $5.6 billion in 1985.

The 1989 combination of Kraft and General Foods (the units still ran independently) created the largest US food maker Kraft General Foods. In the 1990s Kraft General Foods lost market share in areas such as frozen vegetables and processed meat. It introduced "light" meat products and stopped making nearly 300 food items. In 1993 it bought RJR Nabisco's cold cereal business (Shredded Wheat) and sold its Breyers ice-cream business to Unilever.

To streamline management Philip Morris integrated Kraft and General Foods in 1995. Newly named Kraft Foods sold off lower-margin businesses including its bakery unit and its North American table spreads business. Kraft bought Del Monte's shelf-stable pudding business (1995) and Taco Bell's grocery line (1996). It also sold its Lender's bagels (1996) and Log Cabin (1997) lines.

Deciding to eat healthy in early 2000 Kraft bought Boca Burger (soy products) for about $100 million and Balance Bar (meal-replacement snack bars drink mixes and beverages) for $268 million.

In 2000 parent Philip Morris (which renamed itself the Altria Group in 2003) outbid Danone and Cadbury Schweppes (later Cadbury) and agreed to buy Nabisco Holdings. It completed the deal that December for $18.9 billion (including $4 billion in debt) and began integrating those operations into Kraft Foods and Kraft Foods International. Then Philip Morris created a holding company for the newly combined food operations under the Kraft Foods Inc. name in 2001. The original Kraft Foods was renamed Kraft Foods North America.

Kraft Foods International CEO Roger Deromedi was appointed co-CEO of the new holding company along with Betsy Holden. Kraft Foods Inc. was spun off by Altria in 2001 in what was the US's second-largest IPO ever at the time (behind AT&T Wireless now AT&T Mobility).

Kraft cut 7500 jobs in 2002 as a result of the integration of Nabisco operations paying out $373 million in cash for severance and related costs. That year Kraft was also part of a $9 million settlement of a federal lawsuit regarding the use of genetically modified corn in its taco shells.

A strategy to shed brands that do not fit with the rest of the company's portfolio led Kraft to sell Farley's and Sathers in 2002 to FS Partners which renamed the company Farley's & Sathers Candy Company. Later that year Kraft sold some of its candy brands (Now and Later Intense Fruit Chews and Mity Bite) to FS Partners.

In a move to combat the population's growing obesity problem Kraft said in 2003 that it intended to reduce the fat and sugar content and cut the portion sizes of its food products as well as cease marketing in schools.

Deromedi shared the CEO slot with co-CEO Betsy Holden until 2003 at which time Deromedi was named sole CEO. (Holden was demoted to a marketing slot in the company and eventually left Kraft in 2005.) During his tenure as CEO Deromide was dogged by Kraft's looming spinoff from Altria and struggled to improve company profits by selling off underperforming and non-core brands.

The company in 2004 formed an alliance with Dr. Arthur Agatston of low-carb South Beach Diet fame to use the South Beach Diet trademark on some of its products including cereal meal replacements cereal bars refrigerated sandwich wraps and frozen entrees and pizza.

As part of Deromedi's plan to refashion Kraft's product lineup in 2005 the company sold its Altoids breath mints LifeSavers and CremeSavers candies brands whose combined sales were at the time estimated to be about $660 million a year. Wm. Wrigley Jr. Company paid about $1.4 billion for the popular brands.

Despite his best efforts to improve the bottom line Deromedi was shown the door in 2006. He was replaced by Frito-Lay's CEO Irene Rosenfeld (a former top Kraft executive who was instrumental in the company's acquisition and integration of Nabisco). She returned to Kraft after being head of Pepsico's Frito-Lay from 2004 to 2006.

Kraft extricated itself from the haze of second-hand tobacco smoke when it was spun off from Altria in 2007. Having edged toward splitting from its former parent for years the separation relieved the food maker of many headaches. It freed Kraft from any tobacco-related liability that Altria may be found guilty of post-spinoff. It also eliminated a significant layer of management which made it easier for Kraft to improve its sluggish sales.

Focusing on sharpening its brand portfolio Kraft sold off its hot cereals business in 2007. The $200 million sale to B&G Foods included two old favorites Cream of Wheat and Cream of Rice. It also sold its Fruit2O and Veryfine juice brands and operations to Sunny Delight Beverages.

As part of its plan to offer new product categories Kraft entered the lucrative and popular pre-made salad market in 2007 with the introduction of South Beach Living brand chicken-salad kits.

Adding more on the expansion front Kraft bought the Spanish and Portuguese operations of United Biscuits that year; the deal returned to Kraft the rights to Nabisco trademarks such as Oreo Ritz and Chips Ahoy! in Europe the Middle East and Africa.

Kraft further expanded its foreign operations with its 2007 purchase of the cookie/biscuit business of Groupe Danone for some $7.6 billion. The purchase gave the company brands such as LU

Petit Ecolier and Cr¨me Roulée and made biscuits (cookies to us Yanks) the company's largest global business. It also added the Tiger and Prince brands to its Egyptian portfolio.

Billionaire Warren Buffett acquired a small percentage of Kraft in 2007 (less than 5% at the time) joining the also famously rich and famous-on-Wall Street corporate raiders Nelson Peltz (whose estimated Kraft holdings are 3%) and Carl Icahn (who owns about 3%) in ownership of the Velveeta vendor. Peltz and Ichan are typically activist investors making suggestions regarding company operations. Peltz has suggested that Kraft concentrate on its core brands as well as undertake divestitures to fund overseas expansion.

Kraft acquiesced to Peltz on one front agreeing with his investment operations collectively known as Trian Partners by adding two directors (selected by the company and supported by Trian) to its board in 2007. Kraft also signed a "standstill" agreement with Trian agreeing to support the board's full list of nominees at Kraft's next two annual meetings.

Late in 2007 Kraft announced the re-rebranding of its South Beach products from South Beach Diet to South Beach Living saying that it wanted to capture a more positive image for the products. That year the company also sold its Veryfine juice and Fruit2O water brands and operations to the Sunny Delight company.

Kraft's 2008 sale of its slow-growing Post (Shredded Wheat Raisin Bran Honeycomb Grape-Nuts Pebbles and others) to Ralcorp a maker of private-label cereals and other foods is part of Kraft's strategy to pare down its brand offerings and concentrate on high-yield products. Ralcorp paid some $1.6 billion in stock for the acquisition. Post is the #3 US cereal maker by sales after General Millsand Kellogg. Post brought in more than $1 billion for Kraft in both 2006 and 2007.

In February 2010 Kraft acquired Cadbury for about $19 billion of which 60% was cash and 40% was stock. A majority of Cadbury's shareholders (almost 72% according to Kraft) accepted the offer effectively making Cadbury part of Kraft.

EXECUTIVES

Evp Human Resources, Karen J. May, age 60

Evp And Cfo, Brian T. Gladden, age 54, $900,000 total compensation

Ceo And Director, Dirk Van de Put, age 57

Evp And President North America, Glen Walter

Evp Integrated Supply Chain, Daniel Myers, age 64

Evp And President Europe, Hubert Weber, age 56

Evp And General Counsel, Gerhard (Gerd) Pleuhs, age 62

Evp And President Asia Middle East & Africa, Maurizio Brusadelli, age 50

Evp Research Development And Quality, Robin S. (Rob) Hargrove, age 53

Evp And President Latin America, Alejandro R. Lorenzo, age 47

Vice President Sales Channels, David Burns

Vice President Marketing Kraft Singles Natural Cheese And Velveeta, Mary Sagritanti

Senior Vice President And Global Chief Information Officer, Joher Akolawala

Vp Information Systems, David Diedrich

Executive Vice President President North America, Roberto Marques

Senior Vice President And Corporate Controller, Kim Jones

Vice President Human Resources Grocery Bu And Kraft University Relations, Ginny Packer

Evp And Chief Growth Officer, Tim Cofer

Vp Finance And Strategy, Don Valenzano

Vice President Information Technology Group, Ariel Altarriba

Vice President Information Technology Group, Ariel Camacho Perez

Chairman, Irene B. Rosenfeld, age 65

Board Member, Debra Crew

Board Member, Fredric Reynolds

Auditors: PricewaterhouseCoopers LLP

LOCATIONS

HQ: Mondelez International Inc
  Three Parkway North, Deerfield, IL 60015
Phone: 847 943-4000
Web: www.mondelezinternational.com

2018 Sales

	$ mil.	% of total
Europe	10,122	39
North America	6,885	27
AMEA	5,729	22
Latin America	3,202	12
Total	**25,938**	**100**

PRODUCTS/OPERATIONS

2018 Sales

	$ mil.	% of total
Biscuits	11,185	43
Chocolate	8,177	32
Gum & Candy	3,491	13
Cheese & Grocery	1,901	7
Beverages	1,184	5
Total	**25,938**	**100**

COMPETITORS

Associated British Foods	Hershey
Campbell Soup	Kellogg
Coca-Cola	Kerry Group
Dr Pepper Snapple Group	Kraft Heinz
Frito-Lay	Maple Leaf Foods
General Mills	Mars Incorporated
	Nestlé
	Pepperidge Farm

HISTORICAL FINANCIALS

Company Type: Public

Income Statement   FYE: December 31

	REVENUE ($ mil.)	NET INCOME ($ mil.)	NET PROFIT MARGIN	EMPLOYEES
12/19	25,868	3,870	15.0%	80,000
12/18	25,938	3,381	13.0%	80,000
12/17	25,896	2,922	11.3%	90,000
12/16	25,923	1,659	6.4%	90,000
12/15	29,636	7,267	24.5%	99,000
Annual Growth	(3.3%)	(14.6%)	—	(5.2%)

2019 Year-End Financials

Debt ratio: 29.00%
Return on equity: 15.00%
Cash ($ mil.): 1,291
Current ratio: 0.00
Long-term debt ($ mil.): 14,207

No. of shares (mil.): 1,435
Dividends
  Yield: 2.0%
  Payout: 40.0%
Market value ($ mil.): 79,040

	STOCK PRICE ($) FY Close	P/E High/Low		PER SHARE ($) Earnings	Dividends	Book Value
12/19	55.00	21	15	3.00	1.00	19.00
12/18	40.00	20	16	2.00	1.00	18.00
12/17	43.00	24	20	2.00	1.00	18.00
12/16	44.00	43	34	1.00	1.00	16.00
12/15	45.00	10	8	4.00	1.00	18.00
Annual Growth	5.3%	—	—	(12.4%)	14.2%	1.8%

Morgan Stanley

One of the world's top investment banks Morgan Stanley serves up a smorgasbord of financial services. It offers everything from advising corporate clients on mergers & acquisitions to raising capital for large companies to managing real estate investments for wealthy individuals. It boasts one of the largest financial advisor networks which works with clients to pursue their investment goals. Morgan Stanley has more than $470 billion of assets under management. The investment bank is a global enterprise with a presence in more than 40 nations serving corporate institutional government and individual clients.

HISTORY

In 1934 the Glass-Steagall Act required the J. P. Morgan bank (now part of JPMorgan Chase & Co.) to sell its securities-related activities. The next year Henry Morgan Harold Stanley and others established Morgan Stanley as an investment bank. Capitalizing on old ties to major corporations the firm handled $1 billion in issues its first year. By 1941 when it joined the NYSE it had managed 25% of all bond issues underwritten since Glass-Steagall took effect.

In the 1950s Morgan Stanley was known for handling large issues alone. Clients included General Motors U.S. Steel General Electric and DuPont. The firm avoided the merger wave of the 1960s but in the early 1970s it formed Wall Street's first mergers and acquisitions (M&A) department. In 1974 Morgan Stanley handled its first hostile takeover International Nickel's (now Vale Inco) buy of ESB the world's #1 battery maker.

Morgan Stanley went public in 1986. It escaped the carnage of the 1987 crash but a lawsuit arising from investor dissatisfaction with its M&A and LBO activities during that period lasted well into the 1990s.

By 1994 it was talking to possible merger mates including Dean Witter and finally merged with Dean Witter Discover in 1997 creating Morgan Stanley Dean Witter & Co. The San Francisco brokerage founded by Dean Witter in 1924 had remained regional for 40 years serving wealthy customers. In 1977 the firm merged with Reynolds Securities another regional retail brokerage started by Richard Reynolds Jr. the son of the founder of Reynolds Metals (now part of Alcoa) and grandnephew of the founder of R.J. Reynolds Tobacco. The new company Dean Witter Reynolds became the #2 US brokerage after Merrill Lynch and one of the top 10 US underwriters.

Dean Witter needed capital in the early 1980s and sold itself to Sears which hoped to turn it into a financial Allstate. Sears put in a retail-oriented management team and tried to shoehorn Dean Witter into in-store brokerages. Sears' indifference to the investment side hobbled operations.

The Discover card introduced by Sears and Dean Witter in 1986 was a hit but by the late 1980s it was obvious Sears would never be a financial giant. The retailer spun off Allstate Insurance and the newly renamed Dean Witter Discover in 1993.

Amazingly all but six of Morgan Stanley's 3700 World Trade Center employees survived the September 11 2001 terrorist attack on the towers. Hoping to capitalize on deregulations and privatizations in Europe as well as the rise of the individual investor Morgan Stanley acquired UK-based private bank Quilter & Co. in 2001 (then later sold it to Citigroup in 2006). Also that year the firm dropped the public use of "Dean Witter" in 2001 for promotional purposes and then dropped it completely in 2002.

When regulatory scrutiny fell on the mutual fund industry Morgan Stanley was charged with failing to adequately disclose the incentives its brokers and managers received for selling certain funds. In 2003 the firm agreed to pay a $50 million fine and adopt a "plain English" approach to informing investors about its product fees and broker compensation.

In mid-2004 the firm agreed to pay $54 million to settle a sex discrimination lawsuit filed on behalf of more than 300 female employees who claimed they were denied promotions and salary raises.

Unhappy with the firm's performance eight former Morgan Stanley executives (dubbed the Group of Eight) publicly called for the ouster of chairman and CEO Philip Purcell in 2005; Purcell was replaced by John Mack. That year a jury ordered Morgan Stanley to pay more than $1.5 billion to Ronald Perelman now the chairman of cosmetics giant Revlon. (Morgan Stanley in 2003 rejected an offer from Perelman to settle the dispute for $20 million.) Perelman contended that Morgan Stanley withheld knowledge of massive accounting fraud at appliance maker Sunbeam when he sold his camping gear firm Coleman to that company for some $1.5 billion in cash and stock in 1998; a Florida appeals court overturned the verdict in 2007.

In 2006 the firm agreed to pay a $15 million fine to settle charges that it was uncooperative and did not produce documents during investigations performed by the Securities and Exchange Commission (SEC). In addition the company settled charges (while not pleading guilty) that it falsely claimed to arbitration claimants and regulators that it lost e-mails on September 11 2001; it agreed to pay $12.5 million in 2007.

Morgan Stanley had been one of the largest credit card issuers through Discover Financial Services. However it spun those operations off in 2007. Discover was the last remnant of the company's merger with the venerable Dean Witter at the end of the previous century.

After the company wrote down more than $9 billion in mortgage-related investments in 2007 it was compelled to sell part of itself to an investment arm of the Chinese government China Investment Corp. for some $5 billion in order to raise capital. The equity units included in the deal could be converted to a nearly 10% stake in Morgan Stanley.

As its traditional investment banking business faced hard times Morgan Stanley increasingly focused on private equity investing. In 2008 the company's Infrastructure unit teamed up with Ontario Teachers' Pension Plan to acquire electrical services provider SAESA the Chilean subsidiary of Public Service Enterprise Group. In 2007 Morgan Stanley teamed up with Apax Partners Worldwide to buy insurance brokerage Hub International. The previous year Morgan Stanley acquired TransMontaigne a Denver-based oil and gas transportation company (sold 2014) and Heidmar Group a Connecticut-based marine transportation and logistics firm (it later sold Heidmar's lightering business).

In order to shore up the big banks during the financial crisis the US government invested $250 billion in healthy banks to help them jumpstart their operations; Morgan Stanley received about $10 billion of that. The cash — part of the $700 billion taxpayer-fueled bailout in 2008 — came with several stipulations including restrictions on executive pay and the order to use the funds not hoard them. Deciding it didn't need the money that badly Morgan Stanley repaid the $10 billion in 2009. The company announced in late 2008 that it would cut its staff by 10% in an effort to reduce costs.

Also in 2008 the Federal Reserve mandated that Morgan Stanley and Goldman Sachs (the other remaining independent bulge-bracket US investment bank) convert to a bank holding company structure. The structure subjected them to tighter scrutiny but enabled them to acquire a commercial bank to shore up their balance sheets if need be. The move came after rivals Bear Stearns Merrill Lynch and Lehman Brothers were either acquired or went bankrupt.

In 2009 Morgan Stanley sold its remaining stake in investment analysis and market index firm MSCI to raise capital. The deal brought the company some $625 million.

Morgan Stanley also shook up its top leadership. John Mack stepped down as CEO in early 2010; he remained chairman but stepped down at the end of 2011. James Gorman the firm's co-president succeeded Mack at the helm of the company and as chairman. The change marked a significant shift for Morgan Stanley as it scaled back its operations in riskier proprietary trading.

Morgan Stanley's Asian operations got a boost in 2011 when regulators in China gave the go-ahead for the company to begin establishing operations there. It launched a joint securities venture with China Fortune Securities later that year; Morgan Stanley owns a third of the business the maximum stake allowed. China is a strategic market for growth for the company as are the emerging economies of Brazil and India.

The company in 2012 sold its Quilter wealth management division which serves the UK's mass-wealth market to private equity firm Bridgepoint Capital to focus on its wealthiest clients and institutional investors.

EXECUTIVES

Chairman And Ceo, James P. Gorman, age 61, $1,500,000 total compensation
Global Co-head Investment Banking, Franck Petitgas
President, Colm Kelleher, age 62, $1,666,041 total compensation
Co-head Wealth Management, Andy Saperstein
Global Head Sales And Trading, Ted Pick
Evp And Cfo, Jonathan Pruzan, age 51, $1,000,000 total compensation
Evp And Chief Risk Officer, Keishi Hotsuki, age 56
Global Co-head Investment Banking, Mark Eichorn
Global Co-head Of Fixed Income, Robert Rooney
Coo Institutional Securities, Clare Woodman
Head Investment Management, Daniel A. (Dan) Simkowitz, $1,000,000 total compensation
Cima Senior Vice President Wealth Advisor, AL Haddad
Senior Vice President Senior Consultant, David Esham
Vice President Data Center Operations, Christopher Mcdermott
Vice President, Vikas Chawla
Vice President, Desiree Ally
Vice President Morgan Stanley Operations Risk And, Michelle Cuilla
Senior Vice President And Senior Financial Advisor, Lee Corey
Senior Vice President Of Client Services Nationa, Richard French
Vice President Training, Maria Prego
Senior Vice President Portfolio Manager Wealth Advisor, Frank Corrigan
Vice President, Geoffrey Burke
Vice President, Ruben Badar
Vice President, Duncan Fudge
Vice President, Andy Jaglall
National Account Manager, Rosie Bailey
Vice President Information Technology, Anne Egan
First Vice President, Thomas Niles
Senior Vice President And Financial Advisor, Anthony Brock
Vice President Information Technology Department, Francis Rial
Vice President And Financial Advisor, Roger Richard
Vice President Head Of Engineering, Philip O'Dwyer
Vice President Financial Advisor, Douglas Hicks
Vice President Associate Branch Manager Financial, Lisa Kittner
Vice President, Thomas Hartl
First Vice President, Ronald Phelps
Vice President Enterprise Infrastructure And Tech And Info Risk And Qapm, Zhenqin Li
Vice President Information Technology, Richard Wong
Vice President Information Technology, Alex Raykis
Vice President, Wendy Lowe
Vice President In Charge Of European Media And Internet, Fausto Zanetton
Vice President, Andrew Mento
Vice President Risk And Margins, Manu Agarwal
Vice President Network, Nathan Alexander
Senior Vice President, Adam Schur
Certified Wealth Strategist Vice President Morgan Stanley Smith Barney, Brian Weinkle
Vice President, Donny Chia
Vice President, David Collins
Assistant Vice President U.s. Financial Institutions Group, Lisa Kwasnowski
Senior Vice President Financial Advisor, Thomas Bencosme
Vice President, David Cohen
Vice President, Geoffrey Berman
Senior Vice President Advertising Sales, Sean Moran
Vice President Equity Finance Trading, Brian Moran
Senior Vice President Financial Advisor, Byron Hood
Vice President, Gary Soben
Vice President Of Information Technology Vice President Global Pricing Services, Steven Sfiroudis
Vice President, Roxane Rose
Senior Vice President, Kevin Killen
Senior Vice President Human Resources, Christine Discola
Vice President Of Human Resources, Toretha Mcguire
First Vice President And Counsel, Mark A Rhodes
Vice President Technical Support, Steve Mase
Vice President, Klaus Miller
Vice President, Michael Bebawi
First Vice President Investments, Shereen Lakhani
Assistant Vice President, Charles L Wickham
Vice President Finance, Dominick Gallo
Vice President, Jeffrey Krein
Vice President Of Information Systems, Saba Anvar
Vice President, Bruce Morley
Senior Vice President Of The Private Banking And Investment Group, Frank Migliazzo
Vice President Of Technology, Brian McCue
Vice President Desktop Engineering, David Gagliardotto
Vice President Gpc Marketing, Ray Difrancesco
Vice President, Peter C Bernard
Vice President, Gwendolyn Yu
Vice President, Jaymie Wetzel
Vice President, Mary Webb
Vice President, Robert Warznak
Vice President, Gordon Whittaker
Vice President, Steven Warch
Vice President, Douglas Wahl
Vice President, Herman Watson
Vice President, Michael Weissman
Vice President, Kenneth Weitzman

Vice President, Jacqueline West
Executive Vice President, Joseph Grunfeld
Regional Production Manager Assistant Vice
  President, Michael Kiebzak
Vice President Product Management, Bryan
  Thistlethwaite
Vice President, Paul Horowitz
Vice President, Jamie Herring
Vice President Governance Risk And Compliance,
  Bobby Singh
Vice President, Sam Chang
Assistant Vice President, John O'neill
Vice President, Rachel Heidingsfelder
Senior Vice President, James Davis
Vice President Business Operations, David
  Birnbaum
Vice President Financial Advisor, Steven Ernst
Senior Vice President, Doug Mellert
Vice President Interest Rates Trading, Scott Furgal
Vice President Portfolio Manager, Edward Ingold
Vice President, Richard Mejzak
Vice President, Phil Green
Vice President, Jason Devlin
Vice President Market Executive, Edward Luecke
Vice President, Mike Lighthart
Vice President Merrill Lynch Wealth Management,
  Ryan Conners-Copeland
Vice President And Manager Business Analysts,
  Doug Spillane
Vice President Relationship Manager, Matt Parlier
Vice President Fair Lending Director, Kristin M
  Steiner
Vice President Research And Development, Karen
  Definis
Vice President Senior Financial Advisor Pia
  Program Senior Portfolio Advisor Pierce Fenner,
  Sean Morrissey
Vice President Corporate Advisory Services, Vytas
  Maginnis
Senior Vice President, Andrew Gergel
Vice President Client Relationship Manager
  Coastal New England Market, Claire Ponte-
  Goncalves
Vice President Value Add And Retirement
  Marketing, Courtney Golisano
Vice President Investment Knowledge Strategist,
  Brooke Juniper
Vice President Business Finance, Rajiv Khurana
Vice President Defined Contribution Consultant,
  Peter Campagna
Vice President Finance, Jennifer Shoup
Vice President, Bob Christey
Vice President Strategic Initiatives Cash
  Management Marketing, Katlin Mongelluzzo
Senior Vice President And Counsel, Patricia E
  Brigantic
Senior Vice President, Theodore Kornobis
Vice President At Nomura, Krishna Natarajan
Vice President, Derek Cook
First Vice President Pia Portfolio Manager Cfm,
  James Smith
Senior Vice President Wealth Management Senior
  Resident Director Lnternational, Juan Cabanas
Vice President Senior Financial Advisor, Derek
  Rogers
Vice President, Eric Neis
Vice President, Dara Landa
Vice President, Faizan Minhas
Assistant Vice President Financial Advisor,
  Rebecca Connelly
Vice President European Abs Sales, Dana
  Leventhal
Vice President Corporate Finance, Thomas Marcot
Vice President Institutional Client Business
  Institutional Sales, Guido Bridelli
Vice President Defined Contribution, Jeffrey Kern
First Vice President Wealth Management, Will
  Ulbricht
Svp Head Of Asian Sales, Lye Tho
Vice President, Maria Lewis

Vice President, Fuad Mahmood
Senior Vice President Investments, Timothy Owen
Senior Vice President Investments, Stephen Zanolli
Vice President Risk And Quantitative Analysis,
  Ben Wu
Vice President, David Edson
Ishares Governance Vice President, Leah
  Schoellkopf
Vice President Investor Relations, Samantha
  Tortora
Vice President, Uri Morris
Senior Vice President Financial Advisor, Simon
  Lui
Vice President Product Control, Troy Neilsen
Auditors: Deloitte & Touche LLP

LOCATIONS

HQ: Morgan Stanley
  1585 Broadway, New York, NY 10036
Phone: 212 761-4000
Web: www.morganstanley.com

2016 Sales

	% of total
Americas	74
EMEA	14
Asia-Pacific	12
Total	**100**

PRODUCTS/OPERATIONS

2016 Sales

	$ mil.	% of total
Interest income	7,016	19
Non-interest income		
Asset management distribution and administration fees	10,697	28
Trading	10,209	27
Investment banking	4,933	13
Commission and fees	4,109	11
Investments	160	0
Others	825	2
Total	**37,949**	**100**

2016 Sales

	% of total
Institutional Securities	50
Wealth Management	44
Investment Management	6
Total	**100**

COMPETITORS

Brown Brothers Harriman	Lehman Brothers
CIBC	Marsh & McLennan
Charles Schwab	Merrill Lynch
Citigroup	Nomura Securities
Citigroup Global Markets	Oppenheimer Holdings
Deutsche Bank	Raymond James Financial
FMR	State Street
Franklin Templeton	T. Rowe Price
Goldman Sachs	TD Bank
JPMorgan Chase	UBS
	Wells Fargo Securities

HISTORICAL FINANCIALS

Company Type: Public

Income Statement   FYE: December 31

	ASSETS ($ mil.)	NET INCOME ($ mil.)	INCOME AS % OF ASSETS	EMPLOYEES
12/18	853,531	8,748	1.0%	60,348
12/17	851,733	6,111	0.7%	57,633
12/16	814,949	5,979	0.7%	55,311
12/15	787,465	6,127	0.8%	56,218
12/14	801,510	3,467	0.4%	55,802
Annual Growth	1.6%	26.0%	—	2.0%

2018 Year-End Financials

Debt ratio: 22.00%
Return on equity: 11.00%
Cash ($ mil.): 87,196
Current ratio: —
Long-term debt ($ mil.): —

No. of shares (mil.): 1,700
Dividends
  Yield: 3.0%
  Payout: 23.0%
Market value ($ mil.): 67,398

	STOCK PRICE ($) FY Close	P/E High/Low		PER SHARE ($) Earnings	Dividends	Book Value
12/18	40.00	12	8	5.00	1.00	47.00
12/17	52.00	17	13	3.00	1.00	43.00
12/16	42.00	15	7	3.00	1.00	41.00
12/15	32.00	14	10	3.00	1.00	39.00
12/14	39.00	24	17	2.00	0.00	36.00
Annual Growth	0.5%	—		31.1%	33.1%	6.8%

Mosaic Co (The)

Big pieces of the global agricultural chemical
industry come together to form The Mosaic Co. It
ranks as one of the world's largest producers of
phosphate and potash which are used for crop nutrition and as input to animal feed. In North America Mosaic accounts for about 75% of annual phosphate production and about 40% of potash
production. In the rest of the world the company
holds significant market share about 15% of phosphate and 15% of potash production. The raw materials of its products are mined from locations in
Canada and the US. About 70% of Mosaic's sales
are from international customers.

Operations

Mosaic operates three business segments: Phosphates Mosaic Fertilizantes and Potash.

The Phosphates segment which generates about
40% of Mosaic's revenues owns and operates
mines and production facilities in Florida and
Louisiana. It produces concentrated phosphate
crop nutrients and phosphate-based animal feed
ingredients. Its animal feed products are sold under
brand names Biofos and Nexfos. A key phosphate
product is MicroEssentials a fertilizer that is enhanced through a patented process.

The Mosaic Fertilizantes segment 40% of sales
owns and operates mines chemical plants crop nutrients blending and bagging facilities port terminals and warehouses in Brazil and Paraguay. The
segment produces and sells concentrated phosphates crop nutrients phosphate-based animal feed
ingredients and potash fertilizer.

The Potash segment less than 20% of revenue
owns and operates potash mines in Canada
(Saskatchewan province) and New Mexico. Most
of its product is used for crop nutrients and as
input for animal feed. Mosaic's annual potash capacity can produce nearly 9.2 million tons or almost 15% of world capacity and nearly 40% of
North American capacity.

Geographic Reach

Mosaic is headquartered in Plymouth Minnesota
and has customers in about 40 countries. The
company relies on two countries for 70% of its
revenue with Brazil supplying about 40% and the
US providing about 30%.

The company operates phosphate rock mines
in Florida and Brazil and processes the rock into
finished phosphate products at facilities in Florida
Louisiana and Brazil.

Mosaic operates potash mines in Saskatchewan
Canada and Carlsbad New Mexico. The Mosaic
Fertilizantes segment has operations in Brazil and
Paraguay.

Mosaic owns port facilities in Tampa Florida and Houston Texas as well as warehouse distribution facilities in Savage Minnesota Pekin Illinois and Henderson Kentucky.

Its distribution operations also include leased distribution space or contractual throughput agreements in some 15 states including California Indiana Iowa Kentucky and Missouri.

Sales and Marketing

Mosaic sells products to wholesale distributors retail chains cooperatives independent retailers and national accounts.

Phosphate crop nutrient products are marketed worldwide to crop nutrient manufacturers distributors retailers and farmers. Potash products are marketed worldwide to crop nutrient manufacturers distributors and retailers and are also used in the manufacturing of mixed crop nutrients and to a lesser extent in animal feed ingredients. It also sells potash to customers for industrial use.

Mosaic markets its Canadian potash outside of the US and Canada through Canpotex an export association.

Financial Performance

In the past five years Mosaic's revenue declined two years in a row bottoming out at $7.1 billion and then rebounded for two straight years of gains.

In 2018 revenue jumped 29% to $9.6 billion up $2.2 billion from 2017. The increase was driven by changes in operations that made them more efficient and an upturn in the market that included tighter supplies and higher prices. The acquisition of Vale Fertilizantes in Brazil also contributed to the increase.

The company's bottom line turned to a $470 million profit in 2018 from a $107 million loss the year before boosted by higher revenue.

Mosaic held $871 million in cash in 2018 compared to $2.2 billion in the previous year. In 2018 operations generated $1.4 billion investing activities used $1.9 billion and financing activities used $724.8 billion.

Strategy

Mosaic's strategy includes geographic expansion and fulfillment of regulatory mandates in its Florida operations.

The company expanded its South American presence with the 2017 acquisition of Vale Fertilizantes. It paid $2.5 billion for the Brazil-based fertilizer giant gaining several mines in Brazil a potash project in Canada and 40% ownership of a phosphate mine in Peru. Mosaic integrated the operations in 2018 reducing costs by some $158 million and making it an operating segment. Fertilizantes contributed $227 million in operating earnings and $410 million in adjusted earnings in 2018.

The company continues the expansion of its Potash segment with the K3 shafts at its Esterhazy mine which produced mining potash ore in 2018. The ensuing ramp-up will add some 900000 tons to its annual potash capacity with full operations not expected until 2024. The K3 mine supplements existing K1 and K2 mines.

Sales of its MicroEssentials specialty product rose in 2018 shipping a record 3 million tonnes of MicroEssentials (including over 1 million tonnes to Brazil). MicroEssentials sales have grown at a compound rate of 18% over the past decade. The product sells at a premium to other products.

Mosaic ran afoul of US environmental regulators in recent years resulting in the temporary shuttering of its Florida-based Plant City operation. While cost savings is a byproduct of the action the company also is required to inject additional funding into a government-sanctioned environmental reserve to ensure sufficient money exists should future clean-up be necessary.

Mergers and Acquisitions

In 2017 Mosaic acquired Brazil-based Vale Fertilizantes fertilizer business for $2.5 billion. Vale has capacity to produce 4.8 million tons of phosphate fertilizers and half a million tons of potash. It owns five mines in Brazil and four production facilities. As part of the deal Mosaic also acquired the Kronau potash project in Canada and Vale's 40% ownership interest in the Miski Mayo phosphate mine in Peru. Vale gains an 11% ownership interest in Mosaic and has the right to appoint two people to Mosaic's board of directors.

Company Background

Mosaic was created through the merger of IMC Global and Cargill's former crop nutrition unit in 2004. In 2011 Cargill divested its 64% of Mosaic shares to its shareholders and debtholders in a $24 billion transaction splitting off Mosaic and ending its status as a majority-owned company.

EXECUTIVES

Evp And Cfo, Richard L. (Rich) Mack, age 51, $624,000 total compensation
President And Ceo, James (Joc) O'Rourke, age 58, $893,833 total compensation
Svp Potash Operations, Walter F. (Walt) Precourt, age 54
Svp Potash, Bruce Bodine
Assistant Vice President Business Development, Courtney Mattson
Assistant Vice President, David Jellerson
Vice President Information Technology, Ralph Mills
Vice President Procurement, Chris Martus
Vice President Human Resources, Kerrie Campbell
Chairman, Robert L. Lumpkins, age 75
Auditors: KPMG LLP

LOCATIONS

HQ: Mosaic Co (The)
101 East Kennedy Blvd, Suite 2500, Tampa, FL 33602
Phone: 918 918-8270   **Fax:** 763 577-2990
Web: www.mosaicco.com

2018 Sales

	% of total
United States	31
Brazil	39
Canpotex	9
Canada	7
India	3
others regions	11
Total	**100**

PRODUCTS/OPERATIONS

2018 Sales

	$ mil.	% of total
Phosphates	3,886	40
Potash	2,174	22
International distribution	3,747	38
Elimination	(220)	-
Total	**9,587**	**100**

Premium Crop Nutrients

Premium Crop Nutrients
MicroEssentials®; SZ™
MicroEssentials®; S15™
MicroEssentials®; S10™
K-Mag®; Granular
K-Mag®; Premium
K-Mag®; Special Standard
K-Mag®; Standard
Pegasus®; Fine
Pegasus®; Granular
Potash
White Standard 0-0-62
Red Granular 0-0-60
Red Standard 0-0-60
Crystal Granular 0-0-60
Crystal Turf 150
Phosphates

Diammonium Phosphate (DAP) 18-46-0
Monoammonium Phosphate (MAP) 11-52-0
Powdered MAP
Feed Ingredients
Biofos®;
Dyna-K®;
Dynamate®;
Dyna-K White®;
Nexfos®;
Industrial Products
FSA Products
Hydrofluorosilicic Acid (FSA or HFS)
Potash Products
White Fine 0-0-62
White Granular 0-0-62
White Industrial High Quality
White Industrial Special
Red Standard 0-0-60

COMPETITORS

Arab Potash	Potash Corp
CF Industries	Sinofert
Israel Chemicals	Uralkali
K+S	

HISTORICAL FINANCIALS

Company Type: Public

Income Statement				FYE: December 31
	REVENUE ($ mil.)	NET INCOME ($ mil.)	NET PROFIT MARGIN	EMPLOYEES
12/18	9,587	470	4.9%	12,900
12/17	7,409	(107)	—	8,500
12/16	7,163	298	4.2%	8,700
12/15	8,895	1,000	11.2%	8,900
12/14	9,056	1,029	11.4%	9,100
Annual Growth	1.4%	(17.8%)	—	9.1%

2018 Year-End Financials

Debt ratio: 23.00%	No. of shares (mil.): 385
Return on equity: 5.00%	Dividends
Cash ($ mil.): 848	Yield: 0.0%
Current ratio: 2.00	Payout: 8.0%
Long-term debt ($ mil.): 4,492	Market value ($ mil.): 11,260

	STOCK PRICE ($) FY Close	P/E High/Low		PER SHARE ($) Earnings	Dividends	Book Value
12/18	29.00	30	19	1.00	0.00	27.00
12/17	26.00	—	—	(0.00)	1.00	27.00
12/16	29.00	37	26	1.00	1.00	27.00
12/15	28.00	19	10	3.00	1.00	27.00
12/14	46.00	19	15	3.00	1.00	29.00
Annual Growth	(10.6%)	—	—	(17.9%)	(43.8%)	(1.9%)

Motorola Solutions Inc

Do you copy? and "Roger that" might be snippets of conversation heard over two-way radios and other devices made by Motorola Solutions. The company's radios and wireless broadband products are used by government public safety and first-responder agencies for communications and personnel deployment. Commercial and industrial customers use products from Motorola to stay in touch with mobile work forces. Besides two-way radios the company makes vehicle-mounted radios body cameras headsets and other devices and develops software systems to connect them. Some 60% of sales are to customers in the US. Motorola Solutions goes back to the late 1920s when the company made radios for police cars.

Operations

Motorola has two operating segments: Products and Systems Integration and Services and Software.

The Products and Systems Integration segment accounting for about 70% of revenue offers infrastructure devices such as two-way radios and vehicle-mounted radios accessories and video tools as well implementation and integration services. The segment also provides customized radio networks software and applications.

The Services and Software segment about 30% of revenue provides repair technical support and maintenance as well as monitoring and cybersecurity services. Software products include a public safety and enterprise command center software suite unified communications applications and video software delivered on premise and through the cloud.

Geographic Reach

Motorola Solutions operates throughout the world but it relies on the US for about 60% of sales. The UK contributes about 10% of sales and Canada provides about 5% with other countries supplying the remaining 25% of revenue. Motorola runs major facilities for manufacturing and distribution in the US and Germany. The company outsources some of its manufacturing to third-parties outside the US.

Sales and Marketing

Motorola Solutions sells through an in-house sales operation that directly approaches its largest accounts and through channel partners for other accounts. Primary customers are government public safety first-responder agencies and municipalities. Other important customers are commercial and industrial companies that operate private communications networks and manage mobile work forces.

Motorola Solutions depends on agencies in the US federal government for about 10% of sales and the Home Office of the UK for about 5% of sales.

Financial Performance

Motorola Solutions posted a third-straight year of higher revenue in 2018 following four years of falling sales. Net income increased in 2018 reversing a loss in 2017 and two previous years of declining profit.

In 2018 Motorola Solutions' sales rose 14% to $7.3 billion up about $900 million from 2017 driven by sales from the Avigilon and Plant acquisitions made in 2018 and the Kodiak Networks and Interexport acquisitions of 2017. Geographically sales increased in every region.

Net income was $966 million in 2018 compared to a loss of $155 million in 2017 when the company took a $1.2 billion tax hit due to the US Tax Cuts and Jobs Act of 2017.

Motorola Solutions' cash and equivalents were steady at about $1.2 billion year-to-year. In 2018 operations generated $1 billion while investing and financing activities used $1.2 billion and $220 million respectively.

Strategy

Motorola Solutions is moving to increase its revenue from managed and support services and infrastructure- and software-as-a-service offerings by developing and selling cloud-first Software-as-a-Service (SaaS) products and on-premise products.

Acquisitions play an important part in Motorola Solutions' growth plans. It acquired Avigilon Corp. a developer of video security products to enhance offerings that capture and analyze video. The 2019 acquisition of VaaS International Holdings also expanded video capabilities.

Motorola Solutions relies on its workhorse business the land mobile radio (LMR) platform business to generate steady revenue and bring in more. It has an installed base of more than 13000 LMR systems in more than 100 that help drive demand for more devices software upgrades infrastructure improvements and expansion.

Most telecom companies see the faster 5G cellular networks as opportunities to Motorola Solutions they've more of a threat. Such new technologies could reduce sales of the company's traditional products. Even without 5G the company faces more competition from public carriers telecom equipment providers consumer device manufacturers and software companies.

Mergers and Acquisitions

In 2019 Motorola Solutions acquired WatchGuard Inc. which designs and makes mobile video systems. The deal adds to Motorola's video security offerings that include fixed cameras and analytics and license plate recognition cameras and software. WatchGuard's products are in-car video systems body-worn cameras evidence management systems and software.

In 2019 Motorola Solutions acquired VaaS International Holdings which develops video analysis-as-a-service technologies for $445 million. VaaS provides data and image analytics for vehicle location. Its subsidiaries include Vigilant Solutions for law enforcement users and Digital Recognition Network for commercial customers. The acquisition expands Motorola Solutions' command center software portfolio.

Also in 2019 Motorola Solutions acquired Avtec Inc. a provider of voice over internet protocol (VoIP) dispatch services for public safety and commercial customers expanding the company's portfolio for those markets.

Motorola Solutions acquired Avigilon a developer of advanced video surveillance and analytics tools for $1 billion in 2018. Avigilon's products include video analytics network video management software and hardware surveillance cameras and access control tools for commercial and government customers. Motorola is adding Avigilon's products to its public safety products enhancing their video capabilities.

In 2018 Motorola Solutions acquired Airbus DS Communications from Airbus SE which allows Motorola to expand its software for 911 services in North America.

The company acquired Interexport a provider of managed and support services for communications systems for government agencies public safety and enterprise customers in Chile in another 2017 transaction. The deal boosts Motorola's Managed & Support Services business and expands operations in Latin America. Interexport was expected to add about $50 million in revenue in 2017.

Company Background

Motorola got its start in 1928 when Paul Galvin then 33 founded Galvin Manufacturing in Chicago to make battery eliminators so early radios could run on household current instead of batteries. The following year Galvin began making car radio receivers and trying to develop a mobile radio for the police. In 1940 the company developed the first handheld two-way radio for the US Army.

In 1947 Galvin renamed the company Motorola after its car radios. In the late 1950s Motorola started making integrated circuits and microprocessors stepping outside its auto industry mainstay. When Galvin died in 1959 his son Robert became CEO. The company's purchase that year of a hospital communications systems maker led it to produce some of the first pagers.

Over the years the company has expanded and contracted evening launching a satellite system to handle its communications.m An early leader in cell phones the company failed to make the transition to smart phone. Eventually the company divested parts of the business to again focus on communications oriented toward public safety applications.

EXECUTIVES

Chairman And Ceo, Gregory Q. (Greg) Brown, age 60, $1,250,000 total compensation

Evp Strategy And Innovation, Eduardo F. Conrado, age 52, $448,750 total compensation

Evp Products And Services, Bruce W. Brda, age 58, $550,769 total compensation

Evp And Cfo, Gino A. Bonanotte, age 55, $645,385 total compensation

Evp General Counsel And Chief Administrative Officer, Mark S. Hacker, age 48, $526,337 total compensation

Evp Worldwide Sales, John P. (Jack) Malloy, age 48, $497,615 total compensation

Executive Vice President President Global Custo, Joseph M Guglielmi

Corporate Vp Managed And Support Services, Kelly Mark

Vice President Of Environment Health And Safety, Jodi Shapiro

Senior Vice President, Jonathan Meyer

Vice President Of Sales, Edward Fuerst

Vp Systems Integration Program Management, Art Vanags

Vice President Astro Subscriber Products, Steve Young

Svp Sales And Marketing U.s. And Canada, Jim Mears

Vice President, Chris Rapala

Vice President Of Strategic Sales, Patty Holtschneider

Vice President Of Records And Evidence Systems, Alam Ali

Vice President, Chris Kustor

Board Member, Kenneth Denman

Auditors: KPMG LLP

LOCATIONS

HQ: Motorola Solutions Inc
500 West Monroe Street, Chicago, IL 60661
Phone: 847 576-5000 **Fax:** 847 576-3477
Web: www.motorolasolutions.com

2018 Sales

	$ mil.	% of total
US	4,361	59
UK	638	9
Canada	303	4
Other countries	2,097	33
Total	**7,343**	**100**

PRODUCTS/OPERATIONS

2018 Sales

	$ mil.	% of total
Products and Systems Integration	5,100	69
Services and Software	2,243	39
Total	**7,343**	**100**

Selected Products and Services

Devices
  Mobile computers
  Mobile-to-mobile wireless modules
  Public safety LTE infrastructure devices and services (handheld USB modem vehicle modem)
  Radio-frequency identification products (RFID) and accessories
  Two-way radios and pagers
  Two-way radio accessories
Networks
  Mobile broadband (public safety LTE)
  Private broadband networks
  Wireless broadband networks

Services

Enterprise
Enterprise video solutions
Integrated enterprise communications
Managed network infrastructure
Managed security and compliance
Supply chain visibility solutions
Government and Public Safety

Advanced video security systems
Complex network design and integration
Interoperability and unified communications
Next-generation command and control
Public safety managed services
Software
  Application development framework
  Mobility software
  Network design software
  Public sector applications
  Support and help desk applications
Systems
  Dispatch systems
  Enterprise voice systems
  SCADA Systems (real-time facilities monitoring and control)

COMPETITORS

Airbus Group	Intergraph
Cisco Systems	Intermec
EF Johnson	JVC KENWOOD
Technologies	Sepura
Harris Corp.	Tri-Tech
Honeywell	West Corporation
International	

HISTORICAL FINANCIALS

Company Type: Public

Income Statement

FYE: December 31

	REVENUE ($ mil.)	NET INCOME ($ mil.)	NET PROFIT MARGIN	EMPLOYEES
12/18	7,343	966	13.2%	16,000
12/17	6,380	(155)	—	15,000
12/16	6,038	560	9.3%	14,000
12/15	5,695	610	10.7%	14,000
12/14	5,881	1,299	22.1%	15,000
Annual Growth	5.7%	(7.1%)	—	1.6%

2018 Year-End Financials

Debt ratio: 57.00%
Return on equity: ***.***.**%
Cash ($ mil.): 1,257
Current ratio: 1.00
Long-term debt ($ mil.): 5,289

No. of shares (mil.): 164
Dividends
  Yield: 2.0%
  Payout: 38.0%
Market value ($ mil.): 18,809

	STOCK PRICE ($) FY Close	P/E High/Low	Earnings	Dividends	Book Value
12/18	115.00	22 15	6.00	2.00	(8.00)
12/17	90.00	— —	(1.00)	2.00	(11.00)
12/16	83.00	25 18	3.00	2.00	(6.00)
12/15	68.00	24 19	3.00	1.00	(1.00)
12/14	67.00	13 11	5.00	1.00	12.00
Annual Growth	14.4%	— —	1.5%	13.1%	—

MOTT, CHARLES STEWART FOUNDATION INC

EXECUTIVES

Chb-Pres-Ceo, William S White
V Pres-Sec-Treas*, Phillip Peters
V Pres-Invest*, Robert E Swaney Jr
V Pres-Programs*, Maureen Smyth
V Pres-Communications, Marilyn Stein Lefeber
Vce Prsdnt Infrmtn Systms, Gavin T Flint
H Ranalyst, Julie M Flynn
Database Administrator, Karen Poindexter
Communications Officer, Jessica Jones
Auditors: GRANT THORNTON LLP MILWAUKEE

LOCATIONS

HQ: MOTT, CHARLES STEWART FOUNDATION INC
  503 S SAGINAW ST STE 1200, FLINT, MI 485021807
Phone: 810 238-5651
Web: WWW.MOTT.ORG

HISTORICAL FINANCIALS

Company Type: Private

Income Statement

FYE: December 31

	ASSETS ($ mil.)	NET INCOME ($ mil.)	INCOME AS % OF ASSETS	EMPLOYEES
12/17	3,098	43	1.4%	106
12/15	2,721	83	3.0%	
12/09	2,080	0	—	
12/04	2,525	305	12.1%	
Annual Growth	1.6%	(14.1%)	—	—

MPLX LP

MPLX is a diversified master limited partnership formed in 2012 by Marathon Petroleum Corporation (MPC) to own operate develop and acquire midstream energy infrastructure assets. It gathers processes and transports natural gas; gathers transports fractionates stores and markets natural gas liquids (NGLs); and transports stores and distributes crude oil and refined petroleum products. Headquartered in Findlay Ohio MPLX's assets consist of a network of crude oil and products pipeline assets located in the Midwest and Gulf Coast regions of the United States. It owns and operates light-product terminals an inland marine business storage caverns crude oil and product storage facilities (tank farms) a barge dock facility and gathering and processing assets.MPLX went public in 2012. Marathon Petroleum Corporation and MPLX completed another large drop-down deal in 2017 whereby MPLX paid $8.1 billion to obtain refining logistics assets and fuels distribution services from MPC. The transaction increased by 50% the size of MPLX's balance sheet.

EXECUTIVES

Executive Vice President And Chief Commercial Officer Markwest Assets, Randy Nickerson
Vice President And Controller, C Kristopher Hagedorn
Vp Investor Relations Mpc And Mplx, Kristina A Kazarian
Vice President Tax Of Mplx Gp Llc, Frank Quintana
Board Member, Dan Sandman
Auditors: PricewaterhouseCoopers LLP

LOCATIONS

HQ: MPLX LP
  200 E. Hardin Street, Findlay, OH 45840
Phone: 419 421-2414
Web: www.mplx.com

COMPETITORS

American Midstream Partners	Genesis Energy
Blueknight Energy Partners	Holly Energy Partners
	Jayhawk Pipeline
Boardwalk Pipeline	Kinder Morgan
Chevron Pipe Line	Magellan Midstream
Crestwood Midstream Partners LP	Plains All American Pipeline
	Rose Rock Midstream

DCP Midstream Partners	SemGroup
EQT Midstream	Sunoco Logistics
Enterprise Products	TransMontaigne
ExxonMobil Pipeline	Williams

HISTORICAL FINANCIALS

Company Type: Public

Income Statement

FYE: December 31

	REVENUE ($ mil.)	NET INCOME ($ mil.)	NET PROFIT MARGIN	EMPLOYEES
12/18	6,425	1,818	28.3%	—
12/17	3,867	830	21.5%	—
12/16	2,590	256	9.9%	—
12/15	703	156	22.2%	—
12/14	548	121	22.1%	—
Annual Growth	85.0%	96.8%	—	—

2018 Year-End Financials

Debt ratio: 59.00%
Return on equity: 184.00%
Cash ($ mil.): 68
Current ratio: 1.00
Long-term debt ($ mil.): 13,392

No. of shares (mil.): 794
Dividends
  Yield: 8.0%
  Payout: 109.0%
Market value ($ mil.): 24,061

	STOCK PRICE ($) FY Close	P/E High/Low	Earnings	Dividends	Book Value
12/18	30.00	17 13	2.00	2.00	10.00
12/17	35.00	36 29	1.00	2.00	26.00
12/16	35.00	— —	(0.00)	2.00	31.00
12/15	39.00	67 23	1.00	2.00	30.00
12/14	73.00	46 26	2.00	1.00	6.00
Annual Growth	(19.9%)	— —	10.2%	16.8%	14.8%

Mr Cooper Group Inc

EXECUTIVES

Chm, Michael Willingham
Vice President Information Security Officer, Todd Bailey
Auditors: Ernst & Young LLP

LOCATIONS

HQ: Mr Cooper Group Inc
  8950 Cypress Waters Blvd., Coppell, TX 75019
Phone: 469 549-2000
Web: www.mrcoopergroup.com

HISTORICAL FINANCIALS

Company Type: Public

Income Statement

FYE: December 31

	ASSETS ($ mil.)	NET INCOME ($ mil.)	INCOME AS % OF ASSETS	EMPLOYEES
12/18*	16,973	884	5.2%	8,500
07/18	0	154	—	—
12/17	614	26	4.2%	6
12/16	736	202	27.4%	6
12/15	685	(62)	—	6
Annual Growth	191.5%	—	—	1023.1%

*Fiscal year change

2018 Year-End Financials

Debt ratio: 32.00%
Return on equity: 166.00%
Cash ($ mil.): 242
Current ratio: —
Long-term debt ($ mil.): —

No. of shares (mil.): 91
Dividends
  Yield: —
  Payout: —
Market value ($ mil.): 1,060

	STOCK PRICE ($) FY Close	P/E High/Low		PER SHARE ($) Earnings	Dividends	Book Value
12/18*	12.00	2	0	10.00	0.00	21.00
07/18	1.00	1	0	2.00	0.00	(0.00)
12/17	1.00	13	5	0.00	0.00	35.00
12/16	2.00	1	0	4.00	0.00	40.00
12/15	3.00	—	—	(5.00)	0.00	30.00
Annual Growth	65.2%	—	—	—	—	(10.5%)

*Fiscal year change

Murphy USA Inc

It may not be the biggest but Murphy USA is flexing its muscles in the US gas station market. Murphy USA (a former operating unit of Murphy Oil) markets refined products through its network of branded gasoline stations and convenience stores customers and unbranded wholesale customers in more than 25 Southern and Midwestern US states to more than 1.6 million customers. The company's more than 1400 retail gas stations (more than 1150 of which are in Wal-Mart Supercenter parking lots) sell gas under the Murphy USA brand. It also operates about 300 Murphy Express locations and sells some 4 billion gallons of motor fuel through retail outlets.

Operations

The company markets retail motor fuel products and convenience merchandise through its own chain of retail stations almost all of which are in close proximity to Wal-Mart stores. Its business also includes product supply and wholesale assets such as product distribution terminals and pipelines.

Petroleum product sales account for almost 80% of the company's total revenues.

Geographic Reach

Murphy USA has retail stations in more than 25 US states (primarily in the Southeast — Florida and Tennessee) as well as in the Southwest and the Midwest.

Texas Florida Georgia North Carolina and Tennessee together account for about 50% of its total retail outlets with Texas accounting for about 20%.

Sales and Marketing

They sell gasoline under the Murphy USA and Murphy Express brands.

Financial Performance

Murphy's revenue has gone down from 419 billion in 2012 to just under $13 billion in 2017. Net income has been more stable staying mostly above $200 million mark each year.

2017 revenue grew some 10% to $12.9 billion thanks to a 26 cents per gallon increase in retail fuel prices.

Net income grew 10% to $245 million the highest in the last six years mostly from the effects of the deferred tax benefits from the tax reform as well as improvement in the retail fuel margin. This was somewhat offset by a 11% increase in wholesale prices of motor fuel as well as increased in operating expenses due to addition of stores higher labor costs and benefits.

Murphy's cash holdings increased slightly from $154 million to $170 million. Operating activities brought in $284 million. Investment utilized $262 million mostly in purchase of property and plants while a further $5 million went towards financing activities.

Strategy

A strong in-store merchandise sales and fuel distribution sales forecast for 2018 means Murphy USA is well poised for a profitable year despite rising fuel prices. According to the National Association of Convenience Stores (NACS) convenience stores ended 2017 on pace for a 15th straight year of record in-store sales and a 4th straight year of $10 billion-plus in pretax profits.

At Murphy USA sales in first quarter 2018 was up 20% compared to the year before. In 2018 the company also gained $35 million in settlement for the 2010 Deepwater Horizon oil spill. The company has built retail gas stations at Wal-Mart Supercenters and at other standalone locations as a part of an independent growth plan launched in 2016. The convenience store has some 1500 locations consisting of 1158 Murphy USA sites and 290 Murphy Express sites. It plans to build 30 more in 2018.

The company also focuses on improving its infrastructure to lower overhead costs and on long-term investment. It plans to continue to focus its product supply and wholesale efforts on activities that enhance its ability to be a low-price retail fuel leader by optimizing its fuel supply contracts to capitalize on market dynamics whenever possible and minimizing physical product supply and wholesale asset ownership.

Company Background

Boosting its customer offerings in 2010 the company teamed up with Western Union signing a deal to offer online money transfer services at its Murphy USA gas stations and Murphy Express convenience stores across the country.

As part of its former parent's decision to exit the refining business in 2011 MUSA sold its Superior Wisconsin refinery to Calumet Specialty Products Partners for $475 million. It also sold its refinery in Meraux Louisiana to Valero Energy for $625 million. The divestitures transformed MUSA into a pure gas station/convenience store company.

In 2013 Murphy Oil completed the spin-off of its US retail marketing business into an independent public company — Murphy USA Inc. The spin-off was achieved through the distribution to Murphy Oil's shareholders of one share of Murphy USA common stock for every four shares of Murphy Oil stock. It holds through its subsidiaries the US retail marketing business that was separated from its former parent company plus certain ethanol production facilities and other assets and liabilities of Murphy Oil that supported the activities of the US retail marketing operations.

In an effort to exit non-core businesses in the fall of 2013 the company sold underperforming subsidiary Hankinson Renewable Energy LLC (which owns and operates the Hankinson North Dakota ethanol plant) to Guardian Hankinson LLC for $173 million.

EXECUTIVES

Evp And Cfo, Mindy K. West, age 50, $546,083 total compensation
Svp Retail Operations And Support, Marn K. Cheng, age 53, $382,627 total compensation
President And Ceo, R. Andrew Clyde, age 55, $991,667 total compensation
Svp Marketing, Robert J. (Rob) Chumley, $116,667 total compensation
Vice President And Controller, Donnie Smith
Senior Vice President Marketing, Rob Chumley
Chairman, R. Madison Murphy, age 61
Treasurer, Jennifer Bridges
Auditors: KPMG LLP

LOCATIONS

HQ: Murphy USA Inc
200 Peach Street, El Dorado, AR 71730-5836
Phone: 870 875-7600
Web: www.murphyusa.com

2016 Stores

States	no. of stores
Texas	294
Florida	120
Georgia	94
Tennessee	92
North Carolina	86
Alabama	76
Louisiana	75
Arkansas	68
Mississippi	55
South Carolina	56
Oklahoma	53
Missouri	48
Kentucky	47
Ohio	44
Indiana	38
Illinois	37
Michigan	27
Iowa	22
Virginia	22
New Mexico	12
Colorado	12
Minnesota	9
Kansas	5
Utah	4
Nebraska	3
Nevada	2
Total	**1,401**

PRODUCTS/OPERATIONS

2016 Sales

	$ mil.	% of total
Petroleum product sales	9,071	78
Merchandise sales	2,339	20
Other operating revenue	185	2
Total	**11,595**	**100**

COMPETITORS

7-Eleven	Hess Corporation
Alon Brands	QuikTrip
Chevron	Racetrac Petroleum
ConocoPhillips	Royal Dutch Shell
Couche-Tard	Valero Energy
Exxon Mobil	

HISTORICAL FINANCIALS

Company Type: Public

Income Statement   FYE: December 31

	REVENUE ($ mil.)	NET INCOME ($ mil.)	NET PROFIT MARGIN	EMPLOYEES
12/18	14,363	214	1.5%	9,500
12/17	12,827	245	1.9%	9,600
12/16	11,595	221	1.9%	9,100
12/15	12,699	176	1.4%	9,800
12/14	17,210	244	1.4%	9,450
Annual Growth	(4.4%)	(3.3%)	—	0.1%

2018 Year-End Financials

Debt ratio: 37.00%	No. of shares (mil.): 32
Return on equity: 28.00%	Dividends
Cash ($ mil.): 185	Yield: —
Current ratio: 1.00	Payout: —
Long-term debt ($ mil.): 842	Market value ($ mil.): 2,473

	STOCK PRICE ($) FY Close	P/E High/Low	PER SHARE ($) Earnings	Dividends	Book Value
12/18	77.00	14 10	6.00	0.00	25.00
12/17	80.00	12 9	7.00	0.00	22.00
12/16	61.00	14 10	6.00	0.00	19.00
12/15	61.00	18 12	4.00	0.00	19.00
12/14	69.00	13 7	5.00	0.00	19.00
Annual Growth	2.7%	— —	5.4%	—	7.4%

MutualFirst Financial Inc

Before you bank anywhere else this company wants you to head to MutualFirst. MutualFirst Financial is the holding company for MutualFirst Bank which has more than 30 financial centers and trust offices in northern Indiana and a loan production office in southern Michigan. The bankÂ offers standard products and servicesÂ such as checking and savings accounts CDs IRAs and credit cards. More than 40% of the company's loan portfolio is devoted to residential mortgages. Consumer loans including auto boat RV home equity and home improvement loans account for about 25%. Business loans also make up about a quarter of MutualFirst's loan portfolio.

EXECUTIVES

Senior Vice President Business Banking Of Mutualbank, Christopher Caldwell
Vice President Mutual Federal Savings Bank, Shayne Nagy
Assistant Vice President, Susan Smith
Assistant Vice President, Stephanie Salyer
Assistant Vice President, Preston Tollett
Senior Vice President Risk Management, Sharon Ferguson
Vice President, Kathy Balser
Vice President Client Relationship Manager Elkhart County, Vince Turner
Vice President Mutual Federal Savings Bank, Kathy Sears
Vice President Compliance Wealth Management, Martha Oprea
Vice President Mutual Federal Savings Bank, Dorothy Douglass
Vice President And Trust Investment Officer, David Riggs
Assistant Vice President Client Relationship Manager, Michele Banes
Auditors: BKD, LLP

LOCATIONS

HQ: MutualFirst Financial Inc
110 E. Charles Street, Muncie, IN 47305-2419
Phone: 765 747-2800

COMPETITORS

Ameriana Bancorp
Fifth Third
First Financial Bancorp
First Merchants
German American Bancorp
Huntington Bancshares
Old National Bancorp
PNC Financial
STAR Financial Group

HISTORICAL FINANCIALS

Company Type: Public

Income Statement

FYE: December 31

	ASSETS ($ mil.)	NET INCOME ($ mil.)	INCOME AS % OF ASSETS	EMPLOYEES
12/18	2,049	19	0.9%	528
12/17	1,589	12	0.8%	422
12/16	1,553	13	0.9%	442
12/15	1,478	12	0.8%	445
12/14	1,424	11	0.8%	438
Annual Growth	9.5%	14.9%	—	4.8%

2018 Year-End Financials

Debt ratio: 1.00%
Return on equity: 11.00%
Cash ($ mil.): 38
Current ratio: —
Long-term debt ($ mil.): —
No. of shares (mil.): 9
Dividends
  Yield: 3.0%
  Payout: 41.0%
Market value ($ mil.): 229

	STOCK PRICE ($) FY Close	P/E High/Low	PER SHARE ($) Earnings	Dividends	Book Value
12/18	27.00	18 11	2.00	1.00	24.00
12/17	39.00	24 18	2.00	1.00	20.00
12/16	33.00	19 13	2.00	1.00	19.00
12/15	25.00	15 12	2.00	0.00	18.00
12/14	22.00	15 11	1.00	0.00	18.00
Annual Growth	5.0%	— —	10.9%	23.3%	7.5%

NASB Financial Inc

NASB Financial is the holding company for North American Savings Bank which operates about 15 branches and loan offices in the Kansas City and Springfield Missouri areas. Established in 1927 the bank offers standard deposit products to retail and commercial customers including checking and savings accounts and CDs. Mortgages secured by residential or commercial properties make up most of the bank's lending activities; it also originates business consumer and construction loans. Subsidiary Nor-Am sells annuities mutual funds and credit life and disability insurance. Chairman David Hancock and his wife Linda who is also a member of the company's board of directors own about 45% of NASB Financial.

EXECUTIVES

Vice President, Lori West
Vice President Human Resources, Christine M Schaben
Vice President, Ron Stafford
Vice President Construction And Development Lending, Christopher Vick
Assistant Vice President, Carmen Cunningham
Auditors: BKD, LLP

LOCATIONS

HQ: NASB Financial Inc
12498 South 71 Highway, Grandview, MO 64030
Phone: 816 765-2200
Web: www.nasb.com

COMPETITORS

Bank of America
Commerce Bancshares
Dickinson Financial
Guaranty Federal
U.S. Bancorp
UMB Financial

HISTORICAL FINANCIALS

Company Type: Public

Income Statement

FYE: September 30

	ASSETS ($ mil.)	NET INCOME ($ mil.)	INCOME AS % OF ASSETS	EMPLOYEES
09/19	2,605	43	1.7%	—
09/18	2,060	29	1.4%	—
09/17	2,062	29	1.4%	—
09/16	1,950	22	1.1%	—
09/15	1,531	22	1.4%	—
Annual Growth	14.2%	19.0%	—	—

2019 Year-End Financials

Debt ratio: 1.00%
Return on equity: 17.00%
Cash ($ mil.): 65
Current ratio: —
Long-term debt ($ mil.): —
No. of shares (mil.): 7
Dividends
  Yield: 5.0%
  Payout: 46.0%
Market value ($ mil.): 326

	STOCK PRICE ($) FY Close	P/E High/Low	PER SHARE ($) Earnings	Dividends	Book Value
09/19	44.00	8 6	6.00	2.00	36.00
09/18	41.00	11 9	4.00	4.00	31.00
09/17	36.00	10 8	4.00	1.00	32.00
09/16	34.00	11 9	3.00	1.00	29.00
09/15	29.00	11 8	3.00	3.00	27.00
Annual Growth	11.1%	— —	19.2%	(8.1%)	7.5%

National Bank Holdings Corp

National Bank Holdings is the holding company for NBH Bank which operates nearly 100 branches in four south and central US states under various brands including: Bank Midwest in Kansas and Missouri Community Banks of Colorado in Colorado and Hillcrest Bank in Texas. Targeting small to medium-sized businesses and consumers the banks offer traditional checking and savings accounts as well as commercial and residential mortgages agricultural loans and commercial loans. The bank boasted $4.7 billion in assets at the end of 2015 including $2.6 billion in loans and $3.8 billion in deposits. Over 80% of its total revenue is made up of interest income.

Operations
About 63% of the bank's total revenue came from loan interest (including fees) during 2015 while another 19% came from interest on its investment securities. The rest of its revenue came from service charges (7%) bank card fees (5%) and other miscellaneous income sources.

Geographic Reach
National Bank Holdings had a network of 97 banking centers in four states at the end of 2015 with more than half of those in Colorado a third in Missouri nearly a dozen branches in Kansas and two branches in Texas.

Sales and Marketing
The bank serves small- to medium-sized businesses and consumers via its network of banking locations and through online and mobile banking products. It spent $4.3 million on advertising during 2015 down from $4.6 million and $5.3 million in 2014 and 2013 respectively.

Financial Performance

The group's annual revenues and profits have been trending downward over the past few years as it has been selling off branches and loan business to concentrate on the geographic markets and loan types where it carries the most expertise.

National Bank Holdings' revenue rebounded 5% to $192.86 million during 2015 mostly as it earned $21 million in FDIC-related income related to lower indemnification amortization increased FDIC loss-share income and a $5 million gain on an FDIC loss-share agreement termination.

Despite revenue growth in 2015 the group's net income plummeted 47% to $4.9 million mostly on higher loan loss provisions which climbed more than $6.2 million during the year as it increased its specific reserves on non 310-30 loans. National Bank Holdings' operations used $37.65 million compared to just $2.76 million in cash during 2014 mostly after adjusting its earnings for non-cash items mostly related to a decrease in net amounts due to the FDIC.

Strategy

National Bank Holdings has been trimming its branch count in recent years to focus on serving clients through full-service banking centers across its four chief markets of Colorado Kansas Missouri and Texas as well as through online and mobile banking channels. Toward this end in 2013 the bank began integrating its limited-service retirement center locations into its full-service banking centers while also exiting its limited presence in California (its banks there had operated under the Community Banks of California banner).

Meanwhile the regional community bank continues to selectively acquire smaller banks and complementary financial companies that serve small- and medium-sized businesses to grow its loan and deposit business.

Mergers and Acquisitions

In August 2015 National Bank Holdings bought $142 million-asset Pine River Bank in Colorado along with its $64 million in loans and $130 million in deposits for $9.5 million in cash.

Company Background

Formed in 2009 National Bank Holdings went public in 2012. Prior to its filing National Bank Holdings was minority-owned by a number of private shareholders and corporate entities including Taconic Capital Advisors Wellington Management and Paulson & Co.

EXECUTIVES

Chairman President And Ceo, G. Timothy (Tim) Laney, age 59, $500,000 total compensation
Chief Of Enterprise Technology & Integration And Nbh Bank N.a. Midwest/ Texas Division President, Thomas M. (Tom) Metzger, $300,000 total compensation
Chief Financial Officer, Brian F. Lilly, age 60, $295,705 total compensation
Chief Risk Officer, Richard U. Newfield, age 58, $300,000 total compensation
Board Member, Burney Warren
Board Member, Robert Dean
Board Member, Arthur Zeile
Auditors: KPMG LLP

LOCATIONS

HQ: National Bank Holdings Corp
7800 East Orchard Road, Suite 300, Greenwood Village, CO 80111
Phone: 303 892-8715
Web: www.nationalbankholdings.com

PRODUCTS/OPERATIONS

2015 Sales

	$ mil.	% of total
Interest and dividend income:		
Interest and fees on loans	131	63
Interest and dividends on investment securities	38	18
Dividends on non-marketable securities	1	1
Interest on interest-bearing bank deposits	1	-
Total interest and dividend income	171	82
Non-interest income:		
Service charges	15	7
Bank card fees	11	5
Gain on sales of mortgages net	2	1
Bank-owned life insurance income	2	1
Other non-interest income	4	2
Bargain purchase gain	1	1
Gain on previously charged-off acquired loans	1	-
OREO related write-ups and other income	2	1
FDIC indemnification asset amortization net of gain on termination	(15.9)	
FDIC loss sharing income (expense)	0	-
Total non-interest income	21	18
Total	193	100

COMPETITORS

BBVA Compass Bancshares
Bank of America
Bank of the West
Capitol Federal Financial
Central Bancompany
Commerce Bancshares
Enterprise Financial Services
FirstBank Holding Company
JPMorgan Chase
KeyCorp
U.S. Bancorp
UMB Financial
Wells Fargo
Zions Bancorporation

HISTORICAL FINANCIALS

Company Type: Public

Income Statement

FYE: December 31

	ASSETS ($ mil.)	NET INCOME ($ mil.)	INCOME AS % OF ASSETS	EMPLOYEES
12/18	5,677	61	1.1%	1,332
12/17	4,843	15	0.3%	926
12/16	4,573	23	0.5%	1,004
12/15	4,684	5	0.1%	1,042
12/14	4,820	9	0.2%	1,056
Annual Growth	4.2%	60.9%	—	6.0%

2018 Year-End Financials

Debt ratio: —
Return on equity: 10.00%
Cash ($ mil.): 110
Current ratio: —
Long-term debt ($ mil.): —
No. of shares (mil.): 31
Dividends
  Yield: 2.0%
  Payout: 28.0%
Market value ($ mil.): 950

	STOCK PRICE ($) FY Close	P/E High/Low	Earnings	PER SHARE ($) Dividends	Book Value
12/18	31.00	21 15	2.00	1.00	23.00
12/17	32.00	68 56	1.00	0.00	20.00
12/16	32.00	40 23	1.00	0.00	20.00
12/15	21.00	166 127	0.00	0.00	20.00
12/14	19.00	97 84	0.00	0.00	20.00
Annual Growth	12.3%	— —	72.5%	28.2%	2.5%

National General Holdings Corp

Auditors: Ernst & Young LLP

LOCATIONS

HQ: National General Holdings Corp
59 Maiden Lane, 38th Floor, New York, NY 10038
Phone: 212 380-9500
Web: www.nationalgeneral.com

HISTORICAL FINANCIALS

Company Type: Public

Income Statement

FYE: December 31

	ASSETS ($ mil.)	NET INCOME ($ mil.)	INCOME AS % OF ASSETS	EMPLOYEES
12/18	9,439	207	2.2%	8,440
12/17	8,440	106	1.3%	7,570
12/16	7,245	172	2.4%	6,930
12/15	5,563	142	2.6%	4,630
12/14	4,440	102	2.3%	2,980
Annual Growth	20.8%	19.3%	—	29.7%

2018 Year-End Financials

Debt ratio: 7.00%
Return on equity: 10.00%
Cash ($ mil.): 194
Current ratio: —
Long-term debt ($ mil.): —
No. of shares (mil.): 113
Dividends
  Yield: 1.0%
  Payout: 10.0%
Market value ($ mil.): 2,734

	STOCK PRICE ($) FY Close	P/E High/Low	Earnings	PER SHARE ($) Dividends	Book Value
12/18	24.00	17 11	2.00	0.00	20.00
12/17	20.00	36 23	1.00	0.00	18.00
12/16	25.00	18 13	1.00	0.00	18.00
12/15	22.00	18 13	1.00	0.00	14.00
12/14	19.00	18 12	1.00	0.00	11.00
Annual Growth	6.8%	— —	10.4%	33.7%	14.7%

National Oilwell Varco Inc

EXECUTIVES

Chb-Pres-Ceo, Clay C Williams
Sr V Pres-Cfo, Jose A Bayardo
Sr V Pres-General Counsel-Sec, Craig L Weinstock
V Pres-Corp Contrl-Cao, Scott K Duff
Branch Director, Alexander Yudin
Manager, Danny Buck
Workshop Team Leader, Delphine Trebuchet
Administrator, Duane Wolf
Erp Supervisor, Helge Winsvold
Vice President of Sales, Jeff Lambert
Director, Kseniya Tarasenko
Auditors: Ernst & Young LLP

LOCATIONS

HQ: National Oilwell Varco Inc
7909 Parkwood Circle Drive, Houston, TX 77036-6565
Phone: 713 346-7500
Web: www.nov.com

COMPETITORS

Aker Solutions	Halliburton
Baker Hughes	McDermott
Bechtel	Schlumberger
Cameron International	Weatherford
FMC Technologies	International
GE Oil	

HISTORICAL FINANCIALS

Company Type: Public

Income Statement
FYE: December 31

	REVENUE ($ mil.)	NET INCOME ($ mil.)	NET PROFIT MARGIN	EMPLOYEES
12/18	8,453	(31)	—	35,063
12/17	7,304	(237)	—	31,889
12/16	7,251	(2,412)	—	36,627
12/15	14,757	(769)	—	50,197
12/14	21,440	2,502	11.7%	63,642
Annual Growth	(20.8%)	—	—	(13.8%)

2018 Year-End Financials

Debt ratio: 14.00%
Return on equity: (-0.00%)
Cash ($ mil.): 1,427
Current ratio: 3.00
Long-term debt ($ mil.): 2,704

No. of shares (mil.): 383
Dividends
  Yield: 1.0%
  Payout: —
Market value ($ mil.): 9,854

	STOCK PRICE ($) FY Close	P/E High/Low		Earnings	PER SHARE ($) Dividends	Book Value
12/18	26.00	—	—	(0.00)	0.00	36.00
12/17	36.00	—	—	(1.00)	0.00	37.00
12/16	37.00	—	—	(6.00)	1.00	37.00
12/15	33.00	—	—	(2.00)	2.00	44.00
12/14	66.00	15	11	6.00	2.00	49.00
Annual Growth	(20.9%)	—	—	—	(40.9%)	(7.6%)

National Western Life Group Inc

Auditors: BKD LLP

LOCATIONS

HQ: National Western Life Group Inc
10801 N. Mopac Expy Bldg 3, Austin, TX 78759
Phone: 512 836-1010
Web: www.nwlgi.com

HISTORICAL FINANCIALS

Company Type: Public

Income Statement
FYE: December 31

	ASSETS ($ mil.)	NET INCOME ($ mil.)	INCOME AS % OF ASSETS	EMPLOYEES
12/18	11,932	117	1.0%	276
12/17	12,225	110	0.9%	279
12/16	11,895	101	0.8%	265
12/15	11,613	98	0.8%	261
12/14	11,352	106	0.9%	—
Annual Growth	1.3%	2.5%		

2018 Year-End Financials

Debt ratio: —
Return on equity: 6.00%
Cash ($ mil.): 132
Current ratio: —
Long-term debt ($ mil.): —

No. of shares (mil.): 4
Dividends
  Yield: 0.0%
  Payout: 1.0%
Market value ($ mil.): 1,093

	STOCK PRICE ($) FY Close	P/E High/Low		Earnings	PER SHARE ($) Dividends	Book Value
12/18	301.00	10	8	33.00	0.00	523.00
12/17	331.00	12	9	31.00	0.00	504.00
12/16	311.00	11	7	29.00	0.00	474.00
12/15	252.00	10	8	28.00	0.00	443.00
12/14	269.00	6	5	45.00	0.00	428.00
Annual Growth	2.8%	—	—	(7.3%)	—	5.1%

Navient Corp

Navient is a new name for an old business — namely the loan management servicing and asset recovery unit of SLM Corp. (aka Sallie Mae). Navient services a $300 billion student loan portfolio composed of federal and private education loans issued to around 12 million customers. In addition to serving indebted former students Navient provides asset recovery services (collections) to the government higher education institutions and business clients. Navient manages the largest portfolio of Federal Family Education Loan Program (FFELP) loans as well as the largest portfolio of private education loans. Navient began life as an independent company through a strategic divestiture from Sallie Mae which still exists and continues to provide consumer loans.

Operations

Navient operates three business segments: two that own and collect interest on loans and one that services loans and provides loan processing services. The largest segment the Federal Family Education Loan Program (FFELP) brings in more than 50% of total revenue. It collects interest income from its $82 billion portfolio of FFELP loans and adds to its holdings by opportunistically buying FFELP loans from other servicers. More than 95% of FFELP loans are government guaranteed providing Navient a significant buffer against the financial impact of loan losses. Originations of FFELP loans no longer occur replaced with new programs headed by the US Department of Education.

Navient's Private Education Loans segment (more than 30% of revenue) buys finances and services private education loans while also collecting interest on a $23 billion portfolio of such loans. Legal constraints related to the spin-off from Sallie Mae prohibited Navient from originating new private education loans until early 2019.

Business Services (15% of revenue) generates revenue from loan & credit servicing collecting on delinquent loans (asset recovery) and business processing activities. The segment services the company's own FFELP loan portfolio as well as those from other institutions notably the US Department of Education which accounts for more than $300 billion in serviced loans. It also offers asset recovery services for loans and receivables for FFELP loan guarantors higher education institutions and federal state and municipal clients.

Broadly Navient makes about 85% of its revenue from interest income on its FFELP and private education loan portfolios while servicing revenue combined with asset recovery and business processing revenue accounts for another 15%.

Geographic Reach

Wilmington Delaware-based Navient operates throughout the US.

Most of the company's properties are loan servicing and collection centers in the New England and Midwestern regions with additional offices in Virginia Florida Texas and Tennessee. Its largest facility in Fishers Indiana houses 450000 sq. ft. of space representing more than 30% of all owned and leased space.

Sales and Marketing

Navient's sales and marketing model consists of building relationships with the institutions that originate loans - such as universities - as well as bidding for government contracts most notably with the US Department of Education with whom Navient has an existing significant contract through 2019.

The company also sells its services to federal state and local governments; regional authorities; courts; hospitals; health care organizations; and financial services companies.

Financial Performance

Navient's annual revenues and profits have been falling in recent years due to a decline in interest income as its education loans portfolio continues to shrink. At year-end 2017 FFELP loans amounted to $81.7 billion compared to $87.7 billion in 2016.

The company's revenue fell $316 million or 13% to $2.2 billion during 2017 on lower interest income on its shrinking and margin-falling portfolio of student loans as well as from a smaller contribution from gains on derivative and hedging activities.

Revenue declines and an increase in interest expense contributed to a 57% tumble in net income in 2017. Although Navient's debt decreased by about $6 billion between 2016 and 2017 the average interest rate on that debt rose from 2.14% to 2.67% enough to add more than $500 million of interest expense on the borrowings.

Cash and cash equivalents increased by $265 million to $1.5 billion in 2017. The company generated ample cash from customers making loan payments ($14.7 billion) with a further $1.2 billion in cash accumulated from operating activities. Cash uses went primarily to repaying its own borrowings and to acquiring $7.5 billion of education loans from other originators.

Strategy

While Navient's loan holdings generate a large and consistent cash flow from interest income its holdings are shrinking over time and therefore its revenue and income are declining. The company is hindered in that it was not permitted to originate new private student loans until January 2019 as part of its spin-off from Sallie Mae. Additionally the US government modified its student loan programs which precluded issuance of new FFELP loans. All US federal government student loans now originate through the US Department of Education.

Navient's overarching strategy includes both maintenance and growth. It seeks to maintain income streams from its portfolio of loan holdings and from servicing others' loans the latter being heavily dependent on its contracts with the US Department of Education. Keeping default rates low and collecting on delinquent loans are a major focus.

The company seeks to grow its business through opportunistically acquiring existing education loans and branching into new business service markets. It acquired nearly $7 billion in loans from JPMorgan Chase in 2017 for example. Its recent acquisitions of Duncan Solutions (2017) and Xtend Healthcare (2016) allow it to serve clients in the health care toll road authorities and various public-sector markets. In early 2017 the company began collecting overdue US federal tax debts on behalf of the IRS.

A 2017 US Department of Education audit found that Navient may have deceptively steered borrowers into higher-cost repayment plans rather than discussing less costly options. That finding could support federal and state lawsuits against the firm that accuse Navient of boosting profits through unfair and abusive practices. Navient disputes the claims and has said that it is a scapegoat in an industry that has come under fire. Further it says it is not legally obligated to serve as a financial counselor. If Navient is found guilty of unfair practices it could be fined billions of dollars in damages. It could also be required to change the way it handles some 6 million borrowers' accounts.

Mergers and Acquisitions

In late 2017 Navient acquired online lender Earnest which specializes in refinancing student loans. Post-acquisition Earnest remained a distinct brand led by its existing management team. The purchase was important as it provides Navient with an entry to originating student loans.

Also in 2017 the company acquired Duncan Solutions a transportation revenue management firm for $80 million. That deal expanded Navient's municipal and toll relationships.

EXECUTIVES

President And Ceo, John F. (Jack) Remondi, age 56, $1,000,000 total compensation
Evp And Chief Decision Management Officer, Somsak Chivavibul, age 52, $379,999 total compensation
Evp Chief Legal Officer And Secretary, Mark L. Heleen, age 57, $369,357 total compensation
Evp And Chief Risk And Compliance Officer, Timothy (Tim) Hynes, age 50, $370,000 total compensation
Group President Business Processing Solutions, John Kane, age 50, $449,999 total compensation
Evp And Cio, Pat Lawicki
Group President Asset Management And Servicing, John F. (Jeff) Whorley, age 58, $449,999 total compensation
Evp And Cfo, Christian Lown, age 50
Senior Vice President Human Resources, Jon Kroehler
Vice President, Chris Tuten
Vice President Government Relations, Carmen Lowrey
Executive Vice President And Chief Legal Officer, Mark L Heleen
Vice President Financial Planning And Analysis, David Tomkins
Vice President Information Technology Pr, Richard Jackson
Vice President, Stephen Tinney
Vice President Application Development, Carol Swartz
Senior Vice President, Paul Mayer
Vice President; President, Brian Hill
Senior Vice President And Deputy General Counsel, Andrew G Wachtel
Vice President Real Estate, Joseph Muffler
Vice President Of Finance And Information Research, Brian Burgess
Chairman, William M. Diefenderfer, age 74
Auditors: KPMG LLP

LOCATIONS

HQ: Navient Corp
2701 Justison Street, Wilmington, DE 19801
Phone: 302 283-8000
Web: www.navient.com

PRODUCTS/OPERATIONS

2017 Sales

	$ mil.	% of total
Interest		
FFELP loans	2,693	52
Private education loans	1,634	32
Other loans	13	-
Cash & investments	43	1
Non-interest		
Asset recovery & business processing	475	9
Servicing	290	6
Net gains on derivatives & hedging activities	22	-
Gains on sales of loans & investments	3	-
Other	9	-
Adjustments	(2974)	
Total	**2,208**	**100**

COMPETITORS

Bank of America
Brazos Higher Education Service Corp.
Great Lakes Higher Education
Mohela
Nelnet
Pennsylvania Higher Education Assistance Agency
Sallie Mae
Texas Guaranteed

HISTORICAL FINANCIALS

Company Type: Public

Income Statement

FYE: December 31

	ASSETS ($ mil.)	NET INCOME ($ mil.)	INCOME AS % OF ASSETS	EMPLOYEES
12/18	104,176	395	0.4%	6,500
12/17	114,991	292	0.3%	6,700
12/16	121,136	681	0.6%	6,773
12/15	134,112	997	0.7%	7,300
12/14	146,352	1,149	0.8%	6,200
Annual Growth	(8.1%)	(23.4%)	—	1.2%

2018 Year-End Financials

Debt ratio: 90.00%
Return on equity: 11.00%
Cash ($ mil.): 1,286
Current ratio: —
Long-term debt ($ mil.): —
No. of shares (mil.): 247
Dividends
 Yield: 7.0%
 Payout: 69.0%
Market value ($ mil.): 2,180

	STOCK PRICE ($) FY Close	P/E High/Low		PER SHARE ($) Earnings	Dividends	Book Value
12/18	9.00	10	6	1.00	1.00	14.00
12/17	13.00	16	11	1.00	1.00	13.00
12/16	16.00	8	4	2.00	1.00	13.00
12/15	11.00	8	4	3.00	1.00	11.00
12/14	22.00	8	6	3.00	0.00	10.00
Annual Growth	(20.1%)	—		(13.7%)	9.2%	8.0%

Navistar International Corp.

EXECUTIVES

Chb-Pres-Ceo, Troy A Clarke
Exec V Pres-Coo, Persio V Lisboa
Exec V Pres-Cfo, Walter G Borst
Sr V Pres-Gen Counsel, Curt A Kramer
Assoc Gen Counsel-Corp SEC, Richard E Bond
Sr V Pres-Corp Contrl, Samara A Strycker
Procurement Manager De, Lori Anderson

Senior Engineering Manager, Lynn Wolfe
Manager, Macdougall Brad
Manager, Marwan Hallis
Director, Nigel Symons
Auditors: KPMG LLP

LOCATIONS

HQ: Navistar International Corp.
2701 Navistar Drive, Lisle, IL 60532
Phone: 331 332-5000
Web: www.navistar.com

COMPETITORS

All American Group	Hino Motors
BAE SYSTEMS	Isuzu
Blue Bird	Leyland Trucks
Cummins	Mercedes-Benz U.S.
Daimler	International
Deere	Mitsubishi Motors
Detroit Diesel	North America
Eaton	Oshkosh Truck
Fiat	PACCAR
Force Protection	Scania
Ford Motor	Spartan Motors
Forest River	Thor Industries
Freightliner Custom	Tiffin Motorhomes
Chassis	Toyota
General Dynamics	UD Trucks
General Dynamics Land	Volvo
Systems	Winnebago
General Motors	

HISTORICAL FINANCIALS

Company Type: Public

Income Statement

FYE: October 31

	REVENUE ($ mil.)	NET INCOME ($ mil.)	NET PROFIT MARGIN	EMPLOYEES
10/19	11,251	221	2.0%	12,300
10/18	10,250	340	3.3%	13,100
10/17	8,570	30	0.4%	11,400
10/16	8,111	(97)	—	11,300
10/15	10,140	(184)	—	13,200
Annual Growth	2.6%	—	—	(1.7%)

2019 Year-End Financials

Debt ratio: 75.00%
Return on equity: ***,***,**%
Cash ($ mil.): 1,370
Current ratio: 1.00
Long-term debt ($ mil.): 4,317
No. of shares (mil.): 99
Dividends
 Yield: —
 Payout: —
Market value ($ mil.): 3,103

	STOCK PRICE ($) FY Close	P/E High/Low		PER SHARE ($) Earnings	Dividends	Book Value
10/19	31.00	18	10	2.00	0.00	(38.00)
10/18	33.00	14	9	3.00	0.00	(40.00)
10/17	42.00	140	71	0.00	0.00	(46.00)
10/16	22.00	—	—	(1.00)	0.00	(65.00)
10/15	12.00	—	—	(2.00)	0.00	(63.00)
Annual Growth	26.3%			—	—	—

NBT Bancorp. Inc.

NBT Bancorp is the holding company for NBT Bank which operates about 155 branches mainly in suburban and rural areas of central and northern New York northeastern Pennsylvania western Massachusetts southern New Hampshire and northwestern Vermont. The bank offers traditional deposit accounts and trust services and specializes in making business and commercial real estate loans. NBT also holds two main financial services subsidiaries: the EPIC Advisors unit administers retirement plans while Mang Insurance Agency sells personal and commercial coverage. NBT Capital provides venture funding to growing area businesses.

Operations

Other subsidiaries include property manager Broad Street Property Associates title insurance firm NBT Services real estate investment trusts CNB Realty Trust and Alliance Preferred Funding Corp and and equipment leasing services provider Alliance Leasing.

About 63% of the bank's total revenue came from loan interest (including fees) in 2015 while another 7% came from interest on investment securities. The rest of its revenue came from insurance and other financial services fees (6% of revenue) deposit account service charges (4%) ATM and debit card fees (5%) retirement plan administration fees (4%) trust fees (5%) and other miscellaneous sources.

Sales and Marketing

NBT Bancorp serves individuals businesses and municipalities. The bank spent $2.7 million on advertising during 2015 down from $2.8 million and $3.2 million in 2014 and 2013 respectively.

Financial Performance

NBT Bancorp's annual revenue has risen more than 20% since 2011 mostly as bank acquisitions have buoyed its loan business. Meanwhile its annual profit has grown by one-third.

The bank's revenue dipped 2% to $391.7 million during 2015 however mostly as the low-interest environment continued to squeeze its interest margins on its loans and investment securities. It also collected $15 million less in (non-recurring) gains from the sale of its Springtone investment compared to the prior year.

Despite modest revenue declines in 2015 NBT's net income climbed 2% to $76.43 million primarily because in 2014 it had incurred $17.9 million in non-recurring prepayment penalties as it paid down its long-term debt. The company's operating cash levels jumped 42% to $124.54 million for the year mostly as it collected more in net proceeds on the sale of its loans held for sale and sold off more of its non-loan assets.

Strategy

New York-based NBT Bancorp has expanded its financial service lines outside of traditional banking on its own and through acquisitions in recent years.

Mergers and Acquisitions

In October 2015 NBT Bancorp beefed up its Wealth Management and 401(k) recordkeeping businesses after purchasing New Hampshire-based Third Party Administrators Inc which provided administrative services for 401(k) profit sharing and defined benefit plans on behalf of 700 businesses and Section 125 administration. The $4.1 million acquisition helped complement services offered by its Wealth Management division and EPIC Advisors affiliate.

In March 2013 NBT purchased Alliance Financial for $233 million which bolstered its presence in central New York by adding 26 branches in Onondaga Cortland Madison Oneida and Oswego counties. The deal also added $1.4 billion in assets including $920 million in net loans held for investment and $1.1 billion in deposits.

Company Background

NBT Bancorp remained profitable through the recession even as real estate values fell and the number of non-performing loans in its portfolio grew. To do this the company increased its loan collection efforts and focused on selling conforming real estate mortgages. It also stopped originating auto leases.

NBT Bancorp was founded in 1986. However NBT Bank traces its roots to 1856.

EXECUTIVES

Sevp And Cfo, Michael J. Chewens, age 57, $446,610 total compensation

Evp; President Commercial Banking, Jeffrey M. Levy, age 57, $436,000 total compensation

President And Ceo, John H. Watt, age 60

Corporate Svp And Cio, Joseph R. Stagliano

Evp Chief Human Resources Officer And Chief Ethics Officer, Catherine M. Scarlett

Evp; President Wealth Management, Timothy L. Brenner, age 62, $331,050 total compensation

Evp General Counsel And Corporate Secretary, F. Sheldon Prentice

Evp; President New England, Matthew K. Durkee

Evp And President Commercial Banking, Sarah A. Halliday

Vice President And Retirement Plan Services Manager, Peter Kain

Vice President Bank Secrecy Act Officer, James Terry

Assistant Vice President Information Technology Officer Security Officer, Heidi Fisher

Vice President, Karen Sastri

Senior Vice President Southern Tier Regional Commercial Banking Manager Director Of Business Banking, David Theleman

Senior Vice President Product Management, Sharon Horning

Vice President Vice President And Director Of Compliance Risk Man, Patrick Gleason

Vice President, Debra Barker

Vice President Information Processing, Robert Keller

Vice President Market Manager, Lyle Smith

Vice President And Relationship Manager In The Ban, James Sullivan

Vice President Business Development, Debra Turner

Vice President And Commercial Loan Officer Commercial Banking Division Nbt Bank, Mary Ann Hallak-Serwatka

Senior Vice President Administrator, Jeffrey Lake

Vice President Of Information Technology, Robert Hill

Assistant Vice President And Audit Manager, Bryan Green

Director Media Relations, Salvator Arcidiacono

Senior Vice President Director Of Operational Ris, Jim Terry

Vice President Commercial Banking, Bob Vertucci

Vp Svp Commercial Banking Relationship Manager, Joe Delano

Assistant Vice President Security Investigations Officer, Rebecca Powell

Vice President And Relationship Manager, James Antell

Vice President Commercial Loan Officer, Tim Robinson

Vice President, Tom Weingart

Vice President Credit Officer, Jeffrey Rochefort

Chairman, Martin A. Dietrich, age 63

Board Member, Joseph A Santangelo

Auditors: KPMG LLP

LOCATIONS

HQ: NBT Bancorp. Inc.
52 South Broad Street, Norwich, NY 13815
Phone: 607 337-2265   **Fax:** 607 336-7538
Web: www.nbtbancorp.com

PRODUCTS/OPERATIONS

2015 Sales

	$ mil.	% of total
Interest		
Interest and fees on loans	242	63
Securities available for sale	20	5
Securities held to maturity	9	2
Other	2	-
Non-interest		
Insurance and other financial services revenue	24	6
Service charges on deposit accounts	17	4
Trust	19	5
ATM & debit card fees	18	5
Retirement plan administration fees	14	4
Bank-owned life insurance income	4	1
Gain on the sale of Springtone investment	4	1
Net securities gains	3	-
Other	14	4
Total	**392**	**100**

Selected Subsidiaries

Broad Street Property Associates Inc.
CNB Realty Trust
Colonial Finance Services Inc.
EPIC Advisors Inc.
FNB Financial Services Inc.
Hathaway Agency Inc.
LA Lease Inc.
Mang Insurance Agency LLC
NBT Bank National Association
NBT Capital Corp.
NBT Financial Services Inc.
NBT Holdings Inc.
NBT Services Inc.
Pennstar Bank Services Company
Pennstar Financial Services Inc.

COMPETITORS

Astoria Financial	M&T Bank
Community Bank System	Oneida Financial
HSBC USA	Sovereign Bank
KeyCorp	TrustCo Bank Corp NY

HISTORICAL FINANCIALS

Company Type: Public

Income Statement

FYE: December 31

	ASSETS ($ mil.)	NET INCOME ($ mil.)	INCOME AS % OF ASSETS	EMPLOYEES
12/18	9,556	113	1.2%	1,791
12/17	9,137	82	0.9%	1,733
12/16	8,867	78	0.9%	1,704
12/15	8,263	76	0.9%	1,721
12/14	7,798	75	1.0%	1,840
Annual Growth	5.2%	10.7%	—	(0.7%)

2018 Year-End Financials

Debt ratio: 2.00%	No. of shares (mil.): 44
Return on equity: 11.00%	Dividends
Cash ($ mil.): 181	Yield: 3.0%
Current ratio: —	Payout: 43.0%
Long-term debt ($ mil.): —	Market value ($ mil.): 1,511

	STOCK PRICE ($) FY Close	P/E High/Low	PER SHARE ($) Earnings	Dividends	Book Value
12/18	35.00	16 13	3.00	1.00	23.00
12/17	37.00	22 17	2.00	1.00	22.00
12/16	42.00	23 13	2.00	1.00	21.00
12/15	28.00	17 13	2.00	1.00	20.00
12/14	26.00	16 13	2.00	1.00	20.00
Annual Growth	7.1%	— —	10.9%	4.2%	4.3%

NCR Corp

EXECUTIVES

Pres-Ceo, Michael D Hayford
Exec Chb*, Frank R Martire
Coo, Owen J Sullivan
Exec V Pres-Cfo, Andre J Fernandez
Exec V Pres-General Counsel-SE, James M Bedore
Sr V Pres-Chief Hr Officer, Debra Bronder
Cao-Corp Contrl, Beth Potter
Auditors: PricewaterhouseCoopers LLP

LOCATIONS

HQ: NCR Corp
864 Spring Street N.W., Atlanta, GA 30308
Phone: 937 445-5000
Web: www.ncr.com

COMPETITORS

ACI Worldwide	Ingenico
Acxiom	MICROS Systems
BancTec	Motorola Solutions
Cummins-Allison	Netflix
Datalogic Scanning	Oki Electric
De La Rue	Optimal Group
Dell	Oracle
Diebold	Outerwall
Equinox Payments	PAR Technology
Fidelity National	Retalix
Information Services	SANYO
Fiserv	SITA
Fujitsu	Toshiba TEC
Gilbarco	Triton Systems
Hewlett-Packard	Unisys
Honeywell	VeriFone
International	Wincor Nixdorf
IBM	

HISTORICAL FINANCIALS

Company Type: Public

Income Statement

FYE: December 31

	REVENUE ($ mil.)	NET INCOME ($ mil.)	NET PROFIT MARGIN	EMPLOYEES
12/18	6,405	(88)	—	34,000
12/17	6,516	232	3.6%	34,000
12/16	6,543	270	4.1%	33,500
12/15	6,373	(178)	—	32,600
12/14	6,591	191	2.9%	30,200
Annual Growth	(0.7%)		—	3.0%

2018 Year-End Financials

Debt ratio: 39.00%	No. of shares (mil.): 119
Return on equity: (-6.00%)	Dividends
Cash ($ mil.): 464	Yield: —
Current ratio: 1.00	Payout: —
Long-term debt ($ mil.): 2,980	Market value ($ mil.): 2,740

	STOCK PRICE ($) FY Close	P/E High/Low		PER SHARE ($) Earnings	Dividends	Book Value
12/18	23.00	—	—	(1.00)	0.00	11.00
12/17	34.00	49	29	1.00	0.00	13.00
12/16	41.00	24	11	2.00	0.00	12.00
12/15	24.00	—	—	(1.00)	0.00	11.00
12/14	29.00	33	21	1.00	0.00	11.00
Annual Growth	(5.7%)	—	—	—	—	(1.2%)

Nelnet Inc

Got Ivy League tastes on a community college budget? Nelnet may be able to help. The education planning and financing company helps students and parents plan and pay for college educations. Nelnet is mostly known for servicing federal student loans. The firm manages about $76 billion in student loan assets most of which are government loans. However in light of regulatory changes to the student lending market Nelnet is increasingly expanding its fee-based education services. It serves the K-12 and higher education marketplace providing long-term payment plans college enrollment services and software and technology services. It acquired in 2018 Great Lakes Educational Loan Services for $150 million. The firm is part of financial holding company Farmers & Merchants Investment.

Operations

Nelnet provides innovative educational services in loan servicing payment processing education planning and asset management for families and educational institutions. The Company's four operating segments offer a broad range of services designed to simplify education planning and financing for students and families and the administrative and financial processes for schools and financial institutions.

The largest is Asset Generation and Management which acquires and manages Nelnet's student loan holdings. The portfolio includes Nelnet's existing loans originated under the now-defunct Federal Family Education Loan Program (FFELP). However in efforts to diversify its fee-based business and lessen its dependence on student loans the company is focused on developing new products and growing in areas such as tuition payment processing and lead generation products and services such as enrollment management and test prep services.

The three fee-based segments include Student Loan and Guaranty Servicing which services FFELP and other third-party loans writes and services private student loans and provides loan servicing software. (Nelnet is one of four companies providing servicing for the Department of Education.) Tuition Payment Processing and Campus Commerce serves the K-12 market as well as higher education providing financing for families and processing services for schools. Enrollment Services works to connect students with schools by providing marketing for schools and publishing school directories and test preparation study guides for potential students.

Geographic Reach

The company has offices in the US and Canada.

Sales and Marketing

The company's customers include students and families colleges and universities specifically financial aid business and admissions offices K-12 schools lenders state agencies and government entities.

Financial Performance

Nelnet has seen steady growth in revenues in the last few years. In 2013 the company's revenue increased to $1.14 billion (compared to $923.7 million in 2012) primarily due to an increase in Student Loan and Guaranty Servicing (as the result of growth in servicing volume under the company's contract with the Department of Education) and an increase in collection revenues from defaulted FFELP loan assets on behalf of guaranty agencies. Tuition Payment Processing and Campus Commerce revenues grew due to a higher number of managed tuition payment plans as a result of

providing more plans at existing schools and obtaining new school customers.

Net income increased to $302.7 million in 2013 (from $117.8 million in 2012) due to higher revenues and lower operating costs (the result of a decrease in depreciation and amortization costs).

In 2013 Nelnet's operating cash flow increased to $387.2 million (compared to $299.3 million in 2012) due to higher net income and proceeds from the termination of one of the company's cross-currency interest rate swaps. The increase in cash provided by operating activities was partially offset by the impacts of changes in non-cash fair value adjustments for derivatives.

Strategy

The company grows organically and through acquisitions.

Mergers and Acquisitions

To strengthen its student loans business Nelnet purchased in 2018 Great Lakes Educational Loan Services for $150 million and in 2014 acquired CIT's student lending business for $1.1 billion.

In 2014 FACTS Management brand a part of Nelnet's Tuition Payment Processing and Campus Commerce segment and the leader in payment plan services for K-12 schools acquired RenWeb School Management Software one of the leading school information systems for private and faith-based schools. RenWeb currently helps over 3000 schools automate administrative processes like admissions scheduling student billing attendance and grade book management. By automating these tasks RenWeb gives teachers more time to shape the lives of students while saving money and resources. FACTS helps over 6500 schools with tuition management billing and financial aid assessment services.

Company Background

Nelnet has been through a turbulent few years as student loan reform and the financial crisis disrupted business and sent revenues down. The company's ability to adapt to the economic pressures and policy changes have helped it land face-up following the recession. Measures taken including laying off staff and tightening lending practices helped boost profits despite lower revenues. Although non-FFELP servicing income and payment processing revenues grew in 2011 FFELP servicing revenues declined as the portfolio further shrunk and school marketing sales decreased as schools cut back on spending. As a result revenues fell that year by 8% to $979 million. Net income increased 8% (to $204 million) in 2011 compared to 2010 when the company had expenses related to restructuring. Also in 2010 Nelnet paid the US government $55 million to settle a lawsuit claiming it had made false statements to receive extra subsidies.

In a blow to the student lending industry President Barack Obama eliminated the FFELP and prohibited private lenders from making federal student loans in 2010. All new federal student loans began going directly through the Department of Education's Direct Loan Program. As a result Nelnet no longer originates new FFELP loans.

But the change didn't put an end to Nelnet. The company was awarded a five-year servicing contract for federally owned student loans including existing FFELP loans. Nelnet also began servicing new loans generated directly under the Federal Direct Loan Program. The contract was a major win for the company. Nelnet expects that its fee-based revenue will increase as the servicing volume for these loans increases (while the FFELP portfolio declines). The company is also focusing on improving its customer service to increase the allotted percentage of new government loans it services.

CEO Michael Dunlap controls the company holding 68% of the voting power for Nelnet. Dunlap and his family also own Farmers & Merchants Investment.

EXECUTIVES

Coo, Terry J. Heimes, age 55, $550,000 total compensation
Ceo, Jeffrey R. (Jeff) Noordhoek, age 53, $550,000 total compensation
President, Timothy A. (Tim) Tewes, age 60, $375,000 total compensation
Cfo, James D. (Jim) Kruger, $375,000 total compensation
Regional Vice President, Jon Potter
Regional Vice President Of Sales K 12 Mi, Mike Spanier
Regional Vice President, Roy Chernikoff
Vice President Campus Solutions, Anne Delplato
Executive Chairman, Michael S. (Mike) Dunlap, age 56
Vice Chairman, Stephen F. (Steve) Butterfield, age 67
Auditors: KPMG LLP

LOCATIONS

HQ: Nelnet Inc
121 South 13th Street, Suite 100, Lincoln, NE 68508
Phone: 402 458-2370
Web: www.nelnetinvestors.com

PRODUCTS/OPERATIONS

2015 Sales

	$ mil.	% of total
Interest		
Loans	726	60
Investments	8	1
Noninterest		
Loan & guaranty servicing	240	20
Enrollment services	71	6
Tuition payment processing & campus commerce revenue	120	10
Gains on sale of loans & debt repurchases net	5	1
Other	32	2
Total	**1,202**	**100**

COMPETITORS

American Student Assistance
Bank of America
Brazos Higher Education Service Corp.
College Loan Corporation
First Marblehead
Great Lakes Higher Education
JPMorgan Chase
Pennsylvania Higher Education Assistance Agency
Sallie Mae
Texas Guaranteed
Wells Fargo

HISTORICAL FINANCIALS

Company Type: Public

Income Statement				FYE: December 31
	ASSETS ($ mil.)	NET INCOME ($ mil.)	INCOME AS % OF ASSETS	EMPLOYEES
12/18	25,221	228	0.9%	6,200
12/17	23,964	173	0.7%	4,300
12/16	27,180	257	0.9%	3,700
12/15	30,486	268	0.9%	3,400
12/14	30,098	308	1.0%	3,100
Annual Growth	(4.3%)	(7.2%)	—	18.9%

2018 Year-End Financials

Debt ratio: 88.00%
Return on equity: 10.00%
Cash ($ mil.): 121
Current ratio: —
Long-term debt ($ mil.): —
No. of shares (mil.): 40
Dividends
  Yield: 1.0%
  Payout: 12.0%
Market value ($ mil.): 2,107

	STOCK PRICE ($) FY Close	P/E High/Low		PER SHARE ($) Earnings	Dividends	Book Value
12/18	52.00	11	9	6.00	1.00	57.00
12/17	55.00	14	9	4.00	1.00	53.00
12/16	51.00	9	5	6.00	1.00	49.00
12/15	34.00	8	5	6.00	0.00	43.00
12/14	46.00	7	5	7.00	0.00	37.00
Annual Growth	3.1%	—	—	(4.2%)	13.3%	11.3%

NetApp, Inc.

EXECUTIVES

Pres-Ceo, George Kurian
Chb*, T Michael Nevens
Exec V Pres-Cfo, Ronald J Pasek
Exec V Pres, Brad R Anderson
Exec V Pres, Henri Richard
Sr V Pres-Gen Counsel-Sec-Cco, Matthew K Fawcett
Sr V Pres-Cao, Scott R Allen
Svp-Cmo, James Whitemore
Investor Relations Analyst, Billie Fagenstrom
Information Technology Manager, David Mitchell
Network Engineer, Gilbert Juinio
Auditors: DELOITTE & TOUCHE LLP

LOCATIONS

HQ: NetApp, Inc.
1395 Crossman Avenue, Sunnyvale, CA 94089
Phone: 408 822-6000
Web: www.netapp.com

COMPETITORS

Data Domain	Isilon Systems
Dell	LSI Corp.
Dot Hill	Microsoft
EMC	Oracle
Hewlett-Packard	Quantum Corporation
Hitachi Data Systems	XIO
IBM	Xyratex

HISTORICAL FINANCIALS

Company Type: Public

Income Statement				FYE: April 26
	REVENUE ($ mil.)	NET INCOME ($ mil.)	NET PROFIT MARGIN	EMPLOYEES
04/19	6,146	1,169	19.0%	10,500
04/18	5,911	76	1.3%	10,300
04/17	5,519	509	9.2%	10,100
04/16	5,546	229	4.1%	12,030
04/15	6,123	560	9.1%	12,810
Annual Growth	0.1%	20.2%	—	(4.8%)

2019 Year-End Financials

Debt ratio: 18.00%
Return on equity: 74.00%
Cash ($ mil.): 2,325
Current ratio: 1.00
Long-term debt ($ mil.): 1,144
No. of shares (mil.): 240
Dividends
  Yield: 2.0%
  Payout: 41.0%
Market value ($ mil.): 17,256

	STOCK PRICE ($) FY Close	P/E High/Low		PER SHARE ($) Earnings	Dividends	Book Value
04/19	72.00	19	12	5.00	2.00	5.00
04/18	67.00	248	136	0.00	1.00	8.00
04/17	40.00	23	12	2.00	1.00	10.00
04/16	24.00	47	27	1.00	1.00	10.00
04/15	36.00	25	19	2.00	1.00	11.00
Annual Growth	18.8%	—	—	26.7%	24.8%	(20.1%)

Netflix Inc

Netflix and chill? More like Netflix and bill the increasing numbers of global viewers who subscribe to the video streaming service. The world's leading internet streaming company distributes movies and TV shows in a variety of genres and languages to a whopping 139 million monthly (and growing) paid subscribers in more than 190 countries. Netflix creates its own content and strikes deals with other producers for the rights to distribute programming. To keep viewers binging it deploys sophisticated algorithms to predict viewer preferences and make recommendations on what to watch. Netflix still sends DVDs to US customers through the mail though the legacy business gets smaller every year.

IPO

Netflix went public in 2002 when it raised $82.5 million. The company said it would use the funds to pay off debts and boost promotion by offering free trials.

Operations

Netflix's business is organized in three operating segments: domestic streaming (about 48% of revenue) international streaming (about 49% of revenue) and domestic DVD (about 3% of revenue). Domestic streaming derives revenues from monthly membership fees to subscribers in the US while the international streaming segment does the same to subscribers outside of the US. The legacy domestic DVD segment charges a monthly membership fee for DVD rental to US customers via the US Postal Service.

For its streaming services the company offers different subscription plans at various price points based on the quality of streaming (Standard Definition HD or Ultra HD) and the number of internet-connected screens on which a viewer can watch at the same time (one two or four). All plans include unlimited viewing of available TV shows and movies and can be canceled at any time. The company's content is commercial-free giving it a leg up in an increasingly competitive market filled with many advertising-supported rivals.

Geographic Reach

The Los Gatos California-based Netflix has moved beyond the borders of the US to reach more than 190 countries. The company has been busy aggressively expanding its global footprint launching streaming in countries from Cuba to Japan to Australia. Its streaming service is available in all but four or so countries. Netflix has also created and licensed content for local markets across the globe. These moves have paid off with international subscriptions accounting for about 49% of revenue in 2018 compared to about 45% in 2017.

To grow overseas Netflix must contend with international rivals that may offer pirated content via bootleg DVDs illegal downloads or unauthorized streaming. The service is not available in

China one of the few markets it has yet to penetrate. While the nation presents opportunity for significant subscriber growth Netflix faces rigid restrictions there. As a workaround the company has been spending to acquire and produce Mandarin-language content to court Chinese audiences living elsewhere.

Sales and MarketingNetflix has spent increasing amounts of money on advertising surpassing $1.8 billion in 2018 up from about $1 billion in 2017 $842 million in 2016 and some $714 million in 2015. It offers a month-long free trial at sign-up to first-time subscribers a key marketing strategy for the company. In 2019 it rolled out price changes to its US streaming plans raising the Standard plan (two HD streams) from $10.99 to $12.99 per month; the Premium plan (up to four Ultra HD streams) from $13.99 to $15.99 per month; and the Basic plan (with a single non-HD stream) from $7.99 to $8.99 per month.

Financial Performance

The widespread growth of broadband technology and the proliferation of internet-connected devices is driving more audiences to consume digital media content providing ample opportunity for Netflix to grow its streaming business across the globe. Revenues increased an impressive 186% over the past five years jumping from $5.5 billion in 2014 to $15.8 billion in 2018. Over the same period profit levels fluctuated dipping some in 2015 and 2016 but rising higher in 2017 and 2018.

In 2018 revenues increased $4.1 billion or 35% compared to 2017 primarily driven by the growth in average number of streaming paid memberships. Netflix added 29 million paid subscribers in 2018 33% higher than the 22 million it added in 2017. It also raised subscription fees in some markets and shifted to higher priced plans boosting average monthly revenue per paying customer. Domestic streaming revenue increased 24% year-to-year and international streaming grew 53%. Revenue from the legacy DVD business continued to drop.

Net income hit $1.2 billion in 2018 up 117% from the prior year's $559 million. Growth in revenue operating income and operating margin enabled the company to absorb higher expenses as it continued to invest heavily on programming marketing and headcount. Netflix spent $12 billion on content in 2018 up 35% from $8.9 billion in 2017.

Cash at the end of 2018 was $2.6 billion an increase of $500 million from 2017. Cash from operations contributed $2.7 billion to the coffers while investing activities used $33 million. Financing activities used about $4 billion. The company had $10.4 billion in long-term debt versus $6.5 billion the year earlier.

Strategy

The company's strategy is to grow its streaming membership globally improving its members' experience by making massive investments in content. Netflix invested a staggering $12 billion in cash on content in 2018 a figure that analysts expect will grow to around $15 billion in 2019. Netflix is making these investments to face its rivals head on. The company has plenty of existing competition from the likes of Hulu Amazon and YouTube; going forward it faces newer streaming product launches from mega media firms Disney WarnerMedia and NBCUniversal.

The firm continues to explore strategic agreements with TV networks and pay channels while also producing content in-house. Major Hollywood stars including Brad Pitt and Jane Fonda have developed Netflix-only programs and the company has signed successful TV producers like Shonda Rhimes and Ryan Murphy to exclusive development deals. Netflix lures in audiences with new movie releases such as The Irishman a crime drama from Martin Scorsese and breakout TV hits such as Stranger Things.

To stay ahead the company is challenging conventional movie industry norms in more ways than one. Netflix received much criticism from the Hollywood studio system for disrupting the traditional concept of the "release window" (which allows some time to pass after a movie opens in theaters before it becomes available on other viewing platforms) and refusing to grant movie theaters an exclusive release. However it changed its policy in 2019 giving its Oscar nominated film Roma an exclusive (but limited) theatrical run before streaming it into homes in order for it to be considered for an Academy Award.

Mergers and Acquisitions

Netflix has only made a few minor acquisitions since it was founded and its CEO has said the company has no plans to make any major buys in the future. A rare purchase was the 2017 acquisition of Millarworld a comic book publisher whose characters include Kick-Ass and Kingsman. With the transaction Netflix gained access to comics in the popular superhero and science fiction genres. Terms of the deal were not disclosed.

Company Background

Marc Randolph and Reed Hastings founded the DVD-by-mail service in 1997 as a challenge to Blockbuster Video. (Hastings said he got the idea after being hit with a $40 late fee from Blockbuster for failing to return his copy of Apollo 13 which was overdue by about a month.) The company launched its streaming service in 2007 placing a big (and eventually winning) bet on the popularity of accessing entertainment content via subscriptions over the internet.

Netflix released its first original TV series House of Cards in 2013. The critically-acclaimed show was also a hit with audiences putting the streaming company on the map as a producer of high quality content.

EXECUTIVES

Chief Product Officer, Neil Hunt, age 58, $1,000,000 total compensation

Chief Content Officer, Ted Sarandos, age 55, $1,000,000 total compensation

Chief Streaming And Partnerships And International Development Officer, Greg Peters, age 48, $1,000,000 total compensation

Vp Financial Planning And Analysis, David Wells, age 47, $2,400,000 total compensation

Vice President Data Engineering And Analytics, Paul Ellwood

Vice President Global Customer Service And Employee Technology, Brent Wickens

Vice President Of Original Content, Cindy Holland

Vice President Content Planning And Analysis, David Burt

Vice President Information Technology, Eric Pallotta

Vice President Talent (human Resources), Barbie Graver

Vice President Marketing Apac, Jerret West

Vice President Consumer Insights, Adrien Lanusse

Vice President Marketing Latin America, Vinicius Losacco

Vice President User Interface Engineering, Matt Marenghi

Vice President Content Acquisition, Sean Carey

Vice President Originals Marketing, Stephen Bruno

Vp Finance Investor Relations And Corporate Development, Spencer Wang

Vice President Consumer Insights, Zoe Friend

Vice President Of Business Development, Anthony Zameczkowski

Vice President Content, Elizabeth Bradley

Vice President Content Acquisition, Robert Roy

Vice President Of Networks, David Temkin

Vice President Original Film Publicity, Julie Fontaine

Board Member, Jay Hoag

Board Director, Rich Barton

Board Member, Reed Hasting

Board Member, Anne Sweeney

Auditors: Ernst & Young LLP

LOCATIONS

HQ: Netflix Inc
 100 Winchester Circle, Los Gatos, CA 95032
Phone: 408 540-3700
Web: www.netflix.com

PRODUCTS/OPERATIONS

2017 Sales

	$ mil.	% of total
Domestic Streaming	6,153	53
International Streaming	5,089	43
Domestic DVD	451	4
Total	**11,693**	**100**

Selected Netflix Streaming Devices

Apple iPhone
Apple iPad
Apple iPod touch
Apple TV
Blu-ray disc players
Digital video recorders
Google TV
Internet video players
Internet-connected TVs
Home theatre systems
Microsoft Xbox 360 console
Nintendo Wii console
Sony PS3 console

COMPETITORS

AT&T	HBO
Amazon.com	Hastings Entertainment
Apple Inc.	Hulu
Best Buy	Kroger
Charter Communications	Redbox
Columbia House	Showtime Networks
Comcast	Target Corporation
Cox Communications	Time Warner Cable
DIRECTV	Verizon
DISH Network	Wal-Mart
EchoStar	YouTube
Google	

HISTORICAL FINANCIALS

Company Type: Public

Income Statement — FYE: December 31

	REVENUE ($ mil.)	NET INCOME ($ mil.)	NET PROFIT MARGIN	EMPLOYEES
12/19	20,156	1,867	9.3%	8,600
12/18	15,794	1,211	7.7%	7,100
12/17	11,693	559	4.8%	5,500
12/16	8,831	187	2.1%	4,700
12/15	6,780	123	1.8%	3,700
Annual Growth	31.3%	97.5%	—	23.5%

2019 Year-End Financials

Debt ratio: 43.00%	No. of shares (mil.): 439
Return on equity: 29.00%	Dividends
Cash ($ mil.): 5,018	Yield: —
Current ratio: 1.00	Payout: —
Long-term debt ($ mil.): 14,759	Market value ($ mil.): 141,985

NEW YORK CITY HEALTH AND HOSPITALS CORPORATION

New York City Health and Hospitals Corporation (NYC H+H) operates health care facilities in all five boroughs of New York City. As one of the largest municipal health service systems in the US HHC serves 1 million New Yorkers including more than 500000 who are uninsured. It operates a network of around 10 acute care hospitals (including Bellevue the nation's oldest public hospital) large diagnostic and treatment centers skilled nursing centers long-term care facilities and a home health care agency. NYC H+H also operates more than 70 community-based clinics and provides medical services to New York City's correctional facilities. In addition it operates MetroPlus a managed health care plan.

Operations

NYC H+H provides health care services including primary and preventive care emergency care long-term care plant-based nutrition guidance school-based health care and services for victims of domestic violence.

Geographic Reach

NYC H+H operates health care facilities in New York's Manhattan Brooklyn Queens Bronx and Staten Island boroughs.

Sales and Marketing

NYC H+H's MetroPlus health plan provides low to no-cost insurance to more than 500000 customers in New York. It insures many New York City government employees.

Financial Performance

NYC H+H's operating revenue fell in fiscal 2017 (ended June) but recovered the following year surpassing that of fiscal 2016. Operating revenue increased 6% to $7.8 billion in 2018 as net patient service revenue and net appropriations from New York City increased. Those gains were partially offset by a decline in grants revenue.

The company has been losing money for years. In fiscal 2018 it had an operating loss of $57.5 million an improvement over the 2017 operating loss of $272.7 million. That improvement was driven by the higher operating revenue plus certain cost-control measures such as lower other-than-personal services and pension expenses. NYC H+H ended fiscal 2018 with a net deficit of $5.5 billion.

Strategy

NYC H+H has been struggling financially facing a projected $1.8 billion budget gap by 2020. In mid-2017 the system cut 476 positions including nearly 400 management positions. It has closed certain clinics and shuttered its Goldwater specialty care hospital and nursing facility. And although the system has received positive care quality reviews from external organizations it is challenged to attract patients with commercial insurance. To further exacerbate matters the health system has a number of older facilities that would benefit from improvements but it has few resources to allocate to those types of projects.

HISTORY

The City of New York in 1929 created a department to manage its hospitals for the poor. During the Depression more than half of the city's residents were eligible for subsidized care and its public hospitals operated at full capacity.

Four new hospitals opened in the 1950s but the city was already having trouble maintaining existing facilities and attracting staff (young doctors preferred private insurance-supported hospitals catering to the middle class). Meanwhile technological advances and increased demand for skilled nurses made hospitals more expensive to operate. The advent of Medicaid in 1965 was a boon for the system because it brought in federal money.

In 1969 the city created the New York City Health and Hospitals Corporation (HHC) to manage its public health care system — and it was hoped to distance it from the political arena. But HHC was still dependent on the city for funds arousing criticism from those who had hoped for more autonomy. A 1973 state report claimed "the people of New York City are not materially better served by the Health and Hospitals Corporation than by its predecessor agencies."

City budget shortfalls in the mid-1970s led to cutbacks at HHC including nearly 20% of staff. Later in the decade several hospitals closed and some services were discontinued. Ed Koch became mayor in 1978 and gained more control over HHC's operations. Struggles between his administration and the system led three HHC presidents to resign by 1981. That year Koch crony Stanley Brezenoff assumed the post and helped transform HHC into a city pseudo-department.

The early 1980s brought greater prosperity to the system. Reimbursement rates and collections procedures improved allowing HHC to upgrade its record-keeping and its ambulatory and psychiatric care programs. In the late 1980s sharp increases in AIDS and crack addiction cases strained the system and a sluggish economy decreased city funding. Criticism mounted in the early 1990s with allegations of wrongful deaths dangerous facilities and lack of Medicaid payment controls. HHC lost patients to managed care providers and revenues plummeted. In 1995 a city panel recommended radically revamping the system.

Faced with declining revenues and criticism from Mayor Rudolph Giuliani that HHC was "a jobs program" the company began cutting jobs and consolidating facilities in 1996. Under Giuliani's direction HHC made plans to sell its Coney Island Elmhurst and Queens hospital centers. In 1997 the New York State Supreme Court struck down Giuliani's privatization efforts saying the city council had a right to review and approve each sale. In 1998 Giuliani continued to seek to restructure HHC and the agency itself contended it was making progress toward its restructuring goals which were aimed at giving HHC more autonomy as well as more fiscal responsibility. In anticipation of a budget shortfall that year the system laid off some 900 support staff employees. In 1999 the state court of appeals ruled HHC could not legally lease or sell its hospitals.

In 2000 HHC launched an effort to improve its physical infrastructure by beginning the rebuilding and renovation of facilities in Brooklyn Manhattan and Queens. The organization also began converting to an electronic (and thus more efficient) clinical information system. In 2001 HHC forged ahead with further restructuring initiatives. It introduced the Open Access plan a cost-cutting measure designed to expedite the processes involved in outpatient visits.

In 2006 Mayor Michael Bloomberg committed $16 million in funds toward the treatment of those affected by exposure to toxic fumes and dust from the 2001 attacks on the World Trade Center. Together with the city HHC established the WTC Environmental Health Center at Bellevue Hospital; treatment was made available at little or no charge to the patient.

EXECUTIVES

President Ceo And Director, Alan D. Aviles
Acting Svp South Manhattan Health Network; Acting Executive Director Bellevue Hospital Center, Lynda D. Curtis
Svp North Bronx Healthcare Network; Executive Director Jacobi Medical Center, William P. Walsh
Svp Finance And Cfo, Marlene Zurack
Executive Director Queens Hospital Center, Antonio Martin
Executive Director Metropolitan Hospital Center, Meryl Weinberg
Executive Director Elmhurst Hospital Center, Chris Constantino
Executive Director And Cfo Gouverneur Healthcare Services, Mendel Hagler
Executive Director And President Metroplus Health Plan, Arnold Saperstein
Executive Director Sea View Hospital Rehabilitation Center And Home, Angelo Mascia
Svp Queens Healthcare Network, Anne Marie Sullivan
Executive Director Hhc Health And Home Care, Ann Frisch
Svp Information Technology And Cio, Norberto (Bert) Robles
Executive Director Dr. Susan Smith Mckinney Nursing And Rehabilitation Center, Michael Tartaglia
Executive Director Coler-goldwater Specialty Hospital And Nursing Facility, Robert K. Hughes
Svp Quality And Corporate Chief Medical Officer, Ross Wilson
Acting Svp Generations Plus Northern Manhattan Healthcare Network; Executive Director Lincoln Medical And Mental Health Center, Denise C. Soares
Executive Director Kings County Hospital Center, Ernest J. Baptiste
Executive Director Queens Hospital Center, Julius Wool
Assistant Vice President Information Technology Services, Michael Keil
Senior Assistant Vice President, Roslyn Weinstein
Senior Assistant Vice President, Caroline Jacobs
Senior Assistant Vice President, Paul Albertson
Senior Vice President, Arthur Wagner
Senior Assistant Vice President, Maxine Katz
Director Of Admissions, Alex Toro
Assistant Vice President Data Science, Vijay Saradhi
Director Of Pharmacy, Danielle Petrocelli
Director Of Health Information, Stephen Natarajan
Vice President Of Finance And Chief Fina, Tim Buit
Chairman, Michael A. Stocker
Vice Chair, Diane E. Lacey
Auditors: KPMG LLP NEW YORK NY

LOCATIONS

HQ: NEW YORK CITY HEALTH AND HOSPITALS CORPORATION
125 WORTH ST RM 514, NEW YORK, NY 100134006
Phone: 212 788-3321

HHC Networks

Central Brooklyn Family Health Network
  Dr. Susan Smith McKinney Nursing and
  Rehabilitation Center
  East New York Diagnostic & Treatment Center
  Kings County Hospital Center
Generations Plus Northern Manhattan Health Network
  Harlem Hospital Center
  Lincoln Medical and Mental Health Center
  Metropolitan Hospital Center
  Morrisania Diagnostic & Treatment Center
  Renaissance Health Care Network Diagnostic &
  Treatment Center
  Segundo Ruiz Belvis Diagnostic & Treatment Center
North Bronx Healthcare Network
  Jacobi Medical Center
  North Central Bronx Hospital
North Brooklyn Health Network
  Cumberland Diagnostic & Treatment Center
  Woodhull Medical and Mental Health Center
Queens Health Network
  Elmhurst Hospital Center
  Queens Hospital Center
South Brooklyn and Staten Island Health Network
  Coney Island Hospital
  Sea View Hospital Rehabilitation Center & Home
South Manhattan Healthcare Network
  Bellevue Hospital Center
  Gouverneur Healthcare Services

PRODUCTS/OPERATIONS

2018 Sales

	$ mil.	% of total
Net patient services	6,217	80
Net appropriations from City of New York	787	10
Grants	652	9
Other	105	1
Total	**7,761**	**100**

Selected Services

Alcohol and Opioid Use Disorder
Asthma Care
Bariatric Services
Breast Health
Burn Care
Cancer Care
Cardiology
Child Health and Pediatrics
Colon Cancer Screening
Deaf and Hard-of-Hearing
Dental Care
Depression
Diabetes Care
Farmers Market
Flu Vaccination
Geriatric Services
HIV/AIDS Care
HPV Vaccine
Hyptertension
Language/Translation Services
LGBTQ Services
Men's Health
Mental Health
Neonatal Intensive Care
Obstetrics & Gynecology
Palliative Care
Parkinson's Disease
Pediatrics
Quit Smoking
Rehab Services
Victims of Domestic Violence
Sexual Response Assault Teams
Sickle Cell Disease
Sleep Disorder Labs
Stroke Prevention and Care
Telehealth Initiatives
Trauma Centers
Vision Care
Women's Health
WTC Environmental Health Center
Youth Health

COMPETITORS

Beth Israel Medical
  Center
Catholic Healthcare

Lenox Hill Hospital
Memorial
Sloan-Kettering

System
Columbia University
Continuum Health
  Partners
Cornell University

Montefiore Medical
NYU
NewYork-Presbyterian
  Healthcare
Northwell Health

HISTORICAL FINANCIALS

Company Type: Private

Income Statement				FYE: June 30
	REVENUE ($ mil.)	NET INCOME ($ mil.)	NET PROFIT MARGIN	EMPLOYEES
06/17	9,551	(194)	—	35,700
06/02	4,285	(119)	—	
06/01	4,288	(72)	—	
06/00	4,084	9	0.2%	
Annual Growth	**5.1%**	—	—	—

New York Community Bancorp Inc.

It's big banking in the Big Apple and beyond. New York Community Bancorp is the holding company for one of the largest thrifts in the US New York Community Bank as well as New York Commercial Bank (also dba Atlantic Bank) and seven other banking divisions. In its home state New York Community Bank operates through Queens County Savings Bank Richmond County Savings Bank Roosevelt Savings Bank and Roslyn Savings Bank. It serves customers in New Jersey through its Garden State Community Bank division. New York Community Bank also does business as AmTrust Bank which operates in Arizona and Florida and Ohio Savings Bank. Altogether New York Community Bancorp has about 275 bank branches in five states.

Operations

New York Community Bancorp operates two businesses: Banking Operations and Residential Mortgage Banking.

The main banking business generates some 95% of total revenue and serves consumers and businesses with standard services such as checking and savings accounts CDs IRAs credit cards mortgages and loans. It offers life and long-term care insurance through an agreement with third-party provider LPL Financial. New York Community Bancorp typically does not open new stand-alone branches but has been increasing its presence in its market areas by adding locations inside grocery stores and extending business hours. Its commercial arm New York Commercial Bank has 30 branches in Manhattan Queens Brooklyn Westchester County and Long Island including 18 that operate under the name Atlantic Bank. New York Community Bancorp also owns investment advisory firm Peter B. Cannell & Co.

Multifamily mortgage loans (with an emphasis on rent-regulated apartment buildings) are the company's key assets making up more than 70% of its loan book. New York Community Bancorp prefers rent-regulated properties because they tend to have lower-than-average tenant turnover and can often be expected to bring in steady income during economic downturns. The company also focuses on loans secured by commercial real estate in New York and New Jersey.

Geographic Reach

Westbury New York-based New York Community Bancorp has branches in five states: New York home to about 160 community and commercial bank branches; New Jersey with about 45 locations; Ohio and Florida with more than 25 branches each; and Arizona with more than a dozen locations.

Financial Performance

New York Community Bancorp has seen a slow decline in revenue since 2010. In fiscal 2016 sales fell a further 4% to $1.8 billion due to lower returns from securities and money market investments as well as lower mortgage banking income.

Net income was $495.4 in 2016 a sharp increase on the loss of $47.2 million incurred in the previous year. The results reflect a one-off item in 2015 that saw the bank pay $773.8 million to reduce $10.4 billion in wholesale borrowings to a lower cost of debt.

Cash from operations was $755.7 million in 2016 compared to a cash usage of $420.4 million in 2015 primarily for the same reason as changes in net income.

Strategy

To strengthen its balance sheet New York Community Bancorp paid a one-off charge of $773.8 million in 2016 to amend its loan repayment rate from 3.16% to 1.58%. The reduction will save the company $100 million each year.

The company called off its merger with Astoria Bank in later 2016. The deal would have taken the bank over the $50 billion threshold that delineates a systematically important bank and brings tougher regulations and Astoria's more unwieldy footprint would have dragged New York's best-in-class efficiency ratio up.

Company Background

In 2012 it acquired some $2.2 billion in deposits mainly short-term CDs but also money market accounts from Aurora Bank.

New York Community Bank was founded in 1859. New York Community Bancorp was incorporated in 1993.

EXECUTIVES

Sevp And Coo, Robert Wann, age 64, $1,100,000 total compensation
President And Ceo, Joseph R. Ficalora, age 72, $1,400,000 total compensation
Sevp And Cfo, Thomas R. (Tom) Cangemi, age 50, $850,000 total compensation
Evp Chief Corporate Governance Officer And Corporate Secretary, R. Patrick Quinn
Sevp And Chief Lending Officer, James J. Carpenter, age 58, $775,000 total compensation
Evp And Chief Accounting Officer, John J. Pinto, age 48, $575,000 total compensation
Evp And Cio, Robert Brown
Senior Vice President And Controller, James Speranza
Assistant Vice President Regional Human Resources Director, Patricia King
Vice President Risk Management, Debbie Messina
Executive Vice President, Barbara Ann Tosi-Renna
Second Vice President Staff Attorney, Laura Coleman
Senior Vice President Mortgage, Charles Baker
Senior Vice President, Michael Frain
Vice President Loan Review Officer, Ronald Lehrer
Executive Vice President, Andrew Kaplan
Vice President Business Development Officer, Boris Gadol
Underwriter Iii Second Vice President, Tiffany Cohen
First Senior Vice President And Branch Coordinator, Louis Riccio
Assistant Vice President Procurement, Susan Pace-Burke

Erm Governance Manager First Vice President, Olga Collins

Assistant Vice President Of Retail Sales, Edward Day

Application Development Manager First Vice President, Sharon Michitsch

Edandt Training Manager Vice President, Susan Weaver

Vice President Asset Manager, Jeff Roe

Vice President Commercial Lending, John Adams

Senior Vice President Regional Executive, Gail Castellano

Assistant Vice President Manager Of Loan Admin Customer Service, Ken Hsiung

Vice President, Kevin Kaufmann

Vice President Market Manager, Leonard Bosso

Assistant Vice President, Peter Zito

Assistant Vice President, Navia Acosta

Vice President, Ines Kurtov

Vice President, Jeff Lee

First Vice President, Scott Armstrong

Vice President Audit Manager, Adam Sullivan

Vice President, Sonia Holder

Second Vice President, Crocefissa Grima

Senior Vice President, Levi Richardson

Vice President Network Engineering, Michael Mike Gluckman

First Vice President And Sox Compliance Officer, Andrew LaRocca

Vice President Benefits Manager, Frances Kaiser

Assistant Vice President, Cathy Karalis

Vice President, James Drum

Vice President Retail Operations, Jamil Salah

Assistant Vice President Network Engineering, Anthony Ardezzone

Executive Vice President And Chief Human Resources Officer, Eric Kracov

Vice President Systems Engineering, Craig Preiser

Vp It Core Operations Manager, Perry Kaganis

Vice President Branch Manager, Susan Fisher

Assistanty Vice President, Michael Yetemian

Vice President, Kathy Kowler

Assistant Vice President Branch Manager, Vincent Oyola

Vice President Mortgage Lending Officer, Michael Scarola

Assistant Vice President Commercial Lending, Antoinette Difinizio

First Vice President, Douglas Orth

Vice President Regional Business Banker, Petros Messare

Vice President Of Inquiry Management, Kristina Hosea

Vice President Enterprise Risk Asset Liability Management, Tejas Doshi

Assistant Vice President, Beth Gant

Second Vice President, Sarah Artino

Senior Vice President, Frank Macchio

Vp Commercial Lending Officer, Frank Maffei

Assistant Vice President, Angela Gallagher

Vice President And Credit Risk Manager, Jeffrey Roe

Chairman, Dominick Ciampa, age 86

Auditors: KPMG LLP

LOCATIONS

HQ: New York Community Bancorp Inc.
615 Merrick Avenue, Westbury, NY 11590
Phone: 516 683-4100
Web: www.mynycb.com

2016 Locations

	No.
New York Community Bank	
New York	111
New Jersey	45
Ohio	28
Florida	27
Arizona	14
New York Commercial Bank	48
Total	**273**

PRODUCTS/OPERATIONS

2016 Sales

	$ mil.	% of total
Interest		
Mortgage & other loans	1,472	81
Securities & money market investments	203	11
Noninterest		
Fee income	33	2
Bank-owned life insurance	31	2
Mortgage banking income	27	1
Net gain on sale of loans	16	1
Net gain on sales of securities	3	-
Other	42	2
FDIC indemnification expenses	(6.2)	-
Total	**1,820**	**100**

2016 Sales

	% of total
Banking operations	
Interest	89
Non Interest	7
Residential Mortgage banking	
Interest	1
Non Interest	3
Total	**100**

Selected Operations

AmTrust Bank (Arizona Florida)
Atlantic Bank (New York commercial bank)
Garden State Community Bank (New Jersey)
Ohio Savings Bank (Ohio)
Queens County Savings Bank (Queens NY)
Richmond County Savings Bank (Staten Island NY)
Roosevelt Savings Bank (Brooklyn NY)
Roslyn Savings Bank (Long Island NY)

COMPETITORS

Apple Bank for Savings
Astoria Financial
Bank of America
Citigroup
Emigrant Bank
Flushing Financial
HSBC USA
Investors Bancorp
JPMorgan Chase
Provident Financial Services
Ridgewood Savings Bank
Safra Bank
TD Bank USA
Valley National Bancorp
Wells Fargo

HISTORICAL FINANCIALS

Company Type: Public

Income Statement

FYE: December 31

	ASSETS ($ mil.)	NET INCOME ($ mil.)	INCOME AS % OF ASSETS	EMPLOYEES
12/18	51,899	422	0.8%	2,913
12/17	49,124	466	0.9%	3,096
12/16	48,927	495	1.0%	3,487
12/15	50,318	(47)	—	3,448
12/14	48,559	485	1.0%	3,416
Annual Growth	1.7%	(3.4%)	—	(3.9%)

2018 Year-End Financials

Debt ratio: 1.00%
Return on equity: 6.00%
Cash ($ mil.): 1,475
Current ratio: —
Long-term debt ($ mil.): —
No. of shares (mil.): 474
Dividends
  Yield: 7.0%
  Payout: 86.0%
Market value ($ mil.): 4,456

	STOCK PRICE ($) FY Close	P/E High/Low	PER SHARE ($) Earnings	Dividends	Book Value
12/18	9.00	18 11	1.00	1.00	14.00
12/17	13.00	18 13	1.00	1.00	14.00
12/16	16.00	17 14	1.00	1.00	13.00
12/15	16.00	— —	(0.00)	1.00	12.00
12/14	16.00	16 14	1.00	1.00	13.00
Annual Growth	(12.4%)	— —	(7.7%)	(9.2%)	1.8%

NEW YORK COMMUNITY TRUST AND COMMUNITY FUNDS INC

EXECUTIVES

Pres-Exec Dir, Lorie A Slutsky
Sr V Pres*, Joyce Bove
V Pres Donor Rltns*, Robert V Edgar
V Pres of ADM*, Mercedes M Leon
Program Officer, Eve A Stotland
Director of Investments, Ken Beitler
Associate Program Officer, Tonya Thomas
Senior Program Officer, Patricia Swann
Vice President, Shawn V Morehead
Auditors: GRANT THORNTON LLP NEW YORK

LOCATIONS

HQ: NEW YORK COMMUNITY TRUST AND COMMUNITY FUNDS INC
909 3RD AVE FL 22, NEW YORK, NY 100224752
Phone: 212 686-0010
Web: WWW.NYCOMMUNITYTRUST.ORG

HISTORICAL FINANCIALS

Company Type: Private

Income Statement

FYE: December 31

	ASSETS ($ mil.)	NET INCOME ($ mil.)	INCOME AS % OF ASSETS	EMPLOYEES
12/17	2,806	(5)	—	65
12/16	2,552	(6)	—	
12/15	2,473	(100)	—	
12/14	2,571	130	5.1%	
Annual Growth	3.0%	—	—	—

NEW YORK STATE CATHOLIC HEALTH PLAN, INC.

Fidelis Care hopes for always faithful health plan members. The New York State Catholic Health Plan which does business as Fidelis Care serves more than 921000 residents in some 60 counties across the state including the New York City area. The church-sponsored plan's provider network includes more than 63000 physicians hospitals and other health care professionals and facilities. Fidelis Care provides managed Medicaid Medicare and state-sponsored family and children's Health Plus plans as well as long-term care and behavioral health coverage.

Operations

The company boasts an overall statewide member retention rate of more than 78% with a s Child Health Plus retention rate of more than 85%.

Geographic Reach

Fidelis Care's regional offices are located in Rego Park Queens (Greater Metropolitan); Albany (Northeast); Syracuse (Central); and Buffalo (Western) with satellite offices in Poughkeepsie Rochester and Suffern.

Sales and Marketing

The health plan has expanded its membership by seeking new low-income patients who lack coverage. In addition to direct sales efforts Fidelis Care tries to maintain a presence at health centers frequented by its target audience partnering with neighborhood clinics to hold free health screenings and Health Plus enrollment information sessions.

Enroll NY a new website sponsored by not-for-profit organization Hudson Center for Health Equity & Quality is also connecting Fidelis Care and other Medicaid providers with potential customers. In 2013 Fidelis Care began selling through the New York State of Health insurance exchange marketplace.

To bosst membership in 2013 the company ran the "I Want Fidelis Care' campaign (which promoted Fidelis Care as a health care resource) in English and Spanish. TV was added to the media buy in the New York City and Buffalo regions. It also established a social media presence on Facebook Twitter YouTube and Google+.

Financial Performance

Fidelis Care reported gross revenues of $4.1 billion in 2013 up from $3.3 billion in 2012.

Strategy

The company is expanding its office to keep up with demand. In 2014 it opened Ridgewood Community Office; in 2013 it completed of?ce expansion projects in the Albany and Syracuse regional of?ces and the satellite of?ce in Suffern and opened new community of?ces in Flushing (Queens) the Bronx and Bath (Steuben County).

Forecasting substantial growth in 2014 with the enrollment of more than 120000 new members the company announced plans to add more than 75 new information technology jobs at its Buffalo regional office.

In 2013 Fidelis Care moved into 12 new counties with the Medicare Advantage program highlighted by the opportunity to serve residents of western New York for the ?rst time. It also made plans to expand into Seneca Yates and Jefferson counties in 2014 and served additional Managed Long Term Care members as part of the State's phased-in expansion of mandatory enrollment in counties beyond New York City.

Fidelis Care has grown by expanding rapidly into new counties in New York including a number of growth measures in the Medicare marketplace during 2012 and 2013. The health plan's recent activity includes completing construction of Fidelis Care's new operations center and offices in Getzville (Erie County) and the launch of its new provider portal (Provider Access Online). Other growth measures include a 2012 partnership with DentaQuest to promote dental checkups; it also launched a new member portal for members to access benefit information. In 2013 the company gained approval to be a qualified health plan provider on the official New York State of Health marketplace.

Fidelis Care regularly evaluates and broadens its plan offerings. Recent additions include its Fidelis Care at Home managed long-term care offering; the behavioral health and developmental disabilities coverage options; and its fully integrated dual advantage plans (for consumers with both Medicare and Medicaid coverage).

Company Background

The church-sponsored plan was founded in 1993 by the bishops of New York's Roman Catholic dioceses and the Catholic Medical Center of Brooklyn and Queens.

EXECUTIVES

Vice President Network Dev, Pamela Wilkes
Vice President, Carey Shoemaker
Vice President Finance, Dina Soroka
Senior Vice President And Chief Admini, David Thomas
Director Of Government Relations, Colleen Wilson
Vice President, Brian Cummings
Vice President Of Infrastructure, Duncan Ross
Vice President Strategic Planning, James Burnosky
Nursing Director, Margaret Leonard
Vice President Of Information Technology, David Szabad
Medical Director, Camille Pearte
Vice President Product Development And Corporate Innovation Fidelis Care New, Jason Reiser
Assistant Vice President Contract Management, John Place
Senior Medical Secretary, Osvaldo Aquino
Auditors: LB DELOITTE TAX LLP JERICHO

LOCATIONS

HQ: NEW YORK STATE CATHOLIC HEALTH PLAN, INC.
9525 QUEENS BLVD, REGO PARK, NY 113744510
Phone: 888 343-3547
Web: WWW.FIDELISCARE.ORG

PRODUCTS/OPERATIONS

Selected Plans

Child Health Plus
Dual Advantage
Family Health Plus
Fidelis Care at Home (managed long-term care)
Medicaid Advantage Plus (managed long-term care)
Medicaid Managed Care
Medicare Advantage
New York State of Health

COMPETITORS

Aetna
Affinity Health
Anthem
CIGNA
Capital District Physicians' Health Plan
EmblemHealth
Health Net
HealthPlus Amerigroup
Healthfirst
Healthplex
Humana
Independent Health
Lifetime Healthcare
MVP Health Plan
UnitedHealth Group
Vytra Healthcare
healthnow new york inc

HISTORICAL FINANCIALS

Company Type: Private

Income Statement				FYE: December 31
	REVENUE ($ mil.)	NET INCOME ($ mil.)	NET PROFIT MARGIN	EMPLOYEES
12/14	5,305	272	5.1%	1,625
12/10	1,921	51	2.7%	—
12/09	1,435	28	1.9%	—
12/08	1,068	4	0.4%	—
Annual Growth	30.6%	103.1%	—	—

NEW YORK UNIVERSITY

Higher education is at the core of this Big Apple institution. The setting and heritage of New York University (NYU) make it one of the nation's most popular educational institutions. With more thanÂ 50000 students attending its 18 schools and colleges NYU is among the largest private schools in the US. Its Tisch School of the Arts is well-regarded and its law school and Leonard N. Stern School of Business are among theÂ foremost in the country. NYU occupies five major centers in Manhattan; its Washington Square campus is in the heart of Greenwich Village. The school wasÂ founded in 1831. Notable alumni include former Federal Reserve Chairman Alan Greenspan and film producer Oliver Stone.

Operations

NYU reports its financials in two segments — University and NYU Langone Health. The latter segment is composed of the NYU Langone Health System and NYU School of Medicine.

The University includes nearly 20 colleges and divisions including schools of art and sciences law dentistry business mathematical sciences fine arts professional studies public services social work and engineering. NYU also operates NYU Abu Dhabi and NYU Shanghai a joint venture with East China Normal University. The University segment accounts for some 30% of NYU's total revenue.

NYU Langone Health operates two hospitals Kimmel Pavilion and Tisch Hospital which together have some 850 beds. It also operates the 225-bed NYU Langone Orthopedic Hospital the 450-bed NYU Langone Hospital in Brooklyn and several ambulatory care facilities. The segment brings in some 70% of NYU's total revenue.

NYU alumni and faculty boast several prestigious awards including more than a dozen Nobel and Crafoord prizes and another four Pulitzer prizes.

Geographic Reach

Along with its campuses in New York NYU operates degree-granting campuses in Abu Dhabi and Shanghai. It also has more than 10 global academic centers in Africa Asia Europe and the Americas and research programs in more than 25 countries.

Financial Performance

In fiscal 2018 (ended August) NYU's operating revenue increased 17% to $11.6 billion. Driving that gain was an increase in patient care revenue which rose from $5.6 billion to $7 billion that year.

However the university's excess of operating revenue over expenses fell dramatically from $196.8 million to $11.2 million in fiscal 2018. Salaries and medical and pharmaceutical costs rose as did facilities expenses professional services expenses and all other expenses.

NYU ended fiscal 2018 with $1.5 billion in net cash some $217 million more than what it had at the end of 2017. Operating activities provided $941.1 million in net cash financing activities provided another $580.4 million while investing activities used $1.3 billion.

Strategy

In 2018 NYU School of Medicine offered all students full tuition scholarships regardless of merit or financial need. The move was largely designed to promote the training of primary care physicians which is an area of great need in the US. By removing the heavy debt load that medical students typically face the school hopes to encourage students to pursue careers in lower-paying areas such as primary care.

Later that year NYU announced plans to establish a new medical school on Long Island. That campus will also provide full tuition scholarships to students.

HISTORY

New York University was founded by several prominent New Yorkers in 1831. The school held its first classes the following year in rented rooms on the corner of Beekman and Nassau streets then moved to a building in Washington Square in 1835. It established its law school that year. NYU started its school of medicine in 1841 followed by the school of engineering and science (1854). Post-graduate studies in arts and science (its first coeducational program) began in 1886.

NYU's enrollment jumped from fewer than 2000 in 1900 to 28000 in 1930. After a lull during the Depression and WWII the campus boomed again in the postwar years. During the 1950s the university began focusing on improving academics rather than on increasing enrollment. It created a school of the arts in 1965 and in the early 1970s it completed the Elmer Holmes Bobst Library. However a cash crunch during that decade almost forced the school into bankruptcy.

President Jay Oliva took the reins in 1981 and focused on transforming NYU from a largely commuter college into a global university. The school began a campaign to raise $1 billion in 1984 but earmarked the funds for campus improvements rather than swelling its endowment. During the late 1980s NYU opened several new dormitories and conference spaces. In 1994 British historian and collector Sir Harold Acton bequeathed to the school his Tuscany estate — five art-filled villas overlooking Florence Italy.

In 1996 NYU's Medical Center began talks with Mount Sinai Medical Center aimed at merging their hospitals and medical schools. The talks fell apart in early 1997 but the following year the two sides agreed to merge hospitals and keep their medical schools distinct. Also in 1998 NYU formed NYU On-Line Inc. a for-profit subsidiary to develop and sell specialized Internet courses to other schools training centers and students; the venture was subsequently folded in late 2001. During 1999 contributions to the school approached $250 million. That year however two upper-level school officials were fired following allegations of improper use of university money.

Oliva retired as president in 2002 and was replaced by John Sexton former School of Law dean. In 2004 Sexton announced that NYU would give $1 million to New York City towards renovation of Washington Square Park (the school annually gives some $200000 for the park's ongoing maintenance).

EXECUTIVES

Vp Academic And Health Affairs, Robert (Bob) Berne
Vp Information Technology And Chief Information Technology Officer, Marilyn A. McMillan
Provost, David W. McLaughlin
Evp Finance And Information Technology, Martin S. Dorph
Director Global Institute Of Public Health; Dean Of Global Public Health, Cheryl G. Healton
Dean Libraries, Carol A. Mandel
Herman Robert Fox Dean College Of Dentistry, Charles N. Bertolami
Evp Operations, Alison Leary
Director Institute For The Study Of The Ancient World, Roger Bagnall
Director Courant Institute Of Mathematical Sciences, Gérard Ben Arous
Saul J. Farber Dean Nyu School Of Medicine; Ceo Nyu Hospitals Center, Robert I. Grossman

Dean Gallatin School Of Individualized Study, Susanne L. Wofford
Dean Polytechnic School Of Engineering, Katepalli R. (Sreeni) Sreenivasan
Dean Silver School Of Social Work, Lynn Videka
Dean Liberal Studies, Fred Schwarzbach
Judy And Michael Steinhardt Director Institute Of Fine Arts, Patricia Lee Rubin
Dean Leonard N. Stern School Of Business, Peter B. Henry, age 49
Vice Chancellor New York University Abu Dhabi, Alfred H. Bloom
Vp Global Technology And Chief Global Technology Officer, Thomas A. (Tom) Delaney
Dean For Science Faculty Of Arts And Science, Michael D. Purugganan
President, Andrew Hamilton
Gale And Ira Drukier Dean Steinhardt School For Culture Education And Human Development, Dominic Brewer
Anne And Joel Ehrenkranz Dean Faculty Of Arts And Sciences, Thomas J. Carew
Dean For Humanities Faculty Of Arts And Sciences, Joy Connolly
Harvey J. Stedman Dean School Of Professional Studies, Dennis DiLorenzo
Dean Robert F. Wagner Graduate School Of Public Service, Sherry A. Glied
Dean Tisch School Of The Arts, Allyson Green
Dean For Social Sciences Faculty Of Arts And Science, Michael Laver
Vice Chancellor Nyu Shanghai, Jeffrey S. Lehman
Dean Undergraduate College Leonard N. Stern School Of Business, Geeta Menon
Dean School Of Law, Trevor Morrison
Director Marron Institute Of Urban Management, Paul Romer
Seryl Kushner Dean College Of Arts And Science, G. Gabrielle Starr
Dean College Of Nursing, Eileen Sullivan-Marx
Chancellor Nyu Shanghai, Yu Lizhong
Interim Dean Graduate School Of Arts And Science, Anna L. Harvey
Assistant Vice President, Zoe Ragouzeos
Vice President, Marc Wais
Vice Provost, Carol Morrow
Associate Vice President Student Health, Carlo Ciotoli
Vice President Financial Operations And Treasurer, Stephanie Pianka
Assistant Vice President Employee Relations, Barbara Cardeli-Arroyo
Vice President Finance, Harold T Read
Associate Vice President, Deborah Broderick
Assistant Vice President, Allen Mcfarlane
Vice President, Andrew Gordon
Vice President Of Public Relations, Carolynn Choi
Associate Vice President For Stewardship And Events, Gustave Fleury
Medical Director, Marcy Ferdschneider
Chair Department Of Anthropology, Fred Myers
Associate Vice President Campus Planning And Design, Lori Mazor
Vice President Chief Information Security Officer, Mehdi Idrissi
Assistant Vice President Auxiliary Services, Paul Glimcher
Assistant Vice President, Janet Alperstein
Vice President Human Resources, Robert White
Vice President For Budget And Planning, Anthony Jiga
Nursing Director, Mary Gribbin
Director Of Government Relations, Steve Heuer
Vice President For Enrollment Management, Mj Knoll-finn
Vice President For, Robert Campbell
Vice President Human Resources, Sabrina Ellis
Associate Vice President For Global Technologies, Heather Stewart
Vice President Finance, Pamela Morris

Vice President, Robert Levine
Executive Vice President, Tom Jordan
Executive Vice President Research And Innovation Cross Platform, Lisa Sokolov
Vice President And Special Counsel, Leo L Goldsmith
Vice President, Victoria M Mccoy-cosentino
Vice President Director Engineering, Chris Pak
Vice President Global Security And Crisis Management, Jules Martin
Assistant Vice President External Affairs And Protective Services, Carl Barchus
Vice President, Pallavi Sambasivan
Vice President Finance And Administration, Charice Washington-warner
Vice President Sales, Joe Harris
Vice President Council, John Plecnik
Vice President And Manager Raines Perspectives Raines International, Jessica Deoliveira
Senior Vice President Deputy General Counsel Chief Compliance And Ethics Officer, Genie Gavenchak
Senior Vice President And Deputy General Counsel, Lawrence Bunder
Vice President For Operations Capital Projects, Andy Buonpastore
Vice President, Shaila Dani
Vice President For Capital Projects And Facilities, Linda Chiarelli
Executive Vice President, Mandy Hu
Vice President Facilities Management, Debra Berger
Chairman Board Of Trustees, William R. (Bill) Berkley, age 73
Board Director, Christine Trump
Vice Chair President, Peter Romain
Honorary Board Member, John Tintori
Assistant Treasurer, Elisa Cohen
Medical Secretary, Latia Davis
Secretary, Candice Jarvis
Secretary, Jennifer Neuman
Ward Secretary, Mark Brennan
Ms Global Affairs Candidate Treasurer Energy Policy International Club, Jude Buenaseda
Secretary, Lara Maraziti
Treasurer, Daphne Tso
Secretary, Lewis R Steinberg
Secretary Athletic Development, Raffaela Ianniciello
Secretary And Marketing, August Morar
Secretary I, Kelrick Drake
Secretary, Beverly Wideman
Cab Treasurer, Erin Adams
Secretary, Andy Le
College Of Arts And Sciences History Society Treasurer, Samantha Noell
Auditors: PRICEWATERHOUSECOOPERS LLP NE

LOCATIONS

HQ: NEW YORK UNIVERSITY
70 WASHINGTON SQ S, NEW YORK, NY 100121019
Phone: 212 998-1212

PRODUCTS/OPERATIONS

2018 Sales

	$ mil.	% of total
Patient care	6,982	60
Tuition & fees	1,852	16
Grants & contracts	1,012	9
Auxiliary enterprises	505	4
Hospital affiliations	343	3
Endowment distribution	169	2
Contributions	168	2
Net assets from restrictions	122	1
Insurance premiums earned	116	1
Return on short-term investments	16	-
Programs & other	272	2
Total	**11,556**	**100**

Selected Schools and Colleges

College of Arts and Science (founded 1832)
College of Dentistry (1865)
Courant Institute of Mathematical Sciences (1934)
Gallatin School of Individualized Study (1972)
Graduate School of Arts and Science (1886)
Leonard N. Stern School of Business (1900)
Robert F. Wagner Graduate School of Public Service (1938)
School of Continuing and Professional Studies (1934)
School of Law (1835)
School of Medicine (1841)
School of Social Work (1960)
Steinhardt School of Culture Education and Human Development (1890)
Tisch School of the Arts (1965)

HISTORICAL FINANCIALS

Company Type: Private

Income Statement   FYE: August 31

	REVENUE ($ mil.)	NET INCOME ($ mil.)	NET PROFIT MARGIN	EMPLOYEES
08/16	8,500	177	2.1%	21,000
08/11	5,172	564	10.9%	—
08/06	2,148	196	9.1%	—
Annual Growth	**14.7%**	**(1.0%)**	—	—

Newell Brands Inc

Newell Brands is the company behind such household names as Rubbermaid storage boxes Calphalon cookware Graco pushchairs and Sharpie pens. Newell Brands' customers are mainly mass retailers such as Target and home and office supply stores such as Staples in the US which accounts for some two-thirds of total sales. Newell's footprint spans 70 factories and some 120 warehouses and distribution centers. The megabucks acquisition of consumer products giant Jarden brought products such as Bicycle Playing Cards Mr. Coffee Coleman Jostens Oster Rawlings Sunbeam and Yankee Candle under its umbrella.

Operations

Newell Brands structures its operations into three main reporting segments: Learning and Development Food and Appliances and Home and Outdoor Living. Each accounts for roughly a third of sales and includes well-known household brands.

Learning and Development makes pens pencils highlighters and markers glue labels and baby gear and infant care products. Its brands include Aprica Baby Jogger Expo Graco Mr Sketch Parket Sharpie and X-Acto.

The Home and Outdoor Living segment makes products for outdoor activities candles and connected home and security products. Brands include Chespeake Bay Candle Contigo First Alert and Yankee Candle.

Food and Appliances makes slow cookers (Crock-Pot) food storage boxes (Rubbermaid FoodSaver and Sistema) coffee machines (Mr. Coffee) cookware (Calphalon) and jars (Ball).

Geographic Reach

Newell Brands operates in nearly 100 countries in the Americas Europe the Middle East Africa and the Asia Pacific region. Roughly two-thirds of sales come from the US while Europe Middle East and Africa (EMEA) region generates about 15% of sales. Latin America and the Asia Pacific regions both generate 10% of revenue while Canada brings in the remainder of total sales.

Sales and Marketing

Newell Brands reaches consumers through large mass merchandisers such as discount stores home centers warehouse clubs office superstores commercial distributors and e-commerce companies. It also sells direct-to-consumer online while certain brands such as Yankee Candle have dedicated stores.

Newell Brands' biggest customer is Wal-Mart sales to which account for about 10% to 15% of its net sales each year.

Financial Performance

The acquisition of Jarden in 2016 nearly doubled Newell Brands' sales which peaked at $9.6 billion in 2017. However all is not well at Newell as weak cash flow and bankruptcy of key customer Toys "R" Us triggered huge goodwill impairments at the tail end of 2018 and caused the company to accelerate its transformation plan.

In 2018 the company's sales fell 10% to $8.6 billion as the company began selling off non-core brands coupled with general weak sales across all product segments.

Newell reported an $8.3 billion net loss in 2018 compared to a $592.4 million net gain in 2017. It booked an $8.3 billion impairment charge which recorded mainly in the Food and Appliances and Home and Outdoor Living segments while Learning and Development escaped relative unscathed at $351 million.

Newell's cash on hand grew $10 million during 2018 ending the year at $495.7 million. The company's operations generated $680.0 million and its investing activities generated $4.8 billion while financing activities used $5.5 billion. Newell's main cash uses in 2018 were short- and long-term debt repayments dividends and share repurchases while business divestitures generated $5.1 billion.

Strategy

With the brands acquired from Jarden not providing the hoped-for synergies Newell accelerated its transformation plan in 2018. The company plans to sell off big chunks of its portfolio notably its industrial and commercial assets such as Waddington plastic packaging Rubbermaid commercial products Rexair vacuum cleaners Mapa industrial gloves and Spontex cleaning products. It's also selling non-core consumer products such as Rawlings Jostens Pure Fishing among others. The goal is to sell all of them before the end of 2019 and with the capital raised Newell will deleverage its balance sheet strengthen its operations and return cash to shareholders.

Mergers and Acquisitions

Newell Brands made three further acquisitions in the year after its mega-purchase of Jarden in 2016. It acquired Chesapeake Bay Candle a candlemaker for $75 million; New Zealand-based Sistema Plastics which makes airtight food storage boxes for $472 million; and Smith Mountain Industries which also makes candles for $100 million.

HISTORY

Businessmen in Ogdensburg New York advanced curtain rod maker W.F. Linton Co. $1000 to relocate from Rhode Island in the early 1900s. Local wholesaler Edgar Newell signed off on the loan; when the company went bankrupt in 1903 he was forced to take over. The company renamed Newell Manufacturing set up plants in Canada and Freeport Illinois to ease shipping costs and speed delivery.

Production expanded into towel racks ice picks and other items; Woolworth's decision to carry Newell's products turned the company into a national supplier. Edgar Newell died in 1920. The company made its first acquisition in 1938 buying window treatment specialist Drapery Hardware.

The Newell companies were consolidated in the mid-1960s into a single corporation. Daniel Ferguson was named president in 1965 and served alongside his CEO father Leonard one of Newell's original employees. During his tenure Daniel hitched the company's future to the growing dominance of large discount stores. Newell went from a $14 million family business to a global multi-line conglomerate by acquiring products that it distributed to these big buyers. The company went public in 1972.

As for Rubbermaid it was originally a balloon maker in the 1920s called Wooster Rubber. By the mid-1930s Ohio's Wooster Rubber had acquired the Rubbermaid product line of rubber housewares. It went public in 1955 and two years later changed its name to Rubbermaid. During the 1980s the company enjoyed a decade of phenomenal growth. Newell's $6 billion purchase of Rubbermaid in 1999 sealed its biggest deal yet and resulted in a name change: Newell Rubbermaid.

Decades later the company changed its name to Newell Brands in 2016 after it purchased consumer goods giant Jarden in a mega-merger valued at around $15.4 billion.

EXECUTIVES

Evp And Cfo, Ralph J. Nicoletti, age 61, $493,845 total compensation
Ceo, Michael B. (Mike) Polk, age 58, $1,312,500 total compensation
Coo, William A. (Bill) Burke, age 58, $796,053 total compensation
Chief Development Officer, Richard Davies
Chief Customer Officer, Joseph W. Cavaliere
President, Mark S. Tarchetti, age 43, $922,212 total compensation
Svp Information Technology And Cio, Dan Gustafson
Chief Transformation Officer, Russ Torres
Vp Global Ecommerce, Jeremy Liebowitz
Svp Design And Innovation, Nate Young
Vice President Strategy And Analytics, Dan Sedlak
Executive Vice President Chief Human Resources And Communications Officer, Fiona Laird
Vp Marketing Writing And Creative Expression Brands, Victor Misawa
Evp And Cfo, Christopher H Peterson
Senior Business Intelligence Developer, Robert Esteves
Vice President Sales, Mick Piche
Ecommerce Cfo And Vp Analytics, Dan Chun
Chairman, Michael T. Cowhig, age 72
Board Member, Michael Todman
Board Of Directors, Bridget Berman
Board Member, Debra Crew
Auditors: PricewaterhouseCoopers LLP

LOCATIONS

HQ: Newell Brands Inc
6655 Peachtree Dunwoody Road,, Atlanta, GA 30328
Phone: 770 418-7000
Web: www.newellrubbermaid.com

2018 Sales

	$ mil.	% of total
North America		
United States	5,806	67
Canada	397	5
Europe Middle East and Africa	1,096	13
Asia Pacific	685	8
Latin America	648	8
Total	**8,631**	**100**

PRODUCTS/OPERATIONS

2018 sales

	$ mil.	% of total
Learning and Development	2,982	35
Home and Outdoor Living	2,947	34
Food and Appliances	2,699	31
Other	4	-
Total	**8,631**	**100**

Selected Brands & Trade Names

Cleaning organization and decor
  Brute
  Roughneck
  Rubbermaid
  TakeAlongs
Office products
  Accent
  Berol
  DYMO
  Expo
  Liquid Paper
  Paper Mate
  Parker
  Rotring
  Sharpie
  Uni-Ball (under license)
  Waterman
Home and family
  Aprica
  Avex
  Calphalon
  Calphalon One
  Contigo
  Cooking with Calphalon
  Goody
  Graco
  Katana
  Kitchen Essentials
  Teutonia

COMPETITORS

ACCO Brands	Knape & Vogt
Acme United	Lancaster Colony
Alticor	Libbey
Avery Dennison	Lifetime Brands
BIC	Myers Industries
Bridgestone	Owens-Illinois
Coleman	Springs Global US
Crayola	Sterilite
Decorator Industries	Tupperware Brands
Dixon Ticonderoga	Uniek
Faber-Castell	WKI Holding
Home Products	Wilton Brands
International	ZAG Industries
Katy Industries	

HISTORICAL FINANCIALS

Company Type: Public

Income Statement

FYE: December 31

	REVENUE ($ mil.)	NET INCOME ($ mil.)	NET PROFIT MARGIN	EMPLOYEES
12/18	8,631	(6,918)	—	37,000
12/17	14,742	2,749	18.6%	49,000
12/16	13,264	528	4.0%	53,400
12/15	5,916	350	5.9%	17,200
12/14	5,727	378	6.6%	17,400
Annual Growth	10.8%	—	—	20.8%

2018 Year-End Financials

Debt ratio: 40.00%
Return on equity: (-71.00%)
Cash ($ mil.): 496
Current ratio: 2.00
Long-term debt ($ mil.): 6,696
No. of shares (mil.): 423
Dividends
  Yield: 5.0%
  Payout: —
Market value ($ mil.): 7,860

	STOCK PRICE ($) FY Close	P/E High/Low	PER SHARE ($) Earnings	Dividends	Book Value
12/18	19.00	— —	(15.00)	1.00	12.00
12/17	31.00	10 5	6.00	1.00	29.00
12/16	45.00	44 27	1.00	1.00	24.00
12/15	44.00	37 28	1.00	1.00	7.00
12/14	38.00	28 21	1.00	1.00	7.00
Annual Growth	(16.4%)	— —	—	8.7%	15.9%

Newmont Corp

Newmont goes for the gold. Producing close to 6 million ounces of gold annually Newmont Goldcorp Corporation (formerly Newmont Mining Corporation) is one of the top three gold producers in the world. The company has significant operations in the US Australia Peru Ghana and Suriname. Its gold reserves are close to 70 million ounces spread across 23000 square miles of its own land. Newmont also produces some copper principally through Boddington in Australia and Phoenix in the US. Although Newmont makes almost all its sales from refined gold the end-product of its operations is doré bars an alloy consisting primarily of gold but also containing silver and other metals. In 2019 Newmont Mining acquired Goldcorp for $10 billion to create the newly rebranded Newmont Goldcorp Corporation which now holds the world's largest share of gold assets.

Operations

Worldwide Newmont holds mineral rights on about 23000 square miles of land. The company's North American operations include mines in Nevada's Carlin Trend one of the largest gold-mining areas in North America. Other sites in North America reside in Phoenix Twin Creeks and Long Canyon; Nevada. Its Cripple Creek & Victor pit operations are also located in Victor Colorado. In the Asia/Pacific Newmont owns the Boddington project one of Australia's largest gold mining properties. Other holdings include the Tanami and Kalgoorlie sites. Newmont's South America segment operates two sites Yanacocha and Merian and manages the Conga Project.

Geographic Reach

Newmont has operations in North America (Colorado and Nevada) South America (Peru and Suriname) Australia and Africa (Ghana). Around 75% of the company's sale comes from the spot market in London UK with another 10% coming from Switzerland.

Sales and Marketing

Newmont sells more than 5 million ounces of gold at the London bullion spot market which is either used as an investment or finds a variety of end uses including jewelry electronics dentistry industrial and decorative uses.

The company also sells around 120 million pounds of copper a year in the form of concentrate that is sold to smelters for further treatment and refining and cathode. Refined copper is used in wire and cable products for communications electricity transportation industries in addition to equipment and electronic applications.

Financial Performance

Sales increased almost 10% from $6.7 billion in 2016 to $7.3 billion in 2017. This came mostly from the hold segment where higher production volumes and slightly higher prices brought in 10% more revenue year-over-year. Copper sales also increased an impressive 25% in 2017 due to higher average net realized prices partially offset by lower sales volumes.

Despite a sales increase the company posted a loss of $98 million in 2017. This was an improvement over the $627 million in losses posted in 2016 mostly from the absence of $977 million in impairment of long-lived assets posted in 2016.

Operations provided $2.3 billion offset by $961 million going towards investments and a further $864 million used in financing activities.

Strategy

Newport's strategy includes strengthening its portfolio (by building a longer-life lower-cost asset portfolio) and moving on promising exploration project development and inorganic opportunities.

With the world economy in recovery coupled with shortage of mining supply in the international market and an upturn in the demand for gold Newport is planning to produce up to 5.5 million ounces of gold by adding higher-margin assets.

Newmont has strategically accumulated superior assets on four continents giving it a competitive advantage in reserves and marginal growth. However most expansion projects are still in the pipeline. And they span the entire portfolio. This includes Carlin district mine expansions (Twin Underground and Exodus) in North America oxide production enhancement in the Andes as well as a 20% interest acquistion in Continental Gold's high-grade gold in Colombia.

It is already registering volume growth from existing mine expansions (like the Tanami underground extension). A similar underground expansion is planned at Subika mine in Africa. The company also boosted production in 2017 thanks to production from two new mines Merian and Long Canyon.

In 2019 Newmont rejected an unsolicited takeover bid from its competitor Barrick Gold and instead proposed a joint venture in Nevada USA. Meanwhile the company is also looking to create a newly rebranded Newmont Goldcorp corporation by taking over Goldcorp to become a top player in the industry.

Company Background

Colonel William Boyce Thompson a flamboyant trader founded the Newmont Co. in 1916 to trade his various oil and mining stocks. The Newmont name was a combination of New York and Montana where Thompson grew up. The company was renamed Newmont Corporation in 1921 and Newmont Mining Corporation in 1925 when it went public.

In 2019 Newmont Mining became Newmont Goldcorp after its acquisition of Goldcorp Corporation.

HISTORY

The company was founded in 1921 and began publicly trading in 1925. BlackRock Inc. owns 13% of Newmont.

Colonel William Boyce Thompson a flamboyant trader founded the Newmont Co. in 1916 to trade his various oil and mining stocks. The Newmont name was a combination of New York and Montana where Thompson grew up. The company was renamed Newmont Corporation in 1921 and Newmont Mining Corporation in 1925 when it went public. Thompson died five years later. During its first 10 years Newmont focused on investing and trading stocks in promising mineral properties including US copper and gold mines.

Newmont's gold mines bolstered the company throughout the Depression. During the 1940s its focus shifted to copper and Africa. It bought Idarado Mining in 1943 and Newmont Oil in 1944 (sold 1988). The company grew during the 1950s by acquiring stakes in North American companies involved in offshore oil drilling nickel mining and uranium oxide production. It also bought stakes in copper mines in South Africa and South America.

Newmont started producing gold from the Carlin Trend in Nevada in the mid-1960s. It bought a one-third stake in Foote Mineral (iron alloys and lithium) in 1967; by 1974 it controlled 83% of the company (sold 1987). In 1969 Newmont merged with Magma Copper one of the US's largest copper companies. A Newmont-led consortium bought Peabody Coal the US's largest coal producer from Kennecott Copper in 1977 (sold 1990).

After its 1980 discovery of one of the century's most important gold stakes Gold Quarry in the Carlin Trend Newmont spent a decade fending off takeover attempts. The company began selling off noncore operations to focus on gold. Magma Copper was spun off to stockholders in 1988.

A proposed merger with American Barrick Resources a major stockholder collapsed in 1991. Former Freeport-McMoRan VP Ronald Cambre became CEO in 1993 and that year the company began mining in Peru. A 1994 action by the French government one of Newmont's partners in Peru's Yanacocha Mine kicked off a protracted battle over the property's ownership. The claim was upheld in 1998 raising Newmont's stake to more than 50%. Reflecting its increasing interest in Indonesia in 1996 Newmont and Japan's Sumitomo formed a joint venture to exploit gold reserves on Sumbawa Island. In 1997 the company increased its gold reserves and territory by acquiring Santa Fe Pacific Gold for about $2.1 billion.

For years Newmont and Barrick Gold Corporation operated interlocked mining claims in Nevada's Carlin Trend which prevented optimal exploitation by either company. In 1999 both companies agreed to a mutually advantageous land swap in the region.

In 2000 an Indonesian court ordered the closure of the Minahasa mine over a local tax dispute; the company's joint venture agreed to pay a $500000 penalty to settle the matter. Newmont was fined $500000 after a mercury spill at its Yanacocha mine. That year Newmont settled the lingering ownership dispute over the Yanacocha.

Company president Wayne Murdy became CEO early in 2001 (he replaced Cambre as chairman in 2002). Newmont acquired Battle Mountain Gold in 2001 for nearly $600 million. Late that year Newmont moved to acquire Australia's top gold producer Normandy Mining (setting off a bidding war with AngloGold) as well as Canadian gold miner France-Nevada Mining Corp. AngloGold bowed out of the "battle for Normandy" in early 2002 but later completed a three-way deal in which it acquired Normandy and Franco-Nevada.

In 2003 Newmont reduced its stake in Kinross Gold from 14% to 5% and it considered selling off the Ghanaian interests it had gained in the Normandy merger. However in 2004 Newmont literally discovered a gold mine in Ghana — a major district with some 16 million equity ounces of gold.

Murdy retired in 2007; taking the helm was former CEO Richard O'Brien. In 2007 Newmont spun off its royalty assets acquired in 2002 as Franco-Nevada Corporation. Those assets then operated as Newmont Mining Corporation of Canada now a subsidiary of Newmont.

In 2008 Newmont bought Canadian gold producer Miramar Mining which controls the Hope Bay project for about $1.5 billion. It also acquired in 2009 a 33% stake in Boddington from Anglo-Gold Ashanti for about $1 billion giving Newmont 100% of the Boddington project.

In 2011 Newmont acquired Fronteer Gold a Canadian company with properties in the US Turkey and Peru for $2.3 billion. The deal significantly expands Newmont's holdings in Nevada.

EXECUTIVES

Vice President, Sharon Thomas
Svp South America, Trent Tempel
Evp Human Resources, William N. (Bill) MacGowan, age 59, $450,000 total compensation
Vp And Cio, James (Jim) Zetwick
Evp And Cfo, Nancy K. Buese, age 50, $90,865 total compensation
Evp Strategic Development, Randy Engel, age 52, $627,196 total compensation
Evp And General Counsel, Stephen P. Gottesfeld, age 51, $512,074 total compensation
Svp Exploration, Grigore Simon
Evp Technical Services, Scott P. Lawson
President And Ceo, Gary J. Goldberg, age 60, $1,270,742 total compensation
Evp Sustainability And External Relations, Elaine Dorward-King, $468,297 total compensation
Svp Africa, Alwyn Pretorius, age 47
Svp Asia Pacific, Thomas (Tom) Palmer, $615,134 total compensation
Vice President External Relations And Social Responsibilty, Nick Cotts
Senior Vice President Projects, Ramzi Fawaz
Vice President Supply Chain, Ramsey Musa
Vice President Total Rewards And Human Resources Systems, David Kristoff
Vice President Investments And Value Management, David McLaren
Senior Vice President African Operations, Jeffrey Huspeni
Vice President Global Government Relations, Rich Herold
Vice President Marketing And Sales, Edmond Leblanc
Senior Vice President Asia Pacific, Tom Palmer
Vice President Investor Relations, Jessica Largent
Vice President Controller And Chief Accounting Officer, John Kitlen
Vice President Finance And Treasurer, Joshua Hallenbeck
Vice President Operations And Finance Planning, Philip Starkle
Vp Internal Audit, Alison White
Senior Vice President Exploration, Marcelo Godoy
Regional Svp, Alex Bates
Vice President North American Government Relations, Mary Beth Donnelly
Vice President Talent Management, Jennifer Cmil
Vice President Of Supply Chain, Doug Nalbach
Secretary, Lisa Becker
Auditors: Ernst & Young LLP

LOCATIONS

HQ: Newmont Corp
6363 South Fiddlers Green Circle, Greenwood Village, CO 80111
Phone: 303 863-7414   **Fax:** 303 837-5837
Web: www.newmont.com

2017 Sales

	$ mil.	% of total
UK	5,490	74
Switzerland	657	9
Korea	384	5
Philippines	310	5
Germany	168	3
Canada	96	1
US	91	1
Japan	87	1
Other	65	1
Total	**7,384**	**100**

PRODUCTS/OPERATIONS

2017 Sales

	$ mil.	% of total
Gold	7,033	96
Copper	315	4
Total	**7,348**	**100**

COMPETITORS

Agnico-Eagle	Goldcorp
AngloGold Ashanti	Kinross Gold
Barrick Gold	Newcrest Mining
Franco-Nevada	

HISTORICAL FINANCIALS

Company Type: Public

Income Statement   FYE: December 31

	REVENUE ($ mil.)	NET INCOME ($ mil.)	NET PROFIT MARGIN	EMPLOYEES
12/18	7,253	341	4.7%	24,200
12/17	7,348	(98)	—	24,658
12/16	6,711	(627)	—	12,400
12/15	7,729	220	2.8%	15,600
12/14	7,292	508	7.0%	13,700
Annual Growth	(0.1%)	(9.5%)	—	15.3%

2018 Year-End Financials

Debt ratio: 21.00%
Return on equity: 3.00%
Cash ($ mil.): 3,397
Current ratio: 3.00
Long-term debt ($ mil.): 3,608

No. of shares (mil.): 533
Dividends
  Yield: 2.0%
  Payout: 88.0%
Market value ($ mil.): 18,468

	STOCK PRICE ($) FY Close	P/E High/Low	Earnings	Dividends	Book Value
12/18	35.00	66 46	1.00	1.00	20.00
12/17	38.00	— —	(0.00)	0.00	20.00
12/16	34.00	— —	(1.00)	0.00	20.00
12/15	18.00	64 36	0.00	0.00	21.00
12/14	19.00	27 17	1.00	0.00	21.00
Annual Growth	16.4%	—	(11.0%)	25.6%	(1.1%)

News Corp (New)

News Corp is one of the biggest news organizations in the world publishing well-known mastheads such as The Wall Street Journal and New York Post Australia's Herald Sun and The Sun and The Times in the UK. The company owns the Dow Jones and Factiva information services as well as book publisher HarperCollins. In TV News Corp has a majority stake in Foxtel in Australia and owns the Australian News Channel. Other properties are the real estate websites REA Group and Motive. North America supplies about 45% of News Corp's revenue.

Operations

News Corp divides its operations into five segments — news and information services more than 55% of revenue; book publishing about 20% of revenue; digital real estate services about 13%; subscription video services about 10%; and other 2%.

The news and information services segment includes News America Marketing (NAM) a publisher and distributor of coupons in newspapers and on the SmartSource.com website. NAM's customers include many of the largest consumer packaged-goods advertisers in the US and Canada. It reaches 74 million households for its freestanding coupon inserts and about 52500 retail outlets for its in-store advertising.

In book publishing the imprints under Harper Collins include Harper William Morrow Avon and Harlequin. Among its recent best-sellers have been Hillbilly Elegy and The Woman in the Window.

The Digital Real Estate Services segment consists of News Corp's 62% in REA Group a publicly-traded company based in Australia and its 80% interest in Move. The remaining 20% interest in Move is held by REA Group. REA lists properties for sale in Australia and Asia and offers financial services. Move operates the realtor.com website in the US.

The Subscription Video Services segment provides sports entertainment and news services to pay-TV subscribers via cable satellite and over the internet. Properties include the new Foxtel network in Australia of which News Corp owns 65% and the Australian News Channel.

Geographic Reach

News Corp. is based in New York City and has subsidiaries elsewhere in the US Australia and the UK. In addition book publisher HarperCollins has a warehouse in Scotland and Dow Jones runs an office in Hong Kong. North America accounts for more than 45% of News Corp.'s sales followed by the Australasia region with about 35% and Europe (mostly the UK and Ireland) about 20%.

Sales and Marketing

News Corp. spends an average of about $620 million a year on advertising.

Financial Performance

News Corp.'s revenue has been uneven since 2014 and it has lost money for three out of those five years including the last two as sales generated by its news operations have diminished. The news operation's share of revenue fell to 57% in 2018 from 72% in 2014.

In 2018 (ended June) revenue rose 11% to $9 billion from the year before. The increase was driven by the combination of Foxtel in which News Corp. and Telstra held 50% stakes and FOX SPORTS that created the new Foxtel in Australia. The News and Information segment posted slightly higher revenue on a 5% increase in circulation and subscription sales. The Digital Real Estate Services segment also delivered more sales as did the Book Publishing segment which was boosted by strong sales in the general books category and a sublicensing agreement for The Lord of the Rings trilogy. Advertising sales slipped 2% for the year.

In 2018 News Corp.'s net loss about doubled to $1.5 billion from a loss of $738 million in 2017. The 2018 loss included write-offs and other charges related to the Foxtel deal.

News Corp. had about $2 billion in cash and equivalents in its coffers in 2018 about the same as 2017. In 2018 operations generated $757 million while investing activities used $321 million and financing activities used $398 million.

The company's flexibility to maneuver financially might be compromised by an increase in debt that resulted from the Foxtel deal. News Corp's debt jumped to about $1.5 billion in 2018 from $276 million and $369 million in 2017 and 2016 respectively.

Strategy

Revenue from News Corp's News and Information segment has declined in recent years as advertising revenue has shifted from newspapers to companies like Google and Facebook. The challenge for News Corp and other media companies is to find businesses that can produce growth to make up for the news and advertising revenue decline.

In 2018 News Corp and Telstra merged their 50% each ownership in Foxtel with News Corp's FOX SPORTS to create a new version of Foxtel. After the combination Foxtel provides a greater range of programming to viewers in Australia on a wider range of devices.

The digital real estate services segment has become News Corp's fastest-growing business and produces outsized earnings. The segment's sales rose more than 20% in 2018 from 2017 adding four times more revenue than the news and information segment did. The real estate segment provides more than two-thirds of gross earnings while accounting for about 13% of revenue. News Corp beefed up the real estate properties with the acquisitions of Opcity in the US and Hometrack in Australia in 2018.

Mergers and Acquisitions

In 2018 News Corp and Telstra combined their 50% interests in Foxtel and News Corp's ownership of FOX SPORTS Australia into a new company which took the new Foxtel name. Under the new setup News Corp owns 65% of Foxtel and Telstra 45%. The combination helped both entities expand programming and the range of devices on which the service can be accessed.

News Corp. beefed up its real estate-related websites and services with two acquisitions in 2018. It acquired Opcity a real estate technology platform that matches buyers and sellers in real time for $210 million. The acquisition broadened realtor.com's lead generation product portfolio.

REA Group acquired Hometrack Australia provider of property data services to the financial sector for $130 million. The acquisition allows REA to deliver more property data and insights to customers and consumers.

In fiscal 2016 News Corporation spent around $800 million on acquisitions. The company acquired Checkout 51 Mobile Apps ULC Unruly Holdings Limited DIAKRIT International Limited iProperty Group Limited Flatmates.com.au Pty Ltd Australian Regional Media and Wireless Group plc.

EXECUTIVES

Senior Vice President And Deputy General Counsel, Genie Gavenchak
Ceo Harper Collins, Brian Murray, age 52
Chairman And Ceo News America Marketing, Martin (Marty) Garofalo
Ceo News Uk, Rebekah Brooks, age 51
Cto, Marc Frons, age 61
Ceo Unruly, Sarah Wood
Ceo, Robert Thomson, age 59, $2,038,462 total compensation
Cfo, Susan Panuccio
General Counsel And Chief Compliance Officer, David B. Pitofsky, $968,269 total compensation
Ceo The New York Post, Jesse Angelo
Ceo Dow Jones & Company, William (Will) Lewis
Ceo Storyful, Rahul Chopra
Ceo Move Inc., Ryan OA'Hara
Evp And Chief Communications Officer, James E. (Jim) Kennedy
Chairman News Corp Australasia, Michael Miller
Evp And Global Head Government Affairs, Antoinette (Toni) Bush
Vice President, Linden Slaugh
Svp And Treasurer, Rakesh Jobanputra
Senior Vice President, Raju Narisetti
Senior Vice President Head Of Human Resources Coverage Products And Operations, Katie Perdomo
Vice President Telecommunications, Guy Wheaton
Vice President Strategic Sourcing Procurement, Tracey Williamson
Vice President Of Technology, Dan Gould
Vice President Marketing Services At News America Marketing, Marissa Bishop
Senior Vice President, Paula Wardynski, age 63
Senior Vice President Physical Production, Thomas Imperato
Vice President Information Technology, Cindy Schwan
Senior Vice President Strategy And Corporate Development European Television, Marc Heller
Vice President Manager Director, Trista Reiser
Senior Vice President Corporate Affairs, Jim Platt

Vice President Global Transfer Pricing, Kathrin Zoeller
Vice President, Robert Ennis
Executive Vice President Office Of The Chairman, Jeremy Phillips
Vp Group Sales Manager, Christian Lencsak
Senior Vice President Mergers And Acquisitions Strategy, Daniel Costello
Svp Platform And Product Delivery, Andy Nichol
Svp And Global Head Programmatic, Christopher Guenther
Vp Information Governance And Ediscovery Operations, Daniel Mandon
Vice President Group Sales Manager Partnerships, Jacqueline Molligo
Executive Vice President Trade, Marty Garofalo
Information Technology Of Vice President, Laura Richards
Vice President Marketing Services, Mary Mattimore
Senior Vice President, Tom Dittrich
Vice President In Sotre Operations, Bill Schulze
Vice President Human Resources, Theresa Enk
Vice President Marketing Research, Mark Peiser
Vice President Group Sales Manager, Lauren Marglous
Vice President And Senior Account Director Merchandising Sales, Renee Young
Vice President Group Sales Manager Shopper Marketing, Jenna Nudelman
Division Vice President, Kate Ellis
Executive Vice President Finance Execu, Robert Spitz
Vice President, Colleen Moran
Vice President, Stefanie Detwiler
Vice President Channel Expansion, Jon Rubin
Vp Of It, Laura Mcpadden
Vice President Information Security, Janice Clauer
Vice President, Jennifer Hayes
Co-chairman News Corp And 21st Century Fox, Lachlan K. Murdoch, age 46
Chairman, K. Rupert Murdoch, age 88
Assistant Treasurer, Stanley Pauzer
Auditors: Ernst & Young LLP

LOCATIONS

HQ: News Corp (New)
1211 Avenue of the Americas, New York, NY 10036
Phone: 212 416-3400
Web: www.newscorp.com

2018 Sales

	$ mil.	% of total
US & Canada	3,998	44
Europe	1,766	20
Australia and others	3,260	36
Total	**9,024**	**100**

PRODUCTS/OPERATIONS

2018 Sales

	$ mil.	% of total
News & information services	5,119	57
Book publishing	1,758	19
Digital real estate services	1,141	13
Subscription Video Services	1,004	11
Other	2	-
Total	**9,024**	**100**

2018 Sales

	$ mil.	% of total
Advertising	2,799	31
Circulation & subscription	3,021	33
Consumer	1,664	18
Real Estate	858	10
Other	682	8
Total	**9,024**	**100**

List of Items

List of Items
Newspapers
Dow Jones
Barron's (magazine)

Dow Jones Newswires
Factiva (online news and business research)
The Wall Street Journal
The Wall Street Journal Digital Network
MarketWatch
WSJ.com
New York Post
News International Limited (UK)
The Sun
The Sunday Times
The Times
The Advertiser (Adelaide)
The Australian (national daily)
The Courier-Mail (Brisbane)
The Daily Telegraph (Sydney)
Herald Sun (Melbourne)
Sunday Herald Sun (Melbourne)
Sunday Mail (Adelaide)
The Sunday Mail (Brisbane)
The Sunday Telegraph (Sydney)
The Sunday Times (Perth)
Book publishing
HarperCollins Publishers
Cable network programming
Foxtel (65% stake0
Digital real estate services
REA (61.6% stake)
Other
Amplify (digital education)

COMPETITORS

Bloomberg L.P.	LexisNexis
Crain Communications	New York Times
Financial Times	Pearson plc
Forbes	Simon & Schuster
Graham Holdings	Thomson Reuters
Hachette Book Group	Valassis
Hearst Corporation	

HISTORICAL FINANCIALS

Company Type: Public

Income Statement — FYE: June 30

	REVENUE ($ mil.)	NET INCOME ($ mil.)	NET PROFIT MARGIN	EMPLOYEES
06/19	10,074	155	1.5%	28,000
06/18	9,024	(1,514)	—	28,000
06/17	8,139	(738)	—	26,000
06/16	8,292	179	2.2%	24,000
06/15	8,633	(147)	—	25,000
Annual Growth	3.9%	—	—	2.9%

2019 Year-End Financials

Debt ratio: 9.00%
Return on equity: 2.00%
Cash ($ mil.): 1,643
Current ratio: 1.00
Long-term debt ($ mil.): 1,004

No. of shares (mil.): 585
Dividends
Yield: 0.0%
Payout: 77.0%
Market value ($ mil.): 7,894

	STOCK PRICE ($) FY Close	P/E High/Low	PER SHARE ($) Earnings	Dividends	Book Value
06/19	13.00	58 40	0.00	0.00	16.00
06/18	16.00	— —	(3.00)	0.00	16.00
06/17	14.00	— —	(1.00)	0.00	19.00
06/16	11.00	52 35	0.00	0.00	20.00
06/15	15.00	— —	(0.00)	0.00	21.00
Annual Growth	(1.9%)	— —	—	—	(6.6%)

NextEra Energy Inc

NextEra Energy (NEE) owns and operates two businesses: Florida Power & Light (FPL) Florida's largest electric company and NextEra Energy Resources (NEER) one of the world's largest generators of renewable energy. FPL generates more than 24000 MW of electricity and delivers it to more than 5 million mostly residential customers in the state. NEER generates more than 20000 MW of energy via wind and solar sources. NEE operates one of the largest nuclear power fleets in the US with eight commercial nuclear power units in Florida New Hampshire Iowa and Wisconsin. All total the company has assets in nearly 30 US states four Canadian provinces and one province in Spain.

HISTORY

During Florida's land boom of the early 1920s new homes and businesses were going up fast. But electric utilities were sparse and no transmission lines linked systems.

In 1925 American Power & Light Company (AP&L) which operated utilities throughout the Americas set up Florida Power & Light (FPL) to consolidate the state's electric assets. AP&L built transmission lines linking 58 communities from Miami to Stuart on the Atlantic Coast and from Arcadia to Punta Gorda on the Gulf.

FPL accumulated many holdings including a limestone quarry streetcars phone companies and water utilities and purchases in 1926 and 1927 nearly doubled its electric properties. In 1927 the company used an electric pump to demonstrate how swamplands could be drained and cultivated.

During the 1940s and 1950s FPL sold its non-electric properties. The Public Utility Holding Company Act of 1935 forced AP&L to spin off FPL in 1950. The company was listed on the NYSE that year.

FPL grew with Florida's booming population. In 1972 its first nuclear plant (Turkey Point south of Miami) went on line. In the 1980s it began to diversify with the purchase of real estate firm W. Flagler Investment in 1981 and FPL Group was created in 1984 as a holding company. It subsequently acquired Telesat Cablevision (1985) Colonial Penn Group (1985 insurance) and Turner Foods (1988 citrus groves). FPL Group formed ESI Energy in 1985 to develop nonutility energy projects.

Diversification efforts didn't pan out and in 1990 the firm wrote off about $750 million. That year sticking to electricity the utility snagged its first out-of-state power plant in Georgia acquiring a 76% stake (over five years). FPL Group sold its ailing Colonial Penn unit in 1991; two years later it sold its real estate holdings and some of its cable TV businesses.

The utility gave environmentalists cause to complain in 1995. First the St. Lucie nuclear plant was fined by the Nuclear Regulatory Commission for a series of problems. FPL also wanted to burn orimulsion a cheap tar-like fuel. (Barred by the governor the utility gave up the plan in 1998.)

In 1997 FPL Group created FPL Energy an independent power producer (IPP) out of its ESI Energy and international operations; FPL Energy teamed up with Belgium-based Tractebel the next year to buy two gas-fired plants in Boston and Newark New Jersey.

FPL Energy built wind-power facilities in Iowa in 1998 and in Wisconsin and Texas in 1999; it also bought 35 generating plants in Maine in 1999. That year FPL Group sold its Turner Foods citrus unit and the rest of its cable TV holdings. By 2000 FPL Energy owned interests in plants in 12 states.

EXECUTIVES

Chairman And Ceo, James L. (Jim) Robo, age 57, $1,300,000 total compensation

Evp And General Counsel, Charles E. Sieving, age 46, $689,000 total compensation

President And Ceo Nextera Energy Resources, Armando Pimentel, age 57, $838,100 total compensation

President And Ceo Florida Power & Light, Eric E. Silagy, $796,100 total compensation

Evp Human Resources And Corporate Sevices, Deborah H. Caplan

Svp Business Management And Finance Nextera Energy Resources Llc, John Ketchum, $575,000 total compensation

Vp Hr Nextera Energy Resources, Kevin Suncine

Vp Compliance And Corporate Secretary Nextera Energy Inc., Scott Seeley

Vice President Controller And Chief Accounting Officer Nextera Energy Inc., Kirk Crews

Vp External Affairs And Economic Development Florida Power And Light Company, Pamela Rauch

Vp Controller And Chief Accounting Officer Florida Power And Light Company, Kimberly Ousdahl

Treas, Mark Sorensen

Treasurer, Paul Cutler

Auditors: DELOITTE & TOUCHE LLP

LOCATIONS

HQ: NextEra Energy Inc
700 Universe Boulevard, Juno Beach, FL 33408
Phone: 561 694-4000   **Fax:** 561 694-4620
Web: www.nexteraenergy.com

PRODUCTS/OPERATIONS

2016 sales

	$ mil.	% of total
Florida Power & Light	10,895	68
NextEra Energy Resources	4,893	30
Corporate & other	367	2
Total	16	100

Selected Subsidiaries and Divisions

Florida Power & Light Company
Energy Marketing and Trading
NextEra Energy Capital Holdings Inc.
NextEra Energy Resources LLC
NextEra Energy Partners
NextEra Energy Transmission

COMPETITORS

AES	Florida Public
Bangor Hydro-Electric	Utilities
Berkshire Hathaway	JEA
Energy	Oglethorpe Power
CMS Energy	Progress Energy
Calpine	Public Service
Chesapeake Utilities	Enterprise Group
Duke Energy	Seminole Electric
Entergy	Southern Company
Exelon	TECO Energy

HISTORICAL FINANCIALS

Company Type: Public

Income Statement — FYE: December 31

	REVENUE ($ mil.)	NET INCOME ($ mil.)	NET PROFIT MARGIN	EMPLOYEES
12/18	16,727	6,638	39.7%	14,200
12/17	17,195	5,378	31.3%	13,900
12/16	16,155	2,912	18.0%	14,200
12/15	17,486	2,762	15.8%	13,800
12/14	17,021	2,469	14.5%	13,800
Annual Growth	(0.4%)	28.0%	—	0.7%

2018 Year-End Financials

Debt ratio: 36.00%
Return on equity: 21.00%
Cash ($ mil.): 638
Current ratio: 0.00
Long-term debt ($ mil.): 26,782

No. of shares (mil.): 478
Dividends
Yield: 0.0%
Payout: 32.0%
Market value ($ mil.): 83,086

	STOCK PRICE ($) FY Close	P/E High/Low	PER SHARE ($) Earnings	Dividends	Book Value
12/18	174.00	13 10	14.00	4.00	71.00
12/17	156.00	14 10	11.00	4.00	60.00
12/16	119.00	21 16	6.00	3.00	52.00
12/15	104.00	18 15	6.00	3.00	49.00
12/14	106.00	19 15	6.00	3.00	45.00
Annual Growth	13.1%	— —	25.5%	11.2%	12.3%

NGL Energy Partners LP

All hail NGL for providing a secured energy trail. This Master Limited Partnership (MLP) provides transportation storage blending and marketing services for crude oil natural gas refined products and renewables in the US. With the Grand Mesa pipeline seven storage terminals and some 5.5 MMbbls of storage capacity to its name NGL buys refined petroleum in the Gulf Coast Southeast and Midwest regions transports them through the Colonial Plantation Magellan and NuStar pipelines and ultimately sells them to industrial end users or independent retailers and distributors. In addition the company provides water solutions that treats processes and disposes wastewater and solids generated from oil and natural gas production. The company also has a fleet of 160 trucks and 260 trailers as well as 10 tows and 19 barges. In 2018 NGL sold its retail propane delivery business.

Operations

NGL Energy reports four major business segments.

Refined Products and Renewables (70% of sales) buys refined petroleum in the Gulf Coast Southeast and Midwest regions transports them via the Colonial Plantation Magellan and NuStar pipelines and sells to industrial end users or independent retailers and distributors.

The company's crude oil logistics business (approximately 15%) purchases crude oil from producers and transports it for resale at pipeline injection points storage terminals barge loading facilities rail facilities refineries and other trade hubs.

The Liquids segment (10% revenue) supplies natural gas liquids to retailers wholesalers refiners and petrochemical plants throughout the US and in Canada and provides NGL terminaling and storage services through more than 20 terminals throughout the US its salt dome storage facility in Utah and its leased storage and railcar transportation services.

Water Solutions segment revenues (some 1%) are derived from the gathering transportation treatment and disposal of wastewater generated from oil and natural gas production operations. The company owns 75 water treatment and disposal facilities and 100 wells.

The company's retail propane business was sold in 2018. It distributed propane and distillates propane tanks and rental equipment to 320000 customers from 90 service centers and 70 satellite locations. In 2017 it accounted for 5% of annual sales.

Geographic ReachNGL Energy has significant operations in the Bakken Shale Basin of North Dakota the DJ Basin in Colorado the Mississippi Lime shale play in Oklahoma the Permian Basin in Texas and New Mexico the Eagle Ford shale play in Texas as well as the Anadarko Basin in Oklahoma and Texas and southern Louisiana. The company also provides Water Solutions near elevated lands with oil and natural gas production such as the Pinedale Anticline Basin in Wyoming the DJ Basin in Colorado the Permian and Eagle Ford Basins in Texas as well as the Delaware Basin in New Mexico. Its liquid natural gas terminals are in Jefferson City Missouri East St. Louis Illinois and in Ontario Canada. Headquartered in Tulsa Oklahoma the company has corporate offices in Denver and Houston.

Sales and Marketing

NGL Energy sells its refined and renewables products to commercial and industrial end users independent retailers distributors marketers government entities and other wholesalers of refined petroleum products. It also sells its products at TransMontaigne Partners L.P.'s terminals and to third parties. Its liquids business serves national regional and independent retail industrial wholesale petrochemical refiner and natural gas liquids production customers.

Financial Performance

Growth at NGL has skyrocketed over the last decade. In 2009 the company barely had $700 million in annual sales. A decade later it reported more than $17 billion in revenue. Though profits fluctuate wildly the company has posted positive net income in all but two years of the last decade.

Sales at NGL has burgeoned from $13 billion in 2017 to $17.3 billion in 2018. Most of it came from NGL's largest segment Refined Products & renewables ($2.8 billion increase) adding pipeline capacity rights purchased during 2017. Crude oil prices and volumes sold went up adding $600 million more to the coffers over 2016.

Net income fell from $137 million in profits in 2017 to a loss of $71 million in 2018 mostly due to a reduction of special income by $152 million followed by a reduction in gain on sale of property/plant/equipment by $100 million.

The company has $26 million in cash holdings at the end of 2018. Operations provided $138 million and a further $270 million came from investments (mostly from sale of businesses) offset by $394 million used in financing activities mostly going towards long-term debt reduction.

Strategy

NGL Energy has an extensive industry and MLP experience with acquiring integrating operating and growing successful businesses. With the sale of its propane business in 2018 NGL makes clear its strategic priority—use the $1.1 billion in proceeds to immediately repay certain indebtedness (company's debt stands at $2.7 billion) as well as invest in making strategic growth acquisitions in the Water Solutions business which NGL wants to expand (this segment hardly amounts to 1% of its current revenue composition). For 2019 the company wants to grow its Water Solutions business by as much as $450 million.

Additionally the company wants to focus on its core business—crude logistics. An equal emphasis is being given on increasing fee-based business and long-term contracts with high credit quality customers by transitioning a repeatable cash flow model.

NGL Energy is well poised for profits going forward. Its Crude Oil Logistics segment posted exceptional numbers due to increased volumes on Grand Mesa as the pipeline continues to benefit from increased production out of the DJ Basin. Water Solutions business has also continued to benefit from high crude oil prices increased rig counts and increased crude oil production due to price recovery.

Furthermore In the beginning of 2018 NGL and Magnum Liquids formed a joint venture to focus on the storage of natural gas liquids and refined products by combining NGL's Sawtooth Storage Facility with Magnum's refined products rights and adjacent leasehold. NGL will sell an interest in Sawtooth to Magnum for $45 million in cash due at closing.

Mergers and Acquisitions

NGL Energy is focused on expanding its Water Solution business in the Delaware Basin. This included the purchase of 9.6 million barrels of annual fresh water rights from the 36000-acre Beckham Ranch in Lea County New Mexico. The company furthered the strategy in 2019 when it agreed to purchase Hillstone Environmental Partners from Golden Gate capital for about $600 million. Hillstone provides water pipeline services to producers in Eddy and Lea Counties in New Mexico and northern Loving County Texas in the Delaware Basin.

NGL Energy also acquired the McCloy Ranch located in Eddy and Lea Counties which comes with some 87000 acres of land and 2 million barrels of annual water rights. The company now owns 30 million barrels of available freshwater volumes in the Delaware Basin.

Expanding its portfolio in 2017 NGL Energy Partners LP bought assets from Murphy Energy. The assets included the Port Hudson Louisiana Terminal an NGL terminal that supports refined products blending and the Kingfisher Oklahoma Facility a natural gas liquids and condensate facility. The combined purchase price of the assets was $51 million.

In 2016 the company acquired 57% of an existing produced water pipeline company operating in the Delaware Basin portion of West Texas.

Company Background

Formed in 2010 by several investors NGL Energy Partners acquired and combined the assets and operations of NGL Supply a wholesale propane and terminalling business founded in 1967 and Hicksgas a retail propane business founded in 1940.

EXECUTIVES

Vice President Wholesale, Stan Bugh

Ceo, H. Michael Krimbill, age 65, $292,500 total compensation

Evp And Cfo, Robert W. (Trey) Karlovich, age 42

President Retail Division, Shawn W. Coady, age 57, $311,250 total compensation

President Eastern Retail Operations, Vincent J. Osterman, age 62, $250,000 total compensation

President Ngl And President And Ceo High Sierra Energy, James J. (Jim) Burke, age 63, $381,750 total compensation

Evp Ngl Crude Logistics, Don Robinson

Evp Ngl Liquids, Jack Eberhardt

Cio, Jennifer Kingham

Executive Vice President Midstream Division, David Eastin

Senior Vice President Legal, Bill Laughlin

Vice President Rocky Mountain Region, Britt Stephenson

Executive Vice President, Gregory Pound

Executive Vice President Ngl Refined Products, Donald Jensen

Svp Accounting And Corporate Controller, Sharra Straight

Vice President, Mark Mcginty

Evp Ngl Water Solutions, Doug White

Vice President Of Tax, Joel Gustafson

Svp Business Development, Greg Blais

Executive Vice President Operations, Greg Pound

Senior Vice President Asset Management, Todd Tanory

Vice President Eagle Ford, Tim Jurco

Vice President Ngl Water Solutions Formerly High Sierra, Doran Oancia

Vice President Business Development Crude Assets, Derek Graham

Vice President Ngl Marine, Craig Lagrone
Senior Vice President Accounting And Chief Accoun, Larry Thuillier
Vice President Business Development, Carl Peterson
Vp Environmental Compliance, Dudley Tarlton
Vice President Trade Operations, Scott Ernest
Vice President National Accounts, Billy Wilson
Vice President Finance And Treasurer, Linda Bridges
Vice President Credit And Market Risk Management, Thomas Matthews
Vice President Trucking, Willie Seale
Evp Ngl Refined Products, Don Jensen
Senior Vice President Renewable Fuels, Grant Vangilder
Executive Vice President, Greg Piper
Vice President, Mark Mcgrath
Vice President Environmental Health And Safety, Garrett Clemons
Vice President West Texas Region, Wes Pearson
Svp Mergers And Acquisitions, Christian Dobrauc
Senior Vice President, Jeff Pinter
Auditors: Grant Thornton LLP

LOCATIONS

HQ: NGL Energy Partners LP
 6120 South Yale Avenue, Suite 805, Tulsa, OK 74136
Phone: 918 481-1119
Web: www.nglenergypartners.com

PRODUCTS/OPERATIONS

2017 Sales

	$ mil.	% of total
Refined products and Renewables	12,201	71
Crude oil logistics	2,260	13
Liquids	2,070	12
Retail propane	521	3
Water solutions	229	1
Other	1	.
Total	17,283	100

COMPETITORS

AmeriGas Partners	Exxon Mobil
Blueknight Energy Partners	Ferrellgas Partners
Crestwood Midstream Partners LP	Holly Energy Partners
Duke Energy	Huntsman International
Energy Transfer	Martin Midstream Partners
Enterprise Products	Occidental Petroleum
Equistar Chemicals	Williams Companies

HISTORICAL FINANCIALS

Company Type: Public

Income Statement | | | FYE: March 31

	REVENUE ($ mil.)	NET INCOME ($ mil.)	NET PROFIT MARGIN	EMPLOYEES
03/19	24,017	360	1.5%	1,300
03/18	17,283	(71)	—	2,400
03/17	13,022	137	1.1%	2,700
03/16	11,742	(199)	—	3,200
03/15	16,802	17	0.1%	3,100
Annual Growth	9.3%	115.6%	—	(19.5%)

2019 Year-End Financials

Debt ratio: 37.00%
Return on equity: 310.00%
Cash ($ mil.): 19
Current ratio: 1.00
Long-term debt ($ mil.): 2,160
No. of shares (mil.): 125
Dividends
 Yield: 0.0%
 Payout: 78.0%
Market value ($ mil.): 1,749

	STOCK PRICE ($) FY Close	P/E High/Low	PER SHARE ($) Earnings	Dividends	Book Value
03/19	14.00	7 4	2.00	2.00	19.00
03/18	11.00	— —	(1.00)	2.00	17.00
03/17	23.00	26 7	1.00	2.00	18.00
03/16	8.00	— —	(2.00)	3.00	16.00
03/15	26.00	— —	(0.00)	2.00	20.00
Annual Growth	(14.5%)	—	—	(9.9%)	(1.8%)

Nicolet Bankshares Inc

EXECUTIVES

Pres-ceo, Robert Atwell
Vice President Commercial Banking, Trent Willihnganz
Board Member, Michael Gilson
Auditors: Wipfli LLP

LOCATIONS

HQ: Nicolet Bankshares Inc
 111 North Washington Street, Green Bay, WI 54301
Phone: 920 430-1400
Web: www.nicoletbank.com

HISTORICAL FINANCIALS

Company Type: Public

Income Statement | | | FYE: December 31

	ASSETS ($ mil.)	NET INCOME ($ mil.)	INCOME AS % OF ASSETS	EMPLOYEES
12/18	3,097	41	1.3%	550
12/17	2,932	33	1.1%	535
12/16	2,301	18	0.8%	480
12/15	1,214	11	0.9%	280
12/14	1,215	10	0.8%	280
Annual Growth	26.3%	42.5%	—	18.4%

2018 Year-End Financials

Debt ratio: 1.00%
Return on equity: 11.00%
Cash ($ mil.): 250
Current ratio: —
Long-term debt ($ mil.): —
No. of shares (mil.): 9
Dividends
 Yield: —
 Payout: —
Market value ($ mil.): 463

	STOCK PRICE ($) FY Close	P/E High/Low	PER SHARE ($) Earnings	Dividends	Book Value
12/18	49.00	14 11	4.00	0.00	41.00
12/17	55.00	17 13	3.00	0.00	37.00
12/16	48.00	19 12	2.00	0.00	32.00
12/15	32.00	12 9	3.00	0.00	26.00
12/14	25.00	11 7	2.00	0.00	27.00
Annual Growth	18.2%	—	16.3%	—	10.5%

NIELSEN HOLDINGS PLC

EXECUTIVES

Ceo, Mitch Barns

LOCATIONS

HQ: NIELSEN HOLDINGS PLC
 85 BROAD ST, NEW YORK, NY 100042434
Phone: 646 654-5000

HISTORICAL FINANCIALS

Company Type: Private

Income Statement | | | FYE: December 31

	REVENUE ($ mil.)	NET INCOME ($ mil.)	NET PROFIT MARGIN	EMPLOYEES
12/15	6,172	575	9.3%	43,061
12/14	6,288	381	6.1%	—
12/13	5,703	736	12.9%	—
12/12	5,612	273	4.9%	—
Annual Growth	3.2%	28.2%	—	—

NIKE Inc

EXECUTIVES

Ceo-Pres, Mark G Parker
Coo, Eric D Sprunk
Exec V Pres-Cfo, Andrew Campion
Exec V Pres-Chief ADM Officer-, Hilary K Krane
Exec V Pres Global Hr, Monique S Matheson
Exec V Pres Global Sports Mkt, John F Slusher
V Pres-Corp Contrl, Chris L Abston
Human Resources Manager, Shawna Staples
Global Director, Tim Pacholke
Global Senior Director Quality, Ulrike Weiler
Information Technology Manager, Amy Sticksel
Auditors: PricewaterhouseCoopers LLP

LOCATIONS

HQ: NIKE Inc
 One Bowerman Drive, Beaverton, OR 97005-6453
Phone: 503 671-6453
Web: www.nike.com

COMPETITORS

ASICS	Quiksilver
Acushnet	R. Griggs
Amer Sports	Ralph Lauren
Brown Shoe	Rawlings Sporting Goods
Callaway Golf	Rollerblade
Columbia Sportswear	Russell Brands
Deckers Outdoor	Saucony
FUBU	Skechers U.S.A.
Fila Korea	Stride Rite
Fruit of the Loom	Timberland
Hanesbrands	Timex
Juicy Couture	Tommy Hilfiger
K-Swiss	Under Armour
Levi Strauss	VF Corporation
Mizuno	Victoria's Secret Stores
New Balance	Wolverine World Wide
Oakley	adidas
PUMA SE	
Phoenix Footwear	

HISTORICAL FINANCIALS

Company Type: Public

Income Statement | | | FYE: May 31

	REVENUE ($ mil.)	NET INCOME ($ mil.)	NET PROFIT MARGIN	EMPLOYEES
05/19	39,117	4,029	10.3%	76,700
05/18	36,397	1,933	5.3%	73,100
05/17	34,350	4,240	12.3%	74,400
05/16	32,376	3,760	11.6%	70,700
05/15	30,601	3,273	10.7%	62,600
Annual Growth	6.3%	5.3%	—	5.2%

2019 Year-End Financials

Debt ratio: 15.00%   No. of shares (mil.): 1,568
Return on equity: 43.00%   Dividends
Cash ($ mil.): 4,466   Yield: 1.0%
Current ratio: 2.00   Payout: 35.0%
Long-term debt ($ mil.): 3,464   Market value ($ mil.): 120,956

	STOCK PRICE ($) FY Close	P/E High/Low		PER SHARE ($) Earnings	Dividends	Book Value
05/19	77.00	35	26	2.00	1.00	6.00
05/18	72.00	61	43	1.00	1.00	6.00
05/17	53.00	24	19	3.00	1.00	8.00
05/16	55.00	61	25	2.00	1.00	7.00
05/15	102.00	55	39	2.00	1.00	7.00
Annual Growth	(6.7%)	—	—	7.7%	12.3%	(6.1%)

NiSource Inc. (Holding Co.)

Energy holding company NiSource manages rate-regulated natural gas and electric utility companies serving nearly 4 million customers in seven US states making it one the nation's largest natural gas distributors. Its principal subsidiaries include NiSource Gas Distribution Group and NIPSCO. It owns 60000 miles of natural gas pipelines reaching Indiana Ohio Pennsylvania Virginia Kentucky Maryland and Massachusetts. NiSource assets also include power plants that generate close to 3300 MW of electricity annually serving some 479000 customers in northern Indiana.

HISTORY

NiSource's earliest ancestor was the South Bend (Indiana) Gas Light Company founded in 1868 by the Studebaker brothers (of later auto fame) to supply gas. In 1886 a natural-gas discovery near Kokomo Indiana led to a boom in northern Indiana's use of the fuel. By 1900 steel plants and other industries had set up shop along Lake Michigan in northwestern Indiana and in Illinois.

Another NiSource ancestor was formed in 1901 as Hammond Illuminating but it changed its name to South Shore Gas and Electric. In 1909 Northern Indiana Gas and Electric was founded by merging South Shore with other regional utilities. The next year Northern Indiana acquired South Bend.

A third NiSource predecessor Calumet Electric (founded in 1912) had acquired several utilities by the early 1920s when utility magnate Samuel Insull bought it to add to his huge Midland Utilities holding company. In 1923 Insull bought Northern Indiana Gas and Electric which merged three years later with Calumet to form Northern Indiana Public Service Company (NIPSCO). NIPSCO acquired its current service territory in 1930 when it swapped some areas with another Midland subsidiary.

The Public Utility Holding Company Act of 1935 beginning the regulation of regional monopolies forced Midland to divest NIPSCO in 1947. In the 1950s and 1960s NIPSCO built two power plants and tripled its natural gas supply through a contract with a Houston gas company.

Responding to rising demand NIPSCO in 1970 applied to build a nuclear unit at its Bailly plant estimated to cost $180 million. In 1981 the nuke was abandoned after its cost rose to $2.1 billion. Reorganizing in 1987 NIPSCO became part of holding company NIPSCO Industries.

The Energy Policy Act of 1992 ushered in wholesale-power competition. That year NIPSCO acquired Kokomo Gas and Fuel and in 1993 it picked up Northern Indiana Fuel and Light and Crossroads Pipeline.

To prepare for oncoming retail competition NIPSCO in 1993 divided the electric and gas utilities into competing units and increased NIPSCO's marketing force. In 1997 NIPSCO branched out buying water utility holding company IWC Resources and the next year it began a customer choice program for its natural gas customers (all gas was delivered through its distribution lines however).

The company changed its name to NiSource in 1999 but did not alter its acquisition strategy. NiSource entered the US Northeast's gas market where deregulation plans were under way by purchasing New England utility Bay State Gas. A unit of Bay State Gas EnergyUSA bought natural gas marketer TPC and NiSource began integrating its nonregulated operations into EnergyUSA.

After launching a hostile takeover which it later withdrew NiSource purchased natural gas giant Columbia Energy Group for $6 billion in 2000. NiSource then sold its salt cavern gas storage and pipeline construction subsidiaries as well as certain Columbia electric generation and LNG facilities. In 2001 NiSource sold its Columbia Propane unit to AmeriGas Partners; it also agreed to sell water company IWC Resources (and its utility subsidiary Indianapolis Water) to the City of Indianapolis (the sale was completed in 2002).

In 2002 NiSource teamed up with the merchant services unit of Aquila (formerly UtiliCorp) to form an energy marketing and trading joint venture; however NiSource later backed out of the partnership due to instability in the energy trading industry. It also shut down its coal-fired Mitchell Generating Station and sold its SM&P Utility Resources subsidiary to The Laclede Group (renamed Spire).

The following year NiSource sold its Columbia Transmission Communications (Transcom) subsidiary to Neon Communications (which itself was acquired by Globix in 2005).

To pay down debt and focus on its core operations in 2008 NiSource sold Northern Utilities and Granite State Gas Transmission to Unitil for about $202 million. It also sold its Whiting Clean Energy facility to BP Alternative Energy North America for $217 million.

In 2010 the company initiated three separate projects (for a total of $80 million) in the Majorsville Pennsylvania area to aggregate Marcellus Shale gas production for downstream transmission.

To boost its gas transmission and storage assets and take advantage of the burgeoning shale gas market in 2012 the company formed joint ventures with Hilcorp Energy to develop gas production and midstream infrastructure in the Utica shale in Northeastern Ohio and Western Pennsylvania.

In 2013 Lake Erie Land a wholly owned subsidiary of NiSource was pursuing the sale of the real estate assets it owns. NDC Douglas Properties a subsidiary of NiSource Development Company was in the process of exiting its low income housing investments. In addition to raise cash the company sold certain retail services business assets (warranty protection solutions and energy efficiency leasing solutions for residential and small business utility customers) to AGL Resources in 2013. The deal includes 500000 existing customer plans in Indiana Massachusetts Ohio Pennsylvania and Kentucky. The company exited these business lines in 2013. It also sold the commercial and industrial natural gas portfolio of its unregulated natural gas marketing business that year.

EXECUTIVES

Vice President Capital Allocation And Controls, Tim Dehring

Evp And Chief Legal Officer, Carrie J. Hightman, age 61, $490,000 total compensation

President And Ceo, Joseph (Joe) Hamrock, age 56, $858,333 total compensation

Evp; President Nipsco, Violet G. Sistovaris, $360,000 total compensation

Chief Transformation Officer, Mark Kempic

Evp Gas Segment And Chief Customer Officer, Pablo A. Vegas, age 46, $298,295 total compensation

Evp Safety Capital Execution And Technical Services, Mike Finissi

Evp And Cfo, Donald E. Brown, $479,167 total compensation

Evp Regulatory Policy And Corporate Affairs, Carl W. Levander

Vice President, Peter Disser

Vice President, Dick James

Vp Human Resources, Teresa Smith

Senior Vice President Strategic Planning, Guy Ausmus

Vp Investor Relations And Treasurer, Randy Hulen

Vice President And Deputy General Counsel, John Nassos

Vice President Of It Service Performance, Cassandra Pullin

Vice President Financial Planning And Analysis, Tim Tokish

Vice President Total Rewards, Richard Bond

Senior Vice President Safety Environmental And Training, Dave Monte

Vice President, Michael Alverson

Vice President Work Management, Meg Brown

Vice President Of Information Technology, Julie McElmurry

Senior Vice President Field Operations, Keith Wooldridge

Vice President Supply Chain, Scott Kelly

Vp And Gm Columbia Gas Pennsylvania And Columbia Gas Maryland, Michael Davidson

Vice President, Jeff Grossman

Vp It Infrastructure, Greg Skinner

Vp Human Resources And Labor Relations, Edward Santry

Vp And Corporate Secretary, Sam Lee

Vice President Organization And Talent Development, Ken Keener

Vice President Applications, Jennifer Tipton

Vice President And Deputy General Counsel, Maggie Rice

Chairman, Richard L. (Rich) Thompson, age 79

Treasurer And Chief Risk Officer View Bio, Shawn Anderson

Board Member, Carolyn Y Woo

Board Of Directors, Eric L Butler

Auditors: Deloitte & Touche LLP

LOCATIONS

HQ: NiSource Inc. (Holding Co.)
801 East 86th Avenue, Merrillville, IN 46410
Phone: 877 647-5990
Web: www.nisource.com

PRODUCTS/OPERATIONS

2017 sales

	$ mil.	% of total
Gas Distribution	2,063	42
Gas Transportation	1,021	21
Electric	1,786	37
Other	5	0
Total	**4,875**	**100**

Selected Subsidiaries

GAS DISTRIBUTION OPERATIONS
Columbia Gas of Massachusetts
Central Kentucky Transmission Company

Columbia Gas of Kentucky Inc.
Columbia Gas of Maryland Inc.
Columbia Gas of Ohio Inc.
Columbia Gas of Pennsylvania Inc.
Columbia Gas of Virginia Inc.
NiSource Gas Distribution Group Inc.
ELECTRIC OPERATIONS
Northern Indiana Public Service Company

COMPETITORS

AEP	FirstEnergy
Atmos Energy	IPALCO Enterprises
Baltimore Gas and	NSTAR
Electric	National Grid USA
Constellation Energy	New Jersey Resources
Group	Nicor Gas
Dominion Energy	RGC Resources
Duke Energy	Southern Union
EQT Corporation	Unitil
Eversource Energy	Vectren

HISTORICAL FINANCIALS

Company Type: Public

Income Statement				FYE: December 31
	REVENUE ($ mil.)	NET INCOME ($ mil.)	NET PROFIT MARGIN	EMPLOYEES
12/18	5,115	(51)	—	8,087
12/17	4,875	129	2.6%	8,175
12/16	4,493	332	7.4%	8,007
12/15	4,652	287	6.2%	7,596
12/14	6,471	530	8.2%	8,982
Annual Growth	(5.7%)	—	—	(2.6%)

2018 Year-End Financials

Debt ratio: 42.00%	No. of shares (mil.): 372
Return on equity: (-1.00%)	Dividends
Cash ($ mil.): 113	Yield: 3.0%
Current ratio: 1.00	Payout: —
Long-term debt ($ mil.): 7,105	Market value ($ mil.): 9,439

	STOCK PRICE ($) FY Close	P/E High/Low	PER SHARE ($) Earnings	Dividends	Book Value
12/18	25.00	— —	(0.00)	1.00	15.00
12/17	26.00	71 56	0.00	1.00	13.00
12/16	22.00	26 19	1.00	1.00	13.00
12/15	20.00	54 18	1.00	1.00	12.00
12/14	42.00	26 19	2.00	1.00	20.00
Annual Growth	(12.1%)	— —	—	(6.5%)	(5.7%)

Nordstrom, Inc.

Service with a smile is a part of Nordstrom's corporate culture. One of the nation's largest upscale apparel and shoe retailers Nordstrom sells clothes shoes and accessories through about 115 Nordstrom full-line stores and about 240 off-price outlet stores (Nordstrom Rack) in about 40 states and online. It also operates six full-line and six Rack stores in Canada three Jeffrey luxury boutiques six Trunk Club personal clothing service clubhouses three Nordstrom Local hubs two "Last Chance" clearance stores and online private sale site HauteLook. With its easy-return policy and touches such as thank-you notes from employees Nordstrom has earned a reputation for top-notch customer service. Nordstrom family members who own about 30% of the retailer's stock closely supervise the chain.

Operations

Nordstrom's operates two business segments: Retail and Credit. The Retail segment accounts for the vast majority (98%) of Nordstrom's revenue and includes sales from its full-line and Nordstrom Rack stores as well as from its Nordstrom.com nordstromrack.com Hautelook.com Trunk Club.com Jeffrey Nordstrom Local Last Chance and Canadian operations. Nordstrom's Credit segment (2% of total revenue) owns a federal savings bank Nordstrom fsb through which it offers a private-label credit or debit card for Nordstrom purchases and a selection of co-branded Nordstrom VISA cards The cards also include a loyalty program that rewards shoppers depending on their spending levels.Nordstrom's Full Price operations (Nordstrom US full-line stores Nordstrom.com Canadian operations Trunk Club Jeffrey and Nordstrom Local) generate over two-thirds of the retail sales while Off-Price operations (Nordstrom US Rack stores Nordstromrack.com/HauteLook and Last Chance clearance stores) accounts for the remaining sales.By product the company generates nearly a third of its net sales from women's apparel while shoe sales make up nearly a quarter. The rest of its net sales came from men's apparel (more than 15%) women's accessories (more than 10%) cosmetics (some 10%) and kid's apparel and other items (some 5% combined).

Geographic Reach

Based in Seattle Washington Nordstrom has more than 365 full-line and Nordstrom Rack stores in 40 US states as well as about a dozen Nordstrom full-line stores and Rack stores in Canada. California is the retailer's largest market with nearly 90 full-line and Rack stores. Other major markets for the chain include Florida Illinois and Texas. The company also operates six distribution centers in California Florida Iowa Maryland and Oregon; three fulfillment centers in California Iowa and Pennsylvania; and four office facilities in California Colorado Illinois and New York.

Sales and Marketing

Nordstrom processes and ships orders directly to customers through fulfillment centers while its distribution centers process and ship merchandise to its stores and other facilities.The company promotes its products through online marketing magazines store events and other media. Nordstrom's advertising expense totaled $246 million $261 million and $241 million for the years 2018 2017 and 2016 respectively.

Financial Performance

Navigating a challenging retail environment for department stores Nordstrom has seen steady revenue growth in recent years. Its annual revenues have risen close to 20% since 2016.

Revenue increased to $15.8 billion in 2018 an approximately 2.5% increase from the year prior. The increase was driven by new store openings higher digital sales and an increase in credit card revenues.

Net income was $564 million in fiscal year 2018 an increase from $437 million in fiscal year 2017. Selling general and administrative expenses grew 4% in fiscal 2018 to $4.8 billion.

Cash provided by operating activities was $1.2 billion in fiscal 2018 while investing activities used $653 million. Financing activities used another $867 million.

Strategy

While many department stores across the US have failed to keep up as consumers moved toward shopping online and smaller brand-specific stores Nordstrom is proving more adaptable than most.

The company has made many moves to keep up with and ahead of modern consumers who demand omnichannel conveniences and new ways of doing business. Nordstrom is experimenting with new store formats and changing what it means to be a retail store. For example Nordstrom's new smaller Nordstrom Local stores located in urban hubs such as Los Angeles and New York City do not carry retail merchandise. Instead the locations offer customer services such as alterations styling guidance returns and assistance with online shopping.

Nordstrom has expanded its generous return policy to welcome shoppers through its doors. In 2019 the company began accepting merchandise returns from rival stores such as Macy's and Kohl's at its small-format Nordstrom Local locations as a way to drive traffic into stores and offer customers an additional convenience.

It has also found new ways to leverage online such as curbside pickup for online purchases at local stores and same-day shipping for online orders that pull items from local stores. E-commerce has grown to approximately a third of the company's sales.

Nordstrom is looking north for expansion. In 2018 it opened six new Nordstrom Rack discount stores in Canada.

HISTORY

In 1901 John Nordstrom a lumberjack and successful gold miner used his Alaska Gold Rush money to open Wallin & Nordstrom shoe store in Seattle with shoemaker Carl Wallin. Nordstrom retired in 1928 and sold his half of the business which included a second store to his sons Everett and Elmer. Wallin sold his share to the brothers after retiring the following year. A third Nordstrom son Lloyd joined in 1933. The shoe chain thrived and incorporated as Nordstrom's in 1946.

By 1963 Nordstrom's was the largest independent shoe chain in the country. The company diversified by acquiring Best Apparel's stores in Seattle and Portland Oregon. Three years later Nordstrom's bought Portland's Nicholas Ungar a fashion retailer and merged it with one of its shoe stores in Portland under the name Nordstrom Best.

Renaming itself Nordstrom Best in 1966 the company went public in 1971 and changed its name again in 1973 to Nordstrom. The retailer grew steadily throughout the 1970s opening new stores boosting sales in existing stores and diversifying. In 1976 Nordstrom started Place Two featuring apparel and shoes in smaller stores than its traditional department layouts. It moved into Southern California (Orange County) two years later. Buoyed by almost $300 million in new sales Nordstrom executives planned an aggressive expansion.

Nordstrom opened its first store on the East Coast in 1988 in Virginia. The chain continued to expand opening stores in Northern California and in the affluent Washington DC suburbs.

The 1989 San Francisco earthquake along with a national downturn hurt retail sales significantly. Nordstrom's much-touted focus on customer service had a downside: The company was investigated in 1990 for not paying employees for customer services they performed including delivery of merchandise on their own time. (Three years later Nordstrom set aside $15 million to pay back wages to employees who had performed off-the-clock services.)

The company continued to expand in the East and Midwest opening its first store in the New York City area in 1991. In 1993 the retailer opened a men's boutique in New York (Fa Şonnable). Looking for new ways to attract customers Nordstrom introduced a mail-order catalog the next year.

Following the family's business tradition six members of Nordstrom's fourth generation began running the company in 1995. Third-generation members James Nordstrom John Nordstrom Bruce

Nordstrom and Jack McMillan retired as co-chairmen and were replaced by non-family members Ray Johnson and John Whitacre. (Johnson retired in 1996.)

Nordstrom created Nordstrom.com a partnership with Benchmark Capital and Madrona Investment Group in 1999 to consolidate its catalog and Internet operations.

In early 2000 amid slumping sales the company dissolved the co-presidency. Less than a year later however the Nordstroms were back in charge. Chairman and CEO Whitacre resigned and Blake Nordstrom took over running the company as president. His father Bruce came out of retirement to take the chairman's role. Later the company bought the French design company Fa §onnable which supplies the products for its Fa §onnable boutiques.

In May 2002 the company bought out Benchmark's and Madrona's minority stake in Nordstrom.com.

Nordstrom bought a majority interest in August 2005 in luxury specialty stores Jeffrey New York and Jeffrey Atlanta. Terms of the agreement were not disclosed. The Jeffrey stores had about $35 million in sales in 2004. Also in 2005 the company opened stores in Atlanta; Dallas; Irvine California; and San Antonio.

In late 2007 Nordstrom sold its four US Fa §onnable boutiques and 37 European locations to Lebanon-based M1 Group for about $210 million. Overall in 2007 Nordstrom opened three full-line department stores and a single Rack store.

Nordstrom opened its first full-line department store in Hawaii in early 2008. That October amid economic gloom the retailer opened a store in Pittsburgh. Overall the retailer opened eight new Nordstrom stores and half a dozen Rack outlets in 2008. In 2009 it added three full-line Nordstrom locations and 13 Rack outlets.

Nordstrom acquired e-tailer HauteLook for $180 million in stock in March 2011. Based in Los Angeles HauteLook was a leader in online private sales.

EXECUTIVES

Co-president, Blake W. Nordstrom, age 58, $751,152 total compensation

Co-president, Peter E. (Pete) Nordstrom, age 57, $751,152 total compensation

Co-president, Erik B. Nordstrom, age 57, $751,152 total compensation

Evp General Counsel And Secretary, Robert B. Sari, age 63

Evp And Chief Innovation Officer, Geevy S.K. Thomas, age 54

Evp And Cio, Daniel F. (Dan) Little, age 58, $552,806 total compensation

Evp And President Stores, James F. (Jamie) Nordstrom, age 46

Evp And General Merchandise Manager Designer Women's Apparel, Tricia D. Smith, age 48

Evp And Chief Marketing Officer, Scott A. Meden, age 56

Evp Finance And Treasurer, James A. Howell, age 54

Evp And General Merchandise Manager Men's And Kids Wear, Paige L. Thomas, age 48

Evp And President Nordstrom.com, Kenneth J. (Ken) Worzel, age 54, $657,417 total compensation

Evp Nordstrom Merchandising Group, Teri Bariquit, age 53

Evp And General Merchandise Manager Accessories At Home And Beauty, Gemma Lionello, age 54

Evp; Chairman And Ceo Nordstrom Fsb; President Nordstrom Credit, Steven C. Mattics, age 50

Evp Supply Chain, Michael Sato

Cfo, Anne L. Bramman, age 51

Evp Online Merchandising, Kirk M. Beardsley

Evp And President Nordstromrack.com Hautelook And Trunk Club, Terence Boyle

Evp Human Resources, Christine F. Deputy, age 53, $319,206 total compensation

Evp Strategy, Lisa C. Luther

Evp And President Nordstrom Product Group, Jennifer Jackson Brown

Evp And General Merchandise Manager Shoe Division, Kristin Frossmo

Evp And President Nordstrom Rack, Karen S. McKibbin, age 59

Evp And General Merchandise Manager Nordstrom Rack, Brian Roberts

Senior Vice President Customer Experience, Shea Jensen

Vice President Marketing, KRISTEN LAMEY

Vice President Divisional Merchandise Manager, Lori Marten

Vice President Nmg Strategy And Operations, Corinne Copello

Vp Controller, Randy Kanai

Vice President Human Resources Technology Process Insights, Jeff Nelson

Vp Risk Management, Sheryl Garland

Vice President Finance, Mike Bengs

Vice President Payments And New Markets, Bryan Penny

Senior Vice President Human Resources, Lisa V Price

Vp Financial Analytics, Ramin Azerang

Vice President Customer Experience, Shea D Jensen

Vice President Human Resources, Farrell Redwine

Vice President Technology, Joanne Kennedy

Vice President Merchandise Planning, Angie L Caldwell

Vice President Operations Finance, Chris Goelkel

Vice President Corporate Affairs And Public Relations, Gigi Ganatra

Vice President Assistant General Counsel And Aco Nfsb, Janine M Weaver

Vice President Nfsb Senior Vice President Strategic Delivery And Support, Jeanne Muenchau

Vice President Divisional Merch Planning And Inventory, Joe Brazell

Executive Vice President Chief Supply Chain Officer, Brent Beabout

Vice President Nmg Strategy And Operations, Corinne E Copello

Vice President Compensation And Leadership Benefits, Dave Anders

Vp Corporate Tax, Andy Vickers

Vice President Creative Projects, Olivia Kim

Vice President Engineering, Alan John

Vice President Divisional Merchandise Manager Men 's And Kid 's Shoes, Robert Evans

Senior Vice President Human Resources, Lisa Price

Vice President Innovation, Laura Janney

Svp Technology, Brian Gill

Vice President Divisional General Manager Women's Appa, Anita Ortiz

Vice President Strategy, Rebecca Godecke

Vice President, Michelle Sample

Vice President Operations, Jason Trusley

Assistant Treasurer, Daniel Fleming

Board Member, Shellye Archambeau

Auditors: Deloitte & Touche LLP

LOCATIONS

HQ: Nordstrom, Inc.
1617 Sixth Avenue, Seattle, WA 98101
Phone: 206 628-2111
Web: www.nordstrom.com

PRODUCTS/OPERATIONS

2017 Sales

	$ mil.	% of total
Full-line stores US	7,186	48
Nordstrom.com	2,519	17
Nordstrom Rack	3,809	25
Nordstromrack.com/Hautelook	700	4
Other retail	554	4
Corporate/Other	(270)	0
Credit Card revenues net	259	2
Total	**14,757**	**100**

2017 Sales

	$ mil.	% of total
Retail	14,768	98
Credit	259	2
Corporate/Other	(270)	0
Total	**14,757**	**100**

2017 Products category

	% of total
Women's Apparel	32
Shoes	23
Men's Apparel	17
Women's Accessories	11
Beauty	11
Kids' Apparel	3
Other	3
Total	**100**

2017 sales

	No.
Nordstrom full-line stores - U.S.and Canada	123
Nordstrom Rack and others	226
Total	**349**

PRODUCTS OFFERED: Selected
Dresses
Tops
Jeans
Sweaters
Coats
Jackets
Pants
Suits
Skirts
Swimsuits & Cover-Ups
Active Yoga & Outdoor
Bras Panties & Lingerie
Shapewear
Sleep Lounge & Robes
Hosiery Leggings & Socks
Plus-Size Clothing
Petite-Size Clothing
Maternity Clothing
Shoes
Handbags & Wallets
Watches
Jewelry
Fine Jewelry
Optical Frames & Reading Glasses
Sunglasses
Scarves & Wraps
Hats & Hair Accessories
Winter Accessories
Gloves
Belts
Luggage & Travel
Tech Accessories & Cases
Hosiery & Socks

Selected Retail Operations

HauteLook (private-sale website for apparel and home decor)
Jeffrey (boutiques)
Last Chance (clearance store)
Nordstrom (specialty stores selling apparel shoes and accessories for women men and children)
Nordstrom Direct (catalogs and online ordering)
Nordstrom Rack (outlets selling merchandise from Nordstrom specialty stores and manufacturers)

COMPETITORS

Ann Taylor	J. Crew
Astor & Black	Lands' End
Barneys	Macy's
Benetton	Neiman Marcus

Bloomingdale's
Bluefly
Brooks Brothers
Caleres
Dillard's
Donna Karan
Eddie Bauer LLC

Nine West
Tailored Brands
Talbots
The Gap
Tiffany & Co.
Von Maur
Wayfair

HISTORICAL FINANCIALS

Company Type: Public

Income Statement

	REVENUE ($ mil.)	NET INCOME ($ mil.)	NET PROFIT MARGIN	EMPLOYEES
02/19	15,860	564	3.6%	71,000
02/18*	15,478	437	2.8%	72,500
01/17	14,757	354	2.4%	72,500
01/16	14,437	600	4.2%	72,500
01/15	13,506	720	5.3%	67,000
Annual Growth	4.1%	(5.9%)	—	1.5%

FYE: February 2

*Fiscal year change

2019 Year-End Financials

Debt ratio: 34.00%
Return on equity: 61.00%
Cash ($ mil.): 957
Current ratio: 1.00
Long-term debt ($ mil.): 2,677

No. of shares (mil.): 158
Dividends
Yield: 0.0%
Payout: 45.0%
Market value ($ mil.): 7,144

	STOCK PRICE ($) FY Close	P/E High/Low		PER SHARE ($) Earnings	Dividends	Book Value
02/19	45.00	20	13	3.00	1.00	6.00
02/18*	48.00	20	15	3.00	1.00	6.00
01/17	43.00	30	18	2.00	1.00	5.00
01/16	49.00	26	14	3.00	6.00	5.00
01/15	76.00	21	15	4.00	1.00	13.00
Annual Growth	(12.2%)	—	—	(2.8%)	2.9%	(18.9%)

*Fiscal year change

Norfolk Southern Corp

Norfolk Southern Corporation's main subsidiary Norfolk Southern Railway transports freight over a network consisting of about 20000 route miles in 20-plus states (plus DC) in the eastern southeastern and Midwestern US. The rail system is made up of nearly 20000 route miles owned by Norfolk Southern and about 8000 route miles of trackage rights which allow the company to use tracks owned by other railroads. Norfolk Southern transports coal and general merchandise including automotive products and chemicals.

Operations

Norfolk Southern operates some 4200 locomotives and more than 60000 freight cars. It reports through three segments: General Merchandise (60% of net sales) Intermodal (a quarter) and Coal (15%).

The General Merchandise segment is subdivided into five commodity groups: Agriculture/Consumer/Government (such commodities and products as soybeans wheat beverages canned goods ethanol and military items); Chemicals (sulfur petroleum products plastics among others); Metals/Construction (steel aluminum cement bricks etc); Automotive (finished vehicles from and auto parts for such auto OEMs as Ford General Motors and Toyota); and Paper/Clay/Forest (lumber and wood products pulp board and paper products wood fibers wood pulp scrap paper and clay). The General Merchandise segment maintains more than 2.5 million railroad carloads each year.

Intermodal carries about 4 million units for such clients as intermodal marketing companies international steamship lines and truckers.

Coal is Norfolk Southern's single largest commodity group (narrowly ahead of chemicals). The coal segment carries about 115 million tons of coal originating from major coal basins and destined for about 70 coal generation plants as well as export metallurgical and industrial facilities. Operating in the eastern US

Geographic Reach

Norfolk Southern operates in 22 US states and Washington DC and transports overseas freight from several Atlantic and Gulf Coast ports.

Sales and Marketing

Norfolk Southern mainly targets the agriculture metals construction automotive and paper sectors.

Financial Performance

Over the last five years Norfolk Southern's sales dipped then rebounded due to the weakness and subsequent recovery of in hydrocarbon prices which impacted the company's coal business. The main story however is its impressive profitability averaging roughly 15-20% over the period.

In 2018 Norfolk Southern's sales grew 9% to $11.5 billion thanks to broad-based growth across all merchandise categories as well as intermodal and coal. Higher average revenue per unit relating to pricing gains and higher fuel surcharge revenue while volume grew as well. The best-performing categories were chemicals and intermodal.

A huge tax benefit in 2017 from the US Tax Cuts and Job Act meant net income in 2018 fell 51% to $2.7 billion. Setting the tax effect aside earnings grew roughly in line with sales.

Norfolk Southern's cash on hand fell $244 million during 2018 ending the year at $446 million. The company's operations generated $3.7 billion offset by $1.7 billion used in its investing activities and $2.3 billion used in its financing. Norfolk Southern's main cash uses in 2018 were property additions share repurchases and dividends while it took on new borrowing to support liquidity.

Strategy

Norfolk Southern's operations are so strongly cash generative its management doesn't seem to know what to do with it all. While it typically invests around $1.2 billion annually in its railroads Norfolk Southern has been spending even more on buying back shares. Share buybacks reduce the number of shares outstanding and thus "concentrate" a company's share price lifting it — a pointless exercise from an operational standpoint but fantastic for a company's shareholders. In fact the company has been taking on debt to accelerate the program further. Since 2006 Norfolk Southern has spent an eyewatering $14.1 billion on share buybacks (it pays big dividends too) including $2.8 billion in 2018 alone. Its board has authorized the repurchase of a further 50 million shares which would be worth roughly $8 billion at 2018's share price.

If there's a risk to Norfolk Southern's extensive share repurchase program it's that should the good times unexpectedly slow down the company might start to struggle under its debt which stood at $11.1 billion at the end of 2018.

HISTORY

Norfolk Southern Corporation resulted from the 1982 merger of two US rail giants — Norfolk & Western Railway Company (N&W) and Southern Railway Company — which had emerged from more than 200 and 150 previous mergers respectively.

N&W dates to 1838 when one track connected Petersburg Virginia to City Point (now Hopewell). This eight-miler became part of the Atlantic Mississippi & Ohio (AM&O) which was created by consolidating three Virginia railways in 1870.

In 1881 Philadelphia banker E.W. Clark bought the AM&O and renamed it the Norfolk & Western. N&W rolled into Ohio by purchasing two other railroads (1892 1901).

The company took over the Virginian Railway a coal carrier with track paralleling much of its own in 1959. In 1964 N&W became a key railroad in the Midwest by acquiring the New York Chicago & St. Louis Railroad and the Pennsylvania Railroad's line between Columbus and Sandusky Ohio. It also leased the Wabash Railroad with lines from Detroit and Chicago to Kansas City and St. Louis.

Southern Railway can be traced back to the South Carolina Canal & Rail Road a nine-mile line chartered in 1827 and built by Horatio Allen to win trade for Charleston's port. It began operating the US's first regularly scheduled passenger train in 1830 and became the world's longest railway when it opened a 136-mile line to Hamburg South Carolina (1833).

Soon other railroads sprang up in the South including the Richmond & Danville (Virginia 1847) and the East Tennessee Virginia & Georgia (1869) which were combined to form the Southern Railway System in 1894. Southern eventually controlled more than 100 railroads forging a system from Washington DC to St. Louis and New Orleans.

The 1982 merger of Southern and N&W created an extensive rail system throughout the East South and Midwest. Norfolk Southern (a holding company created for the two railroads) also bought North American Van Lines in 1985. Triple Crown Services the company's intermodal subsidiary was started in 1986. The company also made a failed attempt to take over Piedmont Aviation the next year.

Norfolk Southern revived North American Van Lines by selling its refrigerator truck operation Tran-star (1993) and suspending its commercial trucking line. But it later sold the rest of the motor carrier (1998) to focus on rail operations.

When CSX announced its plans to buy Conrail in 1997 Norfolk Southern's counteroffer led to a split of the former Northeastern monopoly between Norfolk Southern (58%) and CSX (42%). Problems with integrating Conrail's assets hurt Norfolk Southern's results. But by 2000 it had regained some of the traffic it had lost to service problems and its intermodal shipping business also gained speed. In 2004 Norfolk Southern and CSX reorganized Conrail to give each parent company direct ownership of the portion of Conrail's assets that it operates. Conrail still operates switching facilities and terminals used by both Norfolk Southern and CSX.

Norfolk Southern got hit in the wallet in 2001: The company agreed to pay $28 million to settle a racial discrimination lawsuit brought by black employees in 1993. Norfolk Southern began rounds of layoffs and closed redundant depots and facilities in 2001.

In 2005 nine people died in South Carolina when chlorine gas leaked from a ruptured car on a Norfolk Southern freight train. The car was breached when the train crashed into a company-owned locomotive and two train cars that were parked on a siding.

Jumping ahead ten years the company in 2015 rejected an unsolicited takeover by Canadian Pacific in a deal worth $37.8 billion.

EXECUTIVES

Vp Government Relations, Bruno Maestri
Evp Cfo And Cio, Cynthia C. (Cindy) Earhart, $600,000 total compensation

Chairman President And Ceo, James A. (Jim) Squires, age 57, $900,000 total compensation

Vp Intermodal Operations, Alan H. Shaw, $500,000 total compensation

Evp And Coo, Michael J. Wheeler, $581,250 total compensation

Vp Business, Robert Martinez

Vp Intermodal And Automotive, Jeffrey Heller

National Account Manager, Rick Lentz

Avp Research And Advanced Technology, Tom Schnautz

National Account Manager, Ty Hildum

Vice President Chief Engineer Design, Dave Becker

National Account Manager, Kevin Fizer

National Account Manager, Brady Daniels

Vice President Inbound Service Ma, Bud Clapp

Group Vice President, Ken Joyner

National Account Manager, Tom Landrum

National Account Manager, Bill Flanagan

Assistant Vice President Industrial Development, Jason Reiner

Vice President Process Engineering, Terry Evans

Vice President, David Dixon

Assistant Vice President Finance, Chris Neikirk

Group Vice President, James Schaaf

Evp And Chief Transformation Officer, Ann Adams

Vp Audit And Compliance, Susan Stuart

Resident Vp Government Relations Pennsylvania And New York, Michael Fesen

Assistant Vice President Transportation Network, Jeff Sliger

Resident Vice President Government Relations, With Gabrielle

National Account Manager, Megan Duperow

National Account Manager, John Reilly

Vp Government Relations, Marque Ledoux

Vice President Human Resources, Annie Adams

Vp Business Development And Real Estate, Robert E Martinez

Assistant Vice President Corporate Accounting, Jason Zampi

Vice President, Nesmith Amanda

Board Member, Thomas Bell

Secretary, Julie Weil

Treasurer, Rachael Sears

Secretary, Donna Coleman

Secretary 1, Heather Faber

Auditors: KPMG LLP

LOCATIONS

HQ: Norfolk Southern Corp
Three Commercial Place, Norfolk, VA 23510-2191
Phone: 757 629-2680
Web: www.norfolksouthern.com

PRODUCTS/OPERATIONS

2018 Sales

	$ mil.	% of total
Merchandise		
Chemicals	1,808	16
Agriculture consumer government	1,674	14
Metals & construction	1,462	13
Automotive	991	8
Paper clay and forest	809	7
Intermodal	2,893	25
Coal	1,821	16
Total	**11,458**	**100**

Selected Facilities Served

Active coal-loading facilities
Auto assembly plants
Auto distribution facilities
Bulk transfer facilities
Coal and iron ore transload facilities
General warehouses/distribution centers
Intermodal terminals
Just-in-time rail auto parts center
Lumber reload centers
Metals distribution centers
Paper distribution centers

Paper mills
Power generation plants served
Steel mills and processing facilities
Triple Crown Service terminals
Vehicle mixing centers

COMPETITORS

APL Logistics	J.B. Hunt
American Commercial Lines	Kansas City Southern
Burlington Northern Santa Fe	Kirby Corporation
	Landstar System
CSX	PVH
Canadian National Railway	Piedmont Natural Gas
	Pier 1 Imports
Canadian Pacific Railway	Pilgrim's Pride
	Pinnacle West
Genesee & Wyoming	Pitney Bowes
Hub Group	Schneider National
Ingram Industries	Union Pacific
	Werner Enterprises

HISTORICAL FINANCIALS

Company Type: Public

Income Statement

	REVENUE ($ mil.)	NET INCOME ($ mil.)	NET PROFIT MARGIN	EMPLOYEES
				FYE: December 31
12/19	11,296	2,722	24.1%	24,587
12/18	11,458	2,666	23.3%	26,662
12/17	10,551	5,404	51.2%	27,110
12/16	9,888	1,668	16.9%	28,044
12/15	10,511	1,556	14.8%	30,456
Annual Growth	**1.8%**	**15.0%**	**—**	**(5.2%)**

2019 Year-End Financials

Debt ratio: 32.00%
Return on equity: 18.00%
Cash ($ mil.): 580
Current ratio: 1.00
Long-term debt ($ mil.): 11,880

No. of shares (mil.): 258
Dividends
  Yield: 2.0%
  Payout: 35.0%
Market value ($ mil.): 50,067

	STOCK PRICE ($) FY Close	P/E High/Low	Earnings	Dividends	Book Value
12/19	194.00	20 14	10.00	4.00	59.00
12/18	150.00	19 13	10.00	3.00	57.00
12/17	145.00	8 6	19.00	2.00	58.00
12/16	108.00	20 12	6.00	2.00	43.00
12/15	85.00	22 14	5.00	2.00	41.00
Annual Growth	**23.1%**	**— —**	**19.1%**	**11.1%**	**9.5%**

Northern Trust Corp

Through its flagship subsidiary The Northern Trust Company Northern Trust provides wealth management brokerage securities lending asset servicing and management and banking and trust services. The firm addresses institutional clients and affluent individuals through around 80 offices in some 20 states and about 20 countries. Operating two main segments?Corporate and Institutional Services (C&IS) and Wealth Management?Northern Trust has approximately $10.1 trillion in assets under custody/administration roughly $7.6 trillion under custody and greater than $1 trillion under direct management. About 65% of company's total revenue comes from the US.

Operations

The firm operates through two segments: Corporate and Institutional Services (C&IS) and Wealth Management. A third business unit Asset Management provides asset management and related services to the two main segments.

The C&IS segment provides asset servicing and related services to endowments sovereign wealth funds corporate and public retirement funds fund managers foundations insurance companies and other institutional investors. Its offerings include investment and treasury management securities lending foreign exchange brokerage and banking. It has roughly $790 billion in assets under management $7 trillion in assets under custody and $9.5 billion in assets under custody/administration. The segment accounts for approximately 60% of Northern Trust's revenue.

The Wealth Management business focuses on high-net-worth individuals and families business owners executives and the like. It provides services such as custody investment and trust management financial and family business consulting estate administration brokerage and banking. The segment has around $280 billion in assets under management $620 billion in assets under custody and $635 billion in assets under custody/administration. It generates the remaining revenue not produced by C&IS.

Trust investment and other servicing fees represent more than 60% of the company's revenue; more than 25% derives from net interest income.

Geographic Reach

Based in Chicago Northern Trust has a presence in some 20 states and about 20 countries through around 80 offices in the Americas Europe the Middle East and the Asia-Pacific region. The US generates roughly two-thirds of company's total revenue and accounts for approximately three-quarters its assets.

Sales and Marketing

The firm serves corporations institutions (such as foundations endowments and sovereign wealth funds) and affluent families and individuals. Relationship management and personalized service are keys to maintaining and growing its client base. The company allocates a significant portion of its capital expenditures for relationship management tools.

Financial Performance

Following the Financial Crisis of 2008 and 2009 Northern Trust saw steep declines in both revenue and net income. Since 2011 however it has stabilized financial performance and experienced steady consistent growth in both metrics. Revenue has expanded by about 40% in the last five years; net income has nearly doubled exceeding $1.5 billion for the first time in 2018.

The company's revenue added 11% to $5.2 billion that year. Trust investment and other servicing fees?its greatest source of revenue?increased 9% due to strong markets and foreign exchange rates new customers and revenue recognition standards and the company's acquisition of the Luxembourg and Switzerland fund administration businesses of UBS's Asset Management unit.

Net income for the year jumped 30% to $1.6 billion as revenue gains outpaced the rate of expense growth.

Cash on hand at the end of 2018 was about $4.6 billion up $64 million from 2017. Operating activities provided $1.8 billion. Investing activities provided $4.3 billion mostly from reducing its deposits with the Fed and other central banks. Reduced total deposits common stock repurchases lower securities sold under repurchase agreements and dividend payments drove financing spend of $5.8 billion.

Strategy

Northern Trust looks to retain and expand its base of private and institutional clients through partnerships and acquisitions that help it serve their greater needs and further its global footprint.

A significant portion of the company's capital expenditures is allocated to software that enhances customer experience. Of its $506 million in 2018 capital expenditures $470 million went to computer software and hardware. In 2019 Northern Trust collaborated with Bloomberg to integrate its Bloomberg AIM order management system with its middle-office technology; the platform provides a smoother investment process for the companies' institutional clients through data synchronization. That year Northern Trust also began using blockchain to deploy legal clauses as smart contracts using software from legal technology startup Avokka. In 2018 the company agreed to acquire BEx a foreign exchange software company that offers a platform for automated algorithmic trading.

Northern Trust continues to expand its geographic footprint across the world. The company has focused on expanding its reach in Europe recently. It launched its Northern Trust Global Services Societas Europaea bank in Luxembourg in 2019. In 2017 it acquired the Luxembourg and Switzerland fund administration units of UBS's Asset Management unit.

Mergers and Acquisitions

In 2018 Northern Trust agreed to acquire foreign exchange software company BEx for $37.6 million. The company's platform facilitates automated algorithmic trading providing faster and more reliable trade execution for its customers.

In a move to expand its presence in Europe Northern Trust acquired the Luxembourg and Switzerland fund administration businesses of UBS's Asset Management unit in 2017 for some $200 million.

Company Background

As part of its international growth plan Northern Trust expanded in Europe with the 2011 purchase of Bank of Ireland's fund administration investment operations outsourcing and custody business. The acquisition was combined with Northern Trust's existing operations in Ireland which is a European hub for cross-border fund administration. The company worked to support European fund managers by expanding its depositary services across multiple fund types asset classes fund locations and investment strategies as well as by implementing the Alternative Investment Fund Managers Directive (AIFMD).

In 2010 Northern Trust expanded its Wealth Management business with the acquisition of Los Angeles-based investment advisory Waterline Partners.

HISTORY

When banker Byron Smith took time off to handle family concerns in 1885 friends turned to him for advice on trust and estate matters. It occurred to him that there was a market for such services within a banking framework.

Smith tested new Illinois banking and trust laws by arranging for state banking authorities to reject his charter application for Northern Trust. As Smith had hoped the charter was upheld by the Illinois Supreme Court.

Northern Trust opened in 1889 in one of Chicago's new skyscrapers the Rookery. With $1 million in capital — about 40% from Smith and the rest from the likes of Marshall Field (retailing) Martin Ryerson (steel) and Philip Armour (meatpacking) — the bank attracted $138000 in deposits its first day.

By 1896 the bank was firmly established; Smith began taking a salary and the company issued its first dividend. Ten years later the firm built its solid granite edifice the "Gray Lady of LaSalle Street" where it still resides.

The bank began buying commercial paper in 1912 joined the Federal Reserve System in 1917 and became a custodian for expropriated German assets during WWI. Byron Smith died in 1914 and was succeeded by his son Solomon.

Northern Trust rejected the get-rich-quick ethos of the 1920s. It was so strong during the Depression that after the 1933 bank holiday people actually clamored to make deposits and the bank administered the Depression-era scholarship fund that helped Ronald Reagan attend college. By 1941 almost half of Northern Trust's commercial deposits originated outside the Chicago area. The bank kept growing during and after WWII.

Solomon Smith retired in 1963; his son Edward took over and launched the company's expansion overseas (Northern Trust International was formed in 1968) and out of state (Florida in 1971 Arizona in 1974). The firm's business was helped by the 1974 passage by Congress of ERISA which required company retirement plans to be overseen by an outside custodian. Edward retired in 1979.

Northern Trust expanded locally when Illinois legalized intrastate branch banking in 1981. In 1987 the company lost money due in part to defaults on loans made to developing countries. It moved into California in 1988 and Texas in 1989.

Northern Trust navigated the early 1990s recession expanded geographically in the mid-1990s and added services through acquisitions. In 1995 the company became the first foreign trust company to operate throughout Canada. That year it bought investment management service RCB International (now Northern Trust Global Advisors). It expanded in the Sun Belt with such acquisitions as Dallas' Metroplex Bancshares and was made first custodian for the Teacher Retirement System of Texas (1997).

In 1998 the company expanded into Michigan and broke into the Cleveland and Seattle markets in 1999. Northern Trust entered cyberspace as well launching a website for its mutual funds. In 2000 the company opened locations in Nevada and Missouri and bought Florida-based investment adviser Carl Domino Associates (renamed Northern Trust Value Investors). Also that year the bank bought Ireland's Ulster Bank Investment Services.

In 2004 Northern Trust bought the fund management custody and trust operations of Baring Asset Management from Amsterdam-based ING Groep.

EXECUTIVES

Senior Vice President Corporate And Institutional Services And Head North American Institutional A, Jeffrey W Conover
Vice President Of Loans, Jean E Sheridan
Vice President, Monique Noblett
Senior Vice President, Donald Berk
Senior Vice President And Senior Portfolio Manager For Northern Trust Global Inv, George Maris
Executive Vice President; Head Capital Markets Group Northern Trust Asset Management, Michael Vardas
Vice President, Allison Coleman
Vice President Administration, Alex Winslow
Evp And President Wealth Management, Steven L. (Steve) Fradkin, age 57, $600,000 total compensation
Evp And President Corporate And Institutional Services, Jeffery D. Cohodes, age 58
Evp And Coo, Jana R. Schreuder, age 60, $693,750 total compensation
Evp And President Asset Management, Stephen N. Potter, age 62, $587,500 total compensation
Evp And Chief Capital Management Officer, Joyce St. Clair, age 59
Evp And President Corporate And Institutional Services, Peter B. Cherecwich, age 54

Evp And Chief Risk Officer, Wilson Leech, age 57
Evp And Cfo, Stephen B. (Biff) Bowman, age 55, $568,750 total compensation
Evp And Chief Investment Officer, Robert P. (Bob) Browne, age 54
President Ceo And Director, Michael G. O'Grady, age 53, $606,250 total compensation
Evp And General Counsel, Susan C. Levy, age 61
Evp Human Resources, S. Gillian Pembleton, age 60
Senior Vice President Technology, Ken Bell
Senior Vice President, Paul D'Ouville
Senior Vice President, Kay Vicino
Senior Vice President Asia Pacific Region, Lawrence Au
Vice President Product Group Investmen, Jim Haran
Vice President Network Services, Peter Poncia
Vice President Content And Social Media Marketing Manager, Mychelle Peterson
Vice President Of Finance, James Heneghan
Senior Vice President Regional Fiduciary Director, Thomas Iskalis
Vice President Information Technology, Ken Le Breux
Vice President International Strategy, Jeremy Baskin
Senior Vice Presiden, Joyce Clair
Senior Vice President, Corinne Mcclintic
Second Vice President Event Marketing Manager, Danielle Czyz
Vice President C And Information Systems Strategic Product Development, Robert Potsic
Vp, Rose Mallon
Vice President, David J Peterson
Executive Vice President, James Mitchell
Senior Vice President, Elizabeth V White
Vice President Portfolio Manager, Chris Fronk
2nd Vp, Annette Daniel
Senior Vice President, Mark Rice
Senior Vice President Managing Director, Scott Roads
Senior Vice President Treasury, Duane Rocheleau
Senior Vice President Northeast Sales Wealth Management Group Northern Trust Company, Ann Zeiler
Executive Vice President Asset Management, Alan Robertson
Vice President, Jon Seele
Vice President Corporate Online Marketing, Tracy Malave
Senior Product Developer Vice President, Rick Clemons
Senior Vice President Relationship Manager, Stephen Kuropas
Vice President Offshore Vendor Manager, Kathryn Furtek
Vice President, Rich Michaels
Senior Vice President, Timothy Geraghty
Vice President Information Technology, Barbara Malinowski
Vice President Division Head, James Monhart
Senior Vice President, Peter Flood
Vice President, Michael Hunniford
Senior Vice President, Molly Drennan
Senior Vice President, John Freel
Vice President, Richard Weiss
Vice President Security Architect, Wendy Betts
Senior Vice President And Managing Director, Gene Harvey
Senior Vice President, Sheldon Woldt
Vice President Portfolio Manager, Michael Chico Michael Chico
Second Vice President Treasury Managemen, Nancy Hamilton
Vice President Database Administration, Santhi Annabathula
Vice President, Janet Schultz
Vice President Senior Consultant, Mark Warner
Senior Vice President Of Marketing, Diane Spradlin

Senior Vice President Mobile Product Manager, Dennis Flowers
Vice President, Felencia Terrell
Vice President, Greg Werra
Vice President Manager Applications, Ann Rogula
Vice President, Deiken Maloney
Vice President Investment Systems Quality Assurance, Cheryl Flack
Second Vice President, Judith Wilson
Vice President Business Services, Matt Adams
Vice President, Patrick Beatty
Senior Vice President, Peter Williams
Vice President Wealth Advisory Private Banking, Holly Brown
Vice President Application Architecture, Nihar Karnik
Senior Vice President, Stephen Brown
Senior Vice President Managing Director Private Client Services, Deb Finnegan
Senior Vice President, Kristin Missil
Second Vice President, Yueru Gu
Vice President Human Resources, Denyse Reese
Executive Vice President, Jennifer Driscoll
Senior Vice President Chief Banking Officer Pfs Central Region, Paul Theiss
Vice President, Andrew Glick
Senior Vice President Worldwide Technologies, John Burke
Senior Vice President, Joseph S Fedacsek
Second Vice President, Karen Smilie
Vice President, Jeffrey Rosenblum
Second Vice President Senior Investment Associate, Jesse Robinett
Vice President Fx Sales Global Foreign Exchange, John Turney
Vice President, Kristina Jakstys
Senior Vice President, James Ferguson
Senior Vice President Senior Relationship Manager, Linda Hansen
Vice President Operations And Technology, Manan Mehta
Senior Vice President Information Technology, Jim Pecyna
Vice President Wealth Advisor (southeast Region), Mike Byrne
Vice President, Jose Aranda
Senior Vice President Risk Management, David Adam
Vice President Wealth Management, Al Combs
Vice President, Rich Teska
Vice President Senior Cash Product Manager, Ellie Dumas
Senior Vice President, Nina Staley
Senior Vice President Senior Investment Officer, Ann Farrall
Vice President Risk Management, Scott Winkates
Vice President Database Administrator, Gary Sako
Second Vice President, Mark Steffen
Vice President, Raje Kantamneni
Senior Vice President, Chris Carlson
Senior Vice President, Scott Hensley
Vice President Corporate Real Estate, Diane Menza
Second Vice President Global Network, Lawrence Walter
Second Vice President Information Technology, Jim Weatherhead
Vice President Administration, Daniel Hintzen
Vice President, Andrew Lewis
Vice President, Matthew Riegel
Vice President, Anita Nikolov
Vice President Global Mobility, Susan Kubiesa
Vice President And Portfolio Manager, Jason A Lawit
Vice President Derivatives Portfolio M, Judson Baker
Second Vice President, Len Soderblom
Vice President Enterprise Banking, Sandy Wiles
Second Vice President, Brent Zonyk
Vice President On Line Product Manager, Mary Jackowiak

Senior Vice President, Thomas James
Senior Vice President, Nancy Lyon
Vice President Operations Risk, Monica Steeg
Vice President Infrastructure Project Management O, Nita Cabuso
Senior Vice President, William Egan
Second Vice President, Amit Dalal
Vice President, David Wicks
Senior Vice President, Kaz Sikora
Vice President, John Brady
Second Vice President, Alex Hingston
Second Vice President, Michelle Bergthold
Vice President, Nicole Bernard
Senior Vice President And Global Head Of Product Development Investment Risk And Analytical Services, Gail Kepley
Vice President Marketing, Kerry Webber
Vice President, Timothy Blair
Senior Vice President Foundation And Institutional, Dave Cyganiak
Vice President Technology, Paul Baldwin
Vice President Information Technology, Bob Schroeder
Vice President Information Technology, Larry Wells
Senior Vice President Pfs Client Servicing Solutions, Julie Sausen
Senior Vice President, Michael Furey
Vice President Of Human Resources, Mae Jones
Senior Vice President, Mark Hardtke
Auditors: KPMG LLP

LOCATIONS

HQ: Northern Trust Corp
50 South LaSalle Street, Chicago, IL 60603
Phone: 312 630-6000
Web: www.northerntrust.com

Selected Operations

US
Arizona
California
Colorado
Connecticut
Delaware
Florida
Georgia
Illinois
Massachusetts
Michigan
Minnesota
Missouri
Nevada
New York
Ohio
Texas
Washington
Wisconsin
International
Africa
Australia
Canada
China
Hong Kong
India
Ireland
Japan
Luxembourg
Middle East
The Netherlands
New Zealand
Saudi Arabia
Singapore
Sweden
UK

PRODUCTS/OPERATIONS

2018 sales

	$ mil.	% of total
US	3,942	66
Non-US	2,018	34
Total	**5,960**	**100**

2018 sales

	$ mil.	% of total
Net interest income	1,623	27
Noninterest expense		
Trust Investment & Other Servicing Fees	3,754	63
Foreign Exchange Trading Income	307	5
Treasury Management Fees	52	1
Security Commissions & Trading Income	98	2
Other Operating Income	128	2
Investment Security Losses net	(1)	-
Total	**5,960**	**100**

Selected Subsidiaries

The Northern Trust Company
MFC Company Inc.
Norlease Inc.
The Northern Trust Company Canada
Northern Trust Holdings Limited
The Northern Trust International Banking Corporation
Northern Trust Cayman International Ltd. (Cayman Islands)
The Northern Trust Company of Hong Kong Limited
Northern Trust Fund Managers (Ireland) Limited
Northern Trust (Ireland) Limited
Northern Trust Fund Services (Ireland) Limited
Northern Trust Management Services Limited (Ireland)
Northern Trust Partners Scotland Limited (UK)
Northern Trust Scottish Limited Partnership (99% UK)
Northern Trust Luxembourg Capital S.A.R.L.
Northern Trust Investments Inc.
The Northern Trust Company of Delaware
NT Global Advisors Inc. (Canada)
Northern Trust Global Investments Japan K.K.
Northern Trust Holdings L.L.C.
Northern Trust Securities Inc.
Northern Trust Services Inc.
Nortrust Realty Management Inc.

COMPETITORS

Bank of America	Goldman Sachs
Bank of New York Mellon	Harris
Barclays	JPMorgan Chase
Citigroup	Morgan Stanley
Deutsche Bank	SEI Investments
Fifth Third	State Street
	Wells Fargo

HISTORICAL FINANCIALS

Company Type: Public

Income Statement

	ASSETS ($ mil.)	NET INCOME ($ mil.)	INCOME AS % OF ASSETS	EMPLOYEES
				FYE: December 31
12/18	132,213	1,556	1.2%	18,800
12/17	138,591	1,199	0.9%	18,100
12/16	123,927	1,033	0.8%	17,100
12/15	116,750	974	0.8%	16,200
12/14	109,947	812	0.7%	15,400
Annual Growth	4.7%	17.7%	—	5.1%

2018 Year-End Financials

Debt ratio: 3.00%
Return on equity: 15.00%
Cash ($ mil.): 38,926
Current ratio: —
Long-term debt ($ mil.): —

No. of shares (mil.): 219
Dividends
  Yield: 2.0%
  Payout: 31.0%
Market value ($ mil.): 18,307

	STOCK PRICE ($) FY Close	P/E High/Low	PER SHARE ($) Earnings	Dividends	Book Value
12/18	84.00	17 12	7.00	2.00	48.00
12/17	100.00	20 17	5.00	2.00	45.00
12/16	89.00	21 13	4.00	1.00	43.00
12/15	72.00	20 15	4.00	1.00	38.00
12/14	67.00	21 17	3.00	1.00	36.00
Annual Growth	5.5%	— —	18.9%	10.5%	7.3%

Northfield Bancorp Inc (DE)

Auditors: KPMG LLP

LOCATIONS

HQ: Northfield Bancorp Inc (DE)
581 Main Street, Woodbridge, NJ 07095
Phone: 732 499-7200
Web: www.eNorthfield.com

HISTORICAL FINANCIALS

Company Type: Public

Income Statement				FYE: December 31
	ASSETS ($ mil.)	NET INCOME ($ mil.)	INCOME AS % OF ASSETS	EMPLOYEES
12/18	4,408	40	0.9%	368
12/17	3,991	25	0.6%	352
12/16	3,850	26	0.7%	366
12/15	3,203	20	0.6%	306
12/14	3,021	20	0.7%	321
Annual Growth	9.9%	18.6%	—	3.5%

2018 Year-End Financials

Debt ratio: 0.00%
Return on equity: 6.00%
Cash ($ mil.): 78
Current ratio: —
Long-term debt ($ mil.): —

No. of shares (mil.): 50
Dividends
Yield: 3.0%
Payout: 67.0%
Market value ($ mil.): 673

	STOCK PRICE ($) FY Close	P/E High/Low	PER SHARE ($) Earnings	Dividends	Book Value
12/18	14.00	20 15	1.00	0.00	13.00
12/17	17.00	37 28	1.00	0.00	13.00
12/16	20.00	35 24	1.00	0.00	13.00
12/15	16.00	36 31	0.00	0.00	12.00
12/14	15.00	36 30	0.00	0.00	12.00
Annual Growth	(2.2%)	— —	20.0%	11.4%	2.3%

Northrop Grumman Corp

Northrop Grumman's major military systems include manned and autonomous aircraft such as the Global Hawk drone a next-generation B-21 Raider bomber and fuselage sections for the F-35 Lightening. Other products and services include various command control communications computer intelligence surveillance and reconnaissance (C4ISR) systems that support the military from the ground the air and space. The company also offers software and services in support of national security for the US and its allies. The 2018 acquisition of Orbital ATK added space vehicles satellites ammunition and missile propulsion systems. The US government accounts for more than 80% of Northrop Grumman's sales.

HISTORY

Huntington Ingalls Industries Jack Northrop co-founded Lockheed Aircraft in 1927 and designed its record-setting Vega monoplane. He founded two more companies — Avion Corporation (formed in 1928 and bought by United Aircraft and Transportation) and Northrop Corporation (formed in 1932 with Douglas Aircraft which absorbed it in 1938) — before founding Northrop Aircraft in California in 1939.

During WWII Northrop produced the P-61 fighter and the famous Flying Wing bomber which failed to win a production contract. In the 1950s Northrop depended heavily on F-89 fighter and Snark missile sales. When Thomas Jones succeeded Jack Northrop as president (1959) he moved the company away from risky prime contracts in favor of numerous subcontracts and bought Page Communications Engineers (telecommunications 1959) and Hallicrafters (electronics 1966) to reduce its dependence on government contracts.

In the early 1970s Northrop was hit with a bribery scandal and the disclosure of illegal payments to Richard Nixon's 1972 campaign fund; Jones was eventually fined for an illegal contribution. As a result a shareholder lawsuit forced Jones to resign as president (he was allowed to remain as chairman). In 1981 the company won the B-2 bomber contract. Jones retired as chairman in late 1990 and under the leadership of Kent Kresa (who became CEO in early 1990 and chairman when Jones retired) Northrop pleaded guilty to 34 counts related to fudging test results on some government projects; it was fined $17 million. In a related shareholders' suit Northrop paid $18 million in damages in 1991.

Northrop and The Carlyle Group bought LTV's Vought Aircraft Industries (now named Triumph Aerostructures - Vought Aircraft Division) in 1992. In 1994 it paid $2.1 billion for Grumman Corporation a premier electronic systems firm and manufacturer of fighter aircraft for the US Navy and changed its name to Northrop Grumman.

In 1929 Roy Grumman Jake Swirbul and Bill Schwendler founded Grumman; within three months it had a contract to design a Navy fighter. Grumman completed its first commercial aircraft (the Grumman Goose) in 1937 and went public in 1938. It soared during WWII on the wings of its Wildcat and Hellcat fighter planes.

Grumman built its first corporate jet (Gulfstream) in 1958 and began work on the Lunar Module for the Apollo space program in 1963. It was near bankruptcy during the 1970s due to costs related to its F-14 Tomcat fighter. Grumman rebuilt its military business in the 1980s and achieved its greatest success in electronic systems.

The UK Ministry of Defence awarded a $279 million contract to Northrop Grumman in 1995 to develop and produce a system to counter infrared missiles. In 1997 Northrop Grumman bought Logicon (information and battle-management systems). It then agreed to an $11.6 billion purchase by Lockheed Martin but the US government citing concerns about increased lack of competition in the defense industry blocked the deal in 1998. As a result Northrop Grumman began a restructuring that cut 10500 defense and aircraft jobs and added 2500 positions to its Logicon subsidiary.

In 1999 Northrop Grumman bought the information systems division of California Microwave for $93 million and Allegheny Teledyne's Ryan Aeronautical (aerial drones) for $140 million. The next year Northrop Grumman sold its underperforming commercial aerostructures business to The Carlyle Group in a $1.2 billion transaction in order to focus on its growing defense electronics and information technology segments. Later in 2000 Northrop Grumman acquired Comptek Research and bought Federal Data (information systems for the US government) from Carlyle in a transaction valued at $302 million. Pension income that year accounted for more than $500 million (about 55%) of the company's pretax profit.

In 2001 the company completed the deal to acquire Litton Industries for $3.8 billion plus $1.3 billion in debt. In the fall Northrop Grumman acquired the electronics and information unit of Aerojet-General Corp. a subsidiary of GenCorp (later renamed Aerojet Rocketdyne) for about $300 million (it became Grumman's Space Systems Division). While its wallet was open the company agreed to match the $2.6 billion that General Dynamics had agreed to pay for submarine and aircraft carrier builder Newport News— a move that the US Defense Department endorsed. In December Honeywell agreed to pay Northrop Grumman $440 million to settle an antitrust and patent infringement lawsuit that Litton had filed against Honeywell in 1990.

The deal to buy Newport News was completed in early 2002. Northrop Grumman then made a hostile $6 billion bid for conglomerate TRW when TRW's stock plunged following the sudden departure of its CEO David Cote to Honeywell. In the wake of Northrop Grumman's spurned initial bid Raytheon General Dynamics and BAE SYSTEMS made offers for TRW's aerospace and defense assets. Finally though TRW accepted a sweetened $7.8 billion offer from Northrop Grumman in July 2002.

The acquisition fortified Northrop Grumman's position in military satellites missile systems and systems integration. In fact Northrop signed a consent decree with the US Justice Department in which the company agreed (under pain of fines) that it wouldn't take unfair advantage of its exclusive position when selling certain components — such as satellite sensors — to competitors.

TRW's Systems unit became Northrop Grumman Mission Systems; TRW's Space and Electronics unit was later known as Northrop Grumman Space Technology. As for TRW's car parts business Northrop sold all but 19.6% of the unit to Blackstone Group for about $4.7 billion to pay down debt; by early 2005 Northrop reduced its stake to 9.9%.

In April 2003 Kresa stepped down as president and CEO and Ronald Sugar took over those roles; Sugar added the chairmanship to his title when Kresa retired in October.

Among Northrop's 2004 contracts were $1.04 billion for X-47B Joint Unmanned Combat Air Systems $1.2 billion (preferred bidder) for E-3D AWACS contract support and $1.4 billion for the CVN 21 generation aircraft carrier. The company also split an $8.4 billion submarine contract with General Dynamics.

Early in 2005 Northrop sold 7.2 million shares of its TRW Automotive stake raising more than $142 million and reducing its stake to 9.9%. It also acquired Integic Corporation an IT company that specialized in business process management and enterprise health applications.

In 2006 Northrop Grumman established Northrop Grumman Technical Services (NGTS) as a separate sector; it was tasked with consolidating Northrop's logistics operations across its various sectors.

Late that same year Northrop Grumman agreed to buy Essex Corporation — a provider of signal image and information processing for defense and intelligence customers in the US. The deal was valued at about $580 million including the assumption of debt. The deal was completed early in 2007 and Essex became a part of Northrop Grumman Mission Systems (now Northrop Grumman Information Systems).

In 2008 the company shed its Electro-Optical Systems business (night vision and applied optics products) to L-3 Communications for $175 million.

In 2009 Northrop Gruman sold its Advisory Services Division comprising subsidiary TASC (engineering and consulting services to the US military and state governments) to private equities General Atlantic LLC and KKR for $1.65 billion. The sale brings Northrop Grumman into compliance with a new federal law that strengthens conflict of interest rules for defense contractors that both sell to and provide consulting for the US military.

Expanding its aerospace and information capabilities the company purchased Sonoma Photonics and assets from Swift Engineering's Killer Bee Unmanned Air Systems lineup for its Aerospace Systems sector (2009). The deal followed its acquisition of 3001 International for $92 million (a nearly three times larger investment) in 2008. The Virginia-based geospatial data collection and analysis provider not only bolstered Northrop Grumman's military offerings but it also reeled in a host of new civilian customers.

Also in 2009 Northrop Grumman settled two decade-old lawsuits with the US government. It agreed to pay $325 million to resolve allegations that it provided defective military satellite parts to the National Reconnaissance Office. The second lawsuit was filed by Northrop Grumman against the US government for uncompensated costs incurred as a result of the cancellation of the Tri-Service Standoff Attack Missile program.

To concentrate more on its core areas Northrop Grumman spun off its shipbuilding business under former subsidiary Huntington Ingalls Industries in 2011. Despite modest increases in year-over-year revenues the shipbuilding sector had struggled to regain profitability after suffering a loss in 2008 attributable to absorbing most of the company's goodwill impairment charge. Also in 2011 the company reduced operations in other segments. It sold its Viper Strike laser-guided bomb operations in Alabama to European consortium MBDA for an undisclosed amount. And it lowered its participation in the National Security Technologies joint venture that manages and operates the Nevada National Security Site.

Focusing on increasing its presence in the Asia/Pacific in 2012 Northrop Grumman purchased M5 Network Security a provider of cyber security and secure mobile communications technology based in Australia.

EXECUTIVES

Chairman President And Ceo, Wesley G. (Wes) Bush, age 57, $1,530,000 total compensation
Vp And Cto, Patrick M. Antkowiak, age 58
Vp And President Technical Services, Christopher T. Jones, age 54
President And Coo, Kathy J. Warden, age 47, $772,500 total compensation
Corporate Vp And President Mission Systems, Mark A. Caylor, age 54
Vp And Cfo, Kenneth L. Bedingfield, age 46, $756,539 total compensation
Chief Executive Northrop Grumman Japan, Stan Crow
General Manager Strategic Systems Aerospace Systems, Janis G. Pamiljans
Vp And Cio, Shawn N. Purvis
Vp James Webb Space Telescope Program, Scott Willoughby
Vp And Deputy General Counsel, Kathryn Simpson
Corporate Vp And Secretary, Jennifer Mcgarey
Vice President Human Resources, Heidi Hendrix
Vice President And Chief Information Officer Of Technology Services, Jim Kane
Vp And Chief Information Security Officer, Mike Papay
Vice President Japan, Curtis Orchard
Security Vice President, Jerry Dodd

Vp Global Cyber Solutions, Bobby Lentz
Vp Tax, Talha Zobair
Vice President Mritime Systems, Todd Leavitt
Vice President Enterprise Communications, Daniel Mcclain
Senior Vice President, Monty Frahm
Vp Of Programs Of Land And Avionics C4isr Division, Robert Fleming
Vice President Business Development Northrop Grumman Space Technology, Jeffrey Grant
Vice President, Bart Lagrone
Vp Contracts And Pricing, Diane Balderson
Vice President, Robert Snodgrass
Vp Information Technology, Martin Bernet
Vice President Government And Industry R, Ryan Casey
Vp Corporate Strategy, Brett Lambert
Government Relations, Robert McCaleb
Vice President Business Management, Joseph Nicolaus
Senior Vice President Executive Assistant, Catherine Fenneman
Vice President Operations Command And Control, Christina Williams
Vice President Middle East, Samir Narmouq
Vice President Strategic Communications, Tim Paynter
Sector Vice President Global Operations Aerospace System, Kevin Mitchell
Vp Missile Defense And Protective Systems, Tarik Reyes
Vice President Associate General Counsel And Sector Counsel Technologyservices Sector, Don Chavez
Vp Nuclear Materials Operations Srns, David Eyler
Vice President Mission Solutions Land And Avionics C4isr Division, Carl Smith
Sector Vp Global Logistics And Operational Support Aerospace Systems, Michelle Scarpella
Vice President Business Management And Cfo, Sunil Navale
Vice President Communications Systems, Cyrus Dhalla
Vp Associate General Counsel And Sector Counsel Mission Systems, Jennifer O'connor
Vp And Cio, Sam Abbate
Vp And Cto Electronic Systems Sector, Eric Reinke Iii
Vp Hr Mission Systems, Milou Carolan
Vice President And Assistant General Counsel, John Cox
Vice President, John Buckley
Vice President, Andrew Reynolds
Sector Vp Of Mission Assurance Of Innovation Systems, Jim Judd
Sector Vp Of Supply Chain Management Of Innovation Systems, Vicky Schumann
Vice President, Simon Mason
Vice President Security, Mary Mccaffrey
Corporate Vice President Communications, Lucy C Ryan
Auditors: DELOITTE & TOUCHE LLP

LOCATIONS

HQ: Northrop Grumman Corp
2980 Fairview Park Drive, Falls Church, VA 22042
Phone: 703 280-2900
Web: www.northropgrumman.com

PRODUCTS/OPERATIONS

2016 Sales

Segments	$ mil.	% of total
Aerospace Systems	10,828	41
Mission Systems	10,928	41
Technology Services	4,825	18
Intersegment eliminations	(2073)	-
Total	**24,508**	**100**

2016 Sales

	$ mil.	% of total
Product	14,738	60
Service	9,770	40
Total	**24,508**	**100**

2016 Sales

	$ mil.	% of total
U.S. Government	20,573	84
International	3,205	13
Other Customers	730	3
Total	**24,508**	**100**

Selected Capabilities

Unmanned Systems
C4ISR
Cyber
Logistics
Advanced Electronics
Commercial Aviation
Directed Energy
IT & Enterprise Solutions
Manned Aircraft
Military Aviation
Missile Defense
Naval Systems
Navigation Systems

COMPETITORS

BAE SYSTEMS	Leonardo
Boeing	Lockheed Martin
Booz Allen	Meggitt
General Dynamics	Raytheon
L3 Technologies	Thales
Leidos	

HISTORICAL FINANCIALS

Company Type: Public

Income Statement

FYE: December 31

	REVENUE ($ mil.)	NET INCOME ($ mil.)	NET PROFIT MARGIN	EMPLOYEES
12/19	33,841	2,248	6.6%	90,000
12/18	30,095	3,229	10.7%	85,000
12/17	25,803	2,015	7.8%	70,000
12/16	24,508	2,200	9.0%	67,000
12/15	23,526	1,990	8.5%	65,000
Annual Growth	9.5%	3.1%	—	8.5%

2019 Year-End Financials

Debt ratio: 31.00%
Return on equity: 26.00%
Cash ($ mil.): 2,245
Current ratio: 1.00
Long-term debt ($ mil.): 12,770
No. of shares (mil.): 168
Dividends
 Yield: 2.0%
 Payout: 27.0%
Market value ($ mil.): 57,735

	STOCK PRICE ($) FY Close	P/E High/Low		PER SHARE ($) Earnings	Dividends	Book Value
12/19	344.00	29	18	13.00	5.00	53.00
12/18	245.00	19	12	18.00	5.00	48.00
12/17	307.00	27	20	11.00	4.00	40.00
12/16	233.00	20	14	12.00	4.00	30.00
12/15	189.00	18	14	10.00	3.00	30.00
Annual Growth	16.2%	—	—	6.2%	13.6%	14.6%

Northwest Bancshares, Inc. (MD)

EXECUTIVES

Chief Executive Officer, Julie McTpavish
Executive Vp, Julia Mctavish
Executive Vice President Commercial Lending, Michael Bickerton
Divisional Avp Office Manager, Mari Pravlik
Senior Vice President District Manager, Kara Odom
Senior Vice President Region Manager Commercial Lending, Richard Cefalo
Assistant Vp Information Security, Lance Spencer
Divisional Vice President And Trust Officer, John Zador
Senior Vice President Commercial Lending Team Leader, Douglas Byers
Senior Vice President, Bradley Chovit
Corporate Assistant Vice President Computer Operations Manager, Robert Pope
Board Member, John Meegan
Auditors: KPMG LLP

LOCATIONS

HQ: Northwest Bancshares, Inc. (MD)
100 Liberty Street, Warren, PA 16365
Phone: 814 726-2140
Web: www.northwestsavingsbank.com

HISTORICAL FINANCIALS

Company Type: Public

Income Statement				FYE: December 31
	ASSETS ($ mil.)	NET INCOME ($ mil.)	INCOME AS % OF ASSETS	EMPLOYEES
12/18	9,608	105	1.1%	2,258
12/17	9,364	94	1.0%	2,254
12/16	9,624	50	0.5%	2,466
12/15	8,952	61	0.7%	2,364
12/14	7,775	62	0.8%	2,220
Annual Growth	5.4%	14.2%	—	0.4%

2018 Year-End Financials

Debt ratio: 2.00%
Return on equity: 9.00%
Cash ($ mil.): 69
Current ratio: —
Long-term debt ($ mil.): —

No. of shares (mil.): 103
Dividends
Yield: 4.0%
Payout: 70.0%
Market value ($ mil.): 1,751

	STOCK PRICE ($) FY Close	P/E High/Low	PER SHARE ($) Earnings	Dividends	Book Value
12/18	17.00	18 15	1.00	1.00	12.00
12/17	17.00	20 16	1.00	1.00	12.00
12/16	18.00	38 24	0.00	1.00	12.00
12/15	13.00	22 18	1.00	1.00	11.00
12/14	13.00	22 18	1.00	2.00	11.00
Annual Growth	7.8%	— —	11.1%	(19.5%)	2.1%

NORTHWEST FARM CREDIT SERVICES

Customer-owned financial cooperative Northwest Farm Credit Services is an agricultural lender that provides financial services to farmers ranchers agribusinesses commercial fishermen timber producers and rural home owners in Alaska Idaho Montana Oregon and Washington. The company has a network of around 45 branches and offers a broad range of flexible loan programs to meet the needs of people in the agriculture business. Northwest Farm Credit also provides leasing services appraisal services and life mortgage disability and crop insurance as well as legal advocacy and assistance to customers in need. It is part of the Farm Credit System a network of lenders serving the US agriculture industry.

Operations

The credit union provides financing and related services to farmers ranchers agribusinesses commercial fishermen timber producers rural homeowners and crop insurance customers. Northwest Farm Credit provides $10.3 billion in loans. Farm Credit System a nationwide network of borrower-owned lending institutions of which it is part provides $205 billion in loans to rural America.

Geographic Reach

Northwest Farm Credit serves customers through 45 offices located in Idaho Alaska Montana Oregon and Washington.

Sales and Marketing

Northwest Farm Credit finances farmers ranchers agribusinesses commercial fishermen timber producers and rural homeowners as well as farm-related businesses agricultural cooperatives and rural utilities.

Financial Performance

In 2015 the company's net revenue increased by 5% due to higher net interest income driven by increased loan volume.

Northwest Farm Credit's net income rose by 12% due to higher net revenues and a decrease in income tax expense.

In 2015 the company's operating cash inflow increased by 19%.

Strategy

The company plans to continue to fund lending operations primarily through its borrowing relationship with CoBank (a fellow Farm Credit System member) and from retained earnings.

Mergers and Acquisitions

In 2014 the company expanded its operations in Montana by buying Culbertson State Agency's crop insurance portfolio.

Company Background

The US Congress created the Farm Credit System in 1916 to meet the financial needs of farmers ranchers and cooperatives who invest as well as borrow from the institutions within the system. All Farm Credit System members are regulated by the Farm Credit Administration.

EXECUTIVES

Evp Financial Services, Fred (Fred) DePell
Evp And General Counsel, Thomas (Tom) Tracy
Evp Corporate Administration And Secretary, Joan E. Haynes
Evp Cfo And Cio, Tom Nakano
Relationship Manager Vice President, Kurt Wittman
Vice President Human Resources, Alice Hardin
Vice President, Carol L Sobson
Vice President Appraisal Services, Joe Moore

Chairman, Drew Eggers
Vice Chairman, Kevin Riel
Auditors: PRICEWATERHOUSECOOPERS LLP S

LOCATIONS

HQ: NORTHWEST FARM CREDIT SERVICES
2001 S FLINT RD, SPOKANE, WA 992249198
Phone: 509 838-2429
Web: WWW.NORTHWESTFCS.COM

PRODUCTS/OPERATIONS

2015 Sales

	$ mil.	% of total
Interest Income	412	82
Patronage income	53	11
Financially Related Services	19	4
loans and other fee	7	1
Other non-interest income	12	2
Total	**502**	**100**

COMPETITORS

Bank of America	U.S. Bancorp
First Interstate	Wells Fargo
Idaho Independent Bank	Zions Bancorporation
KeyCorp	
Northwest Bancorporation	

HISTORICAL FINANCIALS

Company Type: Private

Income Statement				FYE: December 31
	ASSETS ($ mil.)	NET INCOME ($ mil.)	INCOME AS % OF ASSETS	EMPLOYEES
12/14	10,253	228	2.2%	500
12/13	9,605	237	2.5%	—
12/12	9,471	187	2.0%	—
12/11	8,697	159	1.8%	—
Annual Growth	5.6%	12.7%	—	—

NOVARTIS PHARMACEUTICALS CORPORATION

EXECUTIVES

Pres, Marie-France Tschudin
Sr V-Pres-Cmo*, Nancy Lurker
Pres*, Andre Wyss
V Pres*, Yves Teirlynck
V Pres*, Julie Kane
Coo*, Alex Gorsky
V-Pres-Cfo*, Gary E Rosenthal
Cfo*, Helen Boudreau
Vice-President Corporate Commu, Anna Frable
Scientist, Katherine Chan
Manager, Debra Bloodgood
Auditors: PRICEWATERHOUSECOOPERS LLP-BR

LOCATIONS

HQ: NOVARTIS PHARMACEUTICALS CORPORATION
1 HEALTH PLZ, EAST HANOVER, NJ 079361016
Phone: 862 778-8300
Web: WWW.NOVARTIS.COM

Income Statement				FYE: December 31
	REVENUE ($ mil.)	NET INCOME ($ mil.)	NET PROFIT MARGIN	EMPLOYEES
12/16	49,436	6,698	13.5%	7,000
12/15	49,440	17,794	36.0%	—
12/13	58,831	9,292	15.8%	—
Annual Growth	(5.6%)	(10.3%)	—	—

NRG Energy Inc

NRG Energy is a leading power producer with a generating capacity of 28000 MW (including 1600 MW of solar power assets). The vast majority of NRG's power plants are in North America but it also has one in Australia and one in Turkey. Its portfolio includes 50 power plants. It also markets natural gas oil and other commodities. NRG's retail units (including Reliant Energy and Green Mountain Energy) distribute power to about 3 million customers across the US.

Operations

NRG's operating segments are Retail (about 55% of revenues) Generation (over 30%) NRG Yield (about 10%) and Renewables.

NRG's Retail segment is one of the largest in the country. It provides some 63 TWhs of energy and related services under the Business Solutions banner to almost 3 million residential industrial and commercial customers. The segment overlooks several brands that collectively are the largest providers of electricity in Texas.

Wholesale Power Generation a capital-intensive segment is responsible for plant and commercial operations energy services as well as distributed generation business. It has 28000 MW of fossil fuel and nuclear generation capacity at some 50 plants with less than 25% come from coal. Currently it has 500MW of targeted re-powering initiatives for future development.

NRG will sell its Renewables business segment and all interests in NRG Yield Inc. in 2018. The segment focuses on the acquisition development operation and maintenance of utility scale wind and solar community solar and distributed solar generation assets. Including NRG Yield it has a total portfolio of wind and solar assets across 27 states.

NRG Yield is a publicly-traded company through which NRG acquires and operates power generation and thermal infrastructure assets.

Geographic Reach

NRG Energy has generation assets in the US Australia and Turkey. Its retail and thermal subsidiaries serve customers in more than 15 US states. Its NRG Thermal unit provides third-party steam to downtown heating and cooling systems in cities such as Pittsburgh San Diego San Francisco and Harrisburg Pennsylvania.

Most of its retail sales come from Connecticut Delaware Illinois Maryland Massachusetts New Jersey New York Pennsylvania Ohio and Texas.

Sales and Marketing

NRG's retail electricity divisions serve nearly 3 million residential business commercial and industrial customers in all 50 US states and Washington DC.

The company's sales channels include direct sales call centers websites brokers and brick-and-mortar stores. It also sells directly to residential commercial and industrial customers.

Financial Performance

NRG revenue trended upwards from $7 billion in 2008 to $15 billion peak in 2014 before suffering from an oil and gas price downturn and reducing below $11 billion in the following years. Net income has been hit badly due to the commodities price downturn. In the 2015-17 the company has posted a combined three-year loss of $9.3 billion.

Revenue in 2017 grew less than 2% for NRG to $10.6 billion. The slight increase came due to better results from mark to market hedging. Energy revenue the highest company earner reduced by some 20% compared to 2016.

Net loss for 2017 was $2.3 billion compared to a loss of $891 million the year prior mostly due to $1 billion increase in impairment losses from the year prior. In 2017 NRG recorded a loss of $790 million from discontinued operations. This included the deconsolidation of GenOn and its subsidiaries for $208 million (after it filed for bankruptcy).

NRG's cash holdings increased slightly to $1.5 billion. Financing activities used some $485 million while investments utilized more than double that amount at $1 billion mostly in CAPEX. Operations provided a healthy $1.4 billion though greatly reduced by losses on discontinued operations and high impairment charges as well as depreciation and amortization charges.

Strategy

Coming out of three years of massive losses (for a combined $9.3 billion) NRG is in the middle of executing a drastic Transformation Plan. The three-part three-year plan will target portfolio overhaul cost-cutting and capital structure enhancement.

The core of the plan focused on a massive asset sale totaling $3 billion by early 2018. This includes NRG's agreement to sell NRG Yield (along with its renewable platform) in February 2018 for $1.3 billion ownership interests in Buckthorn Solar for $42 million Carlsbad Energy for $365 million and BETM for $70 million.

Despite a tough operational year (Hurricane Harvey further affected 2017 sales by at least $20 million the company calculates) NRG achieved $150 million in cost savings reduced working capital by $221 million is expecting to generate $3.2 billion in cash proceeds from the asset sales and further announced another $1 billion in share buybacks. This would allow the company to pay off $8 billion in debt.

One of the robust performance areas for NRG is its retail sector where customer count is growing from 2.89 million in 2016 to 2.94 in early 2018. Retail's sharing of total earnings has gone up from 25% in 2016 to 60% in first quarter though much of it is due to asset sell offs.

With the power market showing signs of stabilizing and cost-recovery in 2018 the company is pushing for improved retail choices and capacity re-pricing proposal. The company is also exclusively focusing on investing in projects that will have around 15% returns within a maximum 5-year window.

Mergers and Acquisitions

In 2019 NRG agreed to acquire the retail electricity and gas business of Stream Energy for $300 million. The deal adds more than 600000 residential customers in Texas and Pennsylvania and is aligned with NRG's strategy to exit electricity generation and transition to retail sales. The company acquired another retail energy company XOOM Energy in 2018 for $210 million. This acquisition balances NRG's generation portfolio in the East. It also enhances NRG's multi-brand and multi-channel strategy via XOOM's referral-based sales channel.

EXECUTIVES

President And Ceo, Mauricio Gutierrez, age 49, $1,125,000 total compensation

Evp And Cfo, Kirkland B. Andrews, age 52, $642,952 total compensation

Evp Nrg Retail, Elizabeth Killinger, age 49, $504,634 total compensation

Evp National Business Development; President West Region, John Chillemi, age 52, $475,001 total compensation

Evp And General Counsel, David R. Hill, age 56, $500,000 total compensation

Svp Operations, Chris Moser

Svp Information Technology, Donna Benefield

Svp Renewables And President Nrg Renewables, Craig Cornelius

Vice President Strategic Marketing, Virginia Kinney

Senior Vice President Asset Management And Development, Howard Taylor

Vice President Internal Audit, Debra Holmes

Vice President Wholesale Information Technology, Robert Thibeault

Vp Engineering Construction And Project Services, Robert Patrick

Vp Government Affairs, Ray Long

Senior Vice President Business Operations, Jim Ingoldsby

Vice President Reliability Solutions, Phil Kairis

Svp It, Kim Hales

Senior Vice President And Treasurer, Gabriel Garcia

Vp Strategy Business Development, Jim Locher

Chairman, Lawrence S. Coben, age 60

Board Member, William Hantke

Board Member, Anne Schaumburg

Auditors: KPMG LLP

LOCATIONS

HQ: NRG Energy Inc
804 Carnegie Center, Princeton, NJ 08540
Phone: 609 524-4500
Web: www.nrgenergy.com

PRODUCTS/OPERATIONS

2016 Sales

	$ mil.	% of total
Retail revenue	6,274	47
Energy revenue	4,469	34
Capacity revenue	1,970	15
Other revenues	558	4
Mark-to-market activities	(865)	-
Contract amortization	(55)	-
Total	**12,351**	**100**

2016 Sales

	$ mil.	% of total
Retail	6,336	47
Generation	5,679	42
NRG Yield	1,021	7
Renewables	417	3
Corporate	77	1
Other	(1179)	-
Total	**12,351**	**100**

2016 Sales

	$ mil.	% of total
Generation	6,927	51
Retail Mass	4,966	37
NRG Yield	1,021	8
Renewable	417	3
Corporate	137	1
Eliminations	(1117)	-
Total	**12,351**	**100**

Selected Subsidiaries

Energy Plus
Green Mountain Energy Company (retail power)
NEO Corporation (distributed generation; landfill gas hydroelectric and other renewable generation)
NRG Power Marketing Inc. (power sales)
NRG Resource Recovery (waste-to-energy facilities)

NRG Texas LLC (power generation)
NRG Thermal Corporation (district heating and cooling combined heat and power facilities)
Reliant Energy Texas Retail LLC
Texas Genco LP (power generation)
West Coast Power LLC (power generation)

Selected Mergers and Acquisitions

COMPETITORS

AEP	FirstEnergy
AES	Gexa Energy
Accent Energy	Integrys Energy
Alliant Energy	Services
Avista	Nicor Gas
Berkshire Hathaway	PG&E Corporation
Energy	PPL Corporation
Calpine	PSEG Power
Cogentrix Energy	Preferred Energy
Community Energy	Services
Direct Energy	SCANA
Duke Energy	Sempra Generation
Edison International	Tenaska
Entergy	

HISTORICAL FINANCIALS

Company Type: Public

Income Statement
FYE: December 31

	REVENUE ($ mil.)	NET INCOME ($ mil.)	NET PROFIT MARGIN	EMPLOYEES
12/18	9,478	268	2.8%	4,862
12/17	10,629	(2,153)	—	5,940
12/16	12,351	(774)	—	8,763
12/15	14,674	(6,382)	—	10,468
12/14	15,868	134	0.8%	9,806
Annual Growth	(12.1%)	18.9%	—	(16.1%)

2018 Year-End Financials

Debt ratio: 61.00%	No. of shares (mil.): 284
Return on equity: ***,***.**%	Dividends
Cash ($ mil.): 596	Yield: 0.0%
Current ratio: 2.00	Payout: 14.0%
Long-term debt ($ mil.): 6,449	Market value ($ mil.): 11,233

	STOCK PRICE ($) FY Close	P/E High/Low	PER SHARE ($) Earnings	Dividends	Book Value
12/18	40.00	49 27	1.00	0.00	(4.00)
12/17	28.00	— —	(7.00)	0.00	(1.00)
12/16	12.00	— —	(2.00)	0.00	6.00
12/15	12.00	— —	(19.00)	1.00	10.00
12/14	27.00	164112	0.00	1.00	30.00
Annual Growth	10.1%	— —	39.5%	(31.3%)	—

Nucor Corp.

Nucor Corporation is a leading manufacturer trader and seller of steel and steel products in the US. It is also North America's largest recycler of scrap metal and a leading scrap broker. The company produces rolled sheets bars and beams used in the energy automotive transportation and heavy equipment industries. Its other steel products including steel joists electrical conduits and metal building systems are sold to fabricators distributors and metal manufacturers. Subsidiary Harris Steel fabricates rebar for highways and bridges and other construction projects. Another unit the David J. Joseph Company processes and brokers metals pig iron hot briquetted iron and direct reduced iron (DRI).

HISTORY

Nucor started as the second carmaking venture of Ransom Olds who built his first gasoline-powered car in 1897. Two years later Samuel Smith a Detroit copper and lumber magnate put up $199600 to finance Olds Motor Works. A fire destroyed the company's Detroit plant in 1901 so Olds moved production to Lansing Michigan where he built America's first mass-produced car — the Oldsmobile. In 1904 Olds left Olds Motor Works which was bought by General Motors (GM) in 1908 and formed Reo Car Company (renamed Reo Motor Car in 1906). In addition to cars it eventually made trucks and buses.

By the end of the Depression Ford GM and Chrysler commanded over 85% of the US passenger car market. Reo stopped making cars in 1936 and sold its truck manufacturing operations in 1957. Meanwhile it had formed Reo Holding which in 1955 merged with Nuclear Consultants to form Nuclear Corporation of America. The new company offered services such as radiation studies and made nuclear instruments and electronics.

In 1962 Nuclear bought steel joist maker Vulcraft and gained the services of Kenneth Iverson. The diverse company was unprofitable losing $2 million on $22 million in sales in 1965. That year Iverson took over as CEO moved headquarters to Charlotte North Carolina and shut down or sold about half of the company's businesses. By focusing on its profitable steel joist operations the firm ended 1966 in the black. Because the company depended on imports for 80% of its steel needs Iverson decided to move into steel production. Nuclear Corporation built its first minimill in 1969.

The company was renamed Nucor in 1972. It started making steel deck (1977) and cold-finished steel bars (1979). Production tripled and sales more than doubled between 1974 and 1979.

Nucor began to diversify adding grinding balls (used in the mining industry to process ores 1981); steel bolts steel bearings and machined steel parts (1986); and metal buildings and components (1987). Nucor and Japanese steelmaker Yamato Kogyo formed Nucor-Yamato and built a mill in 1988 to produce wide-flange beams (for heavy construction). The following year Nucor opened a state-of-the-art mill in Crawfordsville Indiana and another mill near Hickman Arkansas in 1992.

Iverson turned over his CEO duties to company veteran John Correnti in 1996. The next year Nucor began building a steel beam mill in South Carolina and added a galvanizing facility to its Hickman mill.

In 1998 Nucor announced plans to build its first steel plate mill which became operational in 2000. The company slashed prices twice in 1998 to compete against low-cost imports from Russia Japan and Brazil. Both sales and earnings declined that year due to low metal prices reduced shipments and start-up costs for new plants. The company raised its prices in 1999 and continued its expansion plans. Differences with the board prompted Correnti to resign in 1999; chairman David Aycock assumed his duties. In September 2000 Aycock resigned from the company and Daniel DiMicco formerly an EVP moved up to the rank of CEO.

Nucor along with Australia's Broken Hill Proprietary Corporation and Japan's Ishikawajima-Harima Heavy Industries began a joint venture in 2000 for its technology strip casting. The new technology allows steel production in smaller cheaper plants. In 2001 Nucor purchased a significant amount of assets of Auburn Steel a producer of merchant steel bar for $115 million.

In 2002 Nucor teamed up with Companhia Vale do Rio Doce (Vale) a Brazilian producer and exporter of iron-ore pellets to develop low-cost iron based products. That year Nucor purchased Ala-

bama-based Trico Steel a steel sheet producer for approximately $116 million. In late 2002 Nucor bought financially troubled Birmingham Steel for $615 million in cash and debt.

Nucor Steel Kingman LLC a subsidiary of Nucor Corporation purchased the Kingman Arizona rebar and wire rod rolling unit of North Star Steel for around $35 million in 2003.

Its Vulcraft unit saw an increase in non-residential building construction in 2004 which boosted sales of joist girders steel deck and steel joists. Nucor bought Nucor Tuscaloosa in mid-2004 a producer of coiled plate with an annual capacity of around 700000 tons. The following year saw the company purchase Ohio's Marion Steel for approximately $110 million. The mill was added to Nucor's bar products line.

Record high prices in the industry (led by high demand throughout the world) led to record high sales in 2004. As a matter of fact Nucor's first half of the year outpaced previous annual highs and the company achieved that feat again in the second half.

The company named CEO DiMicco chairman in 2006.

In the latter half of the last decade it started a program of rapid external growth. It acquired the former Connecticut Steel Verco Manufacturing and Canadian steel products maker Harris Steel which like Connecticut Steel had been a customer and partner of Nucor for years. Harris itself made an acquisition in 2008 when it bought rebar fabricator and distributor Ambassador Steel. Nucor also expanded its downstream operations with the 2007 acquisition of building systems maker MAGNA-TRAX for $280 million. Its largest acquisition was that of the David J. Joseph Company a scrap metal broker that had supplied Nucor's minimills for 40 years.

The company has always operated primarily in the US but in 2008 it moved into the international market with the formation of a European joint venture with Duferco. The JV produces steel beams and merchant bar products from manufacturing locations in Italy and serves the European and North African markets. Nucor put about $650 million into the new venture called Nucor S.r.l. Duferdofin.

That year it also expanded considerably in the US by spending $1 billion to buy ferrous and nonferrous metals group The David J. Joseph Company.

In 2010 Nucor formed a US-based joint venture with Mitsui & Co. Nucor paid $225 million for its half of the venture named Steel Technologies.

In 2012 Nucor acquired New Jersey-based Skyline Steel and its subsidiaries from ArcelorMittal for about $605 million. Skyline which has served as a distributor of Nucor's products for more than 20 years accelerated Nucor's growth in steel piling and foundation products. Steel sheet piles are long structural sections having a vertical interlocking system that creates a wall. Skyline's flagship products include hot-rolled and cold-formed sheet piles and pipe piling. A steel foundation distributor in North America Skyline serves industries that include marine construction bridge and highway construction heavy civil construction and underground commercial parking.

In 2011 Nucor sold its NuPro Steel subsidiary to Steel Technologies its joint venture with Mitsui & Co. NuPro produces flat-rolled steel at its plant in Crawfordsville Indiana. Nucor also announced that Steel Technologies would build a steel processing plant in Mexico to serve Japanese electronics and auto companies moving into the region.

In early 2011 Nucor and joint venture partners Rio Tinto Group Mitsubishi and Shougang Corp. permanently closed the high-intensity smelt (his-melt) steel plant in Kwinana Western Australia. Nucor had a 25% stake in the joint venture that was terminated.

Continuing its strategy for key acquisitions in 2013 Nucor acquired Gallatin Steel for $780 million. This addition allowed the company to better serve customers by offering them a wider range of products and further enhancing our reliability. Nucor Steel Gallatin has an annual capacity of 1.8 million tons increasing Nucor's total flat-rolled production to 13 million tons annually. The acquisition also strengthens Nucor's position serving flat-rolled customers in the growing pipe and tube segment.

EXECUTIVES

Evp Flat-rolled Products, Ladd R. Hall, age 62, $463,100 total compensation

Chairman President And Ceo, John J. Ferriola, age 66, $1,300,000 total compensation

Evp Merchant And Rebar Products, James R. Darsey, age 63, $463,100 total compensation

Vp; General Manager Nucor-yamato Steel Company (blytheville Arkansas), R. Joseph Stratman, age 62, $473,914 total compensation

Evp Cfo And Treasurer, James D. (Jim) Frias, age 62, $490,350 total compensation

General Manager Building Systems Division (terrell Texas), Raymond S. Napolitan, age 61

Evp Beam And Plate Products, D. Chad Utermark, age 51

Evp Engineered Bar Products, David A. Sumoski, age 52

Vice President And Gm, K Rex Query

Vice President; General Manager Bar Mill Division Plymouth Utah, David Smith

Executive Vice President, D Utermark

Vice President Communications, Elizabeth Bowers

Vice President And General Manager Vulcraft Division Cold Finish Division, Doyle Hopper

Executive Vice President Beam Plate Products, Chad Utermark

Vice President; Executive Vice President The David J. Joseph Company, James Goetz

Vice President Marketing, Wes Brooker

Vice President General Manager Vulcraft Division Fort Payne Alabama, D Ryan

Evp Engineered Bar Products, Ray Napolitan Jr

Executive Vice President Beam And Plate Products, Douglas Utermark

Board Member, Christopher Kearney

Auditors: PricewaterhouseCoopers LLP

LOCATIONS

HQ: Nucor Corp.
1915 Rexford Road, Charlotte, NC 28211
Phone: 704 366-7000 **Fax:** 704 362-4208
Web: www.nucor.com

PRODUCTS/OPERATIONS

2018 Sales

	$ mil.	% of total
Steel Mills	16,245	65
Steel Products	6,797	27
Raw Materials	2,026	8
Total	**25,067**	**100**

2018 Sales by Product

	$ mil.	% of total
Sheet	7,572	30
Bar	4,709	19
Other Steel products	3,953	16
Plate	2,134	9
Raw Material	2,026	8
Structural	1,831	7
Rebar Fabrication	1,496	6
Tubular products	1,348	5
Total	**25,067**	**100**

Selected Products

Alloy steel
  Cold-drawn steel bars
  Finished hex caps
  Hex-head cap screws
  Locknuts
  Structural bolts and nuts
Carbon steel
  Angles
  Beams
  Channels
  Cold-drawn steel bars
  Finished hex nuts
  Flats
  Floor plate
  Galvanized sheet
  Grinding balls
  Hexagons
  Hot-rolled sheet
  Reinforcing bars
  Structural bolts and nuts
  Wide-range beams
Engineered products
  Composite floor joists
  Floor deck
  Joists
  Joist girders
  Pre-engineered metal buildings
  Roof deck
  Special-profile steel trusses
Stainless steel
  Cold-rolled steel
  Hot-rolled steel
  Pickled sheet

Selected Subsidiaries

Harris Steel Inc.
Harris Steel ULC (Canada)
The David J. Joseph Company
Magnatrax Corporation
Nucor Castrip Arkansas LLC
Nucor Energy Holdings Inc.
Nucor-Yamato Steel Company

COMPETITORS

AK Steel Holding Corporation	Renco
	Steel Dynamics
ArcelorMittal USA	Tata Europe
Arconic	United States Steel

HISTORICAL FINANCIALS

Company Type: Public

Income Statement

FYE: December 31

	REVENUE ($ mil.)	NET INCOME ($ mil.)	NET PROFIT MARGIN	EMPLOYEES
12/18	25,067	2,361	9.4%	26,300
12/17	20,252	1,319	6.5%	25,100
12/16	16,208	796	4.9%	23,900
12/15	16,439	358	2.2%	23,700
12/14	21,105	714	3.4%	23,600
Annual Growth	**4.4%**	**34.8%**	**—**	**2.7%**

2018 Year-End Financials

Debt ratio: 24.00%
Return on equity: 25.00%
Cash ($ mil.): 1,399
Current ratio: 3.00
Long-term debt ($ mil.): 4,233

No. of shares (mil.): 306
Dividends
  Yield: 3.0%
  Payout: 21.0%
Market value ($ mil.): 15,833

	STOCK PRICE ($) FY Close	P/E High/Low		PER SHARE ($) Earnings	Dividends	Book Value
12/18	52.00	9	7	7.00	2.00	32.00
12/17	64.00	16	13	4.00	2.00	27.00
12/16	60.00	27	14	2.00	2.00	25.00
12/15	40.00	45	33	1.00	1.00	23.00
12/14	49.00	26	21	2.00	1.00	24.00
Annual Growth	**1.4%**	**—**	**—**	**35.2%**	**1.0%**	**7.1%**

NVIDIA Corp

NVIDIA is racking up points in computer games logging miles in driverless cars and going deep into data centers. The Santa Clara California-based company's graphics processing units (GPUs) are used to generate computer game images in many PCs and game consoles in the gaming market. What's more its GPUs work well in applications for autonomous vehicles and deep learning a branch of artificial intelligence. NVIDIA's GPU brands are GeForce for games Quadro for designers and digital artists and Tesla and DGX for scientists and researchers. Its Tegra line of system-on-a-chip devices is for mobile gaming and entertainment as well as autonomous robots drones and cars. In 2019 NVIDIA agreed to buy chipmaker Mellanox for $6.9 billion.

Operations

NVIDIA keeps track of its operations by product and market. GPUs account for more than 85% of the company's revenue while the Tegra brand brings in about 15%. In terms of markets gaming produces about 55% of revenue followed by data centers about 25% visualization about 10% and automotive and intellectual property combined more than 10%.

The GPU products include GeForce for PC gaming and GeForce NOW for cloud-based game-streaming services; Quadro for computer-aided design video editing and special effects; Tesla for AI using deep learning and accelerated computing; and GRID for providing NVIDIA graphics capabilities through the cloud and data centers. A new graphics technology NVIDIA RTX produces movie-quality images in real time using ray tracing and AI.

The Tegra line includes DRIVE AGX automotive chip systems that provide self-driving capabilities and SHIELD which includes a family of devices and services for cloud-based mobile applications for home entertainment AI and gaming.

The company also develops software and software libraries for running its chips.

NVIDIA outsources manufacturing to Taiwan Semiconductor Manufacturing Company Limited and Samsung Electronics Co. Ltd. The assembly testing and packaging work is done by independent subcontractors that include Advanced Semiconductor Engineering Inc. BYD Auto Co. Hon Hai Precision Industry Co. and JSI Logistics Ltd.

Geographic Reach

NVIDIA based in Santa Clara California has design centers laboratories and offices in Australia Canada China the Czech Republic Finland France Germany Hong Kong India Israel Italy Japan Poland Russia Singapore South Korea Sweden Switzerland Taiwan United Arab Emirates the UK and the US.

While more than 70% of NVIDIA's sales are to customers in Asia they are spread out over several countries. Customers in Taiwan generate nearly 30% of NVIDIA's revenue followed by customers in China with about 25% and other Asia/Pacific countries about 20%. The US market accounts for just under 15% of NVIDIA's sales.

Sales and Marketing

NVIDIA's sales and marketing team works with end customers and through partner networks that include original equipment manufacturers original device manufacturers system builders add-in board makers and retailers and distributors. As part of its sales and marketing efforts NVIDIA offers rebates to resellers as incentives and it provides marketing development funds to help partners in promoting NVIDIA's products as well as their own.

As NVIDIA products have expanded beyond gaming applications the company has developed more routes to market and a wider more diverse customer roster. No customer accounts for more than 10% or more of sales.

Financial Performance

To say NVIDIA has been on a roll would be an understatement. Over the past five years the company's sales have risen 150% and profit has increased 555% driven by sales of chips for artificial intelligence data centers and more complex gaming applications.

In 2019 (ended January) revenue hit $11.7 billion a $2 billion increase from 2018. A 52% increase in datacenter sales paced by the Tesla GRID and DGX products led the way with help from an 18% improvement in sales of GeForce GPU products for gaming. Professional visualization sales were 21% higher on stronger sales of desktop and mobile workstation products. The lack of Intel licensing revenue nicked PC OEM revenue which slipped 1% year-to-year.

Higher sales combined with a mix of higher-margin products boosted net income to $4.1 billion in 2019 compared to $3 billion in 2018.

Cash and cash equivalents swung to $782 million in 2019 from $4 billion in 2018. Cash use in financing activities was $2.8 billion ($2.5 billion used in 2018) due to higher stock buybacks while cash used in investing activities rose to $4.1 billion in 2019 ($1.2 billion provided in 2018) because of more securities purchases. Cash generated by operations was $3.7 billion in 2019 compared to $3.5 billion the previous year.

Strategy

It takes a lot of computing power to render graphics capable of holding gamers' attention for hours at a time. In providing that power NVIDIA established itself as the dominant player in computer game graphics controlling more than 70% of the market. The company continues to turn out architectures and processors that generate realistic renderings of all kinds of games played on all kinds of platforms. The company sees potential for continued gaming growth in the rise of computer gaming as a spectator sport.

From its gaming base NVIDIA has positioned its GPUs for the artificial intelligence and automotive markets. The high processing power of GPUs enables them to handle the demands of artificial intelligence applications. The biggest cloud infrastructure providers ? Amazon Web Services Microsoft and Google ? use NVIDIA processors in their operations. GPUs also are used to turn analyzed information into graphics through visualization applications.

NVIDIA has plenty of competition with greater overall resources. AMD a long-time player in graphics has released processors recently that rival others in the market. Intel Corp. has used its deep resources to develop and buy technologies to compete in these markets including automotive with its acquisition of Mobileye. Although NVIDIA has grown rapidly over the past five years it cracked the list of Top 10 chipmakers for the first time in 2017.

Mergers and Acquisitions

NVIDIA agreed to buy Mellanox a maker of computer chips and other hardware for data center servers for $6.9 billion in 2019. The companies' say their combined forces will enable them to gain greater market share the growing market for equipping data centers as the use of cloud computing increases. Data center-related products generate about 20% of NVIDIA's sales. The transaction is expected to close by the end of 2019.

Company Background

Taiwan-born and Stanford-trained engineer Jen-Hsun Huang was already a veteran of Advanced Micro Devices and LSI Logic (now just LSI) when he decided to start his own company at age 30. He co-founded NVIDIA in 1992 with fellow engineers and industry veterans Chris Malachowsky (SVP) and Curtis Priem (former CTO). It was incorporated in 1993.

After its first try at a graphics chip failed miserably in 1995 NVIDIA hit the big time in 1997 when it introduced a graphics processor that set a new industry standard for speed. Good product timing and flawless execution kept the company growing: After turning its first profit in 1998 NVIDIA crossed the $100 million $300 million and $700 million sales thresholds in successive years. The company made its IPO in 1999.

EXECUTIVES

Vp Corporate Communications, Bob Sherbin
President And Ceo, Jen-Hsun Huang, age 56, $996,216 total compensation
Evp Operations, Debora C. Shoquist, age 64, $695,131 total compensation
Vp, Chin Shih
Evp Worldwide Field Operations, Ajay K. (Jay) Puri, age 64, $889,573 total compensation
Evp And Cfo, Colette M. Kress, age 51, $769,609 total compensation
Vice President Operations System Engineering, Richard Compton
Svp Content And Technology, Tony Tamasi
Vice President Software Engineering, Dwight Diercks
Vice President Supply Chain Projects, Brian Ebbs
Vice President, Alejandro Troccoli
Vice President Hardware Engineering, John Schafer
Vice President, Jim Vanwelzen
Vp Corporate Affairs, Rebecca Peters
Vice President Software Engineering, Sam Azar
Senior Vice President, Ilyas Elkin
Executive Vice President Business Development, Alban Douillet
Vp Operations, David Miller
Vice President Of Vlsi Engineering, Sameer Halepete
Vice President Automotive Software, Kevin Flory
Vice President Engineering, Laurent Coudrelle
Vice President Of Engineering, Luke Durant
Vice President Of The Investment Group, Shantanu Kalchuri
Vice President, Richard Cameron
Senior Vice President, Jizhi Zhang
National Sales Manager, James Reilley
Vice President World Wide Sales Nvidia Professional Solutions Group, Walter Mundt-Blum
Vp Internal Audit, Bruce Carpenter
Senior Vice President Vlsi Engineering, Joe Grech
Vice President Oem Sales, John Leggio
Vice President Of Gameworks Labs, John Spitzer
Vice President Software Security, Daniel Rohrer
Senior Vice President Geforce Business Unit, Jeff Fisher
Vice President Corporate Marketing, Rob Csonger
Vice President Of Engineering Computer Vision, Ashu Rege
Vice President Gpu Asic Engineering, Arjun Prabhu
Vice President, Rev Lebaredian
Evp Worldwide Field Operations, Jay Puri
Vice President Platform Sales, Stony Peng
Vice President Enterprise Sales, Mark Williams
Senior Vice President Appliances, Ashok Almeida
Vice President Software, Richard Clark
Vice President Enterprise Marketing Corporate Communications And Global Events, Laura Fay
Vice President Americas Partner Organization, Craig Weinstein
Vice President Operations Engineering, Keith Katcher
Vice President Corporate Communications, Robert Sherbin
Vice President Controller, Usman Ahmad
Vice President Of Investor Relations, Simona Jankowski
Vice President Systems Supply Chain, Jeff Whitmer
Senior Vice President Human Resources, Shelly Cerio
Vice President Sales Marketing In Asia Pacific, Raymond Teh
Area Vice President Enterprise Sales, Rima Alameddine
Vice President Product, John Fanelli
Vice President Real Estate, Mike Demuro
Vice President And Treasurer, Chris Ginieczki
Vp Ai Infrastructure, Clment Farabet
Board Member, Darrell Boggs
Board Member, Keegan Brown
Us Treasurer, Jay Landre
Consultant And Member Of The Board, James Forman
Board Member, Hyungon Ryu
Board Member, Mark Perry
Auditors: PricewaterhouseCoopers LLP

LOCATIONS

HQ: NVIDIA Corp
2788 San Tomas Expressway, Santa Clara, CA 95051
Phone: 408 486-2000
Web: www.nvidia.com

2019 Sales

	$ mil.	% of total
Asia/Pacific		
Taiwan	3,360	29
China	2,801	24
Other Asia/Pacific	2,368	20
US	1,506	13
Europe	914	7
Other Countries	767	6
Total	**11,716**	**100**

PRODUCTS/OPERATIONS

2019 Sales

	$ mil.	% of total
GPU	10,175	87
Tegra Processor	1,541	13
Total	**11,716**	**100**

2019 sales by Market

	$ mil.	% of total
Gaming	6,246	53
Datacenter	2,932	25
Professional Visualization	1,130	10
OEM and IP	767	7
Automotive	641	5
Total	**11,716**	**100**

COMPETITORS

AMD	Renesas Electronics
Ambarella	Samsung Electronics
Intel	Texas Instruments
QUALCOMM	Xilinx

HISTORICAL FINANCIALS

Company Type: Public

Income Statement

FYE: January 27

	REVENUE ($ mil.)	NET INCOME ($ mil.)	NET PROFIT MARGIN	EMPLOYEES
01/19	11,716	4,141	35.3%	13,277
01/18	9,714	3,047	31.4%	11,528
01/17	6,910	1,666	24.1%	10,299
01/16	5,010	614	12.3%	6,566
01/15	4,682	631	13.5%	9,228
Annual Growth	**25.8%**	**60.1%**	**—**	**9.5%**

2019 Year-End Financials

Debt ratio: 15.00%
Return on equity: 49.00%
Cash ($ mil.): 782
Current ratio: 8.00
Long-term debt ($ mil.): 1,988

No. of shares (mil.): 606
Dividends
  Yield: 0.0%
  Payout: 9.0%
Market value ($ mil.): 97,051

	STOCK PRICE ($) FY Close	P/E High/Low		PER SHARE ($) Earnings	Dividends	Book Value
01/19	160.00	42	19	7.00	1.00	15.00
01/18	243.00	48	19	5.00	1.00	12.00
01/17	112.00	38	8	3.00	0.00	10.00
01/16	29.00	30	17	1.00	0.00	8.00
01/15	21.00	19	14	1.00	0.00	8.00
Annual Growth	66.8%	—	—	56.0%	15.7%	17.4%

NVR Inc.

From finished lot to signed mortgage NVR offers homebuyers everything?including the kitchen sink. The company builds single-family detached homes townhomes and condominiums?mainly for first-time and move-up buyers?primarily in the eastern US. NVR's houses range in size from 1000 sq. ft. to 9500 sq. ft. and sell for an average price of around $380000. The company's brands include Ryan Homes Heartland Homes and NVHomes. Its largest markets are the Washington DC and Baltimore areas; together they account for around 40% of sales. Its subsidiary NVR Mortgage Finance offers mortgage and title services. The builder was founded in 1980 as NVHomes.

Operations

NVR's Ryan Homes brand is primarily marketed to first-time and first-time move-up buyers. Ryan Homes has operations in more than thirty metropolitan areas along the eastern seaboard and in Illinois Indiana Ohio Pennsylvania Tennessee and West Virginia. NVHomes and Heartland Homes cater to move-up and luxury buyers. NVHomes builds primarily in Delaware and the Baltimore Philadelphia and DC metro areas; Heartland Homes operates in the Pittsburg metro. Homes sell for between $130000 and $1.5 million and at an average of roughly $380000. NVR engages independent subcontractors through fixed-price contracts for its home construction.

To support its homebuilding operations the company offers banking and title services through NVR Mortgage Finance.

Homebuilding accounts for substantially all the builder's total sales; its mortgage banking business?which closes more than 13000 loans totaling about $4.2 billion annually?generates less than 1% of revenue.

Geographic Reach

Reston Virginia-based NVR's homebuilding operations serve more than 30 metropolitan areas in some 15 states in the eastern half of the US. Home sales in the Mid-Atlantic (Maryland Virginia West Virginia Delaware and Washington DC) bring in about 55% of the builder's total sales while Mid-East states (New York Ohio Western Pennsylvania Indiana and Illinois) account for around 20%. The Southeast (North Carolina South Carolina Florida and Tennessee) and Northeast (New Jersey and eastern Pennsylvania) generate about 15% and nearly 10% of revenue respectively. Its largest markets are Washington DC?which produces about 30% of homebuilding sales?and Baltimore Maryland?which provides some 10% of revenue.

Sales and Marketing

NVR markets its homes through sales representatives and model homes converted into temporary offices for salespeople to review alternative floor plans facades and designs for other house models with the client. Its houses are aimed at first-time first-time move-up and upscale buyers.

Financial Performance

NVR's sales and profit boomed in recent years as the residential construction recovery picked up steam. In 2017 the company finally succeeded its peak of $6.1 billion recorded before the financial crash in 2007. Between 2014 and 2018 its net income increased by more than 180%.

Despite a slight decrease in its homes' average selling price the homebuilder's revenue grew 14% to $7.2 billion in 2018 thanks to a 16% increase in units settled. The company began the year with a 24% higher backlog compared with 2017. New orders increased by 4% in 2018.

NVR's net income added a whopping 48% to $797.2 million in 2018 thanks to the strength of its sales performance and a greatly lowered income tax expense slightly offset by a drop in gross profit margin of half a percentage point.

The company added $42.7 million to its cash to end the year with $732.2 million. Operations provided $732.1 million. The company used only $8.1 million on investments?almost entirely on property plant and equipment. Treasury stock purchases pushed outflows from financing activities to $672.3 million.

Strategy

Favorable sales and pricing trends driven by historically low mortgage interest rates and rising rental costs are a boon to NVR and other homebuilders. NVR keeps its profits high by focusing on building in areas where it has a high market share finding it to be more cost-efficient to expand within its existing markets. Higher cash generation in 2018 has been used to fund further homebuilding inventory increases.

Company Background

NVR expanded its portfolio of homebuilding companies in late 2012 when it acquired Heartland Homes the second largest homebuilder in Pittsburgh. NVR continues to use the Heartland Homes name.

HISTORY

NVR got its start when Dwight Schar founded NVHomes Inc. in 1980. Schar had worked for Ryan Homes (founded 1948) since 1969. Like Ryan Homes NVHomes specialized in single-family homes around Washington DC. The strong economy of the 1980s and the deregulation of lending institutions — coupled with favorable partnership and real estate tax laws passed by the Reagan administration — resulted in rapid growth. The company was clearing income of more than $1 million a year by 1983 and soon branched into building townhomes and condominiums.

In 1986 when the company was reorganized as a limited partnership (NVH L.P.) income was up to $14 million. The new entity soon acquired a controlling interest in Ryan Homes; it completed its acquisition of that company in 1987. NVH reorganized as a holding company (NVRyan L.P.) and 1988 profits reached $33.5 million. Over the years the company formed or acquired almost 100 subsidiaries that were involved in all aspects of homebuilding — from land acquisition and construction to home finance and investment advice. It had also branched out into California Florida Indiana Kentucky North Carolina Ohio Pennsylvania and Virginia.

Following an economic recession in 1989 demand for new housing dropped off in the US. The company shortened its name to NVR L.P. and its inventory of unsold land and houses started to grow. The situation was exacerbated by changes in the tax code that made real estate less attractive as an investment; sales from development and construction projects dropped from more than $1 billion in 1988 to about $600 million in 1991. NVR posted a $260 million loss in 1990 as sales and the value of its inventory nose-dived.

NVR reorganized in 1990 and 1991. Focused on eight mid-Atlantic states it put homebuilding under one management structure consolidated its finance activities exited its land-development businesses and offered its mortgage services to customers who weren't NVR homebuyers. It also organized its business into two product lines: upscale (NVHomes) and moderately priced (Ryan Homes) homes. Despite the reorganization and introduction of innovative marketing NVR and several of its subsidiaries filed for Chapter 11 bankruptcy relief in 1992. That year the CFO of NVR's thrift (NVR Savings Bank) went on the lam to Malta after embezzling more than $750000.

The company emerged from bankruptcy as NVR Inc. in 1993 with less debt new owners and a new line of credit; it also had its IPO that year. The next year NVR sold NVR Savings Bank which had four branches in northern Virginia. The robust mid-1990s economy aided NVR; as home sales rose the company entered new markets including the Cleveland and Nashville areas in 1995. To reduce its vulnerability to downturns in the mid-Atlantic area it continued its expansion outside that region buying Fox Ridge Homes (the #2 builder in Nashville) in 1997.

In 1999 it merged its homebuilding subsidiary NVR Homes and mortgage banking holding company NVR Financial Services into NVR. It also acquired Rockville Maryland-based First Republic Mortgage that year but closed the subsidiary's retail operations in 2000 and realigned its mortgage banking business to serve NVR customers exclusively.

From 1994 through 2003 the company benefited from increased housing activity recording steady increases in unit sales backlog and profits for nine years. During the housing downturn that began in 2008 the company performed better than its competitors reporting only one losing quarter in the period.

In late 2012 NVR expanded its portfolio of home-building companies when it acquired Heartland Homes the second-largest homebuilder in Pittsburgh. As part of the purchase NVR planned to continue to use the Heartland Homes name and pair the company with its complementary Ryan Homes.

EXECUTIVES

President Ceo And Director, Paul C. Saville, age 63, $1,566,375 total compensation
President Nvr Mortgage (nvrm), Robert W. Henley, age 52, $460,000 total compensation
Vp Cfo And Treasurer, Daniel D. Malzahn, age 49, $490,000 total compensation
Vp Chief Accounting Officer And Controller, Eugene J. Bredow, $341,250 total compensation
President Homebuilding Operations, Jeffrey D. Martchek, age 54, $539,000 total compensation
Chairman, Dwight C. Schar, age 77
Auditors: KPMG LLP

LOCATIONS

HQ: NVR Inc.
11700 Plaza America Drive, Suite 500, Reston, VA 20190
Phone: 703 956-4000
Web: www.nvrinc.com

2018 Sales

	$ mil.	% of total
Homebuilding		
Mid-Atlantic	3,893	54
Mid-east	1,456	21
Southeast	1,074	15
Northeast	581	8
Mortgage banking		
Fees	159	2
Interest income	12	
Total	**7,175**	**100**

PRODUCTS/OPERATIONS

Selected Brands
Heartland Homes
NVHomes
Ryan Homes

COMPETITORS

Beazer Homes	KB Home
Brookfield Homes	Lennar
Champion Home Builders	M.D.C.
D.R. Horton	M/I Homes
David Weekley Homes	Orleans Homebuilders
Hovnanian Enterprises	PulteGroup
John Wieland Homes	Toll Brothers

HISTORICAL FINANCIALS

Company Type: Public

Income Statement

FYE: December 31

	REVENUE ($ mil.)	NET INCOME ($ mil.)	NET PROFIT MARGIN	EMPLOYEES
12/18	7,190	797	11.1%	5,600
12/17	6,322	538	8.5%	5,200
12/16	5,835	425	7.3%	4,900
12/15	5,170	383	7.4%	4,300
12/14	4,453	282	6.3%	3,942
Annual Growth	12.7%	29.7%	—	9.2%

2018 Year-End Financials

Debt ratio: 19.00%
Return on equity: 47.00%
Cash ($ mil.): 712
Current ratio: 5.00
Long-term debt ($ mil.): 598

No. of shares (mil.): 4
Dividends
 Yield: —
 Payout: —
Market value ($ mil.): 8,719

	STOCK PRICE ($) FY Close	P/E High/Low	PER SHARE ($) Earnings	Dividends	Book Value
12/18	2,437.00	17 10	195.00	0.00	505.00
12/17	3,508.00	24 11	127.00	0.00	435.00
12/16	1,669.00	17 14	104.00	0.00	353.00
12/15	1,643.00	18 13	90.00	0.00	318.00
12/14	1,275.00	19 15	64.00	0.00	278.00
Annual Growth	17.6%	— —	32.3%	—	16.2%

O'Reilly Automotive, Inc.

O'Reilly Automotive has its foot on the gas. The company is the nation's #1 provider of automotive aftermarket parts (both new and remanufactured) maintenance supplies professional service equipment tools and accessories. It also offers customers a range of services including oil and battery recycling battery testing paint mixing and tool rental. O'Reilly operates through a fast-growing network of some 5200 stores across the US as well as online. The family-founded and -operated company wheels and deals with automotive professionals as well as DIY (do-it-yourself) customers.

Operations

O'Reilly stores which average 7400 sq. ft. carry about 23000 SKUs. The stores receive inventory five nights a week from O'Reilly's two dozen-plus regional distribution centers and about 340 Hub stores.

Its products include nationally-known premium brands such as AC Delco Castrol Pennnzoil Turtle Wax and Valvoline as well as private-label brands such as BrakeBest Murray O'Reilly and Ultima.

Beyond its vast array of products O'Reilly's offers a host of services such as used oil oil filter and battery recycling; battery wiper and bulb replacement; battery diagnostic testing; electrical and module testing; and paint mixing.

Geographic Reach

Missouri-based O'Reilly has stores in more than 45 US states including Alaska and Hawaii. Texas and California account for about a quarter of total locations with some 700 stores and 550 stores respectively.

The company's more than two dozen regional distribution centers are located in 20-plus states including Texas (with four locations) Tennessee (three) and Missouri and California (two each).

Sales and Marketing

O'Reilly generates more than 55% of sales from DIY (do-it-yourself) customers and about 40% of sales from professional service providers. It also sells automotive products directly to independently owned parts stores ("jobber stores") in certain markets.

The company maintains a full-time sales staff of about 800. Targeted marketing materials such as flyers quick reference guides and catalogs are produced and distributed on a regular basis to professional service providers paint and body shops and fleet customers.

To stimulate sales among racing enthusiasts O'Reilly sponsors multiple nationally-televised races and more than 700 grassroots local and regional motorsports events across the US.

Financial Performance

O'Reilly's revenue and net income have both seen strong growth over the past decade with revenue nearly doubling and net income up more than 400%. The company has greatly expanded its store network during that time.

In 2018 the company reported record revenue of $9.5 billion up 6% from the prior year. The results were powered by comparable-store sales growth of nearly 4% mostly because of an increase in average ticket values followed by sales from new stores.

Net income also rose that year jumping 16% to $1.3 billion. In addition to increased revenue the growth in net income resulted from a lower provision for income taxes ($370 million compared to $504 million in 2017) related to the Tax Cuts and Jobs Act of 2017.

Cash at the end of 2018 was $31.3 million a decrease of $15 million from the prior year. Cash from operations contributed $1.7 billion to the coffers while investing activities used $534.3 million mainly for capital expenditures. Financing activities used another $1.2 billion primarily for stock repurchase.

Strategy

O'Reilly adheres to a "dual market" strategy by appealing to both do-it-yourself (DIY) and professional service providers. The company believes that its tiered distribution model provides industry-leading parts availability and store in-stock positions while lowering its inventory carrying costs and controlling inventory. To this end the auto parts chain has made significant capital investments in its distribution center network — now with more than two dozen distribution centers across the US — allowing it to efficiently service new stores as well as its existing store network.

Among the investments designed to enhance the company's distribution network are the implementation of voice-picking technology the roll out of enhanced routing software the launch of additional labor management software to improve productivity and efficiency and the continued purchases of material handling equipment such as conveyor systems picking modules and lift equipment.

O'Reilly's aggressive expansion has been a key element of its growth. It opened 200 net new stores in 2018 and has plans for 200-210 more in 2019. New stores are opened in both small and large markets but are strategically located in geographic clusters that complement the company's distribution network to achieve economies of scale.

Mergers and Acquisitions

In late 2018 O'Reilly Automotive purchased the auto parts-related assets of Pompano Beach Florida-based Bennett Auto Supply expanding its footprint in Florida.

Company Background

O'Reilly was founded in 1957 by Charles F. O'Reilly and his son "Chub." It opened a second store in 1965.

In 1978 the company introduced its dual strategy of serving both the professional and DIY retail markets. By 1989 it had 100 stores.

The company went public in 1993 and nearly doubled its size with the 1998 purchase of rival Hi/Lo Auto Supply.

O'Reilly opened its 5000th store in 2017.

EXECUTIVES

President And Ceo, Gregory L. (Greg) Henslee, age 58, $1,238,461 total compensation

Co-president, Jeff M. Shaw, age 56, $396,923 total compensation

Evp Finance And Cfo, Thomas G. (Tom) McFall, age 48, $713,846 total compensation

Co-president, Gregory D. (Greg) Johnson, age 53, $342,308 total compensation

Svp Information Systems, Jeff Lauro

Svp Finance And Controller, Jeremy Fletcher

Vice President Northern Division, Kenny Martin

Senior Vice President Merchandise And Marketing, Mike Swearengin

Co-chairman And Coo, Lawrence P. (Larry) O'Reilly, age 72

Vice Chairman, Charles H. O'Reilly, age 80

Chairman, David E. O'Reilly, age 70

Auditors: Ernst & Young LLP

LOCATIONS

HQ: O'Reilly Automotive, Inc.
 233 South Patterson Avenue, Springfield, MO 65802
Phone: 417 862-6708
Web: www.oreillyauto.com

2018 Stores

	No.
Texas	706
California	553
Missouri	201
Georgia	205
Illinois	203
Ohio	196
Florida	200
Tennessee	176
Michigan	168
North Carolina	173
Washington	156
Arizona	139
Alabama	139
Oklahoma	121
Indiana	137
Minnesota	125

Wisconsin	121
Louisiana	121
Arkansas	112
Colorado	102
South Carolina	108
Other states	1,057
Total	**5,219**

PRODUCTS/OPERATIONS

2018 Sales

	$ mil.	% of total
DIY customers	5,351	56
Professional customers	4,036	42
Other	150	2
Total	**9,536**	**100**

Selected Products

Accessories - Exterior
Accessories - Interior
Air Conditioning
Battery & Accessories
Belts & Hoses
Body & Trim
Brakes
Charging & Starting
Cooling & Heating
Engine Parts & Mounts
Exhaust
Filters & PCV Valves
Fuel & Emissions
Hardware & Fasteners
Ignition & Tune-Up
Lighting & Electrical
Oil Fluids & Chemicals
Performance
Suspension & Steering
Tire & Wheel
Tools & Equipment
Transmission & Transaxle
Truck & Towing
Waxes & Washes
Wipers

COMPETITORS

Advance Auto Parts	Replacement Parts
Amazon.com	Sears
AutoZone	Target Corporation
CARQUEST	U.S. Auto Parts
Genuine Parts	Wal-Mart
Pep Boys	

HISTORICAL FINANCIALS

Company Type: Public

Income Statement
FYE: December 31

	REVENUE ($ mil.)	NET INCOME ($ mil.)	NET PROFIT MARGIN	EMPLOYEES
12/18	9,536	1,324	13.9%	79,174
12/17	8,978	1,134	12.6%	75,289
12/16	8,593	1,038	12.1%	74,715
12/15	7,967	931	11.7%	71,943
12/14	7,216	778	10.8%	67,926
Annual Growth	**7.2%**	**14.2%**		**3.9%**

2018 Year-End Financials

Debt ratio: 43.00%
Return on equity: 263.00%
Cash ($ mil.): 31
Current ratio: 1.00
Long-term debt ($ mil.): 3,417

No. of shares (mil.): 79
Dividends
Yield: —
Payout: —
Market value ($ mil.): 27,217

	STOCK PRICE ($) FY Close	P/E High/Low	PER SHARE ($) Earnings	Dividends	Book Value
12/18	344.00	22 14	16.00	0.00	4.00
12/17	241.00	22 13	13.00	0.00	8.00
12/16	278.00	27 21	11.00	0.00	18.00
12/15	253.00	30 19	9.00	0.00	20.00
12/14	193.00	26 17	7.00	0.00	20.00
Annual Growth	**15.6%**	**— —**	**21.7%**	**—**	**(31.1%)**

O-I Glass Inc

Owens-Illinois (O-I) is one of the world's largest makers of glass containers touting a leading market presence with more than 49000 customers in 85 countries around the world. O-I offers more than 10000 types of glass containers such as bottles in a wide range of shapes sizes and colors used to hold beer wine liquor as well as soft drinks juice and other beverages. It also makes glass containers for foods such as soups salad dressings and dairy products and for pharmaceuticals. Some of its products are made using recycled glass. Major customers have included such heavy hitters as Anheuser-Busch InBev Coca-Cola Diageo H.J. Heinz and Nestle.

Operations

Owens-Illinois is a major glass container manufacturer that caters to many of the world's leading food and beverage brands. It produces glass containers for alcoholic beverages including beer flavored malt beverages spirits and wine. It also produces glass packaging for a variety of food items including soft drinks teas juices and pharmaceuticals.

Geographic Reach

Altogether Owens-Illinois (O-I) operates almost 80 manufacturing plants in 23 countries. It has joint ventures in China Malaysia Mexico the US and Vietnam. Engineering support sites for its glass manufacturing operations are located Australia Columbia France Poland Peru and the US.

O-I divides its operations across four reportable segments based on geography: Europe which generates some 35% of total sales North America (about 33%) Latin America (around 25%) and the Asia/Pacific region (10%).

Sales and Marketing

Owens-Illinois sells most of its glass container products directly to customers under yearly or multi-year supply agreements however some of its products are sold through distributors. Customers range from large multinationals to small local breweries and wineries.Its largest customers are leading global food and beverage manufacturers including Anheuser‑Busch InBev Carlsberg Coca-Cola Constellation Diageo Heineken MillerCoors Nestle Brown Forman and Pernod Ricard.

Financial Performance

Owens-Illinois' revenue has bounced back after a slump in 2014-15. In fiscal 2017 revenue increased 2% to $6.9 billion as gains in Europe Latin America and the Asia/Pacific region were partially offset by weakness in North America. The results largely reflected currency exchange effects which account for $106 million out of the $167 million revenue growth. The other gains came from higher selling prices and a 1% increase in glass shipments partially offset by an unfavorable sales mix.

Net income fell 12% to $202 million as stronger operating income was offset by a $120 million increase in pension settlement charges. As a result cash from operations fell 5% to $831 million.

Strategy

Owens-Illinois (O-I) is placing a priority on winning over customers that have shied away from glass packaging as well as encouraging existing ones to use more. To this end its marketing efforts piggyback on the wave toward sustainable packaging. Along with developing a variety of container features and functions the company highlights the benefits of glass recyclability.O-I also makes investments in its operations to improve efficiency and productivity. In 2018 it invested heavily in repairing assets and improving their flexibility and reliability.

HISTORY

The Owens Bottle Machine Corp. was incorporated in Toledo Ohio in 1907 as the successor to a four-year-old New Jersey company of the same name. It initially grew by acquiring small glass companies. In 1929 Owens bought the Illinois Glass Co. (medical and pharmaceutical glass) and became Owens-Illinois Glass.

The company bought Libbey Glass (tableware) in 1935. Three years later Owens-Illinois and Corning Glass which were both studying uses for glass fiber began Owens-Corning Fiberglass a joint venture with a virtual industry monopoly.

After WWII Owens-Illinois (O-I) started to diversify beyond glass. The company went public in 1952. In 1956 it bought National Container (cardboard boxes). It also created a semi-rigid plastic container that was adopted by bleach and detergent companies.

EXECUTIVES

Svp And Chief Strategy And Innovation Officer, John Haudrich, $334,546 total compensation
Svp And Chief Administrative Officer, Paul Jarrell, $417,000 total compensation
Svp Cto And Supply Chain Officer, Giancarlo Currarino
President O-i North America, Sergio Galindo
Svp And Cfo, Jan A. Bertsch, $650,000 total compensation
Ceo, Andres A. Lopez, $850,000 total compensation
President O-i Europe, Vitaliano Torno, $507,305 total compensation
President O-i Latin America, Miguel I. Alvarez, $380,467 total compensation
President O-i Asia Pacific, Timothy Connors
Svp And General Counsel, James W. (Jim) Baehren, $450,000 total compensation
Vice President Internet Marketing, Benjamin Hagan
Vice President New Business Development, Oscar Enriquez
Vice President Sales Wine North America, Sean Gallagher
Vp Finance And Corporate Controller, Juan Amezquita
Vice President, Steve Gabel
Vp Finance Europe, Robert Gachot
Vice President Global Business Processes, Jim Nordmeyer
Vp Global Engineering, Daniel Murphy
Vice President And Chief Procurement Officer, David Furr
Senior Vice President And Chro, John Webb
Vice President Americas, James Rooney
Vice President Investor Relations, Chris Manuel
Chairman, Carol A. Williams
Assistant Treasurer, Kim Meneilly
Auditors: Ernst & Young LLP

LOCATIONS

HQ: O-I Glass Inc
One Michael Owens Way, Perrysburg, OH 43551
Phone: 567 336-5000
Web: www.o-i.com

2017 Sales

	$ mil.	% of total
Europe	2,375	35
North America	2,160	31
Latin America	1,551	23
Asia Pacific	714	10
Other	69	1
Total	**6,869**	**100**

Selected Subsidiaries

Owens-Illinois Group Inc.
OI General Finance Inc.
OI General FTS Inc.
OI Castalia STS Inc.
OI Levis Park STS Inc.
Owens-Illinois General Inc.
Owens Insurance Ltd.
Universal Materials Inc.
OI Advisors Inc.
OI Securities Inc.
OI Transfer Inc.
Maumee Air Associates Inc.
OI Australia Inc.
Continental PET Holdings Pty. Ltd.
ACI America Holdings Inc.
ACI Ventures Inc.
Owens-Brockway Packaging Inc.
Owens-Brockway Glass Container Inc.
OI Andover Group Inc.
The Andover Group Inc.
Brockway Realty Corporation
NHW Auburn LLC
OI Auburn Inc.
SeaGate Inc.
SeaGate II Inc.

COMPETITORS

Amcor	Plastipak
Anchor Glass	Reynolds Group
AptarGroup	Holdings Limited
Arconic	Saint-Gobain
BWAY	Saint-Gobain
Ball Corp.	Containers
Bemis	Sealed Air Corp.
Berry Global	Silgan
Consolidated Container	Sonoco Products
Crown Holdings	Tetra Pak
Graham Packaging	Tupperware Brands
Newell Brands	Vidrala

HISTORICAL FINANCIALS

Company Type: Public

Income Statement				FYE: December 31
	REVENUE ($ mil.)	NET INCOME ($ mil.)	NET PROFIT MARGIN	EMPLOYEES
12/18	6,877	257	3.7%	26,500
12/17	6,869	180	2.6%	26,500
12/16	6,702	209	3.1%	27,000
12/15	6,156	(74)	—	27,000
12/14	6,784	75	1.1%	21,100
Annual Growth	0.3%	36.1%	—	5.9%

2018 Year-End Financials

Debt ratio: 55.00%
Return on equity: 32.00%
Cash ($ mil.): 512
Current ratio: 1.00
Long-term debt ($ mil.): 5,181

No. of shares (mil.): 156
Dividends
Yield: 0.0%
Payout: 3.0%
Market value ($ mil.): 2,684

	STOCK PRICE ($) FY Close	P/E High/Low	PER SHARE ($) Earnings	Dividends	Book Value
12/18	17.00	14 10	2.00	0.00	5.00
12/17	22.00	23 16	1.00	0.00	5.00
12/16	17.00	16 9	1.00	0.00	2.00
12/15	17.00	— —	(0.00)	0.00	3.00
12/14	27.00	78 51	0.00	0.00	7.00
Annual Growth	(10.6%)	— —	37.1%	—	(8.0%)

Occidental Petroleum Corp

Harnessing its heritage of Western technical know-how Occidental Petroleum engages in oil and gas exploration and production and makes basic chemicals plastics and petrochemicals. It boasts proved reserves of 2.8 billion barrels of oil equivalent primarily from assets in the US the Middle East North Africa and Latin America. Subsidiary Occidental Chemical (OxyChem) produces acids chlorine and specialty products and owns Oxy Vinyls the #1 maker of polyvinyl chloride (PVC) resin in North America. Occidental Petroleum's midstream and marketing units gather treat process transport store trade and market crude oil natural gas NGLs condensate and CO2 and generate and market power. In 2019 it acquired Anadarko for $55 billion.

HISTORY

Founded in 1920 Occidental Petroleum struggled until 1956 when billionaire industrialist Dr. Armand Hammer sank $100000 into the company then worth $34000. It drilled two wells and both came in. Hammer eventually gained control of the company.

Occidental's discovery of California's second-largest gas field (1959) was followed by a concession from Libya's King Idris (1966) and the discovery of a billion-barrel Libyan oil field. In 1968 Occidental bought Signal Oil's European refining and marketing business as an outlet for the Libyan oil. It also diversified buying Island Creek Coal and Hooker Chemical.

In 1969 Occidental sold 51% of its Libyan production to the Libyan government under duress after Idris was ousted. (It suspended operations there in 1986). It soon began oil exploration in Latin America (1971) and in the North Sea (1972-73) where it discovered the lucrative Piper field. Other projects included a 20-year fertilizer-for-ammonia deal with the USSR (1974) and a coal joint venture with China (1985).

During the 1980s Occidental sold some foreign assets and bought US natural gas pipeline firm MidCon (1986). It also bought Iowa Beef Processors (IBP) for stock worth $750 million (1981) and then spun off 49% of it in 1987 for $960 million.

In 1983 Hammer hired Ray Irani to revive Occidental's ailing chemicals business (losses that year: $38 million). Irani integrated operations to ensure higher margins during industry downturns and purchased Diamond Shamrock Chemicals (1986) Shell's vinyl chloride monomer unit (1987) a DuPont chloralkali facility (1987) and Cain Chemical (1988). OxyChem's profits reached almost $1.1 billion by 1989.

Hammer died in 1990 and Irani became CEO. In 1991 to reduce debt Occidental exited the Chinese coal business and sold the North Sea oil properties. Occidental also spun off IBP the largest US red-meat producer to its shareholders.

Occidental paid Irani $95 million in 1997 to buy out his employment contract; instead his compensation (a minimum of $1.2 million a year) was tied to the company's fortunes. That year Occidental's $3.65 billion bid won the US government's auction of its 78% stake in California's Elk Hills petroleum reserve one of the largest in the continental US.

To help pay for Elk Hills the company sold MidCon to K N Energy for $3.1 billion in 1998. Occidental traded its petrochemical operations to Eq-

uistar Chemicals a partnership between Lyondell (now LyondellBasell) and Millennium Chemicals for $425 million and a 29.5% stake.

In a venture with The Geon Company Occidental in 1999 formed Oxy Vinyls the #1 producer of polyvinyl chloride (PVC) resin in North America. That year also brought a windfall: Chevron agreed to pay Occidental $775 million to settle a lawsuit stemming from the 1982 withdrawal by Gulf (later acquired by Chevron) of an offer to buy Cities Service (later acquired by Occidental).

In 2000 Occidental sold its 29% stake in Canadian Occidental back to the company for $828 million to help fund the purchase of oil and gas producer Altura Energy a partnership of BP and Shell Oil for $3.6 billion. Later that year the company sold some Gulf of Mexico properties to Apache for $385 million.

Occidental acquired a new exploration block in Yemen in 2001. The next year it sold its 30% of Equistar Chemicals to Lyondell in exchange for a 21% stake in Lyondell. In 2005 it acquired a stake in a gas and oil production site located in Texas' Permian Basin from ExxonMobil for a reported $972 million. Occidental closed the acquisition of Vintage Petroleum for a reported $3.8 billion in early 2006.

The government of Ecuador seized Occidental Petroleum's Ecuadorian assets in 2006 as part of a nationalization drive. That year Plains Exploration and Production sold non-core oil and gas properties to Occidental for $865 million.

Also in 2006 Occidental reduced its stake in Lyondell from 12% to 8%. The following year Occidental sold its remaining Lyondell shares on the open market.

In North America in 2008 the company bought a 15% stake in the Joslyn Oil Sands project for nearly $500 million. That project is based in Alberta Canada and is operated by Total.

The company re-entered Libya in 2008.

Beefing up its investment vehicles in 2009 the company purchased Citigroup's commodities trading unit (Philbro LLC).

To raise cash to pay down debt in 2011 the company sold its Argentina-based assets to China Petrochemical for $2.45 billion. The deal helped cover some of the costs of Occidental's $3.4 billion acquisition (in late 2010 and early 2011) of safer US-based assets — oil and gas properties in South Texas and North Dakota.

In the US in 2012 Occidental paid $2.3 billion for oil and gas properties in the Permian Basin Williston Basin South Texas and California.

That year Occidental and Magellan Midstream Partners L.P. formed BridgeTex Pipeline Company LLC (BridgeTex) to build the 450-mile-long BridgeTex Pipeline to transport 300000 barrels per day of crude oil between the Permian region and the Gulf Coast refinery markets.

In 2013 OxyChem and Mexichem formed a 50/50 joint venture Ingleside Ethylene LLC to build a 1.2-billion-pound per year capacity ethylene cracker at the OxyChem plant in Ingleside Texas along with pipelines and storage at Markham Texas. As part of a long-term strategic supply relationship between the companies essentially all of the ethylene produced from the cracker will be consumed in the manufacture of vinyl chloride monomer (VCM) utilizing existing VCM capacity. VCM will be delivered to Mexichem to produce polyvinyl chloride (PVC) and PVC piping systems.

Growing it assets in 2013 the company and Qatar Petroleum agreed on the Phase 5 Field Development Plan of the Idd El Shargi North Dome Field offshore Qatar. The project will sustain oil production levels at about 100000 barrels per day through 2019. (In 2011 Occidental also teamed up with ADNOC to develop the major Shah gas field in the UAE).

In 2013 the company paid approximately $500 million to acquire various US-based oil and gas properties.

EXECUTIVES

Svp And Cfo, Cedric W. Burgher, age 59

Svp General Counsel And Chief Compliance Officer, Marcia E. Backus, age 64, $646,970 total compensation

Evp And Group Chairman - Middle East, Edward A. (Sandy) Lowe, age 67, $625,000 total compensation

Svp Marketing And Midstream Operations And Development, Cynthia L. Walker, age 43, $600,000 total compensation

President Ceo And Director, Vicki A. Hollub, age 59, $1,143,314 total compensation

Vp And Cio, Ioannis A. Charalambous

Svp And President Oxy Oil And Gas Domestic, Joseph C. Elliott, age 61

Svp And President Occidental Chemical Corporation, Robert L. Peterson

Vice President Marketing And Asset Optimization, Shawn McGovern

Vice President U.s. Oil Marketing Permian Basin And Hugoton, Steven Rafferty

Vp And Principal Accounting Officer, Jennifer Kirk

Vice President Business Development, Kevin Pilkington

Vice President Health Environment Safety And Security, Wesley Scott

Vice President Government Relations, Ian Davis

Vp Internal Audit, Gary Daugherty

Vice President Exploration And Geoscience, Pedro Romero

Vice President Business Analyst, Eric Wynia

Vice President, Sylvia Low

National Sales Manager, Keith Benn

Chairman, Eugene L. (Gene) Batchelder, age 71

Secretary, Melanie Rome

Auditors: KPMG LLP

LOCATIONS

HQ: Occidental Petroleum Corp
5 Greenway Plaza, Suite 110, Houston, TX 77046
Phone: 713 215-7000
Web: www.oxy.com

2018 Sales

	% of total
US	71
Qatar	9
Oman	9
United Arab Emirates	5
Colombia	4
Other countries	2
Total	**100**

PRODUCTS/OPERATIONS

2018 Sales

	$ mil.	% of total
Oil & gas	10,441	56
Chemicals	4,657	25
Midstream marketing & other	3,656	19
Eliminations	(930)	-
Total		**100**

Selected Subsidiaries

Occidental Chemical Corp. (OxyChem; chemicals polymers and plastics)
Oxy Vinyls LP (76% polyvinyl chloride)
Occidental Energy Marketing Inc. (energy marketing)
Occidental Exploration and Production Company (exploration and production)

COMPETITORS

Apache	Huntsman International
Ashland	Imperial Oil
BP	J.M. Huber
Chevron	Koch Industries Inc.
ConocoPhillips	Marathon Oil
Devon Energy	Olin
Dow Chemical	PEMEX
Eastman Chemical	Royal Dutch Shell
Exxon Mobil	Sunoco
Hess Corporation	TOTAL

HISTORICAL FINANCIALS

Company Type: Public

Income Statement

FYE: December 31

	REVENUE ($ mil.)	NET INCOME ($ mil.)	NET PROFIT MARGIN	EMPLOYEES
12/18	18,934	4,131	21.8%	11,000
12/17	13,274	1,311	9.9%	11,000
12/16	10,398	(574)	—	11,000
12/15	12,699	(7,829)	—	11,100
12/14	21,947	616	2.8%	11,700
Annual Growth	**(3.6%)**	**60.9%**	**—**	**(1.5%)**

2018 Year-End Financials

Debt ratio: 24.00%
Return on equity: 20.00%
Cash ($ mil.): 3,033
Current ratio: 1.00
Long-term debt ($ mil.): 10,201

No. of shares (mil.): 749
Dividends
 Yield: 5.0%
 Payout: 58.0%
Market value ($ mil.): 45,998

	STOCK PRICE ($) FY Close	P/E High/Low		PER SHARE ($) Earnings	Dividends	Book Value
12/18	61.00	16	11	5.00	3.00	28.00
12/17	74.00	43	34	2.00	3.00	27.00
12/16	71.00	—	—	(1.00)	3.00	28.00
12/15	68.00	—	—	(10.00)	3.00	32.00
12/14	81.00	133	93	1.00	3.00	39.00
Annual Growth	**(6.6%)**	**—**	**—**	**61.6%**	**1.9%**	**(7.7%)**

OceanFirst Financial Corp

Ask the folks at OceanFirst Bank for a home loan and they might say "shore." The subsidiary of holding company OceanFirst Financial operates 25 branches in the coastal New Jersey counties of Middlesex Monmouth and Ocean. The community-oriented bank caters to individuals and small to midsized businesses in the Jersey Shore area offering standard products such as checking and savings accounts CDs and IRAs. It uses funds from deposits mainly to invest in mortgages loans and securities. One- to four-family residential mortgages make up more than half of OceanFirst Financial's loan portfolio which also includes commercial real estate (about 30%) business construction and consumer loans.

Operations

The Bank's principal business is attracting deposits from the general public in the communities surrounding its branch offices and investing those deposits primarily in single-family owner-occupied residential mortgage loans and commercial real estate loans. It active subsidiaries include OceanFirst Services LLC OceanFirst REIT Holdings Inc. and 975 Holdings LLC.

Geographic Reach

OceanFirst has operations in the New Jersey counties of Middlesex Monmouth and Ocean.

Financial Performance

OceanFirst's revenues dropped by 4% in 2012 due to decrease in loans and mortgage-backed securities partially offset by higher revenues from investment securities and other.

Net income declined by 3% in 2012 due to an increase in provision for loan losses and non-interest expenses (higher professional fees).

Strategy

OceanFirst seeks to grow commercial loans receivable by offering commercial lending services to local businesses; grow core deposits through broader product offerings andbranch expansion; and increase non-interest income by expanding its fee-based products and services.

Part of the company's strategy for growth includes expanding its fee-based offerings. The bank for example offers trust and asset management services. Company subsidiary OceanFirst Services sells mutual funds annuities and insurance products from third-party vendors. OceanFirst is also seeking opportunities to grow by opening new branch locations within its existing markets.

In 2013 the Bank opened a full service Financial Solutions Center in Red Bank New Jersey offering deposit lending and asset management services. It also opened an additional branch office in Jackson New Jersey.

Since 1995 OceanFirst has opened sixteen branch offices (twelve in Ocean County and four in Monmouth County).

Mergers and Acquisitions

In January 2016 OceanFirst Financial agreed to buy Cape Bancorp— along with its 22 branches in central and southern New Jersey counties $1.1 billion in loans and $1.3 billion in deposits — for $208.1 million. The deal would grow OceanFirst's total total assets by over 60% and nearly double the size of its branch network.

Company Background

OceanFirst Bank's employee stock option plan owns more than 10% of OceanFirst Financial's shares. The company's charitable foundation OceanFirst Foundation owns 7%.

The Bank was founded as a state-chartered building and loan association in 1902. It converted to a Federal savings and loan association in 1945 and became a Federally-chartered mutual savings bank in 1989.

EXECUTIVES

Evp And Cfo, Michael J. Fitzpatrick, age 62, $285,577 total compensation

Evp And Chief Administrative Officer, Joseph R. Iantosca, age 57, $284,808 total compensation

Evp And Chief Lending Officer, Joseph J. Lebel, age 55, $284,808 total compensation

First Svp General Counsel And Corporate Secretary, Steven J. Tsimbinos, $252,798 total compensation

Chairman President And Ceo, Christopher D. Maher, age 51, $566,346 total compensation

Avp Information Technology, Elizabeth Alexander

Vice President Bank Counsel, Denise Horner

Assistant Vice President Oceanfirst Bank, Karen Rack

Vice President Loan Servicing Operations Manager, Christine Schiess

Senior Vice President And Director Human Resources, Anne Johnson

Senior Vice President, Brad Fouss

Assistant Vice President Project Manager, David Mowder

Vice President, Lauren Dezzi

Assistant Vice President Collections Department, Karen Farrell

Vice President Senior Marketing Officer Strategy, Lisa Natale
Senior Vice President, Nancy Mazza
Board Member, Jack Farris
Auditors: KPMG LLP

LOCATIONS

HQ: OceanFirst Financial Corp
110 West Front Street, Red Bank, NJ 07701
Phone: 732 240-4500
Web: www.oceanfirst.com

PRODUCTS/OPERATIONS

2016 sales

	$ mil.	% of total
Interest Income		
Loans	123	80
Mortgage-backed securities	7	4
Investment securities & other	4	2
Non-interest		
Bankcard services revenue	5	3
Wealth management revenue	2	2
Fees & service charges	10	7
Loan Servicing income	0	-
Net gains on sales of loans	1	1
Net loss from other real estate operations	(0.9)	-
Income from Bank owned Life Insurance	2	1
Other	0	-
Total	**154**	**100**

COMPETITORS

Bank of America	PNC Financial
Cape Bancorp	Sovereign Bank
Citibank	TD Bank USA
Hudson City Bancorp	Valley National
Investors Bancorp	Bancorp
JPMorgan Chase	

HISTORICAL FINANCIALS

Company Type: Public

Income Statement				FYE: December 31
	ASSETS ($ mil.)	NET INCOME ($ mil.)	INCOME AS % OF ASSETS	EMPLOYEES
12/18	7,516	72	1.0%	892
12/17	5,416	42	0.8%	684
12/16	5,167	23	0.4%	797
12/15	2,593	20	0.8%	393
12/14	2,357	20	0.8%	376
Annual Growth	33.6%	37.9%	—	24.1%

2018 Year-End Financials

Debt ratio: 1.00%	No. of shares (mil.): 48
Return on equity: 9.00%	Dividends
Cash ($ mil.): 121	Yield: 3.0%
Current ratio: —	Payout: 41.0%
Long-term debt ($ mil.): —	Market value ($ mil.): 1,079

	STOCK PRICE ($) FY Close	P/E High/Low	PER SHARE ($) Earnings	Dividends	Book Value
12/18	23.00	20 14	2.00	1.00	22.00
12/17	26.00	23 18	1.00	1.00	18.00
12/16	30.00	30 16	1.00	1.00	18.00
12/15	20.00	17 13	1.00	1.00	14.00
12/14	17.00	16 13	1.00	0.00	13.00
Annual Growth	7.1%	— —	6.1%	6.1%	13.8%

OCHSNER CLINIC FOUNDATION

EXECUTIVES

Ceo-Pres, Patrick J Quinlan
Exec V Pres-Dir of Fin, B C Brannon
MD, Elizabeth Lapeyre
Supervisor, Jacob Olivares
Project Consultant, Sandy Warren
Endocrinology, Anita Richard
Assistant Vice President, Ann Lockhart
Executive Vice President, Bobby Brannon
Information Technology Manager, Bryan Clark
Senior Executive Assistant, Carol Villafana
Infectious Diseases, Cheryl Balot
Auditors: ERNST & YOUNG US LLP AUSTIN

LOCATIONS

HQ: OCHSNER CLINIC FOUNDATION
1514 JEFFERSON HWY, NEW ORLEANS, LA
701212483
Phone: 504 842-3000
Web: WWW.OCHSNER.ORG

HISTORICAL FINANCIALS

Company Type: Private

Income Statement				FYE: December 31
	REVENUE ($ mil.)	NET INCOME ($ mil.)	NET PROFIT MARGIN	EMPLOYEES
12/17	8,405	129	1.5%	10,500
12/14	2,197	(16)	—	—
12/13	5,550	52	0.9%	—
12/12	4,830	12	0.3%	—
Annual Growth	11.7%	60.1%	—	—

Office Depot, Inc.

Paper and pens have made room for PC repair and point-of-sale services at office products giant Office Depot (#2 worldwide behind Staples). The office supply chain operates nearly 1400 retail stores under the Office Depot and OfficeMax names through which it sells a wide selection of office and school supplies furniture printers and breakroom and cleaning products. It has also moved into IT support and other business-to-business services which it offers through CompuCom and other brands. After divesting all its international holdings Office Depot operates entirely in North America.

HISTORY

Pat Scher Stephen Dougherty and Jack Kopkin opened the first Office Depot one of the first office supply superstores in Lauderdale Lakes Florida in 1986. Scher was selected as chairman. By the end of the year the fledgling company had opened two more stores (both in Florida).

Office Depot opened seven more stores in 1987. When Scher died of leukemia that year the company recruited David Fuente former president of Sherwin-Williams' Paint Store Division as chairman and CEO. Office Depot continued its break-

neck expansion under Fuente. In 1988 — the year the company went public — it opened 16 stores and broke into new markets in four states.

The chain stepped up its pace and by 1990 it had expanded into several other areas including the South and Midwest. Office Depot also added computers and peripherals and opened its first delivery center.

In 1991 the company became North America's #1 office products retailer and expanded its presence in the West through the acquisition of Office Club another warehouse-type office supply chain with 59 stores (most in California). Fuente remained chairman and CEO while former Office Club CEO Mark Begelman became president and COO. (Begelman who left in 1995 and eventually formed the MARS music chain had founded the first Office Club in 1987 in Concord California; he took it public in 1989.)

The company entered the international market with its 1992 purchase of Canada's H. Q. Office International and through licensing agreements in 1993 (in Colombia and Israel). Office Depot created its business services division by acquiring various contract stationers including Eastman Office Products (the West Coast's #1 contract office supplier) in the mid-1990s and added locations in Mexico and Poland; it established a joint venture in France with retailer Carrefour in 1996.

Also in 1996 Office Depot announced a $3.4 billion agreement to be acquired by Staples which would have created a company with more than 1100 stores. However the government blocked the purchase on antitrust grounds in 1997 and the agreement dissolved. Unfettered by merger distractions Office Depot resumed opening stores at a rapid pace including two in Thailand and took its catalog and delivery services online. It then established a joint venture with Japanese retailer Deo Deo.

In 1998 Office Depot acquired Viking Office Products in a $2.7 billion deal. With more than 60% of its sales coming from outside the US Viking augmented Office Depot's already strong delivery network and international expansion. Office Depot acquired the remaining 50% of its French operations from Carrefour in 1998 and the remaining 50% of its Japanese operations from Deo Deo in 1999.

Office Depot started putting Internet kiosks in its US stores in 2000 allowing customers to browse and shop company Web sites. In July 2000 Bruce Nelson CEO of Viking replaced Fuente as CEO of Office Depot. Citing weak computer sales and high warehouse prices the company closed about 70 stores and cut its workforce. In early 2002 Nelson was named chairman as well as CEO after Fuente stepped down.

Office Depot sold its Australian operations to Officeworks a unit of Coles Myer in January 2003. Office Depot used the proceeds to expand its faster-growing European operations. Also that year the company acquired the retail operations of French office supplier Guilbert from Pinault-Printemps-Redoute a move that doubled the company's business in Europe. (Staples had acquired Guilbert's mail-order business the previous year.)

In 2004 the company acquired about 125 retail locations from troubled toy seller Toys "R" Us converting 50 of those into Office Depot locations and selling off the remainder.

Nelson left the company and Neil Austrian served as interim head. Office Depot named AutoZone leader Steve Odland as CEO and chairman in 2005. That year the company shuttered its Viking Office Products brand in the US consolidating its catalog sales under the Office Depot banner. (It still markets products through Viking in international markets.) The business services division also sells technology products through Tech Depot (formerly 4SURE.com).

The company acquired privately held Allied Office Products (AOP) the largest independent dealer of office products and services in the US in 2006. AOP became part of Office Depot's North American Business Solutions Division.

Office Depot opened 70 new stores in 2007 (vs. 115 the previous year).

In mid-2008 the company acquired 13 stores in Sweden through the acquisition of AGE Kontor & Data AB a contract and retail office supply company operating there.

In 2009 the company closed about 125 stores in North America and exited the Japanese market.

CEO Steve Odland resigned in November 2010. In late 2010 Israeli department store operator New Hamashbir Lazarchan acquired Office Depot's operations in Israel for $50 million. New Hamashbir Lazarchan also agreed to pay royalties on revenues generated by Office Depot Israel which has about 45 stores.

Office Depot appointed new leadership in mid-2011 naming interim leader Neil Austrian as the company's permanent replacement for chief executive and chairman. Austrian has served as a director at Office Depot since 1998. He stepped in to lead the office products retailer on a temporary basis following the resignation of Steve Odland in late 2010. Odland's resignation came soon after Office Depot settled Securities and Exchange Commission charges that the company selectively informed analysts and institutional investors that its earnings would fall short of estimates. Office Depot agreed to pay $1 million while Odland and the firm's former CFO agreed to pay $50000.

EXECUTIVES

Evp And Cfo, Joseph T. (Joe) Lower, age 52

Evp Chief Legal Officer And Corporate Secretary, N. David Bleisch, age 60

Evp And Chief Marketing Officer, Jerri L. DeVard, age 59

Ceo And Director, Gerry P. Smith, age 56

Evp Chief Legal Officer Corporate Secretary And President Business Solutions Division, Steve Calkins, age 48

Evp And Chief Administrative Officer, Michael Allison, age 61, $539,423 total compensation

Evp Transformation And Strategic Sourcing, John W. Gannfors

Svp Ecommerce And Chief Digital Officer, Kevin Moffitt

Svp Retail Division, Marko Ibrahim

Senior Vice President North American Business Development, John Lander

Vice President Enterprise Account Management, Steve Dvorchak

Vice President Transformation Delivery, Sharon McGregor

Vice President, Alex Jaime

National Account Manager, David Higgins

Vice President Distribution, Rick DiMaio

Vice President Global Talent Management, Robyn Tyler

Vp Financial Systems And Reporting, Jane Dee

Vice President Information Technology Shared Services, Tonya Peer

Vp It Application Development, Andrew Parry

Evp And Chief Merchandising And Services Officer, Janet Schijns

National Account Manager, Lindsey Trahan

Svp And Chief Accounting Officer, Scott Kriss

Chairman, Joseph S. (Joe) Vassalluzzo, age 71

Board Member, David Szymanski

Board Member, Cynthia Jamison

Board Member, Kristin Campbell

Board Member, Nigel Travis

Auditors: DELOITTE & TOUCHE LLP

LOCATIONS

HQ: Office Depot, Inc.
6600 North Military Trail, Boca Raton, FL 33496
Phone: 561 438-4800   **Fax:** 561 265-4406
Web: www.officedepot.com

PRODUCTS/OPERATIONS

2018 Sales

	$ mil.	% of total
Business Solutions	5,282	48
Retail	4,641	42
CompuCom	1,086	10
Other	6	-
Total	**11,015**	**100**

2018 Sales

	$ mil.	% of total
Products	9,322	85
Services	1,693	15
Total	**11,015**	**100**

COMPETITORS

Amazon.com	HP Enterprise Services
BJ's Wholesale Club	IBM Global Services
Best Buy	Insight Enterprises
CDW	Staples
Costco Wholesale	The UPS Store
Dell	Veritiv
Essendant	Wal-Mart
FedEx Office	

HISTORICAL FINANCIALS

Company Type: Public

Income Statement

FYE: December 29

	REVENUE ($ mil.)	NET INCOME ($ mil.)	NET PROFIT MARGIN	EMPLOYEES
12/18	11,015	104	0.9%	44,000
12/17	10,240	181	1.8%	45,000
12/16	11,021	529	4.8%	38,000
12/15	14,485	8	0.1%	49,000
12/14	16,096	(354)	—	56,000
Annual Growth	**(9.0%)**	—	—	**(5.9%)**

2018 Year-End Financials

Debt ratio: 13.00%	No. of shares (mil.): 544
Return on equity: 5.00%	Dividends
Cash ($ mil.): 658	Yield: 0.0%
Current ratio: 1.00	Payout: 53.0%
Long-term debt ($ mil.): 690	Market value ($ mil.): 1,370

	STOCK PRICE ($) FY Close	P/E High/Low		PER SHARE ($) Earnings	Dividends	Book Value
12/18	3.00	19	11	0.00	0.00	4.00
12/17	4.00	18	9	0.00	0.00	4.00
12/16	5.00	8	3	1.00	0.00	4.00
12/15	6.00	968	533	0.00	0.00	3.00
12/14	9.00	—	—	(1.00)	0.00	3.00
Annual Growth	**(26.9%)**			—	—	**7.1%**

Old National Bancorp (Evansville, IN)

Old National Bank is old but it's not quite national. Founded in 1834 the main subsidiary of Old National Bancorp operates about 200 bank centers across Indiana Kentucky Michigan and Illi-

nois. The bank serves consumers and business customers offering standard checking and savings accounts credit cards and loans. Its treasury segment manages investments for bank and commercial clients. Business loans commercial and residential mortgages and consumer loans account for most of Old National's lending activity. The company also sells insurance manages wealth for high-net-worth clients and offers investment and retirement services through third-party provider LPL Financial.

Operations

Old National Bancorp operates two main segments: Banking which generates the bulk of Old National's revenue and provides traditional loan and deposit products as well as wealth management services; and Insurance which provides commercial property and casualty surety loss control services employee benefits consulting and administration as well as personal insurance.

The bank generated 51% of its revenue from loan interest (including fees) in 2014 while another 14% came from interest on investment securities. Insurance premiums and commissions contributed 7% to the company's total revenues that year while wealth management fees made up another 5%.

Geographic Reach

The bank's nearly 200 banking centers are located across four Midwestern states and Kentucky. Most are in the central northern and southern parts of Indiana; while others are in central Illinois; Western Kentucky and Louisville; Grand Rapids Southeastern and Southwestern Michigan; and Ohio.

Sales and Marketing

Old National has identified metropolitan areas within its market including Indianapolis; Louisville Kentucky; and Lafayette Indiana for growth within its core community banking segment.

The company spent $9.59 million on marketing in 2014 up from $7.21 million and $7.45 million in 2013 and 2012 respectively.

Financial Performance

Old National Bancorp's revenues and profits have been on the uptrend for the past several years thanks to new loan business from a series of bank acquisitions and declining loan loss provisions as its loan portfolio's credit quality has improved with the strengthened economy.

The company's revenue rose by 5% to $554.86 million in 2014 mostly thanks to new loan business stemming from the bank's acquisitions of Tower Financial United Bancorp and LSB Financial during the year along with organic loan growth. Higher revenue in 2014 coupled with strong cost controls lower interest on deposits and a continued decline in loan loss provisions drove Old National's net income higher by 3% to $103.62 million for the year.

Old National's operating cash fell by 21% to $199.72 million after adjusting its earnings for non-cash items related to its net sales proceeds from the sale of its residential real estate loans held-for-sale.

Strategy

Old National continues to seek out additional branch and whole bank acquisitions to grow its loan business and expand its geographic reach. Its acquisition of United Bancorp in mid-2014 for example added nearly $1 billion in new loan business and $869 million in wealth management assets under management while doubling Old National's presence in Michigan to 36 total branches.

The company is also pursuing growth by increasing its focus on commercial banking and cross-selling its insurance and wealth management offerings. To this end Old National in 2014 bought the insurance accounts (consisting of mostly commercial property/casualty accounts) serviced by the Evansville branch office of Wells Fargo Insurance.

Meanwhile it is also selectively exiting markets that haven't been profitable. In early 2015 as part of its ongoing efficiency improvement efforts the bank announced that it would sell 17 of its banking centers including all twelve of its branches in Southern Illinois and close or consolidate another 19 branches in other states over the following months.

Mergers and Acquisitions

In December 2014 Old National agreed to acquire Founders Financial Corporation along with its Founders Bank & Trust subsidiary in Grand Rapids Michigan for $91.7 million which would add nearly $460 million in total assets and four branches in Kent County.

In November 2014 the company purchased LSB Financial and its Lafayette Savings Bank subsidiary for $51.8 million adding five branches near Lafayette Indiana.

In July 2014 the company acquired Ann Arbor-based United Bancorp along with United Bank & Trust for a total of $122 million adding 18 branches in Michigan nearly $919 million in total assets a $963 million loan servicing portfolio and $688 million in trust assets under management.

In April 2014 Old National purchased Indiana-based Tower Financial along with its Tower Bank & Trust subsidiary adding seven new branches and some $556 million in trust assets under management.

In 2013 the bank bolstered its presence in Michigan after acquiring two dozen Bank of America branches in northern Indiana and southwest Michigan. The previous year the bank purchased Indiana Community Bancorp which added 17 branches in the southeastern part of the state. The transaction was valued at nearly $80 million.

EXECUTIVES

Chairman President And Ceo, Robert G. (Bob) Jones, age 62, $668,269 total compensation

Svp And Corporate Secretary, Jeffrey L. (Jeff) Knight, age 59, $321,051 total compensation

Evp And Chief Credit Officer, Daryl D. Moore, age 61, $305,040 total compensation

Ceo North Central Region, Mark D. Bradford, age 61

Evp And Chief Client Services Officer, Annette W. Hudgions, age 61, $250,016 total compensation

President And Ceo Wealth Management, Caroline J. Ellspermann, age 51

Ceo Eastern Region, Dennis P. Heishman

Sevp And Cfo, Christopher A. (Chris) Wolking, age 59, $364,730 total compensation

Evp And Chief Community Relations And Social Responsibility Officer, Kathy A. Schoettlin

Region Ceo Old National Bank, Randall (Randy) Reichmann

Ceo Central And Western Michigan Region, Todd C. Clark, age 49

Evp And Chief Risk Officer, Candice J. Rickard, age 55

Regional Ceo Southern, James Sandgren, $357,673 total compensation

Ceo Central Region, Dan L. Doan

Evp And Director Corporate Strategy, James C. Ryan, age 47

Evp And Cio, John R. Kamin

Evp Associate Engagement And Integrations, Kendra L. Vanzo

Evp Chief Auditing Executive And Chief Ethics Officer, Richard W. (Dick) Dubé

President Onb Investment Services, Kenneth J. Ellspermann

President Old National Insurance, Scott J. Evernham

Ceo Southern Region, Sara L. Miller

President And Coo, Jim Sandgren

President North Central Region, Scott Shishman

Vice President Administration, Gloria Reinhart

Vice President Commercial Banking, Brian Henning

Vice President Associate Counsel, Tom Washburne

Assistant Vice President Mortgage Origination, Lynn Greulich

Vice President Commercial Lending, Kathy Cooper

Vice President Estate And Business Planning, Gary Mccall

Vice President And Client Advisor, Steve Hackman

Senior Vice President Of Marketing, Scott Adams

Assistant Vice President, Sandy Keen

Assistant Vice President, Gidget Rowe

Vice President, Amanda Castaneda

Vice President Sarbanes Oxley Analyst, Denise Rexing

Vice President, Randy Lilly

Assistant Vice President, Jenny Clark

Assistant Vice President Mortgage Loan Officer, Debra Fulkerson

Vp Lpl Financial Advisor, Gary Shelton

Vice President Commercial Banking, Rob Snyder

Vice President Project Manager, Helen Cook

Assistant Vice President Retail Center Manager, Sabrina Mancuso

Private Banker Ii Vice President, Tony Patrick

Vice President Assistant Treasurer, Mike Loyd

Vice President Commercial Lender, Tim Helber

Assistant Vice President Branch Manager, Geoff Thompson

Senior Vice President Treasurer, Jennifer Guzman

Vice President, Jason Etter

Vice President Corporate Banking, James Tutt

Vice President Mortgage Lending, Steve Anderson

Vice President Of Community Banking And Office V, Tammy Hall

Vice President And Trust Officer, Melanie Newkirk

Assistant Vice President Secondary Marketing, Chris Weiberg

Senior Vice President Commercial Banking, James Barnum

Senior Vice President, Lynell Walton

Human Resources Operations Manager Vice President, Ann Claspell

Svp Mortgage Sales Manager, Joel Van Elderen

Vp Client Advisor Corporate Trust Manager, Shannon Perry

Senior Vice President Assistant General Counsel, Gary Case

Vice President And Financial Center Manager, Cathy Stidham

Vice President Treasury Management, Dana Lackey

Vice President Server Systems, John Knight

Senior Vice President, Tommy Elliott

Vice President, Robert Ogburn

Vice President, Rob Triplett

Private Banker L Vice President, Becky Robledo

Vice President Information Technology, Brad Callahan

Senior Vice President And Commercial Relationship Team Leader, Troy Briggs

Vice President Cash Management, Andrea Solis

Volunteer And Work Life Programs Manager Avp, Amy Mpsa

Vp And Commercial Real Estate, Regina Levchets

Senior Vice President, Marty Richardson

Vice President, Jeff Kleinschmidt

Vice President, Jame Tutt

Client Advisor Ll Vice President, Michael Wiederkehr

Client Advisor Ii Vice President, Tamra Inman

Vice President Director And Assistant Controller, Treadweay Todd

Vice President Data Analytics And Loan Acquisition Marketing Manager, Karen Ellison

Executive Vice President And Chief Legal Counsel, Jefferey Knight

Vice President Compliance Audit Manager, Sonja Kriegsmann

Vice President Director Of Information Technology Risk Management, Luke Zeller

Vice President Commercial Relationship Manager, James Kilsdonk

Senior Vice President Security, Shari Krutulis

Vp Portfolio Manager Iii Commercial Real Estate, Dan Ryan

Senior Vice President Operational Risk Director, Sherry Schneider

Vice President Senior Special Assets Officer, Doug Mitcheson

Vice President Client Advisor, Rebecca Grasmeyer

Board Member, Alan Braun

Board Member, Randall Shepard

Board Member, Rebecca Skillman

Board Member, Jerome Henry

Board Member, Katherine White

Auditors: Crowe LLP

LOCATIONS

HQ: Old National Bancorp (Evansville, IN)
One Main Street, Evansville, IN 47708
Phone: 800 731-2265
Web: www.oldnational.com

PRODUCTS/OPERATIONS

2014 Sales

	$ mil.	% of total
Interest		
Loans including fees	306	51
Investment securities	83	14
Noninterest		
Service charges on deposit accounts	48	8
Insurance premiums & commissions	42	7
Wealth management fees	29	5
ATM Fees	26	4
Investment product fees	17	3
Mortgage banking revenue	6	1
Other	42	7
Adjustments	(43.3)	-
Total	**555**	**100**

COMPETITORS

Fifth Third
First Financial (IN)
German American Bancorp
Huntington Bancshares

JPMorgan Chase
PNC Financial
Peoples Bancorp (IN)
U.S. Bancorp

HISTORICAL FINANCIALS

Company Type: Public

Income Statement				FYE: December 31
	ASSETS ($ mil.)	NET INCOME ($ mil.)	INCOME AS % OF ASSETS	EMPLOYEES
12/18	19,728	191	1.0%	2,892
12/17	17,518	96	0.5%	2,801
12/16	14,860	134	0.9%	2,733
12/15	11,992	117	1.0%	2,652
12/14	11,648	104	0.9%	2,938
Annual Growth	14.1%	16.5%	—	(0.4%)

2018 Year-End Financials

Debt ratio: 1.00%	No. of shares (mil.): 175
Return on equity: 8.00%	Dividends
Cash ($ mil.): 317	Yield: 3.0%
Current ratio: —	Payout: 66.0%
Long-term debt ($ mil.): —	Market value ($ mil.): 2,697

	STOCK PRICE ($) FY Close	P/E High/Low	PER SHARE ($) Earnings	Dividends	Book Value
12/18	15.00	17 12	1.00	1.00	15.00
12/17	17.00	27 23	1.00	1.00	14.00
12/16	18.00	17 10	1.00	1.00	13.00
12/15	14.00	15 13	1.00	0.00	13.00
12/14	15.00	16 13	1.00	0.00	13.00
Annual Growth	0.9%	— —	6.5%	4.3%	5.2%

Old Republic International Corp.

Old Republic International keeps pace with changing financial times. With about 140 subsidiaries across North America Old Republic's primary operations are conducted through the Old Republic General Insurance division which offers commercial liability and property/casualty insurance (mostly commercial trucking workers' compensation and general liability policies). In addition the company's Title Insurance group specializes in naturally issuing title insurance to property owners and lenders. Its Old Republic National Title subsidiary is one of the US's oldest and largest title insurance companies with offices throughout the US.

Operations

Old Republic's subsidiaries market underwrite and offer risk management services for insurance products including general and title coverage. Commercial property/casualty policies issued by the general insurance segment account for more than half of the company's sales. Meanwhile the title insurance segment accounts for nearly 40% of revenues and the company's Republic Financial Indemnity Group (RFIG comprising mortgage guaranty and consumer credit indemnity runoff operations) brings in less than 5% of sales. The company also maintains a small life and health insurance business.

More than 70% of the company's consolidated title premium and related fee income comes from independent title agents and underwritten title companies. The rest stems from direct operations including branches of its title insurance businesses and wholly owned agency and service subsidiaries.

Geographic Reach

Through its subsidiaries Old Republic is licensed to do business throughout the US (including the District of Columbia) Puerto Rico the US Virgin Islands Guam and in all Canadian provinces.

Sales and Marketing

While Old Republic does sell some of its property/casualty and specialty products directly it relies on independent agencies brokers and financial institutions to distribute the majority. The company focuses on certain sectors especially transportation commercial construction health care education forest products energy manufacturing retail and wholesale trade and financial services.

Title insurance and related settlement products are sold through some 265 company offices and through agencies and underwritten title companies throughout the US.

Financial Performance

Old Republic's revenues have been steadily rising over the past five years. In 2017 revenue increased 6% to $6.3 billion as net premiums earned fee income and realized investment gains went up.

Both the general insurance and title insurance had higher premium fee and other revenues but this was partially offset by a decline for the run-off RFIG business. However the higher revenue boosted net income which rose 20% to a record $560.5 million.

Despite the increase in profits cash flow from operations fell 29% to $452.8 million that year. That was largely due to negative adjustments to unpaid claims and related items and realized investment gains.

Revenue roller coasters and net income fluctuations don't bother Old Republic as its public filings clearly state that it looks at its business in five-to-10-year intervals and therefore isn't concerned by the ups and downs in shorter cycles. The health of its general insurance business and the fact that it carries very little debt make it easier to take that view.

Strategy

In response to financial strains during the Great Recession Old Republic has chosen to focus on its general and title insurance operations while placing its RFIG mortgage guaranty and consumer credit indemnity operations (which at one point brought in more than 40% of total revenue) in run-off. The firm targets long-term returns on its underwriting operations. As such it spreads its risk over diversified businesses and assets to reduce liability exposures.

After some years of disappointing results Old Republic had a strong performance in 2017 a year in which the company laid the worries of the Great Recession to rest. The rebounding economy has helped drive up the firm's insurance sales: Its General Insurance segment drove the improvement that year. And while underwriting profit rose the company is determined to do even better in that regard. To that end Old Republic will remediate where it is needed most avoiding riskier contracts that are unlikely to deliver strong returns.

Old Republic remains concerned about such factors as ongoing low interest rates and an increase in competitors entering the market. To counteract these factors it plans to carefully explore the markets in which it operates with the intent to diminish its focus on saturated geographies. It also aims to alter and to a certain degree expand its distribution channels.

In mid-2018 the company established Old Republic Residual Market Services which provides specialized services to state-assigned workers' compensation risk plans as well as the National Council on Compensation Insurance Workers Compensation Insurance Plan. It is part of the growing General Insurance segment.

EXECUTIVES

Chairman And Ceo, Aldo C. (Al) Zucaro, age 80, $895,000 total compensation
President And Coo, R. Scott Rager, age 70, $510,000 total compensation
Chairman And Ceo Old Republic Title Companies, Rande K. Yeager, age 70, $510,000 total compensation
Svp And Cfo, Karl W. Mueller, age 59, $465,000 total compensation
President And Coo Old Republic General Insurance Group Inc. (orgig), Craig R. Smiddy, age 55, $485,000 total compensation
Vice President And Associate General Counsel, Kathleen Kumer
Assistant Vice President Commercial Counsel, Avi A Marcus
Vice Chairman, James Kellogg
Auditors: KPMG LLP

LOCATIONS

HQ: Old Republic International Corp.
307 North Michigan Avenue, Chicago, IL 60601
Phone: 312 346-8100
Web: www.oldrepublic.com

PRODUCTS/OPERATIONS

2017 Sales

	% of total
General Insurance	57
Title Insurance	37
Realized investment gains	3
RFIG (run-off)	2
Corporate & other	1
Total	**100**

COMPETITORS

AIG	ING
AXA	Progressive
Allianz	Corporation
Berkshire Hathaway	Stewart Information
CNA Financial	Services
Chubb Limited	The Hartford
Farmers Group	Travelers Companies
Fidelity National	Unum Group
Financial	W. R. Berkley
First American	

HISTORICAL FINANCIALS

Company Type: Public

Income Statement

FYE: December 31

	ASSETS ($ mil.)	NET INCOME ($ mil.)	INCOME AS % OF ASSETS	EMPLOYEES
12/18	19,327	371	1.9%	9,000
12/17	19,404	561	2.9%	8,700
12/16	18,592	467	2.5%	8,500
12/15	17,111	422	2.5%	8,200
12/14	16,988	410	2.4%	8,000
Annual Growth	3.3%	(2.5%)		3.0%

2018 Year-End Financials

Debt ratio: 5.00%	No. of shares (mil.): 303
Return on equity: 8.00%	Dividends
Cash ($ mil.): 100	Yield: 9.0%
Current ratio: —	Payout: 144.0%
Long-term debt ($ mil.): —	Market value ($ mil.): 6,227

	STOCK PRICE ($) FY Close	P/E High/Low	PER SHARE ($) Earnings	Dividends	Book Value
12/18	21.00	18 16	1.00	2.00	17.00
12/17	21.00	10 8	2.00	1.00	18.00
12/16	19.00	11 9	2.00	1.00	17.00
12/15	19.00	12 9	1.00	1.00	15.00
12/14	15.00	11 9	1.00	1.00	15.00
Annual Growth	8.9%	— —	(3.7%)	25.0%	3.1%

Old Second Bancorp., Inc. (Aurora, Ill.)

Old Second won't settle for a silver finish when it comes to community banking around Chicago. Old Second Bancorp is the holding company for Old Second National Bank which serves the Chicago metropolitan area through 25 branches in Kane Kendall DeKalb DuPage LaSalle Will and Cook counties. The bank provides standard services such as checking and savings accounts credit and debit cards CDs mortgages loans and trust services to consumers and business clients. Subsidiary River Street Advisors offers investment management and advisory services. Another unit Old Second Affordable Housing Fund provides home-buying assistance to lower-income customers.

Operations

Commercial real estate loans accounted for 53% of Old Second's loan portfolio at the end of 2015 while residential mortgages made up another 31%. The rest was made up of general commercial loans (12% of loan assets) and construction lending (2%).

Roughly 70% of the bank's revenue comes from interest income. About 54% of its revenue came from loan interest (including fees) during 2015 with another 15% coming from interest on investment securities. The remainder of Old Second's revenue came from deposit account service charges (7%) trust income (6%) mortgage loan sale gains (6%) secondary mortgage fees (1%) and other sources.

Geographic Reach

The bank mostly serves customers in Aurora Illinois (which is 40 miles west of Chicago) and surrounding communities. Its 24 branches are located in the Kane Kendall DeKalb DuPage LaSalle Will and Cook counties of Illinois.

Sales and Marketing

Old Second has been ramping up its advertising spend in recent years. It spent $1.34 million on advertising in 2015 up from $1.28 million and $1.23 million in 2014 and 2013 respectively.

Financial Performance

Old Second's annual revenues have fallen 20% since 2011 as it's had to sell of many of its nonperforming loan assets to de-risk its loan portfolio. The company's profits however have been on the mend as its de-risking measures have led to declining loan loss provisions.

The bank's revenue rebounded by less than 1% to $97.46 million during 2015 as its average loans including loans held for sale grew by 2% for the year.

Revenue growth in 2015 combined with lower interest and amortization costs on deposits drove Old Second Bancorp's net income up by over 50% to $15.39 million. The bank's operating cash levels jumped sharply to $21.14 million (operations had used $6.3 million in 2014) partially thanks to earnings growth but mostly thanks to positive working capital changes related to sales proceeds from loans held for sale and changes in accrued interest payable and other liabilities.

Strategy

Old Second Bancorp continued in 2016 to focus on shedding riskier loan assets that led to deep losses in 2011 while focusing on securing high-quality loans with more creditworthiness. Its efforts began to pay off in 2015 as its average loan balances and revenues began to grow again after years of being in decline.

EXECUTIVES

Assistant Vice President Operations, Brian Bermes
Evp Cfo And Director, J. Douglas Cheatham, age 63, $252,000 total compensation
Ceo And Director Old Second Bancorp Inc. And Old Second National Bank, James L. Eccher, age 54, $325,000 total compensation
Vice President, Jeff Downs
Assistant Vice President, Janet Mutz
Vice President, Robin Hill
Senior Vice President Personal Trust, Andy Roche
Senior Vice President And Treasurer, Stan Faries

Executive Vice President Human Resources, Robert Dicosola
Senior Vice President, Chris Barry
Avp Residential Lender, Terri Hanson
Vice President, Peggy Nelson
Executive Vice President, Don Pilmer
Vice President Treasury Management, John Annis
Vice President, Jocelyn Retz
Vice President, Scott Trandel
Vice President Residential Lending, Michelle Domson
Vice President, Troy Langeness
Vice President, Jeri Ott
Assistant Vice President, Ana Torres
Vice President Commercial Banking, Kristin Zell
Vice President Commercial Banker, Vanessa Aguirre
Senior Vice President Commercial Lending, Mark Fleming
Vice President Residential Lending, Michelle Almond
Assistant Vice President Branch Manager, Nancy Baker
First Vice President, Chris Hainey
Assistant Vice President Retail Manager, Julie Fuller
First Vice President Commercial Banking Director Of Treasury Management, Juwana Zanayed
Senior Vice President, Peter Harrison
Vice President Operations, Carlos Arroyo
Vp, Denise Rogers
Assistant Vice President, Joseph Gordon
First Vice President, Jacqueline Volkert
Vice President Loan Administration, Jason Evans
Chairman Old Second Bancorp Inc. And Old Second National Bank, William B. Skoglund, age 69
Vice Chairman, Gary S. Collins, age 61
Board Member, John Ladowicz
Auditors: Plante & Moran PLLC

LOCATIONS

HQ: Old Second Bancorp., Inc. (Aurora, Ill.)
  37 South River Street, Aurora, IL 60507
Phone: 630 892-0202
Web: www.oldsecond.com

PRODUCTS/OPERATIONS

2015 sales

	% of total
Interest and dividend income	
Loans including fees	54
Taxable	14
Tax exempt	1
Non-interest income	
Service charges on deposits	7
Trust income	6
Net gain on sales of mortgage loans	6
Debit card interchange income	4
Secondary mortgage fees	1
Increase in cash surrender value of bank-owned life insurance	1
Other income	6
Total	**100**

Products/Services

Personal Banking
Card Services
Checking
Loans
Money Services
Online and Mobile Banking
Prime Time Club
Retirement Services
Savings
Loans
Auto and Personal Loans
Home Equity Loans
Home Loans
Mortgage Lenders
Required Documents
SAFE Act
Business Banking

Commercial Banking
Online and Mobile Banking
Small Business Banking
Wealth Management
Business Plan Options
Real Estate Services
Retirement Services

COMPETITORS

Bank of America	Harris
BankFinancial	MB Financial
Fifth Third	Northern Trust
First Midwest Bancorp	West Suburban Bancorp

HISTORICAL FINANCIALS

Company Type: Public

Income Statement — FYE: December 31

	ASSETS ($ mil.)	NET INCOME ($ mil.)	INCOME AS % OF ASSETS	EMPLOYEES
12/18	2,676	34	1.3%	518
12/17	2,383	15	0.6%	450
12/16	2,251	16	0.7%	467
12/15	2,078	15	0.7%	450
12/14	2,062	10	0.5%	485
Annual Growth	**6.7%**	**35.3%**	**—**	**1.7%**

2018 Year-End Financials

Debt ratio: 4.00%	No. of shares (mil.): 30
Return on equity: 16.00%	Dividends
Cash ($ mil.): 55	Yield: 0.0%
Current ratio: —	Payout: 5.0%
Long-term debt ($ mil.): —	Market value ($ mil.): 387

	STOCK PRICE ($) FY Close	P/E High/Low		PER SHARE ($) Earnings	Dividends	Book Value
12/18	13.00	14	11	1.00	0.00	8.00
12/17	14.00	28	20	1.00	0.00	7.00
12/16	11.00	22	12	1.00	0.00	6.00
12/15	8.00	18	11	0.00	0.00	5.00
12/14	5.00	12	10	0.00	0.00	7.00
Annual Growth	**24.7%**	—	—	**24.9%**	**—**	**3.9%**

Olin Corp.

The making of bleach and bullets is all in a day's work for Olin Corporation. The company manufactures chemicals used to make bleach water purification and swimming pool chemicals pulp and paper processing agents and PVC plastics. Olin Chlor Alkali Products is one of the top chlor-alkali producers in North America along with OxyChem. Olin also distributes caustic soda vinyls epoxies chlorinated organics hydrochloric acid and bleach. In addition in a quite divergent business the company's Winchester Ammunition unit makes branded sporting ammunition reloading components small caliber military ammunition and components and industrial cartridges.

Operations

Olin operates three business segments: Chlor Alkali Products and Vinyl (CAPV) Epoxy and Winchester Ammunition.

CAPV accounts for about 55% of total sales and manufactures products including chlorine and caustic soda ethlyene dichloride and vinyl chloride monomers and hydrogen.

The Epoxy segment epoxy materials such as allyl chloride epichlorodydrin and liquid epoxy resins as well as downstream products such as converted epoxy resins and additives. The segment accounts for around a third of sales.

Winchester Ammunition generates more than 10% of sales and manufactures sporting ammunition reloading components small caliber military ammunition and components and industrial cartridges.

Geographic Reach

Olin has plants in across the US (Augusta Georgia; California; Illinois; Mississippi; McIntosh Alabama; Charleston Tennessee; St. Gabriel Louisiana; Henderson Nevada; Niagara Falls New York); and in Canada (Becancour Quebec). It also has a facility in Australia that loads and packs sporting and industrial ammunition. It also has plants and facilities in Germany Brazil South Korea Italy the Netherlands and China.

The US accounts for about 60% of Olin's revenue.

Sales and Marketing

Olin markets most of its products and services through its own sales force and sells directly to various industrial customers mass merchants retailers wholesalers and other distributors as well as the US government and its prime contractors.

The products from Epoxy segment and Chlor Alkali Products and Vinyls are delivered primarily by marine vessels deep-water and coastal barges railcars and trucks.

The end users of products and services of the Epoxy segment are manufacturers of polymers resins and other plastic materials water purification and pesticides adhesives paint and coatings composites and flooring.

Winchester's sales and distribution chain has strong ties to traditional dealers and distributors.

Dow DuPont is Olin's largest customer accounting for about 15% of total sales.

Financial Performance

In the last decade Olin's revenue has gone up steadily from $1.7 billion in 2008 to $2.8 billion in 2015 before an acquisition of Dow Chemical's chlorine and related businesses doubled its revenue to $5.6 billion in 2016. Net income fluctuated in the 2008-14 period between a low of $65 million and a high of $242 million. In 2015-16 the company reported combined losses of $6 million related to acquisition costs.

In 2017 revenue rose 13% to $6.3 billion the highest in company's history thanks to accelerated growth after the Dow acquisition. The growth was triggered by $500 million increase in Chlor Alkali Products and Vinyls sales due to higher caustic soda and EDC product prices as well as volumes. Epoxy sales also increased by $265 million thanks to higher product prices and increased volumes. Despite a boost in revenue Olin's sales volumes were negatively impacted by Hurricane Harvey (approximately $55 million in lost revenue).

Net income rocketed up from a loss of $4 million in 2016 to a profit of half a billion dollars in 2017 the highest in company's history primarily from $400 million in income tax benefit and year-over-year savings of $100 million in restructuring charges and acquisition related costs.

Olin's cash holdings stood at approximately $220 million for 2017. Operations provided $650 million in cash. Investments cost the company half a billion mostly in CAPEX of $250 million as well as $117 million in financing the company's activities.

Strategy

Olin seeks to strengthen its position as a preferred supplier of chlor alkali products to merchant market customers though internal expansion and complementary acquisitions.

The company continues to leverage its legendary Winchester brand with its reputation of innovation (such as introducing reduced-lead and non-lead products) to improve its position as a major supplier of ammunition. To reduce Winchester's annual operating costs by about $30 million the division relocated its centerfire ammunition operations from East Alton Illinois to lower-cost Oxford Mississippi in 2016.

In the epoxy business Olin continues its search for productivity cost improvements throughout its supply chain while making use of its ten sites on four continents to expand into emerging markets.

HISTORY

Vermont-born engineer Franklin Olin founded Equitable Powder in East Alton Illinois in 1892 to make blasting powder for midwestern coal fields. By 1898 the company called Western Cartridge was also making ammunition for small arms. When WWI increased demand for military cartridges Western Cartridge built a brass mill. After the war it began making custom brass and other copper alloys for industrial customers. The company bought Winchester Repeating Arms maker of the famous Winchester Model 1876 repeating rifles in 1931. During WWII Western Cartridge developed the US carbine and M-1 rifles.

The various businesses of Western Cartridge merged as Olin Industries in 1944. Franklin then retired handing the company to sons John and Spencer.

Enriched by the war effort Olin Industries grew. In 1949 it began making cellophane and in 1951 it acquired Frost Lumber Industries and Ecusta Paper a maker of cigarette papers. Olin Industries merged with Mathieson Chemical in 1954 to form Olin Mathieson Chemical the fifth-largest US chemical company.

The Mathieson Alkali Works was founded in Saltville Virginia in 1892 to produce alkalis using a process acquired from English chemical firm Neil Mathieson. By 1909 the company began producing liquid chlorine and in 1923 it built one of the earliest plants for producing synthetic ammonia. During WWII Mathieson manufactured chlorine for water purification and alkali chemicals for sanitation. In 1952 Mathieson acquired drugmaker Squibb.

Olin Mathieson continued to diversify in the mid-1950s buying Blockson Chemical (industrial phosphates) and Brown Paper Mill (kraft paper bags and corrugated cardboard containers). Frost Lumber and Brown Paper Mill formed the Forest Products Division later dubbed Olinkraft. In 1956 Olin Mathieson entered the aluminum business via a joint venture — just in time for a drop in aluminum demand.

In the 1960s the company began making urethane chemicals. It also created Olin-American a subsidiary that built houses and spun off Squibb. In 1969 it shortened its name to Olin Corporation and moved to Stamford Connecticut.

The 1970s saw Olin reining in its diverse businesses. It spun off Olinkraft and sold its aluminum operations. During the 1980s Olin sold its sporting-arms business (but kept Winchester ammunition) as well as its paper housing and cellophane units. John Olin died in 1982. The company acquired Rockcor which included Rocket Research Pacific Electro Dynamics and Physics International in 1985.

Olin moved its headquarters to Norwalk Connecticut in 1995 the same year Spencer Olin died. In 1996 as the earnings potential of its ordnance and aerospace operations lagged Olin spun them off as Primex Technologies. It also sold its isocyanate (used in plastics and adhesives) and other cyclical businesses. Olin bought the remaining 50% of its Niachlor chlor alkali joint venture from DuPont in 1997 after considering putting Niachlor up for sale.

Aspiring to become a leading basic-materials company Olin spun off its specialty chemical business in early 1999 under the name Arch Chemicals. Citing regulatory issues Olin cancelled plans in 2000 to form a chlor alkali chemicals joint venture with Occidental's OxyChem subsidiary. Olin acquired Monarch Brass & Copper Corp. for about $49 million in 2001. The next year it bought brass rod maker Chase Industries. Olin closed its copper and copper alloy sheet plant in Indianapolis in 2003.

In 2007 Olin grew its core chemicals business acquiring chlor-alkali producer Pioneer Companies for about $415 million. To help pay for the deal in late 2007 Olin sold its former Metals unit to investment group KPS Capital Partners for almost $400 million. The Metals unit — which had accounted for about two-thirds of sales — made copper and copper alloy sheets clad metal foil and stainless-steel strips.

In 2011 Olin acquired the balance of the SunBelt Chlor Alkali joint venture it did not own from partner PolyOne Corp. for $175 million in cash and assumed debt. It had held a 50% stake in the venture which produces chlorine and caustic soda. The SunBelt chlor alkali plant located within Olin's McIntosh Alabama facility has approximately 350000 tons of membrane technology capacity and generated some $70 million in earnings in 2010.

The company in 2012 acquired Illinois-based KA Steel for $328 million in cash. KA Steel is one of the largest caustic soda distributors in North America and its acquisition increased Olin's capacity to manufacture bleach by about 20% as well as to sell some of its other products such as hydrochloric acid and potassium hydroxide. A result the purchase Olin formed a chemical distribution segment that year.

EXECUTIVES

Evp Synergies And Systems, John L. McIntosh, age 65, $509,000 total compensation

Chairman President And Ceo, John E. Fischer, age 64, $836,000 total compensation

Vp And Cfo, Todd A. Slater, age 56, $518,000 total compensation

Evp; President Epoxy And International, Pat D. Dawson, age 61, $636,000 total compensation

Svp Ammunition, Thomas J. OÂ'Keefe, age 60

Evp; President Chlor Alkali Vinyls And Services, James A. Varilek, age 60, $447,000 total compensation

Vice President And President Winchester, Brett Flaugher

Vice President Internal Audit, Frank O'Brien

Vice President Human Resources, Dolores Ennico

Vice President Business Integration, Leonard Scott

Vp And Controller, Randee Summer

Vice President Education And Trainning, Mike Gilley

Vice President Finance, Tim Ponsler

Board Member, John O'connor

Board Member, Randall Larrimore

Board Member, William H Weideman

Auditors: KPMG LLP

LOCATIONS

HQ: Olin Corp.
190 Carondelet Plaza, Suite 1530, Clayton, MO 63105
Phone: 314 480-1400
Web: www.olin.com

2016 sales

	$ mil.	% of total
US	3,357	60
Other countries	2,194	40
Total	**5,551**	**100**

PRODUCTS/OPERATIONS

2016 sales

	$ mil.	% of total
Chlor Alkali Products and Vinyls	2,999	54
Epoxy	1,822	33
Winchester	729	13
Total	**5,551**	**100**

Business Segments

Business Segments
Chlor Alkali Products
- Caustic soda
- Chlorine
- Hydrochloric acid
- Sodium hydrochlorite (Industrial and institutional cleaning products)
- Sodium hydrosulfite (bleaching)

Winchester
- Ammunition (shot-shell small-caliber and rimfire)
- Government-owned arsenal operation (maintenance for the US Army)
- Industrial cartridges (eight-gauge loads and powder-actuated tool loads for the construction industry)

Chemical Distribution
- Bleach
- Caustic soda

COMPETITORS

Axiall	Mitsubishi Chemical
Blount International	Occidental Chemical
Brenntag	PPG Industries
FMC	Remington Arms
Formosa Plastics USA	Sumitomo Chemical
Freedom Group	Univar Inc.
Herstal	Westlake Chemical
Huntsman Corp	

HISTORICAL FINANCIALS

Company Type: Public

Income Statement   FYE: December 31

	REVENUE ($ mil.)	NET INCOME ($ mil.)	NET PROFIT MARGIN	EMPLOYEES
12/18	6,946	328	4.7%	6,500
12/17	6,268	550	8.8%	6,400
12/16	5,551	(4)	—	6,400
12/15	2,854	(1)	—	6,200
12/14	2,241	106	4.7%	3,900
Annual Growth	**32.7%**	**32.7%**	**—**	**13.6%**

2018 Year-End Financials

Debt ratio: 36.00%
Return on equity: 12.00%
Cash ($ mil.): 179
Current ratio: 2.00
Long-term debt ($ mil.): 3,104

No. of shares (mil.): 165
Dividends
  Yield: 4.0%
  Payout: 41.0%
Market value ($ mil.): 3,324

	STOCK PRICE ($) FY Close	P/E High/Low		PER SHARE ($) Earnings	Dividends	Book Value
12/18	20.00	20	9	2.00	1.00	17.00
12/17	36.00	11	8	3.00	1.00	16.00
12/16	26.00	—	—	(0.00)	1.00	14.00
12/15	17.00	—	—	(0.00)	1.00	15.00
12/14	23.00	22	16	1.00	1.00	13.00
Annual Growth	**(3.1%)**	—	—	**10.0%**	**(0.0%)**	**7.0%**

Omnicom Group, Inc.

Omnicom Group creates advertising that is omnipresent. The company ranks as the world's #1 corporate media services conglomerate with 1500 agencies across 100-plus countries conducting advertising marketing and public relations operations. It serves global clients through its agency networks BBDO Worldwide DDB Worldwide and TBWA Worldwide. Agencies such as OMD PHD and Hearts & Science comprise the Omnicom Media Group which provides end-to-end data-driven media services. Omnicom's Diversified Agency Services division includes 200 companies providing customer relationship management (CRM) as well as branding and research events and public relations. The US accounts for about 50% of sales.

Operations

Omnicom is active in four primary disciplines: Advertising Customer Relationship Management (CRM) Public Relations and Healthcare.

Advertising accounts for about 55% of Omnicom's total revenue. It includes creative services as well as strategic planning and data analytics.

The CRM segment which accounts for nearly 30% of revenue consists of two units CRM Customer Experience and CRM Execution & Support. CRM Consumer Experience includes Omnicom Precision Marketing Group and digital/direct marketing agencies as well as branding shopper marketing and experiential marketing agencies. CRM Execution & Support carries out field marketing sales support merchandising and point of sale as well as other specialized marketing and custom communications services.

Public Relations services including corporate communications and crisis management generate about 10% of sales while Healthcare-focused marketing and communications provides about 7%.

Geographic Reach

Omnicom has principal corporate offices in New York Connecticut and Florida while it has international offices in London Shanghai and Singapore. The group's network of agencies serves some 5000 clients in more than 100 countries.

About 60% of the company's revenue comes from the Americas while EMEA (Europe Middle East and Africa) contributes around 30%. The remaining 10% or so comes from the Asia-Pacific region.

Sales and Marketing

As a leading global advertising marketing and corporate communications company Omnicom has a large and diverse client base. Often several Omnicom agencies will serve the same client concurrently. None of its clients account for more than 5% of revenue while its top 100 clients account for a little more than 50% of revenue and are served on average by more than 60 Omnicom agencies.

By industry food and beverage companies along with pharmaceutical and healthcare firms account for the largest share of customers with each contributing 15% of the company's total revenue. Omnicom serves other notable industries including consumer products technology financial services and the auto industry each accounting for nearly 10% of sales.

Financial Performance

While Omnicom's net income held steady throughout the most recent five-year period ending in 2018 the company struggled to meaningfully grow its revenue. Challenges include technological disruption from online advertising competitors such as Google and Facebook and changing consumer behavior complicating the marketing environment.

In fiscal 2018 revenue was $15.3 billion representing less than 1% growth from the prior year. Organic revenue growth from advertising PR healthcare and consumer experience services was offset by revenue decreases related to disposals of some of its businesses (primarily in CRM Execution & Support) a negative foreign exchange rate a decrease in acquisition revenue and the adoption of new accounting standards at the start of 2018.

Net income grew slightly to $1.4 billion in 2018 up from $1.2 billion in 2017. Omnicom benefited from a decreased income tax rate and a decrease in operating expenses.

Cash at the end of 2018 was $3.7 billion. Cash from operations was $1.7 billion while investing activities used $221.8 million. Financing activities used $1.4 billion.

Strategy

Omnicom has shifted focus toward high growth digital marketing to better compete with Google and Facebook. To this end the company sold about 20 businesses as it moved to dispose of non-core assets cutting a total of 8400 positions in Q3 of 2018.

Also in 2018 it rolled out its data and analytics platform Omni. The online marketing tool is designed to be a user-friendly one-stop-shop for all Omnicom agencies and clients to plan and create ad campaigns using data from third parties. Users log into Omni to plan and buy media store customer information and track customer sales and other actions.

Mergers and Acquisitions

In 2018 Omnicom acquired Credera a Dallas-based management and IT consulting firm. Credera helps clients such as Southwest Airlines and Chili's with various consulting services including implementing technology for marketing programs and e-commerce.

Another purchase earlier that year was Elsevier's Japanese Pharma Communications business. Pharma Communications delivers medical content for promotional materials and educational programs directed at doctors and patients. Omnicom made the purchase to grow its EMC K.K. healthcare marketing communications agency.

Also in 2018 Omnicom acquired Virginia-based Snow Companies a full-service patient engagement agency that focuses on direct-to-patient (DTP) communications marketing education and patient research initiatives. It primarily serves major pharmaceutical and biotech companies.

Company Background

Omnicom Group was created in 1986 to combine three leading ad agencies ? BBDO Worldwide Doyle Dane Bernbach Group (DDB) and Needham Harper Worldwide ? into a single group capable of competing in the worldwide market.

BBDO Worldwide founded in New York in 1928 as Batten Barton Durstine & Osborn had a huge PepsiCo account and developed the Pepsi Generation campaign.

Doyle Dane Bernbach Group (DDB) which had created the fahrvergn gen ads for Volkswagen had strong ties in Europe.

Needham Harper Worldwide which had served up the "You Deserve a Break Today" commercials for McDonald's had connections in Asia.

Omnicom was established as holding company of independent operating units working together to gain scale.

HISTORY

Omnicom Group was created in 1986 to combine three leading ad agencies into a single group capable of competing in the worldwide market. BBDO Worldwide founded in New York in 1928 as Batten Barton Durstine & Osborn had a huge PepsiCo account and developed the Pepsi Generation campaign. Doyle Dane Bernbach Group (DDB) which had created the fahrvergn gen ads for Volkswagen had strong ties in Europe. And Needham Harper Worldwide which had served up the "You Deserve a Break Today" commercials for McDonald's had connections in Asia. BBDO remained separate but DDB and Needham Harper were merged to form DDB Needham Worldwide. The business services units (public relations firms and direct marketers) of each of these companies were tucked under the Diversified Agency Services (DAS) umbrella.

Bruce Crawford a previous chairman of BBDO who had just finished a stint running New York's Metropolitan Opera became chairman and CEO in 1989. He transformed DAS from a chaotic group of shops into an integrated marketing giant and ran Omnicom as a holding company of independent operating units working together through cross-referrals. By keeping costs low especially interest expenses Omnicom survived the 1990-91 recession with little pain. The company acquired Goodby Berlin & Silverstein (now Goodby Silverstein & Partner s) in 1992. The next year TBWA Advertising (founded in Paris in 1970 by American Bill Tragos) was added to Omnicom's roster.

The merger spree continued in 1994 when Omnicom purchased WWAV Group the largest direct-marketing agency in the UK. In 1995 Omnicom fused TBWA with Chiat/Day (founded in 1968 by Jay Chiat and Guy Day) to form TBWA International Network. Omnicom also acquired Michigan-based Ross Roy Communications (later Interone Marketing Group). In 1997 DDB Needham won back its McDonald's account after a 15-year hiatus. That year Crawford stepped down as CEO (though he remained chairman) and John Wren took control of Omnicom.

In 1998 the company acquired PR firm Fleishman-Hillard adding to the PR clout it established with the acquisition of Ketchum Communications (now Ketchum) in 1996. Omnicom also acquired GGT Group of London for $235 million. (GGT's New York office Wells BDDP had lost a large Procter & Gamble account that year.) It merged GGT's BDDP Worldwide with TBWA to form TBWA Worldwide. BBDO landed a $200 million account with PepsiCo's Frito-Lay that year.

Omnicom's position in Europe was boosted in 1999 when it bought the Abbot Mead Vickers (now Abbot Mead Vickers BBDO) shares it didn't already own. That year TBWA founder William Tragos retired from the company (replaced by Lee Clow) and DDB Needham changed its moniker to DDB Worldwide Communications Group. Omnicom also bought market research firm M/A/R/C for about $95 million and invested $20 million in pharmaceutical clinical trials company SCIREX. In 2000 BBDO scored a major coup over rival FCB Worldwide (now part of Interpublic) by landing the $1.8 billion DaimlerChrysler account. The next year it formed Seneca Investments to hold its stakes in several i-services shops including Agency.com and Organic. (Omnicom acquired the interactive agencies outright in 2003.)

After years of acquisitions and fine-tuning its operating structure Omnicom encountered the effects of the global recession in late 2008. Like most players in the media communications and advertising industries Omnicom experienced declines in revenue and net income at the end of 2009. It attributed the crisis within the automotive industry and declines in the demand for its sports and event marketing services as major reasons for the drops.

In 2010 the company acquired seven companies including Sales Power an in-store promotion company catering to South China and Maslov PR a public relations firm based in Moscow. Among the twelve companies it acquired in 2011 was Nancy Bailey & Associates a corporate licensing and consulting firm.

EXECUTIVES

Evp And Cfo, Philip J. Angelastro, age 55, $850,000 total compensation

Treasurer Omnicom Group And President And Ceo Omnicom Capital, Dennis E. Hewitt, age 74, $395,000 total compensation

President And Ceo, John D. Wren, age 67, $1,000,000 total compensation

Vice Chairman; Chairman Asia Pacific, Serge Dumont

Evp, Asit Mehra

Evp And Dean Omnicom University, Janet Riccio

Evp, Rita E. Rodriguez

Evp, Peter Sherman

Ceo Omnicom Digital, Jonathan B. Nelson, age 51, $850,000 total compensation

Svp General Counsel And Secretary, Michael J. O'Brien, age 57, $700,000 total compensation

Vice President Financial Systems, Allen Flissler

Executive Vice President, Thomas Carey

Vice President Finance Operations, Michael Larson

Senior Vice President And Chief Diversity Officer, Tiffany R Warren

Vice President Of Finance Operations, Brian Sullivan

Senior Vice President, Joe Ricciardi

Vice President Financial Planning And Analysis, Daniel Bearison

Senior Vice President Director Of Global Business Strategy, Celine Vita

Vice President Global Travel, Tony Occhipinti

Vice President Strategy And Operations, Josh Tobey

Senior Vice President Director Of Client Services, Deirdre Eliopoulos

Vice President Of Technology, Pete Donina

Vice President Sports Network, Courtney Leddy

Senior Vice President Senior Account Director, Kathryn Brown

Vice President Account Supervisor Ketchum. Passion And Precision In Communication, Stephanie Buttrill

Vice President Director, Tracey Maffeo

Senior Vice President Director North American Food Practice, Kim Essex

Vice President Associate Media Director, Meredith Reynolds

Vice President Account Director, Amy Hatton

Vice President, Dalya Browne

Vice President Group Account Supervisor, Joseph Bailey

Senior Vice President Group Account Supervisor, Kathleen F Murphy

Senior Vice President Director Brand Practice, Becca Leish

Vice President Group Manager, Kim Assalone

Vice President Social Strategy, Melissa Schreiber

Vice President Director Of Strategy, Kim Ryneska

Vice President Account Director, Natalie Connelly

Executive Vice President Executive Creative Director, Dennis Lim

Vice President Account Director, Allen McCormick

Vice President Group Account Supervisor, Jesse Jenkins

Senior Vice President Account Director, Meg Fitzpatrick

Vice President Group Copy Supervisor, Jessica Krause

Senior Vice President Corporate Practice, Annalise Carol

Vice President, Elizabeth Watters Roberts

Chairman, Bruce Crawford, age 89

Board Member, Linda Johnson Rice

Treasurer, Angie Hickman

Board Member, Debbie Kissire

Auditors: KPMG LLP

LOCATIONS

HQ: Omnicom Group, Inc.
437 Madison Avenue, New York, NY 10022
Phone: 212 415-3600 **Fax:** 212 415-3393
Web: www.omnicomgroup.com

2017 Sales

	$ mil.	% of total
Americas		
North America	8,686	57
Latin America	495	3
EMEA		
Europe	4,128	27
Middle East and Africa	315	2
Asia Pacific	1,650	11
Total	**15,274**	**100**

PRODUCTS/OPERATIONS

2017 sales

	$ mil.	% of total
Advertising	8,142	53
Customer relationship management	4,820	32
Public relations	1,377	9
Specialty communications	935	6
Total	**15,274**	**100**

Selected Operations

Global advertising networks
  BBDO Worldwide
  DDB Worldwide
  TBWA Worldwide
National advertising agencies
  Goodby Silverstein & Partners (San Francisco)
  GSD&M (Austin TX)
  Martin|Williams (Minneapolis)
  Merkley + Partners (New York City)
  Zimmerman Partners Advertising (Fort Lauderdale FL)
Direct response
  Interbrand (brand identity)
  M/A/R/C Research (market research)
  Rapp (direct marketing)
  Targetbase (direct marketing)
Promotional marketing
  The Beanstalk Group (brand licensing and consulting)
  CPM (field marketing)
  The Integer Group (retail marketing)
  Kaleidoscope (sports and event marketing)
  Millsport (sports and event marketing)
Public relations
  Clark & Weinstock
  Cone
  Fleishman-Hillard
  Gavin Anderson & Company
  GPC International
  Ketchum
  Porter Novelli International
  Smythe Dorward Lambert
Specialty communications
  Adelphi Group (health care)
  Corbett Accel Healthcare (health care)
  Dieste (multicultural marketing)
  Doremus (business-to-business advertising)
  SafirRosetti (security and intelligence)
Media services
  Icon International
  Novus Print Media
  OMD Worldwide
  PHD Network

COMPETITORS

Dentsu	Interpublic Group
Dentsu Aegis	Publicis Groupe
Hakuhodo	WPP
Havas	

Company Type: Public

Income Statement FYE: December 31

	REVENUE ($ mil.)	NET INCOME ($ mil.)	NET PROFIT MARGIN	EMPLOYEES
12/18	15,290	1,326	8.7%	70,400
12/17	15,274	1,088	7.1%	77,300
12/16	15,417	1,149	7.5%	78,500
12/15	15,134	1,094	7.2%	74,900
12/14	15,318	1,104	7.2%	74,000
Annual Growth	(0.0%)	4.7%	—	(1.2%)

2018 Year-End Financials

Debt ratio: 20.00%
Return on equity: 51.00%
Cash ($ mil.): 3,652
Current ratio: 1.00
Long-term debt ($ mil.): 4,384

No. of shares (mil.): 224
Dividends
  Yield: 3.0%
  Payout: 41.0%
Market value ($ mil.): 16,398

	STOCK PRICE ($) FY Close	P/E High/Low		PER SHARE ($) Earnings	Dividends	Book Value
12/18	73.00	14	12	6.00	2.00	11.00
12/17	73.00	19	14	5.00	2.00	11.00
12/16	85.00	18	14	5.00	2.00	9.00
12/15	76.00	18	15	4.00	2.00	10.00
12/14	77.00	18	15	4.00	2.00	12.00
Annual Growth	(1.4%)	—	—	8.3%	6.0%	(0.4%)

ON Semiconductor Corp

ON Semiconductor's products manage power use and handle dozens of other functions in an array of electronics. The company designs and manufactures energy efficient low-cost high-volume analog logic and discrete semiconductors ? some 84000 products in all. ON's devices perform power and signal control and interface functions in electronic gear ranging from networking routers and wireless phones and digital cameras to household appliances and electronically controlled operations in vehicles. ON sells directly to manufacturers and to distributors such as Avnet and Arrow Electronics. More than half of ON's sales come from the Asia/Pacific region.

Operations

ON operates through three segments: the Power Solutions Group the Analog Solutions Group and the Image Sensor Group.

The Power Solutions Group accounts for more than 50% of revenue. It offers an array of semiconductor products that regulate power and signal functions including power switching power conversion signal conditioning circuit protection signal amplification and voltage reference functions. Some products help computers use power more efficiently.

The Analog Solutions Group which supplies about 35% of revenue designs and develops processors for specific power-related applications in the automotive consumer computing industrial communications medical and aerospace/defense markets. Some automotive products help reduce emissions.

The Image Sensor Group which generates about 15% of revenue designs and develops products for capturing images. For cameras used in a variety of

settings such as automotive ON's products handle image signal processing and enable auto focus and image stabilization.

ON Semiconductor handles much of its own manufacturing but more than a third of its manufacturing expenses go to contract manufacturers that include Amkor ASE and Kingpak.

Geographic Reach

Headquartered in Phoenix Arizona ON operates distribution centers throughout Asia Europe and the Americas. The company conducts research and development in about 15 countries.

ON Semiconductor's manufacturing plants are in the US the Czech Republic Belgium Malaysia Japan South Korea Canada China Philippines and Vietnam.

Singapore and Hong Kong are the company's largest markets each accounting for about 30% and 25% of sales respectively.

Sales and Marketing

ON's products appear in a wide range of end-user markets including automotive communications computing consumer medical industrial networking telecom and aerospace/defense. Automotive is the largest market generating nearly a third of sales followed by Industrial about 25% and Communications about 20%.

The company relies on 10 customers for about 25% of its revenue.

The company works through several sales channels. Distributors account for almost 60% of revenue while direct sales to original equipment manufacturers account for just less than 35% of revenue. Some customers on the OEM roster are Bosch GmbH Continental Automotive Systems Delphi Hella Huawei Technologies Co. Ltd. Magna International Panasonic Corp. and Samsung Electronics. Direct sales to contract manufacturers supply about 5% of sales.

Financial Performance

ON in 2018 posted its sixth straight year of robust revenue growth driven by the automotive and power markets.

Sales were up 6% to $5.8 billion a $335 million increase from 2017 driven by 8% and 6% increases in Power Solutions Group and Analog Solutions Group revenue respectively. Contributions from the Fairchild acquisition also boosted sales. Image Systems revenue slipped 1% as the company exited the Mobile CIS business.

Net income dropped to $627.4 million in 2018 compared to $810.7 million in 2017. The difference was a tax benefit the company had in 2017 that was not repeated in 2018.

ON's coffers held $1.1 billion in cash and equivalents in 2018 compared to $966.6 million the year before. In 2018 the company's operations generated $1.2 billion in cash while investing activities used $548.9 million and financing activities used $605.1 million.

ON has about $3 billion in debt some of it taken on through the Fairchild acquisition. Paying for its debt could curtail the company's ability to invest in operations.

Strategy

ON wants to make its biggest market automotive electronics even bigger. The company's automotive products do jobs throughout vehicles including reducing emissions improving fuel economy and safety enhancing lighting and controlling brakes and other systems. New automotive products include image sensors for advanced driver assistance systems (ADAS) and LED lighting.

New products for other markets include power integrated modules USB-C power management for server and cloud environments and other power 7 management analog and sensor products for strategic end-markets.

As with other companies ON has found sales with new smartphone platforms for the Chinese

market. Also in the smartphone market the company benefits from the increasing adoption of fast-charging USB-C. On Semiconductor is using its smartphone relationships to cross-sell Fairchild's products into that market.

ON's recent acquisitions have expanded its product portfolio and opened new markets. The acquisitions include Fairchild AXSEM Truesense Imaging and Aptina.

The company added to its manufacturing capacity with the purchase of a 300mm fab in East Fishkill New York from GLOBALFOUNDRIES for $430 million.

Mergers and Acquisitions

In 2019 ON agreed to acquire Quantenna Communications which develops Wi-Fi technology for its connectivity portfolio.

In 2018 ON bought SensL Technologies which makes silicon photomultipliers single photon avalanche diode and LiDAR sending products. The deal extends ON Semiconductor's automotive sensing product offerings.

Company Background

ON Semiconductor and Freescale were both spun off from Motorola in 1999 with On Semiconductor making analog standard advanced logic chips as well as discrete small signal and power components. Investment firm TPG Capital owned 91% of ON Semiconductor and Motorola held the rest. The next year On Semiconductor went public raising more than $500 million in its IPO. Also that year it bought Cherry Semiconductor for about $250 million which expanded it into multiphase controllers drivers and automotive/industrial power management components. In 2005 and 2006 it opened engineering centers in South Korea and Taiwan.

EXECUTIVES

Senior Vice President Human Resources, Colleen McKeown
Vice President And General Manager Of Protection Products Division, Gary Straker
President Ceo And Director, Keith D. Jackson, age 63, $906,154 total compensation
Svp And General Manager Operating Systems And Technology Group, William A. (Bill) Schromm, age 61, $444,800 total compensation
Evp General Counsel Chief Compliance Ethics And Risk Officer And Corporate Secretary, George H. (Sonny) Cave, age 61, $366,653 total compensation
Svp And Cto, Hans Stork
Svp Strategic Business Ventures, Mamoon Rashid, $353,329 total compensation
Evp And General Manager Power Solutions Group, William M. (Bill) Hall, age 63, $394,697 total compensation
Evp Sales And Marketing, Paul E. Rolls, age 56, $446,148 total compensation
Evp And General Manager Analog Solutions Group, Robert A. (Bob) Klosterboer, age 58, $340,337 total compensation
Evp And Cfo, Bernard Gutmann, age 59, $470,848 total compensation
Svp And General Manager Of The Image Sensor Group, Taner Ozcelik, age 51
Senior Vice President Human Resources, Terri Richway
Vice President Of Finance Fpanda Corporate Business Units, Kelly Neagle
Vice President Of Sales And Marketing, Peter Hansen
Senior Vice President Sales Asia Pacific, David Chow
Svp Global Supply Chain Operations, Brent Wilson
Senior Vice President Of Worldwide Operations, Mark Goranson

Vice President And Director Of Manufacturing
Technology, Jimmie Echols
Vice President, Mark Asselberg
Human Resources Director And Vice President,
Robert Wiegand
Executive Vice President Sales And Marketing,
Bob Mahoney
Vice President Human Resources, Colleen McCane
Executive Vice President And General Manager
Power Solutions Group, Bill Hall
Vp Investor Relations And Corporate
Development, Parag Agarwal
Legal Secretary, Susan Galpin
Vice President Operations, Jeff Mendiola
Vice President Of Sales, Dan Olson
Vice President And General Manager High Power
Division, Asif Jakwani
Executive Vice President, Donald Colvin
Vice President Assistant General Counsel
Assistant Compliance And Ethics Officer
Assistant Secretar, Mark Rogers
Vice President Of Human Resources, Mike Lane
Vice President And General Manager, Sergio
Fissore
Vice President Global Solutions Engineering,
Dave Priscak
Evp And Gm Analog Solutions Group, Vincent
Hopkin
Chairman, Alan Campbell, age 60
Board Member, Dodie Hernandez
Board Member, Daryl Ostrander
Board Member, Emmanuel Hernandez
Assistant Treasurer, Matt Brimhall
Board Member, Gilles Delfassy
Board Member, Teresa Ressel
Auditors: PricewaterhouseCoopers LLP

LOCATIONS

HQ: ON Semiconductor Corp
5005 E. McDowell Road, Phoenix, AZ 85008
Phone: 602 244-6600   Fax: 602 244-6071
Web: www.onsemi.com

2018 Sales

	$ mil.	% of total
Singapore	1,955	32
Hong Kong	1,489	26
United Kingdom	947	14
United States	863	12
Other	625	8
Total	**5,878**	**100**

PRODUCTS/OPERATIONS

2018 Sales

	$ mil.	% of total
Power Solutions Group	3,038	52
Analog Solutions Group	2,071	35
Image Sensor Group	769	13
Total	**5,878**	**100**

2018 Sales

	% of total
Automotive	31
Industrial	27
Communications	18
Consumer	13
Computing	11
Total	**100**

Selected Products

Connectivity Custom & SoC
  Audio/Visual ASSP
  Connectivit
  SoC SIP & Custom Products
  Customer Foundry Services
Sensors
  Image Sensors & Processors
  Light & Touch Sensors
  Thermal Management
  Battery-free Wireless Sensors
Power Management

AC-DC Controllers & Regulators
Battery Management
LED Drivers
Analog Logic & Timing
  Amplifiers & Comparators
  Clock Generation
  Clock & Data Distribution
  Interfaces

COMPETITORS

Analog Devices
Cypress Semiconductor
Diodes
Infineon Technologies
Integrated Device
  Technology
Maxim Integrated
  Products
Microchip Technology

Mitsubishi Electric
NXP Semiconductors
Renesas Electronics
STMicroelectronics
Semtech
TSMC
Texas Instruments
Toshiba

HISTORICAL FINANCIALS

Company Type: Public

Income Statement

FYE: December 31

	REVENUE ($ mil.)	NET INCOME ($ mil.)	NET PROFIT MARGIN	EMPLOYEES
12/18	5,878	627	10.7%	35,700
12/17	5,543	811	14.6%	34,000
12/16	3,907	182	4.7%	32,000
12/15	3,496	206	5.9%	24,500
12/14	3,162	190	6.0%	24,500
Annual Growth	**16.8%**	**34.9%**	**—**	**9.9%**

2018 Year-End Financials

Debt ratio: 36.00%
Return on equity: 21.00%
Cash ($ mil.): 1,070
Current ratio: 2.00
Long-term debt ($ mil.): 2,628

No. of shares (mil.): 414
Dividends
  Yield: —
  Payout: —
Market value ($ mil.): 6,832

	STOCK PRICE ($) FY Close	P/E High/Low		Earnings	Dividends	Book Value
12/18	17.00	18	10	1.00	0.00	8.00
12/17	21.00	11	7	2.00	0.00	7.00
12/16	13.00	30	16	0.00	0.00	4.00
12/15	10.00	27	18	0.00	0.00	4.00
12/14	10.00	24	16	0.00	0.00	4.00
Annual Growth	**13.0%**	**—**	**—**	**35.3%**	**—**	**19.6%**

ONEAMERICA FINANCIAL PARTNERS, INC.

EXECUTIVES

Chb-Pres-Ceo, J Scott Davison
Exec V Pres-Cfo, Jeffrey D Holley
Exec V Pres, Mark Roller
Exec V Pres-Sr Clo-SEC, Thomas M Zurek
Sr V Pres-CIO, Gene P Berry
Sr V Pres-Chief Hr Officer, Karin Sarratt
Pres Individual Insurance, Patrick M Foley
Vice President, Angela Trefethen
Consultant, Bartholomew Brown
Manager Public Relations Tax, Christina Cozzolino
Analyst, Christy Wieringa

LOCATIONS

HQ: ONEAMERICA FINANCIAL PARTNERS, INC.
1 AMERICAN SQ, INDIANAPOLIS, IN 462820020
Phone: 317 285-1877
Web: WWW.ONEAMERICA.COM

HISTORICAL FINANCIALS

Company Type: Private

Income Statement

FYE: December 31

	ASSETS ($ mil.)	NET INCOME ($ mil.)	INCOME AS % OF ASSETS	EMPLOYEES
12/16	19,921	88	0.4%	9,875
12/15	18,491	68	0.4%	—
12/14	0	0	—	—
12/04	15,028	56	0.4%	—
Annual Growth	**2.4%**	**3.8%**	**—**	**—**

OneMain Holdings Inc

With more than $21 billion in total assets consumer finance company OneMain Holdings (formerly known as Springleaf Holdings) offers auto loans and personal loans primarily to non-prime customers who have limited access to credit from banks credit card companies and other lenders through more than 1600 branches in around 45 states. It also provides credit insurance non-credit insurance and related products through subsidiaries Merit Life Insurance AHL and Triton. Tracing its roots back to 1920 Springleaf renamed itself in late 2015 after acquiring OneMain Financial.

Operations

OneMain Holdings' operates through its two segments of Consumer and Insurance and Acquisitions and Servicing though about 99% of its revenue derives from the Consumer and Insurance business.

The Consumer and Insurance division mostly makes and services personal and auto loans (typically ranging from $1500 to $30000). It offers credit insurance (also known as payment protection insurance) an optional add-on for borrowers to ensure repayment if they can't repay the loan. It also offers non-credit insurance through auto membership plans. The company has around $16.1 billion in personal loan assets due on about 2.4 million loans.

Geographic Reach

Evansville Indiana-based OneMain Holdings serves customers across the US and has servicing facilities in Mendota Heights Minnesota; Tempe Arizona; London Kentucky; Evansville Indiana; Fort Mill South Carolina; and Fort Worth Texas.

Sales and Marketing

OneMain Holdings is aggressive in targeting high-risk borrowers who might be reluctant to seek financing. It uses direct mail promotions web ads and local marketing to acquire new customers and regain former customers. The company also buys credit data to identify non-prime credit seekers.

Financial Performance

After suffering almost a 30% revenue reduction in 2015 (caused by predecessor company Springleaf's net gain on sale of its real estate loans in 2014) OneMain Holdings bounced back the next year with a near-doubling of its revenue. Less impressive gains the next two years resulted in a five-year improvement of more than 60%. The company's net income has bounced up and down each year since 2014 including to a loss in 2015 when Springleaf acquired OneMain and adopted the OneMain brand.

The company added 13% to its revenue in 2018 to end the year at $3.4 billion. The improvement was driven by growth of and higher yields from its loan portfolio caused mostly by lower amortization of purchase premiums on non-credit impaired finance receivables.

OneMain's net income shot up 144% to $447 million that year thanks to the revenue gains aided by a lower income tax expense.

The company's cash decreased $307 million to $1.2 billion in 2018. Operations provided $2 billion and financing activities generated $44 million. Investments used up $2.4 billion almost all of it for net principal originations of finance receivables held for investment or sale.

Strategy

Since it targets customers who may have trouble paying back their loans OneMain Holdings' origination strategy is to stabilize its portfolio by increasing the percentage of its loans that are secured by titled collateral as opposed to unsecured personal loans. Titled collateral-secured loans generally have lower yields and credit losses. In 2018 48% of its loans were secured by titled collateral compared with 43% the previous year.

The company is also divesting non-core businesses to focus its resources on its most profitable operations. In 2018 the company sold a portfolio of real estate loans for $100 million.

EXECUTIVES

Evp Legal Compliance And Operational Risk, John C. Anderson, age 61, $350,000 total compensation

President And Ceo, Jay N. Levine, age 57, $400,000 total compensation

Evp And Cfo, Scott T. Parker, age 52, $400,000 total compensation

Evp Branch Operations, Bradford D. Borchers, age 55, $350,000 total compensation

Evp Credit And Analytics, David P. Hogan, age 50, $350,000 total compensation

Evp And Coo, Robert A. Hurzeler, age 58, $350,000 total compensation

Evp And Chief Administrative Officer, Lawrence N. Skeats, age 54, $336,539 total compensation

Evp Human Resources, Angela Celestin, age 48, $26,442 total compensation

Vice President Investor Relations, Rohit Dewan

Senior Vice President, Donald Breivogel

Senior Vice President Marketing, Hari Lymon

Vice President Director Marketing, Melody Bateman

Senior Vice President Of Communications, Howard M Schloss

Vice President Director Of Operations, Gary Fulk

Regional Vice President, Daniel Ritenour

Vice President Director, Andrew Mcadoo

Vice President Director Of Operations, Gerald Oslakovic

Vice President Tax, Marianne Ford

Vice President, Scott Bailer

Chairman, Wesley R. (Wes) Edens, age 57

Auditors: PricewaterhouseCoopers LLP

LOCATIONS

HQ: OneMain Holdings Inc
601 N.W. Second Street, Evansville, IN 47708
Phone: 812 424-8031
Web: www.onemainfinancial.com

PRODUCTS/OPERATIONS

2018 Sales

	$ mil.	% of total
Net Interest Income		
Interest Income	3,658	86
Interest Expense	(875)	-
Non-interest Income		
Insurance	429	10
Investment	66	2
Net gain on sale of SpringCastle interests	18	-
Net gain on sales of personal and real estate loans	70	2
Total	**3,366**	**100**

COMPETITORS

Advance America
Atlanticus
Check 'n Go
Check Into Cash
Community Choice Financial
DFC Global
EZCORP
FirstCash
NetSpend
QC Holdings
Regional Management
Security Finance Corporation of Spartanburg
World Acceptance
Xponential

HISTORICAL FINANCIALS

Company Type: Public

Income Statement				FYE: December 31
	ASSETS ($ mil.)	NET INCOME ($ mil.)	INCOME AS % OF ASSETS	EMPLOYEES
12/18	20,090	447	2.2%	10,200
12/17	19,433	183	0.9%	10,100
12/16	18,123	215	1.2%	10,100
12/15	21,056	(242)	—	11,400
12/14	11,058	505	4.6%	5,030
Annual Growth	16.1%	(3.0%)	—	19.3%

2018 Year-End Financials

Debt ratio: 76.00%
Return on equity: 13.00%
Cash ($ mil.): 679
Current ratio: —
Long-term debt ($ mil.): —

No. of shares (mil.): 136
Dividends
 Yield: —
 Payout: —
Market value ($ mil.): 3,299

	STOCK PRICE ($) FY Close	P/E High/Low		PER SHARE ($) Earnings	Dividends	Book Value
12/18	24.00	11	7	3.00	0.00	28.00
12/17	26.00	24	16	1.00	0.00	24.00
12/16	22.00	26	11	2.00	0.00	23.00
12/15	42.00	—	—	(2.00)	0.00	20.00
12/14	36.00	9	5	4.00	0.00	18.00
Annual Growth	(9.5%)	—	—	(6.9%)	—	12.2%

ONEOK Inc

ONEOK ("one oak") is having a gas pursuing its pipeline dreams. ONEOK is an Oklahoma-based midstream natural gas corporation that plays a key role in transforming and transporting natural gas from exploration & producer (E&P) businesses to downstream customers such as refiners and petrochemical companies. Through its primary subsidiary ONEOK Partners its operations include a 38000-mile integrated network of natural gas and natural gas liquid (NGL) pipelines processing plants fractionators and storage facilities in the Mid-Continent Williston Permian and Rocky Mountain regions.

Operations

ONEOK operates three reportable segments: Natural Gas Liquids Natural Gas Gathering and Processing and Natural Gas Pipelines.

The Natural Gas Liquids segment which generates about 75% of revenue owns and operates facilities that gather NGLs and then fractionate and treat them separating them into NGL products. The NGL products are then held in storage facilities or distributed to customers such as petrochemical manufacturers heating fuel users ethanol producers refineries exporters and propane distributors. Its treatment facilities are strategically located in Kansas Oklahoma New Mexico the Rocky Mountain region and Texas.

The Natural Gas Gathering and Processing segment (20% of revenue) serves contracted producers of natural gas in Kansas Montana North Dakota Oklahoma and Wyoming. Producers move their raw (unprocessed) natural gas to ONEOK-run processing facilities which remove contaminants and separate NGLs before delivering the now processed (and compressed) natural gas through more pipelines to end users.

The Natural Gas Pipelines segment (about 5% of revenue) owns and operates nearly 7000 miles of regulated natural gas transmission pipelines and more than 50 billion cubic feet of natural gas storage facilities. It provides interstate natural gas transportation and storage services (underground natural gas storage facilities in Kansas Oklahoma and Texas). It is also part owner of two additional pipelines Northern Border Pipeline located near the US-Canada border and Roadrunner which runs from West Texas to the Mexican border.

Geographic Reach

Tulsa Oklahoma-based ONEOK operates gathering and treatment facilities in well-known natural gas plays such as Bakken Permian Basin and Powder River Basin. It has pipeline and plants in some 15 US states with much of its infrastructure in Oklahoma Kansas and Texas though its operations stretch as far as Tennessee Montana and Wyoming.

Sales and Marketing

The midstream company forms and maintains contractual relationships with hundreds of E&P firms and more than 100 third-party natural gas processing plants. It similarly courts relationships with downstream firms such as natural gas distribution companies electric-generation facilities large industrial firms municipalities refiners and petrochemical companies.

Financial Performance

ONEOK's financial performance over the last five years has fluctuated due to a significant fall in oil prices that began in 2014. As oil prices have since risen ONEOK's fortunes have improved but 2018 revenues were only 3% higher than in 2014.

Sales in 2018 increased 3% to $12.6 billion compared to $12.2 billion in 2017. Growth in 2018 was fueled primarily by a 12% rise in gathered NGL volumes and a 16% increase in natural gas processing volumes.

Net income nearly doubled to $593.5 million in 2018 compared to 2017 mainly due to higher natural gas and NGL volumes in the company's Natural Gas Gathering and Processing and Natural Gas Liquids segments. Improved price differentials in the Natural Gas Liquids segment also helped improve net income.

Cash at the end of 2018 was $11.9 million a decrease of $25.3 million from the prior year. Cash from operations contributed $2.2 billion to the coffers while investing activities used $2.1 billion mainly for capital expenditures. Financing activities used $97 million primarily in the form of dividend payments and repayment of long-term debt.

Strategy

ONEOK's strategy includes growing product volumes adjusting its contractual practices in favor of more predictable revenue flows and leveraging lower funding costs to attain higher return on investment (ROI) on capital expenditure (CAPEX)-based growth opportunities.

Amid rising natural gas production and higher demand for natural gas for export and power generation ONEOK is responding by making big investments to meet the needs of natural gas processors and producers. Investments primarily target the Williston Permian Powder River and DJ Basins and STACK and SCOOP plays in Oklahoma.

In 2018 ONEOK announced $6 billion in capital-growth projects including NGL fractionators natural gas processing plants and NGL pipelines in anticipation of the ongoing rise in demand. The company has already spent about $2 billion and has completed projects in its Natural Gas Gathering and Processing and Natural Gas Liquids segments that increased processing and pipeline capacity.

To ameliorate the effect of swings in natural gas commodity pricing ONEOK has implemented a strategy to offer their services with fee-based pricing (instead of linking to commodity prices) to create a more predictable revenue stream. It receives a percent of proceeds relative to other companies in the value chain (producers refiners etc.). At the end of 2018 nearly 90% of the company's revenue was fee-based up from 66% in 2013.

Mergers and Acquisitions

In August 2018 ONEOK announced the acquisition of the remaining 20% stake in the West Texas LPG Pipeline Limited Partnership from Martin Midstream Partners for $195 million (initial 80% acquired in 2014) which will allow for further integration of its extensive NGL system in the Permian Basin. The system consists of 2600 miles of NGL pipeline in Texas and New Mexico providing transportation services to the Mont Belvieu market center.

HISTORY

In 1906 Oklahoma Natural Gas (ONG) was founded to pipe natural gas from northeastern Oklahoma to Oklahoma City. A 100-mile pipeline was completed the next year. In 1921 ONG created two oil companies to pump out the oil it found as a result of its natural gas exploration.

ONG changed hands many times in the 1920s ending up with utility financier G. L. Ohrstrom and Company which milked it dry by brokering acquisitions (purchasing gas properties and then selling them to ONG) and collecting fees. Stock sales drove revenues inflating the stock's price and the inflated price triggered more stock sales. The bubble burst on October 29 1929. A series of leadership changes ensued and in 1932 the company was dissolved and reincorporated. Under president Joseph Bowes ONG recovered wooing back dissatisfied customers and upgrading its pipelines.

In the late 1930s the company pioneered a type of underground storage that injected gas into depleted gas reservoirs in the summer and withdrew it during winter's peak use times.

The 1950s and 1960s saw the company expand. In 1962 it created its first subsidiary Oklahoma Natural Gas Gathering Company selling gas out of state and therefore subject to federal regulation.

ONG was not affected in the lean 1970s by federal laws that kept wellhead prices low for gas transported across state lines because its main operations were confined to Oklahoma. Congress deregulated wellhead prices in 1978 spurring exploration but causing great price fluctuations in the 1980s. In 1980 ONG changed its name to ONEOK.

In the 1980s ONEOK signed take-or-pay contracts which forced it to pay for gas offered by its suppliers even if it had no customers. When recession in the 1980s caused demand to drop ONEOK had to pay for high-priced natural gas it couldn't sell. In 1988 the company was ordered to pay some $50 million to supplier Forest Oil of Denver. A year later ONEOK was sued for allegedly failing to tell stockholders about the take-or-pay agreements (settled in 1993 for $5.5 million). It later sold more than half of its oil and gas reserves to Mustang Energy for $52 million to finance the Forest Oil court award. The company was still settling lawsuits over the agreements into the 1990s; it settled the last of the claims by 1998.

ONEOK began buying gas transmission and production facilities in Oklahoma and creating drilling alliances in the 1990s. In 1997 ONEOK bought the natural gas assets of Westar Energy formerly Western Resources for $660 million and ONEOK stock worth $800 million. The acquisition doubled the number of ONEOK's customers and increased its gas marketing gathering and transmission operations.

The company also acquired Southern Union's Texas natural gas distribution business (540000 customers) as well as Southern Union's stake in a Mexican gas utility and its propane distribution gas marketing and gas transmission operations in the southwestern US for $420 million.

ONEOK acquired Northern Plains Natural Gas a general partner of pipeline operator Northern Border Partners (later renamed ONEOK Partners) from CCE Holdings (a joint venture of Southern Union and GE Commercial Finance) for $175 million in 2004. The transaction followed CCE Holdings' acquisition of Enron's CrossCountry Energy unit.

Also in 2004 ONEOK changed the name of its wholesale energy unit from ONEOK Energy Marketing and Trading to ONEOK Energy Services.

The company bought Koch Industries' natural gas liquids assets in 2005 for $1.35 billion.

In 2013 the company announced plans to invest $440 million in the natural gas liquids-rich area in the Powder River Basin in Wyoming to by a 50-million cubic feet per day natural gas processing facility in Wyoming (the Sage Creek plant and related infrastructure) for $305 million. It plans to invest $135 million to upgrade and construct natural gas gathering and processing related infrastructure NGL gathering pipelines and well connections.

In 2017 ONEOK completed its $9.3 billion purchase of ONEOK Partners a subsidiary that has and will for the foreseeable future generate the majority of ONEOK's revenue. Prior to the purchase ONEOK owned about 40% of ONEOK Partners and the investing public owned the remaining shares. With the merger complete ONEOK Partners is a wholly owned subsidiary of ONEOK and its shares no longer trade on public markets. ONEOK funded the acquisition with stock doubling its number of issued shares.

EXECUTIVES

Senior Vice President Administrative Services, David Roth

Vice President Of Tax, Tim Blake

Vp Treasury And Risk, Ray Poudrier

Evp And Chief Administrative Officer, Robert F. (Rob) Martinovich, age 61, $500,000 total compensation

Vp Gas Supply And Project Development Energy Division, Terry K. Spencer, age 59, $700,000 total compensation

Svp Operations, Wesley J. Christensen, age 65, $400,000 total compensation

Svp Cfo And Treasurer, Derek S. Reiners, age 48, $375,000 total compensation

Svp Natural Gas Gathering And Processing, Kevin L. Burdick, age 54

Vp And Cio, Brien H. Brown

Svp Natural Gas Pipelines, J. Phillip (Phill) May

Evp Strategic Planning And Corporate Affairs, Walter S. Hulse, age 55, $500,000 total compensation

Svp Natural Gas Liquids Oneok Partners, Sheridan C. Swords

Vice President Commercial G And P, Michael A Fitzgibbons

Vp Ngl Fractionation, Jeremy Wiese

Vice President, Pete Walker

Vice President Investor Relations And Corporate Affairs, Andrew Ziola

Vice President Customer Service, Krystal Parker

Vice President Government Relations, Steve Johnson

Vice President, Walter Allen

Vice President Project Development And Business Analysis, Michael Crisman

Vice President Gas Supply, Christy Williamson

Vice President Sales And Marketing, Carl Holliday

Vp Marketing Oneok Energy Resources, George Drake

Vice President And Chief Accounting Officer, Mike Miers

Vice President Interactive Marketing, Randy Jordan

Vice President Customer Service And Support, James Fallan

Vice President, Donald Jacobsen

Vice President Of Customer Support, William Eliason

Vice President Rates And Regulatory Affairs, Ron Mucci

Senior Vice President Operations, Wesley Christenson

Vp Of It, Jasmin Rea

Manager Government Relations, Michael Gillaspie

Vice President Information Technology, Winsford Spears

Vice President Of Investor Relations And Public Affairs, Dan L Harrison

Vp Commercial Interstate Pipelines Segment, Philip May

Vice President Associate General Counsel, Brandon Watson

Executive Vice President Human Resources, Amber Waid

Vice President Gas Supply (ofs), Greg Lusardi

Chairman Oneok Oneok Partners And One Gas, John W. Gibson, age 66

Board Member, Eduardo Rodriguez

Board Member, Julie Edwards

Board Member, Jim Mogg

Board Member, Randall Larson

Auditors: PricewaterhouseCoopers LLP

LOCATIONS

HQ: ONEOK Inc
100 West Fifth Street, Tulsa, OK 74103
Phone: 918 588-7000   **Fax:** 918 588-7273
Web: www.oneok.com

PRODUCTS/OPERATIONS

2016 Sales

	$ mil.	% of total
Natural Gas Liquids	7,676	76
Natural Gas Gathering and Processing	2,052	20
Natural Gas Pipeline	379	4
Reconciled Intersegment Revenues	(1185.7)	-
Total	**8,921**	**0**

COMPETITORS

BP	Exxon Mobil
DCP Midstream Partners	National Fuel Gas
EQT Corporation	SemGroup
Enable Midstream	Southwest Gas
Partners	TRII
Enterprise Products	Williams Companies

HISTORICAL FINANCIALS

Company Type: Public

Income Statement — FYE: December 31

	REVENUE ($ mil.)	NET INCOME ($ mil.)	NET PROFIT MARGIN	EMPLOYEES
12/18	12,593	1,152	9.1%	2,684
12/17	12,174	388	3.2%	2,470
12/16	8,921	352	3.9%	2,384
12/15	7,763	245	3.2%	2,364
12/14	12,195	314	2.6%	2,269
Annual Growth	0.8%	38.4%	—	4.3%

2018 Year-End Financials

Debt ratio: 51.00%	No. of shares (mil.): 412
Return on equity: 19.00%	Dividends
Cash ($ mil.): 12	Yield: 6.0%
Current ratio: 1.00	Payout: 117.0%
Long-term debt ($ mil.): 8,873	Market value ($ mil.): 22,202

	STOCK PRICE ($) FY Close	P/E High/Low	Earnings	Dividends	Book Value
12/18	54.00	26 18	3.00	3.00	16.00
12/17	53.00	45 36	1.00	3.00	14.00
12/16	57.00	35 12	2.00	2.00	1.00
12/15	25.00	44 16	1.00	2.00	2.00
12/14	50.00	47 30	1.00	2.00	3.00
Annual Growth	2.0%	— —	16.9%	11.2%	54.0%

ONEOK PARTNERS, L.P.

For ONEOK Partners it's OK to have three businesses: natural gas pipelines; gas gathering and processing; and natural gas liquids (NGLs). Its pipelines include Midwestern Gas Transmission Guardian Pipeline Viking Gas Transmission and OkTex Pipeline. The ONEOK affiliate operates 17100 miles of gas-gathering pipeline and 7600 miles of transportation pipeline as well as gas processing plants and storage facilities (with 52 billion cu. ft. of capacity). It also owns one of the US's top natural NGL systems (more than 7200 miles of pipeline). In 2017 41%-owner ONEOK agreed to buy the stock of ONEOK Partners that it did not already own for $9.3 billion in a stock deal. Operations ONEOK Partners operates in three business segments: natural gas gathering and processing; natural gas pipelines; and natural gas liquids. Geographic Reach The company gathers and processes natural gas in the Mid-Continent region which includes the NGL-rich Cana-Woodford Shale and Granite Wash formations the Mississippian Lime formation of Oklahoma and Kansas and the Hugoton and Central Kansas Uplift Basins of Kansas. The Natural Gas Pipelines segment owns and operates regulated natural gas transmission pipelines natural gas storage facilities and natural gas gathering systems for nonprocessed gas. It also provide interstate natural gas transportation and storage service. The company's interstate natural gas pipeline assets transport natural gas through pipelines in North Dakota Minnesota Wis-

consin Illinois Indiana Kentucky Tennessee Oklahoma Texas and New Mexico. Its Natural gas liquids assets provide nondiscretionary services to producers that consist of facilities that gather fractionate and treat NGLs and store NGL products primarily in Oklahoma Kansas and Texas. It also owns or has stakes in natural gas liquids gathering and distribution pipelines in Oklahoma Kansas Texas Wyoming and Colorado and terminal and storage facilities in Missouri Nebraska Iowa and Illinois. In addition it owns natural gas liquids distribution and refined petroleum products pipelines in Kansas Missouri Nebraska Iowa Illinois and Indiana that connect the company's Mid-Continent assets with Midwest markets including Chicago.

Financial Performance

Revenues decreased by 10% in 2012 due to lower net realized natural gas and NGL product prices offset partially by higher natural gas and NGL sales volumes from completed capital projects. The increase in natural gas supply resulting from the development of nonconventional resource areas in North America and a warmer than normal winter caused natural gas prices to drop. NGL prices particularly ethane and propane also decreased in 2012 due primarily to increased NGL production and an increase in available supply. Propane prices also were affected by a warmer than normal winter.

ONEOK Partners' net income grew by 7% in 2012 thanks to lower costs of sales and fuels and lower interest expenses.

Strategy

The company pursues a strategy of building up its fee-based earnings coupled with organic growth and complementary acquisitions in both conventional oil and gas and unconventional (shale plays). It is looking to increase NGL volumes gathered and fractionated in its NGL segment and natural gas volumes processed in its natural gas gathering and processing segment as producers continue to develop NGL-rich resource plays in the Mid-Continent and Rocky Mountain areas.

In 2012 ONEOK Partners announced plans to invest up to $360 million to grow its projects in the Woodford Shale formation.

Company Background

ONEOK Partners was formed in 2006 when ONEOK spun off its gathering and processing NGLs pipelines and storage businesses for $3 billion following that company's acquisition of Northern Border Partners (which was founded in 1993). Building out its assets in 2007 the company acquired an interstate pipeline system from Kinder Morgan Energy Partners for $300 million.

EXECUTIVES

Pres-Ceo, Terry K Spencer
Evp-Cfo, Walter S Hulse III
Svp,naturalgasgathering&procce, Michael A Fitzgibbons
Executive Vice President Opera, Robert F Martinovich

LOCATIONS

HQ: ONEOK PARTNERS, L.P.
100 W 5TH ST STE LL, TULSA, OK 741034298
Phone: 918 588-7000
Web: WWW.ONEOKPARTNERS.COM

PRODUCTS/OPERATIONS

Natural Gas Pipelines
Midwestern Gas Transmission Company
Viking Gas Transmission Company
Guardian Pipeline
OkTex Pipeline Company
ONEOK Gas Transportation

ONEOK Gas Gathering
ONEOK Gas Storage
ONEOK WesTex Transmission
ONEOK Texas Gas Storage
Mid Continent Market Center
ONEOK Transmission Company
Natural Gas Gathering & Processing
Crestone Energy Ventures
ONEOK Field Services
ONEOK Rockies Midstream

COMPETITORS

Enbridge	Panhandle Eastern Pipe
Kinder Morgan Energy	Line
Partners	TransCanada

HISTORICAL FINANCIALS

Company Type: Private

Income Statement — FYE: December 31

	REVENUE ($ mil.)	NET INCOME ($ mil.)	NET PROFIT MARGIN	EMPLOYEES
12/16	8,918	1,072	12.0%	2,364
12/15	7,761	598	7.7%	
12/14	12,192	911	7.5%	—
Annual Growth	(14.5%)	8.5%	—	—

Opus Bank (Irvine, CA)

Auditors: RSM US LLP

LOCATIONS

HQ: Opus Bank (Irvine, CA)
19900 MacArthur Blvd., 12th Floor, Irvine, CA 92612
Phone: 949 250-9800
Web: www.opusbank.com

HISTORICAL FINANCIALS

Company Type: Public

Income Statement — FYE: December 31

	ASSETS ($ mil.)	NET INCOME ($ mil.)	INCOME AS % OF ASSETS	EMPLOYEES
12/18	7,181	31	0.4%	845
12/17	7,487	48	0.6%	797
12/16	7,883	11	0.1%	835
12/15	6,650	60	0.9%	661
12/14	5,085	44	0.9%	585
Annual Growth	9.0%	(8.4%)	—	9.6%

2018 Year-End Financials

Debt ratio: 2.00%	No. of shares (mil.): 36
Return on equity: 3.00%	Dividends
Cash ($ mil.): 255	Yield: 2.0%
Current ratio: —	Payout: 42.0%
Long-term debt ($ mil.): —	Market value ($ mil.): 706

	STOCK PRICE ($) FY Close	P/E High/Low	Earnings	Dividends	Book Value
12/18	20.00	37 22	1.00	0.00	29.00
12/17	27.00	23 14	1.00	0.00	28.00
12/16	30.00	112 58	0.00	1.00	27.00
12/15	37.00	21 13	2.00	0.00	27.00
12/14	28.00	22 18	1.00	0.00	28.00
Annual Growth	(8.8%)	— —	(12.5%)	—	0.4%

Oracle Corp

EXECUTIVES

Ceo, Safra A Catz
Ceo*, Mark V Hurd
Chb-Cto*, Lawrence J Ellison
V Chb*, Jeffrey O Henley
Exec V Pres-General Counsel, Dorian E Daley
Exec V Pres-Corp Contrl-Cao, William Corey West
Director For Java Elec, Dennis Macneil
Director or Senior Director PR, Ed Zou
Director of Technology, Farzin Barazandeh
Senior Director, Glenn Harris
Prinicipal Program Manager, Greg Rogers
Auditors: Ernst & Young LLP

LOCATIONS

HQ: Oracle Corp
　500 Oracle Parkway, Redwood City, CA 94065
Phone: 650 506-7000
Web: www.oracle.com

COMPETITORS

ADP	Manhattan Associates
Accenture	MicroStrategy
BMC Software	Microsoft
CA Inc.	NCR
CDC Software	Novell
Ceridian	Open Text
Cisco Systems	Pegasystems
Courion	Progress Software
Dell Software	Red Hat
EMC	SAP
Fujitsu Technology	SAS Institute
Solutions	SOA Software
HP Autonomy	Sage Group
Hewlett-Packard	Software AG
Hitachi	SuccessFactors
IBM	TIBCO Software
Infor Global	Taleo
Informatica	Teradata
Intel	Workday Inc.
JDA Software	salesforce.com
JasperSoft	

HISTORICAL FINANCIALS

Company Type: Public

Income Statement
FYE: May 31

	REVENUE ($ mil.)	NET INCOME ($ mil.)	NET PROFIT MARGIN	EMPLOYEES
05/19	39,506	11,083	28.1%	136,000
05/18	39,831	3,825	9.6%	137,000
05/17	37,728	9,335	24.7%	138,000
05/16	37,047	8,901	24.0%	136,000
05/15	38,226	9,938	26.0%	132,000
Annual Growth	0.8%	2.8%	—	0.7%

2019 Year-End Financials

Debt ratio: 52.00%—
Return on equity: 33.00%
Cash ($ mil.): 20,514
Current ratio: 2.00
Long-term debt ($ mil.): 51,673
Dividends
　Yield: 2.0%
　Payout: 27.0%
　Market value ($ mil.): —

	STOCK PRICE ($) FY Close	P/E High/Low		PER SHARE ($) Earnings	Dividends	Book Value
05/19	51.00	18	14	3.00	1.00	6.00
05/18	47.00	57	48	1.00	1.00	11.00
05/17	45.00	20	17	2.00	1.00	13.00
05/16	40.00	21	16	2.00	1.00	11.00
05/15	43.00	20	17	2.00	1.00	11.00
Annual Growth	3.9%	—	—	7.7%	12.3%	(12.8%)

Orchid Island Capital, Inc.

No REIT is an island unless your name is Orchid Island Capital. The company which is seeking to become a real estate investment trust invests in residential mortgage-backed securities (RMBS) that are guaranteed by the US government or federally sponsored entities like Fannie Mae Freddie Mac and Ginnie Mae. Its portfolio and principal investment targets consist of pass-through agency RMBS and structured agency RMBS including fixed-rate mortgages adjustable-rate mortgages (ARMs) and hybrid ARMs as well as collateralized mortgage obligations. Formed by mortgage REIT Bimini Capital Management in 2010 Orchid Island Capital filed to go public for the second time in October 2012.

EXECUTIVES

Chairman President And Ceo; Chairman And Ceo Bimini, Robert E. Cauley, age 60
Cfo Chief Investment Officer Secretary And Director; President Cfo And Chief Investment Officer Bimini, G. Hunter Haas, age 43
Auditors: BDO USA, LLP

LOCATIONS

HQ: Orchid Island Capital, Inc.
　3305 Flamingo Drive, Vero Beach, FL 32963
Phone: 772 231-1400
Web: www.orchidislandcapital.com

COMPETITORS

AG Mortgage Investment Trust	Capstead Mortgage
ARMOUR Residential REIT	Hatteras Financial
American Capital Agency Corp.	MFA Financial
Annaly Capital Management	Provident Mortgage Capital
Anworth Mortgage Asset	Redwood Trust
Apollo Residential Mortgage	TMAC Mortgage
	Two Harbors

HISTORICAL FINANCIALS

Company Type: Public

Income Statement
FYE: December 31

	ASSETS ($ mil.)	NET INCOME ($ mil.)	INCOME AS % OF ASSETS	EMPLOYEES
12/18	3,396	(44)	—	—
12/17	4,023	2	0.0%	—
12/16	3,139	2	0.1%	—
12/15	2,242	1	0.0%	—
12/14	1,658	25	1.5%	—
Annual Growth	19.6%	—	—	—

2018 Year-End Financials

Debt ratio: —
Return on equity: (-11.00%)
Cash ($ mil.): 108
Current ratio: —
Long-term debt ($ mil.): —
No. of shares (mil.): 49
Dividends
　Yield: 17.0%
　Payout: —
　Market value ($ mil.): 314

	STOCK PRICE ($) FY Close	P/E High/Low		PER SHARE ($) Earnings	Dividends	Book Value
12/18	6.00	—	—	(1.00)	1.00	7.00
12/17	9.00	2501	84	0.00	2.00	9.00
12/16	11.00	1401	03	0.00	2.00	10.00
12/15	10.00	2841	55	0.00	2.00	12.00
12/14	13.00	6	5	2.00	2.00	13.00
Annual Growth	(16.3%) (14.9%)	—	—	—	(16.1%)	—

Origin Bancorp Inc

Auditors: BKD, LLP

LOCATIONS

HQ: Origin Bancorp Inc
　500 South Service Road East, Ruston, LA 71270
Phone: 318 255-2222
Web: www.origin.bank

HISTORICAL FINANCIALS

Company Type: Public

Income Statement
FYE: December 31

	ASSETS ($ mil.)	NET INCOME ($ mil.)	INCOME AS % OF ASSETS	EMPLOYEES
12/18	4,822	52	1.1%	761
12/17	4,154	15	0.4%	686
12/16	4,071	13	0.3%	—
Annual Growth	8.8%	100.4%	—	—

2018 Year-End Financials

Debt ratio: 1.00%
Return on equity: 11.00%
Cash ($ mil.): 117
Current ratio: —
Long-term debt ($ mil.): —
No. of shares (mil.): 24
Dividends
　Yield: 0.0%
　Payout: 5.0%
　Market value ($ mil.): 809

	STOCK PRICE ($) FY Close	P/E High/Low		PER SHARE ($) Earnings	Dividends	Book Value
12/18	34.00	19	15	2.00	0.00	23.00
12/17	0.00	—	—	1.00	0.00	23.00
12/16	0.00	—	—	0.00	0.00	23.00
Annual Growth	—	—	—	(118.7%)	(13.4%)	0.3%

Oshkosh Corp (New)

EXECUTIVES

Pres-Ceo, Wilson R Jones
Chb, Craig P Omtvedt
Exec V Pres-Coo, John C Pfeifer
Exec V Pres-Cfo, David M Sagehorn
Exec V Pres-General Counsel-SE, Ignacio A Cortina
Exec V Pres-Chief Hr Officer, Robert H Sims
Sr V Pres-Cmo, Bryan K Brandt
Evp-Pres Fire & Emergency, James W Johnson
Evp Gov Oprs & Industry Rel, Joseph H Kimmitt
Evp-Pres Access Equipment, Frank R Nerenhausen
Svp-Chief Information Officer, Anupam Khare
Auditors: DELOITTE & TOUCHE LLP

LOCATIONS

HQ: Oshkosh Corp (New)
P.O. Box 2566, Oshkosh, WI 54903-2566
Phone: 920 502-3009
Web: www.oshkoshcorp.com

COMPETITORS

AM General	Iveco S.p.A.
American LaFrance	J C Bamford Excavators
BAE Systems Land &	L-3 Communications
Armaments	Leyland Trucks
Collins Industries	MAN
Daimler	MANITOU BF
Daimler Trucks North	Mack Trucks
America	Miller Industries
Dover Corp.	Navistar
E-ONE	Navistar International
Federal Signal	PACCAR
Force Protection	Skyjack
General Dynamics Land	Spartan Motors
Systems	Terex
Haulotte	Trinity Industries
Heil Environmental	UD Trucks
Hyundai Motor	Volvo

HISTORICAL FINANCIALS

Company Type: Public

Income Statement				FYE: September 30
	REVENUE ($ mil.)	NET INCOME ($ mil.)	NET PROFIT MARGIN	EMPLOYEES
09/19	8,382	579	6.9%	15,400
09/18	7,706	472	6.1%	15,000
09/17	6,830	286	4.2%	14,000
09/16	6,279	216	3.4%	13,800
09/15	6,098	230	3.8%	13,300
Annual Growth	8.3%	26.1%	—	3.7%

2019 Year-End Financials

Debt ratio: 15.00%	No. of shares (mil.): 68
Return on equity: 23.00%	Dividends
Cash ($ mil.): 448	Yield: 1.0%
Current ratio: 2.00	Payout: 13.0%
Long-term debt ($ mil.): 819	Market value ($ mil.): 5,153

	STOCK PRICE ($) FY Close	P/E High/Low		PER SHARE ($) Earnings	Dividends	Book Value
09/19	76.00	10	6	8.00	1.00	38.00
09/18	71.00	15	11	6.00	1.00	35.00
09/17	83.00	22	14	4.00	1.00	31.00
09/16	56.00	19	10	3.00	1.00	27.00
09/15	36.00	19	12	3.00	1.00	25.00
Annual Growth	20.2%	—	—	29.7%	12.3%	10.8%

Owens & Minor, Inc.

Owens & Minor (O&M) is a leading distributor of medical and surgical supplies. The company carries products from about 1100 manufacturers; those products include surgical dressings endoscopic and intravenous products needles syringes sterile procedure trays gowns gloves and sutures. The firm also provides kitting consulting and other services to help customers manage their supplies. O&M primarily serves hospitals and health systems and the purchasing organizations that serve them. It delivers products to roughly 3000 health care providers across the US (where most of its sales are made).

Operations

O&M operates in three segments: Domestic (more than 90% of revenue) International and Proprietary Products (formerly Clinical & Procedural Solutions).

The Domestic segment provides distribution packaging and logistics services in the US while the International segment comprises its European third-party logistics and packaging businesses. The Proprietary Products segment gathers assembles and delivers procedure kits for surgical specialties (including robotics cardiology and orthopedics) and minor procedures.

In addition to delivering products made by its supply partners the distributor sells value products under its own MediChoice label. To support its distribution operations O&M offers training programs for health professionals on topics ranging from equipment use supply management leadership and safety.

O&M's supply chain management services include third-party logistics services for medical device and pharmaceutical firms. Such services are provided by subsidiaries OM HealthCare Logistics (in the US) and Movianto (in Europe).

Geographic Reach

O&M operates some 50 distribution centers across the US.

Though US operations account for most of O&M's sales (more than 90%) the company is working to branch out into international medical distribution markets including Europe. Its International unit operates 20 logistics centers in about a dozen European countries including Belgium the Czech Republic Denmark France Germany Italy the Netherlands Poland Slovakia Spain Switzerland and the UK.

Sales and Marketing

Most of O&M's sales are attributed to contracts with acute care hospitals which are often represented by group purchasing organizations (GPOs) or integrated delivery networks (IDNs). GPOs Premier and HealthTrust Purchasing Group are the company's largest customers. Additional clients include other government agencies and alternate health care locations such as physician clinics nursing homes and surgery centers. In addition O&M provides outsourced distribution services to suppliers of surgical and medical products.

About 80% of O&M's sales come from the distribution of medical supplies. The company's major product suppliers include Covidien Johnson & Johnson and Becton Dickson; those firms account for some 10% of sales each.

Financial Performance

O&M's revenues have remained relatively static over the past few years. Net income has been a bit more erratic rising and falling as a result of various acquisitions made. The company's long-term debt has been on the rise and it reached $901 million by the end of 2017.

In 2017 revenue dropped 4% to $9.3 billion. The company lost a major customer in 2016 and manufacturer product price changes cut into income. Additionally the International segment has been operating at a loss as O&M invests in building up that business. Finally Proprietary Products production costs increased that year while sales dropped.

Net income fell 33% to $73 million in 2017. In addition to the lower revenue the acquisition of Byram Healthcare and preparation for the acquisition of certain operations of Halyard Health cut into the firm's bottom line. Restructuring costs rose 85% to $43.4 million; these costs were related to workforce reductions and IT restructuring activities. (The company expects these types of expenses to impact earnings in 2018 as well.)

The company ended 2017 with $104.5 million in net cash 44% less than it had at the end of 2016. Financing activities such as the issuance of debt provided $272.8 million and operating activities provided $56.8 million. Investing activities used $416.6 million.

Strategy

As the health care industry has come under pressure so have the industries that serve it. To stay competitive in a struggling market O&M restructured its operations and realigned its leadership team in 2016. Its new strategies for growth include streamlining the distribution of medical supplies by utilizing technology productivity tools and data connectivity. O&M is working to further expand into patient settings beyond hospitals such as surgery centers clinics and other non-acute care facilities that can benefit from its offerings.

The company also works with manufacturers for whom it strives to be the delivery mechanism of choice. Finally O&M complements its product sales services by offering resource management services to care providers including physical inventory reviews inventory tracking and purchasing software.

Mergers and Acquisitions

In 2018 O&M bought the surgical and infection prevention operations of medical supplies maker Halyard Health for $710 million. The purchase included products including sterilization wraps surgical gowns and medical exam gloves.

In 2017 O&M acquired Byram Healthcare for $380 million. Byram is a nationwide distributor of direct-to-patient medical supplies including wound care incontinence and diabetes supplies.

HISTORY

George Gilmer Minor Jr.'s great-grandfather was an apothecary and surgeon in colonial Williamsburg Virginia. His grandfather was Thomas Jefferson's personal physician. Minor himself worked as a wholesale drug salesman in Richmond after the Civil War. In 1882 he and rival wholesaler Otho Owens partnered to form the Owens & Minor Drug Company. The company was both a retail and wholesale business with a storefront that filled prescriptions and sold sundries paints oils and window glass. When Owens died in 1906 Minor became the company's president.

During the 1920s the Owens family sold their stake in the firm. George Gilmer Minor III served briefly as the company's president in the early 1940s; his son George Gilmer Minor IV (called Mr. Minor Jr. to differentiate him from his father) became president in 1947.

In 1954 Owens & Minor installed its first computerized order fulfillment system. The following year the firm became Owens Minor & Bodeker when it bought the Bodeker Drug Company which was both older and larger than Owens & Minor.

After 84 years in the drug wholesale business the company entered the medical and surgical distribution business after buying A&J Hospital Supply in 1966 and Powers & Anderson in 1968. In 1971 Owens Minor & Bodeker went public. By the end of the decade the company had operations in 10 states.

The fourth Minor to run the firm G. Gilmer Minor III (Mr. Minor Jr.'s son) was named president in 1981 (he became CEO in 1984). Under his direction Owens Minor & Bodeker would complete the transition from a drug wholesaler to a medical supplies distributor. In 1981 it purchased the Will Ross subsidiary of G.D. Searle (then the country's #2 medical and surgical supplies distributor).

The company reverted to its original name on its 100th anniversary in 1982. By 1984 medical supplies supplanted wholesale drugs as its primary source of income. In 1988 Owens & Minor listed on the NYSE.

The company passed the $1 billion revenue mark in 1990 and later sold its wholesale drug business. It extended its reach with the purchase of Lyons Physician Supply in 1993 and Stuart Medical (the #3 national distributor) in 1994.

EXECUTIVES

Svp And Chief Of Staff, Erika T. Davis, age 56, $513,719 total compensation
Svp Owens & Minor Europe Operations, Charles C. Colpo, age 62, $453,466 total compensation
Vice President Technology, Charles Eismamn
Evp And Cfo; President International, Richard A. (Randy) Meier, age 59, $648,260 total compensation
Chairman President And Ceo, P. Cody Phipps, age 57, $915,577 total compensation
Evp North American Operations, Rony C. Kordahi, age 55, $328,846 total compensation
Evp Global Manufacturer Services, Stuart Morris-Hipkins
Svp Clinical Procedural Solutions, James S. Glasscock
Svp Manufacturer Services, Geoff T. Marlatt
Svp And Cio, Stephen R. Olive
Svp Strategic Supply Management, Javara D. Perrilliat
Svp Commercial Services, Joseph B. Zaluzney
Vice President Global Tax, Chris McGowan
Board Member, James Rogers
Auditors: KPMG LLP

LOCATIONS

HQ: Owens & Minor, Inc.
9120 Lockwood Boulevard, Mechanicsville, VA 23116
Phone: 804 723-7000 **Fax:** 804 723-7100
Web: www.owens-minor.com

2017 Sales

	$ mil.	% of total
US	8,899	96
UK	176	2
Ireland	57	1
Germany	49	-
France	39	-
Other European countries	98	1
Total	**9,318**	**100**

PRODUCTS/OPERATIONS

2017 Sales by Segment

	$ mil.	% of total
Domestic	8,794	91
International	392	4
Proprietary Products	504	5
Adjustments	(371.8)	-
Total	**9,318**	**100**

Selected Products and Services

Clinical Supply Solutions (inventory and contract management service)
Implant Purchase Manager (utilization contract compliance and billing)
OMDirect (Internet order fulfillment)
OMSolutions (resource management and consulting)
PANDAC system (helps track and control operating room inventories)
QSight (clinical inventory management system)
SurgiTrack (customizable surgical supply service)

COMPETITORS

Alloga UK	FedEx
AmerisourceBergen	Kerma Medical Products
Buffalo Supply	McKesson
Cardinal Health	Medline Industries
Deutsche Post	UPS

HISTORICAL FINANCIALS

Company Type: Public

Income Statement

FYE: December 31

	REVENUE ($ mil.)	NET INCOME ($ mil.)	NET PROFIT MARGIN	EMPLOYEES
12/18	9,839	(437)	—	17,900
12/17	9,318	73	0.8%	6,200
12/16	9,723	109	1.1%	7,900
12/15	9,773	103	1.1%	8,100
12/14	9,440	67	0.7%	5,700
Annual Growth	**1.0%**	**—**	**—**	**33.1%**

2018 Year-End Financials

Debt ratio: 44.00%
Return on equity: (-57.00%)
Cash ($ mil.): 103
Current ratio: 2.00
Long-term debt ($ mil.): 1,651

No. of shares (mil.): 62
Dividends
 Yield: 14.0%
 Payout: —
Market value ($ mil.): 394

	STOCK PRICE ($) FY Close	P/E High/Low		PER SHARE ($) Earnings	Dividends	Book Value
12/18	6.00	—	—	(7.00)	1.00	8.00
12/17	19.00	31	15	1.00	1.00	17.00
12/16	35.00	23	18	2.00	1.00	16.00
12/15	36.00	24	19	2.00	1.00	16.00
12/14	35.00	35	30	1.00	1.00	16.00
Annual Growth (34.8%) (14.7%)		**—**	**—**	**—**	**(3.8%)**	

Owens Corning

Owens Corning (OC) operates in the PINK. Famous for its Pink Panther mascot and its trademarked PINK glass fiber insulation the company is a top global maker of building and composite material systems. The building materials company makes insulation roofing fiber-based glass reinforcements and other materials for the residential and commercial markets. Its composite products business makes glass fiber reinforcement materials for the transportation industrial infrastructure marine wind energy and consumer markets.

Operations

Owens Corning is organized in three business segments: Composites Insulation and Roofing.

Roofing segment (about 40% of revenue) manufactures and sells residential roofing shingles oxidized asphalt materials roofing components used in residential and commercial construction and specialty applications and synthetic packaging materials.

The Composites segment manufactures fabricates and sells glass reinforcements in the form of fiber as well as sell glass fiber products downstream in the form of fabrics mat veil and other specialized products. 30% revenue comes from this segment.

Insulation another 30% of revenue manufactures and sells fiberglass insulation into residential commercial industrial and other markets for both thermal and acoustical applications.

Geographic Reach

Ohio-based Owens Corning has about 100 manufacturing facilities in some 35 countries in the Americas Europe Africa and the Asia/Pacific region. The US generates about 70% of its sales while Europe the Asia/Pacific and Canada and other countries contribute about 10% each.

Sales and Marketing

Owens Corning sells shingles and roofing accessories primarily through home centers lumberyards retailers distributors and contractors in the US Canada Europe and Asia=Pacific. Other asphalt products are sold internally to manufacture residential roofing products and externally to other roofing manufacturers.

The company typically spends around $100 million on advertising each year.

Financial Performance

In the last decade (2008-17) revenue at Owens Corning has been mostly stable in the $5 billion-plus range. For the same period except for a $20 million loss in 2012 the company has posted profits every year with a yearly average above $200 million.

Revenue in 2017 increased some 12% to $6.4 billion the highest in a decade. Insulation brought in $50 million more compared to 2016 primarily due to higher sales and production volumes higher selling prices and the impact of Pittsburgh Corning acquisition. Roofing increased some $50 million more as well mostly due to higher sales volumes.

Net income fell 25% year-over-year to $290 million for 2017 mostly from a $150 million increases in year-over-year operating costs due to acquisitions as well as $150 million increase in combined income tax expenses and loss on debt extinguishment (of 2019 senior notes).

Cash holdings more than doubled to $250 million. Operations from 2017 generated $1 billion in cash offset by $900 million for investment activities (mostly going to subsidiaries). Financing activities had a net positive contribution of $3 million.

Strategy

With steady revenues and increasing in 2017 to cross the $6 billion mark Owens Corning is looking to expand. In early 2018 it acquired the Paroc Group which expands the company's geographic scope to Europe and product portfolio.

Its insulation products now range across the high medium and low temperature ranges in all 3 major markets of North America Europe and China.

The composites segment which has grown for 5 straight years is expanding operations further to India and will start production in late-2018. There is similar performance from other company sectors like its Foamglas business and residential fiberglass insulation. The components business is expected to grow at double-digit rates as well as over 10% growth in composites.

However mineral wool business in the US has underperformed despite improvement measures. Moreover the asphalt market is also likely to further decline and the company is having efficiency problems in its Joplin insulation facility.

Going forward though thanks to several acquisitions and ongoing integration Owens Corning is likely to create strong cash flows.

Mergers and Acquisitions

In 2018 Owens Corning acquired European stone wool insulation producer Paroc Group from CVC Capital Partners for ?900 million (US$ 1 billion). The move expanded Owens' mineral wool technology further entrenched its European presence and shifted its geographic revenue portfolio towards non-North American sources.

In 2016 Owens Corning acquired InterWrap a leading manufacturer of roofing underlayment and packaging materials for US$450 million.

Also in 2016 the company agreed to buy the glass non-wovens and fabrics businesses of Ahlstrom the fiber-based materials company based in Helsinki Finland for US$79.5 million (?73 million).

HISTORY

In the 1930s Corning Glass Works and Owens-Illinois Glass independently found that glass fiber has special resilience and strength. Realizing the potential market they formed joint venture Owens-Corning Fiberglas in 1938. The companies expanded rapidly in the 1940s and 1950s establishing several US plants and one in Canada. Their products included fine fibers thermal wool textiles and continuous filaments.

EXECUTIVES

Chairman President And Ceo, Michael H. (Mike) Thaman, age 55, $1,140,500 total compensation
President Roofing And Asphalt, Brian D. Chambers, age 50, $450,000 total compensation
Svp Organization And Administration, Daniel T. (Dan) Smith, age 54, $527,500 total compensation
President Composite Solutions, Arnaud P. Genis, age 54, $596,667 total compensation
Vp Investor Relations And Treasurer, Michael C. McMurray, age 54, $589,167 total compensation
President Insulation, Julian Francis
Vice President Hr Centers Of Excellence, Suzann Trevisan
Vp Of Network Operations, Tara Silberhorn
Vice President Strategic Marketing, Carmelo Carrubba
Vice President Human Resources (composites Solutions Business), Paula Russell
National Accounts Manager, Chuck Stanislav
Vice President Corporate Affairs, Suzanne Harnett
National Account Manager, Greg Meilinger
Corporate Medical Director, Brian Linder
National Account Manager, Phil Johnson
Treasurer, Victor Defilippis
Auditors: PricewaterhouseCoopers LLP

LOCATIONS

HQ: Owens Corning
One Owens Corning Parkway, Toledo, OH 43659
Phone: 419 248-8000
Web: www.owenscorning.com

2016 Sales

	$ mil.	% of total
United States	3,963	70
Asia Pacific	666	12
Europe	550	10
Canada and other	498	8
Total	**5,677**	**100**

PRODUCTS/OPERATIONS

2016 Sales

	$ mil.	% of total
Roofing	2,194	37
Composites	1,952	33
Insulation	1,748	30
Corporate eliminations	(217)	—
Total	**5,677**	**100**

COMPETITORS

Ball Corp.	Mohawk Industries
CertainTeed	Nippon Electric Glass
China Fiberglass Co.	Owens-Illinois
Ltd.	PPG Industries
Deceuninck	SIG plc
Dow Chemical	Saint-Gobain
GAF Materials	Sherwin-Williams
Johns Manville	Stanley Black and
Knauf Insulation	Decker
Lennox	TAMKO
Louisiana-Pacific	USG
Masco	

HISTORICAL FINANCIALS

Company Type: Public

Income Statement   FYE: December 31

	REVENUE ($ mil.)	NET INCOME ($ mil.)	NET PROFIT MARGIN	EMPLOYEES
12/18	7,057	545	7.7%	20,000
12/17	6,384	289	4.5%	17,000
12/16	5,677	393	6.9%	16,000
12/15	5,350	330	6.2%	15,000
12/14	5,276	226	4.3%	14,000
Annual Growth	**7.5%**	**24.6%**	**—**	**9.3%**

2018 Year-End Financials

Debt ratio: 34.00%	No. of shares (mil.): 110
Return on equity: 13.00%	Dividends
Cash ($ mil.): 78	Yield: 2.0%
Current ratio: 2.00	Payout: 17.0%
Long-term debt ($ mil.): 3,362	Market value ($ mil.): 4,816

	STOCK PRICE ($) FY Close	P/E High/Low		PER SHARE ($) Earnings	Dividends	Book Value
12/18	44.00	20	8	5.00	1.00	39.00
12/17	92.00	36	20	3.00	1.00	37.00
12/16	52.00	16	12	3.00	1.00	34.00
12/15	47.00	17	12	3.00	1.00	32.00
12/14	36.00	24	15	2.00	1.00	31.00
Annual Growth	**5.3%**	**—**	**—**	**26.5%**	**7.0%**	**5.7%**

PACCAR Inc.

PACCAR (named for former rail car manufacturer Pacific Car and Foundry Company) is one of the world's leading designers and manufacturers of big rig diesel trucks. Its lineup of light- medium- and heavy-duty trucks includes the Kenworth Peterbilt and DAF nameplates. The company also manufactures and distributes aftermarket truck parts for these brands. PACCAR's other products include Braden Carco and Gearmatic industrial winches. PACCAR typically sells its trucks and parts through independent dealers. Its PACCAR Financial Services arm offers vehicle financing and its PacLease subsidiary handles truck leasing.

Operations

PACCAR divides its business into three primary segments: Trucks Parts and Financial Services. The Truck segment generates more than 75% of total sales and sells trucks under the Kenworth Peterbilt and DAF brands. The company manufactures trucks in the US Europe Australia Brazil Canada and Mexico. In Europe PACCAR subsidiary Leyland assembles DAF trucks in the UK.

Parts (accounting for nearly 20% of sales) distributes aftermarket parts globally for PACCAR vehicles. PACCAR manufactures its own parts and purchases from suppliers. Financial Services represents about 5% of net revenue and provides financing to independent dealers franchises and directly to customers for trucks and related equipment.

In addition PACCAR's Other business includes the manufacture and marketing of industrial winches; sales in this business are less than 1% of total revenue.

Geographic Reach

PACCAR's headquarters are in Bellevue WA. It operates more than 30 manufacturing plants and distribution centers on four continents including North and South America Europe and Australia.

In North America the company operates four US manufacturing plants in Washington Mississippi Texas and Ohio and one each in Canada and Mexico. In Europe PACCAR owns factories in the Netherlands and the UK and it has one plant each in Australia and Brazil. PACCAR Financial Services operates across the globe in 24 countries. In 2017 the new PACCAR Innovation Center opened in Sunnyvale CA.

About 45% of PACCAR's revenues are generated outside the US with more than 25% coming from Europe.

Sales and Marketing

PACCAR delivers its products and services to customers worldwide in about 100 countries through its dealer network of more than 2200 locations.

Financial Performance

Except for a dip in 2016 PACCAR's revenue has seen steady growth the last five years rising nearly 24% between 2014 and 2018. The company's Trucks segment has been the chief growth driver and helped propel PACCAR's revenue to record levels in both 2017 and 2018.

Sales in 2018 increased 20% to $23.5 billion compared to $19.5 billion in 2017. Growth in 2018 was fueled by PACCAR's Trucks segment which increased 23% over 2017 amid strong demand for both heavy- and medium-duty trucks. The company enjoyed robust growth in truck revenue across all its geographic markets but North America led the way with a sales rise of 29%. The Parts and Financial Services segments also grew sales in 2018.

Net income increased 31% to $2.2 billion in 2018 compared to 2017 primarily due to higher truck delivery volumes and increased sales prices.

Cash at the end of 2018 was $3.4 billion an increase of $1.1 billion from the prior year. Cash from operations contributed $3 billion to the coffers while investing activities used $1.9 billion mainly for originations of retail loans and direct financing leases. Financing activities provided $71 million primarily from term borrowing.

Strategy

PACCAR spent nearly $440 million on capital investments in 2018 and more than $300 million on R&D. To achieve growth it regularly expands its vehicle product range and upgrades its manufacturing and parts distribution facilities.

The company also invests in truck and engine technologies that enhance vehicle fuel efficiency and reliability. PACCAR's Innovation Center in Silicon Valley is developing alternative fuel vehicles including hybrid and electric as well as autonomous technologies.

PACCAR's Information Technology Division (ITD) works with all the company's operating segments to develop software and hardware that increases the efficiency of products as well as company operations. Key ITD initiatives include truck connectivity systems for the DAR Peterbilt and Kenworth brands; working closely with suppliers to develop Advanced Driver Assistance Systems (ADAS); and implementing emerging technologies including autonomous driving and platooning.

Operational efficiency has been improved through the increased use of automated guided vehicles and robotics in manufacturing enhanced algorithms in parts distribution and mobile apps for financial services.

Company Background

William Pigott founded the Seattle Car Manufacturing Company in 1905 to produce railroad cars for timber transport. Finding immediate success Pigott began to make other kinds of railcars in 1906.

In 1917 Seattle Car merged with the Twohy Brothers of Portland. The new company Pacific

Car & Foundry was sold to American Car & Foundry in 1924.

Pacific Car was in decline by 1934 when William's son Paul bought it; since then the company has remained under family management. The company entered the truck-making business with the 1945 purchase of Seattle-based Kenworth.

In the 1950s Pacific Car became the industry leader in mechanical refrigerator car production. It began producing off-road heavy trucks and acquired Peterbilt Trucks of Oakland (1958).

The company moved its headquarters to Bellevue Washington in 1969 and changed its name to PACCAR in 1971.

HISTORY

William Pigott founded the Seattle Car Manufacturing Company in 1905 to produce railroad cars for timber transport. Finding immediate success Pigott began to make other kinds of railcars in 1906. When the Seattle plant burned the next year the company moved near Renton Washington. In 1911 Pigott renamed the company Seattle Car & Foundry.

In 1917 Seattle Car merged with the Twohy Brothers of Portland. The new company Pacific Car & Foundry was sold to American Car & Foundry in 1924. Pacific Car then diversified into bus manufacturing structural steel fabrications and metal technology.

Pacific Car was in decline by 1934 when William's son Paul bought it; since then the company has remained under family management. Paul Pigott added Hofius Steel and Equipment and Tricoach a bus manufacturer in 1936. The company entered the truck-making business with the 1945 purchase of Seattle-based Kenworth.

In the 1950s Pacific Car became the industry leader in mechanical refrigerator car production. It began producing off-road heavy trucks and acquired Peterbilt Trucks of Oakland (1958). To augment its winch business Pacific Car bought Canada's Gearmatic in 1963.

The company moved its headquarters to Bellevue Washington in 1969 and changed its name to PACCAR in 1971.

EXECUTIVES

Ceo, Ronald E. (Ron) Armstrong, age 63, $1,210,000 total compensation

Svp And General Manager Peterbilt, T. Kyle Quinn, age 58, $440,000 total compensation

Evp And Cfo, Harrie C.A.M. Schippers, age 57, $396,022 total compensation

Svp Financial Services, Robert A. Bengston, age 63, $449,615 total compensation

Evp, Gary L Moore, age 63, $547,693 total compensation

Vp And General Manager Kw, C. Michael Dozier

Vp Paccar And President Daf Trucks N.v., R. Preston Feight, age 51

Vp And Cio, A. Lily Ley, age 53

Executive Vice President, Dan Sobic

Vice President And Controller, Michael Barkley

Vice President, James Cardillo

Vp Paccar Brazil, Marco Davila

Vp Manufacturing, George West Jr

Board Member, Alison Carnwath

Chairman And Ceo, Mark C. Pigott, age 66

Board Member, Gregory M Spierkel

Auditors: Ernst & Young LLP

LOCATIONS

HQ: PACCAR Inc.
  777 - 106th Ave. N.E., Bellevue, WA 98004
Phone: 425 468-7400
Web: www.paccar.com

2017 Sales

	$ mil.	% of total
US	10,530	54
Europe	5,355	28
Other regions	3,572	18
Total	**19,456**	**100**

PRODUCTS/OPERATIONS

2017 Sales

	$ mil.	% of total
Truck	14,775	76
Parts	3,327	17
Financial services	1,269	7
Other	86	-
Total	**19,456**	**100**

Selected Divisions and Subsidiaries

DAF trucks
Kenworth Trucks
Peterbilt trucks
Leyland Trucks Limited (UK)
PACCAR Engine Company
PACCAR Financial Corp.
PACCAR Parts
PACCAR Machinery
PACCAR Winch
  Braden winches
  Carco winches
  Gearmatic winches

COMPETITORS

AGCO	Iveco S.p.A.
CNH Industrial	MAN
Caterpillar	Mack Trucks
Cummins	Meritor
Dana	Morris Material
Deere	Handling
Eaton	Navistar International
Fiat Chrysler	Oshkosh Truck
Ford Motor	Scania
General Motors	UD Trucks
Hino Motors	Volvo
Isuzu	

HISTORICAL FINANCIALS

Company Type: Public

Income Statement

FYE: December 31

	REVENUE ($ mil.)	NET INCOME ($ mil.)	NET PROFIT MARGIN	EMPLOYEES
12/18	23,496	2,195	9.3%	28,000
12/17	19,456	1,675	8.6%	25,000
12/16	17,033	522	3.1%	23,000
12/15	19,115	1,604	8.4%	23,000
12/14	18,997	1,359	7.2%	23,300
Annual Growth	5.5%	12.7%	—	4.7%

2018 Year-End Financials

Debt ratio: 39.00%
Return on equity: 26.00%
Cash ($ mil.): 3,436
Current ratio: 2.00
Long-term debt ($ mil.): 9,951
No. of shares (mil.): 347
Dividends
  Yield: 5.0%
  Payout: 49.0%
Market value ($ mil.): 19,805

	STOCK PRICE ($) FY Close	P/E High/Low		PER SHARE ($) Earnings	Dividends	Book Value
12/18	57.00	13	9	6.00	3.00	25.00
12/17	71.00	16	13	5.00	2.00	23.00
12/16	64.00	46	30	1.00	2.00	19.00
12/15	47.00	15	10	5.00	2.00	20.00
12/14	68.00	18	14	4.00	2.00	19.00
Annual Growth	(4.3%)	—	—	13.1%	13.5%	6.8%

Pacific Premier Bancorp Inc

EXECUTIVES

Pres-Ceo, Steven R Gardner
Chb*, Jeff C Jones
Sr V Pres-Cfo*, Kent Smith
Sr Exec Vpres-Cfo*, Ronald J Nicolas Jr
Cro*, Michael Karr
Evp-Cco*, Donn Jakosky
Evp-Chief Acctg Officer*, Lori Wright
Customer Representativ, Leticia Rodriguez
Senior Vice President Director, Thomas Galindo
Vice President, Flo Jenkins
Senior Vice President, Douglas Wolfe
Auditors: Crowe LLP

LOCATIONS

HQ: Pacific Premier Bancorp Inc
  17901 Von Karman Avenue, Suite 1200, Irvine, CA 92614
Phone: 949 864-8000
Web: www.ppbi.com

HISTORICAL FINANCIALS

Company Type: Public

Income Statement

FYE: December 31

	ASSETS ($ mil.)	NET INCOME ($ mil.)	INCOME AS % OF ASSETS	EMPLOYEES
12/18	11,487	123	1.1%	1,030
12/17	8,025	60	0.7%	846
12/16	4,036	40	1.0%	448
12/15	2,791	26	0.9%	335
12/14	2,039	17	0.8%	285
Annual Growth	54.1%	65.1%	—	37.9%

2018 Year-End Financials

Debt ratio: 7.00%
Return on equity: 8.00%
Cash ($ mil.): 210
Current ratio: —
Long-term debt ($ mil.): —
No. of shares (mil.): 62
Dividends
  Yield: —
  Payout: —
Market value ($ mil.): 1,595

	STOCK PRICE ($) FY Close	P/E High/Low		PER SHARE ($) Earnings	Dividends	Book Value
12/18	26.00	20	10	2.00	0.00	32.00
12/17	40.00	26	20	2.00	0.00	27.00
12/16	35.00	24	13	1.00	0.00	17.00
12/15	21.00	20	12	1.00	0.00	14.00
12/14	17.00	18	14	1.00	0.00	12.00
Annual Growth	10.2%	—	—	23.9%	—	27.8%

PACIFIC PREMIER BANK

EXECUTIVES

Pres-Ceo, Steven R Gardner
Chb*, Jeff C Jones
Sr V Pres-Cfo*, Kent Smith
Sr Exec Vpres-Cfo*, Ronald J Nicolas Jr
Cro*, Michael Karr
Evp-Cco*, Donn Jakosky
Evp-Chief Acctg Officer*, Lori Wright
Customer Representativ, Leticia Rodriguez

LOCATIONS

HQ: PACIFIC PREMIER BANK
17901 VON KARMAN AVE, IRVINE, CA 926146297
Phone: 714 431-4000
Web: WWW.PPBI.COM

HISTORICAL FINANCIALS

Company Type: Private

Income Statement				FYE: December 31
	ASSETS ($ mil.)	NET INCOME ($ mil.)	INCOME AS % OF ASSETS	EMPLOYEES
12/17	8,023	68	0.9%	104
12/16	4,035	45	1.1%	—
12/15	2,782	29	1.1%	—
12/14	2,034	19	0.9%	—
Annual Growth	58.0%	54.0%		

Packaging Corp of America

One of the largest containerboard manufacturers in the US Packaging Corporation of America (PCA) produces about 3.9 million tons of containerboard a year most of which is converted into corrugated boxes and ships about 56 billion square feet of corrugated products. PCA's mills also churn out about a million tons of semi-chemical corrugating medium. The company's corrugated packaging includes shipping containers for manufactured goods multi-color boxes and displays for retail locations and honeycomb protective packaging. Its packaging materials also contain food and beverages and other consumer and industrial products. PCA operates manufacturing plants throughout the US.

Operations

PCA operates in three segments: packaging paper and corporate and other. Packaging which accounts for about 85% of sales produces a variety of corrugated packaging products. The paper segment 15% of sales makes and sells a range of papers including communication papers and pressure sensitive papers (collectively white papers). PCA's Paper segment operates under the trade name Boise Paper. Corporate and other includes support staff services and related assets and liabilities transportation assets and activity related to other ancillary support operations.

As a resource-intensive business PCA comes under a number of environmental regulations. The company spends about $40 million a year to comply with regulations and spends another $10 million or so a year on capital expenditures related to environmental concerns.

Geographic Reach

PCA operates eight containerboard mills (five containerboard mills and three paper mills) and about 100 corrugated products plants in about 35 US states. The company's substantial manufacturing footprint is enhanced by a technical and development hub about 10 regional graphic design centers and several printing and distribution sites.

The company also leases cutting rights on 75000 acres of timberland and has supply agreements on an additional 281000 acres — most neighboring its Counce Tennessee and Valdosta Georgia mills. The company operates also has some converting operations in China and Canada.

Sales and Marketing

PCA promotes its products through a direct sales and marketing force as well as independent brokers and distribution partners. It employs a sales manager and sales representatives at most of its corrugated product manufacturing locations. The company serves more than 18000 customers in more than 35000 locations. About three-quarters of sales of corrugated products go to local and regional accounts (located near a single PCA plant); remaining sales come from national accounts (customers who have widespread locations and are served by several PCA plants). Products are distributed by rail or truck. PCA's largest paper segment customer is Office Depot which contributes more than 45% of paper segment sales.

Financial Performance

PCA bounced back with higher sales in 2016 and 2017 after a drop in 2015. Net income followed the same path but with a greater leap in 2017 from 2016.

The company posted a 10% increase in revenue to $6.4 billion in 2017 from 2016 driven by higher sales volumes and prices for containerboard and corrugated products on strong demand. Paper revenue was lower year-to-year with decreased volumes and prices.

Net income jumped 48% to $668 million in 2017 from $449 million in 2016 driven by the higher containerboard and corrugated products sales. Net income included $122 million of estimated income tax benefit related to the US Tax Cut and Jobs Act.

PCA ended 2017 with $217 million in cash about $22 million less than 2016's total. Operating activities generated $856 million in 2017 while investing activities used $609 million and financing activities used $269 million.

Strategy

PCA is definitely thinking inside the box. It is concentrating its resources on building its box business while de-emphasizing the paper side. Its recent acquisitions have focused on expanding its corrugated and containerboard assets and it converted its plant in Wallula Washington to produce only containerboard. The conversion helped improve PCA's overall productivity and enabled it to respond more quickly to customers' needs. The product shift is reflected in PCA's production numbers which show increasing production of corrugated and containerboard while paper production has diminished.

Mergers and Acquisitions

PCA uses acquisitions to bolster its manufacturing capacity and extend its geographic footprint. In 2017 PCA acquired Sacramento Container Corp. Northern Sheets and Central California Sheets for $265 million. The acquired companies which operate two full-line corrugated products operations and sheet feeders in McClellan California and Kingsburg California expanded PCA's West Coast operations.

In 2016 PCA acquired Pennsylvania-based TimBar Corp. for $387 million. TimBar is a corrugated products producer with six corrugated products production facilities.

Also that year PCA picked up Indiana-based Columbus Container for $100 million. Columbus is a corrugated products producer with one corrugated products production facility and five warehousing facilities.

Company Background

PCA was formed by Madison Dearborn in 1999 in order to acquire the containerboard and corrugated product operations of Pactiv. PCA blossomed five years later when it purchased the assets of Acorn Corrugated Box Company a maker of graphics packaging and displays.

EXECUTIVES

Chairman And Ceo, Mark W. Kowlzan, age 64, $1,157,004 total compensation
Evp Corrugated Products, Thomas A. (Tom) Hassfurther, age 63, $913,002 total compensation
Svp General Counsel And Corporate Secretary, Kent A. Pflederer, age 48, $478,002 total compensation
Svp Sales And Marketing Corrugated Products, Thomas W. H. (Tom) Walton, age 59, $361,002 total compensation
Svp Mill Operations, Charles J. (Jack) Carter, age 60, $519,670 total compensation
Svp And Cfo, Robert P. (Bob) Mundy, age 57, $618,000 total compensation
Vice President Engineering, Nam Shin
Vice President White Paper Manufacturing, Jay Thiessen
Vice President Corporate Technology And Engineering, Ray Shirley
Vice President Engineering, Annie Kim
Senior Vice President And Chief Financial Officer, Richard West
National Account Manager, Jeff Harris
Vice President Investor, Minnie Griffin
National Sales Manager, Mike Jarosz
Board Member, Robert Lyons
Assistant Treasurer, Fran Hori
Treas, Pamela Larson
Board Member, James Woodrum
Board Member, Duane Farrington
Board Member, Hasan Jameel
Auditors: KPMG LLP

LOCATIONS

HQ: Packaging Corp of America
1 North Field Court, Lake Forest, IL 60045
Phone: 847 482-3000
Web: www.packagingcorp.com

PRODUCTS/OPERATIONS

2017 Sales

	$ mil.	% of total
Packaging	5,312	73
Paper	1,052	16
Corporate and other	81	1
Total	**64,449**	**100**

Selected Products:
Corrugated Containers
Retail Packaging and Displays
Heavy-Duty Packaging
Produce Packaging
HexacombFalconboard
Tharco Stock Boxes
Record Storage Boxes
Interior Packaging
Packaging Supplies
Freight Saver Dunnage Bags Printing Capabilities
Containe

COMPETITORS

Amcor
Atlas Container
Bio Pappel
Georgia-Pacific
Graphic Packaging Holding
Greif
International Paper
Kapstone Paper and Packaging
Norampac
Pratt Industries USA
Sonoco Products
Southern Container corp

Income Statement   FYE: December 31

	REVENUE ($ mil.)	NET INCOME ($ mil.)	NET PROFIT MARGIN	EMPLOYEES
12/18	7,015	738	10.5%	15,000
12/17	6,445	669	10.4%	14,600
12/16	5,779	450	7.8%	14,000
12/15	5,742	437	7.6%	13,000
12/14	5,853	393	6.7%	14,000
Annual Growth	4.6%	17.1%	—	1.7%

2018 Year-End Financials

Debt ratio: 38.00%
Return on equity: 30.00%
Cash ($ mil.): 362
Current ratio: 3.00
Long-term debt ($ mil.): 2,501

No. of shares (mil.): 94
Dividends
Yield: 4.0%
Payout: 38.0%
Market value ($ mil.): 7,887

	STOCK PRICE ($) FY Close	P/E High/Low	PER SHARE ($) Earnings	Dividends	Book Value
12/18	83.00	17 10	8.00	3.00	28.00
12/17	121.00	17 12	7.00	3.00	23.00
12/16	85.00	18 9	5.00	2.00	19.00
12/15	63.00	19 13	4.00	2.00	17.00
12/14	78.00	20 15	4.00	2.00	15.00
Annual Growth	1.7%	—	18.2%	17.0%	16.3%

PacWest Bancorp

PacWest Bancorp is the holding company for Pacific Western Bank which operates about 80 branches mostly in southern and central California plus an additional branch in Durham North Carolina. The $21 billion-asset bank caters to small and midsized businesses and their owners and employees offering traditional deposit and loan products and services. Commercial real estate mortgages make up more than 30% of its loan portfolio while cash flow- and asset-based business loans make up another 40%. The bank also originates residential mortgage real estate construction and land loans venture capital equipment finance and consumer loans. PacWest offers investment services and international banking through agreements with correspondent banks.

Operations

Like other retail banks PacWest generates the bulk of its revenue from interest income. About 83% of its total revenue came from interest income on loans and leases during 2015 while another 7% came from interest income on investments. The rest of its revenue came from leased equipment income (3% of revenue) deposit account service charges (1%) other commissions and fees (3%) and other miscellaneous income sources.

The bank's Square 1 Bank Division caters to entrepreneurial businesses and their venture capital and private equity investors while its CapitalSource Division provides cash flow asset-based equipment and real estate loans and leases as well as treasury management services to established middle-market businesses across the country.

Geographic Reach

PWB's branches are located across California in Los Angeles Orange Riverside San Bernardino Santa Barbara San Diego San Francisco San Luis Obispo San Mateo and Ventura Counties. It also has a branch in Durham North Carolina.

Financial Performance

PacWest's acquisitions in 2014 and 2015 boosted its interest-earning loan asset balances more than three-fold which sent its revenues and profits soaring during those years.

The bank's revenue jumped 30% to $968.3 million during 2015 mostly as newly acquired loans from its CapitalSource boosted its interest income during the year.

Strong revenue growth coupled with lower acquisition integration and reorganization costs in 2015 drove PacWest's net income up 77% to $300 million. Its operating cash levels spiked 79% to $594 million with the rise in cash-denominated earnings.

Strategy

PacWest has grown its loan and deposit business as well as its branch network through acquisitions of California community banks and specialized financial services companies. It has made 28 acquisitions since 2000 with some of its most recent being the Square 1 acquisition in 2015 and the CapitalSource Inc. acquisition in 2014.

Mergers and Acquisitions

In October 2015 PacWest purchased $4.6 billion-asset Square 1 and its Square 1 Bank subsidiary for $849 million forming the Square 1 Bank Division of the Bank. The deal boosted its core deposits expanded its national lending platform and bolstered its presence in the technology and life-sciences markets.

In April 2014 the bank bought $10.7 billion-asset CapitalSource Inc. and its CapitalSource Bank (CSB) subsidiary.

In May 2013 PacWest acquired $1.7 billion-asset First California Financial Group operator of First California Bank for $237 million. The purchase added six branches (after consolidation) in Los Angeles Orange Riverside San Bernardino San Diego San Luis Obispo and Ventura Counties.

Company Background

During the economic downturn PacWest took advantage of a rash of bank failures through FDIC-assisted transactions. The acquired institutions were merged into Pacific Western Bank. Under the loss-sharing deals the FDIC agreed to reimburse PacWest for future losses tied to the acquisitions. In a 2012 non-FDIC-assisted deal PacWest bought American Perspective Bank adding two branches and a loan office in the Central Coast area.

EXECUTIVES

Evp And Director The Company And Pacific Western Bank, Daniel B. Platt, age 72, $52,500 total compensation
Evp And Chief Risk Officer, Suzanne R. Brennan, age 68, $165,000 total compensation
Ceo, Matthew P. (Matt) Wagner, age 62, $754,167 total compensation
Evp And Cfo Pacific Western Bank, Patrick J. (Pat) Rusnak, age 55
Evp And Chief Accounting Officer, Lynn M. Hopkins, age 51
Evp; Director Human Resources, Christopher D. Blake, age 59, $298,958 total compensation
Evp And Chief Credit Officer, Bryan M. Corsini, age 57, $375,624 total compensation
Evp; President Capitalsource, James J. (Jim) Pieczynski, age 56, $554,539 total compensation
Evp Operations And Systems, Mark Christian
Evp General Counsel And Corporate Secretary, Kori L. Ogrosky
Senior Vice President Information Systems Manager, Norma Lopez
Senior Vice President, Scott Foote
Vice President Operations Manager, Arbi John
Vice President Regional Manager, Shari Schiavone
Vice President, Sue Thomas
Vice President Bsa Officer, Sali Tice
Senior Vice President, John Braunschweiger
Executive Vice President, Jeffrey Lizar
Senior Vice President Financial Planning, Peter Fan
Senior Vice President Group Manager Government Guaranteed Lending Group, Amy Conner
Vice President Business Development Officer, Michelle Coberly
Vice President Operations Executive, Doug Bradley
Senior Vice President Tax, Grace Keegan
Senior Vice President And Controller, Kathy Bailey
Vice President Coml Inv And Asset Manager, Kevin Powelson
Chairman, John M. Eggemeyer, age 73
Treasurer, Victor Santoro
Board Member, Paul Burke
Auditors: KPMG LLP

LOCATIONS

HQ: PacWest Bancorp
9701 Wilshire Blvd., Suite 700, Beverly Hills, CA 90212
Phone: 310 887-8500
Web: www.pacwestbancorp.com

PRODUCTS/OPERATIONS

2015 Sales

	$ mil.	% of total
Interest income		
Loans and leases	819	87
Investment securities & other	65	7
Noninterest income		
Other commissions and fees	32	3
Leased equipment income	24	3
Service charges on deposit accounts	12	1
Other	35	3
FDIC loss sharing expense net	(18.2)	-
Total	**968**	**100**

Selected Mergers & Acquisitions

COMPETITORS

Bank of America	Rabobank America
CVB Financial	San Diego County
California Bank &	Credit Union
Trust	U.S. Bancorp
City National	Wells Fargo
JPMorgan Chase	Westamerica
MUFG Americas Holdings	

HISTORICAL FINANCIALS
Company Type: Public

Income Statement   FYE: December 31

	ASSETS ($ mil.)	NET INCOME ($ mil.)	INCOME AS % OF ASSETS	EMPLOYEES
12/18	25,731	465	1.8%	1,833
12/17	24,995	358	1.4%	1,786
12/16	21,870	352	1.6%	1,669
12/15	21,288	300	1.4%	1,670
12/14	16,235	169	1.0%	1,443
Annual Growth	12.2%	28.8%	—	6.2%

2018 Year-End Financials

Debt ratio: 3.00%
Return on equity: 9.00%
Cash ($ mil.): 386
Current ratio: —
Long-term debt ($ mil.): —

No. of shares (mil.): 123
Dividends
Yield: 7.0%
Payout: 67.0%
Market value ($ mil.): 4,100

	STOCK PRICE ($) FY Close	P/E High/Low	PER SHARE ($) Earnings	Dividends	Book Value
12/18	33.00	15 8	4.00	2.00	39.00
12/17	50.00	20 15	3.00	2.00	39.00
12/16	54.00	19 10	3.00	2.00	37.00
12/15	43.00	17 14	3.00	2.00	36.00
12/14	45.00	25 20	2.00	1.00	34.00
Annual Growth	(7.5%)	— —	18.0%	16.5%	3.6%

Park National Corp (Newark, OH)

Customers can park their money with Park National. The holding company owns Park National Bank which operates more than 120 branches in Ohio and northern Kentucky through 11 community banking divisions. The banks provide an array of consumer and business banking services including traditional savings and checking accounts and CDs. Business loans including commercial leases and mortgages operating loans and agricultural loans account for about 35% of Park National's loan portfolio. The banks also originate consumer residential real estate and construction loans. Park National's nonbank units include consumer finance outfit Guardian Finance Scope Aircraft Finance and Park Title Agency.In 2018 it acquired Charlotte NC-based NewDominion Bank for some $75 million.

Operations

Each of Park National Corporation's bank affiliates specialize in serving specific geographic locations. It's bank divisions include: Century National Bank; Fairfield National Bank; Farmers Bank; First-Knox National Bank; Park National Bank; Richland Bank; Security National Bank; Second National Bank; Unity National Bank; and United Bank.

Geographic Reach

Park National Corporation and its subsidiaries operate in Ohio and northern Kentucky.

Financial Performance

The company's revenue decreased in fiscal 2013 compared to the previous year. It reported $336.2 million in revenue for fiscal 2013 down from $378.1 million in fiscal 2012.

The company's net income dropped slightly in fiscal 2013 compared to the prior period as well. It reported a net income of $77 million in fiscal 2013 after netting a little more than $78 million the prior year.

Park National Corporation's cash on hand increased by almost $10 million in fiscal 2013 compared to fiscal 2012 levels.

EXECUTIVES

President And Ceo, David L. Trautman, age 57, $775,000 total compensation

Cfo Treasurer And Secretary; Svp And Cfo Park National Bank, Brady T. Burt, age 44, $325,000 total compensation

Vice President Commercial Lender, John MacRitchie

Assistant Vice President Retail, Lisa Mcgraw

Chairman, C. Daniel (Dan) DeLawder, age 69

Auditors: Crowe LLP

LOCATIONS

HQ: Park National Corp (Newark, OH)
50 North Third Street, P.O. Box 3500, Newark, OH 43058-3500
Phone: 740 349-8451
Web: www.parknationalcorp.com

PRODUCTS/OPERATIONS

2015 Sales

	$ mil.	% of total
Interest and fees on loans	228	66
Interest and dividends	37	10
Income from fiduciary activities	20	7
Service charges on deposit accounts	15	4
Checkcard fee income	15	4
Other service income	11	3
Other	17	6
Total	**343**	**100**

Selected Affiliates

Century National Bank
Fairfield National Bank
Farmers Bank
First-Knox National Bank
Guardian Finance Company
Park National Bank
Richland Bank
Scope Aircraft Finance
Second National Bank
Security National Bank
United bank
Unity National Bank

COMPETITORS

Bank of America	U.S. Bancorp
Fifth Third	Wayne Savings
Huntington Bancshares	Bancshares
JPMorgan Chase	Wells Fargo
PNC Financial	

HISTORICAL FINANCIALS

Company Type: Public

Income Statement — FYE: December 31

	ASSETS ($ mil.)	NET INCOME ($ mil.)	INCOME AS % OF ASSETS	EMPLOYEES
12/18	7,804	110	1.4%	1,782
12/17	7,538	84	1.1%	1,746
12/16	7,468	86	1.2%	1,726
12/15	7,311	81	1.1%	1,793
12/14	7,003	84	1.2%	1,801
Annual Growth	2.7%	7.0%	—	(0.3%)

2018 Year-End Financials

Debt ratio: 0.00%
Return on equity: 14.00%
Cash ($ mil.): 167
Current ratio: —
Long-term debt ($ mil.): —
No. of shares (mil.): 16
Dividends
  Yield: 5.0%
  Payout: 58.0%
Market value ($ mil.): 1,334

	STOCK PRICE ($) FY Close	P/E High/Low	PER SHARE ($) Earnings	Dividends	Book Value
12/18	85.00	17 11	7.00	4.00	53.00
12/17	104.00	22 17	5.00	4.00	49.00
12/16	120.00	22 14	6.00	4.00	48.00
12/15	90.00	19 15	5.00	4.00	47.00
12/14	88.00	16 13	5.00	4.00	45.00
Annual Growth	(1.0%)	— —	6.7%	2.0%	4.0%

Parker Hannifin Corp

Parker-Hannifin is a leading global manufacturer of motion and control technologies including fluid power systems for the manufacturing and processing industries. It additionally makes hydraulic fuel pneumatic and electromechanical systems and components for the aerospace/defense industry; and motion and control systems for the heating ventilation air conditioning and refrigeration (HVACR) and transportation industries. It owns some 330 manufacturing plants and operates through the two business segments of Diversified Industrial and Aerospace. The company traces its historical roots back to 1918.

Operations

Parker-Hannifin is a worldwide diversified manufacturer of motion and control technologies and systems. It provides precision engineered technologies products and services for a wide variety of mobile industrial and aerospace markets.

Its largest division the Industrial segment is made up of the Automation Filtration Fluid Connectors Hydraulics Instrumentation and Seal groups. Sales of Industrial products in North American and international markets are made primarily to original equipment manufacturers (OEMs) and their replacement markets in various sectors within the manufacturing processing and transportation industries. They include agriculture alternative energy chemical processing construction machinery factory automation food production life sciences material handling paper robotics and water among many others.

Aerospace segment products are sold mainly to commercial and military customers in the OEM and maintenance repair and overhaul end user markets. They are used in aircraft engines missiles unmanned aerial vehicles and in power generation applications.

Geographic Reach

Parker-Hannifin operates more than 330 manufacturing plants and nearly 130 distribution centers and 160 sales and administrative offices in 40 states and in roughly 50 other countries worldwide. North America accounts for roughly 60% of its sales.

Sales and Marketing

Diversified Industrial products are made primarily to original equipment manufacturers (OEM) and their replacement markets in manufacturing packaging processing transportation mobile construction refrigeration and air conditioning agricultural and military machinery and equipment industries. This segment's sales are marketed primarily through field sales employees and approximately 13700 independent distributor locations throughout the world.

Aerospace products cater to the commercial and military aerospace markets to both OEMs and to end-users for spares maintenance repair and overhaul.

Financial Performance

After declining the previous year Parker-Hannifin' revenues spiked by 6% to reach $12 billion in 2017. The growth was primarily a result of acquisitions (contributing almost $560 million in sales) and an increase in volume in both its Diversified Industrial International and Aerospace Systems segment partially offset by the effect of currency rate changes (which decreased net sales in 2017 by almost $85 million).

Its net income also increased 22% to $983 million in 2017 largely due to additional gains made from its CLARCOR acquisition. The rise in net income and additional sales from previous acquisitions also helped Parker-Hannifin's operating cash flow climb from $1.17 billion in 2016 to $1.3 billion in 2017.

Strategy

The company seeks to enhance its operations and profitability through a strategy of identifying and acquiring businesses with complementary products and services and by divesting businesses that are not considered to be a good long-term fit. It also focuses on building up its operations around targeted regions technologies and markets through acquisitions and organic growth.

Mergers and Acquisitions

Parker Hannifin uses acquisitions as a means of enhancing its product portfolio and growing its global footprint.

In 2019 Parker-Hannifin bought Exotic Metals Forming Company for more than $1.7 billion in cash. Exotic is a manufacturer of air and exhaust management systems for aircraft and engines. The deal expands Parker Hannifin's offerings in a high-growth segment of the aircraft engine market.

Also in 2019 the company announced it would buy Lord Corporation for about $3.7 billion. Lord is a privately-held manufacturer of advanced adhesives coatings specialty materials and vibration and motion control technologies. The addition of Lord will grow Parker-Hannifin's material sciences operations that serve key markets including the aerospace and automotive industries.

In a move that significantly expanded its filtration portfolio in early 2017 Parker Hannifin bought CLARCOR a maker of mobile industrial and environmental filtration products in a deal valued at $4.3 billion. The transaction added more than a dozen respected CLARCOR brands including CLARCOR Baldwin Fuel Manager Airguard Altair Hastings and United Air Specialists among others. In addition it gave Parker-Hannifin stronger relationships with original equipment manufacturers and customers in international markets especially for recurring sales in the aftermarket.

HISTORY

Entrepreneurial engineer Arthur Parker founded the Parker Appliance Company in 1918 to make pneumatic brake boosters. Its products were designed to help trucks and buses stop more easily. Unfortunately Parker's own truck slid off an icy road and over a cliff in 1919 destroying the company's inventory and ending that line of business.

Undeterred Parker started a hydraulics and pneumatic components business in 1924 to serve automotive and industrial clients. In 1927 the fuel-linkage system the company developed for the Spirit of St. Louis helped Lindbergh cross the Atlantic. The company prospered during the Depression; sales reached $2 million in 1934. Two of Parker's long-term clients were Douglas Aircraft and Lockheed.

The company went public in 1938. It employed 5000 defense workers during WWII. After Parker died in 1945 his wife Helen hired new management to focus on the automation market. The firm bought cylinder maker Hannifin in 1957 and became Parker-Hannifin.

In 1960 Parker-Hannifin formed an international unit in Amsterdam and it set up a German subsidiary in 1962. Overseas acquisitions and increased demand from the space program and the aviation market spurred growth in the 1960s. Patrick Parker the founder's son became president in 1968 and chairman in 1977. Parker-Hannifin expanded its aerospace business in 1978 with the purchase of Bertea (electrohydraulic flight controls). Patrick Parker continued as CEO until 1983 and as chairman until 1999.

In mid-2016 Parker Hannifin acquired J ¤ger Automobil-Technik GmbH and J ¤ger Automotive Polska Sp. z.o.o headquartered in Hannover Germany. The J ¤ger Group is a pioneer in rubber-to-plastic direct bonded sealing systems for automotive markets and a leading developer of two-component (2K) direct injection molding technology. The deal provided Parker with innovative injection molding technology and businesses with a strong reputation in the automotive industry.

EXECUTIVES

Vp Ebusiness Iot And Services, Robert W. (Bob) Bond, age 61, $548,700 total compensation
President And Coo, Lee C. Banks, age 56, $850,000 total compensation
Vp And Cio, William G. (Bill) Eline, age 63
Vp And President Instrumentation Group, John R. Greco, age 65
Vp And Chief Technology And Innovation Officer, M. Craig Maxwell, age 61
Vp And President Aerospace Group, Roger S. Sherrard, age 53
Chairman And Ceo, Thomas L. (Tom) Williams, age 60, $1,000,000 total compensation
Vp Global Supply Chain And Procurement, John G. Dedinsky, age 62
Vp And President Automation Group, Yoon (Michael) Chung, age 56
Vp And President Asia Pacific Group, Kurt A. Keller, age 61
Cfo, Catherine A. (Cathy) Suever, age 61
Vp And President - Fluid Connectors Group, Andrew D. Ross
Vp And President Latin America Group, Candido Lima
Vp And President Filtration Group, Robert W. Malone
Vp And President Europe Middle East And Africa Group (emea), Joachim Guhe
Evp Human Resources And External Affairs, Mark J. Hart
Vp And President Engineered Materials Group, Jennifer A. Parmentier
Vp And President Hydraulics Group, Andrew M. Weeks, $400,956 total compensation
Vp General Counsel And Secretary, Joseph R. Leonti, $410,400 total compensation
National Sales Manager Automotive, Craig Zardus
Vice President Information Technology Global Finance And Administrative Systems, John Connors
Vice President Human Resources, Kevin Ruffer
Vp Information Technology, Mark Czaja
Vice President Human Resources, Linda Smith
Vice President Of Operations, Jim Rowell
Vice President Of Military And Helicopter Business, Ray Bumpus
Vice President Of Information Technology, Ursula Hartman
National Account Manager, Deirdre Stinson
Vice President Corporate Strategy, Shawn Horner
Vp And Group Controller, Nick Liberatore
Department Head, Steve Bolanos
Vice President Corporate Business Planning And Development, Paul Vallone
Vice President And President Instrumentation Group, William Bowman
Vice President Of Operations North America, Rob Malone
Group Vice President Operations, Colleen Haley
National Accounts Manager, Rachel Hoffman
Vp Sales North America, John Murray
Vp Controller Hydraulics Group, Colin Wilkinson
Vice President Gobal Sales And Marketing, Michael J O'hara
National Sales Manager Life Sciences, Scott Anderson
Group Vice President Supply Chain Management Aerospace Group, Dorith Hakim
Vice President, Greg Parker
Auditors: DELOITTE & TOUCHE LLP

LOCATIONS

HQ: Parker Hannifin Corp
6035 Parkland Boulevard, Cleveland, OH 44124-4141
Phone: 216 896-3000
Web: www.parker.com

2017 Sales

	$ mil.	% of total
North America	7,586	63
International	4,444	37
Total	**12,029**	**100**

PRODUCTS/OPERATIONS

2017 Sales

	$ mil.	% of total
Diversified Industrial		
North America	5,367	45
International	4,378	36
Aerospace Systems	2,285	19
Total	**12,029**	**100**

Selected Brand Names

Atlas Cylinders
Balston
Bayside
Bellows
Cabett
Calzoni
Chelsea
Chomerics
Compumotor
croloop
CTC
Ermeto
Fluid Power
Gold Ring
Greer
Gresen
Hiross
IPS
Jet-Pipe
Lucifer
Miller
Ross
Schrader
Sempress
Skinner
Sporlan
STC

Operating Groups and Selected Products
Aerospace
   Aircraft wheels and brakes
   Flight control components
   Fuel systems
   Pneumatic pumps and valves
Climate and industrial controls
   Expansion valves
   Filter-dryers
   Hose assemblies
   Pressure regulators
   Solenoid valves
Industrial
   Automation
   Air preparation units
   Electric actuators
   Human/machine interface hardware and software
   Indexers
   Multi-axis positioning tables
   Pneumatic valves
   Stepper and servo drives
   Structural extrusions
   Vacuum products
   Filtration
   Cabin air filters
   Compressed-air and gas-purification filters
   Fuel conditioning filters
   Fuel filters/water separators
   Gas generators
   Gas generators
   Hydraulic lubrication and coolant filters
   Lube oil and fuel filters
   Monitoring devices
   Nitrogen and hydrogen generators
   Process chemical and microfiltration filters
   Water desalinization and purification
   Fluid Connectors
   Couplers

Diagnostic equipment
Hoses and hose fittings
Tube fittings
Valves
Hydraulics
Accumulators
Cylinders
Electrohydraulic systems
Hydrostatic steering units
Metering pumps
Motors and pumps
Power units
Rotary actuators
Sensors
Valves
Instrumentation
Ball plug and needle valves
Cylinder connections
Fluoropolymer fittings
Miniature solenoid valves
Multi-solenoid manifolds
Packless ultra-high-purity valves
Quick connects
Regulators
Spray guns
Transducers
Tubing
Ultra-high-purity tube fittings
Seals
Gaskets and packings
Metal and plastic composite seals
Medical devices seals and instruments
O-rings
O-seals
Thermal management products

COMPETITORS

Bosch Rexroth	ITT Corp.
Crane Co.	Moog
Danaher	SMC Corp.
Danfoss	Swagelok
Donaldson Company	Trelleborg
Eaton	Woodward Governor
Emerson Electric	Zodiac Aerospace
Honeywell	
International	

HISTORICAL FINANCIALS

Company Type: Public

Income Statement   FYE: June 30

	REVENUE ($ mil.)	NET INCOME ($ mil.)	NET PROFIT MARGIN	EMPLOYEES
06/19	14,320	1,512	10.6%	55,610
06/18	14,302	1,061	7.4%	57,170
06/17	12,029	983	8.2%	56,690
06/16	11,361	807	7.1%	48,950
06/15	12,712	1,012	8.0%	54,754
Annual Growth	3.0%	10.6%	—	0.4%

2019 Year-End Financials

Debt ratio: 40.00%
Return on equity: 26.00%
Cash ($ mil.): 3,220
Current ratio: 2.00
Long-term debt ($ mil.): 6,521

No. of shares (mil.): 128
Dividends
 Yield: 0.0%
 Payout: 28.0%
Market value ($ mil.): 21,843

	STOCK PRICE ($) FY Close	P/E High/Low	PER SHARE ($) Earnings	Dividends	Book Value
06/19	170.00	16 12	11.00	3.00	46.00
06/18	156.00	26 19	8.00	3.00	44.00
06/17	160.00	22 15	7.00	3.00	40.00
06/16	108.00	20 15	6.00	3.00	34.00
06/15	116.00	19 15	7.00	2.00	37.00
Annual Growth	10.0%	— —	13.3%	7.5%	5.9%

PARTNERS HEALTHCARE SYSTEM, INC.

Partners HealthCare operates two large acute-care medical centers — Brigham and Women's Hospital and Massachusetts General Hospital — and about 15 community hospitals in Boston and surrounding communities. The not-for-profit system also provides primary and specialty care through clinics physician offices rehabilitation centers long-term care facilities and home health and hospice agencies. Subsidiary MassHealth provides medical insurance to state residents. Partners HealthCare also provides medical training and research through an affiliation with Harvard. The organization has additional partnerships with health research and educational organizations around the globe.

Financial Performance

Partners Healthcare reported $13.3 billion in revenue in 2018 a less than 1% decline from 2017 results. Patient service revenue which accounts for about 70% of sales increased 10% but insurance premium revenue (10% of sales) decreased 43% due to membership declines (related to the transition of customers from managed care to accountable care programs). Academic and research revenue (15% of sales) increased 4%.

Excess of revenue over expenses increased 25% to $826.6 million due to lower operating costs related to the insurance business.

The organization ended 2018 with $398.4 million in cash down $340.7 million from 2017. Operating activities contributed $899 million while investing activities used $1.4 billion (mostly for acquisitions property and equipment) and financing activities contributed $140.8 million via long-term debt proceeds and investment income.

Strategy

Partners HealthCare has expanded its operations through a stream of acquisitions and construction efforts. It completed construction of a replacement facility for the Nantucket Cottage Hospital in 2018. The company is also adding three new outpatient care buildings (containing primary women's cancer diagnostic orthopedic physical therapy and surgery care centers) to its Wentworth-Douglass Hospital campus.

Partners HealthCare is investing in new IT tools to improve efficiencies enhance quality and lower the cost of care. The company has installed an electronic health record (EHR) system across all of its facilities; it is also adding a digital imaging platform and a centralized credentialing system.

In addition the company regularly updates medical equipment at its facilities to keep pace with medical innovations. For instance it has added a minimally invasive spine surgery program at Brigham and Women's Faulkner Hospital and robotic surgery centers at two of its community hospitals in recent years.

Mergers and Acquisitions

Partners HealthCare has had two failed efforts to expand beyond Massachusetts. The company's agreement to acquire Care New England was canceled in 2019 after Rhode Island's governor objected to the deal. Partners and Care New England had approached Rhode Island-based Lifespan to also join forces in 2018 but that proposal was subsequently dropped. The organization did successfully acquire specialty hospital Massachusetts Eye and Ear in 2018.

Company Background

Partners HealthCare was founded in 1994 through the merger of Brigham and Women's Hospital and Massachusetts General Hospital.

EXECUTIVES

Vice President Public Affairs Partners Community Benefit Programs, Lee Chelminiak
Vice President Of Finance, David Mcguire
Evp Administration And Finance Cfo And Treasurer, Peter K. Markell, age 63
President And Ceo Massachusetts General Hospital, Peter L. Slavin
Cio, James W. (Jim) Noga
President And Ceo North Shore Medical Center, Robert G. (Bob) Norton, age 69
President And Ceo Neighborhood Health Plan, Deborah C. Enos
President And Ceo Partners Continuing Care, David E. Storto
President And Ceo Brigham And Women's Hospital, Elizabeth G. (Betsy) Nabel
President And Chief Executive Officer, David F. Torchiana
President Of Partners Community, Thomas H. Lee
President And Ceo Spaulding Rehabilitation Network, Maureen Banks
President Mclean Hospital, Scott L. Rauch
President And Ceo Brigham And Women's Physicians Organization, Allen L. Smith
President And Ceo Martha's Vineyard Hospital, Timothy J. Walsh
President And Ceo Mgh Institute Of Health Professions, Janis P. Bellack
President And Ceo, David Torchiana
President And Ceo Nantucket Cottage Hospital, Margot Hartmann
President And Ceo Partners Healthcare At Home, Rod Carnifax
Medical Director, Jane Erb
Vice President Government Affairs, Joseph D Alviani
Medical Director Breast Care Center, Katherina Zabicki
Director Of Nursing, Deborah Morrissey
Medical Director For Population Health Management, Namita Mohta
Nursing Director, Michelle Anastasi
Nursing Director, Lauren Willard
Medical Director Of The Breast And Ovarian Cancer, Paula Ryan
Nursing Director, Elizabeth Mcgrath
Medical Director, David Chen
Clinical Director, Karon Konner
Nursing Director, Janet Quigley
Nursing Director, Mary Sylvia-Reardon
Medical Director, William Holgerson
Senior Vice President Of Clinical Services, David Mccready
Medical Director, Richard Kaufman
Project Manager To Senior Vice President Research, Angela Vail
Medical Director, Sharon Bober
Nursing Director, Michele Ohara
Clinical Director, Martha Kane
Clinical Director Department Of Pt Ot; Clinical Content Lead Partners Ecare, James Zachazewski
Vice President Of Operations, Hofmann Erika
Nursing Director, Peggy Settle
Director Of Medical Records, Doherty Linda
Nursing Director, Lisa Wichmann
Vice President Of Systems, Meg Costello
Nursing Director, Dorothy Parker
Clinical Director, Scott Waugh
Nursing Director, Donna Crown
Senior Vice President Of Clinical Services, Julia Sinclair
Vice President, Anne Fitzgerald

Assistant Vice President Regional Consultant, Viscomi Rudy

Nursing Director, Jennifer Sargent

Vice President Innovation, Chris Coburn

Rsvp Team Leader, Jessica Grajeda

Vice President Of Information Technology, Karl Fitch

Medical Director, Renee Sorrentino

Medical Director, Angelo Volandes

Senior Vice President For Research, Harry Orf

Vice President, Shelly Anderson

Medical Director Emergency Medicine, Patricia Henwood

Clinical Director, Keilty Colleen

Senior Vice President Of Communication And Public Affairs, Erin Mcdonough

Corporate Vice President Clinical Operations And Chief Nursing Officer, Maclauglin Ellen

Senior Vice President Payer Solution Sales, Wilson Caryn

Vice President Of Operations, Ricci Elisabeth

Senior Vice President Research, Richard Bringhurst

Medical Director, Robert Gottlieb

Vice President Operations Mumbai, Prue Stewart

Nursing Director, Kathryn Hall

Senior Vice President, Estrela Rui

Senior Vice President Of Finance And Treasurer, Karen Lavoie

Vice President, Eileen Flaherty

Pharmacy Manager, James Blackwell

Associate Medical Director, R Nicholas Nace Md

Physical Therapy, Tom Rossignoll

Chairman, Edward P. Lawrence, age 77

Secretary, Maria Sanchez

Secretary, Ruth Valdez

Board Member, Warren Foote

Treasurer, Xandra Breakefield

Vice Chair For Radiology Education, Shank Erik

Board Member, Martha Pitman

Secretary Pathology, Mary Niederberger

Department Secretary, Theresa Crotty

Secretary, Evan David

Secretary, Estimable Jerry

Department Secretary, Julie Baratta

Amb. Practice Secretary I, Bertha Taylor

Treasurer, Susanne Churchill

Board Member, Michael Jerosch-herold

LOCATIONS

HQ: PARTNERS HEALTHCARE SYSTEM, INC.
800 BOYLSTON ST STE 1150, BOSTON, MA
021998123
Phone: 617 278-1000

PRODUCTS/OPERATIONS

2014 Sales

	$ mil.	% of total
Net patient service revenue	7,043	65
Premium revenue	1,622	15
Direct academic and research	1,226	11
Indirect academic and research	353	3
Other revenue	662	6
Total	**10,906**	**100**

COMPETITORS

Baystate Health
Boston Medical Center
Cambridge Health Alliance
Cape Cod Healthcare
Cape Cod Hospital
Care New England
CareGroup
Children's Hospital Boston
Milford Regional Medical Center
Northeast Health System
Southcoast Hospitals Group
Steward Health Care
Universal Health Services

HISTORICAL FINANCIALS

Company Type: Private

Income Statement   FYE: September 30

	REVENUE ($ mil.)	NET INCOME ($ mil.)	NET PROFIT MARGIN	EMPLOYEES
09/15	11,666	(916)	—	67,000
09/10	8	(0)	—	
09/08	551	(44)	—	
Annual Growth	54.7%	—	—	—

Patterson Companies Inc

Patterson Companies' catalogs are like wish lists for veterinary and dental practices. The company operates through two primary segments — wholesalers Patterson Animal Health and Patterson Dental. Patterson Animal Health distributes animal supplies including pharmaceuticals parasiticides and equipment in the US Canada and the UK. Patterson Dental distributes products including X-ray film and machines hand instruments sterilization products dental chairs and lights and diagnostic equipment. Patterson Dental serves the US and Canada; some 85% of its sales come from the US.

Operations

Patterson Animal Health is a leading US distributor of health products for companion animals and horses. It sells more than 100000 products including vaccines and drugs consumables and diagnostic supplies and is responsible for nearly 60% of Patterson Companies' revenue.

In business since 1877 Patterson Dental is the second-largest dental supply wholesaler in the US and Canada (after Henry Schein); it accounts for more than 40% of Patterson's sales. The segment offers its customers more than 90000 different items including approximately 3000 private-label products marketed under the Patterson name. In addition to consumables and equipment Patterson Dental offers services such as technology consulting; office design; equipment installation maintenance and repair; and financing for big-ticket purchases.

Geographic Reach

The US market accounts for some 85% of Patterson's annual revenues. Patterson Dental provides dental supplies throughout the US and Canada. Patterson Animal Health distributes items throughout the UK Canada and the US.

Patterson Logistics Services operates distribution centers in Alabama California Colorado Florida Hawaii Indiana Iowa Pennsylvania South Carolina Texas and Washington.

Sales and Marketing

Patterson's products are sold through direct sales and marketing representatives in the US and Canada to over 150000 customers. Marketing is conducted through its website and through catalogs magazines and direct mail. Customers include dentists dental laboratories veterinarian offices laboratories and other health care providers and institutions.

Subsidiary Patterson Logistics Services operates seven primary distribution centers and six smaller facilities in the US that conduct distribution functions for both Patterson segments. Some of the centers stock products from multiple business units while others serve one segment.

Advertising expenses totaled $6926 in fiscal 2018 (ended April) versus $10128 in 2017 and $12113 in 2016.

Financial Performance

Patterson Companies saw rising revenues for years until fiscal 2018 when sales slipped a modest amount. Net income has been more volatile over recent years as the company's expenses have fluctuated.

In fiscal 2018 revenue dropped 2% to $5.5 billion. That decline was led by the Dental segment's sales which fell 8%. Sales of consumables fell 5% as a result of the company's sales team restructuring and the development of new back-end technologies; equipment and software sales fell 15%. These sales declines were partially offset by 3% higher Animal Health sales.

Net income increased 18% to $201 million in 2018 thanks to lower cost of sales and operating expenses.

Patterson ended fiscal 2018 with $63 million in cash some $32 million less than it had at the start of the year. Although operating activities provided $178.9 million in net cash and investing activities provided another $17 million financing activities used $230.3 million.

Strategy

Patterson Companies relies on its ability to provide a diverse platform of products and services in a total-package approach. A key strategy is to promote its value-added services such as equipment installation and maintenance financing and technology guidance.

The company has also invested in its own technology platforms. For example it is building a new enterprise resource planning (ERP) system. The focus on enhancing its online ordering systems has allowed Patterson to build its client base while freeing up sales representatives to spend more time with customers. Additionally the company offers technology troubleshooting claims and electronic statements through its Patterson Technology Center.

Patterson has grown through internal expansion and via acquisitions. It seeks opportunities to take advantage of the fractured markets in which it operates. Such opportunities include buying other distributors or opening new locations to enter additional markets.

Mergers and Acquisitions

In late 2017 Patterson Dental acquired dental office design and equipment dealer Fitzpatrick Dental Design based out of California. That purchase helped build the company's equipment design and sales operations.

HISTORY

In 1877 brothers Myron and John Patterson bought a Milwaukee drugstore and later added dental supplies to the inventory. Myron bought the dental side of the business from his brother in 1891 moved to St. Paul Minnesota and started a dental supply store. His business later became a subsidiary of diversified manufacturer Esmark which sold Patterson to food giant Beatrice in 1982. Recognizing that food and dental supplies were an odd mix Patterson executives initiated a leveraged buyout in 1985.

In an industry as fragmented as some dental patients' smiles the firm used acquisitions to secure a leading position as a full-service provider. In 1987 Patterson bought D.L. Saslow then the #3 distributor. Between 1989 and 1993 it bought smaller distributors in eight states and Washington DC. In 1993 a year after it went public Patterson bought the Canadian arm of bankrupt rival Healthco International.

During the mid- and late 1990s Patterson continued to buy small local dental-supply distributors branching out across the US and Canada. In 1996 and 1997 Patterson expanded into front-office products with the purchase of Colwell Systems and EagleSoft. It took a few more bites out of the market with purchases of two more local distributors in 1998. In 2000 it bought Micheli Dental Supply a dental products distributor in California and eCheck-Up.com an online provider of payroll human resources payables processing and other services.

In 2001 Patterson expanded beyond dental products distribution when it purchased J. A. Webster a distributor of veterinary supplies. Patterson broadened its operations further in 2003 acquiring AbilityOne Products a provider of medical rehabilitation supplies. It also acquired Smith & Nephew's rehab division and with it the Rolyan and Homecraft brand names. The following year the company changed its name from Patterson Dental to Patterson Companies to reflect this expansion.

However returning its focus on its dental and veterinary businesses the firm sold its Patterson Medical unit in 2015.

EXECUTIVES

Western Region President Patterson Dental, Paul A. Guggenheim, age 59, $384,482 total compensation
Evp And Cfo, Ann B. Gugino, age 47, $399,167 total compensation
Vp Operations, Sean M. Muniz
Vp General Counsel And Secretary, Les B. Korsh, age 49, $280,833 total compensation
President Patterson Dental North America And President Patterson Foundation Board Of Directors, Dave Misiak
Cio, Dave Lardy
Interim President Patterson Animal Health, Kevin Pohlman
President Ceo And Director, Mark S. Walchirk
Vice President Security And Infrastructure, Tom Bethke
Vice President Of Marketing, Tim Rogan
Vice President Marketing (equipment And Service), Bob Foss
Vice President Distribution Operations, Mike Grazer
Vice President Of Procurement, Susan Grelling
Chairman, John D. Buck, age 68
Auditors: Ernst & Young LLP

LOCATIONS

HQ: Patterson Companies Inc
1031 Mendota Heights Road, St. Paul, MN 55120
Phone: 651 686-1600
Web: www.pattersoncompanies.com

2018 Sales

	$ mil.	% of total
US	4,537	83
UK	583	11
Canada	345	6
Total	**5,466**	**100**

PRODUCTS/OPERATIONS

2018 Sales by Segment

	$ mil.	% of total
Animal Health	3,243	59
Dental	2,196	40
Corporate	27	1
Total	**5,466**	**100**

2018 Sales

	$ mil.	% of total
Consumables	4,416	81
Equipment & software	709	13
Other	341	6
Total	**5,466**	**100**

COMPETITORS

Benco Dental
Burkhart Dental
Cardinal Health
Carestream Health
Darby Dental
Henry Schein
IDEXX Labs
MWI Veterinary Supply
McKesson
Universal Medical Systems

HISTORICAL FINANCIALS

Company Type: Public

Income Statement — FYE: April 27

	REVENUE ($ mil.)	NET INCOME ($ mil.)	NET PROFIT MARGIN	EMPLOYEES
04/19	5,575	84	1.5%	7,800
04/18	5,466	201	3.7%	7,700
04/17	5,593	171	3.1%	7,500
04/16	5,387	187	3.5%	7,000
04/15	4,375	223	5.1%	7,000
Annual Growth	**6.2%**	**(21.8%)**	**—**	**2.7%**

2019 Year-End Financials

Debt ratio: 23.00%
Return on equity: 6.00%
Cash ($ mil.): 96
Current ratio: 2.00
Long-term debt ($ mil.): 725
No. of shares (mil.): 95
Dividends
  Yield: 0.0%
  Payout: 117.0%
Market value ($ mil.): 2,086

	STOCK PRICE ($) FY Close	P/E High/Low	Earnings	Dividends	Book Value
04/19	22.00	29 21	1.00	1.00	16.00
04/18	24.00	22 10	2.00	1.00	15.00
04/17	44.00	28 22	2.00	1.00	14.00
04/16	43.00	27 20	2.00	1.00	15.00
04/15	48.00	23 17	2.00	1.00	15.00
Annual Growth	**(17.9%)**	**—**	**(20.6%)**	**6.1%**	**1.4%**

PayPal Holdings Inc

Auditors: PricewaterhouseCoopers LLP

LOCATIONS

HQ: PayPal Holdings Inc
2211 North First Street, San Jose, CA 95131
Phone: 408 967-1000
Web: www.paypal.com

HISTORICAL FINANCIALS

Company Type: Public

Income Statement — FYE: December 31

	REVENUE ($ mil.)	NET INCOME ($ mil.)	NET PROFIT MARGIN	EMPLOYEES
12/19	17,772	2,459	13.8%	23,200
12/18	15,451	2,057	13.3%	21,800
12/17	13,094	1,795	13.7%	18,700
12/16	10,842	1,401	12.9%	18,100
12/15	9,248	1,228	13.3%	16,800
Annual Growth	**17.7%**	**19.0%**	**—**	**8.4%**

2019 Year-End Financials

Debt ratio: 10.00%
Return on equity: 15.00%
Cash ($ mil.): 7,349
Current ratio: 1.00
Long-term debt ($ mil.): 4,965
No. of shares (mil.): 1,173
Dividends
  Yield: —
  Payout: —
Market value ($ mil.): 126,883

	STOCK PRICE ($) FY Close	P/E High/Low	Earnings	Dividends	Book Value
12/19	108.00	58 39	2.00	0.00	14.00
12/18	84.00	53 41	2.00	0.00	13.00
12/17	74.00	53 26	1.00	0.00	13.00
12/16	39.00	38 27	1.00	0.00	12.00
12/15	36.00	40 31	1.00	0.00	11.00
Annual Growth	**31.5%**	**—**	**19.9%**	**—**	**6.4%**

PBF Energy Inc

Established US oil refiners meet the new kid on the block. Formed in the first decade of 21st century PBF Energy's five oil refineries are located in California Delaware Louisiana New Jersey and Ohio and have a combined production capacity of about 900000 barrels per day making the company the fourth-largest refiner in the US. PBF's refineries produce gasoline ultra-low-sulfur diesel heating oil jet fuel lubricants petrochemicals and asphalt for the Midwestern and Northeastern US. The company indirectly owns the general partner and approximately 44.2% of the limited partnership interest of PBF Logistics LP. PBF Energy is majority-owned by investment firms The Blackstone Group and First Reserve.

Operations

PBF Energy operates two business segments: Refining which accounts for more than 95% of its sales and Logistics (through PBF Logistics) which accounts for the remaining less-than 5% of sales.;

Refineries in the East Coast (Delaware City and Paulsboro) average total throughput rates of 370000 barrels per day (bpd) and in the Mid-Continent (Toledo) 170000 bpd. Total refined product barrels sold are around 365000 at East Coast refineries; 170000 at Mid-Continent refineries; and 206000 at Gulf Coast refineries.

Gasoline and distillates account for more than 85% of PBF Energy's total sales; chemicals asphalt and blackoils lubricants and feedstocks all account for less than 5% each.

Geographic Reach

PBF Energy operates refineries in Torrance California; Delaware City Delaware; New Orleans Louisiana; Paulsboro New Jersey; and Toledo Ohio and sells its products in Canada and the US.

Sales and Marketing

PBF has product offtake agreements for a large portion of its product sales. The remainder of its refined products are sold through short-term contracts or on the spot market.

Financial Performance

The collapse in the oil price put a severe dent in PBF Energy's revenue in 2015 but in fiscal 2016 the company defied industry trends and grew revenue 21% to $15.9 billion. The increase was primarily a result of contributions from the Torrance refinery acquired from ExxonMobil mid-year. On the downside average selling prices for refined oil fell around $10 per barrel. Volume sales outstripped total throughput meaning the company dipped into inventory.

Net income increased 17% to $170.8 million as changes in the oil price triggered a positive pretax adjustment to inventory value of $521.3 million. Aside from this single large item net income was put under pressure by tighter margins relating to crude oil differentials lower refined selling prices versus raw material costs and increased interest.

Cash from operations increased 16% to $651.9 million due to deferred income taxes worth $244.8 million and changes in inventories.

Strategy

PBF's strategy is to opportunistically acquire refineries. Its latest such acquisition is of the Torrance refinery in California (following the Chalmette acquisition in 2015) which has daily refining capacity of 155000 barrels per day and was bought in 2016. The refinery can process heavy and medium crude oils and has a sophisticated logistics network of crude and products pipelines distribution terminals and refinery crude. Subsequent to its acquisitions PBF targets margin increases by installing new management and carrying out turnarounds.

PBF Logistics PBF's logistics partner acquires new storage capacity and accepts drop-down transactions from PBF. In 2016 it bought four million barrels of capacity in the Philadelphia region and bought from PBF a 50% interest in Torrance Valley Pipeline Company to look after the gathering and pipeline delivery systems hooked up to the Torrance refinery. The two deals increased PBF Logistics' revenue base by 70%. In addition the cash received by PBF accelerates turnaround activities at its acquired refineries.

Mergers and Acquisitions

Expanding to the US West Coast in 2016 PBF Energy acquired the Torrance refinery and related logistics assets from Exxon Mobil for $537.5 million. The Torrance refinery located on 750 acres in Torrance California is a high-conversion 155000 barrel per day delayed-coking refinery.It sold the logistics assets linked to the refinery to its joint venture PBF Logistics.

Company Background

PBF Energy was created in 2008 by Swiss oil refiner Petroplus to help it establish a foothold in the US. Petroplus and The Blackstone Group each invested $667 million to begin buying oil refineries at the height of the global economic recession when larger companies were looking to sell off assets to drum up cash. PBF first bought the Delaware refinery from Valero in 2010 for $220 million. (The low price tag came because the refinery had been shut down since 2009). Next came the New Jersey refinery again purchased from Valero for $358 million.

In 2011 PBF Energy bought an Ohio refinery from Sunoco for $400 million.

PBF Energy went public in 2012 with an IPO that raised $429 million. The IPO came as a quick turnaround before PBF Energy was able to recognize any significant revenue and the company used the $613 million in proceeds to pay back its principal investors Blackstone and First Reserve.

In 2013 PBF Energy signed a deal with Continental Resources for the oil company to supply PBF Energy with Bakken crude oil. The deal marks a shift for the East Coast refinery market - a market that has historically relied on imports of foreign oil.

EXECUTIVES

Chairman And Ceo, Thomas J. Nimbley, age 67, $1,500,000 total compensation

Svp Commercial, Thomas L. O'Connor, age 46, $500,000 total compensation

President, Matthew C. Lucey, age 45, $600,000 total compensation

Cfo, C. Erik Young, age 43, $523,958 total compensation

Svp Refining, Herman Seedorf, age 67

Svp Commercial Western Region, Timothy Paul Davis

Vice President, Clark Wrigley

Auditors: DELOITTE & TOUCHE LLP

LOCATIONS

HQ: PBF Energy Inc
One Sylvan Way, Second Floor, Parsippany, NJ 07054
Phone: 973 455-7500
Web: www.pbfenergy.com

PRODUCTS/OPERATIONS

Products
Clean Fuels
Lubes
Petrochemicals
LPG

2016 sales by segment

	$ mil.	% of total
Refining	15,909	99
Logistics	187	1
Elimination	(175.4)	-
Total	**15,920**	**100**

2016 sales

	$ mil.	% of total
Gasoline & distillates	14,017	88
Asphalt and blackoils	700	5
Chemicals	554	3
Feedstocks and other	388	2
Lubricants	260	2
Total	**15,920**	**100**

COMPETITORS

Alon USA Energy	Motiva Enterprises
CITGO Refining and Chemicals	Paramount Petroleum
	Placid Refining
Chevron	San Joaquin Refining
ConocoPhillips	Shell Oil Products
Exxon Mobil	Sunoco
Flint Hills	Tauber Oil
HollyFrontier	United Refining
Marathon Petroleum	Valero Energy

HISTORICAL FINANCIALS

Company Type: Public

Income Statement   FYE: December 31

	REVENUE ($ mil.)	NET INCOME ($ mil.)	NET PROFIT MARGIN	EMPLOYEES
12/18	27,186	128	0.5%	3,266
12/17	21,787	416	1.9%	3,165
12/16	15,920	171	1.1%	3,165
12/15	13,124	146	1.1%	2,270
12/14	19,828	(38)	—	1,714
Annual Growth	**8.2%**	**—**	**—**	**17.5%**

2018 Year-End Financials

Debt ratio: 24.00%
Return on equity: 5.00%
Cash ($ mil.): 597
Current ratio: 2.00
Long-term debt ($ mil.): 1,931

No. of shares (mil.): 120
Dividends
  Yield: 4.0%
  Payout: 109.0%
Market value ($ mil.): 3,916

	STOCK PRICE ($) FY Close	P/E High/Low		PER SHARE ($) Earnings	Dividends	Book Value
12/18	33.00	48	26	1.00	1.00	22.00
12/17	35.00	9	5	4.00	1.00	21.00
12/16	28.00	22	11	2.00	1.00	19.00
12/15	37.00	25	14	2.00	1.00	17.00
12/14	27.00	—	—	(1.00)	1.00	15.00
Annual Growth	**5.2%**	—	—	—	**(0.0%)**	**10.7%**

Peabody Energy Corp (New)

Peabody likes to be at the pinnacle of the coal industry. One of the world's leading pure-play coal companies Peabody supplies some 190 million tons of coal to major power and steel customers in some 25 countries. With a leading position in the US Powder River and Illinois basins Peabody sits on 5.2 billion tons of coal reserves across 23 mines. US customers primarily power companies account for most of Peabody's sales. Major operations (mainly in the US and Australia) include coal trading and brokering coalbed methane production transportation-related services and development of coal-based generating plants. Facing regulatory pressure and a down market Peabody sought Chapter 11 bankruptcy protection in 2016 from which it emerged in 2017.

Bankruptcy

In the second quarter of 2016 Peabody Energy Corporation and a majority of its wholly owned domestic subsidiaries as well as one international subsidiary in Gibraltar filed voluntary petitions for reorganization under Chapter 11 of US Bankruptcy Court for the Eastern District of Missouri. The company was unable its $10 billion debt due to prolonged losses stemming from low prices and muted energy demand. The company re-emerged in 2017 after successfully raising $1.5 billion in equity financing and nearly $2 billion in debt financing. Its market capitalization improved from $3 billion to $5.1 billion by the end of 2017.

Operations

Peabody conducts business through six operating segments: Powder River Basin Mining Midwestern US Mining Western US Mining Australian Metallurgical Mining Australian Thermal Mining and Trading and Brokerage.

Powder River Basin operations mine for low-sulfur coal through surface mining extraction processes in Wyoming accounting for 30% of sales.

Australian Metallurgical Mining brings in nearly 30% of revenue and consists of the surface and underground extraction of hard semi-hard and semi-soft coking coal as well as low-volatile pulverized coal injection coal. Its mines are mostly in Queensland.

The Australian Thermal Mining segment mines low-sulfur high Btu thermal coal in New South Wales. The segment accounts for almost 20% of the company's total revenue.

The Midwestern US Mining (15% of annual sales) operates mostly in Illinois and Indiana and digs up high sulfur and Btu coal.

Its Western US Mining segment covers operations in New Mexico Arizona and Colorado characterized by mid-range sulfur content. The segment brings around 10% of the revenue.

Peabody also has a Trading & Brokerage segment that brokers coal and freight-related contracts and provides transportation services.

Geographic Reach

Peabody has offices in Australia China the UK and the US. The company serves metallurgical and thermal coal customers in 25 countries on six continents. Its portfolio is largely shaped around its operations in the Powder River Basin of Wyoming the Illinois Basin and the Asia-pacific metallurgical and thermal coal.

About half of Peabody's annual revenue comes from the US.

Sales and Marketing

Coal brokering is conducted both as principal and agent in support of various coal production-related activities that may involve coal produced from their mines coal sourcing arrangements with third-party mining companies or offtake agreements with other coal producers.

Supply agreements are mostly with electricity generators industrial facilities and steel manufacturers. Its international sales are mostly delivered under long-term contracts.

Peabody's five largest customers account for more than 25% of total sales.

Financial Performance

Peabody saw revenue decline precipitously from a $8 billion peak in 2012 to some $4.7 billion in 2016 as a prolonged commodity price downturn severely affected the coal industry. After five straight years of massive losses (2012-16) for a combined $4.5 billion the company was forced to file for bankruptcy in mid-2016. Peabody reemerged from bankruptcy in April 2017 by successfully securing $1.5 billion in equity financing and $2 billion in debt financing.

By the end of the year Peabody turned around its fate dramatically. The company lowered its interest rates by 100 basis points between April and December 2017 lessened its debt load by $500 million while also increasing its liquidity to $1.2 billion. Furthermore the company authorized a $500 million share repurchase program and completed approximately $175 million in share buybacks.

A strong financial performance aided its balance sheet as well. Revenue jumped 18% in 2017 to $5.6 billion thanks to a 5 million ton (3%) increase in coal sold mostly coming from a strong seaborne coal pricing and higher US demand.

Net income improved dramatically from a loss of $729 million for 2016 to about $500 million in profit during seven months of operations (Apr-Dec 2017). The company's Adjusted EBITDA of $1.5 billion for 2017 was the highest since 2012.

Cash holdings improved to $1 billion at the end of 2017. Net cash generated by operations was $214 million with a further $15 million coming from investments offset by $48 million used in financial activities.

Strategy

Faced with declining coal consumption in the US Peabody is pivoting to selling coal in the developing world by prioritizing robust seaborne thermal and metallurgical coal conditions increasing US exports as well as optimizing operations in Australia to cater to the Chinese and Indian markets. In particular the company is hoping to bank on coking coal (Peabody exports around 12 million tons/year from Australia) which has seen a strong up cycle in the last several quarters. However cheap natural gas and stricter regulations around the world will continue to pose serious threats to the company in the future.

More immediately though Peabody holds two strategic advantages over its peers even in tough market conditions. First it has a high reserve-to-production ratio that allows the company for optimizing mine planning solid cost structure and take on expansion projects. Secondly it also has an impressive diversity of revenue streams with a multi-region exposure and extensive experience in demand risks and logistics that positions the company well for seaborne coal demand. Furthermore the company reports a 30% higher margin of earnings than its closest US competitors thanks to its diversified platforms.

Although coal makes up roughly 40% global energy mix (30% share of total US electric output) and remains an essential ingredient in steelmaking—thanks to growing demand in emerging economies like China and India—US

coal demand is projected to decline in the next decade due to gas price stabilization increasing natural gas and other renewable energy consumption and retirement of old coal plants. This is a significant challenge to Peabody which has its prized assets in the US states of Illinois and Wyoming. Though the company claims competitive operations when compared to natural gas competitors a further decline in natural has may change Peabody's position drastically.

A further challenge for Peabody is the increasing coal generation capacity of China. In 2018 Chinese imports were down because Chinese companies are now increasing their use of domestic supplies and scrap. IHS Markit predicts that coal-fueled capacity will decline by 125 GW around the world even though Asian capacity will rise to almost 440 GW. Peabody's tier-one thermal segment boasts quality assets and enjoys strong margins. However to keep up with demand in a low-cost environment the company will have to improve its thermal and met coal production costs.

Mergers and Acquisitions

In December 2018 Peabody acquired the Shoal Creek coal mine from the Drummond Company for $387 million to upgrade its own seaborne metallurgical coal portfolio. The mine produced 2.1 million tons of metallurgical coal in 2017 with a probably reserve of 58 additional million tons. Located in Alabama the mill serves Asian and European steel mills selling at modest discounts to the Australian hard coking coal index.

In October 2018 reports broke that Peabody was eying to buy 80% of Colombia's top coal exporter Drummond International. A month earlier Peabody acquired Drummond's Shoal Creek metallurgical coal mine in central Alabama for $400 million. The Shoal Creek acquistion added two million tons per year of high coke sales for the company and is in line with a metallurgical coal upgrade plan.

The Drummond deal however is a muchbigger deal that is being seen as a a bold move for Peabody which was forced to file for Chapter 11 bankruptcy protection in 2016 after a sharp drop in coal prices left it unable to service its $10 billion debt. However the company has refused to acknowledge the deal yet which is busy dealing with an operational incident at its North Goonyella site in Australia.

In 2017 Drummond produced 32.4 mt of thermal coal some 36% of Colombia's total output. It has major open pits deep-water port and several coal transportation facilities in the country.

Company Background

Peabody was founded in 1883 as a coal supplier but began coal mining in earnest in 1926.

EXECUTIVES

Vice President And Assistant Controller Operations, Gary Kacich
Evp Corporate Services And Chief Commercial Officer, Charles F. Meintjes, age 56, $554,583 total compensation
President Americas, Kemal Williamson, age 59, $504,167 total compensation
Peabody Energy President Australia, George J. Schuller
Evp And Cfo, Amy B. Schwetz, $479,583 total compensation
President And Ceo, Glenn L. Kellow, age 51, $997,896 total compensation
Evp Chief Legal Officer Government Affairs And Corporate Secretary, A. Verona Dorch, $456,667 total compensation
Vice President Trade Operations, Debra Drake
Vp Corporate Development Australia, Miguel Madrigal
Vice President Technical Services, Bill Hall

Vice President And General Manager Of Colorado Operations, Pat Sollars
Vice President Supply Chain Management Americas, Paul Wagner
Senior Vice President Global Government Affairs, Michael Flannigan
Vice President Marketing, Scott Croger
Vice President Business Continuous Improvement, Jeff Maher
Vice President Of Health And Safety, Matt Pedersen-Howard
Vice President And Treasurer, Jim Tichenor
Vice President Btu Conversion, Marty Considine
Chief Human Resource Officer Senior Vice President, Paul Richard
Vice President Human Resources, Gregg Heaton
Senior Vice President And Chief Accounting Officer, Mark Spurbeck
Chairman, Robert A. (Bob) Malone, age 67
Assistant Treasurer, Chino Kim
Board Member, Joe Laymon
Board Member, Stephen Gorman
Board Member, Teresa Madden
Board Member, Nicholas Chirekos
Auditors: Ernst & Young LLP

LOCATIONS

HQ: Peabody Energy Corp (New)
701 Market Street, St. Louis, MO 63101-1826
Phone: 314 342-3400
Web: www.peabodyenergy.com

2017 Sales

	% of total
US	49
Japan	12
Taiwan	9
China	7
India	7
Australia	5
South Korea	1
Other	10
Total	**100**

PRODUCTS/OPERATIONS

2017 Sales

	$ mil.	% of total
Powder River Basin Mining	1,179	28
Australian Metallurgical Mining	1,221	29
Midwestern U.S. Mining	592	14
Australian Thermal Mining	773	18
Western U.S. Mining	441	10
Trading and Brokerage	34	1
Corporate and Other	14	-
Total	**4,253**	**100**

COMPETITORS

Alliance Resource	CONSOL Energy
Alpha Natural Resources	China Coal Energy
	Cloud Peak Energy
Anglo American	Glencore
Arch Coal	North American Coal
BHP Billiton	RAG AG

HISTORICAL FINANCIALS

Company Type: Public

Income Statement

FYE: December 31

	REVENUE ($ mil.)	NET INCOME ($ mil.)	NET PROFIT MARGIN	EMPLOYEES
12/18	5,582	647	11.6%	7,400
12/17*	4,253	678	15.9%	7,100
04/17	1,326	(217)	—	—
12/16	4,715	(740)	—	6,700
12/15	5,609	(1,996)	—	7,600
Annual Growth	**(0.2%)**	**—**	**—**	**(0.9%)**

*Fiscal year change

2018 Year-End Financials

Debt ratio: 18.00%
Return on equity: 18.00%
Cash ($ mil.): 982
Current ratio: 2.00
Long-term debt ($ mil.): 1,331

No. of shares (mil.): 110
Dividends
 Yield: 2.0%
 Payout: 11.0%
Market value ($ mil.): 3,365

	STOCK PRICE ($) FY Close	P/E High/Low		PER SHARE ($) Earnings	Dividends	Book Value
12/18	30.00	11	7	4.00	0.00	31.00
12/17*	39.00	11	6	4.00	0.00	34.00
Annual Growth	(8.2%)	—	—	6.5%	—	(3.6%)

*Fiscal year change

Peapack-Gladstone Financial Corp.

Peapack-Gladstone Financial is the $3.4 billion-asset holding company for the near-century-old Peapack-Gladstone Bank which operates more than 20 branches in New Jersey's Hunterdon Morris Somerset Middlesex and Union counties. Founded in 1921 the bank provides traditional deposit accounts credit cards and loans to individuals and small businesses as well as trust and investment management services through its PGB Trust and Investments unit. Multifamily residential mortgages represent nearly 50% of the company's loan portfolio while commercial mortgages make up around 15%. The bank also originates construction consumer and business loans.

Operations

Peapack-Gladstone Financial operates two main divisions: Banking which offers traditional deposit and loan services merchant card services; and Wealth Management which boasts more than $3.3 billion in assets under administration (as of early 2016) and operates through PGB Trust and Investments which offers asset management services for individuals and institutions as well as personal trust services. More than 80% of the bank's total revenue came from interest income (mostly on its loans) during 2015 while 14% came from its wealth management fee income and 3% came from service charges and fees.

Multifamily residential mortgages represented nearly 50% of the company's loan portfolio at the end of 2015 while commercial mortgages made up another 15%. The rest of its portfolio was made up of construction consumer and business loans.

Geographic Reach

The bank's branches are located across New Jersey in Somerset Morris Hunterdon Middlesex and Union counties Its private banking and wealth management locations are located in Bedminster Morristown Princeton and Teaneck.

Sales and Marketing

The bank's commercial banking business serves business owners professionals retailers contractors and real estate investors. Its wealth management division serves individuals families foundations endowments trusts and estates.

Peapack-Gladstone has been ramping up its advertising spend in recent years. It spent $637000 on advertising during 2015 up from $594000 and $519000 in 2014 and 2013 respectively.

Financial Performance

Peapack-Gladstone's annual revenues and profits have swelled more than 60% since 2011 as its nearly tripled its loan assets to over $2.9 billion.

The bank's revenue jumped 27% to $122.86 million during 2015 mostly thanks to higher interest income as its loan assets grew by 30% with exceptional increases in its multifamily mortgage and commercial loan volumes. Peapack-Gladstone's wealth management division income grew 20% with increases in securities gains service charges and other non-interest income.

Strong revenue growth in 2015 drove Peapack-Gladstone's net income up 34% to $19.97 million. The bank's operating cash levels climbed 11% to $30.31 million thanks to a rise in cash-based earnings.

Strategy

Peapack-Gladstone Financial continued in 2016 to focus on: enhancing its risk management to keep its loan provisions at a minimum and its profits up; expanding its multi-family loans as well as its commercial real estate loans (to a lesser extent); growing its commercial and industrial (C&I) lending business through its private banking divisions; and expanding its wealth management business which now accounts for 15% of its annual revenue.

Mergers and Acquisitions

In May 2015 Peapack-Gladstone bolstered its wealth management division after buying Morristown-based Wealth Management Consultants LLC for $2.8 million. The deal boosted the bank's assets under advisement and administration to $3.5 billion.

EXECUTIVES

Sevp And Cfo Peapack-gladstone Financial And Peapack-gladstone Bank, Jeffrey J. Carfora, age 61
Evp And Coo, Robert A. (Bob) Plante, age 60
President And Ceo Peapack-gladstone Financial And Peapack-gladstone Bank, Douglas L. Kennedy, age 60
Evp Cio And Head Of Banking Services Peapack-gladstone Bank, Kevin B. Runyon
Sevp Chief Strategy Officer And General Counsel, Finn M.W. Casperson, age 49
Evp And Head Of Retail Banking Peapack-gladstone Bank, Anthony V. Bilotta, age 59
Evp And Head Of Commercial Real Estate Peapack-gladstone Bank, Vincent A. Spero
Sevp And President Private Wealth Management, John P. Babcock
Evp And Chief Credit Officer Peapack-gladstone Bank, Lisa Chalkan
Evp And Director Human Capital Peapack-gladstone Bank, Philip Portantino
Evp And President Wealth Management Consultants Peapack-gladstone Bank, Thomas J. Ross
Evp And Head Of Commercial Banking Peapack-gladstone Bank, Eric H. Waser
Svp And Head Of Residential And Consumer Lending Peapack-gladstone, Glenn R. Straffi
Vice President Director Of Corporate Learning, Doreen Macchiarola
Senior Vice President, Charles Adornetto
Vp Sales Distribution Leader, Dominic Sedicino
Vice President, Sean Martin
Vice President And Trust Officer, Kim Czyzewski
Vice President, Glenn Carroll
Private Banker Vice President, Ryan Beltz
Vice President Portfolio Manager, Sarah Krieger
Vice President, Georgette Barnes
Svp Head Of Asset Management At Peapack Capital, David Santom
Assistant Vice President And Senior Loan Administrator, Ana Ribeiro
Assistant Vice President And Senior Custody Officer, Amanda Pullizzi
Svp Senior Underwriter, Christian Gaudioso
Assistant Vice President And Mortgage Consultant, Stephanie Chu
Vice President Financial Analyst, Renee Skuraton
Vice President, David Oddo
Senior Vp Head Of Loan Operations, Lisa Ciampi
Vp Retail Private Banker, Anna Calles
Assistant Vice President And Senior Staff Accountant And Technical Support, Jennifer Greenwood
Chairman, F. Duffield (Duff) Meyercord, age 72
Board Member, Susan Cole
Board Member, Richard Daingerfield
Auditors: Crowe LLP

LOCATIONS

HQ: Peapack-Gladstone Financial Corp.
 500 Hills Drive, Suite 300, Bedminster, NJ 07921-0700
Phone: 908 234-0700
Web: www.pgbank.com

PRODUCTS/OPERATIONS

2015 Sales

	$ mil.	% of total
Interest Income		
Loans including fees	94	77
Securities available for sale	5	4
Other	0	-
Other Income		
Wealth management fee income	17	14
Service charges and fees	3	3
Bank owned life insurance	1	1
Other Income	1	1
Other	1	-
Total	123	100

COMPETITORS

Bank of America	PNC Financial
Hudson City Bancorp	TD Bank USA
JPMorgan Chase	Valley National
MSB Financial	Bancorp

HISTORICAL FINANCIALS

Company Type: Public

Income Statement

FYE: December 31

	ASSETS ($ mil.)	NET INCOME ($ mil.)	INCOME AS % OF ASSETS	EMPLOYEES
12/18	4,618	44	1.0%	409
12/17	4,261	36	0.9%	384
12/16	3,879	26	0.7%	338
12/15	3,365	20	0.6%	316
12/14	2,702	15	0.6%	306
Annual Growth	14.3%	31.2%	—	7.5%

2018 Year-End Financials

Debt ratio: 2.00%
Return on equity: 10.00%
Cash ($ mil.): 161
Current ratio: —
Long-term debt ($ mil.): —

No. of shares (mil.): 19
Dividends
 Yield: 1.0%
 Payout: 9.0%
Market value ($ mil.): 487

	STOCK PRICE ($) FY Close	P/E High/Low		PER SHARE ($) Earnings	Dividends	Book Value
12/18	25.00	16	10	2.00	0.00	24.00
12/17	35.00	18	14	2.00	0.00	22.00
12/16	31.00	20	10	2.00	0.00	19.00
12/15	21.00	18	14	1.00	0.00	17.00
12/14	19.00	18	14	1.00	0.00	16.00
Annual Growth	7.9%	—	—	17.3%	(0.0%)	11.0%

Penney (J.C.) Co.,Inc. (Holding Co.)

J. C. Penney Company is a holding company for department store operator J. C. Penney Corp. One of the largest department store and e-commerce retailers in the US J. C. Penney Corp. operates more than 860 JCPenney department stores across the country and in Puerto Rico. Its stores are mostly found in suburban shopping malls and sell clothing for men women and children as well as footwear accessories homeware and curtains and drapes. Some stores contain styling salons optical centers and portrait studios as well as shop-in-shops such as Sephora cosmetics. J. C. Penney Corp. has been closing stores amid a tough retail environment.

Operations

J. C. Penney Corp. has strength in a broad range of product categories including apparel and footwear accessories fine and fashion jewelry beauty products and home furnishings. Its leading categories are women's and men's apparel together accounting for about 45% of total sales. Home goods and women's accessories (including Sephora cosmetics) account for about 15% of sales each. The last quarter of revenue comes from children's items footwear and handbags jewelry and services such as portrait photography and custom decorating.

The retailer claims more than 650 Sephora shop-in-shop locations and about 750 JCPenney Salons.

Geographic Reach

J. C. Penney Corp. has a presence throughout the continental US Alaska and Puerto Rico. Its top markets include Texas (more than 80 stores) California (about 75) Florida (nearly 55) New York (about 40) and Ohio (more than 35).

Its supply chain network operates about a dozen facilities in California Connecticut Georgia Kansas Ohio Nevada North Carolina Texas and Utah.

Sales and Marketing

J.C Penney Corp. sells merchandise and services to consumers through its department stores and its website (jcpenney.com). The company fulfills online customer purchases by direct shipment to the customer from its distribution facilities and stores or from its suppliers' warehouses and by in-store customer pick up.

The company markets its products via newspaper television programmatic marketing radio and other media.

Financial Performance

Amid a tough retail environment especially for mall-based retailers J. C. Penney's revenue has fallen the past two years after rising for two prior to that. Overall sales are down 2% since fiscal 2014. The company has reported a net loss for each of the last five years.

In fiscal 2018 (ended January 31 2019) the company saw revenue drop 7% from the prior year. Comparable store sales were down 3% that year and J. C. Penney ended the year with about 150 fewer stores than it had at the start of 2017.

Net loss that year was $255 million compared to $118 million in 2017. In addition to the decline in revenue the loss was impacted by a smaller income tax benefit in 2018 ($16 million compared to $126 million the prior year) and a two-point increase in costs of goods sold as a percentage of total sales.

Cash at the end of fiscal 2018 was $333 million a decrease of $125 million from the prior year. Cash from operations contributed $359 million to the coffers while investing activities used $244 million mainly for capital expenditures. Financing activities used another $240 million for payments of long-term debt. J. C. Penney remains highly leveraged however with some $4 billion in total debt.

Strategy

With a new senior leadership team (including a new CEO and a new CFO appointed in late 2018 and early 2019 respectively) J. C. Penney is still working to develop a long-term vision for growth and sustained profitability.

In the short-term however it continues to focus on its omnichannel strategy to create a seamless experience for customers to browse buy pick up and return merchandise online in stores or through a combination of both. The company is improving its website from an assortment and experience standpoint and ensuring it has the right technology platform in place to support it.

The retailer is also optimizing its merchandise assortment and reducing inventory. It is working to revitalize key categories such as women's apparel and has eliminated non-core low-margin categories such as appliances. Overall inventory was reduced by nearly 15% in 2018. In addition J. C. Penney is investing in technology and tools to improve its shrink results (when inventory is lower than reported due to clerical errors or goods being damaged lost or stolen).

The company has reduced its physical footprint significantly in recent years. It ended 2018 with about 865 stores compared to more than 1060 at the end of 2014.

Company Background

J. C. Penney was founded by James Cash Penney in Kemmerer Wyoming in 1902. The first store was named The Golden Rule.

The company was incorporated in 1924 and transitioned to a holding company structure in 2002.

EXECUTIVES

Evp Stores, Joseph M. (Joe) McFarland, age 49, $650,000 total compensation
Svp And General Merchandise Manager Fine Jewelry And Accessories, Pam Mortensen, age 64
Evp Supply Chain, Michael (Mike) Robbins, age 53
Evp Human Resources, Brynn L. Evanson, age 49, $515,937 total compensation
Evp And Cio, Therace M. Risch, age 46, $90,009 total compensation
Svp And Senior General Merchandise Manager Women's Apparel Sephora Salon Women's Specialty Footwear And Handbags, Jodie Johnson
Chairman And Ceo, Marvin R. Ellison, age 54, $1,446,667 total compensation
Evp And Cfo, Jeffrey (Jeff) Davis, age 56
Svp And Group President Northern Stores Division, Sean Lee
Svp And General Merchandise Manager Menâ's Apparel Children Apparel And Jewelry, James Starke
Evp Omnichannel, Michael Amend, age 41
Svp And Group President Southern Stores Division, Jennifer Hipskind
Svp And General Merchandise Manager Sephora Salon & Intimate Apparel And Accessories, Angela Swanner
Evp And Chief Marketing Officer, Marci Grebstein
Svp And General Merchandise Manager Home, Tony Hurst
Svp And General Counsel, Brandy Treadway
Senior Vice President E Commerce, Dennis Johnson
Vice President Custom Decorating And Revenue Services, Ron Brown
Vice President Director Store Environment, Tim Stoller
Vice President Planning And Allocation Ecommerce, Jim Favors
Senior Vice President Planning And Allocation, Brian Greene
Vp Design Trend And Brand Kids, Elizabeth Melley
Executive Vice President For Womens Apparel, Elizabeth Sweney
Vice President Supply Chain Operations, Ron Harper
Vice President Talent Development And Diversity, Miya Maysent
Vp Merchandise Operations, Donna Taylor
Vice President, Eric Blackwood
Vice President Enterprise Support, Gary Maciejewski
Vice President Product Development Des, Valerie Harris
Svp Finance, Trent Kruse
Vice President Brand Trend Design Womens, Nathan Laffin
Legal Secretary, Jo Nolte
Svp Merchandising Home Services Custom Window And Commercial Sales, Katheryn Burchett
Divisional Vice President, Laurie Sutandar
Vice President Information Technology Operations And Support, Steve Martin
Senior Vice President Finance, Jerry Murray
Vice President And Managing Director Global In House Center (gic), Snehil Gambhir
Vice President Information Technology Application Development, Katie Holt
Vice President Information Technology Chief Information Security Officer, David Mcleod
Vice President Information Technology, Raj Lakshmaihgari
Senior Vice President Digital, Dhriti Saha
Svp Information Technology, Melissa Pint
Vice President Infrastructure Engineering, Brian Covert
Svp Price Planning And Allocation, Prosun Niyogi
Svp Global Brand Development, Stephen Budd
Svp Product Development And Design, Val Harris
Svp Planning And Allocation And Pricing, Amy Wooden
Senior Vice President Planning And Allocation, John Welling
Executive Vice President And Chief Merchant, Michelle Wlazlo
Senior Vice President Asset Protection, Mark Stinde
Senior Vice President Chief Accounting Officer Controller, Steven Whaley
Board Member, Paul Brown
Board Member, Debora Plunkett
Board Member, Wonya Lucas
Auditors: KPMG LLP

LOCATIONS

HQ: Penney (J.C.) Co.,Inc. (Holding Co.)
6501 Legacy Drive, Plano, TX 75024-3698
Phone: 972 431-1000
Web: www.jcpenney.com

PRODUCTS/OPERATIONS

2018 Sales

	% of total
Women's apparel	22
Men's apparel and accessories	21
Home	14
Women's accessories including Sephora	13
Children's including toys	9
Footwear and handbags	8
Fine jewelry	7
Services and other	6
Total	**100**

HISTORICAL FINANCIALS

Company Type: Public

Income Statement   FYE: February 2

	REVENUE ($ mil.)	NET INCOME ($ mil.)	NET PROFIT MARGIN	EMPLOYEES
02/19	12,019	(255)	—	95,000
02/18*	12,506	(116)	—	98,000
01/17	12,547	1	0.0%	106,000
01/16	12,625	(513)	—	105,000
01/15	12,257	(771)	—	114,000
Annual Growth	(0.5%)	—		(4.5%)

*Fiscal year change

2019 Year-End Financials

Debt ratio: 52.00%	No. of shares (mil.): 316
Return on equity: (-20.00%)	Dividends
Cash ($ mil.): 333	Yield: —
Current ratio: 2.00	Payout: —
Long-term debt ($ mil.): 3,920	Market value ($ mil.): 417

	STOCK PRICE ($) FY Close	P/E High/Low	PER SHARE ($) Earnings	Dividends	Book Value
02/19	1.00	— —	(1.00)	0.00	4.00
02/18*	4.00	— —	(0.00)	0.00	4.00
01/17	6.00	— —	(0.00)	0.00	4.00
01/16	7.00	— —	(2.00)	0.00	4.00
01/15	7.00	— —	(3.00)	0.00	6.00
Annual Growth	(34.7%)		—	—	(12.4%)

*Fiscal year change

PENNSYLVANIA HOUSING FINANCE AGENCY

Pennsylvania Housing Finance Agency (PHFA) helps residents of the Keystone State obtain keys to their dream homes. The government-owned agency provides financing for low-income home-buyers including the elderly and disabled and participates in rental housing development initiatives. It generates funding from state and federal grants interest earned on investments and loans and the sale of its own securities to private investors.Â The agencyÂ is run by a board which includes Pennsylvania's secretary of banking secretary of community and economic development secretary of public welfare and the state treasurer. The PHFA has funded more than 130000 houses and 54000 apartment units since its founding in 1972.

EXECUTIVES

Vice President Of Information Technology, Kristy Provost

LOCATIONS

HQ: PENNSYLVANIA HOUSING FINANCE AGENCY
211 N FRONT ST, HARRISBURG, PA 171011406
Phone: 717 780-3800
Web: WWW.PHFA.ORG

HISTORICAL FINANCIALS

Company Type: Private

Income Statement   FYE: June 30

	ASSETS ($ mil.)	NET INCOME ($ mil.)	INCOME AS % OF ASSETS	EMPLOYEES
06/18	4,367	21	0.5%	250
06/12	5,593	11	0.2%	—
06/11	6,051	39	0.7%	—
06/10	6,265	25	0.4%	—
Annual Growth	(4.4%)	(2.2%)		

PennyMac Financial Services Inc (New)

If you're thinking residential mortgage this company has more than a penny for your thoughts. The parent of investment management loan services and investment trust companies PennyMac Financial Services (PennyMac) focuses on the US residential mortgage market offering loans and investment management services. Through its Private National Mortgage Acceptance Company the company's PennyMac Loan Services (PLS) originates home loans in 45 states and DC and services loans in 49 states DC and the US Virgin Islands. PLS's counterpart PNMAC Capital Management acts as investment manager and advisor. The companies service and advise PennyMac Mortgage Investment Trust (PMT). PennyMac went public in 2013.

IPO

PennyMac hoped to raise $287.5 million in its IPO but investors responded with $199.9 million. The company plans to use the proceeds to fund growth of its mortgage business through Private National Mortgage Acceptance Company. It will also use the funds for general corporate purposes.

Operations

PennyMac's mortgage banking segment includes correspondent lending retail lending and loan servicing. The correspondent line includes conventional residential mortgages acquired by PMT as well as those guaranteed by FreddieMac FannieMae and other government agencies. The company has more than 140 approved sellers; in 2012 it had $13 billion in conventional loans and $8.4 billion in government-insured loans. Retail lending originates new prime residential conventional and government-backed mortgage loans for purchasing or refinancing homes. PennyMac uses the Internet and a call center rather than traditional branch locations for direct-to-consumer approach. The company's loan servicing business includes the back office work of loan administration collection and default activities. It serves PennyMac subsidiaries and other mortgage companies. The unit handles prime credit and distress loans under the prime servicing and special servicing headings respectively.

PennyMac's investment management segment operates as an investment manager through PNMAC Capital Management (PCM). PCM handles the $1.8 billion in combined assets from PMT and PennyMac's other investment funds. PMT is a publicly traded real estate investment trust (REIT).

Geographic Reach

While PennyMac serves nearly the entire US its portfolio is heavily weighted toward California (38%) Florida (5%) and Colorado (5%).

Financial Performance

The company's revenue has increased on the strength of gains in both the loan servicing and management segments. Other operating metrics include net assets under management total mortgage loans serviced and total mortgage loan production; all have increased in the last three years. PennyMac reported lower net income for 2012 due to amortization and impairment charges and higher spending on compensation. It sold and repurchased loans loans and earned interest on investments to more than double its cash flow for the same period.

Strategy

Since PennyMac was formed during the financial crisis it hasn't had to scramble and adapt like many of its competitors. As many mortgage shoppers turn away from large banks the company believes its poised to take advantage of growth and a lack of stringent regulations imposed on banks. For growth the company intends to focus on expanding its servicing business organically and through acquisitions increasing the number of loan sellers from which it purchases loans and leveraging its servicing portfolio to increase refinance and loan servicing opportunities.

EXECUTIVES

Senior Managing Director And Chief Enterprise Operations Officer, Anne D. McCallion, age 64
President And Ceo, David A. Spector, age 56, $503,370 total compensation
President Pennymac Loan Services, Douglas E. (Doug) Jones, age 62, $325,000 total compensation
Senior Managing Director And Chief Risk Officer, David M. (Dave) Walker, age 63
Senior Managing Director And Chief Mortgage Operations Officer, Steve R. Bailey, age 57
Senior Managing Director And Cfo, Andrew S. Chang, age 41
Senior Managing Director And Chief Capital Markets Officer, Vandad Fartaj, age 44
Senior Managing Director And Chief Administrative And Legal Officer, Jeffrey P. Grogin, age 58
Senior Managing Director And Deputy Cfo, Daniel S. Perotti, age 38
Chairman And Ceo Pennymac Financial Services Inc. And Private National Mortgage Acceptance Company Llc, Stanford L. Kurland, age 66
Auditors: DELOITTE & TOUCHE LLP

LOCATIONS

HQ: PennyMac Financial Services Inc (New)
3043 Townsgate Road, Westlake Village, CA 91361
Phone: 818 224-7442
Web: www.pennymacusa.com

2016 Sales

	$ mil.	% of total
Net gains on mortgage loans held for sale	532	56
Net mortgage loan servicing fees	186	19
Loan origination fees	126	13
Fulfillment fees from PennyMac Mortgage Investment Trust	87	9
Management fees and Carried Interest	24	2
Other	4	1
Net interest expense	-25.1	-
Total	**932**	**0**

COMPETITORS

Bank of America	Quicken Loans
Citigroup	Stonegate Mortgage
JPMorgan Chase	U.S. Bancorp
Nationstar Mortgage	Wells Fargo
Ocwen Financial	

HISTORICAL FINANCIALS

Company Type: Public

Income Statement
FYE: December 31

	ASSETS ($ mil.)	NET INCOME ($ mil.)	INCOME AS % OF ASSETS	EMPLOYEES
12/18	7,479	88	1.2%	3,460
12/17	7,368	101	1.4%	3,189
12/16	5,134	66	1.3%	3,038
12/15	3,505	47	1.3%	2,509
12/14	2,507	37	1.5%	1,816
Annual Growth	31.4%	24.2%	—	17.5%

2018 Year-End Financials

Debt ratio: 17.00%
Return on equity: 8.00%
Cash ($ mil.): 155
Current ratio: —
Long-term debt ($ mil.): —
No. of shares (mil.): 77
Dividends
  Yield: 0.0%
  Payout: 15.0%
Market value ($ mil.): 1,648

	STOCK PRICE ($) FY Close	P/E High/Low		PER SHARE ($) Earnings	Dividends	Book Value
12/18	21.00	9	7	3.00	0.00	21.00
12/17	22.00	5	4	4.00	0.00	20.00
12/16	17.00	6	4	3.00	0.00	15.00
12/15	15.00	9	7	2.00	0.00	12.00
12/14	17.00	11	8	2.00	0.00	10.00
Annual Growth	5.3%	—	—	10.6%	—	21.1%

Penske Automotive Group Inc

Penske Automotive Group has lots of lots. The US' #2 publicly traded auto dealer behind Auto-Nation Penske operates about 155 auto franchises from California to New Jersey and Puerto Rico and another 190 franchises abroad mainly in the UK. It sells more than 40 car brands. Non-US brands including AUDI BMW Land Rover Mercedez-Benz and Porsche generate more than 70% of sales. Penske also sells used vehicles provides financing and runs more than 35 collision repair centers. UK subsidiary Sytner Group operates more than 145 franchises selling 20 brands of mostly high-end models. Additionally Penske holds a nearly 30% stake in Penske Truck Leasing (PTL) known for commercial leasing and contract maintenance. The company is named after its Chairman Roger Penske.

Operations

Penske operates through four reportable segments: Retail Automotive Retail Commercial Truck Non-Automotive Investments and Other. The Retail Automotive segment brings in the vast majority of company revenue (over 90%) and consists of its 345 retail automotive franchises in the US and abroad. It sells new and used cars under around 40 auto brands; around 70% of sales are from premium brands particularly Audi BMW and Porsche. The segment sells over 644000 cars each year. Retail Commercial Truck accounts for over 5% of revenue and consists of the heavy-duty truck dealerships Premier Truck Group. Premier Truck Group has over 25 locations in the US and Canada that offer used trucks servicing and parts. Its service and parts departments are open 24/7. Retail Commercial Truck consists of the company?s retail commercial truck dealership generates over 1% and has operations in the U.S. and Canada.

Penske also has a few other interests such as its commercial vehicle business that imports and distributes Western Star heavy-duty trucks MAN heavy and medium duty trucks and buses and Dennis Eagle garbage trucks in Oceania. Other consists of the company?s commercial vehicle and power systems distribution operations and other non-automotive consolidated operations.

Geographic Reach

Michigan-based Penske rings up some 55% of its sales in the US and Puerto Rico. The remainder comes from its overseas franchises which are predominantly found in the UK but also in Germany Canada and Italy. The company also has operations in Australia and New Zealand.

Sales and Marketing

Penske conducts its advertising and marketing at the local level. In recent years it has concentrated on the internet and other digital media including its own websites. By manufacturer Audi/Volkswagen/Porsche/Bentley franchises brings in about 25% of Penske's total revenue. BMW/MINI brand franchises account for about 25% of revenue Toyota brands (Toyota and Lexus) generate 15% of revenue and Mercedes-Benz brands (Mercedes-Benz/Sprinter/Smart) generate 10%. Advertising expenses were $115 million and $116 million in 2018 and 2017 respectively.

Financial Performance

Penske has seen robust revenue growth in recent years. Its annual revenues have risen more than 32% since 2014. Revenue increased to $22.7 billion in 2018 an approximately 6% increase from the year prior. The increase was driven by higher used vehicles sales higher service and parts sales and dealership acquisitions. Net income was $470.3 million in fiscal year 2018 a drop from $612.8 million in fiscal year 2017. Selling general and administrative expenses grew 5% in fiscal 2018 to $2.6 billion. Cash provided by operating activities was $614.2 million in fiscal 2018 while investing activities used $525.2 million. Financing activities used another $94.3 million.

Strategy

Penske's growth strategy is based on entering new markets increasing digital sales and growing its truck business.

It continues to grow its significant UK operation and has entered into joint ventures and partnerships in Germany Italy Spain and Japan.

The company has increasing its equity in Penske Truck Leasing its joint venture with Penske Corporation and Mitsui. Penske has grown its stake in Penske Truck Leasing from 9% to 28.9%. Penske is expanding into the truck business to tap into the exceptionally good margins available in the truck parts and servicing segment.

Penske is also investing in a digital sales initiative looking to grow its 34% of unit sales in the US that come from e-commerce sources.

Mergers and Acquisitions

In 2017 Penske bought CarShop a UK-based used car dealer expanding its presence in the country. That same year the company acquired CarSense a US-based used car dealer. Additionally it bought Jaguar and Land Rover dealerships from Prestige Family of Fine Cars a New Jersey-based dealership.

EXECUTIVES

Evp Human Resources, Claude H. (Bud) Denker, age 60, $500,000 total compensation
Chairman And Ceo, Roger S. Penske, age 82, $1,200,000 total compensation
President, Robert H. Kurnick, age 57, $700,000 total compensation
Chairman Sytner Group, Gerard Nieuwenhuys, age 58
Evp Investor Relations And Corporate Development, Anthony R. (Tony) Pordon, age 55
Managing Director Sytner Group, Darren Edwards
Evp West Operations, Bernie Wolfe, age 63
Evp Strategic Development, George Brochick, age 71
Evp Central Operations, R. Whitfield Ramonat, age 58
Evp General Counsel And Secretary, Shane M. Spradlin, age 49, $500,000 total compensation
Evp East Operations, John Cragg
Svp And Corporate Controller, J.D. Carlson, age 49, $475,000 total compensation
Evp Marketing And Business Development, Terri Mulcahey
Svp And Cio, Rich Hook
Vice President, Joe Ziniti
Vice President {, Christian Collins
Executive Vice President And General Counsel, Walter P Czarnecki, age 77
Vice President Finance, James Harris
Vice President, Jerry Byrd
Assistant Vice President Business Process Improvement, Matt Gaor
Sr. Vp Human Resources, Tim Roop
Senior Vice President Manufacturer Relations, Robert K Wilshaw
Senior Vice President Of Premium Brands, Michael Famiglietti
Area Vice President, John Sullivan
Senior Vice President Penske Automotive Group, Tony Pordon
Assistant Vice President, Curt Imber
Area Vice President, Bob Miller
Vice President, Sally Hillen
Vice President, Niall Hay
Vice President Manufacturer Relations, Jason Beidelman
Executive Vice President Corporate Development, Tony Pardon
Executive Vice President Operations, Art Vallely
Area Vice President, John Robben
Board Member, Sandra Pierce
Auditors: DELOITTE & TOUCHE LLP

LOCATIONS

HQ: Penske Automotive Group Inc
2555 Telegraph Road, Bloomfield Hills, MI 48302-0954
Phone: 248 648-2500   **Fax:** 248 648-2525
Web: www.penskeautomotive.com

2016 Sales

	$ mil.	% of total
U.S	12,006	60
International	8,113	40
Total	**20,119**	**100**

	No.
U.S	164
U.K	146
Germany	28
Italy	17
Total	**355**

PRODUCTS/OPERATIONS

2016 Sales

	$ mil.	% of total
Retail Automotive	18,673	93
Retail Commercial Truck	1,001	5
Commercial vehicle and Other	449	2
Elimination	(3.9)	-
Total	**20,119**	**100**

COMPETITORS

Asbury Automotive	JM Family Enterprises
AutoNation	Jordan Automotive
Autobytel	Larry H. Miller Group
Avis Budget	Lithia Motors
CarMax	Lookers
Ed Morse Auto	Microsoft
Enterprise Group	National Car Rental
Fletcher Jones	Pendragon
Group 1 Automotive	Potamkin Automotive
Hendrick Automotive	Serra Automotive
Holman Enterprises	Sonic Automotive

HISTORICAL FINANCIALS

Company Type: Public

Income Statement
FYE: December 31

	REVENUE ($ mil.)	NET INCOME ($ mil.)	NET PROFIT MARGIN	EMPLOYEES
12/18	22,785	471	2.1%	27,000
12/17	21,387	613	2.9%	26,000
12/16	20,119	343	1.7%	24,000
12/15	19,285	326	1.7%	22,000
12/14	17,177	287	1.7%	22,100
Annual Growth	7.3%	13.2%	—	5.1%

2018 Year-End Financials

Debt ratio: 55.00%	No. of shares (mil.): 85
Return on equity: 19.00%	Dividends
Cash ($ mil.): 39	Yield: 4.0%
Current ratio: 1.00	Payout: 26.0%
Long-term debt ($ mil.): 2,125	Market value ($ mil.): 3,409

	STOCK PRICE ($) FY Close	P/E High/Low		PER SHARE ($) Earnings	Dividends	Book Value
12/18	40.00	10	7	6.00	1.00	31.00
12/17	48.00	8	5	7.00	1.00	28.00
12/16	52.00	14	8	4.00	1.00	21.00
12/15	42.00	15	12	4.00	1.00	20.00
12/14	49.00	16	12	3.00	1.00	18.00
Annual Growth	(4.8%)	—	—	14.9%	16.2%	13.9%

People's United Financial Inc

People's United Financial is the holding company for People's United Bank (formerly People's Bank) which boasts more than 400 traditional branches supermarket branches commercial banking offices investment and brokerage offices and equipment leasing offices across New England and eastern New York. In addition to retail and commercial banking services the bank offers trust wealth management brokerage and insurance services. Its lending activities consist mainly of commercial mortgages (more than a third of its loan portfolio) commercial and industrial loans (more than a quarter) residential mortgages equipment financing and home equity loans. Founded in 1842 the bank has $36 billion in assets.

Operations

People's United operates two core business segments Retail Banking and Commercial Banking which both share duties of the bank's now-defunct Wealth Management division. The bank also has a non-core Treasury division that manages the company's securities portfolio and other investments.

Commercial Banking which makes up more than half of the company's total revenue provides business loans equipment financing (through People's Capital and Leasing Corp. or PCLC and People's United Equipment Finance Corp or PUEFC) and municipal banking as well as trust services for corporations and institutions and private banking services for wealthy individuals.

Retail Banking which makes up around 20% of total revenues provides deposit services residential mortgages and home equity loans financial advisory and investment management services as well as life insurance through People's United Insurance Agency.

Overall the bank generated 68% of its total revenue from loan interest in 2014 and 7% from interest on securities. About 10% of total revenues came from bank service charges while investment management fees commercial banking lending fees insurance revenue and brokerage commissions each made up less than 3% of overall revenue for the year.

Geographic Reach

People's United has more than 400 branches across Connecticut southeastern New York Massachusetts Vermont New Hampshire and Maine. Connecticut is its largest lending market with 27% of the bank's loan portfolio being extended to consumers and businesses in the region in 2014. New York and Massachusetts are the bank's next largest markets with a 19% and 18% share of its loan portfolio.

Sales and Marketing

The bank sells its products and services through investment and brokerage offices commercial branches online banking and investment trading and through its 24-hour telephone banking service. The company's PCLC and PUEFC affiliates have a sales presence in 16 states to support equipment financing operations throughout the US.

People's United spent $13 million on advertising in 2014 compared to $15.4 million and $17.7 million in 2013 and 2012 respectively.

Strategy

People's United emphasizes cross-selling financial products by developing client relationships and has increasingly tied employee compensation to this ability. The company is particularly focused on building its small business lending wealth management and insurance business. It also continues to open new branches and seeks acquisition targets for further growth.

One other key element of its strategy involves boosting its deposit assets through its expanded convenient store reach. In early 2015 the company boasted nearly 150 full-service branches in Stop & Shop supermarkets across Connecticut and southeastern New York which comprised 36% of the bank's total branch network and held 14% of its total deposits. Much of this is attributed to a key acquisition in 2012 when the company purchased nearly 60 branches (many within Stop & Shop supermarkets) in the New York metro area from RBS Citizens. People's United already had more than 80 Stop & Shop branches in Connecticut so the deal strengthened its relationship with the retailer and expanded its presence in the New York market.

Mergers and Acquisitions

In 2019 People's United Financial acquired BSB Bancorp the holding company for Belmont Savings Bank for about $330 million. Belmont Massachusetts-headquartered Bemont Savings Bank holds about $3 billion in assets and has six branches in the Greater Boston area. The acquisition deepens People's United's presence in the area. That year the company also agreed to buy United Financial Bancorp in a transaction valued at around $760 million. United Financial is the holding company for United Bank a Hartford-based community bank with $7.3 billion in assets and roughly 60 branches in central Connecticut and western Massachusetts.

People's United acquired independent leasing and finance company VAR Technology Finance in early 2019. VAR uses its software platform to finance commercial and public sector customers of large technology manufacturers. The company will maintain its brand but become a division of People's United's LEAF Commercial Capital subsidiary. VAR originated $180 million in loans in 2018.

In 2018 People's United agreed to acquire First Connecticut Bancorp in an all-stock transaction valued at $544 million. The acquisition will further enhance People's United's established presence in the northeastern US. First Connecticut Bancorp is the holding company of Farmington Bank which operates nearly 30 community bank locations across Connecticut and in western Massachusetts.

Company Background

One of the main goals of People's United has been to build its presence in the two largest metropolitan areas in its market New York City and Boston. One of the largest in the Boston area Danvers Bancorp added some 30 branches and carried a price tag of approximately $493 million. People's United also acquired LSB Corporation and Butler Bank the latter in an FDIC-assisted transaction that included a loss-sharing agreement with the regulator covering all acquired loans and foreclosed real estate of the failed bank bringing in another 10 branches in the Boston area. In 2010 People's United bought Bank of Smithtown which had about 30 branches primarily on Long Island in New York.

People's United Financial acquired commercial lender Financial Federal Corporation in 2010 (now People's United Equipment Finance) which provides financing and leasing to small and midsized business nationwide.

People's United Financial underwent significant transformation in past years. The company demutualized and converted to a stock holding company in 2007 and early the following year acquired multibank holding company Chittenden Corporation. The deal added some 140 branches doubling People's United Bank's branch network and expanding its reach beyond Connecticut and New York and into the rest of New England.

EXECUTIVES

Vp Marketing, Cindy Belak
President And Ceo, John P. (Jack) Barnes, age 63, $890,384 total compensation
Sevp Corporate Development And Strategic Planning, Kirk W. Walters, age 64, $468,461 total compensation
Svp And President Merrill Bank, William P. (Bill) Lucy, age 60
Chief Financial Officer, R. David Rosato, age 57

Evp Marketing And Regional Banking People's United Bank, Robert R. (Bob) D'Amore, age 66, $429,323 total compensation

President Vermont, Michael L. Seaver

Sevp Wealth Management, Louise T. Sandberg, age 67

President Massachusetts, Timothy P. Crimmins

Market Leader New York, Sara M. Longobardi

President Northern Connecticut, Michael J. Casparino

Sevp Human Resources, David K. Norton, age 64, $411,231 total compensation

Sevp Commercial Banking, Jeffrey J. (Jeff) Tengel, age 56, $408,654 total compensation

Svp And Division President People's United Bank Southern Connecticut, Armando F. Goncalves

Sevp And General Counsel, Robert E. Trautmann, age 65

Sevp And Chief Administrative Officer, Lee C. Powlus

Svp; President Ocean Bank Division, Dianne M. Mercier

President Southern Maine, Daniel P. (Dan) Thornton

Vice President Information Technology, Carol Anderson

Vice President Information Technology, Roy Allison

Vice President, Kon Khongkham

Vice President Information Technology, Albert Sanna

Vice President Financial Services Manager, Cheryl Nickerson

Vice President Sales Aviation Finance, Jim Pulie

Vice President Of Sales, Jeffrey Morrison

Vice President Market Research, Craig Noble

First Vice President Wealth Management, John Lescure

Senior Vice President Human Resources, Michelle McNeil

Senior Vice President And Market Development Officer, Brian Shea

Vice President, Peter Martinez

Vp Call Center, David Weber

Divisional Vice President, Peter Brestovan

Assistant Vice President, Patrick Talcott

Vice President Capital Markets, Russ Hardy

Svp, Doug Smith

Vice President Customer Experience Manager, Thomas Griesing

Vice President Commercial Relationship Manager, Kasi White

Vice President Director Of Tax, Kathleen Jones

Vp Operations Manager Commercial Services, Keara Piscitelli

Market Manager Assistant Vice President, Alice Baird

Vice President Commercial Lending, Edgar Auchincloss

Senior Vice President And Director Marketing, Kathleen Schirling

Vice President Customer Service Manager, Joan Foster

Senior Vice President, Robert Maquat

Vice President, Daniel Reilly

Vice President Market Manager, David Conner

Vice President, Elaine Khu

Vice President, Patrick Lorent

Vice President Business Banking Portfolio Management, Louis Paffumi

Assistant Vice President Customer Service, Ana Saraiva

Assistant Vice President, Kasey Franzoni

Senior Vice President, Kathleen Lepak

Vice President Financial Analyst, Rita Rivers

Vice President Finance, Brian Connery

Vice President Purchasing, Theresa Knies

Assistant Vice President, David Schalk

Financial Services Mananger Assistant Vice President, Amy Pasquarelli

Assistant Vice President, Francine Grandmaison

Executive Vice President And Market Mana, John Bundschuh

Vice President, Kurtis Denison

Vice President, Bethany Dubuque

Vice President, Lisa Rollins

Senior Vice President, Jody Cole

Vice President Market Manager, David Cavanaugh

Senior Vice President Commercial Lending, Tom Wolcott

Vice President, Michael Ciborowski

Relationship Manager Vice President, Steven Wurtz

Vice President, Rose Morgan

Senior Vice President And Enterprise Security Officer, Jane Stowell

Senior Vice President Senior Commercial Real Estate Lender, Suzanne Wakeen

Vice President Commercial Lending, Debbie Boyle

Vice President Financial Services Manager, Jennifer Lynch

Vice President, Joanne Murgalo

Senior Vice President, Marilyn Hardacre

Vice President, Sheila Moran

Region Manager Senior Vice President Commercial Real Estate Finance, Kathleen Hayes

Senior Lender Vice President, Peter Lange

Svp And Regional Manager Wealth Management, Sylvia Mackinnon

Vice President, Darrin Fodor

Vice President, James Bucko

Assistant Vice President Financial Services Manager, Angela Gallagher

Vice President, Timothy B Hodges

Vice President, Michael Rispoli

Senior Vice President, Mark Leonardi

Vice President Commercial Banking, Deborah Quirk

Senior Vice President Relationship Manager, Vincent Bergin

Executive Vice President Mid Corporate, Dexter Freeman

Financial Services Manager Assistant Vice President, Cheryl Hagmann

Assistant Vice President Financial Services Manager, Robert Duffus

Vice President Customer Service Manager, Scott Zimmerman

Fixed Income Strategist Senior Vice President, Karissa McDonough

Assistant Vice President Branch Manager, Kristen Lavallee

Vice President Financial Services Manager, Kristen Keil

Market Manager Vice President, Renee Goupille

Assistant Vice President Customer Service Manager, Sylvana Chiluisa

Senior Vice President Senior Portfolio Manager, James Witterschein

Vice President Model Validation And Risk Management, Julien Lee

Vice President Financial Services Manager, Joseph Perun

Vice President Senior Market Manager, Christina Veziris

Assistant Vice President Mortgage Account Officer, Richard Klein

Executive Vice President Chief Credit Officer, David Barey

Team Leader Vice President Senior Commercial Review Appraiser, Michelle Gamache

Vice President Comm Lending, Frank Cory

V P Sales, Roger Allcorn

Senior Vice President And Senior Relationship Manager, Ellery Perkinson

Senior Vice President, Patrick Lee

Vice President, Brian Boyaji

Assistant Vice President Customer Service Manager, Krupali Doshi

Vice President Sales And Leasing, Rick Curtiss

Vice President, Tom Emery

Assistant Vice President, Ana Espinal

Vice President, Michael Mancuso

Assistant Vice President, Miriam James

Regional Vice President, Gary Fisher

Vice President And Sr.market Manager Bridgeport Market, Virgilio Lopez

Senior Vice President Senior Relationship Manager New York Cre, Ted Dalton

Vice President, Justin Jennings

Vice President Corporate Communications, Steven Bodakowski

Senior Vice President Head Of Wealth Strategy Product And Marketing, Daniel Darst

Vice President Wealth Management Marketing, Sara Sparks

First Vice President Digital Marketing, James Roy

Vice President Wealth Management Marketing Bank Brand And Advertising, Christine Stafstrom

Senior Market Manager Vice President, Raymond DiPresso

Avp Bank Manager, Flawer Bardales

Assistant Vice President Customer Service Manager, Danielle Lutz

Vice President, Elizabeth Dougherty

Vice President, Justin Mills

Vice President, Kenneth Vaccaro

Vice President Customer Service Manager, Lacey Bicknell

First Vice President, Maria Kastanis

Vice President Information Technology, Michael Kirven

Senior Vice President, Mark Danie

Vice President Treasury Management Sales Officer, Elaine Canton

Senior Vice President Commercial Banking, David Estes

Vice President Market Manager, Benish Shah

Senior Vice President, Phil Cohen

Assistant Vice President Bank Manager, Andrew Matarese

Senior Vice President, Mary McLemore

Senior Portfolio Manager Senior Vice President, Richard Casselman

Senior Vice President Healthcare Financial Services, Walter Unangst

Vice President, Douglas Olsen

Senior Vice President Senior Private Banker, Al Falco

Vice President Senior Private Banker, Sarah Haley

Vice President, Theodore Horan

Assistant Vice President, Rosalind Rubin

N.a. Vice President, Kimberly Alty

Auditors: KPMG LLP

LOCATIONS

HQ: People's United Financial Inc
850 Main Street, Bridgeport, CT 06604
Phone: 203 338-7171   **Fax:** 203 338-2545
Web: www.peoples.com

PRODUCTS/OPERATIONS

2014 Sales

	$ mil.	% of total
Interest & dividends		
Loans		
Commercial real estate	354	26
Commercial	351	26
Residential mortgage	154	12
Consumer	74	5
Securities	97	7
Other	1	-
Noninterest		
Bank service charges	129	10
Investment management fees	42	3
Operating lease income	42	3
Commercial banking lending fees	33	2
Insurance revenue	30	2
Other	77	4
Adjustment	(0.9)	
Total	**1,381**	**100**

COMPETITORS

Bank of America	KeyCorp
Citibank	Liberty Bank
Citizens Financial Group	Sovereign Bank
Fairfield County Bank	TD Bank USA
	Webster Financial

HISTORICAL FINANCIALS
Company Type: Public

Income Statement
FYE: December 31

	ASSETS ($ mil.)	NET INCOME ($ mil.)	INCOME AS % OF ASSETS	EMPLOYEES
12/18	47,877	468	1.0%	5,920
12/17	44,453	337	0.8%	5,584
12/16	40,610	281	0.7%	5,173
12/15	38,877	260	0.7%	5,139
12/14	35,997	252	0.7%	5,397
Annual Growth	7.4%	16.8%	—	2.3%

2018 Year-End Financials

Debt ratio: 2.00%
Return on equity: 8.00%
Cash ($ mil.): 900
Current ratio: —
Long-term debt ($ mil.): —

No. of shares (mil.): 377
Dividends
  Yield: 5.0%
  Payout: 54.0%
Market value ($ mil.): 5,444

	STOCK PRICE ($) FY Close	P/E High/Low	PER SHARE ($) Earnings	Dividends	Book Value
12/18	14.00	16 11	1.00	1.00	17.00
12/17	19.00	20 16	1.00	1.00	17.00
12/16	19.00	22 15	1.00	1.00	16.00
12/15	16.00	20 16	1.00	1.00	15.00
12/14	15.00	19 16	1.00	1.00	15.00
Annual Growth	(1.3%)	— —	11.3%	1.5%	3.6%

People's Utah Bancorp

Auditors: Moss Adams LLP

LOCATIONS

HQ: People's Utah Bancorp
  1 East Main Street, American Fork, UT 84003
Phone: 801 642-3998
Web: www.peoplesutah.com

HISTORICAL FINANCIALS
Company Type: Public

Income Statement
FYE: December 31

	ASSETS ($ mil.)	NET INCOME ($ mil.)	INCOME AS % OF ASSETS	EMPLOYEES
12/18	2,184	41	1.9%	459
12/17	2,124	20	0.9%	483
12/16	1,666	24	1.4%	430
12/15	1,556	20	1.3%	414
12/14	1,367	15	1.1%	367
Annual Growth	12.4%	28.5%	—	5.8%

2018 Year-End Financials

Debt ratio: —
Return on equity: 15.00%
Cash ($ mil.): 47
Current ratio: —
Long-term debt ($ mil.): —

No. of shares (mil.): 19
Dividends
  Yield: 1.0%
  Payout: 25.0%
Market value ($ mil.): 565

	STOCK PRICE ($) FY Close	P/E High/Low	PER SHARE ($) Earnings	Dividends	Book Value
12/18	30.00	18 13	2.00	0.00	15.00
12/17	30.00	30 22	1.00	0.00	14.00
12/16	27.00	21 11	1.00	0.00	13.00
12/15	17.00	15 13	1.00	0.00	12.00
Annual Growth	15.0%	— —	16.3%	22.9%	6.8%

Peoples Bancorp Inc (Marietta, OH)

Peoples Bancorp offers banking for the people by the people and of the people. The holding company owns Peoples Bank which has about 50 branches in rural and small urban markets in Ohio Kentucky and West Virginia. The bank offers traditional services such as checking and savings accounts CDs loans and trust services. Commercial and agricultural loans including those secured by commercial real estate account for the majority of the bank's lending activities. Its Peoples Financial Advisors division offers investment management services while Peoples Insurance sells life health and property/casualty coverage.

Operations
Credit cards and brokerage services are offered through third-party providers.

Financial Performance
The company's revenue increased from $103.7 million in fiscal 2012 up to $104.6 million for fiscal 2013. However despite the slight spike in annual revenue Peoples Bancorp's net income decreased from $29.9 million in fiscal 2012 down to $29 million for fiscal 2013.

The company's cash on hand decreased by about $1 million in fiscal 2013 compared to fiscal 2012 levels.

Strategy
Peoples Bancorp is looking to increase its revenue from service changes and other fees and commissions particularly from insurance and wealth management which are not reliant on fluctuating interest rate margins.

The company is also looking to strengthen its brand and build deeper relationships with its clients.

EXECUTIVES

Evp And Chief Administrative Officer Peoples Bancorp And Evp Chief Administrative Officer And Cashierpeoples Bank N.a., Carol A. Schneeberger, age 62, $233,000 total compensation
Evp And Chief Commercial Lending Officer Peoples Bancorp And Peoples Bank N.a., Daniel K. (Dan) McGill, age 64, $250,000 total compensation
Evp And Chief Credit Officer Peoples Bancorp And Peoples Bank N.a., Timothy H. Kirtley, age 49, $221,500 total compensation
President Ceo And Director Peoples Bancorp And Peoples Bank N.a., Charles W. Sulerzyski, age 61, $500,000 total compensation
Evp Cfo And Treasurer Peoples Bancorp And Peoples Bank N.a., John C. Rogers, age 59, $26,136 total compensation
Vice President, Steven Nulter
Assistant Vice President Branch Market Manager, Candace Frump
Branch Market Manager Assistant Vice President, Peggy Scott-Morgan
Vice President And Controller, Jeffrey Baran
Vice President, Randy Barengo
Chairman Peoples Bancorp And Peoples Bank N.a., David L. Mead, age 64
Auditors: Ernst & Young LLP

LOCATIONS

HQ: Peoples Bancorp Inc (Marietta, OH)
  138 Putnam Street, P.O. Box 738, Marietta, OH 45750
Phone: 740 373-3155
Web: www.peoplesbancorp.com

PRODUCTS/OPERATIONS

2016 Sales

	$ mil.	% of total
Interest Income:		
Interest and fees on loans	94	56
Interest and dividends on taxable investment securities	19	11
Interest on tax-exempt investment securities	3	2
Other Income:		
Insurance income	14	8
Deposit account service charges	11	6
Trust and investment income	11	6
Electronic banking income	10	6
Bank owned life insurance income	1	1
Mortgage banking income	1	1
Commercial loan swap fee income	1	1
Net gain on investment securities	1	1
Net loss on asset disposals and other transactions	(1.1)	-
Other	2	1
Total	166	100

COMPETITORS

1st West Virginia Bancorp	Huntington Bancshares
BB&T	Ohio Valley Banc
Fifth Third	U.S. Bancorp
	United Bankshares

HISTORICAL FINANCIALS
Company Type: Public

Income Statement
FYE: December 31

	ASSETS ($ mil.)	NET INCOME ($ mil.)	INCOME AS % OF ASSETS	EMPLOYEES
12/18	3,991	46	1.2%	871
12/17	3,582	38	1.1%	774
12/16	3,432	31	0.9%	782
12/15	3,259	11	0.3%	817
12/14	2,568	17	0.6%	699
Annual Growth	11.7%	29.0%	—	5.7%

2018 Year-End Financials

Debt ratio: 0.00%
Return on equity: 9.00%
Cash ($ mil.): 78
Current ratio: —
Long-term debt ($ mil.): —

No. of shares (mil.): 20
Dividends
  Yield: 4.0%
  Payout: 51.0%
Market value ($ mil.): 588

	STOCK PRICE ($) FY Close	P/E High/Low	PER SHARE ($) Earnings	Dividends	Book Value
12/18	30.00	16 12	2.00	1.00	27.00
12/17	33.00	16 14	2.00	1.00	25.00
12/16	32.00	19 10	2.00	1.00	24.00
12/15	19.00	42 30	1.00	1.00	23.00
12/14	26.00	20 15	1.00	1.00	23.00
Annual Growth	3.8%	— —	15.4%	16.9%	3.8%

Peoples Financial Services Corp

Power to the Peoples Financial Services. The firm is the holding company for Peoples Security Bank and Trust Company (formerly Peoples National Bank) which operates about 25 branches across northeastern Pennsylvania and neighboring Broome County in New York. Established in 1905 the bank offers standard retail products and services including checking and savings accounts CDs and credit cards to local businesses and individuals. Commercial loans including mortgages construction loans and operating loans make up the greatest portion (40%) of the company's loan book followed by residential mortgages (25%) and consumer loans. The company's Peoples Advisors subsidiary provides investment and brokerage services.

Operations

About 80% of Peoples Financial Services' total revenue came from interest income (mostly on loans) in 2014 while the remainder comes from non-interest income. The bank had a staff of 354 full-time employees at the end of that year.

Geographic Reach

Scranton-based Peoples Security Bank has more than 25 branches across Northeastern Pennsylvania (in the Lackawanna Lehigh Luzerne Monroe Susquehanna Wayne and Wyoming counties) and Broome County in New York state.

Sales and Marketing

The company primarily makes loans to small- and medium-sized businesses. It spent $450 on advertising in 2014 up from $350 and $287 in 2013 and 2012 respectively.

Financial Performance

Peoples has struggled to consistently grow its revenues in recent years due to shrinking interest margins on loans amidst the low-interest environment. Its profits however have been rising thanks to lower interest expenses on deposits and declining loan loss provisions as its loan portfolio's credit quality has improved with higher property valuations in the strengthened economy.

The company enjoyed a breakout year in 2014 however as its revenue jumped 60% to a record $79.21 million mostly as its interest income swelled from new loan business from its 2013 acquisition of Penseco Financial Services. Its service charge fees and commissions merchant services income and commission and fee income from fiduciary services also rose mostly as a result of the significant acquisition.

Higher revenue in 2014 allowed Peoples' net income to more than triple to a record $17.6 million while its operating cash levels more than doubled to $20.6 million on higher cash earnings for the year.

Strategy

Peoples Security Bank occasionally acquires smaller banks to extend its branch network across target markets while adding new loan and deposit business. Its late 2013 acquisition of Penseco Financial Services Corporation for example nearly doubled its loan and deposit business and more than doubled its branch network to 25 branches.

Mergers and Acquisitions

In November 2013 Peoples acquired Penseco Financial Services Corporation along with its Penn Security Bank and Trust subsidiary. The $155 million-deal doubled Peoples' branch network from 12 to 25 branches creating the largest community bank headquartered in Northeastern Pennsylvania.

EXECUTIVES

Ceo And President, Alan W. Dakey, age 67
Evp And Coo Peoples National Bank, Debra E. Dissinger, age 64, $110,000 total compensation
Director, Richard S. Lochen, age 55, $130,000 total compensation
Senior Vice President Chief Financial Officer, Scott Seasock
Chairman, William E. Aubrey, age 56
Auditors: Baker Tilly Virchow Krause, LLP

LOCATIONS

HQ: Peoples Financial Services Corp
150 North Washington Avenue, Scranton, PA 18503
Phone: 570 346-7741

PRODUCTS/OPERATIONS

2014 Sales

	$ mil.	% of total
Interest	64	81
Non-interest	15	19
Total	**79**	**100**

COMPETITORS

Citizens & Northern	HSBC USA
Citizens Financial Services	M&T Bank
	NBT Bancorp
Fidelity D & D	Penns Woods Bancorp
First Keystone	
First National Community Bancorp	

HISTORICAL FINANCIALS

Company Type: Public

Income Statement

FYE: December 31

	ASSETS ($ mil.)	NET INCOME ($ mil.)	INCOME AS % OF ASSETS	EMPLOYEES
12/18	2,289	25	1.1%	390
12/17	2,169	18	0.9%	388
12/16	1,999	20	1.0%	364
12/15	1,819	18	1.0%	348
12/14	1,742	18	1.0%	354
Annual Growth	**7.1%**	**9.0%**	**—**	**2.5%**

2018 Year-End Financials

Debt ratio: —	No. of shares (mil.): 7
Return on equity: 9.00%	Dividends
Cash ($ mil.): 33	Yield: 3.0%
Current ratio: —	Payout: 46.0%
Long-term debt ($ mil.): —	Market value ($ mil.): 326

	STOCK PRICE ($) FY Close	P/E High/Low		PER SHARE ($) Earnings	Dividends	Book Value
12/18	44.00	15	12	3.00	1.00	38.00
12/17	47.00	20	16	3.00	1.00	36.00
12/16	49.00	19	13	3.00	1.00	35.00
12/15	38.00	21	15	2.00	1.00	34.00
12/14	50.00	23	16	2.00	1.00	33.00
Annual Growth	**(3.0%)**	**—**	**—**	**9.5%**	**1.4%**	**3.6%**

PepsiCo Inc

PepsiCo butts heads with its eternal rival The Coca-Cola Company for the title of world's biggest soft drinks maker. PepsiCo's beverage brands include Pepsi Mountain Dew Tropicana Gatorade and Aquafina water. The company also owns Frito-Lay the world's #1 snack maker with offerings such as Lay's Ruffles Doritos and Cheetos. The Quaker Foods unit makes breakfast cereals (Quaker oatmeal Life) Rice-A-Roni and Near East side dishes. Pepsi products are available in 200-plus countries although the US accounts for nearly 60% of total sales. The company operates about half of its bottling plants and distribution facilities.

HISTORY

Pharmacist Caleb Bradham invented Pepsi in 1898 in New Bern North Carolina. He named his new drink Pepsi-Cola (claiming it cured dyspepsia or indigestion) and registered the trademark in 1903. Following The Coca-Cola Company's example Bradham developed a bottling franchise system. By WWI 300 bottlers had signed up. After the war Bradham stockpiled sugar to safeguard against rising costs but in 1920 sugar prices plunged forcing him into bankruptcy in 1923.

Pepsi existed on the brink of ruin under various owners until Loft Candy bought it in 1931. Its fortunes improved in 1933 when in the midst of the Depression it doubled the size of its bottles to 12 ounces without raising the five-cent price. In 1939 Pepsi introduced the world's first radio jingle. Two years later Loft Candy merged with its Pepsi subsidiary and became The Pepsi-Cola Company.

Donald Kendall who became Pepsi-Cola's president in 1963 turned the firm's attention to young people ("The Pepsi Generation"). It acquired Mountain Dew in 1964 and became PepsiCo in 1965 when it acquired Frito-Lay.

In 1972 PepsiCo agreed to distribute Stolichnaya vodka in the US in exchange for being the only Western firm allowed to bottle soft drinks in the USSR. With the purchases of Pizza Hut (1977) Taco Bell (1978) and Kentucky Fried Chicken (1986) it became a major force in the fast-food industry.

When Coca-Cola changed its formula in 1985 Pepsi had a short-lived victory in the cola wars (until the return of Coca-Cola classic the new formula having been a dismal failure). The rivalry was extended to ready-to-drink tea in 1991 when in response to Coca-Cola's Nestea venture with Nestlé PepsiCo teamed up with Lipton.

Between 1991 and 1996 PepsiCo aggressively expanded its overseas bottling operations. However its efforts contrasted markedly with Coca-Cola's well-oiled international distribution machine. The firm then shifted its attention to the organization of its overseas network. Roger Enrico became CEO in 1996.

A year later PepsiCo spun off its $10 billion fast-food unit as TRICON Global Restaurants (now known as YUM! Brands Inc.) putting itself in a better position to sell its soft drinks at other restaurants. Also in 1997 it bought Borden's Cracker Jack snack and Smith's snacks from the UK's United Biscuits.

In 1998 it bought Seagram's market-leading Tropicana juices (rival of Coca-Cola's Minute Maid) for $3.3 billion. The firm sold a 65% stake in its new Pepsi Bottling Group to the public in 1999.

Its more than $13 billion purchase of The Quaker Oats Company in 2001 added the dominant Gatorade sports drink brand to its lineup. To make room for Gatorade PepsiCo sold its competing All Sport energy drink to The Monarch Beverage Company an Atlanta-based soda company later that year.

PepsiCo began a major restructuring of its PepsiCo Beverages & Foods division in 2003. The restructuring resulted in four company divisions: PepsiCo International PepsiCo Beverages North America Frito-Lay North America and Quaker Foods North America.

In 2004 PepsiCo approached juice maker Ocean Spray about a joint venture but was turned away by the cranberry farmers who own the juice manufacturer. The company bought General Mills' stake of their joint venture Snack Ventures Europe (SVE) in 2005 for $750 million. The deal gave Pepsi control of Europe's largest snack food company.

It's also been driving its snack brands to new markets as it bolts on new and more nutritious foods categories through small acquisitions and alliances. In 2013 Muller Quaker Dairy a joint venture between PepsiCo and Theo Muller Group (a Germany-based privately held dairy holding company) opened of its new yogurt manufacturing facility in Batavia New York. It serves as the national production and distribution center for a premium lineup of M ller brand yogurts to US supermarket and club retailers.

EXECUTIVES

Coo Pepsico Beverages And Foods North America, Albert P. (Al) Carey, age 67, $984,615 total compensation

Chairman And Ceo, Indra K. Nooyi, age 63, $1,725,000 total compensation

Evp Human Resources And Chief Human Resources Officer, Cynthia M. Trudell, age 66

Vice Chairman Evp Global Research And Development And Chief Scientific Officer, Mehmood Khan, age 60, $756,731 total compensation

Svp And Cio, Jody R. Davids, age 63

President Essa Category Teams Franchise And Po1 Sub-saharan Africa, Richard D. Evans

Vice Chairman Evp And Cfo, Hugh F. Johnston, age 58, $960,577 total compensation

President Europe Sub-saharan Africa (essa), Silviu Popovici, age 51

President Global Beverages Group, Brad Jakeman

President Pepsico Mexico, Pedro Padierna

President Latin America Beverages, Luis Montoya

President And Coo Frito-lay North America (flna), Vivek Sankaran, age 57

President Global Snacks Group And Global Insights, Simon Lowden

Evp Corporate Strategy And Chief Venturing Officer, Jim Andrew, age 58

President And Coo North America Beverages (nab), Kirk Tanner, age 51

Ceo Asia Middle East And North Africa, Sanjeev Chadha, age 59, $764,423 total compensation

President Pepsico, Ramon Laguarta, age 55, $748,846 total compensation

Evp Global Categories And Franchise Management, Eugene Willemsen

Evp Communications, Jon Banner

Ceo Latin America (latam) And Europe Sub-saharan Africa (essa), Laxman Narasimhan, age 51

Evp Government Affairs General Counsel And Corporate Secretary, Tony West, age 53

Evp Global Operations, Brian Newman

President And Ceo Greater China Region, Mike Spanos

Coo Pepsico North America Foodservice, Anne Fink

Senior Vice President And Controller, Marie Gallagher

Marketing Vice President, Haston Lewis

Vice President Revenue Strategy And Management, Eric Hanson

Senior Vice President, Cynthia Nastanski

Vp Enterprise Architecture, Mike Spies

Vice President Marketing Pepsico Foods, Jason Mcdonell

Vice President Of Lrb Strategy, Brian Kelly

Vice President Human Resources, Dave Moncur

Vp Operations, Gary Murtha

Senior Vice President, Jessica Burt

Finance Senior Vice President, Chris Hall

National Sales Manager, Jill Griffith

Vice President Global Public Policy, Paul Boykas

Vice President Data Analytics And Analytics, Martha Roos

Vice President Technical Accounting And Policy, Lisa Halper

Regional Vice President, Mark Darrow

Vice President Corporate And Commercial Planning Europe, Claire Stone

Vice President, Huw Gilbert

Vice President Selling And Delivery, Greg Moore

Vice President, Shridhar Kulkarni

Sales Vice President, Byron Brooks

Senior Vice President Finance, Nick Dalessandro

Vice President Sales Operations, Kenneth Morgan

Area Vice President, David Laurie

Vice President Finance, Ralph Goedderz

Legal Vice President, Thomas P Schur

Vice President Finance, Christy Jacoby

Vice President, Michael McMahon

Vice President Category Leadership, Mike Gervasio

National Sales Manager, Jennifer Caro

Vice President Information Technology Global Development, Subodh Chawla

Vice President Finance, Mark Beach

Senior Vice President Business Development, Hugh Roth

Vp Of Tax, Christine Griff

Senior Vice President, Jeffrey Coniaris

Vice President Purchase, Ashish Karanjkar

National Sales Manager Restaurant Channel, Christian Duperron

National Account Manager, Lindsay Domaschuk

Vice President Purchasing, Art Schick

Vice President Infrastructure And Engineering, Johnathan Thibodeau

Vice President Consumer Strategy, Tekla Back

Vice President Foodservice Division, Kathryn Matheson

Vice President, Sabrina M Pean

Vice President Strategic Insights, Laura Jones

Vice President Legal India Region, Paul Walton

Vice President, Tarkan Gurkan

Vice President Of Marketing For Atlantic Business Unit, Tammy Sumpter

Vice President Of Consumer Engagement, Anne Howarth

Senior Vice President Customer Supply Chain And Global Go To Market, John Phillips

Vice President Sales National Restaura, Tom Balte

Evp And Chro, Ruth Fattori

Vice President Investor Relations, Ravi Pamnani

Vice President Of Finance, Brent Bracey

Senior Vice President Chief Compliance And Ethics Officer, Debra Torres

Tax Vice President, Jeff Coniaris

Executive Assistant To Robert Mac Kay Vice President And General Auditor, Diana Marra

Sc Vice President, Mark Brinker

Regional Vice President, James Simms

National Sales Manager, Jeff Utne

Vice President And Assistant Treasurer, Jay Laramie

Vice President Human Resources, Jam Johnson

Tax Vice President, Tom Salcito

National Account Manager, Terry Thaden

Sales Vice President, Andy Williams

Sc Cntrct Manufacturing Vice President Naf Cntrct, Karl Schraer

National Account Manager, Jose Abarca

Executive Vice President Global Operations, Grace Puma

Svp And Chro Global Functions And Global Category Groups, Janine Waclawski

Vice President, Denise Lefebvre

National Account Manager, William Leonard

Vice President Asia Middle East And Africa Technical Innovation And Head Greater China Research And Development, Vr Basker

First Vice President Financial Advisor, George Sebastian

Vice President Analytics, Kapil Malhotra

Vice President, Willem Kuzee

Legal Vice President, Timothy F Civil

National Account Manager, Jake Fuller

Vice President Scientific And Regulatory Affairs, Shaminder Singh

National Account Manager, Adam Palmer

National Account Manager, Keesje Kort

Finance Vice President, James Cochrane

National Account Manager, Tyler Lewis

Vice President Marketing Advertising, David Phillips

National Account Manager, Tessa McArthur

Svp Head Of Global Ecommerce, Gibu Thomas

Senior Vice President Global E Commerce Marketing And Product, Michal Geller

Senior Vice President Food Safety Quality Assurance And Scientific And Regulatory Affiars, Mike Liewen

National Account Manager, Brenda Ung

National Account Manager, Megan McCartney

Senior Vice President Global Head Of Information Technology Operations, Majed Sarieddine

Vice President Global Water And Environmental Solutions, Roberta Barbieri

Vice President, David Oliver

Senior Vice President Talent Management Training And Development, Kyle Faulconer

Senior Vice President Chief Insights And Analytics Officer, Stephan Gans

Svp And General Manager Global Pepsico Walmart, Chris Turner

National Sales Manager, Tim Berchtold

Vice President Sales, Scott Sheafe

Regional Vice President, Scott Henzi

National Account Manager Target, Suzanne Rupp

Vice President Global Marketing Hydration Portfolio, Olga OSMINKINA-JONES

Vice President Manufacturing And Engineering Amea, Murat Suer

Senior Vice President, Lily Zaidman

Vice President And General Manager, Joe Mchugh

Vice President Of Global Product Design And Design Innovation, Martin Broen

Senior Vice President And General Manager Quaker Oats Company, Robbert Rietbroek

National Account Manager, Molly Link

Vice President Of Retail Sales, Steve Milonovich

Prod Development Vice President, Kevin Osullivan

Legal Vice President General Cousel, Civil Timothy

National Account Manager, Doug Fowler

Vice President, Gary Ducros

Vp Global Agronomy Solutions, Christine Daugherty

Advisory Board Member, Jayne Vetere

Vice President And Assistant Treasurer For International, Noha Topalian

Board Member, Darren Walker

Secretary, Josefa Brito

Board Member, David Page

Secretary, Carol Hughte

Auditors: KPMG LLP

LOCATIONS

HQ: PepsiCo Inc
700 Anderson Hill Road, Purchase, NY 10577
Phone: 914 253-2000
Web: www.pepsico.com

2018 Sales

	$ mil.	% of total
US	37,148	57
Mexico	3,878	6
Russia	3,191	5
Canada	2,736	4
UK	1,743	3
Brazil	1,335	2
All other countries	14,630	23
Total	**64,661**	**100**

PRODUCTS/OPERATIONS

2018 Sales

	$ mil.	% of total
NAB	21,072	33
FLNA	16,346	25
ESSA	11,523	18
Latin America	7,354	11
AMENA	5,901	9
QFNA	2,465	4
Total	**64,661**	**100**

COMPETITORS

Campbell Soup	Kellogg
Coca-Cola	Kraft Heinz
ConAgra	Mondelez International
Danone	Monster Beverage
Dr Pepper Snapple	Nestlé
Group	Post Holdings
Hain Celestial	Red Bull

HISTORICAL FINANCIALS

Company Type: Public

Income Statement				FYE: December 29
	REVENUE ($ mil.)	NET INCOME ($ mil.)	NET PROFIT MARGIN	EMPLOYEES
12/18	64,661	12,515	19.4%	267,000
12/17	63,525	4,857	7.6%	263,000
12/16	62,799	6,329	10.1%	264,000
12/15	63,056	5,452	8.6%	263,000
12/14	66,683	6,513	9.8%	271,000
Annual Growth	(0.8%)	17.7%	—	(0.4%)

2018 Year-End Financials

Debt ratio: 42.00%
Return on equity: 99.00%
Cash ($ mil.): 10,718
Current ratio: 1.00
Long-term debt ($ mil.): 28,295

No. of shares (mil.): 1,409
Dividends
  Yield: 0.0%
  Payout: 41.0%
Market value ($ mil.): 155,497

	STOCK PRICE ($) FY Close	P/E High/Low		PER SHARE ($) Earnings	Dividends	Book Value
12/18	110.00	14	11	9.00	4.00	10.00
12/17	120.00	35	30	3.00	3.00	8.00
12/16	105.00	25	21	4.00	3.00	8.00
12/15	101.00	28	24	4.00	3.00	8.00
12/14	97.00	23	18	4.00	3.00	12.00
Annual Growth	3.3%	—		19.7%	9.1%	(3.2%)

Performance Food Group Co

Auditors: DELOITTE & TOUCHE LLP

LOCATIONS

HQ: Performance Food Group Co
  12500 West Creek Parkway, Richmond, VA 23238
Phone: 804 484-7700
Web: www.pfgc.com

HISTORICAL FINANCIALS

Company Type: Public

Income Statement				FYE: June 29
	REVENUE ($ mil.)	NET INCOME ($ mil.)	NET PROFIT MARGIN	EMPLOYEES
06/19	19,744	167	0.8%	18,000
06/18*	17,620	199	1.1%	15,000
07/17	16,762	96	0.6%	14,000
07/16	16,105	68	0.4%	13,000
06/15	15,270	57	0.4%	12,000
Annual Growth	6.6%	31.1%	—	10.7%

*Fiscal year change

2019 Year-End Financials

Debt ratio: 29.00%
Return on equity: 14.00%
Cash ($ mil.): 15
Current ratio: 2.00
Long-term debt ($ mil.): 1,332

No. of shares (mil.): 104
Dividends
  Yield: —
  Payout: —
Market value ($ mil.): 4,155

	STOCK PRICE ($) FY Close	P/E High/Low		PER SHARE ($) Earnings	Dividends	Book Value
06/19	40.00	26	18	2.00	0.00	13.00
06/18*	37.00	19	13	2.00	0.00	11.00
07/17	27.00	30	21	1.00	0.00	9.00
07/16	27.00	39	27	1.00	0.00	8.00
Annual Growth	10.4%	—		22.8%	—	11.7%

*Fiscal year change

PETER KIEWIT SONS', INC.

A heavyweight in the heavy construction industry Kiewit is one of North America's largest construction and engineering firms. The company is active in building industrial mining oil gas chemicals power transportation water and wastewater. It builds everything from roads and dams to high-rise office towers and power plants. The company focuses on projects located throughout the US Canada and Mexico. Affiliate Kiewit Mining owns or manages coal mines in Texas and Wyoming and manages a phosphate operation in southeast Idaho. Founded in 1884 Kiewit is owned by employees and Kiewit family members.

Operations

Kiewit's operations are diversified across seven segments: Building; Industrial; Mining; Oil Gas & Chemical; Power; Transportation; and Water/Wastewater.

Kiewit's Transportation segment constructs airport runways bridges marine and port projects rail lines mass transit roads and tunnels. Transportation has completed about 1000 projects which provided nearly $30 billion in revenue over the last 10 years. Kiewit's Power unit is active in gas coal retrofit power delivery renewables nuclear energy and engineering. Over the last 10 years Power has generated almost $20 billion.

Generating $7.5 billion through more than 1100 projects in the last 10 years the company's Building segment builds offices; industrial complexes; education and sports facilities; hotels; hospitals; transportation terminals; science and technology facilities; manufacturing retail and special-use facilities; interior construction; and tenant improvements. Kiewit conducts general construction construction

management design-build and -assist and turnkey project development.

The Mining segment (which has generated nearly $3 billion over more than 100 mining projects in the last 10 years) carries out contract mining mine infrastructure ore processing and owned operations. Kiewit's Oil Gas & Chemical business includes offshore construction oil sands gas processing compressor and pump stations pipelines and terminals liquefied natural gas and refining.

Through its Industrial division the company processes minerals; builds cement plants; treats water; provides engineering procurement and construction for the ferrous and non-ferrous metal industries; installs paper production and packaging machines; and constructs food plants and related structures. Water/Wastewater manages dam water supply and wastewater projects.

Kiewit operates a number of subsidiaries. Kiewit Offshore Services fabricates complex offshore oil production platforms at a facility in Texas. Another subsidiary Kiewit Energy US refines petroleum. Kiewit's TIC subsidiary is a heavy industrial construction and engineering firm based in Colorado.

Geographic Reach

Based in Omaha Nebraska Kiewit operates across the US (more than 80 locations) Canada (more than 10 locations) and Mexico (1 location).

Sales and Marketing

Kiewit's clients include various public and private entities.

Financial Performance

Kiewit doesn't publish financial data but the firm garnered revenue of $8.7 billion in 2017.

Strategy

Kiewit has completed nearly 6000 projects in the last 15 years. Recent major projects include the Air Force Weather Agency headquarters ? a $27 million data center and office building spanning 188000 square feet ? and the National Park Services Regional Headquarters in Omaha Nebraska. The National Park Services Regional Headquarters is a 68000-square-foot mixed private and public office building with exhibits a book store a library and public meeting rooms.

Company Background

The sons of Dutch immigrants Peter and Andrew Kiewit founded masonry contractor Kiewit Brothers in 1884 in Omaha Nebraska. Following the dissolution of the partnership in 1904 Peter continued as the company's sole proprietor. In 1931 ? 17 years after Peter's death ? his son Peter reorganized the business as Peter Kiewit Sons'.

HISTORY

Born to Dutch immigrants Peter Kiewit and brother Andrew founded Kiewit Brothers a brickyard in 1884 in Omaha Nebraska. By 1912 two of Peter's sons worked at the yard which was named Peter Kiewit & Sons. When Peter Kiewit died in 1914 his son Ralph took over and the firm took the name Peter Kiewit Sons'. Another son Peter joined Ralph at the helm in 1924 after dropping out of Dartmouth and later took over.

During the Depression Kiewit managed huge federal public works projects and in the 1940s it focused on war-related emergency construction projects.

One of the firm's most difficult projects was top-secret Thule Air Force Base in Greenland above the Arctic Circle. For more than two years 5000 men worked around the clock beginning in 1951; the site was in development for 15 years. In 1952 the company won a contract to build a $1.2 billion gas diffusion plant in Portsmouth Ohio. It also became a contractor for the US interstate highway system (begun in 1956).

Peter Kiewit died in 1979 after stipulating that the largely employee-owned company should remain under employee control and that no one employee could own more than 10%. His 40% stake when returned to the company transformed many employees into millionaires. Walter Scott Jr. whose father had been the first graduate engineer to work for Kiewit took charge. Scott made his mark by parlaying money from construction into successful investments.

When the construction industry slumped Kiewit began looking for other investment opportunities and in 1984 it acquired packaging company Continental Can Co. (selling off noncore insurance energy and timber assets). Continental was saddled with a 1983 class action lawsuit alleging that it had plotted to close plants and lay off workers before they were qualified for pensions. In 1991 Kiewit agreed to pay $415 million to settle the lawsuit. In the face of a consolidating packaging industry the company sold Continental in the early 1990s.

In 1986 Kiewit loaned money to a business group to build a fiber-optic loop in Chicago; by 1987 it had launched MFS Communications to build local fiber loops in downtown districts. In 1992 Kiewit split its business into two pieces: the construction group which was strictly employee-owned; and a diversified group to which it added a controlling stake in phone and cable TV company C-TEC in 1993. That year Kiewit took MFS public; by 1995 it had sold all its shares and the next year MFS was bought by telecom giant WorldCom.

In 1996 Kiewit assisted CalEnergy (now MidAmerican Energy) in a hostile $1.3 billion takeover of the UK's Northern Electric. Kiewit got stock in CalEnergy and a 30% stake in the UK electric company all of which it sold to CalEnergy in 1998.

That year Kiewit spun off its telecom and computer services holdings into Level 3 Communications. Scott who had been hospitalized the year before for a blood clot in his lung stepped down as CEO and Ken Stinson CEO of Kiewit Construction Group took over Peter Kiewit Sons'.

In 1999 Kiewit acquired a majority interest in Pacific Rock Products a construction materials firm in Canada. Kiewit spun off its asphalt concrete and aggregates operations in 2000 as Kiewit Materials. Also that year the company created Kiewit Offshore Services to focus on construction for the offshore drilling industry. In 2001 the company acquired marine construction firm General Construction Company (GCC). The next year it expanded its offshore business further by buying a Canadian subsidiary from oil and gas equipment services company Friede Goldman Halter which was trying to emerge from bankruptcy.

Kiewit made history in 2002 for the fastest completion of a project of its type when it completed the rebuilding of Webbers Falls I-40 Bridge in Oklahoma at the end of July. (The bridge had collapsed in May after being hit by a pair of barges resulting in 14 fatalities.)

In 2004 Kiewit greatly increased its coal sales and reserves with the acquisition of the Buckskin Mine in Wyoming from Arch Coal.

Kiewit underwent a changing of the guard at the end of 2004 when 22-year veteran Bruce Grewcock took the reins as the company's fourth CEO since its founding. Stinson stayed on as the company's chairman.

In 2008 the group acquired TIC Holdings a heavy industrial construction and engineering firm.

Through its Kiewit Power Engineers Co. the company was contracted by Plutonic Energy Corporation and GE Energy Financial Services to work on the 235 MW hydroelectric Toba Montrose project one of British Columbia's largest renewable energy projects (completed around 2011).

In 2013 Kiewit entered the Australian market through a joint venture agreement that involves as $247 million engineer-procure-construct contract for a wet front end and ore wash plant situated at the Cloudbreak Mine in Northwest Australia. Fortescue Metals Group is the previous owner of Cloudbreak prior to the handover in early 2013.

EXECUTIVES

Svp And Cfo, Michael J. Piechoski, $236,600 total compensation
Chairman President And Ceo, Bruce E. Grewcock, $750,000 total compensation
Evp Energy, Thomas S. Shelby
Cio, Kris Lappala
Vice President For Development, Gerald Pfeffer
Vice President And General Counsel, Sam Gilmore
Vice President Healthcare Services, AJ Klebba
Vice President Finance Canada, Leonardo Morabito
Executive Vice President Operations, Jay Steinmetz
Treasurer, Stephen Thomas
Secretary, Matthew Michler
Auditors: KPMG LLP OMAHA NEBRASKA

LOCATIONS

HQ: PETER KIEWIT SONS', INC.
3555 FARNAM ST STE 1000, OMAHA, NE 681313374
Phone: 402 342-2052
Web: WWW.KIEWIT.COM

Selected Locations

US

Alaska
Arizona
Arkansas
California
Colorado
Florida
Georgia
Hawaii
Idaho
Illinois
Iowa
Kansas
Louisiana
Maryland
Massachusetts
Minnesota
Nebraska
Nevada
New Jersey
New York
North Carolina
Oregon
Tennessee
Texas
Utah
Virginia
Washington
Wyoming
Australia
Western Australia
Canada
Alberta
British Columbia
Manitoba
Newfoundland
New Brunswick
Ontario
Quebec
Saskatchewan

PRODUCTS/OPERATIONS

Selected Locations
US
Alaska
Arizona
California
Colorado
Florida
Georgia
Hawaii
Illinois
Iowa
Kansas
Maryland
Massachusetts
Minnesota
Nebraska
Nevada
New Jersey
New York
North Carolina
Oregon
Texas
Utah
Virginia
Washington
Wyoming
Canada
Alberta
British Columbia
Newfoundland
Ontario
Quebec
Mexico
Mexico City

Selected Subsidiaries and Affiliates
Aero Automatic Sprinkler
Cherne Contracting Corporation
Continental Fire Sprinkler Company
Kiewit Australia
Kiewit Bridge & Marine
Kiewit Building Group
Kiewit Energy Company.
Kiewit Engineering Group Inc.
Kiewit Infrastructure Co.
Kiewit Infrastructure South Co.
Kiewit Infrastructure West Co.
Kiewit Mining Group
Dry Valley/No. Rassmussen Ridge Mines
Buckskin Mining Company
San Miguel Mine
Walnut Creek Mining Company
Kiewit Offshore Services Ltd..
Kiewit Power Constructors Co.
Kiewit Power Engineers
Kiewit Texas Construction L.P.

COMPETITORS

ABB	Lane Construction
Ames Construction	PCL Constructors
Balfour Beatty	Parsons Corporation
Infrastructure	Raytheon
Bechtel	Rio Tinto plc
Black & Veatch	Skanska USA Civil
Fluor	Turner Corporation
Granite Construction	Tutor Perini
Halliburton	Walsh Group
Hubbard Group	Whiting-Turner
Jacobs Engineering	Williams Companies
KBR	

HISTORICAL FINANCIALS

Company Type: Private

Income Statement

	REVENUE ($ mil.)	NET INCOME ($ mil.)	NET PROFIT MARGIN	EMPLOYEES
12/12	11,220	515	4.6%	14,700
12/11	10,381	790	7.6%	—
12/10	9,938	789	7.9%	—
Annual Growth	6.3%	(19.2%)		

FYE: December 29

Pfizer Inc

Pfizer is one of the world's largest research-based pharmaceuticals firms producing medicines for ailments in fields including cardiovascular health metabolism oncology and inflammation and immunology. Its top prescription products include cholesterol-lowering Lipitor pain management drugs Celebrex and Lyrica pneumonia vaccine Prevnar and erectile dysfunction treatment Viagra as well as arthritis drug Enbrel antibiotic Zyvox and high-blood-pressure therapy Norvasc. The firm also makes and sells generic drugs and consumer health products. Pfizer operates around the world but gets half of its revenues from the US.

HISTORY

Charles Pfizer and his cousin confectioner Charles Erhart began making chemicals in Brooklyn in 1849. Products included camphor citric acid and santonin (an early antiparasitic). The company incorporated in 1900 as Chas. Pfizer & Co. was propelled into the modern drug business when it was asked to mass-produce penicillin for the war effort in 1941.

Pfizer discovered Terramycin and introduced it in 1950. Three years later it bought drugmaker Roerig its first major acquisition. In the 1950s the company opened branches in Belgium Canada Cuba Mexico and the UK and began manufacturing in Asia Europe and South America. By the mid-1960s Pfizer had worldwide sales of more than $200 million.

Beginning in the late 1950s Pfizer made Salk and Sabin polio vaccines and added new drugs such as Diabinese (antidiabetic 1958) and Vibramycin (antibiotic 1967). It moved into consumer products in the early 1960s buying BenGay Desitin and cosmetics maker Coty (sold in 1992). It bought hospital products company Howmedica in 1972 (sold in 1998) and heart-valve maker Shiley in 1979. In the 1980s Pfizer expanded its hospital products division buying 18 product lines and companies.

In 1995 Pfizer bought SmithKline Beecham's animal health business and Procter & Gamble's Bain de Soleil skin care line (sold in 1999).

Pfizer made headlines (and lots of men happy) when the company won FDA approval for Viagra in 1998. The little blue pill became a pop icon and made the company a household name.

When Warner-Lambert said in 1999 that it would merge with American Home Products (now Wyeth) Pfizer sued to prevent the union and eventually succeeded with its own hostile bid. The merger with Warner-Lambert was completed and CEO William Steere retired. Pfizer also sold its animal feed additive business.

Pfizer IBM and Microsoft in 2001 formed a joint venture to sell software to automate prescription writing and other administrative procedures in physicians' offices. Determined to narrow its focus on pharmaceuticals the company in 2002 sold its Tetra fish care then sold its Adams confectionery and Schick-Wilkinson Sword shaving products businesses in 2003.

That year Pfizer purchased rival Pharmacia for $54 billion making it the world's largest research-based pharmaceutical company. Following its two giant acquisitions the company trimmed some 20000 people. In 2004 Pfizer acquired the research divisions of QuoreX which develops antibacterial drugs targeting hospital infections. It also purchased Esperion Therapeutics a developer of cholesterol drugs headed by Lipitor discoverer Roger Newton for $1.2 billion. (Pfizer eventually spun Esperion back off into a private independent entity in 2008 after its development drugs didn't pan out as planned although Pfizer retained some assets and a minority stake in the spinoff.)

In the wake of revelations that Merck's Vioxx increased the risk for cardiovascular diseases in 2004 Pfizer reviewed its own COX-2 pain medication Celebrex. Preliminary studies showed Celebrex increased the risk of heart attack; Pfizer didn't pull Celebrex off the market but did add a "black box" warning of possible cardiovascular and gastrointestinal risks. (In 2008 Pfizer reached an agreement in principle to settle for $894 million most of its pending patient lawsuits alleging that Celebrex caused heart attacks and strokes.)

Acquisitions in 2005 included the purchase of Angiosyn a private biotech working on an anti-angiogenesis therapy for macular degeneration (which can lead to blindness) and Idun Pharmaceuticals which was developing apoptosis (programmed cell death) inhibitors to treat liver disease cancer and other diseases.

That year the company scooped up research partner Vicuron Pharmaceuticals which had two anti-infective (anidulafungin and dalbavancin) drugs under review by the FDA and Bioren which has developed a technology that helps drugs last longer through antibody optimization. (Pfizer divested Vicuron as part of its cost-cutting efforts in 2009.)

While acquiring new holdings on the pharmaceutical front Pfizer trimmed its non-pharmaceutical businesses between 2003 and 2005 including operations it acquired with Pharmacia and its European generics portfolio. The company's animal health division sold off its diagnostics products division (which manufactured tests for bovine tuberculosis and paratuberculosis) to Swiss firm Prionics.

On the consumer health care front the population's increased germaphobia translated into high dollars for Pfizer following the acquisition of Purell. However Pfizer later unloaded its consumer unit altogether refocusing efforts onto its core pharmaceutical business. Johnson & Johnson in 2006 acquired the whole consumer caboodle including such brands as Benadryl Listerine Nicorette Rolaids and Sudafed for $16.6 billion. To comply with regulatory requirements for the deal the companies sold Zantac marketing rights in the US to Boehringer Ingelheim for $510 million; they sold the Cortizone Kaopectate and Unisom brands to Chattem.

As part of its ongoing acquisition strategy Pfizer bought biotech firm Rinat Neuroscience which was developing drugs for pain Alzheimer's disease and other neurological disorders in 2006. Pfizer also acquired vaccine technology firm PowderMed that year and it spent $1.4 billion acquiring Sanofi's joint rights to inhaled insulin drug Exubera. (Pfizer dropped Exubera from its product list in late 2007 however due to lukewarm response from physicians and patients. The company took a $2.8 billion charge as a result.)

In 2015 Pfizer completed a $17 billion acquisition of Hospira. Two years later Pfizer sold Hospira Infusion Systems (HIS) to ICU Medical for $1 billion. HIS was Pfizer's global infusion therapy business and included IV pumps and devices. Through the deal Pfizer gained a stake of about 17% in ICU Medical.

In 2016 Pfizer and Ireland-based Allergan terminated their planned merger which would have been the largest-ever health care deal. The $160 billion transaction would have created the world's largest drug maker surpassing Johnson & Johnson.

Also in 2016 Pfizer bought Anacor Pharmaceuticals which has a non-steroid ointment for the treatment of eczema in its pipeline for $5.2 billion. It also acquired biopharmaceutical firm Medivation for $14 billion gaining a pipeline of cancer drugs as well as prostate cancer drug Xtandi.

EXECUTIVES

Evp Corporate Affairs, Sally Susman, age 58
Evp Business Operations And Cfo, Frank A. D'Amelio, age 61, $1,324,000 total compensation
Chairman And Ceo, Ian C. Read, age 65, $1,905,250 total compensation
Evp And Chief Medical Officer, Freda C. Lewis-Hall, age 63, $800,000 total compensation
Evp And President Worldwide Research And Development, Mikael Dolsten, age 60, $1,237,500 total compensation
Evp And General Counsel, Douglas M. (Doug) Lankler, age 53
Evp And Chief Development Officer, Alexander R. (Rod) MacKenzie, age 59
Evp Worldwide Human Resources, Charles H. (Chuck) Hill, age 63
Group President Pfizer Innovative Health, John D. Young, age 54, $1,130,000 total compensation
Evp Strategy And Commercial Operations, Laurie J. Olson, age 55
Coo, Albert Bourla, age 57, $1,117,500 total compensation
Evp And Chief Compliance And Risk Officer, Rady A. Johnson, age 57
Vp Innovative Health Product Portfolio Management And Consumer Operations, Kirsten Lund-Jurgensen, age 59
Global President And General Manager For Pfizer Inflammation & Immunology, Angela Hwang
Vice President Us Primary Care Marketing, James Sage
Vice President Sales, John Zgombic
Vice President Information Management, Craig Barrila
Vice President Manufacturing, Kevin Nepveux
Medical Director, Michael Wajnrajch
Medical Director, Hernan Valdez
Vice President Medical Affairs Platform Strategy Lead, Edith Eby
Senior Vice President Of Product, Chris Hillebrecht
Vice President Us Trade Group, Lou Dallago
Senior Vice President, Stephen Pennacchio
Vice President Compliance Lead Emerging Markets Compliance Division, Jeffrey Liu
Medical Director, Jean Chow
Vice President Of Medical Affairs And, Paul Mensah
Senior Vice President Of Brand, Carey Petersen
National Account Manager, James Dunworth
Senior Vice President Vaccine Clinical Research And Development, William Gruber
Vice President Biopharma Licensing, Robert Smith
Vice President Human Resources, Mario Gagliano
Vice President External Affairs And Worldwide Communications, Elizabeth Golden
Vice President Membership, Steven Hogue
Vice President, Charles Knirsch
Senior Vice President Human Resources Global Human Resources Operations, Tracy Miller
Vice President Finance Onc And Sc, Peter S McGuigan
Senior Medical Director, George Sands
National Account Manager, Teri Kittredge
Vice President And Assistant Treasurer, Brian McMahon
Executive Vice President Development, Shaileen English
Vice President Specialty Biotechnology Operating Unit, Mike McDermott
Commercial Vice President, Nanette Cocero
Medical Director, Charles Tressler
Vp Network Supply Operations Pfizer Innovative Health, Juan Forero
Vice President Global Procurement, Mike Hoffman

Clinical Director, Peter Park
Vice President Nanomedicines And Bioconjugates, Puja Sapra
Medical Director, Alejandra Nieto
Vice President External Supply, Christina Ayllon
National Account Manager, Mark Desantis
Senior Vice President Fin Biopharma And Cons Hlth, Sajal Mitra
Senior Vice President And Portfolio Manager, John Goceljak
Vice President Chief Of Staff To The Chairman And Chief Executive Officer, Navin Katyal
National Account Manager, Alan J Hemler
Senior Vice President, Salomon Azoulay
Vice President Finance, George Eder
Senior Vice President, Peter Honig
Global Medical Director, Leslie Amass
Senior Vice President, Kostas Giamouridis
Vice President, Lynne Handanyan
Vice President, Lisa Housianitis
Senior Vice President, Jaume Pons
Senior Vice President, Rory O'connor
Medical Director, Seth Woodruff
Medical Director, Judith Hadavi
Vice President Human Resources Global Randd, Sander De Beer
Vice President Emea Logistics And Supply Operations, Danny Hendrikse
Associate Medical Director, Silvina Gallo
Medical Director Oncology, Daniel Kalanovic
Medical Director Oncology, Mahmood Alam
Associate Medical Director, Barbara Sleight
Senior Vice President Worldwide Business Development, Doug Giordano
Vice President, Nicola Clear
Senior Vice President, Charles Triano
Vice President Commercial Development, Andy Schmeltz
Medical Director, David Grolman
Senior Vice President Human Resources Gep And Compliance, Don Stewart
Senior Vice President, William Carapezzi
Global Vice President And Head Vaccines Medical Development And Medical Scientific Affairs, Luis Jodar
Vice President, Mark Schneyer
Senior Vice President Wrd Development And Strategic Operations, Evan Loh
Executive Vice President, Karine Gravel
Medical Director Psychiatry And Neurology, Brian Klee
National Sales Manager, Gary Ellis
Vice President Finance, Fergus O'Sullivan
Senior Medical Director, Dan Sheehan
Vice President And Assistant General Counsel, Lindsay Havern
Vice President Scottsdale Operations, Beatrice Colombo
National Sales Manager Immun, Simon Goodger
Vice President Of Marketing, Martina Porru
Vice President Financial Planning And Operations, Toni King
Regional President Emea Pch, Tarek Youssef
Medical Director, Vaibhav Katkade
Vice President And Assistant General Counsel Chief Antit, Marc Brotman
Associate Medical Director, David Witcombe
National Sales Manager, Beatriz Sanchez
Vice President Finance, Serge Roussel
Vice President Established Products Qo, Kevin Jenkins
Vice President, John Hutchison
Vice President Of Pharmaceutical Sciences, Peter Green
Executive Vice President And Co Founder, Cathryn Adams
Vice President Of Clinical Project Management, Dean Gianarkis
Vice President And Team Leader Finance, Michael Vogel

Vice President Gfs Global Shared Services, Terry Wright
Vice President Regulatory Affairs Oncology, Ramzi Dagher
Vice President, Kanwar Nasir Khan
Vice President Global Vac Pneumo, Raul Isturiz
Medical Director, Ioana Russ
Vice President Legal Affairs And General Counsel, Darren Noseworthy
National Sales Manager, Tuncay Ekici
National Sales Manager Consumer Healthcare, Jung-tak Shin
Vice President Regional Head Of Medical Affairs North America, Juan Ovalle
Vice President Of Quality Operations, Steve Brooks
Vice President, Rich Hollander
Board Vice President, Neil Wildman
Medical Director Hematology, Krupa Sivamurthy
Medical Director, Carlos Estevez
Vice President Endocrine Care, Jose Cara
Vice President Sales, Dennis Kozak
Senior Medical Director, Manuela Berger
Vice President, Cory Stiff
Vice President, Kevin Filipski
Senior Vice President Of Sales, Mike Byrne
Vice President For Translational Oncology, Chris Boshoff
Medical Director, Maria Fernanda Velasco
Vice President Payer Accounts, Joseph Kucharski
National Sales Manager Biosimilars, Natalie Bedard
Vice President Corporate Audit, Jennifer Damico
Medical Director, Judith Hey-Hadavi
Vice President Human Resources Medical Corporate Strategy And Human Resources Business Developme, Janice Beauchamp
Vice President, Tracey Boyden
Executive Vice President And Chief Financial Officer, Alan G Levin
Vice President And Chief Counsel Global Business Development, Arthur Cohn
Senior Medical Director, Birgitta Benda
Vice President Bioprocess Services Group, Roberto Silveira
Medical Director Russia, Kirill Tverskoy
National Sales Manager, Leonore JAcobs
Vp And Assistant General Cousel, David Smith
Vice President Medical Affairs, Rochelle Chaiken
Senior Vice President Total Rewards, Steve Pennacchio
National Sales Manager, Tolgay Sevimsavur
Senior Medical Director, Diane Martire
Medical Director Oncology, Subramanian Hariharan
Medical Director Risk Management Lead, Vlad Bykoriz
Senior Medical Director Global Medical Affairs, Gorana Dasic
Vice President And Assistant General Counsel Vaccines, Jason Smith
Vice President Human Resources, Kristin Papesh
Vice President Finance Japan Asia Area, Gordon Loh
Vice President Us Oncology Commercial, Matthew Shaulis
Government Relations, Ryan Bounsy
Auditors: KPMG LLP

LOCATIONS

HQ: Pfizer Inc
235 East 42nd Street, New York, NY 10017
Phone: 212 733-2323
Web: www.pfizer.com

2017 Sales

	$ mil.	% of total
US	26,026	50
Emerging Markets	11,400	21
Developed Europe	8,508	16
Developed Rest of World	6,612	13
Total	**52,546**	**100**

PRODUCTS/OPERATIONS

2017 Sales by Segment

	$ mil.	% of total
Innovative Health	31,422	60
Essential Health	21,124	40
Total	**52,546**	**100**

Selected Products

Pharmaceuticals
Aricept (Alzheimer's disease)
Aromasin (breast cancer)
+Arthrotec (osteoarthritis and rheumatoid arthritis)
BeneFIX (hemophilia)
BMP2 (bone and cartilage development)
Caduet (high cholesterol and blood pressure dual therapy)
Camptosar (colorectal cancer)
Cardura (hypertension and enlarged prostate disease)
Celebrex (arthritis pain)
Chantix/Champix (smoking cessation)
Dalacin/Cleocin (antibiotic for bacterial infections)
Detrol/Detrol LA (overactive bladder)
Diflucan (antifungal)
Effexor (antidepressant and anxiety disorder treatment)
Enbrel (arthritis treatment)
Fragmin (anticoagulant)
Genotropin (growth hormone deficiency)
Geodon/Zeldox (schizophrenia and bipolar disorder)
Inspra (high blood pressure)
Lipitor (cholesterol)
Lyrica (nerve pain)
Medrol (inflammation)
Methotrexate (severe psoriasis)
Neurontin (epilepsy)
Norvasc (hypertension)
Premarin (hormone replacement therapy)
Prevnar (pneumococcus vaccine)
Pristiq (antidepressant)
Protonix (protein pump inhibitor)
Quillivant XR (ADHD)
Rapamune (organ rejection preventative)
Rebif (multiple sclerosis)
ReFacto AF/Xyntha (hemophilia)
Relpax (migraines)
Revatio (hypertension)
Selzentry (HIV)
Skelaxin (muscle relaxant)
Somavert (acromegaly)
Spiriva (chronic obstructive pulmonary disease)
Sulperazon (antibiotic)
Sutent (carcinoma and tumors)
Toviaz (overactive bladder)
Tygacil (anti-infective)
Unasyn (injectable antibacterial)
Vfend (fungal infections)
Viagra (impotence)
Xalatan/Xalacom (glaucoma)
Xanax XR (anti-anxiety treatment)
Zithromax/Zmax (antibiotic)
Zoloft (depression)
Zosyn/Tazocin (anti-infective)
Zyvox (antibiotic)
Animal Health
Cerenia (nausia treatment for canines)
Convenia (canine and feline antibiotics)
Draxxin (cattle antibiotic)
Excede (cattle antibiotic)
Improvac (swine vaccine for boar taint)
Palladia (dog cancer treatment)
Revolution/Stronghold (antiparasitic for dogs and cats)
Rimadyl (canine osteoarthritis treatment)
Suvaxyn (swine vaccine)
Consumer Health
Advil (analgesic)
Anbesol (oral pain relief)
Caltrate (nutritional supplement)
Centrum (vitamins)
ChapStick (lip care)
Dimetapp (cough/cold remedy)
Emergen-C (vitamin C supplement)
FiberCon (laxative)
Nexium (acid reflux)
Preparation H (hemorrhoid treatment)
Robitussin (cough/cold remedy)
ThermaCare (aches and pains)

Allergan plc   Merck
AstraZeneca   Mylan
Boehringer Ingelheim   Novartis
Bristol-Myers Squibb   Roche Holding
Eli Lilly   Sanofi
GlaxoSmithKline   Teva
Johnson & Johnson

HISTORICAL FINANCIALS

Company Type: Public

Income Statement
FYE: December 31

	REVENUE ($ mil.)	NET INCOME ($ mil.)	NET PROFIT MARGIN	EMPLOYEES
12/18	53,647	11,153	20.8%	92,400
12/17	52,546	21,308	40.6%	90,200
12/16	52,824	7,215	13.7%	96,500
12/15	48,851	6,960	14.2%	97,900
12/14	49,605	9,135	18.4%	78,300
Annual Growth	2.0%	5.1%	—	4.2%

2018 Year-End Financials

Debt ratio: 26.00%—
Return on equity: 17.00%
Cash ($ mil.): 1,139
Current ratio: 2.00
Long-term debt ($ mil.): 32,909

Dividends
Yield: 3.0%
Payout: 73.0%
Market value ($ mil.): —

	STOCK PRICE ($) FY Close	P/E High/Low	PER SHARE ($) Earnings	Dividends	Book Value
12/18	44.00	24 18	2.00	1.00	11.00
12/17	36.00	10 9	4.00	1.00	12.00
12/16	32.00	32 24	1.00	1.00	10.00
12/15	32.00	32 27	1.00	1.00	10.00
12/14	31.00	23 19	1.00	1.00	11.00
Annual Growth	8.8%	— —	7.1%	6.9%	(0.5%)

PG&E Corp (Holding Co)

Pacific Gas and Electric Company one of the largest public utility providers in California supplies electricity and natural gas to residential commercial industrial and agricultural customers in northern and central California. It reaches 5.4 million electric customers via 107000 miles of electric distribution lines and 4.5 million gas customers via 43100 miles of gas distribution lines. The company sources its electric and natural gas supply from owned generation facilities (135 electric plants) and through third-party agreements. The utility along with its parent PG&E Corporation filed for Chapter 11 bankruptcy protection in January 2019 as it faced up to $30 billion in damage liabilities related to California wildfires in 2017 and 2018.

Bankruptcy

In January 2019 PG&E filed for Chapter 11 bankruptcy protection as it faces more than $30 billion in liabilities from damages related to massive wildfires that ravaged parts of California in 2017 and 2018. The wildfires killed dozens of people and destroyed thousands of homes. The future of the company is uncertain as it deals with these liability claims from victims bankers and insurance companies.

Operations

Pacific Gas and Electric conducts business through its Electric Utility and Natural Gas Utility segments.

Electric Utility the core business of the company consists of 135 generation facilities in California with a net operating capacity of 7700 MW. This business also includes some 85 electric transmission substations and 18000 circuit miles of transmission lines as well as distribution assets including 107000 miles of distribution lines 50 transmission switching substations and 770 substations. Almost 75% of the company's annual sales comes from its electric business which delivers some 79800 GWh of electricity each year.

The Natural Gas Utility (25% of annual sales) maintains 43100 miles of distribution pipelines more than 6400 miles local transmission pipelines storage facilities and 10 natural gas compressor stations. It also owns three underground natural gas storage fields. The company buys around 287000 MMcf of gas from third-party providers under firm transportation agreements (uninterruptible services for the period specified).

Geographic Reach

Pacific Gas and Electric owns 160000 acres of land in California consisting of its 135 electric power generation facilities three natural gas storage fields and various transmission and distribution properties including more than 150000 miles of electric and natural gas distribution lines. It is headquartered in San Francisco.

Financial Performance

Pacific Gas and Electric has seen revenue decline from $17.1 billion in 2017 to $16.7 billion in 2018 due to a drop in residential and commercial electric sales. Future sales may be seriously affected by two wildfires that affected parts of its service area in 2017 and 2018. The company is also facing lawsuits that accuses the company's poor infrastructure maintenance as the provenance of one of the wildfires.

Net income slipped from a positive $1.6 billion posted in 2017 to a $6.8 billion loss in 2018 as wildfire-related claims that added up to $11.7 billion.

The company's cash and cash equivalents climbed from $447.0 million in 2017 to $1.2 billion in 2018. Cash from operations generated $4.7 billion while cash from investing used $6.5 billion. Financing activities provided $2.7 billion.

Strategy

Pacific Gas and Electric faces an uncertain future as the utility (along with its parent PG&E Corporation) filed for Chapter 11 bankruptcy protection in January 2019. The company is battling lawsuits that allege the company's poor record of infrastructure maintenance (like failure to trim tree branches near power lines) directly led to the wildfires. In April 2019 a federal judge also barred the utility from issuing dividends to the company's stockholders in favor of using the funds for reducing future wildfires.

Having taken a serious hit to its reputation Pacific Gas and Electric has revamped its board with 10 new members (in a 13-member board) and a new CEO (Bill Johnson a former head of Progress Energy) at the helm. It plans to change the current image that the company favors its stockholders over its customers' wellbeing by working closely with the bankruptcy court's judge as well as the state's utilities regulators and the representatives of wildfire victims. This includes cutting back trees near electrical lines submitting to random inspections by the state complying with state environmental laws and improving the company's own fire mitigation plans.

Company Background

Pacific Gas and Electric Company was incorporated in California in 1905. In 1997 the utility company and its subsidiaries started reporting under the holding company PG&E Corporation.

Damage-related liabilities from California wildfires totaling $30 billion forced PG&E Corporation to file for bankruptcy in 2019.

EXECUTIVES

President Electric, Geisha J. Williams, age 57, $634,183 total compensation
Svp And Cio, Karen A. Austin, age 57
Svp Human Resources, Dinyar B. Mistry, age 57, $381,433 total compensation
President Gas, Nickolas (Nick) Stavropoulos, age 60, $613,221 total compensation
Evp Corporate Services And Human Resources, John R. Simon, age 55, $424,994 total compensation
Svp Generation And Chief Nuclear Officer, Edward D. (Ed) Halpin, age 57
Vp Cfo And Controller, David S. Thomason, age 44
Senior Vice President Human Resources, Andrew Williams
Senior Vice President And Chief Supply Officer, Des Bell
Board Member, Allan Smith
Auditors: DELOITTE & TOUCHE LLP

LOCATIONS

HQ: PG&E Corp (Holding Co)
77 Beale Street, P.O. Box 770000, San Francisco, CA 94177
Phone: 415 973-1000   **Fax:** 415 267-7265
Web: www.pgecorp.com

PRODUCTS/OPERATIONS

2018 sales

	$ mil.	% of total
Electric	12,713	75
Natural Gas	4,047	25
Total	16,760	100

COMPETITORS

Edison International   Sempra Energy
PacifiCorp

HISTORICAL FINANCIALS

Company Type: Public

Income Statement
FYE: December 31

	REVENUE ($ mil.)	NET INCOME ($ mil.)	NET PROFIT MARGIN	EMPLOYEES
12/18	16,759	(6,837)	—	24,000
12/17	17,135	1,660	9.7%	23,000
12/16	17,666	1,407	8.0%	24,000
12/15	16,833	888	5.3%	23,000
12/14	17,090	1,450	8.5%	22,581
Annual Growth	(0.5%)	—	—	1.5%

2018 Year-End Financials

Debt ratio: 29.00%
Return on equity: (-43.00%)
Cash ($ mil.): 1,668
Current ratio: 0.00
Long-term debt ($ mil.): —

No. of shares (mil.): 520
Dividends
Yield: —
Payout: —
Market value ($ mil.): 12,358

	STOCK PRICE ($) FY Close	P/E High/Low	PER SHARE ($) Earnings	Dividends	Book Value
12/18	24.00	— —	(13.00)	0.00	24.00
12/17	45.00	22 14	3.00	2.00	37.00
12/16	61.00	23 18	3.00	2.00	35.00
12/15	53.00	33 26	2.00	2.00	34.00
12/14	53.00	18 13	3.00	2.00	33.00
Annual Growth	(18.3%)	— —	—	—	(7.4%)

PHILADELPHIA CONSOLIDATED HOLDING CORP.

Because each industry has its own unique set of risks Philadelphia Insurance Companies and its subsidiaries specialize in designing and underwriting commercial property/casualty insurance. Its niche clients include rental car companies (for that insurance they always want to sell you at the counter) not-for-profits health and fitness centers and day-care facilities. Its specialty lines include loss-control policies and liability coverage for such professionals as lawyers doctors accountants dog groomers and even insurance claims adjusters. Philadelphia Insurance Companies is a subsidiary of Tokio Marine Holdings.

Geographic Reach

Philadelphia Insurance Companies' operating subsidiaries Philadelphia Insurance and Philadelphia Indemnity Insurance sell and service policies through a network of independent agents and about 50 regional offices that stretch across the US. With its new-found backing from Tokio Marine the insurer has access to broader distribution avenues in the US and overseas.

Sales and Marketing

In addition to commercial property and casualty insurance the company also sells personal coverage for collectible cars and homeowners flood insurance.

Strategy

Philadelphia Insurance Companies has been enhancing its information technology systems. The firm is working to upgrade its back-office infrastructure for more efficient handling of billing claims accounting and data management functions.

EXECUTIVES

Regional Vice President, Brent Kruse
Senior Vice President Marketing, Brian O'Reilly
Vice President Assistant Treasurer, Michael Kelly
Vice President Operations, Deborah Sutton
Assistant Vice President, Michael Henk
Vp Marketing, Mike Ricca
Assistant Vice President Human Resources, Laura Boylan
Vice President And Product Manager, Paul Siragusa
Senior Vice President, John Doyle
Regional Vice President, Bill Misita
Assistant Vice President, Liney Kevin
Vice President Commerical Underwriting, Mark Plousis
Avp Contract Surety, Rick Morgan
Vp Accident And Health Division, Michael Flood
Vice President, Robert Morgan
Regional Vice President, Daniel Shea
Assistant Vice President Chief Information Security Officer (ciso), Mark Viola
Vice President, Jon Peeples

LOCATIONS

HQ: PHILADELPHIA CONSOLIDATED HOLDING CORP.
1 BALA PLZ STE 100, BALA CYNWYD, PA 190041401
Phone: 610 617-7900
Web: WWW.PHLY.COM

PRODUCTS/OPERATIONS

Selected Products
Commercial and Personal Property/Casualty Insurance
  Adoption agencies
  Adult day care
  Amateur sports
  Antique collector car
  Apartments
  Auto leasing/rental program
  Boat dealers
  Bowling centers
  Builder's exchange
  Builders' risk
  Business auto fleet
  Camp operators
  Child care centers
  Consulting foresters
  Contractor environmental coverage
  Crime protection plus
  Entertainment
  Environmental
  Fairs and fairgrounds
  Festivals
  Film production
  Flood
  Golf and country clubs
  Health fitness and wellness
  Home health care
  Homeowners association
  Hospice
  Hotels
  Life and business coaches
  Loss control
  Medical facilities and hospitals
  Motorsports
  Museums
  Non-profit and social service organizations
  Nursing homes
  Office parks
  Outdoor recreation
  Performing arts
  Pest control services
  Professional sports
  Public entities
  Real rstate dchedules
  Religious organizations
  RV parks and campgrounds
  Schools
  Security services (The Guardian)
  Shopping centers
  Special events
  Substance abuse rehabilitation facilities
  Temporary staffing agencies
  Volunteer fire department
  Zoos
Liability
  Accountants professional liability
  Allied Health professional liability
  Business owners
  Cyber security liability
  Employed lawyers professional liability
  Employment practices stand alone
  Excess liability
  Miscellaneous professional liability (Affinity Pro)

COMPETITORS

AIG	Liberty Mutual
American Financial Group	Markel
	North Pointe
CNA Financial	RLI
Hagerty Insurance	State Farm
Hanover Insurance	Travelers Companies

HISTORICAL FINANCIALS

Company Type: Private

Income Statement   FYE: December 31

	ASSETS ($ mil.)	NET INCOME ($ mil.)	INCOME AS % OF ASSETS	EMPLOYEES
12/16	9,719	347	3.6%	1,374
12/15	9,047	323	3.6%	—
Annual Growth	7.4%	7.5%	—	—

Philip Morris International Inc

Philip Morris is quitting smoking: The cigarette company is on the long path to a smoke-free product portfolio. In the meantime however Philip Morris International (PMI) is still one of the world's biggest cigarette manufacturers making six of the world's top 15 tobacco brands and laying claim to more than 15% of the cigarette market outside the US. Despite being US-based its sales presence is entirely non-US. Its biggest brands are Marlboro (the world's #1-selling cigarette) which accounts for about a third of PMI's total shipment volume L&M and Bond Street. Top local brands include Fortune Belmont and Dji Sam Soe. PMI was formed when its former parent Altria spun off its international operations.

Operations

Philip Morris International (PMI) operates six segments according to the company's top geographic markets. PMI's European Union segment generates more than 30% of its total revenue East Asia and Australia account for roughly a fifth the South and Southeast Asia and Middle East and Africa segments both account for 15% of sales and the Latin America and Canada and the Eastern Europe segments each represent some 10% of sales.

PMI's international brands make up more than 75% of its shipment volume while the Marlboro brand accounts for more than 35%. PMI's other tobacco products (OTP) primarily include tobacco for roll-your-own and make-your-own cigarettes pipe tobacco cigars and cigarillos.

It has contract manufacturing relationships with more than 25 third-party manufacturers in nearly 25 markets. In addition some 40 third-party operators in Indonesia makes the company's hand-rolled cigarettes. Roughly 25 of PMI's facilities manufacture more than 10 billion cigarettes each year with eight producing more than 30 billion units.

Its international brands are premium price brands Marlboro and Parliament; mid-price brands are L&M Lark and Philip Morris; and low-price brands Bond Street and Chesterfield.

Important local brands include Dji Sam Soe and Sampoerna in Indonesia; Fortune and Jackpot in the Philippines; and Belmont and Canadian Classics in Canada.

PMI's smokeless tobacco portfolio includes IQOS HEETS Marlboro HeatSticks and Parliament HeatSticks. These products described as Reduced Risk Products account for nearly 15% of net sales.

Geographic Reach

New York-based Philip Morris International's (PMI) products are sold in more than 180 markets worldwide. PMI operates more than 45 manufacturing facilities located in Africa Asia Canada Europe Latin America and the Middle East.

PMI's largest factories are based in St. Petersburg and Krasnodar (Russia) Sukorejo and Karawang (Indonesia) Izmir (Turkey) Marikina and Batangas (Philippines) Krakow (Poland) Berlin (Germany) Crespellano (Italy) and Klaipeda (Lithuania).

Sales and Marketing

Philip Morris International's (PMI) products are marketed and promoted through channels such as: point of sale communications brand events access-restricted web sites print and direct communication to verified adult smokers (via mail e-mail and other electronic communication tools). The

Marlboro brand has a long association with motorsports particularly Formula 1 and Moto GP.

PMI distributes its products directly to retailers single independent distributors zonified distribution and national or regional wholesalers. The company's key accounts include gas stations retail chains and supermarkets. It reaches consumers directly through certain own-brand retail and e-commerce operations

Financial Performance

Most of Philip Morris International's (PMI) revenue consists of excise taxes sometimes known as the "vice tax". As these taxes are outside of PMI's control this analysis excludes excise tax revenue.

PMI's sales are growing again after several years of decline. In 2018 the company's sales grew 3% to $29.6 billion thanks to pricing initiatives partially offset by a 3% fall in volumes. By geography the EU grew strongly and Eastern Europe Middle East and Africa South and Southeast Asia and Latin America and Canada grew modestly while East Asia and Australia fell sharply the only segment to shrink. Risk-reduced products continued to grow strongly up 13% to $4.1 billion.

PMI's net income jumped 31% to $7.9 billion due to higher sales and a sharp fall in income taxes relating to a $1.6 billion one-off charge recorded in 2017 relating to the US Tax Cuts and Jobs Act.

PMI's cash on hand fell by $1.9 billion during 2018 ending the year at $6.6 billion. The company's operations generated $9.5 billion offset by $998 million used in its investing and $9.7 billion used in its financing. The company used its strong operating cash flow to repay borrowing and pay a massive $6.9 billion dividend in addition to recording $1.4 billion in capital expenditures.

Strategy

With traditional cigarette sales falling amid decreased tolerance for the health risks posed by cigarettes Philip Morris International (PMI) has partnered with its former parent Altria Group to transition its product commercialization toward more reduced-risk products (RRPs) such as e-cigarettes. PMI has made bold claims about its commitment to a smoke-free future backed up by $6 billion in investment made in the last ten years. PMI now has four smokeless products on the market IQOS HEETS Marlboro HeatSticks and Parliament HeatSticks. IQOS the first to market is now available in nearly 45 markets. RRPs are growing quickly both in real terms and as proportion of PMI's total business.

PMI's smoke-free goal is under threat from the possibility that the US FDA (Food & Drug Administration) could ban flavored e-cigarettes. Nine deaths have been linked to vaping and e-cigarettes in 2019 triggering a crisis for the young industry and causing market leader Juul to suspend all advertising and scale back lobbying. While PMI doesn't have a direct sales presence in the US a $200 billion merger that would reunite PMI with former parent Altria (which owns a big chunk of Juul) was called off in 2019 over fears of a ban. The two companies had planned to launch IQOS in the US.

Company Background

PMI is a result of a spinoff from Altria in 2008. The separation positioned PMI as an independent publicly traded company free from its US branch Philip Morris USA. Altria simultaneously avoided an entanglement in various US legal and regulatory issues.

PMI has made a number of acquisitions to enhance its brand-rich portfolio and geographic presence. In mid-2011 PMI took over a cigarette manufacturer in Jordan. The purchase followed PMI's acquisition of a cigar business comprising trademarks in Australia and New Zealand. During 2011 PMI also revised its joint venture with Vietnam National Tobacco Corp. (Vinataba) in Vietnam open-

ing the door to licensing the Marlboro label as PMI established a local branch to build its brands.

In 2009 PMI acquired the South African tobacco branch of Swedish Match for 1.93 billion ZAR (about $256 million) giving PMI a leg up in producing smokeless tobacco products and builds upon a joint venture between PMI and Swedish Match to market Swedish style snus and other smokeless tobacco lines outside of Scandinavia and the US. (Altria moved to dominate the rapidly rising niche by taking over UST a leader in the US market for smokeless products including the Copenhagen Husky and Skoal brands.) In the same month PMI purchased the Petter̦es tobacco business for $209 million pocketing fine-cut brands popular in Sweden and Norway.

EXECUTIVES

Ceo, André Calantzopoulos, age 61, $1,501,552 total compensation

Cfo, Martin G. King, age 54, $842,239 total compensation

President External Affairs & General Counsel, Marc S. Firestone, age 60, $1,015,680 total compensation

President Science & Innovation, Miroslaw Zielinski, age 58, $943,738 total compensation

Managing Director Germany Austria Croatia And Slovenia, Stacey Kennedy

Coo, Jacek Olczak, age 54, $971,563 total compensation

Svp And Cio, Patrick Brunel, age 53

President European Union Region, Frederic de Wilde, age 51

President Eastern Europe Middle East Africa Region And Pmi Duty Free Including North Africa, Drago Azinovic, age 56

President Latin America And Canada Region, Jeanne Poll̄s, age 54

Svp Commercial, Werner Barth, age 54

President Eastern Europe Region, Marco Mariotti

President Pmi Japan, Paul Riley

Chief Digital Officer, Jaime Suarez

Vice President Information Systems Management, Siegfried Diesch

Vice President Of Supply Chain, Hafed Belhadj

V Pres Controller, Andreas Kurali

Vice President Hr, Charles Bendotti

Vice President Compensation Benefits And International Assignments, Ralf Zysk

Vice President Information Technology, Kamila Masiak

Chairman, Louis C. Camilleri, age 64

Auditors: PricewaterhouseCoopers SA

LOCATIONS

HQ: Philip Morris International Inc
120 Park Avenue, New York, NY 10017
Phone: 917 663-2000   **Fax:** 917 663-5372
Web: www.pmi.com

2018 Sales

	$ mil.	% of total
European Union	9,298	31
East Asia & Australasia	5,580	19
South & Southeast Asia	4,656	16
Middle East & Africa	4,114	14
Eastern Europe	2,921	10
Total	**29,625**	**100**

PRODUCTS/OPERATIONS

Selected Brands

Local brands
  Apollo-Soyuz (Russia)
  Assos (Greece)
  Belmont (Canada)
  Best (Serbia)
  Boston (Colombia)

  Canadian Classics (Canada)
  Champion (Philippines)
  Classic (Serbia)
  Delicados (Mexico)
  Diana (Italy)
  Dji Sam Soe (Indonesia)
  f6 (Germany)
  Fortune (Philippines)
  Hope (Philippines)
  Morven Gold (Pakistan)
  Number 7 (Canada)
  Optima (Russia)
  Petra (Czech Republic and Slovakia)
  Sampoerna A (Indonesia)
  Sampoerna Kretek (Indonesia)
Mid-price brands
  L&M
  Chesterfield
Other international brands
  Benson & Hedges
  Bond Street
  Lark
  Muratti
  Next
  Philip Morris
  Red & White
Premium-price
  Marlboro
  Merit
  Parliament
  Virginia Slims
Other tobacco products
  Interval (France)
  Petterøes (Norway and Sweden)
  Swedish Match snus smokefree tobacco

2018 Shipment Volumes

	% of total
Cigarettes	95
Heated Tobacco Units	5
Total	**100**

COMPETITORS

British American Tobacco	Japan Tobacco
Gudang Garam	Reemtsma
Imperial Brands	Cigarettenfabriken

HISTORICAL FINANCIALS

Company Type: Public

Income Statement

FYE: December 31

	REVENUE ($ mil.)	NET INCOME ($ mil.)	NET PROFIT MARGIN	EMPLOYEES
12/19	29,805	7,185	24.1%	73,500
12/18	29,625	7,911	26.7%	77,400
12/17	28,748	6,035	21.0%	80,600
12/16	26,685	6,967	26.1%	79,500
12/15	26,794	6,873	25.7%	80,200
Annual Growth	**2.7%**	**1.1%**	**—**	**(2.2%)**

2019 Year-End Financials

Debt ratio: 72.00%
Return on equity: ***,***.**%
Cash ($ mil.): 6,861
Current ratio: 1.00
Long-term debt ($ mil.): 26,656

No. of shares (mil.): 1,556
Dividends
  Yield: 5.0%
  Payout: 96.0%
Market value ($ mil.): 132,391

	STOCK PRICE ($) FY Close	P/E High/Low		PER SHARE ($) Earnings	Dividends	Book Value
12/19	85.00	20	14	5.00	5.00	(7.00)
12/18	67.00	22	13	5.00	4.00	(8.00)
12/17	106.00	32	23	4.00	4.00	(8.00)
12/16	91.00	23	19	4.00	4.00	(8.00)
12/15	88.00	20	17	4.00	4.00	(9.00)
Annual Growth	**(0.8%)**	**—**	**—**	**1.1%**	**3.4%**	**—**

Phillips 66

Phillips 66 is a leading marketer of gas aviation fuels crude oil and other refined petroleum products as well as specialty products such as oils waxes solvents and lubricants. It markets in the US under the Phillips 66 Conoco and 76 brands and internationally under the JET and Coop brands. One of the largest crude oil refiners the company processes transports and markets natural gas and natural gas liquids as well as liquefied petroleum gas. It produces olefins and polyolefins and other products through CPChem a joint venture with Chevron. Phillips 66 operates primarily in the US and Europe.

Operations

Of the four segments that Phillips 66 reports Marketing and Specialties is the largest contributing about 65% of sales. It includes sales of refined petroleum products (gasoline distillates aviation fuel) through more than 7500 branded sites in the US and more than 1300 owned leased or joint venture sites in Europe. Specialty products (for example lubricants sold under Phillips 66 Kendall and Red Line brands) and power generation operations also add to this segment's revenue.

The Refining segment which accounts for just roughly 30% of total revenue refines crude oil and other feedstocks into petroleum products (gasoline distillates and aviation fuel). It has a throughput global refining capacity of upwards of 2.1 million barrels per day.

The Midstream segment of Phillips 66 — which gathers transports and markets NGL crude oil and feedstocks — makes up around 5% of total revenue. It includes the company's interest in Phillips 66 Partners LP. A very small fraction of company revenue comes from its equity in CPChem (a joint venture with Chevron) which is one of the world's top producers of olefins and polyolefins and a major supplier of aromatics styrenics and specialty chemicals.

Geographic Reach

Phillips 66 operates primarily in the US. Its presence in Europe is largely concentrated in the UK with some assets in mainland Europe. The US accounts for more than three-quarters of revenue followed by the UK at about 10%.

CPChem is involved in more than 30 global manufacturing facilities in five continents but most significant assets are on the Texas Gulf Coast.

Sales and Marketing

Phillips 66 markets petroleum and specialty products through a network of nearly 8000 marketer-owned or -supplied outlets across the US under brand names 76 Conoco and Phillips 66. It also holds brand-licensing agreements with more than 1100 sites. Its refined products are marketed on both a branded and unbranded basis.

In Europe Phillips 66 sells retail and wholesale products in Austria Germany and the UK under the JET brand and in Switzerland under the Coop brand (equity interest).

Financial Performance

Phillips 66's revenue is closely tied to oil prices meaning its revenue has fallen and risen again over the last five years along with prices. In 2018 the company's sales continued on their upward trajectory growing 9% to $111.5 billion due to higher prices.

Net income grew 10% to $5.6 billion thanks to higher margins in all units partially offset by the absence of a large income tax benefit recorded in 2017 relating to the US Tax Cuts and Jobs Act.

Phillips 66's cash on hand fell $100 million during 2018 ending the year at $3.0 billion. The company's operations generated $7.8 billion offset by the $2.5 billion used in its investing activities and $5.2 billion used in its financing. Phillips 66's main cash uses in 2018 were capital expenditures share repurchases and dividends.

Strategy

Phillips 66 has earmarked capital expenditures of $3.2 billion for 2019 ($2.6 billion in 2018) as improving conditions have increased investment opportunities. The budget includes $900 million designated for midstream subsidiary Phillips 66 Partners LP. Phillips 66 is expanding its logistics infrastructure network including pipelines storage export and fractionation facilities. Much oil and gas activity in the US occurs in the fracking hotspot of the Permian Basin in North Texas; to meet the demands of the growing region Phillips 66 is developing the Gray Oak Pipeline which links the Permian with the Texas Gulf Coast. It has also invested in the expansion of 33%-owned Sand Hills Pipeline that follows the same route.

In the Chemicals business CPChem is continuing to develop a second US Gulf Coast petrochemicals projects as well as pursue debottlenecking on existing assets. The Refining business will target high-returns projects as well as low-capital quick-payout projects. Initiatives to meet air emission reduction targets and environmental standards have been primary recipients of capital spending.

EXECUTIVES

Chairman And Ceo, Greg C. Garland, age 62, $1,616,816 total compensation
Evp And Cfo, Kevin J. Mitchell, $688,448 total compensation
Evp Refining, Lawrence M. (Larry) Ziemba, $690,312 total compensation
Evp Midstream, Robert A. (Bob) Herman, age 61, $661,608 total compensation
Vp Technology, Merl R. Lindstrom
President, Tim G. Taylor, age 65, $1,071,376 total compensation
Evp Legal And Government Affairs General Counsel And Corporate Secretary, Paula A. Johnson, $698,976 total compensation
Evp Marketing And Commercial, Timothy D. (Tim) Roberts
Vp Investor Relations, Jeff Dietert
Vice President State Affairs, Jennifer Stettner
Vice President Of Engineering, Christina Andersen
European Treasurer, John Wallace
Auditors: Ernst & Young LLP

LOCATIONS

HQ: Phillips 66
  2331 CityWest Blvd., Houston, TX 77042
Phone: 281 293-6600
Web: www.Phillips66.com

2016 Sales

	% of total
US	71
UK	12
Germany	7
Other countries	10
Total	**100**

PRODUCTS/OPERATIONS

2016 Sales

	% of total
Refined products	87
Crude oil resales	9
NGL	4
Total	**100**

2016 Sales

	$ mil.	% of total
Marketing and Specialties	63,367	74
Refining	17,948	21
Midstream	2,927	3
Chemicals	5	-
Corporate and Other	32	-
Equity in earnings of affiliates	1,414	2
Net gains of dispositions	10	-
Other income	74	-
Total	**85,777**	**100**

Selected Brands

76
Conoco
Coop
Copylene
JET
Kendall
Phillips 66
Red Line

COMPETITORS

BP	Marathon Petroleum
CITGO	Motiva Enterprises
CVR	NOVA Chemicals
Chevron	National Cooperative
CrossAmerica Partners	Refinery Association
Dow Chemical	Shell Oil Products
Exxon Mobil	Sinclair Oil
Gibson Energy	Sunoco
Hess Corporation	TOTAL
HollyFrontier	Tesoro
LyondellBasell	Valero Energy

HISTORICAL FINANCIALS

Company Type: Public

Income Statement

FYE: December 31

	REVENUE ($ mil.)	NET INCOME ($ mil.)	NET PROFIT MARGIN	EMPLOYEES
12/18	114,217	5,595	4.9%	14,200
12/17	104,622	5,106	4.9%	14,600
12/16	85,777	1,555	1.8%	14,800
12/15	100,949	4,227	4.2%	14,000
12/14	164,093	4,762	2.9%	14,000
Annual Growth	(8.7%)	4.1%	—	0.4%

2018 Year-End Financials

Debt ratio: 21.00%
Return on equity: 22.00%
Cash ($ mil.): 3,019
Current ratio: 1.00
Long-term debt ($ mil.): 11,093

No. of shares (mil.): 456
Dividends
  Yield: 4.0%
  Payout: 23.0%
Market value ($ mil.): 39,299

	STOCK PRICE ($) FY Close	P/E High/Low		PER SHARE ($) Earnings	Dividends	Book Value
12/18	86.00	10	7	12.00	3.00	54.00
12/17	101.00	10	8	10.00	3.00	50.00
12/16	86.00	31	25	3.00	2.00	43.00
12/15	82.00	12	8	8.00	2.00	44.00
12/14	72.00	10	8	8.00	2.00	40.00
Annual Growth	4.7%	—	—	9.1%	13.2%	8.1%

PHILLIPS EDISON - ARC SHOPPING CENTER REIT INC.

EXECUTIVES

Chb- Ceo, Jeffrey S Edison
Co-Chb, Michael C Phillips
Pres, John Bessey
Cfo, Richard J Smith
Coo, R Mark Addy
CIO, Hal Scudder
Cfo-Treas-Sec, Devin I Murphy
Auditors: DELOITTE & TOUCHE LLP CINCINN

LOCATIONS

HQ: PHILLIPS EDISON - ARC SHOPPING CENTER REIT INC.
11501 NORTHLAKE DR FL 1, CINCINNATI, OH 452491667
Phone: 513 554-1110
Web: WWW.PHILLIPSEDISON.COM

HISTORICAL FINANCIALS

Company Type: Private

Income Statement				FYE: December 31
	ASSETS ($ mil.)	NET INCOME ($ mil.)	INCOME AS % OF ASSETS	EMPLOYEES
12/14	2,151	(23)	—	18
12/13	1,722	(12)	—	—
12/12	325	(4)	—	—
12/11	85	(3)	—	—
Annual Growth	193.4%	—	—	—

Pilgrims Pride Corp.

As one of the world's top chicken processors Pilgrim's Pride has a lot to crow about. The company sells fresh frozen and value-added poultry products under a host of brands (Pilgrim's Pride Gold Kist and Moy Park among them) primarily in North America and Europe. Vertically integrated Pilgrim's Pride is involved in breeding hatching raising processing and distributing chicken; it produces some 11 billion pounds of chicken products annually. The company — which serves more than 6000 retail food outlets distributors and food service operators — is majority owned by Brazil's JBS.

Operations

Pilgrim's Pride conducts its operations through a huge network of some 5300 growers nearly 40 feed mills some 50 hatcheries three dozen or so processing plants about 15 prepared foods cook plants and more than 20 distribution centers as well as rendering facilities and pet food plants.

The company's reporting segments are geographic with US Chicken accounting for about two-thirds of sales; UK/European Chicken and Mexican Chicken account for some 20% and more than 10% respectively. Within its largest US segment fresh chicken (refrigerated whole or cut-up chicken marinated or non-marinated) accounts for about 85% of revenue. Prepared chicken (breast filets strips nuggets patties deli products) generates nearly 15% of revenue and export/other (refrigerated for US distributors or frozen for distribution to export markets) accounts for the rest.

Geographic Reach

Customers in the US generate about 65% of Pilgrim's Pride's total revenue with European customers accounting for nearly 20% and Mexican customers accounting for nearly 15%. It exports its products to more than 100 countries worldwide; key areas outside its main three markets include Asia and Central America.

The Colorado-based company has nearly 100 active plants and other facilities in the US as well as about 50 in Mexico 25 in Europe and five in Puerto Rico.

Sales and Marketing

Pilgrim's Pride has some 6000 customers including restaurants and food processors (Chick-fil-A) grocery store chains (Kroger Publix) and wholesale clubs (Costco).

Financial Performance

Pilgrim's Pride has seen strong revenue growth over the past five years for a variety of reasons including acquisitions in the US Mexico and Europe. Sales have increased 27% since 2014. Net income has been somewhat less consistent see-sawing by sometimes 25% or more year-over-year.

In 2018 the company reported revenue of $10.9 billion up 2% from the prior year as it benefited in the UK and Europe from the positive impact of foreign currency translation an increase in net sales per pound and an increase in sales volume. It also saw growth in Mexico while the US segment was flat year-over-year.

Net income plummeted that year falling 65% to $246.8 million as cost of sales grew 9% from 2017.

Cash at the end of 2018 was $361.6 million a decrease of about $288 million from the prior year. Cash from operations contributed $491.7 million to the coffers while financing activities used $384.2 million (a result of payments on its credit line and long-term borrowings) and investing activities used another $338.9 million mainly for capital expenditures.

Strategy

Pilgrim's Pride's strategic focus is on expanding into new geographic markets and product markets (particularly with more differentiated customized offerings) while optimizing its facilities and processes.

Acquisitions represent a key component of this strategy with the late 2017 purchase of Moy Park moving the company into Europe and a pending 2019 acquisition solidifying its operations on the continent. Another acquisition added the Just BARE organic fresh chick brand to the Pilgrim's Pride portfolio; in 2019 through a partnership with a key customer the company significantly expanded distribution of Just BARE and expects to start shipping new prepared food items under the brand later in the year.

As it focuses on this expansion Pilgrim's Pride has also invested in new and existing facilities in recent years.

Mergers and Acquisitions

In 2019 Pilgrim's Pride agreed to acquire Tulip Limited from Danish Crown for around Â 290 million. Tulip is the UK's largest pig rearer with 12 sites around the country and has annual sales of around Â 1 billion from products such as sausages bacon and pre-cooked meats.

EXECUTIVES

Evp Operations - Technical Services And Engineering, Walter F. Shafer
Ceo, Don Jackson, age 68
Svp Commodity Risk Management Feed Ingredient Purchasing And Export Sales, Charles Von Der Heyde
Cfo, Fabio Sandri, age 47, $375,000 total compensation
Evp Sales And Operations, Jayson Penn
Evp Sales And Operations - Prepared Foods, Kevin Miller
Senior Vice President Human Resources, Doug Schult
National Sales Manager Fresh Foodservice, Andrew Hays
Vp Sales, Sidney Prince
Vp Safety Health And Environmental, Rick Stevens
Vp Feed Ingredient Purchasing, Neil Morris
Executive Vice President, Walt Shafer
Senior Vice President Operations, Matthew Herman
Vice President Foodservice Marketing, Keith Arnold
Chairman, Wesley Mendon §a Batista
Board Member, Michael Cooper
Board Member, David Bell
Auditors: KPMG LLP

LOCATIONS

HQ: Pilgrims Pride Corp.
1770 Promontory Circle, Greeley, CO 80634-9038
Phone: 970 506-8000
Web: www.pilgrims.com

2018 Sales

	$ mil.	% of total
US	7,173	66
Europe	2,135	20
Mexico	1,412	13
Asia	159	1
Other locations	59	-
Total	**10,938**	**100**

PRODUCTS/OPERATIONS

2018 Sales

	$ mil.	% of total
US chicken		
Fresh chicken	5,960	55
Prepared chicken	774	7
Export & other chicken	259	2
UK/Europe chicken		
Fresh chicken	925	9
Prepared chicken	866	8
Export & other chicken	304	3
Mexico chicken		
Fresh chicken	1,252	11
Prepared chicken	77	1
Other products		
US	434	4
UK/Europe	54	-
Mexico	34	-
Total	**10,938**	**0**

Selected Brands

Pilgrim's
Pierce Chicken
Gold Kist Farms
County Post
Country Pride
Moy Park

Selected Products

Fresh chicken
Fully cooked
Ready to cook
Individually frozen

COMPETITORS

Allen Family Foods	Noble Foods
Bachoco	Perdue Incorporated
Coleman Natural Foods	Rose Acre Farms
Eberly Poultry	Sanderson Farms
Farmer's Pride	Tecumseh Poultry
Keystone Foods	Tyson Foods

HISTORICAL FINANCIALS

Company Type: Public

Income Statement — FYE: December 30

	REVENUE ($ mil.)	NET INCOME ($ mil.)	NET PROFIT MARGIN	EMPLOYEES
12/18	10,938	248	2.3%	52,100
12/17	10,768	718	6.7%	51,300
12/16	7,931	441	5.6%	39,600
12/15	8,180	646	7.9%	38,850
12/14	8,583	712	8.3%	35,000
Annual Growth	6.2%	(23.2%)	—	10.5%

2018 Year-End Financials

Debt ratio: 39.00%
Return on equity: 13.00%
Cash ($ mil.): 338
Current ratio: 2.00
Long-term debt ($ mil.): 2,295

No. of shares (mil.): 249
Dividends
Yield: —
Payout: —
Market value ($ mil.): 3,881

	STOCK PRICE ($) FY Close	P/E High/Low		PER SHARE ($) Earnings	Dividends	Book Value
12/18	16.00	31	15	1.00	0.00	8.00
12/17	31.00	14	7	3.00	0.00	7.00
12/16	19.00	16	10	2.00	3.00	4.00
12/15	22.00	15	7	3.00	6.00	5.00
12/14	34.00	14	6	3.00	0.00	8.00
Annual Growth	(17.8%)	—	—	(22.3%)	—	(1.2%)

Pinnacle Financial Partners Inc

Pinnacle Financial Partners works to be at the top of the community banking mountain in central Tennessee. It's the holding company for Tennessee-based Pinnacle Bank which has grown to some 40 branches in the Nashville and Knoxville areas since its founding in 2000. Serving consumers and small- to mid-sized business the $9 billion financial institution provides standard services such as checking and savings accounts CDs credit cards and loans and mortgages. The company also offers investment and trust services through Pinnacle Asset Management while its insurance brokerage subsidiary Miller Loughry Beach specializes in property/casualty policies.Pinnacle agreed to merge with North Carolina-based BNC Bancorp in 2017.

Operations

Pinnacle Financial Partners' commercial and industrial loans and commercial real estate loans account for nearly 40% and 20% respectively of its total portfolio of loans.

As part of its primary services to both individual and commercial clients Tennessee-based subsidiary Pinnacle Bank provides core deposits including savings checking interest-bearing checking money market and certificate of deposit accounts.

The bank's lending products include commercial real estate and consumer loans to individuals and small- to medium-sized businesses and professional entities. Pinnacle Bank Partners also offers auto dealer finance services to certain automobile dealers and their customers. Additionally it offers Pinnacle-branded consumer credit cards to select clients.

Its convenience-centered products and services include 24-hour telephone and Internet banking

debit and credit cards direct deposit and cash management services.

Geographic Reach

Based in Tennessee Pinnacle Financial Partners has become the second-largest bank holding company in the state with nearly 35 offices in eight Middle Tennessee counties and four Knoxville offices. It boasts locations in Nashville Knoxville Murfreesboro Dickson Ashland City Mt. Juliet Lebanon Franklin Brentwood Hendersonville Goodlettsville Smyrna and Shelbyville.

Sales and Marketing

Pinnacle Bank traditionally has obtained its deposits through personal solicitation by its officers and directors although it has used media advertising more in recent years due to its advertising and banking sponsorship with the Tennessee Titans NFL Football team. While it would prefer its customers to bank in person the institution allows customers to bank remotely.

Its marketing and other business development costs have risen in recent years: $4.13 million $3.639 million and $3.636 million in 2014 2013 and 2012 respectively.

Financial Performance

Pinnacle Financial Partners has enjoyed steady revenue and profit growth for the past several years thanks to positive loan growth. Revenue in 2014 rose by 9% to a record $258.77 million mostly to thanks to 9% growth in interest income from loans as the bank's loan assets grew by double digits. Pinnacle also saw double-digit growth in its fee income from service charges on deposit accounts as deposit balances grew and double-digit growth in its investment services income and trust fees as brokerage and trust account balances grew.

Higher revenue drove net income up by 22% to a record $70.47 million. Operations provided $95.06 million or 25% less cash than in 2013 primarily because the bank collected roughly $30 million less in proceeds from its mortgage loans held for sale than it did the year before.

Strategy

Pinnacle's goal is to become the dominant bank in its home market of the Southeast. In 2016 it acquired Avenue Financial Holdings for $200 million and followed up the acquisition by agreeing to merge with regional rival BNC Bancorp of North Carolina in 2017. Once the merger completes the combined company will be the biggest in the region.

Pinnacle Financial Partners been looking to diversify its revenue streams through strategic investments in recent years. In early 2015 for example Tennessee-based subsidiary Pinnacle Bank purchased a 30% membership interest in Bankers Healthcare Group LLC which makes term loans to healthcare professionals and practices for $75 million.

Primarily serving small- to medium-sized businesses in the Nashville and Knoxville areas the company in 2013 began extending its reach in its primary markets by opening its fourth full-service banking location in the Knoxville market in the Cedar Bluff area.

Mergers and Acquisitions

In 2017 Pinnacle agreed to merge with BNC Bancorp. The combined company will have assets of some $20 billion and a presence in four states and in 12 of the largest metropolitan markets in the Southeast.

In 2016 Pinnacle acquired Avenue Financial Holdings (holding company of Avenue Bank with-five banking locations in Nashville); the transaction was valued at some $201.4 million. Avenue Bank will operate as a division of Pinnacle Bank for a few months after which the companies will combine operations.

EXECUTIVES

President And Ceo, M. Terry Turner, age 63, $784,700 total compensation

Evp And Chief Administrative Officer, Hugh M. Queener, age 63, $376,700 total compensation

Evp And Senior Lending Officer; Manager Client Advisory Group Nashville, J. Edward (Ed) White, age 69, $145,000 total compensation

Evp And Director Assocaite And Client Experience, Joanne B. Jackson, age 62, $117,000 total compensation

Cfo, Harold R. Carpenter, age 60, $376,700 total compensation

Svp And Manager Trust And Investment Advisory, Robert Newman

President Pinnacle Knoxville, Mike DiStefano

Chief Credit Officer; President Pinnacle Knoxville, J. Harvey White, $283,800 total compensation

Evp And Manager Pinnacle Asset Management, Gary Collier

Svp And Senior Credit Officer Real Estate, Mike Hendren

Svp And Senior Credit Officer, Tim Huestis

Svp And Cio, Randy Withrow

President And Ceo Pnfp Capital Markets, Roger Osborne

Svp And Manager Residential Mortgage Services, Ross Kinney

Evp And Area Executive Rutherford County, Bill Jones

Chief Investment Officer, Mac Johnston

Svp Small Business Banking, Chip Higgins

Evp And Financial Advisor, Jerry Hampton

President Pinnacle Memphis, Damon Bell

Senior Vice President And Financial Advisor In Nashville, Lynn Kendrick

Senior Vice President, Scott Mccabe

Senior Vice President, Kay Mcalister

Financial Advisor Senior Vice President, Brad Byrd

Vice President, Tyane Powell

Senior Vice President, Kevin Marchetti

Senior Vice President Financial Advisor, Cynthia Oliva

Senior Vice President Mortgage Advisor, Jeff Anderson

Senior Vice President Financial Advisor, Lynn Lassiter

Senior Vice President, Michael G Lindseth

Senior Vice President, David Edwards

Senior Vice President, Steve Horn

Senior Vice President, Brande Thomas

Senior Vice President And Mortgage Advisor, Jamie Lacy

Senior Vice President, Eric Kruse

Senior Vice President, Gail Outland

Senior Vice President, Larry Trabue

Senior Vice President, Steve Uebelhor

Senior Vice President, Sarah Teague

Senior Vice President, Kirk Garrett

Senior Vice President Financial Advisor, David Ligon

Senior Vice President, Natalie Readett

Svp And Mortgage Advisor, Laurel Mckenzie

Senior Vice President, Rob Masengill

Credit Advisor Vice President Sba, Pamela Holmes

Sr Vice President, Tina Hoke

Senior Vice President, William Diehl

Senior Vice President Financial Advisor, Kim Ciukowski

Vice President Automotive Finance, Jeff Rhodes

Svp Mortgage Advisor, Luciano Scala

Chief People Officer, Rachel West

Vice President, Shelly Donohoo

Senior Vice President, Todd Carter

Srvp; Mortgage Advisor, Scott Ractliffe

Svp Mortgage Advisor, Deon Ducey

Svp And Office Leader, Sherrie Hicks

Senior Vice President Financial Advisor, Cindy Oliva

Executive Vice President And Chief Financial Officerand#8230, Alan Haefele

Senior Vice President, Sherry McHaffie

Senior Vice President, Clark Cox

Senior Vice President And Financial Adviser In Commercial Real Estate, Thomas Vester

Senior Vice President, Lucy Foutch

Executive Vice President And Senior Credit Officer, Edward White

Senior Vice President, Robert Denovo

Vice President Administration, Beth Hobbs

Senior Vice President, Donna Taylor

Senior Vice President Financial Advisor, Keely Ritchie

Senior Vice President, Allison Jones

Vice President Of Training And Development, Eddie Alford

Senior Vice President Trust And Investment Advisor, Keith B Davis

Senior Vice President Financial Advisor, Stacey Richards

Senior Vice President, Amy Charles

Senior Vice President, Bryan Bean

Vice President, Gary Green

Senior Vice President And Financial Advisor, Samuel King

Senior Vice President, Chris Rippy

Senior Vice President, Nathan Matheson

Senior Vice President And Portfolio Manager, Christopher Bricker

Senior Vice President And Financial Advisor, Ashley Preskenis

Senior Vice President And Financial Advisor, Nancy Benskin

Senior Vice President Credit Advisor, Stacey Fantom

Senior Vice President Credit Advisor, Kendria Northcutt

Senior Vice President, Sam King

Senior Vice President, Tom Dozier

Senior Vice President, Gina Scott

Senior Vice President Private Client Services Community Banker, Janine Stinnett

Senior Vice President And Trust Officer, Scott Lindsey

Senior Vice President, Ron Stinson

Senior Vice President Financial Advisor, Tim Bewley

Senior Vice President, Jason Reierson

Senior Vp, Chris Howe

Executive Vice President, Kent Cleaver

Senior Vice President, Lisa Baskette

Svp Mortgage Advisor, Bridget Mounger

Vice President, Bob Stimson

Senior Vice President, John Douglas

Executive Vice President, Phil Stevenson

Senior Vice President, Cooper Samuels

Senior Vice President Financial Advisor, Amy Campbell

Assistant Vice President, Alan Gauger

Senior Vice President, Diane Jones

Vice President: Treasury Management Advisor, Joy Bowen

Cmb Senior Vice President, Jeff Tucker

Senior Vice President Mortgage Advisor, Clint Porter

Senior Vice President Credit Advisor, Katherine Graham

Senior Vice President, Ryan Murphy

Ctfa Senior Vice President Financial Advisor, Steve Scott

Senior Vice President Financial Advisor, Bryant Lecroy

Svp And Mortgage Advisor, Donathan Cassidy

Senior Vice President, Bob Lawhon

Senior Vice President Mortgage Advisor, Becky Fiedler

Senior Vice President, Debbie Morgan

Senior Vice President Managing Director, Nathan Kurita

Senior Vice President, Jeff East

Senior Vice President, Rick Nelson

Senior Vice President, Jimmy Moncrief

Evp And Music And Entertainment Director, Andy Moats

Senior Vice President, Dan Neumann

Senior Vice President Mortgage Advisor, Todd Flynn

Vice President, Cheryl Plummer

Senior Vice President, Donna Edwards

Senior Vice President, Glenn Layne

Svp Group Banking Manager, Lucy Daugherty

Svp Financial Advisory, Richard Harris

Senior Vice President Financial Advisor, Debbie Indermuehle

Vp Sba Business Development Officer, Janet Matthew

Vice President, Rick Lalance

Mortgage Adv Sor Vice President, Debbie Del Corro

Executive Vice President Director Of Client Services, Andy Boyer

Senior Vice President Financial Advisor, Danny Hester

Svp Fice Leader, Michael Colyer

Senior Vice President Financial Advisor, Bob Johnson

Senior Vice President Credit Advisor, Warren Jackson

Senior Vice President, Regina Jennings

Svp And Area Manager, Eddie Blount

Senior Vice President Financial Advisor, Peggy Hollandsworth

Senior Vice President, Peter Gentry

Senior Vice President, Brad Medcalf

Vice President Mortgage Advisor, Brandon Caldwell

Senior Vice President Financial Consultant, Doug Jones

Senior Vice President Financial Advisor, Edwin Pugh

Senior Vice President, Eric Barrett

Svp Client Service Center Director, Gerry Barber

Senior Vice President Financial Advisor, Jennifer Finnell

Senior Vice President Financial Advisor, John Moore

Svp Area Executive, Mary Garcia

Vp Appraisal Process Manager, Peter Kapetanakis

Credit Advisor Senior Vice President, Rachel Mitchell

Executive Vice President Regional President, Reid Marks

Vp Credit Advisor, Richard Pierce

Senior Credit Officer Vice President, Richmond Moore

Senior Vice President, Ryan Earwaker

Auditors: Crowe LLP

LOCATIONS

HQ: Pinnacle Financial Partners Inc
150 Third Avenue South, Suite 900, Nashville, TN 37201
Phone: 615 744-3700
Web: www.pnfp.com

PRODUCTS/OPERATIONS

2014 Revenue

	% of total
Interest Income	80
Non-interest Income	20
Total	**100**

Selected Subsidiaries

Pinnacle Advisory Services Inc.
Pinnacle Credit Enhancement Holdings Inc.
Pinnacle National Bank
    Miller & Loughry Inc. (dba Miller Loughry Beach)
    PFP Title Company

Pinnacle Community Development Corporation
Pinnacle Nashville Real Estate Inc.
Pinnacle Rutherford Real Estate Inc.
Pinnacle Rutherford Towers Inc.
Pinnacle Service Company Inc.
PNFP Insurance Inc.

COMPETITORS

BB&T	Regions Financial
Bank of America	SunTrust
Fifth Third	U.S. Bancorp
First Horizon	

HISTORICAL FINANCIALS

Company Type: Public

Income Statement
FYE: December 31

	ASSETS ($ mil.)	NET INCOME ($ mil.)	INCOME AS % OF ASSETS	EMPLOYEES
12/18	25,031	359	1.4%	2,297
12/17	22,206	174	0.8%	2,132
12/16	11,195	127	1.1%	1,180
12/15	8,715	96	1.1%	1,065
12/14	6,018	70	1.2%	767
Annual Growth	**42.8%**	**50.3%**	**—**	**31.6%**

2018 Year-End Financials

Debt ratio: 2.00%	No. of shares (mil.): 77
Return on equity: 9.00%	Dividends
Cash ($ mil.): 722	Yield: 1.0%
Current ratio: —	Payout: 16.0%
Long-term debt ($ mil.): —	Market value ($ mil.): 3,572

	STOCK PRICE ($) FY Close	P/E High/Low		PER SHARE ($) Earnings	Dividends	Book Value
12/18	46.00	15	9	5.00	1.00	51.00
12/17	66.00	26	21	3.00	1.00	48.00
12/16	69.00	24	15	3.00	1.00	32.00
12/15	51.00	22	14	3.00	0.00	28.00
12/14	40.00	20	15	2.00	0.00	22.00
Annual Growth	**3.9%**	**—**	**—**	**23.3%**	**16.0%**	**22.9%**

Pioneer Natural Resources Co

Pioneer Natural Resources Company explores for and produces oil gas and NGLs in the Midland Basin of West Texas. With some 680000 net acres containing proved reserves of 1050 million barrels of oil equivalent this independent energy company is one the biggest energy producers in the Midland Basin. Pioneer's production comes mostly from its Spraberry/Wolfcamp oil field which consists of oil (65% of total output) gas (20%) and NGLs (15%). The company reports around 6940 net producing wells. Additionally the company owns interests in two gas processing systems (plants and pipelines) in Texas. Its major customers include Sunoco Logistics Partners Occidental Energy Marketing and Plains Marketing.

Operations

Pioneer's single operating segment engages in oil NGL and gas exploration and production primarily in the Spraberry/Wolfcamp oilfield in the Midland Basin. This oilfield holds 95% of Pioneer's total proved oil and gas reserves (1050 million barrels of oil equivalent). It employs oil drilling and hydraulic fracturing techniques to develop horizontal wells.

In 2018 Pioneer divested its oil gas and liquids fields in South Texas Texas Panhandle and southern Colorado to become a single-asset company focused on the Midland Basin.

Geographic Reach

Pioneer headquartered are in Irving Texas holds 680000 net acres in the Midland Basin in Texas with most of its wells located in the Spraberry/Wolfcamp oil field.

Sales and Marketing

Pioneer transports most of its Permian Basin oil to three Texas Gulf Coast locations: Nederland Houston and Corpus Christi. Some 80% of its oil is exported to international customers. Its three largest customers are Sunoco Logistics Partners L.P. (28% of Pioneer's revenue) Occidental Energy Marketing Inc. (17%) and Plains Marketing L.P. (15%).

Financial Performance

Pioneer's revenue declined from $4.3 billion in 2014 to $3.5 billion in 2016 due to the commodity price downturn only to shoot back up to $9.4 billion by 2018 following the oil price recovery. In the last five years the company's net income has followed a similar trend: it fell from a positive $930.0 million in 2014 to the deep red (losing a combined $829.0 million in 2015 and 2016) before recovering back to healthy profits in the following two years.

Revenue increased some 73% in 2018 to $9.4 billion the highest in five years. A 21% increase in average realized commodity prices per BOE led to this climb. Adoption of new gas and NGL revenue recognition rules in 2018 and increases in sales volumes aided the result.

Net income surged to $978.0 million in 2018 from $833.0 million in 2017. This $145.0 million improvement came primarily from increases in average realized commodity prices per BOE for 2018 as well as increases in net margins from the company's firm transportation agreements that reaped larger margins by moving oil and gas from the company's production sites to price-advantaged markets. These gains were primarily offset by an $800 million increase in income tax provision due to the rules laid out by the 2017 Tax Cuts and Jobs Act.

The company's cash and cash equivalents declined by $71.0 million ending 2018 with $825 million on hand. Cash from operations generated $3.2 billion while cash from investing used $2.6 billion. Financing activities used $703.0 million.

Strategy

Pioneer wants to become a top oil producer in the Midland Basin of West Texas. In 2018 the company divested all its other properties? oil gas and liquids assets in Texas and Colorado? to exclusively focus on the high-return low-cost Spraberry/Wolfcamp oilfield within the Midland Basin. It wants to hit 1 million barrels of oil output a day by 2027 at a 20% compound annual growth rate.

To get there Pioneer plans to use the proceeds from its recent asset sales (some $865.0 million) to crank up operations within its existing asset area as well as acquire more land. It has already spent around $650 million since 2016 to purchase undeveloped acreage in the Spraberry/Wolfcamp oilfield to leverage the region's low breakeven costs.

Simultaneously Pioneer's new operations are focusing on expanding horizontal well drilling activities that can yield high oil percentages. Well productivity has climbed steadily in the last five years encouraging the company to target a daily output of 320-335 thousand barrels of oil equivalent in 2019.

In the near term Pioneer's growing profits may be affected by increasing oil service costs (due to the onset of oil price recovery) charged by vendors like Halliburton and Schlumberger. It plans to use proceeds from recent asset sales to pay for the rising expenses.

Company Background

Pioneer traces its roots back to 1962 when two Texas oilmen Howard Parker and Joe Parsley decided to drill in the US Permian Basin. The company Parker & Parsley quickly gained a reputation for assembling exploration acreage and expanding its drilling activity through conservative hedges and aggressive deals. In 1997 looking to expand into the natural gas business Parker and Parsley merged with MESA Inc. and changed its name to Pioneer Natural Resources.

HISTORY

The 1997 merger of MESA and Parker & Parsley moved quickly to pull itself out of the dry hole created by its own debt and the industry's late-1990s dropoff. Parker & Parsley began in 1962 as a partnership between geologist Howard Parker and engineer Joe Parsley. In 1977 it began drilling wells in West Texas. Southmark a Dallas real estate firm bought the company in 1984; in 1989 management purchased it from Southmark. The company went public in 1991.

T. Boone Pickens founded Petroleum Exploration in 1956. In 1964 Petroleum Exploration and Pickens' Canadian holding Altair Oil and Gas merged as MESA and went public. With gas prices declining in the 1990s MESA began selling assets. Pickens resigned as CEO in 1996.

Richard Rainwater took control of MESA and then merged the firm into Parker & Parsley which became Pioneer Natural Resources. The company moved into Argentina when it paid $1.2 billion for Calgary-based Chauvco Resources in 1997.

To streamline operations and reduce debt Pioneer cut its workforce and in 1999 it sold 400 US properties to Prize Energy.

Pioneer sold oil and gas properties in Texas and Canada in 1999 and moved to consolidate its Permian Basin operations by offering to buy out limited partners. It also drilled its first deepwater well in the Gulf of Mexico and acquired additional properties in Argentina.

In 2000 the company disposed of noncore natural gas assets in Louisiana New Mexico and Oklahoma. At the same time it boosted its deepwater holdings in the Gulf of Mexico. The next year the company announced successful test drilling in its prospects in Argentina and South Africa.

Pioneer also announced an oil discovery in 2001 on its Ozona Deep prospect in the Gulf of Mexico indicating another deepwater production asset for the company. In 2003 Pioneer teamed up with Woodside Energy to conduct a joint exploration program in the shallow-water Texas Shelf region of the Gulf of Mexico.

In 2005 Pioneer sold the Martin Creek Conroy Black and Lookout Butte oil and gas properties in Canada to Ketch Resources for $199 million. That year it acquired oil and gas assets in the Permian Basin and South Texas for a total of $177 million.

Realigning its exploration portfolio the company sold all of its operations in Argentina in 2006 to Apache for $675 million. That year Pioneer sold the bulk of its Gulf of Mexico oil and gas assets to Marubeni Offshore Production for $1.3 billion. In 2007 the company sold its Canadian subsidiary to Abu Dhabi National Energy Company PJSC for $540 million.

In 2009 the company reported a sharp dip in revenues as the result of global recession's impact on lowering commodity prices and weakening demand for oil and gas. Although Pioneer made

about $89 million of property acquisitions (primarily in its South Texas shale) in 2009 financial conditions prompted the company to sell non-core assets to pay down debt. It sold its assets in the Spraberry field in West Texas to a subsidiary Pioneer Southwest Energy Partners for $168.2 million. It also sold its Mississippi and shelf properties in the Gulf of Mexico for about $24 million.

To gain capital to develop its US shale properties in 2010 Pioneer entered a joint venture selling a 45% stake in its southern Texas gas field Eagle Ford Shale to the USA subsidiary of India's Reliance Industries for $1.15 billion.

It has exited higher risk foreign ventures. To raise cash and to focus on its core North American assets in 2011 the company sold its Tunisia-based exploration and production units to OMV for $866 million. It also sold its South African business in 2012 for $38 million.

Securing an industrial sands business to support its hydraulic fracturing drilling activities in the Wolfcamp Shale and Barnett Shale plays in Texas in 2012 Pioneer acquired Carmeuse Industrial Sands for $297 million.

In 2013 it sold its Barnett Shale assets in North Texas to an undisclosed private party for cash proceeds of $155 million.

In 2013 Pioneer Natural Resources sold a 40% stake in 207000 net acres leased in Wolfcamp Shale play (Permian Basin) in the southern portion of the Spraberry Trend Area Field to Sinochem for $1.7 billion.

In 2013 Pioneer Natural Resources Company acquired 52%-owned Pioneer Southwest Energy Partners L.P. which then became a wholly-owned subsidiary of Pioneer Natural Resources USA through a stock-for-unit exchange.

EXECUTIVES

Evp Corporate And Operations, Mark S. Berg, age 60, $437,846 total compensation

President Ceo And Director, Timothy L. (Tim) Dove, age 62, $672,808 total compensation

Evp And Cfo, Richard P. (Rich) Dealy, age 52, $555,131 total compensation

Evp Business Development And Technology, Chris J. Cheatwood, age 58, $440,615 total compensation

Vp Marketing, John C. Distaso

Evp Permian Operations, J. D. Hall, age 53

Evp Stat Wat And Corporate Engineering, Kenneth H. Sheffield, age 58

Vp And Cio, Stephanie D. Stewart, age 50

Vice President Operations Accounting, Teri Pender

Vp Corporate Drilling And Completions, Steve Mamerow

Executive Vice President Operations, J D Hall

Vice President Information Technology, Glen Paris

Vice President Administration And Risk Management, Larry Paulsen

Vice President Environmental, Bonnie Black

Vice President Communications And Government Relations, Thaddeus Owens

Vice President Legal And Chief Compliance Officer, Ron Schindler

Vice President Permian Land, David Sutter

Vice President Investor Relations, Neal H Shah

Chairman, Scott D. Sheffield, age 66

Board Member, Larry Grillot

Auditors: Ernst & Young LLP

LOCATIONS

HQ: Pioneer Natural Resources Co
5205 N. O'Connor Blvd., Suite 200, Irving, TX 75039
Phone: 972 444-9001   **Fax:** 972 969-3587
Web: www.pxd.com

PRODUCTS/OPERATIONS

2018 sales

	$ mil.	% of total
Oil & gas	4,991	52
Sales of purchased oil & gas	4,388	45
Interest & Other	38	-
Derivative gains	(292)	-
Gain from disposition of assets	290	3
Total	**9,415**	**100**

COMPETITORS

Apache	Energen
Chevron	Exxon Mobil
Concho	Kinder Morgan
EOG	Occidental Chemical
Encana Oil & Gas (USA) Inc.	

HISTORICAL FINANCIALS

Company Type: Public

Income Statement

	REVENUE ($ mil.)	NET INCOME ($ mil.)	NET PROFIT MARGIN	EMPLOYEES
12/18	9,415	978	10.4%	3,177
12/17	5,455	833	15.3%	3,836
12/16	3,824	(556)	—	3,604
12/15	4,825	(273)	—	3,732
12/14	5,055	930	18.4%	4,075
Annual Growth	**16.8%**	**1.3%**	**—**	**(6.0%)**

FYE: December 31

2018 Year-End Financials

Debt ratio: 13.00%	No. of shares (mil.): 169
Return on equity: 8.00%	Dividends
Cash ($ mil.): 825	Yield: 0.0%
Current ratio: 1.00	Payout: 6.0%
Long-term debt ($ mil.): 2,284	Market value ($ mil.): 22,293

	STOCK PRICE ($) FY Close	P/E High/Low		PER SHARE ($) Earnings	Dividends	Book Value
12/18	132.00	37	21	6.00	0.00	71.00
12/17	173.00	41	26	5.00	0.00	66.00
12/16	180.00	—	—	(3.00)	0.00	61.00
12/15	125.00	—	—	(2.00)	0.00	56.00
12/14	149.00	36	20	6.00	0.00	58.00
Annual Growth	**(3.0%)**	**—**	**—**	**(2.8%)**	**41.4%**	**5.5%**

Plains All American Pipeline LP

Plains All American Pipeline L.P. owns and operates an extensive network of midstream energy infrastructure that provides logistical and transportation services to oil and gas companies in the US and Canada. With 30 million barrels of active above-ground storage capacity the limited partnership is engaged in the transportation storage terminaling and marketing of crude oil natural gas liquids (NGLs) and natural gas products. Its portfolio includes some 18000 miles of pipelines and a fleet of 830 trailers 50 barges and 20 transport tugs. Plains All American Pipeline has a presence in the major energy market hubs including California Oklahoma Texas and Alberta. Its prominent customers include ExxonMobil and Phillips 66.

Operations

Plains All American Pipeline reports three business segments?Transportation Facilities and Supply and Logistics.

Accounting for 95% of the company's revenue the Supply and Logistics segment makes its money by purchasing crude oil and NGLs from producers and refiners and transporting and reselling these products downstream in the major energy market hubs or directly to end-users in North America. This segment reports 15 million barrels of crude oil storage capacity.

The Transportation segment charges fees for transporting energy products through a combination of tariffs and pipeline capacity agreements. It also invests in transportation assets for equity earnings. Similarly the Facilities business the company's third segment charges fees for the use of its storage terminaling and throughput services. Together these two segments make up the remaining 5% of the company's revenue.

Geographic Reach

Based in Texas Plains All American Pipeline has an extensive network of transportation terminaling and storage facilities at the major energy market hubs in the US including California Louisiana Oklahoma and Texas as well as in the Alberta and Saskatchewan provinces of Canada.

In 2018 the US accounted for more than 80% of company's total revenue.

Sales and Marketing

Plains All American Pipeline collects almost 40% of its annual revenue from just three customers: Marathon Petroleum ExxonMobil and Phillips 66. A loss of these customers may significantly affect the company's revenue.

Financial Performance

In the last five years Plains All American Pipeline saw its revenue decline from $43 billion in 2014 to $26 billion in 2017 only to partially recover to $34 billion in 2018. The 29% year-over-year sales increase from 2017 to 2018 came almost entirely from a $7.8 billion increase in revenue from its Supply and Logistics segment. Results were boosted by favorable regional crude oil differentials and higher lease gathering margins.

Net income bumped up from $856 million in 2017 to $2.2 billion a year later. Though most it came from higher revenue results were aided by a $200 million gain on sale of investments in unconsolidated entities.

The company's cash and cash equivalents increased by $29 million ending 2018 with $66 million on hand. Cash from operations generated $2.6 billion while cash from investing used $813 million. Financing activities used a further $1.7 billion.

Strategy

Plains All American Pipeline's principal business strategy is to provide competitive and efficient midstream transportation and supply and logistics services to producers refiners and other customers while maintaining a healthy margin for itself.

The company has steadily built its portfolio through acquisitions and internal growth making it one of the largest pipeline companies in the US. In recent years the company has been pushing hard to expand its midstream operations. For instance it spent about $1.9 billion in two Permian Basin projects aimed at expanding takeaway capacity in the region. Another $1.1 billion is earmarked for 2019.

However with the commodity price downturn the company's transport volumes fell dramatically in the past five years and remains low; revenue has almost halved since 2014. The company is currently implementing an action plan (adopted in 2017) that aims to reduce the company's debt. By the end of 2018 it reduced its debt by $2 billion under this plan.

Despite such austere times the firm is looking to capture growth opportunities especially in the Permian Basin by increasing its long-haul capacity through two projects the Sunrise II and the Cactus II. A new joint venture Wink-to-Webster (titled after its proposed delivery route) is also in the works.

Company Background

Goodyear Tire & Rubber subsidiary Celeron began designing the All American Pipeline in 1983 to bring heavy crude from California to the less-regulated refineries of Texas. It was completed in 1987 at a cost of $1.6 billion but by 1991 only a trickle of oil was dribbling through as it struggled to attract customers. Prospects began to look up in the mid-1990s when Chevron Texaco and Exxon signed contracts to use the pipeline beginning in 1996. Plains Resources bought the pipeline but then sold off a 43% stake in an IPO.

In 2012 to boost its midstream assets the company bought BP's Canadian NGL operations for $1.7 billion.

HISTORY

Goodyear Tire & Rubber subsidiary Celeron began designing the All American Pipeline in 1983 to bring heavy crude from California to the less-regulated refineries of Texas. It was completed in 1987 at a cost of $1.6 billion but by 1991 only a trickle of oil was dribbling through. The pipeline did not post a profit until 1994.

Prospects began to look up in the mid-1990s when Chevron Texaco and Exxon signed contracts to use the pipeline beginning in 1996. Plains Resources bought the pipeline in 1998 for $400 million; the company created Plains All American Pipeline to acquire and operate the pipeline then sold off a 43% stake in an IPO that raised $260 million. The next year Plains All American bought Scurlock Permian (2300 miles of pipeline) from Marathon Ashland Petroleum for $141 million and the West Texas Gathering System from Chevron (450 miles) for $36 million.

Shareholders sued Plains All American in 1999 after it reported that an employee's unauthorized crude-oil trading would cost the company about $160 million. (In 2000 the company agreed to pay $29.5 million plus interest to settle the cases.)

Plains All American announced plans to mothball all but the California section of the All American Pipeline in 1999. The next year El Paso Energy bought the 1088-mile section of the pipeline that was to be deactivated plus the right to run fiber-optic cable over the entire pipeline for $129 million.

Targeting Canada as part of its expansion strategy in 2001 Plains All American bought about 450 miles of oil pipeline and other midstream assets from Murphy Oil and acquired crude oil and LPG marketing firm CANPET Energy. Also that year Plains Resources reduced its stake in Plains All American from 44% to 29%.

In 2002 the company acquired the Wapella Pipeline System located in southeastern Saskatchewan and southwestern Manitoba. It also bought Shell Pipeline's West Texas crude oil pipeline assets for $315 million. Plains All American Pipeline continued its acquisition streak in 2003 with the acquisitions of the South Saskatchewan pipeline system in Canada and the ArkLaTex pipeline system originating in Sabine Texas.

In 2004 Plains All American continued its expansion with the acquisition of interests in the Capline and Capwood pipeline systems from Shell Pipeline Company for about $158 million. It also acquired the crude oil and pipeline operations of Link Energy for about $330 million and the Cal Ven pipeline system from Unocal Canada for about

$19 million. Later that year the company continued its system expansion by acquiring the Schaefferstown propane storage facility from Koch Hydrocarbon for about $32 million.

In 2006 the company acquired Andrews Petroleum and Lone Star Trucking for $205 million. It also acquired stakes in a number of Gulf Coast crude oil pipeline systems from BP Oil Pipeline Company for $133.5 million. That year in a major deal the company acquired Pacific Energy Partners for $2.4 billion moving the company beyond crude oil and into the refined products and barging businesses.

In 2007 Plains All American Pipeline acquired LPG storage facilities in Arizona and South Carolina.

In 2008 Occidental Petroleum acquired 10% of the company's general partner boosting the amount of new capital available for Plains All American Pipeline to pay down debt and make further acquisitions. It also boosted its Canadian midstream assets with the acquisition of Rainbow Pipeline (crude oil gathering and pipelines).

In 2012 to boost its midstream assets the company bought BP's Canadian NGL operation.

EXECUTIVES

President And Coo, Harry N. Pefanis, age 62, $300,000 total compensation
Evp, Phillip D. (Phil) Kramer, $250,000 total compensation
Chairman And Ceo, Greg L. Armstrong, age 61, $375,000 total compensation
Evp Operations And Business Development, Mark J. Gorman
Evp General Counsel And Secretary, Richard K. McGee, age 58
Svp Technology Process And Risk Management, Alfred A. (Al) Lindseth
Evp And Cfo, Al Swanson, age 55, $250,000 total compensation
President Plains Midstream Canada, W. David (Dave) Duckett, $276,666 total compensation
Evp Commercial Activities, John P. von Berg, $250,000 total compensation
Evp, John R. Rutherford, $62,500 total compensation
President Pngs, Dean Liollio, age 61
Executive Vice President Commercial Activities, John Berg
Vice President, David Wright
Vice President Operations Management System, Stephen Falgoust
Vp Tax, Walter Van Zanten
Vice President, Charles Kingswell-smith
Vice President West Coast Pipelines, Dominic Ferrari
Svp Operations Plains Midstream Canada, Scott Sill
Evp Operations And Engineering, Daniel Nerbonne
Vp Supply Chain Management, James Ferrell
Vp And Treasurer, Sharon Spurlin
Vice President Refinery Supply, Jim Fryfogle
Senior Vice President Commercial Activities, John VonBerg
Vice President Of Operations, Daniel Noack
Vice President Lpg Commercial Plains Midstream Canada, James Shelford
Evp, Phil Kramer
Vp Finance Plains Midstream Canada, Bill Forward
Board Member, Christopher Temple
Assistant Treasurer, Michael McLaughlin
Board Member, John T Raymond
Auditors: PricewaterhouseCoopers LLP

LOCATIONS

HQ: Plains All American Pipeline LP
  333 Clay Street, Suite 1600, Houston, TX 77002
Phone: 713 646-4100
Web: www.plainsallamerican.com

2018 Sales

	$ mil.	% of total
US	28,362	83
Canada	5,693	17
Total	**34,055**	**100**

PRODUCTS/OPERATIONS

2018 Sales

	$ mil.	% of total
Supply and logistics	32,819	96
Transportation	648	2
Facilities	588	2
Total	**34,055**	**100**

COMPETITORS

Buckeye Partners	ONEOK
Enbridge	Sunoco Logistics
Enterprise Products	TransMontaigne
NGL Energy Partners	

HISTORICAL FINANCIALS

Company Type: Public

Income Statement

FYE: December 31

	REVENUE ($ mil.)	NET INCOME ($ mil.)	NET PROFIT MARGIN	EMPLOYEES
12/18	34,055	2,216	6.5%	4,900
12/17	26,223	856	3.3%	4,850
12/16	20,182	726	3.6%	5,100
12/15	23,152	903	3.9%	5,400
12/14	43,464	1,384	3.2%	5,300
Annual Growth	(5.9%)	12.5%	—	(1.9%)

2018 Year-End Financials

Debt ratio: 36.00%
Return on equity: —
Cash ($ mil.): 66
Current ratio: 1.00
Long-term debt ($ mil.): 9,143

No. of shares (mil.): 726
Dividends
  Yield: 6.0%
  Payout: 44.0%
Market value ($ mil.): 14,556

	STOCK PRICE ($) FY Close	P/E High/Low		PER SHARE ($) Earnings	Dividends	Book Value
12/18	20.00	10	7	3.00	1.00	17.00
12/17	21.00	34	19	1.00	2.00	15.00
12/16	32.00	78	36	0.00	3.00	13.00
12/15	23.00	67	24	1.00	3.00	20.00
12/14	51.00	25	19	2.00	3.00	22.00
Annual Growth	(20.9%)	—	—	3.3%	(17.2%)	(6.6%)

Plains GP Holdings LP

EXECUTIVES

MBR, Greg L Armstrong
Pres, Harry N Pefanis
Exec V Pres, Phil D Kramer
Dir, Roy I Lamoreaux
Cfo, Al Swanson
Exec V Pres-MBR, Mark J Gorman
Coordinator, Afton Shelton
Compliance Staff, Chrystah Carter
Vice-President Engineering, Dan Nerbonne
Safety Manager, Beckey Evans
Accounting Staff, Jake Ragle
Auditors: PricewaterhouseCoopers LLP

LOCATIONS

HQ: Plains GP Holdings LP
  333 Clay Street, Suite 1600, Houston, TX 77002
Phone: 713 646-4100
Web: www.plainsallamerican.com

HISTORICAL FINANCIALS

Company Type: Public

Income Statement

FYE: December 31

	REVENUE ($ mil.)	NET INCOME ($ mil.)	NET PROFIT MARGIN	EMPLOYEES
12/18	34,055	334	1.0%	4,900
12/17	26,223	(731)	—	4,850
12/16	20,182	94	0.5%	5,100
12/15	23,152	118	0.5%	5,400
12/14	43,464	70	0.2%	5,300
Annual Growth	(5.9%)	47.8%	—	(1.9%)

2018 Year-End Financials

Debt ratio: 34.00%
Return on equity: —
Cash ($ mil.): 69
Current ratio: 1.00
Long-term debt ($ mil.): 9,143

No. of shares (mil.): 796
Dividends
  Yield: 6.0%
  Payout: 57.0%
Market value ($ mil.): 16,000

	STOCK PRICE ($) FY Close	P/E High/Low		PER SHARE ($) Earnings	Dividends	Book Value
12/18	20.00	13	9	2.00	1.00	2.00
12/17	22.00	—	—	(5.00)	2.00	2.00
12/16	35.00	38	6	1.00	0.00	2.00
12/15	9.00	21	5	1.00	0.00	8.00
12/14	26.00	25	18	1.00	0.00	7.00
Annual Growth	(5.9%)	—	—	13.9%	—	(24.9%)

PNC Financial Services Group (The)

EXECUTIVES

Chb-Pres-Ceo, William S Demchak
Exec V Pres-Coo, E William Parsley III
Exec V Pres-Cfo, Robert Q Reilly
Exec V Pres-Chief ADM Officer-, Gregory B Jordan
Sr V Pres-Contrl, Gregory H Kozich
Information Technology Team ME, Edward Pink
Manager, Jason Donaldson
Director of Security, John Ericksen
Financial Planner, Mary Dinardo
Senior Marketing Research Mana, Mary Metzler
Vice President Marketing, Richard Kopchinski
Auditors: PricewaterhouseCoopers LLP

LOCATIONS

HQ: PNC Financial Services Group (The)
  The Tower at PNC Plaza, 300 Fifth Avenue, Pittsburgh, PA 15222-2401
Phone: 412 762-2000   **Fax:** 412 762-5798
Web: www.pnc.com

COMPETITORS

Bank of America	M&T Bank
Capital One	RBS Citizens Financial
Citigroup	Group
Fifth Third	Sovereign Bank
Harris	TD Bank USA
Huntington Bancshares	U.S. Bancorp
JPMorgan Chase	Wells Fargo
KeyCorp	

Company Type: Public

Income Statement   FYE: December 31

	ASSETS ($ mil.)	NET INCOME ($ mil.)	INCOME AS % OF ASSETS	EMPLOYEES
12/18	382,315	5,301	1.4%	53,063
12/17	380,768	5,338	1.4%	52,906
12/16	366,380	3,903	1.1%	52,006
12/15	358,493	4,106	1.1%	52,513
12/14	345,072	4,184	1.2%	53,587
Annual Growth	2.6%	6.1%	—	(0.2%)

2018 Year-End Financials

Debt ratio: 9.00%
Return on equity: 11.00%
Cash ($ mil.): 16,501
Current ratio: —
Long-term debt ($ mil.): —

No. of shares (mil.): 457
Dividends
  Yield: 3.0%
  Payout: 32.0%
Market value ($ mil.): 53,428

	STOCK PRICE ($) FY Close	P/E High/Low	PER SHARE ($) Earnings	Dividends	Book Value
12/18	117.00	15 10	11.00	3.00	104.00
12/17	144.00	14 11	10.00	3.00	100.00
12/16	117.00	16 10	7.00	2.00	94.00
12/15	95.00	13 11	7.00	2.00	89.00
12/14	91.00	12 10	7.00	2.00	85.00
Annual Growth	6.4%	— —	10.1%	16.0%	5.2%

Polaris Inc

One of the world's top makers of off-road vehicles Polaris Industries makes and sells all-terrain vehicles (ATVs) and side-by-side recreational and utility RANGER-brand vehicles. It also manufactures snowmobiles on-road vehicles such as the Victory and Indian brands motorcycle and small electric vehicles (SEVs). Offerings include replacement parts accessories (covers windshields backrests) garments and riding gear (bags and helmets). Polaris' lineup is sold through dealers and distributors in North America Western Europe and Australia.

OperationsPolaris operates through four chief segments: Off-Road Vehicles (ORV)/Snowmobiles (more than 65% of sales) Aftermarket (more than 15%) Motorcycles (about 110%) and Global Adjacent Markets (less than 110%).Polaris' vehicle lineup includes RANGER RZR and Polaris GENERAL side-by-side off-road vehicles; Sportsman and Polaris ACE all-terrain off-road vehicles; Indian Motorcycle midsize and heavyweight motorcycles; Slingshot moto-roadsters; and snowmobile models that include Titan Switchback RMK and Indy.

Geographic Reach

Polaris based in Hamel Minnesota has about 15 manufacturing locations and five research and development centers as well as 10 distribution facilities in Alabama California Florida Idaho Iowa Minnesota Ohio South Dakota Texas and Wisconsin. International facilities are in Australia Canada China France Mexico and Poland. The US represents around 80% of sales while Canada contributes less than 10%; the remainder comes from other international sales.

Sales and Marketing

Polaris' products are sold through a network of about 1800 independent dealers in North America in addition to almost 30 subsidiaries and some 90 distributors in more than 100 countries outside of North America.

The company advertises its products directly to consumers through print advertising the internet social media billboards television and radio. It also provides media advertising and produces promotional films for its products which are available to dealers for use in showrooms or at special promotions. It provides product brochures posters dealer signs and other miscellaneous promotional items for use by dealers.

Financial Performance

After a 4% revenue decline in 2016 Polaris resumed sales growth in 2107. Net income however slipped for the second year in a row following six years of steady increases.

Revenue jumped 20% in 2017 to $5.4 billion a company high driven by the 2016 Transamerican Auto Parts (TAP) acquisition higher volume and product/price mix. TAP's contribution pushed Aftermarket sales up more than 360% while ORV and snowmobile sales rose 9% and Global Adjacent Market sales edge up 4%. Motorcycle sales fell 16% as the company wound down its Victory line of bikes. Polaris posted sales gains of 22% in the US and Canada while sales classified as international rose 11%.

Polaris' net income fell 19% to $172.5 million in 2017 from 2016. Affecting profit were costs associated with closing the Victory business a non-cash write-down of deferred taxes because of the US Tax Cuts and Jobs Act and expenses from the TAP integration.

The company had about $138 million in cash in 2017 an $11 million increase from 2016. Cash from operations rose about $8 million year-to-year. After paying off debt and issuing net debt Polaris reduced its long-term obligations by about $234 million.

Strategy

Polaris has made several acquisitions to extend its portfolio. The deals include the Transamerican Auto Parts which added significant revenue in aftermarkets parts. In 2018 Polaris added boats to its lineup with the acquisition of Boat Holdings a leader maker of pontoon boats.

The company emphasizes growth outside the US. It has ramped up production of ORVs at its plant in Opole Poland to meet rising demand in Europe. The company intends to make Indian motorcycles for the European market at the plant starting in 2019. The increased overseas production should not have an impact on its US manufacturing operations.

Trade battles with other countries particularly China have challenged Polaris. The impact of higher tariffs through the first half of 2018 was about $40 million and would be more in 2019 if tensions don't ease. The company has raised prices in response to higher tariffs as have competitors.

Mergers and Acquisitions

Acquisitions as well as internal investments and business alliances are fundamental to Polaris' strategy for building its portfolio and market presence.

In 2018 Polaris bought Boating Holdings the largest maker of pontoon boats in the US for about $805 million. Besides pontoon boats Boat Holdings makes deck and cruiser boats and sells through the Bennington Godfrey Hurricane and Rinker brands in the US and Canada. The deal extends Polaris's footprint from off-road to on-water with offerings that brought in about $560 million in revenue in 2017.

In late 2016 Polaris purchased Transamerican Auto Parts a manufacturer distributor retailer and installer of off-road Jeep and truck accessories for $669 million. The deal enhanced Polaris' ecommerce platform and bolstered its ability to serve off-road enthusiasts with a variety of Jeep and truck aftermarket accessories.

Earlier in 2016 Polaris enhanced its Global Adjacent Markets segment through the purchase of California-based Taylor-Dunn Manufacturing Company a provider of industrial vehicles serving a broad range of commercial manufacturing warehouse and ground-support customers.

Company Background

Originally called Hetteen Hoist & Derrick Polaris Industries was founded in Roseau Minnesota in 1945 by Edgar Hetteen and David Johnson. The friends did welding and repair work and made custom machinery for local farmers.

EXECUTIVES

Svp Customer Experience And Chief Marketing Officer, Timothy M. Larson, age 46
President International, Michael D. Dougherty, age 51
Chairman And Ceo, Scott W. Wine, age 51, $985,000 total compensation
Evp Operations Engineering And Lean, Kenneth J. (Ken) Pucel, age 53, $600,000 total compensation
Evp Finance And Cfo, Michael T. (Mike) Speetzen, age 49, $550,000 total compensation
President Parts Garments And Accessories, Stephen L. Eastman, age 54, $391,635 total compensation
Cto, Stephen J. Kemp
Vp And Cio, Matthew J. Emmerich
President Motorcycles, Steven D. Menneto
Vp Snowmobiles, Christopher G. Wolf
Svp Corporate Development And Strategy; President Global Adjacent Markets, Robert P. (Bob) Mack, $295,385 total compensation
President Off-road Vehicles, Chris Musso
Vice President Of Engineering Powertrain, Jeff Matthews
Auditors: Ernst & Young LLP

LOCATIONS

HQ: Polaris Inc
2100 Highway 55, Medina, MN 55340
Phone: 763 542-0500
Web: www.polaris.com

2017 Sales

	$ mil.	% of total
United States	4,328	80
Canada	376	7
Other foreign countries	725	13
Total	5,429	100

PRODUCTS/OPERATIONS

2017 Sales

	$ mil.	% of total
ORV/Snowmobiles	3,571	66
Motorcycles	576	11
Global Adjacent Markets	397	7
Aftermarket	885	16
Total	5,429	100

PRODUCTS

Off-Road Vehicles
RZR Sport Side x Side
General REC Utility Side x Side
RANGER Utility REC Side x Side
RZR Sport Side x Side
Sportsman ATV
Motorcycles
Indian Motorcycle
Victory Motorcycles
Snow
Snowmobiles
Timbersled
Commercial
GEM Electric
Generators
Government & Defense
Lubricants
Slingshot

Arctic Cat
BMW
Deere
E-Z-GO
Harley-Davidson
Honda

Kawasaki Heavy
Industries
Kubota
Suzuki Motor
Triumph Motorcycles
Yamaha Motor

HISTORICAL FINANCIALS

Company Type: Public

Income Statement

FYE: December 31

	REVENUE ($ mil.)	NET INCOME ($ mil.)	NET PROFIT MARGIN	EMPLOYEES
12/18	6,079	335	5.5%	12,000
12/17	5,428	172	3.2%	11,000
12/16	4,517	213	4.7%	8,600
12/15	4,719	455	9.6%	8,100
12/14	4,480	454	10.1%	7,000
Annual Growth	7.9%	(7.3%)	—	14.4%

2018 Year-End Financials

Debt ratio: 48.00%
Return on equity: 37.00%
Cash ($ mil.): 161
Current ratio: 1.00
Long-term debt ($ mil.): 1,896

No. of shares (mil.): 61
Dividends
  Yield: 3.0%
  Payout: 46.0%
Market value ($ mil.): 4,669

	STOCK PRICE ($) FY Close	P/E High/Low	PER SHARE ($) Earnings	Dividends	Book Value
12/18	77.00	25 13	5.00	2.00	14.00
12/17	124.00	49 29	3.00	2.00	15.00
12/16	82.00	31 21	3.00	2.00	14.00
12/15	86.00	23 12	7.00	2.00	15.00
12/14	151.00	23 17	7.00	2.00	13.00
Annual Growth	(15.6%)	— —	(5.8%)	5.7%	2.1%

Popular Inc.

Founded in 1893 Popular is the holding company for Banco Popular de Puerto Rico the largest bank in Puerto Rico with some 170 branches (and around 10 more on the Virgin Islands). In addition to commercial and retail banking services Popular owns subsidiaries that offer vehicle financing and leasing (Popular Auto) insurance (Popular Insurance) financial advisory and brokerage services (Popular Securities) and mortgages (Popular Mortgage). Popular also owns Banco Popular North America (BPNA) which serves the US Hispanic population from about 50 Popular Community Bank branches in New York Florida and New Jersey.

Operations

Commercial real estate and business loans (mostly in Puerto Rico) make up more than 30% of Popular's loan portfolio while residential mortgage loans also account for 30% of loans. Consumer loans make up 20% of the portfolio; the rest of the portfolio comprises lease financing and constructions loans.

The bank generates the bulk of its revenue from interest income. Nearly 70% of its total revenue comes from loan interest while another 10% comes from interest on its investment securities. The remainder of its revenue comes from a mix of credit/debit card insurance trust and other service fees (about 10%); service charges on deposit accounts (10%) and mortgage banking income (1%).

Popular's other financial services include the insurance agency and reinsurance businesses of Popular Insurance Popular Insurance V.I. Popular Risk Services and Popular Life Re. BPNA also owns E-LOAN Popular Equipment Finance and Popular Insurance Agency USA. E-LOAN's sole purpose is to provide an online platform to raise deposits for BPNA.

It has around 640 ATMs in Puerto Rico.

Geographic Reach

Popular operates some 230 branches and almost 50 E-Loan and other subsidiary offices including some 180 Banco Popular de Puerto Rico branches in Puerto Rico 35 branches in New York and others in south Florida New Jersey and the Virgin Islands. About 80% of the bank's loan assets are in Puerto Rico.

Financial Performance

In fiscal 2017 Popular's revenue increased 11% to $2.1 billion due to increases in both interest and non-interest income. Financial results were impacted by the destructive hurricanes that hit Puerto Rico in September 2017. Popular's revenue was affected by reduced merchant transaction activity the waiver of certain late fees and service charges (including ATM fees) to businesses and customers and disruption to mortgage origination servicing and loss mitigation activities.

Net income fell by 50% to $107.7 million. Much of the fall was accounted for by hurricane effects: Popular recorded $88 million in pre-tax hurricane-related expenses including provision for loan losses of $67.7 million. The bank also took a one-off hit from the 2017 US Tax Cuts and Jobs Act which caused a $168.4 million write-down of the deferred tax asset from its US operations.

Cash from operations increased 8% to $635.5 million due to adjustments to reconcile provisions for loan losses partially offset by lower net income.

Strategy

Popular's short-term outlook is dominated by dealing with the effects of Hurricanes Irma and Maria that made landfall in mid and late September 2017. By the end of the year the bank had 92% of its branches and 82% of its ATMs operational up from 31% and 24% one week after the storms respectively. It reestablished call center operations on 25 September and resumed 24/7 operations a month later.

To aid its customers in rebuilding their livelihoods the bank waived ATM fees for 25 days and implemented a payment moratorium for credit cards personal loans auto loans and mortgages. It also set up seven hubs across the territory providing internet access to its commercial clients. Popular also contributed $6.1 million to the Embracing Puerto Rico fund and completed 35 missions distributing 800000 lbs of basic provisions to 140000 people.

Mergers and Acquisitions

In 2018 Popular agreed to acquire Wells Fargo's Puerto Rico Auto Finance Business including $1.5 billion retail auto loans and $340 million in commercial loans for $1.7 billion.

Company Background

To broaden its target audience beyond the Hispanic community Popular rebranded itself in the US switching its name from "Banco Popular" to "Popular Community Bank". The change which was initially begun in pilot markets in 2010 was completed officially in 2012 when the company changed its name in New York City.

EXECUTIVES

Chairman, Richard L. Carri n, age 66, $1,453,846 total compensation

Evp Financial And Insurance, Juan O. Guerrero, age 59, $375,000 total compensation

Evp Administration, Eduardo J. Negr n, age 54, $385,000 total compensation

Evp And Coo Popular Community Bank, Manuel Chinea, age 53

Evp Retail Banking, Néstor O. Rivera, age 72, $375,000 total compensation

Evp And Cfo, Carlos J. V zquez, age 60, $700,962 total compensation

Evp And Chief Risk Officer, Lidio V. Soriano, age 50, $519,231 total compensation

President And Ceo, Ignacio lvarez, age 60, $742,500 total compensation

Evp Commercial Credit, Eli S. Sep lveda, age 56, $420,000 total compensation

Evp Individual Credit, Gilberto F. Monz n, age 59

Evp And Chief Legal Officer, Javier D. Ferrer, age 57, $571,154 total compensation

Evp Cto And Chief Digital Officer, Camille Burckhart, age 40

First Vice President, Jorge Roig

Vice President, Michelle Cianchini

Svp Corporate Communications, Teruca Rullan

Executive Vice President, Liesl A Rodriguez

Senior Vice President, Fabio Garcia

Svp Regulatory Affairs, Fred Teed

Vice President, Franklyn Vargas

First Vice President Banco Popular Fiduciary Services, Javier Rubio

Vice President And Legal Counsel, Angelica Lavergne

Svp Corporate Banking Banco Popular De Puerto Rico, Jose M Pachano

First Vice President Marketing And Advertising Popular Auto, Edouard Lafontant

First Vp Individual Banking Banco Popular Rio Piedras Region, Martiza Mendez

Senior Vice President, David Peters

Vice President Corporate Banking Investor Services Hub, Natalie Claudio

Senior Vice President And Division Manager, Oran Bowry

Vice President International Private Banking, David Hitt

Executive Vice President Of Retail Banking And Operations, Nestor Obie

Vice President, Norberto Prez

Senior Vice President And Manager People Services Division, Douglas Hachenburg

Vice President And Manager Cra Compliance, Vannessa Montes

Vice President Regulatory Compliance Manager, Monica Ledesma

Auditors: PricewaterhouseCoopers LLP

LOCATIONS

HQ: Popular Inc.
Popular Center Building, 209 Munoz Rivera Avenue, Hato Rey, San Juan, PR 00918
Phone: 787 765-9800
Web: www.popular.com

PRODUCTS/OPERATIONS

Sales 2017

	$ mil.	% of total
Interest income:		
Loans	1,479	68
Money market investments	52	2
Investment securities	191	0
Non-interest income:		
Service charges on deposit accounts	154	7
Other service fees	217	10
Mortgage banking activities	26	1
Net gain (loss) and valuation adjustments on investment securities	0	0
Other-than-temporary impairment losses on investment securities	(8.3)	-
Trading account (loss) profit	(0.8)	-
Net gain on sale of loans including valuation adjustments on loans held-for-sale	0	0
Adjustments (expense) to indemnity reserves on loans sold	(22.4)	-
FDIC loss-share (expense) income	(10.1)	-
Other operating income	64	3
Total	2,145	100

Selected Subsidiaries and Affiliates

Banco Popular de Puerto Rico
BP Sirenusa International LLC (US)
Popular Auto Inc.
Popular Mortgage Inc.
Popular Capital Trust I (US)
Popular Insurance Inc.
Popular International Bank Inc.
Banco Popular North America (US)
E-LOA

COMPETITORS

Bank of America	OFG Bancorp
Citigroup	RBC Financial Group
First BanCorp (Puerto Rico)	Santander BanCorp
	Scotiabank
JPMorgan Chase	

HISTORICAL FINANCIALS

Company Type: Public

Income Statement				FYE: December 31
	ASSETS ($ mil.)	NET INCOME ($ mil.)	INCOME AS % OF ASSETS	EMPLOYEES
12/18	47,605	618	1.3%	8,474
12/17	44,277	108	0.2%	7,784
12/16	38,662	217	0.6%	7,828
12/15	35,770	895	2.5%	7,810
12/14	33,097	(313)	—	7,752
Annual Growth	9.5%	—	—	2.3%

2018 Year-End Financials

Debt ratio: 1.00%
Return on equity: 12.00%
Cash ($ mil.): 17,903
Current ratio: —
Long-term debt ($ mil.): —

No. of shares (mil.): 100
Dividends
  Yield: 2.0%
  Payout: 17.0%
Market value ($ mil.): 4,719

	STOCK PRICE ($) FY Close	P/E High/Low		PER SHARE ($) Earnings	Dividends	Book Value
12/18	47.00	9	6	6.00	1.00	54.00
12/17	35.00	45	32	1.00	1.00	50.00
12/16	44.00	22	11	2.00	1.00	50.00
12/15	28.00	4	3	9.00	0.00	49.00
12/14	34.00	—	—	(3.00)	0.00	41.00
Annual Growth	8.5%	—	—	—	—	7.2%

Post Holdings Inc

Breakfast food company Post Holdings has a healthy appetite. The maker of Grape-Nuts Golden Puffs Honey Bunches of Oats Raisin Bran Shredded Wheat Pebbles and Alpha-Bits Post is the third-best-selling breakfast cereal brand in the US (behind Kellogg and General Mills). As well as cereal the company also makes egg products potato products and cheese pasta and other dairy-based products. More recently it has moved beyond the breakfast table by adding snacks active nutrition products and pasta through a series of major acquisitions. It also manufactures nut butters and cereals for private labels. The company has warehouses manufacturing facilities and distribution facilities located throughout the US and Canada.

Operations

Post operates five reportable segments: Post Consumer Brands Weetabix Refrigerated Food Active Nutrition and Private Brands.

The Refrigerated Food segment makes egg products sausage side dishes cheese and other refrigerated products. Egg brands include Papetti's Easy Eggs and Table Ready; and refrigerated side dish brands include Bob Evans Simply Potatoes and Pineland Farms. Cheese and other dairy brands are marketed mainly under the Crystal Farms brand. The segment accounts for more than 35% of sales.

The Consumer Brands segment comprises Post's North America cereal business which makes and sells branded and private-label ready-to-eat cereal products and hot cereal products. Brands include Honey Bunches of Oats Pebbles Oreo O?s Great Grains. Consumer Brands represent 30% of sales.

The Private Brands business pulls in 15% of total sales and makes peanut butter dried fruit and nuts pasta and granola and cereals.

Active Nutrition provides high-protein products including drinks bars and snacks for fitness enthusiasts. Brands include Premier Protein Dymatiza Power Bar Supreme Protein and Joint Juice. It accounts for 15% of sales.

The Weetabix segment is dedicated to sales of the Weetabix brand of wheat-based breakfast products as well as Alpen Weetos Ready Brek and Weetabix on the Go. It generates 5% of total sales from a customer base mainly within the UK and Ireland.

Geographic Reach

Post is headquartered in Missouri. More than 90% of the company's products are sold to customers in the US.

The company's manufacturing footprint spans nine consumer brands facilities eight egg factories and two sausage production plants in the US. Post has Private Brands factories in Georgia (peanut butter) North Dakota and Minnesota (pasta) Oregon (granola) Washington Alabama Ontario and British Columbia (nut butter and dried fruit). Nutrition products are made in Germany and Weetabix products are made at four factories in the UK.

Sales and Marketing

Post Holdings deploys a variety of consumer-targeted marketing campaigns across television digital and print advertisement coupon offers co-op advertising with certain retail customers and co-marketing arrangements with complementary consumer product companies. It also utilizes traditional billboard print digital and social media advertising as well as grass-roots advertising using sampling events and business drops.

Retail giant Wal-Mart Stores is the company's largest customer accounting for around 15% of total sales. Weetabix sells to a narrow customer base of the UK's largest retailers including Tesco Asda Morrison's and Sainsbury's which together account for more than 50% of sales. Nutrition brands are sold in mass merchandise grocery drugstore specialty and convenience stores. Private Brands products are sold in natural and specialty grocery stores such as Whole Foods which accounts for 15% of the segment's sales.

Financial Performance

Post Holding's sales have been growing strongly thanks to a robust acquisition program that has reshaped the company's brand portfolio.

In fiscal 2018 (ended September 30) the company's sales grew 20% to $6.3 billion due to the incremental contribution of Bob Evans and the full-year contribution of Weetabix Group acquired in the previous year. Like-for-like sales were steady across most product categories except Active Nutrition which saw a 26% increase in volume of protein shakes and other ready-to-drink products.

Post's net income has been growing strongly. After a big loss in 2014 it broke even in 2016 and posted a big profit in 2018. Net income of $467.3 million in 2018 represented a near-900% increase on 2017. The change was a result of a $222.9 million loss on debt extinguishment that negatively impacted the previous year coupled with a $204.0 million tax benefit in 2018 relating to the US Tax Cuts and Jobs Act.

Post's cash on hand fell $536.2 million during 2018 ending the year at $1.5 billion. The company's operations generated $719.3 million and its financing yielded $423.4 million offset by $1.7 billion used in its investing activities. Post's main cash uses in 2018 were acquisition share repurchases and debt payments.

After a game-changing fiscal 2015 that saw Post more than double its revenue the company maintained its upward trajectory in fiscal 2016 (ended September) by growing its top line 8% to $5.0 billion.

The growth came from the first full-year contributions from businesses acquired in 2015 particularly MOM Brands and from Willamette Egg Farms acquired part-way through fiscal 2016. Beyond acquisitions Post recorded organic growth in Premier Protein products and ready-to-eat cereal peanut butter and private brand granola. Egg potato cheese pasta products saw sales decline.

Post incurred a net loss of $3.3 million in fiscal 2016 an improvement on the losses of $115 million and $343 million recorded in fiscals 2015 and 2014. The narrowing loss was a result of profit contributions of the acquired businesses.

Cash from operating activities increased 11% or $50.8 million to $502.4 million. As before incremental contributions from the acquired businesses drive operating cash growth as did higher organic earnings from Post Consumer Brands Michael Food and Active Nutrition.

Strategy

Post Holdings has continued to move beyond breakfast cereal into higher-growth categories including snacks sports nutrition supplements and weight loss. The company's recent feeding frenzy of food companies included the $2.45 billion acquisition of Michael Foods its largest-ever which gave it the Simply Potatoes All Whites and Crystal Farms brands. The acquisitions demonstrate its willingness to adapt to shifts in consumer tastes such as capitalizing on the popularity of high-protein products and away-from-home snacks.

Post made a major move into the UK with the purchase of British breakfast food firm Weetabix in 2017. As well as its famous eponymous wheat bricks Weetabix owns Alpen Weetos and Oatibix.

In 2018 the company announced the creation of a new entity for its private brands 8th Avenue Food & Provisions which will be partially owned by private equity firm Thomas H. Lee Partners. The deal allows Post to monetize its investment in the private brands business while still benefiting from any future growth of 8th Avenue.

Post's extensive acquisition activity means it is highly leveraged with total debt of $8 billion.

Mergers and Acquisitions

Post has made a ton of acquisitions in recent years as it reshapes its portfolio to tap into new markets. In 2018 it acquired Bob Evans Farms a maker of various brands of potato pasta and vegetable side dishes pork sausage and convenience food. Post paid around $1.5 billion.

In 2017 it acquired UK cereal maker Weetabix in a $1.76 billion deal. The acquisition which includes the Weetabix Alpen Barbara's Puffins and other cereal brands expands Post's international market presence and bolsters Weetabix's brand presence in the US.

Company Background

Prior to the spinoff Post represented Ralcorp's branded cereal segment which was in decline. (Ralcorp acquired Post from Kraft Foods in 2008 for about $2.7 billion but its success with the brand was sporadic.) In the end Ralcorp decided to launch Post on its own to focus on its own burgeoning private-label food business. The acquisition in 2014 of Michael Foods transformed the business more than doubling its revenue. It followed Michael Foods up with two other major purchases MOM Brands in 2015 and Weetabix in 2017.

EXECUTIVES

Chairman, William P. (Bill) Stiritz, age 84

Evp; President And Ceo Private Brands, Richard R. Koulouris, age 63, $521,875 total compensation

Svp And Cfo, Jeff A. Zadoks, age 54, $462,500 total compensation

Evp; President And Ceo Michael Foods Group, James E. (Jim) Dwyer, $657,692 total compensation

President And Ceo, Robert V. Vitale, $975,000 total compensation

President And Ceo Post Consumer Brands, Christopher J. Neugent, $619,988 total compensation

Svp General Counsel And Chief Administrative Officer, Diedre Gray, $347,083 total compensation

National Sales Manager Specialty Sales, James Budroe

National Account Manager, Gene Streb

Regional Vice President Northwest, Lori Brown

Regional Vice President, Don Larson

Regional Vice President Sales, Bob Burnson

Senior Vice President And Chief Procurement Officer, Brian Palmer

Senior Vice President Quality And Food Safety, Dan Ludwig

Vice President Sales And Marketing, Joe Meehan

Division Vice President Of Information Technology Pcb, Richard E Colestock

Vice President Finance, Craig Shafer

Vice President Supply Chain, Carla E Carver

Vice President Marketing, David Bagozzi

Vice President Of Tax, Edward T Short

Vice President Sales North Central And West Usa Post Consumer Brands, Greg Hasper

Vice President Engineering Attune Food Group, Bill Rogers

Vice President And Treasurer, Matthew Mainer

Vice President, Joseph Boyd

Vice President Supply Chain, Carla Carver

Auditors: PricewaterhouseCoopers LLP

LOCATIONS

HQ: Post Holdings Inc
2503 S. Hanley Road, St. Louis, MO 63144
Phone: 314 644-7600
Web: www.postholdings.com

PRODUCTS/OPERATIONS

2018 Sales

	$ mil.	% of total
Refrigerated Foods	2,338	37
Post Consumer Brands	1,832	29
Private Brands	849	14
Active Nutrition	828	13
Weetabix	423	7
Eliminations	(12.2)	-
Total	**6,257**	**100**

Selected Products

Alpen
Alpha-Bits
Attune
Bran Flakes
Fruity Pebbles
Golden Crisp
golden Temple
Grape-Nuts
Great Grains
Honey Bunches of Oats
Honeycomb
Joint Juice
Peace Cereal
Premier Protein
Raisin Bran

Selects Blueberry Morning
Shredded Wheat
Sweet Home Farm
Toasties
Uncle Sam
Waffle Crisp
Weetabix
Weetos

COMPETITORS

Abbott Nutrition
American Italian Pasta
Clif Bar
ConAgra
Danone
General Mills
Gilster-Mary Lee
Kellogg
NBTY

Nature's Path
Nestlé
New World Pasta
Nissin Food Products
PepsiCo
Weetabix
Wessanen
granoVita

HISTORICAL FINANCIALS

Company Type: Public

Income Statement

FYE: September 30

	REVENUE ($ mil.)	NET INCOME ($ mil.)	NET PROFIT MARGIN	EMPLOYEES
09/19	5,681	125	2.2%	10,100
09/18	6,257	467	7.5%	11,550
09/17	5,226	48	0.9%	11,410
09/16	5,027	(3)	—	8,700
09/15	4,648	(115)	—	8,500
Annual Growth	**5.1%**	**—**	**—**	**4.4%**

2019 Year-End Financials

Debt ratio: 59.00%
Return on equity: 4.00%
Cash ($ mil.): 1,051
Current ratio: 3.00
Long-term debt ($ mil.): 7,066

No. of shares (mil.): 72
Dividends
  Yield: —
  Payout: —
Market value ($ mil.): 7,631

	STOCK PRICE ($) FY Close	P/E High/Low		Earnings	PER SHARE ($) Dividends	Book Value
09/19	106.00	66	49	2.00	0.00	41.00
09/18	98.00	15	10	6.00	0.00	46.00
09/17	88.00	173	139	1.00	0.00	42.00
09/16	77.00	—	—	(0.00)	0.00	46.00
09/15	59.00	—	—	(2.00)	0.00	49.00
Annual Growth	**15.7%**	**—**	**—**	**—**	**—**	**(4.8%)**

PPG Industries Inc

Thanks to its extensive range of paints and coatings you won't catch PPG Industries painting itself into a corner. The company?s Performance and Industrial coatings offerings include paints stains adhesives and sealants for automotive aerospace marine architectural and industrial applications. Well-known paint brands include Glidden Olympic and PPG Pittsburg Paints. Other products include packaging coatings used for the protection and decoration of metal cans closures and plastic tubes. PPG's specialty coatings are used in lighting and lens materials and label substrates. In recent years the company has shed its fiber glass and flat glass businesses to focus on its core coatings operations.

HISTORY

After the failure of his first two plate-glass manufacturing plants John Ford persuaded former rail-

road superintendent John Pitcairn to invest $200000 in a third factory in 1883 in Creighton Pennsylvania. The enterprise Pittsburgh Plate Glass (PPG) became the first commercially successful US plate-glass factory.

Ford left in 1896 after Pitcairn established a company distribution system replacing glass jobbers. Ford went on to found a predecessor of competitor Libbey-Owens-Ford (now owned by glassmaker Pilkington).

Pitcairn built a soda ash plant in 1899 bought a Milwaukee paint company the following year and began producing window glass in 1908. Pitcairn died in 1916 leaving his stock to his sons.

Strong automobile and construction markets in the early 20th century increased demand for the company's products. In 1924 PPG revolutionized glass production with the introduction of a straight-line conveyor manufacturing method. In the 1930s and 1940s PPG successfully promoted structural glass for use in the commercial construction industry.

PPG was listed on the NYSE in 1945. In 1952 it started making fiberglass and in 1968 the company adopted its present name.

Vincent Sarni (CEO 1984-93) recognized that 85% of the company's sales were to the maturing construction and automobile industries. Sarni decided to move the company into growing industries such as electronics.

In 1986 PPG spent $154 million on acquisitions including the medical electronics units of Litton Industries and Honeywell. It acquired the medical technology business of Allegheny International in 1987 and bought Casco Nobel a coatings distributor and the Olympic and Lucite paint lines from Clorox in 1989.

The company which owned one-third of Dutch fiberglass producer Silenka BV acquired the rest in 1991. In 1992 PPG acquired a silica plant in the Netherlands its first in Europe. Two years later it acquired the European automotive coatings business of Netherlands-based Akzo Nobel.

In the 1990s PPG backed away from Sarni's earlier strategies for greater diversification and unloaded a number of high-tech businesses. The firm refocused on its core coatings glass and chemicals operations. PPG acquired Matthews Paints a leading maker of paints for outdoor signs and the refinish coating business of Lilly Industries in 1995.

The company bolstered its chemical operations in 1997 with the addition of France's Sipsy Chime Fine. That same year President and COO Raymond LeBoeuf took over as CEO. In 1998 PPG sold its European flat and automotive glass business to Belgium-based Glaverbel. Acquisitions that year included Australia-based Orica's technical coatings unit and the US paint operations (Porter Paints) of Akzo Nobel.

In 1999 PPG expanded its European coatings business with the purchase of Belgium-based Sigma Coatings' commercial transport coatings unit and Akzo Nobel's aircraft coatings and sealants company PRC-DeSoto International. That year PPG also bought Imperial Chemical Industries' Germany-based coatings business for large commercial vehicles and its US-based auto refinish and industrial coatings businesses. PPG's acquisition spree continued in 2000 with architectural coating maker Monarch Paint.

Early in the new decade PPG suffered from flat or declining earnings from existing operations. Amid falling sales and lower prices for chemicals and glass PPG began to cut jobs and closed some facilities. Still the company recorded its first loss in more than 10 years in 2002 and its second straight year of declining sales.

Like many manufacturers in its industry PPG has been exposed to potentially costly asbestos litigation mainly because of its 50% stake in the bankrupt Pittsburgh Corning a joint venture with Corning that made insulation with asbestos. In 2002 PPG and its insurers agreed to pay roughly $2.7 billion to settle its asbestos claims.

LeBoeuf retired in 2005. He was replaced by president and COO Charles Bunch who had joined the company in 1979 and worked up through the ranks of first the finance department and then the coatings operations.

In 2008 PPG acquired SigmaKalon for $3 billion. SigmaKalon was among the top 10 paint manufacturers in the world and did business almost entirely outside the US. The company now operates as PPG's Architectural Coatings segment. That same year PPG sold its auto glass business to private equity group Kohlberg & Company which set the unit up as a stand-alone company called Pittsburgh Glass Works. PPG received $330 million plus a 40% interest in the company.

In 2011 PPG acquired Equa-Chlor a producer of chlorine caustic soda and muriatic acid for $27 million. Equa-Chlor produces about 220 tons of chlorine per day. In addition to its products PPG also bought Equa-Chlor's distribution system which includes a railcar fleet it integrated into its own. The deal for the Washington state-based company bolsters PPG's chlor-alkali business in the Northwest US and expands its overall supply chain.

As part of its push to expand in emerging markets in 2011 PPG formed a joint venture with an India-based company Harsha Exito Engineering Private to produce fiber glass reinforcement products.

It made two foreign acquisitions to expand its international operations in 2011. First it bought the business assets of Ducol Coatings South Africa Ltd. which had served as an importer and distributor of PPG's automotive refinish products in South Africa since 2003. PPG also expanded its joint venture with India-based Asian Paints (India's largest coatings company) and created a second 50-50 JV in 2012. The deals boosts PPG's position in the Chinese and Asian packaging coatings industry part of its global strategy to expand into emerging regions.

During 2012 the company made four acquisitions related to its coatings business for a total of $288 million including US-based Spraylat Corp. Denmark based Dyrup A/S and the coatings business of Ecuador-based Colpisa Colombiana de Pinturas.

Expanding PPG's architectural coatings business in the US Canada and the Caribbean in 2013 it bought Azko Nobel's North American Decorative Paints business for $1.05 billion.

The company divested flat glass and fiber glass operations in transactions in 2016 and 2017. The sale of flat glass and European fiber glass businesses and the company?s ownership in two Asian fiber glass joint ventures brought in more than $1 billion of cash.

EXECUTIVES

Chairman And Ceo, Michael H. McGarry, age 61, $1,100,000 total compensation

Evp, Viktoras R. Sekmakas, age 58, $646,667 total compensation

Svp Architectural Coatings; President Ppg Emea, Jean-Marie Greindl, age 56

Vp Science And Technology And Cto, David S. Bem

President Ppg Asia Pacific And Vp Protective And Marine Coatings Asia Pacific, Michael Horton

Svp Industrial Coatings, Timothy M. Knavish, age 53, $438,333 total compensation

Vp Coatings Services; President Metokote, Jeffrey J. Oravitz

Chief Commercial Officer Ppg Comex, Henrik Bergstr ¶m, age 48

Svp And Cfo, Vincent J. Morales, age 54

Vp Information Technology, Christopher R. Caruso

Svp Protective And Marine Coatings, Ramaparasad (Ram) Vadlamannati, age 56

Vice President Flat Glass, Richard Beuke

Vice President Global Supply Management, Radhika Batra

Vice President And Treasurer, John Jankowski

Vice President Fiber Glass, Kevin McDonald

Senior Vice President General Counsel Secretary, Anne Foulkes

Vice President Automotive Refinish Europe Middle East And Asia, Jerome Zamblera

National Account Manager, William Dunster

Global Vice President Aerospace, Daniel Korte

Senior Vice President Automotive Coatings, Rebecca Liebert

Vice President And Chief Digital Officer, Devashish Saxena

Board Member, Martin Richenhagen

Board Member, Gary Heminger

Auditors: PricewaterhouseCoopers LLP

LOCATIONS

HQ: PPG Industries Inc
One PPG Place, Pittsburgh, PA 15272
Phone: 412 434-3131
Web: www.ppg.com

2016 Sales

	$ mil.	% of total
United States and Canada	6,595	45
Europe Middle East and Africa	4,304	29
Asia Pacific	2,431	16
Latin America	1,421	10
Total	**14,751**	**100**

PRODUCTS/OPERATIONS

2016 Sales

	$ mil.	% of total
Performance Coatings	8,580	58
Industrial Coatings	5,690	39
Glass	481	3
Total	**14,751**	**100**

Selected Products

Performance Coatings
  Aerospace coatings
  Architectural coatings (Lucite paints Olympic stains)
  Refinish
Industrial Coatings
  Automotive coatings chemicals adhesives and sealants
  Industrial coatings
  Packaging coatings (food and beverage containers)
Commodity Chemicals
  Calcium hypochlorite
  Caustic soda
  Chlorine
  Chlorine derivatives
  Phosgene derivatives
Optical and Specialty Materials
  Optical products (Transitions variable-tint lenses)
  Silica products
Glass
  Aircraft transparencies
  Coated glass
  Continuous-strand fiberglass
  Flat glass

COMPETITORS

3M	KANSAI PAINT CO. LTD.
Akzo Nobel	Kelly-Moore
Axalta Coating Systems	Nippon Paint
BASF Coatings AG	Nippon Sheet Glass
BEHR	Pilkington Group
Benjamin Moore	RPM International
Dow Chemical	Sherwin-Williams
Ferro	

HISTORICAL FINANCIALS

Company Type: Public

Income Statement

FYE: December 31

	REVENUE ($ mil.)	NET INCOME ($ mil.)	NET PROFIT MARGIN	EMPLOYEES
12/18	15,374	1,341	8.7%	27,800
12/17	14,750	1,591	10.8%	47,200
12/16	14,751	877	5.9%	47,000
12/15	15,330	1,406	9.2%	46,600
12/14	15,360	2,102	13.7%	44,400
Annual Growth	0.0%	(10.6%)	—	(11.0%)

2018 Year-End Financials

Debt ratio: 31.00%
Return on equity: 26.00%
Cash ($ mil.): 902
Current ratio: 1.00
Long-term debt ($ mil.): 4,365

No. of shares (mil.): 236
Dividends
  Yield: 2.0%
  Payout: 34.0%
Market value ($ mil.): 24,112

	STOCK PRICE ($) FY Close	P/E High/Low	PER SHARE ($) Earnings	Dividends	Book Value
12/18	102.00	22 17	5.00	2.00	20.00
12/17	117.00	19 15	6.00	2.00	22.00
12/16	95.00	35 27	3.00	2.00	19.00
12/15	99.00	46 16	5.00	1.00	19.00
12/14	231.00	31 23	8.00	1.00	19.00
Annual Growth	(18.5%)	— —	(7.6%)	9.2%	0.8%

PPL Corp

PPL Corporation is one of the largest utility companies in the world delivering electricity to more than 10 million customers through its regulated utility subsidiaries in Kentucky Pennsylvania and Virginia as well as in the UK. It also delivers natural gas to customers in Kentucky Operating as Western Power Distribution in the UK it holds four of the UK's 14 power distribution licenses. The company has more than 8000 MW of electric generating capacity about 220000 miles of electric lines and gas transmission mains and storage fields. PPL was incorporated in 1994.

Operations

PPL has three segments: Kentucky UK and Pennsylvania. While the UK and Pennsylvania each bring in about 30% of total revenue Kentucky is the highest earner bringing in about 40%.

The Kentucky segment includes Louisville Gas and Electric which provides electric services to more than 400000 customers in Kentucky and natural gas service to almost 330000 customers. It also comprises of Kentucky Utility which serves around 560000 customers in Kentucky Virginia and Tennessee.

The UK segment which includes primarily Western Power Distribution's (WPD) regulated electricity distribution operation serves almost 8 million end users in south Wales and southwest and central England. It holds the four of the UK's 14 regulated distribution operator network (DNO) licenses.

The Pennsylvania segment (PPL Electric) delivers electricity to 1.4 million customers in eastern and central Pennsylvania.

Geographic Reach

PPL delivers electricity to customers in Kentucky Pennsylvania Virginia and the UK and natural gas to customers in Kentucky.

The US accounts for 70% of company's revenue; the rest comes from the UK.

Sales and Marketing

PPL Corporation serves some 10 million residential industrial and commercial customers in Kentucky Pennsylvania Tennessee Virginia and the UK.

Financial Performance

Operating in a highly regulated sector PPL's revenue has barely changed in the last five years while net income has alternated between good and bad years due to fluctuations in foreign currency exchange contracts.

In fiscal 2018 the company's sales grew 5% to $7.8 billion a better-than-average result. Growth mostly arose from its UK business which grew its sales 8% while PPL's US operation grew 2%.

Net income jumped 62% to $1.8 billion due to lower income taxes and a positive swing in foreign currency exchange contracts.

PPL's coffers grew $132 million during 2018 ending the year at $643 million. It generated $2.8 billion from its operations and $690 million from its financing activities. Investing activities used $3.4 billion. PPL's main cash uses in 2018 were capital expenditures dividends and long-term debt repayments.

Strategy

Faced with falling revenue and technological disruptions that are rapidly changing the energy grid PPL Corporation is embarking on a long-term core strategy of sustainable production.

Strong cash flows put PPL in a strong investment position. The company plans to invest some $15 billion over the next five years primarily in two ways?technological upgrades especially grid improvements and clean energy production. It is aiming to cut CO2 emissions 70% from 2010 levels by 2050.

HISTORY

PPL's wires reach back to Lehigh Coal & Navigation which was formed in 1822 to mine Pennsylvania coal and build a canal to deliver it to Philadelphia. Heavy industry and steel mills flourished in the Lehigh Valley and Thomas Edison formed small electric companies to serve the area in the early 1880s. Rivals soon followed and by 1900 there were 64 companies in what would become PPL's territory.

EXECUTIVES

President And Coo Lg&e And Ku Energy, Paul W. Thompson

Chairman And Ceo Lg&e And Ku Energy, Victor A. Staffieri, age 63, $811,220 total compensation

Chief Executive Western Power Distribution, Robert A. Symons, age 65, $741,127 total compensation

Chairman President And Ceo, William H. Spence, age 61, $1,154,712 total compensation

President Ppl Electric Utilities, Gregory N. Dudkin, age 61, $524,143 total compensation

Svp And Cfo, Vincent (Vince) Sorgi, age 47, $524,134 total compensation

Vice President Administration And Inside Sales And Marketing Coordinator, Barb Sipe

Vp Business Development, Joseph Clifford

Vp Customer Services, Christopher Cardenas

Vice President, John Barbera

Vice President And Chief Human Resources Officer, Thomas Lynch

Vice President, Bill Riebling

Vice President Finance And Regulatory Affairs And Controller, Marlene Beers

Board Member, Steven G Elliott

Board Member, Craig Rogerson

Board Member, Venkata Madabhushi

Board Member, Rodney Adkins
Confidential Secretary, Linda Brady
Assistant Treasurer, Tadd J Henninger
Board Member, Phoebe Wood
Auditors: DELOITTE & TOUCHE LLP

LOCATIONS

HQ: PPL Corp
  Two North Ninth Street, Allentown, PA 18101-1179
Phone: 610 774-5151
Web: www.pplweb.com

2015 Sales

	$ mil.	% of total
US	5,259	68
UK	2,410	32
Total	7,669	100

PRODUCTS/OPERATIONS

2018 Sales

	$ mil.	% of total
Kentucky Regulated	3,214	42
Pennsylvania Regulated	2,277	29
UK Regulated	2,268	29
Corporate and other	26	-
Total	7,785	100

Selected Subsidiaries

PPL Development Corporation (acquisition and divestiture activities)
PPL Electric Utilities Corporation (electricity distribution)
PPL Energy Supply (nonregulated operations)
  PPL EnergyPlus LLC (wholesale and retail energy marketing)
  PPL Generation LLC (electricity generation)
  PPL Montana LLC (electricity generation)
  PPL Global LLC (international utility operations)
  Western Power Distribution Holdings Limited (formerly WPD Holdings UK electricity distribution)
PPL Services Corporation (shared services for PPL Corp. and other subsidiaries)

COMPETITORS

ABB	Green Mountain Energy
AEP	HC Energ a
Avangrid	Maine & Maritimes
Canadian Utilities	Midwest Generation
Centrica	Ontario Power
Con Edison	Generation
Constellation Energy	Orange & Rockland
Group	Utilities
Covanta	Pepco Holdings
Delmarva Power	Public Service
Dominion Energy	Enterprise Group
Duke Energy	Scottish and Southern
Duquesne Light	Energy
Holdings	South Jersey
EnergySolve	Industries
Exelon	Southern Company
FirstEnergy	TransAlta

HISTORICAL FINANCIALS

Company Type: Public

Income Statement — FYE: December 31

	REVENUE ($ mil.)	NET INCOME ($ mil.)	NET PROFIT MARGIN	EMPLOYEES
12/18	7,785	1,827	23.5%	12,444
12/17	7,447	1,128	15.1%	12,512
12/16	7,517	1,902	25.3%	12,689
12/15	7,669	682	8.9%	12,799
12/14	11,499	1,737	15.1%	17,391
Annual Growth	(9.3%)	1.3%	—	(8.0%)

2018 Year-End Financials

Debt ratio: 51.00%
Return on equity: 16.00%
Cash ($ mil.): 621
Current ratio: 1.00
Long-term debt ($ mil.): 20,069

No. of shares (mil.): 720
Dividends
  Yield: 6.0%
  Payout: 64.0%
Market value ($ mil.): 20,407

	STOCK PRICE ($) FY Close	P/E High/Low		PER SHARE ($) Earnings	Dividends	Book Value
12/18	28.00	12	10	3.00	2.00	16.00
12/17	31.00	24	19	2.00	2.00	16.00
12/16	34.00	14	11	3.00	2.00	15.00
12/15	34.00	36	29	1.00	2.00	15.00
12/14	36.00	14	11	3.00	1.00	20.00
Annual Growth	(6.0%)	—	—	(0.3%)	2.4%	(5.7%)

PRECISION CASTPARTS CORP.

Precision Castparts Corp. (PCC) is a maker of investment castings and forged and airframe products that have applications in industries from aerospace and energy to machinery and medical implants. Products include metal components for aircraft engines industrial gas turbines (IGT) medical implants unmanned aerial vehicles (UAVs) and other industrial applications. The company also makes metal forgings including seamless pipe used in power plants downhole casings and tubing pipe for oil and gas production and aerospace and defense applications. PCC is also a leading manufacturer of fasteners and fastening systems used in the aerospace construction automotive machinery and energy industries. The aerospace sector accounts for most of PCC's sales. The company is a subsidiary of Berkshire Hathaway.

HISTORY

The history of Precision Castparts Corp. (PCC) is not as precise as its castings. The Oregon Saw Company was founded in 1949 and sold in 1953; its buyer wanted neither the future PCC nor a power tools unit so the two became Omark Industries. In 1956 a buyer purchased the power tool business but wasn't interested in castings; that operation was spun off as Precision Castparts Corp.

In the early 1950s a group of Oregon Saw's casting employees developed a process for producing parts as large as 60 inches by use of investment casting making products that rivaled the strength of forged and machined parts at a fraction of the cost. After a two-year search they landed their first aerospace customer — Air Research Corp. — with many to follow. The higher operating temperatures generated by aircraft engines led the company to buy a vacuum furnace in 1959 to fabricate parts that could tolerate greater heat; two more vacuum furnaces were added and sales vaulted toward $10 million by 1967. PCC went public in 1968 and continued to grow. In 1976 the company acquired Centaur Cast Alloys (small investment castings UK) to make parts for the European aerospace industry. By that time General Electric (GE) and Pratt & Whitney accounted for most of PCC's business. Edward Cooley who had masterminded the company's growth since incorporation forged ahead with plans to double production capacity.

In 1980 the airline industry crashed but PCC's sales held at about $90 million. Structural airplane products soon picked up and in 1984 the company bought two titanium foundries in France. To diversify it added TRW's cast airfoils (used in aircraft engines and industrial gas turbines) division in 1986. That acquisition renamed PCC Airfoils increased PCC's annual sales by about 80%; sales reached $443 million by 1989.

The company broadened its offerings again in 1991 when it acquired Advanced Forming Technology which made small complex metal-injection molded parts used in everything from adding machines to military ordnance. The early 1990s recession hit the airline industry and sales dropped. Cooley retired as chairman in 1994 and GE veteran William McCormick replaced him. The next year PCC acquired Quamco Inc. (industrial tools and machines). In 1996 PCC flowed into the fluid management market with the acquisition of NEWFLO for about $300 million.

In 1997 PCC spent $437 million to acquire seven more companies that helped boost sales 75% from 1996 levels. The next year it purchased four metalworking companies that served industries other than aerospace. Having reduced dependence on sales to the aerospace industry to just over 50% PCC began consolidating operations and closing plants to reduce costs.

The company continued to diversify through acquisitions in 1999 but it also expanded its aerospace operations with the purchase of Wyman-Gordon a leading maker of advanced metal forgings for the aerospace market. PCC's 2000 acquisitions included the aerospace division of United Engineering Forgings and Germany-based Convey Engineering (heavy-duty valves). The next year the company bought the assets of Netherlands-based Wouter Witzel and the US's Drop Dies and Forgings Company (renamed Wyman-Gordon Cleveland). In 2002 PCC bought the rest of Western Australian Specialty Alloys (casting and forging alloys) for $27.6 million in cash and PCC shares.

In 2003 Precision Castparts' PCC Structurals unit reached a $400 million agreement with Rolls-Royce to supply large titanium and steel castings. That year the company acquired SPS Technologies a producer of fasteners and other metal components for the aerospace automotive and industrial markets. In 2004 subsidiary SPS Aerospace Fasteners signed a four-year deal with Airbus worth about $72 million to supply collars nuts studs and titanium pins to Airbus plants across Europe.

PCC acquired Air Industries Corporation in early 2005. In 2006 PCC bought Special Metals Corporation (SMC) a maker of nickel alloys and super alloys for $295 million in cash and the assumption of $245 million in SMC debt. PCC intended to use SMC's product as raw materials for its own aircraft engine components. SMC also served the automotive chemical and power generation industries.

Later in 2006 PCC bought Shur-Lok Corporation a manufacturer of aerospace fasteners for about $110 million. The acquisition combined with the 2005 purchase of Air Industries Corporation helped to further PCC's desire to grow its airframe fasteners business.

Early in 2007 PCC completed the purchase of GSC a leading maker of aluminum and steel structural investment casting for the aerospace energy and medical markets. It also acquired Cherry Aerospace which expanded its fastener products portfolio.

In 2009 the company acquired Carlton Forge Works which makes aircraft engines for Boeing and Airbus; California-based Arcturus Manufacturing (hammer forging operations) was included in the transaction. PCC also picked up Airdrome Holdings (fluid fittings) Fatigue Technology (cold expansion technology) and Hackney Ladish (forged pipe fittings) in 2009.

In late summer 2011 PPC purchased Primus International a maker of complex metal industrial parts and assemblies. Its products (machined aluminum and titanium components used in aircraft wings fuselages and engine-related assemblies) cater to Boeing Airbus and other aerospace OEMs. The $900 million deal furthered the company's commitment to the global aerospace industry. In a similar vein the company obtained Unison Engine Components (operating as Tru-Form Rings) from GE Aviation in mid-2011. Tru-Form made flash-welded and cold-rolled rings with jet engine as well as gas turbine applications.

PCC also acquired RathGibson which makes tubing for the oil and gas chemical/petrochemical power-generation and other markets in 2012.

To expand both its Fasteners and Forged Products segments PCC acquired the aerostructures and industrial products businesses of Héroux-Devtek for about CAD$300 million (about $295.5 million) in 2012. Among other benefits the acquisition expanded the company's product line for such OEMs as Lockheed Bombardier and Gulfstream. PCC also inked a deal to purchase the Synchronous Aerospace Group business of private investment firm Littlejohn & Co. in late 2012.

EXECUTIVES

Evp And Cfo, Shawn R. Hagel, $687,500 total compensation
Chairman And Ceo, Mark Donegan, $1,585,000 total compensation
Svp And President Airframe Products, Alan J. (Al) Power
Evp And President Wyman-gordon, Andrew V. Masterman, $592,500 total compensation
Vp And Cio, Byron J. Gaddis
Evp, Steven G. (Steve) Hackett, $708,750 total compensation
Svp And General Counsel, Ruth A. Beyer, $569,000 total compensation
President Aerostructures Products, Joseph I. Snowden, $356,347 total compensation
Svp And President Pcc Airfoils, John P. O'Neill
Svp And President Timet And Special Metals, James R. Pieron
Vice President, Mark Ellis
Vice President, Geoffrey Hawkes
Senior Vice President, Ross Lienhart
Secretary, Russell Pattee
Auditors: DELOITTE & TOUCHE LLP PORTLAN

LOCATIONS

HQ: PRECISION CASTPARTS CORP.
4650 SW MCDAM AVE STE 300, PORTLAND, OR 97239
Phone: 503 946-4800
Web: WWW.PRECAST.COM

PRODUCTS/OPERATIONS

Selected Products and Services

Fasteners
Advanced forming technology
E/One (for the disposal of residential sanitary waste)
J&L fiber services (for pulp and paper industry)
PCC Precision Tool Group
SPS aerospace fasteners (for commercial/military aircraft)
SPS engineered fasteners (high strength for automotive and construction applications)
Forged products
Special Metals Corporation
Wyman-Gordon Forgings
Investment Cast Products
PCC Airfoils (high-temperature blades and vanes)
PCC Structurals (structural investment castings)
Specialty materials and alloys (alloys waxes and metal processing for investment casting)

COMPETITORS

ATI Ladish
Allegheny Technologies
Arconic
Carpenter Technology
Chicago Rivet
Crane Co.
Curtiss-Wright
ESCO
Farwest Steel
  Corporation
Federal Screw Works
Georg Fischer
Haynes International

Hitachi Metals
Kennametal
LISI
Mettis Aerospace
SOURIAU PA&E
Swagelok
Teleflex
ThyssenKrupp
United Technologies
Universal Stainless
V & M Tubes (USA)
Volvo Aero

HISTORICAL FINANCIALS

Company Type: Private

Income Statement				FYE: January 3
	REVENUE ($ mil.)	NET INCOME ($ mil.)	NET PROFIT MARGIN	EMPLOYEES
01/16*	7,002	817	11.7%	30,100
03/15	10,005	1,533	15.3%	—
03/14	9,616	1,784	18.6%	—
03/13	8,378	1,429	17.1%	—
Annual Growth	(5.8%)	(17.0%)	—	—

*Fiscal year change

Preferred Bank (Los Angeles, CA)

Preferred Bank wants to be the bank of choice of Chinese-Americans in Southern California. Employing a multilingual staff the bank provides international banking services to companies doing business in the Asia/Pacific region. It targets middle-market businesses typically manufacturing service distribution and real estate firms as well as entrepreneurs professionals and high-net-worth individuals through about a dozen branches in Los Angeles Orange and San Francisco Counties. Preferred Bank offers standard deposit products such as checking accounts savings money market and NOW accounts. Specialized services include private banking and international trade finance.

Geographic Reach

Preferred Bank markets its services in half a dozen Southern Californian counties: Los Angeles Orange Riverside San Bernardino San Francisco and Ventura.

Financial Performance

In 2013 Preferred Bank reported about $72 million in revenue up just more than 10% from the prior year. The increase was solely from interest income as non-interest income (a very small part of overall revenue anyway) fell more than 40%. The company saw growth in its loan portfolio that year as well as overall deposit growth. Net income fell 20% to $19 million; the decline was primarily related to a boost in net income for 2012 because of a $20 million income tax benefit (compared to income tax expense of $12 million in 2013).

Strategy

Historically the company was focused on the Chinese-American market and although it continues to cater to that clientele most of its current customer base is from the diversified mainstream market.

EXECUTIVES

Evp And Cfo, Edward J. Czajka
President And Coo, Wellington Chen, age 59
Chairman And Ceo, Li Yu, age 78
Vice President Commercial Real Esate Loan Officer, Sally Chang
Vice President, William Ko
Senior Vice President, Jim Belanic
Assistant Vice President Credit Administration, Margaret King
Senior Vice President, John C Stipanov
Vice President, Debbie White
First Vice President, Madelyn Hayashi
Vice President, Barbara Gordon
Vice President Real Estate Industries Group, Greg Hahn
Senior Vice President And Corporate Banking Manager, Christina Ching
Vice President, Craig Miller
Avp Senior Bsa Analyst, Joshua Barron
Vp Assistant Bsa Officer, Kristie Yang
Executive Vice President Head Of Northern California, Alice Huang
Senior Vice President, Pamela Lau
Vice President, Sofia Huang
Vice President Financial Reporting, Brandon George
First Vice President, Johnny Hsu
Vice President Lending, Luey Couto
Senior Vice President, Ann Cheung
Vice President, Wayne Chow
Vice President Human Resources Manager, Karen Cangey
Senior Vice President Internal Audit, Jenny Own
Senior Vice President And Controller, Debbie Kong
Vp Internal Audit Manager, Carlo Garcia
Vice President Commercial Banking, Ricken Li
Vice President Assistant Compliance Officer, Florence Hsu
Vice President, Silvia Espinoza
First Vice President, Philip Wong
Vice President Product Manager, John Wong
Vice President And Portfolio Manager, Welmer Jurado
Senior Vice President, Bill Oberholzer
Executive Vice President Chief Credit Officer, Jonathan Sigal
Assistant Vice President Operations Officer, Patty Artavia
Avp, Xiao Wells
First Vice President, Jean Ou
Vice President Relationship Manager, Eddie Ong
Vice President Financial Intelligence Unit Manager, Krishan Sirimane
Vice President Portfolio Manager, Judy Chang
Senior Vice President Head Of International Banking And Commercial Industrial Lending, Samuel Leung
Vice President, Clara Moore
Vice President, Winny Lo
Senior Vice President, Ann J Cheung
Board Member, Clark Hsu
Fvp Treasurer, Eric Chen
Auditors: Crowe LLP

LOCATIONS

HQ: Preferred Bank (Los Angeles, CA)
601 S. Figueroa Street, 48th Floor, Los Angeles, CA 90017
Phone: 213 891-1188
Web: www.preferredbank.com

PRODUCTS/OPERATIONS

2015 Sales

	mil$ mil.	% of total
Interest income		
Loans and leases	88	90
Investment securities available for sale	6	6
Federal funds sold	0	-
Non-interest income		
Fees and service charges on deposit accounts	1	1
Trade finance income	2	2
BOLI income	0	-
Other income	1	1
Total	**99**	**100**

COMPETITORS

Bank of America	City National
Bank of the West	East West Bancorp
Broadway Financial	Far East National Bank
Cathay General Bancorp	Hanmi Financial
Citigroup	MUFG Americas Holdings

HISTORICAL FINANCIALS

Company Type: Public

Income Statement

FYE: December 31

	ASSETS ($ mil.)	NET INCOME ($ mil.)	INCOME AS % OF ASSETS	EMPLOYEES
12/18	4,216	71	1.7%	263
12/17	3,770	43	1.2%	238
12/16	3,222	36	1.1%	218
12/15	2,599	30	1.1%	205
12/14	2,054	25	1.2%	163
Annual Growth	**19.7%**	**30.3%**	**—**	**12.7%**

2018 Year-End Financials

Debt ratio: 2.00%
Return on equity: 18.00%
Cash ($ mil.): 527
Current ratio: —
Long-term debt ($ mil.): —

No. of shares (mil.): 15
Dividends
  Yield: 2.0%
  Payout: 24.0%
Market value ($ mil.): 664

	STOCK PRICE ($) FY Close	P/E High/Low	Earnings	Dividends	Book Value
12/18	43.00	15 9	5.00	1.00	27.00
12/17	59.00	22 16	3.00	1.00	23.00
12/16	52.00	20 10	3.00	1.00	21.00
12/15	33.00	17 12	2.00	0.00	19.00
12/14	28.00	15 11	2.00	0.00	17.00
Annual Growth	**11.7%**		**27.1%**	**75.1%**	**11.8%**

Primerica Inc

EXECUTIVES

Chb, Rick Williams
Co Chb*, John Addison
Pres*, David T Chadwick
Dir*, Michael K Wells
Coo*, Douglas G Elliott
SEC*, Stacey K Geer
Cfo*, Allison Rand
Director, Glenn Williams
Auditors: KPMG LLP

LOCATIONS

HQ: Primerica Inc
1 Primerica Parkway, Duluth, GA 30099
Phone: 770 381-1000
Web: www.primerica.com

HISTORICAL FINANCIALS

Company Type: Public

Income Statement

FYE: December 31

	ASSETS ($ mil.)	NET INCOME ($ mil.)	INCOME AS % OF ASSETS	EMPLOYEES
12/18	12,595	324	2.6%	2,699
12/17	12,461	350	2.8%	2,718
12/16	11,439	219	1.9%	2,662
12/15	10,612	190	1.8%	2,626
12/14	10,738	181	1.7%	2,579
Annual Growth	**4.1%**	**15.6%**	**—**	**1.1%**

2018 Year-End Financials

Debt ratio: 11.00%
Return on equity: 23.00%
Cash ($ mil.): 262
Current ratio: —
Long-term debt ($ mil.): —

No. of shares (mil.): 43
Dividends
  Yield: 1.0%
  Payout: 14.0%
Market value ($ mil.): 4,172

	STOCK PRICE ($) FY Close	P/E High/Low	Earnings	Dividends	Book Value
12/18	98.00	17 12	7.00	1.00	34.00
12/17	102.00	14 9	8.00	1.00	32.00
12/16	69.00	16 9	5.00	1.00	27.00
12/15	47.00	15 11	4.00	1.00	24.00
12/14	54.00	17 12	3.00	0.00	24.00
Annual Growth	**15.8%**		**22.2%**	**20.1%**	**9.4%**

Principal Financial Group Inc

Founded in 1879 Principal Financial Group (Principal) is a top administrator of employer-sponsored retirement plans offering pension products and services as well as mutual funds annuities asset management trust services and investment advice. Its insurance segment provides group and individual life and disability insurance and group dental and vision coverage. PFG serves 25 million customers and has more than $625 billion in assets under management. Principal operates offices in nearly 25 countries and serves clients in more than 85 countries.

Operations

Principal offers its financial products and services through four business segments: Retirement and Income Solutions US Insurance Solutions Principal International and Principal Global Investors.

The Retirement and Investor Services segment generates about 50% of annual revenue. It provides retirement and other financial products and services such as 401(k) plans Individual Retirement Accounts (IRAs) personal trusts and annuities to individuals and businesses.

The U.S. Insurance Solutions segment (around 30% of revenue) provides individual life insurance and specialty benefits insurance which includes group dental and vision individual and group disability and group life insurance along with non-medical fee-for-service claims administration services.

The Principal International segment (10% of revenue) serves retirement and insurance needs to clients in countries with large middle classes and growing long-term savings. The company typically enters a new market through acquisitions joint ventures and sometimes its own start-up operations.

The Principal Global Investors segment (less than 10% of revenue) offers asset management services to the company's internal asset accumulation business and insurance operations along with third-party clients.

Geographic Reach

Principal Financial Group operates out of offices in nearly 25 countries and serves clients in more than 85 countries. It is headquartered in Des Moines IA.

Its Principal International segment has operations in the Americas (Brazil Chile Mexico) Asia (China Hong Kong India) and Southeast Asia (Singapore Thailand Malaysia Indonesia). The Principal Global Investors segment has offices in a dozen countries across Asia and Europe.

Sales and Marketing

Principal distributes its products and services through institutional and retail sales representatives relationship management and client service professionals who work with consultants and directly with investors to acquire and retain institutional clients retail clients and other investors. The company maintains relationships with independent broker-dealers to distribute its products and services maintaining relationships with over 64000 independent brokers consultants and agents.

The Principal International segment focuses on regions with a growing middle class and demographics that are aligned with Principal's target customer criteria as well as where it is common for workers to contribute to defined contribution retirement plans (similar to 401(k) and IRA plans).

Financial Performance

Over the past five years Principal's financial results continued a long-term upward trend. Its annual revenue has risen more than 35% since 2014 mostly thanks to growing premium income from annuity and life insurance sales.

In 2018 revenue inched up 1% to $14.2 billion its growth slowing compared to the prior two years. Fees were the primary driver of growth rising more than $380 million. Premiums and Net investment income also saw healthy year-over-year increases.

Net income dropped 33% to $1.5 billion in 2018 on the back of higher benefits claims and settlement expenses as well as operating expenses.

Cash at the end of the year was $2.9 billion up $506.7 million from 2017. Cash from operations added $5.2 billion to the coffers while financing activities contributed $1 billion. Investing activities used $5.7 billion.

Strategy

Principal aims to become a global player in retirement services targeting Asian and Latin American countries that rely on private-sector defined-contribution pension plans to accommodate their growing number of retirees. The company typically builds its international business through startups acquisitions and joint ventures.

Principal has exited underperforming businesses such as medical insurance to focus on asset management at home and abroad. It aims to grow its assets under management (AUM) at a 6% compound annual clip with the goal of surpassing $100 trillion AUM in 2020 and $400 trillion by 2050.

In the US Principal courts firms with fewer than 1000 employees for its insurance and pension products; that market is primed for growth as a relatively low percentage of small to mid-sized businesses currently offer these products. Its strategy for growth also includes targeting large institutional clients for its asset management operations which include Principal Global Investors. The company serves approximately 650 institutional investors.

Mergers and Acquisitions

In 2019 Principal Financial Group acquired the Wells Fargo's retirement plan services business for $1.2 billion. With $827 billion in assets under administration the Wells Fargo business unit expanded Principal Financial's 401(k) savings account business. The company indicated the deal transformed it into one of the largest retirement providers. Principal capitalized on the acquisition of the stunted retirement plan services business as Wells Fargo had been prohibited from growing in size by the Federal Reserve following its customer abuse scandals.

The previous year Principal acquired financial technology company RobustWealth. The compay's purchase included RobustWealth's digital advice platform investment tools and client onboarding processes.

Company Background

Principal Financial was founded as the Bankers Life Association in 1879 by Edward Temple a Civil War veteran and banker. Life insurance became popular after the war but some dishonest insurers canceled customers' policies before they had to pay out benefits. Bankers Life an assessable association (members shared the cost of death benefits as the claims arose) was intended to provide low-cost protection to bankers and their families. The company soon after began offering life insurance to nonbankers.

HISTORY

Principal Financial was founded as the Bankers Life Association in 1879 by Edward Temple a Civil War veteran and banker. Life insurance became popular after the war but some dishonest insurers canceled customers' policies before they had to pay out benefits. Bankers Life an assessable association (members shared the cost of death benefits as the claims arose) was intended to provide low-cost protection to bankers and their families. The company soon began offering life insurance to nonbankers but it refused to insure women because of the high mortality rate among mothers during childbirth.

In October 2012 PFG scooped up First Dental Health a California-based preferred provider organization (PPO) with more than 11000 dentists operating in Arizona California and Nevada. The acquisition bolstered PFG's specialty benefits insurance business.

EXECUTIVES

Evp And Cfo, Deanna Strable
Evp And Cfo, Terrance Lillis
Chairman President And Ceo, Daniel J. (Dan) Houston, age 58, $795,192 total compensation
Evp General Counsel And Secretary, Karen E. Shaff, age 65
President Global Asset Management; Ceo Principal Global Investors, James P. (Jim) McCaughan, age 66, $663,500 total compensation
Evp Cio And Chief Digital Officer, Gary P. Scholten, age 62
Svp Retirement And Investor Services; President And Ceo Principal Funds, Nora M. Everett, age 59
Ceo Principal Real Estate Investors, Patrick G. (Pat) Halter
Senior Executive Director And Coo Strategy And Boutique Operations, Barbara A. (Barb) McKenzie
Svp And Controller, Gregory B. (Greg) Elming, age 58
President Principal International, Luis Valdés, age 61, $589,288 total compensation
Chairman Principal Financial Group Asia, Rex Auyeung

Evp Principal Financial Group Inc. And Principal Life And Chief Investment Officer, Timothy M. (Tim) Dunbar, age 61, $483,577 total compensation
Svp; President Principal Financial Group Latin America, Roberto Walker
Svp And Chief Marketing Officer, Elizabeth S. (Beth) Brady
Svp And Chief Investment Officer Principal Life Insurance Company, Dennis Menken
Senior Executive Director And Head Global Fixed Income, David M. Blake
Evp And Cfo, Deanna D. Strable-Soethout, age 50, $488,846 total compensation
President United States Insurance Solutions, Amy C. Friedrich, age 48
Vice President, Debra Stoll
Vice President Sales, Joseph Martin
Vice President, Mihail Dobrinov
Second Vice President, Rajesh Chalamalasetti
Vice President Tax, Rich Wireman
Senior Vice President, Cindy Dicks
Second Vice President, Shelly Meighan
Senior Vice President Risk Management, Lou Flori
Senior Vice President Retirement Distrib, Timothy Minard
Vice President Life, Don Cooper
Vice President Of Annuity Distribution, Steven Becker
Regional Vice President Nonqualified Plans, Jack Leavy
Vice President Operations, Andrea Matson
Regional Vice President, Paul Schreiber
Svp And Deputy General Counsel, Mark Lagomarcino
Vice President Consulting, Joseph Marx
Svp And Deputy General Counsel, Leanne Valentine
Vp And Head Government Relations, Chris Payne
Disability Income Regional Vice President, Justin Harrison
Assistant Vice President And Actuary, Chris Kinnison
Vice President, Cui Sufang
Vice President Of Account, Christine Johnson
Auditors: Ernst & Young LLP

LOCATIONS

HQ: Principal Financial Group Inc
711 High Street, Des Moines, IA 50392
Phone: 515 247-5111
Web: www.principal.com

Selected Geographic Locations

Australia
Brazil
Chile
China
Hong Kong
India
Indonesia
Japan
Malaysia
Mexico
Singapore
Thailand
UK
US

PRODUCTS/OPERATIONS

2016 Sales by Segment

	$ mil.	% of total
Retirement & Investor Services	6,151	49
US Insurance Solutions	3,637	29
Principal International	1,252	10
Principal Global Investors	1,387	11
Corporate	(46.3)	-
Net realized capital gains	81	1
Adjustments	(67.6)	-
Total	**12,394**	**100**

2016 Sales

	% of total
Premiums & other considerations	43
Fees and other revenues	29
Net investment income	27
Net realized capital gains	1
Total	**100**

COMPETITORS

AIG
AXA
Aetna
Allianz
BlackRock
FMR
JPMorgan Chase
John Hancock Financial Services
Lincoln Financial Group
MassMutual
MetLife
Morgan Stanley Investment Management
PIMCO
T. Rowe Price
The Vanguard Group
Unum Group
Voya Financial

HISTORICAL FINANCIALS

Company Type: Public

Income Statement

FYE: December 31

	ASSETS ($ mil.)	NET INCOME ($ mil.)	INCOME AS % OF ASSETS	EMPLOYEES
12/18	243,036	1,547	0.6%	16,475
12/17	253,941	2,310	0.9%	15,378
12/16	228,014	1,317	0.6%	14,854
12/15	218,686	1,234	0.6%	14,895
12/14	219,087	1,144	0.5%	14,873
Annual Growth	**2.6%**	**7.8%**	**—**	**2.6%**

2018 Year-End Financials

Debt ratio: 1.00%
Return on equity: 13.00%
Cash ($ mil.): 2,978
Current ratio: —
Long-term debt ($ mil.): —

No. of shares (mil.): 280
Dividends
  Yield: 5.0%
  Payout: 28.0%
Market value ($ mil.): 12,346

	STOCK PRICE ($) FY Close	P/E High/Low		PER SHARE ($) Earnings	Dividends	Book Value
12/18	44.00	14	8	5.00	2.00	41.00
12/17	71.00	9	7	8.00	2.00	44.00
12/16	58.00	13	8	5.00	2.00	36.00
12/15	45.00	14	11	4.00	2.00	32.00
12/14	52.00	15	11	4.00	1.00	35.00
Annual Growth	**(4.0%)**	**—**	**—**	**10.1%**	**13.2%**	**4.1%**

ProAssurance Corp

ProAssurance protects professional health associates — the doctors dentists and nurses of the US. One of the largest medical liability insurance providers in the nation ProAssurance is the holding company for ProAssurance Indemnity ProAssurance Casualty and other subsidiaries that sell liability coverage for health care providers primarily in the South and Midwest. Its customers include individual doctors in private practice as well as large physician groups clinics and hospitals. Its ProAssurance Specialty Insurance subsidiary writes excess and surplus (higher risk) lines of medical professional liability insurance. ProAssur-ance Casualty also provides some coverage for legal professionals.

Operations

ProAssurance operates through four primary segments: Specialty Property and Casualty (more than half of all sales) Workers' Compensation (about a quarter of sales) Lloyd's Syndicate and Corporate.

Physician policies make up ProAssurance's largest business accounting for about 80% of annual insurance premiums. Other key product groups include policies covering other health professionals medical facilities and legal professionals. Medmarc Casualty Insurance and Noetic Specialty Insurance write products liability coverage for medical technology and life sciences while Eastern Alliance Insurance provides workers' compensation. ProAssurance is also the majority capital provider to Lloyd's of London Syndicate 1729 which began writing business in 2014.

Geographic Reach

Although the company is licensed throughout the US its operations are concentrated in select states in the southern and midwestern US. Its largest markets — Alabama Pennsylvania and Texas — together account for about a third of the company's premiums.

The company owns office facilities in Alabama Michigan Nevada Tennessee and Wisconsin.

Sales and Marketing

ProAssurance employs an internal sales force to write its health care professional liability policies. It also utilizes independent agencies and brokerages.

Customers include physicians dentists specialists (including podiatrists) allied health care professionals medical facilities lawyers life science and medical technology entities.

Financial Performance

ProAssurance is able to sustain financial stability during turbulent market conditions through disciplined underwriting prudent pricing and loss reserve practices and conservative investment strategies. Revenue rose 15% to $852 million in 2014 largely due to the recent addition of workers' compensation business acquired with Eastern Alliance Insurance. The group's participation in the new Lloyd's Syndicate 1729 also drove up earnings. These increases were partially offset by a decline in net premiums for the Specialty Property and Casualty segment.

Net income has been somewhat turbulent over the past five years. It dropped 34% to $196 million in 2014 largely as a result of higher expenses related to the acquisition of Eastern Alliance Insurance and the investment in Lloyd's Syndicate 1729.

Cash flow from operations was on the decline until 2014 when it rebounded by 149% to $96 million. That turnaround was attributed to an increase in cash generated by receivables from reinsurers and a change in unearned premiums.

Strategy

ProAssurance's plans for long-term growth are based on the controlled expansion of its existing operations and by acquiring other specialty insurance companies or books of business. The company looks to expand in both existing and new territories and product lines. For instance the firm is working to grow in fields outside of the medical professional customer base partly due to increasing competition in the physician coverage market.

The company's aggressive acquisitions are part of its strategy to better compete against larger property/casualty insurance firms as well as smaller niche providers. ProAssurance works to provide local services that cater to the liability climates of its core geographies; it also focuses on targeted customer segments (medical and legal) to allow for a deep understanding of the industries' needs. In addition to acquisitions ProAssurance expands through organic growth efforts including new product launches as well as by forming partnerships with professional associations. As part of its strategy to expand geographically its Eastern Alliance Insurance unit opened a new office in Michigan in 2014.

In late 2013 the company became a corporate member of Lloyd's of London becoming the majority capital provider to the new Syndicate 1729. The move provided ProAssurance and its subsidiaries with more direct access to international professional liability opportunities in the health care sector.

Mergers and Acquisitions

In 2013 the company expanded through the purchase of Medmarc Insurance Group a liability underwriter for medical technology and life science policies in a $154 million transaction. The purchase also added some legal professional coverage operations.

EXECUTIVES

Chairman President And Ceo, W. Stancil (Stan) Starnes, age 70, $854,100 total compensation
President Healthcare Professional Liability Group Chief Underwriting Officer And Chief Actuary, Howard H. Friedman, age 60, $476,325 total compensation
Evp And Cfo, Edward L. (Ned) Rand, age 52, $443,475 total compensation
Svp And Chief Marketing Officer Professional Liability Group, Jeffrey L. Bowlby
President Eastern Insurance, Michael L. Boguski, age 56
Evp Corporate Secretary And General Counsel, Jeffrey P. Lisenby, age 50
Svp And Chief Medical Officer, Hayes V. Whiteside
Group Technology Officer Information Systems, Michael Stoeckert
President And Chief Medical Officer Podiatric Insurance Company Of America (pica), Ross E. Taubman
Vice President Information Systems, David Brown
Assistant Vice President External Reporting, Dianne Baldwin
Vice President Actuarial Services, Randy Chaffinch
Regional Vice President Claims, Scott Hunsberger
Regional Vice President Claims, Hal Mcclelland
Senior Vice President Proassurance Risk Solutions, Gregory Cuzzi
Vice President Sales, David Goss
Vice President, Vicky Gould
Vice President Of Operations, Sally Gilmore
Vice President, Tom Langan
Assistant Vice President, Sandy Cook
Regional Vice President Claims, Geri Morrison
Vice President Proassurance Insurance Company, Patrick ODoherty
Assistant Vice President, Tonya Bussey
Auditors: Ernst & Young LLP

LOCATIONS

HQ: ProAssurance Corp
100 Brookwood Place, Birmingham, AL 35209
Phone: 205 877-4400
Web: www.proassurance.com

PRODUCTS/OPERATIONS

2014 Sales by Segment

	$ mil.	% of total
Specialty Property and Casualty	499	58
Workers' Compensation	195	23
Corporate	146	17
Lloyd's Syndicate	13	2
Eliminations	(0.5)	-
Total	**852**	**100**

2014 Sales

	$ mil.	% of total
Net premium earned	700	82
Net investment	130	15
Net realized investment gains	15	2
Other income	8	1
Total	**852**	**100**

COMPETITORS

Berkshire Hathaway	NCMIC
CNA Financial	Physicians' Reciprocal
COPIC	Insurers
Coverys	Princeton Insurance
Dentists Insurance	Company
Company	State Volunteer Mutual
EDIC	Insurance
Markel	The Doctors Company
Medical Liability	Travelers Companies
Mutual Insurance	White Mountains
Monitor Liability	Insurance Group
Managers Inc.	

HISTORICAL FINANCIALS

Company Type: Public

Income Statement

FYE: December 31

	ASSETS ($ mil.)	NET INCOME ($ mil.)	INCOME AS % OF ASSETS	EMPLOYEES
12/18	4,601	47	1.0%	991
12/17	4,929	107	2.2%	994
12/16	5,065	151	3.0%	965
12/15	4,908	116	2.4%	938
12/14	5,169	197	3.8%	967
Annual Growth	(2.9%)	(30.1%)	—	0.6%

2018 Year-End Financials

Debt ratio: 6.00%	No. of shares (mil.): 54
Return on equity: 3.00%	Dividends
Cash ($ mil.): 80	Yield: 3.0%
Current ratio: —	Payout: 198.0%
Long-term debt ($ mil.): —	Market value ($ mil.): 2,176

	STOCK PRICE ($) FY Close	P/E High/Low	PER SHARE ($) Earnings	Dividends	Book Value
12/18	41.00	64 40	1.00	2.00	28.00
12/17	57.00	31 26	2.00	6.00	30.00
12/16	56.00	22 16	3.00	6.00	34.00
12/15	49.00	25 21	2.00	2.00	37.00
12/14	45.00	15 13	3.00	4.00	38.00
Annual Growth	(2.6%)	—	— (28.1%)	(18.1%)	(7.1%)

Procter & Gamble Company (The)

The Procter & Gamble Company (P&G) boasts billion-dollar brands for home and health. The world's largest maker of consumer packaged goods divides its business into five global segments that comprise its vast portfolio of hair skin and personal oral family feminine and baby care product lines. Its dozens of brands include Ace Bounce Crest Gillette Pampers Pepto Bismol Puffs Old Spice Swiffer and Tide. Fabric and home care is P&G's leading product category accounting for about a third of sales. The company sells products in 180-plus countries although the US is its largest market.

HISTORY

Candle maker William Procter and soap maker James Gamble merged their small Cincinnati businesses in 1837 creating The Procter & Gamble Company (P&G) which incorporated in 1890. By 1859 P&G had become one of the largest companies in Cincinnati with sales of $1 million. It introduced Ivory a floating soap in 1879 and Crisco shortening in 1911.The Ivory campaign was one of the first to advertise directly to the consumer. Other advertising innovations included sponsorship of daytime radio dramas in 1932. P&G's first TV commercial for Ivory aired in 1939.

Family members headed the company until 1930 when William Deupree became president. In the 29 years that Deupree served as president and then chairman P&G became the largest US seller of packaged goods.

After years of researching cleansers for use in hard water P&G introduced Tide detergent in 1947. It began a string of acquisitions when it picked up Spic and Span (1945; sold 2001) Duncan Hines (1956; sold 1998) Charmin Paper Mills (1957) and Folgers Coffee (1963 sold 2008). P&G launched Crest toothpaste in 1955 and Head & Shoulders shampoo and Pampers disposable diapers in 1961.

Rely tampons were pulled from shelves in 1980 when investigators linked them to toxic shock syndrome. In 1985 P&G moved into health care when it purchased Richardson-Vicks (NyQuil Vicks) and G.D. Searle's nonprescription drug division (Metamucil). The acquisitions of Noxell (1989; CoverGirl Noxzema) and Max Factor (1991) made it a top cosmetics company in the US. (It sold Noxzema in 2008.)

P&G began a major restructuring in 1993 cutting 13000 jobs and closing 30 plants. The firm acquired Eagle Snacks from Anheuser-Busch in 1996 and sued rival Amway over rumors connecting P&G and its moon-and-stars logo to Satanism. (The suit was dismissed in 1999.) Also in 1996 the FDA approved the use of olestra a controversial fat substitute developed by P&G.

In 1997 it acquired Tambrands (Tampax tampons) making P&G #1 in feminine sanitary protection. Impatient with progress on its sales goals in 1998 P&G began restructuring to focus on global business units rather than geographic regions. Chairman John Pepper handed over his chairman and CEO title in 1999 to president Durk Jager who promised five new products a year and a shakeup of the corporate culture.

In 1999 the company announced further reorganization plans including 15000 job cuts worldwide by 2005. That same year P&G bought The Iams Company (maker of Eukanuba- and Iams-brand dog and cat foods).

With earnings flat Jager resigned in 2000. P&G insider Alan G. Lafley immediately assumed the president and CEO duties and Pepper returned to succeed Jager as chairman.

In 2001 P&G announced job cuts for 9600 employees to further reduce costs. It also sold its Comet cleaner business. That year P&G completed its purchase of the Clairol hair care company from Bristol-Myers Squibb for nearly $5 billion.

In 2002 P&G closed three Clairol plants one warehouse and one distribution center — eliminating about 750 jobs. Production of Clairol products was moved to existing P&G plants. It also sold its olestra plant in Cincinnati to Twin Rivers Technologies but retained ownership of the Olean brand and technology. Additionally it sold its Jif peanut butter and Crisco shortening brands to J.M. Smucker and several personal care brands (including Sea Breeze and Vitalis) to Helen of Troy.

In 2002 P&G branched out in a joint venture with Clorox to help it improve the Glad-brand plastic bags and wraps. P&G held a 10% stake in the Glad venture until late 2004 when the company invested another $133 million to boost its stake to 20% the limit allowed by the agreement.

Also that year Lafley announced that P&G had completed its multiyear restructuring and would stop reporting two sets of results (one with restructuring charges and one without).

Further expanding its hair care segment and building on its successes with Clairol P&G purchased the first of several stakes in Wella in 2003 (it now owns the entire company). That year P&G also entered the premium pet food market with its purchase of The Iams Company for $2.3 billion. And to secure its foothold in China P&G bought the remaining 20% stake in its joint venture with partner Hutchison Whampoa China Ltd. in 2004 for $1.8 billion.

P&G bought four brands to sell in Southeast Asia in its effort to erode market share from Unilever. In 2005 P&G purchased Fab Trojan Dynamo and Paic laundry brands sold in Hong Kong Singapore Thailand and Malaysia from Colgate-Palmolive.

The company reached its lofty spot as the world's largest consumer products company in 2005 through one of its boldest moves — buying Boston-based The Gillette Company for about $57 billion. Overnight the ambitious deal gave P&G the golden ticket to leapfrog over former #1 supplier Unilever. P&G's purchase of Gillette added well-known complementary brands to its already vast portfolio such as Gillette razors and blades Duracell batteries Oral-B oral care items and Braun appliances.

In 2006 P&G paired up with ARYx Therapeutics to develop that company's gastrointestinal disorder treatment.

In 2007 P&G paired its marketing savvy with the diagnostics expertise of Inverness Medical Innovations to form a joint venture company called SPD Swiss Precision Diagnostics. The joint venture makes and markets in-home diagnostic products including pregnancy tests and ovulation/fertility monitoring products under the Clearblue PERSONA Accu-Clear and other names. P&G paid $325 million for its 50% stake in the venture.

EXECUTIVES

Group President Global Grooming, Charles E. Pierce, age 63

Chairman President And Ceo, David S. Taylor, age 61, $1,393,333 total compensation

Global Customer Development Officer, Carolyn Tastad, age 56

Vp North American Region, Steven D. (Steve) Bishop, age 55, $796,667 total compensation

Vp Uk And Ireland, Giovanni Ciserani, age 57, $845,833 total compensation

Group President Global Family Care, Mary L. Ferguson-McHugh, age 60

President Global Personal Health Care, Thomas M. Finn, age 57

Vice Chairman And Cfo, Jon R. Moeller, age 55, $950,000 total compensation

Global Design Officer, Philip J Duncan, age 54

Cio, Linda W. Clement-Holmes, age 57

Global Product Supply Officer, Yannis Skoufalos, age 61

President Beauty Specialty Businesses, Colleen E. Jay, age 57

President Europe Selling & Market Operations, Gary Coombe

Cto, Kathleen B. (Kathy) Fish

President India Middle East And Africa Selling And Market Operations, Mohamed Samir

President Global Home Care And P&g Professional, George Tsourapas, age 59

President Global Fabric Care And Brand Building
Organization Global Fabric And Home Care,
Shailesh G. Jejurikar
President Global Skin And Personal Care, R.
Alexandra Keith
President Global Business Services, Julio Nemeth
President Latin America Selling And Market
Operations, Juan F. Posada
President Greater China Selling And Market
Operations, Matthew S. Price
President Asia/pacific Selling And Market
Operations, Magesvaran Suranjan
Vice President, Charlene Patten
Vice President, Jerry Vikara
Vice President Of Human Resources, Giorgio
Siracusa
Vice President, Ajit Nayak
Chief Sales Officer Reinvention Training
Developer, Ryan P Siereveld
Vp And Associate General Counsel, Ken Patel
Vice President Of Communications, Lisa Bartz
Chief Sales Officer Team Operations Leader, Kelly
Horton
Vice President, Dicky Kho
Vice President Sales, Frank Craft
Vice President Global Investor Relations, John T
Chevalier
Vice President, Patrick Conklin
Vice President Operations, Dawn Seiler
Call Center Customer Service Director Vice
President, Ron Chisholm
Director Managed Care, Debbie Burge
National Sales Manager Canada, David Roberts
Chief Sales Officer Om Analyst, Greg Ribeiro
Vice President Product Supply Baby Care, Eric
Hagemeister
Vice President And General Manager Research
And Development, Petra Hanke-baier
Chief Sales Officer Manager Romania, Georgeta
Parchisanu
Vice President Corporate Solutions, Bob Martindale
Vice President Corporate Development And
Strategic Planning, Becky Frayer
Vice President And General Manager Asia Pacific,
Omar Channawi
National Account Manager, Shelagh Clark
Vice President Management Systems, Frank
Caccamo
Vp Hr, Bryan Thompson
National Sales Manager, Lisa Richards
Vice President Human Resources India Middle
East Africa And Global Fabric And Home Care,
Jamal Berradia
Senior Vice President Go To Market China, Henry
Karamanoukian
Vice President, Kim Kraus
Vice President, Luis Amaro
Vice President, Denise Crookshanks
Vice President Strategic Initiatives, Mei Khoo
Sr V Pres-comptroller-treas, Valarie Sheppard
Board Member, Mike Eftink
Shs Band Booster Treasurer, Lisa Hennessy
Board Member, Bob Kruthaupt
Board Member, BO Passey
Secretary, Jenny Tan
Abm, Christina Morazzani
Assistant Treasurer, Douglas Gerstle
Abm, Marta Roballo
Secretary Treasurer, Dave Seidel
Board Member, John Biscotti
Auditors: DELOITTE & TOUCHE LLP

LOCATIONS

HQ: Procter & Gamble Company (The)
One Procter & Gamble Plaza, Cincinnati, OH 45202
Phone: 513 983-1100
Web: www.pg.com

2019 Sales

	% of total
North America	45
Europe	23
Asia Pacific	10
Greater China	9
India Middle East and Africa (IMEA)	7
Latin America	6
Total	**100**

PRODUCTS/OPERATIONS

2019 Sales

	$ mil.	% of total
Fabric & Home Care	22,080	33
Baby Feminine & Family Care	17,806	26
Beauty	12,897	19
Health Care	8,218	12
Grooming	6,199	9
Corporate	484	1
Total	**67,684**	**100**

Selected Segments and Brands

Fabric Care & Home Care
  Ariel
  Dawn
  Downy
  Febreze
  Gain
  Tide
Beauty
  Head & Shoulders
  Olay
  Old Spice
  Pantene
  SK-II
Baby Feminine & Family Care
  Always
  Bounty
  Charmin
  Luvs
  Pampers
  Tampax
Health Care
  Crest
  Oral-B
  Vicks
Grooming
  Braun
  Fusion
  Gillette
  Mach3
  Venus

COMPETITORS

Alticor	Kao
Amway	Kimberly-Clark
Church & Dwight	S.C. Johnson
Clorox	Shiseido
Colgate-Palmolive	Tom's of Maine
Edgewell Personal Care	Unilever NV
Henkel	Unilever PLC
Johnson & Johnson	

HISTORICAL FINANCIALS

Company Type: Public

Income Statement

FYE: June 30

	REVENUE ($ mil.)	NET INCOME ($ mil.)	NET PROFIT MARGIN	EMPLOYEES
06/19	67,684	3,897	5.8%	97,000
06/18	66,832	9,750	14.6%	92,000
06/17	65,058	15,326	23.6%	95,000
06/16	65,299	10,508	16.1%	105,000
06/15	76,279	7,036	9.2%	110,000
Annual Growth	**(2.9%)**	**(13.7%)**	**—**	**(3.1%)**

2019 Year-End Financials

Debt ratio: 26.00%—
Return on equity: 8.00%
Cash ($ mil.): 4,239
Current ratio: 1.00
Long-term debt ($ mil.): 20,395

Dividends
Yield: 0.0%
Payout: 203.0%
Market value ($ mil.): —

	STOCK PRICE ($) FY Close	P/E High/Low	PER SHARE ($) Earnings	Dividends	Book Value
06/19	110.00	77 54	1.00	3.00	19.00
06/18	78.00	25 19	4.00	3.00	21.00
06/17	87.00	16 14	6.00	3.00	22.00
06/16	85.00	22 18	4.00	3.00	21.00
06/15	78.00	37 31	2.00	3.00	23.00
Annual Growth	**8.8%**	**— —**	**(12.5%)**	**2.8%**	**(4.9%)**

Progressive Corp. (OH)

The Progressive Corporation offers personal lines insurance as well as commercial lines and property insurance. Personal auto insurance is Progressive's largest business; it also offers personal-use vehicle policies for motorcycles RVs snowmobiles and other specialty vehicles. The company's commercial policies cover vans and light to heavy trucks. Most of its commercial lines policies are sold to small business owners. The property insurance business writes residential property insurance for homeowners and offers renters insurance. Progressive markets directly to consumers online and by phone and through more than 35000 independent agents.

Operations

Progressive earns revenue through three segments: Personal Lines (the largest segment accounting for some 85% of total revenue) Commercial Lines (10%) Property (5%).

The company primarily offers coverage to auto insurance customers underwritten by third-party insurance carriers. Personal auto insurance accounts for some 95% of its Personal Lines net premiums. Progressive also offers personal umbrella insurance that provides coverage for the extras in life such as personal injury and legal defense.

Geographic Reach

In addition to its Mayfield Village Ohio headquarters Progressive has offices in Colorado Springs Colorado; Tampa and St. Petersburg Florida; and Tempe Arizona.

Sales and Marketing

Progressive sells its personal lines insurance through more than 35000 independent agencies and through partnerships with other insurance companies and financial institutions. It also sells directly to customers online and by telephone. Commercial lines are distributed directly and through independent agencies.

The company's popular television ads featuring perky spokesperson "Flo" have been a boon for the company's brand recognition.

Financial Performance

Organic growth across its Personal Lines Commercial Lines and Property business segment has boosted Progressive's revenue every year since 2008.

Revenue jumped 19% to $31.9 billion in 2018 as net premiums increased across Progressive's business segments.

Net income rose 64% to $2.6 billion a healthy increase driven mostly by the jump in revenue.

Total cash on hand at the end of 2018 sat at a low $75 million ending about $200 million lower than in the previous period. Cash from operations provided $6.2 billion while investing activities used $7.2 billion (purchases of fixed maturities accounted for the largest investment) and financing provided $846 million.

Strategy

Unlike some insurers who in healthy markets earn more from their investments than their premiums more than 90% of Progressive's revenues have historically come from policy premiums.

The company's insurance operations have remained profitable and have grown as the company has entered into new geographic markets and expanded the online distribution of its personal auto products. Already among the leading US auto insurers based on premiums (just behind State Farm and Allstate) Progressive is aiming to be on top.

The auto insurance industry is highly competitive with large carriers and regional carriers competing for market share. Because it is easy for customers to switch auto insurers Progressive competes on price and accessibility. The company also find success through advertising to attract and retain customers. Its television ads featuring its perky spokesperson "Flo" have boosted company's brand recognition.

Progressive is looking to reduce its exposure to the competitive auto insurance industry by growing its property insurance business. It promotes its residential products through bundled packages with lower auto rates and has rebranded its majority-owned homeowners insurance carrier American Strategic Insurance to the Progressive name to make it easier to sell auto and home bundles. This cross-selling strategy comes with a retention benefit as well; once a customer has bought a bundled package of home/auto/umbrella coverage they are less likely to switch insurance providers.

Company Background

Attorneys Jack Green and Joseph Lewis founded Progressive Mutual Insurance in Cleveland in 1937. Initially offering standard auto insurance the company attracted customers through such innovations as installment plans for premiums (a payment method popularized during the Depression) and drive-in claims services headquartered in a garage. Progressive's early years were uncertain — at one point the founders were even advised to go out of business — but the advent of WWII bolstered business. Car and insurance purchases went up but accidents declined as gas rationing limited driving.

HISTORY

Attorneys Jack Green and Joseph Lewis founded Progressive Mutual Insurance in Cleveland in 1937. Initially offering standard auto insurance the company attracted customers through such innovations as installment plans for premiums (a payment method popularized during the Depression) and drive-in claims services (the company was headquartered in a garage). Progressive's early years were uncertain — at one point the founders were even advised to go out of business: but the advent of WWII bolstered business: Car and insurance purchases were up but accidents were down as gas rationing limited driving.

Then came the suburbs and cars of the 1950s. While most competitors sought low-risk drivers Progressive exploited the high-risk niche through careful underwriting and statistical analysis. Subsidiary Progressive Casualty was founded in 1956 (the year after Joseph Lewis died) to insure the best of the worst. Lewis' son Peter joined the company in 1955 and helped engineer its early-1960s expansion outside Ohio. After Green retired in 1965 Peter gained control of the company through a leveraged buyout and renamed it The Progressive Corporation. Six years later Lewis took it public and formed subsidiary Progressive American in Florida.

In the mid-1970s the industry went into a funk as it was hit by a wave of consolidations and rising interest rates. Lewis set a goal for the company to always earn an underwriting profit instead of depending on investments to make a profit. Progressive achieved stellar results during the 1970s es-

pecially after states began requiring drivers to be insured and other insurers began weeding out higher risks.

Competition in nonstandard insurance grew in the 1980s as major insurers such as Allstate and State Farm joined the fray with their larger sales forces and deeper pockets. In 1988 California's Proposition 103 retroactively reduced rates; Progressive fought California's demand for refunds but set aside reserves to pay them.

That year Lewis hired Cleveland financier Alfred Lerner to guide company investments. Lerner invested $75 million in Progressive via a convertible debenture; five years later he converted it to stock half of which he sold for $122 million. Soon after he was asked to resign. In 1993 Progressive settled with California for $51 million and applied to earnings the remaining $100 million in refund reserves. (Company soul-searching related to Proposition 103 led to the launch of Progressive's now-famous "Immediate Response" vehicles which provide 24-hour claims service at accident sites.)

In 1995 Progressive's practice of using consumer credit information to make underwriting decisions drew the attention of Arkansas and Vermont insurance regulators who said the company might be discriminating against people who didn't have the credit cards Progressive used to evaluate creditworthiness. In 1996 insurance regulators in Alaska Maryland and Texas also began probing Progressive's credit information practices.

In 1997 Progressive bought nonstandard auto insurer Midland Financial Group. As competition grew in 1999 the company cut rates and said it would write no new policies in Canada. In 2000 — with underwriting margins dropping industrywide — the company continued advertising aggressively. Progressive stopped writing new homeowners insurance in 2002 instead concentrating on its core operations. In 2006 the company began offering personal umbrella coverage.

The company took a bold international expansion measure in 2009: Launching personal auto insurance online in Australia. International expansion has not been a key strategy for Progressive but apparently the time was right for such growth. And apparently the company is prepared to give the new operation time to grow which is good considering that it has not yet made significant contributions to overall revenues.

EXECUTIVES

Chief Investment Officer, William M. (Bill) Cody, age 57, $463,269 total compensation
President And Ceo, S. Patricia (Tricia) Griffith, age 55, $616,346 total compensation
President Commercial Lines Group, John A. Barbagallo, age 60, $463,269 total compensation
Cfo, John P. Sauerland, age 55, $546,538 total compensation
Chief Legal Officer, Dan Mascaro
President Personal Lines, Patrick K. (Pat) Callahan, age 48
President Claims, Michael D. (Mike) Sieger, age 57
Cio, Steven A. (Steve) Broz, age 48
Customer Relationship Management President, John Murphy, age 49
National Sales Manager, Eric Brunelle
Vice President Information Technology, Edward Fowler
Vice President Information Technology, Kerry Breitenbach
Vice President Marketing, Carlton Spencer
President Ceo And Director; Chairman And Ceo Progressive Casualty Insurance Company, Glenn M. Renwick, age 64
Treasurer, David Krew
Auditors: PricewaterhouseCoopers LLP

LOCATIONS

HQ: Progressive Corp. (OH)
6300 Wilson Mills Road, Mayfield Village, OH 44143
Phone: 440 461-5000 **Fax:** 440 446-7168
Web: www.progressive.com

PRODUCTS/OPERATIONS

2018 Premium Revenue

	% of total
Personal Lines	85
Commercial Lines	10
Property	5
Total	**100**

Selected Insurance Options

Auto Insurance
Local Car Insurance
Motorcycle Insurance
Boat Insurance
RV Insurance
Commercial Insurance
Snowmobile Insurance
PWC Insurance
Homeowners Insurance
Renters Insurance
ATV Insurance
Life Insurance
Health Insurance
Umbrella Insurance

COMPETITORS

21st Century Insurance	Liberty Mutual
Allstate	Nationwide
American Family Insurance	Old Republic
	State Auto Financial
Cincinnati Financial	State Farm
Farmers Group	Travelers Companies
GEICO	USAA
Infinity Property & Casualty	

HISTORICAL FINANCIALS

Company Type: Public

Income Statement				FYE: December 31
	ASSETS ($ mil.)	NET INCOME ($ mil.)	INCOME AS % OF ASSETS	EMPLOYEES
12/18	46,575	2,615	5.6%	37,346
12/17	38,701	1,592	4.1%	33,656
12/16	33,428	1,031	3.1%	31,721
12/15	29,819	1,268	4.3%	28,580
12/14	25,788	1,281	5.0%	26,501
Annual Growth	15.9%	19.5%	—	9.0%

2018 Year-End Financials

Debt ratio: 9.00%	No. of shares (mil.): 583
Return on equity: 26.00%	Dividends
Cash ($ mil.): 75	Yield: 2.0%
Current ratio: —	Payout: 25.0%
Long-term debt ($ mil.): —	Market value ($ mil.): 35,184

	STOCK PRICE ($) FY Close	P/E High/Low		PER SHARE ($)		
				Earnings	Dividends	Book Value
12/18	60.00	17 11		4.00	1.00	19.00
12/17	56.00	21 13		3.00	1.00	16.00
12/16	36.00	20 17		2.00	1.00	14.00
12/15	32.00	16 12		2.00	1.00	12.00
12/14	27.00	13 10		2.00	1.00	12.00
Annual Growth	22.3%	— —		19.7%	(6.8%)	12.0%

ProSight Global Inc

Auditors: Ernst & Young LLP

LOCATIONS

HQ: ProSight Global Inc
412 Mt. Kemble Avenue, Suite 300C, Morristown, NJ 07960
Phone: 973 532-1900
Web: www.prosightspecialty.com

HISTORICAL FINANCIALS

Company Type: Public

Income Statement

FYE: December 31

	ASSETS ($ mil.)	NET INCOME ($ mil.)	INCOME AS % OF ASSETS	EMPLOYEES
12/18	2,577	55	2.1%	392
12/17	2,409	(44)	—	—
12/16	0	(100)	—	—
Annual Growth	—	—	—	—

2018 Year-End Financials

Debt ratio: 7.00%
Return on equity: 14.00%
Cash ($ mil.): 22
Current ratio: —
Long-term debt ($ mil.): —

No. of shares (mil.): 6
Dividends
Yield: —
Payout: —
Market value ($ mil.): —

	STOCK PRICE ($) FY Close	P/E High/Low	PER SHARE ($) Earnings	Dividends	Book Value
12/18	0.00	— —	9.00	0.00	65.00
12/17	0.00	— —	(8.00)	0.00	63.00
Annual Growth	—	— —	—	—	1.6%

Prosperity Bancshares Inc.

Prosperity Bancshares reaches banking customers across the Lone Star State. The holding company for Prosperity Bank operates about 230 branches across Texas and about 15 more in Oklahoma. Serving consumers and small to midsized businesses the bank offers traditional deposit and loan services in addition to wealth management retail brokerage and mortgage banking investment services. Prosperity Bank focuses on real estate lending: Commercial mortgages make up the largest segment of the company's loan portfolio (33%) followed by residential mortgages (24%). Credit cards business auto consumer home equity loans round out its lending activities.

Operations

About 63% of Prosperity's total revenue came from loan interest (including fees) in 2014 while another 22% came from interest on its investment securities. The rest of its revenue came from non-sufficient fund fees (4%) credit and debit card income (3%) deposit account service charges (2%) trust income (1%) mortgage income (1%) and brokerage income (1%).

Geographic Reach

Prosperity Bancshares operates 230 Texas banking locations across Houston South Texas the Dallas/Fort Worth metroplex East Texas Bryan/College Station Central Texas and West Texas. It also has 15 branch locations in Oklahoma (including Tulsa).

Sales and Marketing

The bank mainly targets consumers and small and medium-sized businesses and tailors its products to the specific needs of a given market.

Financial Performance

Prosperity's revenues and profits have been prospering thanks to loan and deposit business growth from acquisitions and declining loan loss provisions as its loan portfolio's credit quality has improved with higher property valuations in a strengthened economy.

The company's revenue jumped by 32% to $837.7 million in 2014 mostly as its loan interest income swelled by 40% on loan asset growth from its F&M acquisition. The bank's non-interest income rose by 29% as well from new deposit account service fees from the acquisition and additional income from its newly added brokerage and trust business.

Higher revenue and strong operating cost controls in 2014 drove Prosperity's net income higher by 34% to $297.4 million while its operating cash levels rose by 13% to $348.3 million on higher cash earnings.

Strategy

Prosperity Bancshares bases its growth strategy on three key elements: Internal loan and deposit business growth through "individualized customer service" and service line expansion opportunities; cost controls to maximize profitability; and acquisitions.

Toward its internal business growth initiatives Prosperity spent 2012 and 2013 launching its new trust brokerage mortgage lending and credit card products and services to customers for the first time.

With cost-controls in mind the bank tracks its branches "as separate profit centers" noting each branch's interest income efficiency ratio deposit growth loan growth and overall profitability. That way it can reward individual branch managers and presidents accordingly by merit rather than giving higher compensation across the board.

The acquisitive Prosperity Bancshares has been buying up small banks in Texas — and now Oklahoma — as it hopes to hit a sweet spot in the market between the national giants that dominate the Texas banking scene and smaller community banks.

Mergers and Acquisitions

In January 2016 furthering its presence in the Houston market Prosperity Bancshares purchased Tradition Bancshares along with its seven branches in the Houston Area (Bellaire Katy and the Woodlands) $540 million in assets $239 million in loans and $483.8 million in deposits.

In April 2014 toward expansion in the Oklahoma and Dallas markets Prosperity purchased Tulsa-based F&M Bancorporation and its subsidiary The F&M Bank & Trust Company. The deal added 13 branches including nine in Tulsa and surrounding areas three in Dallas and a loan production office in Oklahoma City.

In April 2013 it acquired Coppermark Bank one of Oklahoma City's largest banks with six branches in Oklahoma City and three locations in North Dallas for $194 million. The deal also added the credit card and agent bank merchant processing business from its subsidiary Bankers Credit Card Services.

In January 2013 the company boosted its market share in East Texas after buying East Texas Financial Services and its four First Federal Bank Texas branch locations including three branches in Tyler and one in Gilmer.

Company Background

In early 2012 Prosperity acquired Texas Bankers a three-branch Austin bank with some $72 million in assets. The merger increased Prosperity's number of Central Texas branches to 34 banking locations. It followed that deal with the purchase of The Bank Arlington a single-branch bank operating in the Dallas/Ft. Worth area. It acquired single-branch Community National Bank of Bellaire Texas in late 2012.

Also in 2012 Prosperity expanded into West Texas after it merged American State Financial Corporation and its American State Bank subsidiary into its operations. The deal added $3 billion in assets and 37 West Texas banking offices in Lubbock Midland/Odessa and Abilene.

EXECUTIVES

Executive Vice President Cashier Prosperity Bank, Michael Harris
Evp Cashier Prosperity Bank, Mike Harris
Senior Chairman And Ceo, David Zalman, age 62, $851,567 total compensation
Cfo; Evp And Cfo Prosperity Bank, David Hollaway, age 63, $425,000 total compensation
Vice Chairman; Chairman And Coo Prosperity Bank, H. E. (Tim) Timanus, age 75, $452,400 total compensation
Vice Chairman And Area Chairman Central Texas, Edward Z. (Eddie) Safady
Evp Regulatory And Compliance Prosperity Bank, Rhonda L. Carroll
Chief Lending Officer Prosperity Bank, Randy D. Hester, $325,000 total compensation
Sevp Financial Operations And Administration Prosperity Bank, Mike Epps, $327,625 total compensation
Evp And Cio Prosperity Bank, Gisela Riggan
Chief Risk Oficer, Jennifer Willcoxon
Chief Credit Officer Prosperity Bank, Merle Karnes
President Prosperity Bank, Bob Benter
Evp Prosperity Bancshares And Prosperity Bank, Robert (Bob) Dowdell
Chairman Wealth Management, Russell Marshall
Senior Vice President Sba Lending, Beverly Layne
Assistant Vice President Of Technology Procurement, Lausanne Barrett
Assistant Vice President, Debbie Rodriguez
Senior Vice President Lending, Josie Amejorado
Senior Vice President Iso Sponsorship Program, Jamie Bigley
Vice President Manager, Donna Brune
Vice President, Adrian Ozuna
Assistant Vice President Lobby Manager, Barbara Wilsher
Vice President Lobby Manager, Jana Rachunek
Vice President, Bill Hailey
Senior Vice President, Jamie Lander
Vice President, Candi Biggers
Executive Vice President, Cathy Waller
Assistant Vice President Lending Area, Betty Kindred
Vice President, Cecil Childers
Senior Vice President, Tim Cardinal
Senior Vice President, Jim Schroeder
Assistant Vice President, James West
Assistant Vice President Lobby Manager, Vickie Britt
Senior Vice President, Mark Odlis
7 Assistant Vice President, Kimberly Knight
Assistant Vice President, Robyn Totah
Assistant Vice President, Leslie Labrador
Vice President, Susan Rodriguez
Senior Vice President Trust Officer, Wendy Scribner
Vice President Lobby Manager, Bertha Ramos
Vice President, Stacie Akin
Senior Vice President, Charles Stuart
Vice President And Lending Assistant, Laura Wavra
Vice President, James Long
Vice President, Domingo Gonzales

Senior Vice President Backroom Operation, Thomas Petras
Vice President Commercial Lending, Brandon Kidd
Vice President, Yolanda Cox
Vice President, Melissa Owens
Vice President, Brittani Conoley
Senior Vice President Regional Manager, Spiro Petritsis
Board Member, Perry Mueller
Board Member, Leah Henderson
Board Member, Stephanie Collier
Board Member, Jack Lord
Auditors: DELOITTE & TOUCHE LLP

LOCATIONS

HQ: Prosperity Bancshares Inc.
 Prosperity Bank Plaza, 4295 San Felipe, Houston, TX 77027
Phone: 281 269-7199
Web: www.prosperitybankusa.com

PRODUCTS/OPERATIONS

2014 Sales

	$ mil.	% of total
Interest		
Loans including fees	526	63
Securities	189	22
Federal funds sold	0	-
Noninterest		
Non-sufficient funds fees	37	4
Debit card and ATM card income	23	3
Service charges on deposit accounts	17	2
Trust income	8	1
Brokerage income	6	1
Mortgage income	4	1
Other	28	3
Total	838	100

COMPETITORS

Amegy	JPMorgan Chase
BBVA Compass	North Dallas Bank
Bancshares	Texas Capital
Bank of America	Bancshares
Citibank	Wells Fargo
Comerica	Woodforest Financial
Cullen/Frost Bankers	

HISTORICAL FINANCIALS

Company Type: Public

Income Statement   FYE: December 31

	ASSETS ($ mil.)	NET INCOME ($ mil.)	INCOME AS % OF ASSETS	EMPLOYEES
12/18	22,693	322	1.4%	3,036
12/17	22,587	272	1.2%	3,035
12/16	22,331	274	1.2%	3,035
12/15	22,037	287	1.3%	3,037
12/14	21,508	297	1.4%	3,096
Annual Growth	1.4%	2.0%	—	(0.5%)

2018 Year-End Financials

Debt ratio: 5.00%	No. of shares (mil.): 70
Return on equity: 8.00%	Dividends
Cash ($ mil.): 411	Yield: 2.0%
Current ratio: —	Payout: 32.0%
Long-term debt ($ mil.): —	Market value ($ mil.): 4,351

	STOCK PRICE ($) FY Close	P/E High/Low		PER SHARE ($) Earnings	Dividends	Book Value
12/18	62.00	17	12	5.00	1.00	58.00
12/17	70.00	20	14	4.00	1.00	55.00
12/16	72.00	19	9	4.00	1.00	52.00
12/15	48.00	14	11	4.00	1.00	49.00
12/14	55.00	16	12	4.00	1.00	47.00
Annual Growth	3.0%	—	—	1.6%	10.7%	5.7%

Protective Life Insurance Co

Protective Life & Annuity markets and sells financial security in the form of term and universal life insurance policies and fixed and variable annuity products. Although the company is based in Alabama and licensed to sell insurance throughout the US it exclusively serves clients in New York. Sister companies include West Coast Life Insurance (life insurance and annuities) MONY Life Insurance (ditto) and Lyndon Insurance (specialty coverage). Protective Life & Annuity is a unit of Protective Life Insurance which is part of Dai-Ichi Life Holdings subsidiary Protective Life Corporation.

Operations

Every state has unique requirements that insurance companies must meet in order to gain permission to operate there. New York's insurance code has the stiffest requirements and many small companies simply choose not to operate in that market. However the market is so large and tempting that other companies opt to maintain separate subsidiaries that exclusively serve New York. In this instance parent company Protective Life Insurance Company serves the rest of the US while Protective Life & Annuity is strictly focused on New York.

Protective Life Corporation was acquired by Japanese insurer Dai-ichi Life in early 2015.

Sales and Marketing

Protective Life & Annuity sells coverage through independent agents broker-dealers and financial institutions as well as through partnerships with employer groups and through its own sales division.

EXECUTIVES

Evp Chief Legal Officer Secretary And General Counsel, Deborah J. Long, age 65
Chairman And Ceo, John D. Johns, age 66
Evp And Chief Investment Officer, Carl S. Thigpen, age 62
Evp And Chief Administrative Officer, D. Scott Adams, age 54
President And Coo, Richard J. Bielen
Evp Finance And Risk; Chief Risk Officer, Michael G. (Mike) Temple, age 56
Svp Chief Information And Operations Officer, Mark J. Cyphert
Evp Cfo And Controller, Steven G. Walker
Auditors: KPMG LLP

LOCATIONS

HQ: Protective Life Insurance Co
 2801 Highway 280 South, Birmingham, AL 35223
Phone: 205 268-1000
Web: www.protective.com

COMPETITORS

Guardian Insurance and Annuity	Penn Mutual
	Prudential
MetLife	The Hartford
New York Life	

HISTORICAL FINANCIALS

Company Type: Public

Income Statement   FYE: December 31

	ASSETS ($ mil.)	NET INCOME ($ mil.)	INCOME AS % OF ASSETS	EMPLOYEES
12/18	89,383	194	0.2%	2,957
12/17	79,114	1,182	1.5%	2,773
12/16	74,465	353	0.5%	2,719
12/15*	68,032	180	0.3%	2,541
01/15	0	89	—	—
Annual Growth	—	21.7%		

*Fiscal year change

2018 Year-End Financials

Debt ratio: 4.00%	No. of shares (mil.): 5
Return on equity: 3.00%	Dividends
Cash ($ mil.): 151	Yield: —
Current ratio: —	Payout: —
Long-term debt ($ mil.): —	Market value ($ mil.): —

PROVIDENCE HEALTH & SERVICES

EXECUTIVES

Ceo, Rod Hochman
Pres- Chief Dev Officer, Laurie Kelley
Exec V Pres-Cfo, Todd Hofheins
Technology, Henry Morgan
Program Manager, Mark Sizemore
Officer, Matt Price
Director of Operations, Ruth M Arevalo
Administrative Assistant, Alexander Jackson
Coordinator, Mayra Graves
Senior, Alitha Jenkins
Security Engineering Consultan, Diana Bullion
Auditors: KPMG LLP SEATTLE WA

LOCATIONS

HQ: PROVIDENCE HEALTH & SERVICES
 1801 LIND AVE SW, RENTON, WA 980573368
Phone: 425 525-3355
Web: WWW.PROVIDENCE.ORG

HISTORICAL FINANCIALS

Company Type: Private

Income Statement   FYE: December 31

	REVENUE ($ mil.)	NET INCOME ($ mil.)	NET PROFIT MARGIN	EMPLOYEES
12/15	14,434	49	0.3%	9,700
12/12	281	15	5.3%	—
12/08	7,026	(157)	—	—
12/07	6,348	434	6.8%	—
Annual Growth	10.8%	(23.8%)	—	—

Provident Financial Services Inc

Provident wants to be a prominent force in the New Jersey banking scene. Provident Financial Services owns The Provident Bank which serves individuals businesses and families from 85 branches across more than 10 northern and central New Jersey counties. Founded in 1839 the $8.5 billion-bank offers traditional deposit and lending products as well as wealth management and trust services. About 50% of its revenue comes from real estate loan interest while another 25% comes from interest on commercial and consumer loans. Construction loans round out its lending activities. The company's Provident Investment Services subsidiary sells life and health insurance and investment products.

Operations

Provident which staffed more than 1020 employees boasted some $8.5 billion in total assets loans of $6.1 billion and deposits of $5.8 billion at the end of 2014. Mortgages loans made up 70% of its total loan portfolio that year.

Geographic Reach

The bank's 86 branches are located in northern and central New Jersey as well as in Pennsylvania (in the Bucks Lehigh and Northampton counties). Its administrative offices are in Iselin New Jersey while its satellite loan production offices are in Covent Station Flemington Paramus Princeton and West Orange in New Jersey; and in Bethleham and Newtown Pennsylvania.

Sales and Marketing

Provident targets individuals families and businesses in its primary market areas in New Jersey (which covered a population of 6.9 million or 78% of the state's population) and Pennsylvania (where the bank's primary market covered 10% of that state's population).

Provident's primary markets include a mix of urban and suburban communities. It serves companies in a variety of industries including pharmaceutical and other manufacturing companies network communications insurance and financial services healthcare and retail businesses.

Financial Performance

Provident has struggled to consistently grow its revenues in recent years due to shrinking interest margins on loans amidst the low-interest environment. Its profits however have been rising thanks to declining loan loss provisions as its loan portfolio's credit quality has improved with higher property valuations in a strengthened economy.

The bank's revenue rose by 8% to $320.5 million in 2014 mostly thanks to added interest income from loan asset growth — including a 9% rise in real estate secured loan business and a 24% rise in commercial loan business — stemming from its acquisition of Team Capital Bank.

Higher revenue and a continued decline in loan loss provisions in 2014 drove Provident's net income higher by 4% to $73.6 million. Its operating cash levels dipped by 3% to $96.4 million after adjusting its earnings for non-cash items mostly related to an increase in other assets.

Strategy

Provident Financial continues to look for strategic acquisition opportunities of banks and other financial services providers to grow its loan and deposit business and extend its branch network into more of its primary market areas.

The company also remains focused on its conservative lending practices and is seeking to diversify its portfolio and reduce risk by placing more emphasis on commercial real estate multifamily residential and business loans.

Mergers and Acquisitions

In May 2014 Provident Financial Services purchased Team Capital Bank for $115.1 million effectively extending its reach into Eastern Pennsylvania and the affluent counties of Hunterdon and Somerset. The deal also added $964 million in total assets $631 million in loan assets and $770 million in deposits.

Company Background

In 2011 the company acquired Beacon Trust Company an asset manager for individuals municipalities corporations pension funds and not-for-profit organizations. The deal significantly expanded its wealth management business and boosted its assets under management to some $1.5 billion.

EXECUTIVES

Chairman President And Ceo, Christopher P. Martin, age 63, $608,846 total compensation

Evp And Cfo, Thomas M. Lyons, age 55, $349,308 total compensation

Evp And Director Retail Banking The Provident Bank, Michael A. Raimonde, age 67, $238,370 total compensation

Evp General Counsel And Corporate Secretary The Provident Bank, John F. Kuntz, age 64, $312,700 total compensation

Evp And Chief Lending Officer The Provident Bank, Donald W. Blum, age 63, $314,562 total compensation

Evp And Cio The Provident Bank, Jack Novielli, age 60

Evp And And Chief Human Resources Officer The Provident Bank, Janet D. Krasowski, age 66

Evp And Chief Credit Officer The Provident Bank, Brian Giovinazzi, age 65, $161,138 total compensation

Evp And Chief Wealth Officer The Provident Bank, James D. Nesci, age 47, $274,423 total compensation

Svp And Chief Risk Officer The Provident Bank, James Christy

Vice President, Colleen Hanley

Executive Vice President Human Resources, John Falco

First Vice President Marketing Director, Robert Capozzoli

Vice President, Brown Small

Vice President, Charles Pocsi

Assistant Vice President, Joseph Labib

Senior Vice President Director Asset Recovery, Rudolph Nemeth

First Vice President, Diane Conboy

Vice President Commercial Credit Underwriting, Debra Williams

Auditors: KPMG LLP

LOCATIONS

HQ: Provident Financial Services Inc
239 Washington Street, Jersey City, NJ 07302
Phone: 732 590-9200
Web: www.providentnj.com

PRODUCTS/OPERATIONS

2014 Sales

	$ mil.	% of total
Interest		
Real estate secured loans	167	52
Commercial loans	50	16
Consumer loans	24	7
Securities & other	39	12
Non-interest		
Fees	31	10
Other	10	3
Total	321	100

COMPETITORS

Bank of America	PNC Financial
Capital One	TD Bank USA
Citibank	Valley National
Hudson City Bancorp	Bancorp
JPMorgan Chase	
New York Community Bancorp	

HISTORICAL FINANCIALS

Company Type: Public

Income Statement

FYE: December 31

	ASSETS ($ mil.)	NET INCOME ($ mil.)	INCOME AS % OF ASSETS	EMPLOYEES
12/18	9,726	118	1.2%	1,044
12/17	9,845	94	1.0%	1,054
12/16	9,500	88	0.9%	1,057
12/15	8,912	84	0.9%	1,064
12/14	8,523	74	0.9%	1,021
Annual Growth	3.4%	12.6%	—	0.6%

2018 Year-End Financials

Debt ratio: 4.00%
Return on equity: 9.00%
Cash ($ mil.): 143
Current ratio: —
Long-term debt ($ mil.): —

No. of shares (mil.): 66
Dividends
  Yield: 4.0%
  Payout: 53.0%
Market value ($ mil.): 1,600

	STOCK PRICE ($) FY Close	P/E High/Low	PER SHARE ($) Earnings	Dividends	Book Value
12/18	24.00	16 12	2.00	1.00	20.00
12/17	27.00	20 16	1.00	1.00	20.00
12/16	28.00	21 13	1.00	1.00	19.00
12/15	20.00	16 13	1.00	1.00	18.00
12/14	18.00	16 13	1.00	1.00	18.00
Annual Growth	7.5%	— —	10.5%	12.8%	3.8%

Prudential Annuities Life Assurance Corp

Prudential Annuities Life AssuranceÂ hasÂ a name that fits — the companyÂ is theÂ annuities business unit of life insurance giant Prudential Financial. ItÂ offers variable and fixedÂ annuitiesÂ and other retirement and long-term investment products and services.Â Prudential Annuities Life Assurance's products are distributed through independent financial planners brokers and banks. ItÂ holds the lead position in the US variable annuities market; its variable annuities are distributed by Prudential Annuities Distributors. The company which is part of Prudential Financial's US Retirement Solutions and Investment Management DivisionÂ targets US residents with a household income level of above $100000.

EXECUTIVES

Pres-Ceo, Robert F O'Donnell
Exec V Pres-Cfo, Yanela C Frias
Vice-President, Gary Palmer
Vice-President, Jan Hoffmeister
Executive of Sales, Lynn Erikson
Chief Operating Officer, Pelle Wahlstrom
Chief Information Officer, Ulf Tingstrom
Database Administrator, Cheryl Stewart
Software Developer, Dave Gianetti

Chief Investment Officer, Michael Long
Public Relations Executive, Scott Hawkins
Auditors: PricewaterhouseCoopers LLP

LOCATIONS

HQ: Prudential Annuities Life Assurance Corp
One Corporate Drive, Shelton, CT 06484
Phone: 203 926-1888
Web: www.investor.prudential.com

COMPETITORS

American Equity Investment Life Holding Company
Genworth Financial
Great American Financial Resources
John Hancock Financial Services
Kansas City Life
Lincoln Financial Group
MassMutual
MetLife
National Western
Northwestern Mutual
Presidential Life

HISTORICAL FINANCIALS

Company Type: Public

Income Statement				FYE: December 31
	ASSETS ($ mil.)	NET INCOME ($ mil.)	INCOME AS % OF ASSETS	EMPLOYEES
12/18	54,678	1,683	3.1%	—
12/17	59,961	(84)	—	—
12/16	59,822	(1,090)	—	—
12/15	47,255	173	0.4%	—
12/14	52,473	251	0.5%	—
Annual Growth	1.0%	60.9%		

2018 Year-End Financials

Debt ratio: 1.00%	No. of shares (mil.): 0
Return on equity: 26.00%	Dividends
Cash ($ mil.): 4,541	Yield: —
Current ratio: —	Payout: —
Long-term debt ($ mil.): —	Market value ($ mil.): —

Prudential Financial Inc

Prudential Financial wants to make sure its position near the top of the life insurance summit is set in stone. Prudential known for its Rock of Gibraltar logo is one of the top US life insurers and one of the largest life insurance companies worldwide. The firm is perhaps best known for its individual life insurance though it also sells group life and disability insurance as well as annuities. Prudential also offers investment products and services including asset management services mutual funds and retirement planning. In Asia the company operates through its Gibraltar Life Insurance and Life Planner units. Prudential has some $1.4 trillion in assets under management.

Operations

Prudential operates through five primary divisions encompassing seven segments as well as its corporate operations.

The largest division which brings in more than 35% of revenue is International Insurance. That division provides individual life group insurance and retirement products including certain health policies.

Its US Workplace Solutions division — the second-largest bringing in more than 30% of revenue — comprises the Retirement and Group Insurance

segments. The Retirement segment provides investment and income products and services to retirement plan sponsors. The Group Insurance segment offers a full range of group life long-term and short-term group disability and group corporate- bank- and trust-owned life insurance in the US. It primarily sells these to institutional clients.

Next the US Individual Life and Group Insurance division (about 20% of revenue) includes the Individual Life and Group Insurance segments. The Individual Life segment distributes variable life term life and universal life policies largely to middle-class affluent and wealthy clients in the US. The Group insurance segment offers group life group disability and corporate- bank- and trust-owned life insurance to institutional clients who use them in concert with employee plans and affinity groups.

The fourth division Closed Block brings in more than 10% of revenues. It includes certain in-force policies and annuities (issued prior to the group's demutualization in 2001) as well as related assets and liabilities.

Geographic Reach

Prudential's US operations account for nearly two-thirds of sales. The company also offers international products in more than 40 countries in regions including Asia Latin America and Europe.

The International Insurance division owns offices in Argentina Brazil Japan Korea Malaysia and Taiwan; and leases offices in Italy and Mexico. The Asset Management segment which includes international investment operations leases offices in Australia France Germany Hong Kong Japan Luxembourg Mexico Portugal Singapore South Korea Taiwan and the UK.

Sales and Marketing

Prudential distributes its insurance and annuity products through independent brokers and agencies as well as through Allstate and Prudential's own force of internal agents. The company's investment products are marketed through an in-house sales force while its retirement products are primarily sold through third-party financial advisors benefit consultants and brokers.

Individual life products are offered through third-party channels including independent brokers banks general agencies and producer groups.

Gibraltar Life distributes its products through affinity groups banks and from an in-house fleet of Life Planners who target affluent customers and small businesses.

Strategy

The company pursues growth in its current business lines both organically as well as through acquisitions joint ventures and investments.

Prudential has pursued intensive international growth in recent years with a focus on expanding its insurance and retirement operations in emerging markets. It is concentrating on deepening its presence in markets where it already operates such as Japan. To reach that objective the company has spent about a decade building up its holdings in Japan through a series of acquisitions. To expand in China Prudential is also carefully working on a 50/50 joint venture with a unit of the Chinese conglomerate Fosun Group. The company has already established a joint venture in India which it also considers a high-growth market. Expanding in Europe Prudential opened a new office in Milan in 2015.

In the US market Prudential seeks to provide wealth protection products to individual and group customers. It is expanding both its US insurance and its US retirement and investment management divisions through increased distribution and marketing efforts as well as through occasional acquisitions. In 2015 the group's mutual fund business Prudential Investment launched the Prudential Core Bond Fund a fixed-income platform investing

in such assets as US government securities mortgage-related securities and corporate debt.

In mid-2017 the company announced a reorganization of its US operations; its three units will be named Individual Solutions (including annuities and individual life insurance activities) Workplace Solutions (retirement and group insurance) and Investment Management.

Mergers and Acquisitions

In 2015 Prudential acquired a 40% stake in Chilean retirement services provider Administradora de Fondos de Pensions Habitat (AFP Habitat) for some $532 million. Also that year Prudential Real Estate Investors bought a 49-story Class A office building in Chicago and a new residential high-rise in Cambridge Massachusetts.

Prudential Investment Management in 2016 acquired the Indian asset management business of Deutsche Bank expanding its product portfolio and distribution platform in India.

HISTORY

In 1873 John Dryden founded the Widows and Orphans Friendly Society in New Jersey to sell workers industrial insurance (low-face-value weekly premium life insurance). In 1875 it became The Prudential Friendly Society taking the name from England's Prudential Assurance Co. The next year Dryden visited the English company and copied some of its methods such as recruiting agents from its targeted neighborhoods.

Prudential added ordinary whole life insurance in 1886. By 1900 the firm was selling more than 2000 such policies annually and had 3000 agents in eight states. In 1896 the J. Walter Thompson advertising agency (now the WPP Group) designed Prudential's Rock of Gibraltar logo.

The firm issued its first group life policy in 1916 (Prudential became a major group life insurer in the 1940s). In 1928 it introduced an Accidental Death Benefit which cost it an extra $3 million in benefits the next year alone (death claims rose drastically early in the Depression).

In 1943 Prudential mutualized. The company began decentralizing operations in the 1940s. Later it introduced a Property Investment Separate Account (PRISA) which gave pension plans a real estate investment option. By 1974 the firm was the US's group pension leader.

The insurer bought securities brokerage The Bache Group to form Pru Bache (now Prudential Securities) in 1981. Bache's forte was retail investments an area expected to blend well with Prudential's insurance business. Under George Ball Pru Bache tried to become a major investment banker — but failed. In 1991 Ball resigned leaving losses of almost $260 million and numerous lawsuits involving real estate limited partnerships.

Despite the 1992 settlement of the real estate partnership suits Prudential remained under scrutiny by several states because of "churning" a process in which agents generated commissions by inducing policyholders to trade up to more expensive policies. In 1995 new management led by former Chase Manhattanite Arthur Ryan brought sales under control sold such units as reinsurance and mortgage servicing and put its $6 billion real estate portfolio on the block. (In 1997 it sold its property management unit and Canadian commercial real estate unit; in 1998 it sold its landmark Prudential Center complex in Boston.)

In 1996 regulators from 30 states found that Prudential knew about the churning earlier than it had admitted had not stopped the perpetrators and had even promoted them. A 1997 settlement called for the company to pay restitution but the more than $2 billion estimated cost was thought to be less than the losses customers had suffered.

As the financial services industry continued to restructure Prudential in 1998 announced plans to demutualize. To focus on life insurance the company sold its health care unit to Aetna in 1999. The same year Prudential paid $62 million to resolve more churning claims revamped itself into international institutional and retail divisions and trimmed jobs. Ending its attempts to originate business the company cut 75% of its investment banking staff in 2000.

Demutualized Prudential Financial's 2001 IPO — one of the largest ever in the insurance industry — raised more than $3 billion. Prudential Financial became the holding company name for all operations making Prudential Insurance (the company's former name) a subsidiary and pure life insurer.

EXECUTIVES

Vice President Information Systems, Daniel Galvin
Chairman And Ceo, John R. Strangfeld, age 65, $1,400,000 total compensation
Svp Corporate Human Resources And Chair The Prudential Foundation, Sharon C. Taylor, age 65
Evp And Coo International, Charles F. (Charlie) Lowrey, age 61, $770,000 total compensation
Svp And Cio, Barbara G. Koster, age 64
Evp And Coo Us Businesses, Stephen (Steve) Pelletier, age 65, $770,000 total compensation
Evp And Cfo, Robert M. Falzon, age 59, $759,231 total compensation
Svp And Chief Investment Officer, Scott G. Sleyster, age 59
Svp And Chief Risk Officer, Nicholas C. (Nick) Silitch, age 57
Svp And Chief Actuary, Richard F. Lambert, age 62
President And Ceo Prudential Retirement, Phil Waldeck
Evp And General Counsel, Timothy P. Harris, age 58
Vp Enterprise Services And Financial Systems, Victor Ramos
Vice President Information Systems, Michael Falzon
Vice President Information Technology, Jim Tonno
Vice President Individual Life Insurance Technology, Steven Leitman
Vice President Information Technology, Diana D'Amore
Vice President Human Resources, Suzy Burnham
Vice President, Kevin Prue
Vice President Global Marketing Research, Andrea Kasper
Vice President, Francine Boucher
Vice President Corporate Counselor, Lisa Chow
Vice President Investor Relations, Ruth Hiatt
Senior Vice President Human Resources, Sue Taylor
Vice President, Anthony Fontano
Vp Actuarial Talent Management Organization, Michelle Jankowski
Vice President Of International Operations And Systems, Ryugo Toh
Vice President Information Systems And Security, Matt Schuette
Vice President Annuity Product Management, Lorie Lanza
Vice President Business Ethics Officer, Kimberly Tabb
Vice President Corporate Counsel, Daniel Stringham
Senior Vice President Structured Tranactions Derivative Products, Richard Toner
Vice President And Actuary Actuarial Financial Reporting, Michael J Kaufman
Vice President Financial Systems, John Toner
Vice President Corporate Development, Gaurav Wadhwa
Vice President, Rushabh Shah
Vice President Chief Information Security Officer, Thomas Doughty

Vice President Issues Management, Greg Loder
Vice President Marketing, James Irvine
Vice President Process Management, Greg Steffe
Vice President Relationship Management And Key Accounts, Kevin Tigges
Vice President Institutional Investment Products Group, John Bradley
Vice President Corporate Development, Timothy Maroney
Vice President Project Management, Mary Mathern
Vice President Corporate Counsel, Richard Hibbard
Vice President Strategic Relationship Management, John Keenan
M Sales Vice President, Doug Peterson
Vice President National Accounts, David Johnston
Vice President Information Systems, Venkata Natarajan
Svp And Head Global Product And Market Solutions Pension Risk Transfer Business, Rohit Mathur
Vice President, Bernie Oneill
Vice President Marketing Metrics, Bob Conover
Vp Partner Services, Ivan Potje
Vice President Corporate Counsel (1997), William H Bulmer
Vice President Information Technology, Nicholas Defeis
Vice President National Platform Distribution, Rebecca Makas
Vice President Customer Service, Pauline Rossbauer
Vice President Process Management, Noreen Bertscha
Vice President Finance, Jurgen Muhlhauser
Vice President Of Underwriting, Heidi Bartels
Vice President Finance Chief Officer Prudential Group Insurance, Christine Knight
Vice President Marketing, Barbara Ernst
Vp And Controller Individual Life, Jamie Riesterer
Vice President Operational Risk Management, Susanna Davi
Vice President, Barbara Fuchs
Vice President, Brad Wiginton
Vice President Policy And Regulatory Officer, Jennifer Toure
Vice President (capital Markets), Arnaud Bensoussan
Vice President Of Financial Reporting, Stanley Lezon
Territorial Vice President, Mark Sears
Vice President Information Systems, Christopher Winterroll
Vice President Sales And Strategic Relationships Experience, Anne Thibeault
Vice President Of Stable Value Markets, Dylan Tyson
Vice President Data Warehousing, Brian Davenport
Vice President Counsel, Lisa Wolmart
Regional Vice President, Sean Kath
Vice President, Jennifer Finnerty
Vice President Regional Sales Manager, Chris Sheckley
Vice President Investment Operations, Ralph Vasquez
Vice President Recruiting And Development, Catalina Camoscio
Vice President External Affairs, Ron Doughty
Vice President Business Finance, Stephen Durocher
Vice President Demand Management, Beth Abbott
Vice President, Susanna Horng
Vice President, Lily Huang
Senior Vice President Client Relations And Business Development, Sean Mclaughlin
Vice President Strategic Initiatives, Amy Tedesco
Vice President Talent Partner, Matthew Dreyer
Regional Sales Vice President, Scott Daniels
Vice President Accounting Policy, Thomas Karafin
Assistant Vice President Actuary, Hannah Sun

Vice President Applied Technologies, Michael Boatright
Vice President Strategy Execution And Metrics Strategic Relationships, Jennifer Hutton
Regional Vice President External Wholesaler, Kinga Gawron
Vice President Head Of Talent Consulting, John Hom
Regional Sales Vice President, Lawrence Slabosz
Vice President, Knox Kim
Vice President Complaints Appeals And Litigation Group Insurance, Chris Longo
Investment Senior Vice President, Anne Fifick
Vice President Of Global Communications, Linda Fung
Regional Vice President At The Prudential Insurance Company Of America, Teri Sullivan-yelko
Vice President Strategic Sourcing, Mark Vogt
Senior Vice President Business Development, Marc Pester
Regional Sales Vice President, Wai Miks
Vice President And Assistant Treasurer, Kathleen Hoffman
Vice President Human Resources International Hr, Erin Bokina
Vice President Information Systems, Steven Alt
Vice President, Georgia Kingsley
Senior Vice President, Nick Silitch
Vice President, Steve Ahrens
Cfa Vice President Investmetn Strategy, Mark Bojanowski
Vp Human Resources Senior Hr Business Partner, Christina Schelling
Vice President Data Governance And Solutions, John Adamo
Vice President, Donna Dixon
Investment Vice President, Fernando Herrera
Vice President, Jenna Mcneill
Vp Information Systems And Infrastructure, David Quinn
Executive Vice President Head Global Accounts Global Financial Intermediaries, Kimberly Lapointe
Vice President Information Systems, Marion Campbell
Vice President Key Accounts, Darel Eastling
Vice President Business Development Executive, Jason Krasula
Vice President Regulatory Reporting Corporate Cantrollers, Benoit Bosi
Vp Information Systems, Andrew Pu
Vice President Information Systems, Anita Manchandra
Vice President Telecommunications Information Systems, Warren Leary
Vice President Sales, Richard Kinville
Vice President, Jim Street
Vice President Conference And Travel, Joanne Gandolfo
Senior Vice President Sales Manager, Jonathan Cressman
Vice President Asset Management Human Resources, Marni Garfinkle
Vice President Information Technology, Joe Corrato
Vice President Risk And Control, Susanna Banic
Vice President Mutual Fund Product Devel, Christine Grande
Vice President, James Quartuccio
Vice President, Larry Frank
Vice President Service Assurance, Don Healey
Vice President Marketing And Brokerage Services, Michael Kalen
Vice President Administration, Angela Verrios
Vice President Audit, Hai You
Vice President, Brian Cloonan
Vp Institutional Sales, Ann Nanda
Vice President Corporate Counsel (2006), Richard E Buckley

Vice President And Actuary, Sharon S Brody
Regional Vice President, Don Lanham
Vice President Corporate Counsel (1997), Jeffrey H Clott
Vice President Of Strategic Initiatives, Vishal Jain
Investment Sr. Vice President, Husnu Kipcak
Vice President Retirement Sales Southeast Region, Christopher Stout
Vice President Business Solutions Center, Arthur Selverian
Vice President Marketing And Leads, Danielle Elliott
Vice President, Jeff Lee
Auditors: PricewaterhouseCoopers LLP

LOCATIONS

HQ: Prudential Financial Inc
751 Broad Street, Newark, NJ 07102
Phone: 973 802-6000
Web: www.investor.prudential.com

2017 Sales

	$ mil.	% of total
US	36,573	61
Other	23,116	39
Total	**59,689**	**100**

PRODUCTS/OPERATIONS

2017 Sales by Segment

	$ mil.	% of total
International Insurance	21,560	35
US Workplace Solutions	19,314	32
US Individual Solutions	10,084	17
Closed block business	6,601	11
Investment Management	3,355	5
Adjustments	(1225)	-
Total	**59,689**	**100**

2017 Sales

	$ mil.	% of total
Premiums	32,091	54
Net investment income	16,435	27
Policy charges & fee income	5,303	9
Asset management & service fees	4,127	7
Net realized investment gains	432	2
Other	1,301	1
Total	**59,689**	**100**

COMPETITORS

AEGON	ING
AIG	John Hancock Financial
AXA	Services
Aetna	MassMutual
Aflac	Meiji Yasuda Life
Allianz	MetLife
American Life Insurance	Nationwide Life Insurance
Aviva	Nippon Life Insurance
COUNTRY Financial	Northwestern Mutual
Dai-ichi Life	Principal Financial
FMR	Prudential plc
Great-West Lifeco	Zurich Insurance Group

HISTORICAL FINANCIALS

Company Type: Public

Income Statement

FYE: December 31

	ASSETS ($ mil.)	NET INCOME ($ mil.)	INCOME AS % OF ASSETS	EMPLOYEES
12/18	815,078	4,074	0.5%	50,492
12/17	831,921	7,863	0.9%	49,705
12/16	783,962	4,368	0.6%	49,739
12/15	757,388	5,642	0.7%	49,384
12/14	766,655	1,381	0.2%	48,331
Annual Growth	1.5%	31.1%	—	1.1%

2018 Year-End Financials

Debt ratio: 2.00%	No. of shares (mil.): 411	
Return on equity: 8.00%	Dividends	
Cash ($ mil.): 15,353	Yield: 4.0%	
Current ratio: —	Payout: 38.0%	
Long-term debt ($ mil.): —	Market value ($ mil.): 33,494	

	STOCK PRICE ($) FY Close	P/E High/Low		PER SHARE ($) Earnings	Dividends	Book Value
12/18	82.00	13	8	10.00	4.00	118.00
12/17	115.00	6	5	18.00	3.00	128.00
12/16	104.00	11	6	10.00	3.00	107.00
12/15	81.00	7	6	12.00	2.00	94.00
12/14	90.00	29	24	3.00	2.00	92.00
Annual Growth	(2.6%)	—		—	31.0% 13.5%	6.6%

Public Service Enterprise Group Inc

In the Garden State Public Service Enterprise Group's (PSEG) diversified business model has it smelling like a rose. Regulated subsidiary Public Service Electric and Gas (PSE&G) transmits and distributes electricity to 2.2 million customers and natural gas to 1.8 million customers in New Jersey. Subsidiary PSEG Power operates power generating plants and sells its energy wholesale to PSE&G and others. PSEG Power's 11800-MW generating capacity comes mostly from nuclear and fossil-fuel plants in the US Northeast and Mid-Atlantic regions.

HISTORY

Tragedy struck Newark New Jersey in 1903 when a trolley slid down an icy hill and collided with a train killing more than 30 people. While investigating the accident state attorney general Thomas McCarter discovered the mismanagement of the trolley company and many of New Jersey's other transportation gas and electric companies. Planning to buy and consolidate these companies McCarter resigned and established the Public Service Corporation in 1903 with several colleagues.

The company formed divisions for gas utilities electric utilities and transportation companies. The trolley company generated almost half of Public Service's sales during its first year.

In 1924 the gas and electric companies consolidated as Public Service Electric and Gas (PSE&G). A new company was formed that year to operate buses and in 1928 it merged with the trolley company to form Public Service Coordinated Transport (later Transport of New Jersey). PSE&G signed interconnection agreements with two Pennsylvania electric companies in 1928 to form the first integrated power pool — later known as the Pennsylvania-New Jersey-Maryland Interconnection. The Public Utility Holding Company Act of 1935 ushered in the era of regulated regional monopolies ensuring PSE&G a captive market.

During the 1960s PSE&G joined Philadelphia Electric to build its first nuclear plant at Peach Bottom Pennsylvania. The company completed a second plant in 1977 at Salem New Jersey. Its third one went on line at Hope Creek New Jersey. However plant mismanagement earned PSE&G a slew of fines in the 1980s and 1990s.

The company sold its transportation system to the State of New Jersey in 1980. Five years later

PSE&G formed holding company Public Service Enterprise Group (PSEG) to move into nonutility enterprises and created Community Energy Alternatives (CEA now PSEG Global) to invest in independent power projects. In 1989 Enterprise Diversified Holdings (now PSEG Energy Holdings) was formed to handle activities ranging from real estate to oil and gas production.

CEA and three partners acquired a Buenos Aires power plant in 1993. Taking advantage of overseas privatization in the late 1990s it expanded into Asia and with AES purchased two Argentine electric companies.

PSE&G's nuclear problems resurfaced when the Salem plant was shut down in 1995 to rectify equipment breakdowns. In 1997 PSEG paid Salem partners Delmarva Power & Light and PECO Energy $82 million to settle their lawsuits charging mismanagement of Salem; both units were back on line by 1998.

Continuing to diversify in the late 1990s PSEG formed PSEG Energy Technologies in 1997 to market power and acquired five mechanical services companies in 1998 and 1999.

In 1999 PSEG Global teamed up with Panda Energy International to build three merchant plants in Texas (to be completed by 2001). It also planned plants in India and Venezuela and joined Sempra Energy to buy 90% of Chilquinta Energ - a an energy distributor in Chile and Peru. In 2000 it bought 90% of a distributor serving Argentina and Brazil.

New Jersey's electricity markets were deregulated in 1999; a year later the company transferred PSE&G's generation assets to nonregulated unit PSEG Power. PSEG Power also took charge of PSEG Global's plants under development in Illinois Indiana and Ohio; announced plans for new plants in New Jersey; and acquired an Albany New York plant from Niagara Mohawk.

PSEG Global completed a power plant in Texas in 2001. It also bought 94% of generator and distributor Saesa from Chile's largest conglomerate Copec for $460 million; it later acquired the rest of Saesa through a tender offer. It also purchased a Peruvian generation firm ElectroAndes for $227 million.

In 2002 PSEG Power acquired two Connecticut plants from WEC Energy for approximately $270 million.

PSEG had agreed to be acquired by Exelon but both New Jersey and Pennsylvania opposed the merger and the deal fell through in 2006.

In 2006 PSEG Global sold its 32% stake in RGE a Brazilian electric distribution company with approximately 1.1 million customers to Companhia Paulista de For Ṣa e Luz. In 2008 it sold the SAESA Group of Companies (a power distribution group) in southern Chile to a consortium formed by Morgan Stanley Infrastructure and the Ontario Teachers' Pension Plan for $887 million.

In 2013 PSEG Solar Source announced that it purchased two utility-scale solar power plants totaling 4.4 MW from Canadian Solar Inc. The solar installations are the largest in Shasta county California built at more than 3300 feet in elevation.

EXECUTIVES

Vice President Finance (pseandg) Pseg Services Corporation, Scott Jennings
President And Coo Pseg Power Llc, Ralph A. LaRossa, age 56, $684,308 total compensation
Chairman President And Ceo, Ralph Izzo, age 61, $1,298,269 total compensation
Evp And Cfo, Daniel J. (Dan) Cregg, age 55, $520,000 total compensation
Vp Regulatory Pseg Services, Tamara L. Linde, age 54, $533,789 total compensation

Vp Asset Management And Centralized Services
Pse&g, David M. Daly, age 57

President Pseg Services Corporation, Derek M. Di
Risio, age 54

Svp Hr And Chro Pseg Services Corporation,
Sheila Rostiac

Vice President Engineering Pseg Nuclear, Paul J
Davison

Vice President Gas Supply Pseg Energy
Resources And Trade, David Caffery

Vice President Of Employee Benefits Health And
Safety, John Tiberi

Vice President Manager Director, Donald Staudt

Vice President Tax, Robert Krueger

Vice President Of Tax, Norman Chadwick

Vice President Of Tax, Jose M Perez

Vp Internal Auditing Services Pseandg, Courtney
Mccormick

Legal Secretary, June Barnett

Vp Electric Operations Pseandg, John Bridges

Vice President Of Tax, Mark Creely

Legal Secretary, Sandra Mayer

Vice President Procurement Pseg Service Corp.,
Brian Clark

Senior Vice President Delivery Projects And
Construction Pseandg, Kim Hanemann

Vp Transmission And Distribution Pseg Long
Island, John O'Connell

Vp Corporate Communications Pseg Services
Corporation, Karen Cleeve

Vice President Of Compliance, David Mannai

Government Relations, Vincent Frigeria

Board Member, Hak Shin

Treasurer, Bradford Huntington

Board Member, Michael F Percarpio

Board Member, Willie Deese

Auditors: DELOITTE & TOUCHE LLP

LOCATIONS

HQ: Public Service Enterprise Group Inc
80 Park Plaza, Newark, NJ 07102
Phone: 973 430-7000
Web: www.pseg.com

PRODUCTS/OPERATIONS

2016 Sales

	$ mil.	% of total
PSE&G	6,221	59
Power	4,023	38
Others	370	3
Adjustments	(1553)	-
Total	**9,061**	**100**

Selected Subsidiaries

PSEG Energy Holdings Inc. (nonutility companies)
  PSEG Global Inc. (solar plants and other alternative
  energy investments)
  PSEG Resources Inc. (energy infrastructure
  investments)
PSEG Power LLC
  PSEG Fossil LLC (operator of PSEG's fossil fuel
  plants)
  PSEG Nuclear LLC (operator of PSEG's nuclear
  plants)
  PSEG Energy Resources and Trade LLC (energy
  marketing)
PSEG Services Corporation (management and
  administrative services for PSEG)
Public Service Electric and Gas Company (PSE&G
  distribution of electricity and gas)

COMPETITORS

AEP	FirstEnergy
CenterPoint Energy	NRG Energy
Con Edison	National Grid USA
Constellation Energy	New Jersey Resources
Group	NextEra Energy
Delmarva Power	PPL Corporation
Eversource Energy	South Jersey
Exelon	Industries

HISTORICAL FINANCIALS

Company Type: Public

Income Statement   FYE: December 31

	REVENUE ($ mil.)	NET INCOME ($ mil.)	NET PROFIT MARGIN	EMPLOYEES
12/18	9,696	1,438	14.8%	13,145
12/17	9,084	1,574	17.3%	12,945
12/16	9,061	887	9.8%	13,065
12/15	10,415	1,679	16.1%	13,025
12/14	10,886	1,518	13.9%	12,689
Annual Growth	(2.9%)	(1.3%)	—	0.9%

2018 Year-End Financials

Debt ratio: 34.00%
Return on equity: 10.00%
Cash ($ mil.): 177
Current ratio: 1.00
Long-term debt ($ mil.): 13,168

No. of shares (mil.): 504
Dividends
  Yield: 3.0%
  Payout: 64.0%
Market value ($ mil.): 26,233

	STOCK PRICE ($) FY Close	P/E High/Low		PER SHARE ($) Earnings	Dividends	Book Value
12/18	52.00	20	16	3.00	2.00	29.00
12/17	52.00	17	13	3.00	2.00	27.00
12/16	44.00	27	22	2.00	2.00	26.00
12/15	39.00	13	11	3.00	2.00	26.00
12/14	41.00	15	10	3.00	1.00	24.00
Annual Growth	5.9%	—	—	(1.4%)	5.0%	4.3%

Publix Super Markets, Inc.

Publix Super Markets tops the list of privately owned grocery operators in the US. By emphasizing service and a family-friendly image over price Publix has outgrown and outperformed its regional rivals. Some two-thirds of its nearly 1200 stores are in Florida but it also operates in half a dozen other southeastern states. Publix makes some of its own bakery deli dairy goods and fresh prepared foods at its own manufacturing plants in Florida and Georgia. Many stores also house pharmacies and banks. Founder George Jenkins began offering stock to Publix employees in 1930; employees own more than a quarter of the company.

Operations

Publix stores sell grocery products (dairy produce deli baker meat and seafood) health and beauty care products general merchandise pharmacy products flowers and other products and services. Grocery activities account for some 85% of sales.

Geographic Reach

Publix has nearly 1200 supermarkets in Florida (about two-thirds of total) and Georgia (more than 15% of total) as well as Alabama South Carolina Tennessee North Carolina and Virginia.

It restocks store shelves from nine distribution centers — seven in Florida and one each in Georgia and Alabama. The grocer also operates half a dozen dairy bakery and deli facilities four in Florida and two in Georgia.

Financial Performance

Publix has shown solid sales growth over the past five years as it continues to expand and open new stores across the Southeast. Its revenue has risen some 20% since 2013. With profit margins higher than many (if not all) of its grocery com-

petitors the company has also seen increases in its net income in recent years.

In 2017 Publix reported revenue of $34.8 billion up about 1.5% from the prior year. New store openings powered the growth along with a 1.7% increase in comparable-store sales which was helped by customers' stocking up and replenishing before and after Hurricane Irma hit Florida. This was more than enough to offset an additional week of operation in 2016 which was a 53-week fiscal year.

As the dominant grocer in its primary market Florida Publix regularly reports net profit margins of between 5.5%-6% much higher than other super market chains (Kroger for example is in the 1.5%-2% range). In 2017 it had net earnings of $2.3 billion up from $2 billion in 2016. In addition to the increased revenue net earnings were boosted some $224 million by the Tax Cut and Jobs Act of 2017.

Cash at the end of 2017 was $580 million an increase of about $140 million from the prior year. Cash from operations contributed $3.6 billion to the coffers while investing and financing activities used some $3.45 million mainly for expenditures used in new and remodeled stores and for dividends and stock buybacks.

Strategy

Publix's growth strategy is based on investing in its stores and enhancing its customer service.

It plans to spend more than $1.5 billion in 2018 to open new stores remodel existing stores and increase ownership of its store portfolio. The company opened 44 stores in 2017 including its first locations in Virginia. At year's end it had about 35 stores under construction. In addition Publix remodeled more than 130 locations in 2017. It also continues to invest in its real estate portfolio. At the end of 2017 the company owned nearly a third of its stores up from 29% in 2016 and 11% in 2007.

Publix is also focused on keeping up with customer demand for delivery and other advanced services. It began working with grocery delivery firm Instacart in 2016 and currently offers home delivery in more than 90% of its operating area. The company is also testing curbside pickup and its online ordering platform has been expanded with smokehouse meats fried chicken and other items. It has also enhanced its pharmacy offerings through a partnership with BayCare Health System and serves pharmacy patients with new web and mobile applications.

Lastly Publix has announced plans to relaunch its GreenWise Market concept in select locations in 2018. GreenWise Market targets the health-conscious consumer with specialty natural and organic selections.

EXECUTIVES

Evp And Cfo, David P. Phillips, age 59, $1,051,090 total compensation

General Counsel And Secretary, John A. Attaway, age 60, $690,310 total compensation

Svp, David E. Bornmann, age 61, $488,300 total compensation

President Ceo And Director, Randall T. (Todd) Jones, age 56, $1,688,750 total compensation

Svp And Cio, Laurie Z. Douglas, age 55, $890,255 total compensation

Manager Government Relations, Shane Kunze

Pharmacy Manager, Larry Jones

Vice Chairman, Hoyt R. (Barney) Barnett, age 76

President And Director, William E. (Ed) Crenshaw, age 68

Auditors: KPMG LLP

LOCATIONS

HQ: Publix Super Markets, Inc.
  3300 Publix Corporate Parkway, Lakeland, FL 33811
Phone: 863 688-1188
Web: www.publix.com

2017 Supermarkets

	No.
Florida	779
Georgia	186
Alabama	65
South Carolina	58
Tennessee	41
North Carolina	30
Virginia	8
Total	**1,167**

PRODUCTS/OPERATIONS

2017 Sales

	% of total
Grocery	84
Other	16
Total	**100**

Selected Supermarket Departments

Bakery
Dairy
Deli
Floral
Groceries
Health and beauty care
Meat
Pharmacy
Produce
Seafood
Foods Processed
Baked goods
Dairy products
Deli items

COMPETITORS

ALDI	Kroger
CVS	Rite Aid
Costco Wholesale	Sedano's
Food Lion	Southeastern Grocers
IGA	Wal-Mart
Ingles Markets	Walgreen
Kmart	Whole Foods

HISTORICAL FINANCIALS

Company Type: Public

Income Statement   FYE: December 29

	REVENUE ($ mil.)	NET INCOME ($ mil.)	NET PROFIT MARGIN	EMPLOYEES
12/18	36,396	2,381	6.5%	202,000
12/17	34,837	2,292	6.6%	193,000
12/16	34,274	2,026	5.9%	191,000
12/15	32,619	1,965	6.0%	180,000
12/14	30,802	1,735	5.6%	175,000
Annual Growth	**4.3%**	**8.2%**	—	**3.7%**

2018 Year-End Financials

Debt ratio: 1.00%
Return on equity: 21.00%
Cash ($ mil.): 599
Current ratio: 1.00
Long-term debt ($ mil.): 163
No. of shares (mil.): 715
Dividends
  Yield: —
  Payout: 31.0%
Market value ($ mil.): —

	STOCK PRICE ($) FY Close	P/E High/Low	PER SHARE ($) Earnings	Dividends	Book Value
12/18	0.00	— —	3.00	1.00	17.00
Annual Growth		— —	—	—	—

PUBLIX SUPER MARKETS, INC.

Publix Super Markets tops the list of privately owned grocery operators in the US. By emphasizing service and a family-friendly image over price Publix has outgrown and outperformed its regional rivals. Some two-thirds of its nearly 1200 stores are in Florida but it also operates in half a dozen other southeastern states. Publix makes some of its own bakery deli dairy goods and fresh prepared foods at its own manufacturing plants in Florida and Georgia. Many stores also house pharmacies and banks. Founder George Jenkins began offering stock to Publix employees in 1930; employees own more than a quarter of the company.

Operations

Publix stores sell grocery products (dairy produce deli baker meat and seafood) health and beauty care products general merchandise pharmacy products flowers and other products and services. Grocery activities account for some 85% of sales.

Geographic Reach

Publix has nearly 1200 supermarkets in Florida (about two-thirds of total) and Georgia (more than 15% of total) as well as Alabama South Carolina Tennessee North Carolina and Virginia.

It restocks store shelves from nine distribution centers — seven in Florida and one each in Georgia and Alabama. The grocer also operates half a dozen dairy bakery and deli facilities four in Florida and two in Georgia.

Financial Performance

Publix has shown solid sales growth over the past five years as it continues to expand and open new stores across the Southeast. Its revenue has risen some 20% since 2013. With profit margins higher than many (if not all) of its grocery competitors the company has also seen increases in its net income in recent years.

In 2017 Publix reported revenue of $34.8 billion up about 1.5% from the prior year. New store openings powered the growth along with a 1.7% increase in comparable-store sales which was helped by customers' stocking up and replenishing before and after Hurricane Irma hit Florida. This was more than enough to offset an additional week of operation in 2016 which was a 53-week fiscal year.

As the dominant grocer in its primary market Florida Publix regularly reports net profit margins of between 5.5%-6% much higher than other super market chains (Kroger for example is in the 1.5%-2% range). In 2017 it had net earnings of $2.3 billion up from $2 billion in 2016. In addition to the increased revenue net earnings were boosted some $224 million by the Tax Cut and Jobs Act of 2017.

Cash at the end of 2017 was $580 million an increase of about $140 million from the prior year. Cash from operations contributed $3.6 billion to the coffers while investing and financing activities used some $3.45 million mainly for expenditures used in new and remodeled stores and for dividends and stock buybacks.

Strategy

Publix's growth strategy is based on investing in its stores and enhancing its customer service.

It plans to spend more than $1.5 billion in 2018 to open new stores remodel existing stores and increase ownership of its store portfolio. The company opened 44 stores in 2017 including its first locations in Virginia. At year's end it had about 35 stores under construction. In addition Publix re-

modeled more than 130 locations in 2017. It also continues to invest in its real estate portfolio. At the end of 2017 the company owned nearly a third of its stores up from 29% in 2016 and 11% in 2007.

Publix is also focused on keeping up with customer demand for delivery and other advanced services. It began working with grocery delivery firm Instacart in 2016 and currently offers home delivery in more than 90% of its operating area. The company is also testing curbside pickup and its online ordering platform has been expanded with smokehouse meats fried chicken and other items. It has also enhanced its pharmacy offerings through a partnership with BayCare Health System and serves pharmacy patients with new web and mobile applications.

Lastly Publix has announced plans to relaunch its GreenWise Market concept in select locations in 2018. GreenWise Market targets the health-conscious consumer with specialty natural and organic selections.

EXECUTIVES

Evp And Cfo, David P. Phillips, age 59, $1,051,090 total compensation
General Counsel And Secretary, John A. Attaway, age 60, $690,310 total compensation
Svp, David E. Bornmann, age 61, $488,300 total compensation
President Ceo And Director, Randall T. (Todd) Jones, age 56, $1,688,750 total compensation
Svp And Cio, Laurie Z. Douglas, age 55, $890,255 total compensation
Manager Government Relations, Shane Kunze
Pharmacy Manager, Larry Jones
Vice Chairman, Hoyt R. (Barney) Barnett, age 76
President And Director, William E. (Ed) Crenshaw, age 68

LOCATIONS

HQ: PUBLIX SUPER MARKETS, INC.
  3300 PUBLIX CORP PKWY, LAKELAND, FL 338113311
Phone: 863 688-1188
Web: WWW.PUBLIX.COM

2017 Supermarkets

	No.
Florida	779
Georgia	186
Alabama	65
South Carolina	58
Tennessee	41
North Carolina	30
Virginia	8
Total	**1,167**

PRODUCTS/OPERATIONS

2017 Sales

	% of total
Grocery	84
Other	16
Total	**100**

Selected Supermarket Departments

Bakery
Dairy
Deli
Floral
Groceries
Health and beauty care
Meat
Pharmacy
Produce
Seafood
Foods Processed
Baked goods
Dairy products
Deli items

ALDI
CVS
Costco Wholesale
Food Lion
IGA
Ingles Markets
Kmart

Kroger
Rite Aid
Sedano's
Southeastern Grocers
Wal-Mart
Walgreen
Whole Foods

HISTORICAL FINANCIALS

Company Type: Private

Income Statement				FYE: December 31
	REVENUE ($ mil.)	NET INCOME ($ mil.)	NET PROFIT MARGIN	EMPLOYEES
12/16	34,274	2,026	5.9%	193,000
12/15	32,619	1,965	6.0%	—
12/14	30,802	1,735	5.6%	—
12/12	27,707	1,552	5.6%	—
Annual Growth	5.5%	6.9%		—

PulteGroup Inc

PulteGroup targets a cross-section of home buyers nationwide by buying or optioning land to build single-family houses duplexes townhouses and condominiums. Its Centex brand is marketed to entry-level buyers while Pulte Homes aims to capture customers looking to trade up. PulteGroup also builds Del Webb retiree communities for the growing number of buyers in the 55-plus age range. The company sells its homes in some 45 markets across roughly 25 states. Its homes go for an average price of $425000. PulteGroup became one of the top homebuilders in the US by buying rivals John Wieland Homes and Centex Homes.

HISTORY

William Pulte built his first home in Detroit in 1950 and incorporated his business in 1956 as William J. Pulte Inc.

In 1961 the company built its first subdivision in Detroit. During that decade Pulte moved into Washington DC (1964) Chicago (1966) and Atlanta (1968). In 1969 Pulte merged with Colorado's American Builders to form the Pulte Home Corporation a publicly traded company.

Originally a builder of high-priced single-family homes Pulte began expanding into affordable and midrange housing markets. To lower costs it pioneered modular designs and prebuilt components. Pulte architects designed the Quadrominium a large structure with four separate two-bedroom units each with its own entrance and garage (priced at a mere $20000 per unit in the 1970s).

Pulte formed Intercontinental Mortgage (later renamed ICM Mortgage) and began making home loans in 1972. The company ran into trouble in 1988 when it was accused of forcing Pulte homebuyers in Baltimore to use ICM financing instead of cheaper loans from the county. Pulte settled by repaying the difference in loan costs.

By the mid-1980s Pulte was one of the US's largest on-site homebuilders. PHM Corporation was created in 1987 as a holding company for the Pulte group of companies. That year PHM entered the thrift business by assisting the Federal Savings and Loan Insurance Corp.'s S&L bailout. It acquired five Texas S&Ls (with assets of $1.3 billion)

for $45 million and eventually combined them to form First Heights (finally discontinuing the business in 1994).

Pulte Homes' Quality Leadership customer satisfaction program introduced in the early 1990s paid off in 1991 as Pulte enjoyed record sales despite a depressed home market. Renamed Pulte Corporation in 1993 the company soon faced rising interest rates which dampened the US housing market and affected the Mexican peso. Pulte recorded a $2 million foreign-currency loss on an affordable-housing venture in Mexico in 1994. Nonetheless it began a second joint venture in that country in 1995 and helped form mortgage bank Su Casita with nine Mexican homebuilders to finance home construction on its border. That year it also started developing retirement communities when it bought the Ponds at Clearbrook in New Jersey.

In 1996 its Mexican joint venture Condake-Pulte began building thousands of affordable homes for General Motors and Sony employees in maquiladora residential areas near the US-Mexico border. The company also bought Rhode Island's top homebuilder LeBlanc.

Pulte restructured in 1997 and a year later shed its manufactured housing and building supply business. It also acquired DiVosta one of Florida's largest homebuilders and Tennessee-based Radnor Homes.

The company's 1988 foray into S&Ls came back to haunt it in 1998: The Federal Deposit Insurance Corp. won a lawsuit that accused the builder of abusing tax benefits associated with the S&Ls. (Pulte settled the case in 2001 by paying $41.5 million.) In 1999 Pulte bought the interest held by investment firm Blackstone Group its partner in active-adult homebuilding.

The next year Pulte joined other builders in an Internet-based building materials cooperative. Also in 2000 the company began dealings to expand its homebuilding operations into Argentina.

The company changed its name to Pulte Homes in 2001. That year Mark O'Brien became the company's CEO. He directed Pulte through the major acquisition of retirement community developer Del Webb for about $800 million in stock and $950 million in assumed debt. The combined company became the largest US homebuilder. In 2002 Pulte reorganized the structure of its operations in Mexico and created Pulte Mexico S. de R.L. de C.V. one of the largest builders in that country.

Adding to its portfolio of accolades Pulte was named 2002 "Builder of the Year" by Professional Builder magazine and in 2003 Pulte ranked 19th among the "Top 50 Best-Performing Companies" in Business Week's performance rankings of the Standard & Poor's 500-stock index.

Pulte expanded its operations in the fast-growing San Diego area in 2003 by purchasing assets of ColRich Communities which included about 500 entitled lots in five communities in the South Bay and Coastal North areas of San Diego. It boosted its presence in the Albuquerque Phoenix and Tucson markets by acquiring Sivage-Thomas Homes (Albuquerque) with about 7000 lots in the region and Del Webb entered the Reno Nevada market with its Sierra Canyon active adult community. O'Brien left the company in June 2003 after having served in senior management positions for six years (and 21 total years) within the company. EVP and COO Richard Dugas stepped up to become the company's president and CEO at that time.

In September 2003 the US Court of Federal Claims awarded Pulte and related parties $48.7 million as a result of a breach of contract by the US government related to Pulte's acquisition of five savings and loans in 1988.

J.D. Power and Associates recognized Pulte as a top performer for its fifth consecutive year in its "2004 New Home Builder Customer Satisfaction Study." Out of the 25 markets it surveyed Pulte ranked highest in 14 markets #2 in nine markets and #3 in six markets.

At the close of 2004 Pulte sold some operations in Argentina to real estate developer Grupo Farallon. The next year it sold its Mexican and remaining Argentine homebuilding enterprises to focus exclusively on US operations.

The downturn in the US housing market — due to a toxic cocktail of higher home prices increased foreclosures high unemployment and constraints on mortgage lending — led to weakened demand for new homes and higher cancellation rates. For Pulte this trend meant decreased profitability and a decline in homebuilding activity. Pulte responded to the downturn and adjusted its operations by cutting jobs and shuttering plants to meet lower demand levels.

The company bought rival Centex in 2009. The acquisition made Pulte the largest homebuilder in the US and also strengthened Pulte's offerings in the lower-priced home segment.

A year following the Centex merger founder William Pulte retired from the company and from its board of directors. He was named chairman emeritus.

EXECUTIVES

Evp And Coo, Harmon D. Smith, age 55, $688,462 total compensation

Vp And Cio, Joseph L. Drouin

Evp Human Resources, James R. (Jim) Ellinghausen, age 61, $546,154 total compensation

Evp And Cfo, Robert T. (Bob) O'Shaughnessy, age 53, $742,307 total compensation

President Ceo And Director, Ryan R. Marshall, age 44, $738,462 total compensation

Evp General Counsel And Corporate Secretary, Todd N. Sheldon

Vp And Chief Marketing Officer, Manish M. Shrivastava

Area Vice President Of Finance, Rick Wiles

Vice President Marketing Communications, James VanKirk

Vice President Of Sales And Marketing, Sean Clancy

Senior Vice President Human Resources, Michelle Hairston

Svp Finance, James Ossowski

Vice President Of Procurement, Ryan Rossiter

Vice President Finance, Michael Hyland

Vice President Information Security And Chief Information Security Officer, Alex Wood

Senior Vice President Operations Pulte Mortgage, Wyvetter Livingston

Vice President Tax And Assistant Secretary, Kimberly Hill

Vice President Investor Relations And Corporate Communications, Jim Zeumer

Vice President Of Construction Operations, Chris Edwards

Vice President Land Acquisition, Brad Piroli

Vice President Finance, John Evans

Division Vice President Of Land Acquisition, Matt Callahan

Vice President Construction Operations Middle Atlantic Division, Brad Nicholas

Senior Vice President Capital Markets, Jeff Moran

Vice President Human Resources, Sharyn Torrisi-Cartwright

Vice President And Treasurer, D Bryce Bryce Langen

Regional Vice President Of Sales, Lindsay Motley

Vice President, David Demarco

Sr.vice President Operations, Leslie Devera-duncan

Vice President Regional Service Manager, Paul Harris
Vice President Sales And Marketing, Matt Roesch
Vice President Land Planning And Development, Robert Holmes
Area Vice President Southeast, Paul Johnson
Division Vice President Construction Operations, Rick Kyle
Board Member, Thomas Folliard
Board Member, Richard Dreiling
Board Member, John Peshkin
Auditors: Ernst & Young LLP

LOCATIONS

HQ: PulteGroup Inc
3350 Peachtree Road N.E., Suite 150, Atlanta, GA 30326
Phone: 404 978-6400
Web: www.pultegroupinc.com

Selected Homebuilding Regions

Florida
North (IL IN MI MN MO Northern CA OH OR WA)
Northeast (CT DE MD MA NJ NY PA RI VA)
Southeast (GA NC SC TN)
Southwest (AZ CO HI NV NM Southern CA)
Texas

PRODUCTS/OPERATIONS

2018 Sales

	$ mil.	% of total
West	2,655	26
Florida	1,944	19
Southeast	1,746	17
Midwest	1,497	15
Texas	1,301	13
Northeast	840	8
Financial Services	205	2
Total	**10,188**	**100**

2018 Sales

	$ mil.	% of total
Home building		
Home Sales 96	9818.4	
Land Sales 2	164.5	
Financial Services	205	2
Total	**10,188**	**100**

Selected Brands

Centex (entry-level buyers)
Del Webb (active-adult buyers)
DiVosta (Florida)
Pulte Homes (move-up buyers)

COMPETITORS

Beazer Homes	M.D.C.
CalAtlantic	Meritage Homes
D.R. Horton	NVR
Hovnanian Enterprises	Pardee Homes
KB Home	Toll Brothers
Lennar	

HISTORICAL FINANCIALS

Company Type: Public

Income Statement

FYE: December 31

	REVENUE ($ mil.)	NET INCOME ($ mil.)	NET PROFIT MARGIN	EMPLOYEES
12/19	10,213	1,017	10.0%	5,245
12/18	10,188	1,022	10.0%	5,086
12/17	8,573	447	5.2%	4,810
12/16	7,668	603	7.9%	4,623
12/15	5,982	494	8.3%	4,542
Annual Growth	**14.3%**	**19.8%**	**—**	**3.7%**

2019 Year-End Financials

Debt ratio: 29.00%	No. of shares (mil.): 270
Return on equity: 20.00%	Dividends
Cash ($ mil.): 1,218	Yield: 1.0%
Current ratio: 10.00	Payout: 14.0%
Long-term debt ($ mil.): 3,092	Market value ($ mil.): 10,485

	STOCK PRICE ($) FY Close	P/E High/Low		PER SHARE ($) Earnings	Dividends	Book Value
12/19	39.00	11	7	4.00	0.00	20.00
12/18	26.00	10	6	4.00	0.00	17.00
12/17	33.00	24	13	1.00	0.00	14.00
12/16	18.00	13	9	2.00	0.00	15.00
12/15	18.00	17	12	1.00	0.00	14.00
Annual Growth	**21.5%**	—	—	**28.1%**	**8.1%**	**10.3%**

PVH Corp

PVH has the buttoned-up look down. A top global apparel player PVH is the world's largest dress shirt and neckwear company. The company owns three titans of the apparel industry: Calvin Klein Tommy Hilfiger and Heritage Brands. The former two are multi-billion dollar global lifestyle brands while Heritage Brands is a luxury apparel wholesaler that owns the brands Van Heusen IZOD ARROW Warner's Olga and True&Co. PVH is also has licenses for third-party brands such as DKNY Speedo Kenneth Cole Reaction Michael Kors Collection and others. The company generates sales from multiple channels including about 1700 company-operated retail stores 1500 concession stands retail partners and licensees. It also charges royalty and advertising fees.

Operations

PVH organizes its business into three main areas: Tommy Hilfiger Calvin Klein and Heritage Brands.

Tommy Hilfiger split into Tommy Hilfiger North America and Tommy Hilfiger International contributes some 45% to PVH's revenue. The brand makes everyday and formalwear for the upper-middle class characterized by its classic American preppy stylings. It runs a number of sub-brands such as Hilfiger Collection Tommy Hilfiger Tailored Tommy Hilfiger Tommy Jeans and Tommy Sport. It sells its products wholesale to third party retailers and at retail via a network of owned outlets and has around 30 license agreements with third parties in Australia Brazil India and Mexico among other countries.

Calvin Klein accounts for nearly 40% of revenue and runs a number of sub-brands alongside its Calvin Klein "master" brand: Calvin Klein By Appointment Calvin Klein Jeans CK Calvin Klein and Calvin Klein Jeans. Together they fill various product niches categories and price points. As with Tommy Hilfiger Calvin Klein has around 50 licensing and other arrangements across its brands including JVs in Australia India and Mexico

Heritage Brands accounts for around 20% of revenue and makes shirts neckwear sportswear swimwear intimates underwear and accessories through a range of owned brands and licensed brands. Its licensed brands are DKNY Speedo Kenneth Cole New York Kenneth Cole Reaction MICHAEL Michael Kors Michael Kors Collection and Chaps. It sells wholesale and through Heritage Brands retail outlets across the United States and Canada. Some of its stores stock IZOD Golf Warner's and Speedo products. Heritage Brands

has licensing agreements with around 90 US and international companies.

PVH also completes e-commerce sales through its various brand websites.

Geographic Reach

PVH's products are made in more 1200 factories in some 50 countries worldwide. PVH maintains wholesale and retail warehousing and distribution centers in the US Canada Japan and the Netherlands. The centers inspect sort pack and ship goods to customers.

The company sells products in the US Canada Europe Asia Mexico and Brazil. Its US business accounts for about 45% of sales and Europe 35%. Asia and Canada bring in the rest.

Sales and Marketing

PVH has a relatively concentrated customer base. Its five largest customers including Macy's J. C. Penney account for a fifth of sales.

PVH targets the marketing of its brands at distinct consumer demographics. The company advertises its brands through digital media (including its e-commerce and social media sites) national print media television outdoor signage special events promotions and store locations. It also advertises through product tie-ins and sport sponsorships (Calvin Klein/basketball Van Heusen/football and IZOD/golf). The Tommy Hilfiger marketing team also coordinates appearances by the designer himself Tommy Hilfiger at runway shows special events and flagship store openings.

Financial Performance

PVH's sales stalled in 2015-17 but have grown strongly since while net income has followed a similar pattern.

In fiscal 2019 (ended March 29) PVH's sales grew 8% to $9.7 billion a company record thanks to strong growth in Tommy Hilfiger and Calvin Klein both domestically and abroad. By comparison the Heritage Brands segment was flat.

Net income grew 39% to $746 million as the company kept a lid on selling general and administrative (SG&A) expenses while growing sales. The decrease in SG&A expenses related to the absence of costs recorded in 2017 in connection with the Mr Hilfiger brands the Li & Fung termination and the move to a new New York office.

PVH's cash on hand fell $41.9 million during fiscal 2019 standing at $452.0 million at year's end. The company's operations generated $852.5 million offset by $395.4 million used in investing activities and $478.5 million used in financing activities. PVH's main cash uses in fiscal 2019 were capital expenditures debt repayments and share repurchases.

Strategy

PVH is unifying Calvin Klein under one creative vision. The process began when it took back full control of its jeans and underwear businesses in 2013 and has steadily progressed. It will consolidate its Calvin Klein Sportswear and Calvin Klein Jeans brands in North America close the Calvin Klein 205W39NYW brand close its flagship Madison Avenue store in Manhattan and restructure its creative and design teams globally. The changes should help become Calvin Klein operate more effectively and push PVH's sales towards its $12 billion goal.

Mergers and Acquisitions

Bringing some of its international businesses under direct control in 2019 PVH spent $90 million on acquiring the remaining 78% of Gazal Corporation PVH's long-term Australian partner that it did not already own. PVH also paid $75 million to acquire the Tommy Hilfiger business in Hong Kong.

HISTORY

Moses Phillips came to America from Poland in 1881. While living in a one-room apartment in Pottsville Pennsylvania he sold flannel shirts (which his wife sewed) to coal miners from a push-cart. He soon brought the rest of his family to the US and upgraded the pushcart to a horse and buggy. Business continued to grow and the Phillips-Jones Corporation was formed in 1907.

The company moved to New York in 1914 and control passed from father to son for four generations. Isaac followed Moses then Seymour took over in 1941 until he handed the reins to Lawrence who joined the company in 1948 and became president and CEO in 1969. Ads in the 1950s featured such actors as Anthony Quinn Burt Lancaster and Ronald Reagan in Van Heusen shirts. In 1957 the company received its new name Phillips-Van Heusen (PVH). It grew via acquisitions throughout the 1970s and began selling its merchandise at its own outlet stores in 1979 but it didn't want its products sold at the off-price outlets that became popular in the early 1980s. The company stopped doing business with stores and distributors that allowed PVH merchandise to reach cut-price vendors.

In 1987 PVH bought back more than 5 million shares of stock in order to fend off an acquisition bid by the Hunt family of Texas. Lawrence stepped down in 1993 ending the unbroken chain of Phillipses at the helm. In 1995 the Phillips family sold its stake in the business. In June 2011 the company renamed itself PVH Corp. officially dropping the Phillips-Van Heusen moniker to emphasize its diversified portfolio of brands.

EXECUTIVES

President Geoffrey Beene Retail, Margaret P. (Meg) Lachance

Executive Vice President Finance And Risk, Bruce Goldstein

Chairman And Ceo, Emanuel (Manny) Chirico, age 62, $1,350,000 total compensation

Evp Chief Operating And Financial Officer, Michael A. (Mike) Shaffer, age 57, $891,667 total compensation

Ceo Heritage Brands And North America Wholesale, Francis K. (Ken) Duane, age 63, $1,091,667 total compensation

President Licensing, Kenneth L. (Ken) Wyse

Ceo Tommy Hilfiger And Pvh Europe, Daniel Grieder, age 57, $937,209 total compensation

Evp The Marketing Group, Michael (Mike) Kelly

Ceo Tommy Hilfiger Americas, Gary Sheinbaum

President Van Heusen Retail, Steven B. (Steve) Shiffman, age 61, $908,333 total compensation

President Heritage Sportswear, Geoffrey (Geoff) Barrett

Evp Logistics Services, Kevin J. Urban

President Calvin Klein Retail, Barrie Scardina, age 55

President Calvin Klein 205w39nyc And Calvin Klein By Appointment, Michelle Kessler-Sanders

President Calvin Klein North America Design And Product Development, Alexander (Alex) Cannon

Svp And Chief Risk Officer, Melanie Steiner

President Neckwear, David Sirkin

President Core Intimates, Leslie (Les) Hall

President The Underwear Group, Cheryl Abel-Hodges

Group President Calvin Klein The Americas, Nicholas (Nick) Strange

Regional President Pvh Asia Pacific, Frank Cancelloni

Evp General Counsel And Secretary, Mark D. Fischer, age 57

Evp And Chief Human Resources Officer, David F. (Dave) Kozel, age 63

Evp And Cio, Eileen Mahoney

Chief Supply Chain Officer, William (Bill) McRaith

Evp Wholesale Canada, Richard Deck

President Calvin Klein Europe Brand Management, Marcela Wartenbergh

Country Manager Calvin Klein Brazil, Fábio Vasconcellos

Svp Sales Speedo, John Graham

President Pvh Japan, Tom Chu

Managing Director Calvin Klein Asia Pacific Korea, You Hyun-Ko

Managing Director Calvin Klein Asia Pacific China, Hanson Gu

Managing Director Calvin Klein Asia Pacific Commercial, Annie Wong

Managing Director France, Laurent Albouy

Managing Director Turkey, Hakan Atalay

Managing Director Russia, Georg Faisst

Managing Director Middle East Africa And The Netherlands, Maela Mandelli

Managing Director Uk And Ireland, David Pyne

Managing Director Nordic, Jesper Waerum

Svp And Controller, James Holmes

Vice President, Tom Whitmer

Group Vice President Womens Sourcing, Susan Parson

Vp Purchasing, Jason Zuckerman

Group Vice President Human Resources, Danielle Korins

Vice President Of Mens Design Van Heusen Retail, Jeanne Clarke

Senior Vice President Planning, Steve Leibow

Executive Vice President Pvh Supply, Matthew Wallace

Vice President Merchandising, Gladys Yu

Vice President Planning Process And Technology Integration, Jennifer Taras

Vice President Information Technology, Camille Szczecina

Vice President Of Planning And Analysis Calvin Klein, Pamela Silverstein

Svp Real Estate And Leasing, Natalie Turpan

Executive Vice President Sales And Marketing, Jarratt John

Vp Human Resources, Danielle Bernier

Vice President Distribution, Richard Vuich

Vice President Investor Relations, Nicole Shevins

Vice President Of Planning Calvin Klein, Milena Schaefer

Vice President Human Rights, Roopa Nair

Assistant Vice President Human Resources Learning And Development, Brian Paich

Vice President Marketing Operations, Kathleen Livingston

Dvp Core Brands, Dan Bowe

Vice President Of Creative Design For Warner's Olga Core Brands, Don Allen

Vice President Of Design, Kevin Michales

Senior Vice President, Jillian Zino

Vice President Of Design For Timberland Apparel, Michael Flynn

Vice President Finance Global Supply Chain, John Benz

Evp Integrated Global Marketing, Michael Delellis

Vice President Finance And Operations, Guilford Robinson

Vice President Real Estate, Lauren Kinder

Group Vice President Wholesale Information Technology, Debbie Beer-christensen

Vice President Marketing And Communications, Leslie Davenport

Senior Vice President Tax, Elizabeth Maguire

Vice President Dmm Vh Men's Sportswear Dress, Donna Williams

Vice President Creative Services, Andrea Murray

Vice President Replenishment Planning Calvin Klein, Stefanie Pagovich

Senior Vice President Of Communications, Tiffin Jernstedt

Vice President Retail Planning Calvin Klein Underwear, Marci Glicksman

Vice President, Marissa Pagnani

Svp Accounting, Erik Graf

Vice President Construction X 6306, Susan Pierce

Vice President, Larry Meltzer

Vice President Sales, Rebecca Lucas

Executive Vice President, Franck Belochi

National Sales Manager, Ray Hennessy

Vice President Communications, Lauren Mcclain

Vice President Dmm Sportswear And Accessories, Judith Colaiacovo

Vice President Technical Sevices, Mark Charlton

Vice President Distribution And Cs, Douglas Christian

Vice President, Marion Stienemeier

Vice President Human Resources, MaryAnn Vale

Vice President Global Financial Systems And Sap, Raj Varughese

Vice President Ecommerce (tommy Hilfiger), Sean Reynolds

Vice President Communications North America (tommy Hilfiger), Pearl Lee

Executive Vice President Ecommerce (calvin Klein), Mike Dupuis

Senior Vice President Marketing And Communications (tommy Hilfiger), Abdel Hamri

Senior Vice President Europe Calvin Klein Underwear Pvh, Melanie Gallop

Vice President Of Merchandising Sportswear, Thomas Chanthaphasouk

Executive Vice President Operations And Chief Financial Officer Calvin Klein, Gene Gosselin

Divisional Vice President Store Operations, David Herridge

Vice President Business Planning Store Planning And Analytics, Kristie Tippner

Grp Vice President Infrastructure Services, Dan Quigley

Vice President Global Supply Chain, Sanjeev Shrivastava

Vice President Strategy And Business Development, Candice Baseden

Senior Vice President Infrastructure And Operations, Joe Melfi

Senior Vice President Marketing, Jill Krizelman

Vice President Ecommerce (dmm Calvin Klein), Jimmy Carter

Vice President Of Business Development, Jay Fitzgerald

Vice President Tech Services, Ada Suneson

Senior Vice President Technical Design And Quality Assurance, Michael Collinson

Group Vice President International Information Technology, Fabrizio Zanardo

Vice President Of Communications, Timothy Robertson

Vice President Sales And Mark, Bill Kluber

Vice President Technical Accounting, Mark Green

Vice President Business Planning Store Planning And Analytics, Kathleen Tobi

Vice President Retail Marketing (tommy Hilfiger), Rich Lampmann

Executive Vice President Managing Director Commercial, Andy Wong

Svp Planning And Allocation, James Buehler

Vice President Planning And Operations, Lisa Kilgallon

Senior Vice President Business Process And Project Portfolio Management, Scott Lamb

Grp Vice President Business Development, Lina Yoo

Vice President Retail Development, Sean Osullivan

Vice President, Shawn Ricker

Vice President, Linda Davidson

Vice President, Yvonne Anderson

Senior Vice President Controller, Jim Holmes

Assistant Secretary, Michelle Odonnell

Auditors: Ernst & Young LLP

LOCATIONS

HQ: PVH Corp
200 Madison Avenue, New York, NY 10016
Phone: 212 381-3500
Web: www.pvh.com

2019 Sales

	$ mil.	% of total
U.S.	4,481	46
Canada	529	6
Europe	3	35
Asia	1,164	12
Other	121	3
Total	**9,657**	**100**

PRODUCTS/OPERATIONS

2019 Sales

	$ mil.	% of total
Calvin Klein North America	1,793	18
Calvin Klein International	1,938	20
Tommy Hilfiger North America	1,669	17
Tommy Hilfiger International	26,753	28
Heritage Brands Wholesale	1,317	14
Heritage Brands Retail	264	3
Total	**9,657**	**100**

2019 Sales

	$ mil.	% of total
Wholesale	4,970	52
Retail	4,185	43
Royalty	376	4
Advertising and other	127	1
Total	**9,657**	**100**

Selected Brands

Owned
ARROW
Bass
Calvin Klein
Eagle
IZOD
Tommy Hilfiger
Van Heusen
Licensed
Chaps
Claiborne
DKNY
Kenneth Cole New York
Kenneth Cole Reaction
MICHAEL Michael Kors
Michael Kors Collection
Robert Graham
Sean John

COMPETITORS

Allen-Edmonds	Kellwood
Armani	Kenneth Cole
Caleres	Levi Strauss
Capital Mercury	Nine West
Apparel	Oxford Industries
Donna Karan	Perry Ellis
Eddie Bauer LLC	International
Genesco	Prada
Gucci	Ralph Lauren
Haggar	Reebok
Hugo Boss	The Gap
J. Crew	Timberland
Kate Spade	VF Corporation

HISTORICAL FINANCIALS

Company Type: Public

Income Statement

FYE: February 3

	REVENUE ($ mil.)	NET INCOME ($ mil.)	NET PROFIT MARGIN	EMPLOYEES
02/19	9,657	746	7.7%	38,000
02/18*	8,915	538	6.0%	36,500
01/17	8,203	549	6.7%	44,500
01/16	8,020	572	7.1%	34,200
02/15	8,241	439	5.3%	34,100
Annual Growth	**4.0%**	**14.2%**	**—**	**2.7%**

*Fiscal year change

2019 Year-End Financials

Debt ratio: 24.00%
Return on equity: 13.00%
Cash ($ mil.): 452
Current ratio: 2.00
Long-term debt ($ mil.): 2,819

No. of shares (mil.): 75
Dividends
  Yield: 0.0%
  Payout: 2.0%
Market value ($ mil.): 8,201

	STOCK PRICE ($) FY Close	P/E High/Low	PER SHARE ($) Earnings	Dividends	Book Value
02/19	109.00	17 9	10.00	0.00	77.00
02/18*	151.00	23 12	7.00	0.00	72.00
01/17	90.00	17 10	7.00	0.00	61.00
01/16	73.00	17 10	7.00	0.00	56.00
02/15	110.00	25 20	5.00	0.00	53.00
Annual Growth	**(0.3%)**	**— —**	**16.3%**	**(0.0%)**	**9.9%**

*Fiscal year change

QCR Holdings Inc

Quad City is muscling in on the community banking scene in the Midwest. QCR Holdings is the holding company for Quad City Bank & Trust Cedar Rapids Bank & Trust Rockford Bank & Trust and Community State Bank. Together the banks have about 20 offices serving the Quad City area of Illinois and Iowa as well as the communities of Cedar Rapids Iowa; Rockford Illinois; and Milwaukee. The banks offer traditional deposit products and services and concentrate their lending activities on local businesses: Commercial real estate loans make up about half of the loan portfolio; commercial loans and leases make up another third.

Operations

QCR Holdings' Bancard subsidiary provides credit card processing services; its majority-owned M2 Lease Funds leases machinery and equipment to commercial and industrial businesses.

Strategy

QCR Holdings has grown by launching operations in new geographic markets and then building upon them. It also expands through acquisitions. In mid-2016 the company acquired Iowa-based Community State Bank which operates some 10 branches in the Des Moines area.

EXECUTIVES

Senior Vice President And Director Dep, Kathleen M Francque
President And Ceo, Douglas M. (Doug) Hultquist, age 64, $290,000 total compensation
Director; President And Ceo Cedar Rapids Bank And Trust, Larry J. Helling, age 63, $251,899 total compensation
Evp And Chief Credit Officer, Dana L. Nichols

Evp Coo And Cfo, Todd A. Gipple, age 56, $251,899 total compensation
Evp Corporate Strategy Human Resources And Branding, Cathie Whiteside, $162,000 total compensation
President And Ceo Rockford Bank And Trust, Thomas D. Budd, $172,000 total compensation
President And Ceo Quad City Bank And Trust, John H. Anderson, $200,000 total compensation
Evp Deposit Operations And Information Services, John A. Rodriguez
Svp And Cio, Michael J. Wyffels
Evp And Chief Operations Officer, John R. McEvoy
President And Ceo Community Bank And Trust, Stacey Bentley
President M2 Lease Funds, Richard W. Couch
Chairman And Ceo M2 Lease Funds, John R. Engelbrecht
Evp And Chief Investment Officer, M. Randolph (Rand) Westlund
Vice President Operations Manager, Sherrie L Larson
Senior Vice President Director Of Hum, Jill Dekeyser
Senior Vice President Marketing And Co, Cathy Whiteside
Vice President Controller, Jeri Vandervinne
Vice President And Controller, Nick Anderson
Assistant Vice President Compliance, Thomas King
Vice President, William Grimes
Vice President Product, Gregory Braid
Senior Vice President Treasury Management, Lori Diaz
Assistant Vice President Marketing And Public Relations Officer, Stacey L Keller
Assistant Vice President Marketing And Public Relations Officer, Stacey Keller
Executive Vice President Corporate Strategy And Branding, S Whiteside
Chairman, Patrick S. (Pat) Baird, age 66
Vice Chairman Of The Board, Marie Ziegler
Board Member, Donna Sorensen
Auditors: RSM US LLP

LOCATIONS

HQ: QCR Holdings Inc
3551 7th Street, Moline, IL 61265
Phone: 309 736-3580
Web: www.qcrh.com

PRODUCTS/OPERATIONS

2015 Sales

	$ mil.	% of total
Quad City Bank & Trust	53	46
Cedar Rapids Bank & Trust	38	32
Rockford Bank & Trust	15	13
Wealth Management	9	8
All other	1	1
Inter-company Eliminations	(0.4)	-
Total	**115**	**100**

COMPETITORS

Bank of America	First National of
Blackhawk Bancorp	Nebraska
First Business	MidWestOne
Financial	U.S. Bancorp
First Midwest Bancorp	

Income Statement   FYE: December 31

	ASSETS ($ mil.)	NET INCOME ($ mil.)	INCOME AS % OF ASSETS	EMPLOYEES
12/18	4,950	43	0.9%	755
12/17	3,983	36	0.9%	641
12/16	3,302	28	0.8%	572
12/15	2,593	17	0.7%	406
12/14	2,525	15	0.6%	409
Annual Growth	18.3%	30.3%	—	16.6%

2018 Year-End Financials

Debt ratio: 2.00%
Return on equity: 10.00%
Cash ($ mil.): 219
Current ratio: —
Long-term debt ($ mil.): —

No. of shares (mil.): 16
Dividends
Yield: 1.0%
Payout: 9.0%
Market value ($ mil.): 504

	STOCK PRICE ($) FY Close	P/E High/Low	PER SHARE ($) Earnings	Dividends	Book Value
12/18	32.00	17 10	3.00	0.00	30.00
12/17	43.00	18 15	3.00	0.00	25.00
12/16	43.00	20 10	2.00	0.00	22.00
12/15	24.00	15 11	2.00	0.00	19.00
12/14	18.00	10 10	2.00	0.00	18.00
Annual Growth	15.8%	— —	13.6%	31.6%	13.5%

Qualcomm Inc

QUALCOMM is a leading designer and supplier of computer chips that mobile phone and wireless carriers depend on to get signals straight. The company pioneered the commercialization of the code-division multiple access (CDMA) technology used in digital wireless communications equipment and satellite ground stations mainly in North America. It generates most of its sales through the development and marketing of semiconductor chips such as its Snapdragon line and system software based on CDMA and other technologies. Its biggest customers have been suppliers to mobile phone makers Samsung and Apple. In 2018 QUALCOMM ended its $47 billion bid to buy NXP Semiconductors after the Chinese government failed to approve the deal.

Operations

While CDMA is QUALCOMM's flagship technology it has makes products based on Orthogonal Frequency Division Multiple Access (OFDMA) which allows multiple access on the same channel and Wideband Code Division Multiple Access (WCDMA) designed to ease the transmission of multimedia content.

QUALCOMM CDMA Technologies (QCT) is the company's biggest business segment generating more than 75% of revenue. Its QUALCOMM Technology Licensing (QTL) unit brings in the rest.

The company outsources manufacturing to contractors primarily Global Foundries Inc. Samsung Electronics Semiconductor Manufacturing International Corp. Taiwan Semiconductor Manufacturing Co. and United Microelectronics Corp.

Geographic Reach

QUALCOMM based in San Diego California gets about two-thirds of its revenue from customers based in China (including Hong Kong) while customers based in South Korea supply about 15% of revenue.

Sales and Marketing

More than 50% of QUALCOMM's revenue come from five customers: Apple Inc. (and its supplier Hon Hai Precision) Samsung Electronics Guang-Dong OPPO Mobile Telecommunications Ltd. and Vivo Communication Technology Co.

Financial Performance

QUALCOMM halted a three-year string of falling revenue in 2018 (ended September) but the company's bottom line took a hit from the US Tax Cuts and Jobs Act of 2017.

Sales edged 2% higher to $22.7 billion in 2018 from $22.3 billion in 2017 on a 4.5% increase in QCT sales while licensing sales fell about 5%. The company reported higher sales of radio frequency front-end (RFFE) components and Mobile Station Modem (MSM) integrated circuits. The company's products fetched lower prices on average in 2018 compared to 2017.

QUALCOMM had a net loss of about $4.9 billion due to a $5.7 billion charge for income tax expense for repatriated earnings and profits of US-owned foreign subsidiaries. Also included were a $2 billion fee paid to NXP for terminating the acquisition and a $1.3 billion fine paid to the European Commission.

The company's cash and equivalent balance dropped to $11.8 billion in 2018 from about $35 billion in 2017 because of costs related to the proposed NXP acquisition and an increased in money spent on stock buybacks year-to-year. In 2018 operations generated $3.9 billion and investment activities provided $4.4 billion while investing activities used $31.5 billion.

Strategy

QUALCOMM's revenue suffered when Apple went with another manufacturer for mobile phone modems. What's more the companies have been in court suing and counter-suing over who owns what technology. They continued the courtroom battle into 2019.

Two other corporate battles were settled in 2018 leaving the company with one win and one loss. The win came when Broadcom dropped its bid to buy QUALCOMM when the US government rejected it on national security concerns. In a different takeover battle QUALCOMM ended its pursuit of NXP due to a slow by regulatory review and tepid response from NXP shareholders. QUALCOMM had to cough up a $2 billion termination fee.

On the product side QUALCOMM is ready to furnish manufacturers with technology for 5G wireless networks which are to be much faster and more powerful than previous wireless technologies. The company has worked to develop 5G technology for about a decade (it holds 15% of 5G patents a higher percentage than any other company) and the toil is nearing payoff. The next generation of wireless networking has promise of providing faster communication with less latency unleashing a host of new and powerful applications. The first 5G networks could launch in 2018 with more rolling out over the next several years. If it plays out like previous wireless generations it means big business for QUALCOMM.

Mergers and Acquisitions

QUALCOMM acquired Scyfer B.V. a company that developed artificial intelligence technologies in 2017. Qualcomm added Scyfer's applications to end-use devices such as smartphones cars and robotics to ensure that processing can be done with or without a network

QUALCOMM and TDK formed a joint venture in 2017 to provide chips for mobile devices and internet of things applications. The entity called RF360 Holdings combines QUALCOMM's chip expertise with that of TDK in filters. Application areas are mobile devices automotive and drones. The ownership of the joint venture is split 51% by QUALCOMM and 49% by TDK.

Company Background

Professors Irwin Mark Jacobs and Andrew Viterbi founded digital signal processing equipment company Linkabit in 1968. M/A-COM acquired the company in 1980. Led by Jacobs Viterbi and five other executives left M/A-COM Linkabit in 1985 to start engineer-focused QUALCOMM (for "quality communications") to provide contract R&D services. The company's first home was located above a strip mall pizza parlor in San Diego. CEO Jacobs dreamed of modifying code-division multiple access (CDMA) — a secure wireless transmission system developed during WWII — for commercial use.

In 1988 QUALCOMM introduced OmniTRACS a satellite-based system that tracks the location of long-haul truckers. By 1989 when QUALCOMM unveiled its version of CDMA the company was working on military contracts worth $15 million.

In 1990 the company interrupted the Cellular Telecommunications Industry Association's (CTIA) plans to adopt a rival technology called time-division multiple access when communications service providers NYNEX (now part of Verizon) and Ameritech (later part of SBC Communications and now part of AT&T) adopted QUALCOMM's maverick technology. QUALCOMM initiated a CDMA public relations blitz and by 1991 Motorola AT&T Clarion and Nokia had signed product development and testing agreements.

The company went public in 1991 and introduced the Eudora e-mail software program (named for "Why I Live at the P.O." author Eudora Welty) which it licensed from the University of Illinois. That year QUALCOMM and Loral Corporation unveiled plans for Globalstar a satellite telecommunications system similar to the Iridium system. The CTIA adopted CDMA as a North American standard for wireless communications in 1993.

EXECUTIVES

Senior Vice President, Greg Rose
Svp Government Affairs, William Bold
Senior Vice President And General Manager, Neville Meijers
Senior Vice President Engineering, Edward Tiedemann
Evp And Cfo, George S. Davis, age 62, $760,011 total compensation
Svp And Chief Marketing Officer, Penny Baldwin
Evp General Counsel And Corporate Secretary, Donald J. Rosenberg, age 68, $675,002 total compensation
Ceo And Director, Steven M. (Steve) Mollenkopf, age 50, $1,138,694 total compensation
Evp Technology, Matthew S. (Matt) Grob, age 52
Evp Engineering Qualcomm Technologies Inc. And Cto, James H. (Jim) Thompson, age 55
President, Cristiano R. Amon, age 49, $523,090 total compensation
Evp Human Resources, Michelle Sterling, age 52
Evp Strategy And M&a, Brian T. Modoff, age 59, $542,324 total compensation
Evp And President Qualcomm Technology Licensing (qtl), Alexander H. (Alex) Rogers, age 62
Vice President Of Sales, Eddie Chang
Vice President Engineering, Walid Hamdy
Vp Information Technology, Bob Gentile
Vp Technology, Dom Farmer
Vice President Marketing, Pete Lancia
Senior Vice President Government Affairs, Mark Koro
Vice President Product Management, Kedar Kondap
Vice President Strategy And Analysis, Mauricio Lopez-Hodoyan
Senior Vice President, Laura Sand

Vice President Engineering Linux Android Snapdragon Ioe, Chidu Krishnan
Vice President Strategic Development, Ed Charbonneau
Senior Vice President Of Product Management, Jeff Lorbeck
Vice President Technology, Surya Ganti
Vice President And General Manager Xiam Technologies, Colm Healy
Vice President Engineering, Sanjay Kasturia
Vice President, Mike Spartz
Vice President, Roawen Chen
Vice President And Legal Counsel, Adam Schwenker
Vice President Engineering, Arul Ananthanarayanan
Vice President Information Technology And Software Development, Paul Bender
Vice President, Jl Park
National Account Manager, Leslie Perretti
Vice President Engineering, Andrew Chiu
Senior Vice President Engineering, Gil Sih
Senior Vice President Engineering, Susie Armstrong
Vice President Business Development, Vikas Jain
Vp Of Engineering, Dennis Cashen
Senior Vice President Technology, Peter Black
Vice President (engineering), Sudarshan Keshava
Vp Operations, Malcangio Frank
Vice President Of Engineering, Brian Banister
Senior Vice President Government Affairs, Dean Brenner
Vice President Compensation And Benefits, Michelle Mckinney
Vice President Engineering, King-chung Lai
Vice President Of Technology, Sherman Gregory
Vice President And Treasurer, Dick Grannis
Vp Legal Counsel, Diane Mack
Vice President Engineering, Vladimir Aparin
Vice President 2net Business Qualcomm Life, Chris Talbot
Vice President Of Marketing, Charlotte Lamprecht
Vice President Of Product Management, Tim Leland
Senior Vice President Engineering, Pankaj Kukkal
Vice President Learning And Development, Tamar Elkeles
Vice President Engineering, Brian K Harms
Senior Vice President Strategy And Corporate Development, Matt Eichenberger
Vice President Engineering Ams Design, Gene McAllister
Executive Vice President Of The Americas And India, Peggy L Johnson
Vice President Marketing, Jenny Beneke
Vice President Of Technology, Rob Gilmore
Vice President Government Affairs, Steve Crout
Senior Vice President And General Manager, Rick Valencia
Vice President Product Management, Francesco Grilli
Vice Presidentengineering, Rashmi Char
Vice President Patent Counsel, Timothy Loomis
Executive Vice President, Andrew Gilbert
Vice President Finance, Akash Palkhiwala
Vice President, Cliff Ficke
Vp Intellectual Property Operations, Manjit Gill
Senior Vice President Engineering, Ron Tessitore
Vice President Engineering, Daniel Waldburger
Vp Engineering; Head Of Product Security, Alex Gantman
Vice President Of Government Affairs, Alice Tornquist
Vice President Engineering, Dan Waldburger
Vice President Engineering, Ajay Bawale
Vice President Of Technology, Geoffrey Yeap
Vice President Global Technical Education, Dana Yuan
Vice President Engineering, Eric Tallet
Vice President Sales, Curt Thornton
Vice President Engineering, Benny Malekkhosravi

Vice President Business Development, Jeffery Torrance
Vice President Engineering Qct Software, Tony Schwarz
Vp Engineering, Gene Hnatek
Vice President Engineering, Samir Kapoor
Executive Vice President And President Qualcomm Technology Licensing, Alex Rogers
Vice President, Jeremiah Golston
Vice President Technology, Walid Ali-Ahmad
Vice President Product Management, Mitch Oliver
Vice President Hardware Engineering Group Corpor, Ernie Ozaki
Vice President Of Engineering, Jose Corleto
Svp Finance, Sanjay Mehta
Senior Vice President, Chuck Wheatley
Svp Engineering, Bill Earnshaw
Vice President Modem Senior Writer Engineering, Vanitha Kumar
Vice President Software Product Management, Nancy Fares
Vice President Package Engineering, Raj Pendse
Vice President Business Operations, Laura Hart
Vice President Technology, Ken Wiseman
Vice President Of Engineering, Sathyadev Uppala
Vp Strategic Programs, Edward Charbonneau
Vice President Global Technical Education, Sei Seung Yoon
Vice President Engineering, Len Sheynblat
Vice President Of Business Development, James Cathey
Vice President Of Technology, Steve Dorner
Assistant To Don Rosenberg Executive Vice President And General Counsel, Sylvie Julian
Vp Of Sales And Marketing, Tom Wrappesenior
Vice President And President Of Qualcomm Korea Yh, Oh Hyung Kwon
Vice President Engineering, Frederic Darguesse
Executive Chairman, Paul E. Jacobs, age 57
Secretary, Maria Terris
Secretary Executive, Laurie Mee
Secretary Senior, Joann Carter
Board Member, Barbara Alexander
Board Member, Dirk Stein
Secretary Executive, Cynthia Almazan
Secretary Executive, Gloria Holmes
Secretary Executive, Wendy Walsh
Senior Secretary, Lori Freeman
Secretary Executive, Maria Mackinnon
Secretary Senior, Katy Martin
Board Member, Aurora Fields
Secretary Senior, Heather Gallegos
Secretary Executive, Robin Frampton
Senior Secretary, Jan Harris
Board Member, Anthony Vinciquerra
Board Member, Clark Randt
Board Member, Harish Manwani
Board Member, Francisco Ros
Secretary Executive, Linda Chinn
Auditors: PricewaterhouseCoopers LLP

LOCATIONS

HQ: Qualcomm Inc
5775 Morehouse Dr., San Diego, CA 92121-1714
Phone: 858 587-1121
Web: www.qualcomm.com

2018 Sales

	$ mil.	% of total
China (including Hong Kong)	15,149	67
South Korea	3,173	14
United States	603	2
Other foreign	3,805	17
Total	**22,732**	**100**

PRODUCTS/OPERATIONS

2018 Sales

	$ mil.	% of total
QCT (Qualcomm CDMA Technologies)	17,282	76
QTL (Qualcomm Technology Licensing)	5,163	23
QSI (Qualcomm Strategic Initiatives)	100	-
Adjustments	187	1
Total	**22,732**	**100**

2018 Sales

	$ mil.	% of total
Equipment & services	17,400	77
Licensing	5,332	23
Total	**22,732**	**100**

Selected Operations and Products

Code-Division Multiple Access (CDMA) Technologies Group
  Integrated circuits
  Baseband
  Intermediate-frequency
  Power management
  Radio-frequency
  Systems software
Engineering Services Group
Enterprise Services
Firethorn Holdings
Flarion Technologies
Government Technologies
Innovation Center
Internet Services
MediaFLO Technologies
MEMS Technologies
Qualcomm Ventures
Strategic Initiatives
Technology Licensing Group
  CDMA technologies and patents (cdmaOne CDMA2000 WCDMA TD-SCDMA)
  Royalties from products incorporating CDMA technology
Wireless and Internet Group
  Digital Media
  Digital motion picture delivery systems (under development)
  Government systems (development and analysis services; wireless base stations and phones)
  Internet Services
  Applications development software for wireless devices (BREW)
  Wireless Systems
  Low-Earth-orbit satellite-based telecommunications system (Globalstar)

COMPETITORS

Broadcom	REALTEK SEMICONDUCTOR
Cirrus Logic	CORP.
InterDigital	Renesas Electronics
Marvell Technology	STMicroelectronics
Maxim Integrated Products	Samsung Electronics
MediaTek	Sequans Communications
Murata Manufacturing	Spreadtrum
NVIDIA	Texas Instruments

HISTORICAL FINANCIALS

Company Type: Public

Income Statement				FYE: September 29
	REVENUE ($ mil.)	NET INCOME ($ mil.)	NET PROFIT MARGIN	EMPLOYEES
09/19	24,273	4,386	18.1%	37,000
09/18	22,732	(4,864)	—	35,400
09/17	22,291	2,466	11.1%	33,800
09/16	23,554	5,705	24.2%	30,500
09/15	25,281	5,271	20.8%	33,000
Annual Growth	(1.0%)	(4.5%)	—	2.9%

2019 Year-End Financials

Debt ratio: 48.00%
Return on equity: 151.00%
Cash ($ mil.): 11,839
Current ratio: 2.00
Long-term debt ($ mil.): 13,437

No. of shares (mil.): 1,145
Dividends
  Yield: 0.0%
  Payout: 69.0%
Market value ($ mil.): 87,741

	STOCK PRICE ($) FY Close	P/E High/Low		PER SHARE ($) Earnings	Dividends	Book Value
09/19	77.00	25	14	4.00	2.00	4.00
09/18	72.00	—	—	(3.00)	2.00	1.00
09/17	52.00	42	30	2.00	2.00	21.00
09/16	63.00	17	11	4.00	2.00	22.00
09/15	53.00	24	16	3.00	2.00	21.00
Annual Growth	9.5%	—	—	2.8%	8.3%	(32.5%)

Quanta Services, Inc.

Quanta Services is a specialty contractor that designs installs repairs and maintains network infrastructure across North America and abroad. The company serves the electric power oil and natural gas and communication industries mainly in the US Canada and Australia. Capabilities include pylon construction distribution infrastructure and emergency response among much more. Its oil and gas business offers onshore and offshore services. Quanta's other services include outsource management and other specialty work such as installing traffic and light rail control systems directional drilling and constructing wind and solar power facilities. The company was founded in 1997.

Operations

Quanta operates through two primary segments: Electric Power Infrastructure which generates some 60% of revenue; and Oil and Gas Infrastructure Services (40% of revenue).

The Electric Power segment offers a vast array of physical infrastructure construction and maintenance. Services include transmission construction distribution construction substations power generation emergency response EPC (engineering procurement and construction) services helicopter services and more.

Oil and Gas Infrastructure Services designs installs and maintains pipelines and has horizontal drilling trenching and mechanized welding capabilities. It serves the offshore sector with services including mechanical installation commissioning coatings shallow-water pipeline installation fabrication and marine asset repair.

Geographic Reach

Houston-based Quanta Services generates around 75% of its revenue in the US. Its next largest market is Canada which accounts for about 20% of its business followed by Australia. Other international offices are in South Africa India and Latin America (Chile Colombia Costa Rica Ecuador Guatemala Mexico Panama and Peru).

Sales and Marketing

Quanta mostly serves companies in the electric power oil & gas and communications markets though it also serves commercial industrial and governmental organizations. Around three-quarters of its revenue base is recurring in nature.

Quanta's customer base is relatively well diversified: Its largest customer accounts for 5% of sales and its ten largest combined account for 30%. Clients include American Electric Power Duke Energy PG&E Corp. and TransCanada Corp ITC Holdings and Exelon Corp. among others.

Financial Performance

Apart from a blip in 2015 Quanta's revenue has been on an upward trajectory.

In fiscal 2017 revenue leaped 24% to $9.4 billion. Activity in the oil and gas industry kicked into gear as the oil price rebounded helping Quanta's oil and gas revenue grow $1.1 billion. Customer capital spending on midstream gas pipeline transmission projects was the primary growth driver while the Stronghold acquisition added $190 million to oil and gas sales as well. The electric power infrastructure segment also performed strongly growing $749 million as customers increased spending on transmission projects. Emergency restoration spending in the aftermath of the two major hurricanes to hit Texas in 2017 Irma and Harvey also contributed to electric power sales.

Quanta's net income also grew although it lagged the strident revenue growth up $118 million to $318 million. In fact most of the growth came from a $71.7 decrease in provision for income taxes relating to the 2017 Tax Cuts and Jobs Act: Profit margins were down due to disruption from the two hurricanes partially offset by the higher prices charged for emergency restoration services.

Cash from operations fell 5% to $372.5 million as higher earnings were offset by increased working capital requirements and changes in accounts receivable from the emergency restoration work.

Strategy

With activity in the oil industry ramping up on the back of higher oil prices Quanta is increasing its investment capital. In 2017 it invested $575.8 billion a $309 million increase on 2016 on acquisitions and capital expenditures. As part of its broader strategy to provide fully integrated differentiated solutions to its customers Quanta established energy investment vehicle First Infrastructure Capital in 2017. In partnership with select infrastructure investors it will invest in concessions public-private partnerships and private infrastructure projects. A significant chunk of Quanta's investment budget went on acquiring Stronghold which provides high-pressure solutions to the oil and gas industry.

Mergers and Acquisitions

In 2018 Quanta acquired Northwest Lineman College (NLC) an educational and training institution serving the electric power industry. NLC is based in Boise Idaho with additional campuses in California Florida and Texas. The college will enhance the quality of Quanta's talent.

In July 2017 Quanta acquired Stronghold a specialized services company that provides high-pressure and critical path solutions to the downstream and midstream energy markets for $450 million. The acquisition opens up new niches in the industrial services market. Also in 2017 Quanta acquired a communications infrastructure services contractor and an electrical and communications contractor both based in the US.

In 2016 Quanta completed five acquisitions including an Australian electrical infrastructure services company a Canadian utility contracting company an American medium- and high-voltage powerline contracting company and a telecommunications company located in Canada. In 2015 it made 11 acquisitions.

EXECUTIVES

Cfo, Derrick A. Jensen, age 48, $600,000 total compensation

President Ceo And Coo, Earl C. (Duke) Austin, age 49, $979,924 total compensation

Evp Corporate Development And President Infrastructure Solutions, Jesse E. Morris, age 51, $466,900 total compensation

Evp Operations And Health/safety And Environmental, Randall C. Wisenbaker, age 54, $475,625 total compensation

President Electric Power, Dale L. Querrey, age 55, $595,880 total compensation

President Oil And Gas Division And Chief Strategy Officer, Paul C. Gregory, age 55

Senior Vice President, Bengt Jarlsjo

Vice President Of Operations, Dan Govin

Vp Operations And Business Development, Bj Ducey

Executive Vice President, Ron Tagliapietra

Quanta Vice President, Jody Shea

Vice President Project Development, Richard Vaughan

Vice President Health Safety And Environmental, Matt Compher

Executive Vice President Operations, David Meisel

Vice President Executive Pastry Chef, Kevin Cater

Vicepresident Vice President Operationsproductionmfg Vice President Operat, Tom Rupp

Chairman, Bruce E. Ranck

Auditors: PricewaterhouseCoopers LLP

LOCATIONS

HQ: Quanta Services, Inc.
2800 Post Oak Boulevard, Suite 2600, Houston, TX 77056
Phone: 713 629-7600
Web: www.quantaservices.com

PRODUCTS/OPERATIONS

2017 sales

	$ mil.	% of total
Electric power infrastructure	5,600	59
Oil and gas infrastructure	3,467	41
Total	**9,467**	**100**

COMPETITORS

Cable Com	MDU Construction
Comm-Works	Services
Dycom	MYR Group
EMCOR	MasTec
Goldfield	Mass Electric
Henkels & McCoy	Pike Corporation
IES Holdings	Tetra Tech

HISTORICAL FINANCIALS

Company Type: Public

Income Statement   FYE: December 31

	REVENUE ($ mil.)	NET INCOME ($ mil.)	NET PROFIT MARGIN	EMPLOYEES
12/18	11,171	293	2.6%	39,200
12/17	9,466	315	3.3%	32,800
12/16	7,651	198	2.6%	28,100
12/15	7,572	311	4.1%	24,500
12/14	7,851	297	3.8%	24,600
Annual Growth	9.2%	(0.3%)	—	12.4%

2018 Year-End Financials

Debt ratio: 15.00%
Return on equity: 8.00%
Cash ($ mil.): 79
Current ratio: 2.00
Long-term debt ($ mil.): 1,041

No. of shares (mil.): 142
Dividends
  Yield: 0.0%
  Payout: 2.0%
Market value ($ mil.): 4,262

	STOCK PRICE ($)	P/E	PER SHARE ($)		
	FY Close	High/Low	Earnings	Dividends	Book Value
12/18	30.00	21 15	2.00	0.00	25.00
12/17	39.00	20 15	2.00	0.00	25.00
12/16	35.00	28 14	1.00	0.00	22.00
12/15	20.00	19 12	2.00	0.00	19.00
12/14	28.00	28 19	1.00	0.00	21.00
Annual Growth	1.5%	— —	8.9%	—	5.3%

Quest Diagnostics, Inc.

Quest Diagnostics is one of the largest clinical labs in the US. The company performs diagnostics on some 150 million specimens each year including routine clinical tests such as cholesterol checks Pap smears and HIV screenings. Quest Diagnostics also performs esoteric testing (such as genetic screening) and anatomic pathology testing (such as tissue biopsies for cancer testing). Its Quest Diagnostic Nichols Institute develops new diagnostics. In all the company serves about half of the physicians and hospitals and about a third of the adult population in the US per year. Quest Diagnostics has more than 2200 patient service centers where samples are collected.

Operations
Quest Diagnostics operates through two primary segments — Diagnostic Information Services (DIS) and Diagnostic Solutions.

More than 95% of Quest's revenue comes from its DIS segment which includes its routine clinical anatomic pathology gene-based esoteric and drugs-of-abuse testing businesses. In the realm of diagnostic testing Quest strives to make itself ubiquitous with a comprehensive menu of tests and a network of labs and collection sites that blanket the US. In addition to its more than 2200 patient service centers where samples are collected the company maintains a staff of thousands of field phlebotomists who collect blood samples in physicians' offices. It also maintains a nationwide network of labs including advanced and rapid-response labs. Routine tests account for more than half of Quest's total sales; gene-based and esoteric tests account for more than 30% and pathology tests account for nearly 10%.

The Diagnostic Solutions segment offers risk assessment services for life insurers. It also offers health information technology systems including the MyQuest patient health care portal and the Quanum electronic health record platform.

Quest's logistics holdings include approximately 3700 courier vehicles and some 25 aircraft that combined make more than 7000 stops daily.

Geographic Reach
Quest Diagnostics has labs in California (3) Florida Georgia Illinois (2) Kansas Maryland Massachusetts New Jersey North Carolina Ohio Pennsylvania Texas (2) and Virginia. It also has labs in Mexico and Puerto Rico as well as a majority interest in a drug testing venture in Brazil.

Sales and Marketing
Quest's customers include health plans and other insurers physicians hospitals accountable care organizations employers individual patients retail health care providers government agencies pharmaceuticals and other commercial laboratories.

The company maintains a sales force which markets its diagnostic products drug testing services and other offerings.

Financial Performance
Quest's revenues have been relatively static over the past few years. Net income has been more volatile rising and falling from year to year but generally trending upward.

In 2018 revenue rose 2% to $7.5 billion. The core DIS segment's revenue increased 2% to $7.2 billion; that increase was driven by growth from acquisitions but partially offset by a decrease in organic revenue. The much smaller DS segment's revenue fell 2% largely due to the absence of royalty revenues received the prior year.

Net income fell 5% to $736 million in 2018. Both operating and non-operating expenses rose that year including cost of services and net interest expenses.

The company ended 2018 with $135 million in net cash $2 million less than it had at the end of 2017. Operating activities provided $1.2 billion that year while investing activities used $801 million and financing activities used another $401 million.

Strategy
Quest has been refocusing on its core testing offerings and simplifying its operations.

Key lines of business include general diagnostics advanced diagnostics (genetic advanced molecular testing) and diagnostic services. Its approaches for these lines range from making acquisitions to partnering with health plans and other risk-bearing organizations. The company has made numerous acquisitions recently including fertility testing firm ReproSource and anatomical pathology firm PhenoPath and it plans to continue seeking buying opportunities. And in 2018 Quest established a long-term partnership with UnitedHealthcare through which it will serve the insurance giant's members on a nationwide basis

The company is also focused on scientific and product innovation. Its 2018 acquisition of the US lab operations of Oxford Immunotec provided it with tuberculosis and tick-borne disease testing services. Also that year it introduced the Cardio IQ Insulin Resistance Panel with Score offering.

Narrowing its focus on its core diagnostic information services operations the company has stopped selling diagnostic products. It also sold its India business to Strand Life Sciences in 2019.

To expand its customer base Quest's recent initiatives include introducing electronic check-in opening new patient service centers in grocery stores and introducing self-collection technology that engages customers at home.

Although testing volume has increased for Quest revenue by requisition has fallen slightly as the company faces competitive pricing pressure. The Protecting Access to Medicare Act has also had a negative impact on revenue by requisition as reimbursement denials have increased.

Mergers and Acquisitions
Quest has traditionally looked to grow its reach by acquiring firms with complementary locations or testing capabilities. To that end the company has made a number of acquisitions that have increased its presence in specific testing categories such as cancer biopsy tests.

In late 2018 Quest bought ReproSource which provides specialty fertility diagnostic services; it will use that addition to build up its comprehensive women's health offerings for obstetricians gynecologists fertility specialists and other providers.

Also that year it acquired PhenoPath a provider of specialized anatomic pathology services. PhenoPath now operates as part of Quest's AmeriPath business. In another deal the company purchased Mobile Medical Examination Service (MedXM) which provides home-based health risk assessments. That purchase expanded the company's presence in the mobile and home markets.

In 2017 it purchased Cleveland HeartLab the outreach lab operations of two Connecticut hospitals the outreach lab operations of Cape Cod Healthcare and certain assets of California Laboratory Associates.

Company Background
Quest Diagnostics was incorporated in 1990 but its predecessors date their history back to 1967.

HISTORY

Quest Diagnostics began as one man's quest to make clinical tests more affordable. Pathologist Paul Brown started Metropolitan Pathological Laboratory (MetPath) in his Manhattan apartment in 1967. To help his business take off in 1969 he bought two $55000 blood analyzers that could automatically perform a dozen common tests; the machines allowed him to charge patients $5.50 while hospitals and other labs were charging upwards of $40. Investments in emerging lab technology helped MetPath continue to beat competitors' prices and grow its business. It made its first profit in 1971 and eventually attracted the attention of Corning Glass Works which bought 10% of the company in 1973.

MetPath's growth was due in part to investments in technology. The company built a state-of-the-art central lab in New Jersey in 1978 that could process some 30000 specimens daily; it also went on an acquisition spree to expand across the US. These investments left the firm swamped with debt and Corning bought the company in 1982.

An autonomous unit of Corning MetPath continued to grow as Medicare reimbursement for lab tests went up and more doctors ordered more tests to catch and prevent disease before it happened. To cut costs in the mid-1980s the company reorganized its facilities to create a regional lab network. A reorganization in 1990 at its parent placed MetPath in the Corning Lab Services subsidiary.

Corning Lab Services strengthened its operations in the early 1990s by buying labs from regional operators. In 1994 MetPath became Corning Clinical Laboratories. Around the same time the company found itself besieged with demands from HMOs and other managed care providers to lower its costs. Also during this time the company settled a handful of federal suits accusing it of fraudulent Medicare billing. In the face of increasing pressure parent Corning spun off its lab testing business to the public as Quest Diagnostics in 1996.

On its own Quest aimed to grow through acquisitions. In 1999 it bought rival SmithKline Beecham Clinical Laboratories from GlaxoSmithKline. (GSK gained a minority stake in Quest through the deal; it gradually sold off all shares in Quest by 2011.) Continuing its growth strategy in the 21st century it bought American Medical Laboratories to expand its esoteric testing operations in 2002. The company was finally able to close its acquisition of Unilab in early 2003 after the deal ran into delays with the FTC. Quest sold some labs and service contracts in northern California to LabCorp to appease FTC regulators.

To expand internationally the company began providing testing services in India in 2008 including esoteric testing for hospitals tests for the life insurance industry and diagnostics for global clinical trials.

EXECUTIVES

Chairman President And Ceo, Stephen H. (Steve) Rusckowski, age 61, $1,100,000 total compensation
Svp And Group Executive Diagnostic Solutions, Jon R. Cohen, age 64, $575,000 total compensation

Svp And Group Executive Clinical Franchise Solutions And Marketing, Catherine T. Doherty, age 56, $575,000 total compensation
Svp Commercial, Everett V. Cunningham, age 52
Vp Global Markets And Chairman Q2 Solutions, John B. Haydon
Evp And Cfo, Mark J. Guinan, age 57, $586,538 total compensation
Evp General Diagnostics, James E. Davis, age 56, $586,538 total compensation
Svp Research And Development And Medical And Chief Medical Officer, Jay G. Wohlgemuth
Svp And Cio, Lidia Fonseca
Vp And Treasurer, Tracy Cinco-abela
Vice President Clinical Trials, Christopher Fikry
Svp Strategy Mergers And Acquisitions And Ventures, Dermot Shorten
Regional Vice President Commercial, Geoffrey Albrecht
Vp Marketing, James Humphreys
Auditors: PricewaterhouseCoopers LLP

LOCATIONS

HQ: Quest Diagnostics, Inc.
500 Plaza Drive, Secaucus, NJ 07094
Phone: 973 520-2700
Web: www.QuestDiagnostics.com

PRODUCTS/OPERATIONS

2018 Sales

	$ mil.	% of total
Diagnostic Information Services		
Routine clinical testing services	4,217	56
Gene-based & esoteric testing services	2,409	32
Anatomic pathology testing services	578	8
Other	327	4
Total	**7,531**	**100**

Selected Products and Services

Clincial laboratory testing
  Routine clinical testing (body fluid testing)
  Alcohol and other substance-abuse tests
  Allergy tests (ImmunoCap)
  Blood cholesterol
  Complete blood cell counts
  Pap smears
  Pregnancy testing
  Urinalyses
  Gene-based and esoteric testing
  Endocrinology
  Cancer monitoring (gene-based)
  Cellular immunology
  Genetics
  Hematology
  Microbiology
  Molecular diagnostics
  Oncology
  Protein chemistry
  Serology
  Toxicology
  Anatomic pathology testing (AmeriPath Dermpath Diagnostics and Quest Diagnostics brands)
  Cancer biopsies
  Tissue and cell testing
Other products and services
  Clinical trials testing
  Diagnostic products
  Medical data management systems
  Life insurance risk assessment services

Selected Subsidiaries

American Medical Laboratories Incorporated
AmeriPath Inc.
Celera Corporation
Enterix Inc.
Focus Diagnostics Inc.
HemoCue Inc.
LabOne Inc.
MedPlus Inc.
OralDNA Labs Inc.
Quest Diagnostics Nichols Institute

COMPETITORS

Arup Laboratories	Pathology Associates
Bio-Reference Labs	Medical Laboratories
Genomic Health	Psychemedics
LabCorp	Solstas
Medtox Scientific	Sonic Healthcare
Oncolab	

HISTORICAL FINANCIALS

Company Type: Public

Income Statement
FYE: December 31

	REVENUE ($ mil.)	NET INCOME ($ mil.)	NET PROFIT MARGIN	EMPLOYEES
12/18	7,531	736	9.8%	46,000
12/17	7,709	772	10.0%	45,000
12/16	7,515	645	8.6%	43,000
12/15	7,493	709	9.5%	44,000
12/14	7,435	556	7.5%	45,000
Annual Growth	0.3%	7.3%	—	0.6%

2018 Year-End Financials

Debt ratio: 35.00%
Return on equity: 15.00%
Cash ($ mil.): 135
Current ratio: 1.00
Long-term debt ($ mil.): 3,429
No. of shares (mil.): 135
Dividends
  Yield: 2.0%
  Payout: 37.0%
Market value ($ mil.): 11,241

	STOCK PRICE ($) FY Close	P/E High/Low		PER SHARE ($) Earnings	Dividends	Book Value
12/18	83.00	21	15	5.00	2.00	39.00
12/17	98.00	20	16	6.00	2.00	36.00
12/16	92.00	20	13	5.00	2.00	34.00
12/15	71.00	16	12	5.00	1.00	33.00
12/14	67.00	18	13	4.00	1.00	30.00
Annual Growth	5.6%	—	—	8.6%	10.9%	6.6%

Qurate Retail Inc

Liberty Interactive Corp. stands by your right to shop at home and online. The company owns and operates market-leading home shopping channel QVC which sells 770 products each week across the home apparel beauty and accessories jewelry and electronics categories. QVC also sells online. Liberty Interactive also runs online businesses including Zulily and online invitation site Evite. It also holds equity stakes in FTD Companies HSN Interval Leisure and LendingTree among others. Liberty Interactive acquired the long-standing rival of its QVC business HSN Inc. for around $2.1 billion in 2017. Liberty Interactive Corp. was formed in 2011 when its predecessor restructured and split off its Liberty Capital and Liberty Starz businesses as Liberty Media.

Operations

Liberty Interactive operates through two main business divisions: QVC Group and Liberty Ventures.

The QVC Group consists of QVC Zulily and Liberty's interest in HSN. QVC is the company's cash cow subsidiary accounting about 80% of its sales. The television brand broadcasts live shopping programs and sells merchandise online in the US and abroad. QVC classifies its products into six groups: home beauty apparel jewelry accessories and electronics. Home is the biggest earner at around one third of sales followed by apparel at nearly 20% and beauty at more than 15%.

Zulily brings in 15% of sales sells products in the US and elsewhere online through flash sales events primarily through its desktop and mobile websites and mobile applications.

Liberty Ventures consists of e-card website Evite and interests in Liberty Broadband FTD Interval Leisure Group Time Warner Charter Communications Britco and LendingTree.

Geographic Reach

Liberty Interactive rings up around 75% of its sales in the US. Japan and Germany each account for less than 10% of sales. QVC has shopping channels in Germany Italy Japan France and the UK. The company also has a joint venture in China.

Sales and Marketing

Flagship subsidiary QVC distributes its television programs through satellite and optical fiber to cable and satellite system providers in the US Germany Japan the UK and neighboring countries. It also transmits programs via digital terrestrial broadcast television to viewers in Italy the UK and certain parts of the US and Germany. Additionally QVC offers a web-based catalog for retailers.

Some of QVC's clients include Comcast Time Warner Cable Cox Dish Network DirecTV Verizon and AT&T.

Financial Performance

After a bad 2015 Liberty Interactive's revenue bounced back in fiscal 2016 growing 7% to $10.6 billion. Growth was concentrated in Zulily which gained more than $1 billion due to its first full-year contribution. QVC's sales declined $61 million while the sales of Backcountry and Bodybuilding in 2015 and 2016 also weighed on sales.

Net income increased 40% to $1.3 billion thanks to higher revenue decreases in stock-based compensation and gains on the Right Start sale in January 2016.

Cash form operations increased 39% to $1.4 billion due to higher net income and changes in deferred income tax expense offset by realized losses on financial instruments.

Strategy

Liberty Interactive has been busy reshaping its business. In the last few years it has pared down its number of activities particularly in online retail — in 2015-16 it has sold or spun off Backcountry.com Bodybuilding.com Expedia and CommerceHub.com; the year before that it sold Provide Commerce to floral and gift retailer FTD Companies and spun off TripAdvisor and the Buy-Seasons group as TripAdvisor Holdings.

The sales paved the way for the $2.1 billion acquisition of QVC's archrival HSN Inc. agreed in 2017. With both QVC and HSN recording unfavorable revenue trends in recent years the acquisition reflects that the former rivals' biggest competitors are no longer each other but e-commerce giants such as Amazon. QVC HSN and Zulily will be bundled up as QVC Group.

Mergers and Acquisitions

Liberty Interactive agreed to buy the 62% of the Home Shopping Network Inc. (HSNi) that it didn't own for about $2.1 billion in stock. The deal would unite HSNi with Liberty's QVC in an effort to combat Amazon.com and other online retailers. Liberty plans to package QVC HSNi and Zulily.com into an asset-backed spinoff in late 2017. The acquisition of HSNi was expected to close by the end of the year.

HISTORY

The man who would be king of cable programming got his start on the hardware end of the business. In 1970 John Malone became president of General Instrument's Jerrold Communications subsidiary which supplied equipment to the then-new cable TV industry. One of Jerrold's customers was Bob Magness a former Texas rancher who in the

1950s started the company that eventually became Denver-based cable operator Tele-Communications Inc. (TCI). In the early 1970s TCI struggled in need of leadership. In 1973 the 32-year-old Malone was named CEO of TCI.

Malone restructured TCI's debt in 1977 paving the way for expansion into bigger cable markets after deregulation in 1984. He also acquired programming buying stakes in Black Entertainment Television (33% 1979 sold to Viacom in 2001) the Discovery Channel (14% 1986) and American Movie Classics (50% 1986). In 1987 TCI helped save debt-plagued Turner Broadcasting and came away with 12% of Turner Broadcasting's stock.

Due in part to antitrust pressure from government regulators in 1991 TCI spun off much of its programming assets along with interests in 14 cable systems as Liberty Media. Malone became chairman and principal shareholder. In its first year the company launched Court TV in a joint venture and introduced film channel Encore. The next year it bought an interest in the Home Shopping Network (which became USA Networks in 1998 and later changed names to USA Interactive in 2002 InterActiveCorp in 2003 and finally IAC/InterActiveCorp in 2004).

In 1994 TCI reacquired Liberty Media; it issued a tracking stock the next year to reflect the value of Liberty's program assets. Also in 1995 Liberty Media and News Corp. joined forces to create FOX/Liberty Networks a national sports network designed to compete with Disney's ESPN.

In 2011 Liberty Media Corp. changed its name to Liberty Interactive Corp. following the split-off of its Liberty Capital and Liberty Starz tracking stocks.

EXECUTIVES

President And Ceo, Gregory B. (Greg) Maffei, age 58, $1,045,739 total compensation
Chief Corporate Development Officer, Albert E. Rosenthaler, age 59, $336,031 total compensation
Chief Legal Officer, Richard N. (Rich) Baer, age 62, $327,307 total compensation
Cfo Liberty Media Corporation Liberty Interactive Corporation And Liberty Broadband Corporation, Mark D. Carleton, age 58, $127,147 total compensation
Chairman, John C. Malone, age 78
Auditors: KPMG LLP

LOCATIONS

HQ: Qurate Retail Inc
12300 Liberty Boulevard, Englewood, CO 80112
Phone: 720 875-5300
Web: www.qurateretail.com

2016 Sales

	$ mil.	% of total
US	7,979	75
Japan	900	8
Germany	866	8
Other countries	902	9
Total	**10,647**	**100**

PRODUCTS/OPERATIONS

2016 Sales

	$ mil.	% of total
QVC	8,682	81
zulily	1,547	15
Ventures Group	428	4
eliminations	(10)	-
Total	**10,647**	**100**

2016 Sales

	% of total
Home	33
Apparel	19
Beauty	17
Accessories	13
Jewelry	9
Electronics	9
Total	**100**

COMPETITORS

Amazon.com	Orbitz Worldwide
American Express	Priceline
EVINE Live	Travelocity
IAC	Wal-Mart

HISTORICAL FINANCIALS

Company Type: Public

Income Statement — FYE: December 31

	REVENUE ($ mil.)	NET INCOME ($ mil.)	NET PROFIT MARGIN	EMPLOYEES
12/18	14,070	916	6.5%	27,226
12/17	10,404	2,441	23.5%	28,255
12/16	10,647	1,235	11.6%	21,080
12/15	9,989	869	8.7%	22,080
12/14	10,499	537	5.1%	20,078
Annual Growth	**7.6%**	**14.3%**	**—**	**7.9%**

2018 Year-End Financials

Debt ratio: 41.00%
Return on equity: 12.00%
Cash ($ mil.): 653
Current ratio: 1.00
Long-term debt ($ mil.): 5,963
No. of shares (mil.): 439
Dividends
 Yield: —
 Payout: —
Market value ($ mil.): 8,572

	STOCK PRICE ($) FY Close	P/E High/Low		Earnings	PER SHARE ($) Dividends	Book Value
12/18	20.00	20	13	1.00	0.00	13.00
12/17	24.00	10	7	3.00	0.00	18.00
12/16	20.00	28	18	1.00	0.00	12.00
12/15	27.00	10	9	3.00	0.00	11.00
12/14	29.00	—	—	(0.00)	0.00	9.00
Annual Growth	**(9.7%)**			**—**	**—**	**8.7%**

Qurate Retail Inc

Auditors: KPMG LLP

LOCATIONS

HQ: Qurate Retail Inc
12300 Liberty Boulevard, Englewood, CO 80112
Phone: 720 875-5300
Web: www.libertymedia.com

HISTORICAL FINANCIALS

Company Type: Public

Income Statement — FYE: December 31

	REVENUE ($ mil.)	NET INCOME ($ mil.)	NET PROFIT MARGIN	EMPLOYEES
12/17	10,381	1,208	11.6%	28,255
12/16	10,219	473	4.6%	21,080
12/15	9,169	640	7.0%	22,080
12/14	10,028	520	5.2%	20,078
12/13	10,307	438	4.2%	23,079
Annual Growth	**0.2%**	**28.9%**	**—**	**5.2%**

2017 Year-End Financials

Debt ratio: 39.00%
Return on equity: 21.00%
Cash ($ mil.): 330
Current ratio: 1.00
Long-term debt ($ mil.): 6,686
No. of shares (mil.): 479
Dividends
 Yield: —
 Payout: —
Market value ($ mil.): 11,686

	STOCK PRICE ($) FY Close	P/E High/Low		Earnings	PER SHARE ($) Dividends	Book Value
12/17	24.00	10	7	3.00	0.00	14.00
12/16	20.00	28	18	1.00	0.00	11.00
12/15	27.00	23	19	1.00	0.00	11.00
12/14	29.00	28	22	1.00	0.00	9.00
12/13	29.00	35	23	1.00	0.00	13.00
Annual Growth	**(4.5%)**			**34.3%**	**—**	**2.8%**

Qwest Corp

EXECUTIVES

Exec V Pres-cao-contrl, David D Cole
Executive Vice President Product Management, Shaun Andrews
Vice President And General Manager, Alison Greenwood
Senior Business Intelligence Developer, Scott Reames
Auditors: KPMG LLP

LOCATIONS

HQ: Qwest Corp
100 CenturyLink Drive, Monroe, LA 71203
Phone: 318 388-9000
Web: www.centurylink.com

HISTORICAL FINANCIALS

Company Type: Public

Income Statement — FYE: December 31

	REVENUE ($ mil.)	NET INCOME ($ mil.)	NET PROFIT MARGIN	EMPLOYEES
12/18	8,493	1,665	19.6%	19,000
12/17	8,550	1,657	19.4%	22,000
12/16	8,910	1,085	12.2%	22,000
12/15	8,964	1,074	12.0%	22,000
12/14	8,838	970	11.0%	23,000
Annual Growth	**(1.0%)**	**14.5%**	**—**	**(4.7%)**

2018 Year-End Financials

Debt ratio: 34.00%
Return on equity: 17.00%
Cash ($ mil.): 5
Current ratio: 1.00
Long-term debt ($ mil.): 5,948
No. of shares (mil.): 0
Dividends
 Yield: 9.0%
 Payout: 77.0%
Market value ($ mil.): 0

	STOCK PRICE ($) FY Close	P/E High/Low		Earnings	PER SHARE ($) Dividends	Book Value
12/18	19.00	—	—	(0.00)	2.00	
*** *** *** **						
12/17	23.00	—	—	(0.00)	1.00	
*** *** *** **						
Annual Growth	**(4.6%)**			**—**	**12.1%**	**1.4%**

R. DIRECTIONAL DRILLING & UNDERGROUND TECHNOLOGY, INC.

EXECUTIVES

Pres-Ceo, Jose M Ruiz
V Pres of Oprs*, Aurelio Ruiz
Vice President of Sales*, Derek Reeve
Auditors: KEN DUSSEAU PC

LOCATIONS

HQ: R. DIRECTIONAL DRILLING & UNDERGROUND
TECHNOLOGY, INC.
8560 N 77TH DR, PEORIA, AZ 853457969
Phone: 602 374-3173

HISTORICAL FINANCIALS
Company Type: Private

Income Statement · FYE: December 31

	REVENUE ($ mil.)	NET INCOME ($ mil.)	NET PROFIT MARGIN	EMPLOYEES
12/12	7,668	(1,040)		61
12/11*	8	2	29.9%	—
09/10	3	1	27.4%	—
Annual Growth	5174.7%	—	—	—

*Fiscal year change

Radian Group, Inc.

Radian Group is glowing from a conflagration of private mortgage insurance claims. Through subsidiaries Radian Guaranty Radian Mortgage Assurance and Radian Insurance Radian Group provides traditional private mortgage insurance coverage to protect lenders from defaults by borrowers who put down a deposit of less than 20% when buying a home. Such coverage provides protection on individual loans and covers unpaid loan principal and delinquent interest. Its pool insurance covers limited exposure on groups of loans. Radian still insures municipal bonds written before 2008 through its financial guaranty business. Radian Group's customers include mortgage bankers commercial banks and savings institutions.

Operations

Radian operates in two segments: The mortgage insurance division offers credit-related insurance coverage primarily private mortgage insurance as well as risk services for lending agencies. These operations are primarily conducted through the Radian Guaranty subsidiary. The company also provides mortgage and real estate services through its principal services subsidiary Clayton as well as Green River Capital Red Bell Real Estate and ValuAmerica.

Meanwhile the financial guaranty segment — handled by the Radian Asset Assurance unit — insures a runoff portfolio of public finance and structured finance credits. The unit which no longer actively markets policies historically offered direct insurance or reinsurance for credit based risks as well as credit protection through default swaps and financial guaranty transactions.

During headier days the government encouraged lenders to turn more Americans into homeowners and Radian made a steady diet of insuring subprime mortgages. However that strategy meant that it was among the first to be hit and hit hard when the housing market imploded and mortgage defaults piled up.

Geographic Reach

Headquartered in Philadelphia Radian has offices across the US as well as in Hong Kong and in Bristol UK.

Sales and Marketing

The principal customers of Radian's mortgage insurance business are mortgage originators such as mortgage bankers mortgage brokers commercial banks savings institutions credit unions and community banks.

Financial Performance

In fiscal 2015 Radian's revenue climbed 11% to $1.2 billion due mainly to a 101% increase in revenue from the Services segment. It also recorded higher net premiums in the year. Net income dropped however by 70% to $286.9 million due to a large income tax benefit in the prior fiscal year. The company's cash position strengthened with cash from operating activities climbing to $15.5 million from a loss of $153.2 million in 2014.

Strategy

Radian is looking to expand the depth and breadth of its mortgage offering as the housing market in the US continues to strengthen.

Mergers and Acquisitions

In 2017 Radian consulting subsidiary Clayton Holdings acquired California-based ValuEscrow which continues to operate under its own brand name. The following year Radian acquired Independent Settlement Services a national appraisal and title management firm. That company will continue to operate under its current brand but will eventually transition to the Radian name.

HISTORY

Radian Group was born from the ashes of the 1987 stock crash and the rubble of the natural disasters of the early 1990s. Parent insurance company Reliance Group was deep in debt and desperately in need of cash. To raise money Reliance separated CMAC Investment (and operating subsidiary Commonwealth Mortgage Assurance) from subsidiary Commonwealth Land Title and took the company public in 1992.

In 1994 after two years of lackluster stock performance the board promoted CFO Frank Filipps (an American International Group veteran) to CEO. Filipps limited commissions to new policies rather than retained business. The pokey stock nosed up with some help from low interest rates and high numbers of new mortgage loans. Despite a raise in interest rates in 1995 the company continued to expand its market share.

In 1996 the company launched Prophet Score a new risk-assessment model that allowed CMAC to expand its coverage to include subprime loans. These measures jump-started sales to new highs in 1997 and 1998. Nevertheless CMAC (and its competitors) suffered in the market because of negative publicity: private mortgage (PMI) insurers were slammed for keeping quiet when borrowers' equity rose to 20% the point when PMI is usually considered unnecessary. In 1999 CMAC bought former rival Amerin and changed the name of the combined company to Radian Group.

Radian diversified its operations through the 2001 acquisition of credit-based insurance and financial services provider Enhance Financial (renamed Radian Reinsurance and later merged into Radian Asset Assurance Inc.) In 2002 Radian sold off the Enhance Consumer Services subsidiary.

In 2005 Filipps departed to join Clayton Holdings. Sanford Ibrahim was then named CEO.

The company expanded into Asia in 2005 through a partnership with Standard Chartered Bank (Hong Kong) with Radian as the exclusive provider of residential mortgage insurance to the lender. However the deal did not take root and Standard Chartered Bank yanked their contract in early 2008.

As the credit markets went into meltdown that year the company began pulling back on the riskiest of bonds (such as second-liens) by mid-2007 but by early 2008 its ratings had been lowered.

In response to the market troubles Radian stopped insuring certain types of higher-risk home loans and began working with existing mortgage services to help distressed borrowers modify their loan terms. The company's Radian Asset Assurance operations in the US and UK also stopped accepting new business as part of its general hunkering down to ride out the storm and in 2010 it put the UK unit into liquidation.

EXECUTIVES

Ceo, Richard G. (Rick) Thornberry
President Radian Guaranty, Teresa A. Bryce Bazemore, age 59, $550,000 total compensation
Evp And Cfo, J. Franklin (Frank) Hall, age 51, $400,000 total compensation
Evp And Cio, Richard I. (Rick) Altman, age 52
Evp And Chief Risk Officer, Derek V. Brummer, $415,000 total compensation
President Clayton Holdings, Jeff Tennyson
Vice President Marketing And Communications, Elizabeth Emmons
Assistant Vice President Risk Manager, Richard Mcveigh
Assistant Vice President Manager Information Technology Administration, Nicole Phillipine
Senior Vice President Capital Markets Risk And Operations, Susan Kropp
Senior Vice President, Robert Quigley
Vice President, John Castiello
Vice President National Account Manager, Todd Ebert
Vice President, Colleen Teears
Senior Vice President And Deputy General Counsel, Glenn Davis
Vice President Business Development, Shelley Duffy
Assistant Vice President Corporate Accounting, Abigail Rodriguez
Assistant Vice President Human Resources Business Partner, Karen L Chung
Senior Vice President, Michael Dziuba
Divisional Vice President, PJ Harrigan
Vice President, John Damian
Vp Security Assurance, Lucas Burke
Avp Security Assurance, Brad Bowers
Vp Operations Training, Matthew Carroll
Vp Business Technology Partners, Theresa Kelems
Director, Herbert Wender, age 82
Board Member, Howard Culang
Auditors: PricewaterhouseCoopers LLP

LOCATIONS

HQ: Radian Group, Inc.
1500 Market Street, Philadelphia, PA 19102
Phone: 215 231-1000
Web: www.radian.biz

PRODUCTS/OPERATIONS

2016 Revenues

	$ mil.	% of total
Net premiums earned—insurance	922	74
Services revenue	169	14
Net investment income	114	9
Net gains (losses) on investments and other financial instruments	31	3
Other income	4	-
Total	**1,239**	**100**

COMPETITORS

Assured Guaranty	Old Republic
Genworth Financial	Triad Guaranty
MGIC Investment	US Department of
National Mortgage	Veterans Affairs
Insurance	United Guaranty

HISTORICAL FINANCIALS

Company Type: Public

Income Statement				FYE: December 31
	ASSETS ($ mil.)	NET INCOME ($ mil.)	INCOME AS % OF ASSETS	EMPLOYEES
12/18	6,315	606	9.6%	1,942
12/17	5,901	121	2.1%	1,887
12/16	5,863	308	5.3%	1,971
12/15	5,642	287	5.1%	1,881
12/14	6,860	960	14.0%	1,702
Annual Growth	(2.0%)	(10.9%)	—	3.4%

2018 Year-End Financials

Debt ratio: 18.00%	No. of shares (mil.): 213
Return on equity: 19.00%	Dividends
Cash ($ mil.): 95	Yield: 0.0%
Current ratio: —	Payout: 0.0%
Long-term debt ($ mil.): —	Market value ($ mil.): 3,492

	STOCK PRICE ($) FY Close	P/E High/Low		PER SHARE ($) Earnings	Dividends	Book Value
12/18	16.00	8	5	3.00	0.00	16.00
12/17	21.00	40	28	1.00	0.00	14.00
12/16	18.00	13	6	1.00	0.00	13.00
12/15	13.00	13	9	1.00	0.00	12.00
12/14	17.00	3	2	4.00	0.00	11.00
Annual Growth	(0.5%)	—	—	(9.7%)	(0.0%)	9.5%

Ralph Lauren Corp

Ralph Lauren Corporation is galloping at a faster clip than when its namesake founder first entered the arena over 45 years ago. With golden mallet brands such as Polo by Ralph Lauren Chaps RRL Club Monaco and RLX Ralph Lauren the company designs and markets apparel and accessories home furnishings and fragrances. Its collections are available at more than 13000 retail locations worldwide including many upscale and mid-tier department stores (Macy's contributes 25% to RL's wholesale revenue). It operates 465-plus Ralph Lauren and Club Monaco retail stores worldwide as well as 615-plus concession-based shops-within-shops and 10 e-commerce sites.

HISTORY

Ralph Lauren a suave Manhattanite was actually born Ralph Lifschitz in the Bronx New York. It is said that his father Frank an immigrant Russian housepainter and muralist informally changed the family's name to Lauren and inspired his son to recreate himself in the image of a mythic upper class.

After high school Ralph who formally changed his name to Lauren became a salesman at Brooks Brothers and then a sales representative for Rivetz a Boston tie maker. In 1967 he landed a job as a tie designer for Beau Brummel of New York. The company gave him his own style division which he named Polo because of the sport's refined image. The next year Lauren started Polo Fashions to make tailored menswear. Partner Peter Strom teamed up with Lauren in the early 1970s. Although its designs received critical acclaim Polo Fashions had a bumpy start as Lauren adjusted to the business aspect of his fashion label.

Lauren's profile rose in the 1970s when he won three Coty Awards for design and produced costumes for the movie The Great Gatsby. In 1971 Lauren adopted his polo-player-on-a-horse logo and introduced a line for women. That year the first licensed Polo store opened (on Rodeo Drive in Beverly Hills) along with his first in-store boutique (at Bloomingdale's in New York City). He added shoes to the lineup in 1972 licensed his womenswear line the next year and launched a licensed fragrance line in 1978.

By 1980 Polo Fashions had become Polo Ralph Lauren. Encouraged by the success of the licensed products Lauren led the designer charge into home furnishings introducing his Home Collection in 1983. He opened his flagship store in New York City three years later. The company expanded upmarket with its Purple Label and downmarket with Polo Jeans denims and a line of paints in 1996.

Following the stampede of fashion-house IPOs Polo went public in 1997. The next year moving to reduce expenses the company restructured its divisions. In 1999 Polo paid $85 million for hip Canadian retailer Club Monaco to compete in the burgeoning youth market. It also opened RL a fine-dining restaurant adjacent to its retail outlet in Chicago's famed shopping district.

In early 2000 Polo purchased its European licensee Poloco for $230 million giving the company greater control of its brand. Then in a 50-50 joint venture with NBC and its affiliates Polo formed Ralph Lauren Media Company to sell its products via the Internet as well as broadcast cable and print media. Also that year the company closed 11 underperforming Club Monaco locations and announced plans to shut down all of its jeans stores. To extend its European reach even further Polo bought its Italian licensee PRL Fashions of Europe in 2001.

Polo Ralph Lauren inked one of the most significant licensing deals in company history — and what it considers to be a great match to boot — in 2005. The firm paired with the United States Tennis Association (USTA) to form a four-year global partnership and was designated the official apparel sponsor of the US Open through 2008. The agreement involved among other things an official shirt designed by Lauren for on-court officials co-branded US Open/Polo Ralph Lauren merchandise and joint marketing programs. In 2006 the company entered a licensing agreement with Luxottica valued at more than $1.75 billion over a 10-year period.

The company's agreement with the USTA gave it the momentum to seal a deal with The All England Club and Wimbledon in 2006 that extends through 2010. Polo Ralph Lauren as part of the agreement became the exclusive outfitter of Wimbledon — the first official designer in the 129-history of the games. Polo Ralph Lauren creates and outfits on-court officials and sells its Wimbledon collection at its freestanding stores as well as through select retailers and Polo.com.

Initiatives for 2007 included the launch of a new group named Global Brand Concepts formed to develop lifestyle brands for specialty and department stores including J.C. Penney's American Living Collection. The group designs and markets new products including accessories home decor and women's men's and children's apparel.

That year Polo Ralph Lauren purchased the remaining 50% stake in Polo.com from both Ralph Lauren Media a unit of NBCUniversal and Value-Visions Media for about $175 million. The move gave Polo full control over its plans to develop its online presence domestically and abroad.

The company brought its East Coast lifestyle brand to Asia when it opened its first freestanding flagship store in Tokyo in 2006. The next year Polo Ralph Lauren secured a foothold in the Japanese apparel and accessories market by purchasing the 50% balance of Polo Ralph Lauren Japan for some $23 million and making it a wholly owned subsidiary. The company also increased its stake in Impact 21 Co. a Japanese sub-licensee from 20% to 97% in. Impact 21 operates the company's men's women's and jeans apparel and accessories business in Japan.

Founder Ralph Lauren stepped down as CEO in November 2015 but remained involved with the company as chairman and chief creative officer.

During 2013 RLC brought several licensing arrangements in-house. In April 2013 it acquired the Chaps Menswear Business from PVH for about $18 million. In July it bought the Australia and New Zealand licensed operations from its licensee for about $15 million.

EXECUTIVES

President Ceo And Director, Patrice J. L. Louvet, age 55
President Global Brands, Valérie Hermann, age 56, $917,308 total compensation
Cfo, Jane H. Nielsen, age 55
Brand President Men's Polo Purple Label And Double Rl, Tom Mendenhall
Senior Vice President Merchandising And Manufacturing, Benny Lin
Vice President Store Development, Rick Farrar
Vice President Of Construction, Deidre Dunne
Vice President Sales, Allison Cappello
Vice President Of Merchandising Blue Label, Brooke Allinson
Vice President Gmm Ralphlauren Com, Flo Dessen
Senior Vice President Marketing Communications And International Business Development, William Li
Vice President, Michel Botbol
Vp Global Brand Marketing Ralph Lauren Home, Daniel Strassburger
Vice President Planning And Allocation Factory Store Concept, Bradley Eckhart
Vice President, Kim Babka
Vice President, Maureen Whitaker
Vice President, Ralf Dremel
Vice President Design, Daniele Marin
Vice President Technical Manufacturing, Paul Haffner
Vice President Head Of Stores, Marc Tenebruso
Vice President Information Technology Infrastructure, Jonathan Zwang
Vpcredit And Trade Finance, Kenneth Cruz
Vp Asset Protection, Chris Hinger
Vice President Knit Design And Development, Julie Mastrarrigo
Vice President Store Operations, Scott Link
Senior Vice President Retail Europa, Alessandro Valenti
Vice President, Jay Kimpton
Senior Vice President Production, Lisa Aiosa
Vice President Mens Production, Cindy Tse

Svp Supply Chain And Logistics Operations, Freida Bailey
Vice President, Bryan Fogg
Vice President, Vince Dellosa
Senior Vice President Sales Footwear, Geoffrey Ward
Vice President Store Development Architect, John Heist
Vice President Of Merchandising Dresses, Kathy Pastorius
Vice President, Pamela Flynn
Vice President Of Product Development, Melissa Schirripa
Senior Vice President, Wendy Berloe-Buch
Vice President, Dan McCampbell
Vice President Of Design, Callery McGee
Vice President Design And Development, Peter Sjonell
Vice President Of Asset Protection Global Supply Chain, Chris Aye
Vice President: Planning, Dan Greenberg
Vice President Of Production, Michael Marafioti
Executive Vice President Manufacturing, Richard Bangs
Vice President Corporate Business Development, Andrew Nkongho
Vice President Global Human Resources Systems Solutions, Dean Dellantonia
Vice President Us Distribution Ops Global Supply Chain, George Clopton
Vice President Finance, Paul Wickman
Vice President Financeand Operations, Richard Foggio
Vice President, Patricia Faz
Corporate Vice President, Robert Grecco
Vice President Women 's Marketing, Amy Fisher
Vice President, Dara Miller
Vice President Of Woven Production, Patgun Chen
Vice President Of Design Womens Footwear, Nancy Boas
Senior Vice President Mens Specialty Store Division, Tom Cush
Vice President Platform Engineering, Atif Khan
Vice President Sales Polo Ralph Lauren Tailored Clothing, Phil Faust
Vice President Digital Product Management, Samantha Starmer
Vice President Of Licensed Business, Meegan Colgan
Vice President, Elise Schneider
Senior Vice President Of Merchandising Lauren Collection And Women's Licensed Businesses, Sandy Aronson
Vice President Merchandising, Christine Imundi
Vice President Marketing, Lisa Pillette
Vice President Global Marketing, Tom Jarrold
Vice President Human Resources, Patricia Moffett
Senior Vice President Advertising, Mary Randolph Carter
Executive Assistant To The Senior Vice President Of Interactive Technology, Erika Keller
Assistant Vice President Of Mis, Peggy Love
Vice President Home Design, Stavros Garger
Vice President Production And Sourcing, Hannah Bradford
Vice President Internal Audit, Amy Cheema
Senior Vice President Sales, Richard Sementelli
Vice President Of Creativeservice, Salvatore Disanto
Corporate Vice President Global Ecommerce Operatio, Ralph Wear
Vice President Human Resources, Andrea Carter
Vice President Merchandising, Michael Reinhart
Vice President, Angela Cohen
Senior Vice President Global Manufacturing, Don Baum
Vice President, David G Rush
Vice President Retail Development, George Rakotci
Vice President, Hilary Berger
Vice President Of Menswear Design, John Varvatos
Executive Vice President, Alfredo Paredes

Vice President Product Presentation And Training Polo Retail Group, Baldo LaRussa
Senior Vice President Accessories Merchandising, Louise Mimicopoulos
Senior Vice President Chief Of Staff, Robbin Mitchell
Vice President, Moira Taylor
Vice President Creative Services, Sarah O'reilly
Vice President Regional Controller Europe, Marta Wilczewska
Vice President Creative Services, Quinn Pofahl
Vice President Of Specialty Store Planning, Matthew Sanders
Vice President Taxes, Bob Alexander
Vice President Of Account Services And Business In, Thomas Zente
Vp Sales Ralph Lauren Childrenswear, Howard Bronstein
Senior Vice President Global Creative Services, Karen Ford
Vice President Sales, Cameron Lambert
Vice President Financial Planning And Analysis, Gernot Senke
Vice President Marketing, Liz Carey
Vice President Customer Operations, Cathy Houlihan
Senior Vice President Product Innovation, Jason Berns
Vice President Design Sweaters, Susann Epperlein
Vice President, Barry Jordan
Vice President Intellectual Property, Anna Dalla
Vice President Compensation And International Total Rewards, Danielle Moss
Vice President Global Manufacturing, Lance Baran
Vice President Of Merchandise Planning, Sandra Cooper
Executive Vice President, Birrittella Buffy
National Sales Manager Mens, Thomas Cush
Vice President Marketing Asia Pacific, Larry Feng
Vice President Global Merchandising European Menswear, Martin Roos
Vice President Marketing, Michele Rast
Vice President Assistant Treasurer, Tom Lynch
Vice President Creative Services, Francis Power
Senior Vice President Of Childrenswear Sales, Regan Romei
Vice President Information Technology Infrastructure, Alex Santillana
Senior Vice President Marketing And Communications Asia Pacific, Jason Beckley
Regional Vice President, Ben Lisi
Vice President, Abby Curley
Vice President Production, Lisa Ruland
Senior Vice President, Kim Di
Vice President Of Design Womens Collection, Daniela Kamiliotis
Vice President Advertising Design, Lisa Curtiss
Vice President Art Acquisitions, Donald Nowicki
Vice President Of Advertising Set Design, John Devitt
Vp Tax Compliance And Controversy, Michele Garofalo
Senior Vice President Haberdashery, Mike Cohen
Vice President Assistant Corporate Controller, Caroline Tung
Chairman And Chief Creative Officer, Ralph Lauren, age 79
Vice Chairman And Chief Innovation Officer, David Lauren, age 47
Board Member, John R Alchin
Board Member, Hubert Joly
Board Member, Robert C Wright
Senior Vice President General Counsel And Secretary, Avery Fischer
Board Member, Joyce Brown
Auditors: Ernst & Young LLP

LOCATIONS

HQ: Ralph Lauren Corp
650 Madison Avenue, New York, NY 10022
Phone: 212 318-7000
Web: www.RalphLauren.com

2016 Sales

	$ mil.	% of total
Americas	4,938	67
Europe	1,573	21
Asia	894	12
Total	**7,405**	**100**

PRODUCTS/OPERATIONS

2016 Sales

	$ mil.	% of total
Retail	3,933	53
Wholesale	3,297	45
Licensing	175	2
Total	**7,405**	**100**

Selected Brand Names & Licenses
Wholesale
Lauren by Ralph Lauren
Pink Pony
Polo Ralph Lauren
Ralph by Ralph Lauren
Ralph Lauren Black Label
Ralph Lauren Blue Label
Ralph Lauren Purple Label
Ralph Lauren Polo Sport
Retail
Club Monaco
Ralph Lauren
Polo Ralph Lauren
Polo Sport
Licensing Partners
Fitz and Floyd Inc.
Hanesbrands
Kohl's Department Stores Inc.
L'Oréal S.A.
Luxottica Group
Peerless Inc.
The Warnaco Group
WestPoint Home Inc.

COMPETITORS

Abercrombie & Fitch
American Eagle Outfitters
Ann Taylor
Armani
Benetton
Brand Matter
Burberry
Calvin Klein
Christian Dior
Coach Inc.
Donna Karan
Ermenegildo Zegna
Escada
Estée Lauder
Gianni Versace
Gucci
Guess?
H&M
Haggar
Herm ̈s
Hugo Boss
J. Crew

Jos. A. Bank
Kate Spade
Kenneth Cole
Kering
L.L. Bean
LVMH
Lands' End
Laura Ashley
Levi Strauss
Martha Stewart Living
Michael Kors Holdings
Nautica Apparel
Nine West
PVH
Perry Ellis International
Richemont
St. John Knits
The Gap
Tiffany & Co.
Tommy Bahama
Tommy Hilfiger
VF Corporation

HISTORICAL FINANCIALS

Company Type: Public

Income Statement

FYE: March 30

	REVENUE ($ mil.)	NET INCOME ($ mil.)	NET PROFIT MARGIN	EMPLOYEES
03/19	6,313	431	6.8%	24,300
03/18*	6,182	163	2.6%	23,500
04/17	6,653	(99)	—	23,300
04/16	7,405	396	5.3%	26,000
03/15	7,620	702	9.2%	25,000
Annual Growth	(4.6%)	(11.5%)	—	(0.7%)

*Fiscal year change

2019 Year-End Financials

Debt ratio: 16.00%
Return on equity: 13.00%
Cash ($ mil.): 584
Current ratio: 3.00
Long-term debt ($ mil.): 902

No. of shares (mil.): 78
Dividends
 Yield: 0.0%
 Payout: 47.0%
Market value ($ mil.): 10,128

	STOCK PRICE ($) FY Close	P/E High/Low		PER SHARE ($) Earnings	Dividends	Book Value
03/19	130.00	27	18	5.00	3.00	42.00
03/18*	112.00	60	33	2.00	2.00	43.00
04/17	82.00	—	—	(1.00)	2.00	41.00
04/16	97.00	30	18	5.00	2.00	45.00
03/15	131.00	23	16	8.00	2.00	45.00
Annual Growth	(0.3%)		—	(9.6%)	7.8%	(1.7%)

*Fiscal year change

RAYMOND JAMES & ASSOCIATES INC

Does everybody love Raymond James & Associates (RJA)? Raymond James Financial hopes so. RJA is that company's primary subsidiary and one of the largest retail brokerages in the US. The unit provides brokerage financial planning investments and related services to consumers. It performs equity and fixed income sales trading and research for institutional clients in North America and Europe. Its investment banking group provides corporate and public finance debt underwriting and mergers and acquisitions advice. RJA also makes markets for approximately 1000 stocks including thinly traded issues. Planning Corporation of America a wholly-owned subsidiary of RJA sells insurance and annuities.

Operations

RJA is engaged in most aspects of securities distribution and investment banking.

Geographic Reach

The company has more than 200 branches and satellite offices concentrated in the Mid-Atlantic Midwest Southeast and Southwest portions of the US in addition to ten institutional sales offices in Europe.

Sales and Marketing

RJA has many big name clients across dozens of industries. In 2013 Titan Medical announced that it has retained RJA to provide advisory services and present options which could include a possible sale.

Strategy

In 2012 the company's parent completed its acquisition of Morgan Keegan & Co. and MK Holding Inc. from Regions Financial Corporation. Some

of the equity capital markets and fixed income operations of were integrated into RJA.

EXECUTIVES

Vice President, Scott Cutliff
Vice President Investments Financial Advisor,
 Aamsa Zuniga
Auditors: KPMG LLP TAMPA FL

LOCATIONS

HQ: RAYMOND JAMES & ASSOCIATES INC
 880 CARILLON PKWY, SAINT PETERSBURG, FL
 337161100
Phone: 727 567-1000
Web: WWW.RAYMONDJAMES.COM

COMPETITORS

Ameriprise	Janney Montgomery
Charles Schwab	Scott
E*TRADE Financial	Merrill Lynch
Edward D. Jones	Scottrade
Edward Jones	TD Ameritrade
FMR	Wells Fargo Advisors

HISTORICAL FINANCIALS

Company Type: Private

Income Statement

FYE: September 30

	ASSETS ($ mil.)	NET INCOME ($ mil.)	INCOME AS % OF ASSETS	EMPLOYEES
09/17	9,918	198	2.0%	10,000
09/16	10,689	146	1.4%	—
09/15	7,894	168	2.1%	—
09/14	6,956	183	2.6%	—
Annual Growth	12.6%	2.8%	—	—

Raymond James Financial, Inc.

Diversified financial services company Raymond James Financial offers financial advice to retail clients and corporations alike. The brokerage house has more than 7800 advisors and nearly $800 billion in total client assets held in about 3 million client accounts. Raymond James offers investment and asset management services for retail and institutional clients; underwriting distribution trading and brokerage of equity and debt securities; sale of mutual funds and other investment products; corporate and retail banking services; and trust services. It has an extended geographic reach with more than 3100 locations in the US Canada and Europe although the US accounts for most of revenue.

HISTORY

Robert James often called the "founder of financial planning" first started a construction business in Ohio after his WWII service in the US Navy and then began a Florida home-building company. He got into the financial services business in 1954 with Florida Mutual Fund a company he and Gerard Jobin formed that eventually became American National Growth Fund. But when most companies were selling just stocks or mutual funds James

saw a need for a more comprehensive approach to investing. He decided to focus on helping individual clients learning about their financial needs and goals and then working with them on everything from investments to taxes. To that end he began offering seminars for retirees.

In 1960 those seminars had turned into a new company James and Associates which two years later became Robert A. James Investments. In 1964 James acquired Raymond and Associates a firm started by Edward Raymond in 1962; the newly merged firm was renamed Raymond James & Associates (RJA).

James' son Thomas joined the firm in 1966 the year the company's revenues first surpassed $1 million. Over the next several years the company expanded its investment offerings and set up new divisions. It added Investment Management & Research as an affiliate broker/dealer in 1967 and Planning Corporation of America as a general insurance agency in 1968.

Raymond James Financial incorporated as a holding company in 1969 and Thomas James became CEO the next year. RJA formed Eagle Asset Management in 1975 RJ Oil & Gas (subsidiary for oil and gas limited partnerships) in 1977 securities and real estate subsidiaries in 1980 (Robert Thomas Securities and RJ Properties respectively) and an equipment leasing subsidiary (RJ Leasing) in 1982.

Raymond James Financial went public in 1983 the year Robert James died. Two years later the company organized its Heritage Family of Funds. RJA became an international company in the late 1980s opening an office in Paris in 1987 and in Geneva the next year. It also began offering a cash management program in 1988 and began its Stock Loan Department. Trust and banking subsidiaries were begun in 1992 and 1994 respectively followed by the creation of Equity Capital Markets Group in 1996.

In 2000 Raymond James Financial crossed the billion-dollar-mark hitting $1.7 billion in sales. That year it acquired Canadian investment firm Goepel McDermid (renamed Raymond James Ltd.) to offer individual and institutional investment services to the Canadian market and it launched Raymond James Killik a UK joint venture that became Raymond James Investment Services in 2002.

In 2006 Raymond James Financial reduced front-end commissions with variations of variable annuity products; the next year it kicked off its Wealth Solutions department a unit designed to help high-net-worth clients and their advisors. Also that year Raymond James Financial extended its deal to attach its name to the home stadium of the NFL's Tampa Bay Buccaneers through 2015.

In 2012 to build its capital markets business in one of its largest purchases to date the company bought the investment banking and brokerage business of Morgan Keegan from Regions Financial for $1.2 billion and integrated the Morgan Keegan platform into its RJ&A platform. Raymond James Financial previously purchased boutique investment bank Lane Berry & Co. International in Boston in 2009 and Chicago-based investment bank and brokerage Howe Barnes Hoefer & Arnett in 2011.

To boost its large-cap investments the firm in 2012 acquired a 45% interest in ClariVest Asset Management.

RJ Bank acquired the Canadian operations of Allied Irish Banks in 2012 adding a portfolio of approximately $430 million in loan commitments. In conjunction with the deal RJ Bank launched a new finance company in Canada which will help the company grow its corporate and real estate banking business. It's part of Raymond James Financial's strategy of expanding its corporate lending business to additional markets.

EXECUTIVES

President Global Equities And Investment Banking Raymond James & Associates, Jeffrey E. (Jeff) Trocin, age 59, $305,000 total compensation

Evp Finance Cfo And Treasurer, Jeffrey P. (Jeff) Julien, age 62, $280,000 total compensation

Coo Raymond James Financial And Ceo Raymond James & Associates, Dennis W. Zank, age 64, $330,000 total compensation

Vice President Human Resources Executive, Michael Girolamo

President Raymond James Financial And Fixed Income Capital Markets, John C. Carson, age 62, $300,000 total compensation

President Planning Corporation Of America, Scott A. Curtis, age 56

Chairman And Ceo, Paul C. Reilly, age 64, $445,000 total compensation

President And Ceo Raymond James Bank, Steven M. (Steve) Raney, age 53

Chairman And Ceo Raymond James Ltd., Paul D. Allison, age 62

President Raymond James & Associates Private Client Group, Tashtego S. (Tash) Elwyn, age 47

Evp Technology And Operations, Bella Loykhter Allaire, age 65

Evp And President Asset Management Group, Jeffrey A. (Jeff) Dowdle, age 54

Evp General Counsel And Secretary, Jonathan N. Santelli, age 47

Senior Vice President; Director European Equities, Mark Abbott

Senior Vice President Communications, Tracey Bustamante

Vice President Investments, Greg Williams

Senior Vice President Fixed Income Sales, Gerard Buquicchio

Vice President And Managing Director Acquisitions Northeast Raymond James Tax Credit Funds, Darryl Seavey

Vice President Corporate Client Services, Hunt James

Vice President And Managing Director Acquisitions West Raymond James Tax Credit Funds, Kevin Kilbane

Senior Vice President, Mark Mchugh

Senior Vice President Financial Planning Raymond James And Associates, Charles J Bauder

Vice President, David Thomas

Vice President Institutional Equity Sales, Rob Mills

Vp Asset Management Raymond James Tax Credit Funds, Brian Lynch

Vice President Client Communications Technology, Randy McGlothin

Vice President, Mark Matheson

Vice President, Ed Cashman

Vice President Deposit Operations, Barbara Shore

Senior Vice President Investments, Roger Grefe

Vice President Investments, Sandy Martin

First Vice President, Beth Smith

Vice President Of Investments Programs And Services Committee Chair, Linda Larkin Smith

Senior Vice President, Scott Brinner

Senior Vice President, Sandy Webb

Vice President Variable Annuity Sales, Vanessa Marcos

Senior Vice President, Steve Shapiro

Senior Vice President Investments, John Reuter

Vice President Mortgage Consultant, Valerie Pratt

Vice President Information Technology, Frank Bugh

Senior Vice President And Head Corporate Development, Alexandra Band

National Sales Manager, Peter Delahunt

Vice President Sales Trader International, Sharon Agudio

Vice President Operations, Tim Bradford

Vice President, Christine Holder

Assistant Vice President Of Information Technology, Brian Miller

Vice President Regulatory Reporting, Marshall Ollia

Senior Vice President Of Operations, Denise Samson

First Vice President Investments, Robert Hodgson

Vice President Investments, Sonya Choeff

Vice President, Peter Gairing

Senior Vice President, Roxanne Post

Vice President Syndicate Operations, Andrea Borum

Senior Vice President Institutional Equity Sales, Zachary Taylor

Vice President Acquisitions Southeast, John Colvin

Senior Vice President Office Services, Raymond Lacour

Vice President Agency Trader Team Lead, Allen Spence

Vice President For Investments, Brian Rimel

Senior Vice President Equity Research Infrastruct, Michael Turits

Senior Vice President Of Investments And Branch Manager, Mark K Mekler

Vice President Investment Banking, Justin Cadman

Associate Vice President, Nick Roederer

Associate Vice President Investments, Elizabeth Aulick Robertson

Vice President, Trey Haydon

Vice President, Stacy W Houston

Senior Vice President Fi Trading, Randall Hawkins

Vice President Investments, Mark Mazman

Senior Vice President, Fred Coble

Vice President Regional Manager, Angela Nye

Vice President Fi Trading, Chad Runnels

Associate Vice President, Daniel Allen

Vice President, Christine Pedrick

Corporate Bond Trader And Vice President, Mark Schreiner

Vice President Investments, Brent Carlton

Assistant Vice President, Ruth Quinlan

First Vice President, Kenny Mcclain

Fvp Fi Trading, Edward Wildrick

Vice President Investments, Gregory Majors

Senior Vice President Investments, Michael Mccall

Vice President Investments, Robert Peabody

Vice President Fi Strategies, Emilio Garma-Fernandez

Assistant Vice President Lending Solutions Consultant, Dino Martinbianco

Senior Vice President, Jeff Harring

Vice President Investments, Patrick Dowden

Vice President, Michael Mobley

Assistant Vice President Internal Sales, Samantha Fernandez

First Vice President Investments, Tom Mahoney

Vice President Of Operations, Jesus Cruz

Senior Vice President Fi Trading, BEN LAPOINTE

Vice President, Al Caudullo

Senior Vp Investments, Jason Pucci

Assistant Vice President Corporate Loan Operations, Tonia Armes

Executive Vice President And Senior Corporate And Real Estate Banking Executive Raymond James Bank, Tom Macina

Vice President, Scott Englehardt

Vice President, Lee Morthland

Senior Vice President Healthcare Public Finance New York, Dean Scarano

Vice President, Sasha Stipanovich

Senior Vice President Financial Advisor, Chip Lee

First Vice President, Tom Owens

Vice President, Chris Cowing

Assistant Vice President Application Development, John D'Agostino

Associate Vice President Investments, Michael Lowe

Senior Vice President Investments Branch Manager, Matt Quigley

Vice President Compliance, Brad Cole

Senior Vice President Investments, Bob Taylor

Senior Vice President Fixed Income Sales, Geoffrey Waters

Senior Vice President Fi Trading, Gail Tyler

Vice President Fi Trading, Ben Streed

Vice President, Bob Jones

Assistant Vice President Asset Management Services, Robert Lyublanovits

Vice President Public Finance, Ogden Kniffin

Senior Vice President Real Estate Investment Banking St. Petersburg, Jozsi Popper

Vice President, Holly Hayes

Senior Vice President Listed And Otc And International Trading, Terri Stewart

Certified Financial Planner??? Senior Vice President Investments, Frank Maurno

Associate Vp Wealth Management, Mark Canavesio

Senior Vice President, Chad Puryear

Associate Vice President, Kristin Smith

First Vice President, Eduardo Bonilla

Associate Vice President Investments Sim, Lynn T Shaw

Vice President Asset Management Services, George Raffa

Vice President, Matt Ransom

First Vice President Brokered Cds, Joseph Evans

Vice President Investments, James Evans

Vice President Investments, Tom Lamacchio

Vice President, Landon Myers

Vice President, Jamie Kosharek

Vice President, Donna Loufman

Assistant Vice President Of Asset Managment Services, Andrew Keil

Vice President Corporate Banking, Daniel Gendron

Wms Senior Vice President Investments, James McLean

Vice President Banking Consultant, Chris Drennen

Vice President Energy Investment Banking Dallas, Kyle Gunnison

Associate Vice President Investments, Joe Zaiter

Vice President Sales, Alec Levine

Vice President, Carla Hargett

Vice President, Neil Tagaras

Vice President, Ted Long

Vice President, Tim Hansen

Senior Vice President Investments, Terry Mcmahon

First Vice President Investments, Keith Dubauskas

Senior Vice President Government Guaranteed Desk, Michelle Shadix

Senior Vice President, Doug Marron

Senior Vice President Investments, Travis McAfee

Senior Vice President Investments, Alan Spilker

Assistant Vice President Credit Risk Officer, Sloan Yadley

Auditors: KPMG LLP

LOCATIONS

HQ: Raymond James Financial, Inc.
880 Carillon Parkway, St. Petersburg, FL 33716
Phone: 727 567-1000
Web: www.raymondjames.com

2018 Sales

	$ mil.	% of total
US	6,914	92
Canada	423	6
Europe	139	2
Other	- -	
Total	**7,476**	**100**

PRODUCTS/OPERATIONS

2018 Sales By Segment

	$ mil.	% of total
Private Client Group	5,121	67
Capital Markets	992	13
RJ Bank	654	8
Asset Management	815	11
Other	60	1
Eliminations	(166.3)	-
Total	**7,476**	**100**

Selected Subsidiaries

Alex. Brown
Eagle Asset Management Inc.
Eagle Boston Investment Management Inc.
Eagle Fund Distributors Inc.
Howe Barnes Hoefer & Arnett Inc.
Lane Berry & Co. International
Planning Corporation of America
Raymond James & Associates
Raymond James Asset Management International S.A. (France)
Raymond James Bank FSB (dba RJ Bank)
Raymond James Canada LLC
Raymond James Capital Partners L.P.
Raymond James European Holdings Inc.
Raymond James Financial Services Inc.
Raymond James Financial Services Advisors
Raymond James Investment Services Limited (UK 75%)
Raymond James Ltd. (Canada)
Raymond James Tax Credit Funds Inc.
Raymond James Trust N.A.
Reams Asset Management
Scout Investments

COMPETITORS

Charles Schwab
E*TRADE Financial
Edward Jones
FMR
LPL Financial
Legg Mason
Merrill Lynch
Morgan Stanley
National Financial Partners
Oppenheimer Holdings
Piper Jaffray
Stifel Financial
TD Ameritrade
Wells Fargo Advisors

HISTORICAL FINANCIALS

Company Type: Public

Income Statement

FYE: September 30

	REVENUE ($ mil.)	NET INCOME ($ mil.)	NET PROFIT MARGIN	EMPLOYEES
09/19	8,023	1,034	12.9%	18,910
09/18	7,476	857	11.5%	18,550
09/17	6,525	636	9.8%	17,000
09/16	5,520	529	9.6%	15,900
09/15	5,308	502	9.5%	14,850
Annual Growth	10.9%	19.8%	—	6.2%

2019 Year-End Financials

Debt ratio: 6.00%	No. of shares (mil.): 138
Return on equity: 16.00%	Dividends
Cash ($ mil.): 6,562	Yield: 2.0%
Current ratio: 0.00	Payout: 19.0%
Long-term debt ($ mil.): 2,444	Market value ($ mil.): 11,366

	STOCK PRICE ($) FY Close	P/E High/Low	PER SHARE ($) Earnings	Dividends	Book Value
09/19	82.00	13 10	7.00	1.00	48.00
09/18	92.00	17 14	6.00	1.00	44.00
09/17	84.00	19 13	4.00	1.00	39.00
09/16	58.00	16 11	4.00	1.00	35.00
09/15	50.00	17 14	3.00	1.00	32.00
Annual Growth	13.5%	— —	20.2%	17.2%	10.8%

Raytheon Co.

Raytheon Company regularly places among the Pentagon's top ten prime contractors. Its air land sea space and cyber defense offerings include reconnaissance targeting and navigation systems as well as missile systems (Patriot Sidewinder and Tomahawk) unmanned ground and aerial systems sensing technologies and radars. Additionally Raytheon makes systems for communications (satellite) and intelligence radios cybersecurity and air traffic control. The company serves both domestic and international customers primarily as a prime contractor or subcontractor on a broad portfolio of defense and related programs for government customers. The US government accounts for about 70% of sales. In early 2019 Raytheon agreed to merge with leading aerospace and defense giant United Technologies Corporation (UTC). The combined company will be renamed Raytheon Technologies Corporation.

Operations

To support its customers worldwide Raytheon serves defense and intelligence markets via five business segments: Integrated Defense Systems (IDS) Intelligence Information and Services (ISS) Missile Systems (MS) Space and Airborne Systems (SAS) and Forcepoint.

Missile Systems represents about 30% of the company's revenue. It develops missile and combat systems for US armed forces and those of its allies. It provides and supports advanced weapon systems including missiles smart munitions close-in weapon systems projectiles kinetic kill vehicles and advanced combat sensor solutions.

Space and Airborne Systems (about 25%) makes integrated sensor and communication systems for advanced missions. These include but are not limited to civil and military electro-optical/infrared (EO/IR) sensors airborne radars for surveillance and fire control applications lasers precision guidance systems electronic warfare systems; and tactical and strategic communications.

The Intelligence Information and Services segment accounts for about 25% of revenue and provides technical and professional services to intelligence defense federal and commercial customers worldwide. It specializes in things like global intelligence surveillance and reconnaissance (ISR) navigation DoD space and weather solutions and domestic air traffic management (ATM) systems.

Integrated Defense Systems (20%) delivers products that protect against airborne and ballistic missile threats and develops and produces products such as large land- and sea-based radar solutions cyber and intelligence solutions and naval combat and ship electronic and sensing systems.

Forcepoint (less than 5%) develops cybersecurity products and serves commercial and government organizations worldwide. It makes a range of human-centric cybersecurity capabilities that incorporate behavior-based insights including data loss prevention user and entity behavior analytics (UEBA) and cloud and on-premise web and email security to name a few.

Geographic Reach

Raytheon maintains offices in nearly 20 countries and has established global subsidiaries to serve customers in Australia Canada Germany the US and the UK. It sells products and services to customers in about 80 countries although the US primarily the US government accounts for about 70% of net sales.

Sales and Marketing

Although more than 70% of Raytheon's products are sold to the US government the company also counts among its customers the US Federal Aviation Administration (FAA) the Federal Bureau of Investigation (FBI) and NASA as well as members of the US military and US intelligence communities. In addition Raytheon has some key international customers.

Financial Performance

Raytheon has seen steady and significant revenue growth over the last several years with an increase of 19% since 2014.

Sales in 2018 reached a record $27.1 billion a 7% increase from $25.4 billion in 2017. The increase was a result of higher net sales in on classified programs particularly in the cyber and space divisions in the Intelligence Information and Services (ISS) segment. Two large programs were for the Department of Homeland Security (DHS) and the US Army's Warfighter Field Operations Customer Support (Warfighter FOCUS) program.

Profits in 2018 spiked 44% to $2.9 billion after hovering just above the $2 billion level in previous years. This was primarily due to a decrease of $850 million in income tax expenses due to the Tax Cuts and Jobs act.

Cash at the end of fiscal 2018 was $3.6 billion an increase of $209 million from the prior year. Cash from operations contributed $3.4 billion to the coffers while investing activities used $521 million mainly for additions to property plant and equipment. Financing activities used another $2.4 billion for dividends to stockholders and the company's stock repurchase program.

Strategy

Raytheon's diverse product lineup puts it in a better position to weather budget cuts than some of its competitors that handle a limited number of defense products and services. Its business is also contingent to a great extent on the federal defense budget. Besides focusing resources on emerging opportunities within the Department of Defense Raytheon aims to extend sales of its cyber solutions capabilities beyond the US government and target key countries as individual markets with multiple customers.

Within the Air and Missile Defense segment the company continues to capitalize on its Patriot Air and Missile Defense System program internationally with bookings in the three new countries of Romania Poland and Sweden. In 2018 the company opened a new 30000 square foot radar development facility that uses advanced automation technology for building and testing complex radar integrations.

Raytheon's commercial arm Forcepoint sells cybersecurity products for enterprises defense departments and civil agencies. To grow this business the company established its global Cyber Academy program that provides education and training to help governments organizations and large-scale companies protect themselves against increasing cyber threats.

Mergers and Acquisitions

In early 2019 Raytheon agreed to merge with leading aerospace and defense giant United Technologies Corporation (UTC) in an all-stock transaction valued at $121 billion. The combined company is projected to have combined sales of $74 billion and create a systems provider with advanced technologies for both the defense and aerospace industries that are platform-agnostic. The new company will be named Raytheon Technologies Corporation and would take United's Collins Aerospace and Pratt & Whitney units and pair them with Raytheon's defense products which include the Patriot and Sidewinder missile systems. It does not include UTC's Otis and Carrier divisions which UTC still plans to spin off as separate companies in 2020.

Company Background

In 1922 Laurence Marshall and several others founded American Appliance Company to produce home refrigerators. When their invention failed Marshall began making Raytheon (meaning "light of/from the gods") radio tubes. Raytheon was adopted as the company's name in 1925. It bought the radio division of Chicago's Q. R. S. Company in 1928 and formed Raytheon Production Company with National Carbon Company (makers of the Eveready battery) to market Eveready Raytheon tubes in 1929.

It entered the defense technology business in 1940 when it began developing magnetrons (tubes used in microwave radar systems) and contracted with the US Navy for 100 ship radar systems.

In 1965 the company acquired Amana Refrigeration and developed the first countertop microwave (it later divested its home appliances business).

Raytheon's Patriot missile defense systems program began operations in 1976 and is still one of the main components of its product portfolio.

In 2019 the company agreed to merge with leading aerospace systems manufacturer United Technologies Corporation. The combined entity will be renamed Raytheon Technologies Corporation.

HISTORY

In 1922 Laurence Marshall and several others founded American Appliance Company to produce home refrigerators. When their invention failed Marshall began making Raytheon (meaning "light of/from the gods") radio tubes. Raytheon was adopted as the company's name in 1925. It bought the radio division of Chicago's Q. R. S. Company in 1928 and formed Raytheon Production Company with National Carbon Company (makers of the Eveready battery) to market Eveready Raytheon tubes in 1929.

EXECUTIVES

Vp; President Intelligence Information And Services, David C. Wajsgras, age 60, $971,943 total compensation

Vp; President Global Business Services, Rebecca B. Rhoads, age 61

Vp Business Development And Ceo Raytheon International, John D. Harris, age 57

Vp; President Space And Airborne Systems, Richard R. (Rick) Yuse, age 68, $792,506 total compensation

Chairman And Ceo, Thomas A. (Tom) Kennedy, age 64, $1,299,979 total compensation

Vp; President Missile Systems, Taylor W. Lawrence, age 56, $728,151 total compensation

Vp General Counsel And Corporate Secretary, Frank R. Jimenez, age 54, $627,706 total compensation

Cio, Kevin T. Neifert

Vp And Cfo, Anthony F. OA'Brien, $608,510 total compensation

Vp; President Integrated Defense Systems, Wesley D. Kremer, age 54

Chief Executive Raytheon Arabia, Kurt Amend

Vice President, Roger W Anderson

Vp Legal, Mark D Nielsen

Vice President, Mark Kampf

Vice President Communication And Public Affairs Space And Airborne Systems, Trudy Sullivan

Assistant Vice President Risk, Diane Murphy

Vice President Account Services, Glenn D Henseler

Vice President; Program Management Excellence, Larry Briggs

Business Development Vice President, David Scott

Vice President, Rebecca Ransom

Vice President Employee Relations And Human Resourcesms, James Cronin

Vice President Of Human Resour, Cathy Murphy

Vice President Manager Director, David Veit

Senior Vice President Human Resources, Jeff Wolske

Vice President, Kathryn A Dirkschneider

Vice President Integrated Defense Systems Seapower Capability Systems, Paul Ferraro

Vice President Corporate Affairs, Pam Erickson

Senior Vice President Enterprise Information Technology, Tenesha Harris

Vice President Of Operations, Kim Ernzen

Vice President Navigation Weather And Services, Matt Gilligan

Senior Vice President Information Technology, Thomas Madison

Vice President Raytheon Company Evaluation Team, Edward Miyashiro

Vice President Special Programs, Joseph Maggio

Vp And Chief Diversity Officer, Emanuel Brady

Government Relations, Tim Delgiudice

Vice President Digital Social Marketing, Allison Jeannotte

Vp Integrated Air And Missile Defense Integrated Defense Systems, Tom Laliberty

Vice President Special Projects, John Nannen

Vice President Raytheon Company Evaluation Team, Rudy Lewis

V P Of Finance, Toby O'brien

Vice President Capture Management Excellence Business Development, John Letendre

Vp Raytheon Electronic Warfare Systems, Travis Slocumb

Vice President Cybersecurity And Special Missions, John Desimone

Vice President And Principal Scientist Network And Communications Technologies, Jason Redi

Vice President Of Prime Contracting, Joel Taves

Vp Engineering Technology And Mission Assurance, Mark Russll

Vp And Cto, William Kiczuk

Vice President Of Supply Chain Management, Michael Shaughnessy

Vice President Strategy Integrated Communications Systems And Space And Airborne Systems M And A, John Oglesby

Vice President Engineering Raytheon Missile Systems, Bernard Merwald

Vice President International Operations And Disclosure, Christopher Haave

Vice President Operations, Barbara Borgonovi

Vice President Pension Investments, Scott Lupkas

Vice President Business Development Executive, Matthew Lambert

Senior Vice President Enterprise Information Technology, Robert Pierce

Vice President And General Manager, Raphael Cronin

Board Member, Stephen Hadley

Board Member, William Spivey

Board Member, James M Reed

Board Member, George Oliver

Secretary, Eugene Smith

Auditors: PricewaterhouseCoopers LLP

LOCATIONS

HQ: Raytheon Co.
870 Winter Street, Waltham, MA 02451
Phone: 781 522-3000
Web: www.raytheon.com

2018 Sales

	$ mil.	% of total
US	18,953	70
Middle East & North Africa	3,986	15
Asia Pacific	2,723	10
Europe & other regions	1,396	5
Total	**27,058**	**100**

PRODUCTS/OPERATIONS

2018 Sales

	$ mil.	% of total
Products	22,633	84
Services	4,425	16
Total	**27,058**	**100**

2018 Sales

	$ mil.	% of total
Missile Systems	8,298	29
Space & Airborne Systems	6,748	24
Intelligence & Information Systems	6,722	23
Integrated Defense Systems	6,180	22
Forcepoint	634	2
Adjustments	(1524)	-
Total	**27,058**	**100**

Selected Products

Integrated Defense Systems (IDS)
  Aegis Weapon Systems radar equipment
  AN/AQS Minehunting Sonar System
  Joint Land Attack Cruise Missile Defense Elevated Netted Sensor (JLENS)
  Landing Platform Dock Amphibious Ship LPD-17
  Patriot Air and Missile Defense System
  Sea-Based X-Band Radar (SBX)
  Ship Self-Defense System (SSDS)
  Surface-Launched AMRAAM (SLAMRAAM)
  Terminal High Altitude Area Defense (THAAD) Radar
Intelligence and Information Systems (IIS)
  Army Research Lab
  Communications systems
  Department of Education programs
  Distributed Common Ground System
  Emergency Patient Tracking System
  Global Broadcast Service
  Global Hawk Ground Segment
  Information solutions programs
  Managed data storage solutions
  Mobile Very Small Aperture Satellite Terminal
  National Polar-Orbiting Operational Environmental Satellite System Program
  RedWolf telecommunications surveillance
  Signal and imagery intelligence programs
  Supercomputing
  U-2 (field support)
  UAV systems and ground stations
Missile Systems (MS)
  Advanced Medium-Range Air-to-Air missile (AMRAAM)
  AIM-9X Sidewinder
  Evolved SeaSparrow (ESSM)
  Excalibur long-range artillery system
  Exoatmospheric Kill Vehicle
  Extended Range Guided Munition (ERGM)
  High-Speed Anti-Radiation Missile Targeting System
  Paveway laser-guided bombs
  Maverick AGM-65 missiles
  Tomahawk and Tactical Tomahawk cruise missiles
  TOW Javelin Phalanx Standard and SeaRAM missiles
Network Centric Systems (NCS)
  Airspace management and homeland security
  Command and control systems
  Combat systems
  Integrated communications systems
  Precision technologies and components
Space and Airborne Systems (SAS)
  Active electronically scanned array radars
  Airborne radars and processors
  Electronic warfare systems
  Electro-optic/infrared sensors
  Intelligence surveillance and reconnaissance systems
  Space and missile defense technology
Technical Services (TS)
  Base operations
  Logistics support
  Maintenance support
  Professional services
  Treaty compliance monitoring
  Weapons security and destruction

Selected Markets

Command Control Communication and Intelligence (C3I)
  Systems provide integrated real-time support for on- and off-battlefield and transform raw data into actionable intelligence
Cybersecurity

Provides cyber capabilities to the Intelligence DoD and DHS markets as well as embedding cybersecurity in Raytheon's products and IT infrastructure

Effects

Achieves specific military actions or outcomes from force protection to theater/national missile defense

Homeland Security

Domestic and international homeland security markets especially transportation security immigration control/identity management critical infrastructure protection maritime security energy security intelligence program support law enforcement solutions a

Mission Support

Provides total life-cycle and training system engineering logistics and maintenance support to customer

Sensing

Acquires precise situational data across air space ground and underwater domains and generates information needed for effective battlespace decisions

COMPETITORS

BAE Systems Inc.	Harris Corp.
Boeing	Honeywell Aerospace
Crane Aerospace & Electronics	Interstate Electronics
	Lockheed Martin
Emerson Electric	Northrop Grumman
Exelis	Rockwell Collins
Fluor	Saab AB
GE	Sierra Nevada Corp

HISTORICAL FINANCIALS

Company Type: Public

Income Statement   FYE: December 31

	REVENUE ($ mil.)	NET INCOME ($ mil.)	NET PROFIT MARGIN	EMPLOYEES
12/18	27,058	2,909	10.8%	67,000
12/17	25,348	2,024	8.0%	64,000
12/16	24,069	2,211	9.2%	63,000
12/15	23,247	2,074	8.9%	61,000
12/14	22,826	2,244	9.8%	61,000
Annual Growth	4.3%	6.7%	—	2.4%

2018 Year-End Financials

Debt ratio: 16.00%
Return on equity: 27.00%
Cash ($ mil.): 3,608
Current ratio: 1.00
Long-term debt ($ mil.): 4,755

No. of shares (mil.): 282
Dividends
 Yield: 2.0%
 Payout: 34.0%
Market value ($ mil.): 43,245

	STOCK PRICE ($) FY Close	P/E High/Low	PER SHARE ($) Earnings	Dividends	Book Value
12/18	153.00	22 14	10.00	3.00	41.00
12/17	188.00	27 21	7.00	2.00	35.00
12/16	142.00	20 16	7.00	4.00	34.00
12/15	125.00	19 14	7.00	3.00	34.00
12/14	108.00	15 12	7.00	2.00	31.00
Annual Growth	9.1%	— —	9.0%	10.1%	7.0%

RBB Bancorp

Auditors: Eide Bailly LLP

LOCATIONS

HQ: RBB Bancorp
1055 Wilshire Blvd., Suite 1200, Los Angeles, CA 90017
Phone: 213 627-9888
Web: www.royalbusinessbankusa.com

HISTORICAL FINANCIALS

Company Type: Public

Income Statement   FYE: December 31

	ASSETS ($ mil.)	NET INCOME ($ mil.)	INCOME AS % OF ASSETS	EMPLOYEES
12/18	2,974	36	1.2%	365
12/17	1,691	26	1.5%	203
12/16	1,396	19	1.4%	177
12/15	1,023	13	1.3%	—
12/14	0	10		—
Annual Growth	—	36.4%		—

2018 Year-End Financials

Debt ratio: 4.00%
Return on equity: 11.00%
Cash ($ mil.): 148
Current ratio: —
Long-term debt ($ mil.): —

No. of shares (mil.): 20
Dividends
 Yield: 2.0%
 Payout: 21.0%
Market value ($ mil.): 351

	STOCK PRICE ($) FY Close	P/E High/Low	PER SHARE ($) Earnings	Dividends	Book Value
12/18	18.00	16 8	2.00	0.00	19.00
12/17	27.00	15 12	2.00	0.00	17.00
Annual Growth	(10.5%)	— —	4.6%	52.3%	3.0%

Realogy Group LLC

EXECUTIVES

Chb-Pres- Ceo, Richard A Smith
Exec V Pres-Cfo-Treas, Anthony E Hull
Exec V Pres-General Counsel-Co, Marilyn J Wasser
Sr V Pres-Cao-Contrl, DEA Benson
Exec V Pres-Chief Hr Officer, Sunita Holzer
Sr V Pres-Cao-Contrl, Timothy B Gustavson
Customer Support Manager, Shane Anderson
Director, Travis Bailey
Application Business, Virag Gutgutia
It Security, Ashley Vanderhoof
Senior Vice-President, Dina Dimaria
Auditors: PricewaterhouseCoopers LLP

LOCATIONS

HQ: Realogy Group LLC
175 Park Avenue, Madison, NJ 07940
Phone: 973 407-2000
Web: www.realogy.com

HISTORICAL FINANCIALS

Company Type: Public

Income Statement   FYE: December 31

	REVENUE ($ mil.)	NET INCOME ($ mil.)	NET PROFIT MARGIN	EMPLOYEES
12/18	6,079	137	2.3%	11,400
12/17	6,114	431	7.0%	11,800
12/16	5,810	213	3.7%	11,800
12/15	5,706	184	3.2%	11,400
12/14	5,328	143	2.7%	10,700
Annual Growth	3.4%	(1.1%)		1.6%

2018 Year-End Financials

Debt ratio: 52.00%
Return on equity: 6.00%
Cash ($ mil.): 225
Current ratio: 1.00
Long-term debt ($ mil.): 2,800

No. of shares (mil.): 115
Dividends
 Yield: —
 Payout: —
Market value ($ mil.): —

Realogy Holdings Corp

Realogy Holdings is one of the largest franchisors of residential real estate offices in the world with about 16600 offices in around 115 countries. Its brands include Century 21 Coldwell Banker ERA Better Homes and Gardens Real Estate and Sotheby's. In addition to franchising the company owns and operates about 760 offices under those brands and the Corcoran Group and Citi Habitats labels. It also provides relocation title and settlement services and mortgages. The company derives almost all its revenue from its US operations.

Operations

Realogy Holdings operates through the four business segments: Company Owned Real Estate Brokerage Services (known as NRT) Real Estate Franchise Services (called Realogy Franchise Group or RFG) Title and Settlement Services (entitled Title Resource Group or TRG) and Relocation Services (dubbed Cartus).

Realogy's revenue is heavily weighted in its NRT segment; it provides some 75% of sales. The segment houses the company's real estate brokerage business under the Coldwell Banker Corcoran Sotheby's International Realty Citi Habitats and ZipRealty brands in many of the largest metropolitan areas in the US.

RFG generates about 15% of the company's revenue. It franchises the Century 21 Coldwell Banker Coldwell Banker Commercial ERA Sotheby's International Realty Better Homes and Gardens Real Estate brand names.Representing around 10% of Realogy's revenue TRG offers full-service title and settlement services to real estate companies affinity groups corporations and financial institutions. Those services are often rendered in conjunction with the company's real estate brokerage and relocation business.

Cartus accounts for roughly 5% of Realogy's revenue. It markets home sale assistance client-guaranteed home equity advances for transferees home finding intercultural and language training and group move management.

Approximately 75% of the company's revenue derives from gross commission income; about 15% comes from services.

Geographic Reach

Based in Madison New Jersey Realogy operates through 16600 offices in about 115 countries; however substantially all its revenue comes from the US.

Sales and Marketing

Realogy's franchise system has nearly 300000 independent sales associates worldwide including more than 190000 independent sales agent in the US. Its largest brand is Century 21 with roughly 9600 global offices and 127500 brokers and agents. Its other brands include Coldwell Banker Era Real Estate Sotheby's International Realty and Better Homes and Gardens Real Estate.

Financial Performance

In tandem with the strengthening US housing market Realogy's revenue grew steadily for the last several years until 2018 when it ticked down 1% compared to the year prior. Since 2015 its net income has slipped 4% due to a large reduction in 2018.

Realogy's revenue fell to $6.1 billion in 2018. Sales were depressed by stagnancy in US home purchase volumes which the company attributed to limited inventory and higher average prices and mortgage rates.

The company's net income slid 68% to $137 million that year due to the weakened revenue combined with a high income tax expense (compared to a benefit in 2017) higher commission and agent-related costs restructuring costs and interest expense. At the beginning of 2018 the company began a restructuring which included employee terminations facility closures and technology investment.

Realogy added $4 million to the top of its cash in 2018. Operations contributed $394 million. Financing activities?mainly common stock repurchases?used $297 million; the company spent $91 million on investments primarily additions to property and equipment.

Strategy

Embracing the rapidly expanding role of new technologies in business applications Realogy Holdings' strategy in recent years has centered on launching software platforms that improve the productivity of its independent sales associates.

In 2019 the company announced that it would begin offering two new technology platforms to its agents: OfferBOOST and Fast Track. OfferBOOST facilitates cash home buying by qualified buyers. Fast Track speeds closings to as little as a week by preparing house-specific mortgage and title work in advance. Realogy launched its Social Ad Engine in partnership with Facebook that year. The program generates ads for agents' listings on social media based on users' data analytics. The company also announced a partnership with OJO Labs through which it is introducing an AI-driven mobile and digital customer support assistant.

Realogy partnered with Home Partners of America in 2018 to offer the company's cataLIST program via Coldwell Banker. cataLIST gives property owners the option of a cash offer for their home purchase within one business day. The owner may accept the offer within five days of receipt; closing can occur in as little as 10 days.

The company also expanded its franchise lineup in 2018 with the additions of Corcoran and Climb Real Estate.

Mergers and Acquisitions

One of the ways Realogy Holdings has achieved record-setting revenue growth over the years is through the use of acquisitions. In 2015 Realogy acquired Coldwell Banker United realtors in the active markets of Texas Florida North Carolina and South Carolina. Coldwell brought 60 offices staffed by 2000 affiliated sales associates to Realogy. It continues to operate under the Coldwell Banker brand.

Company Background

In 2012 Realogy Holdings raised $1 billion in its IPO a vote of confidence in the recovery of the residential real estate market in the US. Realogy used the IPO proceeds to reduce its more than $7 billion in debt. Despite losing $540 million in the two years prior to its IPO the firm believed the real estate market was poised for recovery. Its strategy included growing all segments of its business though it offered no specifics on that front. The company's name changed from Domus to Realogy in 2012.

EXECUTIVES

Evp General Counsel And Corporate Secretary, Marilyn J. Wasser, age 63

Chairman President And Ceo, Richard A. Smith, age 65, $1,000,000 total compensation

President And Ceo Nrt, Bruce G. Zipf, age 62, $625,000 total compensation

President And Ceo Cartus, Kevin J. Kelleher, age 64, $475,000 total compensation

Evp And Chief Human Resources Officer, Sunita Holzer

Evp Cfo And Treasurer, Anthony E. (Tony) Hull, age 60, $675,000 total compensation

President And Ceo Title Resource Group, Donald J. (Don) Casey, age 57, $450,000 total compensation

Svp And Cio, Stephen Fraser

President And Ceo Realogy Franchise Group, John Peyton

Vice President Of Information Technology, Neil Stanton

Senior Vice President Of Learning, Bryon Ellington

Senior Vice President Ethics And Compliance, Kimberly Toomey

Vice President, John Ferrie

Senior Vice President Strategic Initiatives, Monty Smith

Vice President Sales Development And Operations, Peter Karpiak

Vice President Consulting Operations, Donna Burke

Senior Vice President Operations Americas Cartus, William Wilson

Vice President Of Relocation Services, Dennie Howard

Auditors: PricewaterhouseCoopers LLP

LOCATIONS

HQ: Realogy Holdings Corp
175 Park Avenue, Madison, NJ 07940
Phone: 973 407-2000
Web: www.realogy.com

2018 Sales

	$ mil.	% of total
US	5,961	98
All other countries	118	2
Total	**6,079**	**100**

PRODUCTS/OPERATIONS

2018 Sales

	$ mil.	% of total
Company-owned real estate brokerage services	4,607	72
Real estate franchise services	820	13
Title and settlement services	580	9
Relocation services	378	6
Corporate and other	(306)	-
Total	**6,079**	**100**

2018 Sales

	$ mil.	% of total
Gross commission income	4,533	75
Service revenue	947	16
Franchise fees	393	6
Other	206	3
Total	**6,079**	**100**

Selected Brands

Better Homes and Gardens Real Estate
Century 21
Coldwell Banker
Coldwell Banker Commercial
ERA
Sotheby's International Realty
Corcoran
Citi Habitats
ZipRealty

COMPETITORS

Brookfield Global Relocation	Keller Williams
Ebby Halliday Realtors	Move Inc.
HomeServices	NRT LLC
HomeVestors of America	RE/MAX
Jones Lang LaSalle	SIRVA
	Weichert Realtors

HISTORICAL FINANCIALS

Company Type: Public

Income Statement

FYE: December 31

	REVENUE ($ mil.)	NET INCOME ($ mil.)	NET PROFIT MARGIN	EMPLOYEES
12/18	6,079	137	2.3%	11,400
12/17	6,114	431	7.0%	11,800
12/16	5,810	213	3.7%	11,800
12/15	5,706	184	3.2%	11,400
12/14	5,328	143	2.7%	10,700
Annual Growth	**3.4%**	**(1.1%)**	**—**	**1.6%**

2018 Year-End Financials

Debt ratio: 52.00%	No. of shares (mil.): 115
Return on equity: 6.00%	Dividends
Cash ($ mil.): 238	Yield: 2.0%
Current ratio: 1.00	Payout: 33.0%
Long-term debt ($ mil.): 2,800	Market value ($ mil.): 1,683

	STOCK PRICE ($) FY Close	P/E High/Low		PER SHARE ($) Earnings	Dividends	Book Value
12/18	15.00	25	14	1.00	0.00	20.00
12/17	27.00	11	8	3.00	0.00	20.00
12/16	26.00	25	15	1.00	0.00	18.00
12/15	37.00	39	29	1.00	0.00	16.00
12/14	44.00	51	35	1.00	0.00	15.00
Annual Growth	**(24.2%)**	**—**	**—**	**3.0%**	**—**	**7.9%**

RECKSON OPERATING PARTNERSHIP, L.P.

EXECUTIVES

Pres-Ceo, Marc Holliday
Cfo-Cao-Treas, Matthew J Diliberto
Gen Ptnr, Wyoming Acquisition GP LLC

LOCATIONS

HQ: RECKSON OPERATING PARTNERSHIP, L.P.
420 LEXINGTON AVE, NEW YORK, NY 101700002
Phone: 212 594-2700
Web: WWW.SLGREEN.COM

HISTORICAL FINANCIALS

Company Type: Private

Income Statement

FYE: December 31

	ASSETS ($ mil.)	NET INCOME ($ mil.)	INCOME AS % OF ASSETS	EMPLOYEES
12/18	7,009	199	2.8%	279
12/17	8,542	198	2.3%	—
12/16	8,755	313	3.6%	—
12/15	8,859	363	4.1%	—
Annual Growth	**(7.5%)**	**(18.1%)**	**—**	**—**

REDWOOD CREDIT UNION

EXECUTIVES

Pres-Ceo, Brett Martinez
Programmer, Sky Walker
Consultant, Carrie Bruce
Assistant Manager, Earl Chavez
Manager, Stephen Hazard
Information Specialist, Jonathan Busch
Assistant Manager, Amy Murphy
Coordinator, Crickett Green
Accountant, Catharine Lyne
Business Manager, Jana Beatty
Senior Web Developer, David Gindy
Auditors: CLIFTONLARSONALLEN LLP PHOENI

LOCATIONS

HQ: REDWOOD CREDIT UNION
 3033 CLEVELAND AVE # 100, SANTA ROSA, CA
 954032126
Phone: 707 545-4000
Web: WWW.REDWOODCU.ORG

HISTORICAL FINANCIALS

Company Type: Private

Income Statement				FYE: December 31
	ASSETS ($ mil.)	NET INCOME ($ mil.)	INCOME AS % OF ASSETS	EMPLOYEES
12/17	4,047	68	1.7%	390
12/16	3,288	57	1.7%	—
12/14	2,468	47	1.9%	—
12/13	2,271	49	2.1%	—
Annual Growth	15.5%	8.6%	—	—

Redwood Trust Inc

Redwood Trust is cultivating a forest of real estate mortgage assets. The real estate investment trust (REIT) finances manages and invests in residential real estate mortgages and securities backed by such loans. It also invests in commercial real estate loans and securities. Redwood acquires assets throughout the US but has a concentration of credit risk in California Texas Massachusetts Florida and New York which hold some of the US' most active real estate markets. Redwood Trust slowed loan origination acquisition and securitization during the most recent recession but has picked up those activities as the economy has recovered.

Operations

Redwood Trust invests in real estate related assets that have the potential to provide attractive cash flows over a long time period and distribute attractive levels of dividends to stockholders. The mortgage-backed securities the company typically invests in include senior securities. Redwood Trust also invests in other assets securities and instruments that are related to residential and commercial real estate.

About 43% of Redwood's total revenue came from interest income on its real estate securities in 2014 while interest income on its residential loans

and commercial loans made up 24% and 16% of total revenue that year respectively. The rest of its revenue (about 12%) came from its mortgage banking activities which involves buying and selling mortgage loans. The bank had a staff of 221 people at the end of 2014.

Geographic Reach

Redwood primarily concentrates on supplying loans to the markets of California Texas Massachusetts Virginia Florida and New York — which held 70% of its credit held for sale and 53% of its credit held-for-investment in 2014. The REIT has offices in California Colorado and New York.

Financial Performance

Redwood Trust has struggled to grow its revenues and profits over the past few years mostly as its mortgage banking business and other noninterest income sources have declined (an industry-wide problem for mortgage banking businesses). Its interest income however has been on the rise as it's acquired more interest-earning assets over time.

The company's revenue fell 25% to $278.1 million in 2014 mostly as its residential mortgage banking income declined by $67 million with fewer originations as potential interest rate hikes scared borrowers away during the year and put "pressure on margins and profitability" according to the company.

Revenue declines in 2014 caused Redwood's net income to plummet 42% to $100.6 million. Its cash levels fell further than in the prior year with operations using $1.79 billion mostly because the the REIT used more of its cash toward purchasing loans and generated less from proceeds from loan sales.

Strategy

Redwood Trust continues to acquire prime jumbo residential loans on a flow basis for the subsequent securitization of those loans and to a lesser extent for sale to third parties. The company is focusing on building a franchise business model that would get it ready to capitalize on the expected eventual reform of government agencies Fannie Mae and Freddie Mac.

The company has shifted its strategy in recent years to transition toward originating senior commercial loans and increasing gain-on-sale or fee income. Its long-term strategy is to to add additional loan sellers loan products and capital sources. To this end in mid-2014 Redwood Trust established a new subsidiary that could access "attractive long-term financing from the Federal Home Loan Bank of Chicago (FHLBC) for residential mortgage loans" with the intention to acquire residential mortgage loans to hold as long-term investments.

EXECUTIVES

Ceo, Martin S. (Marty) Hughes, age 61, $750,000 total compensation
President, Christopher J. Abate, age 39, $425,000 total compensation
Evp General Counsel And Secretary, Andrew P. Stone, age 48, $375,000 total compensation
Cfo, Collin Cochrane, age 43
Evp Commercial Investments And Finance, Fred J. Matera, age 55, $500,000 total compensation
Evp, Dashiell Robinson
Vice President, Fred Ty
Vice President Credit Policy Manager, Jennifer Adams
Assistant Vice President, Jason Moutray
Associate Vice President, Jennifer Wolff
Vice Chairman, Douglas B. Hansen, age 61
Chairman, Richard D. Baum, age 72
Auditors: Grant Thornton LLP

LOCATIONS

HQ: Redwood Trust Inc
 One Belvedere Place, Suite 300, Mill Valley, CA 94941
Phone: 415 389-7373
Web: www.redwoodtrust.com

PRODUCTS/OPERATIONS

2014 Sales

	$ mil.	% of total
Interest income		
Real estate securities	126	43
Residential loans	69	24
Commercial loans	48	16
Others	0	—
Non-interest income		
Mortgage banking activities	35	12
Realized Gains	16	5
Adjustments	(14.4)	—
Total	**278**	**100**

COMPETITORS

Annaly Capital Management	MFA Financial
Bank of America	Main Street Capital
Capstead Mortgage	NewStar Financial
Duff & Phelps	Starwood Property
Dynex Capital	Triangle Capital
Hercules Technology	iStar Financial Inc

HISTORICAL FINANCIALS

Company Type: Public

Income Statement				FYE: December 31
	ASSETS ($ mil.)	NET INCOME ($ mil.)	INCOME AS % OF ASSETS	EMPLOYEES
12/18	11,937	120	1.0%	149
12/17	7,040	140	2.0%	120
12/16	5,483	131	2.4%	125
12/15	6,231	102	1.6%	211
12/14	5,919	101	1.7%	221
Annual Growth	19.2%	4.4%	—	(9.4%)

2018 Year-End Financials

Debt ratio: 22.00%
Return on equity: 9.00%
Cash ($ mil.): 176
Current ratio: —
Long-term debt ($ mil.): —

No. of shares (mil.): 85
Dividends
 Yield: 8.0%
 Payout: 88.0%
Market value ($ mil.): 1,279

	STOCK PRICE ($) FY Close	P/E High/Low		PER SHARE ($) Earnings	Dividends	Book Value
12/18	15.00	12	10	1.00	1.00	16.00
12/17	15.00	10	8	2.00	1.00	16.00
12/16	15.00	10	6	2.00	1.00	15.00
12/15	13.00	17	10	1.00	1.00	15.00
12/14	20.00	18	14	1.00	1.00	15.00
Annual Growth	(6.5%)	—	—	3.9%	1.3%	1.4%

Regeneron Pharmaceuticals, Inc.

Regeneron is fighting some serious enemies. Regeneron Pharmaceuticals develops protein-based drugs used to battle a variety of diseases and conditions including cancer high cholesterol inflammatory ailments and eye diseases. The biotechnology company has a handful of products on the market including eye disease treatment EYLEA (aflibercept) cholesterol lowering drug Praluent rare inflammatory disease treatment ARCALYST rheumatoid arthritis drug Kevzara and cancer treatment ZALTRAP. Regeneron has 15 more candidates in clinical development.

Operations

Regeneron operates in one business segment which includes all activities from discovery and development through commercialization of its pharmaceutical products. Most of the segment's revenue comes from EYLEA sales followed by ARCALYST sales. The company also has development candidates in areas including hypercholesterolemia oncology rheumatoid arthritis asthma and atopic dermatitis. This segment brings in more than 60% of total revenue.

The rest of the company's revenue comes from development collaborations. Regeneron has collaborations with Sanofi and Bayer HealthCare to develop aflibercept for additional indications including cancerous tumors as well as obtain approvals outside of the US. The company also has a partnership with Teva to develop fasinumab for chronic pain in patients with osteoarthritis. And in mid-2018 it established two new partnerships that employ Regeneron's antibody technology platform. It is collaborating with Zoetis to discover new veterinary treatments and with bluebird bio to develop new cell therapies for cancer.

Geographic Reach

Regeneron has its corporate and R&D headquarters in Tarrytown New York and a satellite office in Basking Ridge New Jersey. It manufactures bulk drug materials in Renssalaer New York and has additional office space in Sleepy Hollow and Troy New York.

Internationally Regeneron is headquartered in Dublin Ireland and has a manufacturing facility in Limerick Ireland as well as an office in London.

Sales and Marketing

Regeneron uses distributors and specialty pharmacies to sell its products directly to health care providers. ARCALYST is sold directly to patients.

The company's largest customers are AmerisourceBergen subsidiary Besse Medical McKesson and Express Scripts subsidiary Curascript SD Specialty Distribution. They account for virtually all gross product revenue. Regeneron also collaborates with Bayer and Sanofi for global sales of EYLEA Dupixent Praluent and Keyzara.

Financial Performance

Thanks to the launching of about a half-dozen products since 2011 Regeneron has reported strong revenue growth over the last few years. Net income has also been rising steadily.

In 2017 revenue increased 21% to $5.9 billion thanks primarily to higher sales of EYLEA and higher collaboration revenue from Sanofi and Bayer. Overall net product sales increased 11% that year.

With that higher revenue net income rose 34% to $1.2 billion in 2017. Higher sales of EYLEA helped fund activities such as an expansion of manufacturing capabilities to support the company's other product candidates.

The company ended 2017 with $812.7 million in net cash nearly $300 million more than it had at the end of 2016. This was largely due to operating cash inflow totaling $1.3 billion. Investing activities primarily the purchases of investment securities used $1 billion and financing activities used $24.4 million.

Strategy

Regeneron has expanded the applications of its protein-based technology to include the creation of human monoclonal antibodies (laboratory-produced cloned proteins). It has a pipeline of 15 clinical-stage antibodies with programs in eye disease infectious disease cancer pain management cardiovascular disease and inflammation. The company also licenses its human antibody technology out to drug developers who then use Regeneron's technology in researching their own antibody drugs.

With its development partners Regeneron has been successful in obtaining expanded approvals for its existing products. In late 2018 Sanofi and Regeneron won US approval for Dupixent as an asthma treatment adding to its previously approved use for dermatitis. Dupixent is expected to reach blockbuster status and the asthma indication will only help boost its sales. However Dupixent for asthma has a relatively high list price of $36000 per year and it faces competition from other drugs.

Also in 2018 Sanofi and Regeneron's Libtayo received FDA clearance to treat patients with metastatic cutaneous squamous cell carcinoma (CSCC which accounts for about 20% of skin cancer cases) who are not candidates for curative surgery or radiation. Libtayo is also under review in Europe.

Regeneron faces competition from Novartis which is hoping to launch its EYLEA competitor in 2019. Novartis' RTH258 is not yet approved by the FDA but it has shown to perform better than EYLEA in clinical trials.

In 2017 and 2016 Regeneron spent $2.1 billion on R&D expenses up from $1.6 billion in 2015.

Company Background

Regeneron was founded in New York City in 1988.

ARCALYST (rilonacept) was approved by the FDA in 2008 and subsequently became the company's first market-stage product.

EXECUTIVES

Evp Research And Development, Neil Stahl, age 62, $619,300 total compensation

Chief Scientific Officer; President Regeneron Laboratories, George D. Yancopoulos, age 59, $1,055,700 total compensation

President And Ceo, Leonard S. Schleifer, age 66, $1,242,000 total compensation

Evp Commercial, Robert J. Terifay, age 59, $550,700 total compensation

Svp Finance And Cfo, Robert E. Landry, $585,600 total compensation

Evp; General Manager Industrial Operations And Product Supply, Daniel P. Van Plew, age 46, $349,200 total compensation

Medical Director, Mark Ballard

Medical Director Immunology And Inflammation, Gregory St John

Vice President Strategic Program Direction Oncology, Robert Charnas

Medical Director, Brad Shumel

Vice President Early Clinical Development, Olivier Harari

Chairman, P. Roy Vagelos, age 89

Board Member, Bonnie Bassler

Board Member, Huda Zoghbi

Auditors: PricewaterhouseCoopers LLP

LOCATIONS

HQ: Regeneron Pharmaceuticals, Inc.
777 Old Saw Mill River Road, Tarrytown, NY 10591-6707
Phone: 914 847-7000
Web: www.regeneron.com

PRODUCTS/OPERATIONS

2017 Sales

	$ mil.	% of total
Net product sales		
EYLEA	3,702	63
ARCALYST	17	-
Bayer collaboration	938	16
Sanofi collaboration	877	15
Other	339	6
Total	**5,872**	**100**

COMPETITORS

Allergan Limited	GlaxoSmithKline
Amgen	Merck
AstraZeneca	Novartis
Bristol-Myers Squibb	Pfizer
Eli Lilly	Roche Holding
Genentech	Teva

HISTORICAL FINANCIALS

Company Type: Public

Income Statement · FYE: December 31

	REVENUE ($ mil.)	NET INCOME ($ mil.)	NET PROFIT MARGIN	EMPLOYEES
12/19	7,863	2,116	26.9%	8,100
12/18	6,711	2,444	36.4%	7,400
12/17	5,872	1,199	20.4%	6,200
12/16	4,860	896	18.4%	5,400
12/15	4,104	636	15.5%	4,300
Annual Growth	17.7%	35.1%	—	17.2%

2019 Year-End Financials

Debt ratio: 5.00%	No. of shares (mil.): 110
Return on equity: 21.00%	Dividends
Cash ($ mil.): 1,618	Yield: —
Current ratio: 4.00	Payout: —
Long-term debt ($ mil.): 714	Market value ($ mil.): 41,407

	STOCK PRICE ($) FY Close	P/E High/Low	Earnings	Dividends	Book Value
12/19	375.00	23 14	18.00	0.00	101.00
12/18	374.00	18 13	21.00	0.00	80.00
12/17	376.00	47 30	10.00	0.00	57.00
12/16	367.00	63 39	8.00	0.00	42.00
12/15	543.00	96 64	6.00	0.00	35.00
Annual Growth	(8.8%)	— —	35.2%	—	30.3%

REGENTS OF THE UNIVERSITY OF MICHIGAN

Ranking among the top US public universities Regents of the University of Michigan (or simply University of Michigan) boasts more than 60000 students and about 8000 faculty members in southeast Michigan. Its three campuses in Ann Arbor Dearborn and Flint offer more than 260 undergraduate and graduate degree programs in fields including architecture education law medicine music and social work. The university has a student to faculty ratio of 15:1. The vast University of Michigan Health System which includes four hospitals and numerous outpatient centers provides about half of annual revenue. The university is supported by an $11.9 billion endowment.

Financial Performance

University of Michigan's revenue for operating activities was $8.7 billion for the 2018-2019 year. Operating revenue was $7.5 billion in fiscal 2018 (ending June 30) up 5% from 2017. Patient care revenue increased 6% tuition and fees rose 7% and federal grants and contracts grew 4%.

The university ended 2018 with $133.4 million in cash up $28.2 million from 2017. Operating activities used $411.1 million while investing activities contributed $299.3 million (from investment proceeds).

Strategy

University of Michigan strives to maintain national standards for academics research and health care. The university also works to recruit qualified faculty and health care staff and to attract high-performing students. Recent investments include expanding educational and health facilities and conducting enterprise-wide IT system upgrades. It completed construction of the Brighton Center for Specialty Care and launched construction of a new robotics engineering research and teaching facility in 2018.

University of Michigan has been conducting cost-cutting and productivity enhancement programs to combat the effects of reduced state educational appropriations and rising health care and facility costs.

EXECUTIVES

Vp Government Relations, Cynthia H. Wilbanks
Vp Development, Jerry A. May
Chancellor University Of Michigan-dearborn, Daniel Little
Evp And Cfo, Kevin P. Hegarty, age 63
Chairman Victors For Michigan, Stephen M. Ross
President, Mark S. Schlissel
Dean School Of Public Health, Martin Philbert
Vp Information Technology And Cio, Kelli Trosvig
Dean Stamps School Of Art And Design, Gunalan Nadarajan
Dean School Of Dentistry, Laurie McCauley
Dean Law School, Mark D. West
Chancellor University Of Michigan-flint, Susan E. Borrego
Interim Provost And Evp Academic Affairs, Paul N. Courant
Evp Medical Affairs; Dean Medical School; Ceo Michigan Medicine, Marschall S. Runge
Vp And General Counsel, Timothy G. Lynch
Vp Research, S. Jack Hu
Interim Dean Taubman College Of Architecture And Urban Planning, Robert Fishman
Edward J. Frey Dean Ross School Of Business, Scott DeRue
Dean School Of Education, Elizabeth Birr Moje
Dean School Of Engineering, Alec D. Gallimore
Dean School Of Information, Thomas A. Finholt
Dean School Of Kinesiology, Lori Ploutz-Snyder
Dean College Of Literature Science And The Arts, Andrew D. Martin
Dean College Of Music Theatre And Dance, Aaron Dworkin
Interim Dean School Of Natural Resources And Environment, Dan Brown
Dean School Of Nursing, Patricia D. Hurn
Dean College Of Pharmacy, James T. Dalton
Dean School Of Social Work, Lynn Videka
Dean Rackham Graduate School; Vice Provost Academic Affairs Graduate Studies, Carol A. Fierke
Assoc Vice President Development, Dondi Cupp
Assoc Vice President For Human Rscs, Laurita Thomas
Associate Vice President And Executive Director For Research Administration, Marvin Parnes

Associate Vice President Development, Julie Sparkman
Vice President Marketing, Rachelle Caoagas
Assistant Vice President Estate, Diane Tracy
Vice President Research, Stephen Forrest
Associate Vice President For Research Douvan Collegiate Professor Of Psychology Research Professor, Toni Antonucci
Vp Finance, Elizabeth Bills
Vice President Technology, Jamila Power
Vice President Technology, Mehra Rohit
Vice President Of Finance, Ruohao Li
Vice President Of Administration, Andy White
Vice President Student Government Budget Allocations Committee, Mackenzie Swart
Director Of Admissions And Orientation, Deb Peffer
Vice President Of Sales, Bill Bobrowsky
Vice President Finance Technology, William Hausman
Int Assistant Vice President Academic Human Resources, Donna Lartigue
Interim Vp Information Technology And Cio, Andrew Rosenberg
Vice President Of Resource Development Chief Fundrasing Officer, Darci Hoag
Director Of Clinical Services And Research; Assistant Professor Of Psychiatry, Renee Hoste
Office Of The Vice President For Student Affairs Student Aid, Michael Chrzan
Interim Vice President For Communications, Kate Michael
Vice President Of Finance, Morgan Slaff
Uofm Emba Vice President, Eric James Forster
Dance Student Assembly Vice President, Kelli Yapp
Vice President, Mohammed Islam
Vice President Finance, Dennis Diebolt
Vice President Of Projects Net Impact Advanced Fellow, Charlene Franke
Vice President Corporate Relations, Brandon Meloche
Vice President, Olivia Herron
Vice President And Corporate Counsel, Gael Tisack
Vice President, Shiuh Lee
Vice President, Beatrice Thaman
Vp Of Women In Mathematics, Vijita Kamath
Executive Vice President, David Witters
Vice Chairman, Michael J. Behm
Chairman, Mark J. Bernstein
Program Secretary, Frances Liao
Secretary Senior, Dawn Schulz
Senior Business Analyst Treasurers Office Department, Kristopher Covietz
Secretary Iv Law School Department, LauraA Shiltz
Secretary Iii Department Of Family Medicine Department, SophiaS Scoma
Board Member, Shary Balius
Board Member, Neil Elkin
Secretary Office Of Early Childhood Education And Family Services, Martin Stroud
Secretary, Mary Burton
Secretary Iii, Qiana London
Secretary Iv Pediatrics Ambulatory Care Pgm Department, CynthiaLynn Ellis
Treasurer, Eleonore Edgell
Senior Secretary, Andrew Mcintyre
Treasurer, Nahiyan Bakr
Treasurer, Alex Darr
Secretary B Temp Flint Ecdc, Kristina Russo
Secretary Of The University Office Of, Roberta Ruth Palmer
Lead Secretary, Amber French
Board Member, Ellen Toronto
Assistant Secretary Of The University, Erin Katz
Secretary Office Of The Vice President For Government Relations, Jill Crane
Auditors: PRICEWATERHOUSECOOPERS LLP DE

LOCATIONS

HQ: REGENTS OF THE UNIVERSITY OF MICHIGAN
503 THOMPSON ST, ANN ARBOR, MI 481091340
Phone: 734 764-1817
Web: WWW.UMICH.EDU

PRODUCTS/OPERATIONS

Selected Academic Units
Architecture and urban planning
Art and design
Business administration
Dentistry
Education
Engineering
Kinesiology
Law
Literature science and the arts
Medicine
Music
Natural resources and environment
Nursing
Pharmacy
Public health
Public policy
Social work

HISTORICAL FINANCIALS

Company Type: Private

Income Statement — FYE: June 30

	REVENUE ($ mil.)	NET INCOME ($ mil.)	NET PROFIT MARGIN	EMPLOYEES
06/18	7,467	920	12.3%	34,624
06/17	7,080	1,276	18.0%	—
06/16	6,278	(295)		—
06/14	5,535	1,575	28.5%	—
Annual Growth	7.8%	(12.6%)	—	—

Regions Financial Corp (New)

The holding company for Alabama-chartered Regions Bank Regions Financial boasts around $125 billion in total assets. With some 1500 branches and more than 1900 ATMs across 15 states in the South Midwest and Texas Regions offers banking services for large corporations middle market companies and real estate investors on top of its main business of standard banking products for retail customers and small businesses. The company's smaller wealth and asset management operations target affluent private individuals. Formed in 1971 as First Alabama Bancshares Regions was Alabama's first multibank holding company.

Operations

Regions Financial operates through three segments: Corporate Bank Consumer Bank and Wealth Management.

The Consumer Bank accounts for about 55% of revenue and encompasses the company's branch and ATM network. Through its physical locations as well as internet and telephone channels Regions provides consumer banking products including small business loans home mortgages and equity lines and credit cards.

Regions' Corporate Bank generates more than 30% of the company's revenue. The segment's main operations focus on industrial lending?including equipment lease financing?and commercial and investment real estate loans. Its capital markets offerings include securities underwriting and placement as well as advisory services for foreign exchange derivatives and mergers and acquisitions.

Providing nearly 10% of Regions' revenue the holding company's Wealth Management division's activities span trust asset and investment management and retirement and estate planning.

Regions' main source of income is interest on loans including fees which accounts for more than 60% of its revenue. Taxable debt securities and deposit account service charges each contribute more than 10%. Card and ATM fees provide more than 5%.

Nearly half of Regions' portfolio is made up of commercial and industrial loans. Consumer loans mostly residential first mortgages and home equity lines comprise almost 40%. Owner-occupied commercial real estate and commercial investor real estate mortgages each account for more than 5%.

Geographic Reach

Birmingham Alabama-based Regions Financial runs some 1500 branches and more than 1900 ATMs across 15 southern midwestern and central states. More than half its branches are in Florida Tennessee and Alabama; nearly 25% are in Mississippi Georgia and Louisiana. The rest are in Arkansas Texas Missouri Indiana Illinois South Carolina Kentucky Iowa and North Carolina.

Sales and Marketing

Regions Financial markets its products directly via physical branches and internet and mobile banking apps. Its Wealth Management customers are affluent individuals while its business customers include corporate middle market small business and commercial real estate developers and investors. Corporate Bank customers include corporate middle market and commercial real estate developers and investors.

Financial Performance

Buoyed by improving economic conditions that bolstered credit metrics Regions Financial's revenue has inched up each of the last five years for overall growth of about 10%. Despite a loss in 2015 the company's net income added more than 50% in that time?mostly from gains in 2018. Regions has grown its debt more than 250% since 2014 primarily due to increased Federal Home Loan Banks (FHLB) advances in 2015 and 2018.

Driven entirely by a rise in net interest income the holding company's revenue added 4% in 2018 to end the year at $5.8 billion. Despite slowing credit improvement pushing up its loan loss provision higher yields on earning assets?primarily loans?increased the company's net interest income.

Net income grew by 39% to $1.8 billion in 2018 following the company's sale of its insurance business. A reduced income tax expense related to US tax reform contributed similarly to the increase.

Regions depleted its cash stores by $443 million in 2018 finishing the year with $3.5 billion. Operations contributed $2.3 billion while financing activities?primarily proceeds from long-term borrowings?provided $327 million. The $3 billion it lost on investments was primarily attributable to net changes in loans.

Strategy

In early 2019 Regions Financial presented its three-year growth strategy. The company aims to open new branches and hire more corporate bankers wealth managers and mortgage loan originators in its key growth markets of Atlanta Houston and Orlando. The holding company also vowed to invest in digital banking?including online account openings digital loan applications and digital wealth management advisory.

Under the plan Regions is allocating $625 million for tech investment. The company expects to add voice banking to its service roster increase utilization of AI for customer-facing and back-office systems and use data and analytics to improve the quality of its customer financial advice and its credit risk management.

The company's expense control measures center on reducing its real estate through branch and back-office consolidation introducing collaborative workspaces and providing more remote work options. The company expects to reduce its branch and non-branch real estate by 15% or 2.1 million square feet by 2021. By that time the company also expects to save another $60 million through reorganization of its third-party vendor purchases.

In an effort to focus on its best-performing segments Regions sold off its Regions Insurance Group subsidiary in 2018.

Company Background

One of Regions Financial's precursors The Northern Bank of Alabama opened in 1852. The second and third banks which would later combine to form Regions First National Bank of Montgomery and Exchange Bank in Birmingham opened in 1871 and 1928 respectively. The banks combined in 1970 to create a holding company with assets of $446 million?First Alabama Bancshares. Regions had $4.4 billion in assets by 1987. In 1998 its assets reached $32.8 billion and its branch network totaled 667.

HISTORY

Regions Financial was created out of three venerable Alabama banks. The oldest First National Bank of Huntsville was founded in 1855. When 10 years later the bank was besieged by Union troops a loyal cashier hid securities in the chimney and refused to tell the soldiers where they were. A few years later it was robbed by Jesse James (for years the bank kept in its vaults a gun purported to belong to a James gang member). First National Bank of Montgomery was founded in 1871 and Exchange Security Bank in 1928.

Banking veteran Frank Plummer consolidated the three banks to form Alabama's first multibank holding company First Alabama Bancshares in 1971. The combined firm then became the bank that ate Alabama. But even as it gobbled up other banks its diet remained bland: Its lending programs were modest and focused on a narrow range of business.

The bank's growth in the 1980s was solid if unexciting as it picked up community banks in Alabama (Anniston National Bank and South Baldwin Bank among others) and Georgia (Georgia Co. a mortgage subsidiary of Columbus Bank and Trust). Before he died in 1987 Plummer brought in Willard Hurley as chairman. Hurley put the brakes on acquisitions when they overloaded the bank's data-processing systems. He also put the company up for sale igniting its stock price for a while but there were no serious suitors.

When Hurley passed the baton to Stanley Mackin in 1990 the bank was still rumored to be for sale. But Mackin had other ideas. He put the bank back on its acquisition track and raised the bar on profitability expectations for each department. In 1993 Mackin orchestrated First Alabama's purchase of Secor a failed New Orleans thrift outbidding rival AmSouth Bancorporation. The Secor purchase raised eyebrows but First Alabama sold some branches and folded other operations into its organization.

In 1994 First Alabama changed its name to Regions Financial in order to reflect its out-of-state operations. The next year Regions rolled into Georgia in a big way leaping from a few banks to holdings with approximately $4 billion in assets. Rumors of a merger with either Wachovia or SunTrust Banks popped up in 1996 but the bank continued on its independent course. The next year the company's tank-like progress was halted when it was outbid for Mississippi's Deposit Guaranty Corp. by First American.

By way of consolation Regions in 1998 bought First Commercial Corp. of Little Rock paying a premium price for its 26 banks mortgage company and investment company. Regions also acquired 13 other companies that year and began a major overhaul of its systems concurrently with the assimilation of these operations. This effort included the consolidation of the back-office aspects of its retail and indirect lending operations.

Mackin retired in 1998 and banking veteran Carl Jones Jr. became CEO. Under his direction the bank continued its geographic infill strategy with acquisitions of banks and branches in Arkansas Florida Louisiana Tennessee and Texas in 1999 and 2000. The company also sold its credit card portfolio to MBNA (since acquired by Bank of America) and in 2001 acquired Memphis-based investment bank Morgan Keegan.

Regions Financial has looked for acquisitions in order to grow geographically and diversify its product and services mix. It fortified its foothold in the South and expanded into the Midwest with its blockbuster merger with Union Planters in 2004. Roughly two years later the company acquired fellow Birmingham-based bank AmSouth for nearly $10 billion in stock. The latter deal created one of the 10 largest banks in the US and helped Regions Financial keep pace with other megabanks in its markets such as Bank of America and SunTrust. The deals also helped entrench the company in states such as Alabama Arkansas Mississippi and Tennessee where it is a market leader.

EXECUTIVES

President Chief Executive Officer Regions Bank And Regions Financial Corporation Director, John M. Turner, age 59

Sevp Coo, John B. Owen, $659,816 total compensation

Sevp General Counsel And Corporate Secretary, Fournier J. (Boots) Gale, $570,554 total compensation

Sevp Head Of Corporate Banking Group, Ronald G. (Ronnie) Smith

Sevp Head Of Commercial Banking, William E. (Bill) Horton

Sevp Head Of Corporate Responsibility And Community Engagement, C. Keith Herron

Sevp Head Of Corporate Real Estate And Procurement, Brett D. Couch

Sevp And Head Of Consumer Banking Group, Scott M. Peters

Sevp And Head Of Wealth Management, William D. (Bill) Ritter

Sevp And Cfo Regions Bank And Regions Financial Corporation, David J. Turner, $644,062 total compensation

Sevp Chro, David R. (Dave) Keenan

Sevp And Chief Risk Officer, C. Matthew Lusco, $566,308 total compensation

Sevp Head Of Strategic Performance And Alignment, Ellen S. Jones

Evp Of Regions Bank And Executive Managing Director Of Regions Securities Llc And Group Head Of Healthcare, John Barton

Senior Vice President Senior Credit Officer Commercial Real Estate, Aubrey Martin

Executive Vice President Of Marketing, Cindy Kloak

Vice President Information Technology Manager, Kristopher Bridges

Vp Firewall, Jeff Green

Vice President, Jackson Parrish

Senior Vice President And Head Consumer Collections And Asset Recovery, Brent Pyatt

Evp Stateic And Corporate Planning, Houston Cook

Vice President And Technology Contract Manager, Mike Ritchie

Vice President, Joe Massery

Vice President Commercial Real Estate, Todd Harris

Senior Vice President Consumer Sales Manager, Ken Knapp Ken Knapp

Vice President, Brandon Pettagrue

Senior Vice President, Donald Sinclair

Vice President Information Technology Risk Manager, Rusk Feltman

Senior Vice President Of Mortg, Ginger Ricchetti

Assistant Vice President Business Systems Analyst, Tim Boles

Vice President Secondary Marketing, Jonathan Loukotka

Sr. Vice President Credit Process Manager, Scott Underberg

Vice President Branch Sales Manager, Cathy Cosey

Senior Vice President Mortgage Division Controller, Rita Young

Vice President And Financial Consultant, Kevin Carnathan

Senior Vice President Consumer Sales Manager Regions Bank, Cedric Oliver

Vice President, William Laenger

Vice President Business Banking, Keith Boling

Vice President, Kenneth Bizzard

Vice President Relationship Manager, Cory Guillory

Executive Vice President Of Commercial Banking, Tammi Sanchez

Assistant Vice President And Branch Manager And Small Business Lender, Bryan Furlong

Vice President North Central Alabama Marketing And Event, Joy Parker

Assistant Vice President Branch Manager, Linda Barton

Vp Community Affairs Manager Ga Sc, Tiffany Kirk

Vice President Global Trade Finance, Chuck Youngerman

Vice President Florida Market, Lisa Fulghum

Regulatory Operations Vp, Rodney Ford

Senior Vice President Corporate Financial Planning And Analysis, Becky Crain

Senior Vice President And Texas Market Manager, Wendel Pardue

Vice President, Eric Hinkle

Senior Vice President Program Development Manager, David Fron

Vice President Of Information Technology, Adrian Castanon

Vice President Relationship Manager, Franklin Reyes

Vice President Mortgage Loan Officer, Mary Ethridge

Vice President Manager Of Special Projects And Incentive Compensation Modeling, Matthew Bledsoe

Assistant Vice President Of In, Don Turrentine

Vice President Mortgage Production Manager, Alan Noe

Vice President Escrow Manager, Kathy Schwartz

Senior Vice President, Glenn Little

Evp Corporate Security, William Burch

Executive Assistant To Bill Askew Senior Executive Vice President And Chris Ewing Executive Vice President, Pamela Ashley

Vice President Business Banking, Brian Brooks

Vice President, Barrett Vawter

Vice President Loss Mitigation Manager, Rebecca Leon

Vice President, Tanya Noletto

Vice President, Stan Gist

Evp Corporate Hr, Janet Parker

Senior Executive Vice President And Chief Credit Officer, Barb Godin

Assistant Vice President Branch Manager, Patrick Cayson

Vice President Information Technology Manager, Kris Bridges

Senior Vice President Corporate Banking, JP Hickey

Vice President Wealth Management, Leslie G Stricklin

Vice President, Bryan Cheek

Vice President And Trust Advisor, Conor Duggan

Vice President Human Resources, Ellie Long

Vice President Private Wealth Management, Patty Franco

Vice President Manager Of Tax Compliance, Pamela Taylor

Senior Vice President And Assistant General Counsel, Judd Anderton

Svp And Assistant General Counsel, Bradley Blair

Senior Vice President Wealth Management Compliance, Aneidre Amerson-Allman

Vice President, Jennifer Jackson

Senior Vice President Regional Manager, Jeff Bradley

Senior Vice President Wealth Management, Lisa Harless

Executive Vice President Human Resources Regions Bank, Anthony Hernandez

Executive Vice President And Chief Audit Executive, Michael Balbirnie

Senior Vice President, James Watkins

Vice President And Mortgage Operations Manager Regions Bank, Matthew Knueven

Vice President, Patti Maner

Vice President, Michael Harrington

Vice President Enterprise Risk Management, James Madden

Vice President Credit Portfolio Manager Regions Bank, Suresh Nair

Vp Mobile, Greg Melville

Vice President, Bruce Paterson

Vice President, Becky Sullivan

Vice President, Susan Clowdus

Executive Vice President, Pam Davis

Senior Vice President Senior Credit Officer, Mike Crosson

Senior Vice President, Bill Robertson

Vice President And Commercial Relationship Manager, Pat Brandenburg

Vice President Estate Administration, Judi Wurm

Vice President Trust Advisor, Natalie Mann

Senior Vice President, Barry Musselman

Senior Vice President, Edward Ryrie

Vice President, Carl Taube

Vice President Commercial And Industrial, Philip Ugalde

Vice President Private Banking Custom Underwriter, Heather Helms

Vice President, Ryanne Santurio

Vice President Senior Commercial Credit Portfolio Manager, Hongfei Zhang

Vice President Business Banking, Sandy Salyers

Senior Vice President, Redmond Taylor

Senior Vice President And Regional Sales Director Regions Investment Services, Alex Sarafianos

Vice President, Laura Bynum

Senior Vice President Special Assets Division Regions Bank, Gray Ives

Senior Vice President Commercial Banking, Alicia McCory

Executive Vice President, Tammi Calvo-sanchez

Vice President Consumer Lending, Kandy Shirley

Assistant Vice President, Tammy Simmons

Senior Vice President Ebusiness, Joe Jordan

Vice President Communications Management, Veleka Finch

Assistant Vice President, Ella Shakeel

Senior Vice President, Philip Bittel

Assistant Vice President, Zachary Dark

Avp Manager Of Security Analytics And Orchestration, Sean Maher

Vice President Culture Communications Training And Administration, Candace Higginbotham

Senior Vice President Director Of Sec Reporting, Chris Lollar

Vice President Branch Manager, Cathy Haywood

Senior Vice President, Jonathan Tutor

Senior Vice President, James Rowland

Vice President Client Acquisition Program Manager, Karen Blumensaadt

Vp Branch Manager, Juanita Shope

Vp Bi And Database Research Marketing, Sudarsan Thopay

Evp And Head Of Diversity And Inclusion Of Regions Bank, Clara Green

Vice President, Chris Fitz

Vice President, Brent Goers

Vice President Regional Portfolio Manager, Sue Schmidt

Senior Vice President, Shawn Coard

Senior Vice President, Fernanda Hailey

Vp Branch Manager, Miles Victor

Executive Vice President And Treasurer, M Deron Smithy

Vice President Trust Advisor, Marlin Evans

Vice President Financial Consultant, Andrew George

Vice President, Chase Frost

Vice President, Allison Aicher

Senior Vice President, Sandra K Howell

Senior Vice President, Charlie Page

Assistant Vice President, James Garner

Vice President Mortgage Banking Manager, Lacy Husk

Vice President Cra Development Manager, Hanai Sablich

Auditors: Ernst & Young LLP

LOCATIONS

HQ: Regions Financial Corp (New)
1900 Fifth Avenue North, Birmingham, AL 35203
Phone: 205 581-7890
Web: www.regions.com

2018 Branch Locations

	No.
Florida	307
Tennessee	220
Alabama	211
Mississippi	126
Georgia	116
Louisiana	99
Arkansas	82
Texas	80
Missouri	64
Indiana	52
Illinois	48
South Carolina	23
Kentucky	11
Iowa	8
North Carolina	7
Total	**1,454**

PRODUCTS/OPERATIONS

2018 Sales

	$ mil.	% of total
Interest income		
Loans including fees	3,613	56
Debt securities - taxable	625	10
Operating lease assets	70	1
Loans held for sale	15	-
Other earning assets	70	1
Interest Expense	(658.0)	-
Non-interest income		
Service charges on deposits	710	11
Card and ATM fees	438	7
Investment management and trust fee income	235	4
Capital markets income	202	3
Mortgage income	137	2
Securities gains (losses) net	1	-
Others	296	5
Total	**5,754**	**100**

2018 Sales

	$ mil.	% of total
Consumer Bank	3,405	58
Corporate Bank	1,931	33
Wealth Management	510	9
Other	(92.0)	—
Total		**100**

Selected Products

Banking
  Checking
  Money Market
  Savings
  CDs
  Regions Visa CheckCard
  Business Checking
  Business Savings
  Merchant Services
  Treasury Management
  Payroll
  Audit Confirmations
Commercial Banking
  Deposit Services
  Treasury Management
  Online Services
  Merchant Services
  Global Trade Finance
  Corporate Trust
Private Wealth Management
  Solutions for Individuals
  Credit and Risk Management
  Wealth Management
  Solutions for Professionals

COMPETITORS

Arvest Bank	First Horizon
BB&T	Investar
BBVA Compass	JPMorgan Chase
Bancshares	SunTrust
Bank of America	Synovus
Capital One	Trustmark
Citigroup	Wells Fargo
First Citizens	Woodforest Financial
BancShares	

HISTORICAL FINANCIALS

Company Type: Public

Income Statement

FYE: December 31

	ASSETS ($ mil.)	NET INCOME ($ mil.)	INCOME AS % OF ASSETS	EMPLOYEES
12/18	125,688	1,759	1.4%	19,969
12/17	124,294	1,263	1.0%	21,714
12/16	125,968	1,163	0.9%	22,166
12/15	126,050	1,062	0.8%	23,916
12/14	119,679	1,155	1.0%	23,723
Annual Growth	1.2%	11.1%	—	(4.2%)

2018 Year-End Financials

Debt ratio: 4.00%
Return on equity: 11.00%
Cash ($ mil.): 3,538
Current ratio: —
Long-term debt ($ mil.): —

No. of shares (mil.): 1,025
Dividends
  Yield: 3.0%
  Payout: 30.0%
Market value ($ mil.): 13,712

	STOCK PRICE ($) FY Close	P/E High/Low		PER SHARE ($) Earnings	Dividends	Book Value
12/18	13.00	13	8	2.00	0.00	15.00
12/17	17.00	17	13	1.00	0.00	14.00
12/16	14.00	17	8	1.00	0.00	14.00
12/15	10.00	14	12	1.00	0.00	13.00
12/14	11.00	14	11	1.00	0.00	13.00
Annual Growth	6.1%	—	—	17.8%	26.4%	4.1%

Reinsurance Group of America, Inc.

Just what is reinsurance? Here hold this pile of insurance risk while we explain that holding company Reinsurance Group of America (RGA) is one of the largest life reinsurers in the US. RGA provides insurance companies with reinsurance on the risks they've taken on allowing them to reduce their liability and increase their business volume. Its operations are organized into two large groups: Traditional and Financial Solutions. Traditional reinsurance includes individual and group life and health disability and critical illness coverage while Financial Solutions includes longevity financial and asset-intensive products. RGA operates in more than 25 countries in the Americas the Asia/Pacific region Europe and South Africa. The US and Latin America account for some 55% of RGA's total sales.

Operations

RGA's Traditional group which accounts for about 90% of its total sales provides both traditional life reinsurance and reinsurance on investment assets such as annuities and corporate-owned life insurance policies. In addition to its traditional mortality-risk and asset reinsurance the group offers financial reinsurance to help its customers meet regulatory requirements.

The Financial Solutions unit (some 10% of total sales) consists of four businesses: asset-intensive reinsurance (full-risk coinsurance of annuities or reinsurance with a large investment component) financial reinsurance (involving ceding companies) stable value products (guaranteed investment contracts) and longevity reinsurance (employee retirement benefits).

The company also provides e-underwriting solutions to help customers write policies better and more quickly.

RGA has life reinsurance in force valued at about $3.3 trillion and about $64.5 billion in consolidated assets.

Geographic Reach

RGA organizes its operating segments by geographic region: US and Latin America; Canada; Europe Middle East and Africa; and Asia Pacific. The US and Latin America segment accounts for about 55% of total sales.

The company has offices in Australia Barbados Bermuda Brazil Canada China France Germany Hong Kong India Ireland Italy Japan Malaysia Mexico the Netherlands New Zealand Poland Singapore South Africa South Korea Spain Taiwan the United Arab Emirates the UK and the US.

Sales and Marketing

RGA primarily provides reinsurance to large US-based life insurance companies. Its top five customers generate some $2.2 billion representing about one-fifth of its gross premiums.

Financial Performance

RGA's revenue has been trending upward over the past five years. Net income has also been rising although 2017 was an outlier year in which the company netted $1.8 billion — about triple what it typically nets — thanks to a tax benefit of around $1 billion.

In 2018 revenue increased 3% to $12.9 billion. Consolidated net premiums increased 7% that year as the company secured more life reinsurance in force. Increased global business in particular drove growth. The gain was partially offset by a small decrease in consolidated investment income.

Net income fell 61% to $715.8 million compared to the prior year when RGA had significantly higher earnings. However net income increased 2% when compared to 2016.

The company ended 2018 with $1.9 billion in net cash about $600 million more than it had at the end of 2017. Operating activities provided $1.6 billion while investing activities used $636.6 million and financing activities used $322 million.

Strategy

RGA's strategy for growth has positioned the company well for harsh economic times and industry challenges. To achieve profitable results the company relies on its strong underwriting capabilities and disciplined pricing as well as geographic expansion and diversification in the products and services it offers. It is especially widening its mortality offerings in North America including facultative automatic and in-force block reinsurance. It also looks to leverage existing client relationships. In addition the company is looking to profit from the aging US population of baby boomers which is concerned with retirement income and estate planning.

As part of its efforts to diversify RGA has been seeking new longevity risk contracts. (Longevity risk refers to the risk of having to make payments to a retiree for a longer period than planned for if the person lives longer than expected.) For example in 2019 the company signed a deal with Manulife to reinsure longevity risk from an in-force block of Canadian annuities.

It is a successful mature company offering reinsurance products and expanding into new markets. However RGA is less nimble than some of its competitors as it lags behind in developing innovative new products and in investing in its technological capabilities.

Mergers and Acquisitions

In early 2018 RGA acquired LOGiQ3 a group of firms that provide technology outsourcing and consulting services to North American insurance and reinsurance providers. The deal included LOGiQ3 Corp. APEXA Cookhouse Lab and Tindall Associates Inc. (TAI).

Company Background

General American Life Insurance launched a life reinsurance division in 1973. General American Re became a top 10 US reinsurer by the 1980s and it started doing business in Canada and Europe in 1989. It went public as Reinsurance Group of America in 1993.

EXECUTIVES

Evp General Counsel And Secretary, William L. Hutton
Sevp And Cfo, Todd C. Larson, age 56, $472,428 total compensation
Evp And Chief Of Staff, Robert M. Musen
Evp Global Financial Solutions; President Rga Financial Group, John P. Laughlin
Interim Ceo Rgax Americas And Chief Solutions Officer Rgax, Mark E. Showers
Evp And Chief Human Resources Officer, Gay Burns
President And Ceo, Anna Manning, $750,000 total compensation
Evp Global Acquisitions, Scott D. Cochran
Sevp And Coo, Alain P. Néemeh, $563,750 total compensation
Evp And Chief Investment Officer, Timothy (Tim) Matson
Evp And Cio, Suzy Scanlon
Evp And Global Chief Risk Officer, Jonathan Porter
Senior Vice President Long Term Care And U.s. Individual Health, Wayne Adams
Vice President Global Human Resources Business Partner, Marcia Bequette
Vice President Compensation And Benefits, Pat Grube

Senior Vice President And Chief Actuary, Doug Knowling
Vice President Deputy Compliance Counsel, Robert Jett
Regional Vice President, Joseph Klimchak
Vice President Information Management And Analytics Services, Mike Foster
Vice President And Actuary Financial M, Christopher Clark
Senior Vice President Public Relations, Yuko Oshima
Vice President Actuary, Julie Decker
Senior Vice President, Brian Haynes
Vice President Finance, John Hayden
Senior Vice President Valuation And Financial Analysis, James Kellett
Evp International Business Development, Brendan Galligan
Senior Vice President Global Acquisitions, Richard Leblanc
Vice President Aura Client Services, Mike Casale
Vice President And Assistant General Counsel, Christopher Rickey
Vice President Life Product Services, David Burgoon
Sales Vice President U S Individual Health, Winona Berdine
Vice President Business Development, Quentin Marsh
Senior Vice President And Director Global Tax, Kent Zimmerman
Vice President Global Underwriting Quality And Risk Assurance, Stephanie Williams
Senior Vice President Of The Latin American Division, Jaime Correa
Vice President Underwriting, Kim Lancaster
Vice President Valuation And Financial Analysis, Chris Murphy
Vice President For Financial Markets, Mark M Hopfinger
Senior Vice President Heathcare, Steven Abood
Vice President And Director, Keiko Imuro
Senior Vice President Of Quota Share Healthcare Reinsurance, David Vnenchak
Vp And Managing Actuary, Hezhong Ma
Vice President Structured Finance, Rose Vogan
Vice President Business Development, Lisa Renetzky
Vice President And Actuary, Dustin Hetzler
Vice President Of Operations, Anne Riley
Vice President Corporate Underwriting Auditor, Pat Bradley
Senior Vice President, Dave Fischer
Vice President Credit Research And Risk Management, Scott Stone
Vice President Manufacturing, Ray Keefe
Senior Vice President And Associate Gc, Dana Wiele
Vice President, Doris Jackson
Vice President Global Compensation And Benefits, Ray Stengel
Svp And Chief Actuary U.s. Group Reinsurance, Dean Abbott
Vp Stable Value Marketing, Kara Marr
Vice President And Assistant General Counsel Corporate, Cliff Jenks
Vp Global Asset Liability Management, Chris Dignam
Vp And Sr. Actuary Rgax, Derek Kueker
Vice President Business Development, Mike Choate
Senior Vice President Global Acquisitions, Matthew Easley
Vice President Underwriting, Scott Grandmont
Vice President Risk Management, Sarah Maune
Vice President Director Of Investment Strategy And Research, Amy Gibson
Vice President Global Marketing, Sue Carrillo
Vice President And Actuary Head Of Global Experience Analytics, Michael Lane

Senior Vice President Business Operations Program Lead Tom Program, Jeff Birkholz
Vice President And Medical Director, Valerie Kaufman
Vice President Director Of Non U.s. Portfolio Management, Daniel Collins
Vice President Corporate Communications, Lynn Phillips
Vice President Business Initiatives, Peter Schindler
Svp Group Life Accident And Disability Reinsurance U.s. Group Reinsurance, Jim Rathbum
Vice Pr, Alka Gautam
Svp Investor Relations, Jeffrey Hopson
Vice President Innovation Studio Lead, Farron Blanc
Vice President Aura Product Management, Brad Butler
Svp And Chief Risk Officer Global Financial Solutions, Jeff Nordstrom
Svp And Chief Medical Director Of U.s. Mortality Markets, Holowaty Carl
Senior Vice President Head Of Asset Liability Management, Brad Barks
Regional Vice President And Underwriting Manager, Brent Hoehne
Vp Valuation And Financial Analysis, Eric Walta
Vice President Business Initiatives, Daniel Lyons
Assistant Vice President International Treaties, Diane Hare
Vice President Corporate Modeling, Steve Pummer
Vp Head Of U.s. Portfolio Management, Christopher Quallen
Senior Vice President And Chief Pricing Actuary, Alissa Holz
Senior Vice President Erm, Robert Lamarche
Vice President And Senior Actuary Business Initiatives, Stephanie Grass
Chairman, J. Cliff Eason
Assistant Treasurer, Jeffrey Boyer
Auditors: DELOITTE & TOUCHE LLP

LOCATIONS

HQ: Reinsurance Group of America, Inc.
16600 Swingley Ridge Road, Chesterfield, MO 63017
Phone: 636 736-7000
Web: www.rgare.com

2018 Sales

	$ mil.	% of total
US & Latin America	7,203	56
Asia/Pacific	2,471	19
Europe Middle East and Africa	1,845	14
Canada	273	10
Corporate & other	84	1
Total	12,876	100

Selected Countries of Operation

Australia
Barbados
Bermuda
Canada
China
France
Germany
Hong Kong
India
Ireland
Italy
Japan
Malaysia
Mexico
Netherlands
New Zealand
Poland
Singapore
South Africa
South Korea
Spain
Taiwan
Turkey
United Arab Emirates
UK
US

PRODUCTS/OPERATIONS

2018 Sales by Segment

	$ mil.	% of total
Traditional	11,432	89
Financial Solutions	1,360	10
Corporate & other	84	1
Total	12,876	100

2018 Sales

	$ mil.	% of total
Net premiums	10,544	81
Investment income	2,139	16
Other	364	3
Adjustments	(505.1)	-
Total	12,876	100

Selected Products and Services

e-Underwriting solutions
Facultative and underwriting expertise
Financial solutions
Group reinsurance
Individual life reinsurance
Individual living benefits reinsurance
Product development

Selected Subsidiaries

Reinsurance Company of Missouri Incorporated (RCM)
RGA Americas Reinsurance Company Ltd. (RGA Americas)
RGA Atlantic Reinsurance Company Ltd. (RGA Atlantic)
RGA International Reinsurance Company (RGA International)
RGA Life Reinsurance Company of Canada (RGA Canada)
RGA Reinsurance Company (Barbados) Ltd. (RGA Barbados)
RGA Reinsurance Company (RGA Reinsurance)
RGA Reinsurance Company of Australia Limited (RGA Australia)

COMPETITORS

General Re	Prudential
Hannover Re	SCOR Reinsurance
Munich Re Group	Swiss Re
Pacific Life	XL Group plc

HISTORICAL FINANCIALS

Company Type: Public

Income Statement				FYE: December 31
	ASSETS ($ mil.)	NET INCOME ($ mil.)	INCOME AS % OF ASSETS	EMPLOYEES
12/18	64,535	716	1.1%	2,767
12/17	60,515	1,822	3.0%	2,640
12/16	53,098	701	1.3%	2,482
12/15	50,383	502	1.0%	2,201
12/14	44,680	684	1.5%	2,070
Annual Growth	9.6%	1.1%	—	7.5%

2018 Year-End Financials

Debt ratio: 5.00%
Return on equity: 8.00%
Cash ($ mil.): 1,890
Current ratio: —
Long-term debt ($ mil.): —
No. of shares (mil.): 63
Dividends
Yield: 2.0%
Payout: 20.0%
Market value ($ mil.): 8,808

	STOCK PRICE ($) FY Close	P/E High/Low		PER SHARE ($) Earnings	Dividends	Book Value
12/18	140.00	15	11	11.00	2.00	135.00
12/17	156.00	6	4	28.00	2.00	148.00
12/16	126.00	12	7	11.00	2.00	110.00
12/15	86.00	13	11	7.00	1.00	94.00
12/14	88.00	9	7	10.00	1.00	102.00
Annual Growth	12.5%	—	—	3.0%	15.0%	7.1%

Reliance Steel & Aluminum Co.

Reliance Steel & Aluminum shows its mettle as North America's largest metals service center company. Operating in the US (about 300 service centers in 40 states) and a dozen other countries it processes and distributes more than 100000 metal products (bars beams pipes tubes plates coils etc.) to 125000-plus customers in industries like aerospace energy construction manufacturing semiconductor and electronics and transportation. Carbon steel is its top product; Reliance also markets alloy stainless and specialty steel as well as aluminum brass copper and titanium products. The company's trade names include Earle M. Jorgensen Metals USA and Precision Strip.

Operations

Reliance operates under several brand names including Earle M. Jorgensen Metals USA Precision Strip Phoenix Metals Reliance Metalcenter and Yarde Metals.

Reliance purchases a variety of metals from primary producers converts them to specialty products through various processing services and advanced technique (like bending coiling polishing etc.) and sells them in small quantities to customers through a network of metals service centers.

Although Reliance has only one reportable operating segment Metal Service Centers it earns revenue through six products and services. Carbon steel is its highest revenue earner accounting for more than 50% of total sales followed by Aluminum at 20%. The rest (Stainless Steel Alloy and Other) make up just over 25% of company revenues.

Geographic Reach

Reliance operates in about 40 US states and Australia Belgium Canada China France India Malaysia Mexico Singapore South Korea Turkey the UAE and the UK.

The company purchases inventory from US metals producer and some international suppliers.

The US is by far Reliance's largest market accounting for more than 90% of revenue. Sales mostly arise from the Midwest (more than 30%) and Southeast.

Sales and Marketing

Reliance has some 125000 customers active in a wide range of industries including general manufacturing non-residential construction (including infrastructure) transportation (rail truck trailer and shipbuilding) aerospace and defense energy (oil and natural gas) electronics and semiconductor fabrication and heavy industry (agricultural construction and mining equipment).

Reliance focuses on smaller customers and order sizes with quick turnarounds although it serves large original equipment manufacturers as well. About 95% are repeat customers. Products are delivered via a fleet of nearly 1800 trucks. The company has around 2100 sales personnel in about 45 states and a dozen other countries.

The company believes the diversity of its customer and product base and wide geographic footprint mitigates volatility and provides a competitive advantage.

Financial Performance

Reliance Steel's sales and general health fluctuate with steel prices. Its recent history has been characterized by declining sales for several years up to 2016 after which an uptick in the global price of steel has lifted sales once more.

In fiscal 2018 the company's sales grew 19% to $11.5 billion thanks to a 17% increase in the average selling price and a 1% increase in volume sold.

Net income grew a less impressive 3% to $633 million as a strong increase in operating profits was partially offset by a $246 million increase in tax expense (the 2017 US Tax Cuts and Jobs Act bestowed a $37.2 million tax credit in the previous financial year). Operating profits were boosted by investment in value-added processing equipment and a focus on specialty products.

Reliance's cash position weakened slightly in 2018 ending the year $26.2 million lower at Å 128.2 million. The company generated $664.6 million from its operating activities while investing activities used $281.0 million and financing activities used $403.9 million. The company's main cash uses in 2018 were debt repayments share repurchases and capital expenditures.

Strategy

Reliance's strategic priorities are building up high-margin specialty businesses and growing its product and geographic base including abroad. It pursues these goals via internal investment and numerous acquisitions.

The company has spent $1 billion in the past six years developing technologies to enable value-added processing capacity. The strategy seems to have been a success: in 2018 nearly half Reliance's total orders included value-added processing. As a result Reliance boasts extremely impressive gross margins: it targets 27% to 29% each year (in 2018 gross margins were 28.4%).

Reliance's acquisition strategy is to buy up specialty steel suppliers that enhance product customer and geographic diversification then invest in their operating performance and integrate them into Reliance's operating model. The wide product and customer base shields Reliance somewhat from commodity price volatility and cyclical customer demand. On the other hand Reliance's 24-delivery proposition makes geographic growth slow as it needs sufficient density to meet its requirements. It still generates 90% of sales in the US.

Additionally Reliance focused on servicing customers with small order sizes (average order is just over $1000) and quick turnaround by expanding its service network to ensure the proximity of its metal service centers to its customers.

Mergers and Acquisitions

Reliance has been prolific in acquiring companies?almost 70 since 1994.

In 2018 Reliance acquired a number of companies.

It acquired All Metals Holdings a South Carolina-based toll processing specialist for the automotive construction and appliance markets among others. All Metal provides value-added transportation and logistics from six terminals located in the southeastern US.

It acquired the remaining 40% it did not already own of Acero Prime a Mexican toll processing business in order to grow its volume sales to the automotive market.

In August 2018 Reliance acquired two KMS companies (Pennsylvanian and South Carolina) specializing in precision sheet metal fabrication. Terms of the transaction were not disclosed.

Early 2018 Reliance acquired DuBose National Energy Services and its affiliate DuBose National Energy Fasteners & Machines Parts. DuBose Energy and DuBose Fasteners make metal and metal products for the nuclear industry including utilities component manufacturers and contractors. DuBose Energy is headquartered in Clinton North Carolina and DuBose Fasteners is headquartered in Cleveland Ohio.

In 2017 Reliance spent $162 million in acquisition costs. In October of the same year the company acquired Ferguson Perforating Company (net sales $8 million) headquartered in Providence Rhode Island. Ferguson's specialized services in producing highly engineered and complex perforated metal for diverse end markets including automotive and aerospace increases Reliance's processing capacity and adds product diversification.

In 2016 Reliance acquired three companies for a combined value of nearly $350 million.

The acquisition of Tubular Steel in St. Louis Missouri strengthened Reliance's foothold in the energy end market.

Best Manufacturing Inc headquartered in Arkansas was acquired for high margin value added processing capabilities.

The third Alaska Steel marks the company's entry into the Alaska market broadening its market reach while increasing access to diverse industries like energy and infrastructure.

Company Background

The company was founded in 1939 by Thomas Neilan as Reliance Steel Products Company a distributor of steel reinforcing bar in Los Angeles California. In 1956 the company is renamed for a second time to reflect its expanding product lines assuming the name it holds today: Reliance Steel & Aluminum Co.

EXECUTIVES

President Ccc Steel, Brian M. Tenenbaum

Sevp And Cfo, Karla R. Lewis, age 54, $604,250 total compensation

Executive Svp Operations, William K. Sales, age 62, $550,000 total compensation

President And Ceo, Gregg J. Mollins, age 64, $1,025,000 total compensation

Managing Director All Metal Services, David L. Potts

President Ami Metals, Scott A. Smith

Executive Svp Operations, James D. Hoffman, age 60, $577,500 total compensation

President Allegheny Steel Distributors, Bernie J. Herrmann

President Aluminum And Stainless, Joseph B. Wolf

President Pacific Metal, John S. Nosler

President Infra-metals, Mark A Haight, age 60

President Earle M. Jorgensen Co., James Desmond

Svp Operations, Stephen P. (Steve) Koch, age 52, $486,250 total compensation

President Siskin Steel & Supply, Paul J. Loftin

President Yarde Metals, Matthew L. (Matt) Smith

President Sugar Steel, Robert J. Sugar

President Chapel Steel, Stanley J. (Stan) Altman

President Clayton Metals, Brian K. Cleveland

Cio, Susan C. Borchers, age 58

President Feralloy, Carlos Rodriguez-Borjas

President American Metals, Nicole Heater

President Crest Steel, Kristofer M. Farris

President Delta Steel, Eric J. Offenberger

President Diamond Manufacturing, David L. Simpson

President National Specialty Alloys, Mark Russ

President Service Steel Aerospace, Douglas Nesbitt

President Viking Materials, Michael E. Allen

President Chatham Steel, Jerome Rooney

President Precision Strip, Joseph P. Wolf

President Continental Alloys & Services, Randall C. (Randy) Zajicek

President Liebovich Bros., David Corirossi

President Northern Illinois Steel Supply, Michael J. Ruth

President Pdm Steel Service Centers, Sean Mollins

President Phoenix Metals, Barry L. Epps

President Best Manufacturing, James Best

President Precision Flamecutting And Steel, Susan McKay

President Valex, Steve Simon

Managing Director Metalweb Limited, Karl Weston
Vice President Tax, Silva Yeghyayan
Vice President Health Safety And Human
  Resources, Don Prebola
Svp General Counsel And Corporate Secretary,
  William Smith Ii
Chairman, Mark V. Kaminski, age 64
Board Member, Andrew Sharkey
Secretary, Yvette M Schiotis
Board Member, John Figueroa
Auditors: KPMG LLP

LOCATIONS

HQ: Reliance Steel & Aluminum Co.
  350 South Grand Avenue, Suite 5100, Los Angeles, CA
  90071
Phone: 213 687-7700
Web: www.rsac.com

2018 Sales

	$ mil.	% of total
United States	10,638	92
Foreign Countries	896	8
Total	**11,535**	**100**

2018 Sales

	% of total
Midwest	32
West/Southwest	22
Southeast	18
International	8
Mid-Atlantic	6
Northeast	6
Pacific Northwest	5
Mountain	3
Total	**100**

PRODUCTS/OPERATIONS

2018 Sales

	% of total
Carbon steel	54
Aluminum	19
Stainless steel	14
Alloy	6
Toll processing	4
Other	3
Total	**100**

PRODUCTS

Alloy Steel
Aluminum
Brass & Copper
Carbon Steel
Stainless Steel
Titanium

COMPETITORS

A. M. Castle	Ryerson
O'Neal Steel	Steel Technologies
Olympic Steel	Ternium Mexico
Russel Metals	Worthington Industries

HISTORICAL FINANCIALS

Company Type: Public

Income Statement — FYE: December 31

	REVENUE ($ mil.)	NET INCOME ($ mil.)	NET PROFIT MARGIN	EMPLOYEES
12/18	11,535	634	5.5%	15,600
12/17	9,721	613	6.3%	14,900
12/16	8,613	304	3.5%	14,500
12/15	9,351	312	3.3%	14,000
12/14	10,452	372	3.6%	14,900
Annual Growth	**2.5%**	**14.3%**	**—**	**1.2%**

2018 Year-End Financials

Debt ratio: 27.00%
Return on equity: 14.00%
Cash ($ mil.): 128
Current ratio: 5.00
Long-term debt ($ mil.): 2,139
No. of shares (mil.): 67
Dividends
  Yield: 3.0%
  Payout: 23.0%
Market value ($ mil.): 4,760

	STOCK PRICE ($) FY Close	P/E High/Low		PER SHARE ($) Earnings	Dividends	Book Value
12/18	71.00	11	8	9.00	2.00	70.00
12/17	86.00	10	8	8.00	2.00	64.00
12/16	80.00	21	12	4.00	2.00	57.00
12/15	58.00	16	12	4.00	2.00	55.00
12/14	61.00	16	12	5.00	1.00	53.00
Annual Growth	**3.8%**	**—**		**16.6%**	**9.3%**	**7.1%**

Renasant Corp

Those who are cognizant of their finances may want to do business with Renasant Corporation. The holding company owns Renasant Bank which serves consumers and local business through about 80 locations in Alabama Georgia Mississippi and Tennessee. The bank offers standard products such as checking and savings accounts CDs credit cards and loans and mortgages as well as trust retail brokerage and retirement plan services. Its loan portfolio is dominated by residential and commercial real estate loans. The bank also offers agricultural business construction and consumer loans and lease financing. Subsidiary Renasant Insurance sells personal and business coverage.Shareholders approved a merger with Metropolitan Bank in mid-2017.

Financial Performance

The company's revenue increased in fiscal 2013 compared to the prior year. It reported revenue of $252.6 million for fiscal 2013 up from $228 million in revenue for fiscal 2012.

Renasant's net income also went up in fiscal 2013 compared to the previous fiscal period. It reported net income of about $33.5 million for fiscal 2013 up from net income of $26.6 million in fiscal 2012.

The company's cash on hand decreased by about $24 million in fiscal 2013 compared to fiscal 2012 levels.

Strategy

Renasant has looked to diversify its loan portfolio. The bank has reduced its amount of loans for construction and land development — a sector that has been hit particularly hard — by tightening its underwriting standards.

It's also been growing through acquistions. In late 2014 for example Renasant purchased Heritage Financial Group in an all stock merger deal that amounted to $258 million. The move added $1.9 billion in assets $1.2 billion in loan assets and $1.3 billion in deposit assets to Renasant's collection. In addition the move significantly expanded the bank's geographic reach adding 48 banking mortgage and investment offices in Alabama Florida and Georgia. All told the deal made Renasant one of the largest community banks in the Southeast region of the United States.

Mergers and Acquisitions

In 2017 Renasant agreed to a $190 million merger with Metropolitan Bank.

EXECUTIVES

Evp, Stuart R. Johnson, age 66, $250,000 total compensation
Chairman President And Ceo, E. Robinson (Robin) McGraw, age 72, $750,000 total compensation
Evp, James W. Gray, age 63, $230,000 total compensation
President And Coo, C. Mitchell (Mitch) Waycaster, age 61, $450,000 total compensation
Evp, Mary J. Witt, age 60
Evp, W. Mark Williams, age 56
Evp, R. Rick Hart, age 71, $496,000 total compensation
Evp And General Counsel, Stephen M. Corban, age 64, $75,000 total compensation
Evp; President Eastern Region Renasant Bank, O. Leonard (Len) Dorminey, age 66, $213,285 total compensation
Evp And Cfo, Kevin D. Chapman, age 44, $375,000 total compensation
Evp; President Western Region Renasant Bank, J. Scott Cochran, age 56
First Vice President Director Of Corporate Communication And Ir Contact, John Oxford
Executive Vice President, Danny Gladney
Assistant Vice President, Kent Dees
Vice President And Trust Officer, Allison Youngblood
Executive Vice President, Craig Gardella
Senior Vice President Corporate Banking, Will Smithhart
Assistant Vice President Account Executive, Brian Gagel
Vice President, Josh Sullivan
Senior Vice President, Donna Wade
Senior Vice President, Robert Hankins
Senior Vice President And Business Development Officer, Bobby Harper
Vice President Commercial Banker, Larry Finkel
Executive Vice President Credit Administration, Stuart Weise
Senior Vice President, Scott Rossman
Vice President, Jack Stuart
Vice President Relationship Officer, Danny Crabtree
Senior Vice President Commercial Banking, David Harwell
Senior Vice President, Jason McClimans
Division President Executive Vice President, Raymond Vannorman
Vice President Client Portfolio Manager Asset Manage Ement Renasant Asset Management, Matt Legg
Vice President Appraisal Officer Card, Lisa Wells
Central Monitoring Department Manager Vice President, Tracey Aldridge
Senior Vice President Director Of Senior Business Analyst Lending, John Daly
Vice President, Raakhi Phillips
First Vice President Associate Counsel, Jared Carrubba
Vice President, Brian Porter
Vice President, Michael Wiegert
Small Business Lending Division Manager Senior Vice President, Butch Lyle
Assistant Vice President Senior Business Analyst Portfolio Manager, Kathy Davis
Senior Vice President, Phil Smith
Executive Vice President, Mark Jeanfreau
Assistant Vice President And To, Crystal Tucker
Senior Vice President, Melanie Kurn
Division President Senior Vice President, Ed Hutchinson
Senior Vice President Mortgage Controller, Bryan Morelli
Vice President, Jon Appel
Senior Vice President, John Temple
Assistant Vice President Mortgage Lender, Brenda Pearce

Assistant Vice President Treasury Management
Specialist, Chrissy Aubin
Vice President Special Assets Officer, Scott
Williams
Board Member, Richard Heyer
Auditors: Horne LLP

LOCATIONS

HQ: Renasant Corp
209 Troy Street, Tupelo, MS 38804-4827
Phone: 662 680-1001
Web: www.renasant.com

PRODUCTS/OPERATIONS

2015 Sales

	$ mil.	% of total
Interest income		
Loans	236	64
Securities	27	7
Other	0	-
Non-interest income		
Mortgage banking income	36	10
Service charges on deposit accounts	29	8
Fees and commissions	16	4
Wealth management	10	3
Other	17	4
Total	**371**	**100**

COMPETITORS

BBVA Compass
Bancshares
BancorpSouth
Citizens Holding
Citizens National Bank
of Meridian

First Horizon
Hancock Holding
Regions Financial
Trustmark

HISTORICAL FINANCIALS

Company Type: Public

Income Statement

FYE: December 31

	ASSETS ($ mil.)	NET INCOME ($ mil.)	INCOME AS % OF ASSETS	EMPLOYEES
12/18	12,935	147	1.1%	2,359
12/17	9,830	92	0.9%	2,102
12/16	8,700	91	1.0%	1,965
12/15	7,926	68	0.9%	1,996
12/14	5,805	60	1.0%	1,471
Annual Growth	22.2%	25.3%		12.5%

2018 Year-End Financials

Debt ratio: 2.00%
Return on equity: 8.00%
Cash ($ mil.): 569
Current ratio: —
Long-term debt ($ mil.): —

No. of shares (mil.): 59
Dividends
Yield: 3.0%
Payout: 34.0%
Market value ($ mil.): 1,767

	STOCK PRICE ($) FY Close	P/E High/Low	PER SHARE ($) Earnings	Dividends	Book Value
12/18	30.00	18 10	3.00	1.00	35.00
12/17	41.00	23 19	2.00	1.00	31.00
12/16	42.00	20 14	2.00	1.00	28.00
12/15	34.00	20 14	2.00	1.00	26.00
12/14	29.00	17 14	2.00	1.00	23.00
Annual Growth	1.1%	— —	10.4%	4.1%	11.5%

Republic Bancorp, Inc. (KY)

As one of the top five bank holding companies based in Kentucky $4 billion-asset Republic Bancorp is the parent of Republic Bank & Trust (formerly First Commercial Bank) which offers deposit accounts loans and mortgages credit cards private banking and trust services through more than 30 branches in across Kentucky and around 10 more in southern Indiana Nashville Tampa and Cincinnati Ohio. About one-third of the bank's $3 billion-loan portfolio is tied to residential real estate while another 25% is made up of commercial real estate loans. Warehouse lines of credit home equity loans and commercial and industrial loans make up most of the rest. The company also offers short-term consumer loans and tax refund loans.

Operations

Republic Bancorp operates three "core banking" segments: Traditional Banking which generated more than 80% of the company's total profit during 2015; Warehouse (almost 20% of profit) and Mortgage Banking (less than 1%). Its Warehouse lending business offers short-term credit facilities secured by single-family residences to mortgage bankers nationwide. Its Republic Processing Group segment offers short-term consumer loans prepaid debit cards and tax refund loans.

The bank made 75% of its total revenue from interest income almost entirely from loans during 2015 though a small percentage came from taxed investments and Federal Home Loan Bank stock. The rest of its revenue came from net refund transfer fees from its Republic Processing Group segment (9% of revenue) deposit account service charges (7%) interchange fee income (4%) mortgage banking income (2%) and other miscellaneous income sources.

Subsidiary Republic Insurance Services (also known as the Captive) provides property and casualty insurance coverage to the company and eight other third-party insurance captives for which insurance may not be available or cost effective.

Geographic Reach

The company had 40 RB&T branches at the end of 2015 including 32 in Kentucky mostly in the Louisville Metro area and others in the Central Western and Northern parts of the state. It had 3 branches in southern Indiana (in Floyds Knobs Jeffersonville and New Albany); two branches in the Tampa Florida metro area; two branches in the Nashville Tennessee metro area; and one more in the Cincinnati Ohio metro area.

Sales and Marketing

Republic spent $3.16 million on marketing and development expenses during 2015 compared to $3.26 million and $3.11 million in 2014 and 2013 respectively.

Financial Performance

Republic Bancorp's revenues and profits have been trending higher since 2013 as its loan assets have risen more than 30% over the period.

The company's revenue climbed 9% to $190 million during 2015 mostly thanks to higher interest income as its loan assets grew by 9% to $3.33 billion with commercial loans (real estate and business loans) and residential mortgage loans and lines of credit driving most of the growth.

Strong revenue growth in 2015 drove Republic's net income up 22% to $35 million for the year. The company's operating cash levels nearly doubled to $50 million after adjusting its earnings for non-cash items related to mortgage loan sales and

thanks to favorable working capital changes related to changes in other liabilities.

Strategy

Republic Bancorp is moving toward building its commercial loans business launching a Corporate Banking division in 2015 to originate commercial loans with amounts ranging from $2.5 million to $25 million to borrowers with the highest credit ratings in its existing geographic markets. It also acquires smaller community banks to expand into new geographic markets while building its loan and deposit business.

Additionally Republic Bancorp has been moving into other revolving credit lines while also looking to take advantage of the rapidly growing prepaid card market. During 2015 for example it partnered with netSpend to become a pilot issuer of netSpend-branded prepaid cards; and partnered with ClearBalance to originate revolving lines of credit nationally for hospital receivables.

Mergers and Acquisitions

In October 2015 Republic Bancorp expanded its presence in Florida and grew its loan business after agreeing to buy $250 million-asset Cornerstone Bancorp along its four Cornerstone Community Bank branches in the Tampa Florida metro area $190 million in loans and $200 million in deposits. The deal was expected to be completed in the first half of 2016.

Company Background

In 2012 Republic Bancorp entered the Nashville and Minneapolis market through the FDIC-assisted acquisitions of the failed Tennessee Commerce Bank and First Commercial Bank respectively.

EXECUTIVES

Vice Chairman; President Republic Bank & Trust, A. Scott Trager, age 66, $350,000 total compensation
President And Ceo; Ceo Republic Bank & Trust, Steven E. (Steve) Trager, age 58, $353,000 total compensation
Evp Cfo And Chief Accounting Officer Republic Bancorp And Republic Bank & Trust, Kevin Sipes, age 47, $281,500 total compensation
Vice President And Risk Manager, Bryan Hendrick
Assistant Vice President, Mike Long
Vice President, Susan Smith
Assistant Vice President Accounting Supervisor, Denise Witten
Senior Vice President, Lisa Butcher
Assistant Vice President Technology Services Managerand#8230;, Scott Estes
Vice President Project Services Manager, Michelle Cunningham
Vice President Retail Collections, Lori Forbes
Executive Vice President And Chief Risk Officer Of Republic Bank And Trust Company, John Rippy
Avp Banking Center Supervisor, Robin Verenna
Vice President Retail Collections Supervisor, Jaree Glass
Senior Vice President, David Buchanon
Vice President Director Of Business Intelligence, Deb Reese
Assistant Vice President, Philip Thomas
Vice President, Karen McGee
Vice President Senior Manager Of Technology Services, Sean O'Mahoney
Assistant Vice President, Amy Quinn
Vice President Mortgage Warehouse Lending, Tim Poole
Vice President Senior Private Banking Officer, Steven Sharp
Senior Managing Director Business Development Vp, Leslie Raeber
Vice President Contact Center Director Of Client Experience, Robinson Damion
Vice President Treasury Management, Tamara McCain

718

Vice President, Scott Lee
Vice President Mortgage Warehouse Lending, Scott Davis
Assistant Vice President Business Development Manager, Wende Cosby
Vice President Relationship Manager, Steven Shields
Vice President Loan Operations, Donna Blincoe
Chairman, Bernard M. Trager, age 90
Auditors: Crowe LLP

LOCATIONS

HQ: Republic Bancorp, Inc. (KY)
601 West Market Street, Louisville, KY 40202
Phone: 502 584-3600
Web: www.republicbank.com

PRODUCTS/OPERATIONS

2015 Sales

	$ mil.	% of total
Interest		
Loans including fees	134	70
Taxable investment securities	7	4
Other	1	1
Noninterest		
Net refund transfer fees	17	9
Service charges on deposit accounts	13	7
Interchange fee income	8	4
Mortgage banking	4	2
Other	5	3
Adjustments	(0.3)	-
Total	**190**	**100**

Selected Services

Checking
Credit & Debit Cards
Internet & Mobile Banking
Lending
Private Banking & Wealth Management
Savings & Investing

COMPETITORS

BB&T	KeyCorp
Bank of America	PNC Financial
Community Trust	Stock Yards Bancorp
Fifth Third	U.S. Bancorp
Home Federal	

HISTORICAL FINANCIALS

Company Type: Public

Income Statement · FYE: December 31

	ASSETS ($ mil.)	NET INCOME ($ mil.)	INCOME AS % OF ASSETS	EMPLOYEES
12/18	5,240	78	1.5%	1,064
12/17	5,085	46	0.9%	1,009
12/16	4,816	46	1.0%	954
12/15	4,230	35	0.8%	799
12/14	3,747	29	0.8%	735
Annual Growth	8.7%	28.2%	—	9.7%

2018 Year-End Financials

Debt ratio: 1.00%
Return on equity: 12.00%
Cash ($ mil.): 351
Current ratio: —
Long-term debt ($ mil.): —

No. of shares (mil.): 21
Dividends
Yield: 3.0%
Payout: 26.0%
Market value ($ mil.): 809

	STOCK PRICE ($) FY Close	P/E High/Low		PER SHARE ($) Earnings	Dividends	Book Value
12/18	39.00	7	5	4.00	1.00	33.00
12/17	38.00	19	15	2.00	1.00	30.00
12/16	40.00	18	11	2.00	1.00	29.00
12/15	26.00	16	13	2.00	1.00	28.00
12/14	25.00	18	16	1.00	1.00	27.00
Annual Growth	11.9%	—	—	28.3%	7.1%	5.4%

Republic First Bancorp, Inc.

Republic First Bancorp is the holding company for Republic Bank which serves the Greater Philadelphia area and southern New Jersey from more than 15 branches. Boasting over $1 billion in assets the bank targets individuals and small to midsized businesses offering standard deposit products including checking and savings accounts money market accounts IRAs and CDs. Commercial mortgages account for more than 70% of the company's loan portfolio which also includes consumer loans business loans and residential mortgages. Republic has been transitioning from a commercial bank into a major regional retail and commercial bank.

Operations

The bank's loan portfolio is made up of mostly commercial loans including commercial real estate loans construction and land development loans commercial and industrial loans as well as owner occupied real estate loans consumer-related loans and residential mortgages. As of 2015 each its commercial loans typically ranged from $250000 to $5 million though it sometimes lent up to its legal limit of $19.9 million.

About 72% of Republic First Bancorp's total revenue came from loan interest (including fees) in 2014 while another 11% came from interest and dividends on its taxable and tax-exempt investment securities. The rest of its revenue came from gains on sales of SBA loans (10%) loan advisory and servicing fees (3%) service fees on deposit accounts (3%) and other miscellaneous income sources. The bank had a staff of 235 full-time employees at the end of 2014.

Geographic Reach

Republic First boasts more than 15 branch offices in Pennsylvania (in Abington Ardmore Bala Cynwyd Plymout Meeting Media and Philadelphia) and New Jersey (in Berlin Cherry Hill Glassboro Haddonfield Marlton and Voorhees).

Sales and Marketing

The bank's commercial loans are mostly made to small and medium-sized businesses as well as professionals who need working capital financing for asset acquisitions or other financial services.

Republic First has been ramping up its advertising spend in recent years. It spent $597 thousand on advertising in 2014 compared to $447 thousand and $307 thousand in 2013 and 2012 respectively.

Financial Performance

The company has struggled to consistently grow its revenues in recent years due to shrinking interest margins on loans amidst the low-interest environment. Republic First has been steadily climbing out from prior years of losses (2013 2011 2010) however thanks to declining interest expenses and lower loan loss provisions as its loan portfolio's credit quality has improved with higher property valuations in the strengthened economy.

Republic First's revenue rose by 4% to $48.4 million in 2014 mostly thanks to an 8% jump in interest income as loan balances increased during the year. The bank's non-interest income fell on lower sales of SBA loans with fewer SBA loan originations which offset some of its top-line growth.

The company shot back into the black with a $2.4 million profit in 2014 (compared to a net loss of $3.5 million in 2013) mostly because in 2013 it had suffered a non-recurring $3.6 million loan loss on a bad loan as well as a non-recurring $1.9 million charge related to a legal settlement. Republic First's operating cash levels also skyrocketed to $9.7 million mostly on higher cash earnings.

Strategy

Republic Bank which had historically been known for its business and commercial lending has been focused on retail banking in the past few years and is working to become a major regional retail and commercial bank. As part of this strategy the bank has restructured its loan portfolio to reduce its emphasis on commercial real estate loans and has pursued a "retail-focused" strategy by offering customers "extended store hours absolutely free checking and coin counting more than 55000 surcharge ATMs and free VISA gift cards" according to the company's CEO letter included in the 2014 annual report.

The company has been expanding organically through new branch openings in recent years. In 2015 for example Republic Bank opened three new branches in South New Jersey in Berlin Marlton and Glassboro. In April of that year the company also sold $45 million in common stock through a private placement offering to cover its "aggressive expansion plans in 2015 and beyond."

EXECUTIVES

Assistant Vice President Network Engineer, John Rudolph
Svp Human Resources Director, Janine Zangrilli
Senior Vice President Chief Risk Officer, Tracie Young
Vice President And Marketing Manager, Katie Michaleski
Vice President Loan Administration, Lisa Iannello
Vice President Of Consumer Lending, Dan Charyna
Senior Vice President And Retail Market Manager, Leslie DiLuigi
Vice President Senior Business Development Officer, Judy Rosner
Vice President, Krista Collings
Vice President, Amy Osborn
Senior Vice President, Brennan Charlene
Assistant Vice President Loan Closer Sba Division, Camille Oldenburg
Board Member, Brian Tierney
Board Member, Theodore Flocco
Auditors: BDO USA, LLP

LOCATIONS

HQ: Republic First Bancorp, Inc.
50 South 16th Street, Philadelphia, PA 19102
Phone: 215 735-4422
Web: www.myrepublicbank.com

PRODUCTS/OPERATIONS

2014 Sales

	$ mil.	% of total
Interest income		
Interest and fees on taxable loans	35	71
Interest and dividends on taxable investment securities	5	10
Interest and fees on tax-exempt loans	0	1
Interest and dividends on tax-exempt investment securities	0	1
Interest on federal funds sold and other interest-earning assets	0	0
Non interest		
Gain on sales of SBA loans	5	10
Loan advisory and servicing fees	1	3
Service fees on deposit accounts	1	3
Gain on sale of investment securities	0	1
Legal settlements	0	0
Other-than-temporary impairment	0	0
Portion recognized in other comprehensive income (before taxes)	(0.03)	0
Net impairment loss on investment securities	0	0
Bank owned life insurance income	0	0
Other non-interest income	0	0
Total	**49**	**100**

Bank of America
Citizens Financial
  Group
PNC Financial
Prudential Bancorp
Royal Bancshares

Sovereign Bank
Sun Bancorp (NJ)
TD Bank USA
TF Financial
Wells Fargo

HISTORICAL FINANCIALS

Company Type: Public

Income Statement

FYE: December 31

	ASSETS ($ mil.)	NET INCOME ($ mil.)	INCOME AS % OF ASSETS	EMPLOYEES
12/18	2,753	9	0.3%	531
12/17	2,322	9	0.4%	448
12/16	1,924	5	0.3%	306
12/15	1,439	2	0.2%	277
12/14	1,215	2	0.2%	235
Annual Growth	22.7%	37.1%	—	22.6%

2018 Year-End Financials

Debt ratio: 0.00%
Return on equity: 4.00%
Cash ($ mil.): 72
Current ratio: —
Long-term debt ($ mil.): —

No. of shares (mil.): 59
Dividends
  Yield: —
  Payout: —
Market value ($ mil.): 351

	STOCK PRICE ($) FY Close	P/E High/Low		PER SHARE ($) Earnings	Dividends	Book Value
12/18	6.00	62	39	0.00	0.00	4.00
12/17	8.00	62	47	0.00	0.00	4.00
12/16	8.00	69	29	0.00	0.00	4.00
12/15	4.00	77	55	0.00	0.00	3.00
12/14	4.00	76	43	0.00	0.00	3.00
Annual Growth	12.3%	—	—	21.0%	—	8.8%

Republic Services Inc

Republic Services is the second-largest nonhazardous waste management provider in the US behind leader Waste Management in terms of revenue and geographic coverage. Republic provides waste disposal services for commercial industrial municipal and residential customers through its network of 350 collection firms. It owns or operates some 190 solid waste landfills more than 200 transfer stations and about 90 recycling centers. Other assets include seven treatment recovery and disposal facilities and 10 salt water disposal wells. It also has about 75 landfill-to-gas and a handful of other renewable energy projects.

Operations

Republic Services divides its operations into two broad geographic categories Group 1 and Group 2. Group 1 covers the western US and parts of the Midwest. Group 2 covers the remaining portion of the Midwest the eastern US and Texas. Group 2 accounts for more than 50% of revenue.

Solid waste collection operations is Republic Services' largest revenue generator. Small-container collection brings in 30% of revenue while residential and large containers account for more than one-fifth each. Its landfill disposal services generate 15% of revenue.

Geographic Reach

Phoenix Arizona-based Republic Services operates throughout the US. The company has collection businesses transfer stations active solid waste landfills and recycling centers in about 40 US states and Puerto Rico. Its active solid waste landfills total 109000 acres including nearly 38000 permitted acres.

Sales and Marketing

Republic Services employs municipal marketing representatives responsible for working with municipalities or communities seeking Republic's residential services. It also employs a National Accounts selling organization.

The company interacts directly with customers through its My Resource customer portal and mobile app. Republic serves than 14 million residential/municipal commercial and industrial customers.

Financial Performance

In the past five years Republic Services' revenue has trended upwards.

The exception was 2018 when Republic Services reported no revenue growth ($10.40 million in 2018 vs. $10.41 million in 2017). The even results were due in large part to revenue recognition changes the company made in 2018 which shifted the timing of when in the customer contract cycle Republic records revenue. Excluding the new revenue recognition approach the company's revenue increased 4% an uptick driven by price increases (including fuel recovery fees charged) and revenue added from acquisitions.

Republic Services' net income dropped 19% to $1 billion from 2017 results of $1.2 billion due in large part to higher income taxes than in the prior period.

Total cash on hand at the end of 2018 increased $66.1 million to $179.1 million. Cash from operations contributed $2.2 billion while investing activities used $1.2 billion for capital expenditures and other investments. Financing used $1 billion to repay debt repurchase stock and pay dividends.

Strategy

Perhaps the most visible reminder of a waste company is the truck making its rounds. Likewise for Republic Services it finds cost savings by investing in modernizing its fleet. About three-quarters of the company's fleet is automated which means a truck needs only a driver while a mechanical arm hoists the trash receptacle to and from the truck. The company has also shifted 20% of its fleet to using compressed natural gas which burns cleaner and is usually cheaper than gasoline. It continues to invest in converting trucks and refilling stations to use and supply compressed natural gas.

Republic Services snaps up local and regional waste services through acquisitions. In 2017 and 2018 the company acquired hauling landfill and recycling operations and related assets; this includes the purchase of ReCommunity Holdings and its recycling centers in 14 states. Republic's acquisitions help it expand into and enter markets where populations are rising which translates into higher waste volume and ultimately more revenue.

Company Background

Republic Services began in 1980 as Republic Resources an oil exploration and production company. In 1989 after a stockholder group tried to force Republic into liquidation Browning-Ferris (BFI) founder Thomas Fatjo stepped in gained control of Republic Resources and refocused it on a field he knew well — solid waste. Renamed Republic Waste the company began making acquisitions.

In 1990 Michael DeGroote founder of BFI competitor Laidlaw bought into Republic Waste. In 1995 Wayne Huizenga — who co-founded Waste Management in 1971 and was beginning to develop a national auto sales organization in the mid-1990s after his tenure as chairman and CEO of Blockbuster Entertainment — approached DeGroote about a deal. They rejected an immediate merger of the waste and auto businesses because the latter was not well-enough developed and would drag down Republic's numbers. Instead they agreed to merge Republic and the Hudson Companies (a trash business owned by Huizenga's brother-in-law Harris Hudson) to sell Huizenga a large interest in Republic through a private offering and to give him control of the board (in 1995). The company became Republic Industries.

Republic Industries spun off about 30% of its waste business as Republic Services in 1998; the IPO raised $1.3 billion. Republic's acquisition trend continued as it agreed to buy 16 landfills 136 commercial collection routes and 11 transfer stations from Waste Management for $500 million. Later that year Waste Management veteran James O'-Connor succeeded Huizenga as CEO although Huizenga continued as chairman.

HISTORY

Republic Services began in 1980 as Republic Resources an oil exploration and production company. In 1989 after a stockholder group tried to force Republic into liquidation Browning-Ferris (BFI) founder Thomas Fatjo stepped in gained control of Republic Resources and refocused it on a field he knew well — solid waste. Renamed Republic Waste the company began making acquisitions.

In 1990 Michael DeGroote founder of BFI competitor Laidlaw bought into Republic Waste. In 1995 Wayne Huizenga — who co-founded Waste Management in 1971 and was beginning to develop a national auto sales organization in the mid-1990s after his tenure as chairman and CEO of Blockbuster Entertainment — approached DeGroote about a deal. They rejected an immediate merger of the waste and auto businesses because the latter was not well-enough developed and would drag down Republic's numbers. Instead they agreed to merge Republic and the Hudson Companies (a trash business owned by Huizenga's brother-in-law Harris Hudson) to sell Huizenga a large interest in Republic through a private offering and to give him control of the board (in 1995). The company became Republic Industries.

Huizenga's investment brought a flood of new investors. With new resources Republic Industries became a driving force in the garbage industry's consolidation binge and the company bought more than 100 smaller waste haulers between 1995 and 1998. Republic Industries spun off about 30% of its waste business as Republic Services in 1998; the IPO raised $1.3 billion. Republic's acquisition trend continued as it agreed to buy 16 landfills 136 commercial collection routes and 11 transfer stations from Waste Management for $500 million. Later that year Waste Management veteran James O'Connor succeeded Huizenga as CEO although Huizenga continued as chairman.

Investors filed class-action lawsuits against Republic in 1999 claiming the Waste Management purchases held far more integration problems than the company admitted. In 2000 Republic swapped nine of its solid-waste operations for eight Allied Waste businesses which Allied needed to divest in order to gain federal approval for its merger with BFI.

While many firms in the industry were selling off assets in 2001 Republic was expanding its operations in the Northern California market by acquiring Richmond Sanitary Services. Huizenga retired as chairman at the end of 2002 and was once again succeeded by O'Connor. Huizenga stayed on the board as a director until May 2004.

In 2007 the company sold Living Earth Technology Company (a noncore stand-alone business in Texas) for about $37 million. In 2008 prior to its megadeal with Allied Waste Republic rebuffed a takeover bid by industry leader Waste Management.

In late 2008 Republic Services the once #3 industry player acquired #2 company Allied Waste for $6 billion to place it closer to industry leader Waste Management in terms of revenues and geographic coverage. Following the acquisition Republic divested assets in seven markets (six municipal solid waste landfills six collection businesses and three transfer stations) in order to meet US antitrust regulations.

During 2012 the company invested $76 million on five recycling centers and plans to continue to look for opportunities to expand its recycling capabilities.

In 2013 the company dedicated a 2037 acre state-of-the-art landfill and transfer station in Texas to meet the Rio Grande Valley's waste needs for the next 100 years. The new La Gloria landfill replaced Republic's Rio Grande Valley Landfill in Donna Texas that had reached full capacity.

EXECUTIVES

President And Ceo, Donald W. (Don) Slager, age 57, $1,100,000 total compensation
Evp And Chief Development Officer, Brian A. Bales
Evp Chief Legal Officer Chief Ethics And Compliance Officer And Corporate Secretary, Catharine D. Ellingsen, age 55, $395,107 total compensation
Evp And Chief Administrative Officer, Jeffrey A. (Jeff) Hughes, age 63, $482,061 total compensation
Evp Operations, Jon Vander Ark
Evp Operations, Tim Stuart
Svp And Cio, Bill Halnon
Svp And Chief Accounting Officer, Charles F. (Chuck) Serianni, age 57, $511,779 total compensation
Evp Operations Support, Nathan Cabbil
Evp And Chief Transformation Officer, Stuart Levy
Evp And Chief Customer Officer, Tom Lynch
Evp And Chief Marketing Officer, Sue Klug
Senior Vice President Treasurer, Edward A Lang
Executive Vice President General Counsel And Corporate Secretary, Michael Rissman
Chairman, Manuel Kadre, age 53
Auditors: Ernst & Young LLP

LOCATIONS

HQ: Republic Services Inc
18500 North Allied Way, Phoenix, AZ 85054
Phone: 480 627-2700
Web: www.republicservices.com

2018 Sales

	$ mil.	% of total
Group2	5,071	50
Group1	4,812	48
Corporate entities	158	2
Total	**10,041**	**100**

PRODUCTS/OPERATIONS

2018 Sales

	$ mil.	% of total
Small-container	3,058	31
Residential	2,235	22
Large-container	2	22
Other	44	0
Transfer	538	5
Landfill	1	13
Energy services	195	2
Other	520	5
Total	**10,041**	**100**

COMPETITORS

Casella Waste Systems	Waste Connections
Recology	Waste Connections US
Rumpke	Waste Industries USA
Safety-Kleen	Waste Management
WCA Waste	

HISTORICAL FINANCIALS

Company Type: Public

Income Statement

FYE: December 31

	REVENUE ($ mil.)	NET INCOME ($ mil.)	NET PROFIT MARGIN	EMPLOYEES
12/18	10,041	1,037	10.3%	36,000
12/17	10,042	1,278	12.7%	35,000
12/16	9,388	613	6.5%	33,000
12/15	9,115	750	8.2%	33,000
12/14	8,788	548	6.2%	31,000
Annual Growth	**3.4%**	**17.3%**	**—**	**3.8%**

2018 Year-End Financials

Debt ratio: 39.00%	No. of shares (mil.): 323
Return on equity: 13.00%	Dividends
Cash ($ mil.): 71	Yield: 2.0%
Current ratio: 1.00	Payout: 46.0%
Long-term debt ($ mil.): 7,647	Market value ($ mil.): 23,249

	STOCK PRICE ($) FY Close	P/E High/Low	PER SHARE ($) Earnings	Dividends	Book Value
12/18	72.00	24 20	3.00	1.00	25.00
12/17	68.00	18 15	4.00	1.00	24.00
12/16	57.00	32 24	2.00	1.00	23.00
12/15	44.00	21 18	2.00	1.00	22.00
12/14	40.00	27 20	2.00	1.00	22.00
Annual Growth	**15.7%**	**— —**	**19.9%**	**7.5%**	**2.9%**

Rite Aid Corp

While Rite Aid ranks a distant third (behind Walgreen and CVS) in the US retail drugstore business it nevertheless boasts a formidable presence with nearly 2500 drugstores in almost 20 states and the District of Columbia. Rite Aid stores generate roughly 70% of their sales from filling prescriptions while the rest comes from selling health and beauty aids convenience foods greeting cards and more including Rite Aid brand private-label products. Some 60% of all Rite Aid stores are freestanding more than half have drive-through pharmacies and more than 60% have a GNC store within them. Rite Aid sold some 1900 stores to Walgreens in 2018 for around $4 billion.

HISTORY

Wholesale grocer Alex Grass founded Rack Rite Distributors in Harrisburg Pennsylvania in 1958 to provide health and beauty aids and other sundries to grocery stores. He offered the same products at his first discount drugstore Thrif D Discount Center opened in 1962 in Scranton Pennsylvania. Four years later the company began placing pharmacies in its 36 stores. Rite Aid went public and adopted its current name in 1968 and the next year it made the first of many diverse acquisitions: Daw Drug Blue Ridge Nursing Homes and plasma suppliers Immuno Serums and Sero Genics.

Purchases in the 1970s included Sera-Tec Biologicals of New Jersey (blood plasma) and nearly 300 stores. By 1981 Rite Aid was the #3 drugstore

chain and sales exceeded $1 billion. In 1984 it bought the American Discount Auto Parts chain and Encore Books discount chain and spun off its wholesale grocery operation in 1984 as Super Rite retaining a 47% stake (sold 1989).

Acquisitions added almost 900 stores during the 1980s. Expansion costs eroded Rite Aid's profit margins and the company focused on integrating its buys in 1990.

As part of a major restructuring in 1994 the company began selling its non-drugstore assets. Also in 1994 Rite Aid acquired Pharmacy Card and Intell-Rx and merged the two to form Eagle Managed Care.

Martin Grass took Rite Aid's reins from his dad in 1995. That year the company agreed to buy Revco at the time the #2 drugstore operator but the deal was derailed by FTC and Department of Justice objections in 1996. Rite Aid bounced back and acquired Thrifty PayLess (with more than 1000 stores) for about $2.3 billion in 1996. The deal gave the company more than 3600 stores and a presence in the western US. Also in 1996 Rite Aid exited several markets. In 1998 it closed many smaller stores and bought PCS Health Systems (the #1 US pharmacy benefits manager) from drug maker Eli Lilly and merged its Eagle Managed Care division into PCS.

In 1999 after a Wall Street Journal investigation Rite Aid revealed that Martin Grass Alex Grass and other family members held stakes in several suppliers and real estate interests doing business with the company. That year Rite Aid partnered with General Nutrition Companies Inc. (GNC) and took a 25% stake in the Internet retailer drugstore.com. Later in 1999 Rite Aid began slashing its $5.1 billion debt by cutting corporate staff and selling off some stores in California and the Pacific Northwest. CEO Martin Grass resigned and a team of former Fred Meyer officers — led by Robert Miller — took over.

In 2000 the company secured $1 billion from Citibank to reduce debt and provide capital. In July 2000 the company announced it would restate profits that over the past two years had been inflated in excess of $1 billion. Later that year Rite Aid sold PCS Health Systems to pharmacy benefits manager Advance Paradigm for more than $1 billion (about $500 million less than what Rite Aid originally paid for it). Rite Aid announced plans in 2001 to expand GNC concessions to additional stores.

To raise cash Rite Aid sold large blocks of its drugstore.com stock trimming its original 25% stake to less than 10% by April 2002. Former chairman and CEO Martin Grass former general counsel and vice chairman Franklin Brown and former CFO Frank Bergonzi among others were indicted in June 2002 for allegedly falsifying Rite Aid's books.

In April 2003 former chairman and CEO Martin Grass agreed to pay nearly $1.5 million to settle a lawsuit in which shareholders alleged that Rite Aid's books were falsified inflating the stock's value. In June Grass and former CFO Franklyn Bergonzi both pleaded guilty to conspiracy to defraud shareholders. Eric Sorkin Rite Aid's former VP of pharmacy services pleaded guilty to conspiring to obstruct justice. The following month Rite Aid began mailing checks totaling nearly $140 million to thousands of its current and former shareholders damaged by the accounting scandal at the company. In October former chief counsel Franklin Brown was convicted of conspiracy and lying to the Securities and Exchange Commission among other charges.

Despite its high debt load Rite Aid reportedly made a $4 billion cash-and-stock offer for struggling rival Eckerd but lost out to CVS and

Canada's Jean Coutu Group who divvied up Eckerd in mid-2004.

In May 2004 Grass whose father founded Rite Aid struck a plea deal with prosecutors under which he was sentenced to eight years in prison. Also in May several other former company executives including Sorkin and ex-CFO Frank Bergonzi were sentenced in the accounting scandal. In June Rite Aid agreed to pay the US government $5.6 million (plus another $1.4 million to more than 20 states) to settle a federal lawsuit alleging the drugstore chain submitted false prescription claims to government insurance programs. In October former vice chairman Brown was sentenced to 10 years in prison the longest sentence of six Rite Aid officials charged in the accounting scandal.

CFO John Standley resigned in 2005 to join supermarket operator Pathmark Stores as its CEO. Standley joined Rite Aid as its CFO in 1999.

In April 2007 the company agreed to a store swap with California-based Longs Drug Stores. Under the terms of the agreement Rite Aid acquired six Longs stores in Northern California Oregon and Washington in exchange for giving Longs six of its stores in Nevada.

In its first major deal since its brush with bankruptcy in 1999 Rite Aid acquired more than 1850 Brooks and Eckerd drugstores and six distribution centers from Canada's Jean Coutu Group in a cash-and-stock deal valued at about $4 billion in June 2007.

Rite Aid exited the Las Vegas market in 2008 saying it was not a core market and had not contributed to overall results. It sold 27 of its Las Vegas stores to Walgreens. It March 2009 Rite Aid made a similar disposal of all seven of its stores in San Francisco and five locations in eastern Idaho when it sold them to Walgreen. Rite Aid said the stores were in areas with too light a store presence to operate efficiently. In July Rite Aid agreed to pay $500000 in consumer refunds to settle charges by the FTC that the company falsely advertised its Germ Defense line of cold-and-flu remedies as preventing illness or reducing the severity and duration of symptoms. The FTC said Rite Aid did not have evidence to support its Germ Defense product claims. Rite Aid founder Alex Grass died in August 2009 at the age of 82.

President and CEO John Standley added the title of chairman in mid-2012.

EXECUTIVES

Chairman And Ceo, John T. Standley, age 56, $1,184,500 total compensation
Svp Ny Metro Division, Mark Kramer, age 69
Sevp Cfo And Chief Administrative Officer, Darren W. Karst, age 59, $809,751 total compensation
Evp Merchandising And Distribution, Enio A. (Tony) Montini, age 67, $471,500 total compensation
President And Coo, Kermit R. Crawford, age 60
Coo Rite Aid Stores, Bryan Everett, age 46, $461,250 total compensation
Evp Marketing, David Abelman, age 60
Svp Mid-atlantic Division, Scott Bernard
Svp Western Division, Bill Romine
Svp Northeast Division, Derek Griffith
Svp And Cio, Steve Rempel
Evp Pharmacy, Jocelyn Konrad, age 49
Svp Southern Division, Bill Jackson
Svp General Counsel And Secretary, Jim Comitale
Svp And Chief Human Resources Officer, Ken Black
Pharmacy Manager, John Stanbrough
Rph, Rajesh Kumar
Vice President And Chief Information Security Officer, Robert Lautsch
Pharmacy Manager, Ana Miladinovic
Pharmacy Manager, Kari McCabe
Pharmacy Manager, Ngozi Onumonu

Group Vice President Real Estate, Raymond Payne
Pharmacy Manager, Mark Hanna
Vice President Pharmacy Operations, Scott Jacobson
Vice President Indirect Procurement, Frank Ho
Pharmacist Manager, Mandy Hoysan
Rph, Rangaraju Saripalli
Director Of Pharmacy Acquisitions, Todd Rossi
Group Vice President Category Management Administration Financial Analysis And Replenishment, Nate Newcomer
Vice President, Doug Riden
Vice President Litigation And Commercial Law, Ron Chima
Divisional Pharmacy Vice President Rite Aid Corp, Margherita Cardello
Pharmacy Manager, Viljan Kristollari
Senior Vice President Pharmacy Regulatory Affairs, Daniel Miller
Vice President Remodel Construction, Paul Davidovicz
Vice President Regulatory Affairs, Amanda Glover
Pharmacy Manager, Fiona Richardson
Pharmacy Manager, Rosa Azadian
Vice President Pharmacy Operations, Dennis Yoney
Vp Operations, Brian Dein
Pharmacy Manager, Tri Vo
Group Vp Loss Prevention, Bob Oberosler
Pharmacy Manager, Donald Brensinger
Pharmacy Manager, Nilay Parikh
Vice President Corporate Development, Paul Krueger
Vice President Store Operations, Tony Sadler
Rph, Fady Soliman
Pharmacy Manager, Farnaz Heidari
Pharmacy Manager, Vickie-hanh Le
Pharmacy Manager, Daniela Gurian
Pharmacy Manager, Katerina Stefanou
Pharmacy Manager, Kristina Mironichenko
Vice President Managed Care, Alison Farrell
Pharmacy Manager, Stephanie Eng
Pharmacy Manager, Diane Brown
Senior Vice President And Chief Communications Officer, Susan Henderson
Regional Vice President Administration, Nancy Wight-Tally
Vice President Pharmacy Services, Peter Bonnick
Vp Federal Affairs And Public Policy, Yong Choe
Pharmacy Manager, Helen Rey
Pharmacy Manager, Tina-shai Quallis
Pharmacy Manager, Dante Lanzillo
Pharmacy Manager, Amrita Prasad
Pharmacy Manager, Jugraj Johl
Pharmacist Manager, Denise Mercuri
Pharmacy Manager, Andre Leandro
Vice President Financial And Labor Analysis, Dave Markley
Vice President Pharmacy Services, Mike Podgurski
Pharmacy Manager, Joshua Maher
Regional Vice President, Kirt Patel
Vice President Distribution Operations, Robert Shovel
Group Vice President Category Management Consumables General Merchandise And Seasonal, Ted Williams
Vice President Private Brand Development, Bob Himler
Vp Human Resources, Michael Atcovitz
Pharmacy Manager, Bhaveer Dhanjee
Rph, Hanna Nguyen
Vice President Information Technology Development, Robert A Kostosky
Pharmacy Manager, Anand Mangu
Group Vice President And Controller, Brian Hoovers
Pharmacy Manager, Soheila Zahedpour
Pharmacy Manager, Marina Gerr
Group Vice President Pharmaceutical Purchasing And Clinical Services, Ernest Richardsen
Pharmacy Manager, Michael Kippenberger

Pharmacy Manager, Jill Watters
Auditors: Deloitte & Touche LLP

LOCATIONS

HQ: Rite Aid Corp
30 Hunter Lane, Camp Hill, PA 17011
Phone: 717 761-2633   **Fax:** 717 975-5905
Web: www.riteaid.com

2016 Stores

	No.
New York	604
California	580
Pennsylvania	537
Michigan	275
New Jersey	257
North Carolina	225
Ohio	224
Virginia	190
Georgia	179
Massachusetts	146
Maryland	140
Washington	139
Kentucky	116
West Virginia	104
Alabama	93
South Carolina	91
Tennessee	81
Maine	79
Connecticut	77
Oregon	72
New Hampshire	68
Louisiana	62
Rhode Island	44
Delaware	42
Vermont	37
Mississippi	26
Utah	22
Colorado	20
Idaho	13
Indiana	10
District of Columbia	7
Nevada	1
Total	**4,561**

PRODUCTS/OPERATIONS

2019 Sales

	$ mil.	% of total
Retail Pharmacy	15,757	72
Pharmacy Services	6,094	28
Inter-segment elimination	(211.3)	—
Total	**21,640**	**100**

2019 Sales

	% of total
Prescription drugs	66
General merchandise & other	18
Over-the-counter medications & personal care	11
Health & beauty aids	5
Total	**100**

Selected Merchandise and Services

Beverages
Convenience foods
Cosmetics
Designer fragrances
Greeting cards
Health and personal care products
Household items
Over-the-counter drugs
Photo processing
Prescription drugs
Private-label products
Seasonal merchandise
Vitamins and minerals

COMPETITORS

A&P	Kroger
BJ's Wholesale Club	Marc Glassman
CVS	Medicine Shoppe
Costco Wholesale	Publix
Dollar General	Safeway
Family Dollar Stores	Target Corporation
Kinney Drugs Inc.	Wal-Mart
Kmart	Walgreen

HISTORICAL FINANCIALS

Company Type: Public

Income Statement   FYE: March 2

	REVENUE ($ mil.)	NET INCOME ($ mil.)	NET PROFIT MARGIN	EMPLOYEES
03/19	21,640	(422)	—	53,100
03/18	21,529	943	4.4%	59,000
03/17*	32,845	4	0.0%	87,000
02/16	30,737	165	0.5%	88,000
02/15	26,528	2,109	8.0%	89,000
Annual Growth	(5.0%)	—	—	(12.1%)

*Fiscal year change

2019 Year-End Financials

Debt ratio: 46.00%	No. of shares (mil.): 54
Return on equity: (-30.00%)	Dividends
Cash ($ mil.): 144	Yield: —
Current ratio: 2.00	Payout: —
Long-term debt ($ mil.): 3,479	Market value ($ mil.): 39

	STOCK PRICE ($) FY Close	P/E High/Low	PER SHARE ($) Earnings	Dividends	Book Value
03/19	1.00	— —	(8.00)	0.00	22.00
03/18	2.00	0 0	18.00	0.00	30.00
03/17*	5.00	— —	(0.00)	0.00	12.00
02/16	8.00	3 2	3.00	0.00	11.00
02/15	8.00	0 0	42.00	0.00	1.00
Annual Growth	(45.0%)	— —	—	—	(108.9%)

*Fiscal year change

RiverSource Life Insurance Co

EXECUTIVES

Chb-pres, John R Worner
Rvp Insurance, Michele Turner
Executive Vice President Human Resources, Kelli Hunter
Auditors: PricewaterhouseCoopers LLP

LOCATIONS

HQ: RiverSource Life Insurance Co
1099 Ameriprise Financial Center, Minneapolis, MN 55474
Phone: 612 671-3131
Web: www.riversource.com

HISTORICAL FINANCIALS

Company Type: Public

Income Statement   FYE: December 31

	ASSETS ($ mil.)	NET INCOME ($ mil.)	INCOME AS % OF ASSETS	EMPLOYEES
12/18	110,073	905	0.8%	—
12/17	120,440	741	0.6%	—
12/16	114,053	686	0.6%	—
12/15	113,356	895	0.8%	—
12/14	118,136	965	0.8%	—
Annual Growth	(1.8%)	(1.6%)	—	—

2018 Year-End Financials

Debt ratio: —	No. of shares (mil.): 0
Return on equity: 24.00%	Dividends
Cash ($ mil.): 1,085	Yield: —
Current ratio: —	Payout: 83.0%
Long-term debt ($ mil.): —	Market value ($ mil.): —

RLI Corp

You might wonder what folks in Illinois know about earthquake insurance but as a specialty property/casualty insurer Peoria-based RLI knows how to write such policies. Through its subsidiaries the company mainly offers coverage for US niche markets — risks that are hard to place in the standard market and are otherwise underserved. It focuses on public and private companies as well as non-profit organizations. RLI's commercial property/casualty lines include products liability property damage marine cargo directors and officers liability medical malpractice and general liability. It also writes commercial surety bonds and a smattering of specialty personal insurance.

Operations

RLI's specialty commercial property/casualty operations are conducted through its RLI Insurance Mt. Hawley Insurance Contractors Bonding and Insurance Company and RLI Indemnity subsidiaries. Personal offerings account for small portion of RLI's revenues and include homeowners insurance in Hawaii home business coverage pet insurance and personal umbrella (supplemental property/casualty) policies.

Geographic Reach

While the company operates in all 50 US states the District of Columbia and Puerto Rico California is RLI's largest market accounting for about 20% of the company's premiums.

Sales and Marketing

RLI markets its products to brokers and independent agents through branch offices scattered across the US.

Financial Performance

Like many insurers RLI's finances took a negative hit from the economic turmoil of 2008 and 2009. The company improved its returns as of 2010 and hasn't looked back. In 2013 it reported a 7% increase in revenue from $661 million to $706 million due to increased net premiums especially in the casualty segment. New products also made strong contributions. Net income grew 33% from $103 million to $126 million on increased revenue and decline in losses. Cash from operations a category that has fluctuated for RLI improved by $99 million due to investments.

Strategy

The company has gradually expanded its range of products with an emphasis on property insurance. In 2012 RLI entered the recreational vehicle (RV) insurance market by forming an underwriting partnership with Recreation Insurance Specialists. In 2013 it saw growth in its casualty business in transportation professional liability umbrella and admitted package businesses.

Mergers and Acquisitions

In 2014 the company purchased 20% of Prime Holdings Insurance Services for $5.3 million. The Utah-based company sells excess and surplus lines insurance in 49 states through a network of brokers; it specializes in hard-to-place risks (underwater hotels English Channel swims bungee jumps from helicopters).

In 2012 RLI moved into the field of medical malpractice coverage through the acquisition of Rockbridge Underwriting Agency. Two years later it launched RLI Healthcare a healthcare liability division serving hospital systems long-term and outpatient care facilities and clinical research providers with surplus lines in all 50 states.

Company Background

Gerald Stephens founded the company in 1961 and served as its chairman from 2001 until his retirement in 2011.

EXECUTIVES

Vice President, Paul Dietrich
Chairman And Ceo, Jonathan E. Michael, age 65, $775,000 total compensation
President And Coo, Craig W. Kliethermes, age 54, $473,269 total compensation
Vp And Chief Investment Officer, Aaron P. Diefenthaler, age 45
Svp And Cfo, Thomas L. Brown, age 62, $417,308 total compensation
President Rli Transportation Division, Dan Meyer
Svp Operations Rli Product Divisions, Jennifer L. Klobnak, age 47, $298,462 total compensation
Vice President Information Technology, Murali Natarajan
Assistant Vice President Commercial, Martha Weissbaum
Vice President, Brent Flanigan
Avp Internal Audit Services, Patrick Ferrell
Assistant Vice President Specialty Markets, Paul V Harris
Vice President Ocean Marine, Lenny Pekola
Assistant Vice President Fidelity Group, Thomas Huber
Vpres Casualty Brokerage, Dennis Drees
Vice President Passenger Transportation, Tim Hathy
Vice President, Chris D Randall
Vice President Contract Surety, Bart Davis
Vice President, Terry Driggs
Senior Vice President, Blake Ahrens
Assistant Vice President Claims, Andrea Dean
Vice President General Counsel Corporate Secretary, Aniel O Kennedy
Vice President Commercial Specialty Auto Program, John Terlisner
Assistant Vice President, Brian Combs
Assistant Vice President Executive Products Group, Kerrick Porter
Vice President Operations, Richard W Quehl
Assistant Vice President Technology, Karl Flower
Vice President Communications, Greg Tiemeier
Vice President Finance, Jonathan Micheal
Vice President Underwriting, Carol Denzer
Vice President, Paul Vendetti
Assistant Vice President, Ted McGrath
Assistant Vice President, Philip Abellera
Vice President Underwriting, John Stenhouse
Vice President Business Development And Retention, Mike Haswell
Assistant Vice President, Don Johnson
Vice President And Healthcare Product Leader, Scott Ducey
Assistant Vice President Underwriting And Senior Business Analyst, Steven Cave
Assistant Vice President Surety And Director Surety Automation, Sandy Swinford
Assistant Vice President Underwriting, Brian Schick
Vice President, William J Irish
Vice President National Fidelity Practice Leader, Tom Huber
Vp Energy Casualty, Jeff Foering
Board Member, Barbara Allen
Board Member, Kaj Ahlmann
Board Member, Robert Viets
Board Member, Michael Angelina
Board Member, Charles Link
Auditors: DELOITTE & TOUCHE LLP

LOCATIONS

HQ: RLI Corp
9025 North Lindbergh Drive, Peoria, IL 61615
Phone: 309 692-1000   **Fax:** 309 692-1068
Web: www.rlicorp.com

PRODUCTS/OPERATIONS

2016 Revenues

	$ mil.	% of total
Net premiums earned		
Casualty	455	56
Property	152	19
Surety	122	15
Net investment income	53	6
Net realized gains	35	4
Total	**816**	**100**

Selected Products

Commercial
  Casualty
  Contractors bonding and insurance
  Executive products liability
  Marine
  Professional services
  Property
  Reinsurance
  Specialty programs
  Transportation
Personal
  Homeowners (Hawaii)
  Home business owners
  Personal umbrella
Surety Bonds

COMPETITORS

Arch Insurance Group
Baldwin & Lyons
CNA Financial
Chubb Limited
Crum & Forster
Great American Insurance Company
Great West Casualty
HCC Insurance
James River Group
Lancer Insurance
Lexington Insurance
Markel
Meadowbrook Insurance
Navigators
Philadelphia Insurance Companies
Safeco
Sompo International
The Hartford
Travelers Companies
United States Liability Insurance Group

HISTORICAL FINANCIALS

Company Type: Public

Income Statement
FYE: December 31

	ASSETS ($ mil.)	NET INCOME ($ mil.)	INCOME AS % OF ASSETS	EMPLOYEES
12/18	3,105	64	2.1%	912
12/17	2,947	105	3.6%	902
12/16	2,778	115	4.1%	943
12/15	2,737	138	5.0%	902
12/14	2,776	135	4.9%	882
Annual Growth	2.8%	(17.0%)	—	0.8%

2018 Year-End Financials

Debt ratio: 5.00%
Return on equity: 8.00%
Cash ($ mil.): 30
Current ratio: —
Long-term debt ($ mil.): —

No. of shares (mil.): 45
Dividends
  Yield: 1.0%
  Payout: 131.0%
Market value ($ mil.): 3,070

	STOCK PRICE ($) FY Close	P/E High/Low		PER SHARE ($) Earnings	Dividends	Book Value
12/18	69.00	55	40	1.00	2.00	18.00
12/17	61.00	26	21	2.00	3.00	19.00
12/16	63.00	27	21	3.00	3.00	19.00
12/15	62.00	20	15	3.00	3.00	19.00
12/14	49.00	31	13	3.00	4.00	20.00
Annual Growth	8.7%	—		(17.5%)	(15.7%)	(1.9%)

ROBERT BOSCH LLC

Robert Bosch LLC is your one-stop shop for German-engineered auto parts appliances and power tools. The North American subsidiary of German giant Robert Bosch GmbH Bosch LLC makes and markets automotive original equipment and aftermarket products industrial drive and control technology packaging technology power tools home appliances security and communication systems thermotechnology and software solutions. Robert Bosch LLC's biggest area Mobility Solutions makes products aimed at the next generation of automobiles particularly around connectivity automation and electrification. Active since 1906 Bosch LLC has grown to around 70 primary North American locations.

Operations

Robert Bosch LLC comprises four reporting segments Mobility Solutions Industrial Technology Consumer Goods and Energy and Building Technology.

The Mobility Solutions segment represents two-thirds of sales and is active in injection technology and powertrain peripherals for internal-combustion engines powertrain electrification steering systems safety and driver-assistance systems car multimedia vehicle-to-vehicle and vehicle-to-infrastructure communication repair-shop concepts and technology and services.

The Industrial Control segment produces drive and control products and packaging technology and generates around 10% of sales. The Consumer Goods segment accounts for around a fifth of sales and consists of Robert Bosch's US power tools home appliances business. Energy and Building Technology segment (5% of sales) outfits buildings with heating ventilation and lighting infrastructure.

Geographic Reach

Robert Bosch LLC accounts for 15% of global sales. It has around 70 primary facilities in the US Canada and Mexico

Financial Performance

Robert Bosch LLC's sales grew 6% to $14.5 billion in 2018.

Strategy

One of Robert Bosch's major markets North America continues to receive substantial investment. It has expanded Mobility Solutions plants in Charleston and Anderson South Carolina and a dishwasher factory and central distribution center in New Bern North Carolina. It has also broke earth in the construction of a $120 million plant in Celaya Mexico. The 225000 sq. ft. factory will produce electronic control units which are used in connected mobility for the American market. Most recently Bosch opened a technology and innovation hub in Guadalajara Mexico.

EXECUTIVES

President Bosch Security Systems Inc., Christopher P. Gerace
Cfo; Evp Controlling Finance And Administration, Maximiliane Straub
President And Ceo Bosch Rexroth Corporation, Berend Bracht
Regional President Gasoline Systems North America, Sujit Jain
Regional President Chassis Systems Control, D. Scott Winchip
Evp Original Equipment Sales Chrysler, Juergen Peters
Evp Original Equipment Sales Ford, Manfred Mueller
President And Ceo Bsh Home Appliances Corporation, Michael Traub
Regional President Automotive Electronics North America, Timothy (Tim) Frasier
Regional President Diesel Systems North America, Bernd Boisten
President, Mike Mansuetti
Regional President Robert Bosch Automotive Aftermarket Division, Odd Joergenrud
Evp Original Equipment Sales General Motors, Clesio Honma
Regional President Electrical Drives, Peter Denk
Regional President Starter Motors And Generators North America, Pres Lawhon
Regional President Bosch Engineering Group North America, Wayne (Keith) Andrews
President Robert Bosch Healthcare Systems Inc., Micha Kirchhoff
Vp Original Equipment Sales Chrysler, Paul Thomas
Vice President Business Development, Michael Barhaug
Vice President Purchasing, Scott Schafer
Vice President, Tim Williams
Vp Human Resources, Michael Mckenna
Vice President, Christine Zimmerman
Executive Vice President Finance And Administ, Cara Reynolds
Senior Vice President, Martin Kueper
Vice President, Heiko Weller
Vice President Of Sales, Doug Arnold
Vice President Automotive Aftermarket, Karen Folger
Vice President Of Information Technology, James Puttick
National Sales Manager, Robert Dono
Vice President Operations, Scott Langston
Vice President Of Sales, Rajesh Darji
Vice President Operations, Charles Miklich
Vice President Marketing And Business Strategy, Andreas Sambel
Vice President Sales Marketing And Aftermarket, Ross Long
Vice President Mergers And Acquisitions, Marcia Medendorp
Chairman, Werner Struth

LOCATIONS

HQ: ROBERT BOSCH LLC
2800 S 25TH AVE, BROADVIEW, IL 601554532
Phone: 248 876-1000
Web: WWW.BOSCHTECHINFO.COM

PRODUCTS/OPERATIONS

2019 Sales

	% of total
Mobility Solutions	66
Consumer Goods	18
Industrial Technology	10
Energy and Building Technology	6
Other	3
Total	**100**

Selected Products

Automotive Technology
  Aftermarket
  Alternators
  Brake pads
  Car audio products
  Diesel parts
  Filters
  Fuel pumps
  Ignition products
  Oxygen sensors
  Spark plugs
  Spark plug wire sets
  Starters
  Wiper blades
  Original equipment
  Actuators
  Braking and chassis systems

Car multimedia
Electrical systems
Electronic systems
Powertrain systems - diesel
Powertrain systems - gasoline
Consumer Goods and Building Technology
Household appliances
Cooktops
Dishwashers
Ovens
Washers and dryers
Power tools
Angle grinders
Belt sanders
Circular saws
Drill bits
Drills
Drywall drivers
Impact wrenches
Jigsaws
Orbit sanders/polishers
Planers
Reciprocating saws
Rotary hammers
Routers
Screwdriver bits and accessories
Wet/dry vacuums
Security Systems
Access control
Communications
Fire detection
Security management
Video surveillance
Thermotechnology
Indoor climate control (heating and cooling and hot
water production)
Industrial Technology
Drive and control
Assembly
Electric drives and controls
Gears
Hydraulics
Linear motion
Pneumatics
Packaging
Confectionary cosmetics and chemicals
Packaging machines
Packaging services
Pharmaceuticals
Production tools
Air assembly tools
Cordless assembly tools
DC electric assembly tools
Electric assembly tools
Solar Energy
Crystalline PV modules
Solar cells
Thin-film modules
Wafers

COMPETITORS

AISIN World Corp.	LG Electronics
Advanced Security &	Makita
Controls	Molins
DENSO America	Motorcar Parts
Dana	NGK Spark Plugs
Delphi Automotive	Neaton Auto Products
Systems	Stanley Black and
GE	Decker
Hitachi Automotive	Visteon
Systems Americas	Whirlpool

HISTORICAL FINANCIALS

Company Type: Private

Income Statement
FYE: December 31

	REVENUE ($ mil.)	NET INCOME ($ mil.)	NET PROFIT MARGIN	EMPLOYEES
12/14	10,474	181	1.7%	12,986
12/10	6,810	326	4.8%	—
12/09	5,464	59	1.1%	—
Annual Growth	13.9%	25.1%		—

Robert Half
International Inc.

Robert Half International carries the full load of personnel services. The company places temporary and permanent staff through eight divisions: Accountemps Robert Half Finance and Accounting Robert Half Legal OfficeTeam (general administrative) Robert Half Technology (information technology) Robert Half Management Resources (senior level professionals) and The Creative Group (advertising marketing and Web design). The firm also publishes job reports and surveys on the latest employment trends and annual salary guides to track pay trends and has an internal audit and risk consulting division in Protiviti. The US accounts for three-quarters of sales.

Operations

Robert Half operates in three business segments: temporary and consultant staffing risk consulting and internal audit services and permanent placement staffing.

Temporary and consulting is Robert Half's biggest business at roughly 75% of total sales. It provides specialized staffing in the accounting and finance administrative and office and information technology legal advertising marketing and web design fields.

Risk consulting & internal audit accounts some 15% of sales and provides business and technology risk consulting and internal audit services.

The Permanent place staffing segment brings in about 10% sales and provides full-time personnel in the accounting and finance administrative and office and information technology fields.

Geographic Reach

Headquartered in Menlo Park in California Robert Half's temporary and permanent staffing services business has some 325 offices in more than 40 states Washington DC and more than 15 international markets. Protiviti has more than 60 offices in some 25 states and 10 foreign countries. The firm's domestic segment accounts for about 75% of total sales.

Sales and Marketing

Robert Half recruits via direct marketing and print radio and internet advertising. Robert Half also has joint marketing agreements with many tech-related companies to coordinate joint mailings cooperative advertising and other promotions. The firm typically spends around $50 million on advertising annually.

Financial Performance

Robert Half returned to strong sales growth in 2018 after an interruption in 2017 in which revenue grew less than 1%.

In 2018 the company's sales grew 10% to $5.8 billion — a new high — amid strong performances in all three reportable segments. Growth was strongest internationally particularly in Europe with international sales up 2 percentage points to 24%. Robert Half's temporary and consultant staffing services realized higher hourly rates and higher hours worked by temporary staff.

Robert Half's net income surged 49% to $434.3 million thanks to expanded gross margins and a reduction in income taxes. Gross margins in the temporary and consultant staffing segment were boosted by higher bill-pay spreads and conversion revenue rising from 37.2% to 37.6%. The risk consulting and internal audit segment's gross margins fell due to higher pay rates for professional staff and headcount.

Robert Half's cash on hand fell $18.2 million during 2018 ending the year at $276.6 million.

The company's operations generated $572.3 million while its investing activities used $88.5 million and its financing used $490.1 million. Thanks to healthy operating cash flows Robert Half returned a ton of cash to shareholders in 2018 in the shape of share repurchases ($353.5 million) and dividends ($136.4 million). Capital expenditures were $42.5 million by comparison.

Strategy

Robert Half prefers to grow organically rather than by making material acquisitions. The majority of Robert Half's capital spending in the last few years was for technological infrastructure and software. The firm has recently completed the installation upgrades to its enterprise resource planning and project management applications and it continues to invest in further digital initiatives to improve its service offerings to clients and candidates. In recent years strong performances and healthy operating cash flows have allowed the board to reward shareholders generously. It disbursed more than $1.1 billion on dividends and share repurchases between 2016 and 2018.

Company Background

Robert Half was founded in 1948 by Bob and Maxine Half. In early 1970s Robert Half opens its first international branch in London UK. Around the same time it also launched Accountemps a professional staffing division. Max Messmer purchased Robert Half in 1986; it floated on the New York Stock Exchange in 1990.

HISTORY

Robert Half founded Robert Half Inc. in 1948 as an employment agency for accountants. He developed Accountemps on the side to supply firms with accountants and other finance professionals on a temporary basis. His concept was a hit and Half became known as a pioneer in the specialized employment services industry. He started franchising his business nationwide. The temp industry grew slowly in the 1960s and 1970s until the 1980s brought a rapid expansion. By 1985 there were 150 independent Accountemps and Robert Half franchises.

Harold "Max" Messmer joined the company in 1985 for what would prove to be a tumultuous first couple of years. In 1986 Boothe Financial Corporation bought all of Robert Half's outstanding stock and Messmer launched a program to buy all the Robert Half franchises. A year later Boothe sold Robert Half which then went public as Robert Half International placing Messmer at the helm as CEO and president.

EXECUTIVES

Evp Corporate Development, Robert W. Glass, age 60, $245,000 total compensation

Vice Chairman President And Cfo, M. Keith Waddell, age 62, $265,000 total compensation

Chairman And Ceo, Harold M. Messmer, age 73, $525,000 total compensation

President And Coo Staffing Services, Paul F. Gentzkow, age 63, $265,000 total compensation

Evp Chief Administration Officer And Treasurer, Michael C. Buckley, age 53, $265,000 total compensation

Svp And Cio, Sean Perry

Vice President And Associate General Counsel, Ava Chan

Regional Vice President, Tama Emery

Regional Vice President, Sherri Bohlke

Vice President Perm Placement, John Bresnahan

Regional Vice President, Paul Flaharty

Division Director Assistant Vice President Accountemps, Aja Romain

Assistant Vice President, Isaac Polanco

Regional Vice President, Joe Gonzales

Regional Vice President, Alan Reisinger
Vice President, Shawn Surkosky
Vice President, Antoine Roberts
Senior Vice President, Robin Cohen
Assistant Vice President And Division Director Robert Half Finance And Accounting, Todd Ison
Vice President Tss Strategic Accounts, Jimmy Holbrook
Vice President Finance And Accounting Permanent Placement Services, Tracy Kaszuba
Chicago Region Vice President, Ryan Skubis
Vice President Staffing Recruiting, Joseph Abbondante
Vice President Technology Sales, Joey Langone
Senior Regional Vice President, Phil Willingham
Regional Vice President, Michelle Reisdorf
Vice President, Justin Berg
Regional Vice President, Mary Kim
Regional Vice President Robert Half Technology And The Creative Group, Nicole Sims
Vice President Major Accounts, Sheron Hindley-smith
Vice President Enterprise Solutions, John Wallace
Avp Division Director, Shawna Dunn
Regional Vice President, Jennifer Elmore
Assistant Vice President, Nelvin Moss
Assistant Vice President Senior Staffing Manager, David Song
Senior Regional Vice President, Deborah Bottineau
Vice President, Susan Chesney
Evp Professional Staffing Services, Andrew Denka
Assistant Vice President, Kimberly Kasper
Senior Vice President, Melissa Shipman
Vice President Managed Technology Solutions, Jason Schnur
Vice President Technology Staffing Services, Tim Johnson
Vice President Professional Staffing Services, Sandra Giberson
Auditors: PricewaterhouseCoopers LLP

LOCATIONS

HQ: Robert Half International Inc.
2884 Sand Hill Road, Suite 200, Menlo Park, CA 94025
Phone: 650 234-6000
Web: www.roberthalf.com

2018 sales

	$ mil.	% of total
Domestic	4,434	76
Foreign	1,367	24
Total	**5,800**	**100**

PRODUCTS/OPERATIONS

2018 sales

	$ mil.	% of total
Temporary & consultant staffing	4,331	74
Risk consulting & internal audit services	958	17
Permanent placement staffing	512	9
Total	**5,800**	**100**

Selected Operating Units

Accountemps (temporary accounting and finance personnel)
The Creative Group (advertising marketing and Web design)
OfficeTeam (temporary administrative and office personnel)
Protiviti (internal audit and risk consulting)
Robert Half Finance and Accounting (temporary accounting and finance personnel)
Robert Half Legal (temporary and full-time legal support personnel)
Robert Half Management Resources (senior-level accounting and finance personnel)
Robert Half Technology (temporary and contract IT personnel)

COMPETITORS

Adecco	Kelly Services
Deloitte Consulting	Kforce
Ernst & Young Global	ManpowerGroup
General Employment	PricewaterhouseCoopers
Enterprises	Randstad Holding
Headway Corporate	Solomon Page
Resources	Winston Resources
KPMG	

HISTORICAL FINANCIALS

Company Type: Public

Income Statement				FYE: December 31
	REVENUE ($ mil.)	NET INCOME ($ mil.)	NET PROFIT MARGIN	EMPLOYEES
12/18	5,800	434	7.5%	231,600
12/17	5,267	291	5.5%	228,600
12/16	5,250	343	6.5%	231,400
12/15	5,095	358	7.0%	236,000
12/14	4,695	306	6.5%	225,000
Annual Growth	5.4%	9.2%	—	0.7%

2018 Year-End Financials

Debt ratio: 0.00%	No. of shares (mil.): 119
Return on equity: 40.00%	Dividends
Cash ($ mil.): 277	Yield: 2.0%
Current ratio: 2.00	Payout: 31.0%
Long-term debt ($ mil.): 0	Market value ($ mil.): 6,811

	STOCK PRICE ($) FY Close	P/E High/Low	PER SHARE ($) Earnings	Dividends	Book Value
12/18	57.00	22 15	4.00	1.00	9.00
12/17	56.00	24 18	2.00	1.00	9.00
12/16	49.00	18 13	3.00	1.00	9.00
12/15	47.00	23 17	3.00	1.00	8.00
12/14	58.00	26 17	2.00	1.00	7.00
Annual Growth	(0.5%)	— —	12.1%	11.7%	5.3%

ROBERT W. BAIRD & CO. INCORPORATED

Employee-owned Robert W. Baird & Co. bringsÂ midwestern sensibility to the high-flying world of investment banking. The company offers brokerage asset management and investment banking services to middle-market corporations institutional clients and wealthy individuals and families.Â Its investment banking activities include underwriting and distributing corporate securities mergers and acquisition advisory and institutional sales and trading. The company also conducts equity research on more than 600 US firms.Â Baird manages more than $97 billion in client assets.

Operations

The companyÂ manages aboutÂ 10 bond and equity mutual funds: Baird Advisors manages fixed income investments while Baird Investment Management handles the equities side. Baird also invests in private equity and venture capital.

Geographic Reach

The firm has more than 100Â officesÂ in North America Asia and Europe where it ownsÂ 48% of Baird UK. More than half of Baird's locations areÂ wealth management offices in the US.

Sales and Marketing

Baird is the marketing name for Robert W. Baird & Co. Incorporated and its subsidiaries and affiliates worldwide.

Financial Performance

The company's revenues increased by 9% in 2011 and net incomeÂ grew by 2%.

Strategy

The driving forces for the company's growth have been its wealth management and investment banking operations. Unlike many financial services firms Baird has been adding staff and opening new offices in the US.

The company has also turned to the East for its fortunes. Its private equity group recently has an office in Shanghai hoping to capitalize on China's increasingly business-friendly environment.Â The outpost focuses on small high-growth businesses that have been overlooked by other venture capitalists.Â Baird hasÂ also expanded its investment banking operations in the region.

In 2012 Baird formed a strategic alliance with Axis Capital the investment banking subsidiary of Axis Bank with an initial focus on cross-border mergers and acquisitions between India and Europe and India and the US.

Company Background

Founded in 1919 Baird had been majority-owned by Northwestern Mutual since 1982. However employees bought back the company's stock in a series of purchases that culminated in 2004.

EXECUTIVES

Coo, Russell P. (Russ) Schwei
Chief Investment Officer, Mary Ellen Stanek
Cfo, Terrance P. (Terry) Maxwell
President Private Wealth Management, Michael J. (Mike) Schroeder
Director Fixed Income Capital Markets, Patrick S. (Pat) Lawton
Managing Director And Director Institutional Equity Services, William W. (Bill) Mahler
Co-head Global Investment Banking, Brian S. Doyal
President And Ceo, Steven G. (Steve) Booth
Co-head Global Investment Banking, Brian McDonagh
Director Risk Management, Mark A. Roble
Managing Partner Baird Capital, Gordon G. Pan
Head Global Equities And Director Equity Research, Jon A. Langenfeld
Cio, Timothy (Tim) Byrne
Senior Vice President, Jay Schwister
Vice President, Mark Zalewski
Vice President, Peter Klode
Vice President Vice President Administration, Thomas Seidcheck
Vice President, Joseph G Verdi
Senior Vice President, Dustin Hutter
Vice President, Florian Stoeger
Senior Vice President, Karen Heintz
Vice President Technology Product Manager, Lesley Augustine
Vice President, Tom Coburn
Senior Vice President Of Wealth Management Office, Paul McWane
Senior Vice President Supervisory Analyst, Keith Dorris
Vice President Information Technology Architect, Jim Cornelius
Vice President, Charles Galarza
Vice President, Robert Ferriman
Senior Vice President, Peter Hammond
Vice President, Tim Duchow
Vice President, John W Diemer
Vice President Financial Analyst, Lori Jackson
Vp, Owen Wrassman
Senior Vice President Investments, Cory Davis
Senior Vice President, Jayson C Bales

Senior Vice President And Senior Portfolio Manager, Daniel Tranchita
Senior Vice President, Michael Chorley
Vice President, Janet Holsclaw
Vice President, Marla Regan
First Vice President Purchase And Sales, Dean Markofski
Vice President, Charles Narmi
Vice President, Dalena Welkomer
Vice President, Adrianne Limjoco
Vice President, Ryan Unthank
Assistant Vice President, Tonia G Morris
Senior Vice President, Richard Palm
Vice President, Dale Rudow
Assistant Vice President Compliance Officer, Heidi Mclemore
Senior Vice President, Mark Kindler
Assistant Vice President Private Asset Management, Robert Filetti
Vice President, Mike Monfeli
Vice President Financial Advisor, Dan Koth
Vice President Private Wealth Management, Rebecca Ross
Senior Vice President Private Wealth Management, Matthew H Schmitt
Senior Vice President, Shawn B Smith
Senior Vice President Public Relations, Angela Pittman Taylor
Assistant Vice President, Dominic Burrescia
Vice President, Abhishek Pulakanti
Senior Vice President, Douglas Stencel
First Vice President Tech And Systems, Dennis Weishan
Vice President Financial Advisor, Jeff Pedersen
First Vice President, Guy Sawyer
Vice President And Art Director, Virginia Sunu
Vice President, Mike Malone
Vice President Wealth Management, Theresa Rynaski
Vice President Transition Process Manager, Denise Renner
Vice President Information Technology Project Services, Jim Whittet
Senior Vice President, Chuck Cairns
Vice President, Frank Downey
Vice President, Dawn Decicco
Vice President Financial Advisor, Blaine Gibson
Assistant Vice President And Marketing Specialist, Karen Sweeney
First Vice President, Bryan Fiene
Vice President, Mary E Levar
Vice President, Michael Halloran
Assistant Vice President, Genise Brandt
Private Equity Finance Manager Vice President, Erin Jelenchick
Senior Vice President, Rob Zwiebel
Assistant Vice President, Heather Melzer
Assistant Vice President, Kathy Cobb
Vice President Cash Management, Stephanie Ray-kuczynski
Senior Vice President Private Wealth Management, Bryan Sampson
Senior Vice President Internal Audit Director, David Cook
Vice President Investments, Thomas Olson
Senior Vice President Director Of Application Development, Jason Montague
Vice President Investment Banking, Christopher Hildreth
Vice President, Alex Ballantine
Vice President Portfolio Analyst, Aaron Benson
Vice President, Suzanne King
Vice President, John P Campbell
Senior Vice President, Gail Bivens-rose
Vice President, Jessica Stamm
First Vice President, Terry Lineberger
Vice President And Financial Advisor, Jon Bolton
Vice President, Rich Nigro
Senior Vice President Investments, Ronald Christian

Vice President, Marcy Finley
Senior Vice President, Mike Parrott
Vice President Equity Research, Mircea Dobre
Senior Vice President, David Schwarz
Vice President, Greg Pauly
Vice President Senior Research Associate, Luke Junk
Senior Vice President, Mark Falci
Vice President, Chase Hinderstein
Vice President, Joe Vruwink
Vice President, Brian Ellenbecker
Assistant Vice President, Stacey Leigh
Assistant Vice President, Deanne Soetenga
Vice President, Frederick Jetter
Vice President Private Wealth Management, Robert King
Assistant Vice President, Bernadette Ross
Vice President Investment Banking, Matthew Tingler
Vice President, Ryan Cox
Senior Vice President, Douglas Crandall
Senior Vice President, Timothy Butler
Vice President, Randall McLaughlin
Vice President, Richard Roesch
Senior Vice President, Orlando C Montesino
First Vice President Research, Ron Freisleben
Vice President Private Wealth Management, Phyllis Lovrien
Vice President Investment Banking, John Sun
Vice President, Brian Kelso
Vice President, Justin Albert
Assistant Vice President Andamp; Administrative Office M, Sandra Gary
Vice President Investments, John Barnefield
Senior Vice President, Andy Roed
Vice President, Gavin Amato
Vice President Private Wealth Management, Larry Magid
Vice President Senior Estate Planner, Rick Holman
Assistant Vice President, Brian Hanrahan
Vice President, Dawn Mattrisch
Vice President, Alex Lawhorn
Vice President Investments, Frances D Bobbie
Assistant Vice President, Ginny Moye
Vice President, Peter Philpott
Senior Vice President, Mary Howard
Vice President, James Cain
Vice President Private Wealth Management, Wes Oliver
Assistant Vice President, Dale Jacques
Senior Vice President, Gerald Jarzabek
Senior Vice President, Jan Bayle
Assistant Vice President, Mary Zavaglia
Assistant Vice President, Judie Meriweather
Vice President Pwm, Clay Ryan
Assistant Vice President, Mary Walters
First Vice President, Thomas Hayden
Senior Vice President And Associate General Counsel, Andrew Ketter
Vice President Resources Consultant Business Partner Human Capital, Lynn Rudolph
Senior Vice President Investments, Lewis Krinsky
Assistant Vice President, Michelle Hernandez
Vice President, Alice Ambrowiak

LOCATIONS

HQ: ROBERT W. BAIRD & CO. INCORPORATED 777 E WISCONSIN AVE FL 29, MILWAUKEE, WI 532025391
Phone: 414 765-3500
Web: WWW.RWBAIRD.COM

PRODUCTS/OPERATIONS

Business Groups
Asset Management
Equity Capital Markets
Fixed Income Capital Markets
Private Equity
Private Wealth Management

COMPETITORS

Citigroup Global Markets	Piper Jaffray
Cowen Group	Raymond James Financial
Goldman Sachs	Stephens
Greenhill	Stifel Financial
Jefferies Group	Thomas Weisel Partners
Morgan Stanley	William Blair

HISTORICAL FINANCIALS
Company Type: Private

Income Statement — FYE: December 31

	ASSETS ($ mil.)	NET INCOME ($ mil.)	INCOME AS % OF ASSETS	EMPLOYEES
12/09	2,064	42	2.0%	5,215
12/08	1,080	37	3.4%	—
12/07	1,713	50	2.9%	—
Annual Growth	9.8%	(8.6%)	—	—

Robinson (C.H.) Worldwide, Inc.

C.H. Robinson Worldwide (CHRW) keeps merchandise moving. A third-party logistics (3PL) provider the company contracts with more than 73000 carriers including trucks trains ships and airplanes to arrange freight transportation for its 120000-plus customers in the the food and beverage manufacturing and retail industries. Using its proprietary Navisphere platform CHRW can handle more than 45 million digital transaction per month and close to 20 million shipments per year. Besides transportation the company also offers logistics supply chain management and transportation management services. C.H. Robinson operates worldwide but generates about 90% of total revenue in the US.

HISTORY

In the early 1900s Charles H. Robinson began a produce brokerage in Grand Forks North Dakota. Robinson entered a partnership in 1905 with Nash Brothers the leading wholesaler in North Dakota and the company C.H. Robinson was born.

Robinson became president but soon relinquished control under mysterious circumstances (rumor had it he ran off with Annie Oakley). H. B. Finch took charge and by 1913 a new company Nash Finch became C.H. Robinson's sole owner.

As a subsidiary C.H. Robinson primarily procured produce for Nash Finch which helped it expand into Illinois Minnesota Texas and Wisconsin. To avoid FTC scrutiny over preferential treatment Nash Finch split CHR in two: C.H. Robinson Co. owned by C.H. Robinson employees which sold produce to Nash Finch warehouses; and C.H. Robinson Inc. owned by Nash Finch.

After WWII the interstate highway system and refrigerated trucks changed the industry. No longer dependent on railroads C.H. Robinson began charging for truck brokerage of perishables. The two companies formed by the 1940s split reunited under the C.H. Robinson name in the mid-1960s; Nash Finch kept a 25% stake in the company and sold the rest to employees. Not surprisingly Nash Finch wanted to divert C.H. Robinson profits to its other businesses so in 1976 C.H. Robinson employees bought out Nash Finch.

The next year D. R. "Sid" Verdoorn was named president and Looe Baker became chairman. They focused on increasing C.H. Robinson's data-processing capability and adding branch offices. In 1980 the Motor Carrier Act deregulated the transportation industry and C.H. Robinson entered the freight-contracting business acting as a middleman for all types of goods. The company grew rapidly from about 30 offices in 1980 to more than 60 in 1990.

As part of its overall effort to become a full-service provider C.H. Robinson formed its Intermodal Division (more than one mode of transport) in 1988. It also established an information services division (1991) and bought fruit juice concentrate distributor Daystar International (1993). By this time the company was working with more than 14000 shippers and moving more than 500000 shipments a year.

Meanwhile C.H. Robinson had ventured overseas with the launch of its international division in 1989. It entered Mexico in 1990 and added airfreight operations and international freight forwarding through the 1992 purchase of C.S. Green International. In 1993 C.H. Robinson picked up a 30% stake in French motor carrier Transeco (acquiring the rest later) and opened offices in Mexico Chile and Venezuela.

The company went public in 1997 and became C.H. Robinson Worldwide (CHRW). The next year Verdoorn who was CEO assumed the additional role of chairman. The following year the company acquired Argentina's Comexter transportation group to gain market share in South America and it expanded its European operation in 1999 through the purchase of Norminter a French third-party logistics provider. Much closer to home CHRW bought Eden Prairie-based Preferred Translocation Systems a logistics provider to LTL carriers and Chicago-based transportation provider American Backhaulers.

In 2000 CHRW partnered with PaperExchange.com Inc. the global e-business marketplace for the pulp and paper industry to provide an exclusive logistics service to PaperExchange.com members. CHRW continued to expand in 2002 with the purchase of Miami-based Smith Terminal Transportation Services. Verdoorn stepped down as CEO that year and company president John Wiehoff was promoted to replace him. Verdoorn retired at the end of 2006 and Wiehoff succeeded him as chairman.

The company acquired three US-based produce sourcing and marketing companies — FoodSource Inc. FoodSource Procurement and Epic Roots — in 2004 for a reported $270 million. That year CHRW added seven offices in China by acquiring a Dalian-based freight forwarder and in 2005 it gained operations in Germany Italy and the US by buying two freight forwarding companies Hirdes Group Worldwide and Bussini Transport. Also in 2005 CHRW bought US-based freight broker Payne Lynch & Associates as well as an India-based freight forwarder Triune. The following year (2006) the company acquired US-based LXSI Services a specialist in domestic airfreight and expedited ground transportation management that had gross revenue of about $25 million.

In mid-2008 CHRW acquired Transera International Holdings a project forwarding business based in Canada. Transera has office locations in Canada Dubai Singapore and the US and has annual revenues of about $125 million.

In 2009 the company purchased London-based Walker Logistics Overseas an international freight forwarder serving primarily the electronics telecommunications medical sporting goods and military industries. The acquisition expanded its capabilities in Asia-to-Europe trade and brought two key distribution gateways — London and Amsterdam. CHRW then expanded its produce distribution business even further in 2009 by opening a European-based produce sourcing company in France which will focus on bringing fresh produce from France Italy and Spain to North and South America Europe Asia and Middle Eastern countries. That same year CHRW acquired certain assets of International Trade & Commerce (ITC) a US customs brokerage company that specializes in warehousing distribution and services between the US and Mexico. Also in 2009 the company bought Rosemont Farms as well as Quality Logistics which provides logistics for produce transportation; both companies are based in Florida.

In 2010 CHRW expanded its transportation management services to India by building a new facility and control tower operations. The India-based facility was established to serve customers in South and Southeast Asia as well as in Pakistan and the Middle East.

CHRW divested its former payment services segment T-Chek (only 1% of total sales in 2012) in October 2012 to Electronic Funds Source LLC for $303 million in cash. The T-Chek unit provided such services as funds transfer and fuel purchasing management and CHRW made the deal to focus on its core transportation and logistics services.

In late 2012 CHRW acquired Phoenix International a provider of international ocean air and customs brokerage freight forwarding services. CHRW bought Phoenix for nearly $572 million in cash and roughly $63.5 million in newly-issued CHRW stock in a deal that sizably enhanced its international freight forwarding capabilities.

During that same time period CHRW swallowed up Apreo Logistics S.A. a freight forwarding firm based in Poland. The acquisition strengthened the company's toehold in Europe and further diversified its modal offering.

EXECUTIVES

Cio, Chad M. Lindbloom, $590,000 total compensation
Chairman President And Ceo, John P. Wiehoff, $1,167,000 total compensation
Cfo, Andrew C. Clarke, $525,000 total compensation
President Robinson Fresh, James P. (Jim) Lemke, $210,000 total compensation
Chief Commercial Officer, Christopher J. (Chris) O'Brien, $500,000 total compensation
President Asia, Andy Wang
Vp Global Forwarding North America, Michael J. (Mike) Short, $500,000 total compensation
Vp Management Services, Jordan T. Kass
President North American Surface Transportation, Robert C. Biesterfeld
President Europe, Jeroen Eijsink
Vice President Key Account Manager, Jay Commesser
Vice President Global Forwarding Sales, Matt Mcinerney
Vice President Global Accounts, Richard Kapsner
National Account Manager, Jen Theisen
Vice President, Terry Bigaouette
Vice President Information Technology, Steve Enberg
National Account Manager, Andy Hutson
National Account Manager, Matt Lapolice
Vice President And General Mgr, Rob Pierson
National Account Manager, Michelle Clayton
Vice President Asia Global Forwarding, John Chen
Vice President Global Sales, Brian Tonn
Vice President Investor Relations And Treasury, Robert Houghton
Vp Ir And Treasury, Bob Houghton
Vice President Oceana, Andrew Coldrey
Vice President Corporate Business Development, Francisco Guzman

Treasurer, Troy A Renner, age 55
Board Member, Trey Bullard
Board Member, James Stake
Board Member, Scott Anderson
Auditors: DELOITTE & TOUCHE LLP

LOCATIONS

HQ: Robinson (C.H.) Worldwide, Inc.
14701 Charlson Road, Eden Prairie, MN 55347
Phone: 952 937-8500   **Fax:** 952 937-6714
Web: www.chrobinson.com

2017 Sales

	$ mil.	% of total
United States	12,865	87
Other locations	2,004	13
Total	**14,869**	**100**

PRODUCTS/OPERATIONS

2017 Sales

By Segment	$ mil.	% of total
NAST	10,191	65
Robinson Fresh	2,583	14
Global Forwarding	2,171	17
All Other & Corporate	602	4
Eliminations	(678.0)	-
Total	**14,869**	**100**

2017 Sales

By Product	$ mil.	% of total
Transportation	13,503	91
Sourcing	1,366	11
Total	**14,869**	**100**

Selected Products
Navisphere Vision
Navisphere Carrier
Navisphere Driver

Selected Services
Air
Intermodal
Less-than-truckload
Logistics
    Customs brokerage
    Transportation management services
    Warehousing services
Ocean
Truckload

COMPETITORS

ALC	Hub Group
APL Logistics	J.B. Hunt
BNSF Logistics	Kuehne + Nagel
CEVA Logistics	International
Cass Information	Landstar Inway
Systems	MIQ Logistics
Chiquita Brands	Panalpina
Comdata	Penske Truck Leasing
CorTrans Logistics	Ryder System
DHL	Schneider Logistics
Dole Food	TLC
Exel	Transplace
Expeditors	UPS Supply Chain
FedEx Trade Networks	Solutions
Fresh Del Monte	
Produce	

HISTORICAL FINANCIALS

Company Type: Public

Income Statement				FYE: December 31
	REVENUE ($ mil.)	NET INCOME ($ mil.)	NET PROFIT MARGIN	EMPLOYEES
12/18	16,631	665	4.0%	15,262
12/17	14,869	505	3.4%	15,074
12/16	13,144	513	3.9%	14,125
12/15	13,476	510	3.8%	13,159
12/14	13,470	450	3.3%	11,521
Annual Growth	5.4%	10.3%	—	7.3%

2018 Year-End Financials

Debt ratio: 30.00%
Return on equity: 44.00%
Cash ($ mil.): 379
Current ratio: 2.00
Long-term debt ($ mil.): 1,341

No. of shares (mil.): 137
Dividends
  Yield: 2.0%
  Payout: 42.0%
Market value ($ mil.): 11,544

	STOCK PRICE ($) FY Close	P/E High/Low		PER SHARE ($) Earnings	Dividends	Book Value
12/18	84.00	21	17	5.00	2.00	12.00
12/17	89.00	25	18	4.00	2.00	10.00
12/16	73.00	22	17	4.00	2.00	9.00
12/15	62.00	22	17	4.00	2.00	8.00
12/14	75.00	25	17	3.00	1.00	7.00
Annual Growth	2.9%	—	—	11.6%	7.1%	12.9%

HISTORICAL FINANCIALS

Company Type: Public

Income Statement				FYE: September 30
	REVENUE ($ mil.)	NET INCOME ($ mil.)	NET PROFIT MARGIN	EMPLOYEES
09/19	6,695	696	10.4%	23,000
09/18	6,666	536	8.0%	23,000
09/17	6,311	826	13.1%	22,000
09/16	5,880	730	12.4%	22,000
09/15	6,308	828	13.1%	22,500
Annual Growth	1.5%	(4.2%)	—	0.6%

2019 Year-End Financials

Debt ratio: 37.00%
Return on equity: 69.00%
Cash ($ mil.): 1,018
Current ratio: 2.00
Long-term debt ($ mil.): 1,956

No. of shares (mil.): 116
Dividends
  Yield: 2.0%
  Payout: 46.0%
Market value ($ mil.): 19,067

	STOCK PRICE ($) FY Close	P/E High/Low		PER SHARE ($) Earnings	Dividends	Book Value
09/19	165.00	32	24	6.00	4.00	3.00
09/18	188.00	49	38	4.00	4.00	13.00
09/17	178.00	28	18	6.00	3.00	21.00
09/16	122.00	22	16	6.00	3.00	15.00
09/15	101.00	21	16	6.00	3.00	17.00
Annual Growth	12.9%	—	—	(1.1%)	10.5%	(32.7%)

Rockwell Automation, Inc.

EXECUTIVES

Chb-Pres-Ceo, Blake D Moret
Sr V Pres-Cfo, Patrick Goris
Sr V Pres-Cto, Sujeet Chand
Sr V Pres-General Counsel-Sec, Rebecca W House
V Pres-Treas, Steven W Etzel
V Pres-Contrl, David M Dorgan
Hw Engineering Manager, Mark Bjerke
Director, Mike Sparger
Senior Project Engineer, Pete Klein
Global Program Manager In, Rob Swim
Human Resources, Roy Schultz
Auditors: DELOITTE & TOUCHE LLP

LOCATIONS

HQ: Rockwell Automation, Inc.
  1201 South Second Street, Milwaukee, WI 53204
Phone: 414 382-2000
Web: www.rockwellautomation.com

COMPETITORS

ABB	Mitsubishi Corp.
Danaher	OMRON
Dematic SARL	Schneider Electric
Eaton	Select Business
Emerson Electric	Solutions
FANUC	Siemens AG
Hitachi	Toshiba
Honeywell ACS	Weiss Instrument
Invensys	Wonderware
Metso	Yokogawa Electric

Roper Technologies Inc

Roper Technologies is an industrial manufacturer and technology company providing a diverse set of offerings such as industrial controls water meter reading products and measurement instrumentation as well as application management software. Its business segments include RF Technology (toll and traffic systems RFID card readers and software) Medical and Scientific Imaging (digital imaging products and software) Industrial Technology (pumps leak testing fluid measurement) and Energy Systems and Controls (controls and sensors testing and inspection equipment). Roper's lines are used in niche markets engaged in RF (radio frequency) water energy research and medical education transportation and security applications. The company targets end-markets seeking value-added engineered products. About 80% of total sales come from the US.

HISTORY

George Roper founded the company in 1919 in Rockford Illinois to make gas stoves and gear pumps. In the late 1950s the stove works were spun off to Sears as the Roper Corporation and the pump-making operations were moved to Georgia. Roper was a public company until a 1981 leveraged buyout (a takeover of a company using borrowed funds.) UK-born Derrick Key who joined Roper in 1982 became CEO in 1991. The company went public again the next year as Roper Industries.

During the 1990s Roper grew by acquisitions both at home and abroad. However it gained entry into Eastern Europe in 1993 by winning a seven-year contract worth $350 million with Russian gas czar OAO Gazprom to install advanced control systems across Russia's vast pipeline system.

The company added digital-imaging and analytical systems for electron microscopes in 1996 by purchasing Gatan International a California company with branches in Germany and the UK. Roper's 1997 purchases included Industrial Data Systems (leak-testing equipment Utah); Petrotech (systems integration for fluid-control products; Louisiana with an Indonesian unit); and Princeton Instruments (spectral and imaging cameras; New Jersey with locations in France and the UK).

Roper expanded its digital-imaging line in 1998 by acquiring Photometrics Ltd. (digital cameras and detectors) and PMC/Beta Limited (vibration sensing and control equipment). Roper's bid to buy Leach Holding fell through impeding its effort to boost its industrial components offerings. In 1999 it bought Varlen's petroleum analysis instrumentation unit and Eastman Kodak's motion analysis operations (digital video equipment).

Roper's focus on providing high-margin products to niche markets spurred growth through acquisitions that included Eastman Kodak's high-speed and high-resolution digital video equipment unit as well as makers of testing equipment for the petroleum industry. the company bought Struers Holdings' two operating units which provided preparation equipment used in quality inspection (Struers A/S) and material shaping equipment used to make semiconductors and optoelectronics (Logitech).

Roper acquired Hansen Technologies in 2001 and added Struers' operating units in 2001; in 2002 it spent about $83 million on Zetec (industrial testing equipment) Duncan Technologies (industrial digital cameras) AiCambridge/"Qualitek" (leak detection equipment) Quantitative Imaging (industrial and scientific digital cameras) and Definitive Imaging (image analysis software). At the same time however Roper exited some of its Petrotech businesses and was hit by the downturn in the semiconductor industry the oil and gas exploration markets and the generally weak economy.

At the end of 2003 Roper acquired Neptune Technology Group Holdings (meter-reading technology) for $475 million. Expanding beyond its core controls pumps and analytical tools businesses Roper acquired radio-frequency identification technology and related services provider TransCore Holdings for $597 million in 2004.

The company purchased Louisville Colorado-based security applications technologies provider Inovonics Wireless Corporation for $45 million in 2005. That same year Roper strengthened its presence in the medical imaging market by acquiring Kalona Iowa-based CIVCO Medical Instruments Co. a supplier of specialized medical products from KRG Capital Partners LLC. It also bought Orange City Iowa-based MEDTEC a maker of technology used in diagnosing and treating cancer for about $150 million to fold into its CIVCO operations.

The company acquired Dynisco LLC in 2006 for $243 million from the Audax Group a private equity investment firm. Also known as Dynisco Instruments the business made pressure and temperature measurement and control instruments primarily for the plastics industry with applications in life sciences. In recent years Dynisco acquired Alpha Technologies and Viatran Corp. suppliers of analytical instruments and sensors for various applications. Dynisco became part of Roper's Energy Systems and Controls segment.

Acquisitions in 2007 were less costly totaling $106 million and largely benefited the company's Energy Systems and Control segment; four businesses were acquired that brought on board pressure measurement sensors air intake-cut off devices audio recording vibration monitoring and process control equipment. The RF Technology segment gained a rugged mobile computers provider and Scientific and Industrial Imaging obtained a manufacturer of computers and software for mobile computing.

Between 2007 and 2011 the company has averaged more than four acquisitions a year with six each in 2007 and 2008. The largest of the 2008 acquisitions was the purchase of The CBORD Group for $375 million. CBORD makes electronic ID and debit cards for colleges and universities hospitals supermarkets and other businesses and institutions. The acquisition diversified the company's RF Technology interests beyond transportation and water utilities to health care and education end-markets.

Cumulatively Roper's other acquisitions in 2008 ran to $331 million with the RF Technology segment receiving additional boosts with Getloaded.com Technolog and Horizon Software. Horizon Software builds upon the capabilities previously brought in by CBORD. A provider of software Horizon captures corporate dining health care K-12 education military and senior living markets. The two other deals in 2008 (Tech-Pro and Chalwyn) grew the company's Energy Systems and Controls portfolio with industrial test instruments and software and air shut-off valves.

Other acquisitions over the years included Heartscape which developed a technology that can detect heart attacks quicker and with more accuracy; iTradeNetwork a provider of Software-as-a-Service (SaaS)-based trading network and information services used by the food industry; and United Toll Services which made toll and traffic systems and software vital to transportation infrastructure projects that are anticipated to receive an uptick in funding.

In 2012 the company acquired Sunquest Information Systems a provider of health care software catering to more than 1700 large and midsized hospitals and laboratories for about $1.4 billion. The deal allowed it to broaden its product portfolio into new areas. The prior year it snapped up Northern Digital (NDI) a Canada-based 3-D technology provider for the medical industry. Seen as a growth industry NDI's products are used in computer-assisted medical procedures. As with the other acquisitions NDI became part of Roper's medical operations.

EXECUTIVES

Chairman President And Ceo, Brian D. Jellison, age 73, $1,225,000 total compensation

Evp, Paul J. Soni, age 61, $475,000 total compensation

Evp, L. Neil Hunn

Vp And Cfo, Robert Crisci, age 43

Vice President General Counsel, David Liner

Group Vice President Scientific And Industrial Imaging, Ben Wood

Vp Hr, Greg Anderson

Group Vp, Claude Pumilia

Vice President Finance Andamp; Investor Relations, Rob Crisci

Group Vp, Christopher Kreips

Auditors: PricewaterhouseCoopers LLP

LOCATIONS

HQ: Roper Technologies Inc
6901 Professional Parkway East, Suite 200, Sarasota, FL 34240
Phone: 941 556-2601
Web: www.ropertech.com

2018 Sales

	$ mil.	% of total
United States	4,176	80
Non-U.S.	1,015	20
Total	**5,191**	**100**

PRODUCTS/OPERATIONS

2018 Sales

	$ mil.	% of total
RF Technology	2,168	42
Medical & Scientific Imaging	1,522	29
Industrial Technology	900	17
Energy Systems & Controls	600	12
Total	**5,191**	**100**

Selected Products

Energy Systems and Controls
  Control systems
  Fluid properties testing equipment
  Industrial valves and controls
  Non-destructive inspection and measurement instrumentation
  Sensors and controls
Industrial technology
  Flow measurement equipment
  Industrial leak testing equipment
  Industrial pumps
  Materials analysis equipment and consumables
  Water meter and AMR products and systems
RF Technology
  Card systems/integrated security solutions
  Freight matching
  Toll and traffic systems
Scientific and Industrial Imaging
  Digital imaging products and software
  Handheld and vehicle mount computers and software
  Medical products and software

COMPETITORS

ABB	IBM Software
AMETEK	IDEX
Agilent Technologies	IMI plc
Crane Co.	Itron
Curtiss-Wright	NN Inc.
Danaher	Parker-Hannifin
Dover Corp.	Pentair
Emerson Electric	PerkinElmer
Flowserve	SPX
Haskel	Schneider Electric
Honeywell	Thermo Fisher
International	Scientific

HISTORICAL FINANCIALS

Company Type: Public

Income Statement

FYE: December 31

	REVENUE ($ mil.)	NET INCOME ($ mil.)	NET PROFIT MARGIN	EMPLOYEES
12/18	5,191	944	18.2%	15,611
12/17	4,607	972	21.1%	14,236
12/16	3,790	659	17.4%	14,155
12/15	3,582	696	19.4%	10,806
12/14	3,549	646	18.2%	10,137
Annual Growth	**10.0%**	**10.0%**	—	**11.4%**

2018 Year-End Financials

Debt ratio: 32.00%	No. of shares (mil.): 103
Return on equity: 13.00%	Dividends
Cash ($ mil.): 364	Yield: 1.0%
Current ratio: 1.00	Payout: 18.0%
Long-term debt ($ mil.): 4,940	Market value ($ mil.): 27,558

	STOCK PRICE ($) FY Close	P/E High/Low	PER SHARE ($) Earnings	Dividends	Book Value
12/18	267.00	34 27	9.00	2.00	75.00
12/17	259.00	28 19	9.00	1.00	67.00
12/16	183.00	29 24	6.00	1.00	57.00
12/15	190.00	28 21	7.00	1.00	53.00
12/14	156.00	25 20	6.00	1.00	47.00
Annual Growth	**14.3%**	— —	**9.0%**	**19.8%**	**12.0%**

Ross Stores Inc

Ross wants you to dress for less. A leading off-price apparel retailer (behind TJX Cos. and Kohl's) Ross operates some 1340 Ross Dress for Less and more than 190y 200 dd's Discounts stores that sell closeout merchandise including men's women's and children's clothing at prices well below those of department and specialty stores. While apparel accounts for more than half of sales it also sells small furnishings toys and games luggage and jewelry. Featuring the Ross "Dress for Less" trademark the chain targets 18- to 54-year-old white-collar shoppers from primarily middle-income households. Ross and dd's stores are located in strip malls in over 35 states and mostly in the western US and Guam.

Operations

Ross Stores operates two brands of off-price retail apparel and home fashion stores: Ross Dress for Less and dd's DISCOUNTS. Ross does a roaring trade in off-price apparel and home fashion chain offering first-quality in-season name-brand and designer apparel as well as accessories footwear and home decor at between 20%-60% off department and specialty store regular prices.

Launched in 2004 dd's DISCOUNTS serves one of the fastest-growing demographic markets in the US. The ultra-low-price spinoff which offers brand-name apparel at a 20%-70% discount has grown to almost 200 locations in about 15 states including big ones such as California Florida and Texas. The stores which average 23200 square feet are located in strip shopping centers in urban and suburban neighborhoods.

The retailer operates six distribution processing facilities: three in California two in South Carolina and one in Pennsylvania. These distribution centers are the sole source of its stores merchandise. Additionally the discounter owns four and leases three other warehouse facilities for packaway storage. To distribute merchandise to stores on a regular basis Ross Stores enlists the help of third-party cross docks. Shipments are made by contract carriers to stores between three and six times per week depending on the location.

Geographic Reach

Half of California-based Ross' stores are located in the states of California Texas and Florida. The company's distribution centers and warehouses are in Pennsylvania South Carolina and California.Aside from the territory of Guam Ross does not have an international presence.

Sales and Marketing

Ross Stores relies primarily on television as a medium to share the Ross Dress for Less value proposition with its current and potential customers. The company believes that television advertising is the most efficient and cost-effective medium while it continues to use additional channels to build brand awareness. However advertising for its dd's DISCOUNTS stores is focused on new store grand openings and local grass roots initiatives.It also employs social media to communicate its brand position.

Financial Performance

Ross Stores' annual sales have risen more than 40% since 2011 thanks to rapid store expansion and steady same-store sale growth of between 3% and 7% per year. Its annual profits have kept pace with top line growth over the period as the chain has managed to slow its overhead cost growth.

The fast-growing chain's sales jumped 8% to $12.9 billion — a $1 billion gain — during fiscal 2017 (ended January) mostly thanks to continued store growth. Comparable store sales also increased a solid 4%.

Net income was up 10% to $1.1 billion due to lower cost of goods sold partially offset by higher selling general and administrative expenses. Cash from operating activities grew 14% to $1.6 billion due to higher net income.

Strategy

Ross Stores continues its aggressive retail expansion strategy opening additional stores based on market penetration local demographic characteristics competition expected store profitability and the ability to leverage overhead expenses. The company anticipates room in the US to support at least 2000 Ross locations and 500 dd's DISCOUNTS locations.

Indeed the chain has expanded its store count by 40% to 1533 at the end of 2016 from 1125 at the end of 2011. During 2016 alone the retailer added 87 net new stores (including 71 Ross stores) in established regions and in the less-tapped Midwest markets (including its first stores in the Dakotas). It plans to open a further 90 stores in 2017.

Other objectives the discount chain emphasized in 2016 included: maintaining a sufficient library of well-known brands labels and fashions sold with strong discounts; meeting customer needs on a local basis; delivering an "off-price customer" suited shopping experience; and managing effective and competitive store growth in all of its markets.

To boost its relationships with suppliers Ross does not require them to provide markdown/promotional allowances or return privileges. This combined with opportunistic purchases (closeouts such as manufacturer overruns and canceled orders) allows the company to obtain large discounts on merchandise. As a result Ross Stores' customers typically pay 20% to 60% less than department and specialty store prices. Ross holds down costs by offering minimal service and few frills inside its stores.

HISTORY

In 1957 the Ross family founded Ross Stores and opened its first junior department store; by 1982 there were six of the stores in the San Francisco area. That year two retailing veterans Stuart Moldaw (founder of Country Casuals and The Athletic Shoe Factory) and Donald Rowlett (creator of Woolworth's off-price subsidiary J. Brannam) led the acquisition of the company. Moldaw (chairman) and Rowlett (president) wanted to create an off-price chain in California where — despite the success such endeavors were having in the rest of the country — such stores were largely absent. The duo intended to establish a foothold by saturating California markets before competitors muddied the waters.

They restocked the stores with brand-name men's women's and children's apparel shoes accessories and domestics merchandise at reduced prices. Before the end of 1982 they opened two more Ross "Dress for Less" stores; the next year 18 more were added including the chain's first non-California store in Reno Nevada (much of the chain's expansion came through the acquisition of existing strip mall stores). Another 40 stores were added in 1984.

The company went public in 1985 to help fund its expansion and extended its reach to include Colorado Florida Georgia New Mexico and Oregon; that year it opened 41 stores.

In August 2004 Ross opened its first three dd's DISCOUNTS stores in Vallejo San Leandro and Fresno California. The retailer moved its headquarters from Newark California to Pleasanton in mid-2004 and then sold the Newark property for about $17 million.

EXECUTIVES

Ceo, Barbara Rentler, age 61, $1,301,875 total compensation
President And Coo, Michael B. O'Sullivan, age 55, $1,147,250 total compensation
President And Chief Merchandising Officer Ddâ's Discounts, Brian R. Morrow, age 59
President Merchandising Ross Dress For Less, Bernard (Bernie) Brautigan, age 54, $1,070,750 total compensation
Group Svp And Cfo, Michael J. Hartshorn, age 51, $651,375 total compensation
Vice President Store Initiatives, Kelly West
Vp And Dmm Housewares, Shannon Lauzon
Vice President Dmm, Valorie Donato
Evp Planning, Vanessa Baque-stanton
Vice President Property Management, John Fox
Svp Human Resources, Deon Riley
Evp Stores And Loss Prevention, Gary Cribb
Vice President Dmm, Veronica Valencia
Vice President Of Planning, Melanie Allaire
Vice President Planning, Kristin Kuster
Svp Strategy And Marketing, Delaney Steele
Vp Executive Recruiting, Cathy Kiliper
Ciso And Vice President Enterprise Architecture, Elwin Wong
Group Vice President Total Rewards And Human Resources Initiatives, Kevin Reimann
Gvp West Coast Operations, Kevin Garst
Vp Of Regional And Store Planning, Angela Menziuso Menziuso
Group Vp Allocation, Mary Danner
Vp And Dmm Tabletop, Chris Agate
Chairman, Michael A. Balmuth, age 69
Auditors: Deloitte & Touche LLP

LOCATIONS

HQ: Ross Stores Inc
5130 Hacienda Drive, Dublin, CA 94568-7579
Phone: 925 965-4400
Web: www.rossstores.com

2017 Stores

	No.
California	364
Texas	222
Florida	185
Arizona	74
Illinois	62
Georgia	56
North Carolina	45
Pennsylvania	44
Washington	42
Virginia	38
Colorado	33
Nevada	33
Tennessee	31
Oregon	30
Maryland	24
Oklahoma	23
South Carolina	23
Alabama	23
Missouri	21
Louisiana	18
Hawaii	17
Utah	17
New Jersey	13
Wisconsin	13
New Mexico	12
Idaho	11
Kansas	10
Kentucky	9
Indiana	9
Mississippi	8
Arkansas	8
Montana	6
Wyoming	3
Delaware	2
District of Columbia	1
Guam	1
North Dakota	1
South Dakota	1
Total	**1,533**

PRODUCTS/OPERATIONS

2017 Sales

	% of total
Women's apparel	28
Home accents bed & bath	25
Accessories lingerie fine jewelry & fragrances	13
Men's apparel	13
Shoes	13
Children's apparel	8
Total	**100**

2017 Stores

	No.
Ross Dress for Less	1,340
dd's DISCOUNTS	193
Total	**1,533**

Selected Merchandise

Bed and bath
Children's apparel
Cookware
Educational toys
Fine jewelry
Fragrances
Gourmet foods
Home accents
Ladies' apparel
  Accessories
  Dresses
  Junior
  Lingerie
  Maternity
  Misses sportswear
  Petites
  Women's World
Luggage
Men's apparel
  Traditional men's
  Young men's
Shoes
Small electronics
Small furnishings
Sporting goods and exercise equipment

COMPETITORS

Ascena Retail	Kmart
Big Lots	Kohl's
Burlington Coat	Sears
Factory	TJX Companies
Cato	Tailored Brands
Charming Shoppes	Target Corporation
Family Dollar Stores	Wal-Mart
Fred's	

HISTORICAL FINANCIALS

Company Type: Public

Income Statement

FYE: February 2

	REVENUE ($ mil.)	NET INCOME ($ mil.)	NET PROFIT MARGIN	EMPLOYEES
02/19	14,984	1,587	10.6%	88,100
02/18*	14,135	1,363	9.6%	82,700
01/17	12,867	1,118	8.7%	78,600
01/16	11,940	1,021	8.5%	77,800
01/15	11,042	925	8.4%	71,400
Annual Growth	**7.9%**	**14.5%**	**—**	**5.4%**

*Fiscal year change

2019 Year-End Financials

Debt ratio: 5.00%
Return on equity: 50.00%
Cash ($ mil.): 1,413
Current ratio: 2.00
Long-term debt ($ mil.): 312
No. of shares (mil.): 368
Dividends
Yield: 0.0%
Payout: 21.0%
Market value ($ mil.): 33,779

	STOCK PRICE ($) FY Close	P/E High/Low	PER SHARE ($) Earnings	Dividends	Book Value
02/19	92.00	24 17	4.00	1.00	9.00
02/18*	79.00	24 15	4.00	1.00	8.00
01/17	65.00	24 18	3.00	1.00	7.00
01/16	56.00	42 18	3.00	0.00	6.00
01/15	92.00	43 28	2.00	0.00	5.00
Annual Growth	0.0%	— —	17.8%	22.5%	13.1%

*Fiscal year change

RPM International Inc (DE)

RPM International's products like Rust-Oleum Zinsser and DAP are familiar sites on shelves of home improvement stores and consumers' workshops. Its products also are used by industrial manufacturers and contractors for bigger jobs. The company's consumer brands include do-it-yourself caulks and sealants rust preventatives and general-purpose paints repair products personal care items and hobby paints. Beyond those consumer-related products RPM offers industrial-grade products for waterproofing corrosion resistance floor maintenance and wall finishing. RPM also offers industrial cleaners restoration services equipment and colorants. The company gets two-thirds of its sales from US customers.

HISTORY

Frank Sullivan founded Republic Powdered Metals in 1947 to make an industrial aluminum paint. The company went public in 1963 and three years later it bought Reardon Co. (household coatings) the first of more than 50 acquisitions. After his father's death in 1971 Thomas Sullivan took over and reorganized RPM as a holding company.

By 1979 RPM though successful was taken to task by its board for lack of formal planning. In 1985 it bought Sun Oil's Carboline coating and tank-lining subsidiary. This purchase forced RPM to lay off employees for the first time.

RPM bought Rust-Oleum in 1994. In its largest acquisition at that time the company bought roofing-product expert Tremco in 1996 for $236 million. The purchase amassed debt and to compensate RPM sold its Craft House hobby activity subsidiary and Swiggle Insulating Glass in 1997.

The company resumed acquisitions and overseas expansion in 1998 by purchasing Flecto (wood finish) the UK's Nullifire (fireproof coatings) and Germany's Alteco Technik (floors); it also established joint ventures in Russia and China. In 1999 RPM paid $290 million for UK-based Wassall's DAP adhesives division. Softer sales in the Americas and Asia plus increased distribution expenses that fiscal year prompted the company to begin restructuring its operations.

RPM sold its Alox metalworking additive business to Lubrizol in 2000. The next year the company finished its restructuring — which had resulted in 17 plant closures and a 10% workforce reduction — and set its sights on reducing debt.

Thomas C. Sullivan's son — and grandson of the company's founder — Frank Sullivan took the chief executive reins in 2002; Thomas Sullivan remained with the company as chairman.

The company went through a spate of acquisitions in the middle of the decade. Its flooring services division has acquired National Building Facilities Services and Harsco's fiberglass-reinforced plastics business and its corrosion control division has acquired AD Fire Protection Systems. Tremco has acquired German sealant manufacturer Illbruck Sealant Systems. In early 2007 Rust-Oleum acquired the UK's Tor Coatings in an effort to grow the unit's European coatings operations. Later that year the company sold its auto restoration products subsidiary Bondo to 3M.

In 2010 two RPM subsidiaries Bondex International and its holding company Specialty Products Holding Corp. filed for Chapter 11 reorganization in a move to resolve asbestos claims against Bondex. The process allowed the companies to establish a trust fund and a court order directing all present and future claims to the fund for compensation.

The company also went on an international shopping trip in 2010. RPM acquired Hummervoll Industribelegg AS a Norway-based supplier and installer of industrial flooring systems; UK-based Pipeline & Drainage Systems a supplier of curb bridge and channel drainage products; and Turkish company Park Dis Ticaret AS a provider of sealant tapes and membranes.

RPM subsidiary Euclid Chemical acquired PSI Packaging in 2011. PSI is a producer of micro- and macro-fibers for the ready-mixed and pre-cast concrete market. The PSI deal will expand both Euclid and RPM's manufacturing and sales capacity for concrete reinforcement fibers particularly in the international market.

In 2011 the company expanded further internationally when its Performance Coatings Group acquired API an Italian flooring and deck coatings company. The buy also complemented RPM's Flowcrete and Stonhard commercial flooring businesses. That year the company's Performance Coatings Group acquired Spanish company Grupo P&V a top European supplier of fire protection and insulation products. Grupo P&V manufactures sells and installs expanded perlite and vermiculite used in passive fire protection soundproofing and heat insulation. The acquisition fits in with RPM's Carboline product line and expands the company's fire protection market in Europe.

In 2012 the company purchased nail care enamel and related products maker Kirker Enterprises for an undisclosed amount. Kirker became part of the consumer segment. Earlier in the year RPM's Rust-Oleum Group acquired Australia-based HiChem Paint Technologies which makes automotive aftermarket coatings and specialty coatings for both industrial applications and home use.

That year it also acquired Brazilian building materials and construction products company Viapol for an undisclosed amount. Viapol has brand-leading products in Brazil including its rolled asphalt roofing materials waterproofing products concrete admixtures and retail paints and varnishes. The buy broadens RPM's global footprint by moving the company into the Brazilian market South America's largest economy.

In 2013 RPM's Performance Coatings Group acquired Expanko a producer of FritzTile brand terrazzo tile (as well as cork rubber and rubber/cork floor tiles) for the education health-care hospitality and sports/entertainment markets.

EXECUTIVES

President And Coo, Ronald A. Rice, age 56, $720,000 total compensation

Chairman And Ceo, Frank C. Sullivan, age 58, $960,000 total compensation

President Tremco Incorporated, Paul G. P. Hoogenboom, age 58, $425,000 total compensation

Svp Manufacturing Supply Chain Logistics And Operations, John J. McLaughlin

President Rpm Industrial Segment, David P. Reif

Vp Information Technology, Lonny R. DiRusso

President And Ceo Dap, Terry Horan

Svp General Counsel And Chief Compliance Officer, Edward W. Moore, age 62, $360,000 total compensation

Vp And Cfo, Russell L. Gordon, age 53, $465,000 total compensation

Vp Corporate Benefits And Risk Management, Janeen B. Kastner, age 52, $295,000 total compensation

Vp Associate General Counsel And Assistant Secretary, Tracy Crandall

Vice President Information Technology Rpm Speciality Products Group, Mark Rankin

Vice President Information Technology, Matthew Franklin

Vice President Global Tax Treasurer, Matthew Ratajczak

Auditors: DELOITTE & TOUCHE LLP

LOCATIONS

HQ: RPM International Inc (DE)
P.O. Box 777, 2628 Pearl Road, Medina, OH 44258
Phone: 330 273-5090   Fax: 330 225-8743
Web: www.rpminc.com

2019 Sales

	$ mil.	% of total
US	3,677	66
Europe	1,029	19
Canada	390	7
Latin America	219	4
Asia Pacific	178	3
Other regions	72	1
Total	5,565	100

PRODUCTS/OPERATIONS

2019 Sales

	$ mil.	% of total
Industrial	2,890	52
Consumer	1,888	34
Specialty	787	14
Total	5,565	100

Selected Products

Industrial
  Carboline (industrial coatings)
  Chemspec (commercial carpet cleaning chemicals)
  Day-Glo (fluorescent colorants and pigments)
  Dryvit (exterior finishing systems)
  Dymeric (sealants)
  Fibergrate (reinforced plastic grating)
  Flowcrete (polymer flooring system)
  Nullifire (fireproofing coatings)
  Republic (roofing products)
  Stonhard (flooring products)
  Tremco (industrial and commercial sealants)
  Woolsey/Z-Spar (marine coatings)
Consumer
  DAP (sealants caulks and patch and repair products)
  OKON (sealants and stains)
  Painter's Touch (general purpose coatings)
  Rust-Oleum (rust preventative coatings)
  Testors (hobby and leisure products)
  Tremclad (coatings)
  Varathane (wood finishes)
  Watco (wood finishes)
  Zinsser (primer-sealers and wallcovering removers)

COMPETITORS

3M	H.B. Fuller
Akzo Nobel	Henkel
Ameron	Masco
Axalta Coating Systems	PPG Industries
Benjamin Moore	Sherwin-Williams
Ferro	

Company Type: Public

Income Statement				FYE: May 31
	REVENUE ($ mil.)	NET INCOME ($ mil.)	NET PROFIT MARGIN	EMPLOYEES
05/19	5,565	267	4.8%	14,957
05/18	5,322	338	6.3%	14,540
05/17	4,958	182	3.7%	14,318
05/16	4,814	355	7.4%	13,394
05/15	4,595	239	5.2%	12,864
Annual Growth	4.9%	2.7%	—	3.8%

2019 Year-End Financials

Debt ratio: 46.00%	No. of shares (mil.): 131
Return on equity: 18.00%	Dividends
Cash ($ mil.): 223	Yield: 3.0%
Current ratio: 2.00	Payout: 68.0%
Long-term debt ($ mil.): 1,973	Market value ($ mil.): 7,011

	STOCK PRICE ($) FY Close	P/E High/Low	PER SHARE ($) Earnings	Dividends	Book Value
05/19	54.00	34 24	2.00	1.00	11.00
05/18	50.00	22 18	3.00	1.00	12.00
05/17	54.00	41 34	1.00	1.00	11.00
05/16	50.00	19 14	3.00	1.00	10.00
05/15	50.00	29 22	2.00	1.00	10.00
Annual Growth	1.7%	—	3.1%	7.7%	2.6%

Rush Enterprises Inc.

Rush Enterprises has been truckin' along as a heavy-duty commercial vehicle dealer since 1965. The company operates a growing network of more than 100 commercial vehicle and service dealerships under the name Rush Truck Centers in some 21 states. It is one of the largest Peterbilt truck dealers in the US but it also sells trucks manufactured by Blue Bird Ford Isuzu Hino Mitsubishi Fuso and IC Bus. Additionally Rush offers aftermarket parts and services such as body shop repairs insurance and third-party financing and rentals and leasing. Founded in 1965 Rush's reach has spread as far as California and Florida. Late chairman W. Marvin Rush's family control the rapidly growing company.

Operations

Rush Truck Centers dealerships that sell new and used commercial vehicles are its largest business accounting for more than two thirds of Rush Enterprises' total sales. The company also sells aftermarket parts and services representing about 30% of annual sales and third-party financing. Of its vehicle sales about 80% are new and 20% used.

The company runs a number of other small businesses such as World Wide Tires which operates two locations in Texas and sells tires for commercial use and Momentum Fuel Technologies which manufactures compressed natural gas fuel systems and related parts.

Geographic Reach

New Braunfels Texas-based Rush Enterprises' Rush Truck Centers are located in Alabama Arizona California Colorado Florida Georgia Idaho Illinois Indiana Kansas Missouri Nevada New Mexico North Carolina Nebraska Ohio Oklahoma Pennsylvania Tennessee Texas Utah and Virginia.

Sales and Marketing

Rush Enterprises promotes it products through its sales personnel advertisements in trade magazines and online and at industry shows. Customers include owner operators regional and national truck fleets corporations and local governments. Its customer base is diversified and it does not rely on any customer for more than 10% of total sales.

The company purchases vehicles parts and accessories directly from manufacturers wholesale distributors or other sources that provide the most favorable pricing.

Financial Performance

Rush Enterprises had a rough time in 2016 amid industry-wide malaise but recovered in 2017. The company's revenue grew 12% or $499.3 million to $4.7 billion on the back of growth in new vehicle sales and aftermarket products and services. Used vehicle sales growth was materially flat.

Net income jumped from $40.6 million to $172.1 million due to stronger operating profits and a net tax benefit of $35.7 million relating to the 2017 US Tax Cuts and Jobs Act.

Rush's cash positioned strengthened in 2017 its coffers growing by $42.5 million to $124.5 million.

Strategy

Rush has stated its ambition to grow its revenue to $7 billion by 2020 by investing heavily in its business particularly the parts and service business. Rusty Rush the chairman and CEO views the segment as having the most potential in terms of revenue and profit growth. The windfall from the 2017 US Tax Cuts and Jobs Act will be pumped into the business including an extensive salespeople and technician recruitment drive.

Rush markets its dealership network as "one-stop shops" where customers can purchase new and used commercial vehicles (ranging from heavy- and medium-duty trucks to buses); finance lease or rent vehicles and equipment; buy aftermarket parts and accessories; and have warranty and non-warranty service performed by certified technicians. Its customer base includes regional and national truck fleets (typically those that buy more than five trucks in any one-year period) owner operators corporations and local governments.

Geographically the company's strategy is to expand this network either by organically opening new centers in existing areas of operation or by acquiring additional dealerships that are located adjacent to its current operations. Rush also grows by adding complementary product lines including truck-mounted cranes refuse vehicles and towing vehicles.

To combat a shortage of truck technicians Rush is investing in training programs for new recruits with the goal of reducing first-year turnover. The program will aim to attract more women; historically truck technicians have been predominantly men.

Mergers and Acquisitions

Rush regularly buys up truck dealerships to expand its size. In late 2017 the company acquired Transwest San Diego which sells Ford trucks for $2.2 million. It had acquired another Transwest dealer in Las Vegas the year before for $0.8 million.

EXECUTIVES

Senior Vice President Marketing Fleets And Specialized Equipment Sales, David Orf
Chairman President And Ceo, W. M. (Rusty) Rush, age 60, $1,437,000 total compensation
Evp, Derrek Weaver, age 46, $369,468 total compensation
Svp Cfo And Treasurer, Steven L. (Steve) Keller, age 49, $395,604 total compensation
Svp Navistar Dealerships, Richard J Ryan, age 51
Svp Peterbilt Dealerships, Corey H. Lowe, age 43

Svp And Coo, Michael J. McRoberts, age 60, $456,515 total compensation
Vice President Medium Duty Sales, Steven Taylor
Vice President, Lynn Cornelius
Senior Vice President Operations, Jody Pollard
Auditors: Ernst & Young LLP

LOCATIONS

HQ: Rush Enterprises Inc.
555 I.H. 35 South, Suite 500, New Braunfels, TX 78130
Phone: 830 302-5200
Web: www.rushenterprises.com

PRODUCTS/OPERATIONS

2017 Sales

	$ mil.	% of total
New & used commercial vehicle sales	2,993	64
Parts & service sales	1,471	31
Lease & rental	217	5
Finance & insurance	18	0
Other	14	0
Total	**4,714**	**100**

2017 Sales

	$ mil.	% of total
Truck Segment	4,698	100
All Other	16	0
Total	**4,714**	**100**

2017 Unit Vehicle Sales

	$ mil.	% of total
New vehicles	25,696	78
Used vehicles	7,060	22
Total	**32,756**	**100**

Selected Businesses and Brands

Custom Vehicle Solutions
Momentum Fuel Technologies
Rig Tough Truck Parts
Rig Tough Used Trucks
Rush Bus Centers
Rush Crane Systems
Rush Refuse Systems
Rush Towing Systems
Rush Truck Centers
Rush Truck Financing
Rush Truck Insurance
Rush Truck Leasing

COMPETITORS

Freightliner Sterling Western Star	Penske Truck Leasing
Holman Enterprises	RDO Equipment
Hunter's Truck Sales & Service	Rip Griffin Truck Service Center
Midway Ford Truck Center	Ryder System
Murphy-Hoffman	W.D. Larson
Palm Truck Centers	Worldwide Equipment Inc.
Penske Automotive Group	

HISTORICAL FINANCIALS

Company Type: Public

Income Statement				FYE: December 31
	REVENUE ($ mil.)	NET INCOME ($ mil.)	NET PROFIT MARGIN	EMPLOYEES
12/18	5,506	139	2.5%	7,214
12/17	4,714	172	3.7%	6,825
12/16	4,215	41	1.0%	6,180
12/15	4,980	66	1.3%	6,700
12/14	4,727	80	1.7%	6,297
Annual Growth	3.9%	14.8%	—	3.5%

Debt ratio: 53.00%		No. of shares (mil.): 37		
Return on equity: 13.00%		Dividends		
Cash ($ mil.): 132		Yield: 1.0%		
Current ratio: 1.00		Payout: 7.0%		
Long-term debt ($ mil.): 489		Market value ($ mil.): 1,276		

	STOCK PRICE ($) FY Close	P/E High/Low		PER SHARE ($) Earnings	Dividends	Book Value
12/18	34.00	16	9	3.00	0.00	29.00
12/17	51.00	12	7	4.00	0.00	26.00
12/16	32.00	33	14	1.00	0.00	22.00
12/15	22.00	20	13	2.00	0.00	21.00
12/14	32.00	19	13	2.00	0.00	19.00
Annual Growth	1.8%	—	—	15.2%	—	10.8%

Ryder System, Inc.

When it comes to commercial vehicles and distribution Ryder System wants to be the designated driver. The company's Fleet Management Solutions (FMS) segment acquires manages and maintains fleet vehicles for commercial customers. Similarly the Supply Chain Solutions (SCS) segment provides logistics and supply chain services from industrial start to finish?raw material supply to product distribution. SCS also offers dedicated contract carriage service by supplying trucks drivers and management and administrative services to customers on a contract basis. Ryder's worldwide fleet of more than 270000 vehicles ranges from tractor-trailers to light-duty trucks and more recently electric trucks. The majority of its revenue comes from the US.

Operations

Ryder operates through three main divisions: Fleet Management Solutions (FMS) Supply Chain Solutions (SCS) and Dedicated Transportation Solutions (DTS).

Fleet Management Solutions provides full-service leasing contract maintenance and contract-related maintenance for commercial truck fleets as well as commercial truck tractor and trailer rentals. FMS accounts for nearly 30% of revenue and operates in North America and the UK.

Supply Chain Solutions offers integrated logistics solutions including distribution management dedicated transportation and professional services primarily in North America. It accounts for about 25% of revenue. Dedicated Transportation Solutions accounts for about 15% of sales and provides vehicles and drivers as part of a dedicated transportation solution in the US.

Overall revenue from services represents about 50% of Ryder's total sales; lease and rental revenue accounts for more than 40%; and the remaining revenue comes from fuel services sales.

Geographic Reach

Based in Miami FL Ryder operates in North America (the US Canada Mexico and Puerto Rico) Europe (Germany and the UK) and Asia (Singapore). The US accounts for around 90% of its revenue.

Sales and Marketing

Ryder's Fleet Management Services customers in the US range from small businesses to large national enterprises operating in a wide variety of industries the most significant of which are food and beverage industrial transportation and warehousing and business and personal services.

Financial Performance

Ryder System has grown significantly over the last several years with a 27% increase in sales since 2014.

Sales in 2018 leaped to $8.4 billion compared with $7.3 billion in 2017 a 15% increase. Ryder attributes the growth to new business and higher volumes in all segments as well as higher fuel costs passed on to customers and sales from the acquisition of MXD. Increases in revenue were offset by a downturn in used vehicle sales.

The company posted $273 million in net income about a third that of $791.8 million the previous year mainly due to a non-recurring tax benefit of $477.7 million in 2017 (due to the Tax Cuts and Jobs Act).

Cash at the end of fiscal 2018 was $68.1 million a decrease of $14.9 million from the prior year. Cash from operations contributed $1.6 billion to the coffers while investing activities used $2.7 billion mainly for purchases of property plant and equipment and acquisitions. Financing activities provided $1.1 billion from borrowings offset by dividends paid to stockholders and the company's stock repurchase program.

Strategy

Ryder has several strategic initiatives in place to drive growth across all its segments.

In its Fleet Management Services (FMS) division Ryder is currently running sales and marketing campaigns targeting the large non-outsourced transportation and logistics market. It's leveraging trends like driver and technician shortages complex regulations and higher vehicle maintenance costs to sway these businesses to outsource their fleet management to Ryder. The company has expanded services in its Dedicated Transportation Solutions (DTS) business by adding drivers as well as routing scheduling and administrative activities.

In the Supply Chain Solutions segment the company aims to capitalize on the growing e-commerce and e-fulfillment space. After acquiring MXD in 2018 Ryder is rebranding MXD's last mile service offering as Ryder Last Mile which includes delivery of big and bulky goods direct to consumers' homes. Ryder Last Mile can now deliver to 95% of the US and Canada within a two-day time frame.

Other investments Ryder hopes will increase sales are the launch of COOP by Ryder a commercial truck sharing platform where fleet owners can list and rent underused vehicles and the continued development of its RyderShare cloud-based platform for load visibility and tracking and its Ryder-Gyde fleet management app. It also recently purchased 1000 Class 5 electric vehicles; it will lease 900 to FedEx and keep 100 for the company's use.

Mergers and Acquisitions

In 2018 Ryder System acquired Metro Truck & Tractor Leasing a full-service leasing rental and maintenance company for $52 million. The addition of Metro Truck increases Ryder's geographic footprint in the US particularly in the Baltimore MD area.

Also in 2018 the company purchased e-commerce fulfillment provider MXD Group for $20 million. MXC has a national network of facilities and specializes in last mile capabilities throughout the US and Canada. The acquisition allows Ryder to serve manufacturers retailers and their customers who have come to expect quick delivery of supplies and merchandise.

Company Background

Ryder Truck Rental was founded in Miami by Jim Ryder in 1933. It was the first truck leasing company in the US with operations in four southern states until 1952 when it bought Great Southern Trucking (renamed Ryder Truck Lines) and doubled its size. In 1955 the year it went public as Ryder System Ryder bought South Carolina-based Carolina Fleets and Yellow Rental (a leasing service operating in the Northeast). More acquisitions over the next decade extended Ryder's truck rental business across the US and into Canada. Ryder Truck Lines was sold to International Utilities in 1965.

HISTORY

Ryder Truck Rental founded in Miami by Jim Ryder in 1933 was the first truck leasing company in the US. It rented trucks in four southern states until 1952 when it bought Great Southern Trucking (renamed Ryder Truck Lines) doubling its size. In 1955 the year it went public as Ryder System Ryder bought Carolina Fleets (a South Carolina trucking company) and Yellow Rental (a northeastern leasing service). More purchases over the next decade extended its truck rental business across the US and into Canada. Ryder Truck Lines was sold to International Utilities in 1965.

EXECUTIVES

Evp And Cfo, Art A. Garcia, age 57, $479,783 total compensation
Chairman And Ceo, Robert E. Sanchez, age 53, $785,225 total compensation
Evp And Chief Marketing Officer, Karen M. Jones, age 56
Evp Chief Legal Officer And Secretary, Robert D. Fatovic, age 53, $392,650 total compensation
President Global Fleet Management Solutions, Dennis C. Cooke, age 54, $543,750 total compensation
Evp And Chief Sales Officer, John J. Gleason, age 63
President Dedicated Transport Solutions, John J. Diez, $411,000 total compensation
Vp And General Manager High-technology Supply Chain Solutions, J. Steven (Steve) Sensing
Svp And Cio, Melvin (Mel) Kirk
Vice President Technical Services And Operations, Michael Pivowar
Vice President Audit Services, Clifford Zoller
Vice President Information Technology, Greg Knott
Senior Vice President And Treasurer, Daniel Susik
Vice President Global Compliance Officer, Celeste Lipworth
Vice President Compensation And Benefits, Boon Ooi
Vice President Sales Hci, Dave Sims
Vice President And Deputy General Counsel, Alena Brenner
Vice President Corporate Communications And Community Relations, David Bruce
Vice President Talent Management And Human Resources, Amparo Bared
First Vice President, Tammy Megowan
Vice President Operations, Albert Pinto
Vice President Asset Management, Eugene Tangney
Vice President Business Development, Mark Swenson
Vice President Business Development, Ron Mullowney
Vice President Of Tax, Ben Schmoyer
Vice President Of Sales, Alex Madrinkian
Vice President Information Technology, Mike Parvor
Vice President Information Technology, Stephen Hitchings
Vice President Business Development, Paul Skinner
Executive Vice President Chief Human Resources Officer, Gregory Greene
Vice President Automotive, Dick Jennings
Executive Vice President Sales And Marketing, Greg Greene
Senior Vice President National Sales, John Deris
Vice President Of Sales, Chris Fairey

Vice President National Sales, William Toerpe

Senior Vice President Sales And Solutions, Todd Skiles

Senior Vice President And General Manager, Tom Pettit

Vice President Business Development And Marketing, Jeffrey Boudreau

Vice President, Eugenio Sevilla-Sacasa

Vice President Supply Chain Excellence, Gary Allen

Vice President Supply Chain Solutions, Steve Thoke

Vp Operations, Bryce Kinsley

Vice President Of Business Development, Dave Walby

Vice President Sales And Marketing, Chuck Lounsbury

Senior Vice President And General Manager Supply Chains Solutions, Tom Jones

Vice President International Supply Chain Solutions, Gene Sevilla

Vice President Information Technology Strategic Operations, Jonathan Mish

Vice President Andamp; Global Product Manager Rental Operations, Rick Mohr

Vp National Sales, Bill Toerpe

Vice President And General Manager, Gerald Brown

Director Of Government Relations, Joshua Grodin

Vice President Audit Services, Sanjay Singh

Vice President Technical Services And Operations, Mike Pivower

Vice President And Controller, Frank Mullen

Vice President Global Marketing, Samuel H Johnson

Vice President Director Of Business Development Lease Finance, Scott M Mishoe

Senior Vice President Of Quality, Roger Ciccini

Senior Vice President And Chief Information Officer, Rajeev Ravindran

Senior Vice President Sales And Marketing Supply Chain Solutions, Steve Dean

Vice President And Managing Director Latin America, Eugene Sevilla-Sacasa

Executive Vice President Tech Corporate, Alva Way

Vice President Compensation And Benefits, Nicole Turner

Executive Vice President, Patrick Floyd

Vice President Operations Ryder Last Mile, Frank Gaura

Board Member, Robert Eck

Board Member, Luis Nieto

Board Member, Abbie Smith

Board Member, Michael Hilton

Board Member, Tamara Lundgren

Board Member, Hansel Tookes

Board Member, John Berra

Board Member, Emily Smith

Board Member, Robert Hagemann

Board Member, Follin E Smith

Member Board Of Directors, Dmitri Stockton

Auditors: PricewaterhouseCoopers LLP

LOCATIONS

HQ: Ryder System, Inc.
11690 N.W., 105th Street, Miami, FL 33178
Phone: 305 500-3726
Web: www.ryder.com

2018 Sales

	$ mil.	% of total
US	7,387	88
Canada	465	5
Europe	335	4
Mexico	198	3
Singapore	24	-
Total	8,409	100

PRODUCTS/OPERATIONS

2018 Sales

	$ mil.	% of total
Fleet Management Solutions	5,255	58
Supply Chain Solutions	2,398	27
Dedicated Transportation Solutions	1,333	15
Eliminations	(577.5)	-
Total	8,409	100

2017 Sales

	$ mil.	% of total
Services revenue	4,281	51
Lease and rental revenue	4	42
Fuel services revenue	620	7
Total	8,409	100

Selected Services

Fleet Management Solutions
  Commercial rental
  Contract maintenance
  Full service leasing
  Used vehicles
Supply Chain Solutions
  Distribution management
  Transportation management
Dedicated Contract Carriage

COMPETITORS

ArcBest
Barloworld Handling
C.H. Robinson Worldwide
FedEx
J.B. Hunt
Landstar System

Penske Truck Leasing
Schenker Inc.
Schneider National
UPS
UniGroup
YRC Worldwide

HISTORICAL FINANCIALS

Company Type: Public

Income Statement   FYE: December 31

	REVENUE ($ mil.)	NET INCOME ($ mil.)	NET PROFIT MARGIN	EMPLOYEES
12/18	8,409	273	3.3%	39,600
12/17	7,330	791	10.8%	36,100
12/16	6,787	262	3.9%	34,500
12/15	6,572	305	4.6%	33,100
12/14	6,639	219	3.3%	30,600
Annual Growth	6.1%	5.7%	—	6.7%

2018 Year-End Financials

Debt ratio: 51.00%
Return on equity: 10.00%
Cash ($ mil.): 68
Current ratio: 1.00
Long-term debt ($ mil.): 5,694

No. of shares (mil.): 53
Dividends
  Yield: 4.0%
  Payout: 41.0%
Market value ($ mil.): 2,558

	STOCK PRICE ($) FY Close	P/E High/Low		PER SHARE ($) Earnings	Dividends	Book Value
12/18	48.00	17	9	5.00	2.00	55.00
12/17	84.00	6	4	15.00	2.00	54.00
12/16	74.00	17	10	5.00	2.00	38.00
12/15	57.00	17	9	6.00	2.00	37.00
12/14	93.00	23	17	4.00	1.00	34.00
Annual Growth	(15.1%)	—	—	5.9%	10.5%	12.4%

RYMAN HOSPITALITY PROPERTIES, INC.

Ryman Hospitality Properties (formerly Gaylord Entertainment) may be hollerin' for attention in the hospitality game but it's no corporate hayseed. Its properties consist of resort hotels tethered closely to attractions that appeal to the meetings and conventions market. They include the Gaylord Opryland Resort & Convention Center in Nashville the Gaylord Palms Resort in Florida (close to Disney World) the Gaylord Texan Resort near Dallas and the Gaylord National Resort and Convention Center in the Washington DC area. Ryman's hotels are managed by hotel giant Marriott. In 2012 the company changed its name convered to a REIT and sold its hotel brand and management business to Marriott.

HISTORY

The origins of Gaylord Entertainment can be traced back to the Oklahoma Publishing Co. a newspaper publishing company founded by Edward K. Gaylord Ray Dickinson and Roy McClintock in 1903. The publisher of The Daily Oklahoman Oklahoma Publishing branched into radio in 1928 with the purchase of Oklahoma City radio station WKY. With its 1949 creation of Oklahoma City television station WKY-TV Oklahoma Publishing made the leap into television.

Edward K. Gaylord died in 1974 at the age of 101 and his son Edward L. Gaylord was appointed CEO. Under his leadership the company purchased Opryland USA in 1983 — an acquisition that netted it the Grand Ole Opry Opryland Themepark and the Opryland Hotel. Opryland USA also launched country music cable network The Nashville Network that year.

In 1991 the increasingly diverse Oklahoma Publishing spun off its entertainment and broadcast holdings in the form of public company Gaylord Entertainment which established its headquarters in Nashville Tennessee. Gaylord Entertainment acquired a majority interest in cable music network Country Music Television (CMT) the same year. It later expanded CMT into Latin America Asia and the Pacific Rim. CMT also made a brief foray into Europe but that initiative was ended in 1998.

Facing a consolidating entertainment and media landscape Gaylord sold The Nashville Network and the US operations of CMT to Westinghouse (now CBS) in 1997. It also sold television station KSTW that year. The company expanded its reach into Christian music with the purchase of Word Entertainment and its 1997 acquisition of Blanton Harrell Entertainment gave Gaylord a presence in artist management. Terry London was appointed CEO in 1997.

The company closed its Opryland theme park in 1998 in the face of declining attendance and broke ground at the same site for the Opry Mills entertainment shopping and restaurant complex (opened 2000). Gaylord also purchased a Nashville Ramada Inn in 1998 (later renaming it Radisson Hotel at Opryland). With its 1998 acquisition of Paris-based Pandora Investment Gaylord branched into film distribution.

In 1999 the company formed Opryland Hospitality Group to oversee expansion of the Opryland hotel concept across the US. It also sold its last television station KTVT in Dallas/Fort Worth to CBS. Edward K. Gaylord II succeeded his father as chairman in 1999. That year the company launched its Internet division GETdigitalmedia (later renamed

Gaylord Digital) and moved online with the purchase of Christian Web sites Musicforce.com and Lightsource.com. Later the same year the company expanded its Internet presence with the purchase of Songs.com a music Web site focused on independent artists. But in late 2000 the company announced it would close its Internet unit. Also in 2000 the company bought Corporate Magic a firm focused on producing entertainment events for corporate audiences.

At the end of 2000 Gaylord sold Musicforce.com to Christian Book Distributors. Following that sale it sold Lightsource.com to LifeAudio.com in early 2001. That year the company sold its film and television production units and announced a restructuring in order to cut costs. It also renamed Opryland Hotels to Gaylord Opryland while expanding into Texas and Florida. Colin Reed was appointed CEO in 2001.

Between 2001 and 2003 Gaylord Entertainment sold Word Entertainment to Warner Music Group the Opry Mills shopping and restaurant complex to The Mills Corporation the Acuff-Rose Music Publishing business to Sony/ATV two of its Nashville radio stations to Cumulus Media and its majority interest in the Oklahoma City Redhawks minor league baseball team.

Edward L. Gaylord officially retired from the company in 2003 at age 83. Also that year the company significantly expanded its hospitality business with the purchase of ResortQuest a vacation and condominium property management firm. In 2004 the Gaylord family sold more than half its shares in the company making Gabelli Funds the majority owner.

In 2005 Gaylord acquired 50% of Corporate Magic a Dallas-based provider of production support for corporate meetings and events. It did so to support its meeting and convention facilities.

The company unloaded its minority interest in minor league hockey team the Nashville Predators in 2005. Two years later it sold ResortQuest to a subsidiary of Leucadia National Corp. for $35 million. Also in 2007 it sold its interest in sporting goods store operator Bass Pro Group. In 2008 the company opened the Gaylord National Resort and Convention Center in the Washington DC area. The property has some 2000 rooms and approximately 450000 square feet of meeting space.

Also in 2008 Gaylord terminated plans to acquire the Westin La Cantera Resort in San Antonio for about $253 million citing a tough economic environment. In addition the 2008 sale of its ResortQuest subsidiary an online booking service in vacation rentals property management and resort real estate sales fit the company's strategy of selling off assets that aren't related to its Grand Ole Opry or its operations in the meetings and convention market.

In 2009 the company responded to weak earnings by cutting approximately 500 jobs across all areas of the business. Gaylord reported steep dip in profits in 2010 primarily due to harsh flooding in Nashville when the Cumberland River rose to historic levels flowing over protective levees. The flood resulted in property damage and temporary closures at its properties in Nashville causing lost revenues and an increase in expenses. Also in 2010 Gaylord sold its 50% stake in Corporate Magic back to that company's CEO.

The company changed its name to Ryman Hospitality Properties in 2012. It also converted to an REIT and sold the Gaylord brand to Marriott which now manages Ryman's hotel properties and certain other entertainment holdings.

EXECUTIVES

Evp Ryman Hospitality Properties; President Opry Entertainment Group, Stephen G. (Steve) Buchanan

Chairman And Ceo, Colin V. Reed, age 71, $782,830 total compensation

Svp Investments Design And Construction, Bennett D. Westbrook, age 52, $318,447 total compensation

President And Cfo, Mark Fioravanti, age 57, $469,407 total compensation

Svp Asset Management, Patrick Chaffin, age 45, $274,975 total compensation

Svp General Counsel And Secretary, Scott J. Lynn, age 45, $364,876 total compensation

Senior Vice President And Corporate Controller, Jennifer Hutcheson

Vice President Information Technology, Sharon Asmus

Vice President, James Chamblin

Vice President Human Resources, Shawn Smith

Svp Of Marketing, Laura Hollingsworth

Board Member, Michael J Bender

Member Board Of Directors, Fazal Merchant

Auditors: ERNST & YOUNG LLP NASHVILLE

LOCATIONS

HQ: RYMAN HOSPITALITY PROPERTIES, INC.
1 GAYLORD DR, NASHVILLE, TN 372141207
Phone: 615 316-6000
Web: WWW.RYMANHP.COM

PRODUCTS/OPERATIONS

2015 Sales

	$ mil.	% of total
Hospitality	995	91
Entertainment (previously Opry and Attractions)	98	9
Total	**1,092**	**100**

2015 Sales

	$ mil.	% of total
Food and beverage	461	42
Rooms	405	37
Other hotel revenue	129	12
Entertainment (previously Opry and Attractions)	98	9
Total	**1,092**	**100**

Select Operations

Hospitality
Gaylord Opryland Resort & Convention Center (Tennessee)
Gaylord Palms Resort & Convention Center (Florida)
Gaylord Texan Resort & Convention Center
Radisson Hotel at Opryland (Tennessee)
Attractions
Gaylord Springs Golf Links (golf club Tennessee)
General Jackson Showboat
Grand Ole Opry
Ryman Auditorium
Wildhorse Saloon
WSM-AM

COMPETITORS

CKX
Caesars Entertainment
Disney Parks & Resorts
Elvis Presley Enterprises
Herschend Entertainment
Hershey Entertainment
Hilton Worldwide
Kennywood
Las Vegas Sands
Live Nation Entertainment
MGM Resorts
Marriott
New York Convention Center Operating Corporation
SeaWorld
Welk Group

HISTORICAL FINANCIALS
Company Type: Private

Income Statement   FYE: December 31

	ASSETS ($ mil.)	NET INCOME ($ mil.)	INCOME AS % OF ASSETS	EMPLOYEES
12/16	2,406	159	6.6%	1,000
12/15	2,331	112	4.8%	—
12/14	2,413	126	5.2%	—
12/13	2,425	113	4.7%	—
Annual Growth	(0.3%)	12.0%	—	—

S & T Bancorp Inc (Indiana, PA)

S&T Bancorp is the bank holding company for S&T Bank which boasts nearly $5 billion in assets and serves customers from some 60 branch offices in western Pennsylvania. Targeting individuals and local businesses the bank offers such standard retail products as checking savings and money market accounts CDs and credit cards. Business loans including commercial mortgages make up more than 80% of the company's loan portfolio. The bank also originates residential mortgages construction loans and consumer loans. Through subsidiaries S&T Bank sells life disability and commercial property/casualty insurance provides investment management services and advises the Stewart Capital Mid Cap Fund.

Operations

S&T Bancorp operates through three main business segments: Community Banking which offers traditional banking services and commercial and consumer loans; Wealth Management which boasts $2 billion in assets under management and administration and provides brokerage services trust and custodial services and investment advisory for affluent individuals and institutions; and Insurance which offers commercial property and casualty insurance group life and health coverage employee benefit services and personal insurance products through S&T Insurance Group LLC.

Its S&T Bancholding subsidiary provides investment services in the Wealth Management segment while its Stewart Capital Advisors subsidiary provides investment advisory services in the segment.

Overall S&T Bancorp generated 72% of its total revenue from loan interest (including fees) in 2014 plus another 6% from interest on its investment securities. About 10% of its total revenue came from debit and credit card fees and deposit account service charges while wealth management fees and insurance fees made up 6% and 3% of total revenue that year respectively.

Geographic Reach

Headquartered in Indiana Pennsylvania S&T Bancorp boasts branches in a dozen counties in the state including: Allegheny Armstrong Blair Butler Cambria Centre Clarion Clearfield Indiana Jefferson Washington and Westmoreland counties. It also has loan production offices in northeast and central Ohio and in western New York.

Sales and Marketing

Targeting both individuals and local businesses S&T Bancorp spent $3.32 million on marketing in 2014 up from the $2.93 million and $3.21 million it spent in 2013 and 2012 respectively.

Financial Performance

S&T Bancorp's revenue has slowly declined in recent years due to shrinking interest margins on loans amidst the low-interest environment. The firm's profits however have been rising thanks to declining loan loss provisions as its loan portfolio's credit quality has improved with the strengthened economy.

Following several years of top-line declines the bank's revenue inched up by nearly 1% to $206.86 million in 2014. The rise was mostly thanks to higher interest income as overall earning-asset balances grew by nearly 7% during the year reflecting the bank's growing loan business and increased investment securities assets. Wealth Management fees also continued to grow rising by 6% during the year.

Higher revenue coupled with lower interest expenses on deposits and a $6.6 million reduction in loan loss provisions in 2014 drove S&T Bancorp's net income higher by 15% to $57.91 million. S&T's operating cash levels fell by 9% to $78.1 million for the year after adjusting its earnings for non-cash items mostly related to its net proceeds from sales of its mortgage loans originated-for-sale.

Strategy

S&T Bancorp reiterated in 2015 that its growth strategy is centered around organic growth in existing and new markets and growth through strategic acquisitions that introduce new lines of business. Its 2015 acquisition of Integrity Bancshares for example expanded S&T's footprint eastward across four counties in Pennsylvania and added millions of dollars worth of new loan business. Also that year the bank entered the western part of New York for the first time with the opening of a new loan production office in the region.

In late 2012 the bank extended its operations into its neighbor Ohio when it opened a handful of branches in Akron. That same year the bank acquired Mainline Bancorp and Gateway Bank of Pennsylvania bolstering its presence in its core western Pennsylvania market.

Mergers and Acquisitions

In March 2015 S&T Bancorp purchased Camp Hill-based Integrity Bancshares for $155 million adding $860 million in assets and eight branches expanding S&T's geographic footprint eastward into Cumberland Dauphin Lancaster and York counties in Pennsylvania. S&T added that the acquisition positioned the bank in high-growth markets within the state and added experienced members to the bank's loan team.

In 2012 the bank acquired Mainline Bancorp and Gateway Bank of Pennsylvania. Both transactions served to expand S&T's presence in western Pennsylvania.

EXECUTIVES

Sevp And Coo, David P. Ruddock, age 57, $265,000 total compensation

President And Ceo S&t And S&t Bank, Todd D. Brice, age 56, $525,000 total compensation

Evp And Retail Banking Division Manager, Richard A. (Rich) Fiscus

Sevp And Cfo, Mark Kochvar, age 58, $278,000 total compensation

Sevp And Chief Lending Officer, David G. Antolik, age 52, $302,000 total compensation

Evp And Chief Investment Officer Wealth Management, Malcolm E. Polley, age 56

Sevp Chief Risk Officer And Secretary, Ernest J. Draganza

Evp And Deputy Chief Credit Officer, William (Bill) Kametz

Sevp And Chief Credit Officer, Patrick Haberfield

Sevp And Chief Banking Officer, Rebecca Stapleton

Evp And Commercial Loan Officer, Steve Drahnak

Evp And Chief Audit Executive, LaDawn D. Yesho

Evp, David Richards

Evp Marketing Division Manager, Rob Jorgenson

Evp And Cio, Jim Mill

Evp And Manager, Robert Jogrenson

Sevp And Market Executive, Thomas J. Sposito

Market President Central Pennsylvania, Jordan Space

Market President Northeast Ohio, Steve Hendricks

Vice President Mortgage Underwriting Manager, Christine Rumbaugh

Vice President Marketing, Kelly Thomas

Vice President Credit Analysis Operation Manager, Dennis Scott

Senior Vice President Banking Operations, Robert Coleman

Vice President Marketing, Kelly Corrinne

Evp And Chief Risk Officer, Ernie Draganza

Vice President Of Information Technology, Ron Rodman

Vice President Regional Manager, Megan White

Assistant Vice President Sba Commercial Loan, Becky Oldenski

Evp And Chief Security Officer, Kevin Dodds

Svp Regional Busines Banking Sandt Bank, Sean Dockery

Svp Commercial Banker Sandt Bank, Jeffrey Bierlein

Svp Commercial Banker Sandt Bank, David D'angelo

Vice President Special Assets Officer, Peter Talarovich

Vice President Business Banker, Cathleen Campriani-square

Vice President And Relationship Manager, Ronald Barner

Assistant Vice President Data Management Manager, Matthew Mann

Senior Vice President Commercial Banker, Paul Kelly

Assistant Vice President Senior Operations Accountant, Travis Mazon

Vice President, Kevin Hurley

Vice President Platforms Support Manager, Debbie Silveri

Chairman S&t And S&t Bank, Charles G. Urtin

Vice Chairman S&t And S&t Bank, Christine J. Toretti, age 62

Auditors: Ernst & Young LLP

LOCATIONS

HQ: S & T Bancorp Inc (Indiana, PA)
800 Philadelphia Street, Indiana, PA 15701
Phone: 800 325-2265
Web: www.stbancorp.com

PRODUCTS/OPERATIONS

2014 Sales

	$ mil.	% of total
Interest		
Loans including fees	147	72
Investment securities & other	13	6
Noninterest		
Wealth management fees	11	6
Debit and credit card fees	11	5
Service charges on deposit accounts	11	5
Insurance fees	6	3
Others	8	3
Total	**207**	**100**

Selected Subsidiaries

9th Street Holdings Inc.
Commonwealth Trust Credit Life Insurance Company (50%)
S&T Bank
S&T Insurance Group LLC
S&T-Evergreen Insurance LLC
S&T Bancholdings Inc.
S&T Professional Resources Group LLC
S&T Settlement Services LLC
Stewart Capital Advisors LLC

COMPETITORS

AmeriServ Financial	First Commonwealth
Citizens Financial	Financial
Group	Northwest Bancshares
F.N.B. (PA)	PNC Financial
Fidelity Bancorp (PA)	

HISTORICAL FINANCIALS

Company Type: Public

Income Statement

FYE: December 31

	ASSETS ($ mil.)	NET INCOME ($ mil.)	INCOME AS % OF ASSETS	EMPLOYEES
12/18	7,252	105	1.5%	1,040
12/17	7,060	73	1.0%	1,080
12/16	6,943	71	1.0%	1,080
12/14	4,965	58	1.2%	945
12/13	4,533	51	1.1%	948
Annual Growth	9.9%	15.8%	—	1.9%

2018 Year-End Financials

Debt ratio: 2.00%	No. of shares (mil.): 35
Return on equity: 12.00%	Dividends
Cash ($ mil.): 155	Yield: 3.0%
Current ratio: —	Payout: 33.0%
Long-term debt ($ mil.): —	Market value ($ mil.): 1,312

	STOCK PRICE ($) FY Close	P/E High/Low	PER SHARE ($) Earnings	Dividends	Book Value
12/18	38.00	16 12	3.00	1.00	27.00
12/17	40.00	21 16	2.00	1.00	25.00
12/16	39.00	19 11	2.00	1.00	24.00
12/14	30.00	16 11	2.00	1.00	20.00
12/13	25.00	15 10	2.00	1.00	19.00
Annual Growth	8.4%	— —	12.1%	10.2%	7.0%

S&P Global Inc

Say "AAA!". One of the big-three credit ratings agencies S&P Global (formerly McGraw-Hill Financial) assigns companies local governments and countries its well-known credit scores ranging from D (lowest) to AAA (highest). It also assigns ratings to corporate or municipal bonds and other individual debt issues. S&P Global's other businesses include S&P Global Market Intelligence S&P Dow Jones Indices and S&P Global Platts. Its largest market is the US which generates around 60% of the company's revenue. After it sold its education and construction businesses in 2016 the company changed its name from McGraw-Hill Financial to S&P Global.

Operations

S&P Global has four reportable segments: Ratings; Market and Commodities Intelligence; S&P Dow Jones Indices; and Global Platts.

The Ratings segment generates roughly 50% of S&P Global's total sales and provides credit ratings research and analytics to investors issuers and other market participants.

The Market and Commodities Intelligence accounts for around 40% of sales and helps the financial community track performance improve investment returns perform risk analysis and develop mitigation strategies. It comprises three business lines: Desktop Data Management Solutions and Risk Services.

S&P Dow Jones accounts for around 10% of sales and maintains a range of stock indices for investors including the Dow Jones Industrial Average and S&P 500.

S&P Global Platts a separate division since the start of 2018 provides information and benchmark prices for the commodity and energy markets.

Geographic Reach

New York-based S&P Global has more than 100 offices worldwide including around 30 in the US. The US is S&P Global's largest market at around 60% of sales. Europe generates some 25% and the Asia/Pacific region more than 10%. The Global Platts division is headquartered in London.

Sales and Marketing

S&P Global's Ratings segment serves investors corporations governments municipalities commercial and investment banks insurance companies asset managers and other debt issuers.

The company's Market and Commodities Intelligence segment serves investment managers investment banks private equity firms insurance companies commercial banks corporations professional services firms and government agencies and regulators; as well as producers traders and intermediaries within energy metals and agriculture markets.

S&P Global Platts markets to traders analysts risk managers and purchasing agents in public and private sector organizations.

The company spends millions per year on advertising and promotional costs.

Financial Performance

S&P Global's revenue has been growing year on year in all segments and major territories.

In fiscal 2017 sales grew a further 7% to $6.1 billion. Higher bank loan and corporate bond ratings revenue drove strong growth in the Ratings segment while Indices grew its revenue 15% thanks to an increase in assets under management for exchange traded funds and mutual funds. Gains in Ratings and Indices were partially offset by disposals in the Market and Commodities Intelligence segment which saw revenue shrink 5% as a result. During 2017 it sold S&P Securities Evaluations S&P Credit Market Analysis and J.D. Power.

Net income fell to $1.5 billion from a high of $2.1 billion in 2016 largely a result of the $1.1 billion gain on the sale of the J.D. Power and Associates business recorded in 2016. Underlying profitability was slightly stronger in 2017 than 2016 due to lower expense relating to disposals.

Cash from operations increased 29% to $2.0 billion due higher results from operations partially offset by the timing of tax payments.

Strategy

Over the last several years S&P Global has sold off all its businesses not relating to its core mission of providing financial and credit information. Disposals have included its education business its construction business and J.D. Power (marketing information services). In 2019 the company agreed to sell its model portfolio business to Goldman Sachs. The unit uses ETFs and mutual funds to build portfolios for financial advisers. The division also manages equity portfolios using a rules-based investment process and advises on assets of more than $33 billion.

Strong demand for S&P's Global Platts services led the company separating it out as a distinct reportable segment. It will continue to develop its product offerings and analytic capabilities and pursue growth in new markets and geographies.

Mergers and Acquisitions

In April 2018 S&P Global completed its acquisition of Kensho Technologies a provider of analytics artificial intelligence machine learning and data visualization systems. Its primary customers are Wall Street banks investment institutions and the National Security community.

In February 2018 the company acquired Panjiva Inc. a privately-held company that provides global supply chain insights by leveraging data science and technology to make sense of large unstructured datasets.

EXECUTIVES

Vice President Technology, Rosalin Danner
President And Ceo, Douglas L. (Doug) Peterson, age 60, $1,000,000 total compensation
President S&p Global Platts, Martin Fraenkel
Evp And Chief Economist, Paul Sheard, age 65
President S&p Global Ratings, John L. Berisford, age 55, $600,000 total compensation
Evp And General Counsel, Steven J. (Steve) Kemps, age 55, $204,167 total compensation
Managing Director And Ceo Crisil, Ashu Suyash, age 52
Evp And Cfo, Ewout L. Steenbergen, age 50, $99,432 total compensation
Ceo S&p Dow Jones Indices, Alexander J. (Alex) Matturri, age 60, $493,750 total compensation
Evp Public Affairs, Courtney Geduldig
President S&p Global Market Intelligence, Michael A. (Mike) Chinn, $152,308 total compensation
Svp Human Resources, France M. Gingras, age 54
Cio, Swamy Kocherlakota
Svp Of Global Real Estate Services, Mitra Meshginpoosh
Vice President Strategy And Finance, Cari Lawless
Vice President Of Marketing, Connie Howard
Vice President International Affairs, Cynthia Baraddon
Senior Vice President And Chief Financial Officer Of Ratings, Elizabeth O'melia
Vice President, Maryann Johnston
Senior Vp Corporate Strategy Financial Planning And Analysis, Saugata Saha
Senior Vice President Chief Risk, Nancy Luquette
Senior Vice President, Peter Scheschuk
Senior Vice President And Treasurer, Edward Haran
Vice President Human Resources Ratings, Sheila O'Neill
Vice President Human Resources Platts, Stacey Follon
Vice President Information Technology Infrastructure Engineering And Operations, Ron Chiang
Vice President Index Services, Roby Muntoni
National Accounts Manager, Nicole Nicdao
Vice President Sales And Relationship Management, Ari Greenberg
Vice President Marketing, Cynthia Sejas
Vice President Content Specialists, Shyam Wadhwa
Senior Vice President Chief Accounting Officer Controller, Christopher Craig
Vice President Client Development, Rosemarie Dezenzo
Vp And Global Auditor, Wale Akinwande
Vice President Human Resources, Marie Rabb
Vice President Finance, Mark Simonton
Chairman, Charles E. (Ed) Haldeman, age 70
Board Member, Kurt Schmoke
Board Member, Michael Rake
Board Member, Richard Thornburgh
Board Member, William Green
Board Member, Edward Rust
Board Member, Monique Leroux
Board Member, Rebecca Jacoby
Board Member, Stephanie Hill
Auditors: Ernst & Young LLP

LOCATIONS

HQ: S&P Global Inc
55 Water Street, New York, NY 10041
Phone: 212 438-1000
Web: www.spglobal.com

2017 Sales

	$ mil.	% of total
US	3,658	60
Europe	1,473	24
Asia	594	10
Other regions	338	6
Total	**6,063**	**100**

PRODUCTS/OPERATIONS

2017 Sales

	$ mil.	% of total
Market and Commodities Intelligence	2,452	40
Ratings	2,988	48
Indices	733	12
Adjustments	(110)	-
Total	**6,063**	**100**

COMPETITORS

A.M. Best	Fitch Ratings Inc.
Bloomberg L.P.	MSCI
D&B	Moody's
DBRS	Morningstar
Fair Isaac	Thomson Reuters

HISTORICAL FINANCIALS

Company Type: Public

Income Statement

FYE: December 31

	REVENUE ($ mil.)	NET INCOME ($ mil.)	NET PROFIT MARGIN	EMPLOYEES
12/19	6,699	2,123	31.7%	22,500
12/18	6,258	1,958	31.3%	21,200
12/17	6,063	1,496	24.7%	20,400
12/16	5,661	2,106	37.2%	20,000
12/15	5,313	1,156	21.8%	20,400
Annual Growth	**6.0%**	**16.4%**	**—**	**2.5%**

2019 Year-End Financials

Debt ratio: 35.00%
Return on equity: 384.00%
Cash ($ mil.): 2,866
Current ratio: 2.00
Long-term debt ($ mil.): 3,948

No. of shares (mil.): 244
Dividends
  Yield: 1.0%
  Payout: 27.0%
Market value ($ mil.): 66,624

	STOCK PRICE ($) FY Close	P/E High/Low	PER SHARE ($) Earnings	Dividends	Book Value
12/19	273.00	32 19	9.00	2.00	2.00
12/18	170.00	28 20	8.00	2.00	3.00
12/17	169.00	30 19	6.00	2.00	3.00
12/16	108.00	16 10	8.00	1.00	3.00
12/15	99.00	25 20	4.00	1.00	1.00
Annual Growth	**29.0%**	**— —**	**19.6%**	**14.6%**	**28.0%**

Salesforce.Com Inc

Salesforce.com Inc. is the top developer and seller of customer relationship management software with more than 150000 users. The company offers cloud-based applications that manage customer relationships including Sales Cloud Marketing and Commerce Cloud and Service Cloud (for customer support) as well as the Salesforce Platform. Other products offer e-commerce analytics and social media tools through cloud-based applications. Salesforce's customers come from a variety of industries including financial services telecommunications manufacturing entertainment and government. It generates most of its revenue in the US. Salesforce bought Tableau for about $15.7 billion in 2019.

Operations

Besides its big three cloud products ? Sales Cloud Service Cloud and Marketing and Commerce Cloud Salesforce offers several others that help companies manage their relationships with customers.

They include: Community Cloud which helps companies create and manage branded digital destinations for customers partners and employees; IoT (Internet of Things) Cloud which helps companies collect information from connected devices products sensors and apps; Analytics Cloud which helps an employee explore business data from any device; and Salesforce Quip a productivity tool designed for teams.

Salesforce also offers consulting services for deployment training and design and integration.

Most of the company's revenue comes from its subscription and support segment which accounts for nearly 95% while the rest comes from professional and other services.

The company runs many of its cloud services on Amazon Web Services Google and IBM in international markets.

Geographic Reach

Salesforce relies on customers in the US for more than two-thirds of its revenue while customers in Europe account for about 20% of revenue and those in the Asia/Pacific region generate about 10%.

Sales and Marketing

Salesforce.com counts more than 150000 users from small businesses with one subscription to large enterprises with thousands. With such a large customer base no one customer counts for more than 5% of sales.

The company uses a direct sales force made up of telephone sales reps based in regional hubs and field sales reps in territories close to their customers. It also works with consulting firms systems integrators and others to find customers. For successful sales Salesforce pays a fee based on the first-year subscription revenue generated by the referred customers.

Salesforce spends about 45% of revenue on sales and marketing a level the company expects to maintain as it seeks more customers and builds awareness.

Financial Performance

Salesforce has turned in a fast-growing revenue line for the past five years averaging a 30% annual increase as the company has added more applications to its basic customer relationship management offerings.

In 2019 (ended January) revenue hit about $13.3 billion up some $2.7 billion and a 26% increase from 2017. The growth was driven by higher subscription and support revenue from new business which includes new customers upgrades and additional subscriptions from existing customers. MuleSoft acquired in May 2018 contributed $431 million in revenue. Sales rose 24% in the Americas 33% in Europe and 28% in the Asia/Pacific region year-over-year.

Salesforce's net income leaped to $1.1 billion in 2019 from $360 million in 2018. As a percentage of revenue expenses were about the same allowing more of the higher revenue to flow to the bottom line.

Salesforce has cash and equivalents of $2.5 billion in 2019 compared to $1.6 billion in 2018. In 2019 the company's operations generated $3.4 billion while investing activities used $5.3 billion and financing activities provided $2 billion.

Strategy

Salesforce continued to generate higher revenue in 2019. Its biggest business Sales Cloud accounted for $4 billion in revenue by itself making it bigger than some independent cloud software companies. The company's other strong performer

Service Cloud brought in another $3.6 billion. While those are the big moneymakers Salesforce's customers generally buy services from more than one of the company's clouds.

To strengthen those clouds Salesforce has injected artificial intelligence into them. Called Einstein the AI element helps Salesforce's customers more effectively analyze data that help them better understand their customers. Salesforce sees Einstein as an advantage in attracting new customers as well as tempting current customers to upgrade their services.

The acquisition of MuleSoft in May 2018 added capabilities to help customers link their Salesforce applications. The unit added about $341 million to Salesforce's sales in 2019.

Salesforce went that deal one better with its proposed acquisition of Tableau Software for $15.3 billion in 2019. The deal would strengthen Salesforce's data analysis and presentation capabilities.

Salesforce and Apple reached an agreement in September 2018 to develop Salesforce apps for Apple's mobile operating system iOS. Third-party developers also can develop Salesforce-related apps for iOS. The agreement could spur salespeople wielding iPads and iPhones to use more Salesforce products.

Mergers and Acquisitions

In 2019 Salesforce in its biggest deal acquired Tableau Software which develops applications for analyzing and presenting data for $15.7 billion. With Tableau's products in its software arsenal Salesforce offers customers a more comprehensive package for data collection and analysis.

In another 2019 deal Salesforce agreed to acquire ClickSoftware a developer of field service management software for $1.35 billion in cash and shares to speed growth of its cloud-based products for customer service operations. ClickSoftware's offerings would become part of Salesforce's Service Cloud. The transaction was expected to close in the Salesforce quarter ending Oct. 31 2019.

In 2019 Salesforce agreed to buy privately held Bonobo AI which develops artificial intelligence software to gather insight on customers by analyzing phone calls texts and chats. Salesforce is to add the Bonobo software to its Salesforce Sales Cloud. Terms were not disclosed.

Salesforce acquired MapAnything also in 2019. The company markets software for map-based visualization asset tracking and route optimization to improve field sales and service team efficiency. The purchase complements Salesforce.com's Sales Cloud and Service Cloud programs.

In 2018 Salesforce bought MuleSoft which develops software for linking applications for about $6.5 billion. With the addition of MuleSoft's technologies Salesforce can help its customers connect information throughout their companies across public and private clouds and data sources. MuleSoft which went public in 2017 posted higher annual revenue but did not make a profit as an independent company.

Acquisitions in the company's 2017 fiscal year (ended January) were SteelBrick Inc. which automates the quote-to-cash process; MetaMind Inc. natural language processing and image recognition across the Salesforce clouds; BeyondCore Inc. smart data discovery technology for structured data sources; Quip Inc. productivity software; and Krux Digital Inc. a data management platform.

EXECUTIVES

Chairman And Ceo, Marc Benioff, age 54, $1,550,000 total compensation

President And Chief Strategy Officer, Alexandre (Alex) Dayon, age 51, $900,000 total compensation

Vice Chairman President And Coo, Keith G. Block, age 57, $1,150,000 total compensation

Evp Customers For Life And Chief Growth Officer, Maria Martinez, age 61

President And Cfo, Mark J. Hawkins, age 59, $750,000 total compensation

Evp Global Real Estate, Elizabeth Pinkham

President And Chief Product Officer, Bret Taylor

President Legal And General Counsel, Amy E. Weaver, age 51

Evp Corporate Relations And Chief Philanthropy Officer, Suzanne DiBianca

President And Chief People Officer, Cindy Robbins, age 46

Senior Vice President Engineering, Emin Gerba

Regional Vice President Brazil, Manny Martinez

Regional Vice President Sales Salesforce. Experience Success, Julie Hall

Regional Vice President Sales Cloud, Bhavin Shah

Vice President Reporting And Technical Accounting, Hubert Ban

Senior Vice President Internal Audit, John Beeler

Executive Vice President Operations And Mobility, Todd Pierce

Vice President Global Operations Salesforce University, Shane Anastasi

Vp Customer Success Group, Greg Tate

Vice President Sales Engineering, Mike Booth

Area Vice President, Philip Klebba

Area Vice President Automotive And Manufacturing, Paul Culpepper

Senior Vice President Central Europe, Joachim Schreiner

Vp Tpm Infrastructure Engineering, Mauricette Forzano

Senior Vice President Customer Success, Manjula Talreja

Vice President, Anil Dindigal

Senior Vice President, Jon Sigler

Vice President Enterprise Sales, Dallas Stonhaus

Vice President Of Engineering At Salesforce, Ramesh Ragineni

Area Vice President Global Strategic Accounts, Larry Shurtz

Regional Vice President Enterprise Sales, Stacy Parker

Senior Vice President Employee Marketing And Engag, Jody Kohner

Vice President Commercial Sales, Dean Tobe

Vp Esbp, Stephanie Orth

Senior Vice President Manufacturing And Consumer Goods Industries Salesforce.com, Cynthia Bolt

Svp Communities Engineering, Stephen Ayers

Area Vice President Federal Sales, Dan Davis

Regional Vice President Enterprise Sales, Charlie Rapier

Regional Vice President, Jeffrey Pope

Vice President Salesforce, Dan Whalen

Vice President, Mary Heston

Regional Vice President Customer Success, Israel Forst

Regional Vice President, Craig Lashmet

Regional Vice President, Sheldon Buytenhuys

Regional Vice President Enterprise Accounts, Dick Cotter

Vice President Customer Intelligence, Ashfaq Mohiuddin

Regional Vice President Public Sector Customers For Life, Tom Gardner

Area Vice President, Steve Moroski

Regional Vice President, David Rubinstein

Regional Vice President, Joe Haney

Regional Vice President Success Services, Jon Lokay

Regional Vice President, Tim Murdoch

Regional Vice President Commercial Sales, David Jeffrey

Regional Vice President, Andrew Bearese

Svp Smb Marketing, Marie Rosecrans

Senior Vice President Strategic Planning, Peter Schwartz

Regional Vice President Enterprise Sales, Scott Duval

Vp Product Management, Amruta Moktali

Regional Vice President Corporate Sales, Andrew Oconnor

Svp Enterprise Americas, John Vitalie

Regional Vice President Marketing Cloud, Garner White

Vice President Northern Europe, Renzo Taal

Regional Vice President, Yasuhide Inoue

Svp And Gm Salesforce Marketing Cloud Japac, Lee Hawksley

Regional Vice President Middle East And Africa, Richard McGuinness

Regional Vice President Asia Pacific Platform Analytics Service Cloud, Robert Wickham

Regional Vice President Commercial Sales Latam, Fernando Bertolla

Vp Revenue Operations Products And Enablement, Heather Atkinson

Area Vice President Sales Marketing Cloud East, Edward Mcdonnell

Vice President Marketing Cloud Experience, Mike Kaplan

Area Vice President Partner Sales, Julia Fare

Senior Vice President Communications Field Marketing, Bill Taylor

Svp Product Design And User Experience, Justin Maguire

Area Vice President, Eric Eyken-sluyters

Svp Gm Messaging, Joanna Milliken

Regional Vice President, Norman Gallagher

Regional Vice President Enterprise Sales, Reed Overby

Senior Vice President Infrastructure, Vijay Gill

Assistant Vice President Ecs West, Bruce Fiscus

Regional Vice President Enterprise Sales, Jerry Schorn

Regional Vice President Marketing Cloud, James Bishop

Regional Vice President Salesforce Marketing Cloud, Roman Howe

Vice President, Johnny Khoury

Regional Vice President Uk Commercial Sales, Conor O'malley

Vice President Enterprise Sales, Jennifer Birnie

Vice President Sales Financial Services, John Messina

Regional Vice President Enterprise Sales, Greg Rakauskas

Regional Vice President Enterprise Sales, David Chatterton

Regional Vice President, Ryan Nelson

Regional Vice President Alliances And Channels Southern Europe, Pascal Voirand

Senior Avp North America Platform Cloud Sales, Mark Desrosiers

Vice President Business Development, Brian Remmel

Regional Vp Salesforce Commerce Cloud, Charles Ellis

Vice President Platform User Experience, Guy Jenkins

Regional Vice President Of Commercial Sales, Daisuke Yasuda

Regional Vice President Sales Italy, Ezio Russo

Regional Vice President Social Sales, Sheehan Murphy

Regional Vice President Marketing Cloud, David Mcnally

Vice President Associate General Counsel Emea, Adam Burrows

Regional Vice President Alliances And Channels Gtm Asia, Francis Chong

Regional Vp Smb Asia, Chris Yio

Vice President Marketing, Sara Varni

Regional Vice President Commercial Sales, Laurent Malpeli

Rvp Sales Data And Audiences, Frederick Stanichev

Vice President Area, Markus Ehrle

Area Vice President Of Sales, Christina Meitus

Regional Vice President Sales, Federico Casa

Senior Vice President Government Affairs And Public Policy, Jim Green

Vice President Compliance, Perez Art

Assistant Vice President Retail, Gibson Scott

Svp Total Rewards And Mobility, Stan Dunlap

Vice President And Associate General Counsel Corporate And Securities, Sarah Dods

Regional Vice President Sales (marketing Cloud), Mike Silvester

Vice President Data Science Apps, Robin Glinton

Regional Vice President Co Prime Sales, Alwin Schauer

Regional Vice President Strategic Sales, Sebastien Zins

Vice President Gtm Alliances Apac, Charles Woodall

Regional Vice President Platform, Biliouris Mike

Regional Vice President West, John Danahy

Vice President Employee Success, Mark Gundacker

Regional Vice President Enterprise Sales, Brad Hanggi

Vice President Global Sales Strategy And Planning, Ozlem Yuksel

Vice President Global Sales Strategy And Planning, Randy Stone

Vp Customer Success, Michael Rouleau

Vp Product Infrastructure, Kartik Chandrayana

Vice President Public Sector Solution Engineering, Todd Lesser

Area Vice President Sales, Jeremy Thies

Vice President Enterprise Retail, Christian Conway

Senior Vice President, Lauren Cannizzo

Regional Vice President Enterprise Sales, Lobdell Chris

Vp Product Management, Kathryn Murphy

Senior Vice President And General Manager, Mike Milburn

Vice President Global Recruiting Futureforce, Dellisanti Suzana

Vice President Voting Systems, Bill Pessin

Senior Vice President Product Management, Liam Doyle

Senior Vice President, Kori Obrien

Auditors: Ernst & Young LLP

LOCATIONS

HQ: Salesforce.Com Inc
Salesforce Tower, 415 Mission Street, 3rd Fl, San Francisco, CA 94105
Phone: 415 901-7000
Web: www.salesforce.com

2019 Sales

	$ mil.	% of total
Americas	9,445	71
Europe	2,553	19
Asia/Pacific	1,284	10
Total	13,282	100

PRODUCTS/OPERATIONS

2019 Sales

	$ mil.	% of total
Subscription & support	12,413	93
Professional services & other	869	7
Total	13,282	100

COMPETITORS

CDC Software	Microsoft Dynamics
Google	NetSuite
Hewlett Packard Enterprise	Oracle
	SAP
IBM	Sage Software
Infor Global	ServiceNow
KANA	SugarCRM

HISTORICAL FINANCIALS

Company Type: Public

Income Statement   FYE: January 31

	REVENUE ($ mil.)	NET INCOME ($ mil.)	NET PROFIT MARGIN	EMPLOYEES
01/19	13,282	1,110	8.4%	35,000
01/18	10,480	127	1.2%	29,000
01/17	8,392	180	2.1%	25,000
01/16	6,667	(47)	—	19,000
01/15	5,374	(263)	—	16,000
Annual Growth	25.4%	—	—	21.6%

2019 Year-End Financials

Debt ratio: 10.00%
Return on equity: 9.00%
Cash ($ mil.): 2,669
Current ratio: 1.00
Long-term debt ($ mil.): 3,173

No. of shares (mil.): 770
Dividends
Yield: —
Payout: —
Market value ($ mil.): 117,017

	STOCK PRICE ($) FY Close	P/E High/Low	PER SHARE ($) Earnings	Dividends	Book Value
01/19	152.00	108 70	1.00	0.00	20.00
01/18	114.00	632437	0.00	0.00	13.00
01/17	79.00	322208	0.00	0.00	11.00
01/16	68.00	— —	(0.00)	0.00	7.00
01/15	56.00	— —	(0.00)	0.00	6.00
Annual Growth	28.1%	— —	—	—	35.0%

Sandy Spring Bancorp Inc

Sandy Spring Bancorp is the holding company for Sandy Spring Bank which operates around 50 branches in the Baltimore and Washington DC metropolitan areas. Founded in 1868 the bank is one of the largest and oldest headquartered in Maryland. It provides standard deposit services including checking and savings accounts money market accounts and CDs. Commercial and residential real estate loans account for nearly three-quarters of the company's loan portfolio; the remainder is a mix of consumer loans business loans and equipment leases. The company also offers personal investing services wealth management trust services insurance and retirement planning.

Operations

Sandy Spring Bancorp's nonbank subsidiaries include money manager West Financial Services and Sandy Spring Insurance which sells annuities and operates insurance agencies Chesapeake Insurance Group and Neff & Associates.

Financial Performance

The company's revenue increased in fiscal 2013 compared to the previous year. It reported $196.9 million in revenue for fiscal 2013 after bringing in revenue of $190.8 million in fiscal 2012.

The company's net income also went up in fiscal 2013 compared to the prior period. It claimed a profit of about $44 million in fiscal 2013 after netting a little more than $36 million in fiscal 2012.

Sandy Spring Bancorp's cash on hand increased by about $43 million in fiscal 2013 compared to fiscal 2012 levels.

Mergers and Acquisitions

In 2012 Sandy Spring Bancorp acquired CommerceFirst Bancorp a small Maryland bank with a strong Small Business Administration lending practice. The $25.4 million transaction added five branches to Sandy Spring Bank's network.

EXECUTIVES

Evp General Counsel And Secretary, Ronald E. Kuykendall, age 66, $279,039 total compensation

Evp Wealth Management Insurance Mortgage, R. Louis (Lou) Caceres, age 56, $333,865 total compensation

President And Ceo Bancorp And Bank, Daniel J. (Dan) Schrider, age 54, $600,692 total compensation

Evp And Cfo Bancorp And Bank, Philip J. Mantua, age 60, $333,192 total compensation

Evp And Cio, John D. Sadowski, age 55

Evp Commercial And Retail Banking, Joseph O'Brien, $355,038 total compensation

Evp And Chief Credit Officer, Ronda M. McDowell

Vice President, Brian Schott

Vice President Private Banking Relationship Manager, Victor Emeogo

Vice President, Christopher Huang

Senior Business Analyst Assistant Vice President, Stephen Marsico

Vice President Marketing Communications Manager, Jennifer Schell

Assistant Vice President Team Leader, Tamika Daniels

Vice President, Denise Kratz

Vice President Hris Project Administrator, Patti Boyle

Vice President, Isaac Sterbenz

Vice President Commercial Lending, Heather Burke

Assistant Vice President Public Relations Specialist, Amanda Walsh

Senior Vice President, Scott Sims

Vice President, William Grahe

Senior Vice President Commercial Relatio, Wendy Lance

Senior Vice President, Glen Buco

Vice President Ecommerce, Lisa Johnson

Assistant Vice President Branch Manager, Phil Hicks

Vice President And Underwriter, Jacqueline Gerhart

Vice President, James Holochuk

Vice President Facilities, Thomas Gemmell

Senior Vice President Alternative Delivery, Don Haasen

Vice President Debit And Credit Card Product Manager, Ron Waters

Vice President, Michael Mckeon

Vice President Commercial Relationship Manager, James Bear

Executive Vice President, Lou Caceres

Senior Vice President, Laurie Kramer

Vice President, Christine Wilson

Vice President Corporate Paralegal, Lori Shipley

Vice President, Cave Katie

Vice President And Insurance And Surety Bonding, Fred Hildebrand

Senior Vice President Director Of Regulatory Management, Diane Slack

Senior Vice President Marketing, Amalia G Kastberg

Assistant Vice President, Alexis Vining

Vice President, Todd Levine

Vice President Mortgage Banker, Jeff Starcher

Senior Vice President Marketing, Amalia Kastberg

Senior Vice President, Michael Acton

Senior Vice President Financial Reporting, Joseph Dennis

Vice President, Philip Fish

Vice President, Jackie Yankanich

Vice President, Asma Iqbal

Vice President, Dushanti Peiris

Vice President, Michael Groft

Vice President Commercial Banking Treasury Management Division, Monica Tressler

Vice President Senior Mortgage Banker, Doug Benner

Senior Vice President, Michelle Levenson

Chairman, Robert L. Orndorff, age 63

Auditors: Ernst & Young LLP

LOCATIONS

HQ: Sandy Spring Bancorp Inc
17801 Georgia Avenue, Olney, MD 20832
Phone: 301 774-6400
Web: www.sandyspringbank.com

PRODUCTS/OPERATIONS

2015 Sales

	$ mil.	% of total
Interest Income:		
Interest and fees on loans and leases	135	65
Interest and dividends on investment securities	23	11
Other	1	-
Non-interest Income:		
Wealth management income	20	10
Service charges on deposit accounts	8	4
Insurance agency commissions	5	2
Bank card fees	5	2
Mortgage banking activities	3	2
Other Income	9	4
Total	**208**	**100**

COMPETITORS

BB&T	Fulton Financial
Bank of America	OBA Financial Services
Bay Bancorp	PNC Financial
Capital One	SunTrust

HISTORICAL FINANCIALS

Company Type: Public

Income Statement

FYE: December 31

	ASSETS ($ mil.)	NET INCOME ($ mil.)	INCOME AS % OF ASSETS	EMPLOYEES
12/18	8,243	101	1.2%	932
12/17	5,447	53	1.0%	754
12/16	5,091	48	0.9%	752
12/15	4,655	45	1.0%	737
12/14	4,397	38	0.9%	727
Annual Growth	17.0%	27.5%	—	6.4%

2018 Year-End Financials

Debt ratio: 0.00%	No. of shares (mil.): 36
Return on equity: 12.00%	Dividends
Cash ($ mil.): 101	Yield: 4.0%
Current ratio: —	Payout: 45.0%
Long-term debt ($ mil.): —	Market value ($ mil.): 1,114

	STOCK PRICE ($) FY Close	P/E High/Low	PER SHARE ($) Earnings	Dividends	Book Value
12/18	31.00	15 11	3.00	1.00	30.00
12/17	39.00	21 17	2.00	1.00	23.00
12/16	40.00	20 12	2.00	1.00	22.00
12/15	27.00	16 13	2.00	1.00	22.00
12/14	26.00	18 15	2.00	1.00	21.00
Annual Growth	4.7%	— —	16.7%	9.7%	9.6%

Sanmina Corp

Contract manufacturer Sanmina makes the boards and components that make up many an electronic device. Starting with the design stage the company makes assembles and tests printed circuit boards. It also makes backplanes cable assemblies radio frequency and optical components and modules and memory modules. Besides products Sanmina provides services such as engineering materials management and order fulfillment. Its customers are OEMs in the healthcare defense medical aerospace telecommunications and technology industries among others. Sanmina operates about 25 manufacturing facilities on six continents. The California-based company gets more than 80% of its sales from outside the US.

Operations

Sanmina's Integrated Manufacturing Solutions unit (about 80% of sales) makes printed circuit boards optical and radio frequency modules and conducts assembly and testing. The Components Products and Services unit (about 20% of sales) makes interconnect systems and mechanical systems components in addition to memory and storage products.

The company has more than 12.5 million sq.ft. of manufacturing space.

Geographic Reach

Sanmina based in San Jose California operates nearly 75 facilities in some 25 countries. Mexico is the company's largest geographic segment accounting for about 30% of revenue. US customers account for 20% of revenue while China generates about 15%.

Sales and Marketing

Sanmina supplies OEMs primarily in the communications networks defense and aerospace industrial and semiconductor systems medical computing automotive sectors. The industrial medical defense and automotive market accounts for more than half of the company's sales communication network customers generate nearly 40% and the company's cloud business supplies some 10%.

The company depends on 10 customers for half of its sales. Two of them Nokia and Motorola Solutions each account for about 10% of Sanmina's revenue.

Sanmina sells through its direct sales force as well as representative sales firms.

Financial Performance

Sanmina posted higher revenue for the fifth year in a row with a 3.5% rise to $7.1 billion in 2018 (ended September) from 2017. In 2018 sales in the industrial medical defense and automotive end market increased about 8% on growth in medical products and automotive products while industrial products sales were lower. Sales were up 1.3% in the communications networks business but the cloud segment's sales fell 9.5%.

The company recorded a net loss of $95.5 due to about $30 million in restructuring charges and a $161 million tax expense related to the US Tax Cuts and Jobs Act.

Sanmina held $420 million in cash and equivalents at the end of 2018 compared to $407 million for 2017. The company's operating activities generated $156 million in 2018 while investing and financing activities used $116 million and $28 million respectively.

Strategy

As Sanmina pursues new business the company targets work with higher system complexity in heavily regulated markets. Those jobs carry higher margins and allow Sanmina to use the expertise it's built up in developing and making higher-end systems. As part of that strategy the company combined its medical business with its defense industrial and automotive segment.

In the communication networks business Sanmina expects that the arrival of 5G networks will create opportunities for growth. The company looks for demand for its capabilities in optical components and switches.

The company in 2018 began a restructuring in which it closed some facilities with more actions to follow.

The company maintains it is positioned to deal with trade tensions between the US and China saying that its worldwide footprint enables it to switch manufacturing locations to avoid tariffs. A prolonged trade dispute could stretch its coping strategy which has included passing on higher costs to customers.

Company Background

Jure Sola and Milan Madaric founded Sanmina in 1980 as Sanmina. Sola still serves as executive chairman of the company.

EXECUTIVES

Ceo, Robert K. (Bob) Eulau, age 57, $510,000 total compensation

Evp Europe And Asia Sales, Dennis R. Young, age 68, $350,000 total compensation

Svp And Cio, Manesh Patel

Evp Global Human Resources, Alan M. Reid, age 56, $290,000 total compensation

Evp And Cfo, David Anderson, age 59

Vp Business Development, Charlie Mason

Vice President Of Sales, Darryl Smith

Vp Hr Emea, Lindsey Tullett

Vice President Of Finance, Sonia Ng

Vice President Business Development, James Murphy

Vp Global Supply Management, John Yapp

Executive Vice President Sanmina China, Edmund Yuen

Vice President Corporate Development, George Chen

Vice President Quality Assurance And Ra, Tim McGinnis

Vice President Supply Chain, Tom Pendergrass

Vice President And General Manager Sanmina Global Services, Adolfo Anzaldua

Vice President Embedded Connected And Cloud Solutions, Brad Draves

Vice President Manufacturing, Norman Evans

Vice President Global Operations, Levente Szekely

Vice President, George Korolog

Senior Vice President Corporate Devel, Robin Walker

Vice President And Plant Manager, Carl Duckett

Senior Vice President Of Worldwide Med, Seamus Grady

Senior Vice President Of Sales Western Region, Ed Archer

Vice President Finance Tcg, Ted Wilson

Vice President, Michael Sparacino

Executive Vice President, Robert Alberico

Senior Vice President Sales And Marketing Optical And Micro Electronics, Nat Mani

Vice President Internal Audit, Aroon Gudibande

Vice President Global Business Services, Jean-Marc Orozco

Senior Vice President Pcb Operations, Steve Bruton

Vice President Tech, Dale Kersten

Svp East Coast Operations, Jose Carrasquillo

Vice President Global Strategic Accounts, Pierre Atchison

Senior Vice President, Bob Moffat

Senior Vice President Of Global Sales, Kevin Walkup

Vice President Business Development, David Roeloffs

Vp Gsm, Ivy Ong

Vice President Of Operations, Jay Caton

Server Development Vice President, Rick Kumar

Chairman, Jure Sola, age 68

Board Member, John Goldsberry

Board Member, Wayne Shortridge

Board Member, Joseph Licata

Board Of Director, Gene Sapp

Board Member, William Delaney

Auditors: PricewaterhouseCoopers LLP

LOCATIONS

HQ: Sanmina Corp
2700 N. First St., San Jose, CA 95134
Phone: 408 964-3500
Web: www.sanmina.com

2018 Sales

	$ mil.	% of total
Mexico	2,068	29
China	1,196	17
US	1,338	19
Malaysia	688	10
Other countries	1,820	25
Total	**7,110**	**100**

PRODUCTS/OPERATIONS

2018 Sales

	$ mil.	% of total
Industrial Medical Defense and Automotive	3,682	52
Communications Networks	2,685	38
Cloud Solutions	744	10
Total	**7,110**	**100**

2018 Sales

	$ mil.	% of total
IMS	58,485	80
CPS	1,459	20
Inter segment Revenue	(196.7)	.
Total	**7,110**	**100**

Selected Services

Backplane assembly
Cable assembly
Circuit assembly
Circuit fabrication
Configuration
Distribution
Enclosures
Engineering
Forward logistics
In-circuit testing
Inventory management
Materials management
Order fulfillment
Printed circuit board design
Reverse engineering
Sustaining engineering
System assembly and testing

COMPETITORS

Benchmark Electronics	Nam Tai
Celestica	Plexus
Flextronics	SMTC Corp.
Hon Hai	SYNNEX
Jabil	TTM Technologies
Lexmark	Venture Corp.
Molex	
Multi-Fineline	
Electronix	

HISTORICAL FINANCIALS

Company Type: Public

Income Statement   FYE: September 28

	REVENUE ($ mil.)	NET INCOME ($ mil.)	NET PROFIT MARGIN	EMPLOYEES
09/19	8,234	142	1.7%	43,000
09/18	7,110	(96)	—	47,000
09/17*	6,869	139	2.0%	47,000
10/16	6,481	188	2.9%	45,397
10/15	6,375	377	5.9%	43,854
Annual Growth	**6.6%**	**(21.7%)**	**—**	**(0.5%)**

*Fiscal year change

2019 Year-End Financials

Debt ratio: 10.00%
Return on equity: 9.00%
Cash ($ mil.): 455
Current ratio: 2.00
Long-term debt ($ mil.): 347

No. of shares (mil.): 70
Dividends
  Yield: —
  Payout: —
Market value ($ mil.): 2,239

	STOCK PRICE ($) FY Close	P/E High/Low		PER SHARE ($) Earnings	Dividends	Book Value
09/19	32.00	17	11	2.00	0.00	24.00
09/18	28.00	—	—	(1.00)	0.00	22.00
09/17*	37.00	23	15	2.00	0.00	23.00
10/16	28.00	12	7	2.00	0.00	22.00
10/15	21.00	6	4	4.00	0.00	19.00
Annual Growth	**10.7%**	—	—	**(18.2%)**	—	**4.9%**

*Fiscal year change

Santander Consumer USA Holdings Inc

This auto finance company aims to put credit-impaired car buyers in the driver's seat. Santander Consumer USA (SCUSA) makes subprime new and used vehicle loans to buyers at more than 14000 Chrysler Ford GM and Toyota dealerships throughout the US. The technology-driven company also originates loans through independent dealers such as CarMax banks and its direct-to-consumer website Roadloans.com. SCUSA also provides refinancing and cash-back refinancing services. While subprime loans make up more than 80% of its loan portfolio the company is looking to increase its prime loan business. Founded in 1995 SCUSA is owned by Spanish banking giant Banco Santander SA. The company went public in 2014.

IPO

Santander Consumer USA (SCUSA) went public in January 2014 with an offering valued at $1.5 billion. The IPO capitalizes on the rebound in auto sales as credit-impaired borrowers return to the car market. Post IPO Banco Santander owns 61% of SCUSA.

Financial Performance

The auto lender reported more than $2.9 billion in finance and other interest income in 2012 a 14% increase versus 2011.

Strategy

SCUSA is looking to expand its portfolio of prime loans through partnerships with automakers. To that end in February 2013 SCUSA entered into a 10-year agreement with Chrysler whereby it originates private-label loans and leases under the Chrysler Capital brand. The company relies on third-party banks and parent company Banco Santander for approximately $12 billion and $5 billion respectively in committed financing. It also has agreements with Bank of America and Sovereign to fund the Chrysler Capital business.

Company Background

In 2006 Banco Santander acquired a 90% stake in Drive Financial from HBOS and the company's founding partners for $651 million. Drive changed its name to Santander Consumer USA in 2008.

EXECUTIVES

Board Member, Edith Holiday
Auditors: PricewaterhouseCoopers LLP

LOCATIONS

HQ: Santander Consumer USA Holdings Inc
1601 Elm Street, Suite 800, Dallas, TX 75201
Phone: 214 634-1110
Web: www.santanderconsumerusa.com

COMPETITORS

Ally Bank	Credit Acceptance
Bank of America	Ford Motor Credit
Capital One Auto Finance	GM Financial
	Toyota Motor Credit

HISTORICAL FINANCIALS

Company Type: Public

Income Statement

FYE: December 31

	ASSETS ($ mil.)	NET INCOME ($ mil.)	INCOME AS % OF ASSETS	EMPLOYEES
12/18	43,960	916	2.1%	4,952
12/17	39,422	1,188	3.0%	5,076
12/16	38,539	766	2.0%	5,100
12/15	36,570	827	2.3%	5,100
12/14	32,342	766	2.4%	4,400
Annual Growth	8.0%	4.6%	—	3.0%

2018 Year-End Financials

Debt ratio: 79.00%
Return on equity: 14.00%
Cash ($ mil.): 148
Current ratio: —
Long-term debt ($ mil.): —

No. of shares (mil.): 352
Dividends
Yield: 3.0%
Payout: 20.0%
Market value ($ mil.): 6,197

	STOCK PRICE ($) FY Close	P/E High/Low		PER SHARE ($) Earnings	Dividends	Book Value
12/18	18.00	9	6	3.00	1.00	20.00
12/17	19.00	6	3	3.00	0.00	18.00
12/16	14.00	7	4	2.00	0.00	15.00
12/15	16.00	11	7	2.00	0.00	12.00
12/14	20.00	12	8	2.00	0.00	10.00
Annual Growth	(2.7%)	—	—	4.3%	35.1%	18.2%

Santander Holdings USA Inc.

Santander Holdings USA is the parent company of Sovereign Bank which reigns in the Northeast with more than 700 branch locations. TheÂ bankÂ caters to individuals and small to midsized businesses offeringÂ deposits creditÂ cards insurance and investmentsÂ as well as commercial loans and mortgages (which together account for nearlyÂ half of its total portfolio) and residential mortgages and home equity loansÂ (more than a quarter).Â Santander Holdings also owns a majority of Santander Consumer USA which purchases and services subprime car loans made byÂ auto dealerships and other companies.Â Spain-based banking giant Banco Santander acquired the rest of Sovereign BancorpÂ it didn't already own in 2009.

EXECUTIVES

Vice President And Manager Commercial Real Estate Department, Frank Picone
Vice President, Donna Valente
Vice President, Matthew Bartlett
Vice President Market Planner Real Estate Strategy Branch Transformation, David Kurnik
Assistant Vice President And Credit Officer, Ligerta Vezuli
Auditors: PricewaterhouseCoopers LLP

LOCATIONS

HQ: Santander Holdings USA Inc.
75 State Street, Boston, MA 02109
Phone: 617 346-7200
Web:
www.santanderus.com/us/investorshareholderrelations

Selected Locations

Connecticut

Delaware

Maryland

Massachusetts
New Hampshire
New Jersey
New York
Pennsylvania
Rhode Island

PRODUCTS/OPERATIONS

2013 Sales

	$ mil.	% of total
Interest		
Loans	1,959	58
Investment securities	331	10
Deposits	7	.
Noninterest		
Equity method investment	427	12
Consumer banking fees	229	7
Commercial banking fees	200	6
Mortgage bankin revenue	122	4
Bank owned life insurance	57	3
Others	54	.
Total	3,384	100

COMPETITORS

Bank of America	M&T Bank
Citibank	PNC Financial
Citizens Financial Group	People's United Financial
Fulton Financial	TD Bank USA
HSBC USA	Webster Financial
JPMorgan Chase	Wells Fargo
KeyCorp	

HISTORICAL FINANCIALS

Company Type: Public

Income Statement

FYE: December 31

	REVENUE ($ mil.)	NET INCOME ($ mil.)	NET PROFIT MARGIN	EMPLOYEES
12/18	11,313	707	6.3%	16,700
12/17	10,716	561	5.2%	17,000
12/16	10,745	363	3.4%	16,500
12/15	10,474	(1,455)	—	15,150
12/14	11,919	2,335	19.6%	14,000
Annual Growth	(1.3%)	(25.8%)	—	4.5%

2018 Year-End Financials

Debt ratio: 33.00%
Return on equity: 3.00%
Cash ($ mil.): 7,791
Current ratio: 0.00
Long-term debt ($ mil.): 44,954

No. of shares (mil.): 530
Dividends
Yield: 0.0%
Payout: 58.0%
Market value ($ mil.): —

	STOCK PRICE ($) FY Close	P/E High/Low		PER SHARE ($) Earnings	Dividends	Book Value
12/18	0.00	—	—	(0.00)	1.00	40.00
12/17	26.00	—	—	(0.00)	2.00	40.00
12/16	26.00	—	—	(0.00)	2.00	37.00
12/15	26.00	—	—	(0.00)	2.00	32.00
Annual Growth	—	—	—	—	(6.9%)	5.6%

Schein (Henry) Inc

From Poughkeepsie to Prague Henry Schein outfits dental offices around the world with everything they need. The company is a leading global distributor of dental supplies equipment and pharmaceuticals. Henry Schein provides everything from delicate hand-held tools up to X-ray equipment and patient chair accessories as well as office supplies and anesthetics. But the company isn't only interested in teeth: It also supplies doctors' offices and other office-based health care providers with diagnostic kits surgical tools drugs and vaccines. Other offerings include practice management software repair services and financing. The US accounts for about 65% of revenue.

Operations

Henry Schein's health care distribution segment accounts for more than 95% of the company's sales and is divided into three smaller divisions: global dental (accounting for around half of sales) medical (20%) and animal health (more than 25%). Altogether Henry Schein offers more than 120000 branded and private-label products as well as 180000 special order offerings.

The company spun off its animal health business in 2019.

Henry Schein also has a health care technology and value-added services segment which provides practice management software hardware and other technology systems as well as e-commerce and financial services.

Geographic Reach

Henry Schein is headquartered in Melville New York and has locations across the US. It also has dental and medical distribution operations or affiliates in more than 30 countries in the Asia/Pacific region Europe the Americas and Africa.

The company invests in building its business in China Brazil and South Africa but it depends on the US market to supply about 65% of annual revenue.

Sales and Marketing

Henry Schein markets health care products to office-based dentists and physicians as well as dental labs surgery centers government and community clinics and other alternative care locations. The company's field sales force of more than 3600 sales consultants (including equipment sales specialists) and about 1900 telesales representatives primarily serve the North American and European markets as well as other select international regions. The firm also sells through social media and e-commerce platforms.

Henry Schein's global dental group serves office-based dental practitioners laboratories schools and other institutions. Its medical group serves office-based medical practitioners ambulatory surgery centers and other care settings.

Financial Performance

Henry Schein has grown through acquisitive and organic measures which has led to an average revenue increase of about 5% over the last five years.

In 2018 sales rose about 6% to $13.2 billion from 2017 boosted by higher revenue in each segment. In the dental business sales of equipment and consumable merchandise were higher. Acquisitions also contributed.

The company's net income jumped $129 million to $535.9 million in 2018 from 2017 with help from a lower tax bill in 2018 compared to 2017.

Henry Schein's coffers held $80.2 million in cash and equivalents in 2018 some $94 million less than in 2017. Operations generated about $648.7 million in 2018 while investing and financing activities used $193 million and $603.8 million respectively.

Strategy

Henry Schein is a leader in the North American dental supply market. One root of its success is its extensive network of distribution centers for quickly filling and delivering orders to nearby customers.

In 2019 Henry Schein spun off its animal health business into a separate company Covetrus allowing each company to focus on its key markets. Henry Schein received $1.1 billion cash distribution from the transaction that it used to pay down debt.

Branching out beyond dental and medical tools Henry Schein and Internet Brands formed a joint venture Henry Schein One to provide practice management tools to dentists. Henry Schein looks for organic growth from the business as well for opportunities to expand it through acquisitions.

Through the acquisition of North American Rescue (NAR) the company got access to NAR's customer roster of defense and public safety customers for medical supplies.

Henry Schein plans to invest in the growing dental specialty areas for implants bone regeneration and endodontic and orthodontic products. Geographically the company invests in increasing its reach in China where it had about $60 million in sales in 2018. It also expanded in Brazil with several aquisitions.

The company faces new competition from Amazon which is sourcing dental supplies directly from Dentsply Sirona. Although Amazon is not a major player in the dental supply business it has become increasingly involved in health care and could pose a threat to Henry Schein should it decide to penetrate the market further.

Mergers and Acquisitions

In early 2019 Henry Schein acquired North American Rescue which supplies medical products used by first responders. The purchase expanded its domestic and foreign military businesses.

In 2019 Henry Schein acquired Lighthouse 360 through its Henry Schein One joint venture with Internet Brands. Lighthouse 360 provides dental practice management and patient communication software that will expand Lighthouse 360's offerings.

In 2018 the company acquired a majority stake in Brazilian veterinary products distributor ABASE. In early 2017 the company bought a majority stake in Brazilian distributor Dental Cremer which serves some 90000 dental practitioners. It also acquired a 51% stake in Tecnew which distributes animal health products in Brazil.

Also that year it bought South Carolina-based Merritt Veterinary Supplies which serves clinics across the US's eastern region as well as Southern Anesthesia + Surgical (also based in South Carolina) which distributes products across the US.

Henry Schein ended 2017 with the acquisition of Georgia-based eVetPractice which provides cloud-based practice management solutions to veterinary clinics. That purchase included AVImark and ImproMed in North America as well as Vision RxWorks and RoboVet in international markets.

Company Background

For more than 50 years Henry Schein distributed drugs made by Schein Pharmaceuticals. In 1992 management spun off the drug business and led by former accountant Stanley Bergman began acquiring other dental supply companies at a terrific rate: 34 between 1994 and 1996 alone.

The company went public in 1995 and bought more than a dozen businesses. These purchases which included product marketer Vertex Corp.'s distribution unit moved Henry Schein into the medical and veterinary supply fields. The purchase of Schein Dental Equipment (founded by Marvin

Schein) boosted per-customer sales by adding big-ticket merchandise to the product mix.

HISTORY

For more than 50 years Henry Schein distributed drugs made by Schein Pharmaceuticals. In 1992 management spun off the drug business and led by former accountant Stanley Bergman began acquiring other dental supply companies at a terrific rate: 34 between 1994 and 1996 alone.

The company went public in 1995 and bought more than a dozen businesses. These purchases which included product marketer Vertex Corporation's distribution unit moved Henry Schein into the medical and veterinary supply fields. The purchase of Schein Dental Equipment (founded by Marvin Schein) boosted per-customer sales by adding big-ticket merchandise to the product mix.

Acquisitions continued hot and heavy as the company boosted operations abroad. The purchases hit the bottom line; Schein avoided bloat by restructuring operations closing facilities and developing new systems. The company consolidated 13 distribution centers into five in 1997. The following year the firm expanded into Canada and bought a controlling stake in UK direct marketer Porter Nash.

To boost profits the company announced in 2000 that it would cut 5% of its workforce. It also shut down some facilities and sold its software development business as part of its overall restructuring plan. In 2001 the firm resumed its acquisitions when it bought the dental supply business of drug maker Zila. Over the next few years it expanded internationally when it bought up firms in the Czech Republic Germany Italy New Zealand and the UK.

Choosing to focus on supplying office-based health care practitioners in 2006 it sold its hospital supply business for $36.5 million. Other dispositions have included the sale of its oncology and specialty pharmaceutical businesses (2007) and a dental products wholesaler (2009). In 2009 Henry Schein acquired a majority stake in Butler Animal Health tripling the size of its domestic animal health operations; the unit was renamed Butler Schein Animal Health following the deal. (The company increased its stake in Butler Schein Animal Health to about 72% in 2012.)

Henry Schein expanded its health care technology segment in 2010 through the acquisition of majority ownership of ImproMed and McAllister Software Systems both developers of veterinary practice management systems in the US. In 2011 the company entered the veterinary market in Australia and New Zealand with the $92 million buy of Provet Holdings. The purchase helped Henry Schein cement its strategy to expand its international health care distribution unit.

EXECUTIVES

Evp And Chief Strategic Officer, Mark E. Mlotek, age 63, $555,962 total compensation

Evp And Chief Administrative Officer, Gerald A. Benjamin, age 66, $551,308 total compensation

President; Ceo Global Dental Group, James P. Breslawski, age 65, $698,769 total compensation

Evp And Cfo, Steven Paladino, age 62, $551,308 total compensation

Chairman And Ceo, Stanley M. Bergman, age 70, $1,342,385 total compensation

Svp And Chief Merchandising Officer, Michael Racioppi, age 64, $340,275 total compensation

President Henry Schein Europe, Robert (Bob) Minowitz, age 60

Chief Commercial Officer; President Corporate Commercial Development Group, David C. (Dave) McKinley, age 66

Svp And Cto, James A. (Jim) Harding, age 63

Evp; Ceo Global Animal Health Medical And Dental Surgical Group, Karen Prange, age 55, $410,000 total compensation

President Global Animal Health Group, Peter McCarthy

President Global Medical Group, Bridget A. Ross, age 54

Vice President Global E Commerce, Robert Lamb

Vice President Corporate Finance, Ronald South

Vice President Investor Relations, Carolynne Borders

Vice President Finance, Charles Crawford

Vice President, Patrick Allen

Sales Vice President, Gerard Metselaar

Vice President Product Merchandising, Marguerite Walsh

Vice President Business Planning And Development, Rich Miranda

Vice President And General Manager, Rita Acquafredda

Vice President Of Technology Sales, John Cox

Vice President, Marie Woods

Vice President Regulatory Affairs, Jeff Peacock

Vp European Purchasing And Inventory Management, Lezlee Blackburn

Vice President North American Distribution, Michael Richardson

Vice President Marketing Canada, Peter Jugoon

Vice President Sales Midwest, Cy Elborne

Vice President Of Customer Services And Technical Support, Genevieve Tap

Vice President Business Development, Edward L Mohr

Vice President Business Development, Richard Miranda

National Sales Manager, Deanna Evans

Vice President National Telesales Operations, Jim Loiacono

National Sales Manager, Bill Nixon

Vice President Corporate Business Development, Scott Sanders

Vice President Director Of Operations, Ravi Bhir

Vice President, Jesse Garringer

Vice President, Don Cohen

Vp And General Auditor, James Patterson

Vice President, Gene Heller

Vice President Customer Service And Facilities, Jim Mullins

National Sales Manager, Deanna Wright

Vice President Dental Marketing, Joachim Feldmer

Vice President Global Marketing, Shirley Stanley

Vice President Technology Global Prosthetic Solutions, Patrick Thurm

Vp Safety, Shirley Taylor

Vice President Supply Chain Services, Jurgen Debrier

Vp Us Distribution, Jeff Reade

Vice President Business Development And Strategic Relationships, David Chen

Vice President Data And Business Analytics, Diana Friedman

Vice President Financial Reporting Taxation, Reid Arstark

National Sales Manager, Eve Ohea

Vice President Corporate Business Development, Jd Friedland

Vp Process Improvement; Vp Administration North America, Jim Huether

Vice President Corporate Business Development An, John Kristich

National Sales Manager, Christian Marsolais

National Account Manager, John Ballarin

Vice President And General Manager Pharmaceutical And Nutritional Products Global Animal Health, Gilles Guillemette

Vp Europe Dental Western Region; Managing Director France, Vincent Junod

Vp Marketing North America Dental Group, Mark Hillebrandt

Vice President Global Supply Chain Europe, Axel Pfitzenreiter
Vice President, Brian Peterson
Senior Vice President And Chief Executive Officer Global Dental Group, Jonathan Koch
Vice President, Howard Tapler
Vice President North America Digital Dental Marketing, Leigh Benowitz
National Sales Manager U.s, John Stango
Vice President Global Compensation And Benefits, Jonathan Lee
Executive Vice President Of Sales, Ann Gothard
Auditors: BDO USA, LLP

LOCATIONS

HQ: Schein (Henry) Inc
135 Duryea Road, Melville, NY 11747
Phone: 631 843-5500
Web: www.henryschein.com

2018 Sales

	$ mil.	% of total
US	8,348	63
Other countries	4,854	37
Total	**13,202**	**100**

PRODUCTS/OPERATIONS

2018 Sales by Segment

	$ mil.	% of total
Health Care Distribution		
Dental	6,349	48
Animal health	3,683	28
Medical	2,661	20
Technology and Value-Added Services	509	4
Total	**13,202**	**100**

COMPETITORS

Allscripts	McKesson
Benco Dental	Medline Industries
Burkhart Dental	NextGen
Cardinal Health	Patterson Companies
Carestream Health	Sybron Dental
Darby Dental	athenahealth
IDEXX Labs	eClinicalWorks
MWI Veterinary Supply	

HISTORICAL FINANCIALS

Company Type: Public

Income Statement — FYE: December 29

	REVENUE ($ mil.)	NET INCOME ($ mil.)	NET PROFIT MARGIN	EMPLOYEES
12/18	13,202	536	4.1%	18,000
12/17	12,462	406	3.3%	22,000
12/16	11,572	507	4.4%	21,000
12/15	10,630	479	4.5%	19,000
12/14	10,371	466	4.5%	17,500
Annual Growth	**6.2%**	**3.6%**		**0.7%**

2018 Year-End Financials

Debt ratio: 23.00%
Return on equity: 19.00%
Cash ($ mil.): 80
Current ratio: 1.00
Long-term debt ($ mil.): 1,004
No. of shares (mil.): 151
Dividends
  Yield: —
  Payout: —
Market value ($ mil.): 11,797

	STOCK PRICE ($) FY Close	P/E High/Low	PER SHARE ($) Earnings	Dividends	Book Value
12/18	78.00	26 18	3.00	0.00	20.00
12/17	70.00	72 26	3.00	0.00	18.00
12/16	152.00	58 46	3.00	0.00	18.00
12/15	157.00	55 44	3.00	0.00	17.00
12/14	137.00	50 40	3.00	0.00	17.00
Annual Growth	**(13.2%)**	— —	**6.4%**	—	**4.0%**

Schwab (Charles) Corp (The)

The once-rebellious Charles Schwab is all grown up: the discount broker now offers the same traditional brokerage services it shunned over three decades ago. Schwab manages more than $3.4 trillion in assets for some 13.8 million individual investors and institutional clients. Traders can access its services via telephone the internet-enabled devices and through more than 345 offices in 45-plus states as well as London Hong Kong Singapore and Australia. Besides discount brokerage the firm offers financial research advice and planning investment management and retirement and employee compensation plans.It also operates Charles Schwab Bank a federal savings bank and Charles Schwab Investment Management an investment advisor for Schwab's mutual finds and exchange-traded funds.

Operations

Charles Schwab firm operates through two business segments. Its Investor Services segment generates some 70% of company revenue and offers retail brokerage and banking services to individual investors as well as retirement plan and corporate brokerage services. Its Advisor Services segment generating nearly 30% of revenue provides custodial trading and support services to institutional investors.

About half of Charles Schwab's revenue comes from interest income on cash investment securities brokerage-related receivables and loans to banking clients. Nearly 40% of its revenue comes from asset management and administration fees which consist of mostly mutual fund service fees advice solutions fees and other fees. Trading revenue makes up 10% of its total revenue and consists of commission and principal transaction income.

The company's OneSource service offers investors access to more than 3000 no-load funds. Schwab also provides access to nearly 50000 bonds bond funds and other fixed income investment products from more than 200 dealers. Additional services include futures and commodities trading access to IPOs and educational investment materials including ratings of more than 3000 stocks. Schwab provides trading and support services to independent investment advisors as well.

Geographic Reach

San Francisco-based Charles Schwab has more than 345 branch offices in more than 45 US states as well as offices in London Hong Kong Singapore Australia and Puerto Rico.

Sales and Marketing

Charles Schwab provides financial services to both individuals and institutional clients. Its Advisor Services segment provides custodial trading and support services to independent investment advisors and retirement business services to independent retirement plan advisors and record keepers with assets plans held at Schwab Bank.Its Investor Services provides retail brokerage and banking services to individual investor and retirement plan services as well as other corporate brokerage services to businesses and employees.

Charles Schwab has around $3.4 trillion in client assets across 10.8 million active brokerage accounts more than 1.2 million banking accounts and 1.6 million corporate retirement plan participants.

Financial Performance

Thanks to a rising stock market and a growing investor base Charles Schwab has boosted its average client assets by more than 60% since 2013

from $2.1 trillion to almost $3.4 trillion at the end of 2017. The resulting rise in asset-based fees and related trading revenue and interest income from receivables has led to strong revenue and profit growth over the past few years.

Charles Schwab had a very good 2017. The company's revenue increased 15% to $8.6 billion as it grew its managed assets by 21% and client base by one million. Brokerage accounts grew 32% and net new client assets grew 86%.

Net income surged 25% to $2.4 billion as its expanded revenue while keeping costs down partially offset by a one-off $46 million charge relating to the US Tax Cuts and Jobs Act introduced at the end of 2017.

Cash inflow from operations increased $742 million to $897 million due to higher net income and changes in equity in undistributed earnings of subsidiaries.

Strategy

Charles Schwab's strategy is relatively straight-forwards: deliver high quality service and advice and leverage scale to operate efficiently and offer low prices. In 2017 the company shared its impressive economies of scale with its clients by aggressively reducing pricing in a variety of areas ranging from online equity commissions to index mutual funds to purchased money market funds.The approach reaped rewards as the company hit record levels in 2017 in active brokerage accounts net new assets and client assets while strongly growing profits. Clients opened more than 100000 accounts in each month of the year and brought in nearly $200 billion in core net new assets. Charles Schwab also achieved industry-leading Net Promoter Scores of 63 and 57 in its Retail and Advisory Services businesses respectively.

Its success in 2017 put Charles Schwab in a position to keep its foot on the gas. The company will make significant investments in digital its technology infrastructure and business process redesign to improve its customer proposition further.

HISTORY

During the 1960s Stanford graduate Charles Schwab founded First Commander Corp. which managed investments and published a newsletter. But he failed to properly register with the SEC and after a hiatus he returned to the business under the name Charles Schwab & Co. in 1971. Initially a full-service broker Schwab moved into discount brokerage after the SEC outlawed fixed commissions in 1975. While most brokers defiantly raised commissions Schwab cut its rates steeply.

From 1977 to 1983 Schwab's client list increased thirtyfold and revenues grew from $4.6 million to $126.5 million enabling the firm to automate its operations and develop cash-management account systems. To gain capital Charles sold the company to BankAmerica (now Bank of America) in 1983. Schwab grew but federal regulations prevented expansion into such services as mutual funds and telephone trading. Charles bought his company back in 1987 and took it public. When the stock market crashed later that year trading volume fell by nearly half from 17900 per day. Stung Schwab diversified further offering new fee-based services. Commission revenues fell from 64% of sales in 1987 to 39% in 1990 but by 1995 the long bull market had pushed commissions to more than 50%.

In 1989 Schwab introduced TeleBroker a 24-hour Touch-Tone telephone trading service available in English Spanish Mandarin or Cantonese.

Schwab continued to diversify courting independent financial advisors. Other buys included Mayer & Schweitzer (1991 now Schwab Capital

Markets) an OTC market maker that accounted for about 7% of all NASDAQ trades. In 1993 the firm opened its first overseas office in London but traded only in dollar-denominated stocks until it bought Share-Link (later Charles Schwab Europe) the UK's largest discount brokerage in 1995. It subsequently sold the British pound sterling brokerage business to Barclays PLC although it has maintained its US dollar business in the UK.

During the next year Schwab made a concerted effort to build its retirement services by creating a 401(k) administration and investment services unit. In 1997 Schwab allied with J.P. Morgan Hambrecht & Quist and Credit Suisse First Boston (CSFB) to give its customers access to IPOs; the next year the relationship with CSFB deepened to give Schwab access to debt offerings. In late 1997 and early 1998 Schwab reorganized to reflect its new business lines. The firm also began recruiting talent rather than promoting from within.

Expansion was key at the turn of the century. In 1999 Schwab moved toward more broker-advised investing: It inked a deal (geared toward its retirement products customers) with online financial advice firm Financial Engines and introduced Velocity a desktop system designed to make trading easier for fiscally endowed investors. In 2000 Schwab bought online broker CyBerCorp (later CyberTrader) as well as U.S. Trust which markets to affluent clients.

While Schwab's World Trade Center offices were destroyed by the September 11 terrorist attacks the company did not lose any of its New York staff.

To pare expenses Schwab reduced its workforce by about 35% between 2000 and 2003. Founder and chairman Charles Schwab relinquished his role of co-CEO in early 2003 only to move back into the driver's seat in mid-2004 when former CEO David Pottruck was asked to step down by the company's board.

One of Schwab's first orders of business was to reexamine the company's 2004 acquisition of SoundView Technology Group which was combined with its Capital Markets operations to form Schwab SoundView Capital Markets. While the purchase was intended to help the company beef up its services for institutional investors Schwab said that SoundView lacked "synergy" with the company's tradition of supporting the individual investor and sold the business to Swiss bank UBS.

Schwab acquired The 401(k) Companies from Nationwide Financial Services in 2007. The addition became part of the company's existing Charles Schwab Trust subsidiary which serves as a trustee for employee benefit plans. Also that year Schwab sold U.S. Trust to Bank of America for some $3.3 billion in cash and shut down its CyberTrader day trading arm merging the direct-access brokerage's business with its own.

In 2011 Charles Schwab acquired retail brokerage optionsXpress. The $1 billion deal expanded its client base and online equity options and futures trading business and it has already boosted the company's trading revenues.

In another 2011 transaction Charles Schwab acquired Compliance11 which allowed the company to offer compliance monitoring and reporting services.

In December 2012 the firm purchased Massachusetts-based ThomasPartners a dividend income-focused asset management firm with some $2.3 billion in assets under management for $85 million in cash.

EXECUTIVES

Cfo, Peter Crawford, age 51

President And Ceo, Walter W. (Walt) Bettinger, age 58, $1,041,667 total compensation

President And Ceo Charles Schwab Bank, Paul V. Woolway

Evp Client Solutions, G. Andrew (Andy) Gill, age 56

Evp Corporate Initiatives, James D. McCool, age 60, $550,000 total compensation

President And Ceo Charles Schwab Investment Management, Marie A. Chandoha, age 58, $572,500 total compensation

Evp International Services And Special Business Development, Lisa Kidd Hunt

Svp Advisor Services, Bernard J. Clark, age 60, $525,000 total compensation

Evp Operational Services, Ron Carter

Evp And Chief Marketing Officer, Jonathan M. Craig

Evp Corporate Risk, Nigel J. Murtagh, age 56

Evp Retirement Plan Services, Steven H. (Steve) Anderson

Evp Technology Services, Jim McGuire

Evp General Counsel And Corporate Secretary, David R. Garfield, age 63

Evp Investor Services, Terri R. Kallsen, age 51, $450,000 total compensation

Evp Investor Services Strategy Segments And Platforms, Neesha Hathi

Evp And Cto, Timothy C. Heier

Evp And Cio, Dennis Howard

Evp Internal Audit, Mitch Mantua

Vice President Managing Director Relationship Management New York Metro Region, Tom Cantillon

Vice President Financial Consultant, Rich Kahan

Vice President Financial Consultant, Martin Kurtz

Vice President Senior Financial Consultant, Jerry Santoro

Vice President Financial Consultant, Darren Wilcox

Vice President Financial Consultant, Brian Tveter

Vice President Financial Consultant, Anthony Price

Senior Vice President, Jonathan Beatty

Vice President Global Compliance, Janet Epstein

Vice President Retirement Plan Sales, Michael E Filbin

Vice President Senior Financial Consultant, Stephen Liepold

Vice President Financial Consultant, Anthony Zeller

Vice President Retirement Plan Sales, Luis R Arellano

Vice President Financial Consultant, Greg Frelka

Vice President Information Technology, Ed Fulkerson

Vice President Financial Consultant, Shelley Helmerick

Vice President Financial Consultant, Luiz Soutomaior

Vice President Compliance And Monitoring, Mike Marsh

Vice President Senior Financial Consultant, Ming Chen

Vice President Financial Consultant Executive Services, David Findlow

Vice President Financial Consultant, Jacob Peroceschi

Vice President Financial Consultant, Gary Libler

Vice President Senior Financial Consultant, Brian Rogers

Vp Sr Financial Consultant, Mike Elam

Vice President Of Marketing Active Trader Market, Karen Cashen

Vice President Financial Consultant, Brandon Setlock

Vice President Financial Consultant Atlanta Lenox, Rick Groff

Vice President Financial Consultant, Jesus Arroyo

Vice President Financial Consultant, David Mattox

Vice President, Olivier Guerin

Vice President Financial Consultant, Chad Vidovich

Vice President Financial Consultant, JAMES SALUS

Vice President Financial Consultant, John Curren

Vice President Financial Consultant, Shelley Chidley

Vice President Plan Sponsor Services, Ben Sheppard

Vice President Financial Consultant, David Bernstein

Vice President Financial Consultant, Ari Strait

Vice President Financial Consultant, Jane Gudgel

Vice President, Dana Ecker

Vice President Internal Audit, Shayne Zundel

Vice President Financial Consultant, Eric Flynn

Vice President Financial Consultant, Michael Castro

Vice President Financial Consultant, James Kukurin

Vice President Financial Consultant, Ben Gongora

Vice President Financial Consultant, Jason Blum

Vice President Financial Consultant, Tim Thomas

Vice President Financial Consultant, Jonathan Harel

Vice President Senior Financial Consultant, Douglas Kaminski

Vice President Financial Consultant, Tamara Blue

Vice President Financial Consultant, Wes Honnold

Vice President Financial Consultant, Tatum Schuler

Vice President Financial, James Riefe

Vice President Model Risk Management, Marc Bourzutschky

Vice President, James Westbay

Vice President, John Gutierrez

Vice President Financial Consultant, Michael Klebba

Vice President Financial Consultant, Hans Raymond

Senior Vice President Financial Consultant, Sean Reeves

Vice President, William Parrott

Vice President Financial Consultant, Selene Argao

Vice President Financial Consultant, Bill Schwind

Vice President Financial Consultant, Timothy Harker

Vice President, Matthew Heck

Vice President Financial Consultant, Rick Fine

Vice President Senior Financial Consultant, John Khoury

Vice President Finance Transformation, Brian Godfrey

Vice President Sales Retirement Plan Services, Jen Papay

Vice President Financial Consultant, Christian Beck

Vice President Financial Consultant Dallas Tx Park Cities, Jason Dugdale

Vice President Branch Manager At Charles Schwab, Todd Storrs

Vp And Managing Director Services Schwab Advisor, Scot Kobashigawa

Vice President, Dennis Mojares

Vice President Financial Consultant, Tristyn Eames

Vp Sr Financial Consultant, Jason Burke

Vice President Financial Consultant Schwab Private Client, Jess Ramos

Vice President And Branch Manager International Schwab International Orlando, Cynthia Paul

Vice President Financial Consultant, Patrick Means

Vp Financial Consultant, Teb Yu

Vice President Financial Consultant, Robert Freddino

Vice President Financial Consultant, Jennifer Depriest

Vice President Financial Consultant, Brandon Lilley

Vice President Financial Consultant, German Ramirez

Vice President Financial Consultant, Drake Beck

Vice President, Erick Ibarra

Vice President, Jake King

Vice President Financial Consultant, Justin Sinnott
Vice President Financial Consultant Ca Insurance
  License #0b27845, Cynthia Leal
Vice President Financial Consultant, Denise
  Patridge
Vice President Financial Consultant Carlsbad
  Branch, Ron Scherdorf
Vice President Financial Consultant, Carter Taylor
Vice President Financial Consultant, Garrett Sloan
Executive Vice President Retirement Plan
  Services, Steve Anderson
Vice President Financial Consultant, Michael
  Murray
Vice President Financial Consultant, Travis Nelson
Vp Financial Consultant, Kristin Hayes
Vice President Financial Consultant, Michael Cook
Vice President, Deborah Pritchard
Vice President And Branch Manager, Francisco J
  Vivas
Vice President, Lisa Quartarone
Vice President Financial Consultant, Mark Findling
Vice President Financial Consultant, Trent Fifield
Vice President Financial Consultant, Angie Krylo
Vice President Talent Acquisition, Robert Mundell
Vice President Associate General Counsel, Steve
  Johnson
Vice President Financial Consultant, Chris
  Terebessy
Svp Financial Consultant, Aaron Olson
Vice President Distributor And Business
  Oversight Regulatory Communications, Jennifer
  Hafner
Vice President Financial Consultant, Nicholas
  Sexauer
Vice President Financial Consultant, Linda Tarbet
Vice President Financial Consultant, Sue Cheung
Vice President Financial Consultant, Grant Seaton
Vice President Branch Manager, Whitney Fletcher
Vice President Branch Manager, Joe Benvenuto
Vice President Financial Consultant, Kenneth
  Jorgenson
Vice President Financial Consultant, Brian Mitchell
Vice President Financial Consultant, Gary Hettler
Vice President Financial Consultant, Jeff Han
Senior Vice President And Head Office Legislative
  And Regulatory Affairs, Jeff Brown
Vice President Financial Consultant, Karl Michael
  Lulu
Vice President Financial Consultant, Phillip
  Thanawiwat
Vice President Financial Consultant, Scott Alers
Vice President Financial Consultant, David Bubb
Vice President Financial Consultant, Anthony
  Khavarani
Vice President Financial Consultant Provo Orem,
  Taylor Caron
Senior Vice President Infrastructure, Dustin Yates
Senior Vice President Compensation And
  Benefits, David Callahan
Vice President Human Resources, Sarah Stanson
Executive Vice President Human Resources, Katie
  Casey
Vice President Financial Consultant, Scott Jeamel
Vice President Financial Consultant, Stella Hui
Vice President Finacial Consultant, Dan Weisman
Vice President Senior Financial Consultant, Ryan
  Kaplan
Auditors: DELOITTE & TOUCHE LLP

LOCATIONS

HQ: Schwab (Charles) Corp (The)
  211 Main Street, San Francisco, CA 94105
Phone: 415 667-7000   **Fax:** 415 627-8894
Web: www.aboutschwab.com

PRODUCTS/OPERATIONS

2017 Sales

	$ mil.	% of total
Investor Services	6,200	72
Advisor Services	2,418	28
Total	**8,618**	**100**

2017 Sales

	$ mil.	% of total
Interest	4,282	50
Asset management & administration fees	3,392	39
Trading	654	8
Provision for loan losses	- -	
Other	290	4
Total	**8,618**	**100**

Selected Subsidiaries

Charles Schwab Bank
Charles Schwab Investment Management Inc. (mutual
  fund investment adviser)
Schwab Holdings Inc.
  Charles Schwab & Co. Inc. (securities broker-dealer)

COMPETITORS

Ameriprise	Morgan Stanley
Bank of America	Principal Financial
E*TRADE Financial	Raymond James
Edward Jones	Financial
FMR	Scottrade
Franklin Templeton	ShareBuilder
John Hancock Financial	T. Rowe Price
Services	TD Ameritrade
Legg Mason	The Vanguard Group

HISTORICAL FINANCIALS

Company Type: Public

Income Statement				FYE: December 31
	REVENUE ($ mil.)	NET INCOME ($ mil.)	NET PROFIT MARGIN	EMPLOYEES
12/18	10,989	3,507	31.9%	19,500
12/17	8,960	2,354	26.3%	17,600
12/16	7,649	1,889	24.7%	16,200
12/15	6,512	1,447	22.2%	15,300
12/14	6,160	1,321	21.4%	14,600
Annual Growth	15.6%	27.6%	—	7.5%

2018 Year-End Financials

Debt ratio: 2.00%
Return on equity: 18.00%
Cash ($ mil.): 27,938
Current ratio: 0.00
Long-term debt ($ mil.): 6,878

No. of shares (mil.): 1,332
Dividends
  Yield: 1.0%
  Payout: 19.0%
Market value ($ mil.): 55,336

	STOCK PRICE ($) FY Close	P/E High/Low	PER SHARE ($) Earnings	Dividends	Book Value
12/18	42.00	24 15	2.00	0.00	16.00
12/17	51.00	32 23	2.00	0.00	14.00
12/16	39.00	31 17	1.00	0.00	12.00
12/15	33.00	34 25	1.00	0.00	10.00
12/14	30.00	32 25	1.00	0.00	9.00
Annual Growth	8.3%	— —	26.7%	17.7%	14.6%

Seaboard Corp.

With pork and turkey from the US flour from Haiti and sugar from Argentina Seaboard has a lot on its plate. The diversified agribusiness and transportation firm has operations in some 45 countries in the Americas the Caribbean and Africa. Seaboard sells its pork and poultry in the US and abroad. Overseas it trades grain (wheat soya) operates power plants and feed and flour mills and grows and refines sugar cane. Seaboard owns a shipping service for containerized cargo between the US the Caribbean and South America; it has shipping terminals in Miami and Houston and a fleet of about 20 vessels (two owned the rest chartered) and ships to ports worldwide. Seaboard is run by descendants of founder Otto Bresky.

Operations

Seaboard operates in five segments.

The company's Pork Division about a quarter of revenue is a vertically integrated pork producer and one of the largest producers and processors in the US. The unit works through the lifecycle of a hog from research in nutrition and genetics and extending to production of meat products.

The Commodity Trading and Milling (CT&M) Division about 50% of revenue trades processes and moves agricultural commodities such as wheat corn soybeans soybean meal and others. The primary destinations for the ag products are Africa South America the Caribbean and Asia.

Seaboard's Marine Division some 15% of revenue provides cargo shipping services between the US the Caribbean and Central and South America. The company has major facilities at Port Miami and the Port of Houston.

The rest of Seaboard's revenue comes from its operations in sugar which are mostly in Argentina power generation in the Dominican Republic and its 50% non-controlling interest in Butterball LLC the largest producer of turkeys and turkey products in the US.

Geographic Reach

Kansas-based Seaboard is a global company that serves several segments such as agribusiness and ocean cargo transportation in about 45 countries specifically in the Americas the Caribbean and Africa. Its largest market is Central and South America and the Caribbean representing about 35% of annual sales. Africa and the US are other big markets for the company.

Financial Performance

After several years of consistent growth Seaboard's sales have stumbled in the past three years. Revenue dipped 4% in 2016 to $5.4 billion from 2015 with lower sales in five of its six segments and all but one of its geographic areas. Sales were down 8% in the Commodity Trading & Milling unit which is responsible for half the company's revenue) on lower commodity prices and the mix of products. Sales rose 8% for the Pork unit as acquisitions increased the sales volume of market hogs and the acquisition of a second biodiesel plant produced higher biodiesel volumes.

Seaboard's net income jumped to $312 million in 2016 an 82% increase from 2015. The company reduced the cost of sales 6% in 2016 from the year before boosting net income.

Higher net income helped pushed cash flow from operations to $427 million in 2016 from $416 million in 2015.

Strategy

Seaboard seeks growth by expanding operations in several areas.

The company continues to beef up its pork division. With its partner Triumph Seaboard opened a new Daily's bacon plant in St. Joseph Missouri that has a production capacity of 60 million pounds a year. Seaboard and Triumph followed in 2017 with another new pork processing plant in Sioux City Iowa. But pork is more than bacon and Seaboard rehabilitated a closed biodiesel plant in St Joseph Missouri. That plant along with the one on Guymon Oklahoma gives Seaboard capacity to produce 64 million gallons of biodiesel fuel per year.

In 2016 Seaboard gain took over day-to-day work of the Brazilian flour milling operations by restructuring and consolidation. The company expects to reduce the operation's costs by focusing on single site production.

Seaboard could face challenges if US trade agreements are renegotiated or abrogated. If the US charges higher tariffs on foreign goods entering the country other nations could retaliate by putting higher tariffs on US goods. Agricultural products are some of the US's biggest goods for export and would be likely targets for retaliation which could increase prices reduce exports or both.

Mergers and Acquisitions

In September 2014 Seaboard's processed meats division sold a 50% stake in Daily's Premium Meats to its processing partner Triumph Foods for $72.5 million making Seaboard and Triumph co-owners of the business. The sale provided additional capital to expand production and geographic reach of the Daily's brand.

In July 2013 Seaboard acquired a 50% stake in a flour milling business in Gambia for about $9.1 million.

HISTORY

Otto Bresky founded his company as a flour broker in 1916. He acquired his first flour mill in Atchison Kansas in 1918 and the following year purchased the Imperial Brewery Co. in Kansas City and converted it to a flour mill. Over the next four decades Bresky ground out a series of acquisitions of milling companies. In 1928 he purchased Rodney Milling Co. and retained the name as the identity for the family business. The company then purchased Ismert-Hincke Milling Co. (1938) and the Consolidated Flour Mills Co. (1950). In 1959 Rodney Milling merged with publicly traded Hathaway Industries and changed its name to Seaboard Allied Milling Corp.

In the 1960s Seaboard Allied became one of the first millers to shift flour milling from the source of the raw materials (the wheat fields of the Great Plains) to the population centers in the Southeast and on the East Coast. In 1962 Seaboard Allied built a flour mill in Chattanooga Tennessee. It then purchased George Urban Milling Company in Buffalo New York (1965) and built a flour mill in Jacksonville Florida (1966). But Bresky's expansionist strategy did not stop at the Atlantic Seaboard. The company acquired a flour mill in Guayaquil Ecuador in 1966 (a joint venture with Continental Grain Co.) then constructed flour mills in Freetown Sierra Leone (1968) and Georgetown Guyana (1969).

Bresky retired in 1973 and was succeeded by his son Harry. A chip off the old block Harry acquired a flour mill in Cleveland Tennessee and built flour mills in Buchanan Liberia and in Sapele Nigeria that year. In 1978 Seaboard Allied acquired Mochasa Ecuador's leading producer of animal feed and launched Top Feeds a mixed-feed plant in Sapele.

Facing stiff competition in the mill business from agribusiness giants in 1982 Seaboard Allied sold all its US flour mills to Cargill. The company changed its name to Seaboard that year and began expanding outside the US. In 1983 the company formed Seaboard Marine a shipping business in Florida to serve its increasingly far-flung enterprises.

In addition to geographic diversification the company expanded into new agribusiness areas. Seaboard acquired Central Soya's poultry unit in 1984 and it bought the Elberton Poultry Company the next year. Seaboard commenced shrimp farming operations in Ecuador in 1986 and in Honduras in 1987. Two years later Transcontinental Capital Corporation (Bermuda) a subsidiary began

supplying power from a floating power barge to the Dominican Republic.

Seaboard entered the hog business in 1990 by acquiring a pork-processing plant in Albert Lea Minnesota. It opened a hog-processing facility in Guymon Oklahoma in 1996 and closed the Minnesota plant. That year the company bought a stake in Ingenio y Refinerio San Martin del Tabacal an Argentina-based sugar cane and citrus company. It then acquired flour-mill pasta-plant and cookie operations in Beira Mozambique.

After serving as CEO for more than 30 years in 2006 Harry Bresky stepped down as CEO (but remained as chairman) and turned over the company's reins to his son Steven. Harry Bresky died in 2007.

In 2010 Seaboard acquired a 50% stake in Butterball LLC.

EXECUTIVES

Vice President, David Becker
Svp Finance And Treasurer, David Oswalt
Svp Engineering, James L. (Jim) Gutsch, age 65
Evp And Cfo, Robert L. Steer, age 60, $763,000 total compensation
Chairman President And Ceo, Steven J. Bresky, age 66, $942,000 total compensation
Ceo Pork, Terry J. Holton, age 59, $552,000 total compensation
Ceo Marine, Edward A. (Eddie) Gonzalez, age 54, $472,000 total compensation
Ceo Commodity Trading And Milling, David M. Dannov, age 58, $472,000 total compensation
Ceo Sugar, Hugo Rossi
Ceo Power, Armando G. Rodriguez
Vice President Audit Services, TY Tywater
Vice President Operations Foods Divisi, Marty Hast
Svp Taxation And Business Development, David Rankin
Executive Vice President Seaboard Marine, Bruce Brecheisen
Assistant Secretary, Zachery Holden
Assistant Treasurer, Katie Verschelden
Auditors: KPMG LLP

LOCATIONS

HQ: Seaboard Corp.
9000 West, 67th Street, Merriam, KS 66202
Phone: 913 676-8800
Web: www.seaboardcorp.com

2016 Sales

	$ mil.	% of total
Caribbean Central & South America	1,990	37
Africa	1,572	29
US	1,161	22
Pacific Basin & Far East	309	6
Canada/Mexico	236	4
Europe	40	1
All other	71	1
Total	**5,379**	**100**

PRODUCTS/OPERATIONS

2016 Sales

	$ mil.	% of total
Products	4,334	80
Services	961	18
Other	84	2
Total	**5,379**	**100**

2016 Sales

	$ mil.	% of total
Commodity Trading & Milling	2,778	52
Pork	1,443	27
Marine	916	17
Sugar	147	3
Power	79	1
All other	16	-
Total	**5,379**	**100**

Selected Operations
Cargo shipping
Citrus production and processing
Commodity merchandising (wheat corn and soybean meal)
Domestic trucking transportation
Electric power generation
Flour maize and feed milling
Jalape?o pepper processing
Pork production and processing
Sugar production and refining

COMPETITORS

ADM	Imperial Sugar
APL	Jennie-O
American Crystal Sugar	Johnsonville Sausage
Bay State Milling	Louis Dreyfus Group
Bunge Limited	M. A. Patout
CGC	Makino
CHS	Mondelez International
CSX	NYK Line
Cargill	Neptune Orient
Carr's Milling	Nicor Gas
Chelsea Milling	Nutreco
Chiquita Brands	Organic Milling
Colonial Group	Overseas Shipholding
Crowley Maritime	Group
Dole Food	Smithfield Foods
Evergreen Marine	Southern States
Evergreen Mills	Star of the West
Farmers Rice Milling	Sunkist
Fresh Del Monte	S dzucker
Produce	Tate & Lyle
Genco Shipping and	Tyson Foods
Trading	U.S. Sugar
Horizon Milling	Western Sugar
Hormel	Cooperative

HISTORICAL FINANCIALS

Company Type: Public

Income Statement

FYE: December 31

	REVENUE ($ mil.)	NET INCOME ($ mil.)	NET PROFIT MARGIN	EMPLOYEES
12/18	6,583	(17)	—	12,600
12/17	5,809	247	4.3%	11,800
12/16	5,379	312	5.8%	12,000
12/15	5,594	171	3.1%	10,772
12/14	6,473	365	5.6%	10,778
Annual Growth	**0.4%**	**—**	**—**	**4.0%**

2018 Year-End Financials

Debt ratio: 17.00%
Return on equity: (-1.00%)
Cash ($ mil.): 194
Current ratio: 4.00
Long-term debt ($ mil.): 739

No. of shares (mil.): 1
Dividends
 Yield: 0.0%
 Payout: —
Market value ($ mil.): 4,137

	STOCK PRICE ($) FY Close	P/E High/Low	PER SHARE ($) Earnings	Dividends	Book Value
12/18	3,538.00 2,838.00	— —	(15.00)	6.00	
12/17	4,410.00 2,902.00	22 17	211.00	6.00	
12/16	3,952.00 2,701.00	17 9	267.00	0.00	
12/15	2,895.00 2,457.00	32 20	146.00	0.00	
12/14	4,198.00 2,320.00	13 8	310.00	0.00	
Annual Growth	**(4.2%)**	**— —**	**—**	**—**	**5.2%**

Seacoast Banking Corp. of Florida

Seacoast Banking Corporation is the holding company for Seacoast National Bank. It operates some 50 branches in Florida with a concentration in four large city markets. Serving individuals and businesses the bank offers a range of financial products and services including deposit accounts credit cards trust services and private banking. Commercial and residential real estate loans make up most of the bank's lending activities; to a lesser extent it also originates business and consumer loans.

Operations

Seacoast Bank offers traditional banking products such as deposit accounts checking & savings accounts CDs business loans home mortgages and the like. It also makes available to its customers brokerage and annuity services along with insurance products. A division of the bank Seacoast Marine Finance specializes in boat loans which it typically originates itself and then sells into the secondary market.

Geographic Reach

Seacoast National Bank has some 50 branches in 14 counties across Florida stretching from Broward County north through the Treasure Coast and into Orlando and west to Okeechobee and surrounding counties. Its primary markets are Tampa Orlando Port St. Lucie and West Palm Beach/Ft. Lauderdale.

Financial Performance

Seacoast Banking Corporation has done well in recent years steadily growing interest income to nearly $200 million in 2017 up from a low of $70 million just four years prior. The bank registered positive earnings from 2013 forward albeit the results fluctuated wildly.

In 2017 interest income grew 30% to $192 million and non-interest income improved by 25% to $170 million. Its loan portfolio grew ? through organic means as well as via acquisitions ? by almost 30% against which it earned additional interest income. The bank's average net interest margin rose 10 basis points to 3.73%.

Net income also lodged an excellent year increasing 48% from the prior year to $43 million. Although the company incurred an $8.6 million impairment of its deferred tax assets due to the change in US Federal tax law the increase in revenue along with a $15 million gain on the sale an investment it made in Visa company stock pushed up yearly earnings.

Cash at the end of the year was $109 million unchanged from 2016. Financing activities contributed $196 million mostly from an increase in deposits from acquisitions. Investing activities used $246 million in the process of buying and selling securities and originating new loans. Operating activities added $49 million.

Strategy

Seacoast Bank has grown mostly through acquisitions in recent years. Since 2014 it opened one new office and acquired 49 branches (19 of which were subsequently shuttered). Orlando has been a hot destination for it as it transformed its presence there just a few branches to the largest Florida-based bank in the market by 2017. The bank anticipates continued geographic growth in Florida through organic means but also through acquisition if the right opportunity arises as with the 2017 purchases of NorthStar Banking and Palm Beach Community Bank.

Although it caters to personal customers as well as business clients the focus on businesses has sparked significant growth in the associated loan portfolio. The company tends to commercial clients with revenues exceeding $5 million in specific industry verticals. It takes a comprehensive relationship approach by providing business treasury lending and wealth management services. The commercial loan portfolio grew nearly 300% between year-end 2013 and year-end 2017 from $632 million to $2.5 billion.

The bank significantly expanded its banking technology platform by introducing digital deposit capture on smartphones updating its mobile platforms for consumer and business customers and enhancing its ATM capabilities. Customers have taken to the online functionality and in 2017 the bank processed more digital transactions than it did through its physical branch network.

Mergers and Acquisitions

In 2017 Seacoast purchased NorthStar Banking Corporation adding more than $200 million in assets $170 million in deposits and nearly $140 million in loans to Seacoast's balance sheet. In the same year it acquired Palm Beach Community Bank for some $70 million adding $270 million in loans and four bank branches to Seacoast's operations.

EXECUTIVES

Chairman And Ceo, Dennis S. (Denny) Hudson, age 63, $537,852 total compensation
Evp And Residential Lending Executive, Michael J. (Mike) Sonego
Evp And Commercial Banking Executive, Charles K. Cross, age 61, $273,333 total compensation
Evp And Chief Risk And Credit Officer, David D. Houdeshell, age 58, $262,500 total compensation
Evp Enterprise Services And Initiatives, Kathleen (Kathy) Cavicchioli
Evp And Chief Marketing Officer, Jeffery (Jeff) Lee
Evp Service And Operations, Jeffery (Jeff) Bray
Evp And Chief Human Resources Officer, Daniel G. (Dan) Chappell
Cfo And Head Of Strategy, Charles M. (Chuck) Shaffer, age 45, $248,333 total compensation
Evp Community Banking, Julie Kleffel
Senior Vice President Marketing Director, Susan Bergstrom
Senior Vice President Human Resources Director, Charles Olsson
Vp Sba Portfolio Manager, Maureen Swierkowski
Executive Vice President Chief Human Resources Officer, Dan Chappell
Executive Vice President, William Hahl
Assistant Vice President And Call Center Manager, Joni Wyszkowski
Vice President Financial Advisor, Carl Newton
Executive Vice President, Tom Hall
Senior Vice President Community Banking Director, Eileen Hatt
Vice President Business Banking Manager, Theresa Vazquez
Svp Senior Fiduciary And Risk Officer Cfp Clu, Peter Lowery
Avp Banking Center Manager, Amber Shirk
Senior Vice President Commercial Banking, Thomas Dargan
Assistant Vice President Corporate Finance, Zev Zaretsky
Vice President Commercial Banking, David Beckey
Vice President Cra Officer, Iris Jones
Vice President And Treasury Management, Jacci Watson
Vice President Leadership Development Manager, Angel Birch
Vice President Senior Market Leader, Tom Popieski
Vice President Market Manager, Hart Donovan
Vice President, Travis Engebretsen

Vice President Business Banker, Stephen Markham
Senior Market Manager Vice President, Monika Krumbock
Vice President Senior Small Business Banker, Jack Gould
Vice President Collection And Recovery Manager, Gary Albert
Vice President Residential Lending, Steve Bilbo
Vp Of Seacoast Bank Commercial Banking, Greg Peters
Vice President Commercial Banking, Daniel Lightfritz
Vice President And Market Manager, Lee Jeff
Vice President Mortgage Banking Officer, Grace Monforte
Vice President Mortgage Lending Area Manager, Megan Martinez
Vice President Commercial Banking, Brian Wickman
Assistant Vice President Commercial Loan Officer, Ronnie Houck
Vice President Business Banker, Joe Ritchie
Vp Small Business Banking And Commercial Banking, Gilbert Russell
Vp Regional Business Banking Manager, Phil Fitzpatrick
Senior Vice President Commercial Banker, Jennifer Potter
Vice President Commercial Banker, Shane McCutchen
Board Director, Dennis Arczynski
Board Member, Maryann Goebel
Board Member, Herbert Lurie
Board Member, Jacqueline Bradley
Board Member, Tim Huval
Auditors: Crowe LLP

LOCATIONS

HQ: Seacoast Banking Corp. of Florida
815 Colorado Avenue, Stuart, FL 34994
Phone: 772 287-4000
Web: www.seacoastbanking.com

PRODUCTS/OPERATIONS

Selected Services
Commercial and retail banking
Mortgage services
Wealth management

COMPETITORS

BB&T	PNC Financial
BBX Capital	Regions Financial
Bank of America	SunTrust
BankUnited	Suncoast Schools FCU
CenterState Banks	Wells Fargo
EverBank Financial	

HISTORICAL FINANCIALS

Company Type: Public

Income Statement				FYE: December 31
	ASSETS ($ mil.)	NET INCOME ($ mil.)	INCOME AS % OF ASSETS	EMPLOYEES
12/18	6,748	67	1.0%	902
12/17	5,810	43	0.7%	805
12/16	4,681	29	0.6%	725
12/15	3,535	22	0.6%	665
12/14	3,093	6	0.2%	579
Annual Growth	21.5%	85.4%		11.7%

2018 Year-End Financials

Debt ratio: 1.00%	No. of shares (mil.): 51
Return on equity: 9.00%	Dividends
Cash ($ mil.): 116	Yield: —
Current ratio: —	Payout: —
Long-term debt ($ mil.): —	Market value ($ mil.): 1,336

	STOCK PRICE ($) FY Close	P/E High/Low	Earnings	Dividends	Book Value
12/18	26.00	24 17	1.00	0.00	17.00
12/17	25.00	26 21	1.00	0.00	15.00
12/16	22.00	29 17	1.00	0.00	11.00
12/15	15.00	25 18	1.00	0.00	10.00
12/14	14.00	68 48	0.00	0.00	9.00
Annual Growth	17.3%	— —	60.1%	—	15.6%

Sears Holdings Corp

Once a retail giant Sears Holdings is growing smaller and leaner these days. The company is a retailer of appliances and tools as well as lawn and garden fitness and automotive repair equipment. With about 425 retail stores across the US Sears Holdings operates through subsidiaries Sears Roebuck and Co. and Kmart offering proprietary Sears brands including Kenmore and DieHard. Beyond retail Sears Holdings is a leading provider of home installation and product repair services. In response to plummeting sales in a tough retail climate Sears Holdings has been forced to sell assets and close hundreds of stores in recent years. In 2019 it emerged from Chapter 11 bankruptcy protection owned by an affiliate of hedge fund ESL Investments controlled by former Sears chairman Eddie Lampert.

Bankruptcy

After months if not years of speculation Sear Holdings filed for Chapter 11 bankruptcy in October 2018. It had been a long decline for the retailer which first had to contend with the lower prices and convenience offered by Walmart Target and Home Depot among other big-box stores and later with Amazon and other e-commerce sites.

In early 2019 the retailer emerged from bankruptcy with a new owner — Transform Holdco an affiliate of hedge fund ESL Investments which is controlled by former Sears chairman Eddie Lampert. The newly slimmed-down company for which Transform Holdco paid some $5.2 billion includes 425 stores (about half Sears half Kmart) and prominent brands such as Kenmore DieHard and Sears Auto Centers.

Geographic Reach

Illinois-based Sears Holdings has some 425 stores half Sears-branded and half Kmart-branded across the US.

Strategy

Sears Holdings' new parent Transform Holdco hopes the leaner organization can capitalize on its long retail history to return to growth. It will remain focused on two key strategies — Shop Your Way a social shopping program where members can earn points and receive benefits both in stores and online and Integrated Retail the seamless connection of digital and physical shopping experiences to better serve customers.

In mid-2019 Transform Holdco announced that it would acquire Sears Hometown and Outlet Stores which was spun off from Sears Holdings in 2012 and reunite the business with Sears and Kmart. Sears Holdings is also launching new much smaller stores focused on home goods services and appliances. A handful of these new Home and Life Stores opened during Memorial Day weekend in 2019.

The company's strategy however could be complicated by a lawsuit brought by Sears Holdings (filed by the restructuring team) accusing majority owner Eddie Lampert and others of illegally siphoning billions of dollars of assets from the retailer prior to its bankruptcy filing.

Company Background

Sears Holdings was created in 2005 as a result of the $11.9 billion mega-merger of Sears and struggling Kmart masterminded by chairman and CEO Edward Lampert.

EXECUTIVES

Chairman And Ceo, Edward S. (Eddie) Lampert, age 56, $1 total compensation
Cfo, Robert A. Riecker, age 54
President Fulfillment Supply Chain And Sourcing, Girish Lakshman, age 54, $794,444 total compensation
Svp Customer Experience And Integrated Retail, Leena Munjal, age 42, $568,750 total compensation
Svp Shop Your Way, Eric D. Jaffe, age 31
President Apparel, David Pastrana Benito, age 42
President Home Services, Sean Skelley, age 52, $794,444 total compensation
President Home And Footwear, Kurt C. Staelens
Vice President Sales And Business Development, Chris Granger
Divisional Vice President Core Ecommerce Integrated Retail Product Management, Rob Hudson
Divisional Vice President, Carlos Fojo
Divisional Vice President Chief Marketing Officer Grocery And Drug, R Whitton
Dvp Kenmore Product Development, Tom Desalvo
Divisional Vice President Home Services Online, Sandeep Patil
Chief Marketing Officer Of Home Appliances And Vice President Of, Kevin Brown
Div Vice President Ny Technical Design, Vanessa Allen
Vice President Space Management And Analytics, Amy Higgins
Vice President Ecommerce Program And Product Management, Christopher Kraft
Vice President Chief Financial Officer Grocery Drug And Rx, Jonathan Carpenter
Dvp Human Resources Retail Services, Megan Van Pelt
Divisional Vice President Head Of Sears Retail Human Resources, Colleen Kozak
Vice President Media Services, Perianne Grignon
Dvp Supply Chain, Brandon Cates
Divisional Vice President Consumer Insight And Analytics, Geoff Day
Executive Vice President Real Estate And Strategic Opportunities, Stephen Champion
Chief People Officer, Julie Ainsworth
Vp And Gmm Of Mens Apparel And Team Licensed Sports Kmart Sears, John Pfabe
Auditors: DELOITTE & TOUCHE LLP

LOCATIONS

HQ: Sears Holdings Corp
3333 Beverly Road, Hoffman Estates, IL 60179
Phone: 847 286-2500
Web: www.sears.com

COMPETITORS

Amazon.com	Kohl's
AutoZone	Lowe's
Bed Bath & Beyond	Macy's
Best Buy	Office Depot
Dillard's	Target Corporation
Home Depot	The Gap
Hudson's Bay	Wal-Mart

HISTORICAL FINANCIALS

Company Type: Public

Income Statement   FYE: February 3

	REVENUE ($ mil.)	NET INCOME ($ mil.)	NET PROFIT MARGIN	EMPLOYEES
02/18*	16,702	(383)	—	89,000
01/17	22,138	(2,221)	—	140,000
01/16	25,146	(1,129)	—	178,000
01/15	31,198	(1,682)	—	196,000
02/14	36,188	(1,365)	—	249,000
Annual Growth	(17.6%)	—		(22.7%)

*Fiscal year change

2018 Year-End Financials

Debt ratio: 57.00%	No. of shares (mil.): 108
Return on equity: ***,***.**%	Dividends
Cash ($ mil.): 182	Yield: —
Current ratio: 1.00	Payout: —
Long-term debt ($ mil.): 2,249	Market value ($ mil.): 254

	STOCK PRICE ($) FY Close	P/E High/Low	Earnings	Dividends	Book Value
02/18*	2.00	— —	(4.00)	0.00	(34.00)
01/17	7.00	— —	(21.00)	0.00	(36.00)
01/16	17.00	— —	(11.00)	0.00	(18.00)
01/15	32.00	— —	(16.00)	0.00	(9.00)
02/14	36.00	— —	(13.00)	0.00	16.00
Annual Growth	(49.6%)	— —	—	—	—

*Fiscal year change

SECURITIES INVESTOR PROTECTION CORPORATION

Securities Investor Protection Corporation (SIPC) is an industry-financed insurance plan that protects clients of most broker-dealers registered with the US Securities and Exchange Commission (SEC). SIPC insures customers' securities (up to $500000 per account) against losses due to the financial failure of brokerage firms. Losses caused by fluctuations in market value are not protected. The not-for-profit membership corporation was mandated by the Securities Investor Protection Act and has more than 6000 members. Its board is appointed by the US president the treasury secretary and the Federal Reserve Board. Assessments from members and investments in government securities provide money for the SIPC Fund.

EXECUTIVES

Vice President Operations, Karen Saperstein
Auditors: GRANT THORNTON MCLEAN VA

LOCATIONS

HQ: SECURITIES INVESTOR PROTECTION CORPORATION
1667 K ST NW STE 1000, WASHINGTON, DC 200061620
Phone: 202 371-8300
Web: WWW.SIPC.ORG

HISTORICAL FINANCIALS

Company Type: Private

Income Statement

	ASSETS ($ mil.)	NET INCOME ($ mil.)	INCOME AS % OF ASSETS	EMPLOYEES
12/16	2,945	362	12.3%	39
12/15	2,653	169	6.4%	—
12/14	2,363	307	13.0%	—
12/11	1,606	132	8.2%	—
Annual Growth	12.9%	22.4%	—	—

SEFCU SERVICES, LLC

EXECUTIVES

Mng MBR, Michelle Raymond
MBR*, Robert Maclasco
Loan Officer, Donn Luthanen
Senior Manager, Ellyn Bolduc
Loan Officer Assistant, Alexandra Agnos
Manager, Erin Buckley
Senior Consultant, Joanne Lashin
Loan Officer, Linda Deluke
Senior Loan Officer, Mary Duhamel
Assistant Manager Loan Servici, Monique Haller
Vice President, Nancy Brown

LOCATIONS

HQ: SEFCU SERVICES, LLC
700 PATROON CREEK BLVD, ALBANY, NY 122061067
Phone: 518 783-1234
Web: WWW.SEFCUMORTGAGESERVICES.COM

HISTORICAL FINANCIALS

Company Type: Private

Income Statement   FYE: December 31

	ASSETS ($ mil.)	NET INCOME ($ mil.)	INCOME AS % OF ASSETS	EMPLOYEES
12/17	3,555	22	0.6%	102
12/16	3,329	19	0.6%	
Annual Growth	6.8%	16.0%	—	—

Selective Insurance Group Inc

Property/casualty insurance holding company Selective Insurance Group's reach primarily covers the entire eastern US seaboard and much of the Midwest. Commercial policies sold by its 10 subsidiaries include workers' compensation and commercial automobile property and liability insurance. Personal lines include homeowners and automobile insurance. The company also offers federal flood insurance administration services throughout the US and some excess and surplus (E&S nonstandard) insurance. Selective Insurance Group operates through four reportable segments: Stan-

dard Commercial Lines Standard Personal Lines E&S Lines and Investments.

Operations

Selective's Standard Commercial Lines segment which serves business not-for-profit organizations and government agencies accounts for about three-fourths of Selective's net premiums written. Standard Personal Lines — including flood insurance coverage — follows representing more than 10% of net premiums written. The E&S Lines segment which covers more unusual risks than standard insurance accounts for nearly 10% of net premiums written.

The company's flood insurance is sold to businesses and individuals through the National Flood Insurance Program.

Geographic Reach

Selective primarily writes commercial policies in 25 eastern midwestern and southwestern states plus Washington DC. Personal policies are primarily sold in 13 states in the East and Midwest. The company also offers flood and E&S insurance policies in all 50 states plus Washington DC.

While its native New Jersey market still accounts for about 20% of Selective's net written premiums the company has successfully become a "super-regional" insurer. By doing business in a wider geographic range Selective is better able to spread out its catastrophic risk exposure. It maintains its headquarters in New Jersey and regional branch offices in New Jersey Indiana Maryland North Carolina Pennsylvania and Arizona.

Sales and Marketing

Some 1250 independent retail agents sell Selective's Standard Commercial Lines products with a focus on providing policies to small and mid-sized businesses and government entities. The company's nationwide flood protection products are sold by a network of some 5800 retail agents while E&S policies are sold through about 90 wholesale agencies and brokers.

Target clients include manufacturing and wholesale contractor community and public services and mercantile and services customers.

Promotional efforts are conducted through radio television billboard and other advertising venues including sporting events.

Financial Performance

Selective's revenue has been rising since 2010 and in general net income has also been rising. These gains have largely been driven by growth in the core commercial lines segment as well as solid retention rates.

Revenue increased 8% to $2.5 billion in 2017. Net premiums earned and investment income both grew that year and the company realized net gains of $6.4 billion versus net realized losses of $4.9 billion in 2016.

With the higher revenue net income rose 6% to $168.8 million in 2017.

The company ended 2017 with $0.5 million in net cash the same total it had at the end of 2017. Operating activities provided $370.7 million in cash that year. Investing activities used $331.1 million and financing activities used $39.6 million.

Strategy

Selective's three primary areas of interest are improving its overall customer experience refining its underwriting tools and enhancing its technological capabilities. The group focuses on organic business growth and activities to become more customer-centric. It has primarily been building up its portfolio of personal and commercial E&S insurance products. The company has established regional business teams with full underwriting authority in order to build up its presence in local markets.

Selective has also continued its expansion into new markets. In mid-2017 it began offering commercial lines in Arizona and New Hampshire. The

following year it introduced commercial lines in Colorado New Mexico and Utah. The company intends to offer personal coverage in Arizona and Utah as well.

Additionally Selective has invested in technology that speeds up the process of writing new commercial business policies to improve customer and agency services. In 2017 it deployed a new underwriting platform that helps analyze new business in comparison to its existing portfolio. The following year it launched a commercial driver-sensor offering to promote safe driving. However Selective has lagged somewhat behind its competitors in launching new types of products (such as the Selective Drive application) in a timely fashion.

The company works with what it refers to as "ivy league" distribution partners who have a strong presence in Selective's key markets. Among its goals are to increase the amount of business it does with those partners and to represent a bigger business share of those partners' operations.

Like all insurers Selective relies on data to manage risk and add new business. The company has access to less data than some of its larger competitors many of whom have built up massive stores of data over decades. Because of this it has fewer capabilities to assess risk profitability adverse claim potential fraudulent activities and customer buying habits.

Company Background

In the 1920s Daniel L.B. Smith was a general store operator in Sussex County New Jersey. Almost by accident he began selling insurance out of one of his store locations and he decided that the area needed a local insurance company. With an initial investment of $20000 Smith and several partners opened Selected Risks Insurance Company. The company expanded beyond its New Jersey origins over the next several decades.

EXECUTIVES

Vice President, Eric Thiessen
Assistant Vp And Regional Safety Operations Manager, Alan Null Costa
Chairman And Ceo, Gregory E. Murphy, age 64, $946,923 total compensation
Vice President Operations, Yanina Hupka
Evp And Chief Actuary, Ronald J. Zaleski, age 65, $437,692 total compensation
Evp General Counsel And Chief Compliance Officer, Michael H. Lanza, age 58, $536,923 total compensation
President And Coo, John J. Marchioni, age 49, $793,846 total compensation
Evp And Cfo, Mark A. Wilcox, age 51
Evp And Chief Claims Officer, George A. Neale
Evp And Chief Human Resources Officer, Angelique Carbo
Evp And Cio, Gordon J. Gaudet
Svp And Chief Marketing Officer, Rohit Mull
Vice President, Dennis L Barger
Assistant Vice President Bond Underwriting Manager, Debra Paziora
Assistant Vice President, Robert Mitchell
Senior Vice President Personal Lines, Allen Anderson
Assistant Vice President It Selective Insurance Company Of America, Cynthia Sanchez
Commercial Auto Underwriting Assistant Vice President, Stan Willey
Vice President Application Development, Richard Agresta
Vice President, Christopher Nickol
Vice President Office Automation, Kathy Koval
Legal Secretary, Maria Rodriguez
Assistant Vice President Business Case Manger, Sue Insalaco
Vice President Field Operations Manager, Tony Miller

Vice President, Jim Klotz

Assistant Vice President, Deborah Dickens-hunter

Vice President Personal Lines Pricing, Mindy Oosten

Assistant Vice President Application Architecture, Kevin Vieten

Vice President, Carol Ryan

Assistant Vice President Property Line, Scott Crump

Assistant Vice President Assistant Controller, Angelo Mastrolia

Assistant Vice President Workers Compensation, Joe Greco

Vice President Government Affairs And Compliance, Jeff Beck

Assistant Vice President Northeast Regional Manager Claims, Vincent Disimone

Assistant Vice President, Haide Krygoski

Vice President Specialty Programs, Lorraine Miller

Vice President Field Operations, Steven Bennett

Assistant Vice President, Robert L Redden

Assistant Vice President Claims Service Center, Susan L Brown

Vice President Of Flood Operat, Cassie Masone

Vice President Commercial Lines Underwriting Line Of Business And Product Development, Vere Bryan

Vice President Bonds East Hanover Nj, Timothy Marchio

Senior Vice President Actuarial Reserving, Vincent Senia

Senior Vice President And Deputy General Counsel, Maria Orecchio

Assistant Vice President Director Of Communications, Jamie Morgan

Vice President And Director Communications, Jamie Beal

Assistant Vice President Corporate Systems Applica, Gary Beumee

Vice President Information Technology, Harikrishna Raghumandala

Vp Underwriting, John Rhodes

Vice President Underwriting, Mike Lucas

Vp Field Operations Manager, Wesley Riley

Legal Secretary, Lori Coyle

Senior Vice President, Martin Hollander

Assistant Vice President Contractors Strategic Business Unit Leader, Nicole Hayes

Avp Property Claims, Christopher Carpenter

Vp Regional Claims Operations, Carlos Lewis

Avp Claims Application Delivery, Kevin Forrey

Vp And Regional Manager, Deneen Dallago-lohan

Assistant Vice President Regional Claim Manager, Stephen Bartholomew

Legal Secretary, Liliana Vasquez

Executive Vice President, Chuck Chapman

Assistant Vice President Corporate Claims, Peyton Artz

Vp Director Of Safety Management, David Colarusso

Auditors: KPMG LLP

LOCATIONS

HQ: Selective Insurance Group Inc
40 Wantage Avenue, Branchville, NJ 07890
Phone: 973 948-3000   Fax: 973 948-0282
Web: www.selective.com

PRODUCTS/OPERATIONS

2017 Sales by Segment

	$ mil.	% of total
Standard Commercial Lines	1,798	73
Standard Personal Lines	291	12
E&S Lines	213	8
Investments	168	7
Total	2,470	100

2017 Sales

	$ mil.	% of total
Net premiums earned	2,291	93
Net investment income earned	162	7
Other	11	-
Net realized gains	6	-
Total	2,470	100

COMPETITORS

Allstate	Progressive Corporation
Chubb Limited	State Farm
Cincinnati Financial	The Hartford
Erie Indemnity	Travelers Companies
GEICO	United Fire
Hanover Insurance Company	W. R. Berkley
Liberty Mutual	Zurich Insurance Group
Nationwide	

HISTORICAL FINANCIALS

Company Type: Public

Income Statement

FYE: December 31

	ASSETS ($ mil.)	NET INCOME ($ mil.)	INCOME AS % OF ASSETS	EMPLOYEES
12/18	7,953	179	2.3%	2,290
12/17	7,686	169	2.2%	2,260
12/16	7,356	158	2.2%	2,250
12/15	6,904	166	2.4%	2,200
12/14	6,582	142	2.2%	2,200
Annual Growth	4.8%	6.0%	—	1.0%

2018 Year-End Financials

Debt ratio: 6.00%
Return on equity: 10.00%
Cash ($ mil.): 1
Current ratio: —
Long-term debt ($ mil.): —
No. of shares (mil.): 59
Dividends
Yield: 1.0%
Payout: 27.0%
Market value ($ mil.): 3,592

	STOCK PRICE ($) FY Close	P/E High/Low	PER SHARE ($) Earnings	Dividends	Book Value
12/18	61.00	22 18	3.00	1.00	30.00
12/17	59.00	21 14	3.00	1.00	29.00
12/16	43.00	16 11	3.00	1.00	26.00
12/15	34.00	13 9	3.00	1.00	24.00
12/14	27.00	11 9	2.00	1.00	23.00
Annual Growth	22.4%	— —	5.0%	8.7%	7.8%

Sempra Energy

Sempra Energy makes sure the lights are always on. The company provides natural gas to nearly 7 million customers and electricity to nearly 3.5 million in California via its two primary subsidiaries Southern California Gas (SoCalGas) and San Diego Gas & Electricity (SDG&E). SoCalGas operates more than 100000 miles of combined pipeline and four natural gas storage facilities while SDG&E operates 15000 miles of pipeline. Sempra also owns Oncor the largest electricity transmission firm in Texas. Sempra is selling its South America holdings which include Chilquinta Energia in Chile and Luz del Sur in Peru to focus exclusively on North America.

HISTORY

Sempra Energy is the latest incarnation of some of California's leading lights. Formed by the $6.2 billion merger between Enova and Pacific Enter-

prises the company traces its roots back to the 1880s.

Enova began as San Diego Gas which lit its first gaslights in 1881 and added electricity in 1887 (when it became San Diego Gas & Electric Light). Massive utility holding company Standard Gas & Electric bought the company in 1905 and renamed it San Diego Consolidated Gas & Electric. Over the next few decades San Diego Consolidated expanded through acquisitions and even stayed profitable during the Depression. But the 1935 Public Utilities Holding Company Act forced Standard to divest many of its widespread utilities and in 1940 San Diego Consolidated went public as San Diego Gas & Electric (SDG&E).

SDG&E grew quickly until the 1970s when new environmental laws slowed plans to build more power plants and rates soared because the company had to purchase power. The company finally added more generating capacity in the 1980s and the state of California allowed SDG&E to diversify into real estate software and oil and gas distribution. In 1995 it created Enova to serve as its holding company.

Meanwhile up the coast in San Francisco Pacific Enterprises began as gas lamp rental firm Pacific Lighting in 1886; it quickly moved into gas distribution to defend its market against electricity. The firm bought three Los Angeles gas and electric utilities in 1889 and continued to grow through acquisitions; it consolidated all of its utilities in the 1920s. Pacific Lighting sold its electric properties to the city of Los Angeles in 1937 in exchange for a long-term gas franchise.

The company entered oil and gas exploration in 1960. A decade later it merged its gas utility operations into Southern California Gas (SoCalGas). Pacific Lighting continued to diversify in the 1980s buying two oil and gas companies and three drugstore chains. Renamed Pacific Enterprises in 1988 the company launched an unsuccessful diversification effort that cost it $88 million in 1991. Over the next two years it sold off noncore businesses to focus on SoCalGas and in the mid-1990s it began moving into South and Central America. This included a joint venture with Enova and Mexico's Proxima SA to build and operate Mexico's first private utility.

Pacific Enterprises and Enova agreed in 1997 to a $6.2 billion merger; Sempra Energy was born in 1998. That year California began deregulating its retail power market. In response Sempra sold SDG&E's non-nuclear power plants (1900 MW) in 1999. It used the proceeds to eliminate its competitive transition charge and in turn lowered its electric rates.

But under deregulation rates tripled by mid-2000; that summer the California Public Utilities Commission (CPUC) implemented a rate freeze for electric customers. Wholesale power prices soared and rolling blackouts occurred in 2000 and 2001 as a result of the state's inadequate energy supply. In 2001 the CPUC began allowing utilities to increase their rates and SDG&E agreed to sell its transmission assets to the state for about $1 billion.

Sempra sold its 72.5% share in power marketing firm Energy America to British energy company Centrica in 2001. In 2002 the company purchased bankrupt utility Enron's London-based metals trading unit for about $145 million; later that year it purchased Enron's metals concentrates and metals warehousing businesses.

The company restructured its competitive energy business units in 2005 renaming several divisions and dividing the former Sempra Energy Solutions operations (retail energy marketing and services for commercial and industrial customers) under the Commodities and Generation divisions. That year Sempra sold one of its gas storage units to Vulcan's investment company for a reported $250 million.

In 2006 the company settled class-action litigation that claimed that two of its subsidiaries Southern California Gas and San Diego Gas & Electric had helped to create the 2000-2001 energy crises in California by restricting the supply of natural gas to the state.

In 2007 Sempra was awarded a $172 million settlement arising from a 2002 dispute over the company's minority stakes in two Argentine natural gas holding companies.

In 2008 Sempra Energy formed a commodities marketing joint venture with The Royal Bank of Scotland RBS Sempra Commodities.

In a move to expand its midstream and distribution assets in the southeastern US in 2008 the company acquired EnergySouth for $510 million.

The company reported a jump in its revenues in 2010 thanks to a recovering global economy that drove up energy demand along with higher oil and gas prices and increased rates. Losses related to winding down its commodities unit trimmed Sempra Energy's net income for the year.

In 2013 Sempra U.S. Gas & Power acquired the Broken Bow 2 wind project in Nebraska. When Broken Bow 2 is completed Sempra U.S. Gas & Power will have joint-venture projects totaling more than 1000 MW of wind generating capacity. Sempra U.S. Gas & Power also agreed to purchase 43 1.7-MW General Electric wind turbines to power the 75-MW wind farm. Located in Custer County the wind farm will generate enough renewable power for 30000 Nebraska homes.

Building its midstream portfolio in 2010 the company acquired El Paso's Mexico-based pipeline and compression assets for $300 million.

In 2010 and 2011 Sempra Energy exited the commodities trading business. (In 2008 Sempra Energy had formed a partnership with The Royal Bank of Scotland to operate RBS Sempra Commodities including Sempra Energy Trading which traded and markets wholesale energy commodities in Asia Europe and North America. However to refocus its operations around its more financially reliable North American businesses to pay down debt and to meet EU antitrust requirements in 2010 the company sold the European and Asian segments of this partnership to JP Morgan Chase for about $1.6 billion. It also sold that unit's retail commodity operations to Noble Group for $318 million and eventually wound down its joint venture with The Royal Bank of Scotland.)

In early 2012 the company consolidated Sempra Generation Sempra Pipelines & Storage and Sempra LNG (together formerly Sempra Global) into Sempra International and Sempra US Gas & Power to improve its management and pursue strategic initiatives. Sempra US Gas & Power includes natural gas and renewables while Sempra International includes subsidiaries Sempra Mexico and Sempra South American Utilities.

Taking advantage of abundant natural gas supply from US shale plays In 2013 Sempra Energy teamed up with GDF SUEZ Mitsubishi and Mitsui & Co. to design and build an LNG export facility at the Cameron LNG receipt terminal in Hackberry Louisiana capable of processing 13.5 million tons per year.

To raise cash to fund its growth initiative the company sold one 625-MW block of Sempra U.S. Gas & Power's 1250-MW Mesquite Power natural gas-fired power plant to Salt River Project Agricultural Improvement and Power District for $371 million.

In 2012 BP Wind Energy and Sempra U.S. Gas & Power expand their strategic relationship by agreeing to jointly develop the Mehoopany Wind Farm in Pennsylvania and the Flat Ridge 2 Wind Farm in Kansas (a combined investment of more than $1 billion).

Growing its natural gas footprint in the Southeast US in 2012 Sempra U.S. Gas & Power agreed to buy Hattiesburg Mississippi-based Willmut Gas & Oil Company a natural gas utility which provides service to about 20000 customers in Hattiesburg and the surrounding area.

EXECUTIVES

Evp And General Counsel, Martha B. Wyrsch, age 61, $577,900 total compensation
Chairman President And Ceo, Debra L. (Debbie) Reed, age 62, $1,391,900 total compensation
Chairman President And Ceo Southern California Gas, Dennis V. Arriola, age 58
Corporate Group President Infrastructure, Joseph A. (Joe) Householder, age 63, $700,000 total compensation
Chairman And Ceo Infraestructura Energética Nova (ienova), Carlos Ruiz Sacristᴬn, age 69
President Coo And Director Socalgas, J. Bret Lane, age 60
Ceo Southern California Gas Company (socalgas), Patricia K. (Patti) Wagner, age 57
Svp And Chief Human Resources And Administrative Officer, G. Joyce Rowland, age 64, $405,000 total compensation
Corporate Group President Of Utilities, Steven D. Davis, age 63, $541,400 total compensation
Evp And Cfo, Jeffrey W. Martin, age 57
President San Diego Gas & Electric (sdg&e), Scott D. Drury, age 53
Cio, P. Kevin Chase, age 50
Vp Enterprise Risk Management And Compliance Sdgande And Socalgas, Diana Day
Regional Vice President Commercial Development Sempra U.s. Gas And Power, Sue Bradham
Vice President Business Origination, Michael Sliwowski
Senior Vice President Regulatory And Finance, Schavrien Lee
Vp Controller And Chief Accounting Officer, Peter Wall
Vp Major Project Controls, Ryan O'neal
Vice President Federal Government Affairs, Maryam Brown
Vp Compliance And Governance And Corporate Secretary, M Angelica Espinosa
Board Member, William Jones
Auditors: DELOITTE & TOUCHE LLP

LOCATIONS

HQ: Sempra Energy
488 8th Avenue, San Diego, CA 92101
Phone: 619 696-2000
Web: www.sempra.com

2018 Sales

	$ mil.	% of total
US	8,840	76
South America	1,585	13
Mexico	1,262	11
Total	**11,687**	**100**

PRODUCTS/OPERATIONS

2018 Sales

	$ mil.	% of total
SDG&E	4,568	38
SoCalGas	3,962	33
Sempra South American Utilities	1,585	13
Sempra Mexico	1,376	11
Sempra LNG & Midstream	472	4
Sempra Renewables	124	1
Adjustments and eliminations	(400)	-
Total	**11,687**	**100**

2018 Sales

	$ mil.	% of total
Utilities:		
Electric	5,506	47
Natural gas	4,540	39
Energy-related businesses	1,641	14
Total	**11,687**	**100**

COMPETITORS

AEP	IBERDROLA
AES	Los Angeles Water and
AT&T	Power
Avista	NRG Energy
CMS Energy	NV Energy
Calpine	PG&E Corporation
CenterPoint Energy	PacifiCorp
Constellation Energy	Public Service
Group	Enterprise Group
Dominion Energy	Sacramento Municipal
Duke Energy	Utility
Edison International	Southern Company
Endesa S.A.	Southwest Gas
Entergy	Tenaska
Exelon Energy	Williams Companies
FirstEnergy	

HISTORICAL FINANCIALS

Company Type: Public

Income Statement

FYE: December 31

	REVENUE ($ mil.)	NET INCOME ($ mil.)	NET PROFIT MARGIN	EMPLOYEES
12/18	11,687	1,050	9.0%	4,015
12/17	11,207	257	2.3%	16,046
12/16	10,183	1,371	13.5%	16,575
12/15	10,231	1,350	13.2%	17,387
12/14	11,035	1,162	10.5%	17,046
Annual Growth	**1.4%**	**(2.5%)**	**—**	**(30.3%)**

2018 Year-End Financials

Debt ratio: 42.00%
Return on equity: 7.00%
Cash ($ mil.): 190
Current ratio: 0.00
Long-term debt ($ mil.): 21,611

No. of shares (mil.): 274
Dividends
Yield: 3.0%
Payout: 105.0%
Market value ($ mil.): 29,619

	STOCK PRICE ($) FY Close	P/E High/Low		PER SHARE ($) Earnings	Dividends	Book Value
12/18	108.00	34	29	3.00	4.00	63.00
12/17	107.00	120	99	1.00	3.00	50.00
12/16	101.00	21	16	5.00	3.00	52.00
12/15	94.00	21	17	5.00	3.00	48.00
12/14	111.00	25	19	5.00	3.00	46.00
Annual Growth	**(0.7%)**	**—**	**—**	**(7.3%)**	**7.9%**	**8.0%**

SENTARA HEALTHCARE

Sentara Healthcare is not-for-profit operator of more than 300 health facilities in Virginia and North Carolina. The system includes a dozen acute care hospitals housing a total of more than 2000 beds including Sentara Norfolk Sentara RMH and Sentara Virginia Beach. Several of its hospitals contain specialist facilities such as the Sentara Heart Hospital the Hospital for Extended Recovery and two orthopedic hospitals. In addition the company operates medical practices urgent care clinics imaging centers rehab facilities nursing homes hospice and home health agencies and ambulance providers. Its Optima Health unit provides HMO

PPO and other health insurance products to about 450000 Virginians.

Financial Performance

Sentara Healthcare reports more than $5 billion in annual revenue. About three-fourths of earnings come from patient services (mostly from inpatient care); insurance premiums and capitation revenue make up most of the rest.

The company spends more than $350 million annually on community benefits primarily for uncompensated care of uninsured patients. It also supports community education and screening programs as well as professional education programs at the Eastern Virginia Medical School.

Strategy

While it is already one of the largest health care organizations in the state Sentara Healthcare continues to grow through acquisitions construction efforts (both expansions and new buildings) and mergers.

In 2018 the company broke ground on its new $93.5 million Sentara Cancer Center in Norfolk VA. The facility scheduled for completion in 2020 will bring together medical teams from Sentara Medical Group and affiliates Virginia Oncology Associates and Eastern Virginia Medical School. The company is also building a new 20-bed hospital in Suffolk Virginia at the Sentara BelleHarbour outpatient campus.

As the health care industry shifts towards less-expensive outpatient settings Sentara is working to upgrade some ambulatory care facilities to provide more convenient care options for patients.

The company has worked to stay ahead of information technology trends that help improve operational efficiencies and quality of care. It has invested in fields such as population health management telehealth (Sentara MDLIVE) advanced patient monitoring (Sentara eICU) and workflow productivity and healthcare analytics (in partnership with Medstreaming).

Company Background

Sentara Healthcare was founded in 1888 as Norfolk's 25-bed Retreat for the Sick. Norfolk General and Leigh Memorial merged in 1972.

Additional hospitals were acquired over the years including Hampton General Hospital (1988) Bayside Hospital (1991) Virginia Beach General Hospital (1998) Williamsburg Community Hospital (2002) Obici Hospital (2006) Potomac Hospital (2009) RMH Healthcare (2011) Martha Jefferson Hospital (2011) and Halifax Regional Health System (2013). Construction of the Sentara Princess Anne Hospital was completed in 2011.

In 2014 it acquired the assets and operations of Albemarle Hospital Albemarle Physician Services and Regional Medical Services through a 30-year capital lease agreement with Pasquotank County and Albemarle Hospital Authority. The businesses were combined into newly formed subsidiary SAMC.

EXECUTIVES

Vice President Human Resources, Michael Taylor
Ceo, Howard P. Kern
Svp And Cio, Bertram S. (Bert) Reese
Svp And Cfo, Robert A. (Rob) Broerman
Svp; President Sentara Health Plans And Optima Health, Michael M. Dudley
President Sentara Leigh Hospital, Teresa L. (Terrie) Edwards
President Sentara Careplex Hospital, Debra A. Flores
Corporate Vp Sentara Norfolk General Hospital Sentara Careplex Hospital And Sentara Williamsburg Regional Medical Center, Mary L. Blunt
President Sentara Martha Jefferson Hospital, Jonathan S. Davis
President Sentara Virginia Beach General Hospital, Elwood B. (Bernie) Boone
Chief Nursing Officer, Genemarie McGee
Svp And Chief Medical Officer, Terry Gilliland
President Sentara Williamsburg Regional Medical Center, David J. (Dave) Masterson
President Sentara Norfolk General Hospital, Kurt Hofelich
President Sentara Life Care Corporation, Bruce Robertson
President Sentara Princess Anne Hospital, Thomas B. Thames
Corporate Vp; President Sentara Rmh Medical Center, Jim Krauss
Corporate Vp; President Sentara Medical Group, Robert (Doug) Culling
Corporate Vp, Michael Gentry
President Sentara Enterprises, Linda R. Huffer
President Sentara Obici Hospital, Steve Julian
President Sentara Halifax Regional Hospital, Chris A. Lumsden
Corporate Vp; President Sentara Northern Virginia Medical Center, Stephen D. Porter
President Sentara Albemarle Medical Center, Coleen Santa Ana
Medical Director, Frank Barch
Vice President Finance, Lester Eljaiek
Director Of Pharmacy, Betsy Early
Medical Director, Carl Hartman
Vice President Operations, Robert Firestone
Vice President Operations, Valerie Keane
Vice President And Chief Information Security Officer, Daniel Bowden
Vice President Government Relations And Health Policy, Paul Speidell
Vice President For Clinical Informatics And Transformation, David Mohr
Vice President Patient Care Nurse Executive, Peggy Braun
Medical Director, Steve Fisher
Vice President Information Technology, Kris Clickner
Vice President Of Medical Affairs, Dennis Szurkus
Vice President Operations, Allura Kemick
Vice President Medical Affairs, Michael Ashby
Vp Clinical Services Optima, Karen Bray
Vice President Hospital Finance, Leo Deleon
Chairman, Bob Fort
Vice Chairman, Henry (Sandy) Harris
Auditors: KPMG LLP NORFOLK VIRGINIA

LOCATIONS

HQ: SENTARA HEALTHCARE
  6015 POPLAR HALL DR, NORFOLK, VA 235023819
Phone: 800 736-8272
Web: WWW.SENTARA.COM

PRODUCTS/OPERATIONS

Selected Hospitals

Charlottesville
  Martha Jefferson Hospital
  MJH Outpatient Care Center
  Health Services at Proffit Road
  Health Services at Spring Creek
  Sentara Home Care Services
  Optima Health
Hampton Roads
  Sentara CarePlex Hospital
  Sentara Heart Hospital
  Sentara Leigh Hospital
  Sentara Norfolk General Hospital
  Sentara Obici Hospital
  Sentara Princess Anne Hospital
  Sentara Virginia Beach General Hospital
  Sentara Williamsburg Regional Medical Center
  Orthopaedic Hospital at Sentara CarePlex
  Sentara Northern Virginia Medical Center

Martha Jefferson Hospital
  RMH Healthcare
Harrisonburg
  RMH Healthcare
  Optima Health
Northern Virginia
  Sentara Northern Virginia Medical Center
  Sentara Lake Ridge
  Sentara Medical Group physicians
  Sentara Home Care Services
  Sentara Heart and Vascular Center
  Optima Health

Selected Services

Cancer
Cardiac (Heart)
Digestive (Colorectal)
Home Care
Imaging
Maternity
Neurosciences
Rehabilitation
Seniors
Thoracic
Transplant
Trauma/Emergency Services
Urology
Vascular
Weight Loss Surgery
Women's

COMPETITORS

Aetna
Anthem Health Plans of Virginia
Bon Secours Health
CIGNA
Carilion Clinic
Centra Health Inc.
Children's Hospital of The King's Daughters
Franklin Hospital Corp.
HCA Capital Division
Humana
Inova
Kaiser Foundation Health Plan of the Mid-Atlantic
Norton Community Hospital
Novant Health
Riverside Health System (Virginia)
Twin County Regional Healthcare
UnitedHealth Group

HISTORICAL FINANCIALS

Company Type: Private

Income Statement   FYE: December 31

	REVENUE ($ mil.)	NET INCOME ($ mil.)	NET PROFIT MARGIN	EMPLOYEES
12/17	5,298	580	11.0%	28,000
12/16	5,083	329	6.5%	—
12/15	4,834	139	2.9%	—
12/14	4,694	360	7.7%	—
Annual Growth	4.1%	17.3%	—	—

ServisFirst Bancshares Inc

ServisFirst Bancshares is a bank holding company for ServisFirst Bank a regional commercial bank with about a dozen branches located in Alabama and the Florida panhandle. The bank also has a loan office in Nashville. ServisFirst Bank targets privately-held businesses with $2 million to $250 million in annual sales as well as professionals and affluent customers. The bank focuses on traditional commercial banking services including loan origination deposits and electronic banking services such as online and mobile banking. Founded in 2005 by its chairman and CEO Thomas Broughton III the bank went public in 2014 with an offering valued at nearly $57 million.

IPO
ServisFirst Bancshares sold 625000 shares priced at $91 per share. Proceeds from the May 2014 IPO will be used to support the bank's growth plans both in Alabama and in other states.

Geographic Reach
Birmingham-based ServisFirst Bank has branches in Birmingham Huntsville Montgomery Mobile Dothan Pensacola and Nashville.

Financial Performance
The bank reported net income of $41.2 million in 2013 compared with $34 million in 2012. The increase was primarily due to an increase in net interest income which rose nearly 20% to $112.5 million. Noninterest income increased 4% to $10 million in 2013.

As of March 2014 the bank had total assets of approximately $3.6 billion total loans of $2.9 billion and total deposits of about $3.0 billion.

EXECUTIVES

President And Ceo Servisfirst Bancshares And Servisfirst Bank, Thomas A. (Tom) Broughton, age 63, $350,000 total compensation

Evp And Coo Servisfirst Bancshares And Servisfirst Bank, Clarence C. Pouncey, age 62, $263,000 total compensation

Evp Cfo Treasurer And Secretary Servisfirst Bancshares And Servisfirst Bank, William M. Foshee, age 64, $230,000 total compensation

Evp Servisfirst Bancshares And President And Ceo Servisfirst Bank Of Huntsville, Andrew N. (Andy) Kattos, age 49

President And Ceo Servisfirst Bank Of Mobile, William (Bibb) Lamar, age 75

Evp Servisfirst Bancshares And President And Ceo Servisfirst Bank Of Montgomery, G. Carlton (Carl) Barker, age 64

Evp Servisfirst Bancshares And President And Ceo Servisfirst Bank Of Pensacola, Rex D. McKinney, age 56

Evp Correspondent Banking Servisfirst Bancshares And Servisfirst Bank, Rodney E. Rushing, age 61, $245,000 total compensation

Svp And Chief Credit Officer Servisfirst Bancshares And Servisfirst Bank, Don G. Owens, age 67, $187,200 total compensation

President And Ceo Servisfirst Bank Of Atlanta, Ken Barber

Evp And Chief Lending Officer, Doug Rehm

Ceo Servisfirst Bank Dothan, B. Harrison Morris, age 42

First Vice President, Lee McKinnon

Senior Vice President Commercial Lending, Chad Thomason

Senior Vice President Of Commerical Banking, David Hearne

Senior Vice President Commercial Banking, Jeff Johnson

Vice President, John Peacock

Senior Vice President Commercial Banking Team Lead, Lawson Kirkland

Vice President Retail Banking Center Manager, Crystal Lee

Senior Vice President Commercial Relationship Manager, Jim Gardner

Senior Vice President, Justin Fontenot

Vice President, Kiley Elmore

Senior Vice President Of Commercial Banking, Walter Brand

Senior Vice President Private Banking, Patricia Griner

Assistant Vice President, Debbie Crook

Vice President Portfolio Manager, Gary Allen

Fvp Commercial Banking, Cheryl Dunn

Executive Vice President, Brad Armagost

Vice President, Barry Devane

Vice President, Bart Mcbride

Vice President Correspondent Banking, Andrew Barrett

Vice President And Commercial Lender, Max Coblentz

Vice President Commercial Banking, Marshall Darneille

Senior Vice President, Samantha S Curd

Vice President Credit Officer, Stacy B Suddeth

Vice President, Sam Scott

Senior Vice President, Hill Womble

Senior Vice President Commercial Banking, Will Clay

Senior Vice President, Michael Stephens

Assistant Vice President Cash Management Services, Loretta Shapiro

Vice President Credit Officer, Stacy Suddeth

Senior Vice President, Bryan Neth

Vice President Portfolio Manager, Jill Alvarez

Vice President Of Cash Management, Delbert Madison

Chairman Servisfirst Bancshares And Servisfirst Bank, Stanley M. (Skip) Brock, age 68

Auditors: Dixon Hughes Goodman LLP

LOCATIONS

HQ: ServisFirst Bancshares Inc
2500 Woodcrest Place, Birmingham, AL 35209
Phone: 205 949-0302
Web: www.servisfirstbank.com

2013 Branches

	No.
Alabama	10
Florida	2
Total	**12**

COMPETITORS

Bank of America	Wells Fargo
Bank of the Ozarks	

HISTORICAL FINANCIALS

Company Type: Public

Income Statement

FYE: December 31

	ASSETS ($ mil.)	NET INCOME ($ mil.)	INCOME AS % OF ASSETS	EMPLOYEES
12/18	8,007	137	1.7%	473
12/17	7,082	93	1.3%	434
12/16	6,370	81	1.3%	420
12/15	5,096	64	1.2%	371
12/14	4,099	52	1.3%	298
Annual Growth	18.2%	27.2%	—	12.2%

2018 Year-End Financials

Debt ratio: 1.00%	No. of shares (mil.): 53
Return on equity: 21.00%	Dividends
Cash ($ mil.): 458	Yield: 2.0%
Current ratio: —	Payout: 21.0%
Long-term debt ($ mil.): —	Market value ($ mil.): 1,701

	STOCK PRICE ($) FY Close	P/E High/Low		PER SHARE ($) Earnings	Dividends	Book Value
12/18	32.00	17	12	3.00	0.00	13.00
12/17	42.00	25	19	2.00	0.00	11.00
12/16	37.00	48	23	2.00	0.00	10.00
12/15	48.00	40	24	1.00	0.00	9.00
12/14	33.00	83	26	1.00	0.00	8.00
Annual Growth	(0.8%)		—	24.7%	32.0%	13.0%

Sherwin-Williams Co (The)

For roughly 150 years Sherwin-Williams has maintained its position as one of the world's top paint manufacturers (along with Akzo Nobel PPG Industries and Henkel). Sherwin-Williams' products include a variety of paints finishes coatings applicators and varnishes sold under brands such as Dutch Boy Krylon Sherwin-Williams and Valspar The company operates mostly in the US Canada Latin America and the Caribbean through about 4700 paint stores and sells automotive finishing and refinishing products through wholesale branches. Its other outlets include home centers independent dealers and automotive retailers. More than 90% of US residents live within 50 miles of one of the company's retail locations.

HISTORY

In 1870 Henry Sherwin bought out paint materials distributor Truman Dunham and joined Edward Williams and A. T. Osborn to form Sherwin Williams & Company in Cleveland. The business began making paints in 1871 and became the industry leader after improving the paint-grinding mill in the mid-1870s patenting a reclosable can in 1877 and improving liquid paint in 1880.

In 1874 Sherwin-Williams introduced a special paint for carriages beginning the concept of specific-purpose paint. (By 1900 the company had paints for floors roofs barns metal bridges railroad cars and automobiles.) Sherwin-Williams incorporated in 1884 and opened a dealership in Massachusetts in 1891 that was the forerunner of its company-run retail stores. The company obtained its "Cover the Earth" trademark in 1895.

Before the Depression Sherwin-Williams bought a number of smaller paint makers: Detroit White Lead (1910) Martin-Senour (1917) Acme Quality Paints (1920) and The Lowe Brothers (1929). Responding to wartime restrictions the company developed a fast-drying and water-reducible paint called Kem-Tone and the forerunner of the paint roller the Roller-Koater.

Sales doubled during the 1960s as the company made acquisitions including Sprayon (aerosol paint 1966) but rising expenses kept earnings flat. In 1972 the company expanded its stores to include carpeting draperies and other decorating items. But long-term debt ballooned from $80 million in 1974 to $196 million by 1977 when the company lost $8.2 million and suspended dividends for the first time since 1885.

John Breen became CEO in 1979 reinstated the dividend purged over half of the top management positions and closed inefficient plants. He also focused stores on paint and wallpaper merchandise and purchased Dutch Boy (1980).

In 1990 Sherwin-Williams began selling Dutch Boy in Sears stores and Kem-Tone in Wal-Marts. Acquisitions that year included Borden's Krylon and Illinois Bronze aerosol operations and DeSoto's architectural coatings segment which made private-label paints for Sears and Home Depot. In 1991 Sherwin-Williams bought two coatings business units from Cook Paint and Varnish and the Cuprinol brand of coatings.

Sherwin-Williams purchased paint manufacturer Pratt & Lambert in 1996. That year it introduced several new products including Low Temp 35 a paint for low temperatures; Healthspec a low-odor paint; and Ralph Lauren designer paints. Prep-Rite do-it-yourself interior primers debuted in

1997. Also that year Sherwin-Williams bought Thompson Minwax (Thompson's Water Seal Minwax Wood Products) from Forstmann Little and Chile-based Marson Chilena a spray paint maker.

The company streamlined some of its business segments and trimmed jobs in 1998. Christopher Connor president of the Paint Stores group replaced Breen as CEO in 1999 and chairman in 2000. Also in 2000 Sherwin-Williams moved into the European automotive coatings market by acquiring Italy-based ScottWarren.

In late 2001 the company acquired Wisconsin-based Mautz Paint Company.

After a rough but still profitable 2001 the company grew revenues and profits for its consumer units (consumer paints and paint stores) in 2002 thanks largely to a healthy do-it-yourself market. Sales for its automotive finishes and international units however were down because of a slow collision-repair market and currency-exchange effects.

In 2010 Sherwin-Williams bought Arch Chemicals' Sayerlack a leading Italian wood care coating company and acquired Becker Acroma Industrial Wood Coatings a Swedish manufacturer of industrial wood coatings. It also acquired all shares of AlSher Titania (a joint venture with Altair Nanotechnologies) it did not already own giving it a 100% stake in the technology company. AlSher Titania is developing a promising titanium dioxide technology that Sherwin-Williams plans to commercialize.

That same year the company also acquired Pinturas C "ndor an Ecuadorian diversified coatings supplier with $60 million in annual sales bolstering its market share in architectural paint in Latin America.

Among its acquisitions in 2011 was UK-based Leighs Paints a leader in fire-protectant (intumescent) coatings. (Because the intumescent technology prolongs the structural integrity of steel and concrete in a catastrophic fire more people are able to evacuate.)

In 2012 Sherwin-Williams made a significant purchase in the buyout of Jiangsu Pulanna Coating Co. headquartered in Changzhou China. Pulanna is an automotive refinishes coatings manufacturer and the deal improved Sherwin-Williams' presence in the most populous country in the world.

Also in 2012 Sherwin-Williams picked up Geocel Holdings a maker of caulks sealants and adhesives serving construction and repair applications. Geocel has locations in the US and the UK and the deal strengthened Sherwin-Williams' Consumer Group segment.

In a major geographic expansion in late 2012 the company agreed to acquire Grupo Comex a leader in the paint and coatings market in Mexico for $2.34 billion. However Mexico's antitrust regulator blocked the deal in mid-2013 stating the new company could artificially set higher prices at its discretion. Sherwin-Williams subsequently terminated the proposed deal.

However in 2013 the company acquired the US/Canada business of Comex. Sherwin-Williams paid $90 million in cash and assumed liabilities in the range of $75 million. Comex operations in the US and Canada consist of 314 company operated stores (234 in the US and 80 in Canada) and 8 manufacturing sites (5 in the US and 3 in Canada). In addition Comex supplies paint and coatings products to 1500 external retail locations.

2013 product launches included Sherwin-Williams Protective & Marine Coatings' Magnalux 404 FF the first styrene-free vinyl ester for use with steel and concrete substrates in the oil and gas market; Fast Clad 105ER a 100% solids tank lining for crude oil and ethanol storage; and Nova-Plate 325 an extended lifecycle 100% solids tank lining for high-temperature crude oil produced water and frac tank applications.

In 2013 Sherwin-Williams teamed up with Williams-Sonoma to create seasonal palettes of Sherwin-Williams paint colors that coordinate with the Pottery Barn Pottery Barn Kids PBteen and West Elm collections.

EXECUTIVES

Chairman President And Ceo, John G. Morikis, age 56, $1,095,795 total compensation
President And General Manager Latin America Division The Americas Group, Paul R. Clifford
Cio, Thomas J. (Tom) Lucas
President The Americas Group, Robert J. Davisson, age 59, $611,936 total compensation
President And General Manager South Western Division The Americas Group, Monty J. Griffin, age 59
President And General Manager Diversified Brands Division Consumer Group, Cheri M. Phyfer, age 48
President And General Manager Automotive Division Global Finishes Group, Thomas C. Hablitzel, age 57
President And General Manager Global Supply Chain Division Consumer Group, Joel D. Baxter, age 59
President And General Manager Mid Western Division The Americas Group, Peter J. Ippolito, age 55
President And General Manager Protective And Marine Coatings Division Global Finishes Group, Ronald B. Rossetto
President Global Finishes Group, David B. Sewell, age 51
President Southeastern Division Paint Stores Group, Todd V. Wipf
President And General Manager Product Finishes Division Global Finishes Group, Bruce G. Irussi
Svp Finance And Cfo, Allen J. Mistysyn, age 50
President And General Manager Eastern Division The Americas Group, Justin T. Binns
Vice President Sales, Brian Padden
Senior Vice President Of Human Resources For Gsc, Matt Schupp
National Account Manager, Vincent Barone
Vice President Of Sales, Jim Sinko
National Account Manager, Pat Busch
National Accounts Manager, Harvey Kulkin
National Sales Manager, Bill Deckard
National Sales Manager, Christopher Olden
Vice President Human Resources, Scott Gradert
Vice President Finance And Controller Diversified Brands Division, Dan Scalabrino
National Account Manager, Richard May
Vice President Taxes And Assistant Secretary Sherwin Williams Company, Michael Cummins
Vice President Global Sourcing, David Ash
Corporate Medical Director, Gregory Ornella
Vp Of Human Resources, Susan − Keough
Vice President Of Sales, Cj Dibattista
Senior Vice President Of Sales, Todd Stephenson
Vice President Sales, Doug Henson
Vice President Executive Compensation, Greg Sofish
National Account Manager, John Hackett
Vice President, Brett White
Vice President Human Resources Paint Stores Group, Thomas Gilligan
Vice President Human Resources, Lonnie McGowen
Vice President Of Information Security, Karen Gabel
National Account Manager, Tiffany Tryon-smith
Svp Corporate Communications And Public Affairs, Robert Wells
National Account Manager, Randy Scott
National Accounts Manager, Zach Wechter
Vice President Of Regional Operations, Phil Matisak
Vice President Global Sourcing, Jose Aravena
Vice President Merchandising, Kevin Madigan
National Account Manager, Mike Pinedo
Senior Vice President, Tom Liebhardt
Board Member, Joseph Banks
Treasurer, Scott McVeigh
Board Member, Chris Pluta
Treasurer, Isaac Blaylock
Auditors: Ernst & Young LLP

LOCATIONS

HQ: Sherwin-Williams Co (The)
  101 West Prospect Avenue, Cleveland, OH 44115-1075
Phone: 216 566-2000   **Fax:** 216 566-3310
Web: www.sherwin.com

PRODUCTS/OPERATIONS

2018 sales

	$ mil.	% of total
The Americas Group	9,625	55
Performance Coatings Group	5,166	29
Consumer Brands Group	2,739	16
Administrative	4	-
Total	**11,856**	**100**

Operations

Operations
Paint Stores
  Products
  Architectural coatings
  Industrial maintenance
  Marine products
  Brands
  ArmorSeal
  Brod-Dugan
  Con-Lux
  FlexBon Paints
  Hi-Temp
  Kem
  Mautz
  Mercury
  Old Quaker
  Powdura
  Pro-Line
  SeaGuard
  Sherwin-Williams
Consumer
  Products
  Architectural paints
  Industrial maintenance
  Paints
  Private-label coatings
  Stains
  Wood finishings
  Varnishes
  Brands
  Cabot
  Cuprinol
  Dupli-color
  Dura Clad
  Dutch Boy
  EverLast
  Formby's
  H&C
  Krylon
  Martin Senour
  Maxwood Latex Stains
  Minwax
  Plastic Kote
  Pratt & Lambert
  Red Devil
  Rubberset
  Signature Select
  Thompson's WaterSeal
  Valspar
  White Lightning
Automotive Finishes
  Products
  Finishing refinishing and touch-up products for motor vehicles
  Brands
  Baco
  Excelo
  Lazzuril
  Martin Senour
  ScottWarren
  Sherwin-Williams

Western
International Coatings
  Products
  Architectural paints
  Industrial maintenance products
  Stains
  Varnishes
  Wood finishing products
Brands
  Andina
  Colorgin
  Dutch Boy
  Globo
  Kem-Tone
  Krylon
  Marson
  Martin Senour
  Minwax
  Pratt & Lambert
  Pulverlack
  Ronseal
  Sherwin-Williams
  Sumare

COMPETITORS

Akzo Nobel	Dunn-Edwards
BASF SE	Ferro
Benjamin Moore	H.B. Fuller
California Products	Kelly-Moore
Comex Group	Masco
Coronado Paint	PPG Industries
Diamond Vogel Paint	RPM International

HISTORICAL FINANCIALS
Company Type: Public

Income Statement   FYE: December 31

	REVENUE ($ mil.)	NET INCOME ($ mil.)	NET PROFIT MARGIN	EMPLOYEES
12/18	17,534	1,109	6.3%	53,368
12/17	14,984	1,772	11.8%	52,695
12/16	11,856	1,133	9.6%	42,550
12/15	11,339	1,054	9.3%	40,706
12/14	11,130	866	7.8%	39,674
Annual Growth	12.0%	6.4%	—	7.7%

2018 Year-End Financials

Debt ratio: 49.00%
Return on equity: 30.00%
Cash ($ mil.): 156
Current ratio: 1.00
Long-term debt ($ mil.): 8,708

No. of shares (mil.): 93
Dividends
  Yield: 1.0%
  Payout: 29.0%
Market value ($ mil.): 36,638

	STOCK PRICE ($) FY Close	P/E High/Low	PER SHARE ($) Earnings	Dividends	Book Value
12/18	393.00	40 31	12.00	3.00	40.00
12/17	410.00	22 14	19.00	3.00	39.00
12/16	269.00	25 19	12.00	3.00	20.00
12/15	260.00	26 19	11.00	3.00	9.00
12/14	263.00	30 20	9.00	2.00	11.00
Annual Growth	10.6%	— —	7.4%	11.8%	39.7%

SHI INTERNATIONAL CORP.

Businesses that need more than boxes of hardware and software can call SHI International. The company distributes scores of computer hardware and software products from suppliers such as Adobe Cisco Microsoft VMware Symantec and Lenovo. It resells PCs networking products data storage systems printers software and keyboards among other items. SHI offers a range of professional services including software licensing asset management managed desktop services systems integration and vocational training. The company serves corporate government and health care customers from more than 30 offices across the US Canada the UK Germany France and Hong Kong. SHI was founded in 1989 by Chairman Koguan Leo.

Operations
SHI serves several sectors and verticals. The company specializes in software and hardware procurement deployment planning configuration data center optimization IT asset management and cloud computing as well as custom IT solutions.

Geographic Reach
Based in Somerset New Jersey SHI has a global reach through its 30-plus offices located across the US Canada the UK Germany France and Hong Kong. In the US the company operates primarily in Texas and California but also in Arizona Colorado Florida Georgia Illinois Indiana Kansas Massachusetts Michigan Minnesota Missouri New Jersey New York Pennsylvania Virginia and Washington. Specifically its cloud briefing center is housed in New York City and its corporate call center runs from Austin Texas. The company's 420000-sq.-ft. headquarters operates beside its 305000-sq.-ft. Integration Center in Somerset New Jersey.

Financial Performance
SHI International rang up $6.8 billion in sales in 2015 a 14% increase versus the prior year. SHI's Strategic Enterprise Commercial Enterprise Corporate and Public Sector divisions contributed nearly equally to the revenue total for the year and growth outside the U.S. was steady with SHI's Canada U.K. and France divisions each posting double-digit growth. In addition SHI recognized over $1 billion in revenue from cloud products and solutions.

The seller of IT products and services boasts a 99% annual customer retention rate.

Strategy
The company has transformed itself from a $1 million regional reseller of software to a $5 billion global provider of information technology products and services.To this end SHI has invested some $20 million in a new data center that provides cloud services specifically what the company terms infrastructure-as-a-service (IaaS). The data center is one of six in the US that houses virtual machines for IT professionals to provide services such as application deployment disaster recovery software-as-a-service (SaaS). It also offers on-demand burst computing services where customers use the additional bandwidth to handle peaks in demand.

SHI's professional services unit already provides some cloud services and data center consulting. SHI sees IaaS as a logical extension of the software asset management (SAM) service it already provides. Under the SAM program SHI handles software deployment licensing compliance and inventories across a business.

SHI partners with Omaha Nebraska-based information security software specialist Solutionary to manage data security services using its ActiveGuard software product to block computer network security breaches as data center security is one of the biggest concerns for businesses in a cloud computing environment. Awards and Recognition

SHI is the largest minority and women-owned Business Enterprise (MWBE) in the US. The company's ranked 13th on CRN's 2015 Solution Provider 500 list of the largest IT solution providers in North America.

EXECUTIVES

President And Co-ceo, Thai Lee, age 62
Vp And General Manager, Hal Jagger
Vice President Internal Audit And Finance Operations, Kevin Boyles
Vice President, Melissa Graham
Chairman, Koguan Leo
Auditors: COHNREZNICK LLP NEW YORK NEW

LOCATIONS

HQ: SHI INTERNATIONAL CORP.
  290 DAVIDSON AVE, SOMERSET, NJ 088734145
Phone: 732 764-8888

PRODUCTS/OPERATIONS

Selected Products
Accessories
Peripherals
Hardware
Memory
Software

Selected Services
Cloud services
Computer vocational training services
Data center services
Events
Hardware services
Networking
POLARIS Software asset management
Storage
Strategic consulting
Webinars

COMPETITORS

ASI Computer Technologies	Computacenter
Agilysys	Ingram Micro
Arrow Electronics	Insight Enterprises
Avnet	PC Mall
CDW	Softchoice
CompuCom	Tech Data

HISTORICAL FINANCIALS
Company Type: Private

Income Statement   FYE: December 31

	REVENUE ($ mil.)	NET INCOME ($ mil.)	NET PROFIT MARGIN	EMPLOYEES
12/18	9,767	246	2.5%	4,500
12/17	8,244	198	2.4%	—
12/16	7,269	105	1.4%	—
12/15	6,540	70	1.1%	—
Annual Growth	14.3%	52.1%	—	—

Sierra Bancorp

Sierra Bancorp is the holding company for the nearly $2 billion-asset Bank of the Sierra which operates approximately 30 branches in Central California's San Joaquin Valley between (and including) Bakersfield and Fresno. The bank offers traditional deposit products and loans to individuals and small and mid-size businesses. About 70% of its loan portfolio is made up of real estate loans while another 15% is made up of mortgage warehouse loans and a further 10% is tied to commercial and industrial loans (including SBA loans and direct finance leases). The bank also issues agricultural loans and consumer loans.

Operations
Bank of the Sierra makes almost 80% of its revenue from interest income. About 64% of its total revenue came from interest income on loans and leases (including fees) during 2015 while another 14% came from interest income on taxed and tax-exempt securities. The rest of its revenue came from deposit account service charges (12% of revenue) checkcard fees (5%) and other non-interest income sources.

Geographic Reach
The Porterville California-based bank operates branches and offices mostly in the San Joaquin Valley in Porterville Arroyo Grande Atascadero Bakersfield California City Clovis Delano Dinuba Exeter Farmersville Fillmore Fresno Hanford Lindsay Oxnard Paso Robles Reedley San Luis Obispo Santa Clarita Santa Paula Selma Tehachapi Three Rivers Visalia and Tulare.

Sales and Marketing
Bank of the Sierra has been gradually increasing its advertising spend in recent years. It spent $2.3 million on advertising and promotion in 2015 up from $2.2 million and $1.9 million in 2014 and 2013 respectively.

Financial Performance
The bank's revenue has been steadily rising over the past few years mostly as bank acquisitions and organic loan business growth has spurred higher interest income. Meanwhile its profits have more than doubled since 2011 thanks to declining loan loss provisions as its loan portfolio's credit quality has improved with higher property valuations in the strengthened economy.

Sierra Bancorp's revenue jumped 13% to $80.4 million during 2015 thanks to higher interest income from continued double-digit loan asset growth led by a jump in mortgage warehouse lines from increased line utilization a first-quarter purchase of residential mortgage loans and strong organic growth in non-farm real estate and agricultural production loans. Deposit account service fees also grew thanks to organic deposit client growth.

Strong revenue growth and lower acquisition costs in 2015 drove the bank's net income up 19% to $18 million. Sierra's operating cash levels rose 4% to $29.78 million during the year as its cash-based earnings increased.

Strategy
While the Bank of Sierra has traditionally grown organically by opening around one new branch per year in the Central Valley it has more recently acquired small area banks and individual branches to bolster its deposit and loan business while expanding into untapped markets such as further south into the Santa Clara Valley.

Mergers and Acquisitions
In July 2016 the bank bought $145 million-asset Coast Bancorp and its Coast National Bank branches in San Luis Obispo Paso Robles Arroyo Grande and Atascadero California.

In November 2014 Sierra Bancorp bought $129 million-asset Santa Clara Valley Bank N.A. and its branches in Santa Paula Santa Clarita and Fillmore in California for $15 million. the deal expanded Sierra's reach outside of its traditional market for the first time more south into the Santa Clara Valley of California.

EXECUTIVES
Evp And Cfo, Kenneth R. (Ken) Taylor, age 59, $242,500 total compensation

Evp And Chief Credit Officer, James F. (Jim) Gardunio, age 68, $197,600 total compensation

Vp And Manager Hanford Bank Of The Sierra, Kevin J. McPhaill, age 46, $185,000 total compensation

Senior Vice President Specialized Lending, Michael McLennan

Senior Vp, Matthew Hessler

Senior Vice President Of Tulare County And Manager Of Tulare County, David Soares

Vice President Assistant Risk Manager, Cyndi Carmichael

Chairman, Morris A. Tharp, age 79

Auditors: Eide Bailly LLP

LOCATIONS
HQ: Sierra Bancorp
86 North Main Street, Porterville, CA 93257
Phone: 559 782-4900
Web: www.bankofthesierra.com

COMPETITORS

Bank of America	MUFG Americas Holdings
Bank of the West	United Security
Central Valley	Bancshares
Community Bancorp	Wells Fargo
Citibank	Westamerica
Comerica	Zions Bancorporation
JPMorgan Chase	

HISTORICAL FINANCIALS
Company Type: Public

Income Statement				FYE: December 31
	ASSETS ($ mil.)	NET INCOME ($ mil.)	INCOME AS % OF ASSETS	EMPLOYEES
12/18	2,523	30	1.2%	556
12/17	2,340	20	0.8%	576
12/16	2,033	18	0.9%	497
12/15	1,797	18	1.0%	431
12/14	1,637	15	0.9%	437
Annual Growth	11.4%	18.1%	—	6.2%

2018 Year-End Financials
Debt ratio: 1.00%
Return on equity: 11.00%
Cash ($ mil.): 74
Current ratio: —
Long-term debt ($ mil.): —

No. of shares (mil.): 15
Dividends
 Yield: 3.0%
 Payout: 38.0%
Market value ($ mil.): 368

	STOCK PRICE ($) FY Close	P/E High/Low		PER SHARE ($)		
				Earnings	Dividends	Book Value
12/18	24.00	16	12	2.00	1.00	18.00
12/17	27.00	21	17	1.00	1.00	17.00
12/16	27.00	20	12	1.00	0.00	15.00
12/15	18.00	14	11	1.00	0.00	14.00
12/14	18.00	16	14	1.00	0.00	14.00
Annual Growth	8.2%	—	—	15.5%	17.1%	6.9%

Signature Bank (New York, NY)

Signature Bank marks the spot where some professional New Yorkers bank. The institution provides customized banking and financial services to smaller private businesses their owners and their top executives through 30 branches across the New York metropolitan area including all five boroughs Long Island and affluent Westchester County. The bank's lending activities mainly entail real estate and business loans. Subsidiary Signature Securities offers wealth management financial planning brokerage services asset management and insurance while its Signature Financial subsidiary offers equipment financing and leasing. Founded in 2001 the bank now boasts assets of roughly $29 billion.

Operations
Mortgage loans including commercial real estate loans multifamily residential mortgages home loans and lines of credit and construction and land loans comprise the bulk of Signature Bank's loan portfolio (and much of its asset base as well).

The bank which staffed some 1010 employees at the end of 2014 generated 68% of its revenue from interest on loans and leases that year while 20% came from interest on its securities available-for-sale and 7% came from securities held-to-maturity. The remainder of its revenue came from fees and service charges (2%) and various other miscellaneous sources.

Geographic Reach
The bank's nearly 30 branch offices are mostly in the New York metropolitan area which includes Manhattan Brooklyn Westchester Long Island Queens the Bronx Staten Island and Connecticut.

Sales and Marketing
Signature Bank mostly serves privately-owned businesses their owners and senior managers (typically with a net worth between $500000 and $20 million).

Financial Performance
The company's revenues and profits have risen in recent years thanks to strong organic loan business growth and declining loan loss provisions as its loan portfolio's credit quality has improved with higher property valuations in the strengthened economy.

Signature's revenue jumped by 22% to a record $959.3 million in 2014 mostly as loan interest (on commercial loans mortgages and leases) and security interest income continued to grow as the bank built up its interest-earning assets during the year.

Higher revenue and a continued decline and loan loss provisions in 2014 boosted the bank's net income by 30% to a record $296.7 million. Signature's operating cash levels more than doubled to $421 million on higher cash earnings.

Strategy
Signature Bank has long targeted privately-held businesses that have fewer than 1000 employees and revenues of less than $200 million. Some of its target clients include real estate owners/companies law firms accounting firms entertainment business managers medical professionals retail establishments money management firms and non-profit foundations.

The bank continues to expand its service lines particularly focusing on specialty financing to grow its business organically. In 2015 it planned to offer direct commercial vehicle financing through a network of approved commercial vehicle dealerships in New York's Tri-State area with loans targeting small and mid-size business borrowers looking to acquire commercial vehicles and fleets. Also that year it formed its Maryland-based Signature Public Funding Corp subsidiary to provide municipal finance and tax-exempt lending and leasing products to local state and federal government agencies nationwide.

Company Background
The bank's emphasis on personal service helped it to grow its deposit base and loan portfolio in 2011. During a time when many other banks struggled under the weight of bad loans in a bad economy Signature Bank achieved record earnings for the fourth consecutive year.

Founded in 2001 as an alternative to mega-banks Signature Bank was spun off from Bank Hapoalim in 2004.

EXECUTIVES

President Ceo And Director, Joseph J. DePaolo,
  $577,500 total compensation
Svp And Cfo, Vito Susca
President Ceo And Director, Michael G. O'Rourke
Evp, Kevin P. Bastuga
Evp, Bryan D. Duncan
Vp Retail Operations Manager, Ella Riordan-Pacheco
Vice President, John C Spagnuolo
Vice President, Joseph Fingerman
Group Director Senior Vice President, Kevin
  Hardiman
Vice President Commercial Banking, Ross
  Thomson
Senior Vice President Group Director, Salvatore
  Costa
Svp, Maria Hegi
Chairman And Director, Leonard S. Caronia
Auditors: KPMG LLP

LOCATIONS

HQ: Signature Bank (New York, NY)
  565 Fifth Avenue, New York, NY 10017
Phone: 646 822-1500
Web: www.signatureny.com

PRODUCTS/OPERATIONS

2014 Sales

	$ mil.	% of total
Interest		
Loans net	656	68
Securities available for sale	194	20
Securities held to maturity	70	7
Other	5	1
Noninterest		
Fees & service charges	19	2
Commissions	11	1
Net gains on sales of loans	5	1
Net gains on sales of securities	5	-
Other	2	-
Adjustments	(7.8)	-
Total	**959**	**100**

COMPETITORS

Apple Bank for Savings	Herald National Bank
Astoria Financial	JPMorgan Chase
Bank Leumi USA	New York Community
Capital One	Bancorp
Citigroup	Safra Bank
HSBC USA	TD Bank USA

HISTORICAL FINANCIALS

Company Type: Public

Income Statement — FYE: December 31

	ASSETS ($ mil.)	NET INCOME ($ mil.)	INCOME AS % OF ASSETS	EMPLOYEES
12/18	47,365	505	1.1%	1,393
12/17	43,118	387	0.9%	1,305
12/16	39,048	396	1.0%	1,218
12/15	33,451	373	1.1%	1,122
12/14	27,319	297	1.1%	1,010
Annual Growth	14.7%	14.2%	—	8.4%

2018 Year-End Financials

Debt ratio: 1.00%	No. of shares (mil.): 55
Return on equity: 12.00%	Dividends
Cash ($ mil.): 317	Yield: 1.0%
Current ratio: —	Payout: 13.0%
Long-term debt ($ mil.): —	Market value ($ mil.): 5,659

Stock Price / P/E / Per Share data:

	STOCK PRICE ($) FY Close	P/E High/Low	Earnings	Dividends	Book Value
12/18	103.00	17 11	9.00	1.00	80.00
12/17	137.00	23 17	7.00	0.00	73.00
12/16	150.00	21 15	7.00	0.00	66.00
12/15	153.00	22 16	7.00	0.00	57.00
12/14	126.00	22 17	6.00	0.00	50.00
Annual Growth	(5.0%)	— —	11.6%	—	12.7%

SIGNATURE FINANCIAL LLC

EXECUTIVES

Ceo-MBR, Joseph J Depaolo
MBR, Eric Howell
Senior Vice President, Ann Buzzo
Senior Vice President, Anne Doligale
Senior Vice President, Lisa Wente
Senior Vice President, Marietta Mullane
Executive Sales Officer, Stephen Port

LOCATIONS

HQ: SIGNATURE FINANCIAL LLC
  565 5TH AVE AT46TH, NEW YORK, NY 100172413
Phone: 646 865-0767
Web: WWW.SIGNATUREBANK.BANK

HISTORICAL FINANCIALS

Company Type: Private

Income Statement — FYE: December 31

	ASSETS ($ mil.)	NET INCOME ($ mil.)	INCOME AS % OF ASSETS	EMPLOYEES
12/17	43,120	387	0.9%	11
12/16	39,048	396	1.0%	
12/15	33,451	373	1.1%	
Annual Growth	13.5%	1.9%	—	—

Silvergate Capital Corp

Auditors: Crowe LLP

LOCATIONS

HQ: Silvergate Capital Corp
  4250 Executive Square, Suite 300, La Jolla, CA 92037
Phone: 858 362-6300
Web: www.silvergatebank.com

HISTORICAL FINANCIALS

Company Type: Public

Income Statement — FYE: December 31

	ASSETS ($ mil.)	NET INCOME ($ mil.)	INCOME AS % OF ASSETS	EMPLOYEES
12/18	2,004	22	1.1%	209
12/17	1,892	8	0.4%	
Annual Growth	5.9%	192.2%	—	—

2018 Year-End Financials

Debt ratio: 1.00%	No. of shares (mil.): 18
Return on equity: 17.00%	Dividends
Cash ($ mil.): 674	Yield: —
Current ratio: —	Payout: —
Long-term debt ($ mil.): —	Market value ($ mil.): —

	STOCK PRICE ($) FY Close	P/E High/Low	Earnings	Dividends	Book Value
12/18	0.00	— —	1.00	0.00	11.00
12/17	0.00	— —	1.00	0.00	8.00
/0.00	—	—(0.00)	0.00	(0.00)	
Annual Growth	—	— —	—	—	—

Simmons First National Corp

Simmons First National thinks it's only natural it should be one of the largest financial institutions in The Natural State. The $8.1 billion-asset holding company owns Simmons First National Bank and seven other community banks that bear the Simmons First Bank name and maintain local identities; together they operate around 150 branches throughout Arkansas and in Kansas Tennessee and Missouri. Serving consumers and area businesses the banks offer standard deposit products like checking and savings accounts IRAs and CDs. Lending activities mainly consist of commercial real estate loans single-family mortgages and consumer loans such as credit card and student loans.

Operations

In addition to Simmons First National Bank the company owns Simmons First Bank of Jonesboro Simmons First Bank of South Arkansas Simmons First Bank of Northwest Arkansas Simmons First Bank of Russellville Simmons First Bank of Searcy Simmons First Bank of El Dorado and Simmons First Bank of Hot Springs. Simmons First Trust Company a subsidiary of Simmons First National Bank provides trust and fiduciary services; Simmons First Investment Group offers broker-dealer services.

Like other retail banks Simmons makes the bulk of its money from interest income. About 65% of its total revenue came from loan interest during 2015 while another 8% came from interest on investment securities. The rest of its revenue came from service charges on deposit accounts (8% of revenue) debit and credit card fees (6%) mortgage lending income (3%) trust income (2%) investment banking income (1%) and other non-interest income sources.

Geographic Reach

The bank has around 150 branches mostly in Arkansas but also in Kansas Missouri and Tennessee.

Financial Performance

Simmons First National Bank's annual revenues and profits have been rising mostly thanks to new loan business from rapid bank expansion (mostly stemming from acquisitions).

The bank's revenue jumped 60% to $396.8 million during 2015 mostly thanks to 58% growth in legacy loans and growth in acquired loan business from the acquisitions of Liberty and Community First. Non-interest income grew 54% thanks to rising trust service charges deposit fees mortgage lending income all also tied to its recent acquisitions.

Revenue growth in 2015 more than doubled Simmons' net income to $74.36 million. The bank's operating cash levels spiked eight-fold to $88.7 million for the year thanks to a rise in cash-based earnings and favorable changes in working capital.

Strategy

Simmons tries to differentiate itself from smaller competitors by offering a wider array of products while striving to provide more personalized service than larger regional banks. The company also likes to acquire banks to grow its loan and deposit business while expanding into new geographic markets. Between 1990 and 2015 Simmons made 11 whole bank acquisitions and a handful of branch deals with other banks adding some 125 branches to its total branch network.

Mergers and Acquisitions

In 2019 Simmons First National acquired Reliance Bancshares a bank holding company with more than 20 branches in the St. Louis Missouri metropolitan area. The acquisition brings Simmons total assets to $17.6 billion and its total number of branches to more than 200 across Arkansas Colorado Illinois Kansas Missouri Oklahoma Tennessee and Texas. That year the company also purchased The Landrum Company the parent of Landmark Bank. Landrum brings with it approximately $3.3 billion in assets $2.1 billion in loans $3 billion in deposits and 40 branches in Missouri Oklahoma and Texas.

EXECUTIVES

Evp Organizational Development, Stephen C. Massanelli, age 63
Chairman And Ceo, George A. Makris, age 62, $502,500 total compensation
Sevp Cfo And Treasurer, Robert A. Fehlman, age 54, $306,614 total compensation
Evp And Central And Northeast Arkansas Regional Chairman Simmons First National Bank, Barry K. Ledbetter
President And Chief Credit Officer Simmons First National Bank, N. Craig Hunt
Evp And South Arkansas Regional Chairman Simmons First National Bank, Freddie G. Black
Evp Corporate Strategy And Performance And Secretary, Susan F. Smith, age 57
President Chief Banking Officer And Director, David L. Bartlett, age 67, $376,142 total compensation
Evp, Marty D. Casteel, age 67, $304,180 total compensation
Evp Controller Chief Accounting Officer And Investment Relations Officer, David W. Garner, age 49
Evp Of Marketing, Robert C. Dill, age 76, $179,393 total compensation
Evp And Chief Risk Officer, Tina M. Groves, age 49
Evp Technology And Operations Simmons First National Bank, Lisa W. Hunter
Svp And Marketing Director Simmons First National Bank, Amy W. Johnson
President El Dorado Community Bank, Robert L. Robinson
Chairman Russellville Community Chairman, Ronald B. (Ron) Jackson
President Hot Springs Community Bank, Steven W. (Steve) Trusty
President Conway Community Bank, Jason Culpepper
Evp And General Counsel, Patrick A. Burrow, age 65
Evp Specialty Lending Simmons First National Bank, Larry L. Bates
Evp And Tennessee Regional Chairman Simmons First National Bank, John C. Clark
Evp And Kansas And Missouri Regional Chairman Simmons First National Bank, Gary E. Metsger

Vice President, Clint Parton
Vice President And Personnel Manager, Leigh Cockrum
Vice President, Pam Lawshe
Vp Of Mortgage, Deana Powell
Assistant Vice President Branch Manager, Emily Ferguson
Assistant Vice President Loans, Esther Chapman
Senior Vice President Director Of Marketing And Communications, Elizabeth Machen
Vice President, Chad Pittillo
Executive Vice President Operations, Glenda Tolson
Vice President Regional Manager, Zilpha Wilson
Vice President, Rick Pierce
Senior Vice President, Adam Mitchell
Vice President Financial Analysis Manager, Donna Renfro
Senior Vice President Regulatory And Consumer Affairs, Kevin Archer
Vice President Market Manager, Dorvan Wiley
Vice President And Trust Officer, Robin Thornton
Vice President Administration, David Rushing
Vice President Equipment Finance, Michael Childers
Assistant Vice President And Trust Officer, Karen Cash
Vice President Customer Service, Barbara Jacks
Vice President Mortgage Lending Manager, Justin Moore
Assistant Vice President And Investment Officer, Kelton Harrison
Vice President Administration, Brent Martin
Senior Vice President, Steve Landry
Assistant Vice President, Chris Rittelmeyer
Vice President Commercial Lending, Vernon Scott
Assistant Vice President Atm Operations, Karla Dial
Vice President Facilities Management, Anita Murrell
Executive Vice President Financial Services, Phillip Tappan
Vice President Manager Personal Trust, Cathy Roper
Svp Dtr Of Community Dev, Martie North
Vice President Financial Advisor, James Watkins
Senior Vice President And Senior Credit Officer, Stephen Landry
Executive Vice President Chief People Marketing Officer Assistant General Counsel, Jennifer Compton
Executive Vp, Tina Graves
Senior Vice President, David Seal
Senior Vice President Commercial Lending, Shane Strahl
Auditors: BKD, LLP

LOCATIONS

HQ: Simmons First National Corp
501 Main Street, Pine Bluff, AR 71601
Phone: 870 541-1000
Web: www.simmonsbank.com

PRODUCTS/OPERATIONS

2015 Sales

	$ mil.	% of total
Interest Income		
Loans	268	65
Investment securities	31	8
Others	2	-
Non-interest income		
Service charges on deposit accounts	31	8
Debit and credit card fees	27	6
Mortgage lending income	11	3
Trust income	9	2
Other service charges and fees	10	2
others	22	6
Net (loss) gain on assets covered by FDIC loss share agreements	(14.8)	-
Total	**397**	**100**

COMPETITORS

Arvest Bank	Bear State Financial
BOK Financial	Home BancShares
BancorpSouth	IBERIABANK
Bank of America	Regions Financial
Bank of the Ozarks	U.S. Bancorp

HISTORICAL FINANCIALS

Company Type: Public

Income Statement				FYE: December 31
	ASSETS ($ mil.)	NET INCOME ($ mil.)	INCOME AS % OF ASSETS	EMPLOYEES
12/18	16,543	216	1.3%	2,654
12/17	15,056	93	0.6%	2,640
12/16	8,400	97	1.2%	1,875
12/15	7,560	74	1.0%	1,946
12/14	4,643	36	0.8%	1,331
Annual Growth	37.4%	56.8%		18.8%

2018 Year-End Financials

Debt ratio: 2.00%	No. of shares (mil.): 92
Return on equity: 10.00%	Dividends
Cash ($ mil.): 833	Yield: 2.0%
Current ratio: —	Payout: 26.0%
Long-term debt ($ mil.): —	Market value ($ mil.): 2,228

	STOCK PRICE ($) FY Close	P/E High/Low		PER SHARE ($)		
				Earnings	Dividends	Book Value
12/18	24.00	26	10	2.00	1.00	24.00
12/17	57.00	47	37	1.00	1.00	23.00
12/16	62.00	42	25	2.00	0.00	18.00
12/15	51.00	44	27	1.00	0.00	18.00
12/14	41.00	41	31	1.00	0.00	14.00
Annual Growth	(12.2%)	—	—	21.8%	8.1%	15.5%

Simon Property Group, Inc.

Simon Property Group is the largest shopping mall and retail center owner in the US. The self-managed self-administered real estate investment trust (REIT) owns develops and manages regional shopping malls outlet malls (under the Premium Outlet and The Mills brands) boutique malls and shopping centers. Its real estate portfolio is composed of some 230 retail properties totaling approximately 190 million sq. ft. of leasable space. Its portfolio covers 35 states and Puerto Rico though much is concentrated in the US Southeast Midwest and Northeast. The REIT also has stakes in outlet centers in Canada Mexico Europe and Asia. The company is still run by the founding family.

Operations

Simon Property's primary operations are the ownership development leasing and management of its retail real estate portfolio. The extend of its involvement and revenue generation varies by its degree of ownership. In addition to owning some 200 properties in the US it is a joint-venture partner in about 80 mostly international properties. It also uses joint ventures to hold equity investments in several European real estate holding companies. It manages the day-to-day operations of its owned properties as well as about 60 of its joint-venture properties. The remaining properties all of which are located outside the US are managed through joint ventures in which Simon shares but does not have majority control.

The company makes about 60% of its revenue from rental income just less than 30% from tenant recoveries (reimbursements to Simon Properties for common area maintenance real estate taxes etc.) and the rest from overage rents management fees and other corporate revenue.

Geographic Reach

Indianapolis Indiana-based Simon Property Group owns and operates ? wholly or as part of joint ventures ? retail real estate properties in the Americas Europe and Asia.

By far its largest market is the US where it generates over 95% of its revenue and holds nearly 95% of its long-lived assets.

Sales and Marketing

Simon Property enters long-term tenancy contracts with retailers to fill its properties. Its lease terms must be competitive to attract desirable tenants and its management services provide postsale customer care to its lessees and also strive to pull consumer traffic into its properties with local advertising and special events (Santa Claus at the Mall for example).

Many of its properties are anchored by major tenants such as JCPenney Macy's Dillard's Neiman Marcus and Bloomingdale's and supplemented with smaller stores like Dick's Sporting Goods Nordstrom Kohl's and AMC Theatres. Its Premium Outlets are home to a variety of popular retailers including Adidas American Eagle Outfitters Ann Taylor Columbia Sportswear Michael Kors Tommy Hilfiger and The North Face.

Occupancy for its US malls Premium Outlets and Mills-branded properties remain above 95%. No one tenant accounts for more than 5% of its consolidated revenue.

Financial Performance

The long-term trend in revenue has been positive over recent years. Revenue has climbed steadily since 2014 growing from $4.9 billion in that year to $5.7 billion in 2018. Net income has grown in parallel jumping from $1.4 billion to $2.4 billion over the five-year period.

Simon Property's 2018 revenue of $5.7 billion grew about 2% from 2017's $5.5 billion in part as a result of higher occupancy rates rents and dollar-per-square-foot sales number from its tenants. In 2018 net income from continuing operations was $2.4 billion compared to $1.9 billion in 2017.

Cash at the end of 2018 was $514.3 million. Cash from operations contributed $3.8 billion to the coffers while investing activities used $236.5 million mainly for capital expenditures. Financing activities used another $4.5 billion for mortgage and unsecured debt payments and partnership distributions.

Strategy

The retail industry is encountering both cyclical and structural changes including a younger demographic that prefers to spend their disposable income on experiences over material goods and internet-based e-commerce that emphasizes convenience for the consumer. Simon Property is changing with the times by reformulating the tenant mix in its properties to bring more experiential options and addressing new and redevelopment needs in growth markets. Although internet-based retail presents challenges to many of Simon's typical tenants the REIT maintains the relevance of a brick-and-mortar presence. Still it is modifying its store mix within its properties to include more entertainment and residency offerings while still working with its long-standing clients to fill space in its retail properties.

Acknowledging the changing retail dynamic Simon is diversifying its properties away from apparel-heavy approaches by transitioning its tenant base to include residential space hotels entertainment options restaurants and wellness centers. The idea is to entice consumers to its property not only to shop but to be entertained and possibly even spend the weekend. Centers such as The Domain in Austin TX and the jointly-developed Brickell City Centre in Miami FL exemplify this new approach.

Simon is averaging $1 billion in annual investments to build new or redevelop existing properties. In 2018 Simon opened the Denver Premium outlets in Colorado and acquired the remaining 50% in a joint venture at The Outlets at Orange in Los Angeles. In 2018 Simon invested $600 million in redevelopment projects at sites including at Aventura Mall in Miami and Desert Hills Premium Outlets in Cabazon California. The company's approach is to start with the aesthetic and functional appeal and then to add on-site customer service and technology to make the shopping experience easier and more efficient for shoppers and retailers.

Branching out into new areas the company has launched a new online shopping platform for its premium outlets featuring more than 300000 products from 2000 brands. It is also embracing the growing popularity of cannabis-based products with a new partnership in 2019 with Green Growth Brands to open about 110 shops within its malls selling CBD-infused products.

Company Background

Simon Property Group helped change the face of the US retail landscape from mom-and-pop stores to shopping malls. The original Simon Property Group (formed in 1993) was the offshoot of brothers Melvin and Herbert Simon's Melvin Simon & Associates (MSA founded in 1959).

To get started the Simons sometimes borrowed cash from friends but during the 1960s and 1970s developers could usually borrow 100% of a shopping center's construction costs after securing an anchor tenant. Leases then provided money to repay debt and make a down payment on the next project. The Simons consistently retained equity developing a huge asset base that they used as collateral for larger projects.

The new strip malls boasted retail's two most important virtues — price and convenience — and in time they developed into the modern mall. MSA built its first indoor mall in the mid-1960s in snowy Fort Collins Colorado. By the late 1960s MSA and other developers were consumed with mall projects.

As the 1989 real estate slump hit the Simons were busy building the largest mall in the country just outside Minneapolis. Completed in 1992 the Mall of America included a roller coaster a two-story miniature golf course and a walk-through aquarium. In 1993 Simon Property Group went public in one of the largest IPOs of its time.

EXECUTIVES

Evp And Cfo, Andrew A. (Andy) Juster, age 67, $500,000 total compensation
President Coo And Director, Richard S. (Rick) Sokolov, age 69, $800,000 total compensation
Chief Administrative Officer; President Malls, John Rulli, $463,500 total compensation
Chairman And Ceo, David Simon, age 57, $1,250,000 total compensation
Svp And Cio, David Schacht
President The Mills, Gregg M. Goodman
Ceo Premium Outlets, Stephen J. Yalof
Chief Marketing Officer; President Simon Brand Ventures, Mikael Thygesen
Sevp; President Simon Malls, David J. Contis, age 60, $750,000 total compensation
Chief Investment Officer, Stanley Shashoua
Vice President, Paul Ajdaharian

Regional Vp Mid Atlantic And Midwest Region, David Johnson
Vice President Of Acquisitions And Asset Intensification, Patrick Peterman
Assistant Vice President Digit, Stephanie Jenkins
Assistant Vice President, Drew Steele
Vice President Of Architecture, Gaylon Melton
Vice President Legal Leasing, Woodrow Stone
Regional Vice President, Brian Nelson
Vice President Property Tax, Michael Larson
Vicepresident, Donna Vosper
Vice President Marketing And Strategic Partnerships, Ed Vittoria
Senior Vice President Of Operations, Stephen Kingsley
Regional Vice President Financial Reporting, Julie Leer
Senior Vp Of Leasing, Robert Alexander
Vice President, Teresa Tom
Senior Vice President Risk Management, Michael Horvath
Vice President, Jodi Calisto
Regional Vice President, Adam Pisano
Vp Corporate Security Emergency Management, Russ Tuttle
Vice President, Cathy Iunghuhn
Senior Vice President, Ronald Hanson
Vice President Leasing, Tim Cutting
Executive Vice President And Chief, Greg Null Neeb
Regional Vice President, Melissa Palencia
Portfolio Vice President Of Marketing, Lynnette Lauria
Regional Vice President, Robert Guerra
Senior Vice President, Michael Gaffney
Vice President Business Development, Josh Ginsburg
Vice President Business Development, Shelly Drapkin
Evp Luxury Leasing Premium Outlets, Peter Baxter
Vice President Development, Jocelyn Gubler
Vice President, Paula Weant
Evp Leasing Premium Outlet, Larry Weinstein
Assistant Vice President Leasing, Carolyn Preston
Vice President Local Leasing, Shannon Shinn
Senior Vice President Investor Relations, Thomas Ward
Vice President Leasing, Stacey Lewis
Senior Vice President, Deborah Simon
Vice President Managing Counsel Legal Leasing, Gregory Lowe
Senior Vice President, Greg Vlahos
Assistant Vice President Of Business Development, Aaron Casteel
Regional Vice President Development, Kevin Compton
Executive Vice President Leasing, Michael Nevins
Vice President, Roach Heather
Vice President Anchor Leasing, Christine Schnauffer-mansfield
Regional Vice President Development, Rod Vosper
Vice President Of Operations, Rob Courtney
Vp Digital Strategy, Patrick Flanagan
Senior Vice President Development Malls, Charles Davis
Vice President, John Steen
Senior Vice President And Leasing Counsel, Matthew Broas
Vice President Project Management, Jeffrey Jones
Treasurer, Robert Demchak
Board Member, Christopher Smith
Auditors: Ernst & Young LLP

LOCATIONS

HQ: Simon Property Group, Inc.
225 West Washington Street, Indianapolis, IN 46204
Phone: 317 636-1600   **Fax:** 317 685-7336
Web: www.simon.com

2016 Sales

	$ mil.	% of total
Minimum rent	3,359	62
Tenant reimbursements	1,495	28
Overage rent	162	3
Management fees & other revenues	144	2
Other income	277	5
Total	**5,435**	**100**

2016 US Properties

	No.
Malls	108
Premium outlets	67
Mills	14
Lifestyle centers	4
Other shopping centers	13
Total	**206**

Selected Properties

Aventura Mall Miami
Burlington Mall Boston
Copley Place Boston
Dadeland Mall Miami
Desert Hills Premium Outlets Cabazon CA
Fashion Centre at Pentagon City Washington DC
Fashion Valley San Diego
The Florida Mall Orlando
The Forum Shops at Caesars Las Vegas
The Galleria Houston
Gotemba Premium Outlets Gotemba (Tokyo) Japan
King of Prussia Mall Philadelphia
Las Vegas Premium Outlets(2) Las Vegas
Lenox Square and Phipps Plaza Atlanta
Orlando Premium Outlets(2) Orlando
Roosevelt Field New York
Sawgrass Mills Ft. Lauderdale
SouthPark Charlotte
Stanford Shopping Center Palo Alto
Town Center at Boca Raton Boca Raton
Walt Whitman Shops New York
The Westchester New York
Woodbury Common Premium Outlets New York
Woodfield Mall Chicago

COMPETITORS

Belz	Kimco Realty
CBL & Associates	Macerich
Properties	Taubman Centers
Cadillac Fairview	Vornado Realty
GGP	Westfield Corporation
Horizon Group	
Properties	

HISTORICAL FINANCIALS

Company Type: Public

Income Statement   FYE: December 31

	REVENUE ($ mil.)	NET INCOME ($ mil.)	NET PROFIT MARGIN	EMPLOYEES
12/18	5,658	2,440	43.1%	6,700
12/17	5,539	1,948	35.2%	5,000
12/16	5,435	1,839	33.8%	5,000
12/15	5,266	1,828	34.7%	5,000
12/14	4,871	1,409	28.9%	5,250
Annual Growth	**3.8%**	**14.7%**	**—**	**6.3%**

2018 Year-End Financials

Debt ratio: 76.00%	No. of shares (mil.): 320
Return on equity: 66.00%	Dividends
Cash ($ mil.): 514	Yield: 5.0%
Current ratio: 0.00	Payout: 100.0%
Long-term debt ($ mil.): 23,306	Market value ($ mil.): 53,827

	STOCK PRICE ($) FY Close	P/E High/Low		PER SHARE ($)		
			Earnings	Dividends	Book Value
12/18	168.00	24 19	8.00	8.00	11.00
12/17	172.00	30 24	6.00	7.00	12.00
12/16	178.00	39 30	6.00	7.00	14.00
12/15	194.00	35 29	6.00	6.00	15.00
12/14	182.00	41 33	5.00	5.00	16.00
Annual Growth	**(2.0%)**	**—**	**14.9%**	**11.3%**	**(9.6%)**

Sirius XM Holdings Inc

You might say radio programming from this company comes from a higher plane. SIRIUS XM Holdings operating through SIRIUS XM Radio manages satellite radio systems under the SIRIUS and XM brands that together boast more than 25 million subscribers. Each service offers more than 150 channels of CD-quality music news and talk shows. Programming includes National Football League Major League Baseball and college games as well as talk shows featuring hosts Howard Stern Martha Stewart and Oprah Winfrey. The company has equipment alliances with several automakers; it also sells satellite radio equipment through its website and through such retail outlets as Best Buy and WalMart. In 2018 SiriusXM offered $3.5 billion for music streaming company Pandora.

Operations

In addition to its domestic radio services SiriusXM has interests in the Canadian market. It owns 50% of SIRIUS Canada a joint venture with the Canadian Broadcasting Corporation (CBC). SIRIUS Canada merged with Canadian Satellite Radio (XM Canada) in 2011 giving SiriusXM a solid foundation in the Canadian market.

Sales and Marketing

Subscription satellite radio has proven to be quite popular thanks to the wealth of programming options available beyond the limited content offered by advertising-supported terrestrial radio broadcasters.

With its large subscriber base SiriusXM has stolen away many listeners from traditional broadcast stations operated by major radio companies such as Clear Channel and Cumulus Media. Providing all that content though is quite expensive due to rights fees for sports and exclusive talk shows as well as the satellite equipment needed to reach listeners across the country.

During fiscal 2013 the company spent about $180000 on advertising after spending roughly $140000 on advertising during fiscal 2012.

Financial Performance

SiriusXM has been experiencing a positive trend in its revenue since 2008. The company's fiscal 2013 revenues increased by 12% compared to fiscal 2012 primarily due to increases in its subscriber revenues advertising revenues agency fees and equipment revenues.

SiriusXM saw its net income nosedive in 2013. Net income decreased 98% from $3.47 billion in fiscal 2012 to only $377.2 million in fiscal 2013. The huge drop was largely due to drastically increased expenses for things such as royalties and taxes.

Even with its net income dropping so dramatically during fiscal 2013 the company's cash from operations increased due to improved operating performance lower interest payments and higher collections from subscribers and distributors.

Strategy

SiriusXM is dependent on automobile makers. The company works hard to convert customers who received a promotional subscription as part of the purchase or lease of a new vehicle to a self-paying subscription.

Mergers and Acquisitions

In 2018 SIRIUS XM agreed to buy Pandora Media Inc. for $3.5 billion. In 2013 SIRIUS XM purchased connected vehicle business Agero Inc. Agero's connected vehicle business provides services to several automakers including Acura BMW Honda Hyundai Infiniti Lexus Nissan and Toyota.

EXECUTIVES

Evp And Cfo, David J. Frear, age 63, $850,000 total compensation
Evp And General Counsel, Patrick L. Donnelly, age 57, $575,000 total compensation
Evp Sales And Automotive, Stephen R. (Steve) Cook, age 63, $518,583 total compensation
Svp And Cio, William C. (Bill) Pratt
Ceo, James E. (Jim) Meyer, age 65, $1,468,590 total compensation
President And Chief Content Officer, Scott A. Greenstein, age 60, $1,224,520 total compensation
Evp And Chief Administrative Officer, Dara F. Altman, age 61, $500,000 total compensation
Evp Operations And Products, Enrique Rodriguez, $531,827 total compensation
Senior Vice President Promotions Event Marketing And Talent Relations, Ross Zapin
Vp It Systems, Donna Colorito
Vice President Of Application Development, Daniel Eccles
Vice President Purchasing And Procurement, Larry Simon
Corporate Vice President And Chief Engineering Officer, Terry Smith
Vice President, Denise Stevens
Executive Vice President Sales And Development, Joseph A Verbrugge
Vice President Business Solutions Management, Mike Leary
Vice President Information Technology And Corporate Solutions, Moshe Pridan
Corporate Vice President And Chief Innovation Officer, Stell Patsiokas
Senior Vice President Sports Programming, Steve Cohen
Vice President Marine And Aviation, Craig Correa
Vice President Human Resources, Walt Sanderson
Vice President Interactive, Patrick Fitzgerald
Senior Vice President Platform Software, Stuart Cox
Vice President Programming, Trinity Colon
Senior Vice President Advertising Sales, Bette Rockmore
Vice President Information Security And Compliance, Patricia Edfors
Vice President Market Research, Kathie Mahoney
Vice President Process And Information Management, Evelyn Sasmor
Senior Vice President Automotive Partnerships, Rodney Pickett
Vice President It Infrastructure Engineering And Operations, Scott Evon
Senior Vice President Comedy Programming, Jack Vaughn
Vice President Marketing Operations, James Dunn
Vice President And General Manager Talk Prgrmg, Dave Gorab
Vice President Consumer Electronics Prod, Sean Gibbons
Chairman, Gregory B. (Greg) Maffei, age 58
Board Member, James F Mooney
Board Member, James Holden
Board Member, George Bodenheimer
Auditors: KPMG LLP

HQ: Sirius XM Holdings Inc
1221 Avenue of the Americas, 35th Floor, New York, NY 10020
Phone: 212 584-5100
Web: www.siriusxm.com

COMPETITORS

CBS Radio	Saga Communications
Cox Radio	Spanish Broadcasting
Cumulus Media	Townsquare Media
Emmis Communications	Univision Radio
Entercom	WestwoodOne
Entravision	iHeartCommunications
Radio One Inc.	

HISTORICAL FINANCIALS

Company Type: Public

Income Statement				FYE: December 31
	REVENUE ($ mil.)	NET INCOME ($ mil.)	NET PROFIT MARGIN	EMPLOYEES
12/19	7,794	914	11.7%	4,534
12/18	5,771	1,176	20.4%	2,699
12/17	5,425	648	11.9%	2,575
12/16	5,017	746	14.9%	2,402
12/15	4,570	510	11.2%	2,323
Annual Growth	14.3%	15.7%	—	18.2%

2019 Year-End Financials

Debt ratio: 70.00%—
Return on equity: ***,***.**%
Cash ($ mil.): 106
Current ratio: 0.00
Long-term debt ($ mil.): 7,842

Dividends
Yield: 1.0%
Payout: 25.0%
Market value ($ mil.): —

	STOCK PRICE ($) FY Close	P/E High/Low	PER SHARE ($) Earnings	Dividends	Book Value
12/19	7.00	36 26	0.00	0.00	(0.00)
12/18	6.00	29 20	0.00	0.00	(0.00)
12/17	5.00	42 32	0.00	0.00	(0.00)
12/16	4.00	31 22	0.00	0.00	(0.00)
12/15	4.00	47 37	0.00	0.00	(0.00)
Annual Growth	15.1%	—	—	22.1%	

SLM Corp.

If SLM doesn't seem familiar perhaps you know it by its more common moniker Sallie Mae. Holding more than $8 billion in student loans SLM's main subsidiary Sallie Mae Bank is one of the nation's largest education loan providers and specializes in originating acquiring financing and servicing private student loans which are not guaranteed by the government. The company also earns fees for its processing and administrative offerings through various subsidiaries.

HISTORY

The Student Loan Marketing Association was chartered in 1972 as a response to problems in the Guaranteed Student Loan Program of 1965. For years the GSL program had tinkered with rates to induce banks to make loans but servicing the small loans was expensive and troublesome. Sallie Mae began operations in 1973 buying loans from their originators; its size provided economies of scale in loan servicing.

Originally only institutions making educational or student loans were allowed to own stock in Sallie Mae. This was later changed so that anyone could buy nonvoting stock. In 1993 voting stock was listed on the NYSE.

Sallie Mae was always a political football altered again and again to reflect the education policies of the party in power. When it was founded during the Nixon administration its loans were restricted by a needs test which was repealed during the Carter years. The Reagan administration reimposed the needs test and at the same time sped up the schedule under which the company was to become self-supporting which it did by late 1981.

Forced to rely on its own resources Sallie Mae turned to creative financing. One of its traditional advantages was that its loan interest rates were linked to Treasury bills traditionally about 3% above the T-bill rate. The company became a master at riding the spread between its cost of funds and the interest rates it charged.

Between 1983 and 1992 Sallie Mae's assets swelled by more than 400% and its income rose by almost 500%. As the firm grew management became more visible with high pay and extravagant perks. Although salaries were not inconsistent with those of executives at comparable private corporations the remuneration level and perks irked Congress. But Sallie Mae kept growing — in 1992 it expanded its facilities and added 900 new staff members.

The 1993 Omnibus Budget Reconciliation Act with its transfer of the student loan program directly to the government and its surcharge on Sallie Mae began to adversely affect earnings in 1994. While awaiting permission to alter its charter the company stepped up its marketing efforts especially to school loan officers who advised students on loan options.

In 1995 then-COO Albert Lord led a group of stockholders in a push to cut operating expenses and repackage student loans as securities à la Freddie Mac and Fannie Mae. Lord and some of his supporters won seats on the board (as well as the enmity of Lawrence Hough who resigned as CEO in the midst of the melee). That year Sallie Mae bought HICA Holding one of two private insurers of education loans. In 1996 Congress passed legislation forcing Sallie Mae's privatization.

Despite SLM's rising stock shareholders were unhappy with chairman William Arceneaux's status quo business plan. Lord gained control in 1997.

In 1998 the organization became SLM Holding. Assets and earnings were muted that year when unfavorable market conditions prevented Sallie Mae from securitizing its loans.

The firm the next year expanded its lending operations by buying Nellie Mae. Also in 1999 Sallie Mae teamed with Answer Financial to sell insurance. Growth continued in 2000 when the company bought loan servicer Student Loan Funding Resources as well as the marketing student loan servicing and administrative operations of USA Group; the company changed its name to USA Education following the acquisition. The company also cut some 1700 jobs approximately 25% of its workforce.

The following year Sallie Mae teamed with Intuit allowing the financial software company access to Sallie Mae's 7 million customers. It also launched online recruiting service TrueCareers that year.

In 2002 it bought Pioneer Credit Recovery and General Revenue Corporation two of the nation's largest student loan collection agencies. It also reverted to the SLM moniker to reconnect with the name by which it has so long been known.

The privatization plan put into place in the mid-'90s (orchestrated in large part by then-CEO Lord) came to fruition nearly four years ahead of schedule when SLM transitioned to a private organization in December 2004.

In 2007 SLM saw its stock values plummet to their lowest levels in about a decade. A number of industry-wide factors figured into the losses not the least of which was the downturn in the credit market. Also affecting the company was the signing into law of the College Cost Reduction and Access Act (CCRAA). Intended to reform student lending and cut costs for borrowers the act slashed subsidies for lenders participating in the Federal Family Education Loan Program (FFELP). The reform cut into the company's interest-earning operations. As a result SLM increased its focus on higher-yielding private education loans which carry a lower risk.

Additionally SLM that year became ensnared in a student-lending industry probe led by New York attorney general Andrew Cuomo. The company agreed to a $2 million settlement and to abide by a code of conduct regarding its dealings with college employees.

One of the most dramatic results of the troubles was the collapse of a planned acquisition by a consortium of investment firms. The planned $8.8 billion deal included buyers J.C. Flowers (which was to own about a half of SLM) Bank of America and JPMorgan Chase. In the midst of the industry probe J.C. Flowers sought a change in SLM's leadership in an effort to secure regulatory approval for the acquisition; Thomas J. (Tim) Fitzpatrick was ousted as CEO. Ultimately the buyers canceled the deal citing the reduced potential value of SLM. The student lender filed a lawsuit to challenge the termination but eventually dropped the suit. It later cut more than 10% of its workforce.

EXECUTIVES

Vp Federal Government Relations, Tim Morrison
Senior Vice President Loan Operations, Michael Maier
Chairman And Ceo, Raymond J. Quinlan, $600,000 total compensation
Evp And General Counsel, Laurent C. Lutz, $525,000 total compensation
Evp And Cfo, Steven J. McGarry, $375,000 total compensation
Svp And Chief Risk Officer, Jeffery F. Dale, age 57, $400,000 total compensation
Evp And Chief Marketing Officer, Charles P. Rocha, $375,000 total compensation
Svp And Chief Compliance Officer, Jim Truitt
Vice President West Region Head, Robin Famiglietti
Svp Corporate Development, Paul Mayer
Svp And Chief Risk Officer, Jeffrey Dale
Assistant Vice President Network Services, Peter Tropf
Vice President, Jonathan Boyles
Senior Vice President General Counsel, Nicolas Jafarieh
Vice President Finance Other Credit, Doug Maurer
Vice President Finance And Treasurer, Christopher Lynch
Vice President And Associate General Counsel, Anne Milem
Executive Vice President Administration, Joni Reich
Vice President, Lynn M Langdon
Vice President Information Technology Credit Origination, Michael Migliore
Senior Executive Administrative Assistant For Senior Vice President Corporate Finance, Kathleen Mullaney
Svp Banking And Campus Solutions, Kelly Christiano
Vice President Information Technology Risk And Compliance, Karen Delozier
Svp And Chief Security Officer, Jerry Archer

Vice President Product Development, John Lazzati
Senior Vp, Tamara Belkin
Senior Vice President Chief Regulatory Counsel And Assistant Corporate Secretary, Rick Nelson
Auditors: KPMG LLP

LOCATIONS

HQ: SLM Corp.
  300 Continental Drive, Newark, DE 19713
Phone: 302 451-0200
Web: www.salliemae.com

PRODUCTS/OPERATIONS

2016 Sales

	$ mil.	% of total
Interest		
Lons	1,061	79
Investments	9	1
Cash & cash equivalents	8	1
Non-Interest income		
Gain on sale of loans	0	14
(Losses) gains on derivatives and hedging activities net	(0.9)	5
Other income	70	-
Total	**1,146**	**100**

Selected Subsidiaries

HICA Holding
Sallie Mae Bank
Sallie Mae Inc.
SLM Education Credit Finance Corporation
  Bull Run I LLC
  SLM Education Credit Funding LLC
SLM Investment Corporation
Southwest Student Services Corporation

COMPETITORS

Bank of America
Brazos Higher Education Service Corp.
Citizens Financial Group
Discover
Educational Funding of The South
First Marblehead
FirstCity Financial
Great Lakes Higher Education
KeyCorp
Mohela
Nelnet
PNC Financial
Pennsylvania Higher Education Assistance Agency
SunTrust
Texas Guaranteed

HISTORICAL FINANCIALS

Company Type: Public

Income Statement
FYE: December 31

	ASSETS ($ mil.)	NET INCOME ($ mil.)	INCOME AS % OF ASSETS	EMPLOYEES
12/18	26,638	487	1.8%	1,700
12/17	21,780	289	1.3%	1,500
12/16	18,533	250	1.4%	1,300
12/15	15,214	274	1.8%	1,200
12/14	12,972	194	1.5%	1,000
Annual Growth	19.7%	25.9%	—	14.2%

2018 Year-End Financials

Debt ratio: 16.00%	No. of shares (mil.): 436
Return on equity: 18.00%	Dividends
Cash ($ mil.): 2,559	Yield: —
Current ratio: —	Payout: —
Long-term debt ($ mil.): —	Market value ($ mil.): 3,621

(Sallie Mae / SLM stock table)

	STOCK PRICE ($) FY Close	P/E High/Low	PER SHARE ($) Earnings	Dividends	Book Value
12/18	8.00	11 8	1.00	0.00	7.00
12/17	11.00	20 16	1.00	0.00	6.00
12/16	11.00	21 10	1.00	0.00	5.00
12/15	7.00	18 11	1.00	0.00	5.00
12/14	10.00	63 19	0.00	1.00	4.00
Annual Growth	(5.0%)	— —	26.3%	—	12.1%

(Smucker stock table)

	STOCK PRICE ($) FY Close	P/E High/Low	PER SHARE ($) Earnings	Dividends	Book Value
12/18	18.00	19 12	1.00	0.00	20.00
12/17	22.00	47 33	1.00	0.00	18.00
12/16	19.00	24 18	1.00	0.00	18.00
12/15	16.00	46 9	0.00	0.00	17.00
12/14	3.00	93 58	0.00	0.00	25.00
Annual Growth	53.3%	— —145.4%	—	—	(4.6%)

SmartFinancial Inc

Cornerstone Bancshares is the holding company for Cornerstone Community Bank which operates about five locations in Chattanooga Tennessee and surrounding communities in addition to two loan production offices in Knoxville Tennessee and Dalton Georgia. The bank offers standard retail and commercial services including checking and savings accounts money market accounts and CDs. Its lending activities primarily consist of commercial real estate loans residential mortgages real estate construction loans and business and agricultural loans. Another subsidiary of Cornerstone Bancshares Eagle Financial purchases accounts receivable and acts as a conduit lender.

EXECUTIVES

Senior Vice President Knoxville Area Market Executive, Mike Honeycutt
Regional President Alabama And Florida, Robert Kuhn
Auditors: Dixon Hughes Goodman LLP

LOCATIONS

HQ: SmartFinancial Inc
  5401 Kingston Pike, Suite 600, Knoxville, TN 37919
Phone: 865 437-5700
Web: www.smartfinancialinc.com

COMPETITORS

Bank of America	Regions Financial
First Horizon	SunTrust
First Security Group	Tennessee Valley
Home Federal Bank (TN)	Financial Holdings

HISTORICAL FINANCIALS

Company Type: Public

Income Statement
FYE: December 31

	ASSETS ($ mil.)	NET INCOME ($ mil.)	INCOME AS % OF ASSETS	EMPLOYEES
12/18	2,274	18	0.8%	387
12/17	1,721	5	0.3%	343
12/16	1,062	6	0.5%	222
12/15	1,024	2	0.1%	225
12/14	416	2	0.4%	104
Annual Growth	52.9%	82.3%	—	38.9%

2018 Year-End Financials

Debt ratio: 2.00%	No. of shares (mil.): 14
Return on equity: 7.00%	Dividends
Cash ($ mil.): 116	Yield: —
Current ratio: —	Payout: —
Long-term debt ($ mil.): —	Market value ($ mil.): 255

Smucker (J.M.) Co.

The J. M. Smucker Company gets its bread and butter from more than just jelly. The food and beverage company known for its namesake Smucker's fruit spread has an extended product portfolio that includes Folgers coffee (the top brand in the US) Jif peanut butter (the top brand in the US) and Milk-Bone dog snacks (the top brand in the US); other products include shortening and oils frozen sandwiches and juices. It generates roughly equal parts of its revenue from pet foods coffee and consumer foods. Smucker's generates more than 90% of its sales in the US.

Operations

Smucker's operations are divided among four business segments: US Retail Pet Foods US Retail Coffee and US Retail Consumer Foods (which each account for nearly 30% of revenue) and International/Away from Home (which accounts for about 15%).

The company's growing pet food business includes mainstream pet food (Meow Mix 9Lives Rachael Ray Nutrish Nature's Recipe) premium pet food (Natural Balance) and pet snacks (Milk-Bone Pup-Peroni). Its coffee operations include mainstream ground single-serve and premium coffee (Folgers Dunkin Donuts Cafe Bustelo 1850) and its consumer foods operations include peanut butter (Jif) fruit spreads (Smucker's) and shortening and oils (Crisco).

Smucker's international segment primarily includes coffee for Canadian and other non-US markets as well as Canadian flour (Robin Hood Five Roses) and Smucker's and Jif products.

Overall coffee is the company's leading product category generating about a third of sales; dog food cat food pet snacks and peanut butter each contribute about 10%.

Geographic Reach

Ohio-based Smucker's generates more than 90% of revenue in the US with Canada accounting for about 5%.

The company has manufacturing and processing facilities in about a dozen US states and one Canadian province. It has sales and administrative offices in the US Canada China and Mexico.

Sales and Marketing

In the US retail market segments Smucker's products are primarily sold through direct sales and brokers to food retailers supermarkets food wholesalers drug stores club stores mass merchandisers discount and dollar stores military commissaries natural foods stores and distributors pet specialty stores and online retailers. Its International products are distributed through retail channels and foodservice distributors and operators (e.g. restaurants lodging schools and universities health care operators).

Walmart and subsidiaries account for about 30% of the company's sales. Indeed its top 10 customers generate some 60% of the company's revenue.

Advertising expense as a percent of net sales has been rising in recent years; costs were $194 million in fiscal 2018 compared to about $170 million each of the prior two years.

Financial Performance

Since jumping nearly 40% in fiscal 2016 because of the acquisition of Big Heart pet food maker Smucker's revenue has been on the decline. It has fallen some 6% over the past two years. Net income has seen a bit more irregular growth but recorded a huge jump in the most recent fiscal year.

In fiscal 2018 (ended April 2018) the company reported revenue of $7.4 billion down about half a percent from the prior year as increases in the pet food and international categories were not enough to offset a decline in consumer foods (primarily from the oils & baking categories).

Net income however more than doubled in 2018 to $1.3 billion. An income tax benefit of more than $475 million (compared to an expense of nearly $300 million the year before) related to 2017 US tax reform led to the rise.

Cash at the end of fiscal 2018 was $193 million an increase of $26 million from the prior year. Cash from operations contributed $1.2 billion to the coffers while investing activities used $278 million mainly for capital expenditures. Financing activities used another $922 million for dividends to stockholders and repayments of short-term borrowings and long-term debt.

Strategy

Smucker's strategy focuses on growth through owning and marketing the #1 brand name food products (both people and pet) in North America with potential for worldwide appeal. Acquisitions and manufacturing and distribution agreements underpin these ends. As part of the company's long-term growth objectives it is working to increase sales by 3% and earnings per share by more than 8% annually on average. While the sales contribution from acquisitions will vary from year to year it expects organic growth including new products to drive much of the growth.

Along those lines in fiscal 2018 the company launched canisters of 1850 and Dunkin' Donuts coffee as well as Jif PowerUps peanut butter snacks and Pup-Peroni jerky bites. Products introduced in the last three years represent about $500 million in revenue.

As a result of this focus on top brands particularly pet food and snacks and coffee the company in 2018 agreed to sell its US baking business (Pillsbury Martha White Hungry Jack and other brands) to investment firms for $375 million. It previously divested its US canned milk brands (Eagle Brand Magnolia) and operations.

With the acquisition of Big Heart Pet Brands the company instantly became a player in the growing pet food and snacks market. The pet segment is now Smucker's largest.

Mergers and Acquisitions

In 2018 Smucker's paid nearly $2 billion for premium pet food company Ainsworth Pet Nutrition. The deal adds a handful of pet food and snack brands including fast-growing Rachel Ray Nutrish to Smucker's pet food division which already includes Meow Mix Milk-Bone and 9Lives among other brands.

HISTORY

Jerome Smucker began operating a steam-powered cider mill in 1897 for farmers in Orrville Ohio but he found that his biggest business was selling apple butter made using a secret Smucker family recipe. By the 1920s The J. M. Smucker Company had begun producing a full line of preserves and jellies and in 1935 it acquired its first fruit-processing operations.

Under Jerome's grandson Paul Smucker the company gained widespread national distribution by the mid-1960s. Tim Smucker succeeded his father Paul as president in 1981 then as chairman in 1987 when his brother Richard became president.

The company's growth has been enhanced through the development of its industrial fruit fillings business and acquisitions of domestic natural juice and peanut butter companies including Knudsen & Sons (1984) After the Fall (1994) and Laura Scudder's (from National Grape Co-op 1994). It has gradually expanded internationally through acquisitions. In 1993 it acquired the jam preserves and pie-filling unit of Canada's Culinar. In a 1998 deal Smucker purchased Australia's Allowrie jam and Lackersteens marmalade lines.

Smucker sold its flagging Mrs. Smith's frozen pie business to Flowers in 1997 less than two years after buying the unit from Kellogg. It bought Kraft's domestic fruit spread unit in 1997 and in 1999 purchased the northwestern Adams peanut butter business from Pro-Fac Cooperative. Smucker kept the Adams name but shifted packaging to its Pennsylvania peanut butter plant.

Spreading into retail the company opened a store in 1999 in its hometown of Orrville and then launched online and catalog sales. Also that year Smucker bought a fruit filling plant in Brazil from Groupe Danone a major customer. During 2000 the company's Henry Jones Foods subsidiary (Australia) purchased Taylor Foods (sauces marinades).

Smucker acquired International Flavors & Fragrances' formulated fruit and vegetable preparation businesses in 2001. Moving beyond its stronghold in natural peanut butter brands the next year Smucker purchased the Jif peanut butter and Crisco cooking oil and shortening brands from Procter & Gamble. The $670 million purchase price for Jif and Crisco included shifting 53% of Smucker stock into the hands of P&G shareholders.

A decision to concentrate on North America led to the $37 million sale of Australian subsidiary Henry Jones Foods in 2004. Also that year Smucker sold its operations in Brazil to Cargill and closed down two fruit processing plants in California and Oregon. Its purchase of International Multifoods that year added an array of US brands to the Smucker family including Pillsbury flour baking mixes and ready-to-spread frostings; Hungry Jack pancake mixes syrup and potato side dishes; Martha White baking mixes and ingredients; and PET evaporated milk brands. Canadian brands included Robin Hood flour and baking mixes Bick's pickles and condiments and Golden Temple flour and rice.

To further its strategy of concentrating on its core retail brands in 2005 Smucker sold its US foodservice and bakery business and the Canadian operations of Gourmet Baker (all part of its International Multifoods acquisition) to Value Creation Partners. The following year the company sold its Canadian grain-based foodservice operations and industrial businesses to Cargill and CHS Inc. The operations were integrated into leading US flour miller Horizon Milling (which is jointly owned by Cargill and CHS). Adding to its name-brand offerings in 2006 Smucker acquired the White Lily brand of flours baking mixes and frozen biscuits from C.H. Guenther.

The company extended its baking offerings with the 2007 acquisition of sweetened condensed and evaporated milk producer Eagle Family Foods Holdings. Smucker paid $133 million in cash and $115 million in assumed debt for it. Eagle is a good fit with Smucker's PET milk products. Given Smucker's size and subsequent bargaining power with food retailers (including Wal-Mart the giant in US food retailing) and Eagle's domination of the North American canned-milk sector (it is the largest producer of evaporated and sweetened condensed milk in the US and Canada) the pairing of the two companies was a sensible move for both.

EXECUTIVES

Vice Chairman And Cfo, Mark R. Belgya, age 58, $545,962 total compensation
Senior Vp, Chris Resweber
Vice Chairman; President U.s. Food And Beverage, Steven T. Oakland, age 58, $623,077 total compensation
President Pet Food And Pet Snacks, Barry C. Dunaway, age 56, $330,000 total compensation
President And Ceo, Mark T. Smucker, age 50, $355,000 total compensation
President Canada And International, David J. Lemmon
Vp Marketing Services, Tamara J. Fynan
Svp Operations, J. Randal Day
Vice President Of Marketing, Kent Wadsworth
Vp Commodities Purchasing Consumer Foods, Dan Nowicki
Vice President, Sonal Robinson
Senior Vice President Human Resources And Corporate Communications, Jill Penrose
Svp General Counsel And Secretary, Jeannette Knudsen
Vice President Sales And Trade Marketing, Stephen Kouri
Vice President Finance, Mark Draa
National Sales Manager, Mike Workman
Vice President Market Research, Jill Boyce
Vp Government Relations And Corporate Sustainability, Julia Sabin
Vp Sales And Marketing, John Hall
Vice President Of Supply Chain And Operations, Todd Campbell
Vice President Sales And Support, Chantel Meza
National Account Manager, Matt Kleinhenz
National Account Manager, Scott Dacus
Senior Vice President Growth And Consumer Engagement, Geoff Tanner
Svp Operations, J Randal Day
National Account Manager, Mike Freitas
Vice President Green Coffee, Roger Larsh
Vice President Ecommerce, Daniel Cooke
Chairman, Richard K. Smucker, age 71
Board Member, Dan Russell
Auditors: Ernst & Young LLP

LOCATIONS

HQ: Smucker (J.M.) Co.
One Strawberry Lane, Orrville, OH 44667-0280
Phone: 330 682-3000
Web: www.jmsmucker.com

2018 Sales

	$ mil.	% of total
Domestic	6,786	92
International		
Canada	432	6
Other countries	139	2
Total	**7,357**	**100**

PRODUCTS/OPERATIONS

2018 Sales

	$ mil.	% of total
US Retail Pet Foods	2,169	30
US Retail Coffee	2,092	28
US Retail Consumer Foods	2,001	27
International and Away From Home	1,095	15
Total	**7,357**	**100**

Selected Products

Coffee
Frozen sandwiches
Fruit spreads
Juices and beverages
Peanut butter
Pet food
Pet snacks
Pickles and condiments
Shortening and oils
Syrups
Toppings

Selected Brands

Canadian brands
  Adams
  Bick's
  Carnation (under license)
  Double Fruit
  Five Roses
  Golden Temple
  Robin Hood
  Smucker's
Coffee
  Café Bustelo
  Café Pilon
  Dunkin' Donuts (under license)
  Folgers
  kava
  Medaglia D'oro
Consumer and natural foods
  Adams
  Crisco
  Dickinson's
  Jif
  Knott's Berry Farm
  Laura Scudder's
  Smucker's
Pet food and snacks
  9Lives
  Dad's
  Gravy Train
  Kibbles 'n Bits
  Meow Mix
  Milk-Bone
  Natural Balance
  Nature's Recipe
  Rachel Ray Nutrish
  Snausages

COMPETITORS

B&G Foods	Hormel
Caribou Coffee	Kraft Heinz
Community Coffee	Mars Incorporated
ConAgra	National Grape
Cranberries Limited	Cooperative
E.D. Smith	Nestlé Purina PetCare
Farmer Bros.	Pinnacle Foods
Ferrero	Snyder's-Lance
General Mills	Starbucks
Hain Celestial	Tata Global Beverages
Hershey	Welch's
Hill's Pet Nutrition	

HISTORICAL FINANCIALS

Company Type: Public

Income Statement   FYE: April 30

	REVENUE ($ mil.)	NET INCOME ($ mil.)	NET PROFIT MARGIN	EMPLOYEES
04/19	7,838	514	6.6%	7,400
04/18	7,357	1,339	18.2%	7,000
04/17	7,392	592	8.0%	7,140
04/16	7,811	689	8.8%	6,910
04/15	5,693	345	6.1%	7,370
Annual Growth	8.3%	10.5%	—	0.1%

2019 Year-End Financials

Debt ratio: 35.00%   No. of shares (mil.): 114
Return on equity: 6.00%   Dividends
Cash ($ mil.): 101   Yield: 3.0%
Current ratio: 1.00   Payout: 74.0%
Long-term debt ($ mil.): 4,686 Market value ($ mil.): 13,948

	STOCK PRICE ($) FY Close	P/E High/Low	PER SHARE ($) Earnings	Dividends	Book Value
04/19	123.00	27 21	5.00	3.00	70.00
04/18	114.00	11 8	12.00	3.00	69.00
04/17	127.00	31 24	5.00	3.00	60.00
04/16	127.00	23 18	6.00	3.00	60.00
04/15	116.00	35 29	3.00	3.00	59.00
Annual Growth	1.4%	— —	7.9%	7.4%	4.3%

SOLSTICE HOLDINGS INC.

EXECUTIVES

Pres, Mr Doug L Devos
Chm, Stephen Van Andel
Exec V Pres-Cfo, Russ Evans
Exec V Pres-Coo, Alvin Koop
V Pres, Mr Michael Mohr
Cntrl, Mr Craig V Witcher

LOCATIONS

HQ: SOLSTICE HOLDINGS INC.
  7575 FULTON ST E, ADA, MI 493550001
Phone: 616 787-1000

HISTORICAL FINANCIALS

Company Type: Private

Income Statement   FYE: December 31

	REVENUE ($ mil.)	NET INCOME ($ mil.)	NET PROFIT MARGIN	EMPLOYEES
12/08	8,235	0	—	14,000
12/07	7,168	0	—	—
12/06	6,387	0	—	—
Annual Growth	13.5%	—	—	—

Sonic Automotive, Inc.

Sonic Automotive is one of the leading US auto dealers just behind rivals like AutoNation and Penske Automotive. Sonic operates 100 new and used vehicle franchises about 10 company-owned used vehicle stores and about 15 collision repair centers in major markets in more than a dozen states including California Texas the Carolinas Alabama and Tennessee. The company sells some 25 brands of cars and light trucks including Honda Ford and Subaru and offers extended aftermarket services. Chairman O. Bruton Smith is also the majority owner of Speedway Motorsports which operates eight NASCAR auto racetracks.

Operations

Sonic Automotive sells new vehicles including luxury cars (BMW Lexus Land Rover and Volvo) mid-line imports (Honda Nissan and Toyota) and domestic brands (Ford and General Motors). Luxury brands account for more than 55% of new vehicle sales mid-line brands bring in about one third of new vehicle sales and domestic brands more

than 10%. Sonic operates in two segments: Franchised Dealership segment and EchoPark segment. The Franchised Dealership segment operate more than 95 stores and accounts for the vast majority of company?s sales. It also offers a range of after-market services including vehicle financing replacement parts performance of vehicle maintenance paint and collision repair services and arrangement of extended warranty contracts and insurance.

Its EchoPark segment which accounts for 7% of sales operates about eight stores that buy and sell pre-owned vehicles and arrange finance and insurance products.

Geographic Reach

Sonic is headquartered in Charlotte North Carolina. California is Sonic's #1 market accounting for around 30% of sales followed closely by Texas at more than a quarter of total sales. EchoPark's retail units are clustered in Colorado and Texas.

Sales and Marketing

Sonic?s advertising expenses were $63.1 million $61.6 million and $61.7 million for 2018 2017 and 2016 respectively. The increased spending has come primarily from marketing efforts related to establishing the new EchoPark locations.

Financial Performance

Sonic Automotive has seen healthy revenue growth in recent years through a strategy of new stores and acquisitions. Its annual revenues have risen close to 10% since 2014.

Revenue increased to $9.9 billion in 2018 a slight increase from the year prior. Net income was $52 million in 2018 a drop from $93 million in 2017.

Selling general and administrative expenses fell slightly in fiscal 2018 to $1.1 billion.

Cash at the end of 2018 was $5.8 million a decrease of 7% from the prior year. Cash provided by operating activities was $143.7 million in fiscal 2018 while investing activities used $15.3 million. Financing activities used another $128.8 million.

Strategy

As part of the company's strategic plans Sonic is primarily focused on growing its operations in large metropolitan markets in the Southeast Texas and California. The company plans to grow its new-vehicle franchise business both organically and opportunistically through acquisitions.

The company's long-term growth strategy is to target luxury or mid-line import brands in regions where it already operates. Nearly 90% of total new vehicle revenue was generated by luxury and mid-line import dealerships which usually have higher operating margins lower associate turnover and lower inventory levels.

Sonic is also counting on its EchoPark business to be a growth engine. Its EchoPark used car business expansion is based on operating larger EchoPark dealerships that serve as a destination point for shoppers. The stores are company-owned and not franchised. The company sees used vehicle sales as more stable than new vehicle sales because they are less sensitive to economic cycles and seasonal influences.

Company Background

O. Bruton Smith and his son Scott control the company through their ownership of about 40% of Sonic Automotive's voting stock.

EXECUTIVES

President And Ceo, B. Scott Smith, age 51, $1,085,438 total compensation
Evp Operations, Frank J. (Jeff) Dyke, age 52, $969,179 total compensation
Vp And Chief Marketing Officer, Rachel M. Richards
Evp And Cfo, Heath R. Byrd, age 52, $677,327 total compensation

Vp Information Technology, Christopher (Chris) Maritato
Vice President Of Finance And Insurance, Richard O'Connor
Vice President, John Russ
Vice President Tax, Joseph Oconnor
Vice President, William Sullivan
Senior Regional Vice President, Karen McKemie
Vice President Manufacturer Relations, Raymond Valentine
Regional Vice President Tn Dc, Kevin Gaither
Senior Business Intelligence Developer, Jonathan Henin
Regional Vice President, Steve Prather
Regional Vice President, Tasos Theodorou
Vice President, James Brannon
Chairman, O. Bruton Smith, age 91
Vice Chairman, David B. Smith, age 44
Board Member, William Belk
Assistant Treasurer, Chris Cellini
Auditors: KPMG LLP

LOCATIONS

HQ: Sonic Automotive, Inc.
   4401 Colwick Road, Charlotte, NC 28211
Phone: 704 566-2400   **Fax:** 704 536-5116
Web: www.sonicautomotive.com

PRODUCTS/OPERATIONS

2016 sales

	$ mil.	% of total
Franchised Dealerships	9,603	99
EchoPark	129	1
Total	**9,732**	**100**

2016 sales

	$ mil.	% of total
New vehicles	5,235	54
Used vehicles	2,533	26
Wholesale vehicles	211	2
Parts service and collision repair	1,410	14
Finance insurance and other	343	4
Total	**9,732**	**100**

Services Center List-Selected:
Acura of Serramonte Service Center
Audi West Houston Service Center
BMW of Birmingham Service Center
Cadillac of Las Vegas Service Center
Capitol Chevrolet of Columbia Service Center
Fort Mill Ford Service Center
Honda of Santa Monica Service Center
Momentum Volkswagen Service Center
North Central Ford Service Center
Toyota of Fort Worth Service Center
Volkswagen of Fort Myers Service Center
Brands
BMW
Mercedes
Lexus
Audi
Land Rover
Cadillac
Porsche
Honda
Toyota
Volkswagen
Hyundai
Ford
General Motors

COMPETITORS

Asbury Automotive	Enterprise Rent-A-Car
AutoNation	Group 1 Automotive
AutoTrader	Gunn Automotive
Autobytel	Internet Brands
CarMax	JM Family Enterprises
Darcars	Penske Automotive
David McDavid Auto	Group
Group	Sewell Automotive
DriveTime Automotive	

HISTORICAL FINANCIALS

Company Type: Public

Income Statement   FYE: December 31

	REVENUE ($ mil.)	NET INCOME ($ mil.)	NET PROFIT MARGIN	EMPLOYEES
12/18	9,952	52	0.5%	9,700
12/17	9,867	93	0.9%	9,750
12/16	9,732	93	1.0%	9,800
12/15	9,624	86	0.9%	9,800
12/14	9,197	97	1.1%	9,300
Annual Growth	**2.0%**	**(14.6%)**	**—**	**1.1%**

2018 Year-End Financials

Debt ratio: 65.00%	No. of shares (mil.): 43
Return on equity: 6.00%	Dividends
Cash ($ mil.): 6	Yield: 2.0%
Current ratio: 1.00	Payout: 20.0%
Long-term debt ($ mil.): 919	Market value ($ mil.): 588

	STOCK PRICE ($) FY Close	P/E High/Low	PER SHARE ($) Earnings	Dividends	Book Value
12/18	14.00	19 11	1.00	0.00	19.00
12/17	18.00	12 8	2.00	0.00	18.00
12/16	23.00	12 8	2.00	0.00	16.00
12/15	23.00	16 12	2.00	0.00	15.00
12/14	27.00	15 11	2.00	0.00	13.00
Annual Growth	**(15.5%)**	**—**	**(10.1%)**	**24.5%**	**10.1%**

Sonoco Products Co.

Sonoco Products is a manufacturer of industrial and consumer packaging used by the food consumer goods construction and automotive industries. The company makes composite cans for things like snack foods powdered beverages and pet foods and produces flexible and rigid packaging (paper and plastic) for food personal care items and chemicals. Sonoco also manufactures point-of-sale displays protective packaging and paperboard tubes for industrial processes. Other services include fulfillment and supply chain management. About two-thirds of Sonoco's revenues are generated in the US.

Operations

Sonoco divides its business into four chief business segments. Consumer Packaging is its largest segment and accounts for roughly 45% of sales. It produces items such as composite cans paperboard containers caulk tubes trays cups and packaging films. Within the Consumer Packaging business paper-based rigid packaging is the company's largest revenue-producing group of products and represents 20% of consolidated sales.

The Paper and Industrial Converted Products segment generates 35% of sales and includes recycled paper products and other recyclable materials as well as paperboard tubes and cores. Display and Packaging (more than 10%) includes point-of-purchase displays custom and retail packaging and fulfillment. Protective Solutions (10%) comprises paperboard-based and expanded foam protective packaging and temperature-assured packaging.

Geographic Reach

Based in Hartsville SC Sonoco operates more than 310 locations around the world in about 35 countries concentrated in Canada Europe and the US. The US generates around 65% of sales annually. Sonoco's international sales are concentrated in Europe (20%) followed by Canada (around 5%).

Sales and Marketing

Each of Sonoco's operating units has its own sales staff and maintains direct sales relationships with its customers.

Financial Performance

Sonoco's revenue has rebounded in the last two years after consecutive declines in both 2015 and 2016. Overall sales have increased about 7% over the past five years.

Revenue hit a record high of $5.4 billion in 2018 up 7% from 5.0 billion in 2017. The increase was due to sales from acquisitions higher selling prices and modest volume growth.

Net income in 2018 soared to $313.6 million from $175.3 million the previous year - a 79% increase. This was largely due to a tax benefit posted in 2017 from the Tax Cuts and Jobs Act.

Cash at the end of fiscal 2018 was $120.4 million a decrease of $134.5 million from the prior year. Cash from operations contributed $589.9 million to the coffers while investing activities used $444.1 million mainly for property plant and equipment and acquisitions. Financing activities used another $273.7 million for dividends to stockholders and the company's stock repurchase program.

Strategy

Sonoco is implementing key initiatives to drive growth in both its consumer packaging and industrial businesses. The company is also addressing some manufacturing inefficiencies with automation and robotics to reduce the unit cost to produce each of its products.

In the consumer packaging business Sonoco is responding to trends such as shifting demographics digital disruption health and wellness and social consciousness. For example older baby boomers want easy to open packaging while millennials are looking for speed and convenience. The company is developing packaging features that address both needs. The increase in e-commerce has driven the need for more protective packaging. Sonoco now provides specially certified packaging for shipments through Amazon ? Amazon Packaging Support and Supplier Network (APASS) ? which ensures packaging passes a physical performance test. Sonoco is also making more transparent packaging highlighting fresh and natural ingredients and implementing new PET recycled plastic in its clamshell packaging. The company aims to expand its consumer business with new operations starting up in Brazil and Southeast Asia as well as other growth projects in the US and Europe.

In the industrial business Sonoco has improved the stability of its TrueCore products reducing core chewout and spinout and its new EcoSPAN core product is now recyclable. The 2018 acquisition of 100% of its Conitex Sonoco joint venture is helping the company's industrial business penetrate emerging markets in Asia.

Mergers and Acquisitions

Sonoco also looks to acquisitions as a means for growth. In 2019 the company purchased Corenso Holdings America Inc. from a private equity firm for about $110 million. Corenso makes uncoated recycled paperboard (URB) and other products used in the paper packaging films and tape industries. The acquisition broadens Sonoco's customer base and adds valuable core converting equipment to its operations.

In 2018 the company paid $143 million for the remaining 70% interest in its Conitex Sonoco joint venture originally formed in 1998 with Spain-based packaging company Texpack Inc. The same year Sonoco acquired Florida-based Highland Packaging Solutions a manufacturer of thermoformed packaging for fresh fruits vegetables and eggs for $148.5 million. Through this acquisition

Conoco is targeting higher sales in the fast-growing perimeter of retail supermarkets.

Company Background

Sonoco was originally founded as the Southern Novelty Company in Hartsville South Carolina in 1899. Its first product was a paper cone-shaped yarn carrier used in the textile industry. The company went on to add paper tubes to its product line and added new operations throughout the US. In 1923 the name was changed to Sonoco Products Company using the first two letters from each word of the original name.

In 1950 Sonoco expanded into Mexico. In the 1960s it made several acquisitions and branched out to make spiral tubes fiber drums and composite containers with metal ends. In the 1970s the company began operations in Canada as well as Puerto Rico. The company later diversified into the wastepaper collection and processing business and the manufacture of plastic grocery bags (The company exited the plastic bag business in 2003.) and rigid and flexible packaging.

HISTORY

Sonoco Products originated during the South's industrial renewal after the Civil War. Major James Coker and son James Jr. (who had been badly wounded at the Battle of Chickamauga) founded the Carolina Fiber company in Hartsville South Carolina to make pulp and paper from pine trees. The business was based on a thesis James Jr. wrote in 1884 at Stevens Institute of Technology in Hoboken New Jersey. The essay explained how to make paper pulp using the sulfite process.

After failing to sell the pulp commercially the Cokers decided to use it to make paper cones for the textile industry which was seeing rapid growth in the southern US. In 1899 Major Coker and investor W. F. Smith formed the Southern Novelty Company. Major Coker's son Charles became president in 1918. As sales neared $1 million in 1923 the company changed its name to Sonoco.

EXECUTIVES

President Ceo And Director, M. Jack Sanders, age 65, $1,039,817 total compensation

Svp Plastic Packaging And Protective Solutions, Vicki B. Arthur, age 60

Svp Paper/engineered Carriers U.s./canada And Display And Packaging, Rodger D. Fuller, age 57, $473,319 total compensation

Vp Global Flexibles, Robert L. Puechl, age 63

Svp And Cfo, Barry L. Saunders, age 59, $548,759 total compensation

Vp Tubes And Cores U.s. And Canada, James A. Harrell, age 57

Svp Rigid Paper Containers And Paper/engineered Carriers International, R. Howard Coker, age 56, $471,695 total compensation

Evp Coo And Ceo-elect, Robert C. (Rob) Tiede, age 60, $567,741 total compensation

Vp Marketing And Innovation, Marcy J. Thompson, age 57

Vp Human Resources, Allan H. McLeland, age 52

Vp Paper And Industrial Converted Products Emea Asia Australia And New Zealand, Adam Wood, age 50

Division Vice President And General Manager Protective Solutions Industrial Business Segment, Carl Kraus

Vice President Manufacturing, Chuck Redfearn

National Account Manager, Paul Dejong

Senior Vice President Of Corporate Planning, Kevin Mahoney

Vice President, Jeff Tedder

Corporate Vice President General Counsel Secretary, John Florence

Vice President Investor Relations And Corporate Affairs, Roger Schrum

Vp Consumer Protective Packaging Solutions, Greg Powell

Vice President, Rhett Mitchell

Vice President, Harold Cummings

Chairman, Harris E. DeLoach, age 73

Board Member, James Micali

Treasurer, Julie Albrecht

Secretary Iv, Connee Grantham

Secretary Iv, Allison Eddins

Board Member, Blythe Mcgarvie

Board Member, Harry Cockrell

Board Member, Sundaram Nagarajan

Auditors: PricewaterhouseCoopers LLP

LOCATIONS

HQ: Sonoco Products Co.
1 N. Second St., Hartsville, SC 29550
Phone: 843 383-7000   **Fax:** 843 383-7008
Web: www.sonoco.com

2018 Sales

	$ mil.	% of total
US	3,490	65
Europe	1,093	20
Canada	246	5
Other	562	10
Total	**5,391**	**100**

PRODUCTS/OPERATIONS

2018 Sales

	$ mil.	% of total
Consumer Packaging	2,360	44
Paper & Industrial Converted Products	1,911	35
Display & Packaging	592	11
Protective Solutions	528	10
Total	**5,391**	**100**

Selected Products and Services

Paper and Industrial Converted Products
  Tubes and cores
  Concrete forms
  Molded plugs
  Pallets
  Pallet components
  Paperboard tubes cores
  Roll packaging
  Rotary die boards
  Void forms
  Paper
  Boxboard
  Chipboard
  Corrugating medium
  Lightweight corestock
  Linerboard
  Recovered paper
  Recycled paperboard
  Specialty grades
  Tubeboard
  Sonoco Recycling
  Collection processing and recycling of old corrugated containers paper plastic metal glass other recyclable materials
Consumer Packaging
  Ends and closures
  Aluminum steel and peelable membrane easy-open closures for composite metal and plastic containers
  Printed flexible packaging
  Thin-gauge rotogravure flexographic and combination printed film (laminations and rotogravure cylinder engraving brand artwork management)
  Thin-gauge packaging
  Rigid packaging - blow molded plastics
  Monolayer and multilayer bottles and jars
  Rigid packaging - paper
  Composite paperboard cans (round and shaped)
  Fiber cartridges
  Single-wrap paperboard packages
  Rigid packaging - thermoformed plastic
  Mono coated and barrier and non-barrier laminated tubs cups spools consumer and institutional trays
Packaging Services
  Paperboard specialties

Rixie coasters
Stancap glass covers
Other paper amenities
Point-of-purchase (P-O-P)
Contract packaging co-packing and fulfillment services
Designing manufacturing assembling packing and distributing temporary semi permanent and permanent P-O-P displays
Service centers
Packaging supply chain management (custom packing fulfillment primary package filling scalable service centers)
Protective Packaging
  Molded and extruded plastics (product design tool design and fabrication; manufacturing in both injection molding and extrusion technologies)
  Protective packaging
  Contract package testing
  Sonopost technology
  Sonobase carriers
  Sonopop systems

COMPETITORS

AptarGroup	Greif
Avery Dennison	International Paper
Ball Corp.	Owens-Illinois
Bemis	Packaging Corp. of
Crown Holdings	America
Graphic Packaging	Sealed Air Corp.
Holding	Silgan

HISTORICAL FINANCIALS

Company Type: Public

Income Statement

FYE: December 31

	REVENUE ($ mil.)	NET INCOME ($ mil.)	NET PROFIT MARGIN	EMPLOYEES
12/18	5,391	314	5.8%	23,000
12/17	5,037	175	3.5%	21,000
12/16	4,783	286	6.0%	20,000
12/15	4,964	250	5.0%	21,000
12/14	5,015	239	4.8%	20,800
Annual Growth	1.8%	7.0%	—	2.5%

2018 Year-End Financials

Debt ratio: 30.00%	No. of shares (mil.): 100
Return on equity: 18.00%	Dividends
Cash ($ mil.): 120	Yield: 3.0%
Current ratio: 1.00	Payout: 52.0%
Long-term debt ($ mil.): 1,190	Market value ($ mil.): 5,304

	STOCK PRICE ($) FY Close	P/E High/Low		PER SHARE ($) Earnings	Dividends	Book Value
12/18	53.00	19	15	3.00	2.00	18.00
12/17	53.00	32	27	2.00	2.00	17.00
12/16	53.00	20	13	3.00	1.00	15.00
12/15	41.00	19	15	2.00	1.00	15.00
12/14	44.00	19	16	2.00	1.00	15.00
Annual Growth	5.0%	—	—	7.5%	6.3%	4.1%

South Plains Financial Inc

Auditors: Weaver and Tidwell, L.L.P

LOCATIONS

HQ: South Plains Financial Inc
5219 City Bank Parkway, Lubbock, TX 79407
Phone: 806 792-7101
Web: www.city.bank

HISTORICAL FINANCIALS

Company Type: Public

Income Statement

FYE: December 31

	ASSETS ($ mil.)	NET INCOME ($ mil.)	INCOME AS % OF ASSETS	EMPLOYEES
12/18	2,713	29	1.1%	684
12/17	2,573	24	0.9%	—
Annual Growth	5.4%	23.9%	—	—

2018 Year-End Financials

Debt ratio: 6.00%
Return on equity: 14.00%
Cash ($ mil.): 246
Current ratio: —
Long-term debt ($ mil.): —

No. of shares (mil.): 15
Dividends
Yield: —
Payout: 103.0%
Market value ($ mil.): —

	STOCK PRICE ($) FY Close	P/E High/Low	PER SHARE ($) Earnings	Dividends	Book Value
12/18	0.00	— —	2.00	2.00	14.00
12/17	0.00	— —	2.00	1.00	15.00
/0.00	—	—(0.00)	0.00	(0.00)	
Annual Growth	—	—	—	—	—

South State Corp

South State Corporation (formerly First Financial Holdings) is the holding company for South State Bank (formerly South Carolina Bank and Trust and South Carolina Bank and Trust of the Piedmont both known as SCBT). The bank operates branches throughout the Palmetto state as well as in select counties in Georgia and North Carolina. Serving retail and business customers the banks provide deposit accounts loans and mortgages as well as trust and investment planning services. More than half of the firm's loan portfolio is devoted to commercial mortgages while consumer real estate loans make up more than a quarter. South State plans to merge with Southeastern Bank Financial parent of Georgia Bank & Trust.

Operations

Beyond its retail and commercial banking mortgage lending consumer finance and trust and investment businesses the bank operates registered investment advisors Minis & Co. and First Southeast 401K Fiduciaries as well as limited-purpose broker-dealer First Southeast Investor Services.

South State Corporation generated 70% of its total revenue from loan interest (including fees) in 2014 while another 4% came from interest income on investment securities. Service charges and Bankcard services income made up another 14% of total revenue while trust and investment services income and mortgage banking income each contributed roughly 4% during the year.

Geographic Reach

South State Corporation boasts nearly 130 branches across nearly 20 counties in South Carolina a handful of counties in North Carolina and about a dozen counties in the northeast and coastal regions of Georgia.

Financial Performance

South State Corporation's revenues and profits have been on the rise over the past few years mostly thanks to continued growth of its loan business and declining loan loss provisions as its loan portfolio's credit quality has improved with the strengthened economy.

The company's revenue jumped by 28% to $436.72 million in 2014 which was mostly driven by 20% growth in its loan interest income as its average loan asset balances swelled by a similar percentage. South State's non-interest income also swelled by 76% thanks to higher deposit account service charge bankcard service trust and investment service and mortgage banking fees from overall growth in the business through acquisitions and organic initiatives.

Higher revenue and controlled operating costs in 2014 drove the bank's net income higher by 53% to $75.44 million. South State's operating cash levels declined by 51% to $118.65 million for the year after adjusting its earnings for non-cash net sales proceeds from its mortgage loans held-for-sale and as the bank spent more cash toward its accrued income taxes.

Strategy

Though it does sometimes expand or relocate its existing branches to better position its locations for more growth South State Corporation has been mostly growing its loan business and branch network through strategic bank and branch acquisitions. Its 2015 acquisition of 13 branch locations from Bank of America for example extended South State's reach into six new markets and three existing markets while adding millions of dollars worth of new loan business. Then in mid-2016 South State Corporation agreed to buy Southeastern Bank Financial the holding company of Georgia Bank & Trust (which also operates in South Carolina as Southern Bank & Trust). The combined company will operate more than 130 branches in Georgia and the Carolinas.

Mergers and Acquisitions

In 2015 South State Corporation agreed to purchase 12 South Carolina branches and one Georgia branch from Bank of America expanding its reach into six new markets. The acquired branches were located in Hartwell Georgia; as well as Florence Greenwood Orangeburg Sumter Newberry Batesburg-Leesville Abbeville and Hartsville in South Carolina.

Company Background

South State Corporation and South State Bank changed their names from First Financial Holdings and South Carolina Bank and Trust respectively in 2014. The change was designed to better promote the South State brand with customers.

EXECUTIVES

Ceo, Robert R. Hill, age 52, $645,000 total compensation
Vice President Of Public Relations, Donna Pullen
Cfo And Coo, John C. Pollok, age 53, $442,000 total compensation
Regional President Upstate, John F. Windley, age 67, $315,000 total compensation
Chief Credit Officer And Chief Risk Officer, Joseph Burns, $295,000 total compensation
President, R. Wayne Hall, $203,405 total compensation
Evp And Corporate Secretary, William C. Bochette
Vice President, Reid Davis
Senior Vice President Technology, Ross Bagley
Senior Executive Vice President, Dane H Murray
Vice President, Stacy Cannon
Senior Vice President Corporate Counsel, Nici Comer
Senior Vice President Chief Compliance Officer, Lora Jex
Chairman, Robert R. Horger, age 68
Vice Chairman, Paula Harper Bethea
Board Member, Kevin Walker
Board Member, Cynthia Hartley
Board Member, Robert Demere
Auditors: Dixon Hughes Goodman LLP

LOCATIONS

HQ: South State Corp
520 Gervais Street, Columbia, SC 29201
Phone: 800 277-2175
Web: www.southstatebank.com

PRODUCTS/OPERATIONS

2011 Sales

	$ mil.	% of total
Interest		
Loans including fees	320	70
Investment securities	20	4
Other	2	-
Noninterest		
Service charges on deposit accounts	36	10
Bankcard services income	30	6
Trust and investment services income	18	4
Mortgage banking	16	4
Securities gains net	-	0
Amortization of FDIC indemnification asset	(21.9)	0
Other	16	4
Total	437	100

COMPETITORS

BB&T
Bank of America
Bank of South Carolina
First Citizens
 Bancorporation

Regions Financial
Security Federal

HISTORICAL FINANCIALS

Company Type: Public

Income Statement

FYE: December 31

	ASSETS ($ mil.)	NET INCOME ($ mil.)	INCOME AS % OF ASSETS	EMPLOYEES
12/18	14,676	179	1.2%	2,602
12/17	14,467	88	0.6%	2,719
12/16	8,901	101	1.1%	2,055
12/15	8,557	99	1.2%	2,058
12/14	7,826	75	1.0%	2,081
Annual Growth	17.0%	24.1%	—	5.7%

2018 Year-End Financials

Debt ratio: 1.00%
Return on equity: 8.00%
Cash ($ mil.): 376
Current ratio: —
Long-term debt ($ mil.): —

No. of shares (mil.): 36
Dividends
Yield: 2.0%
Payout: 39.0%
Market value ($ mil.): 2,148

	STOCK PRICE ($) FY Close	P/E High/Low	PER SHARE ($) Earnings	Dividends	Book Value
12/18	60.00	19 12	5.00	1.00	66.00
12/17	87.00	32 27	3.00	1.00	63.00
12/16	87.00	22 14	4.00	1.00	47.00
12/15	72.00	19 14	4.00	1.00	44.00
12/14	67.00	22 18	3.00	1.00	41.00
Annual Growth	(2.8%)	— —	12.1%	13.9%	12.8%

Southern California Edison Co.

One of the Golden State's largest utilities Southern California Edison (SCE) distributes power to 5.1 million customers in central coastal and southern California (excluding Los Angeles and some other cities). The utility's system consists of more than 12600 miles of transmission lines and some 91400 miles of distribution lines. SCE has about 6900 MW of generating capacity from stakes in nuclear hydroelectric fossil-fueled and solar power plants. The utility also has power purchase agreements and sells excess power to wholesale customers. SCE is a unit of utility and competitive power holding company Edison International.

Geographic Reach

SCE supplies electricity to a 50000 square-mile area of central coastal and southern California. This service area contains a population of nearly 15 million people and SCE serves the population via about 5.1 million customer accounts.

Sales and Marketing

SCE generates about 45% of its revenues from commercial customers and about 40% from residential customers. Other revenue comes from agricultural and industrial customers public authorities and resale.

Financial Performance

SCE reported moderate but steady revenue growth between 2016 and 2018 following a considerable decline in 2015. Net income remained in the $1.1 billion to $1.6 billion range between 2014 and 2017 but then dipped into the red in 2018.

SCE's revenue increased 3% to some $12.6 billion in 2018.

The company reported a net loss of $189 million in 2018 due to $1.8 billion in wildfire-related claims charges.

The company ended 2018 with $22 million in cash down $493 million from 2017. Operating activities contributed $3.2 billion while investing activities used $4.3 billion (mostly capital expenditures) and financing activities contributed $616 million via an expanded credit line.

Strategy

SCE is focused on modernizing its electric grid to improve system safety and reliability and to better integrate renewable resources. The utility is ramping up its green energy programs to comply with the state of California's aggressive long-term renewable energy goals. SCE has signed contracts with new solar and geothermal energy producers and is investing heavily in battery storage projects. It has also reduced its fossil-fuel power plant holdings.

SCE is installing solar photovoltaic installations on commercial and residential rooftops. It is also installing electric vehicle charging stations at apartment complexes and office buildings. In addition the utility has installed smart electric meters — digital two-way communication devices which allow customers and the utility to better manage energy use.

A recent uptick in wildfires in California has prompted scrutiny into utilities' liability for wildfire-related damages. SCE and parent Edison International face several lawsuits claiming that the utility caused or contributed to damages from fires that occurred in 2017 and 2018. The firm took a $1.8 billion charge for existing and expected claims in 2018 which resulted in a net financial loss. The company is working on wildfire safety measures including line inspection and tree-trimming programs and the installation of fire-resistant poles insulated lines and high-risk monitoring cameras.

Company Background

Southern California Edison was founded in 1896 as West Side Lighting. It later merged with Los Angeles Edison Electric and became Southern California Edison in 1909. Holding company SCEcorp was formed in 1987 and was renamed Edison International in 1996.

EXECUTIVES

Svp And Cio, Todd L. Inlander

Ceo, Kevin M. Payne, age 58
Svp Power Supply, Stuart R. Hemphill
Vp Operational Services And Chief Procurement Officer, Douglas R. Bauder
Svp Transmission And Distribution, Peter T. Dietrich
Vp Distribution, Gregory M. Ferree
Vp Transmission Substations And Operations, Paul J. Grigaux
President, Ronald O. (R.O.) Nichols, age 65
Vp Decommissioning And Chief Nuclear Officer San Onofre Nuclear Generating Station, Thomas J. (Tom) Palmisano
Vp And Treasurer, William (Tres) Petmecky, age 50
Vice President And Treasurer, Robert C Boada
Vice President, Anthony Blakemore
Vice President, Debbie Rodgers
Government Relations, Karen Cadavona
Vice President, Dawn Anaiscourt
Vice President General, Robert Baldwin
Vice President And Treasurer Sce, Daniel Wood
Vice President Distribution Sce, Greg Ferree
Vice President, Mark Carter
Senior Vice President Power Supply Sce, Kevin Walker
Vice President, Jill Anderson
Treasurer, Jonathan Rumble
Secretary, Darin Hester
Auditors: PricewaterhouseCoopers LLP

LOCATIONS

HQ: Southern California Edison Co.
2244 Walnut Grove Avenue, P.O. Box 800, Rosemead, CA 91770
Phone: 626 302-1212
Web: www.sce.com

PRODUCTS/OPERATIONS

2015 Sales

	% of total
Commercial customers	43
Residential customers	38
Industrial customers	5
Public authorities	5
Agriculture & other operating revenue	9
Total	**100**

2015 Sales

	$ mil.	% of total
Utility Earning Activities	6,305	55
Utility Cost- Recovery Activities	5,180	45
Total	**11,485**	**100**

COMPETITORS

American States Water	Portland General Electric
Avista	
Bonneville Power	Sacramento Municipal Utility
Calpine	
Imperial Irrigation District	San Diego Gas & Electric
NV Energy	SoCalGas
PacifiCorp	
Pacific Gas and Electric	

HISTORICAL FINANCIALS

Company Type: Public

Income Statement

FYE: December 31

	REVENUE ($ mil.)	NET INCOME ($ mil.)	NET PROFIT MARGIN	EMPLOYEES
12/18	12,611	(189)	—	12,219
12/17	12,254	1,136	9.3%	12,234
12/16	11,830	1,499	12.7%	11,947
12/15	11,485	1,111	9.7%	12,678
12/14	13,380	1,565	11.7%	13,600
Annual Growth	**(1.5%)**	**—**	**—**	**(2.6%)**

2018 Year-End Financials

Debt ratio: 24.00%
Return on equity: (-1.00%)
Cash ($ mil.): 21
Current ratio: 1.00
Long-term debt ($ mil.): 12,892

No. of shares (mil.): 435
Dividends
 Yield: 6.0%
 Payout: —
Market value ($ mil.): 7,950

	STOCK PRICE ($) FY Close	P/E High/Low		PER SHARE ($)		
				Earnings	Dividends	Book Value
12/18	18.00	—	—	(0.00)	1.00	32.00
12/17	24.00	—	—	(0.00)	1.00	34.00
12/16	24.00	—	—	(0.00)	1.00	33.00
12/15	24.00	—	—	(0.00)	1.00	31.00
12/14	23.00	—	—	(0.00)	1.00	31.00
Annual Growth	**(5.1%)**	**—**	**—**	**(0.5%)**	**0.9%**	

Southern Company (The)

Southern Power provides power for the burgeoning population in the South. The company owns builds acquires and markets energy in the competitive wholesale supply business. It develops and operates independent power plants in the southeastern US. The company which is part of Southern Company's generation and energy marketing operations has more than 10500 MW of primarily fossil-fueled facilities generating capacity operating or under construction in Alabama California Florida Georgia Nevada North Carolina Texas and New Mexico. Southern Power's electricity output is marketed to wholesale customers in the region. It is growing by acquiring and developing solar power facilities.

Operations

The company is a wholesale energy provider serving electricity needs of municipalities electric cooperatives and investor-owned utilities. Southern Power and its subsidiaries owns and/or operates 35 facilities in nine states. Its renewable assets include biomass and solar.

Thanks to solar facilities under construction and the acquisitions of Calipatria Solar and Grant Wind as well as other capacity and energy contracts the Southern Power has an average of 75% of its available demonstrated capacity covered through 2020 and an average of 70% of its available demonstrated capacity covered through 2025.

Geographic Reach

Southern Power has operations Alabama California Florida Georgia Nevada New Mexico North Carolina Oklahoma and Texas.

Financial Performance

In fiscal 2015 Southern Power's net sales decreased by $111 million compared to 2014. Power purchase agreements (PPA) energy revenues declined due to lower energy prices driven by a drop in natural gas prices which was passed through in fuel revenues.

Wholesale revenues and non-affiliates revenues declined due to lower energy and capacity revenues.

In 2015 net income increased by 25% due to lower fuel expenses and purchased power partially offset by decreased sales.

Fuel expense decreased due to lower natural gas generation costs.

Purchased power expenses decreased primarily due to a drop in volume of KWhs purchased as well as a decrease associated with the average cost of purchased power.

Net cash provided by the operating activities increased by 66% due to higher income tax benefits received and higher revenues from new PPAs including solar PPAs.

Strategy

The company is expanding its regional generation portfolio (primarily with solar power plants) in order to boost its overall generating capacity to almost 10000 MW.

Mergers and Acquisitions

Growing its solar power assets in 2016 Southern Power acquired the 120-MW East Pecos solar facility (Southern Power's second solar project in Texas).

That year Southern Power and Turner Renewable Energy jointly bought the 20-MW Calipatria solar facility from Solar Frontier Americas. (Southern Power's 10th solar facility in California).

In 2015 Southern Power acquired a controlling interest in the 200-MW Garland solar facility under construction in California from Recurrent Energy a subsidiary of Canadian Solar Inc.

In 2014 Southern Power and Turner Renewable Energy acquired the largest solar facility in New Mexico the 50-MW Macho Springs Solar Facility. The Southern Power-Turner Renewable Energy partnership's seventh solar project and its second-largest overall the plant is expected to generate enough electricity to power more than 18000 homes.

EXECUTIVES

Svp And Coo, John G. Trawick
Vice President Of Construction, Keith Russell
Senior Vice President Compliance Officer, Thomas Bishop
Board Member, Larry Thompson
Auditors: Deloitte & Touche LLP

LOCATIONS

HQ: Southern Company (The)
30 Ivan Allen Jr. Boulevard, N.W., Atlanta, GA 30308
Phone: 404 506-5000   **Fax:** 404 506-0455
Web: www.southerncompany.com

PRODUCTS/OPERATIONS

2015 Sales

	$ mil.	% of total
Wholesale revenues non-affiliates	964	69
Wholesale revenues affiliates	417	30
Other revenues	9	1
Total	**1,390**	**100**

COMPETITORS

AEP	Duke Energy
AES	Entergy
Calpine	NextEra Energy

HISTORICAL FINANCIALS

Company Type: Public

Income Statement

FYE: December 31

	REVENUE ($ mil.)	NET INCOME ($ mil.)	NET PROFIT MARGIN	EMPLOYEES
12/18	23,495	2,242	9.5%	29,192
12/17	23,031	880	3.8%	31,344
12/16	19,896	2,493	12.5%	32,020
12/15	17,489	2,421	13.8%	26,703
12/14	18,467	2,031	11.0%	26,369
Annual Growth	**6.2%**	**2.5%**	**—**	**2.6%**

2018 Year-End Financials

Debt ratio: 38.00%	No. of shares (mil.): 1,034
Return on equity: 9.00%	Dividends
Cash ($ mil.): 1,396	Yield: 5.0%
Current ratio: 1.00	Payout: 110.0%
Long-term debt ($ mil.): 40,736	Market value ($ mil.): 45,404

	STOCK PRICE ($) FY Close	P/E High/Low	PER SHARE ($) Earnings	Dividends	Book Value
12/18	44.00	23 20	2.00	2.00	24.00
12/17	48.00	63 56	1.00	2.00	24.00
12/16	49.00	21 18	3.00	2.00	26.00
12/15	47.00	20 16	3.00	2.00	23.00
12/14	49.00	23 18	2.00	2.00	23.00
Annual Growth	**(2.8%)**	**—**	**(0.1%)**	**3.4%**	**0.8%**

Southern Copper Corp

EXECUTIVES

Pres-Ceo, Oscar Gonzalez Rocha
Chb, German Larrea Mota-Velasco
V Pres Fin-Cfo-Treas, Raul Jacob Ruisanchez
General Counsel, Andres Carlos Ferrero Ghislier
Comptroller, Lina Vingerhoets Vilca
SEC, Julian Jorge Lazalde Psihas
V Pres Exploration, Edgard Corrales Aguilar
Gen Auditor, Rafael Lopez Abad
Secretary, Julian Lazalde Psihas
Auditors: Galaz, Yamazaki, Ruiz Urquiza, S.C.

LOCATIONS

HQ: Southern Copper Corp
1440 East Missouri Avenue, Suite 160, Phoenix, AZ 85014
Phone: 602 264-1375   **Fax:** 602 264-1397
Web: www.southerncoppercorp.com

HISTORICAL FINANCIALS

Company Type: Public

Income Statement

FYE: December 31

	REVENUE ($ mil.)	NET INCOME ($ mil.)	NET PROFIT MARGIN	EMPLOYEES
12/18	7,097	1,543	21.7%	13,899
12/17	6,655	729	10.9%	13,140
12/16	5,380	777	14.4%	13,414
12/15	5,046	736	14.6%	13,024
12/14	5,788	1,333	23.0%	12,735
Annual Growth	**5.2%**	**3.7%**	**—**	**2.2%**

2018 Year-End Financials

Debt ratio: 41.00%	No. of shares (mil.): 773
Return on equity: 24.00%	Dividends
Cash ($ mil.): 845	Yield: 5.0%
Current ratio: 3.00	Payout: 70.0%
Long-term debt ($ mil.): 5,960	Market value ($ mil.): 23,787

	STOCK PRICE ($) FY Close	P/E High/Low	PER SHARE ($) Earnings	Dividends	Book Value
12/18	31.00	29 15	2.00	1.00	8.00
12/17	47.00	51 34	1.00	1.00	8.00
12/16	32.00	35 22	1.00	0.00	8.00
12/15	26.00	36 26	1.00	0.00	7.00
12/14	28.00	21 16	2.00	0.00	7.00
Annual Growth	**2.2%**	**—**	**5.6%**	**32.1%**	**4.2%**

Southern Missouri Bancorp, Inc.

Southern Missouri Bancorp isÂ the holding company for Southern Bank (formerly Southern Missouri Bank and Trust) which serves localÂ residents and businesses in southeastern Missouri and northeastern ArkansasÂ through more than 10 branches.Â Residential mortgages account for the largest percentage of the bank's loan portfolio followed by commercial mortgages and business loans. Construction and consumer loans round out its lending activities. Deposit products include checking savings andÂ money market accounts CDs and IRAs. The bankÂ also offers financial planning and investment services. Originally chartered in 1887 Southern Bank acquired Arkansas-based Southern Bank of Commerce in 2009.

EXECUTIVES

Vice President, Mel Jackson
Vice President Loan Officer, Jon Holman
Vp, Tiffany Jenkins
Vice President Of Deposit Operations, Tiffany Beaton
Board Member, John Abercrombie
Auditors: BKD, LLP

LOCATIONS

HQ: Southern Missouri Bancorp, Inc.
2991 Oak Grove Road, Poplar Bluff, MO 63901
Phone: 573 778-1800
Web: www.bankwithsouthern.com

COMPETITORS

Bank of America	Regions Financial
Commerce Bancshares	U.S. Bancorp
IBERIABANK	UMB Financial

HISTORICAL FINANCIALS

Company Type: Public

Income Statement

FYE: June 30

	ASSETS ($ mil.)	NET INCOME ($ mil.)	INCOME AS % OF ASSETS	EMPLOYEES
06/19	2,214	29	1.3%	470
06/18	1,886	21	1.1%	415
06/17	1,708	16	0.9%	390
06/16	1,404	15	1.1%	342
06/15	1,300	14	1.1%	327
Annual Growth	**14.2%**	**20.6%**	**—**	**9.5%**

2019 Year-End Financials

Debt ratio: 1.00%
Return on equity: 13.00%
Cash ($ mil.): 36
Current ratio: —
Long-term debt ($ mil.): —

No. of shares (mil.): 9
Dividends
  Yield: 0.0%
  Payout: 17.0%
Market value ($ mil.): 324

	STOCK PRICE ($) FY Close	P/E High/Low		PER SHARE ($) Earnings	Dividends	Book Value
06/19	35.00	13	10	3.00	1.00	26.00
06/18	39.00	17	13	2.00	0.00	22.00
06/17	32.00	18	11	2.00	0.00	20.00
06/16	24.00	12	9	2.00	0.00	17.00
06/15	19.00	22	10	2.00	0.00	18.00
Annual Growth	16.6%			15.1%	11.2%	9.5%

Southern National Bancorp Of Virginia Inc

Southern National Bancorp of Virginia isÂ the holding company forÂ Sonabank which hasÂ some 20 locations inÂ central and northern Virginia and southern Maryland. Founded in 2005 the bank servesÂ small and midsized businesses their owners andÂ retail consumers. It offers standard deposit products includingÂ checking savings and money market accounts and CDs.Â TheÂ bank'sÂ lending is focused on commercial real estate single-family residential construction and single-family homes as well asÂ other types of consumer and commercial loans.Â In 2009 Southern National Bancorp acquired the failed Greater Atlantic Bank in an FDIC-assisted transaction; in 2012 it acquired the loans and deposits of HarVest Bank of Maryland.

EXECUTIVES

Senior Vice President, Linda Sandridge
Vice President Senior Lending Officer, Marie Leibson
Senior Vice President And Chief Credit Officer Of The Company And The Bank, Tom Baker
Assistant Vice President, Sharon Tyson
Auditors: Dixon Hughes Goodman LLP

LOCATIONS

HQ: Southern National Bancorp Of Virginia Inc
  6830 Old Dominion Drive, McLean, VA 22101
Phone: 703 893-7400
Web: www.sonabank.com

COMPETITORS

BB&T
Bank of America
Burke & Herbert Bank
Capital One
PNC Financial

SunTrust
Virginia Commerce
  Bancorp
Wells Fargo

HISTORICAL FINANCIALS

Company Type: Public

Income Statement

FYE: December 31

	ASSETS ($ mil.)	NET INCOME ($ mil.)	INCOME AS % OF ASSETS	EMPLOYEES
12/18	2,701	34	1.2%	348
12/17	2,614	2	0.1%	393
12/16	1,142	10	0.9%	162
12/15	1,036	9	0.9%	181
12/14	917	7	0.8%	173
Annual Growth	31.0%	45.7%	—	19.1%

2018 Year-End Financials

Debt ratio: 2.00%
Return on equity: 10.00%
Cash ($ mil.): 28
Current ratio: —
Long-term debt ($ mil.): —

No. of shares (mil.): 24
Dividends
  Yield: 2.0%
  Payout: 32.0%
Market value ($ mil.): 318

	STOCK PRICE ($) FY Close	P/E High/Low		PER SHARE ($) Earnings	Dividends	Book Value
12/18	13.00	13	9	1.00	0.00	14.00
12/17	16.00	142	118	0.00	0.00	13.00
12/16	16.00	20	14	1.00	0.00	10.00
12/15	13.00	17	15	1.00	1.00	10.00
12/14	11.00	19	16	1.00	1.00	9.00
Annual Growth	3.9%			21.9%	(14.5%)	11.6%

Southside Bancshares, Inc.

Southside Bancshares is the holding company for Southside Bank which boasts nearly 65 branches across East North and Central Texas with many around the cities of Tyler and Longview. About one-third of its branches are located in supermarkets (including Albertsons and Brookshire stores) and 40% are motor bank facilities. The bank provides traditional services such as savings money market and checking accounts CDs and other deposit products as well as trust and wealth management services. Real estate loans primarily residential mortgages make up about half of the company's loan portfolio which also includes business consumer and municipal loans. The bank has total assets exceeding $4.8 billion.

Operations

Southside generated 48% of its total revenue from loan interest in 2014 while interest income on taxable investment securities and mortgage-backed securities made up 16% and 19% respectively. About 9% of its revenue came from deposit service fees and another 2% came from trust income.

Geographic Reach

The bank's branches are located in East North and Central Texas. Its main markets are in East Texas the greater Fort Worth area and the greater Austin area. It is also an affiliate with more than 55000 foreign ATMs worldwide.

Sales and Marketing

Southside which staffed 813 employees at 2014's end serves individuals businesses municipal entities and non-profit organizations in local communities.

Financial Performance

Southside Bancshares' revenues and profits have been falling over the past several years despite consistent growth in loan and investment interest income mostly because the bank's gains on securities held-for-sale have declined.

The company's revenue dipped by 4% to $148.3 million in 2014 mostly due to a $5.6 million decline in gains on the sale of its AFS securities and a $2.8 million impairment of equity related to its investment in SFG Finance stemming from the sale of loans purchased by SFG and the repossessed assets.

Lower revenue and an uptick in loan loss provisions in 2014 caused Southside's net income to tumble 49% to $20.8 million for the year while its operating cash levels dipped by 6% to $56 million on lower cash earnings.

Strategy

Southside looks to acquire financial institutions to grow its loan business and expand its geographic reach outside of its existing markets. Its 2014 acquisition of OmniAmerican Bank alone helped boost its loan assets by more than 60% to $2.17 billion while adding 14 branches in a new market (Dallas/Fort Worth).

To grow its deposits and deepen its presence in the markets it serves the company has also been expanding its network of banking locations — both in-store and full-service branches.

Mergers and Acquisitions

In December 2014 the company acquired OmniAmerican Bank to boost its loan business and expand its footprint to the Dallas area. The deal added 14 full-service branches in the 12-county Dallas/Fort Worth metroplex and more than $763 million in new loan business.

EXECUTIVES

Senior Executive Vice President, Jeryl Story
President And Ceo Southside Bancshares And Southside Bank, Lee R. Gibson, age 62, $493,325 total compensation
Regional President North Texas Southside Bank, Tim Carter, age 64
Regional President Central Texas Southside Bank, Peter M. Boyd, age 63, $435,510 total compensation
Evp And Chief Credit Officer Southside Bank, Earl W. (Bill) Clawater, age 65, $265,000 total compensation
Evp And Chief Analytics Officer Southside Bank And Company Secretary, Brian K. McCabe, age 58, $228,385 total compensation
Regional President East Texas Southside Bank, Tim Alexander, age 62
Evp And Cfo, Julie N. Shamburger, age 56
Assistant Vice President Marketing, Jill Payne
Assistant Vice President, Julie A Brown
Vice President, Jeff Quesenberry
Vice President, Cindy Davis
Senior Vice President, Michael Custer
Senior Vice President, Kim Partin
Vice President Branch Manager, Tara Suttle
Executive Vice President, Debra Rutledge
Vp Of Information Technology, Gina Heppel
Senior Vice President, Zelton Harvey
Senior Vice President, Doug Cassidy
Vice President, Julie Hunter
Assistant Vice President, Tanya Merritt
Senior Vice President, Mary Mclarry
Vp Internal Audit, Misty de Wet
Vice President Business Services, Grant Williams
Senior Vice President, Landon Brim
Senior Vice President Loan Operations, Krystyna Alexander
Vp Sr. Credit Analyst, Ken Hetherington
Vp Commercial Lending, Ryan Reeve
Executive Vice President, Brad Browder

Vice President Special Assets, Ginger Hines
Vp Mortgage Loan Officer, Gary Gardner
Assistant Vice President Project Management, Niki Hughes
Vice President, Bradan Myrick
Vice Chairman, John R. (Bob) Garrett, age 66
Chairman, W.D. (Joe) Norton, age 82
Board Member, Elaine Anderson
Auditors: Ernst & Young LLP

LOCATIONS

HQ: Southside Bancshares, Inc.
1201 S. Beckham Avenue, Tyler, TX 75701
Phone: 903 531-7111
Web: www.southside.com

PRODUCTS/OPERATIONS

2014 Sales

	$ mil.	% of total
Interest		
Loans	71	48
Mortgage-backed & related securities	28	19
Investment securities	25	16
Other	0	-
Non-interest		
Deposit services	15	9
Gain on sale of securities	3	2
Trust income	3	2
Back owned life insurance income	1	1
Gain on sale of loans	0	-
Other	4	3
Adjustments	(2.8)	-
Total	**148**	**100**

COMPETITORS

Bank of America
Capital One
East Texas Financial
Jacksonville Bancorp of Illinois
Regions Financial

HISTORICAL FINANCIALS

Company Type: Public

Income Statement				FYE: December 31
	ASSETS ($ mil.)	NET INCOME ($ mil.)	INCOME AS % OF ASSETS	EMPLOYEES
12/18	6,123	74	1.2%	820
12/17	6,498	54	0.8%	855
12/16	5,564	49	0.9%	679
12/15	5,162	44	0.9%	683
12/14	4,807	21	0.4%	813
Annual Growth	6.2%	37.3%	—	0.2%

2018 Year-End Financials

Debt ratio: 3.00%
Return on equity: 10.00%
Cash ($ mil.): 111
Current ratio: —
Long-term debt ($ mil.): —

No. of shares (mil.): 34
Dividends
  Yield: 4.0%
  Payout: 62.0%
Market value ($ mil.): 1,071

	STOCK PRICE ($) FY Close	P/E High/Low		PER SHARE ($) Earnings	Dividends	Book Value
12/18	32.00	17	14	2.00	1.00	22.00
12/17	34.00	21	17	2.00	1.00	22.00
12/16	38.00	21	11	2.00	1.00	18.00
12/15	24.00	19	15	2.00	1.00	16.00
12/14	29.00	36	26	1.00	1.00	16.00
Annual Growth	2.4%	—	—	21.6%	9.3%	8.6%

Southwest Airlines Co

EXECUTIVES

Chb-Ceo, Gary C Kelly
V Chb*, Ron Ricks
Pres, Thomas M Nealon
Coo, Michael G Van De Ven
Exec V Pres-Cfo, Tammy Romo
Exec V Pres-Cro, Andrew M Watterson
Cto, Tom Merritt
Evp-Chief Legal & Reg Officer, Mark R Shaw
Managing Director, Dave Harvey
Vp Supply Chain Mngt, Stacy Malphurs
Vp Marketing, Bill Tierney
Auditors: Ernst & Young LLP

LOCATIONS

HQ: Southwest Airlines Co
P.O. Box 36611, Dallas, TX 75235-1611
Phone: 214 792-4000   **Fax:** 214 792-5015
Web: www.southwest.com

COMPETITORS

Alaska Air
American Airlines Group
Delta Air Lines
Frontier Airlines
JetBlue
US Airways
United Continental

HISTORICAL FINANCIALS

Company Type: Public

Income Statement				FYE: December 31
	REVENUE ($ mil.)	NET INCOME ($ mil.)	NET PROFIT MARGIN	EMPLOYEES
12/19	22,428	2,300	10.3%	60,800
12/18	21,965	2,465	11.2%	58,800
12/17	21,171	3,488	16.5%	56,100
12/16	20,425	2,244	11.0%	53,500
12/15	19,820	2,181	11.0%	49,583
Annual Growth	3.1%	1.3%	—	5.2%

2019 Year-End Financials

Debt ratio: 10.00%
Return on equity: 23.00%
Cash ($ mil.): 2,548
Current ratio: 1.00
Long-term debt ($ mil.): 1,846

No. of shares (mil.): 519
Dividends
  Yield: 1.0%
  Payout: 16.0%
Market value ($ mil.): 28,019

	STOCK PRICE ($) FY Close	P/E High/Low		PER SHARE ($) Earnings	Dividends	Book Value
12/19	54.00	14	11	4.00	1.00	19.00
12/18	46.00	15	10	4.00	1.00	18.00
12/17	65.00	11	9	6.00	0.00	18.00
12/16	50.00	14	10	4.00	0.00	14.00
12/15	43.00	15	10	3.00	0.00	11.00
Annual Growth	5.8%	—	—	6.9%	25.2%	13.6%

SpartanNash Co.

Grocery wholesaler and retailer SpartanNash distributes some 60000 nationally branded and private-label products to more than 2100 independent grocery retail locations across all 50 US states through some 20 distribution centers. It also services national retailers such as Family Dollar. In addition the company distributes goods to 600- plus US military commissaries and exchanges in the US and several other countries. On the retail side SpartanNash operates about 160 supermarkets under the Family Fare Supermarkets D&W Fresh Market VG's Food and Pharmacy Martin's and Sun Mart banners among others. The company traces its roots to 1917.

HISTORY

Making dinner in the early 1900s often required several shopping stops: the grocer for canned goods a butcher for meat and yet another place for produce. Eventually the big grocery chains began offering one-stop shopping not to mention better prices due to greater buying power. Worrying about how to compete in 1917 approximately 100 small grocers met in Grand Rapids Michigan to discuss organizing a cooperative; almost half of those formed the Grand Rapids Wholesale Grocery Co. The stores remained independent operating under different names but achieving economies of scale and volume buying through the co-op. They also began developing a variety of services for member stores. Sales topped $1 million in 1934.

Over the years the company expanded beyond its Grand Rapids origins. In 1950 it formed subsidiary United Wholesale which served independent grocers on a cash-and-carry basis. It acquired the Grand Rapids Coffee Company in 1953. The next year the co-op launched its first private-label item Spartan Coffee with a green Spartan logo reminiscent of the Michigan State University mascot. The company changed its name to Spartan Stores in 1957.

Spartan Stores entered retailing in the early 1970s when it bought 19 Harding's stores. It became a for-profit company in 1973 but continued to provide rebates to customers based on their purchases. Spartan Stores began offering insurance to its customers in 1979.

Concerned about the direction of the company customers named Patrick Quinn formerly a VP at a small chain of grocery stores as president and CEO in 1985. To focus on the wholesale business and to avoid any appearance of conflict of interest in both supplying member stores and operating competing stores Spartan Stores sold its 23 retail stores between 1987 and 1994 giving customer stores the first option on them. It entered the convenience store wholesale business with its 1987 acquisition of L&L/Jiroch. Two years later the co-op acquired Associated Grocers of Michigan (later known as Capistar closed in 1996).

Sales topped $2 billion in 1991. Spartan Stores expanded its convenience store operations in 1993 by buying wholesaler J.F. Walker. Despite record sales in 1996 a $46 million restructuring charge that included extensive technological improvements led to a $21.7 million loss the largest in the company's history. The following year Jim Meyer who had joined Spartan Stores in 1973 replaced the retiring Quinn as president and CEO. Also in 1997 the company stopped giving its customers rebates finally doing away with the last remnants of its co-op years.

To keep Michigan customers out of the clutches of its wholesaling rivals Spartan Stores re-entered retailing in 1999 by acquiring eight Ashcraft's Markets. It bought 13 Family Fare stores and 23 Glen's grocery stores that year. In early 2000 the company sold off its insurance business. Later that year Spartan Stores acquired food and drug chain Seaway Food Town (Michigan and Ohio) for about $180 million and began publicly trading.

In 2001 the company purchased longtime customer Prevo's Family Markets a supermarket chain with 10 stores in western Michigan. In an effort to reduce debt and improve profitability in mid-2002 the company announced plans to close its Food

Town stores which suffered from competitors such as Meier Kroger and Farmer Jack's. (By mid-2003 Spartan had sold the last of its 26 Food Town stores. Spartan Stores' retail operations had accounted for about 40% of the company's sales.)

In 2003 Spartan Stores sold seven shopping centers in Michigan for $46 million as part of its strategy to sell noncore properties and focus on its retail and distributions businesses. That year James Meyer retired as president and CEO of Spartan Stores and was succeeded by Craig Sturken a former executive of the Great Atlantic & Pacific Tea Company. Later the company sold convenience store suppliers L&L/Jiroch and J.F. Walker to Knoxville Tennessee-based distributor H.T. Hackney Co.

Spartan Stores sold the assets of United Wholesale Grocery Co. a privately held firm in Michigan for about $10 million in 2004. The sale marked Spartan's exit from the convenience store distribution business. The company also closed or sold all of its Food Town stores for $42.1 million.

In 2005 the company opened three fuel centers in Michigan under the Family Fare Quick Stops and Glen's Quick Stop banners. The company acquired D&W Food Centers the following year and purchased about 20 stores from G&R Felpausch in 2007. Spartan Stores' retail expansion continued in 2008 when it acquired more than 15 stores from V.G.'s Food Center. Sturken stepped down as CEO that year and was replaced by Dennis Eidson. In early 2011 Sturken took a less responsible role as chairman and advisor as he looked to transition out of the business.

EXECUTIVES

Vp Information Technology And Cio, David deS. (Dave) Couch, age 68, $205,920 total compensation
President And Ceo, David M. (Dave) Staples, age 56, $600,000 total compensation
Evp Retail Operations, Theodore C. (Ted) Adornato, age 65, $369,308 total compensation
Evp And Cfo, Mark E. Shamber, age 51
Evp Merchandising And Marketing, Larry Pierce, age 64
Evp Chief Legal Officer And President Mdv, Kathleen M. (Kathy) Mahoney, age 64, $415,000 total compensation
Evp; Ceo Caito Foods, Bob Kirch
Vice President Sales Great Lakes Region, Jim Gohsman
Vice President Corporate Affairs, Jeanne Norcross
Divisional Vice President Of West, Bruce Emery
Vice President South Heartland Regions, Joe Hermes
Vice President Logistics Military And National Accounts Logistics, Mitch Cadlo
Vice President Of Inventory Management, Jason Burnett
Senior Vice President And General Manager, Pat Weslow
Vice President Of Marketing, Brian Holt
Senior Vice President Supply Chain, Tom Lee
Chairman, Dennis Eidson, age 65
Treasurer, Bill Jacobs
Auditors: DELOITTE & TOUCHE LLP

LOCATIONS

HQ: SpartanNash Co.
850 76th Street, S.W., P.O. Box 8700, Grand Rapids, MI 49516
Phone: 616 878-2000
Web: www.spartannash.com

COMPETITORS

Alex Lee	IGA
Associated Wholesale	Kroger
Grocers	McLane
C&S Wholesale	Meijer
Coastal Pacific Food	Miner's
Distributors Inc.	S. Abraham & Sons
Core-Mark	SUPERVALU
Costco Wholesale	Wal-Mart

HISTORICAL FINANCIALS
Company Type: Public

Income Statement
FYE: December 29

	REVENUE ($ mil.)	NET INCOME ($ mil.)	NET PROFIT MARGIN	EMPLOYEES
12/18	8,065	34	0.4%	14,000
12/17	8,128	(53)	—	14,800
12/16*	7,735	57	0.7%	14,700
01/16	7,652	63	0.8%	15,200
01/15	7,916	59	0.7%	16,100
Annual Growth	0.5%	(13.0%)		(3.4%)

*Fiscal year change

2018 Year-End Financials

Debt ratio: 35.00%	No. of shares (mil.): 36
Return on equity: 5.00%	Dividends
Cash ($ mil.): 19	Yield: 0.0%
Current ratio: 2.00	Payout: 77.0%
Long-term debt ($ mil.): 680	Market value ($ mil.): 607

	STOCK PRICE ($) FY Close	P/E High/Low	Earnings	PER SHARE ($) Dividends	Book Value
12/18	17.00	29 18	1.00	1.00	20.00
12/17	27.00	— —	(1.00)	1.00	20.00
12/16*	40.00	26 12	2.00	1.00	22.00
01/16	22.00	20 13	2.00	1.00	21.00
01/15	26.00	17 12	2.00	0.00	20.00
Annual Growth	(10.1%)	— —	(12.0%)	10.7%	(0.0%)

*Fiscal year change

SPECTRUM HEALTH SYSTEM

EXECUTIVES

Pres, Richard C Breon
Svp-Cfo, Matthew Cox
Coordinator, Josh Miller
Administrative Director, Larry Genzink
Director, Cynthia Pollock
Fleet Staff, Greg Elderkin
Administrator, Jodi Scully
Director, Alan Kranzo
Project Manager, Amy Robertson
Software Developer, Brett Vanderhaar
Neurologist, Jason Umfleet

LOCATIONS

HQ: SPECTRUM HEALTH SYSTEM
100 MICHIGAN ST NE, GRAND RAPIDS, MI 495032560
Phone: 616 391-1774
Web: WWW.SPECTRUMHEALTH.ORG

COMPETITORS

Ascension Health	HealthPlus of Michigan
Blue Cross Blue Shield	McLaren Bay
of Michigan	McLaren Health Care

Borgess Health	Mercy Health Hackley
Bronson Battle Creek	Munson Healthcare
Bronson Health Care	OmniCare Health Plan
CareSource	Sheridan Community
Covenant HealthCare	Hospital
Great Lakes Health	Total Health Care
Plan	Zeeland Community
Hayes Green Beach	Hospital
Memorial Hospital	
Health Alliance Plan	
of Michigan	

HISTORICAL FINANCIALS
Company Type: Private

Income Statement
FYE: June 30

	REVENUE ($ mil.)	NET INCOME ($ mil.)	NET PROFIT MARGIN	EMPLOYEES
06/18	6,004	333	5.5%	16,996
06/17	5,681	357	6.3%	—
06/10	1,446	143	9.9%	—
06/09	1,266	0	—	—
Annual Growth	18.9%	—	—	—

Spirit AeroSystems Holdings Inc

EXECUTIVES

Pres-Ceo, Thomas C Gentile
Chb, Robert Johnson
Sr V Pres-Chief ADM Officer, Samantha J Marnick
Sr V Pres-Cfo, Jose Garcia
Sr V Pres-Chief Technology & Q, John Pilla
Sr V Pres-Cco-General Counsel-, Stacy Cozad
Sr V Pres Dfnce Prgrms, Krisstie Kondrotis
Sr V Pres-Gen Mgr, Michelle J Lohmeier
Sr V Pres Fabrication & Supply, Ron Rabe
Tech Designer, Aaron Kitterman
Integrated Corrective Action T, Amy Bedard
Auditors: Ernst & Young LLP

LOCATIONS

HQ: Spirit AeroSystems Holdings Inc
3801 South Oliver, Wichita, KS 67210
Phone: 316 526-9000
Web: www.spiritaero.com

COMPETITORS

Airbus
Beechcraft
Boeing
Bombardier
Dassault Aviation
Embraer
Finmeccanica
Fuji Heavy Industries
GKN
Goodrich Corp.
Gulfstream Aerospace
Kawasaki Heavy Industries
Lockheed Martin
Mitsubishi Heavy Industries
Northrop Grumman
Saab AB
Snecma
Textron
Triumph Aerostructures - Vought Aircraft Division
Triumph Group
United Technologies

HISTORICAL FINANCIALS

Company Type: Public

Income Statement

	REVENUE ($ mil.)	NET INCOME ($ mil.)	NET PROFIT MARGIN	EMPLOYEES
12/18	7,222	617	8.5%	17,000
12/17	6,983	355	5.1%	15,500
12/16	6,793	470	6.9%	14,400
12/15	6,644	789	11.9%	15,200
12/14	6,799	359	5.3%	15,402
Annual Growth	1.5%	14.5%	—	2.5%

2018 Year-End Financials

Debt ratio: 33.00%
Return on equity: 41.00%
Cash ($ mil.): 774
Current ratio: 2.00
Long-term debt ($ mil.): 1,864

No. of shares (mil.): 105
Dividends
  Yield: 1.0%
  Payout: 8.0%
Market value ($ mil.): 7,603

	STOCK PRICE ($) FY Close	P/E High/Low		PER SHARE ($) Earnings	Dividends	Book Value
12/18	72.00	18	12	6.00	0.00	12.00
12/17	87.00	29	17	3.00	0.00	16.00
12/16	58.00	16	11	4.00	0.00	16.00
12/15	50.00	10	7	6.00	0.00	16.00
12/14	43.00	18	10	3.00	0.00	11.00
Annual Growth	13.8%	—	—	22.2%	—	0.5%

SPIRIT REALTY CAPITAL, INC.

EXECUTIVES

Pres-Ceo, Jackson Hsieh
Exec V Pres-Cfo, Phillip D Joseph Jr
Exec V Pres-Chief Acquisitions, Boyd Messmann
Exec V Pres Asset Management, Mark L Manheimer
Sr V Pres-Chief Hr Officer, Michelle M Greenstreet
Sr V Pres-Cao, Prakash J Parag
Chb, Richard I Gilchrist
Evp-Cfo, Michael Hughes
Asset Management Analyst, Charlie Bernet
Accounts Payable Specialist, Carina Cabalitasan
Information Technology Directo, Colin Lane
Auditors: ERNST & YOUNG LLP DALLAS TEX

LOCATIONS

HQ: SPIRIT REALTY CAPITAL, INC.
  2727 N HARWOOD ST STE 300, DALLAS, TX
  752012407
Phone: 480 606-0820
Web: WWW.SPIRITREALTY.COM

HISTORICAL FINANCIALS

Company Type: Private

Income Statement

FYE: December 31

	ASSETS ($ mil.)	NET INCOME ($ mil.)	INCOME AS % OF ASSETS	EMPLOYEES
12/17	7,264	77	1.1%	71
12/16	7,678	97	1.3%	—
12/14	8,017	(34)	—	—
12/13	7,231	2	0.0%	—
Annual Growth	0.1%	160.4%	—	—

Sprint Corp (New)

EXECUTIVES

Branch Manager, Mark Kline
Manager, Scott North
Manager, Paul Hall
Auditors: Deloitte & Touche LLP

LOCATIONS

HQ: Sprint Corp (New)
  6200 Sprint Parkway, Overland Park, KS 66251
Phone: 913 794-1091
Web: www.sprint.com

HISTORICAL FINANCIALS

Company Type: Public

Income Statement

FYE: March 31

	REVENUE ($ mil.)	NET INCOME ($ mil.)	NET PROFIT MARGIN	EMPLOYEES
03/19	33,600	(1,943)	—	28,500
03/18	32,406	7,389	22.8%	30,000
03/17	33,347	(1,206)	—	28,000
03/16	32,180	(1,995)	—	30,000
03/15	34,532	(3,345)	—	31,000
Annual Growth	(0.7%)	—	—	(2.1%)

2019 Year-End Financials

Debt ratio: 47.00%—
Return on equity: (-7.00%)
Cash ($ mil.): 6,982
Current ratio: 1.00
Long-term debt ($ mil.): 35,366

Dividends
  Yield: —
  Payout: —
Market value ($ mil.): —

	STOCK PRICE ($) FY Close	P/E High/Low		PER SHARE ($) Earnings	Dividends	Book Value
03/19	6.00	—	—	(0.00)	0.00	6.00
03/18	5.00	5	3	2.00	0.00	7.00
03/17	9.00	—	—	(0.00)	0.00	5.00
03/16	3.00	—	—	(1.00)	0.00	5.00
03/15	5.00	—	—	(1.00)	0.00	5.00
Annual Growth	4.5%	—	—	—	—	3.9%

Sprouts Farmers Market Inc

A fast-growing natural foods retailer Sprouts Farmers Market operates more than 310 stores in about 20 US states including Arizona California Colorado Nevada New Mexico Oklahoma Texas and Utah. The stores (ranging from 28000 to 30000 sq. ft.) sell organic and local produce baked goods all-natural meats and seafood imported cheeses bulk foods and vitamins and supplements. Stores also offer more than 450 bins of bulk rice spices nuts and grains. Sprouts also sells its own private label brand of groceries.

Operations

Sprouts sources its products from more than 780 vendors and suppliers (domestically and internationally). KeHE Distributors LLC is its primary supplier of dry grocery and frozen food products making up nearly 35% of total purchases in Sprouts stores. Overall the company?s Perishable products (produce meat seafood deli bakery floral and dairy and dairy alternatives) account for about 60% of the company?s revenue. The remainder is generated from Non-Perishable goods (grocery vitamins and supplements bulk items frozen foods beer and wine and natural health and body care).

Geographic Reach

Sprouts operates more than 310 stores in nearly 20 US states. Over 35% of its stores are located in California while another over 35% of stores are spread fairly evenly across the states of Arizona Colorado and Texas. The remaining Sprouts stores are located in the states of Alabama Florida Georgia Kansas Maryland Missouri Nevada New Mexico Oklahoma North Carolina Pennsylvania South Carolina Tennessee Washington and Utah.

Sales and Marketing

Sprouts touts its position as the value-oriented neighborhood grocery store for natural and organic products through a marketing and promotional strategy that includes print (flyers and newspaper inserts) digital and social media platforms. The chain sends about 20 million weekly advertisement circulars that focus on product education and offerings to entice the customer and also uses local radio television and billboards to promote sales and support its brand image.

Financial Performance

Sprouts has seen soaring revenue growth in recent years thanks to the grocers' aggressive expansion and the continued popular demand for organic food in the US. Its annual revenues have risen more than 75% since 2014. Revenue increased to $5.2 billion in fiscal 2018 an approximately 12% increase from the year prior. The increase was driven by solid performance by new stores opened in the previous year and same-store sales growth. Net income was $158.5 million in 2018 a slight increase from the $158.4 million in 2017. Selling general and administrative expenses grew 13% in fiscal 2018 to $1.4 billion primarily related to the 30 new stores that opened in 2018. Total cash at the end of 2018 was $2.2 million a decrease of $17 million compared to the prior year. Cash provided by operating activities was $294.4 million in 2018 while investing activities used $177.1 million mainly for capital expenditures and sales enhancing initiatives. Financing activities used another $134.5 million.

Strategy

Fast-growing Sprouts Farmers Market continues to boost its store count and extend its retail reach mostly through new store openings (though it will consider acquisitions in suitable target markets with acceptable terms and conditions).

The chain has increasingly accelerated its store expansion to successfully fuel growth over the past few years opening 30 stores in 2018. It plans for another approximately 30 new stores in 2019. Sprouts has been expanding into new states including Pennsylvania Washington and South Carolina in 2018 and Louisiana New Jersey and Virginia in 2019.

Capitalizing on the popularity of online ordering the retailer has seen its online grocery delivery sales grow more than 60% in the first quarter of 2019 year over year. Sprouts is also expanding its click-and-collect program which allows online ordering and store pickup of groceries.

Sprouts' private label line of groceries half of which are organic or non-GMO accounts for about 14% of the company's revenues. The company plans to grow its private label sales to 16% of sales by 2021.

The company has also launched a new store format that emphasizes its enhanced deli meat and seafood departments. Its new freestanding deli offers made-to-order sandwiches sushi made in the store and fresh juices.

EXECUTIVES

Cio, Daniel J. Bruni, age 61, $318,077 total compensation
Chief Operations Officer, Dan Sanders
President And Coo, James L. (Jim) Nielsen, age 47, $522,596 total compensation
Ceo, Amin N. Maredia, age 46, $644,309 total compensation
Chief Development Officer, Theodore E. (Ted) Frumkin, age 57, $292,942 total compensation
Cfo, Bradley S. (Brad) Lukow, age 55, $386,846 total compensation
Senior Vice President, Mark Miale
Vice President Store Operations Field Capability, Cindy Chikahisa
Vice President, Terry Gibbons
Vice President Human Resources, Gwynn Simpson
Vice President Of Produce And Bulk, Tom Foulds
Vice President Business Intelligence, Gaurav Narwani
Vice President Store Development, Seth Brown
Vice President Of Merchandising Services, Thomas Hurley
Vp And Controller, Robyn O'Brenden
Chairman, Joseph Fortunato
Auditors: PricewaterhouseCoopers LLP

LOCATIONS

HQ: Sprouts Farmers Market Inc
5455 East High Street, Suite 111, Phoenix, AZ 85054
Phone: 480 814-8016
Web: www.sprouts.com

2016 Stores

	No.
California	96
Texas	40
Arizona	32
Colorado	30
Georgia	12
Oklahoma	10
New Mexico	7
Nevada	6
Utah	5
Alabama	4
Kansas	4
Tennessee	4
Missouri	3
Total	**253**

PRODUCTS/OPERATIONS

Sales 2016

	% of total
Perishables	50
Non-Perishables	50
Total	**100**

Selected Product category

Bakery
Beer
Body care
Bulk items
Dairy
Dairy alternatives
Deli
Frozen foods
Grocery
Meat
Natural health &
Seafood
Vitamins and supplements
Wine

COMPETITORS

Bashas'
Costco Wholesale
H-E-B
Kroger
Natural Grocers by
Vitamin Cottage
Safeway
Target Corporation
Trader Joe's
Wal-Mart
Whole Foods

HISTORICAL FINANCIALS

Company Type: Public

Income Statement

FYE: December 30

	REVENUE ($ mil.)	NET INCOME ($ mil.)	NET PROFIT MARGIN	EMPLOYEES
12/18	5,207	159	3.0%	30,000
12/17*	4,665	158	3.4%	27,000
01/17	4,046	124	3.1%	24,000
01/16	3,593	129	3.6%	20,000
12/14	2,967	108	3.6%	17,000
Annual Growth	**15.1%**	**10.2%**	**—**	**15.3%**

*Fiscal year change

2018 Year-End Financials

Debt ratio: 35.00%
Return on equity: 26.00%
Cash ($ mil.): 2
Current ratio: 1.00
Long-term debt ($ mil.): 573

No. of shares (mil.): 125
Dividends
  Yield: —
  Payout: —
Market value ($ mil.): 2,898

	STOCK PRICE ($) FY Close	P/E High/Low		PER SHARE ($) Earnings	Dividends	Book Value
12/18	23.00	24	17	1.00	0.00	5.00
12/17*	24.00	21	15	1.00	0.00	5.00
01/17	19.00	35	23	1.00	0.00	5.00
01/16	27.00	46	23	1.00	0.00	5.00
12/14	33.00	55	36	1.00	0.00	5.00
Annual Growth	**(8.3%)**	**—**	**—**	**14.9%**	**—**	**1.1%**

*Fiscal year change

SSM HEALTH CARE CORPORATION

The mission of SSM Health began with five nuns who fled religious persecution in Germany in 1872 only to arrive in St. Louis in the midst of a smallpox epidemic. They formed their first hospital there in 1877. Today the Midwest-based not-for-profit system sponsored by the Franciscan Sisters of Mary owns some 25 acute care hospitals with about 4500 licensed beds; it also has management or affiliation agreements with a number of other area hospitals. Additionally the company offers more than 300 outpatient facilities including physicians' practices home care and hospice services post-acute facilities and an insurance company.

Operations

In southern Wisconsin SSM Health facilities include St. Clare Hospital in Baraboo St. Mary's Janesville Hospital in Janesville and St. Mary's Hospital in Madison. Southern Illinois locations include St. Mary's Good Samaritan Hospital in Mount Vernon and St. Mary's Hospital in Centralia. The company owns and operates about 10 hospitals in Missouri; these include Cardinal Glennon Children's Hospital and DePaul Hospital. Oklahoma hospitals include St. Anthony Hospital in Oklahoma City and St. Anthony Shawnee Hospital in Shawnee.

SSM Health has some 9500 physicians on its staff. The system has some 176000 inpatient admissions and some 1.6 million outpatient visits each year.

The system participates in a Medicare Accountable Care Organization (ACO). It also has a pharmacy benefit arm.

Geographic Reach

SSM Health's facilities are located in Illinois Missouri Oklahoma and Wisconsin.

Sales and Marketing

Managed care payments account for about half of SSM Health's net patient revenue before provision for uncollectible accounts; Medicare accounts for about 30% and Medicaid accounts for about 15%.

The system spent $20666 on advertising on 2016 up from $17956 in 2015.

Financial Performance

SSM Health's operating revenue increased 12% to $6.1 billion due largely to a rise in net patient service revenues and an increase in other revenue. Premiums earned and investment income also rose that year.

However operating expenses increased across most areas and the system reported a decrease in excess of revenues over expenses which fell 52% to $99.4 million. Similarly operating cash flow fell 51% to $220.4 million in 2016. Factors contributing to that drop included an increase in pension-related changes and in provisions for uncollectible accounts and bad debts.

Strategy

SSM Health often partners with other care providers which helps it expand without having to invest in new facilities from the ground up.

Like most health systems SSM has been challenged with lower government reimbursement rates. It is implementing a financial improvement initiative which includes some company layoffs.

Mergers and Acquisitions

SSM Health has been making a number of acquisitions to expand its network. For example in 2016 it doubled its stake in St. Clare Surgical Center to 60% and acquired the rest of Physicians Surgery Center at DePaul it didn't already own. SSM also took over the operations of about 25 health clinics located in Walgreens stores in Greater St. Louis.

In early 2018 the system acquired Agnesian HealthCare and Monroe Clinic (both based in Wisconsin) adding four hospitals eight post-acute facilities and several outpatient facilities.

EXECUTIVES

President And Ceo, William P. Thompson
Svp Finance, Kris A. Zimmer
President Hospital Operations, Chris Howard
Evp; President Health Care Delivery Finance And Integration, Gaurov Dayal
Svp Strategy Communications And Marketing, Paula J. Friedman
President Ssm St. Joseph Health Center, Mike Bowers
Evp; President Physician And Ambulatory Operations, Shane Peng
Chief Nursing Officer, Maggie Fowler
Svp And Cio, Phillip Loftus
President St. Maryâ's Hospital, Jon Rozenfeld
President Ssm Health At Home, Alison Ruehl
Auditors: DELOITTE & TOUCHE LLP ST LOU

LOCATIONS

HQ: SSM HEALTH CARE CORPORATION
10101 WOODFIELD LN # 100, SAINT LOUIS, MO 631322944
Phone: 314 994-7800
Web: WWW.SSMHEALTH.COM

PRODUCTS/OPERATIONS

Selected Facilities

Illinois
St. Mary's Good Samaritan (joint sponsorship with Felician Services two hospitals in Mt. Vernon and Centralia)

Missouri
St. Francis Hospital & Health Services (Maryville)
St. Mary's Health Center (Jefferson City)
SSM Cardinal Glennon Children's Medical Center (St. Louis)
SSM DePaul Health Center (Bridgeton)
SSM St. Clare Health Center (St. Louis)
SSM St. Joseph Health Center (St. Charles)
SSM St. Joseph Health Center (Wentzville)
SSM St. Joseph Hospital West (Lake St. Louis)
SSM St. Mary's Health Center (Richmond Heights)

Oklahoma
Bone & Joint Hospital (Oklahoma City)
Shawnee Medical Center Clinic (Shawnee)
St. Anthony Hospital (Oklahoma City)
Unity Health Center (Shawnee)

Wisconsin
Boscobel Area Health Care (managed hospital and clinics Boscobel)
Columbus Community Hospital (affiliate Columbus)
Edgerton Hospital and Health Services (Edgerton)
St. Clare Hospital (Baraboo)
St. Clare Meadows Care Center (nursing home Madison)
St. Mary's Care Center (nursing home Madison)
St. Mary's Hospital (Madison)
St. Mary's Janesville Hospital (Janesville)
Stoughton Hospital (affiliate Stoughton)
Uplands Hill Health (affiliate hospital and nursing care Dodgeville)

COMPETITORS

Adventist Health System Sunbelt Healthcare
Advocate Health Care
Allina Hospitals
Ascension Health
BJC HealthCare
Carle Physician Group
Community Health Systems
HCA
Hospital Sisters Health System
Mayo Clinic
Mercy Health
Meriter Health Services
MetroSouth Medical
Rush System for Health
Tenet Healthcare
University of Wisconsin Hospital and Clinics
VITAS Healthcare

HISTORICAL FINANCIALS

Company Type: Private

Income Statement				FYE: December 31
	REVENUE ($ mil.)	NET INCOME ($ mil.)	NET PROFIT MARGIN	EMPLOYEES
12/17	6,497	246	3.8%	24,230
12/16	6,109	(31)	—	—
12/13	1,178	32	2.8%	—
Annual Growth	53.3%	65.9%	—	—

Stanley Black & Decker Inc

Stanley Black & Decker has all the tools of the trade. A leading global toolmaker the company generates more than two-thirds of sales from a plethora of tools (hand mechanics' power pneumatic hydraulic) and related accessories. In addition to its well-known namesake brands it sells other top brands such as Bostitch Mac Tools and DEWALT directly to consumers as well as through distributors home centers and mass-merchant distributors. Stanley Black & Decker also sells engineered fastening and infrastructure products to customers in the automotive manufacturing and oil & gas industries among others and designs and installs electronic security systems and automatic doors to commercial customers. It generates nearly half of sales outside the US.

Operations

Stanley Black & Decker operates its business through three segments: Tools & Storage (which generates about 70% of sales) Security (about 15%) and Industrial (about 15%).

The Tools & Storage segment includes professional and consumer power tools (saws drills grinders nail guns lawn mowers vacuums and cleaning tools) and accessories hand tools and storage products such as tool boxes and sawhorses. The products are mostly available via home centers hardware stores mass merchants and other retailers.

The company's Security segment includes Convergent Security Solutions which designs and installs electronic security systems and provides monitoring surveillance and other services and Mechanical Access Solutions which sells automatic doors. These products are primarily sold directly to commercial customers.

Stanley Black & Decker sells rivets inserts weld studs and other fastening products through its Industrial segment. The segment also includes infrastructure equipment used by the oil & gas industry and hydraulics tools and accessories.

Geographic Reach

Stanley Black & Decker operates primarily in the Americas Europe and Asia. The US is its largest market accounting for about 55% of sales. Europe led by France generates about a quarter of sales and Asia brings in about 10%.

Headquartered in New Britain Connecticut the company has major facilities for manufacturing distribution and sales in some 20 countries including locations in about 20 US states.

Sales and Marketing

The Tools & Storage segment sells its products to professional end users industrial users distributors and retail consumers. The majority of sales are distributed through retailers including home centers mass merchants hardware stores and retail lumber yards. US and international mass merchants and home centers collectively account for nearly 30% of sales; home improvement giant Lowe's accounts for just more than 10%.

Stanley Black & Decker markets it other products and services directly and through third-party distributors to customers in a host of industries including automotive manufacturing oil & gas electronics and aerospace.

Advertising cost was $123.3 million in 2017 compared to $124.1 million in 2016 and $101.7 million in 2015.

Financial Performance

Stanley Black & Decker has seen solid revenue and strong net income growth over the past five years as the company has pursued acquisitions and manufacturing and supply chain efficiencies. Revenue is up nearly 20% since 2013 and net income is up about 250%.

In 2017 the company reported revenue of $12.7 billion up 12% from the prior year. The results were driven almost entirely by the Tools & Storage segment fueled in equal parts by organic growth (innovative new products and a strong overall tool market) and acquisitions (mostly Newell).

Net income that year jumped more than 25% to $1.2 billion on the increased revenue and a gain on the sale of the company's mechanical security business.

Cash at the end of fiscal 2017 was $637 million a decrease of $494 million from the prior year. Cash from operations contributed $1.4 billion to the coffers while investing activities used $2.3 billion mainly for acquisitions. Financing activities added some $295 million because of proceeds from the issuance of preferred stock.

Strategy

Stanley Black & Decker's overarching strategy which it calls 22/22 Vision is the build to $22 billion in revenue by the year 2022. As part of that strategy the company is focused on industry geographic and customer diversification through both innovative organic growth and acquisitions.

Operational excellence and product innovation is enabled by its Stanley Fulfillment System (SFS 2.0) which resulted in the mid-2016 launch of the FlexVolt variable-voltage battery system that has helped power organic growth in the years since. Stanley Black & Decker continues to show its commitment to product innovation with increased research and developments costs (up 25% in 2017) and innovation center openings in Germany (Stanley Engineered Fastening Breakthrough Innovation Center) and the US (Futures Innovation Factory). An advanced manufacturing center which will test new technologies such as 3-D metal printing is opening in Connecticut in the second half of 2018. SFS 2.0 also enables cost-cutting with a focus on sales and operations planning (S&OP) operational lean complexity reduction global supply management and order-to-cash excellence.

Merger and acquisition activity has played a huge role in Stanley Black & Decker's buildup over the past decade-plus and will continue to be important in getting the company to $22 billion in revenue. It started its acquisition spree in 2002 and has made some $9 billion in purchases since then adding new products to its portfolio and expanding its market and geographic reach. Along the way the company has divested non-core and/or low-margin businesses including its early 2017 disposal of the mechanical security business (which included commercial hardware brands Best Access phi Precision and GMT).

Mergers and Acquisitions

In late 2018 Stanley Black & Decker announced that it would acquire 20% of outdoor power equipment maker MTD Products for $234 million. The deal wihch includes the option of purchasing the rest of MTD beginning in July 2021 strengthens the company's presence in the growing lawn and garden market.

Earlier that year the company closed on the $440 million purchase of Nelson Fastener Systems from the Doncasters Group in the UK. The deal brings a host of complementary products and expands the company's presence in general industrial end markets. Also that year it announced plans to buy International Equipment Solutions Attachments Group (IES Attachments) for $690 million. IES Attachments makes performance-driven heavy equipment attachment tools for off-highway applications under such names as Paladin Genesis and Pengo; the deal expands Stanley Black & Decker's presence in industrial markets.

The prior year Stanley Black & Decker acquired Sears Holdings Corp.'s iconic Craftsman tool brand for $900 million. The acquisition expands Black & Decker's product line up and allows the company to increase sales by expanding distribution of Craftsman tools into more international markets. Also in 2017 Stanley Black & Decker bought the tools business (Irwin Lenox) from consumer products company Newell Brands for $1.95 billion.

Company Background

Stanley Black & Decker traces its roots back to 1843 when Frederick Stanley opened a bolt shop in a converted early-19th-century armory in New Britain Connecticut. In 1852 he teamed with his brother and five friends to form The Stanley Works to cast form and manufacture various types of metal. In 2010 it merged with The Black & Decker Corporation a company founded by S. Duncan Black and Alonzo G. Decker and incorporated in Maryland in 1910 and changed its name to Stanley Black & Decker.

EXECUTIVES

President And Ceo, James M. (Jim) Loree, age 60, $992,500 total compensation

Vp And Cio, Rhonda O. Gass, age 55

Svp And Group Executive Global Tools And Storage, Jeffery D. (Jeff) Ansell, age 52, $660,833 total compensation

Svp And Cfo, Donald (Don) Allan, age 54, $671,667 total compensation

Svp And President Global Emerging Markets, Jaime A. Ramirez, age 51, $425,000 total compensation

President Sales And Marketing Global Tools And Storage, John H. A. Wyatt, age 60, $541,667 total compensation

President Hand Tools Accessories And Storage, Lee B. McChesney, age 47

Cto, Mark T Maybury

President Stanley Security Europe, Aru Bala

President Stanley Oil And Gas, Pete Morris

President Asia, Yingli (Christine) Yan

President Power Tools And Equipment Global Tools And Storage, Frank A. Mannarino

President Emerging Markets Group, Bart Muller

President Sales And Marketing Global Tools And Storage, James P. OÁ'Sullivan

President Hydraulics, J. Douglas Redpath

National Account Manager, Allison Lawrence

Vice President, Debi Geyer

Vice President Compensation Benefits And Hris, Michele Webster

Vice President Manufatura Latin America, Domingos Dragone

Vp Sales, Kirk Starr

Vice President And Chief Accounting Officer, Jocelyn Belisle

Vice President And Managing Director Europe And Asia, Ned Urschel

National Account Manager, John Murray

Vp Labor And Employee Relations, Jim Tallaksen

Vp Hr, Carlos Apollonio

Vice President Real Estate, Gregory Smulski

National Account Manager, Dennis Kellagher

Vice President Assistant, Catherine Ennis

Vice President Digital Product Innovation And Marketing, Robert Ross

Vp Environment Health Safety And Corporate Social Responsibility, Deb Geyer

Vice President Of North American Sales, Martin Guay

Vp Corporate Tax And Treasurer, Michael Bartone

Vp Public Affairs, Tim Perra

National Account Manager, Daniel Wegrzyn

National Account Manager, Dan Costanzo

Vp Business Development, Marty Guay

Senior Vice President Human Resources, Joseph Voelker

Senior Vice President General Counsel, Janet M Link

Vice President And General Manager, Jim Gillis

National Sales Manager, Dan Miller

National Sales Manager, Jevri Christanto

Vice President Of Human Resources, Rodney Hobbs

National Account Manager, Greg Glenn

Vice President And General Manager, Saad Malik

Vice President Engineering, Colin Dyke

Vice President Global Operations And Integrated Supply Chain Spectrum Brands, David Booher

Chairman, George W. Buckley, age 72

Board Member, Carlos Cardoso

Executive Board Member, Stanley Doors

Board Member, James Scholefield

Board Of Directors, Robert Blackburn

Auditors: Ernst & Young LLP

LOCATIONS

HQ: Stanley Black & Decker Inc
1000 Stanley Drive, New Britain, CT 06053
Phone: 860 225-5111   **Fax:** 860 827-3895
Web: www.stanleyblackanddecker.com

2017 Sales

	$ mil.	% of total
Americas		
US	6,916	54
Canada	578	5
Other	774	6
Europe		
France	609	5
Other	2,742	21
Asia	1,128	9
Total	**12,747**	**100**

PRODUCTS/OPERATIONS

2017 Sales

	$ mil.	% of total
Tools & Storage	8,862	70
Security	1,939	15
Industrial	1,946	15
Total	**12,747**	**100**

Product and Services

Commercial Security
Fastening Solutions
Hospital & Healthcare Services
Infrastructure Products
Pipeline Services
Tools & Storage

Selected Brand Names

Black & Decker
Bostitch
Craftsman
DEWALT
FatMax
LaBounty
Mac Tools
Proto
Stanley
Vidmar

COMPETITORS

ASSA ABLOY	Klein Tools
Atlas Copco	Makita
Fortune Brands Home & Security	Robert Bosch Tool
Husqvarna	Snap-on
Illinois Tool Works	Techtronic

HISTORICAL FINANCIALS

Company Type: Public

Income Statement

FYE: December 29

	REVENUE ($ mil.)	NET INCOME ($ mil.)	NET PROFIT MARGIN	EMPLOYEES
12/18	13,982	605	4.3%	60,767
12/17	12,747	1,226	9.6%	57,765
12/16*	11,407	965	8.5%	54,023
01/16	11,172	884	7.9%	51,250
01/15	11,339	761	6.7%	50,400
Annual Growth	**5.4%**	**(5.6%)**	**—**	**4.8%**

*Fiscal year change

2018 Year-End Financials

Debt ratio: 22.00%	No. of shares (mil.): 151
Return on equity: 8.00%	Dividends
Cash ($ mil.): 289	Yield: 0.0%
Current ratio: 1.00	Payout: 65.0%
Long-term debt ($ mil.): 3,820	Market value ($ mil.): 17,979

	STOCK PRICE ($) FY Close	P/E High/Low		PER SHARE ($) Earnings	Dividends	Book Value
12/18	119.00	43	27	4.00	3.00	52.00
12/17	170.00	21	14	8.00	2.00	54.00
12/16*	115.00	19	14	7.00	2.00	42.00
01/16	107.00	18	15	6.00	2.00	38.00
01/15	96.00	20	16	5.00	2.00	41.00
Annual Growth	**5.5%**	**—**	**—**	**(4.3%)**	**6.0%**	**6.1%**

*Fiscal year change

Starbucks Corp.

Wake up and smell the coffee — Starbucks is everywhere. The world's #1 specialty coffee retailer Starbucks has more than 29300 coffee shops in 80 countries. The shops offer coffee drinks and food items as well as roasted beans coffee accessories and teas. Starbucks operates more than 15300 of its own shops which are located mostly in the US while licensees and franchisees operate roughly 14000 units worldwide (including many locations in shopping centers and airports). In addition Starbucks markets its coffee through grocery stores food service customers and licenses its brand for other food and beverage products. The US accounts for the majority of Starbucks' revenue.

HISTORY

Starbucks was founded in 1971 in Seattle by coffee aficionados Gordon Bowker Jerry Baldwin and Ziv Siegl who named the company for the coffee-loving first mate in Moby Dick and created its famous two-tailed siren logo. They aimed to sell the finest-quality whole bean and ground coffees. By 1982 Starbucks had five retail stores and was selling coffee to restaurants and espresso stands in Seattle. That year Howard Schultz joined Starbucks to manage retail sales and marketing. In 1983 Schultz traveled to Italy and was struck by the popularity of coffee bars. He convinced Starbucks' owners to open a downtown Seattle coffee bar in 1984. It was a success; Schultz left the company the following year to open his own coffee bar Il Giornale which served Starbucks coffee.

Frustrated by its inability to control quality Starbucks sold off its wholesale business in 1987. Later that year Il Giornale acquired Starbucks' retail operations for $4 million. (Starbucks' founders held on to their other coffee business Peet's Coffee & Tea.) Il Giornale changed its name to Starbucks Corporation prepared to expand nationally and opened locations in Chicago and Vancouver. In 1988 the company published its first mail-order catalog.

Starbucks lost money in the late 1980s as it focused on expansion (it tripled its number of stores to 55 between 1987 and 1989). Schultz brought in experienced managers to run Starbucks' stores. In 1991 it became the nation's first privately owned company to offer stock options to all employees.

In 1992 Starbucks went public and set up shops in Nordstrom's department stores. The following year it began operating cafes in Barnes & Noble bookstores. The company had nearly 275 locations by the end of 1993. Starbucks inked a deal in 1994 to provide coffee to ITT/Sheraton hotels (later acquired by Starwood Hotels & Resorts). The next year it capitalized on its popular in-house music selections by selling compact discs. Also in 1995 Starbucks joined with PepsiCo to develop a bottled coffee drink and agreed to produce a line of premium coffee ice cream with Dreyer's.

Starbucks expanded into Japan and Singapore in 1996. Also that year the company created Caffe Starbucks an online store located on AOL's marketplace. In 1997 Starbucks began testing sales of whole-bean and ground coffees in Chicago supermarkets.

In 1998 Starbucks expanded into the UK when it acquired that country's Seattle Coffee Company chain (founded in 1995) for about $86 million and converted its stores into Starbucks locations. It also announced plans to sell coffee in supermarkets nationwide through an agreement with Kraft Foods. In 1999 Starbucks bought Tazo an Oregon-based tea company as well as music retailer Hear Music and opened its first store in China. Schultz toned down his Internet plans in late 1999 after investors and analysts voiced skepticism.

In 2000 Schultz ceded the CEO post to president Orin Smith remaining chairman but focusing primarily on the company's global strategy. Starbucks jumpstarted its worldwide expansion the next year opening about 1100 stores worldwide including locations in a handful of new European countries such as Austria and Switzerland. It also spun off its Japanese operations as a public company. The following year the company opened its first shop in Spain and went on to open Starbucks locations in Greece and Germany. Later in 2002 it announced large-scale expansion plans in Mexico and Latin America.

The next year Starbucks acquired Seattle Coffee Company (and its Seattle's Best Coffee brand) from Popeyes for $72 million. The deal gave Starbucks an additional 150 coffee shops (as if it needed them) but more importantly it gave the coffee giant the Seattle's Best Coffee brand and wholesale coffee business. It also got something new out of the deal: franchised locations.

Starbucks was one of the first national retailers to jump on the Wi-Fi bandwagon teaming with Hewlett-Packard and Deutsche Telekom's T-Mobile unit to offer high-speed wireless Internet access at 1200 of its locations in the US London and Berlin. In 2004 Starbucks and Hewlett-Packard unveiled their Hear Music service which allows Starbucks customers to create custom music CDs in some locations. It later premiered the Hear Music channel on XM Satellite Radio (later SIRIUS XM Radio) and launched a new Hear Music CD-burning media bar (co-developed with HP) in selected stores.

In 2005 the company began offering a hot chocolate in its US and Canada markets and in conjunction with Jim Beam Brands (now Beam) it introduced Starbucks Coffee Liqueur and Starbucks Cream Liqueur. That year Starbucks signed agreements with Suntory in Japan and Uni-President in Taiwan to sell its ready-to-drink coffees in those countries. Additionally Smith retired as president and CEO in 2005; he was replaced by Starbucks' North American president Jim Donald.

The company acquired full ownership of joint ventures Coffee Partners Hawaii and Cafe del Caribe (Puerto Rican outlets) in 2006. While Starbucks continued to dominate the coffee business traffic at its stores began to decline in 2007. The company brought Schultz back as CEO in 2008 replacing Donald.

Starbucks acquired fruit and vegetable juice maker Evolution Fresh in 2011 for $30 million in cash. In December 2012 the company purchased Teavana Holdings Inc. for $620 million in cash. Teavana operates some 300 Heaven of Tea retail stores.

In 2012 Starbucks agreed to acquire San Francisco-based Bay Bread LLC and its La Boulange bakery brand. It made the purchase to try its hand in the French bakery market. The previous year Starbucks acquired fruit and vegetable juice maker Evolution Fresh for $30 million as part of an effort to push itself as a healthy lifestyle brand.

EXECUTIVES

Evp And Cto, Gerri Martin-Flickinger

President And Coo, Kevin R. Johnson, age 58, $576,923 total compensation

Group President Us And Americas, Clifford (Cliff) Burrows, age 60, $796,300 total compensation

Group President China And Asia/pacific Channel Development And Emerging Brands, John Culver, age 58, $633,300 total compensation

Svp And President Europe Middle East And Africa (emea), Martin Brok

Evp Us Retail Store Operations, Cosimo LaPorta

Evp And Global Chief Marketing Officer, Sharon Rothstein

Svp; President Teavana, Bernard Acoca

Chief Creative Officer; President Global Innovation, Arthur Rubinfeld, age 65, $484,058 total compensation

Evp Licensed Stores Us And Americas, Chris Carr

Svp Global Business, Lucy Lee Helm, $493,172 total compensation

Evp Public Affairs, Vivek Varma

Evp And Chief Partner Resources Officer, Scott Pitasky

Evp And Cfo, Scott H. Maw, $632,500 total compensation

Evp Global Coffee, Craig Russell

Svp; President Starbucks Canada, Rossann Williams

President Starbucks Global Channel Development, Michael Conway

Evp And Chief Digital Officer, Adam Brotman

Evp And Global Chief Strategy Officer, Matthew Ryan

President Starbucks Europe Middle East And Africa, Kris Engskov

President Starbucks China, Belinda Wong

Senior Vice President Deputy General Counsel Chief Ethics And Compliance Officer, Matthew Swaya

Senior Vice President Chief Design Officer, Liz Muller

Vice President And Assistant General Counsel, Mark Fordham

Vice President Global Sourcing And Supplier Relations, Jonathan Gardner

Vice President Of Partner Resources, Angel Yu

Senior Vice President Operations Services And U.s. Alignment, Denise Nelsen

Senior Vice President Food Evenings And Licensed Stores, Christine Barone

Senior Vice President Customer Relationship Management, Aimee Johnson

Vp Assistant General Counsel Global Commercial Marcom And Regulatory, Kenneth Wan

Vice President Operations Implementation, Steve Figliola

Vice President Global Operations Innovation, Dennis Mcgrath

Vp Payments And Cards, Ryan Records

Senior Vice President Partner Resources Global Retail, Angela Lis

Vice President, Pablo Arizmendi

Vice President Manager Director, Lesley Blyth

Senior Vice President Chief Procurement Officer Global Sourcing, Kelly Bengston

Vice President Software Engineering, Marianne Marck

Vice President Channel Operations, Jennifer Gamage

Vice President Global Coffee, Andrew Linnemann

National Account Manager, Hamilton Seale

Vice President Of Digital Products, Ben Straley

Vice President Operations Southeast Region, Sharon Powell

Regional Vice President Operations, Camille Hymes

Vice President, William Mcnichols

Senior Vice President Gbl Design And Construction Execution, Bill Transue

Vice President Corporate Facilities, Eric Jensen

Senior Vice President Research And Development Qandr, Mary Wagner

Vp Global Supply Chain Store Delivery, Tiffany Broderson

Vp Of Operations, Miguel Lozano

Vice President And Treasurer, Drew Wolff

Vice President Corp. Social Responsibility, Sue Mecklenburg

Senior Vice President Store Development And Design, Scott Keller

Vice President Zone Licensed Stores East, Lisa Compton

Senior Vice President Finance, David Chichester

Svp Siren Retail Operations, Katie Seawell

Gm And Vice President Latin America, Ricardo Rico

Vice President Of Global Public Affairs, Cathy Heseltine

Regional Vice President, Suzanne Dechant

Vice President Field Information Technology, Lisa Orchard

Vice President, James Koster

Vice President Global Learning, Stephen Krempl

Vice President, Doug Wayles

Senior Vice President Southeast Plains, Paul Twohig

Vice President Business Intelligence, Mike Manzano

Vice President, Sophie Hume

Senior Vice President Partner Resources U.s. And Americas, Marissa Andrada

Svp Global Strategy Insights And Analytics, Pam Greer

Vice President Of Sales Operations And Learning And Development Teavana, Catherine McCabe

Senior Vice President Public Affairs, Rajiv Chandrasekaran

Vice President Retail Technology, Courtney Kissler

Senior Vice President Infrastructure And Enablement, Jeff Wile

Senior Vice President Partner Resources And Human Resources, Lucy Hur

Senior Vice President Executive Creative Director Starbucks Global Creative, Leanne Fremar

Executive Vice President Global Supply Chain, Hans Melotte

Senior Vice President Global Integrated Logistics, Ash Walia

Divisional Senior Vice President East Division, Zeta Smith

Senior Vice President Engineering And Architecture Starbucks Technololgy, Tal Saraf

Senior Vice President Entrepreneur In Residence,
Richard Tait
Senior Vice President Corporate Development
And Business Alliances, Bill McNichols
Svp Global Coffee And Tea, Michelle Burns
Vice President Finance, Robert Dilworth
Vice President Global Engineering, Jeff Juneau
Senior Vice President Logistics And Us Retail
Supply Chain, Carl Mount
Vp Global Security And Resilience, Garrett Petraia
Senior Vice President Sirenideas, Mesh Gelman
Vice President Partner Resources, Heather Newton
Vp Partnerships, Maria Smith
Vice President Information Technology, Tammy
Green
Vice President Information Technology, Georg
Gorostiza
Co Managing Director At Starbucks, Matthew
Courtney
Vice President Store Development Support
Services, Ray Silverstein
Senior Vice President Global Supply Chain
Finance And Shared Services, Sena M Kwawu
Vice President Food Safety And Quality, Stephen P
Graham
Senior Vice President Supply Chain Finance And
Shared Services, Sena Kwawu
Vice President Business Systems Development,
Wouleta Ayele
Vice President Marketing, Rebekah Lyle
Senior Vice President U.s. Marketing, Emily Chang
Senior Vice President Global Total Rewards, Holly
May
Senior Vice President Deputy General Counsel
And Chief Ethics And Compliance Officer, Ashish
Mishra
Vice President Total Rewards, Julie Ann Overcash
Chairman And Ceo, Howard D. Schultz, age 66
Board Member, Jorgen Knudstorp
Auditors: DELOITTE & TOUCHE LLP

LOCATIONS

HQ: Starbucks Corp.
2401 Utah Avenue South, Seattle, WA 98134
Phone: 206 447-1575
Web: www.starbucks.com

2018 Sales

	% of total
Americas	68
China/Asia Pacific	18
EMEA	4
Channel Development	9
Corporate and Other	1
Total	**100**

PRODUCTS/OPERATIONS

2018 Sales

	$ mil.	% of total
Company-owned stores	19,690	80
Licensed stores	2,652	11
Other	2,377	9
Total	**24,720**	**100**

2018 Sales

	% of total
Beverage	59
Food	18
Package and single-serve coffees and teas	11
Other	12
Total	**100**

Brand Portfolio

Brand Portfolio
Starbucks Coffee
Seattle's Best Coffee
Teavana
Evolution Fresh
La Boulange
Ethos Water
Torrefazione Italia Coffee

Selected Products

Coffee
Handcrafted Beverages
Merchandise
Fresh Food

COMPETITORS

Cinnabon	Nestlé
Community Coffee	Panera Bread
Dunkin	The Coffee Bean
Einstein Noah	Tim Hortons
Restaurant Group	Whitbread
Farmer Bros.	illy
McDonald's	

HISTORICAL FINANCIALS

Company Type: Public

Income Statement

FYE: September 29

	REVENUE ($ mil.)	NET INCOME ($ mil.)	NET PROFIT MARGIN	EMPLOYEES
09/19	26,509	3,599	13.6%	346,000
09/18*	24,720	4,518	18.3%	291,000
10/17	22,387	2,885	12.9%	277,000
10/16	21,316	2,818	13.2%	254,000
09/15	19,163	2,757	14.4%	238,000
Annual Growth	**8.5%**	**6.9%**	**—**	**9.8%**

*Fiscal year change

2019 Year-End Financials

Debt ratio: 58.00%
Return on equity: ***,***.**%
Cash ($ mil.): 2,687
Current ratio: 1.00
Long-term debt ($ mil.): 11,167

No. of shares (mil.): 1,185
Dividends
  Yield: 0.0%
  Payout: 29.0%
Market value ($ mil.): 104,683

	STOCK PRICE ($) FY Close	P/E High/Low		PER SHARE ($) Earnings	Dividends	Book Value
09/19	88.00	34	19	3.00	1.00	(5.00)
09/18*	57.00	19	15	3.00	1.00	1.00
10/17	54.00	32	26	2.00	1.00	4.00
10/16	54.00	33	28	2.00	1.00	4.00
09/15	58.00	53	26	2.00	1.00	4.00
Annual Growth	**11.1%**	**—**	**—**	**12.5%**	**22.5%**	**—**

*Fiscal year change

Starwood Property Trust Inc.

Starwood Property Trust hopes to shine brightly in the world of mortgages. A real estate investment trust (REIT) the company originates finances and manages US commercial and residential mortgage loans commercial mortgage-backed securities and other commercial real estate debt investments. It acquires discounted loans from failed banks and financial institutions some through the FDIC which typically auctions off large pools of loan portfolios. Starwood Property Trust is externally managed by SPT Management LLC an affiliate of Starwood Capital Group. As a REIT the trust is exempt from paying federal income tax so long as it distributes quarterly dividends to shareholders.

Financial Performance

Overall revenues grew 63% in 2012 to $327 million up from $201 million in 2011. The trust primarily earns money on interest income from mortgage-backed securities and loans.

Mergers and Acquisitions

In 2013 Starwood Property Trust bought LNR Property LLC a real estate investment finance management and development firm. The trust paid $862 million for LNR's US special servicer the US investment securities portfolio Archetype Mortgage Capital (now Starwood Mortgage Capital) Archetype Financial Institution Services LNR Europe and 50% of LNR's interest in Auction.com.

Later that year it moved to spin off its single-family residential business as a new REIT named Starwood Waypoint Residential Trust. The trust which will be affiliated with Waypoint Homes will invest own and operate single-family rental homes and non-performing residential mortgage loans in the US.

EXECUTIVES

Chb-Ceo, Barry S Sternlicht
Pres, Jeffrey F Dimodica
Exec V Pres-Gen Counsel-Coo-Cc, Andrew J Sossen
Cfo-Treas-Cao, Rina Paniry
Chief Originations Officer, Dennis Schuh
Senior Sales Manager, Corinna Aguilar
Sales, Elise Welsh
Catering Sales Manager, Emily Isabell
Auditors: Deloitte & Touche LLP

LOCATIONS

HQ: Starwood Property Trust Inc.
591 West Putnam Avenue, Greenwich, CT 06830
Phone: 203 422-7700
Web: www.starwoodpropertytrust.com

COMPETITORS

American Capital Agency Corp.	JER Investors Trust
	MFA Financial
Annaly Capital Management	PennyMac Mortgage
	Petra Real Estate
Arbor Realty Trust	RAIT Financial Trust
Colony Northstar	Realty Finance
Drive Shack	Corporation
Hatteras Financial	Redwood Trust
Invesco Mortgage Capital	Two Harbors
	iStar Financial Inc

HISTORICAL FINANCIALS

Company Type: Public

Income Statement

FYE: December 31

	ASSETS ($ mil.)	NET INCOME ($ mil.)	INCOME AS % OF ASSETS	EMPLOYEES
12/18	68,262	386	0.6%	290
12/17	62,941	401	0.6%	312
12/16	77,256	365	0.5%	340
12/15	85,738	451	0.5%	450
12/14	116,099	495	0.4%	468
Annual Growth	**(12.4%)**	**(6.0%)**	**—**	**(11.3%)**

2018 Year-End Financials

Debt ratio: 16.00%
Return on equity: 8.00%
Cash ($ mil.): 240
Current ratio: —
Long-term debt ($ mil.): —

No. of shares (mil.): 276
Dividends
  Yield: 10.0%
  Payout: 135.0%
Market value ($ mil.): 5,433

	STOCK PRICE ($) FY Close	P/E High/Low		PER SHARE ($) Earnings	Dividends	Book Value
12/18	20.00	16	13	1.00	2.00	17.00
12/17	21.00	15	14	2.00	2.00	17.00
12/16	22.00	15	11	2.00	2.00	17.00
12/15	21.00	13	10	2.00	2.00	17.00
12/14	23.00	13	10	2.00	2.00	17.00
Annual Growth	**(4.0%)**	**—**	**—**	**(10.8%)**	**(0.0%)**	**(0.8%)**

State Auto Financial Corp.

Thanks to State Auto Financial the state of auto insurance is healthy in the Midwest. The company sells property/casualty policies through several subsidiaries writing personal commercial and specialty coverage including automobile homeowners multi-peril and workers' compensation insurance. It also participates in an insurance pool through its parent company State Auto Mutual Insurance which owns more than 60% of State Auto Financial and provides the offices for its headquarters. Subsidiary Stateco Financial Services manages the company's invested assets. State Auto Financial is the only part of State Auto Mutual that is publicly traded.

Operations

State Auto Financial has four reportable segments: personal insurance commercial insurance specialty insurance and investment operations.

The personal insurance segment provides primarily personal automobile and homeowners to the personal insurance market. It brings in some 40% of State Auto's total revenue.

The commercial insurance segment provides commercial automobile commercial multi-peril property data compromise and risk control insurance covering small-to-medium sized commercial exposures in the business insurance market. That segment accounts for about a third of total revenue.

The specialty insurance segment provides commercial coverage — including workers' compensation — requiring specialized product underwriting claims handling or risk management services. It brings in more than 15% of total revenue. State Auto exited the specialty insurance business in 2018 so that segment will be eliminated in future reporting periods.

The investment operations segment managed by subsidiary Stateco provides investment services. It represents some 10% of total revenue.

Geographic Reach

State Auto Financial operates in about 35 states. Ohio Kentucky and Texas are its biggest markets accounting for almost 25% of its annual premiums.

Sales and Marketing

Through the mutual pool State Auto Financial and its sister companies known collectively as State Auto Group market products through retail agents and wholesale brokers. It works with some 2800 retail agencies. The company focuses its business insurance sales on small-to-medium-sized companies.

Financial Performance

State Auto Financial's revenue has been growing steadily over the past five years but net income has been falling since 2014 due to its high expense ratio. The company lost money in 2017.

Revenue increased 1% to $1.4 billion in 2017 thanks to increases in net written premiums for personal auto and homeowners insurance and (to a lesser extent) commercial insurance. That was partially offset by a decline in the discontinued specialty segment.

The company had a $10.7 million net loss that year after netting $21 million in 2016. This was largely due to a $44.1 federal income tax expense related to a change in tax laws.

State Auto ended 2017 with $91.5 million in net cash some $40 million more than it had at the end of 2016. Operating activities provided $67.9 million while investing activities and financing activities used $20.5 million and $7 million respectively.

Strategy

While its revenues have grown steadily with personal and standard commercial products State Auto Financial has struggled with underwriting and pricing issues that have impacted its results. To counter those issues the company has been focused on improving its rates (which has resulted in a drop in retention) and securing new business. It offers discounts to auto customers who sign up for telematics driving habit tracking and to homeowners customers who use smart home technologies. Additionally it has been rolling out its State Auto Connect digital platform for new personal policies and new commercial auto policies. With these initiatives the company saw its first increase in homeowners policies-in-force in eight years in 2017.

To hone its focus on its core personal and commercial insurance offerings the company has shut down its specialty insurance units: It exited the programs business in 2016 and in 2017 it exited the excess and surplus property and excess and surplus casualty businesses. Other recent exits include the large commercial health care and trucking businesses.

EXECUTIVES

Svp And Chief Risk Officer, Cynthia A. Powell, age 58

President And Ceo, Michael E. (Mike) LaRocco, age 62

Svp And Cfo, Steven E. English, age 58, $447,231 total compensation

Vp And Director Operation Effectiveness, Lyle D. Rhodebeck, age 61

Svp Secretary And General Counsel, James A. (Jay) Yano, age 68, $357,692 total compensation

Svp Standard Lines, Joel E. Brown, age 61

Svp And Director Specialty Lines, Jessica E. Buss, age 47, $372,692 total compensation

Svp And Chief Claims Officer, Stephen P. Hunckler, age 60

Vice President Chief Risk Officer, Bill Cody Bill Cody

Rvp Personal Underwriting, Amy L Skaggs

Assistant Vice President Actuarial Department, Alp Can

Senior Vice President And Chief Information And Strategy Officer Of Stfc And State Auto Mutual, Greg Tacchetti

Assistant Vice President Risk Engineering, Tom Mullaney

Vice President Specialty Programs, Greg Scullans

Assistant Vice President Reinsurance, Cpcu Olmstead

Senior Vice President Personal Lines, Jason E Berkeu

Director Of Government Relations, Elise Spriggs

Vice President Legal, Perry Fioravanti

Senior Vice President Chief Information And Strategy Officer, Gregory Tacchetti

Evp, Ryan Helon

Evp, Wayne Embree

Chairman, Robert P. (Bob) Restrepo, age 68

Auditors: Ernst & Young LLP

LOCATIONS

HQ: State Auto Financial Corp.
518 East Broad Street, Columbus, OH 43215-3976
Phone: 614 464-5000
Web: www.stateauto.com

2017 Direct Written Premiums

	% of total
Ohio	9
Texas	9
Kentucky	6
California	5
Minnesota	4
Tennessee	4
Georgia	4
Indiana	4
Mississippi	4
South Carolina	4
Illinois	3
Maryland	3
Pennsylvania	3
North Carolina	3
Other	36
Total	**100**

PRODUCTS/OPERATIONS

2017 Sales

	$ mil.	% of total
Personal insurance premiums	580	41
Commercial insurance premiums	456	32
Specialty insurance premiums	239	17
Investment income & other	146	10
Total	**1,421**	**100**

COMPETITORS

AIG	National General
Allstate	Holdings
American Family	Nationwide
Insurance	Progressive
American Southern	Corporation
GEICO	State Farm
Kentucky Employers'	The Hartford
Mutual	Travelers Companies

HISTORICAL FINANCIALS

Company Type: Public

Income Statement

FYE: December 31

	ASSETS ($ mil.)	NET INCOME ($ mil.)	INCOME AS % OF ASSETS	EMPLOYEES
12/18	2,896	13	0.4%	1,854
12/17	3,014	(11)	—	1,962
12/16	2,959	21	0.7%	2,020
12/15	2,829	51	1.8%	2,065
12/14	2,767	107	3.9%	2,274
Annual Growth	1.1%	(41.2%)	—	(5.0%)

2018 Year-End Financials

Debt ratio: 4.00%
Return on equity: 2.00%
Cash ($ mil.): 60
Current ratio: —
Long-term debt ($ mil.): —

No. of shares (mil.): 43
Dividends
 Yield: 1.0%
 Payout: 56.0%
Market value ($ mil.): 1,471

	STOCK PRICE ($) FY Close	P/E High/Low	PER SHARE ($) Earnings	Dividends	Book Value
12/18	34.00	117 92	0.00	0.00	19.00
12/17	29.00	— —	(0.00)	0.00	21.00
12/16	27.00	54 37	1.00	0.00	21.00
12/15	21.00	22 16	1.00	0.00	21.00
12/14	22.00	9 7	3.00	0.00	21.00
Annual Growth	11.3%	—	(42.2%)	(0.0%)	(2.9%)

STATE OF CALIFORNIA

EXECUTIVES

Governor, Gavin Newsom
Lt. Governor*, Eleni Kounalakis
Consultant, A Kirk McKenzie
Chief Licensing/Information Te, Brian Desmarais
Chief Information Security Off, Carol Kelly
Budgets and Fiscal STA, Caroline McNeil
Computer Support Staff Represe, Cheryl Drefs
Budgets and Fiscal STA, Diane Herteg
Chief Technology Support Servi, Jim Rengstorff
AG Technician II, Jose Antonio Diaz
Analyst, Karen Bianchi Walsh
Auditors: JOHN F COLLINS II CPA DEPUTY

LOCATIONS

HQ: STATE OF CALIFORNIA
STATE CAPITAL, SACRAMENTO, CA 95814
Phone: 916 445-2864
Web: WWW.CA.GOV

HISTORICAL FINANCIALS

Company Type: Private

Income Statement — FYE: June 30

	REVENUE ($ mil.)	NET INCOME ($ mil.)	NET PROFIT MARGIN	EMPLOYEES
06/16	255,725	4,799	1.9%	208,580
06/15	249,923	6,252	2.5%	—
06/14	219,871	8,082	3.7%	—
06/13	205	8	3.9%	—
Annual Growth	976.7%	742.3%	—	—

STATE OF NEW YORK MORTGAGE AGENCY

The State of New York Mortgage Agency (SONYMA pronounced "Sony Mae") is a public benefit corporation of the State of New York that makes homebuying more affordable for low- and moderate-income residents of the state. SONYMA has two program divisions: Its single-family programs and financing division provides low-interest rate mortgages to first-time homebuyers with low and moderate incomes through the issuance of mortgage revenue bonds while its mortgage insurance fund provides mortgage insurance and credit support for multi-family affordable residential projects and special care facilities throughout the state.

EXECUTIVES

Vice President, Daniel Murphy
Assistant Vice President, Robert Rosado
Vice President Special Projects, Mark Flescher
Vice President Internal Audit, Stephen Chopey
Senior Vice President, Michael Friedman
Vice President, Michael Esposito
Assistant Vice President, Olivia Jervis
Avp Originations Project Set Aside Director, Marie Cammarata
Auditors: ERNST & YOUNG LLP NEW YORK N

LOCATIONS

HQ: STATE OF NEW YORK MORTGAGE AGENCY
641 LEXINGTON AVE FL 4, NEW YORK, NY 100224503
Phone: 212 688-4000
Web: WWW.NYSHCR.ORG

HISTORICAL FINANCIALS

Company Type: Private

Income Statement — FYE: October 31

	ASSETS ($ mil.)	NET INCOME ($ mil.)	INCOME AS % OF ASSETS	EMPLOYEES
10/18	5,324	148	2.8%	221
10/17	5,229	35	0.7%	—
10/16	5,187	64	1.2%	—
10/09	5,225	162	3.1%	—
Annual Growth	0.2%	(1.0%)	—	—

STATE OF OKLAHOMA

EXECUTIVES

Governor, Kevin Stitt
Lt Gov*, Todd Lamb
General Counsel-Sec*, James Williamson
Sec, Science and Innovation, Kayse Shrum
Sec, Health and Mental Health, Jerome Loughridge
Contracting Andamp, Kathy Hallum
Sales Representative, Amanda Porter
Coordinator Mark, Barbara Charlet
Personnel Director, Barbara Jones
Assistant Professor, Blaine Mooers
Senior Vice President, Brian Maddy
Auditors: GARY A JONES CPA CFE OKLAH

LOCATIONS

HQ: STATE OF OKLAHOMA
421 NW 13TH ST STE 220, OKLAHOMA CITY, OK 731033784
Phone: 405 521-2342
Web: WWW.OK.GOV

HISTORICAL FINANCIALS

Company Type: Private

Income Statement — FYE: June 30

	REVENUE ($ mil.)	NET INCOME ($ mil.)	NET PROFIT MARGIN	EMPLOYEES
06/18	17,806	602	3.4%	37,613
06/17	17,175	48	0.3%	—
06/16	16,789	(1,026)	—	—
06/15	17,331	314	1.8%	—
Annual Growth	0.9%	24.2%	—	—

STATE OF RHODE ISLAND AND PROVIDENCE PLANTATIONS

EXECUTIVES

Gov, Gina M Raimondo
Lt Gov, Daniel J McKee
State Controller, Lawrence C Franklin Jr
Research Scientist, Adam Miller
Grant Manager, Andrea Creach
Control Administrator, Arthur Sheridan
Research Technician, Caitlin Oconnor
Human Resources Manager, Cecille Antonelli
Associate Director, Cheryl Burrell
Human Resources Rep, Crystine Marandola
Manager, David Salvatore
Auditors: DENNIS E HOYLE CPA-OFFICE OF

LOCATIONS

HQ: STATE OF RHODE ISLAND AND PROVIDENCE PLANTATIONS
82 SMITH ST STE 102, PROVIDENCE, RI 029031121
Phone: 401 222-2080
Web: WWW.GOPROVIDENCE.COM

HISTORICAL FINANCIALS

Company Type: Private

Income Statement — FYE: June 30

	REVENUE ($ mil.)	NET INCOME ($ mil.)	NET PROFIT MARGIN	EMPLOYEES
06/17	7,013	215	3.1%	13,535
06/16	6,860	(10)	—	—
06/15	6,788	161	2.4%	—
06/14	6,282	(47)	—	—
Annual Growth	3.7%	—	—	—

STATE OF TEXAS

EXECUTIVES

Governor, Greg Abbott
Chief of Staff*, Luis Saenz
Deputy Chief of Staff*, David Whitley
Chief Operating Officer*, Reed Clay
Deputy Chief of Staff*, Jordan Hale
Senior Adviser For State Opera, Steven Albright
Texas District Attorney, Andria Bender
Senior Adviser, Sarah Hicks
Deputy Director, Aimee Snoddy
Regional Manager, Alan Piller
Computer Operator, Allan Bagby
Auditors: JOHN KENT CPA AUSTIN TEXAS

LOCATIONS

HQ: STATE OF TEXAS
CAPI BLDG 1100 N CONG AVE, AUSTIN, TX 78701
Phone: 512 463-2000

HISTORICAL FINANCIALS

Company Type: Private

Income Statement   FYE: August 31

	REVENUE ($ mil.)	NET INCOME ($ mil.)	NET PROFIT MARGIN	EMPLOYEES
08/17	115,336	1,883	1.6%	144,175
08/15	107,351	1,993	1.9%	—
08/14	109,861	8,184	7.4%	—
08/13	0	0	—	—
Annual Growth	—	—	—	—

State Street Corp.

Through its flagship State Street Bank and other subsidiaries State Street provides investment servicing (including clearing settlement payment brokerage and trading and risk and compliance analytics) and investment management services (which include core and enhanced indexing multi-asset strategies environment and social investing and ETFs). The holding company's primary clientele comprises investment managers mutual funds corporate and public retirement plans collective investment funds and other investment pools foundations endowments and insurance companies. Founded in 1792 as Union Bank State Street has some $31.6 trillion in assets under custody and administration and roughly $2.5 trillion in assets under management.

HISTORY

The US's chaotic post-revolutionary era gave birth to the first ancestor of State Street Corporation. Union Bank was founded in 1792 by Boston businessmen breaking the eight-year monopoly held on Boston banking by Massachusetts Bank (a forerunner of FleetBoston which was acquired by Bank of America in 2004). Governor John Hancock's distinctive signature graced Union's charter; the bank set up shop at 40 State Street near the port and enjoyed the glory days of New England's shipping trade.

In the mid-19th century Boston's financial eminence faded as New York flexed its economic muscle. In 1865 the bank was nationally chartered and changed its name to National Union Bank of Boston. It got a new neighbor in 1891: Directors of Third National Bank set up State Street Deposit & Trust to engage in the newfangled business of trusts.

In 1925 National Union Bank merged with State Street and inherited its custodial business. The bank grew through the 1950s; acquisitions included the Second National Bank and the Rockland-Atlas National Bank.

In 1970 State Street converted to a holding company — the State Street Boston Financial Corp. (State Street Boston Corp. as of 1977). The company also went international that decade opening an office in Munich Germany.

Soaring inflation and the recession of the 1970s forced the company to radically rethink its mission. The 1974 passage of the Employee Retirement Income Security Act changed the laws governing the management of pension funds and created an opportunity. State Street was one of the first banks to move aggressively into high-tech information processing and affiliate Boston Financial Data Services began servicing pension assets in 1974.

Encouraged by that success in 1975 new CEO William Edgerly (who served until 1992) steered State Street away from branch banking and into investments trusts and securities processing. An early achievement was designing PepsiCo's retirement plan. Fee-based sales approached 50% of revenues; the company could now quit focusing on lending. In the 1980s and 1990s the company built its administration and investment management businesses overseas and moved into software.

Evolving in the late 1990s State Street left non-core businesses but expanded globally. In 1997 it formed European Direct Capital Management to invest in eastern and central Europe. State Street Global Advisors opened a London office in 1998 to serve wealthy individuals outside the US.

The company sold its commercial banking business to Royal Bank of Scotland in 1999 signaling an exit from that business and narrowing State Street's scope to the asset and investment management businesses. The company also bought Wachovia's custody and institutional trust business and teamed with Citigroup to sell 401(k) retirement products.

In 2000 State Street created FX Connect an electronic foreign exchange trading system. Also that year David Spina took over as CEO from the retiring Marshall Carter.

The firm bought Bel Air Investment Advisors and its broker/dealer affiliate Bel Air Securities in 2001 to cater to the ultrawealthy. In 2003 State Street sold its corporate trust business to U.S. Bancorp and its private asset management business to Charles Schwab's U.S. Trust. Spina retired in 2004; his protégé Ron Logue stepped in as chairman and CEO.

In 2007 State Street added bulk by acquiring another Boston-based fund accounting and servicing provider Investors Financial Services. The company boosted its foreign exchange offerings with the acquisition of Currenex. The following year State Street and Citigroup sold their CitiStreet retirement and pension plan management joint venture to ING Groep for some $900 million.

The US Treasury invested some $2 billion in the company in 2008 as part of a broader bailout plan to restore confidence and increase liquidity. State Street was among eight other top banks that received a combined $250 billion; the company repaid the full amount within months.

In the distressed economic climate State Street's servicing and management revenues declined due to lower equity market valuations and lending volumes and an increase in bankruptcies. The company hit its nadir in 2009 when it reported more than $2 billion in losses.

EXECUTIVES

President And Coo, Ronald P. (Ron) O'Hanley, age 62, $784,615 total compensation
Evp And Global Head State Street Alternative Investment Solutions, George E. Sullivan
Chairman And Ceo, Joseph L. (Jay) Hooley, age 62, $980,769 total compensation
Evp And Head Of Regulatory Industry And Government Affairs, Stefan M. Gavell
Evp And Head Global Markets And Global Services Asia Pacific, Wai Kwong Seck, age 63
Evp And Chief Legal Officer, Jeffrey N. Carp, age 62, $675,000 total compensation
Evp, Maria F. Dwyer
Evp And Head Securities Finance And Portfolio Solutions, Nicholas T. (Nick) Bonn
Evp And Global Cio, Antoine Shagoury
Evp And Chief Administrative Officer State Street Global Advisors, Marc P. Brown
Evp Corporate Advisory Services, James C. Caccivio

Global Head Of Operations Infrastructure And Business Transformation, Jeffrey D. Conway, age 53
Evp And Cto, Albert J. (Jerry) Cristoforo
Evp, Sharon E. Donovan Hart
President And Ceo State Street Global Advisors, Cyrus Taraporevala
Evp And Head State Street Global Exchange, Lou Maiuri
Evp And Head Global Operations, Robert Kaplan
Evp And Head Sector Solutions Sales Emea, Stefan Gmuer
Evp And Head Tax And Tax Advantaged Investments, Dennis E. Ross
Evp Chief Human Resources And Corporate Citizenship Officer, Kathryn M. (Kathy) Horgan
Evp, Richard G. Taggart, age 59
Evp And General Counsel, David C. Phelan
Evp Trading And Clearing, Martine Bond
Evp, Tracy Atkinson
Evp And Chief Investment Officer, Paul J. Selian
Evp And Chief Marketing Officer, Hannah Grove
Evp And General Counsel, Phillip S. Gillespie
Evp And Chief Risk Officer, Andrew Kuritzkes, age 58
Evp Alternative Asset Managers Solutions, Maria Cantillon
Evp And Coo State Street Global Services Emea, Anthony Carey
Global Chief Investment Officer, Rick Lacaille
Evp And Chief Compliance Officer, Cuan Coulter
Evp, David Crawford
Evp And Head Application Development And Maintenance, Ali El Abboud
Evp And Chief Data Officer, James Hardy
Evp And Head Specialized Products Group State Street Global Services Investment Services Americas, Brenda Lyons
Evp Head Of Institutional Investor Services, Stephen F. (Steve) Nazzaro
Evp And International Chief Risk Officer, David Suetens
Evp And Cfo, Eric Aboaf, age 54
Evp And Managing Director State Street Bank Gmbh, Jorg Ambrosius
Evp Global Markets Sales And Trading And Research, Anthony C. Bisegna
Evp State Street Global Advisors And Cio Global Equity Beta Solutions, Lynn S. Blake
Evp And Head State Street Global Services Ireland, Susan Dargan
Evp Chief Innovation Officer And Head Advisory And Information Solutions, Jessica Donohue
Evp And Head Of Global Services, Andrew Erickson
Evp And Head Sector Solutions Americas And Global Alternatives, Scott R. FitzGerald
Evp And Head Global Total Rewards And Human Resources, Todd Gershkowitz
Evp And Head Derivatives Securities Valuation And Internal Recon Centers Of Excellence, John Griffin
Evp And Head Emea State Street Global Advisors, Mike Karpik
Evp International Finance And Treasury, Mark R. Keating
Evp State Street Global Markets, Karen D. Keenan
Evp State Street Global Markets, Ian Martin
Evp, Ivan Matviak
Evp And General Auditor, Michael Richards
Evp Ssga And Global Head Spdr Exchange Traded Funds Business And Head Intermediary Distribution United States; Chairman Ssga Funds Management Inc., James E. (Jim) Ross
Evp And Head Global Markets Emea, Rajen Shah
Evp State Street Global Advisors And Cio Investment Solutions Group, Dan Farley
Evp And Global Head Of State Street Securities Finance, Paul Fleming
Evp State Street Global Services Investment Services Americas, Michael Fontaine

Evp Legal State Street Global Markets State Street Global Exchange State Street Global Operations And Credit Service, R. Bryan Woodard
Evp, Aunoy Banerjee
Evp And Head Asia Pacific Ssga, Lochiel Crafter
Evp, Pinar Kip
Evp, Jon Lehner
Evp And Head State Street Global Exchange, John Plansky
Evp, Liz Roaldsen
Evp And Treasurer, John Slyconish
Ceo Emea, Elizabeth Nolan
Senior Vice President, Martin Sullivan
Vice President Of Information Technology, Phil Pengeroth
Vice President Information Technology, Chandra Busannagari
Vice President Information Technology, Siddharth Jeevan
Executive Vice President, Gunjan Kedia
Vice President March Mondiaux, Gaetan Reid
Vice President Director, Lou Adreani
Vice President It Business Project Analysis, Michael Tarpey
Vice President, Mark Massaro
Assistant Vice President, Christina Daniels
Vice President Product Manager Etf Operations, Adam Hicks
Assistant Vice President, Joanne Farrington
Assistant Vice President, Dennis Shea
Vice President, Kevin Miley
Senior Vice President, Susan Luo
Senior Vice President, Mark Schafer
Assistant Vice President, Diane Matusic
Vice President; Mutual Fund Administration, Scott Jenkins
Vice President Of Creative, John Mcclain
Vice President Information Technology, Srihari Valiveti
Vice President, Allan Lewis
Vice President Otc Derivatives And Collateral Management, Ed Matuga
Assistant Vice President Mutual Fund Tax, Adriana Grossi
Assistant Vice President, Ed Alter
Assistant Vice President, Susan Mccusker
Senior Vice President And Chief Applications Architect, Chris Mccarthy
Vice President Derivatives Program Manager, Michael Derr
Vice President Investor Services, Dori J Samia
Vice President, Travis Calabio
Avp Gcs, Andrew Cammorata
Assistant Vice President, Mike Manganaro
Vice President Financial Reporting, Winnie Lam
Vice President, Paul Branzburg
Vice President, Michael Cogliano
Senior Counselvice President, Veronica Greenbaum
Senior Vice President, Chris Malley
Vice President Adm Testing, Irina Reznikova
Senior Vice President And Chief Scientist, David Saul
Senior Vice President, Paul Connolly
Vice President Human Resources Business Partner, Tammy Chojnowski
Senior Vice President Corporate Audit Chief Administrative Officer, Shannon Groppi
Avp, Raquel Ellis
Vice President, Diane Webber
Vice President, Ravi Bandaru
Assistant Vice President Ta Operations, Stephanie Babou
Vice President Information Systems, Scott Wheeler
Assistant Vice President Relationship Management, Tara Stevens
Vice President, Mike Irwin
Vice President, Jason Bittarelli
Vice President, Mary Phillips
Assistant Vice President, Keri Lanzetta

Vice President Strategy Consultant, JONATHAN NESBIT
Vice President, Michelle Hayward
Assistant Vice President, Karen Mcinnis
Vice President Fx Trading And Sales, Conor Keane
Vice President Global Agile Product Owner, Lawrence Perreira
Assistant Vice President, Lokesh Aggarwal
Vice President, Kevin Moss
Assistant Vice President, Gregory Mullen
Vice President, Daniel Mazza
Vice President And Senior Counsel, Francine Hayes
Senior Vice President Privacy Officer, Gerald Spada
Vice President, James Callahan
Vice President, Gopal Balasubramanian
Avp, Nicole Souza
Vice President Project Team Manager, Karen Rodeo
Vice President, Michael Mccarthy
Assistant Vice President, Renee Hickey
Assistant Vice President, Bimal Patel
Vice President Corporate Citizenship, Wayne Young
Vice President Vdi Infrastructure Architecture, Bruce Lyons
Senior Vice President State Street Bank Gmbh, Evert Van Den Brink
Vice President, Erin Rodriguez
Vice President, Gene Morris
Vice President, Lawrence Giampietro
Vice President, Awanish Choudhury
Vp Application Construction Manager, Rob Donelson
Vice President, Anand Rangana
Vice President Architecture, Steve Kiernan
Assistant Vice President Ims, Peter Kiely
Vice President State Government Relations, Jeevan Ramapriya
Vp It Vendor Management, Mark Fratus
Vice President Community Event Sponsorship Manager, Laura O'Keefe
Auditors: Ernst & Young LLP

LOCATIONS

HQ: State Street Corp.
One Lincoln Street, Boston, MA 02111
Phone: 617 786-3000
Web: www.statestreet.com

2016 Assets Mix

	% of total
North America	75
Europe/Middle East/Africa	20
Asia/Pacific	5
Total	**100**

PRODUCTS/OPERATIONS

2018 Assets Mix

	% of total
North America	73
Europe/Middle East/Africa	21
Asia/Pacific	6
Total	**100**

2018 Revenue

	$ mil.	% of total
Fees:		
Servicing fees	5,421	45
Management fees	1,851	16
Foreign exchange trading services	1,201	10
Securities finance	543	5
Processing fees and other	289	2
Net interest revenue	2,671	22
Gains (losses) related to investment securities net	6	-
Total	**11**	**100**

2018 Sales

	$ mil.	% of total
Investment Servicing	10,034	84
Investment Management	1,956	16
Elimination	(8.0)	-
Total	**11,982**	**100**

Selected Capabilities

Data and Analytic
Investment Management
Investment Research and Trading
Investment Servicing

COMPETITORS

Bank of New York Mellon	JPMorgan Chase
Citigroup	Morgan Stanley
Credit Suisse (USA)	Northern Trust
Deutsche Bank	Principal Financial
First Data	SEI Investments
Fiserv	UBS Financial Services

HISTORICAL FINANCIALS

Company Type: Public

Income Statement
FYE: December 31

	ASSETS ($ mil.)	NET INCOME ($ mil.)	INCOME AS % OF ASSETS	EMPLOYEES
12/18	244,626	2,599	1.1%	40,142
12/17	238,425	2,177	0.9%	36,643
12/16	242,698	2,143	0.9%	33,783
12/15	245,192	1,980	0.8%	32,356
12/14	274,119	2,037	0.7%	29,970
Annual Growth	**(2.8%)**	**6.3%**	**—**	**7.6%**

2018 Year-End Financials

Debt ratio: 5.00%
Return on equity: 11.00%
Cash ($ mil.): 77,497
Current ratio: —
Long-term debt ($ mil.): —

No. of shares (mil.): 380
Dividends
  Yield: 3.0%
  Payout: 28.0%
Market value ($ mil.): 23,963

	STOCK PRICE ($) FY Close	P/E High/Low		PER SHARE ($) Earnings	Dividends	Book Value
12/18	63.00	17	9	6.00	2.00	65.00
12/17	98.00	19	14	5.00	2.00	61.00
12/16	78.00	16	10	5.00	1.00	56.00
12/15	66.00	18	14	4.00	1.00	53.00
12/14	79.00	17	14	5.00	1.00	52.00
Annual Growth	**(5.3%)**			**8.8%**	**11.3%**	**6.0%**

STATE UNIVERSITY OF NEW YORK

SUNY days are ahead for many New Yorkers seeking higher education. With an enrollment of more than 460000 students The State University of New York (SUNY) is vying with California State University System for the title of largest university system in the US. Most students are residents of New York State. Students come from all 50 states as well as 160 countries. SUNY maintains 64 campuses around the state including four university centers about two dozen university colleges 30 community colleges and a handful of technical colleges as well as medical centers. The system has a student-teacher ratio of about 16:1.

Operations

The school offers more than 7500 undergraduate programs of study — including engineering business literature medicine agriculture performing arts and human services. SUNY also offers about 400 study abroad programs.

Steel Dynamics Inc.

Steel Dynamics may operate mini-mills but it produces steel on a large scale. Steel Dynamics operates electric arc furnace mini-mills steel scrap processing and metals recycling centers and steel fabrication facilities. The company sells to companies in the automotive construction and manufacturing industries as well as to steel processors and service centers primarily in the Midwestern and eastern US. Among its mini-mill output are beams rails and other products used in the construction industrial machinery and transportation industries. Steel Dynamics' annual steel shipping capacity is 11 million tons.

Operations

Steel Dynamics has three reporting segments: Steel Metals Recycling and Steel Fabrication.

Its Steel operations have six electric-arc furnace mini-mills producing steel from steel scrap using continuous casting automated rolling mills and some 10 downstream steel coating lines and Iron Dynamics (IDI). Its Flat Roll Division sheet steel products such as hot rolled cold rolled and coated steel products are used by automakers and other industries. The Long Products Division sells structural steel beams and pilings for the construction industry and industrial quality grade rail for the railroad industry. The Steel operations account for about three-quarters of sales.

The Metals Recycling operations (about 15% of revenue) consist solely of OmniSource which includes ferrous and nonferrous scrap metal processing transportation marketing brokerage and consulting services. In addition OmniSource designs installs and manages customized scrap man-

agement programs for industrial manufacturing companies.

The company's Steel Fabrication operations (about 10% of revenue) include seven New Millennium Building Systems plants which fabricate steel joists trusses girders and decking used by the non-residential construction industry.

All told Steel Dynamics operates six electric-arc-furnace steel mills steel coating lines a downstream engineered bar (SBQ) processing facility an iron production facility multiple metals recycling operations and seven steel fabrication plants.

Geographic Reach

Steel Dynamics has operations in Indiana (Butler Columbia City Jeffersonville and Pittsboro) Mississippi (Columbus) Pennsylvania (Pittsburgh) Virginia (Roanoke) and West Virginia (Huntington). It also serves the Southern US Canada and Mexico.

Sales and Marketing

Steel Dynamics' primary customers for structural steel products are steel service centers steel fabricators and a range of other manufacturers including metal building firms general construction contractors developers brokers agriculture consumer goods and governmental entities. The company's steel operation's biggest customers are construction about 40% manufacturing nearly 32% and automotive about 15%.

Financial Performance

In the last decade revenue at Steel Industries has more or less remained stable around the $8 billion mark despite a plunge in 2009 when it posted just below $4 billion in earnings. Net income has been much less predictable. It has had two years of losses (2009 2015) and mostly profits below $200 million though the company has fared better in the last couple of years.

2017 was one of the best years for the company. Revenue increased 20% to $9.5 billion the highest in a decade. The record level of steel operation and fabrication shipments (close to 10 million tons combined) and improved demand in the domestic steel market followed by selling price hikes contributed to the revenue growth. Metals recycling operations increased earnings by almost 250%.

Steel Dynamics profits in 2017 grew some 80% again the highest in a decade to $813 million mostly from the absence of $133 million asset impairment charge as well as a $20 million gain in other expenses compared to 2016.

Company's cash holdings increased from $840 million to $1 billion. Operations generated $740 million. Investment activities took up some $140 million while financing activities utilized $415 million majority of which went towards long-tern debt reduction. CAPEX in 2017 was $165 million.

Strategy

Steel Dynamics is seeking to maintain and enhance one of the lowest operating cost structures in the North American steel industry by optimizing the use of its equipment enhancing productivity and exploring new technologies to lower production costs. It is looking to enter new markets in strategic geographic locations that offer attractive growth opportunities by acquiring new businesses or by entering joint ventures or alliances.

The company has improved at several plants to bring on more capacity and make operations more efficient. The company is investing millions of dollars in improvements at the Butler Flat Roll division and the Gavalume line at the Columbus Flat Roll division which serve the automotive market.

The company collaborates with customers to expand its range of products as illustrated by expansions at its Engineered Bar Products Division (high-quality smaller-diameter SBQ bars) and at its Structural and Rail Division (premium grade rails).

Mergers and Acquisitions

In September 2018 Steel Dynamics acquired almost all assets of Kentucky Electric Steel a wholly-owned subsidiary of Specialty Steel Works for $5 million. The Ashland area operations which will be integrated into Steel Dynamics' West Virginia segment include a rolling mill with an annual capacity of 250000 tons that produces flats and specialty alloy bars.

In 2016 Steel Dynamics acquired Vulcan Threaded Products for $114 million. The Birmingham Alabama-based company makes and supplies threaded rod products and also cold draws and heat-treated steel bar. The deal is an example of Steel Dynamics pursuing higher-margin downstream business opportunities that use its steel products in manufacturing processes.

Company Background

Growing its share of the rail market in 2012 Steel Dynamics announced plans to install a heat-treating system (capable of producing up to 350000 tons of standard strength and head hardened plain carbon steel rails for North America's railroad industry) at its Columbia City Indiana Structural and Rail Division.

Steel Dynamics entered a joint venture in 2011 with Spain's Lafarga Group to construct a $39 million facility which will produce copper wire rod from recycled copper.

Steel Dynamics was incorporated in 1993.

EXECUTIVES

Vice President Human Resources, Benjamin Eisbart
President And Ceo, Mark D. Millett, age 60, $1,010,000 total compensation
Evp Metals Recycling And President And Coo Omnisource, Russell B. (Russ) Rinn, age 62, $510,000 total compensation
Svp Long Products Steel Group, Glenn A. Pushis, age 53, $393,750 total compensation
Manager Information Technology, Robert E. (Bob) Francis
Evp And Cfo, Theresa E. Wagler, age 49, $580,000 total compensation
Vp And General Manager Engineered Bar Products Division, Barry T. Schneider, age 50, $363,750 total compensation
Vp And President Steel Of West Virginia, Timothy R. (Tim) Duke
Svp Downstream Manufacturing Group, Christopher A. (Chris) Graham, age 56, $322,500 total compensation
Vp And Corporate Controller, Brent Ritenour
Vice President Finance, John Morris
Vp And General Manager Roanoke Bar Division, Joe Crawford
Vice President Business Development, Alex Hoffman
Vice President, Boudler Noelle
Chairman, Keith E. Busse, age 77
Vice President Treasurer And Risk Manager, Richard Poinsatte
Board Member, Richard T Teets
First Secretary Of Desi, Antoniak Renee
Treasurer Chapter, Bob Barrick
Auditors: Ernst & Young LLP

LOCATIONS

HQ: Steel Dynamics Inc.
7575 West Jefferson Blvd., Fort Wayne, IN 46804
Phone: 260 969-3500
Web: www.steeldynamics.com

PRODUCTS/OPERATIONS

2016 sales

	$ mil.	% of total
Steel	5,871	65
Metals Recycling	2,172	24
Steel Fabrication	704	8
Other	277	3
Eliminations	(1246.1)	
Total	**7,777**	**100**

Selected Products

Cold-rolled galvannealed
Cold-rolled hot-dipped galvanized
Direct reduced iron
Fully processed cold-rolled sheet
Hot-rolled galvannealed
Hot-rolled hot-dipped galvanized
Hot-rolled pickled and oiled
Liquid pig iron
Structural products (steel joists trusses)
Steel Operations
  Sheet Products
    Hot rolled Products
    Cold Rolled Products
  Long Products
    Structural
    Wide flange American Standard and miscellaneous beams
    H piling
    Channel sections
  Rail Products
    Engineered Bar Products
    Merchant Bar Products
    Specialty Shapes
Metals Recycling   No. 2 shredded
  No. 1 bundles
  Plate and structural
  No. 1 busheling
  Turnings
  Heavy melt
  Briquettes
  Copper granules
  Stainless steel bundles
Steel Fabrication Operations Joists
  Decking
  Castellated beams
  Cambered beams

COMPETITORS

AK Steel Holding Corporation	Evraz
ArcelorMittal USA	Gerdau Ameristeel
Canam Steel Corporation	Nucor
Commercial Metals	Timken
	United States Steel
	Wheeling Corrugating

HISTORICAL FINANCIALS

Company Type: Public

Income Statement

FYE: December 31

	REVENUE ($ mil.)	NET INCOME ($ mil.)	NET PROFIT MARGIN	EMPLOYEES
12/18	11,822	1,258	10.6%	8,200
12/17	9,539	813	8.5%	7,635
12/16	7,777	382	4.9%	7,695
12/15	7,594	(130)	—	7,500
12/14	8,756	157	1.8%	7,780
Annual Growth	**7.8%**	**68.3%**	**—**	**1.3%**

2018 Year-End Financials

Debt ratio: 31.00%
Return on equity: 35.00%
Cash ($ mil.): 828
Current ratio: 4.00
Long-term debt ($ mil.): 2,352
No. of shares (mil.): 225
Dividends
  Yield: 2.0%
  Payout: 14.0%
Market value ($ mil.): 6,767

	STOCK PRICE ($) FY Close	P/E High/Low		PER SHARE ($) Earnings	Dividends	Book Value
12/18	30.00	10	5	5.00	1.00	17.00
12/17	43.00	13	10	3.00	1.00	14.00
12/16	36.00	25	10	2.00	1.00	12.00
12/15	18.00	—	—	(1.00)	1.00	11.00
12/14	20.00	37	23	1.00	0.00	12.00
Annual Growth	**11.1%**			**68.1%**	**13.0%**	**9.7%**

Sterling Bancorp (DE)

Sterling Bancorp is the holding company for Sterling National Bank a community-based thrift operating dozens of offices in New York's Hudson Valley region and Greater New York City area. Founded in 1888 the bank attracts consumers and business clients by offering traditional deposit products such as checking and savings accounts and CDs. It uses funds from deposits to originate primarily real estate loans and mortgages. Sterling Bancorp which has assets of more than $7 billion was formerly Provident New York Bancorp; Provident acquired the former Sterling Bancorp in late 2013 and changed its name as well as the name of its banking subsidiary to Sterling. In 2017 the bank agreed to acquire Astoria Financial for $2.2 billion.

EXECUTIVES

Chief Administrative Officer Senior Executive Vice President, Rodney Whitwell
Executive Vice President General Counsel Chief Legal Officer, James Blose
Executive Vice President Marketing, Anthony Burke
Senior Managing Director And Svp, Tammy Leisen
Vice President Managing Director, Michael Gogitidze
Assistant Vice President Client Service Manager, Jason Solow
Vice President Managing Director, Lisa Congemi-doutney
Vp And Director Compliance Assurance, Dawn Arenella
Vp Director Facilities Procurement And Vendor Management, Michele Miuta
Svp Director Consumer Banking Network, James Griffin
Svp Director Consumer Banking Administration, Michael Lechleider
Vice President And Managing Director, Craig Levy
Vice President Senior Credit Officer Leg, James Schanter
Assistant Vice President Secondary Marketing Analyst, Michelle Bobrow
Operations Workflow Integration Leader Vp, Krista Gulalo
Auditors: Crowe LLP

LOCATIONS

HQ: Sterling Bancorp (DE)
400 Rella Boulevard, Montebello, NY 10901
Phone: 845 369-8040
Web: www.sterlingbancorp.com

COMPETITORS

Capital One	JPMorgan Chase
Citibank	KeyCorp
HSBC USA	M&T Bank

HISTORICAL FINANCIALS

Company Type: Public

Income Statement

FYE: December 31

	ASSETS ($ mil.)	NET INCOME ($ mil.)	INCOME AS % OF ASSETS	EMPLOYEES
12/18	31,383	447	1.4%	1,907
12/17	30,360	93	0.3%	2,076
12/16	14,178	140	1.0%	970
12/15	11,956	66	0.6%	1,089
12/14	7,425	17	0.2%	829
Annual Growth	**43.4%**	**126.5%**	**—**	**23.2%**

2018 Year-End Financials

Debt ratio: 1.00%
Return on equity: 10.00%
Cash ($ mil.): 438
Current ratio: —
Long-term debt ($ mil.): —
No. of shares (mil.): 216
Dividends
  Yield: 2.0%
  Payout: 14.0%
Market value ($ mil.): 3,570

	STOCK PRICE ($) FY Close	P/E High/Low		PER SHARE ($) Earnings	Dividends	Book Value
12/18	17.00	13	8	2.00	0.00	20.00
12/17	25.00	45	36	1.00	0.00	19.00
12/16	23.00	23	13	1.00	0.00	14.00
12/15	16.00	29	22	1.00	0.00	13.00
12/14	14.00	72	63	0.00	0.00	12.00
Annual Growth	**3.5%**			**76.7%**	**(0.0%)**	**15.2%**

Sterling Bancorp Inc (MI)

Auditors: Crowe LLP

LOCATIONS

HQ: Sterling Bancorp Inc (MI)
One Towne Square, Suite 1900, Southfield, MI 48076
Phone: 248 355-2400
Web: www.sterlingbank.com

HISTORICAL FINANCIALS

Company Type: Public

Income Statement

FYE: December 31

	ASSETS ($ mil.)	NET INCOME ($ mil.)	INCOME AS % OF ASSETS	EMPLOYEES
12/18	3,197	63	2.0%	352
12/17	2,962	38	1.3%	308
12/16	2,164	33	1.5%	294
12/15	1,712	23	1.3%	
Annual Growth	**23.1%**	**41.3%**	**—**	**—**

2018 Year-End Financials

Debt ratio: 2.00%
Return on equity: 21.00%
Cash ($ mil.): 54
Current ratio: —
Long-term debt ($ mil.): —
No. of shares (mil.): 53
Dividends
  Yield: 1.0%
  Payout: 4.0%
Market value ($ mil.): 368

	STOCK PRICE ($) FY Close	P/E High/Low		PER SHARE ($) Earnings	Dividends	Book Value
12/18	7.00	12	6	1.00	0.00	6.00
12/17	13.00	16	15	1.00	0.00	5.00
12/16	0.00	—	—	1.00	0.00	4.00
Annual Growth	**—**			**18.0%**	**(40.5%)**	**20.8%**

Stifel Financial Corp

Through subsidiaries Stifel Nicolaus (founded 1890) Thomas Weisel Century Securities Associates Stifel Bank & Trust and others Stifel Financial provides asset management financial advice and banking services for private individuals corporations municipal and institutional clients in the US. Stifel also offers brokerage and mergers and acquisitions advisory services for corporate clients underwrites debt and equity and provides research on more than 1000 US and European equities. The firm boasts nearly 360 US offices with a concentration in the Midwest and mid-Atlantic regions and additional offices in the UK and the rest of Europe.

Operations

Stifel Financial operates two main business segments.

The Global Wealth Management segment which generates more than 60% of the firm's total revenue consists of two businesses: Stifel Bank which provides traditional banking products and services and the Private Client Group which is made up of offices across the US that provide securities brokerage services and insurance products.

The Institutional Group segment (almost 40% of revenue) provides securities brokerage trading and research services to institutions and specializes in the sale of equity and fixed-income products.

Geographic Reach

The company is headquartered in Missouri with about 360 private client offices and more than 35 Institutional Group offices mostly across the US as well as in certain foreign locations in the UK and the rest of Europe. About 95% of its revenue stems from the US.

Sales and Marketing

With its 2280-plus financial advisors and 125 independent contractors Stifel serves individuals corporations municipalities and institutions. Its broker-dealer subsidiaries boast more than 1.5 million accounts from customers based in the US and Europe.

Financial Performance

Stifel's revenues have been growing at a healthy clip in recent years thanks to business-boosting acquisitions combined with growth across all business lines as the financial markets have appreciated and demand for investor capital has strengthened.

The firm's revenues climbed 11% to peak at a record-setting $2.6 billion during 2016. This historic growth was driven by a 64% surge from interest revenue generated from the growth in interest-earning assets of Stifel Bank. In addition principal transactions revenues spiked 22% in 2016 due to higher institutional fixed income brokerage revenues as a result of increased volumes. The firm also generated additional revenue from several previous acquisitions.

Despite revenue growth in 2016 Stifel's net income dipped 12% to $82 million as the company spent more on compensation benefits and office space to support future revenue growth. In addition Stifel experienced negative cash flow of $349 million in 2016 as the firm used more cash to purchase operating assets.

Strategy

Stifel has fortified its operations and extended its national footprint mainly through strategic acquisitions as well as through organic growth. It plans to further expand its domestic private client footprint by recruiting experienced financial advisors and continuing to selectively consider acquisitions as they arise.

Mergers and Acquisitions

Stifel Financial has achieved historic revenue growth over the years by using acquisitions primarily to fortify its wealth management business.

Stifel acquired mergers and acquisitions and private capital advisory firm Mooreland Partners in 2019. The company serves the technology industry through its offices in New York Silicon Valley London and Frankfurt. It has completed more than 250 M&A and capital raising transactions for mid-market companies primarily in North America and Europe.

In late 2017 it agreed to acquire the wealth management business belonging to B.C. Ziegler & Company. The business Ziegler Wealth Management was established in 1902 and has nearly 60 private client advisors in 12 branches across five. It manages approximately $4.8 billion in client assets.

In 2017 Stifel picked up investment bank City Financial Corporation and its City Securities subsidiary. City Financial primarily operates in Indiana and the Midwest specializing in wealth management and public finance.

EXECUTIVES

Vice Chairman Svp And Director Stifel Financial Corp. And Evp Investment Banking Stifel Nicolaus & Co., Richard J. Himelfarb, age 78, $250,000 total compensation

Chairman President And Ceo, Ronald J. (Ron) Kruszewski, age 60, $200,000 total compensation

President Cfo And Director, James M. Zemlyak, age 59, $250,000 total compensation

Evp; President And Co-director Institutional Group, Thomas P. Mulroy, age 57, $250,000 total compensation

Svp And Director Stifel Financial Corp. And President And Ceo Keefe Bruyette And Woods, Thomas B. (Tom) Michaud, age 54, $250,000 total compensation

Evp; President And Co-director Institutional Group, Victor J. Nesi, age 59, $250,000 total compensation

Vice President Mortgage Banker, Dan Bayer

Vice President Investments Sarasota, Brad Wilson

Senior Vice President Investments Charleston, Park Smith

Senior Vice President Investments Walnut Creek, Chris Thompson

Senior Vice President Investments Minneapolis, Dee Ray

Senior Vice President Investments Atlanta, Brad Simmons

Svp And Sr Mortgage Loan Officer, Kent Hackstadt

Vice Chairman; Evp Stifel Nicolaus & Co., Ben A. Plotkin, age 63

Co-chairman, Thomas W. (Thom) Weisel, age 77

Auditors: Ernst & Young LLP

LOCATIONS

HQ: Stifel Financial Corp
501 North Broadway, St. Louis, MO 63102-2188
Phone: 314 342-2000
Web: www.stifel.com

2016 Sales

	% of total
US	94
UK	5
Other European countries	1
Total	**100**

PRODUCTS/OPERATIONS

2016 Sales

	$ mil.	% of total
Commissions	730	28
Asset management and service fees	583	22
Investment banking	513	19
Principal transactions	475	18
Interest	294	11
Others	47	2
Total	**2,642**	**100**

Selected Services

Individual
Bonds
Corporate Executive Services
Estate Planning
Exchange Traded Funds
Financial And Wealth Planning
Insurance
Investment Advisory Services
Market News
Mutual Funds
Options
Portfolio Tracker
Prospectus
Retirement Plans
Stifel Bank & Trust
Stifel Cash Management Accounts
Stifel Mobile Announcement
Stifel Trust
Institutions
Asset Management
Conferences & Events
Equity Capital Markets
Equity Sales & Trading
Fixed Income Sales & Trading
Investment Banking
Public Finance
Research
Senior Management

Selected Subsidiaries

Broadway Air Corp.
CSA Insurance Agency Incorporated
Choice Financial Partners Inc.
Stifel Bank & Trust
Stifel Nicolaus Limited (UK)
Stifel Nicolaus & Company Incorporated
Ryan Beck Holdings LLC
Thomas Weisel Partners Group Inc.

COMPETITORS

Edward Jones	Oppenheimer Holdings
FBR	Piper Jaffray
Goldman Sachs	Raymond James
JMP Group	Financial
Lazard	Wells Fargo Advisors
Morgan Stanley	

HISTORICAL FINANCIALS

Company Type: Public

Income Statement				FYE: December 31
	ASSETS ($ mil.)	NET INCOME ($ mil.)	INCOME AS % OF ASSETS	EMPLOYEES
12/18	24,520	394	1.6%	7,500
12/17	21,384	183	0.9%	7,100
12/16	19,129	82	0.4%	7,100
12/15	13,336	92	0.7%	7,100
12/14	9,518	176	1.8%	6,200
Annual Growth	26.7%	22.3%	—	4.9%

2018 Year-End Financials

Debt ratio: 5.00%
Return on equity: 13.00%
Cash ($ mil.): 2,069
Current ratio: —
Long-term debt ($ mil.): —
No. of shares (mil.): 71
Dividends
Yield: 1.0%
Payout: 10.0%
Market value ($ mil.): 2,933

STOCK PRICE ($) FY Close	P/E High/Low		PER SHARE ($) Earnings	Dividends	Book Value
12/18	41.00	13 7	5.00	0.00	45.00
12/17	60.00	24 17	2.00	0.00	40.00
12/16	50.00	45 23	1.00	0.00	41.00
12/15	42.00	44 30	1.00	0.00	37.00
12/14	51.00	20 16	2.00	0.00	35.00
Annual Growth	(5.1%)	— —	19.6%	—	6.3%

Stock Yards Bancorp Inc

Stock Yards Bancorp is the holding company of Stock Yards Bank & Trust which operates about 35 branches mostly in Louisville Kentucky but also in Indianapolis and Cincinnati. Founded in 1904 the $3 billion-asset bank targets individuals and regional business customers offering standard retail services such as checking and savings accounts credit cards certificates of deposit and IRAs. It also provides trust services while brokerage and credit card services are offered through agreements with other banks. Commercial real estate mortgages make up 40% of the bank's loan portfolio which also includes commercial and industrial loans (30%) residential mortgages (15%) construction loans and consumer loans.

Operations

Stock Yards Bank & Trust operates two main business lines: Commercial Banking which provides loans and deposits to individual consumers and businesses as well as mortgage origination and company brokerage activity; and Investment Management and Trust which provides wealth management services such as investment management trust estate administration and retirement plan services.

About 63% of the company's total revenue came from loan interest during 2015 while another 7% came from interest income on its securities. The rest came from its investment management and trust services (13% of revenue) deposit account service charges (7%) bankcard transaction revenue (4%) mortgage banking revenue (3%) brokerage commissions and fees (1%) and other non-interest sources.

Geographic Reach

Kentucky-based Stock Yards Bancorp had 37 branches at the end of 2015 including 28 branches in the Louisville Kentucky metro area and the rest in the Indianapolis Indiana and Cincinnati Ohio metro areas.

Financial Performance

Stock Yards' annual revenues have risen 11% since 2011 thanks to a combination of mostly organic loan growth and investment management and trust services fee growth. Meanwhile its annual profits have grown more than 55% on declining loan loss provisions as its loan portfolio's credit quality has improved with higher property valuations in the strengthened economy.

The bank's revenue climbed 4% to a record $133.12 million during 2015 on higher interest income mostly as its loan assets grew 9% to $2 billion with record loan production.

Revenue growth and a decline in interest expense on deposits in 2015 drove Stock Yard's net income up 7% to a record $34.82 million. The bank's operating cash levels jumped 8% to $43.17 million mostly thanks to the increase in cash-based earnings.

Strategy

Stock Yards outlined its plans for 2016 and beyond to maintain stable net interest margins achieve near-double digit loan growth manage credit quality to keep loan loss provisions down and increasing its regulatory readiness.

Mergers and Acquisitions

In 2013 the bank extended the reach of its operations into Oldham County through its purchase of $146 million-asset The BANcorp Inc. and its five THE BANK branches in the region for $19.9 million.

EXECUTIVES

Sevp, Kathy C. Thompson, age 57, $345,000 total compensation

Chairman And Ceo, David P. Heintzman, age 59, $535,000 total compensation

Evp Secretary Treasurer And Cfo, Nancy B. Davis, age 63, $232,000 total compensation

Evp And Chief Lending Officer, Philip S. Poindexter, age 53, $270,000 total compensation

President, James A. (Ja) Hillebrand, age 50, $375,000 total compensation

Evp And Chief Risk Officer, William M. Dishman, age 57

Evp And Chief Strategic Officer, Clay Stinnett

Evp Retail Banking Brokerage And Business Banking, Michael J. Croce

Assistant Vice President Deposit Operations, Marcia Sweat

Vice President Private Banking, Dan Thacker

Vice President Commercial Lending, Kevin Mccullough

Assistant Vice President, June Schenk

Vice President Commerical Lending, Jason Morgan

Board Member, Richard Northern

Auditors: BKD LLP

LOCATIONS

HQ: Stock Yards Bancorp Inc
1040 East Main Street, Louisville, KY 40206
Phone: 502 582-2571
Web: www.syb.com

PRODUCTS/OPERATIONS

2015 Revenues by Category

	$ mil.	% of total
Interest income	93	70
Non-interest income	40	30
Total	**133**	**100**

Selected Products & Services

Personal Banking
  Banking
  Personal Lending
  Personal Investing & Wealth Management Services
Business Banking
  Credit Loans & Leasing
  Deposit Services
  Treasury Management
  Business Retirement Plans
Wealth Management Services
  Investment Management
  Financial Planning
  Trust & Estate Services
  Brokerage Service

COMPETITORS

Fifth Third	Porter Bancorp
First Capital	Republic Bancorp
Home Federal	U.S. Bancorp
PNC Financial	

HISTORICAL FINANCIALS

Company Type: Public

Income Statement

FYE: December 31

	ASSETS ($ mil.)	NET INCOME ($ mil.)	INCOME AS % OF ASSETS	EMPLOYEES
12/18	3,303	56	1.7%	591
12/17	3,240	38	1.2%	580
12/16	3,039	41	1.3%	578
12/15	2,817	37	1.3%	555
12/14	2,564	35	1.4%	524
Annual Growth	6.5%	12.4%	—	3.1%

2018 Year-End Financials

Debt ratio: —
Return on equity: 16.00%
Cash ($ mil.): 199
Current ratio: —
Long-term debt ($ mil.): —
No. of shares (mil.): 23
Dividends
  Yield: 3.0%
  Payout: 48.0%
Market value ($ mil.): 746

	STOCK PRICE ($) FY Close	P/E High/Low		PER SHARE ($) Earnings	Dividends	Book Value
12/18	33.00	17 12		2.00	1.00	16.00
12/17	38.00	28 19		2.00	1.00	15.00
12/16	47.00	26 15		2.00	1.00	14.00
12/15	38.00	24 18		2.00	1.00	13.00
12/14	33.00	21 17		2.00	1.00	12.00
Annual Growth	(0.4%)	— —		11.4%	13.1%	8.2%

Stryker Corp

Is this an operating room or Dad's workshop? Stryker's surgical products include such instruments as drills saws and even cement mixers. The company operates through three primary segments — MedSurg Orthopaedic and Neurotechnology & Spine. MedSurg's products include microsurgery instruments endoscopy equipment communications systems emergency medical equipment and patient handling tools. The Orthopaedic segment makes artificial hip and knee joints trauma implants bone cement and other orthopedic supplies. The Neurotechnology & Spine segment provides rods screws and artificial discs for spinal surgeries as well as coils and stents for cerebral vascular procedures. Stryker's products are marketed globally to doctors hospitals and other health care facilities via direct sales personnel and distributors.

Operations

Stryker's MedSurg segment is the largest unit bringing in about 45% of total revenues. Its MedSurg Equipment division provides surgical navigation systems endoscopic systems emergency medical equipment and other medical devices. Its biggest customers are hospitals and other care providers who have to invest a decent chunk of cash in order to upgrade their surgical equipment.

Stryker's Orthopaedic segment is nearly as large accounting for about 40% of annual revenues. The division's products include the Triathlon and Scorpio knee implant systems Simplex bone cement the VariAx and Hoffman systems and the Oasys spinal implant.

The company's smallest segment — Neurotechnology & Spine — accounts for some 15% of sales. It provides both neurosurgical and neurovascular devices for minimally invasive surgical procedures. Spinal implant products include cervical thoracolumbar and interbody systems used in various therapies.

Geographic Reach
Stryker operates more than 40 manufacturing facilities in the Americas; Europe the Middle East and Africa (EMEA); and the Asia/Pacific region. While it markets its products in more than 85 countries and is looking to grow in international markets sales in the US continue to make up the majority (about 75%) of annual revenues.

Sales and Marketing
In the US Stryker uses its own sales and marketing force maintaining separate dedicated sales teams for each of its core product lines to doctors hospitals and other care providers. By allowing for specialization each team can provide expertise and guidance directed specifically to customers in each of the medical specialties Stryker serves. In markets outside the US Stryker's products are sold through company-owned subsidiaries and branch locations as well as through third-party distributors and medical device dealers.

Financial Performance
Stryker's revenues have increased steadily over the last five years (and in have risen for nearly 40 years straight) both as a result of organic growth in the medical technology sector and through its excellent track record with acquisitions. Net income has been somewhat more volatile though falling in 2013 and 2014 and again in 2017.

In 2017 revenue grew 10% to a record $12.4 billion due to growth across all segments especially the MedSurg division. That unit saw 14% growth through increased sales volume. Its rapidly growing Medical division which makes patient handling emergency medical equipment and intensive care disposable products led the segment's sales that year. Other strong performers included MedSurg's Endoscopy unit the Neurotechnology business and the Orthopaedics segment's Trauma & Extremities operations. Geographically sales in the US Europe Canada and Australia performed well while emerging markets also showed growth.

Despite the rising revenues net income slipped 38% to $1.0 billion. This was largely due to higher operating expenses and an increase in income taxes.

Stryker ended 2017 with $2.5 billion in cash and cash equivalents. That figure was a 23% decline from what it had at the end of 2016. Cash provided by operations declined due to product recalls and foreign exchange rates while cash used by investing activities (e.g. acquisitions) totaled $1.6 billion. Financing activities used another $794 million.

Strategy
Stryker's strategy for growth centers around strengthening its position in the high end of the medical technology industry. The company works toward that goal by combining internal R&D programs partnerships and a steady stream of acquisitions. Focus areas of growth including widening its presence geographically and expanding its product offerings in core and complementary fields of medicine. Geographically the company targets emerging markets including China through both its standard line of products and its lower-cost Trauson brand.

Overall the company follows the strategy of staying on top of the latest technology by consistently upgrading and introducing new versions of its popular brands. Within the past couple of years it has launched such products as the robotic-arm assisted Mako Total Knee the Neptune 3 Waste Management System and the Tritanium interbody spinal device.

Acquisitions are another important strategy for growth. In 2017 the company spent nearly $1 billion to acquire firms including Novadaq Technologies and Vexim.

In terms of partnerships in 2017 the company formed an alliance with GE unit GE Additive to expand Stryker's additive manufacturing (or industrial 3D printing) capabilities. The companies are working together to develop new additive products and materials including metal.

Cost-cutting initiatives include rationalizing product lines implementing a global enterprise resource planning system and consolidating manufacturing sites as possible. But the company has a number of new facilities open or under construction including sales and customer service offices in numerous countries a manufacturing plant in Utah a technology center in Ireland an R&D centers in Michigan and Germany.

The company spends between 5% and 7% of annual revenues on R&D programs each year.

Mergers and Acquisitions
Purchases in recent years have brought Stryker new software and manufacturing technologies and entered it into new lines of business such as surgical imaging and minimally invasive devices for treatment of stroke and brain conditions.

In 2019 Stryker agreed to buy TSO3 which develops sterilization technology for medical devices for about $52 million. TSOP3 makes the STERIZONE VP4 a low-temperature sterilizer that is cleared for use in the US Canada and Europe.

In 2019 the company acquired Israel-based OrthoSpace for $110 million plus up to $110 million in milestone payments. OrthoSpace makes balloons that prevent friction during minimally invasive bone procedures; it is approved in Europe and being tested in the US.

In 2018 Stryker bought K2M which specializes in spinal surgery products for $1.4 billion. The deal broadened Stryker's presence in the spinal and complex spine market and added a portfolio of minimally invasive spine devices. K2M became part of Stryker's Spine division.

Also that year Stryker acquired ear nose and throat products specialist Entellus Medical in a $662 million transaction.

In a smaller deal Stryker acquired HyperBranch Medical Technology for $220 million in October 2018. The purchase included the Adherus AutoSpray Dural Sealant for the spinal cord and brain. HyperBranch joined the company's Neurotechnology business. Stryker also acquired Invuity which makes single-use lighted surgical instruments and illumination devices for $190 million.

In 2017 Stryker bought Canadian medical imaging products firm Novadaq Technologies for $716 million. Novadaq makes fluorescence imaging technology that shows blood flow during surgeries. The purchase expanded Stryker's reach into the open and plastic reconstructive surgery market.

Also in 2017 the company acquired control of French spinal implant manufacturer Vexim for some $216 million. It bought the rest of Vexim which is looking to launching its SpineJack device in the US in 2018.

In 2016 Stryker bought personal products maker Sage Products for $2.8 billion. Sage which specializes in items that prevent hospital-acquired conditions is now part of Stryker's MedSurg segment. The firm also purchased UK company Stanmore Implants Worldwide which makes orthopedic devices to help treat bone cancer.

Also that year the company purchased Physio-Control for almost $1.3 billion and Instratek for an undisclosed amount. Physio-Control develops and manufactures monitors/defibrillators and CPR-assist devices which serve as fitting add-ons to Stryker's Emergency Medical Services (EMS) business. Instratek is a Texas-based maker of orthopedic implants and endoscopic instruments for use in hand and foot procedures.

Company Background
Stryker was founded in 1941 by Dr. Homer Stryker.

HISTORY
Stryker was founded in 1941 by Dr. Homer Stryker an orthopedic surgeon who had invented several orthopedic devices. It was incorporated in 1946 as a Michigan company. The company expanded through organic measures and occasional acquisitions over the following decades while the Stryker family kept a hand in its operations.

Beginning in 2009 Stryker set out to further diversify its operations through acquisitions. In 2010 Stryker purchased supportive surface maker (think: beds and tables) Gaymar Industries for approximately $150 million in cash. The two companies were already well-acquainted through a long-standing supply and sales agreement in the US.

Its $1.5 billion acquisition of Boston Scientific's neurovascular division in 2011 added minimally invasive devices (such as coils stents and balloon catheters) for the treatment of cerebral conditions such as brain aneurysms and hemorrhagic and ischemic strokes.

Stryker further boosted its neurovascular operations later that year when it acquired Concentric Medical a maker of clot removal products for use in ischemic stroke procedures for some $135 million. Following these acquisitions Stryker rearranged its operating structure from two divisions into three: Reconstructive MedSurg Equipment and Neurotechnology and Spine.

The company's OP-1 bone growth product was so successful that in 2011 the company sold the product franchise to Olympus for $60 million. During 2011 Stryker acquired synthetic bone graft material maker Orthovita for some $304 million in cash. It also spent $150 million to purchase France's Memometal Technologies for its in hand and foot device products.

EXECUTIVES
Vp Regulatory Affairs Quality, Elizabeth Staub
Vice President, Bronwen Taylor
Group President Orthopaedics, David K. Floyd, $575,000 total compensation
Chairman President And Ceo, Kevin A. Lobo, $1,129,167 total compensation
Group President Global Quality And Operations, Lonny J. Carpenter, $497,500 total compensation
Group President Medsurg And Neurotechnology, Timothy J. Scannell, $610,333 total compensation
Vp And Cio, Bijoy Sagar
Vp Communications Public Affairs And Strategic Marketing, Yin C. Becker
Group Cfo Medsurg & Neurotechnology (msnt), Glenn Boehnlein, $517,333 total compensation
President Asia Pacific, Graham A. McLean
Vice President Information Technology, Justin Ritchie
Marketing Vice President, Stewart Simpson
Vice President International Regulatory Affairs, Brad Hossack
Vp Finance And Business Development, Rod Macleod
Vice President Healthcare Systems, Lara Latham
Vice President Marketing And Education Services, Lori Quigley
Area Vice President Stryker Orthopaedics, Eric Tamweber
Mvp Manager, Nicole Westin
Vice President Human Resources, Art Hartman
Vp Global Supply Chain Operations, John Lebowitz
Vice President Operations, Mike Vanvleet
Vp Finance And Treasurer, Jeanne Blondia
Vp Alignment Strategy And Reform, Geoffrey Walton

Area Vice President, William Fain
Vp Corporate Controller, William Berry Jr
Vice President Global Infrastructure Services,
  Michael Doyle
Vp Hr Joint Replacement, Karen Bick
Regional Vice President, Jonathan Lehmann
Vice President And General Manager, Gordon Van
  Ummersen
Board Of Director, Louise Francesconi
Board Of Director, Ronda Stryker
Board Director, Srikant Datar
Board Member, Andrew Silvernail
Board Member, Mary Brainerd
Auditors: Ernst & Young LLP

LOCATIONS

HQ: Stryker Corp
  2825 Airview Boulevard, Kalamazoo, MI 49002
Phone: 269 385-2600 **Fax:** 269 385-1062
Web: www.stryker.com

2017 Sales

	$ mil.	% of total
US	9,059	73
Europe Middle East & Africa	1,567	13
Asia/Pacific	1,413	11
Other	405	3
Total	**12,444**	**100**

PRODUCTS/OPERATIONS

2017 Sales by Segment

	$ mil.	% of total
MedSurg		
Medical	1,969	16
Instruments	1,678	14
Endoscopy	1,652	13
Sustainability	258	2
Orthopaedics		
Knees	1,595	13
Trauma & Extremities	1,478	12
Hips	1,303	10
Other	337	3
Neurotechnology & Spine		
Neurotechnology	1,423	11
Spine	751	6
Total	**12,444**	**100**

COMPETITORS

Arthrex	Olympus
CONMED Corporation	Penumbra
DePuy	Philips Electronics
DePuy Spine	STERIS
Globus Medical	Smith & Nephew
Hill-Rom Holdings	Synthes
Medline Industries	Terumo Medical
Medtronic	Corporation
Medtronic Sofamor	ZOLL
Danek	Zimmer Biomet
NuVasive	

HISTORICAL FINANCIALS

Company Type: Public

Income Statement

FYE: December 31

	REVENUE ($ mil.)	NET INCOME ($ mil.)	NET PROFIT MARGIN	EMPLOYEES
12/19	14,884	2,083	14.0%	40,000
12/18	13,601	3,553	26.1%	36,000
12/17	12,444	1,020	8.2%	33,000
12/16	11,325	1,647	14.5%	33,000
12/15	9,946	1,439	14.5%	27,000
Annual Growth	10.6%	9.7%	—	10.3%

2019 Year-End Financials

Debt ratio: 37.00%
Return on equity: 17.00%
Cash ($ mil.): 4,337
Current ratio: 3.00
Long-term debt ($ mil.): 10,231

No. of shares (mil.): 375
Dividends
  Yield: 1.0%
  Payout: 24.0%
Market value ($ mil.): 78,623

	STOCK PRICE ($) FY Close	P/E High/Low		PER SHARE ($) Earnings	Dividends	Book Value
12/19	210.00	40	27	5.00	2.00	34.00
12/18	157.00	19	15	9.00	2.00	31.00
12/17	155.00	59	43	3.00	2.00	27.00
12/16	120.00	28	20	4.00	2.00	25.00
12/15	93.00	27	24	4.00	1.00	23.00
Annual Growth	22.6%	—	—	9.7%	10.8%	10.6%

Summit Financial Group Inc

Summit Financial Group is at the peak of community banking in West Virginia and northern Virginia. The company owns Summit Community Bank which operates about 20 branches that offer standard retail banking fare such as deposit accounts loans and cash management services. Commercial real estate loans including land development and construction loans account for about 40% of Summit Financial Group's loan portfolio which also includes residential mortgages and a smaller percentage of business and consumer loans. The bank's Summit Insurance Services unit sells both commercial and personal coverage.

EXECUTIVES

Senior Vice President And Chief Of Credit Administration, Patrick Frye
Senior Vice President Commercial Lending, Jason Hicks
Senior Vice President Commercial Lending, Lisa Dennison
Executive Vice President Of Business Development, Jack Rossi
Senior Vice President And Trust Officer, Julie H Johnson
Vice President Commerical Loans, Anna B Abbey
Vice President Of Mortgage Originations, Oguz Sengul
Vice President Commerical Loans, Anna Abbey
Senior Vice President And Trust Officer, Julie Johnson
Senior Vice President Commercial Lending, Jim Rodgers
Secretary Independent Director, Phoebe Heishman
Board Member, Scott Bridgeforth
Auditors: Yount, Hyde & Barbour, P.C.

LOCATIONS

HQ: Summit Financial Group Inc
  300 North Main Street, Moorefield, WV 26836
Phone: 304 530-1000
Web: www.summitfgi.com

COMPETITORS

Allegheny Bancshares	Highlands Bankshares
BB&T	Inc.
F & M Bank	SunTrust
Fauquier Bankshares	

HISTORICAL FINANCIALS

Company Type: Public

Income Statement

FYE: December 31

	ASSETS ($ mil.)	NET INCOME ($ mil.)	INCOME AS % OF ASSETS	EMPLOYEES
12/18	2,201	28	1.3%	371
12/17	2,134	12	0.6%	349
12/16	1,759	17	1.0%	251
12/15	1,492	16	1.1%	231
12/14	1,444	11	0.8%	222
Annual Growth	11.1%	25.4%	—	13.7%

2018 Year-End Financials

Debt ratio: 1.00%
Return on equity: 13.00%
Cash ($ mil.): 60
Current ratio: —
Long-term debt ($ mil.): —

No. of shares (mil.): 12
Dividends
  Yield: 3.0%
  Payout: 29.0%
Market value ($ mil.): 238

	STOCK PRICE ($) FY Close	P/E High/Low		PER SHARE ($) Earnings	Dividends	Book Value
12/18	19.00	12	8	2.00	1.00	18.00
12/17	26.00	28	19	1.00	0.00	16.00
12/16	28.00	18	7	2.00	0.00	14.00
12/15	12.00	8	7	2.00	0.00	13.00
12/14	12.00	9	7	1.00	0.00	16.00
Annual Growth	12.9%	—	—	17.9%	—	3.0%

Sunoco LP

Sunoco LP (formerly Susser Petroleum Partners) pairs with its parent to proffer petroleum. It operates about 900 convenience stores and retail fuel sites and distributes motor fuel to convenience stores independent dealers commercial customers and distributors in more than 30 US states at 6800 sites both directly and through its 32% stake in in Sunoco LLC owned in partnership with Energy Transfer Partners (ETP). Energy Transfer Equity owns 's general partner and incentive distribution rights. ETP owns a 38.4% limited partner interest in the company. In 2016 Sunoco LP bought the fuels business of Emerge Energy Services LP for $167.7 million.In 2017 Japan-based Seven & i Holdings agreed to buy 1100 convenience stores and gas stations from Sunoco LP for about $3.3 billion.

EXECUTIVES

Vp Retail Company Operations, Paul A Brzezicki
Board Member, James Bryant
Auditors: Grant Thornton LLP

LOCATIONS

HQ: Sunoco LP
  8111 Westchester Drive, Suite 400, Dallas, TX 75225
Phone: 214 981-0700
Web: www.sunocolp.com

COMPETITORS

CITGO	Shell Oil Products
Chevron	Sinclair Oil
ConocoPhillips	Sunoco
Exxon Mobil	TOTAL
Hess Corporation	Valero Energy
Royal Dutch Shell	

HISTORICAL FINANCIALS

Company Type: Public

Income Statement   FYE: December 31

	REVENUE ($ mil.)	NET INCOME ($ mil.)	NET PROFIT MARGIN	EMPLOYEES
12/18	16,994	(207)	—	3,622
12/17	11,723	149	1.3%	
12/16	15,698	(406)	—	
12/15	16,935	237	1.4%	
12/14	1,890	35	1.9%	
Annual Growth	73.2%	—	—	—

2018 Year-End Financials

Debt ratio: 61.00%	No. of shares (mil.): 99
Return on equity: (-14.00%)	Dividends
Cash ($ mil.): 56	Yield: 12.0%
Current ratio: 1.00	Payout: —
Long-term debt ($ mil.): 2,980	Market value ($ mil.): 2,694

	STOCK PRICE ($) FY Close	P/E High/Low	PER SHARE ($) Earnings	Dividends	Book Value
12/18	27.00	— —	(3.00)	3.00	8.00
12/17	28.00	93 67	0.00	3.00	19.00
12/16	27.00	— —	(5.00)	3.00	19.00
12/15	40.00	48 28	1.00	3.00	31.00
12/14	50.00	70 38	1.00	2.00	33.00
Annual Growth	(14.0%)	—	—	12.6%(29.8%)	

SUTTER HEALTH

Whether you drink too much in Wine Country hit some rough waters off the Marin Headlands or trip during a hike through the redwood forest it's likely Sutter Health is just a stone's throw away. The Northern California not-for-profit health care system is one of the nation's largest with more than 4250 acute care beds. After being formed through the merger of Sutter Health and California Healthcare System Sutter Health now caters to residents of more than 100 communities from the California Bay Area to the beaches of Hawaii. Its services are provided through affiliated doctors from a host of health care facilities including acute care hospitals home health networks and skilled nursing facilities.

Operations

Sutter Health affiliates provide acute care services health education home health care hospice care adult day care prenatal clinics immunization services and other specialized health care services.

The system's health plan network includes about 25 hospitals and campuses and dozens of other facilities with more than 5000 providers serving some 40000 members throughout Northern California.

In 2017 the system reported more than 11 million outpatient visits; more than 190000 discharges; and some 870000 emergency room visits.

Sutter reports its revenue in four categories: patient service revenue (more than 85% of total) premium revenue (around 10%) contributions and other (combined less than 5%)

Geographic Reach

Sutter Health structures its governance into two geographic regions across Northern California: the Bay Area (which also includes Hawaii) and the Valley.

Sales and Marketing

Sutter Health earns its revenue through patient care with payers including health insurers and government programs.

Financial Performance

In 2018 Sutter Health reported $12.7 billion in operating revenue a 2% increase over the prior year. However operating expenses increased and investment income fell 44% to $187 million that year. The company reported a $198 million net loss versus income of $893 million in 2017.

Sutter ended 2018 with $362 million in net cash $33 million less than it had at the end of 2017. Operating activities provided $758 million and financing activities provided another $574 million but investing activities used $1.4 billion.

Strategy

As a not-for-profit system Sutter Health reinvests its earnings into the communities it serves. For example it recently built the new two-campus California Pacific Medical Center in San Francisco; the facilities opened their doors in 2018. It also has construction projects to expand its network of clinics.

Like most other health care organizations across the country Sutter Health is using technology to improve the quality of care given to patients. In 2019 it began a partnership with digital scribe firm Suki to pilot an AI-powered digital assistant for doctors. The voice-enabled tool will integrate with Sutter's existing electronic health records system allowing doctors to spend more quality time with their patients and giving patients access to updated care data. Suki will learn each doctor's preference and clinical practice guidelines and ultimately will be able to create an actionable plan of care.

Company Background

Although it traces its roots back to the 1800s Sutter Health was officially formed through the 1996 merger of Sacramento's Sutter Health and the Bay Area's California Healthcare System.

EXECUTIVES

Ceo Sutter Health Sacramento-sierra Region, Sarah Krevans, age 60
Svp And Cfo, Robert D. (Bob) Reed, age 67
President Sutter Health Central Valley Region, David P. Benn
President Sutter Health East Bay Region, David Bradley
Svp And Cio, Jonathan (Jon) Manis
Svp; Executive Officer Sutter Medical Network, Jeffrey Burnich
President Sutter Health West Bay Region, Mike Cohill
President Sutter Health Sacramento Sierra Region, James E. Conforti
President Sutter Health Peninsula Coastal Region, Jeff Gerard
Ceo Sutter Solano Medical Center, Abhishek Dosi
Vice President Finance And Treasurer, Svend Ryge
Vice President, Theresa Frei
Vice President Of Construction, Melinda Dow
Vice President And Medical Director, Joan Etzell
Vice President Is Corporation Client Services, Jennifer Sierras
Senior Vice President And General Counse, Florence Di Benedetto
Vice President Total Rewards, Diane Schnabel
Vice President Legal Operations, Pamela Marino
Vice President Strategy And Business Development Sutter Health Medical And Markets Network, Todd Smith
Vice President, Tom Hart
Regional Vice President, Jodi Davis
Vice President Talent And Change Management, Christopher Henry
Medical Director, Jeff Jenkins
Medical Director, Gina Bell
Vice President Chief Nursing Informatics Officer, Donna Woelfel
Vice President Managed Care, Karrie Abe
Vice President Clinical Informatics And Electronic Health Records, Howard Landa
Chair, Geraldine R. Brinton
Board Member, Portia Diwa
Unit Secretary, Vicki Pugh
Unit Secretary, Alicia Marzan-goble

LOCATIONS

HQ: SUTTER HEALTH
2200 RIVER PLAZA DR, SACRAMENTO, CA 958334134
Phone: 916 733-8800
Web: WWW.SUTTERHEALTH.ORG

Selected Hospitals

Alta Bates Summit Medical Center (Berkeley Oakland)
California Pacific Medical Center (San Francisco)
Eden Medical Center (Castro Valley)
Kahi Mohala (Ewa HI)
Marin General Hospital (Greenbrae)
Memorial Hospital Los Banos (Los Banos)
Memorial Medical Center (Modesto)
Menlo Park Surgical Hospital
Mills-Peninsula Health Services (Burlingame)
Novato Community Hospital (Novato)
Sutter Amador Hospital (Jackson)
Sutter Auburn Faith Hospital (Auburn)
Sutter Coast Hospital (Crescent City)
Sutter Davis Hospital (Davis)
Sutter Delta Medical Center (Antioch)
Sutter Lakeside Hospital (Lakeport)
Sutter Maternity & Surgery Center of Santa Cruz
Sutter Medical Center (Sacramento)
Sutter Medical Center of Santa Rosa
Sutter Roseville Medical Center
Sutter Solano Medical Center (Vallejo)
Sutter Tracy Community Hospital (Tracy)

PRODUCTS/OPERATIONS

2018 Sales

	$ mil.	% of total
Patient service revenue	10,957	86
Premium revenue	1,383	11
Contributions	6	-
Other	351	3
Total	12,697	100

Selected Services

Allergy Care
Alzheimer's and Brain Health
Arthritis and Rheumatology
Asthma Care
Back and Spine Services
Behavioral Health Care
Bioethics Services
Cancer Services
Cosmetic Surgery
Dermatology Services
Diabetes Services
Ear Nose and Throat Services
Emergency Services
Endocrinology
Fertility Services
Gastroenterology
Gynecology and Women's Health
Health Education
Heart and Vascular Services
Holistic and Integrative Medicine
Home Health and Hospice Care
Imaging
Kidney Disease and Nephrology
Lab and Pathology
Liver Care
Neuroscience
Occupational Health
Orthopedic Services
Palliative Care and Advanced Illness Management
Pediatric Services
Physical Therapy and Rehabilitation
Podiatric Services
Pregnancy and Childbirth Services
Primary Care
Pulmonary Care

Reconstructive Plastic Surgery
Senior Services and Geriatric Care
Surgical Services
Transplant Services
Urgent Care
Urology
Vision Care
Weight Loss Services
Long-Term Care Centers
Irene Swindells Alzheimer's Residential Care Center San Francisco
Sutter Oaks Nursing Center Sacramento
Sutter Senior Care PACE Program Sacramento
Cancer Centers
Alta Bates Summit Comprehensive Cancer Center Berkeley and Oakland
California Pacific Medical Center San Francisco
Dorothy E. Schneider Cancer Center at Mills-Peninsula Health Services Burlingame
Eden Medical Center Castro Valley
Memorial Regional Cancer Center Modesto
Sutter Auburn Faith Hospital Auburn
Sutter Cancer Center Sutter Medical Center Sacramento
Sutter Cancer Center Sutter Roseville Medical Center Roseville
Sutter Solano Cancer Center Vallejo
Programs listed above are approved by the American College of Surgeons' Commission on Cancer.
Research Institutes
California Pacific Medical Center San Francisco
Palo Alto Medical Foundation Research Institute Palo Alto
Sutter Health Institute for Research and Education San Francisco
Sutter Institute for Medical Research Sacramento
Home Health and Hospice Services
Coming Home Hospice
Cohen Cormier Home Attendant & Care Management
Sutter Auburn Faith VNA & Hospice
Sutter Care at Home
Sutter Coast Home Care
Sutter Infusion & Pharmacy Services / Emeryville and Sacramento
Sutter Lakeside Home Medical Services
Sutter Lifeline / Sacramento
Sutter North Home Health Agency
VNA of the Central Valley
VNA of Santa Cruz County
Express Medical Clinics
Sutter Express Care (Three locations in Sacramento & Placer counties)

COMPETITORS

Adventist Health System West
Alta Bates Summit Medical Center
Ascension Health
Children's Hospital & Research Center at Oakland
HCA
Hawai'i Pacific Health
Kuakini Health System
Providence St. Joseph Health
Rehabilitation Hospital of the Pacific
Stanford Health Care
Tenet Healthcare
UCSF Medical

HISTORICAL FINANCIALS

Company Type: Private

Income Statement   FYE: December 31

	REVENUE ($ mil.)	NET INCOME ($ mil.)	NET PROFIT MARGIN	EMPLOYEES
12/18	12,697	(447)	—	48,000
12/17	12,444	1,060	8.5%	—
12/16	11,873	422	3.6%	—
12/15	10,998	84	0.8%	—
Annual Growth	4.9%	—	—	—

SVB Financial Group

SVB Financial Group is the holding company for Silicon Valley Bank which serves emerging and established companies involved in technology life sciences and private equity and provides customized financing to entrepreneurs executives and investors in those industries. It also offers deposit accounts loans and international banking and plays matchmaker for young firms and private investors. SVB also provides investment advisory brokerage and asset management services and markets credit and banking services to wealthy individuals. Founded in 1983 SVB has $60 billion in assets and holds $29 billion in deposits.

Operations

SVB Financial Group has four reporting segments: Global Commercial Bank SVB Leerink SVB Capital and SVB Private Bank.

SVB's revenue derives heavily from its Global Commercial Bank segment; it accounts for about 85% of the total. The division comprises five subunits: Commercial Bank Private Equity Division SVB Wine SVB Analytics and Debt Fund Investments. The Commercial Bank provides financial services including credit treasury management and foreign exchange to commercial clients in the technology venture capital and private equity life science and healthcare industries. SVB Analytics offers research to innovation economy investors and companies while Debt Fund Investments houses SVB's investments debt fund investments.

Healthcare- and life science-focused investment bank SVB Leerink offers biotechs pharmas and medical device and diagnostic companies capital raising and sales and trading services merger and acquisition advisory and equity research. It also sponsors private investment funds. The segment generates roughly 10% of SVB's revenue.

SVB Capital and SVB Private Bank each bring in less than 5% of the company's revenue. The former manages third parties' venture capital funds. The latter markets banking products to the private equity and venture capital community.

Roughly 85% SVB's $29 billion loan portfolio is dedicated to commercial loans; about 50% of the total portfolio is allocated to private equity and venture capital entities and some 25% of the total is to software and internet companies. Loans to life science and healthcare companies make up about 10%.

Geographic Reach

Santa Clara California-based SVB Financial has more than 25 regional offices in California Arizona Colorado Georgia Illinois Massachusetts New York North Carolina Oregon Pennsylvania Texas Utah Virginia and Washington. It has international offices in Hong Kong China Germany India Israel and England.

Sales and Marketing

Clients to SVB Financial Group's Global Commercial Bank primarily encompass technology life science healthcare private equity and venture capital entities. The company's technology clients typically include semiconductor data and storage companies; software and internet companies; and innovators in energy and resources. SVB Leerink's customers include biotechs pharmas medical device and diagnostic makers healthcare services and digital health firms and life science tool companies.

Financial Performance

Against the backdrop of the Silicon Valley tech boom SVB Financial Group's asset and loan base has grown steadily over the last five years as has its revenue?which posted overall growth of some 85%. The company's net income fared even better soaring about 270% in that time.

SVB's revenue jumped 34% to $2.6 billion in 2018. Increased average loan balances and yields and fixed income investment balances and securities yield drove a net interest income gain of $479.7 million. Fee income rose $136.9 on additions across all of SVB's fee sources particularly client investments.

The company's net income shot up 99% to $974 million that year on the strength of its revenue.

SVB infused its cash stores with $648.5 million in 2018 to end the year with $3.6 billion. Operations provided $933.6 million. It used $4.8 billion on investments (mostly increased net loans and held-to-maturity securities) and received $4.5 billion from its investing activities (stemming from net increased deposits).

Strategy

SVB Financial Group adjusts its business strategy according to each of its client niches including life science healthcare and technology companies; private equity and venture capital firms; premium wine producers; and private bank and wealth management customers.

The holding company's most robust strategy is centered on technology and life science companies. SVB seeks to develop relationships with such clients early in their development and continually offer them expanded services as they mature. Its SVB Accelerator offers banking and financial services to pre-revenue or low-revenue (less than $5 million annually) startups primarily performing research and development that have brought few if any products to market. SVB Growth addresses mid- and late-stage companies?mostly private entities dependent on venture capital that may be poised for an IPO. They typically have yearly revenue of between $5 and $75 million. SVB Corporate Finance serves established large corporations with advanced products or services and annual revenue of more than $75 million.

In a move to expand its operations in the growing life science and healthcare industries in 2019 SVB purchased Leerink Partners?an investment bank serving biotechs pharmas and other healthcare-centric companies. Leerink's operations remain largely unchanged under the SVB Leerink banner.

SVB relies on strong relationships with the private equity and venture capital communities cultivated over its three decades of existence to maintain its client base in those sectors.

Mergers and Acquisitions

In January 2019 SVB Financial Group acquired Boston-based Leerink Holdings the parent company of healthcare and life science investment bank Leerink Partners. SVB paid $280 million up front and created a retention pool for employees of $60 million to be paid over five years. The deal greatly expanded its operations and client base among biotechs pharmas and medical device and diagnostic companies.

Company Background

Established in 1983 SVB Financial Group went public on Nasdaq five years later. By 1996 it had expanded to 15 US states.

HISTORY

Silicon Valley Bank was founded in 1983 by Roger Smith to provide banking services to tech startups in San Jose. The bank boomed along with tech companies during the 1980s lending to the likes of Cisco Systems.

In 1990 the bank spread east to Boston's burgeoning technology alley. It also expanded into residential and commercial real estate lending. The recession of 1989 to 1991 found Silicon Valley Bancshares with an overextended loan portfolio and in 1992 the bank booked a loss due to non-performing loans; the next year it was put under federal supervision.

To rally stockholder confidence the company brought in new management and demoted Smith from chairman to vice chairman; he left the in 1995. The bank reduced its real estate lending and diversified into factoring foreign exchange and executive banking for venture capitalists and clients' upper management.

The 1995 IPO frenzy aided the company's turn-around. Silicon Valley cashed in on warrants it had taken as collateral from young companies. Regulatory supervision was lifted in 1996 and the bank soon opened offices in the Atlanta; Austin Texas; Boulder Colorado; Phoenix; and Seattle areas.

In 1999 Silicon Valley Bancshares created a website targeted at technology firms in need of financing employees office space and equipment. However nonperforming loans began to dog the bank once again affecting profits and bringing a regulatory request to boost capital reserves.

In 2000 despite being hammered by the high-tech stock selloff the company continued to expand opening offices in West Palm Beach Florida and North Carolina's Research Triangle and successfully capitalizing its first venture fund. The following year it bought tech-focused investment bank Alliant Partners (later renamed SVB Alliant) to broaden its service offerings.

Still licking its wounds from the tech bust the company ceased lending to the entertainment industry and to churches in 2002. Silicon Valley Bancshares changed its name to SVB Financial Services in 2005.

SVB Alliant struggled with losses for years and SVB Financial explored its options including spinning the unit off to management. It ultimately decided to shut down the division which ceased operations in 2008.

EXECUTIVES

Coo, Michael L. Dreyer, age 55
Chief Digital Officer, Bruce E. Wallace, age 54, $398,113 total compensation
President And Ceo Svb Financial Group And Silicon Valley Bank, Gregory W. (Greg) Becker, age 52, $925,904 total compensation
President Silicon Valley Bank, Michael R. (Mike) Descheneaux, age 52, $602,308 total compensation
Head Of Technology Banking, John D. China, $498,385 total compensation
Head Of Europe Middle East And Africa (emea) And President Uk Branch, Philip C. Cox, age 52
Chief Credit Officer Silicon Valley Bank, Marc C. Cadieux, age 52, $447,308 total compensation
Cfo, Daniel Beck
Chief Risk Officer, Laura Izurieta, age 58
Cio, Roger E. Leone, age 65
Vice President, Vincent Vallejos
Senior Vice President, Dave Bhagat
Vice President Relationship Manager, Don Chandler
Vice President, Suzann Russell
Vice President Manager Of Sales And Business Product Management, Dennis Corbett
Vice President Relationship Manager Corporate Technology, Phil Silvia
Vice President, Damarie Rodriguez
Vice President, Sam Subilia
Vice President And Relationship Managersouth Bay Region, Jacob Moseley
Vice President And Foreign Exchange Trader, Patrick Chin
Senior Vice President, Li Song
Vice President Regional Director, Carmella Montesdeoca
Vice President, Lauren Cole
Vice President, Alina Zinchik

Vice President Corporate Finance, Andrea Jones
Vice President, Ann Kim
Senior Vice President And Senior Relationship Manager, Matt Maloney
Vice President, Patrick Haggerty
Vice President, Austin Badger
Vice President Software, Alex Choy
Vice President, Bailey Morrow
Vice President, Jigar Patel
Senior Vice President, Andy Tsao
Vice President Relationship Manager, John Peck
Vice President, Benjermin Colombo
Vice President, Patrick Scheper
Senior Vice President, Michael Tramack
Senior Vice President, Chris Stoecker
Vice President Foreign Exchange, Joseph Landers
Vice President, Raj Morey
Executive Vice President And Founder, Rob Mcmillan
Vice President Relationship Manager Cleantech, Jordan Kanis
Vice President Leveraged Finance, Jordan Samiljan
Vice President, Ellen Ayoub
Vice President Ii, Ryan Kirschling
Vice President, Cody Nenadal
Vice President, Max Lautmann
Vice President Corporate Finance, Will Deevy
Vice President, Tom Gordon
Vice President, Paula Sen
Vice President, Kyle Swan
Vice President I, Russell Follansbee
Vice President, Dennis He
Vice President, Chelsea Hakso
Vice President Structured Finance, James Caron
Vice President Relationship Manager, Glenn Marasigan
Vice President, Matt Kelty
Vice President, Marc Neri
Vice President, Kelly Belcher
Vice President, Steve Lyons
Vice President Structured Finance, Derek Almeida
Vice President, Erin Angerer
Vice President Early Stage Banking, Navid Shahrestani
Vice President Global Fund Banking, Robert Pyke
Vice President, Jordan Parcell
Vice President Partnerships, George Hotarek
Vice President, William Robinson
Vice President, Carly Kiser
Vice President, Aerin Lim
Vice President, AJ Fang
Vice President, Frank O'brien
Vice President Life Sciences, Kristina Peralta
Vice President Corporate Finance, Ted Bell
Vice President Technology Banking, Patrick Johnson
Vice President, Janice Ahn
Chairman Svb Financial Group And Silicon Valley Bank, Roger F. Dunbar, age 73
Assistant Secretary And Treasurer, Lori De Leon
Board Member, Chris Canazaro
Auditors: KPMG LLP

LOCATIONS

HQ: SVB Financial Group
3003 Tasman Drive, Santa Clara, CA 95054-1191
Phone: 408 654-7400
Web: www.svb.com

Selected Offices

US
Atlanta
Austin TX
Broomfield CO
Chicago
Dallas
Irvine CA
Menlo Park CA
Minnetonka MN
New York

Newton MA
Palo Alto CA
Philadelphia
Phoenix
Pleasanton CA
Portland OR
Raleigh NC
Salt Lake City
San Diego
San Francisco
Santa Rosa CA
Seattle
St. Helena CA
Tysons Corner VA
International
Bangalore India
Beijing
Herzliya Pituach Israel
London
Mumbai India
Shanghai

PRODUCTS/OPERATIONS

2016 Sales

	$ mil.	% of total
Interest		
Loans	834	51
Investment securities	359	22
Noninterest		
Net gains on investment securities	52	3
Net gains on derivative instruments	49	3
Foreign exchange fees	104	6
Credit card fees	68	4
Deposit service charges	53	3
Lending related fees	33	2
Letters of credit	26	2
Client investment fees	32	2
Other	40	2
Total	**1,650**	**100**

Selected Subsidiaries and Affiliates

Silicon Valley Bank
SVB Analytics Inc.
SVB Asset Management
SVB Business Partners (Beijing) Co. Ltd.
SVB Business Partners (Shanghai) Co. Ltd.
SVB Global Financial Inc.
SVB Global Investors LLC
SVB Growth Investors LLC
SVB India Advisors Pvt. Ltd.
SVB Israel Advisors Ltd.
SVB Qualified Investors Fund LLC
SVB Real Estate Investment Trust
SVB Securities
SVB Strategic Investors LLC
SVB Strategic Investors Fund L.P.
Venture Investment Managers L.P.

COMPETITORS

Bank of America	Heritage Commerce
Citigroup	MUFG Americas Holdings
City National	U.S. Bancorp
Comerica	

HISTORICAL FINANCIALS

Company Type: Public

Income Statement				FYE: December 31
	ASSETS ($ mil.)	NET INCOME ($ mil.)	INCOME AS % OF ASSETS	EMPLOYEES
12/18	56,928	974	1.7%	2,900
12/17	51,214	491	1.0%	2,438
12/16	44,684	383	0.9%	2,311
12/15	44,687	344	0.8%	2,089
12/14	39,345	264	0.7%	1,914
Annual Growth	9.7%	38.6%	—	10.9%

2018 Year-End Financials

Debt ratio: 1.00%
Return on equity: 21.00%
Cash ($ mil.): 3,448
Current ratio: —
Long-term debt ($ mil.): —

No. of shares (mil.): 53
Dividends
Yield: —
Payout: —
Market value ($ mil.): 9,987

	STOCK PRICE ($) FY Close	P/E High/Low	PER SHARE ($) Earnings	Dividends	Book Value
12/18	190.00	18 10	18.00	0.00	97.00
12/17	234.00	26 17	9.00	0.00	79.00
12/16	172.00	24 11	7.00	0.00	70.00
12/15	119.00	22 15	7.00	0.00	62.00
12/14	116.00	25 18	5.00	0.00	55.00
Annual Growth	13.1%	— —	35.9%	—	15.2%

Synchrony Financial

Auditors: KPMG LLP

LOCATIONS

HQ: Synchrony Financial
777 Long Ridge Road, Stamford, CT 06902
Phone: 203 585-2400
Web: www.synchronyfinancial.com

HISTORICAL FINANCIALS

Company Type: Public

Income Statement   FYE: December 31

	ASSETS ($ mil.)	NET INCOME ($ mil.)	INCOME AS % OF ASSETS	EMPLOYEES
12/18	106,792	2,790	2.6%	16,500
12/17	95,808	1,935	2.0%	16,000
12/16	90,207	2,251	2.5%	15,000
12/15	84,135	2,214	2.6%	12,000
12/14	75,707	2,109	2.8%	11,000
Annual Growth	9.0%	7.2%	—	10.7%

2018 Year-End Financials

Debt ratio: 22.00%
Return on equity: 19.00%
Cash ($ mil.): 9,396
Current ratio: —
Long-term debt ($ mil.): —

No. of shares (mil.): 719
Dividends
 Yield: 3.0%
 Payout: 19.0%
Market value ($ mil.): 16,862

	STOCK PRICE ($) FY Close	P/E High/Low	PER SHARE ($) Earnings	Dividends	Book Value
12/18	23.00	11 6	4.00	1.00	20.00
12/17	39.00	16 11	2.00	1.00	18.00
12/16	36.00	14 9	3.00	0.00	17.00
12/15	30.00	14 11	3.00	0.00	15.00
12/14	30.00	11 8	3.00	0.00	13.00
Annual Growth	(5.8%)	— —	7.7%	—	12.9%

Synnex Corp

SYNNEX connects technology sellers with buyers and helps with customer service after the sale. The company distributes PCs peripherals software and consumer electronics from manufacturers that include HP Inc. Hewlett-Packard Enterprise Google Panasonic Lenovo Asus and Microsoft. Its Concentrix segment offers customer support services using phone chat web e-mail and digital print. The company's online services include parts catalogs configuration and ordering. In addition the company offers contract design and assembly build-to-order and configure-to-order services for manufacturers and systems integrators. SYNNEX depends on the US for 70% of sales.

Operations

SYNNEX operates through two segments: Technology Solutions (TS) and Concentrix. The TS segment which accounts for about 90% of the company's revenue distributes IT systems peripherals system components software networking equipment CE and complementary products. It also offers data center server and storage.

Concentrix accounting for the remaining sales offers a range of business process outsourcing (BPO) services such as technical support renewals management lead management direct sales customer service back office processing and IT outsourcing. Concentrix's operations significantly expanded in 2018 with the addition of Convergys a BPO provider that SYNNEX bought in 2018.

Geographic Reach

SYNNEX headquartered in Fremont California gets 70% of sales from the US and 10% from Canada.

The company has about 60 distribution and administrative facilities in the US US Canada Japan China and Central and South America. Concentrix operates more than 275 delivery centers and administrative facilities in 40 countries throughout the world.

Sales and Marketing

SYNNEX sells to its large commercial government reseller and retail customers through its own sales force. SYNNEX markets its products and services to smaller resellers and OEMs through regional sales teams. The company also employs product management and business development specialists who focus on selling and promoting the products and services of selected suppliers or for specific end-market verticals.

SYNNEX relies on one customer and one supplier for a significant portion of revenue. The customer accounts for more than 15% of SYNNEX's revenue while HP Inc. is its biggest OEM supplier providing an eighth of revenue.

Financial Performance

SYNNEX has achieved unprecedented growth over the past four years with revenue reaching a company high of $20 billion in 2018 an 18% increase from 2017 boosted by contributions from acquisitions.

The Technology Solutions segment's revenue rose about 18% in 2018 from 2017 mostly from the full-year impact of the Westcon-Comstor Americas acquisition in September 2017. The segment also saw strength in sales of peripherals IT systems software and networking products in the US. The Concentrix segment's revenue jumped about 24% in 2018 from 2017 aided by about $440 million in sales from Convergys which was acquired in October 2018. Also contributing to higher sales were volume growth and expansion of services with consumer electronics technology and travel transportation and tourism customers.

Net income was relatively at about $300 million in 2018 and 2017. The company had higher interest expense and finance charges in 2018 from 2017 because of borrowing money to pay for acquisitions and support growth of the Technology Solutions business.

SYNNEX had $454.7 million in cash and equivalents in 2018 compared to $550.7 million in 2017. In 2018 cash from operations stood at $100.7 million while investing activities used $1.2 billion and financing activities provided about $1 billion.

Strategy

SYNNEX has made acquisitions in the past few years to strengthen the Technology Solutions and the Concentrix segments. The deals for Westcon-Comstor Americas' distribution business for $526.7 million in 2017 and Convergys for $2.3 billion in 2018 helped push SYNNEX over the $20 billion revenue mark in 2018. The deals also bolstered the company as competitors like Avnet and Tech Data also made acquisitions to expand.

SYNNEX has invested in making its operations more efficient increasing the amount of automation and adding more digital practices with higher margins.

SYNNEX's Hyve data center business hasn't performed to expectations and the company continues to work to diversify Hyve's customers and improve its profitability.

Mergers and Acquisitions

In 2018 SYNNEX acquired Convergys a competitor in business processing outsourcing (BPO) for $2.8 billion. Convergys became part of SYNNEX's Concentrix BPO operation. The expanded BPO unit within SYNNEX provides services in more than 70 languages from about 275 offices in some 40 countries around the world.

In 2017 SYNNEX acquired the Westcon-Comstor operations in North America and South America from Datatec Ltd. for about $800 million. SYNNEX also bought a a 10% stake in Datatec's Westcon International operations in Europe and the Asia/Pacific regions for about $30 million. The deal adds Westcon-Comstor's products and services in security unified communications and collaboration and networking to SYNNEX's operations.

In late 2016 the company acquired Canada-based The Minacs Group Pte for $420 million which is being integrated into its Concentrix business segment. The additional revenue from Minacs helped SYNNEX to achieve record revenue growth for its fiscal 2016.

Company Background

Robert Huang founded SYNNEX in 1980. The company has grown with the help of acquisitions; it bought about 25 companies from 1997-2018. The company's name comes from the combination of synergy and nexus.

EXECUTIVES

President And Ceo, Kevin M. Murai, age 56, $633,794 total compensation
Senior Vice President Corporate Finance And Treasurer, Mike Vaishnav
President Hyve Solutions, Stephen Ichinaga, age 58
President North American Technology Solutions, Peter Larocque, age 58, $459,499 total compensation
President Synnex Canada, Mitchell P. Martin, age 56
Svp And Cio, Gary Gulmon, age 58
Svp Marketing North America, Robert L. (Bob) Stegner
Coo, Dennis Polk, age 53, $459,499 total compensation
Cfo, Marshall Witt, $437,986 total compensation
President New Age Electronics, Fred Towns
Svp And General Manager Global Business Services, Christopher (Chris) Caldwell, $441,670 total compensation
Corporate Vice President Business Operations, Gina Rugani
Vice President, Steve Heslop
Vice President Of Procurement, Cynthia Su
Vice President Sales, Bruce Holappa
Senior Vice President Information Technology, Robert Sturycz
Vice President Sales, Willa Flemate
Vice President Internal Audit, Dana Aghai-Yazdy
Vice President Hp Enterprise Sales, Peter Montana
National Account Manager, Keith Cox
Assistant Vice President Commercial Sales Smb, John Phillips
Senior Vice President Sales New Age Electronics, Eric Kirkendall

Senior Vice President Systems Integration, Steve
Ichinaga
Vice President Marketing Technology Solutions
Divi, Denna Mensch
Vice President Of Enterprise Products, Doug Bone
Senior Vice President Operations, Tim Rush
Senior Vice President Marketing North America,
Bob Stegner
Senior Vice President Sales And Account
Management Concetrix Corporation, Rick Rosso
Senior Vice President Europe Global Applications
Development Solutions Pricing And Strategic
Pro, Philip Cassidy
Senior Vice President Operations And Delivery
Concentrix Corporation, Winnie Sun
Senior Vice President Information Systems And
Infosec Security Concentrix Corporation, Guy
Brosseau
Vice President Finance, Charlie Spano
Vice President Of Enterprise Sales, Synnex
Hpenterprise
Vice President Retail Product Management, Pierre
Montminy
Svp Concetrix Insurance Solutions, Marc Fedor
Svp High Value Services Concentrix Corporation,
Kathy Juve
Board Member, Andrea Zulberti
Chairman, Dwight Steffensen, age 76
Vice Chairman, Calvin Currie
Auditors: KPMG LLP

LOCATIONS

HQ: Synnex Corp
44201 Nobel Drive, Fremont, CA 94538
Phone: 510 656-3333
Web: www.synnex.com

2018 Sales

	$ mil.	% of total
United States	14,352	72
Canada	1,802	9
Other	3,898	19
Total	**20,054**	**100**

PRODUCTS/OPERATIONS

2018 Sales

	$ mil.	% of total
Technology solutions	17,609	88
Concentrix	2,463	12
Inter-segment	(18.4)	-
Total	**20,054**	**100**

2018 Sales

	$ mil.	% of total
Products	17,609	88
Services	2,445	12
Total	**20,054**	**100**

Selected Subsidiaries

Concentrix Technologies
ComputerLand Corporation
Concentrix Technologies (India) Private Limited
Concentrix Corporation
Concentrix Costa Rica S.A.
Concentrix Free Trade Zone S.A.
Concentrix HK Limited
Concentrix Nicaragua S.A
Sennex Enterprises Limited
SIT Funding Corporation
SYNNEX Canada Limited
SYNNEX Information Technologies (Beijing) Ltd
SYNNEX Information Technologies (Chengdu) Ltd
SYNNEX Information Technologies (China) Ltd
SYNNEX Infotec Corporation
SYNNEX de México S.A. de C.V
SYNNEX Software Technologies (HK) Limited
SYNNEX-Concentrix Corporation
SYNNEX-Concentrix UK Limited

Selected Services

Distribution
Contract assembly
Distribution services
Logistics services
Global Business Services
Automated service renewals software
Customer services
Hosted renewals services software in Europe
(RenewalsManager)
Financing services
Marketing services
Outsourced back-office services
Technical support services

COMPETITORS

Accenture	Plexus
Arrow Electronics	Premier Farnell
Avnet	Sanmina
Benchmark Electronics	ScanSource
Conduent	Tech Data
Hon Hai	Teleperformance
Ingram Micro	Wistron
Jabil	

HISTORICAL FINANCIALS

Company Type: Public

Income Statement
FYE: November 30

	REVENUE ($ mil.)	NET INCOME ($ mil.)	NET PROFIT MARGIN	EMPLOYEES
11/19	23,757	501	2.1%	240,900
11/18	20,054	301	1.5%	231,600
11/17	17,046	301	1.8%	113,600
11/16	14,062	235	1.7%	110,000
11/15	13,338	209	1.6%	72,500
Annual Growth	**15.5%**	**24.5%**	**—**	**35.0%**

2019 Year-End Financials

Debt ratio: 26.00%
Return on equity: 14.00%
Cash ($ mil.): 226
Current ratio: 2.00
Long-term debt ($ mil.): 2,718
No. of shares (mil.): 51
Dividends
　Yield: 0.0%
　Payout: 15.0%
Market value ($ mil.): 6,233

	STOCK PRICE ($) FY Close	P/E High/Low		PER SHARE ($) Earnings	Dividends	Book Value
11/19	123.00	13	8	10.00	2.00	75.00
11/18	81.00	19	10	7.00	1.00	68.00
11/17	136.00	18	14	8.00	1.00	58.00
11/16	117.00	20	13	6.00	1.00	50.00
11/15	94.00	18	13	5.00	1.00	46.00
Annual Growth	**6.8%**	**—**	**—**	**16.8%**	**27.1%**	**12.9%**

Synovus Financial Corp

Synovus Financial has a nose for community banking. The holding company owns flagship subsidiary Synovus Bank and more than 25 locally branded banking divisions that offer deposit accounts and consumer and business loans in Alabama Florida Georgia South Carolina and Tennessee. Through more than 280 branches the bank provides checking and savings accounts loans and mortgages and credit cards. Other divisions offer insurance private banking wealth and asset management and other financial services. Nonbank subsidiaries include Synovus Mortgage Synovus Trust investment bank and brokerage Synovus Securities and GLOBALT which provides asset management and financial planning services.

Geographic Reach

Georgia-based Synovus Financial has about 130 bank branches in Georgia. Florida is the bank's second largest market with nearly 50 branches while Alabama and South Carolina are home to more than 40 each.

Financial Performance

While the bank reported a 10% decline in revenue in 2013 versus 2012 to $1.18 billion and an 81% plunge in net income (to $159.4 million) it did make some progress on the long road to recovery. Significantly the bank redeemed its obligations under TARP (troubled asset relief program) in July 2013 funding more than two-thirds of the TARP redemption with internally available funds. The firm redeemed the remainder with proceeds from offerings of its common and preferred stock. Its loan portfolio grew by about $516 million up nearly 3% versus 2012. Credit quality also continued to improve while the bank lowered expenses.

Synovus blamed its continuing revenue slide on lower interest and non-interest income in 2013 versus 2012. Interest income fell on lower income on loans and investment securities. Non-interest income suffered relative to 2012 when the bank experienced higher levels of investment securities gains and gains on private equity investments as well as a decline in income from mortgage banking.

Strategy

Synovus has been cutting costs raising capital and improving efficiency in the aftermath of the residential and commercial real estate bust that hit the southeastern US particularly hard. During the dark days of the banking crisis (2008 to 2009) the company slashed about 10% of its workforce and it cut approximately 10% more in 2010 and 2011. It also closed nearly 40 branches and consolidated others.

Also Synovus which has traditionally maintained separate charters and local boards of directors for its subsidiary banks consolidated all of its charters into one in 2010 in order to reduce complexity and improve efficiency. Synovus also consolidated by merging some of its banks in Georgia and Florida; two of its Florida banking subsidiaries (one de novo and the other formed in the merger of three subsidiaries' banking charters) have taken the Synovus Bank brand a new strategy for the company.

The company returned to profitability in 2012 and remained profitable (although considerably less so) in 2013. To right itself Synovus has deemphasized commercial real estate lending and increased its focus on commercial and industrial banking including specialized services such as asset-based lending international banking and treasury management in an effort to increase revenue. The company is courting large corporate clients in the health care manufacturing distribution financial services natural resources and transportation sectors. Among smaller enterprises it targets professional practices such as physicians attorneys and accountants particularly for its private banking business.

Mergers and Acquisitions

In May 2013 Synovus assumed $56.8 million in deposits that belonged to failed Sunrise Bank from its receiver the FDIC. As part of the deal the bank acquired $492000 in loans.

The company bought specialty finance firm Entaire Global in October 2016. Entaire a private life insurance premium finance lender primarily serves small businesses. Synovus which is aiming to diversify its loan portfolio with the purchase paid an initial $30 million; it will pay extra earnings-based payments over a period of up to five years.

EXECUTIVES

Evp And Coo, Allen J. Gula, age 64, $434,192 total compensation

Evp And Chief Risk Officer, Mark G. Holladay, age 63, $428,454 total compensation

Evp And Chief Retail Banking Officer, D. Wayne Akins, age 56

Chairman And Ceo, Kessel D. Stelling, age 63, $962,269 total compensation

Evp Financial Management Services, J. Barton Singleton, age 55, $390,606 total compensation

Evp And Chief Credit Officer, Kevin J. Howard, age 54

Evp And Chief Community Banking Officer, R. Dallis (Roy) Copeland, age 50, $412,336 total compensation

Evp And Chief Corporate Banking Officer, Curtis J. Perry, age 56

Evp And Cfo, Kevin S. Blair

Cio, Renee S. Roth

Cto, Santosh Kokate

Evp General Counsel And Secretary, Allan E. Kamensky, age 58, $417,229 total compensation

Chief Information Security Officer, Kevin P. Gowen

Vice President Of Regional Sales, Ron Ward

Executive Vice President Corporate Affairs, Calvin Smyre

Senior Vice President Deputy General Counsel, Michael Smith

Senior Vice President Diversity And Career Resources, Audrey Hollingsworth

Senior Vice President Private Wealth Advisor, Michelle Mcclellan

Senior Vice President, Edward Deitz

Executive Vice President Risk And Compliance, John Latimer

Vice President, Susan Pitts

Vice President Product Management, Lynn White

Executive Vice President Retail Branches Columbus Band And Trust, Carolynn Obleton

Senior Vice President And Chief Audit Executive, Stephen Sawyer

Vice President Accounting Manager, Liz Gobbel

Vice President Tax Compliance Manager, Jim Buchs

Senior Vice President, Robbie Jones

Vice President And Director Compliance, Deborah Kent-Cochran

Senior Vice President, Brick F Luke

Executive Vice President, Jon Dodds

Senior Vice President, Jason Ninas

Executive Vice President, David Kimrey

Senior Vice President Facility Management Division, Mike Webb

Vice President Of Human Resources, Ronald Carr

Senior Vice President, Eric Tikkanen

Vice President Commercial Banking, Michael Harley

Vice President Retail Market Manager, Stephan Hollis

Vice President Finance Account Manager, Richard Pettit

Vice President Senior Business Analyst Lender, Alvena Pareja

Senior Vice President, Dan Summers

Vice President Commercial Real Estate, Mark Mathews

Senior Vice President Director Of Correspondent Banking, Richard Lane

Senior Vice President And Director Lcbg East, Michael Sawicki

Vice President, Phyllis Lyons

Vice President, Sandy Gowan

Evp Commercial Real Estate Division, Paige Collier

Vice President Commercial Banking, Patrick Ahern

Senior Vice President, David O'rear

Senior Vice President, Jeff Bauer

Evp And President Florida, Kent Ellert

Assistant Vice President Retail Market Manager, Leteria Waters

Senior Vice President, Wayne Gray

Vp And Commercial Banker, Gregory Alt

Senior Vice President Corporate Banking, Brad Beard

Assistant Vice President Branch Manager, Eileen Burton

Senior Vice President Market President, Patrick Murphy

Assistant Vice President, Janice Vagner

Treasurer, Joseph Lowery

Board Member, Jennifer Brooke

Auditors: KPMG LLP

LOCATIONS

HQ: Synovus Financial Corp
1111 Bay Avenue, Suite 500, Columbus, GA 31901
Phone: 706 649-2311
Web: www.synovus.com

Bank Branch Locations

	No.
Georgia	114
Florida	48
South Carolina	38
Alabama	37
Tennessee	11
Total	**248**

PRODUCTS/OPERATIONS

2016 Sales

	$ mil.	% of total
Interest income:		
Loans including fees	944	73
Investment securities available for sale	68	5
Trading account assets	0	-
Mortgage loans held for sale	3	-
Federal Reserve Bank balances	4	-
Other earning assets	4	-
Non-interest income:		
Service charges on deposit accounts	81	6
Fiduciary and asset management fees	47	4
Bankcard fees	33	3
Other non-interest income	34	3
Brokerage revenue	27	2
Mortgage banking income	24	2
Other fee income	20	2
Investment securities gains net	6	-
Total	**1,296**	**100**

COMPETITORS

BB&T	First Citizens
BBVA Compass	BancShares
Bancshares	First Horizon
BBX Capital	Regions Financial
BancorpSouth	SunTrust
Bank of America	Trustmark
Citigroup	Wells Fargo

HISTORICAL FINANCIALS

Company Type: Public

Income Statement   FYE: December 31

	ASSETS ($ mil.)	NET INCOME ($ mil.)	INCOME AS % OF ASSETS	EMPLOYEES
12/18	32,669	428	1.3%	4,651
12/17	31,222	275	0.9%	4,541
12/16	30,104	247	0.8%	4,436
12/15	28,793	226	0.8%	4,452
12/14	27,051	195	0.7%	4,511
Annual Growth	**4.8%**	**21.7%**	**—**	**0.8%**

2018 Year-End Financials

Debt ratio: 2.00%
Return on equity: 14.00%
Cash ($ mil.): 488
Current ratio: —
Long-term debt ($ mil.): —

No. of shares (mil.): 116
Dividends
 Yield: 3.0%
 Payout: 29.0%
Market value ($ mil.): 3,707

	STOCK PRICE ($) FY Close	P/E High/Low	PER SHARE ($) Earnings	Dividends	Book Value
12/18	32.00	16 9	3.00	1.00	27.00
12/17	48.00	23 18	2.00	1.00	25.00
12/16	41.00	22 14	2.00	0.00	24.00
12/15	32.00	21 15	2.00	0.00	23.00
12/14	27.00	21 2	1.00	0.00	22.00
Annual Growth	**4.2%**	**— —**	**27.1%**	**42.9%**	**4.9%**

Sysco Corp

Sysco is the #1 food distributor in the US. The company serves more than 650000 customer locations in the US and internationally in the restaurant (standalone and chain) healthcare and education and hotel industries among others. Its 330-plus distribution centers and some 14000 delivery vehicles deliver branded and private-label food — including fresh frozen and canned foods and specialty and meat products — as well as non-food items such as silverware and utensils. The SYGMA Network focuses on supplying specific chain restaurants. Sysco also offers technology services and management consultancy services such as menu analysis and inventory management. The US accounts for about 80% of sales.

Operations

Sysco operates through three primary segments: US Foodservice International Foodservice and SYGMA.

The US Foodservice business generates some 70% of total sales and consists of its food and non-food delivery operations in the US including its custom-cut meat and seafood companies specialty produce business and specialty imports. The International Foodservice segment which generates another 20% of sales delivers similar product lines to its customers in Canada Europe (primarily the UK France Ireland and Sweden) the Bahamas Mexico Costa Rica and Panama.

The SYGMA segment accounts for about 10% of sales and consists of Sysco's customized distribution to select chain restaurants.

Overall the fresh and frozen meats category accounts for about 20% of sales with the canned and dry products and frozen produce bakery other categories each bringing in about 15%.

Geographic Reach

Houston-based Sysco operates some 170 US distribution facilities more than half its total; the country accounts for around 80% of sales.

Its other facilities are found in about a dozen other countries notably Canada (about 35 sites and nearly 10% of sales) the UK (65 sites and about 5% of sales) and France (nearly 30 sites and just under 5% of sales).

Sales and Marketing

Sysco has a huge client base with more than 650000 customer locations including restaurants (more than 60% of revenue) hospitals nursing homes schools hotels and motels industrial caterers and other foodservice providers.

On a national scale the company jockeys for customers with rivals U.S. Foods and Performance Food Group. It claims to serve more than 15% of the estimated $300 billion foodservice market.

Financial Performance

Amid a growing industry and consistent acquisitions Sysco has seen solid growth in both revenue and net income over the past five years. Sales are up 23% since fiscal 2015 (ended June) and net income is up about 140%.

In fiscal 2019 the company reported revenue of $60.1 billion up 2% from the prior year. The growth is almost entirely attributable to the US Foodservice segment which saw an increase in case volume and impacts from product cost inflation.

Net income that year was also up jumping 17% to $1.7 billion because of the increase in revenue and lower income taxes.

Cash at the end of fiscal 2019 was $532.2 million a decrease of $183.6 million from the prior year. Cash from operations contributed $2.4 billion to the coffers while investing activities used $742.9 million mainly for capital expenditures. Financing activities used another $1.8 billion for dividends to stockholders stock repurchase and debt repayments.

Strategy

To accelerate growth Sysco is generally focused on two broad areas — customer experience and operational excellence.

On the former the company is working to improve customer-facing technology (including its online ordering process) and support the continued growth of Sysco-branded products through new product launches and product innovation. Its product innovation platform Cutting Edge Solutions has delivered 1 million-plus cases of new on-trend products to customers. Expanding its reach beyond the US and Canada (which currently account for about 90% of sales) is also a key element of the customer experience strategy.

On the latter Sysco has several cost-saving and optimization initiatives on tap including modernizing its global financial platform reducing overall general and administrative spend transforming its UK supply chain and streamlining the leadership and administrative support for its Canadian operations. The company hopes to reinvest savings from these initiatives back into the business to facilitate continued growth.

Mergers and Acquisitions

Sysco is an acquisitive company using purchases to bolster its market strength add to its product portfolio and expand geographically.

In 2019 it bought J. Kings Food Service Professionals a New York broadline distributor; California distributors J & M Wholesale Meats and Imperio Foods; Waugh Foods an Illinois broadline distributor; and Ireland-based wine and spirits distributor Classic Drinks.

Company Background

Sysco was founded in 1969 when John Baugh a Houston wholesale food distributor formed a national distribution company with the owners of eight other US wholesalers. The company went public in 1970 and has grown organically as well as through major acquisitions.

HISTORY

Sysco was founded in 1969 when John Baugh a Houston wholesale food distributor formed a national distribution company with the owners of eight other US wholesalers. Joining Baugh's Zero Foods of Houston to form Sysco were Frost-Pack Distributing (Grand Rapids Michigan) Louisville Grocery (Louisville Kentucky) Plantation Foods (Miami) Thomas Foods and its Justrite subsidiary (Cincinnati) Wicker (Dallas) Food Service Company (Houston) Global Frozen Foods (New York) and Texas Wholesale Grocery (Dallas). The company went public in 1970. Sysco which derives its name from Systems and Services Company benefited from Baugh's recognition of the trend toward dining out. Until Sysco was formed small independent operators almost exclusively provided

food distribution to restaurants hotels and other non-grocers.

In the 2000s Sysco acquired smaller competitors who hadn't fared quite as well during the downturn. In 2013 the company acquired foodservice operations in Nassau Bahamas; San Francisco California; San Jose California; Stockton California; Ontario Canada; Quebec Canada; Orlando Florida; Dublin Ireland; St. Cloud Minnesota; Co. Down Northern Ireland; Greenville Ohio; and Houston Texas.

Its 2012 acquisition of European Imports Ltd. helped it expand into the specialty import products segment. Purchasing Crossgar a leading privately owned foodservice supplier in Northern Ireland strengthened Sysco's presence on the island and complemented its 2009 acquisition of Pallas Foods. Other 2012 conquests include Appert's Foodservice Buchy Food Service Central Seafood Company and Metro Richelieu's Distagro. Their combined annual revenues were about $520 million.

In a sweeping move for the foodservice industry Sysco in late 2013 attempted to acquire its rival U.S. Foods for $3.5 billion. The deal would have boosted its share of the US market to about 25% from about 18%. By combining Sysco and US Foods the company expected to achieve annual synergies of at least $600 million and estimated annual sales of approximately $65 billion. The deal was pushed back due to delays in talks with antitrust regulators and the parties terminated to planned transaction in 2015 after failing to obtain regulator approvals.

EXECUTIVES

Assistant Vp Of Hr, Susan Billiot
Svp Marketing, William W. (Bill) Goetz
Vice President, Charles Staes
Vp Corporate Social Responsibility, Catherine Kayser
Vp Financial Reporting, Bob Culak
Vp Supply Chain, Robert Howell
Vice President Information Technology, John D Holzem
Evp Merchandising And Sysco Business Services, William B. (Bill) Day, age 62, $508,333 total compensation
Evp Supply Chain, R. Scott Charlton, age 60
Svp International Foodservice Operations Americas, Scott A. Sonnemaker
Ceo, William J. (Bill) DeLaney, age 63, $1,245,833 total compensation
President And Coo, Thomas L. (Tom) Bené, age 57, $770,833 total compensation
Evp Human Resources, Paul T. Moskowitz, age 55
Svp U.s. Foodservice Operations, Greg D. Bertrand, age 55
Evp Administration And Corporate Secretary, Russell T. Libby, age 53, $590,125 total compensation
Svp Market Segment Strategy And President Sysco Ventures (cake), Brian C. Beach
Evp And Cfo, Joel T. Grade, age 49, $605,833 total compensation
Evp And Cto, Wayne Shurts, age 60, $621,602 total compensation
Vice President, Loren Gausman
Vice President Human Resources Search, Mark Wisnoski
Vice President Merchandising, Brian Smith
Vice President Supply Chain Operations Enterprise Planning And Design, Theodore Murray
Vice President Information Systems, Ira Wilson
Vice President Sales, Colby Morse
Vice President National Accounts, Justin Hiraki
Vice President, Scott Lesner
Vice President Tax, Barbara Green

Vice President Associate General Counsel Transactions, Carmen Ng
Vice President Merchandising, David Haberkorn
Vice President Merchandising Services, Robert Thurber
Vice President Of Marketing, Chad Lombardo
Vice President Systems, Kristin Lindsay
Executive Vice President, Stephen Smith
Vice President Logistics, Mark Will
Assistant Vice President Of Customer Services, Rita Kolberg
Vice President Of Human Resources, John Fraser
Vice President, Dennis Hernandez
Vp National Sales And Corporate Officer, Rodger Smith
Vice President Information Technology, Danny Byrd
Sr Vp Operations, Chuck Fraser
Vice President Corporate Business Development, Greg Keller
Vice President Operations, Ron Shanks
Vice President Enterprise Asset Management, Dan Bennett
Assistant Vice President Merchandising Center Of The Plate Supply Chain Manager, Jeff Kimmich
Vice President Business Development National Accounts, Amy Davis-Smith
Vice President Merchandising, Gail Mccoy
Vice President Merchandising, Michelle Nielsen
Vice President Of Merchandising And Marketing, Amy Lewis
National Sales Manager, Greg Deboer
Executive Vice President Sysco Food Services, Timothy Peterzen
Vice President Of Marketing, Sharon Armentrout
Reg Vp, Margie Mcallister
Vice President Of Merchandising, Dale Kahn
Vice President Of Information Technology, Lucas Wagner
Vice President Accounts Payable, Alison Peterman
Vp Of Multi Unit Sales, Allan Faneuf
Vice President Revenue Management, Ken Jaycox
Vice President Of Finance, Alma Vega
Vice President Of Territory Sales, Kelly Ferris
Vp Multi Unit Accounts, Skip Fauber
Vice President Of Merchandising, Kurt Chapin
Vice President, Daniel Gentry
National Account Manager, Amy Carman
Senior Vice President Sales And Marketing, Jim Hope
Assistant Vice President Of Marketing, Tracey Mills
Vice President Call Center, Alena Galsnte
Vice President Of Merchandising, Richard Ashlock
National Account Manager, Cindy Rankin
Vice President Supply Chain Management, Masao Nishi
Vice President Human Resources, Michele Giordano
Vp Operations, Gary Licho
Vice President Sales, John Counts
Vice President Sales Marketing, John Miko
Vice President Of Merchandising And Marketing, Bobbie McDonald
Vice President Human Resources, Sabrina Knouse
Vice President, Richard Dachman
Vice President Brand Executive, David Montpetit
Senior Vice President Marketing, Bill Goetz
Vice President Sales, Eric Kane
Vice President Merchandising, Brian R Todd
Principal Vice President Of Finance And Administ Vice President Finance And Administration, Erica Koranda
Vice President Of Merchandising, Tom Johnson
Executive Vice President, Thaire Bryant
Vice President Customer Service, Jackie Mack
Vice President Sales And Marketing, Keith Lusk
Manager Vice President Merchandising, James Brennan
Vice President Warehouse And Logistics Operations, George Moses

Senior Vice President Contract Sales Executive Officer, Kent Humphries
Vice President, Navin Advani
Executive Vice President Supply Chain, Scott Charlton
Vice President Of Operations, Rudy Villanueva
Vice President Merchandising, David Passaro
National Account Manager, Kristin Smith
Vice President Sales, John Woolery
Vp And Treasurer, Greg Keyes
National Sales Manager, Hugh Morgan
Vice President Of Labor Relations, Chuck Munn
National Account Manager, Carol Vogt
Vice President Merchandising And Marketing, Christopher Flint
Vice President, Heike Gillman
Vice President Finance, Enrique Becerra
National Account Manager, Martin Escatel
National Account Manager, Clay Steadham
Market Vp Of Merchandising Northeast, Eric Zeilor
Vp Of Finance And Cfo Of Spokane, Jeff Kolcum
National Account Manager, Tracy Jones
Vice President Human Resources, Brett Appleberg
Vice President, Bob Morgan
Vice President Management Information Systems, Mary Brumbaugh
Vice President Of Sales, Melissa White
Vice President Sales, Walt Sharpless
Vice President Merchandising, Kathleen Griego
Vice President Total Rewards, Erin Packwood
Vp Compliance, Jose Colondres
Vp Government Relations, Gerald Kunde
Vice President Government Relations, Chip Kunde
Vice President Marketing, Maureen Quirk
Vp Sysco Business Services, Chris Davis
Vice President Operations, Justin Dalton
Vice President Merchandising, Debra Morey
Vice President Sales Development And Support, Paul Nasir
Executive Vice President, James Ehlers
Vp Operations, Grady Metoyer
Vp Of Finance And Cfo Of Sysco San Diego, Jim Harlan
Government Relations, Brad Christie
Vice President Operations, John Petrossian
Regional Vice President Multi Unit Healthcare Hospitality Sales, Victoria Gardner
Vp Operations, Kevin Proulx
Vice President Of Sales, Troy S Willis
Regional Vice President Healthcare, Greg Mcculloch
National Sales Manager, Hugh G Morgan
Vice President Marketing, Maureen M Quirk
Vice President Human Resources Business Partner, Douangchan Steele
Vice President And Human Resources Business Partner, Terri L Clark
Vice President Of Purchasing, Robert C Thurber
National Account Manager, Kelly P Garcia
Vice President Of Human Resources, John J Fraser
Vice President And General Manager, Joe Napoli
Vice President And Treasurer, Gregory S Keyes
Vice President Finance, Enrique X Becerra
Regional Vice President Human Resources, Bettina Brayshaw
National Account Manager, Sonnie Broxton
Vice President Of Operations, Michael R Caldwell
Vice President National Accounts Restaurant, Cary T Nelms
Vice President Facilities Construction Real Estate, Theodore W Speas
Vice President Operations, Jim Forant
Senior Vice President, Phillip Waring
Vp Merchandising Pacific Market, Kevin Sloan
Vice President National Accounts Restaurant, Cary Nelms
National Account Manager, Kelly Garcia
Vice President Facilities Construction Real Estate, Theodore Speas
Auditors: Ernst & Young LLP

LOCATIONS

HQ: Sysco Corp
1390 Enclave Parkway, Houston, TX 77077-2099
Phone: 281 584-1390   **Fax:** 281 584-2880
Web: www.sysco.com

2019 Sales

	$ mil.	% of total
US	48,257	80
Canada	4,660	8
UK	3,134	5
France	1,582	3
Other	2,481	4
Total	**60,114**	**100**

PRODUCTS/OPERATIONS

2019 Sales

	$ mil.	% of total
US Foodservice	41,288	69
International Foodservice	11,493	19
SYGMA	6,244	10
Other	1,089	2
Total	**60,114**	**100**

2019 Sales

	$ mil.	% of total
Fresh & frozen meats	11,570	19
Canned & dry food	9,941	16
Frozen fruits vegetables bakery & other	8,978	15
Dairy products	6,114	10
Poultry	5,848	10
Fresh produce	5,066	8
Paper & disposables	3,960	7
Seafood	3,382	6
Beverage products	2,309	4
Other	2,946	5
Total	**60,114**	**100**

COMPETITORS

Ben E. Keith	Performance Food Group
Edward Don	Reinhart FoodService
Golden State Foods	Shamrock Foods
Gordon Food Service	US Foods
MAINES	UniPro Foodservice
McLane Foodservice	
Meadowbrook Meat Company	

HISTORICAL FINANCIALS

Company Type: Public

Income Statement   FYE: June 29

	REVENUE ($ mil.)	NET INCOME ($ mil.)	NET PROFIT MARGIN	EMPLOYEES
06/19	60,114	1,674	2.8%	69,000
06/18*	58,727	1,431	2.4%	67,000
07/17	55,371	1,143	2.1%	66,500
07/16	50,367	950	1.9%	51,900
06/15	48,681	687	1.4%	51,700
Annual Growth	**5.4%**	**25.0%**	—	**7.5%**

*Fiscal year change

2019 Year-End Financials

Debt ratio: 45.00%
Return on equity: 67.00%
Cash ($ mil.): 513
Current ratio: 1.00
Long-term debt ($ mil.): 8,122

No. of shares (mil.): 513
Dividends
  Yield: 0.0%
  Payout: 47.0%
Market value ($ mil.): 36,271

	STOCK PRICE ($) FY Close	P/E High/Low	PER SHARE ($) Earnings	Dividends	Book Value
06/19	71.00	23 19	3.00	2.00	5.00
06/18*	68.00	25 18	3.00	1.00	5.00
07/17	50.00	27 23	2.00	1.00	4.00
07/16	51.00	31 21	2.00	1.00	6.00
06/15	38.00	36 31	1.00	1.00	9.00
Annual Growth	**16.5%**	—	**29.2%**	**6.2%**	**(13.8%)**

*Fiscal year change

T Rowe Price Group Inc.

T. Rowe Price Group administers a family of mutual funds in a variety of investment styles. Traditionally oriented toward growth investing the funds offer products in many risk and taxation profiles including small- mid- and large-cap stock funds; money market funds; and bond funds both taxable and nontaxable. Other services include asset management advisory services (including retirement plan advice for individuals) corporate retirement plan management separately managed accounts variable annuity life insurance plans discount brokerage and transfer agency and shareholder services. Founded in 1937 T. Rowe Price has almost $1.1 trillion in assets under management.

Operations

Investment advisory services (and the fees generated by them) are T. Rowe Price's cash cow accounting for more than 85% of its annual revenue. The company provides these services to its Price Funds to clients on separately managed or subadvised account basis and to other products such as collective investment trusts and target-date retirement trusts.

Administrative fees account for about 10% of total revenue. These fees encompass ancillary services provided to the firm's investment advisory clients. Services include mutual fund transfer agent services record keeping for retirement plans investing in non-T. Rowe Price funds and brokerage services.

Distribution and servicing fees account for less than 5% of the group's revenue.

Geographic Reach

Baltimore-based T. Rowe Price serves clients in about 45 countries around the world from offices in 15-plus countries including locations in London and Hong Kong.

Investment advisory customers from outside the US account for some 6% of the group's assets under management.

Sales and Marketing

T. Rowe Price's clients include individual and institutional investors and financial intermediaries. The company distributes its products through third-party financial intermediaries retirement plan sponsors and directly to individual and institutional investors.

Advertising expenses totaled $92 million in 2017 versus $79.9 million in 2016 and $79.7 million in 2015.

Financial Performance

With the exception of 2016 T. Rowe Price has enjoyed healthy revenue and profit growth over the past few years thanks to a bullish stock market new client inflows and most recently lowered corporate tax rates.

In 2017 revenue increased 13% to $4.8 billion as investment advisory income rose 15%. Driving that increase was an increase in assets under management and the highest net new cash flows since 2012. Administrative fees and distribution and services fees also rose but they didn't recover to the levels reached in 2015.

Despite an increase in operating expenses including compensation costs and facility costs net income grew 23% to $1.5 billion that year. This was due to the higher revenues earned and higher net investment income.

T. Rowe Price ended 2017 with $2 billion a 58% increase over the prior year. Nearly $230 million in net cash was provided by operating activities while $39 million was provided by investing activities and $462 million was provided by financing activities.

Strategy

T. Rowe Price regularly adds to its funds and strategies offerings to attract new investors and their capital. To this end the firm in 2017 added T. Rowe Price US High Yield Fund and in 2016 expanded its quantitative management-style series of strategic funds with three new equity funds.

The company offers its products through a variety of distribution channels to reach more customers. To further pursue growth T. Rowe Price has three broad strategies: expanding its product offerings strengthening its distribution channels. and investing in technology.

As the firm increasingly moves to digital offerings it has been closing certain locations (including investor centers) and consolidating operations. In 2018 it opened an innovation center where data scientists work with people developers and designers to improve its customer interfaces.

HISTORY

Thomas Rowe Price Jr. left a brokerage job at Mackubin Goodrich & Co. to found his own investment advisory firm in 1937. He pushed investing for the long haul choosing stocks of promising young companies (the firm invested in IBM in 1950). Price's company was incorporated in 1947 and was employee-owned until it went public in 1986.

The firm moved into international investments in 1979. T. Rowe Price was primarily an institutional pension fund manager until the 1980s. Creativity lagged as fund managers made investments from a list selected by the research department and the Growth Stock Fund underperformed on the S&P 500. In 1987 the firm opened its funds to individual investors.

Thereafter it introduced a slew of new funds slicing and dicing the market to appeal to the broadest possible industry and risk investment profiles including offerings in emerging market stocks and health and science stocks.

In the late 1990s however the company's value investing strategy brought lagging fund results and a stagnant corporate stock price. Nevertheless cash continued to pour into the company's funds until the collapse of Russian and Asian markets in 1998. US investors got the willies slowing asset flows to T. Rowe Price and other mutual fund managers.

In response Roche began moving the company into overseas asset management markets. In 1999 the firm joined with Sumitomo Bank (later part of Sumitomo Mitsui Financial Group) and Daiwa Securities to form asset manager Daiwa SB Investments in Japan. It also targeted Europe where the growth of private retirement plans opened up new opportunities. Nevertheless the company missed out on many of the explosive returns of the high-tech boom.

In 2000 however the high-tech bubble burst seeming to vindicate T. Rowe Price's conservative approach. That year the company bought out the remaining 50% of its Rowe Price-Fleming International asset management joint venture with Robert Fleming (which later became part of JPMorgan Chase). Also that year the company reorganized itself into holding company T. Rowe Price Group. The company's UK subsidiary received regulatory approval to expand to the European continent in 2001.

EXECUTIVES

Vice Chairman Vp And Ceo T. Rowe Price International Ltd, Edward C. Bernard, age 62, $350,000 total compensation

President And Ceo, William J. (Bil) Stromberg, age 58, $350,000 total compensation

Vp Cfo And Treasurer, Kenneth V. Moreland, age 63, $350,000 total compensation

Head International Equity, Christopher D. Alderson, age 57, $305,057 total compensation

Head Us Investment Services, Scott B. David

Head Global Technology, Nigel Faulkner

Head Global Investment Services, Robert Higginbotham

Head Equity, Eric L. Veiel, $350,000 total compensation

Head Fixed Income, Edward A. Wiese

Vp Cfo And Treasurer, Céline Dufétel

Vice President Global Trading, Ava Rainey

Avp Relationship Manager, Lisa Mcgarvey

Vice President Dcio, Keith Blackmon

Vice President, Bailey Devries

Assistant Vice President Project Lead, Mike Hooper

Avp And Systems Consultant, Charles Popeck

Assistant Vice President, Lora Rosen

Vice President, Tala Boulos

Vice President Enterprise Architecture, Paul Macek

Assistant Vice President, Jason Bandel

Vice President, Leigh Woodworth

Vice President Defined Contribution Investment Specialist, Adam Brown

Vice President Trpa Trpg, Doug Talley

Vice President, Greg Franzoni

Vice President Applications Management, Jennifer Perricone

Vice President And Research Analyst, Steven Boothe

Vice President, Mark Weigman

Vice President And Crm Manager, Steve Larson

Vice President, Laura Chasney

Vice President, Steve Sullivan

Vice President Information Security Manager, Brian Porter

Vice President, Kimberly Oconnor

Vice President, Heather McPherson

Assistant Vice President Customer Sales And Services Channel Manager, Sean Rentch

Vice President, Tom McGuire

Vice President, Paul Wojcik

Vice President And Regional Relationship Manager, David Orlando

Vice President, Chris Dyer

Vice President Director Of Retail Operations, Chris Hufman

Vice President Us Investment Services Financial Institutions, Cima Gordon

Vice President, Jeff Zoller

Vice President Regional Sales Consultant, Alan Valenca

Vice President And Quantitative Analyst, Kim Dedominicis

Vice President, Andy Brooks

Assistant Vice President, Craig Sauerwalt

Vice President, Brian Brennan

Assistant Vice President, Chris Clingenpeel

Vice President International Tax, Rebecca English

Vice President, Joe Vogelpohl

Vice President Of Real Estate, Mark Ruhe

Vice President Credit Research, Ted Robson

Vice President Senior Retirement Sales Executive, Terence Howard

Vice President, Ng Jan

Assistant Vice President Equity Trader, Susan Klein

Assistant Vice President Lead Marketing Manager, Lauren Inskeep

Vice President; Global Head Of Corporate Actions, Larry Robinson

Vice President, Jim Ouartarone

Assistant Vice President Crm Marketing Analytics, Beverly Wisbar

Vice President Dcio Sales Consultant, Michele Giangrande

Vice President, Ricky Smallwood

Assistant Vice President Investment Services, John Ramirez

Avp Business Intelligence And Analytics Manager, Paul Ebert

Vice President Credit Analyst, Colin Bando

Vice President, Mett Kinak

Vice President Equity Trading, Tammy Wiggs

Vice President And Senior Legal Counsel, Terri Doud

Vice President Investment Tax, Paul Krug

Vice President Quantitative Investment Analyst, Yongheon Lee

Vice President Head Of Corporate Communications, Craig Smith

Vice President Regional Sales Consultant, Jonathan Lepore

Vice President Senior Relationship Manager, Guen Toste

Assistant Vice President, Melissa Shank

Vice President, Eric Bolisay

Vice President Territory Sales, Mike Shamburger

Assistant Vice President Tax, Nathan Taylor

Vice President, Dana Morgan

Vice President Senior Legal Counsel, Bryan Venable

Assistant Vice President Project Management Lead Manager, Courtney Knatz

Vice President Senior Relationship Manager, Shaun Mccloskey

Vice President Regional Investment Consultant, Tom Bauer

Vice President Regional Investment Consultant, Derek Fisher

Vp Senior Manager Retirement Plan Services Rps, Kelly Katz

Assistant Vice President, Tim Cannon

Vice President Talent Acquisition, Phr Rundell

Assistant Vice President, Andrea Reed

Vice President Senior Manager, Chris Gaeng

Vice President, Robert Craft

Vice President, Jennifer Richardson

Vice President, David Crotty

Vice President, Anna Dreyer

Assistant Vice President Client Experience And Digital Marketing, David Malone

Assistant Vice President, Nimesh Chheda

Vice President Midwest Retirement Sales Executive, Mike Palace

Vice President, Jim Tzitzouris

Vice President Relationship Manager, Ann Rogers

Vice President Enterprise Data Governance, Shonyel Lyons

Vice President And Group Manager; Real Estate And Workplace Strategy, Chris Calhoun

Vice President Quality Assurance And Testing (gbs Investment Operations Technology), Michael Wasielczyk

Vice President Global Market Research And Insights, Todd Hiller

Vice President And Global Head Of Enterprise Service Desk, LaShaunda Allums

Vice President Architecture Distribution And Marketing, Raman Tallamraju

Vp Senior Retirement Sales Executive, Allen Ehling

Vice President Senior Retirement Sales Executive, Niki Green

Vice President Senior Rates Fx Trader, Geoffrey Hardin

Vice President Solutions Execution Manager, Peter Entner

Assistant Vice President Investment Risk Reporting, Amber Miller

Vice President, Alan Alexander

Vice President National Accounts Manager Broker Dealer Distribution, Jeff Talbott

Vice President, Anjie Kallas

Vice President, Jonathan Wilkinson

Vice President, Karen Glooch

Vice President, Linsley Carruth
Vice President And Senior Product Manager Of Investment Funds, Ian Hoddy
Vice President National Accounts, Mitch Wurzer
Senior Legal Counsel Vice President, Warren Blinder
Vice President Quantitative Developer, John Pirie
Vice President, Vishal Chhikara
Vice President Regional Investment Consultant, Andrew Pizza
Global Portfolio Strategist And Vice President Of T Rowe Price Group, Chris Faulkner-macdonagh
Vice President Senior Retirement Sales Executive, Bryan Mccain
Vice President Operations, William Luecking
Vice President Institutional Sales, Jason Widener
Vice President Credit Analyst, Ramon Decastro
Chairman, Brian C. Rogers, age 64
Secretary Scheduler, Helen Botfield
Board Member, Alan Wilson
Auditors: KPMG LLP

LOCATIONS

HQ: T Rowe Price Group Inc.
100 East Pratt Street, Baltimore, MD 21202
Phone: 410 345-2000   **Fax:** 410 752-3477
Web: www.troweprice.com

Selected Locations

Domestic
 Baltimore
 Colorado Springs CO
 New York
 Owings Mills MD
 Philadelphia
 San Francisco
 Tampa
International
 Amsterdam
 Copenhagen
 Dubai
 Frankfurt
 Hong Kong
 London
 Luxembourg
 Madrid
 Melbourne
 Milan
 Singapore
 Stockholm
 Sydney
 Tokyo
 Toronto
 Zurich
US
 Baltimore
 Colorado Springs CO
 Owings Mills MD
 Tampa
 International Offices
 Amsterdam
 Buenos Aires
 Copenhagen
 Dubai
 Hong Kong
 London
 Luxembourg
 Singapore
 Sydney
 Tokyo
 Toronto
 Zurich

PRODUCTS/OPERATIONS

2017 Sales

	$ mil.	% of total
Investment advisory services	4,288	890
Administrative fees	358	7
Distribution & servicing fees	147	3
Total	**4,793**	**100**

Selected Subsidiaries

T. Rowe Price Advisory Services Inc.
T. Rowe Price Associates Inc.
 T. Rowe Price (Canada) Inc. (US)
 T. Rowe Price Investment Services Inc.
 T. Rowe Price Retirement Plan Services Inc.
 T. Rowe Price Services Inc.
T. Rowe Price International Ltd. (UK)
 T. Rowe Price Hong Kong Limited
 T. Rowe Price Singapore Private Ltd.

COMPETITORS

AllianceBernstein	Invesco
American Century	Legg Mason
Ameriprise	MFS
Capital Group	Northwestern Mutual
FMR	Putnam
Franklin Templeton	The Vanguard Group

HISTORICAL FINANCIALS

Company Type: Public

Income Statement

FYE: December 31

	REVENUE ($ mil.)	NET INCOME ($ mil.)	NET PROFIT MARGIN	EMPLOYEES
12/18	5,373	1,838	34.2%	7,022
12/17	4,793	1,498	31.2%	6,881
12/16	4,223	1,215	28.8%	6,329
12/15	4,201	1,223	29.1%	5,999
12/14	3,982	1,230	30.9%	5,870
Annual Growth	7.8%	10.6%	—	4.6%

2018 Year-End Financials

Debt ratio: —
Return on equity: 31.00%
Cash ($ mil.): 1,425
Current ratio: 2.00
Long-term debt ($ mil.): —

No. of shares (mil.): 238
Dividends
 Yield: 3.0%
 Payout: 39.0%
Market value ($ mil.): 21,979

	STOCK PRICE ($) FY Close	P/E High/Low	PER SHARE ($) Earnings	Dividends	Book Value
12/18	92.00	17 11	7.00	3.00	26.00
12/17	105.00	17 11	6.00	2.00	24.00
12/16	75.00	16 13	5.00	2.00	20.00
12/15	71.00	18 14	5.00	4.00	19.00
12/14	86.00	19 16	5.00	2.00	21.00
Annual Growth	1.8%	— —	12.4%	12.3%	5.6%

T-Mobile US Inc

EXECUTIVES

Ceo, John J Legere
Exec Chb*, Timotheus Hottges
Pres-Coo*, G Michael Sievert
Exec V Pres-Cfo, J Braxton Carter
Exec V Pres-Cto, Neville R Ray
Exec V Pres-General Counsel-SE, David A Miller
Sr V Pres Fin-Cao, Peter Osvaldik
Evp Corp Svcs, David R Carey
Evp Corp Strategy, Peter A Ewens
Pres, Metropcs, Thomas C Keys
Evp Hr, Elizabeth A McAuliffe
Auditors: PricewaterhouseCoopers LLP

LOCATIONS

HQ: T-Mobile US Inc
12920 SE 38th Street, Bellevue, WA 98006-1350
Phone: 425 378-4000
Web: www.T-Mobile.com

HISTORICAL FINANCIALS

Company Type: Public

Income Statement

FYE: December 31

	REVENUE ($ mil.)	NET INCOME ($ mil.)	NET PROFIT MARGIN	EMPLOYEES
12/19	44,998	3,468	7.7%	53,000
12/18	43,310	2,888	6.7%	52,000
12/17	40,604	4,536	11.2%	51,000
12/16	37,242	1,460	3.9%	50,000
12/15	32,053	733	2.3%	50,000
Annual Growth	8.9%	47.5%	—	1.5%

2019 Year-End Financials

Debt ratio: 34.00%
Return on equity: 13.00%
Cash ($ mil.): 1,528
Current ratio: 1.00
Long-term debt ($ mil.): 28,526

No. of shares (mil.): 857
Dividends
 Yield: —
 Payout: —
Market value ($ mil.): 67,199

	STOCK PRICE ($) FY Close	P/E High/Low	PER SHARE ($) Earnings	Dividends	Book Value
12/19	78.00	21 16	4.00	0.00	21.00
12/18	64.00	21 16	3.00	0.00	29.00
12/17	64.00	13 10	5.00	0.00	26.00
12/16	58.00	34 20	2.00	0.00	22.00
12/15	39.00	52 32	1.00	0.00	20.00
Annual Growth	19.0%	— —	48.8%	—	1.3%

Talcott Resolution Life Insurance Co

EXECUTIVES

Pres, Brion S Johnson
Sr V Pres-Cao, Peter F Sannizzaro
Sr V Pres, Mark Niland
Corporate Counsel/Legal, Leslie Soler
Administrative Assistant, Aida Ramos
Manager, Alicia Soucy
Customer Representativ, Alicia Jones
Legal Staff, Nancy Bertucci
Manager, Olivia Caires
Account Executive, Neal McLaughlin
Claim Consultant, Cheryl Braddy
Auditors: DELOITTE & TOUCHE LLP

LOCATIONS

HQ: Talcott Resolution Life Insurance Co
One Griffin Road North, Windsor, CT 06095
Phone: 800 862-6668
Web: www.thehartford.com

HISTORICAL FINANCIALS

Company Type: Public

Income Statement

FYE: December 31

	ASSETS ($ mil.)	NET INCOME ($ mil.)	INCOME AS % OF ASSETS	EMPLOYEES
12/18*	150,146	409	0.3%	—
05/18	0	94	—	—
12/17	168,732	(46)	—	—
12/16	170,346	282	0.2%	—
12/15	175,350	500	0.3%	—
Annual Growth	(5.0%)	(6.5%)	—	—
*Fiscal year change

2018 Year-End Financials

Debt ratio: —	No. of shares (mil.): 0
Return on equity: 16.00%	Dividends
Cash ($ mil.): 221	Yield: —
Current ratio: —	Payout: —
Long-term debt ($ mil.): —	Market value ($ mil.): —

Tapestry Inc

Tapestry is weaving together a collection of leading premium fashion brands. Previously Coach the company designs and makes (mostly through third parties) high-end leather goods and accessories including handbags wallets and luggage under the Coach brand. It also licenses the Coach name for watches eyewear and fragrances. In addition through acquisitions Tapestry owns the Stuart Weitzman (luxury women's shoes) and Kate Spade (women's apparel and accessories) brands. The company sells its wares through department and outlet stores (in the US and globally) and websites. It also operates more than 1500 retail and factory outlet stores in North America Japan China and other countries in the Asia-Pacific region.

Operations

Tapestry reports through three primary segments: Coach (some 70% of revenue) Kate Spade (nearly a quarter) and Stuart Weitzman (about 5%).

The Coach brand include leather goods and accessories such as handbags wallets wristlets and cosmetic cases. It also licenses its name to third parties for watches (Movado) eyewear (Luxottica) and fragrances (Interparfums). The segment's products are sold through some 1600 wholesale and distributor locations as well as about 980 Coach stores.

Kate Spade?s offerings include handbags ready-to-wear jewelry footwear gifts and home décor. The brand is also licensed to third parties for bedding eyewear tableware and a host of other products. The segment's products are sold through some 1200 wholesale and distributor locations as well as more than 400 Kate Spade stores.

Footwear is the domain of Stuart Weitzman although the brand is expanding into handbags and accessories. Its products are sold through some 1100 wholesale and distributor locations as well as some 150 Stuart Weitzman stores.

Direct-to-consumer sales account for about 90% of revenue.

Geographic Reach

Tapestry directly operates more than 1500 stores in North America and the Asia-Pacific region. Leading markets include the US (about 55% of sales) China (about 15%) and Japan (more than 10%).

The New York-based company has distribution product development and quality control locations in the US Canada Hong Kong China Japan South Korea Vietnam the Philippines Singapore Spain the UK and India.

Sales and Marketing

In addition to its own 1500-plus stores Tapestry's products are sold through department stores and other third-party retailers in North America and Europe. Top US wholesale customers include Macy's (including Bloomingdale's) Dillard's Nordstrom Saks Fifth Avenue Lord & Taylor The Bay Belk and Von Maur.

The company also has e-commerce sites in North America Europe Greater China Japan South Korea and Hong Kong.

Tapestry spent $247.1 million for advertising in 2019 up from $228.4 million and $178.3 million in 2018 and 2017 respectively.

Financial Performance

The acquisition of sister fashion brands has boosted Tapestry's revenue some 45% over the past five years. Excluding a dip in fiscal 2018 net income has also shown strong growth up 60% since fiscal 2015.

In fiscal 2019 (ended June) the company reported revenue of $6 billion up 3% from the prior year. Sales increased across all three brands (excluding the effects of foreign currency) although the Kate Spade brand was the primary growth engine due to 60-plus new store openings.

Net income that year was also up jumping 62% to $643.4 million. Lower cost of sales and lower taxes as a result of the 2017 Tax Act powered results.

Cash at the end of fiscal 2019 was $969.2 million a decrease of $274.2 million from the prior year. Cash from operations contributed $791.7 million to the coffers while investing activities used $574.2 million mainly for investments and capital expenditures. Financing activities used another $484.9 million for dividends to stockholders and stock repurchase.

Strategy

Among Tapestry's strategic priorities are brand innovation digital and data analytic investment and global growth with a special emphasis on China.

The company is focused on improving its production planning cycle and speed to market as it accelerates product innovation across its brands including planned customization programs. In a related move in fiscal 2020 Tapestry is bringing in-house the Kate Spade footwear business. It is particularly focused on innovation in the growing premium bags and small leather goods and footwear and outerwear categories.

In fiscal 2019 the company named a new Chief Data Officer and launched its Data Labs portal which includes data science and artificial intelligence (AI) tools to improve the retailer's collection and use of data.

Tapestry has made several moves to expand in China which the company refers to as its ChinaNext agenda. In September 2019 it announced a partnership with Alibaba's Tmall China's largest B2C ecommerce platform. Coach Kate Spade and Stuart Weitzman will all have flagship stores on the Tmall Luxury Pavilion platform.

Mergers and Acquisitions

In fiscal 2018 Tapestry acquired luxury apparel and accessories designer Kate Spade & Co. for $2.4 billion. Upon completion the company changed its name from Coach and organized operations around its three luxury brands.

Company Background

Tapestry traces its roots to the 1941 founding of leather goods maker Coach Inc. which was acquired by Sara Lee Corporation in 1985. It went public in 2000 and Sara Lee divested its remaining ownership in 2001.

Coach acquired Stuart Weitzman a luxury women's footwear firm in fiscal 2015 and Kate Spade a lifestyle accessories and ready-to-wear company in fiscal 2018. That year the company changed its name to Tapestry to reflect its multibrand portfolio.

EXECUTIVES

Cfo, Kevin G. Wills, age 53
Global Head Of Investor Relations And Corporate Communications, Andrea Shaw Resnick, age 58
President Global Business Development And Strategic Alliances, Ian Bickley, age 55, $800,000 total compensation
Ceo And Interim Ceo Kate Spade & Company, Victor Luis, age 53, $1,300,000 total compensation
Brand President Stuart Weitzman, Wendy Kahn
President North America And Global Marketing, Andre Cohen, age 55, $866,667 total compensation
President Chief Administrative Officer And Secretary, Todd Kahn, age 55, $708,333 total compensation
Evp And Cio, Christine (Chris) Putur
Divisional Vice President Glo, Sonia Sparolini
Divisiona Vice President Leather Management, Marzia Bandini
Divisional Vice President, Glenn King
Dvp Corporate And Executive Compensation, Helen Freilich
Divisional Vice President Design Development Women's Rtw, Christina Gradassi
Vp And Associate General Counsel, Suzanne White
Vice President And General Manager Singapore Malaysia, Nicolas Villeger
Vice President Real Estate Construction, Anthony Galvin
Vice President, Sandra Constantine
Executive Vice President Marketing And Strategy, Stephanie Stahl
Dvp Of Store Construction, Scott Till
Vp Sales North America, Dominic Cioffoletti
Divisional Vice President Procurement, Carl Hernas
Vice President Tax, Elizabeth Leete
Senior Vice President Head Of Global Procurement, Scott Easterwood
Vice President Global Merchandising, Nicole Fields
Vice President Of Real Estate, Ira Cohen
Senior Vice President And Controller Coach Greater New York, Melinda Brown
Svp Product Development Coach Leatherware, James Pappas
Divisional Vice President Of Loss Prevention, Daniel Hafford
Vice President And Treasurer, Sue Vo
Divisional Vice President North America Wholesale Footwear, Giovanni Cafiso
Vp Global Visual Experience, Giovanni Zaccariello
Vice President Global Marketing, Katie Gohman
Executive Vice President Chief Information Officer, Michael Braine
Vp Global Head Creative Studio Coach, Jo Baldwin
Senior Vice President Global Chief Marketing Officer Coach Brand, Carlos Becil
Vice President Footwear Designer Coach, Lucio Finale
Divisional Vice President Global And North America Advertising And Digital Marketing, Susan Mccarthy
Vice President, Jane Cho
Svp Global Digital And Customer Experience, Joon Silverstein
Chairman, Jide J. Zeitlin, age 56
Board Member, Susan Kropf
Board Member, Ivan Menezes
Board Member, Andrea Guerra
Auditors: DELOITTE & TOUCHE LLP

LOCATIONS

HQ: Tapestry Inc
10 Hudson Yards, New York, NY 10001
Phone: 212 946-8400   Fax: 212 594-1682
Web: www.tapestry.com

2019 Stores

	% of total
North America	675
International	865
Total	**1,540**

2019 Sales

	$ mil.	% of total
US	3,395	56
Greater China	913	15
Japan	712	12
Other	1,007	17
Total	**6,027**	**100**

PRODUCTS/OPERATIONS

2019 Sales

	$ mil.	% of total
Coach		
Women's Handbags	2,261	38
Men's	862	14
Women's Accessories	767	13
Other Products	381	6
Kate Spade		
Women's Handbags	764	13
Women's Accessories	288	5
Other Products	315	5
Stuart Weitzman	389	6
Total	**6,027**	**100**

2019 Stores

	No.
Coach	986
Kate Spade	407
Stuart Weitzman	147
Total	**1,540**

COMPETITORS

Cole Haan	Mulberry Group
Dooney & Bourke	Nine West
Etienne Aigner Group	Prada
Gucci	Ralph Lauren
Herm ̈s	Samsonite
Kenneth Cole	Tiffany & Co.
LVMH	michael kors
Michael Kors Holdings	

HISTORICAL FINANCIALS

Company Type: Public

Income Statement

FYE: June 29

	REVENUE ($ mil.)	NET INCOME ($ mil.)	NET PROFIT MARGIN	EMPLOYEES
06/19	6,027	643	10.7%	21,000
06/18*	5,880	398	6.8%	20,800
07/17	4,488	591	13.2%	14,400
07/16	4,492	461	10.3%	15,100
06/15	4,192	402	9.6%	15,800
Annual Growth	9.5%	12.4%	—	7.4%

*Fiscal year change

2019 Year-End Financials

Debt ratio: 23.00%
Return on equity: 19.00%
Cash ($ mil.): 969
Current ratio: 3.00
Long-term debt ($ mil.): 1,602

No. of shares (mil.): 287
Dividends
  Yield: 0.0%
  Payout: 61.0%
Market value ($ mil.): 9,100

	STOCK PRICE ($) FY Close	P/E High/Low	PER SHARE ($) Earnings	Dividends	Book Value
06/19	32.00	24 13	2.00	1.00	12.00
06/18*	47.00	39 28	1.00	1.00	11.00
07/17	47.00	22 16	2.00	1.00	11.00
07/16	41.00	25 17	2.00	1.00	10.00
06/15	36.00	30 23	1.00	1.00	9.00
Annual Growth	(3.2%)	— —	11.1%	(0.0%)	8.0%

*Fiscal year change

Targa Resources Corp

Targa Resources Corp. has the energy to deliver natural gas throughout its service territory of Texas Oklahoma and neighboring states. Through its Targa Resources Partners entity it gathers processes transports and sells natural gas natural gas liquids (NGLs) crude oil and refined petroleum products. It owns or operates about 27000 miles of natural gas gathering pipelines and more than 35 processing plants. It has a presence in many shale basins including the Permian Eagle Ford Barnett Anadarko Arkoma and Williston. In early 2016 Targa Resources Corp purchased all un-owned shares of Targa Resources Partners securing complete control of its previously majority-owned subsidiary.

Operations

Targa Resources operates two segments: Gathering and Processing and Logistics and Marketing.

The Logistics and Marketing segment accounting for 85% of total revenue is Targa's downstream business. It converts mixed NGLs into NGL products and provides certain value-added services such as storing terminaling distributing and marketing NGLs; storing and terminaling refined petroleum products and crude oil. It performs marketing activities in support of Targa's other businesses including services to LPG exporters. Assets owned by this segment are generally connected to and supplied in part by the Gathering and Processing segment. It also owns and leases out some 700 railcars to move product.

The Gathering and Processing segment gathers natural gas produced from oil and gas wells and processes this raw natural gas into sellable natural gas by extracting NGLs and removing impurities. It also gathers and terminals crude oil. The segment owns some 27000 miles of gathering pipeline and has a gross processing capacity of 3500 million cubic feet of natural gas per day.

Geographic Reach

Targa Resources is headquartered in Houston TX. The assets owned by the Logistics and Marketing segment are predominantly located in Mont Belvieu and Galena Park Texas in Lake Charles Louisiana in Tacoma Washington and in Baltimore Maryland.

The Gathering and Processing segment's assets are located in the Permian Basin of West Texas and Southeast New Mexico; the Eagle Ford Shale in South Texas; the Barnett Shale in North Texas; the Anadarko Ardmore and Arkoma Basins in Oklahoma and South Central Kansas; the Williston Basin in North Dakota and in the onshore and near offshore regions of the Louisiana Gulf Coast and the Gulf of Mexico.

Sales and Marketing

Targa sells its products to petrochemical companies refineries export companies large commercial and industrial customers as well as to natural gas and electric utilities that serve individual consumers. Targa also earns revenue by purchasing and reselling NGL products in the spot and forward physical markets.

Targa Resources' wholesale propane marketing operations primarily sell propane and related logistics services to major multi-state retailers independent retailers and other end-users.

Financial Performance

In recent years Targa Resources' revenue has been steady with a single positive aberration in 2014. Generally revenue comes in around $6.6 billion. Net income delivered positive though minimal results between 2011 and 2015 (averaging $50 million) before plunging in 2016.

For the year 2017 revenue rose about 30% to $8.8 billion coming entirely from the 38% increase of sale of commodities thanks to higher commodity prices ($2.2 billion) as well as increased petroleum products natural gas and condensate sales volumes ($100 million).

In 2017 net income swung from a sizable loss of $278 million to a profit of $54 million entirely due to income tax benefits stemming from the tax reform. Without it the company would have recorded a loss of $293 million for 2017 $30 million more than the year prior.

Targa's cash holdings increased from $74 million in 2016 to $137 million in 2017. Operations contributed $940 million followed by an even great contribution of $1 billion from financing activities coming from $4 billion in issuance of long-term debt . By contrast investment utilized $1.9 billion mostly in purchase of property plant and equipment.

Strategy

Targa Resources is focused on production from US shale plays and by the deployment of shale exploration and production technologies in both liquids-rich natural gas and crude oil resource plays for driving its growth. It is actively pursuing natural gas gathering and processing and NGL fractionation opportunities associated with liquids-rich natural gas from shale and other resource plays such as portions of the Barnett Eagle Ford Utica and Marcellus Shales and with even richer casinghead gas opportunities from active crude oil resource plays such as the Wolfberry and the Bone Springs Avalon and Bakken Shale plays. Production growth in the major shale plays (overall not just Targa's) is expected to be about 40% between 2016 and 2020 and 30% between 2020 and 2025. Part of Targa's strategy is to merely ensure it has the right assets and operations in place to grow its business along with the increased production (and demand) of these shale plays.

For example in the Permian Basin Targa gathers product from a diverse set of producers spanning 2 million dedicated acres of land. With expansion projects it expects that by the end of 2018 it will have capacity to process 2.5 billion cubic/ft per day of natural gas. It connected its recently acquired Delaware and Midland Basin assets to its existing systems to more efficiently move natural gas among its pipelines and processing plants.

Of its $1.3 billion of 2017 capital expenditures 80% is focused on the Permian Basin including nearly $300 million for its joint-venture project Grand Prix NGL pipeline. The pipeline will transport volumes from the Permian Basin and from Targa's North Texas system to Targa's fractionation and storage complex in the NGL market hub at Mont Belvieu Texas. Grand Prix will be supported by Targa's volumes and other third party customer commitments and is expected to be in service in early 2019. The capacity of the pipeline from the Permian Basin will be approximately 300 thousand barrels per day expandable to 550 thousand barrels per day.

The Permian work not only allows greater acquisition of natural gas but the connection to Mont Belvieu aids its downstream operations by lowering transportation costs and increasing predictability of supply. The Downstream business segment also expects to benefit from higher demand from new petrochemical facilities in the Houston area as well as higher demand from non-US customers wanting to export Targa's excess propane and butanes.

Mergers and Acquisitions

In 2016 Targa Resources completed the acquisition of all of the outstanding common units of Targa Resources Partners LP. As a result of the acquisition Targa improved its credit and coverage profile lowered its cost of capital and simplified its structure thereby improving its access to capital.

EXECUTIVES

Ceo, Joe Bob Perkins, age 58
President Administration, Jeffrey J. (Jeff) McParland, age 64, $500,000 total compensation
Evp Southern Field Gathering And Processing, Patrick J. (Pat) McDonie, age 59
Evp General Counsel And Secretary, Paul W. Chung, age 58, $490,000 total compensation
Evp And Cfo, Mattthew J. (Matt) Meloy, age 41, $450,000 total compensation
Evp Logistics And Marketing, D. Scott Pryor, age 57
Evp Northern Field Gathering And Processing, Dan C. Middlebrooks, age 63
Evp Engineering And Operations, Clark White, age 60
Evp Commercial, Robert Muraro, age 43
Vice President Finance, Howard M Tate
Vp Domestic Marketing Refinery Services And Commercial Transporation, Rob Donaldson
Svp Natural Gas Marketing, Stacey Duke
Chairman, James W. Whalen, age 78
Vice Chairman, Michael A. Heim, age 71
Auditors: PricewaterhouseCoopers LLP

LOCATIONS

HQ: Targa Resources Corp
811 Louisiana St., Suite 2100, Houston, TX 77002
Phone: 713 584-1000   **Fax:** 713 584-1100
Web: www.targaresources.com

PRODUCTS/OPERATIONS

2016 sales

	$ mil.	% of total
Logistics and Marketing	5,520	82
Gathering and Processing	1,109	17
Other	63	1
Total	**6,691**	**100**

COMPETITORS

DCP Midstream Partners	Enterprise Products
Devon Energy	Kinder Morgan
EnLink Midstream Partners	Magellan Midstream
Enbridge	ONEOK Partners
Energy Transfer	Summit Midstream Partners LP

HISTORICAL FINANCIALS

Company Type: Public

Income Statement

FYE: December 31

	REVENUE ($ mil.)	NET INCOME ($ mil.)	NET PROFIT MARGIN	EMPLOYEES
12/18	10,484	2	0.0%	2,460
12/17	8,815	54	0.6%	2,130
12/16	6,691	(187)	—	1,970
12/15	6,659	58	0.9%	1,870
12/14	8,617	102	1.2%	1,350
Annual Growth	**5.0%**	**(64.6%)**	**—**	**16.2%**

2018 Year-End Financials

Debt ratio: 39.00%
Return on equity: 0.00%
Cash ($ mil.): 232
Current ratio: 1.00
Long-term debt ($ mil.): 5,632
No. of shares (mil.): 232
Dividends
 Yield: 10.0%
 Payout: —
Market value ($ mil.): 8,349

	STOCK PRICE ($) FY Close	P/E High/Low	PER SHARE ($) Earnings	Dividends	Book Value
12/18	36.00	— —	(1.00)	4.00	27.00
12/17	48.00	— —	(0.00)	4.00	29.00
12/16	56.00	— —	(2.00)	4.00	29.00
12/15	27.00	98 24	1.00	3.00	26.00
12/14	106.00	62 35	2.00	3.00	4.00
Annual Growth	**(23.7%)**	**— —**	**—**	**8.0%**	**61.3%**

Target Corp

Cheap-but-chic Target is the US's #2 discount chain (behind Wal-Mart). The fashion-forward discounter operates 1800-plus Target and SuperTarget stores across the US as well as an online business at Target.com. It sells a broad range of household goods food and pet supplies apparel and accessories electronics decor and other items under national brands as well as owned and exclusive brands. Target and its larger grocery-carrying incarnation SuperTarget have carved out a niche by offering more upscale trend-driven merchandise than rivals Wal-Mart and Kmart. The company also offers pharmacy and clinic services in its stores through an operating agreement with CVS Pharmacy.

HISTORY

The panic of 1873 left Joseph Hudson bankrupt. After he paid his debts at 60 cents on the dollar he saved enough by 1881 to open a men's clothing store in Detroit. Among his innovations were merchandise-return privileges and price marking in place of bargaining. By 1891 Hudson's was the largest retailer of men's clothing in the US. Hudson repaid his creditors from 1873 in full with interest. When Hudson died in 1912 four nephews expanded the business.

Former banker George Dayton established a dry-goods store in 1902 in Minneapolis. Like Hudson he offered return privileges and liberal credit. His store grew to a 12-story full-line department store.

After WWII both companies saw that the future lay in the suburbs. In 1954 Hudson's built Northland in Detroit then the largest US shopping center. Dayton's built the world's first fully enclosed shopping mall in Edina a Minneapolis suburb in 1956. In 1962 Dayton's opened its first discount store in Roseville (naming the store Target to distinguish the discounter from its higher-end department stores).

Dayton's went public in 1966 the same year it began the B. Dalton bookstore chain. Three years later it merged with the family-owned Hudson's forming Dayton Hudson. Dayton Hudson purchased more malls and invested in such specialty areas as consumer electronics and hard goods. Target had 24 stores by 1970.

The Target chain became the company's top moneymaker in 1977. The next year Dayton Hudson bought California-based Mervyn's (later Mervyns). In the late 1970s and 1980s it sold nine regional malls and several other businesses including the 800-store B. Dalton chain to Barnes & Noble. The Target stores division purchased Indianapolis-based Ayr-Way (1980) and Southern California-based Fedmart stores (1983). In the late 1980s Dayton Hudson took Target to Los Angeles and the Northwest. Robert Ulrich who began with the company as a merchandise trainee in 1967 became president and CEO of the Target stores division in 1987 and chairman and CEO of Dayton Hudson in 1994.

Dayton Hudson opened the first Target Greatland store in 1990. By this time it had 420 Target stores. Also that year Dayton Hudson bought the Marshall Field's chain of 24 department stores from B.A.T Industries. Marshall Field's began as a dry-goods business that Marshall Field bought in 1865 and subsequently built into Chicago's premier upscale retailer.

SuperTarget stores were introduced in 1995. The Target stores division opened stores in the Mid-Atlantic and Northeast the next year while the department store division began selling off its Marshall Field's locations in Texas.

In 1998 Dayton Hudson boosted its Internet presence by purchasing direct-marketing company Rivertown Trading; it also bought apparel supplier Associated Merchandising that year. In 2000 Dayton Hudson renamed itself Target Corporation. In early 2001 the company renamed its Dayton's and Hudson's chains Marshall Field's. Also that year Target acquired the rights to 35 former Montgomery Wards stores from the bankrupt retailer.

The nation's #2 discounter was #1 when it came to corporate giving in 2001. Target topped the Forbes list of America's Most Philanthropic Companies that year donating 2.5% of its 2000 income (nearly $86 million). By comparison Wal-Mart gave away $116.5 million in 2001 less than 1% of its income in 2000.

In 2002 the company reopened 30 of the former Montgomery Ward stores as Target outlets. Net of closings 94 Target stores opened in 2002 while neither Mervyns nor Marshall Field's added to their store counts. In March 2003 three new SuperTarget stores opened in the Dallas/Fort Worth area.

2004 was a year of divestments for Target. In January the discounter announced it was exiting the catalog business. To that end in April Target sold its Signals and Wireless gifts catalogs to Universal Screen Arts for an undisclosed sum. In July Target sold its Marshall Field's business to The May Department Stores Co. for about $3.2 billion in cash. In September Target completed the sale of 257 Mervyns stores in 13 states to an investment group that includes Cerberus Capital Management Lubert-Adler/Klaff and Partners and Sun Capital Partners as well as its Mervyns credit card receivables to GE Consumer Finance for a combined sum of approximately $1.65 billion in cash. (Later Mervyns filed for bankruptcy and closed the last of its stores by the end of 2008.)

In October 2005 vice chairman Gerald Storch resigned unexpectedly after more than a dozen years with the company. No reason was given for his departure. In the largest mass opening in Target's history the retailer opened 60 new stores on October 9.

In July 2006 Target.com extended its partnership with Amazon Enterprise Solutions a unit of online retailer Amazon.com through August 2010. Amazon provides e-commerce technology to the discount chain.

In May 2008 Ulrich who served as chairman and CEO since 1994 handed his CEO title to president Gregg Steinhafel. (Steinhafel joined the retailer in 1979 and worked his way up the executive ranks.) Also in May Target closed on the sale of a 47% stake in its credit-card receivable to JPMorgan Chase for $3.6 billion. The five-year deal allows Target to buy back the stake at the end of the term. In October the company opened a pair of stores in Alaska thereby expanding its retail presence to 48 states. In November Target said no thanks to a plan Ackman had proposed for Target to spin off its real estate holdings in a bid to increase shareholder value citing uncertainty about valuation assumptions and the potential reduction in financial flexibility as a result of spin off.

Ulrich retired from the board in January 2009 and Steinhafel added the chairman's title to his job description.

In April 2010 Target stopped offering new credit card applicants its co-branded Visa credit card.

Chairman president and CEO Steinhafel resigned in May 2014 five months after a massive data breach at the company. In July 2014 the company named retail veteran Brian Cornell as chairman and CEO. Cornell 55 joined Target from PepsiCo Americas Foods where he served as CEO and oversaw the global food business. Before joining PepsiCo Cornell served as president and CEO of Sam's Club a division of Wal-Mart Stores.

EXECUTIVES

Senior Vice President Of Real Estate, Scott Nelson
Evp Chief Legal Officer And Corporate Secretary, Don H. Liu, age 58, $275,000 total compensation
Svp Merchandising, Patricia (Trish) Adams
Evp And Chief Corporate Social Responsibility Office, Laysha L. Ward, age 51
Chairman And Ceo, Brian C. Cornell, age 60, $1,300,000 total compensation
Evp And Coo, John J. Mulligan, age 53, $1,000,000 total compensation
Evp And Chief Merchandising Officer, Mark J. Tritton, age 55, $396,635 total compensation
Evp And Chief Stores Officer, Janna A. Potts, age 51
Evp And Cio, Michael E. (Mike) McNamara, age 54, $468,462 total compensation
Evp And Cfo, Catherine R. (Cathy) Smith, age 55, $798,558 total compensation
President Target Sourcing Services, Kelly Caruso
Evp And Chief Human Resources Officer, Stephanie A. Lundquist, age 43
Evp And Chief Risk And Compliance Officer, Jacqueline Hourigan Rice, age 47
Evp And Chief Marketing Officer, Rick H. Gomez, age 49
Svp Grocery Fresh Food And Beverage, Jeff Burt
President Target Financial And Retail Services, Scott Kennedy
President Target India, Tammy Redpath
Svp Global Sourcing, Cynthia Ho
Senior Vice President Risk And Government Affairs, Matt Zabel
Vp Strategy And Operations Community Relations, Tony Heredia
Pharmacy Manager, Mikel Gilbert
Vice President Technology Services, Tim Milne
Pharmacy Manager, Joseph Legrand
Vice President Assistant, Dana Winkler
Senior Vice President Region Ii, Robert Thompson
Senior Vice President Merchandising Capabilities, Michael Fiddelke
Vice President Administration Property Dvlpt Department, Katy DeLaTorre
Senior Vice President, Stephen Brinkley
Vice President And General Manager, Steve Mattson
Vice President Assistant, Melissa Loth
Senior Vice President Distribution, Carson Landsgard
Vice President Of Marketing, William White
Senior Vice President Enterprise Data Analytics And Business Intelligence, Paritosh Desai
Senior Vice President Administrative Assistant, Nadean Mueller
Senior Vice President, Manojkumar Shah
Pharmacy Manager, Jacqueline Jansen
Vice President, Sarah Arrell
Senior Vice President Talent And Organizational Effectiveness, Tim Curoe
Vice President Creative, Seth Zimmerman
Vice President Of Communications, Dustee T Jenkins

Vice President Administrative Assistant, Vonnie Zuehlke
Senior Vice President Executive Assistant, Tracy Rockholt
Vice President Assistant Corporate Financial Planning, Bethany Borucki
Group Vice President, Stacy Lippa
Vice President Supply Chain Technology, Rachel Whitcomb
Pharmacy Manager, David Cathcart
Senior Vice President Assistant, Amanda Dale
Vice President Human Resources, Ann Florell
Senior Vice President And Manager Financial Institutions, Addison Averett
Executive Vice President Executive Assistant, Kari Meiller
Vice President Finance, Scott Brill
Senior Vice President Business Development, Aaron Alt
Executive Vice President And Chief Human Resources Officer, Melissa Kremer
Senior Vp Vp Technical Architect, Subbarao Gudipalli
Vice President Of Wfm, Daniel Traczyk
Vice President Assistant, Milagros Hanson
Group Vice President, Beth Gates
Vice President Healthcare Operations, John Holcomb
Senior Vice President Owned Brand Management And Product Design, Julie Guggemos
Vice President Of Distribution Operations, Diane Closs
Executive Vice President Merchandising Apparel And Home, Trish Adams
Vice President Assistant, Rhonda Broyles
Senior Vice President Gc Sec'y, TimothyR Baer
Senior Group Vice President, Bill Hall
Vice President Assistant, Christina Hayes
Senior Vice President Home, Cara Sylvester
Vp Engineering And System Operations, Valerie Blihovde
Executive Vice President Chief Legal Officer And Corporate Secretary, Tim Baer
Vp Admin, Lorene Laubach
Senior Vp Vp Technical Architect Enterprise Architecture, Prasanna Singaraju
Vice President Business Development, Pam Tomczik
Senior Vice President Infrastructure And Operations, Tom Kadlec
Vice President Architecture, Joel Crabb
Senior Vice President Operational Excellence, Anu Gupta
Vice President Assistant, Amanda Pellowski
Senior Vp Vp Technical Architect, Dean Mclain
Vp Enterprise Risk Mgmt, Soraya Wright
Senior Vice President Fulfillment Operations, Preston Mosier
Senior Vice President Global Logistics Inventory Allocation And Replenishment, Ben Cook
Senior Vice President Network Planning And Operational Design, Shekar Natarajan
Svp Chief Accounting Officer And Controller, Robert Harrison
Senior Vice President And Chief Information Security Officer, Rich Agostino
Pharmacy Manager, Annie Song
Vice President Assistant, Teresa Bayne
Vice President Internal Innovation And Operations, West Stringfellow
Group Vice President, Amanda Vela
Vice President Assistant Style Marketing, Lindsey Lamppa
Vice President Divisional Meat And Fresh Prepared Food, Mark Kenny
Vice President And Co Founder, Steve Worthy
Senior Vice President Marketing, Michelle Messenberg
Vice President Property Management, John Leisen

Senior Vice President Merchandising Apparel And Accessories, Michelle Wlazlo
Senior Vice President Merchandising And Supply Chain Portfolio Solutions, Brett Craig
Vp Admin, Kim Sorenson
Evp And Chief Supply Chain And Logistics Officer, Arthur Valdez
Vice President Merchandise Manager, Scott Bradley
Pharmacy Manager, Samantha Schrempp
Vp Logistics Strategy And Planning, Sundip Naik
Vice President, Sumesh George
Vice President, Aaron Allen
Svp Assistant, Melissa Scanlon
Senior Vp Vp Lead Technical Specialist, Steve Esslinger
Vice President Of Planning, Joe Shillings
Senior Vice President Food And Beverage Supply Chain, Frank Bruni
Senior Vice President Food And Beverage Supply Chain, Frank Brunl
Senior Vice President Target Properties, Mark Schlndele
Senior Vice President Enterprise Data Analytics And Business Intelligence, Parltosh Desal
Senior Vice President Supply Chain Field Operations, Preston Mosler
Vice President;prin, Rick Harris
Senior Vice President Treasurer, Corey L Haaland
Assistant Treasurer, Sara Ross
Board Member, Rakesh Mishra
Vice Chairman, Mollie McCarty
Board Member, Megan Healey
Auditors: Ernst & Young LLP

LOCATIONS

HQ: Target Corp
1000 Nicollet Mall, Minneapolis, MN 55403
Phone: 612 304-6073
Web: www.target.com

2018 Locations

	No.
California	287
Texas	150
Florida	123
Illinois	94
New York	82
Minnesota	73
Pennsylvania	75
Ohio	63
Virginia	59
Michigan	53
North Carolina	51
Georgia	50
Other	684
Total	**1,844**

PRODUCTS/OPERATIONS

2018 Sales

	$ mil.	% of total
Beauty & household essentials	17,726	24
Apparel & accessories	15,004	20
Food & beverage	14,585	19
Home furnishings & décor	14,298	19
Hardlines	12,709	17
Credit card profit sharing	673	1
Other	250	-
Total	**75,356**	**100**

Selected Exclusive Brands

DENIZEN from Levi's
Genuine Kids from OshKosh
Isabel Maternity by Ingrid & Isabel
Nate Berkus for Target
Oh Joy! for Target

Selected Private Labels

Archer Farms (food)
Cat & Jack (children's apparel)
Market Pantry
Smith & Hawken (garden & outdoor)
Xhilaration (apparel)

COMPETITORS

Amazon.com	Home Depot
BJ's Wholesale Club	J. C. Penney Company
Bed Bath & Beyond	Kohl's
Best Buy	Kroger
Costco Wholesale	Lowe's
Dollar General	Sears Holdings
Dollar Tree	Wal-Mart
Euromarket Designs	

HISTORICAL FINANCIALS

Company Type: Public

Income Statement — FYE: February 2

	REVENUE ($ mil.)	NET INCOME ($ mil.)	NET PROFIT MARGIN	EMPLOYEES
02/19	75,356	2,937	3.9%	360,000
02/18*	71,879	2,934	4.1%	345,000
01/17	69,495	2,737	3.9%	323,000
01/16	73,785	3,363	4.6%	341,000
01/15	72,618	(1,636)	—	347,000
Annual Growth	0.9%	—	—	0.9%

*Fiscal year change

2019 Year-End Financials

Debt ratio: 27.00%	No. of shares (mil.): 518
Return on equity: 26.00%	Dividends
Cash ($ mil.): 1,556	Yield: 0.0%
Current ratio: 1.00	Payout: 46.0%
Long-term debt ($ mil.): 10,223	Market value ($ mil.): 36,849

	STOCK PRICE ($) FY Close	P/E High/Low	PER SHARE ($) Earnings	Dividends	Book Value
02/19	71.00	16 11	6.00	3.00	22.00
02/18*	73.00	15 9	5.00	2.00	22.00
01/17	64.00	18 13	5.00	2.00	20.00
01/16	72.00	16 13	5.00	2.00	22.00
01/15	74.00	— —	(3.00)	2.00	22.00
Annual Growth	(0.8%)	— —	—	7.3%	(0.1%)

*Fiscal year change

TATA AMERICA INTERNATIONAL CORPORATION

Tata America International is the North American holding company for Indian conglomerate Tata Group. In the US the company has about a dozen subsidiaries including offices for Tata Communications IT services firm Tata Consultancy Services (with more than 20 locations) and engineering consultancy Tata Technologies. In the industrial sector Tata America owns steel manufacturing plants in Ohio and Pennsylvania and General Chemical Industrial Products a soda ash plant in Wyoming. Other holdings include hotels (The Pierre in New York the Taj Boston and the Taj Campton Place in San Francisco) and sales offices for its beverage brands Eight O'Clock Coffee Good Earth and Tetley.

EXECUTIVES

President, Surya Kant
Vp Marketing And Communications, John Lenzen
Cfo, S. Mahalingam
Auditors: DELOITTE HASKINS & SELLS LLP

LOCATIONS

HQ: TATA AMERICA INTERNATIONAL CORPORATION
101 PARK AVE RM 2603, NEW YORK, NY 101782604
Phone: 212 557-8038
Web: WWW.TCS.COM

PRODUCTS/OPERATIONS

Selected Subsidiaries

IT Services
  Tata Business Support Services
  Tata Communications
  Tata Consultancy Services
  Tata Elxsi
  Tata Interactive Systems
  Tata Technologies
Engineering
  Tata AutoComp Systems
Services
  Campton Place
  Taj Boston
  The Pierre
Consumer Products
  Eight O'Clock Coffee
  Good Earth
  Tanishq
  Tata Tea Inc.
  Tetley
Chemicals
  General Chemical

COMPETITORS

Accenture	HCL Technologies
Atos North America	HP Enterprise Services
CIBER	IBM Global Services
Capgemini North America	ICP Inc.
	Infosys
Cognizant Tech Solutions	NTT Data
	Syntel
Computer Sciences Corp.	Unisys
	Wipro Technologies
Fujitsu America	Zensar Technologies

HISTORICAL FINANCIALS

Company Type: Private

Income Statement — FYE: March 31

	REVENUE ($ mil.)	NET INCOME ($ mil.)	NET PROFIT MARGIN	EMPLOYEES
03/18	8,197	122	1.5%	1,700
03/17	845	168	19.9%	—
03/16	755	118	15.7%	—
03/15	6,800	111	1.6%	—
Annual Growth	6.4%	3.0%	—	—

TCF Financial Corp (New)

Chemical Financial has banking down to a science. It's the holding company for Chemical Bank which provides standard services such as checking and savings accounts CDs and IRAs credit and debit cards and loans and mortgages to individuals and businesses through nearly 190 branches in the lower peninsula of Michigan. The majority of the bank's loan portfolio is made up of commercial loans while consumer loans make up the remainder. Boasting assets of $9 billion Chemical is the second largest bank in Michigan. The company also offers trust investment management brokerage and title insurance services through subsidiaries.

Operations

Its Wealth Management division which has some $4 billion in assets under custody offers trust services estate planning investment management and employee benefit programs. Chemical Financial Advisors offers mutual funds and marketable securities while CFC Title Services issues title insurance for mortgage properties. CFC Capital manages the company's municipal investment securities portfolio.

About 72% of Chemical Financial's total revenue came from loan interest (including fees) in 2014 while another 6% came from interest on its investment securities. The rest of its revenue came from deposit account service charges and fees (8%) wealth management revenue (6%) mortgage banking income (2%) and other miscellaneous sources of income.

Sales and Marketing

Chemical Financial spent $3.45 million on advertising in 2014 up from $2.97 million and $3.11 million in 2013 and 2012 respectively.

Financial Performance

Chemical Financial's revenues and profits have been rising over the past few years thanks growing loan and deposit business from acquisitions lower interest expenses on deposits and declining loan loss provisions as its loan portfolio's credit quality has improved with higher property valuations in the strengthened economy.

The bank's revenue rose by 6% to $290.4 million in 2014 as the bank as its acquisition of Northwestern Bancorp boosted its loan business during the year. Higher revenue lower interest expenses and a continued decline in loan loss provisions drove the bank's net income up by 9% to a record $62.1 million. The bank's operating cash levels inched higher to $89.9 million on higher cash earnings.

Strategy

The bank follows an aggressive acquisition strategy to boost its loan and deposit business while expanding its branch network into key parts of Michigan. Indeed its acquisitions in 2015 and 2014 boosted the bank's presence in northwestern Michigan and along the Michigan-Indiana border. By the end of 2014 the bank had acquired some 21 community banks and 36 branch bank offices.

Mergers and Acquisitions

Chemical Financial agreed in January 2019 to merge with Minnesota-based TCF Financial to form a Midwest bank with about $45 billion in assets $34 billion in total deposits and more than 500 branches in nine states. TCF's large deposit base and national wholesale lending business will complement Chemical's commercial lending and wealth management activities. The combined company which is to retain the TCF brand will have a more diversified deposit mix between retail and commercial lines and a more balanced loan portfolio across geographies asset classes and industries. Following the merger TCF shareholders will have a controlling interest in the combined company.

Company Background

In late 2012 the company acquired 21 branches in northeastern Michigan and Battle Creek from Independent Bank. That more than $8-million transaction further expands Chemical Bank's presence geographically. Additional acquisitions including FDIC-assisted takeovers of failed banks are possible.

EXECUTIVES

Svp Cfo And Treasurer, Lori A. Gwizdala, age 61, $344,720 total compensation
Vice Chairman And President Chemical Bank, Thomas C. (Tom) Shafer, age 60

Evp And Senior Credit Officer Chemical Bank,
James E. Tomczyk, age 67, $225,504 total
compensation

Vice Chairman Chemical Bank And Ceo Insite
Capital Llc, Thomas W. Kohn, age 65, $329,174
total compensation

Evp Commercial Lending Chemical Bank, Daniel
W. Terpsma, age 65

Evp And Cfo Chemical Financial And Chemical
Bank, Dennis L. Klaeser, age 61, $183,483 total
compensation

President And Ceo, David T. Provost

Director Chemical Financial And Chairman
Chemical Bank, Franklin C. Wheatlake, age 71

Evp And Coo Business Operations Chemical
Bank, Leonardo Amat, age 50, $309,477 total
compensation

Evp And Chief Risk Officer Chemical Bank, Lynn
M. Kerber, age 50

Evp General Counsel And Secretary, William C.
Collins, age 66

Evp And Coo Customer Experience Chemical
Bank, Robert S. Rathbun, age 55, $309,477 total
compensation

Svp And Cio, Greg Meidt

Vice President Of Customer Service, Sue Lynde

Vice President, Robert O Burgess

Assistant Vice President Product Development,
Jim Hubinger

Vice President Commercial Loan Officer, Jeff Hyde

Executive Vice President Chief Operating Officer,
James Milroy

Senior Vice President Of Investments, Pavel
Konecny

Vice President Information Systems, Laurie Soren

Senior Vice President And Trust Officer, Jude
Patnaude

Vice President Information Technology, Gary
Richard

Vice President Senior Financial Advisor East
Region Sales Manager, Brenda Rajewski

Vice President Data Services, Brian Beall

First Vice President, David Vermilye

Vice President, Robin Grove

Vice President And Trust Investment Officer, Glen
Matz

Mortgage Officer Assistant Vice President, Sue
Moody

Vice President Information Technology, Annette
Rus

Executive Vice President, Diane M Schweigert

Vice President And Community Reinvestment Act
Officer, Robert BurgessJr

Vice President Commerical Loans, Scott Harris

Vice President, John Laman

Vice President Commercial Loans, EARL
VANOPSTALL

Vice President Trust Investment Officer, Duane
Carpenter

Vice President Treasury Management And
Business Development, Marc Cesere

Vice President Treasury Management, Tammy Kerr

Vice President Commercial Lending, David
Kiekintveld

Vice President Mortgage Originator, Krista Martiny

Assistant Vice President Electronic Banking
Services, Mary Green

Vice President Commercial Banking Relationship
Manager Commerce Park Interim Vice, Ron
Cordaro

Vice President First, Michael Debo

Assistant Vice President Treasury Management
Sales Advisor, Julie Kuchnicki

Executive Vice President Chief Delivery Officer,
Gregory Bixby

Assistant Vice President And Branch Operations
Specialist, Barb Hartman

Vice President And Trust Officer, Pamela Dolezan

Assistant Vice President Branch Manager, Sharon
Langenberg

Senior Vice President Business Banking Credit
Director, Nita Cohen

Vice President And Personal Trust Officer, Joanna
Keenan

Chairman, Gary H. Torgow, age 61

Treasurer, Cheryl Whitman

Board Member, James Fitterling

Auditors: KPMG LLP

LOCATIONS

HQ: TCF Financial Corp (New)
333 W. Fort Street, Suite 1800, Detroit, MI 48226
Phone: 800 867-9757
Web: www.chemicalbank.com

PRODUCTS/OPERATIONS

2014 Sales

	$ mil.	% of total
Interest		
Loans including fees	209	72
Investment securities	17	6
Other	0	-
Non-interest		
Service charges on deposit accounts	22	8
Wealth management revenue	16	6
Other customer service charges & fees	19	6
Other	6	2
Total	**290**	**100**

COMPETITORS

1st Source Corporation	Flagstar Bancorp
Bank of America	Huntington Bancshares
Comerica	Independent Bank (MI)
Fifth Third	Mercantile Bank
Firstbank	

HISTORICAL FINANCIALS

Company Type: Public

Income Statement				FYE: December 31
	ASSETS ($ mil.)	NET INCOME ($ mil.)	INCOME AS % OF ASSETS	EMPLOYEES
12/18	21,498	284	1.3%	3,100
12/17	19,281	150	0.8%	3,000
12/16	17,355	108	0.6%	3,300
12/15	9,189	87	0.9%	2,100
12/14	7,322	62	0.8%	2,000
Annual Growth	30.9%	46.2%	—	11.6%

2018 Year-End Financials

Debt ratio: 0.00%
Return on equity: 10.00%
Cash ($ mil.): 496
Current ratio: —
Long-term debt ($ mil.): —

No. of shares (mil.): 71
Dividends
  Yield: 3.0%
  Payout: 31.0%
Market value ($ mil.): 2,616

	STOCK PRICE ($) FY Close	P/E High/Low		PER SHARE ($) Earnings	Dividends	Book Value
12/18	37.00	15	9	4.00	1.00	40.00
12/17	53.00	27	21	2.00	1.00	37.00
12/16	54.00	25	13	2.00	1.00	37.00
12/15	34.00	15	12	2.00	1.00	27.00
12/14	31.00	17	13	2.00	1.00	24.00
Annual Growth	4.6%	—	—	18.9%	7.2%	13.0%

TD Ameritrade Holding Corp

Through several subsidiaries TD Ameritrade Holding provides electronic discount brokerage and related financial services that enable retail investors to trade common and preferred stocks of US companies exchange-traded funds (ETFs) mutual funds bonds options futures and foreign currencies. In addition to its online offerings the company provides services through a network of more than 360 retail branches and relationships with more than 6000 independent registered investment advisors (RIAs). TD Ameritrade holds some $1.3 trillion in client assets and supports about half a million client trades per day.

Operations

TD Ameritrade Holding provides securities brokerage services and related technology-based financial services to value-conscious retail investors traders and registered investment advisors (RIAs). It provides its services mainly through the internet its national branch network and via its relationships with RIAs. The company offers its brokerage services under a simple low-cost commission structure and provides to RIAs its brokerage custodial services.

TD Ameritrade Holding operates several trading and investment platforms including tdameritrade.com thinkorswim TD Ameritrade Mobile and TD Ameritrade Institutional (for its RIAs). Beyond its core online services it offers online education investment advice and goal planning sessions and a service that refers retail investors to RIAs.

The company generates about 35% of revenue from commissions and transaction fees and around 30% from account fees from clients of Toronto-Dominion Bank and TD Bank USA with which TD Ameritrade has an insured deposit account agreement. It also produces about 25% of revenue from interest and 10% from investment product fees.

In 2019 TD agreed to sell its retirement plan custody and trust assets to Broadridge Financial Solutions. The deal will allow TD to increase its focus on growing its RIA products and services. The company will continue to offer turnkey retirement plan products to investment advisors through its TD Ameritrade Retirement Plan (TDARP) service.

Geographic Reach

Headquartered in Omaha Nebraska TD Ameritrade Holding has administrative and operational facilities in St. Louis Missouri; Southlake Texas; and Denver Colorado. The company also has an operations center in Jersey City New Jersey; six data center facilities in Texas Missouri Arizona and New Jersey; and smaller administrative and operational facilities in California Colorado Illinois Maryland Massachusetts Michigan Texas and Utah.

The company has more than 360 retail branch offices in 48 states and the District of Columbia.

Sales and Marketing

TD Ameritrade Holding targets a broad market of independent value-conscious retail investors traders financial planners and registered investment advisors (RIAs) and institutions. Clients can access its products and services through channels including the internet its network of retail branches mobile trading applications or over the phone via interactive voice response and registered representatives.

The online securities brokerage promotes its business via online television print website and social media advertising. The company's ads reach retail investors generally through digital channels online searches social media financial news networks and other television and cable networks. The company spends comparatively little on advertising to institutional investors.

TD also models its return on marketing investment to support advertising decisions and uses data analytics to create targeted advertising for clients.

Financial Performance

TD Ameritrade's revenue ticked up only slightly in fiscal years 2015 and 2016 before seeing gains of some 10% and 50% in 2017 and 2018 respectively; all its revenue streams saw gains those years. Net income trended similarly adding less than 5% each year until 2018 when it increased nearly 70% on higher revenue and a lower effective tax rate caused by the Tax Cuts and Jobs. Overall revenue and net income added about 70% and 85% respectively from 2014 to 2018. The company added more than 80% to its cash and nearly doubled its long-term debt in that time.

TD's revenue grew 48% to $5.3 billion in 2018 owing to the addition of about 3.5 million funded accounts from its 2017 acquisition of competitor Scottrade Financial Services.

The holding company's net income added 69% to $1.5 billion in 2018 thanks to the revenue-boosting Scottrade acquisition and US tax reform.

TD's cash stores expanded by $1.2 billion in 2018 to end the period at $2.7 billion. Operations provided $1.9 billion and investments added $92 million. The company's financing activities particularly dividend payments and treasury stock purchases used $782 million.

Strategy

TD Ameritrade Holding is in an enviable position as retail interest in stock investing is on the rise. Following tepid and sometimes volatile performance caused by the 2009 Financial Crisis retail investors are engaged in and curious about their investments. TD Ameritrade along with its expanded presence from the Scottrade Financial Services acquisition is poised to capture increasing revenue from increased trading volume. The company facilitated 811000 average trades per day in 2018 up nearly 60% from the previous year.

The organic growth of increased trading volume will be supplemented with higher interest revenue due to the rising interest rate environment brought about by the US Fed's interest rate hikes. As well as client assets grow so too will the deposits held at affiliate banks Toronto-Dominion Bank and TD Bank USA which it in turn invest to generate their own interest income.

The company is also working to branch out from its traditional products and services. In 2018 the company tripled its number of commission-free exchange-traded funds available to clients through an expanded ETF Market Center to aid client education about integrating ETFs into their investment portfolios. That year the company also reintroduced its Model Market Center an open-architecture model portfolio marketplace used by RIAs to assist their clients' investment needs.

TD is also expanding the channels by which its clients can make trades. The company was the first to launch trading via chatbot on Facebook Messenger and Twitter implement 24/5 trading and provide voice-activated trading through Amazon's Alexa.

Furthermore TD is growing its international network especially in Asia: In 2018 the company opened a branch in Hong Kong to complement its Singapore office.

Mergers and Acquisitions

In 2017 TD Ameritrade Holding and Toronto-Dominion Bank (which owns some 45% of TD Ameritrade) bought online brokerage rival Scottrade in a $4.3 billion two-stage transaction. Scottrade merged into TD Ameritrade while its Scottrade Bank subsidiary became part of Toronto-Dominion Bank. The acquisition more than quadrupled TD Ameritrade's retail branch network and gave the company about 3.5 million funded client accounts.

Company Background

Begun as a local investment banking firm in 1971 TD Ameritrade Holding became a retail discount securities brokerage firm in 1975. In 1988 the company became the first to offer touch-tone phone trading and in 1995 it acquired K. Aufhauser & Co. which is credited with performing the first online trade in 1994.

Following a 1997 IPO the company combined its brokerage units into one broker dealer Ameritrade. The company quadrupled its retail branch network and added 3.5 million client accounts with the $4.3 billion purchase of rival Scottrade in 2017.

HISTORY

Ameritrade began in 1971 as investment bank TransTerra. Dean Witter veteran Joe Ricketts transformed the firm into a discount broker in 1975. TransTerra formed Televest/Bancvest (now AmeriVest) in 1982 and Ameritrade Clearing (now TD Ameritrade Clearing) in 1983.

In 1988 the company became the first to offer Touch-Tone telephone trading and added Internet trading in 1994. TransTerra formed Ceres Securities a deep-discount brokerage service that added research to its services when it bought brokerage firms K. Aufhauser and All American in 1995. The company formed its eBroker all-Internet brokerage service in 1996 and became Ameritrade late that year.

In 1997 the company went public and combined its service-oriented subsidiaries. It also formed an alliance that directed users of America Online's investor site to Ameritrade's websites. The company grew rapidly in the late 1990s but like most technology-based companies suffered the impact of the subsequent tech wreck and the struggling economy.

Later TD Ameritrade led a wave of consolidation within the electronic brokerage industry. It purchased rivals National Discount Brokers and Datek in 2001 and 2002 but didn't stop there. In 2003 the company acquired the accounts of Mydiscountbroker.com from SWS Group and the retail accounts of BrokerageAmerica which together helped push the company's account base past the 3 million mark. It gained another 145000 accounts from brokerage firms Bidwell & Company and JB Oxford Holdings in 2004 and 2005.

E*TRADE offered to buy Ameritrade for more than $6 billion in mid-2005 but the company refused saying it wasn't up for sale. The following year Ameritrade made its own purchase. It bought the US operations of TD Waterhouse and added the "TD" to its name as well as some 100 branch locations. As part of the deal Canada-based TD Bank assumed about a 45% stake in the firm.

EXECUTIVES

Evp General Counsel And Secretary, Ellen L. S. Koplow, age 59
Ceo, Timothy D. (Tim) Hockey, age 56
Evp And Cfo, Stephen J. (Steve) Boyle, age 58, $96,923 total compensation
Evp And Chief Human Resources Officer, Karen Ganzlin
Evp And Chief Risk Officer, David Kimm
President Td Ameritrade Institutional, Thomas A (Tom) Nally, age 47, $450,000 total compensation
Evp Trader Group, Steven (Steve) Quirk

Managing Director Corporate Strategy And Business Development, Prashant Bhatia
Cio, Vijay Sankaran
President Retail Distribution, Peter deSilva
Senior Vice President And Director Of Technology, Lawson McClellan
Vice President Strategic Relationship Management, Bob Campione
Vice President Institutional Sales, Erik Blankmeyer
Vice President Services, James Watts
First Vice President Human Resources, Jessica Bednarovsky
Vice President Of Sales Td Ameritrade Institutional, Greg Mayes
Vice President, Bryan Louie
Regional Vice President, Gary Ausman
Vice President Institutional Sales, Kevin Peterson
Vice President Institutional Sales, Ryan Moeller
Senior Vice President, Gwen Parker
Chairman, Joseph H. (Joe) Moglia, age 69
Board Member, Todd Ricketts
Auditors: Ernst & Young LLP

LOCATIONS

HQ: TD Ameritrade Holding Corp
200 South 108th Avenue, Omaha, NE 68154
Phone: 402 331-7856   **Fax:** 402 597-7789
Web: www.amtd.com

PRODUCTS/OPERATIONS

2018 Sales

	$ mil.	% of total
Commissions & transaction fees	1,969	36
Insured deposit account fees	1,541	28
Net interest revenue	1,272	24
Investment product fees	557	10
Other	113	2
Total	5,452	100

Selected Subsidiaries

Ameritrade Advisory Services LLC
Ameritrade International Company
Amerivest Investment Management LLC
Financial Passport Inc.
Futures Forex Trading LLC
Investools Inc.
TD Ameritrade Clearing Inc.
TD Ameritrade IP Company Inc.
TD Ameritrade Mobile LLC
TD Ameritrade Online Holdings Corp.
TD Ameritrade Services Company Inc.
TD Ameritrade Trust Company
TD Ameritrade Inc.
TD Waterhouse Canadian Call Center Inc.
The Insurance Agency of TD Ameritrade LLC
thinkorswim Advisors Inc.
thinkorswim Group Inc.
thinkorswim Holdings Inc.
thinkorswim Singapore Pte. Ltd.
ThinkTech Inc.

COMPETITORS

Charles Schwab	Morgan Stanley
E*TRADE Financial	Raymond James
Edward Jones	Financial
FMR	ShareBuilder
LPL Financial	The Vanguard Group
Merrill Lynch	Wells Fargo Advisors

Income Statement   FYE: September 30

	REVENUE ($ mil.)	NET INCOME ($ mil.)	NET PROFIT MARGIN	EMPLOYEES
09/19	6,016	2,208	36.7%	9,226
09/18	5,452	1,473	27.0%	9,183
09/17	3,676	872	23.7%	10,412
09/16	3,327	842	25.3%	6,010
09/15	3,247	813	25.0%	5,690
Annual Growth	16.7%	28.4%	—	12.8%

2019 Year-End Financials

Debt ratio: 8.00%	No. of shares (mil.): 544
Return on equity: 26.00%	Dividends
Cash ($ mil.): 2,852	Yield: 3.0%
Current ratio: 1.00	Payout: 32.0%
Long-term debt ($ mil.): 3,594	Market value ($ mil.): 25,405

	STOCK PRICE ($) FY Close	P/E High/Low		PER SHARE ($) Earnings	Dividends	Book Value
09/19	47.00	14	11	4.00	1.00	16.00
09/18	53.00	24	18	3.00	1.00	14.00
09/17	49.00	30	20	2.00	1.00	13.00
09/16	35.00	22	16	2.00	1.00	10.00
09/15	18.00	—	—	1.00	1.00	9.00
Annual Growth	26.3%		—	27.7%	18.9%	15.0%

Tech Data Corp.

One of the world's largest wholesale distributors of technology products Tech Data Corp. provides thousands of items to more than 125000 resellers in 100-plus countries. Its catalog of products includes computer components (disk drives keyboards and video cards) networking equipment (routers and bridges) peripherals (printers modems and monitors) systems (PCs and servers) and software. Tech Data also offer products and services geared to data centers that include storage networking servers and cloud infrastructure. Other services are technical support configuration integration financing and logistics and product fulfillment. More than 60% of Tech Data's revenues are generated outside the US.

Operations

Tech Data operates as a distributor of technology products logistics management and other value-added services in North America South America (grouped under its Americas segment) the Asia/Pacific region and Europe.

The company's Endpoint Solutions portfolio includes PC systems mobile phones and accessories printers peripherals supplies endpoint technology software and consumer electronics.

The Advanced Solutions portfolio includes data center technologies such as storage networking servers advanced technology software and converged and hyper-converged infrastructure.

Geographic Reach

Clearwater Florida-based Tech Data sells to customers in more than 100 countries throughout North America South America Europe the Middle East and Africa and Asia/Pacific region. Europe is the company's largest market accounting for about 55% of sales with the Americas supplying more than 40%. The company has underperformed in the Asia/Pacific region which delivers less than 5% of its revenue. Its progress in the re-

gion has been slowed by challenging operating environments in some countries and higher-than-anticipated investments leading to a non-cash goodwill impairment charge of $47 million.

Sales and Marketing

Tech Data is one of the world's largest technology distributors helping companies like Apple Cisco HP Inc. and hundreds of others bring their products to market. It also offers a wide range of technical and business support services. It purchases equipment directly from vendors in significant quantities.

Products purchased from Apple accounted for more than 15% of Tech Data's sales while HP and Cisco each accounted for more than 10%.

The company's customers include approximately 125000 value-added resellers direct marketers retailers and corporate resellers.

Financial Performance

Tech Data's revenue rose robustly in 2018 and again in 2019 boosted by the acquisition of the Technology Solutions division of Avnet following two years of declining sales.

In 2019 (ended January) sales increased about 11% to $37.2 billion from 2018. Higher sales of data center products pushed Tech Data's sales higher around the world. In the Americas sales of software products and personal computer systems rose as did software and mobility products in Europe.

Net income jumped to $340.6 million in 2019 up $224 million from the previous year. Higher revenue and lower taxes following implementation of the US Tax Cuts and Jobs Act combined to drive profit higher.

Tech Data had $799.1 million in cash in 2019 compared to $955.6 million in 2018. Operations generated $380 million in 2019 while investing and financing activities used $171.7 million and $332.2 million respectively.

Tech Data has incurred substantial debt about $1.4 billion. The debt and terms of financing could limit the company's ability to obtain additional financing working capital capital expenditures or acquisitions make it more difficult to obtain trade credit from vendors and limits its flexibility to plan for and adjust to changing business and market conditions.

Strategy

Tech Data is moving to provide higher value products and services. In delivering higher value offerings to its customers the company can charge more and increase its operating margins and strengthen its balance sheet.

The acquisition of Avnet's Technology Solutions (TS) unit for $2.6 billion arms Tech Data was a step in providing higher value products. TS added a broader higher-value added range of products to offer customers who might want someone else to take over tasks like data center management. It also brought products and services from Hewlett-Packard Enterprise and IBM into Tech Data's arsenal.

In its 2019 fiscal year Tech Data introduced a higher value product called the cloud solutions factory which simplifies some time-consuming and complicated parts of cloud deployments. The factory offers tools designed to reduce costs and improve efficiency.

The company also expanded its security and analytics and the Internet of Things businesses establishing them as global practices and gathering expertise from across the company to build on its current offerings.

Company Background

Tech Data grew out of an electronics distribution business founded by Edward Raymund a University of Southern California graduate who started out as a representative for electronics manufacturers. By the early 1960s he had established an

industrial electronics distribution business in Florida. In 1974 he incorporated that business as Tech Data.

HISTORY

Tech Data grew out of an electronics distribution business founded by Edward Raymund a University of Southern California graduate who started out as a representative for electronics manufacturers. By the early 1960s he had established an industrial electronics distribution business in Florida. In 1974 he incorporated that business as Tech Data.

In 1981 Raymund's 25-year-old son Steven who had earned master's degrees in economics and international politics from Georgetown University's School of Foreign Service joined Tech Data on a temporary basis to work on the company's catalog. At that time Tech Data sold diskettes and other computer supplies to local companies and had about $2 million in sales.

Steven Raymund's favored status at the company angered a group of managers. Shortly after he arrived at Tech Data they copied the company's client list and walked out. The defection nearly sank Tech Data but Steven Raymund stayed on when his father handed him two-thirds of the company.

With the PC industry beginning to take off Steven Raymund positioned Tech Data as a middleman between computer and peripheral manufacturers and resellers. Steven was named COO in 1984. He became CEO in 1986 the year the company went public.

Tech Data began to distribute software in 1992 and a year later the company signed up Microsoft and inked a distribution deal for IBM computer systems. In 1994 Tech Data purchased U.S. Software Resource a California-based distributor of more than 500 business and entertainment software titles thereby increasing its software list and gaining high-profile publishers such as Borland International (now Borland Software) and Corel as suppliers.

Also in 1994 Tech Data began a global expansion when it bought France's largest distributor of wholesale computer products Softmart International.

To further build its business in Europe Tech Data in late 2012 acquired several distribution companies owned by UK-based Specialist Distribution Group (SDG) in the UK France and the Netherlands. Combined the acquired businesses generate sales of about ?1.4 billion ($1.75 billion). Previously Tech Data bought Triade Holding a Netherlands-based distributor of consumer electronics and IT products in 2010. The purchase strengthened Tech Data's IT business and accelerated its diversification into consumer electronics in the Netherlands Denmark and the Benelux region; it also supported operations across Europe by adding new specialty products vendors and customers. As part of the transaction Tech Data's joint venture with Brightstar Brightstar Europe (formed in 2007) acquired Triade subsidiary Mobile Communication Company (MCC) a mobility products distributor in Benelux. Total value of both deals was ?83 million (about $123 million). (Later Tech Data in 2012 bought its joint venture partner Brightstar's 50% ownership in Brightstar Europe for more than $165 million as well as several distribution companies in the UK from the distribution arm of IT services company Specialist Computer Holdings.)

EXECUTIVES

Evp And Chief Legal Officer, David R. (Dave) Vetter, age 59, $490,522 total compensation

Chairman And Ceo, Robert M. Dutkowsky, age 64, $1,122,124 total compensation

President Americas, Joseph H. Quaglia, age 54, $526,885 total compensation

President Europe, Patrick Zammit, age 52

Evp And Cio, John Tonnison, age 50, $433,495 total compensation

Evp And Cfo, Charles V. (Chuck) Dannewitz, age 65, $579,863 total compensation

Evp And Coo, Richard T. (Rich) Hume, age 60, $547,500 total compensation

Vp Product Marketing Client And Mobile Solutions, Linda Rendleman

Evp And Chief Human Resources Officer, Beth E. Simonetti

Vice President Sap Development And Operations, Tammy Gardner

Vice President Of Information Technology, Scott Moore

Vp Security Solutions, Heather Murray

Vice President Sales Eastern U.s, Marc McClure

Vp Gm Latin America Caribbean, Deena Piquion

Vp And Treasurer, Scott Walker

Vice President And General Manager Iscs Americas, Shaun Sinden

Vice President Of It, Marlene Perez

Vp Information Technology, Pete Story

Senior Vice President Mobile Solutions And Retail, Patrick Stokes

Vice President Tax, Cary Gums

Vice President Marketing, Wendy Linsky

Vp Technology, Jeff Tadeo

Vice President Of Networking Marketing, Charles Bartlett

Senior Vice President Us Accounting, Tracy Hummel

Vice President Manager Director, Cathy Clark

Vice President Global Business Development, John O'Shea

Vice President Product Marketing, Sid Earley

Vice President Streamone, Bob Kruger

Senior Vice President Finance, Cookie Serrano

Vice President Of Credit The Americas, Jay Snyder

Vice President Global Cisco Strategy And Americas Iot, Angie McCourt

Vice President Data Analytics Iot And Cognitive Computing, Colin Blair

Senior Vice President Advance Solutions, Kevin Kennedy

Vice President Of Sales Services, Ron Brinckerhoff

Vice President Vendor Marketing Enterprise Solutions, Anne Devine-Pride

Vice President Sales Operations, Christy Anderson

Vice President And General Manager Retail Meeting And Direct Marketers, Bob Johnson

Vice President Enterprise Sales, Eric Barnhart

Vp Data And Networking, Cheryl Neal

Vice President Sales Enterprise Solutions, Patty Gorman

Vp Cisco Solutions Tech Data Ts, Phillip Privett

Vice President Human Resources, John Trifone

Board Member, Charles Adair

Board Member, Kathleen Misunas

Treasurer, Gael Manzo

Vp Assistant Treasurer, David Childers

Board Member, Harry J Harczak

Auditors: Ernst & Young LLP

LOCATIONS

HQ: Tech Data Corp.
5350 Tech Data Drive, Clearwater, FL 33760
Phone: 727 539-7429
Web: www.techdata.com

2019 Sales

	$ mil.	% of total
Europe	20,026	54
Americas	16,041	43
Asia/Pacific	1,172	3
Total	**37,239**	**100**

PRODUCTS/OPERATIONS

Solutions
Credit Services
Marketing Services
Education & Training
Technical Services
Products and services
Logistics & Warehousing
Supply Chain Services
Technical Services
Marketing Services
Solutions Center

COMPETITORS

ALSO Holding AG	Avnet
ASI Computer Technologies	ESPRINET SPA
Agilysys	Ingram Micro
Arrow Electronics	SYNNEX
	Westcon

HISTORICAL FINANCIALS

Company Type: Public

Income Statement
FYE: January 31

	REVENUE ($ mil.)	NET INCOME ($ mil.)	NET PROFIT MARGIN	EMPLOYEES
01/19	37,239	341	0.9%	14,000
01/18	36,775	117	0.3%	14,000
01/17	26,235	195	0.7%	9,500
01/16	26,380	266	1.0%	9,000
01/15	27,671	175	0.6%	8,900
Annual Growth	**7.7%**	**18.1%**	**—**	**12.0%**

2019 Year-End Financials

Debt ratio: 11.00%
Return on equity: 12.00%
Cash ($ mil.): 799
Current ratio: 1.00
Long-term debt ($ mil.): 1,301

No. of shares (mil.): 37
Dividends
Yield: —
Payout: —
Market value ($ mil.): 3,533

	STOCK PRICE ($) FY Close	P/E High/Low	Earnings	Dividends	Book Value
01/19	96.00	12 8	9.00	0.00	79.00
01/18	100.00	36 27	3.00	0.00	77.00
01/17	86.00	16 11	6.00	0.00	62.00
01/16	62.00	11 7	7.00	0.00	57.00
01/15	57.00	15 11	5.00	0.00	52.00
Annual Growth	**13.8%**	**— —**	**18.1%**	**—**	**11.0%**

Telephone & Data Systems Inc

Telephone and Data Systems (TDS) is one of the largest US phone companies that's not descended from Ma Bell. The company has about 6.2 million local phone wireless and cable connections in about 35 states. The company's core business unit U.S. Cellular serves about 5 million customers in more than 20 states with key markets the central US and the mid-Atlantic region. The company also offers fixed-line and broadband internet services in rural and suburban markets in some 25 states through its TDS Telecom subsidiary which provides local service to 1.2 million access lines through incumbent local-exchange carriers (ILEC). Data networking and hosted telecom services are provided to business clients through the TDS Business unit.

Operations

TDS is more telephone than data systems with about 80% of revenue generated by wireless services sold by US Cellular. TDS owns more than 80% of US Cellular's stock.

About 20% of revenue comes from TDS Telecom which operates wireline and cable subsidiaries that provide communications services. Wireline operations provides telecommunication services such as voice broadband and video.

The rest of the company's revenue is supplied by its cable operations that offer advanced broadband video and voice services multi-line phone systems data networking Ethernet and VoIP services through its two brands: TDS Cable and Bend-Broadband.

TDS also owns OneNeck a provider of IT services such as management and hosting of a customer's IT infrastructure and applications.

Geographic Reach

Headquartered in Chicago Illinois TDS's US Cellular provides service in more than 20 states mostly in the Midwest but also in the east along the Atlantic seaboard and in the Northwest. The wireline unit operates in around 25 states and as a Competitive Local Exchange Carrier (CLEC) in Illinois Michigan Minnesota New Hampshire and Wisconsin. The cable brands operate in New Mexico Texas Utah and Oregon.

Sales and Marketing

US Cellular sells its services through distribution channels that include retail sales and service centers direct sales third-party national retailers independent agents and its website and telesales. It focuses on retail consumers government entities and small-to-mid-sized business customers in industries such as construction retail agriculture professional services and real estate.

Wireline operations provide telecommunications services to residential and commercial customers. Wireline also provides services to wholesale customers which are primarily interexchange carriers (companies that provide long-distance telephone and data services between local exchange areas) and wireless carriers.

Financial Performance

TDS's annual revenue has hovered around $5 billion a year for a decade as the company has tried to generate new revenue to replace declining wireline sales. The company has maintained a fluctuating profit for nine of 10 years.

In 2018 revenue inched 2% higher to about $5.2 billion from 2017 breaking a two-year revenue slide. US Cellular's revenue was 2% higher despite 49000 fewer retail connections in 2018 from 2017. Customers switching to smartphones from feature phones helped drive revenue higher. Average revenue per user increased to $44.98 in 2018 from $44.38 in 2017. Telecom revenue edged up 1% in 2018 from 2017 on the strength of a 12% rise in cable revenue while wireline revenue was down 2%.

TDS posted a profit of $135 million in 2018 compared to a $153 million profit the year before. Although the company had lower costs in 2018 it received a sizable tax benefit in 2017.

The company's cash and equivalents stood at $927 million in 2018 compared to $622 million in 2017. Operations generated $1 billion in 2018 while investing activities used $680 million and financing activities used $32 million.

TDS has a significant amount of indebtedness about $2.4 billion in long-term debt which could affect its ability to respond to market opportunities and threats. The company's interest expense was $172 million in 2018.

Strategy

TDS introduced new calling plans in 2017 and 2018 was the first year to show full results. Unlimited calling plans account for more than 25% of its postpaid connection base. Continuing adoption of unlimited plans helped drive the increases in ARPU as did sales of device protection plans and accessories and roaming revenue.

The company continues to invest in its network capacity increasing capital spending to $767 million in 2018 up $73 million from 2017. The company expanded VoLTE service in Iowa Wisconsin California Washington and Oregon in 2018 and plans to complete coverage in New England and the Mid-Atlantic areas in 2019.

Part of the company's capital spending has gone to develop 5G technology. The fifth generation of wireless service 5G technology is expected to provide higher speed and reliability as well as low latency. In the fourth quarter of 2018 US Cellular began conducting a trial using 5G standards and equipment on its core LTE network. In 2019 the company bought spectrum at an FCC auction that would enhance its 5G service in its service areas.

As a regional telecommunications provider TDS's U.S. Cellular unit goes against national carriers such as AT&T and Verizon as does TDS Telecom. The national carriers have more extensive networks and advertise heavily. With its smaller more rural customer bases TDS deals with some higher expenses that its competitors do.

Mergers and Acquisitions

In 2017 Telephone and Data Systems acquired K2 Communications a provider of broadband video and voice products to residential customers. The deal added more than 1200 service addresses to nearby TDS services areas in Colorado. Also in 2017 TDS bought Crestview Communications Sun Prairie Utilities and InterLinx Communications to bolster its fiber-based broadband networks.

Company Background

LeRoy Carlson Sr. learned the ins and outs of rural phone operators when he owned a small firm that supplied equipment and forms to independent phone companies. In the mid-1950s he began buying some of these small phone companies which he consolidated with a phone book publisher and his equipment company to form Telephones Inc. Carlson sold the company to Contel in 1966.

Carlson continued to buy and sell rural carriers allowing them to retain local management while he provided centralized purchasing and system upgrades. In 1969 he bought 10 rural providers in Wisconsin and consolidated all of his companies into Telephone and Data Systems (TDS).

HISTORY

LeRoy Carlson Sr. learned the ins and outs of rural phone operators when he owned a small firm that supplied equipment and forms to independent phone companies. In the mid-1950s he began buying some of these small phone companies which he consolidated with a phone book publisher and his equipment company to form Telephones Inc. Carlson sold the company to Contel in 1966.

Carlson continued to buy and sell rural carriers allowing them to retain local management while he provided centralized purchasing and system upgrades. In 1969 he bought 10 rural providers in Wisconsin and consolidated all of his companies into Telephone and Data Systems (TDS).

Between 1970 and 1975 TDS acquired 32 rural phone companies. When smaller companies in its established regions became scarce TDS bought rural phone providers from large independents. As TDS diversified the wireline subsidiary became TDS Telecommunications.

The company began offering paging services in Wisconsin in 1972 and later created subsidiary American Paging (1981). In 1975 TDS moved into cable TV service eventually creating TDS Cable Communications (1984) but it sold the holdings in 1986.

Getting a head start on the big Bells in the cellular race TDS began seeking licenses in the early 1980s eventually winning a 5% stake in the Los Angeles market. Although buffeted by larger independents it placed a high priority on cellular operations and formed subsidiary United States Cellular Corporation in 1983. Two years later US Cellular launched services in Tennessee and Oklahoma.

EXECUTIVES

Svp Acquisitions And Corporate Development, Scott H. Williamson, age 68, $663,000 total compensation

Vp And Treasurer, Peter L. Sereda, age 57

Vice President And Assistant Treasurer, John Toomey

President And Ceo, LeRoy T. (Ted) Carlson, age 73, $1,352,700 total compensation

Svp And Cio, Kurt B. Thaus, age 61

Svp Technology Services And Strategy, Joseph R. Hanley, age 53

Svp Finance And Chief Accounting Officer, Douglas D. Shuma, age 57, $432,500 total compensation

Vp Information Technology Operational Services And Chief Information Security Officer, Theodore E. Wiessing

Vice President Information Technology Strategy Quality And Application Services, Laurie Ruchti

Vice President Internal Audit, Frieda Ireland

Vp Tax, David D Gillman

Vp, Miriam Oberbruner

Vice President Strategy, Peter Taft

Svp Of Marketing Of Sales And Customer Operations Of Tds Telecom, Shane West

Vp And Chro Of Tds Telecoms, Kathy Cefalu

Vice President And Controller, Kroll Anita

Chairman, Walter C. D. Carlson, age 66

Board Member, Gary Sugarman

Auditors: PricewaterhouseCoopers LLP

LOCATIONS

HQ: Telephone & Data Systems Inc
30 North LaSalle Street, Suite 4000, Chicago, IL 60602
Phone: 312 630-1900   **Fax:** 312 630-1908
Web: www.teldta.com

PRODUCTS/OPERATIONS

2018 Sales

	$ mil.	% of total
U.S. Cellular	3,967	78
TDS Telecom	927	18
All Other	255	4
Total	**5,109**	**100**

2018 Sales

	$ mil.	% of total
Service	3,999	78
Equipment and product sales	1,110	22
Total	**5,109**	**100**

COMPETITORS

AT&T	HC2 Holdings
ATN International	NII Holdings
Cavalier Telephone	Sprint Communications
CenturyLink	Suddenlink
Cincinnati Bell	Communications
Cricket	T-Mobile USA
FairPoint Communications Inc.	Verizon

HISTORICAL FINANCIALS

Company Type: Public

Income Statement   FYE: December 31

	REVENUE ($ mil.)	NET INCOME ($ mil.)	NET PROFIT MARGIN	EMPLOYEES
12/18	5,109	135	2.6%	9,400
12/17	5,044	153	3.0%	9,900
12/16	5,104	43	0.8%	10,300
12/15	5,176	219	4.2%	10,400
12/14	5,009	(136)	—	10,600
Annual Growth	0.5%	—	—	(3.0%)

2018 Year-End Financials

Debt ratio: 25.00%   No. of shares (mil.): 114
Return on equity: 3.00%   Dividends
Cash ($ mil.): 921   Yield: 2.0%
Current ratio: 3.00   Payout: 55.0%
Long-term debt ($ mil.): 2,418   Market value ($ mil.): 3,710

	STOCK PRICE ($) FY Close	P/E High/Low		PER SHARE ($) Earnings	Dividends	Book Value
12/18	33.00	30	20	1.00	1.00	40.00
12/17	28.00	24	18	1.00	1.00	38.00
12/16	29.00	81	54	0.00	1.00	38.00
12/15	26.00	15	12	2.00	1.00	38.00
12/14	25.00	—	—	(1.00)	1.00	36.00
Annual Growth	6.5%			—	4.5%	2.4%

TENASKA MARKETING VENTURES

EXECUTIVES

Chm, Howard L Hawks
Pres, Fred R Hunzeker
V Pres, David N Schettler
Mgr-Dir, Janet Corritore
Mgr-V Pres, Mike Metzler
Sr V Pres, Terry K Cameron
Sr V Pres, Lori A Bruck
Mgr-V Pres, John Obermiller
Mgr-V Pres, Martin E Titus
Mrg-Dir, John G Hall
V Pres, Terry Clarke

LOCATIONS

HQ: TENASKA MARKETING VENTURES
14302 FNB PKWY, OMAHA, NE 681544446
Phone: 402 691-9500
Web: WWW.TENASKA.COM

HISTORICAL FINANCIALS

Company Type: Private

Income Statement | | | | FYE: December 31

	REVENUE ($ mil.)	NET INCOME ($ mil.)	NET PROFIT MARGIN	EMPLOYEES
12/07	10,310	0	—	91
12/05	9,471	0	—	
12/04	0	0	—	
12/03	4,940	0	—	
Annual Growth	20.2%	—	—	—

Tenet Healthcare Corp.

Tenet Healthcare is a for-profit company operating about 65 acute care hospitals with some 18000 beds in about 10 US states including California Florida and Texas. Its operations range from small community facilities offering basic care to major hospitals such as the 600-bed Brookwood Baptist Medical Center in Birmingham Alabama. In addition to its acute care holdings Tenet operates outpatient centers imaging centers and other health care units that form regional networks around its main hospitals. Its United Surgical Partners International (USPI) division operates ambulatory surgery centers and surgical hospitals. Tenet is spinning off its Conifer unit which provides patient billing and communications.

HISTORY

Hospital attorney Richard Eamer along with attorneys Leonard Cohen and John Bedrosian founded National Medical Enterprises (NME) in 1969. After its IPO NME bought 10 hospitals nursing homes an office building and land in California. Within six years the company owned operated and managed 23 hospitals and a home health care business. It sold medical equipment and bottled oxygen and provided vocational training for nurses.

In the 1970s NME expanded into hospital construction and bought five Florida hospitals. By 1981 NME was the #3 health care concern in the US owning or managing 193 hospitals and nursing homes. In the 1980s NME diversified further buying nursing homes and mental health centers. By the end of the decade the company's Specialty Hospital Group brought in more than 50% of revenues. NME was the second-largest publicly owned health care company in the US (after HCA) by 1985.

In 1990 NME reversed course spinning off most of its long-term-care businesses but kept 19 UK nursing facilities operated by its Westminster Health Care subsidiary (sold 1996). In 1992 the company acquired an Australian hospital management firm.

That year several insurance companies sued NME alleging fraudulent psychiatric claims; NME settled the suits in 1993. Federal agents later raided company headquarters seizing papers related to the suspected fraud. That year investment banker Jeff Barbakow took over as CEO forcing out Eamer and Cohen.

In 1993 and 1994 NME dumped most of its psychiatric and rehabilitation facilities using the proceeds to help pay penalties stemming from the federal investigation into alleged insurance fraud kickbacks and patient abuse at its psychiatric units.

NME paid another $16 million in related state fines. (Related civil lawsuits were settled in 1997.)

The company's name change to Tenet Healthcare coincided with new purchases throughout the South in 1995 and 1996.

The next few years were mixed for Tenet. On the upside it bought OrNda HealthCorp which complemented Tenet's existing networks. Tenet and MedPartners (now Caremark Rx) then the #1 practice management firm formed a Southern California hospital-doctor network in 1997 that gave both companies heft in dealing with HMOs (the partnership crumbled in 1999 when MedPartners exited practice management to focus on pharmacy benefits management and ceased operations in California). Merger discussions began with embattled market leader Columbia/HCA (now HCA) but fizzled.

In 1998 Tenet bought eight Philadelphia hospitals owned by the bankrupt Allegheny Health Education & Research Foundation. The company was dogged by another investigation this time by the Health and Human Services Inspector General's office over allegations the company paid more than fair market value for a physician practice in return for kickbacks. Tenet in 2004 agreed to pay about $31 million to settle two lawsuits stemming from these allegations.

Like many companies in the industry in 1999 Tenet began feeling the effects of the Balanced Budget Act of 1997 which mandated more scrutiny of Medicare expenditures to health care providers. In response the company began divesting some of its hospitals; it also shed its practice management business and reorganized its corporate structure.

Tenet rebounded and acquired hospitals in 2001 and 2002 but the next year proved not so kind. Federal investigations into the company's billing practices particularly those related to Medicare began late in 2002. In 2003 the company settled claims brought by the Department of Justice that doctors performed unnecessary cardiac surgeries at its Redding Medical Center (now Shasta Regional Medical Center) in California; the settlement cost Tenet $54 million (plus millions more to settle patients' claims). Tenet sold the facility in 2004 and also disposed of more than a dozen other facilities cutting its holdings from 115 to 100.

An even larger sell-off began in 2004 and included nearly 20 hospitals in California and others in Louisiana Massachusetts (all three were sold to Vanguard Health Systems in early 2005) Missouri and Texas. The company also exited the Nevada market when it sold Lake Mead Hospital Medical Center in Las Vegas in early 2004. Additionally the company ended some operating leases and joint ventures primarily in California; sold its Barcelona Spain hospital; and sold about a dozen home health agencies and hospice providers to Amedisys.

Tenet Healthcare moved its headquarters from Santa Barbara California to Dallas in 2005. The move was intended to streamline operations and save money.

Tenet saw some hard times in 2005 and spent years struggling to emerge from several subsequent years of investigations lawsuits and bad publicity. Its New Orleans and Mississippi facilities were hit hard by Hurricane Katrina in 2005 and its Memorial Medical Hospital in New Orleans became a symbol of the city's devastation after several dozen bodies were found there in the aftermath of the storm. The company has since sold both locations.

In 2006 it resolved multiple federal investigations regarding its billing practices by agreeing to a $900 million deal with the Justice Department. Its sale of hospitals post-Katrina was part of a larger plan announced in 2006 to sell off about a dozen facilities ridding itself of some low-performing operations partly to pay its $900 million bill to government investigators and partly so it could invest in equipment upgrades at its remaining hospitals. (The sales followed a larger-scale divestiture of about 25 facilities begun earlier.) In 2009 Tenet sold the USC University Hospital and Kenneth Norris Jr. Cancer Hospital to the University of Southern California for $275 million.

In 2010 Tenet sold its stake in supply chain and clinical workforce management firm Broadlane to MedAssets for some $159 million.

In late 2010 fellow hospital operator and rival Community Health Systems(CHS) made an unsolicited bid to acquire Tenet in a deal worth some $7.3 billion ($3.3 billion in cash and stock plus the assumption of $4 billion in debt). Tenet responded with a resounding "thanks but no thanks" saying the bid undervalued the company. CHS remained persistent despite a "poison pill" plan Tenet adopted and a volley of lawsuits. After Tenet's board rejected a plumped up offer of $4.1 billion in cash CHS formally withdrew all offers in 2011.

EXECUTIVES

Chairman And Ceo, Ronald A. (Ron) Rittenmeyer, age 72

Ceo Doctors Medical Center, Warren J. Kirk

Ceo San Antonio Market, Trip Pilgrim

Ceo Western Region, Jeffrey (Jeff) Koury

Vp Patient Financial Services, Stephen M. (Steve) Mooney

Svp And Chief Managed Care Officer, Clint Hailey

Svp And Controller, Daniel J. (Dan) Cancelmi, age 56, $618,000 total compensation

Ceo Desert Market, Michele Finney

Ceo Eastern Region – Central Division, Garry Gause

Ceo Philadelphia Market, Michael P. (Mike) Halter

Ceo Texas Region, Tim Adams

Ceo Eastern Region – Coastal Division, Marsha Powers

Ceo Texas Region, J. Eric Evans, age 41, $626,538 total compensation

Svp Applied Informatics And Cio, Paul T. Browne

Ceo South Texas Market, Manuel R. (Manny) Vela

Ceo Memphis Market, Audrey Gregory

Ceo United Surgical Partners International, William H. (Bill) Wilcox

Ceo El Paso Market, Sally Deitch

Ceo Detroit Market, Anthony Tedeschi

Svp And Chief Compliance Officer, Howard Hacker

Vp Patient Care Services And Chief Nursing Officer, Dian Adams

Chief Medical Officer, Octavio J. (Tavi) Diaz

Ceo Phoenix Market, Frank Molinaro

Ceo Birmingham Market, Keith Parrott

Vice President Construction And Design, Kenneth Sutherland

Regional Vice President Chief Financial Officer, Bill Durham

Vice President And Assistant General Counsel, Paul Castanon

Vice President Chief Financial Officer Central Region At Tenet Healthcare, Kathryn Engstrom

Blood Bank Director, Melanie Orourke

Vice President Government Relations, Corey Davison

Vice President Health Plans, Ron Rosenberger

Vice President Financial Information Systems, Michael Hongola

Vp Finance And Accounting Conifer, James Enna

Rph, Lisa Jesse

Assistant Vice President Regional Operations Managed Care, Dawn Cirri

Vice President Managed Care, Mike Blerman

Director Of Nursing, Terraca Holmes

Vice President And Chief Of Staff Executive Office, Katy Black

Svp Of Chief Human Resources Officer, Robb Webb
Vice President Of Finance Tenet Physician Resources, Debra Lee
Vp And Cio Of Conifer Health Solution, Chris Tyler
Svp And Cfo Of Conifer Health Solutions, Daniel Karnuta
Svp And Chief Compliance Officer Of Conifer Health Solutions, Dan Feldman
Director Of Him, Amy Bolin
Senior Vice President Global Services, Rod Fomby
Medical Director, Cathy Novakovich
Vp Financial Planning And Analysis, Michael B Rice
Vice President Graduate Medical Education Dio, Victor Jaffe
Vp Talent Management And Development, Greg Miller
Secretary, Sonia Carcache
Board Member, Tammy Romo
Unit Secretary, Erica Roche
Board Member, Richard Mark
Board Member, James Bierman
Board Member, Richard Fisher
Auditors: DELOITTE & TOUCHE LLP

LOCATIONS

HQ: Tenet Healthcare Corp.
1445 Ross Avenue, Suite 1400, Dallas, TX 75202
Phone: 469 893-2200
Web: www.tenethealth.com

Selected Hospitals

Alabama
Brookwood Medical Center (Birmingham)
California
Desert Regional Medical Center (Palm Springs)
Doctors Hospital of Manteca
Doctors Medical Center (Modesto)
Emanuel Medical Center (Turlock)
Fountain Valley Regional Hospital and Medical Center
John F. Kennedy Memorial Hospital (Indio)
Lakewood Regional Medical Center
Los Alamitos Medical Center
Placentia Linda Hospital
San Ramon Regional Medical Center
Sierra Vista Regional Medical Center (San Luis Obispo)
Twin Cities Community Hospital (Templeton)
Florida
Coral Gables Hospital
Delray Medical Center (Delray Beach)
Good Samaritan Medical Center (West Palm Beach)
Hialeah Hospital
North Shore Medical Center (Miami)
Palm Beach Gardens Medical Center
Palmetto General Hospital (Hialeah)
St. Mary's Medical Center (West Palm Beach)
West Boca Medical Center (Boca Raton)
Missouri
Des Peres Hospital (St. Louis)
South Carolina
Coastal Carolina Hospital (Hardeeville)
East Cooper Regional Medical Center (Mt. Pleasant)
Hilton Head Hospital
Piedmont Medical Center (Rock Hill)
Tennessee
Saint Francis Hospital (Memphis)
Saint Francis Hospital-Bartlett
Texas
Centennial Medical Center (Frisco)
Cypress Fairbanks Medical Center (Houston)
Doctors Hospital at White Rock Lake (Dallas)
Houston Northwest Medical Center
Lake Pointe Medical Center (Rowlett)
Nacogdoches Medical Center
Park Plaza Hospital (Houston)
The Hospitals of Providence Memorial Campus (El Paso)
Texas Regional Medical Center (Sunnyvale)

PRODUCTS/OPERATIONS

2017 Sales by Segment

	$ mil.	% of total
Hospital Operations	16,260	82
Ambulatory Care	1,940	10
Conifer		
Tenet	618	3
Other customers	979	5
Adjustments	(618)	-
Total	**19,179**	**100**

COMPETITORS

Adventist Health System Sunbelt Healthcare
Ascension Health
Banner Health
CHRISTUS Health
Carolinas HealthCare System
Catholic Health Initiatives
Community Health Systems
Dignity Health
Encompass Health
HCA
LifePoint Health
Memorial Health Services
Mercy Health
SSM Health Care
Sutter Health
Texas Health Resources
Universal Health Services
University Health Services

HISTORICAL FINANCIALS

Company Type: Public

Income Statement

FYE: December 31

	REVENUE ($ mil.)	NET INCOME ($ mil.)	NET PROFIT MARGIN	EMPLOYEES
12/18	18,313	111	0.6%	115,500
12/17	19,179	(704)	—	125,820
12/16	19,621	(192)	—	130,000
12/15	18,634	(140)	—	134,630
12/14	16,615	12	0.1%	108,989
Annual Growth	**2.5%**	**74.4%**	**—**	**1.5%**

2018 Year-End Financials

Debt ratio: 66.00%
Return on equity: ***.***.**%
Cash ($ mil.): 411
Current ratio: 1.00
Long-term debt ($ mil.): 14,644
No. of shares (mil.): 103
Dividends
 Yield: —
 Payout: —
Market value ($ mil.): 1,757

	STOCK PRICE ($) FY Close	P/E High/Low		PER SHARE ($) Earnings	Dividends	Book Value
12/18	17.00	36	14	1.00	0.00	(1.00)
12/17	15.00	—	—	(7.00)	0.00	(1.00)
12/16	15.00	—	—	(2.00)	0.00	4.00
12/15	30.00	—	—	(1.00)	0.00	7.00
12/14	51.00	527	323	0.00	0.00	7.00
Annual Growth	**(23.7%)**			**—**	**72.8%**	**—**

Tenneco Inc

Tenneco is a global auto parts manufacturer that designs and distributes ride-control and emissions control products. It makes ride control equipment such as shock absorbers struts and steering stabilizers under brands like Monroe and Quick-Strut and emissions-control systems including catalytic converters exhaust pipes and mufflers under the Walker Tru-Fit Fonos and DynoMax brands.

It also makes Clevite elastomer products (bushings mounts and exhaust isolators) for vibration control in cars and heavy trucks. It supplies both the original equipment (OE) and replacement markets worldwide. Major customers Ford Motor and General Motors account for more than 10% of sales. Tenneco operates worldwide on six continents.

Operations

Tenneco divides its operations across five segments. These are Clean Air Ride Performance Aftermarket Powertrain and Motorparts.

Clean Air products and systems generate more than 55% of the company's revenue and help global OE manufacturers in light vehicle commercial truck and off-highway markets meet global emissions regulations anywhere in the world. Products are broken into four key areas: emissions control products such as gas and diesel filters and catalytic converters; lightweighting and thermal management which includes thermo-electric generators heat exchangers and manifolds; acoustic products like mufflers; and products to reduce noise vibration and harshness (NVH).

The Ride Performance segment represents more than 15% of revenue and is organized by product (shocks struts and vibration control products) and includes computer-controlled and conventional machine centers. Ride Performance has made such technological advances as adaptive damping systems which adapt to an individual vehicle's motion to provide a smoother ride; electronically adjustable suspensions based on things like steering braking and speed; and air leveling systems to automatically adjust the height of the vehicle.

The company's Aftermarket segment primarily sells products for ride control NVH performance and emission control. The Powertrain segment includes pistons piston rings cylinder liners valve seats and guides bearings and spark plugs. Aftermarket and Powertrain each generate around 10% of revenue.

Through its Motorparts segment the company manufactures and distributes a broad portfolio of products for the global vehicle aftermarket as well as for the vehicle service market. Products include parts for braking systems wipers and some chassis components. The Motorparts segment accounts for the remaining 5%-plus of the company's revenue.

Geographic Reach

In addition to key alliances and joint ventures Tenneco operates more than 90 manufacturing facilities on six continents throughout the world including Argentina Brazil India China and Thailand.

The Clean Air segment operates about 65 manufacturing facilities worldwide some of which are joint ventures. About 15 are in North and South America 20 are in Europe and close to 30 are in Asia Pacific. Ride Performance has 25 manufacturing facilities with ten in North and South America seven in Europe and South Africa and eight in Asia Pacific. Tenneco has five Aftermarket production facilities worldwide?two in North America one in Europe and two in Asia Pacific. Aftermarket also operates 22 distribution centers worldwide; eight of these are third party logistics providers.

Tenneco's major geographic segments are the US which represents almost 40% of its total sales followed by China with almost 15% and Germany with around 10%.

Sales and Marketing

Tenneco has separate sales and marketing staffs for original equipment (OE) and aftermarket customers. For OE the sales team includes engineers and program managers and are organized by customer business unit and product type (ride performance clean air and powertrain).

For aftermarket sales the sales force is organized by region and covers multiple product lines. It sells aftermarket products through a combination of full-line warehouse distributors direct sales to retailers and service providers and direct sales through online channels.

GM and Ford each account for more than 10% of Tenneco's total revenue. Other customers include Nissan BMW Navistar PSA Peugeot FAW Toyota and Jaguar among others. In addition to the motor vehicle industry the company also serves the agricultural (John Deere and Caterpillar) marine railroad aerospace power generation and industrial markets.

Financial Performance

Tenneco has seen a general upward trend in sales over the last several years.

The company enjoyed unprecedented growth in 2018 with revenues peaking at a record-setting $11.8 billion a 27% hike from $9.3 billion in 2017. The revenue growth for 2018 was fueled by the acquisition of Federal-Mogul which contributed $1.9 billion in revenue. Excluding the acquisition organic sales grew by 7% driven by growth in both the Clean Air and Ride Performance segments.

The company's profits however dropped to $55 million in 2018 compared with $198 million the prior year. The decrease was primarily due to increased costs associated with the integration of Federal-Mogul including restructuring charges.

Cash at the end of fiscal 2018 was $702 million an increase of $384 million from the prior year. Cash from operations contributed $439 million to the coffers while investing activities used $2.5 billion mainly for the acquisition of Federal-Mogul. Financing activities provided $2.5 billion from the proceeds from term loans to finance the acquisition.

Strategy

The company focuses on growth through increased production volumes new technologies and geographic expansion?both organically and via strategic acquisitions and alliances. Tenneco is also eying adjacent markets to expand its portfolio of products and systems. Not limiting itself to passenger cars or medium-size trucks the company is positioning its emissions and ride control systems for heavy-duty trucks buses and agricultural and construction equipment. Tenneco is also in the throes of integration activities with recently-acquired Federal-Mogul which the company expects will provide opportunities for cost reduction and increased profits.

As stricter environmental standards are enacted Tenneco finds itself well positioned as a supplier of emission control systems. The company has developed diesel particulate filters (DPFs) for passenger cars and medium-duty trucks both in Europe and North America. The filters when used with converters can reduce emissions of particulates by as much as 90% and nitrogen oxide by up to 95%.

Another trend in the automotive industry that is building Tenneco's business is OEMs simplify their assembly process thus reducing costs and development times. To achieve this they are outsourcing more of the design and manufacturing of vehicle parts as well as fully-integrated systems that support emission control anti-lock braking roll-control and powertrains. This trend has given rise to Tier 1 systems integrators in addition to Tier 1 suppliers. Tenneco fits the bill for both roles. To boost its position even further the company offers just-in-time (JIT) systems for its emission control operations and has built JIT facilities close to customers' plants for quick delivery of product components.

Mergers and Acquisitions

In 2018 Tenneco completed the acquisition of aftermarket parts supplier Federal-Mogul (Icahn Enterprises was the majority shareholder) for $5.4 billion. Tenneco intends to split the combined businesses into two publicly traded companies—an aftermarket and ride performance company that will include Tenneco Ride Performance and Federal-Mogul Motorparts and a powertrain technology company which will include Tenneco Clean Air and Federal-Mogul Powertrain. The deal gives Tenneco the opportunity to capture the market in both business areas.

Also in 2018 the company acquired Ohlins Racing A.B. a Swedish technology company that develops premium suspension systems and components for the automotive and motor sport industries. Tenneco believes Ohlins will increase its share in developing mobility markets and accelerate the development of advanced original equipment (OE) intelligent suspension solutions.

HISTORY

Tennessee Gas and Transmission began in 1943 as a division of the Chicago Corporation headed by Gardiner Symonds and authorized to build a pipeline from West Virginia to the Gulf of Mexico. With the US facing WWII fuel shortages the group finished the project in 11 months.

After WWII Tennessee Gas went public with Symonds as president. It merged its oil and gas exploration interests into Tennessee Production Company (1954) which with Bay Petroleum (bought 1955) became Tenneco Oil in 1961. Symonds acquired complementary firms and entered the chemical industry by buying 50% of Petro-Tex Chemical in 1955.

Tenneco Oil moved its headquarters to Houston in 1963 to better ship natural gas from the Texas Gulf Coast. Symonds bought Packaging Corporation of America a maker of shipping containers pulp and paperboard products in 1965. A year later the company which had become a conglomerate adopted the Tenneco name.

EXECUTIVES

Vice President Human Resources, Mike Schneider
Evp And Cfo, Kenneth R. (Ken) Trammell, age 58, $625,000 total compensation
Vp And Cio, H. William Haser, age 58
Ceo, Brian Kesseler, age 53, $895,000 total compensation
Evp And President Asia/pacific, Peng (Patrick) Guo, age 53
Svp And General Manager Global Aftermarket, Joseph A. (Joe) Pomaranski, age 63
Vp And General Manager North America Aftermarket, Jeff Koviak
Vp And General Manager North America Clean Air, Michael Seurynck
Vp And General Manager North America Ride Performance, Jack Hall
Vp And General Manager Europe Aftermarket, Bruce Ronning
Vp And General Manager China Clean Air, Yih Sng
Vp And General Manager China Aftermarket, Edward Hang
Vp And General Manager Global Elastomers, Steve Pohlman
Managing Director India, Sagar Hemade
General Manager Japan, Yasuhara Shimonishi
Vp And Cto, Ben Patel
Evp And President Ride Performance, Martin Hendricks, age 56
Vp And General Manager Europe Ride Performance, Jean-Luc Desire
Vp And General Manager Europe Clean Air, Traci Melville
Vp And General Manager China Ride Performance, Yi Ren
Vice President General Manager, Alex Gelbcke
Vp Global Communications, Jane Ostrander
Svp, Gregg Bolt
Vice President, Richard Wambold
Vice President Finance, Leo Waner
Vp And Gm Aftermarket Europe, Maurits Binnendijk
Vp Business Management Systems, Steve Vielmetti
Vice President Of Human Resources, Brian Boukalik
Senior Vice President Strategy And Corporate Development, Elizabeth Williams
Vice President Finance Global Clean Air Division, Steven Darwin
Executive Vice President, Rainer Jueckstock
Vice President, Kaled Awada
Vice President Of South America Aftermarket, Antonio Teodoro
Vp Global Communications, Chris Brathwaite
Executive Vice President, Brad Norton
Vice President Of Investor Relations, Richard Kwas
Chairman And Ceo, Gregg M. Sherrill, age 66
Auditors: PricewaterhouseCoopers LLP

LOCATIONS

HQ: Tenneco Inc
500 North Field Drive, Lake Forest, IL 60045
Phone: 847 482-5000
Web: www.tenneco.com

2018 Sales

	$ mil.	% of total
US	4,488	38
China	1,553	13
Germany	1,212	10
Poland	731	6
Mexico	543	5
United Kingdom	499	4
India	316	3
Turkey	7	-
Other Foreign	2,414	21
Total	**11,763**	**100**

PRODUCTS/OPERATIONS

2018 Sales

	$ mil.	% of total
Clean Air Products & Systems	6,707	57
Ride Performance	1,949	17
Aftermarket	1,221	10
Powertrain	1,112	9
Motorparts	774	7
Total	**11,763**	**100**

Selected Brands and Products

Emission control systems (DynoMax Fonos Thrush and Walker)
  Aftertreatment control units
  Burner systems
  Catalytic converters and diesel oxidation catalysts
  Diesel particulate filters (DPFs)
  Exhaust manifolds
  Hangers and isolators
  High-frequency turbo decoupler
  Hydrocarbon vaporizers and injectors
  Lean NOx traps
  Mufflers
  Pipes
  Resonators
  Selective catalytic reduction (SCR)
Ride control systems (Fric-Rot Monroe and Rancho)
  Coil and leaf springs
  Computerized electronic suspension (CES)
  Corner and full axle modules
  Heavy duty truck and train shocks
  Kinetic suspension technology
  Shock absorbers and struts
  Suspension systems
  Top mounts
  Vibration control components (Clevite Elastomers)
  Engine and body mounts
  Exhaust isolators
  Leaf and coil springs
  Spring seats
  Suspension control arm link and stabilizer bar bushings

COMPETITORS

Benteler Automotive
Cooper-Standard
Automotive
Edelbrock
Faurecia Exhaust
Systems

Kolbenschmidt Pierburg
Letts Industries
Meritor
Wescast Industries
ZF Group NAO

HISTORICAL FINANCIALS

Company Type: Public

Income Statement				FYE: December 31
	REVENUE ($ mil.)	NET INCOME ($ mil.)	NET PROFIT MARGIN	EMPLOYEES
12/18	11,763	55	0.5%	81,000
12/17	9,274	207	2.2%	32,000
12/16	8,599	363	4.2%	31,000
12/15	8,209	247	3.0%	30,000
12/14	8,420	226	2.7%	29,000
Annual Growth	8.7%	(29.8%)	—	29.3%

2018 Year-End Financials

Debt ratio: 41.00%
Return on equity: 5.00%
Cash ($ mil.): 697
Current ratio: 1.00
Long-term debt ($ mil.): 5,340

No. of shares (mil.): 81
Dividends
Yield: 4.0%
Payout: 108.0%
Market value ($ mil.): 2,215

	STOCK PRICE ($) FY Close	P/E High/Low		PER SHARE ($) Earnings	Dividends	Book Value
12/18	27.00	70	28	1.00	1.00	21.00
12/17	59.00	17	13	4.00	1.00	14.00
12/16	62.00	10	5	6.00	0.00	11.00
12/15	46.00	15	10	4.00	0.00	8.00
12/14	57.00	18	13	4.00	0.00	8.00
Annual Growth	(16.6%)	—	—	(29.0%)	—	27.3%

Tennessee Valley Authority

Tennessee Valley Authority (TVA) is a US government-owned corporation and the largest public power producer in the country. It sells wholesale electricity to more than 150 municipal and cooperative power distributors which serve nearly 10 million people in Tennessee and parts of Alabama Georgia Kentucky Mississippi North Carolina and Virginia. It also sells power directly to large industrial customers and federal agencies. In addition TVA provides flood control and land management for the Tennessee River system and assists utilities and state and local governments with economic development.

Operations

Tennessee Valley Authority operates six fossil plants three nuclear plants more than 15 natural gas or oil-fired plants and about 30 hydroelectric plants. TVA provides electric power through a network of nearly 20000 miles of transmission line which delivers more than 160 billion kWh of electricity annually. While most of its power comes from traditional generation sources it also operates nearly 15 solar energy sites. Other facilities include a diesel generator plant digester gas co-firing capacity at one coal-fired plant and biomass co-firing potential located at its coal-fired sites.

TVA's power generation mix includes nuclear (about 40% of sales) coal and natural gas (about

20% each) hydro (10%) and the rest from purchased renewable and non-renewable power.

TVA also has an agreement with the US Department of Energy (DOE) to produce tritium a radioactive gas that boosts the power of nuclear weapons at its Watts Bar TN nuclear plant.

Geographic Reach

TVA supplies power in large parts of Tennessee Alabama Mississippi and Kentucky and in portions of Georgia North Carolina and Virginia. Tennessee accounts for 65% of the company's revenue Alabama around 15% and Mississippi about 10%.

Sales and Marketing

Tennessee Valley Authority provides electricity to large industrial customers federal agencies and local power companies (LPCs) serving nearly 10 million people in parts of seven southeastern states. Two of the largest LPCs served by TVA are the Memphis Light Gas and Water Division and Nashville Electric Service.

Financial Performance

TVA has seen fluctuations in revenue over the last several years as the company is dependent on the weather for both demand for electricity as well as the price for that power.

Revenue for TVA increased 5% in 2018 primarily due to colder than normal temperatures and an increase in total degree days (measured by how many degrees the temperature fluctuates from 65Å F in the five largest cities in its service area).

Net income almost doubled to $1.1 billion in 2018 compared with $685 million the previous year. This was primarily due to increased sales and lower operating and fuel costs. Operating costs in 2017 included a one-time $500 million contribution to the TVA's pension plan.

Cash at the end of fiscal 2018 was $299 million a decrease of $1 million from the prior year. Cash from operations contributed $4.0 billion to the coffers while investing activities used $2.3 billion mainly for construction and nuclear fuel expenditures. Financing activities used another $1.7 billion for bond repurchases.

Strategy

TVA is changing its power generation mix to become a cleaner producer of energy. It has closed or is closing several older less efficient coal-generated power units while putting more natural gas-fired units online as well as increasing nuclear generation capabilities. The authority is working toward obtaining 50% of its power supply from low- or zero-carbon-emitting or renewable sources by 2020.

In 2019 the company released a draft of its Integrated Resource Plan (IRP). The document outlines the company's long-term operational and financial plan to provide reliable electric power and support environmental stewardship while creating a flexible operating model that takes into account increasing amounts of renewable energy sources and distributed energy resources (DER).

HISTORY

TVA was established by Congress in 1933 primarily to reduce flood damage improve navigation on the Tennessee River and promote agricultural and industrial development in the region. In 1999 government appropriations for the authority ceased.

In 1924 the Army Corps of Engineers finished building the Wilson Dam on the Tennessee River in Alabama to provide power for two WWI-era nitrate plants. With the war over the question of what to do with the plants became a political football.

An act of Congress created the Tennessee Valley Authority (TVA) in 1933 to manage the plants and Tennessee Valley waterways. New Dealers saw TVA as a way to revitalize the local economy

through improved navigation and power generation. Power companies claimed the agency was unconstitutional but by 1939 when a federal court ruled against them TVA had five operating hydroelectric plants and five under construction.

During the 1940s TVA supplied power for the war effort including the Manhattan Project in Tennessee. During the postwar boom between 1945 and 1950 power usage in the Tennessee Valley nearly doubled. Despite adding dams TVA couldn't keep up with demand so in 1949 it began building a coal-fired unit. Because coal-fired plants weren't part of TVA's original mission in 1955 a Congressional panel recommended the authority be dissolved.

Though TVA survived its funding was cut. In 1959 it was allowed to sell bonds but it no longer received direct government appropriations for power operations. In addition it had to pay back the government for past appropriations.

TVA began to build the first unit of an ambitious 17-plant nuclear power program in Alabama in 1967. However skyrocketing costs forced it to raise rates and cut maintenance on its coal-fired plants which led to breakdowns. In 1985 five reactors had to be shut down because of safety concerns.

In 1988 former auto industry executive Marvin Runyon was appointed chairman of the agency. "Carvin' Marvin" cut management sold three airplanes and got rid of peripheral businesses saving $400 million a year. In 1992 Runyon left to go to the postal service and was replaced by Craven Crowell who began preparing TVA for competition in the retail power market.

TVA ended its nuclear construction program in 1996 after bringing two nuclear units on line within three months a first for a US utility. The next year it raised rates for the first time in 10 years planning to reduce its debt. In response to a lawsuit filed by neighboring utilities it agreed to stop "laundering" power by using third parties to sell outside the agency's legally authorized area.

In 1999 the authority finished installing almost $2 billion in scrubbers and other equipment at its coal-fired plants so that it could buy Kentucky coal along with cleaner Wyoming coal. That year however the EPA charged TVA with violating the Clean Air Act by making major overhauls on some of its older coal-fired plants without getting permits or installing updated pollution-control equipment. It ordered TVA to bring most of its coal-fired plants into compliance with more current pollution standards. The next year TVA contested the order in court stating compliance would jack up electricity rates.

TVA was fined by the US Nuclear Regulatory Commission in 2000 for laying off a nuclear plant whistleblower.

In 2008 a holding pond at TVA's coal-burning Kingston Fossil Plant failed and dumped some 5.4 million cu. yd. of fly ash over 400 acres in eastern Tennessee's Roane County. The slide knocked down utility poles and trees and damaged at least a dozen homes (some beyond repair). Although no one was hurt some residents were cut off by the spill prompting officials to build a new road. The flooding was the pond's third reported incident in six years. The cleanup will likely cost more than $1 billion. Some 14 lawsuits were filed against the TVA as a result of the incident.

William D. Johnson former chairman president and CEO of Progress Energy was named president and CEO of TVA in 2013.

EXECUTIVES

Evp And Cfo, John M. Thomas, age 56, $577,212 total compensation

Evp And Chief Nuclear Officer, Joseph P. (Joe) Grimes, age 62, $557,135 total compensation

Svp Distributed Energy Resources, Jay C. Stowe

Evp And Coo, Charles G. (Chip) Pardee, age 59, $647,481 total compensation

Evp External Relations, Van M. Wardlaw, age 59

Svp Watts Bar Operations And Construction, Michael D. (Mike) Skaggs, $446,712 total compensation

President Ceo And Director, William D. (Bill) Johnson, age 64, $998,827 total compensation

Svp Chief Communications And Marketing Officer, Janet J. Brewer

Evp And General Counsel, Sherry A. Quirk, age 64

Senior Vice President Human Resources And Communication, Katherine Black

Executive Vice President And Chief Nuclear Officer, Joe Grimes

Chair, V. Lynn Evans

Auditors: Ernst & Young LLP

LOCATIONS

HQ: Tennessee Valley Authority
400 W. Summit Hill Drive, Knoxville, TN 37902
Phone: 865 632-2101
Web: www.tva.gov

2018 Sales

	$ mil.	% of total
Tennessee	7,350	65
Alabama	1,600	14
Mississippi	1,052	9
Kentucky	696	6
Georgia	267	2
North Carolina	66	1
Virginia	48	1
Off-system sales	7	.
Other revenues	158	2
Revenue capitalized during pre-commercial plant operations	(11)	-
Total	**11,233**	**100**

PRODUCTS/OPERATIONS

2018 Sales

	$ mil.	% of total
Electricity sales:		
Local power companies	10,262	91
Industries directly served	695	6
Federal agencies and other	129	1
Other revenues	158	2
Revenue capitalized during per-commercial plant operations	(11)	-
Total	**11,233**	**100**

HISTORICAL FINANCIALS

Company Type: Public

Income Statement   FYE: September 30

	REVENUE ($ mil.)	NET INCOME ($ mil.)	NET PROFIT MARGIN	EMPLOYEES
09/19	11,318	1,417	12.5%	10,009
09/18	11,233	1,119	10.0%	10,023
09/17	10,739	685	6.4%	10,092
09/16	10,616	1,233	11.6%	10,691
09/15	11,003	1,111	10.1%	10,918
Annual Growth	**0.7%**	**6.3%**		**(2.1%)**

2019 Year-End Financials

Debt ratio: 44.00%—
Return on equity: 13.00%
Cash ($ mil.): 299
Current ratio: 1.00
Long-term debt ($ mil.): 20,183

Dividends
Yield: 3.0%
Payout: —
Market value ($ mil.): —

	STOCK PRICE ($) FY Close	P/E High/Low	Earnings	Dividends	Book Value
09/19	25.00	— —	(0.00)	1.00	(0.00)
09/18	25.00	— —	(0.00)	1.00	(0.00)
09/17	25.00	— —	(0.00)	1.00	(0.00)
09/16	26.00	— —	(0.00)	1.00	(0.00)
09/15	24.00	— —	(0.00)	1.00	(0.00)
Annual Growth	**0.7%**	— —	—	**(3.1%)**	

Terex Corp.

Terex Corporation makes a variety of cranes aerial platforms and materials processing equipment. The company makes aerial lifts from articulating to telescopic booms used in industrial and construction overhead jobs. It also makes all sort of cranes and specialty equipment such as wood processing biomass and recycling equipment. Terex products are sold in more than 100 countries around the globe to the construction forestry recycling and utility industries under the Terex Genie and Powerscreen brands. About 55% of Terex's sales come from North America.

Operations

Terex makes and sells its construction and materials processing equipment across three operating segments.

Aerial Work Platforms (AWP) generates about 50% of net sales and designs manufactures and services aerial work platform equipment telehandlers and light towers. Cranes (more than 25%) makes and refurbishes a wide range of cranes as well as related components and replacement parts. In 2019 the company sold off parts of its crane business. Materials Processing (MP) accounts for less than 25% of sales and makes materials processing and specialty equipment including crushers washing systems screens apron feeders and material handlers among other equipment.

Through Terex Financial Services the company offers rental and leasing services and financing for equipment purchases.

Geographic Reach

Headquartered in Westport CT Terex sells its products in more than 100 countries. The company has manufacturing and other facilities in the US as well as Europe South America and Asia.

North America is the company's largest market accounting for about 55% of sales. Western Europe accounts for about 25% and Asia Pacific roughly 15%. The remaining sales are made throughout the rest of the world.

Sales and Marketing

Terex sells its products through a worldwide network of dealers rental companies independent distributors major accounts and direct sales to clients.

The company's broad range of equipment is used by various industries including construction manufacturing transportation and energy. Terex's top ten customers account for close to 25% of total sales.

Financial Performance

Although the heavy construction equipment industry has improved over the past few years Terex's revenue has been slow to recover. The company posted three consecutive years of declining sales from 2014 to 2017.

Revenue rebounded by 17% to $5.1 billion in 2018 up from almost $4.4 billion in 2017 but still below the company's past sales figures. The increase in 2018 was due to higher demand for equipment in all its segments and favorable currency translation.

Net income amounted to $113.7 million in 2018 down from $128.7 million the previous year. Contributing to the decrease in 2018 was a loss of about $67 million related to the settlement of its US benefit pension plan. The previous year also saw a net gain of $42 million from the sale of part of its Konecranes business.

Cash at the end of fiscal 2018 was $372.1 million a decrease of $258.0 million from the prior year. Cash from operations contributed $94.2 million to the coffers while investing activities used $85.9 million mainly for capital expenditures for investment in the business. Financing activities used another $244.9 million for dividends to stockholders and the company's stock repurchase program.

Strategy

Amid a global climate of weak demand for heavy machinery Terex is working to adjust its cost structure and reduce costs. It continues to take actions to optimize its manufacturing footprint consolidate facilities across all three of its core segments and reduce its workforce. It has closed facilities and sold off some of its non-core business to generate cash. In 2019 it sold its boom truck truck crane and crossover product lines to Load King a subsidiary of Custom Truck One Source and the Demag mobile crane business to Tadano.

In addition to facilities consolidation and restructuring activities Terex continues to implement several initiatives to drive growth and is finally seeing an upward trend in sales. To simplify its financial reporting the company is consolidating its financial performance figures to one chart of accounts across the company. It has deployed a customer relationship management (CRM) system including pricing and dealer management tools and developed a global parts and service organization and a new parts pricing system. To lower costs in its supply chain Terex is continuing to deploy an enterprise-wide strategic sourcing process (including reviewing some of its supplier contracts) and has initiated a supplier awards program.

Company Background

Real estate entrepreneur Randolph Lenz moved into heavy equipment manufacturing with the purchase of bankrupt snowplow maker FWD Corporation in 1981. That was followed the same year with the acquisition of Northwest Engineering a maker of construction equipment started in the 1920s.

In 1986 the company acquired Terex USA the North American distributor of parts for off-highway Terex trucks from General Motors and later Terex Equipment the UK-based truck maker. The company changed its corporate name to Terex Corporation in 1987. That year Terex entered the mobile-crane market with the purchase of Koehring Cranes. Terex acquired mining-truck maker Unit Rig in 1988 and trailer maker Fruehauf in 1989. It moved into aerial work platforms in 1991 with the acquisition of Mark Industries and picked up the forklift business of Clark Equipment the following year. (Clark invented the forklift truck in 1928.)

EXECUTIVES

Svp Secretary And General Counsel, Eric I. Cohen, age 60, $563,890 total compensation

President And Ceo, John L. Garrison, $882,692 total compensation

Svp And Cfo, John D. Sheehan, age 58

President Terex Cranes Material Handling And Port Solutions, Stoyan (Steve) Filipov, age 50, $566,075 total compensation

President Terex Materials Processing, Kieran
 Hegarty, age 52
President Terex Construction, George Ellis, age 58,
 $369,000 total compensation
President Terex Aerial Work Platforms, Matthew
 (Matt) Fearon, age 57, $510,000 total compensation
Vp And Cio, Andrew Campbell
President Terex Financial Services, Linda McAvoy
Vice President Global Supply Chain, Jeremy Rife
Vice President Terex Transformation Program,
 Derek Everitt
Vice President Of Sales For Europe Middle East
 Africa, Phil Graysmark
National Sales Manager, Craig Hain
Vice President Information Technology
 Infrastructure, Damian Kitson
Vice President Finance China, Angel Tian
Vice President Of Human Resources Mining, Peter
 Rall
Vice President Of Global Sales And Marketing
 And Commercial Operations, Jim Lohan
Vice President, Robert Brown
National Sales Manager, Chris Johnson
Vp Controller And Chief Accounting Officer, Mark
 Clair
National Account Manager, Anthony Laslavic
Vice President Information Technology Awp
 Genie, Scott Mcneal
Vp Of Global Sales And Marketing Of Terex Aerial
 Work Platforms (awp), Simon Meester
Chairman, David A. Sachs, age 59
Board Member, Geert Hansen
Auditors: PricewaterhouseCoopers LLP

LOCATIONS

HQ: Terex Corp.
 200 Nyala Farm Road, Westport, CT 06880
Phone: 203 222-7170   Fax: 203 222-7976
Web: www.terex.com

2018 Sales

	$ mil.	% of total
North America	2,826	55
Western Europe	1,179	23
Asia-Pacific	646	13
Rest of World	474	9
Total	**5,125**	**100**

PRODUCTS/OPERATIONS

2018 Sales

	$ mil.	% of total
Aerial Work Platforms	2,560	50
Cranes	1,315	26
Material Processing	1,257	24
Eliminations	(6.5)	-
Total	**5,125**	**100**

Selected Brands

Genie
Powerscreen
Terex

Selected Products

Cranes
 Lattice boom crawler cranes
 Lattice boom truck cranes
 Mobile telescopic cranes
 Specialized port and rail equipment
 Gantry cranes
 Lift trucks and forklifts
 Mobile harbor cranes
 Reach stackers
 Replacement parts and components
 Ship-to-shore cranes
 Straddle and sprinter carriers
 Tower cranes
 Truck-mounted cranes (boom trucks)
Aerial Work Platforms
 Aerial work platform equipment
 Light towers
 Material lifts
 Portable aerial work platforms

 Replacement parts
 Scissor lifts
 Self-propelled articulating and telescopic booms
 Telehandlers
 Trailer-mounted articulated booms
 Trailer-mounted light towers
 Utility equipment
Materials processing
 Apron feeders
 Components and replacement parts
 Crushers (mobile base)
 Screens (mobile base)
 Washing systems
Material Handling and Port Solutions
 Crane components and equipment
 Process cranes
 Rope and chain hoists
 Standard cranes

COMPETITORS

AICHI CORPORATION
Altec Industries
Astec Industries
Doosan Heavy Industries
Generac Holdings
Haulotte
Hitachi Construction Machinery
JLG Industries
Kobelco Construction Machinery America
Legris Industries Group
Manitex International
Manitowoc
Metso
Sandvik
Sany Heavy Industry
Skyjack
TADANO LTD.
WESCO INC.
Wacker Neuson
Zoomlion Heavy Industry Science and Technology Co.

HISTORICAL FINANCIALS

Company Type: Public

Income Statement

FYE: December 31

	REVENUE ($ mil.)	NET INCOME ($ mil.)	NET PROFIT MARGIN	EMPLOYEES
12/18	5,125	114	2.2%	11,700
12/17	4,363	129	2.9%	10,700
12/16	4,443	(176)	—	11,300
12/15	6,543	146	2.2%	20,400
12/14	7,309	319	4.4%	20,400
Annual Growth	(8.5%)	(22.7%)	—	(13.0%)

2018 Year-End Financials

Debt ratio: 35.00%
Return on equity: 11.00%
Cash ($ mil.): 368
Current ratio: 2.00
Long-term debt ($ mil.): 1,215

No. of shares (mil.): 70
Dividends
 Yield: 1.0%
 Payout: 27.0%
Market value ($ mil.): 1,919

	STOCK PRICE ($) FY Close	P/E High/Low		PER SHARE ($) Earnings	Dividends	Book Value
12/18	28.00	33	17	1.00	0.00	12.00
12/17	48.00	35	21	1.00	0.00	15.00
12/16	32.00	—	—	(2.00)	0.00	14.00
12/15	18.00	21	12	1.00	0.00	17.00
12/14	28.00	15	9	3.00	0.00	19.00
Annual Growth	(0.3%)		—	(14.7%)	12.5%	(10.2%)

Territorial Bancorp Inc

Territorial Bancorp serves its customers island-style. It is the financial holding company for Territorial Savings Bank which provides standard products and services such as checking and savings accounts money market accounts CDs IRAs and loans from its nearly 30 branch locations across Hawaii. Its Territorial Financial Services subsidiary sells insurance while LPL Financial offers Mutual funds and annuities. Territorial Savings Bank targets the territorial nature of its customers — one- to four-family residential mortgages account for 95% of its loan portfolio. Multifamily and commercial mortgages and construction and home equity loans round out its lending activities.

Operations

Territorial Bancorp generated 61% of its total revenue from loan interest in 2014 with another 31% coming from interest on its investment securities. About 3% of its revenue came from service fees on loan and deposit accounts while 2% came from gains on its investment security sales.

Sales and Marketing

The bank provides financial services to individuals families and small- to medium-sized businesses from its 28 branches spread across the state of Hawaii.

Financial Performance

Territorial's revenues and profits have been slowly declining in recent years mostly as its margins have been squeezed in the low-interest environment and as its gains on its held-for-sale loans have been shrinking.

The company's revenue ended mostly flat around $64.8 million in 2014 with mixed results. The bank's loan and investment security interest grew by 7% thanks to asset growth though these improvements were offset by lower gains on investment securities and loans compared to the year before.

Lower revenue in 2014 coupled with a slight uptick in loan loss provisions and equipment investment costs caused Territorial Bancorp's net income to tumble by 4% to $14.1 million. Its operating cash levels also fell by 19% to $14.1 million after adjusting its earnings for non-cash items mostly related to its net proceeds on its held-for-sale loans.

Strategy

Territorial Bancorp relies on its competitive rates and pricing to grow its loan and deposit business. During 2014 its deposit business grew organically by nearly 6% mostly as the bank promoted its higher-than-market rates for its passbook and statement savings accounts.

Company Background

Founded in 1921 Territorial Savings was mutually owned until 2009 when its former parent Territorial Mutual Holding Company converted to a stock form of ownership and sold shares in itself to the public. The move allowed the company to offer other financial services in addition to banking.

EXECUTIVES

Chairman President And Ceo Territorial Bancorp
 Inc. And Territorial Savings Bank, Allan S.
 Kitagawa, age 73, $766,080 total compensation
Vice Chairman Co-coo General Counsel And
 Corporate Secretary Territorial Bancorp Inc. And
 Territorial Savings Bank, Vernon Hirata, age 66,
 $269,100 total compensation
Svp Business Development And Marketing, Denise
 Takashima
Svp Branch Administration, Robert Costa

Vice Chairman And Co-coo Territorial Bancorp Inc. And Territorial Savings Bank, Ralph Y. Nakatsuka, age 63, $269,100 total compensation
Vice President, Karen Lam
Assistant Vice President Branch Manager Loan Officer, Geoffrey Baricaua
Board Of Directors, David Murakami
Auditors: Moss Adams LLP

LOCATIONS

HQ: Territorial Bancorp Inc
1132 Bishop Street, Suite 2200, Honolulu, HI 96813
Phone: 808 946-1400
Web: www.territorialsavings.net

PRODUCTS/OPERATIONS

2014 Sales

	$ mil.	% of total
Interest and dividend income		
Loans	40	61
Investment securities	20	31
Others	0	—
Non-interest income		
Service fees on loan and deposits	2	3
Income on bank owned life insurance	1	2
Others	2	3
Total	65	100

COMPETITORS

American Savings Bank
Bank of Hawaii
Central Pacific Financial

HISTORICAL FINANCIALS

Company Type: Public

Income Statement
FYE: December 31

	ASSETS ($ mil.)	NET INCOME ($ mil.)	INCOME AS % OF ASSETS	EMPLOYEES
12/18	2,069	19	0.9%	285
12/17	2,004	15	0.7%	283
12/16	1,878	16	0.9%	276
12/15	1,821	15	0.8%	280
12/14	1,692	14	0.8%	272
Annual Growth	5.2%	8.0%	—	1.2%

2018 Year-End Financials

Debt ratio: —
Return on equity: 8.00%
Cash ($ mil.): 47
Current ratio: —
Long-term debt ($ mil.): —
No. of shares (mil.): 10
Dividends
Yield: 4.0%
Payout: 64.0%
Market value ($ mil.): 251

	STOCK PRICE ($) FY Close	P/E High/Low	PER SHARE ($) Earnings	Dividends	Book Value
12/18	26.00	15 12	2.00	1.00	24.00
12/17	31.00	21 18	2.00	1.00	24.00
12/16	33.00	18 14	2.00	1.00	23.00
12/15	28.00	18 13	2.00	1.00	23.00
12/14	22.00	15 13	2.00	1.00	22.00
Annual Growth	4.8%	— —	7.7%	13.0%	2.8%

Tesla Inc

Founded in 2003 the company designs manufactures and markets high-performance technologically advanced electric cars and solar energy generation and energy storage products. Tesla sells three fully electric models: the Model S sedan and the Model X SUV and the Model 3 sedan which is among the world's top-selling electric cars. The fuel-efficient fully electric vehicles recharge their lithium-ion batteries from an outlet. Tesla's Autopilot self-driving technology hardware has been available on all Tesla models since late 2016. US customers generate about 70% of Teslós sales. CEO Elon Musk founded PayPal and also runs SpaceX.

Operations

Tesla designs makes and sells the Model S Model X and Model 3 electric vehicles. The company also offers leasing and services. The automotive segment generates just under 95% of sales. The division's operations also include an international network of company-owned stores and used car sales. Tesla's network of Supercharger and Destination Charging stations in North America Europe and Asia provides fast convenient charging locations for Tesla owners to recharge their vehicles.

The company's energy generation and storage segment (just over 5% of revenue) makes and sells stationary energy storage products and solar energy systems to residential and small commercial customers. Its Powerwall 2 lithium-ion battery system is designed to store electricity for use as backup power in the event of an outage and to optimize self-consumption of solar power generation. Tesla's commercial and utility offering Powerpack 2 is an energy storage system that offers features like peak shaving load shifting emergency backup and self-consumption of solar generation.

Tesla's solar energy systems include solar panels inverters and rack systems. The company's Solar Roof gathers solar energy from glass tiles that aim to be more architecturally pleasing than traditional roof-mounted solar panels.

Geographic Reach

Tesla operates vehicle manufacturing facilities in Fremont and Lathrop California; Tilburg the Netherlands; and its Gigafactory 1 near Reno Nevada. Energy storage products are manufactured at its Gigafactory 1. Solar products are made primarily at Tesla's Gigafactory 2 site in Buffalo New York. The US accounts for about 70% of sales. Other markets for which the company breaks out sales include China (about 10% of sales) and Norway (about 5%).

Sales and Marketing

Tesla markets and sells cars directly to consumers through an international network of company-owned stores and galleries. Tesla is notable in that it does not use dealerships (due in some states to legal restrictions).

The company's solar energy and storage products are typically sold directly to residential customers through the company's stores and galleries and through channel partners. An international sales organization markets Powerpack 2 systems and residential energy storage products outside the US.

Financial Performance

Teslós revenue growth has accelerated like its first car the Roadster sportscar (0-60 in 1.9 seconds) driven by the rising number of vehicles sold each year. Between 2014 and 2018 sales have grown a whopping 570%. The company however has posted a string of net losses as it pours money into research and development and manufacturing.

Teslós revenue jumped 83% to $21.5 billion in 2018 driven by an 87% increase in automotive revenue. The number of vehicles sold in 2018 rose 138% to about 245500 compared to 2017. Automotive sales revenue rose 107% but leasing revenue was down 20% in 2018. Service revenue increased about 39%. The energy generation and storage segment contributed about 5% of total revenue.

As fast as the company?s sales are moving forward its bottom line is stuck in reverse. The company lost about $976 million in 2018 which was an improvement over the nearly $2 billion lost in 2017. The cost of automotive revenue rose 91% in 2018. However the rise in unit sales is outpacing production cost growth which may indicate manufacturing is becoming more efficient. Tesla also had higher expenses for R&D sales general and administrative and interest in 2018 but these expenses grew at a slower pace than in 2017.

Cash at the end of 2018 was $4.3 billion an increase of about $300 million from the prior year. Cash from operations contributed $2.1 billion to the coffers while investing activities used $2.3 billion mainly for capital expenditures. Financing activities used $573.8 million primarily in the form debt repayments.

Strategy

Tesla's Model 3 was the US's top-selling luxury car in 2018 the first full year of its production. But production has still struggled to keep pace with demand. During 2018 the company managed to turn out about 7000 Model 3 vehicles per week. Tesla hopes to accelerate production to 10000 Model 3s per week by early 2020.

To help meet that goal and ramp up sales in overseas markets Tesla's Gigafactory 3 in Shanghai China broke ground in early 2019. Gigafactory 3 passed a government inspection that was necessary to begin production in September 2019 and full production is expected to soon follow. Model 3s rolling out of Gigafactory 3 is pivotal to Tesla's play in the world's largest electric car market and will help it gain ground in China while avoiding import tariffs.

Tesla is also busy advancing its autonomous car technology. The company's Autopilot driver assist system includes auto-steering traffic-aware cruise control automated lane changing and other features that together offer a complete self-driving experience while keeping the driver in ultimate control of the car.

Electricity isn't just for cars as far as Tesla is concerned. The company is developing Tesla Semi an electric version of diesel-powered semis built for hauling heavy payloads. The company said it will have a 500-mile battery range. Tesla intends to use the truck for its own logistics but PepsiCo Anheuser Busch J.B. Hunt UPS and FedEx have placed orders for the trucks. Tesla plans to begin production of the Semi in 2020.

While most automakers have generated armies of suppliers providing parts Tesla tries to handle as much manufacturing as it can in-house including batteries and drive trains. The company spreads production costs for batteries across its energy and storage unit but the costs of funding such manufacturing operations eat up a lot of cash.

Tesla pioneered the electric car market of the 21st century but other automakers are appearing bigger in the rearview mirror. Companies such as Honda Toyota Ford GM Nissan BMW Daimler are investing in development programs designed to shift large parts in some cases all of their fleets to electric power in the coming years. Tesla has delivered highly ranked vehicles so far but traditional automakers can call on deep resources extensive supply chains and global markets in developing and selling their vehicles.

Mergers and Acquisitions

Late in 2019 Tesla acquired Canada-based Hibar Systems a manufacturer of battery systems for electric automobiles laptops and other products. Industry watchers believe the deal is part of Tesla's strategy to reduce its dependence on its third-party battery partners. Around the same time Tesla bought computer vision start-up DeepScale. The purchase of DeepScale is expected to accelerate Tesla's autonomous driving technology efforts.

Earlier in 2019 Tesla acquired energy technology company Maxwell Technologies in an all-stock deal valued at more than $200 million. Maxwell develops and makes ultracapacitors devices that can store and quickly deliver surges of energy. Tesla would use the technology to increase battery capacity while reducing weight in its vehicles.

Company Background

Tesla Motors is named for Nikola Tesla (1856-1943) the renowned Serbian-American engineer and inventor. Tesla Motors was incorporated in July 2003.

EXECUTIVES

Chairman Ceo And Product Architect, Elon Musk, age 48, $45,936 total compensation
Cfo, Deepak Ahuja, age 56, $338,000 total compensation
Cto, Jeffrey B. (JB) Straubel, age 43, $250,560 total compensation
Vice President Power Electronics, Nick Kalayjian
Vice President Global Investor Relations, Jeff Evanson
Vice President Of Regulatory Affairs And Associate General Counsel, James Chen
National Sales Manager, Christine Moore
Vice President Engineering, Steve Macmanus
Vice President, Nancy Yan
Vp Business Development, Diarmuid O'connell
Vice President Global Recruiting, Cindy Nicola
Vp Asia Pacific, Robin Ren
Chief People Officer, Gaby Toledano
Vice President Ir And Strategy, Jeff K Evanson
Vice President Autopilot Engineering, David Nister
Svp Energy Operations, Sanjay Shah
Vice President Ehs, Laurie Shelby
Svp People Partner, Gillian Davis
Board Member, Ira Ehrenpreis
Corporate Treasurer And Vice President Global Tax Trade Treasury And New Ventures At Tesla Motors, Susan J Repo
Auditors: PricewaterhouseCoopers LLP

LOCATIONS

HQ: Tesla Inc
3500 Deer Creek Road, Palo Alto, CA 94304
Phone: 650 681-5000
Web: www.teslamotors.com

2017 Sales

	$ mil.	% of total
US	6,221	53
China	2,027	17
Norway	823	7
Other	2,687	23
Total	**11,759**	**100**

PRODUCTS/OPERATIONS

2017 Sales

	$ mil.	% of total
Automotive	10,625	91
Energy generation & storage	1,116	9
Total	**11,759**	**100**

COMPETITORS

AES	Mitsubishi Motors
BMW	Nissan
BYD	Samsung Electronics
Daimler	Siemens Energy
FCA US	Subaru of America
Ford Motor	SunPower
General Motors	Sunrun
Honda	Suzuki Motor
Hyundai Motor	Toyota
Isuzu	Vivint Solar Inc.
Kia Motors	Volkswagen
LG Chem	VydroTech

HISTORICAL FINANCIALS

Company Type: Public

Income Statement   FYE: December 31

	REVENUE ($ mil.)	NET INCOME ($ mil.)	NET PROFIT MARGIN	EMPLOYEES
12/18	21,461	(976)	—	48,817
12/17	11,759	(1,961)	—	37,543
12/16	7,000	(675)	—	30,025
12/15	4,046	(889)	—	13,058
12/14	3,198	(294)	—	10,161
Annual Growth	**60.9%**			**48.1%**

2018 Year-End Financials

Debt ratio: 40.00%
Return on equity: (-21.00%)
Cash ($ mil.): 3,686
Current ratio: 1.00
Long-term debt ($ mil.): 9,404

No. of shares (mil.): 173
Dividends
  Yield: —
  Payout: —
Market value ($ mil.): 57,442

	STOCK PRICE ($) FY Close	P/E High/Low	PER SHARE ($) Earnings	Dividends	Book Value
12/18	333.00	— —	(6.00)	0.00	29.00
12/17	311.00	— —	(12.00)	0.00	25.00
12/16	214.00	— —	(5.00)	0.00	29.00
12/15	240.00	— —	(7.00)	0.00	8.00
12/14	222.00	— —	(2.00)	0.00	7.00
Annual Growth	**10.6%**	**— —**	**—**	**—**	**40.8%**

Texas Capital Bancshares Inc

Texas Capital Bancshares is the parent company of Texas Capital Bank with more than 10 branches in Austin Dallas Fort Worth Houston and San Antonio. The bank targets high-net-worth individuals and Texas-based businesses with more than $5 million in annual revenue with a focus on the real estate financial services transportation communications petrochemicals and mining sectors. Striving for personalized services for its clients the bank offers deposit accounts Visa credit cards commercial loans and mortgages equipment leasing wealth management and trust services. Its BankDirect division provides online banking services. Founded in 1998 Texas Capital Bancshares has about $11.7 billion in assets.

Financial Performance

The bank reported $488.6 million in revenue in 2013 an nearly 11% increase versus 2012. Net income was flat at about $121 million after posting three consecutive years of gains. Cash flow from operations continued its steep three year decline. The bank's total assets increased 11% from about $10.5 billion in 2012 to $11.7 billion in 2013. Total deposits increased 24% year over year to about $9.3 billion.

Strategy

Headquartered in Dallas Texas Capital Bank (TCB) believes that its Texas roots give it a competitive advantage over larger competitors that are headquartered out of state. Indeed TCB is gaining market share and is expanding by hiring experienced bankers and support staff. The bank is looking to grow within its main metropolitan markets but has also branched out beyond the borders of its home state. The bank has an Cayman Islands branch to offer offshore cash management and deposit products to it core clientele.

EXECUTIVES

President And Ceo Texas Capital Bancshares Inc. President And Ceo Texas Capital Bank, C. Keith Cargill, age 66, $825,000 total compensation
Evp And Chief Lending Officer Dallas Region, Vince A. Ackerson, age 62, $454,166 total compensation
Managing Director Regional And Specialty Banking Texas Capital Bank Austin Fort Worth And San Antonio And Commercial Real Estate And Builder Finance, Mark M. Johnson
Evp Austin Region Texas Capital Bank, Kerry L. Hall
Regional President Texas Capital Bank Dallas, Russell Hartsfield
Chief Risk Officer Texas Capital Bancshares Inc. And Texas Capital Bank, John D. Hudgens, age 63, $455,833 total compensation
Managing Director Specialty And Regional Banking Texas Capital Bank Dallas And Syndicated Finance Lender Finance Leasing And Financial Institutions, James D. (Jim) Recer
Regional Chairman Texas Capital Bank Houston, Bill Wilson
Regional President Texas Capital Bank San Antonio, David Pope
Managing Director Regional And Specialty Banking Texas Capital Bank Houston, John C. Sarvadi
Controller And Chief Accounting Officer Texas Capital Bancshares And Cfo Texas Capital Bank, Julie L. Anderson, age 50, $355,000 total compensation
Regional Chairman Texas Capital Bank San Antonio, Shaun Kennedy
Regional Chairman Texas Capital Bank Fort Worth, Robin Hamilton
Regional President Texas Capital Bank Fort Worth, David Williams
Evp Builder Finance, Melissa Abel
Evp Asset Based Lending, Chris Capriotti
Evp Commercial Real Estate, Rob Delph
Evp Lender Finance, David Fricke
Evp Energy/oil And Gas Syndicated Finance And Financial Institutions, Lester Keliher
Evp Financial Institutions, Peter Stringer
President Mortgage Finance, Gary Ort
Evp Technology Operations Enterprise Planning And Information Security Texas Capital Bank, Kirk Coleman
Evp Sba Lending, John Gannon
Evp Public Finance, Paul Howell
Evp Strategic Sales And Marketing, Greg Lewis
President Private Wealth Advisors, Alan L. Miller
Vice President Manager Credit Underwriting, Anthony Violi
Senior Vice President Compensation Director, Chris Gullo
Vice President, Lela Naggar
Vice President, Raul Cantu
Vice President Deposit Operations, Leslie Marsh
Vice President Of Information Technology Infrastructure, Randy Tiegs
Senior Vice President And Deposit Operation, Connie Couch
Vice President, Jenny Downey
Vice President Corp Security And Investigations, Cary Wicker
Vice President Fraud Investigator, Jamie Burud
Vice President Security, Neal Baker
Executive Vice President, Brent Johnston
Executive Vice President, Ronald Baker
Vice President Planning, Prasad Varma
Executive Vice President Human Resources And Ld, Cara McDaniel
Executive Vice President Director Of Operations, James White
Senior Vice President And Cra Manager, Phil Aslin
Chairman, Larry L. Helm, age 71

LOCATIONS

HQ: Texas Capital Bancshares Inc
  2000 McKinney Avenue, Suite 700, Dallas, TX 75201
Phone: 214 932-6600
Web: www.texascapitalbank.com

PRODUCTS/OPERATIONS

2015 Sales

	$ mil.	% of total
Interest income		
Interest and fees on loans	595	92
Other	8	1
Non-interest income		
Brokered loan fees	19	3
Service charges on deposit accounts	8	1
Trust fee income	5	1
Swap fees	4	1
Other	12	1
Total	**651**	**100**

Selected Services

Association capital bank
Bankdirect
Business services
Mortgage business finance
Online services
Personal banking
Private wealth advisors
Treasury and liquidity

COMPETITORS

Amegy	Comerica
BBVA Compass	Cullen/Frost Bankers
Bancshares	JPMorgan Chase
BOK Financial	Prosperity Bancshares
Bank of America	Wells Fargo

HISTORICAL FINANCIALS

Company Type: Public

Income Statement   FYE: December 31

	ASSETS ($ mil.)	NET INCOME ($ mil.)	INCOME AS % OF ASSETS	EMPLOYEES
12/18	28,258	301	1.1%	1,641
12/17	25,076	197	0.8%	1,564
12/16	21,697	155	0.7%	1,442
12/15	18,909	145	0.8%	1,329
12/14	15,900	136	0.9%	1,142
Annual Growth	15.5%	21.9%	—	9.5%

2018 Year-End Financials

Debt ratio: 15.00%	No. of shares (mil.): 50
Return on equity: 13.00%	Dividends
Cash ($ mil.): 3,030	Yield: —
Current ratio: —	Payout: —
Long-term debt ($ mil.): —	Market value ($ mil.): 2,565

	STOCK PRICE ($) FY Close	P/E High/Low		PER SHARE ($) Earnings	Dividends	Book Value
12/18	51.00	18	8	6.00	0.00	50.00
12/17	89.00	25	19	4.00	0.00	44.00
12/16	78.00	26	10	3.00	0.00	41.00
12/15	49.00	21	14	3.00	0.00	35.00
12/14	54.00	23	17	3.00	0.00	32.00
Annual Growth	(1.5%)	—	—	19.1%	—	11.3%

TEXAS COUNTY AND DISTRICT RETIREMENT SYSTEM

EXECUTIVES

Exec Dir, Gene Glass
Cao*, Ray Smith
Deputy Dir*, Amy Bishop
Staff, Brad Eddins
Network Analyst, Brad Watkins
Contrl, Vincent Prendergast
Manager of Human Resources, David Redd
Director, Kim Kizer
General Counsel, Ann McGeehan
Hedge Associate, Derek Bergquist
Benefits Team Leader, Gina Pax
Auditors: KPMG LLP AUSTIN TX

LOCATIONS

HQ: TEXAS COUNTY AND DISTRICT RETIREMENT SYSTEM
  901 S MO PAC EXPY IV500, AUSTIN, TX 787465776
Phone: 512 328-8889
Web: WWW.TCDRS.ORG

HISTORICAL FINANCIALS

Company Type: Private

Income Statement   FYE: December 31

	ASSETS ($ mil.)	NET INCOME ($ mil.)	INCOME AS % OF ASSETS	EMPLOYEES
12/16	26,387	1,761	6.7%	108
12/15	24,654	(182)	—	—
12/14	24,832	0	—	—
12/10	18,117	2,178	12.0%	
Annual Growth	6.5%	(3.5%)	—	—

Texas Instruments Inc.

Texas Instruments sticks to basics — producing analog and embedded processors the workhorses of the industry. The company's analog chips manage power in electronic equipment and its embedded processors handle specific tasks in electronic devices. TI's customers which number about 100000 use the company's chips for applications that include autos industrial machinery consumer electronics communications devices and calculators. The company also sticks to basics in production operating its own manufacturing plants which it places around the world. International customers generate about 85% of revenue. Another TI basic: TI engineer Jack Kilby was credited as co-inventor of the integrated circuit in the late 1950s.

Operations

Texas Instruments operates through two segments: Analog and Embedded Processing.

The Analog business which accounts for about two-thirds of sales includes high-volume analog and logic products power management semiconductors and amplifiers and data converters. The company's analog products are used in the personal electronics automotive and industrial markets as well as others.

The Embedded Processing segment which generates about a quarter of sales makes digital signal processors (DSPs) and microcontrollers. TI's embedded processors range from low-cost microcontrollers used in products such as electric toothbrushes to complex devices used in automotive applications such as infotainment and advanced driver assistance systems.

The remaining revenue comes from the Other segment which includes digital light processors (DLP) used in projectors to create high-definition images calculators application specific integrated circuits (ASICs) and custom semiconductors.

Geographic Reach

China is the biggest single market for Texas Instruments accounting for about 45% of revenue with other Asia/Pacific countries (including Japan) accounting for nearly 15% of revenue. The US generates more than 15% of TI's sales. The company has facilities for service sales and other functions in the US Europe and Asia and operates 20 manufacturing sites in 10 countries.

Sales and Marketing

Texas Instruments has a wide representation of sales channels as well as customers. About 65% of the company's revenue comes through distributors who keep inventory of TI products on hand. As for customers its 100 biggest account for about two-thirds of TI's sales.

In terms of markets TI gets about a third of revenue from industrial about 25% from personal electronics about a fifth from automotive and more than 10% from communications with enterprise systems and calculators accounting for the remaining revenue.

Financial Performance

After several years of fluctuating revenue TI has posted three straight years of solid gains.

In 2018 TI's revenue rose 6% to $15.8 billion compared to $14.9 billion in 2017. Growth in its Power and Signal Chain products fueled Analog sales while higher sales of Connected Microcontrollers boosted Embedded Processing revenue. Other revenue was 9% lower in 2018 from 2017.

Net income increased to $5.6 billion in 2018 from $3.7 billion in 2017. TI paid half as much in federal taxes in 2018 than 2017 because of the Tax Cuts and Jobs Act.

The company's coffers held $2.4 billion in cash and equivalents in 2018 compared to $1.6 billion a year earlier. TI's operations generated $7.2 billion in 2018 while investing activities used $78 million and financing activities used $6.3 billion.

Strategy

Texas Instruments' focus on its Analog and Embedded Processing units is paying off. They combined to produce 90% of the company's revenue almost double since 2004. The company believes that analog and embedded processors offer diversity of applications long product life cycles and lower-cost manufacturing processes.

More narrowly TI has identified two markets where analog and embedded processes can generate growing sales over time: industrial and automotive. In 2018 automotive and industrial combined to provide about 55% of TI's revenue up from 42% in 2013.

On the manufacturing end TI is moving to produce more chips on 300-millimeter wafers which have a 40% cost advantage over standard 200-millimeter wafers. The 300-millimeter operations generated about $4.8 billion in revenue in 2018 some $800 million more than in 2017.

TI faces strong competition around the world from other chipmakers. The industry consolidation that TI has avoided has created bigger competitors with wider ranges of products and deeper resources. On the other side of the spectrum small companies with innovative products are capable of snatching market share away.

Trade tensions between the US and China which accounts for 45% of TI's sales resulted in slower sales late in 2018. Higher tariffs levied in 2019 could heighten the impact on TI.

Company Background

Clarence "Doc" Karcher and Eugene McDermott founded Geophysical Service Inc. (GSI) in Newark New Jersey in 1930 to develop reflective seismology a new technology for oil and gas exploration. In 1934 GSI moved to Dallas. The company produced military electronics during WWII including submarine detectors for the US Navy. GSI changed its name to Texas Instruments (TI) in 1951.

TI began making transistors in 1952 after buying a license from Western Electric. The company went public on the New York Stock Exchange in 1953. In 1954 it introduced the Regency Radio the first pocket-sized transistor radio. (That year TI also produced the first commercial silicon transistor.)

TI engineer Jack Kilby invented the integrated circuit (IC) in 1958. Working independently Intel co-founder Robert Noyce developed an IC at the same time while working at Fairchild Semiconductor; the two men are credited as co-inventors. In 2000 Kilby was awarded the Nobel Prize in Physics for his work.

EXECUTIVES

Chairman President And Ceo, Richard K. (Rich) Templeton, age 60, $1,164,083 total compensation

Svp High-volume Analog And Logic Central Analog Services Dlpâ® Products And Education Technology, Stephen A. (Steve) Anderson, age 57, $616,500 total compensation

Svp Analog Power Products, Niels Anderskouv, age 49

Svp Technology And Manufacturing, Kevin J. Ritchie, age 63, $688,333 total compensation

Svp Embedded Processing, R. Gregory (Greg) Delagi, age 56, $622,917 total compensation

Evp And Coo, Brian T. Crutcher, age 46, $822,917 total compensation

Svp Information Technology Services And Cio, Ellen L. Barker, age 56

Svp Worldwide Sales And Applications, Bing Xie, age 51

Svp Cfo And Chief Accounting Officer Finance And Operations, Rafael R. Lizardi, age 46

Svp Analog Signal Chain, Haviv Ilan, age 50

Vice President Connected Microcontrollers, Ray Upton

National Sales Manager, Dennis Smith

Senior Vice President High Volume Analog And Logic Centeral Analog Services Dlp Products And Educ, Hagop Kozanian

Board Member, Carrie Cox

Board Member, Robert Sanchez

Auditors: Ernst & Young LLP

LOCATIONS

HQ: Texas Instruments Inc.
12500 TI Boulevard, Dallas, TX 75243
Phone: 214 479-3773
Web: www.ti.com

2018 Sales

	$ mil.	% of total
US	2,288	14
Asia	9,240	59
EMEA	3,047	19
Japan	869	6
Rest of World	340	2
Total	**15,784**	**100**

PRODUCTS/OPERATIONS

2018 Sales

	$ mil.	% of total
Analog	10,801	68
Embedded processing	3,554	23
Other	1,429	9
Total	**15,784**	**100**

2018 Sales by Market

	% of total
Industrial	36
Personal electronics	23
Automotive	20
Communications equipment	11
Enterprise sytems	7
Calculators	3
Total	**100**

Selected Products

Semiconductors
  Analog and mixed-signal
  Amplifiers and comparators
  Clocks and timers
  Data converters
  Power management chips
  Radio-frequency (RF) chips
  Application-specific integrated circuits (ASICs)
  Digital light processors (DLPs micro-mirror-based devices for video displays)
  Digital signal processors (DSPs)
  Microcontrollers
  Microprocessors
  Standard logic
Educational Technology
  Calculators (including graphing handheld and printing models)

COMPETITORS

AMD	Maxim Integrated
ARM Holdings	Products
Analog Devices	Microchip Technology
Atmel	Microsemi
CASIO COMPUTER	NVIDIA
Canon	NXP Semiconductors
Fairchild	ON Semiconductor
Semiconductor	QUALCOMM
Infineon Technologies	Renesas Electronics
Intel	STMicroelectronics
Intersil	Samsung Electronics
Marvell Technology	

HISTORICAL FINANCIALS

Company Type: Public

Income Statement   FYE: December 31

	REVENUE ($ mil.)	NET INCOME ($ mil.)	NET PROFIT MARGIN	EMPLOYEES
12/18	15,784	5,580	35.4%	29,888
12/17	14,961	3,682	24.6%	29,714
12/16	13,370	3,595	26.9%	29,865
12/15	13,000	2,986	23.0%	29,977
12/14	13,045	2,821	21.6%	31,003
Annual Growth	**4.9%**	**18.6%**	**—**	**(0.9%)**

2018 Year-End Financials

Debt ratio: 30.00%
Return on equity: 58.00%
Cash ($ mil.): 2,438
Current ratio: 3.00
Long-term debt ($ mil.): 4,319

No. of shares (mil.): 945
Dividends
  Yield: 3.0%
  Payout: 47.0%
Market value ($ mil.): 89,317

	STOCK PRICE ($) FY Close	P/E High/Low		PER SHARE ($) Earnings	Dividends	Book Value
12/18	95.00	21	15	6.00	3.00	10.00
12/17	104.00	28	20	4.00	2.00	11.00
12/16	73.00	21	14	3.00	2.00	11.00
12/15	55.00	21	15	3.00	1.00	10.00
12/14	53.00	21	16	3.00	1.00	10.00
Annual Growth	**15.3%**		**—**	**21.4%**	**20.7%**	**(1.1%)**

TEXAS PERMANENT SCHOOL FUND MANAGEMENT COMPANY, INC.

EXECUTIVES

Prin, Elizabeth Jones
Senior Real Estate Portfolio M, Nick Tramontana
Auditors: LISA R COLLIER CPA CFE CID

LOCATIONS

HQ: TEXAS PERMANENT SCHOOL FUND MANAGEMENT COMPANY, INC.
1701 CONGRESS AVE, AUSTIN, TX 787011402
Phone: 512 463-1814
Web: WWW.TEA.TEXAS.GOV

HISTORICAL FINANCIALS

Company Type: Private

Income Statement   FYE: August 31

	ASSETS ($ mil.)	NET INCOME ($ mil.)	INCOME AS % OF ASSETS	EMPLOYEES
08/17	44,517	4,155	9.3%	4
08/16	38,821	1,520	3.9%	—
Annual Growth	**14.7%**	**173.4%**	**—**	**—**

Textron Inc

Texton's products help customers across the globe get on the move — by air land or sea. The company is known for its Beechcraft and Cessna aircraft and Bell military and commercial helicopters. It also services Hawker business jets. In addition Textron provides parts repair and other after-market services. The company also makes specialty vehicles (E-Z-GO golf carts Arctic Cat ATVs) fuel systems land and marine systems unmanned aerial vehicles and simulation and training products. Textron which generates about 60% of revenue from the US serves government industrial and commercial clients.

Operations

The company operates through five segments: Textron Aviation Industrial Bell Textron Systems and Finance.

Textron Aviation (36% of company revenue) manufactures and services Beechcraft and Cessna aircraft and provides service for Hawker brand business jets. Aircraft offerings include business jets and turboprop piston engine military trainer and defense airplanes. Textron Aviation also sells aircraft parts and offers maintenance inspection and repair services through a global network of 18 service centers. Through subsidiary Able Aerospace Services Textron Aviation provides maintenance repair and overhaul (MRO) services to military and commercial aircraft.

The Industrial segment (31% of sales) operates two products lines: fuel systems and functional components (sold through its German-based Kautex subsidiary) and specialized vehicles (such as E-Z-GO golf carts and recently-acquired Arctic Cat snowmobiles and ATVs).

The Bell segment (23% of sales) supplies the US military with the V-22 tilt rotor aircraft which can operate with the features of both a fixed-wing craft and a helicopter and the H-1 helicopter. Bell produces and supports the V-22 program through a partnership with Boeing. Bell also manufacturers a range of commercial helicopters. Through five service centers four parts distribution centers and some 100 independent dealers Bell provides repair and overhaul and customizing services for an installed base of 13000 helicopters.

Textron Systems (10% of sales) provides unmanned systems marine and land systems and simulation and training solutions. It serves markets that include aerospace defense and general aviation. Besides the US military the segment sells to foreign military organizations approved by the US government.

Finance (less than 1% of sales) consists of Textron Financial Corporation (TFC) and offers financing mainly for new and used Textron Aviation aircraft and Bell helicopters.

Geographic Reach

The company operates about 55 plants in the US and another 50 outside the US. The US account for more than 60% of sales. Other major markets include Europe (about 15%) and Asia Pacific (nearly 10%). Other international sales account for about 15% of sales.

Sales and MarketingTextron Aviation sells through its own sales force as well as through a network of authorized independent sales representatives. Post-sale support and service is offered though global service and parts distribution centers. It sells to US government customers (about 25% of consolidated revenues results from US government contracts) to customers outside the US through foreign military sales sponsored by the US government and directly through commercial sales channels. The Industrial segment sells through a combination of factory direct resources and a worldwide network of independent distributors and dealers.

Financial Performance

Textron's revenue has been uneven the last five years rising less than 1% between 2014 and 2018. Annual fluctuations in aircraft deliveries have contributed to the ups and downs of Textron's revenue.

Sales in 2018 decreased 2% to $14 billion compared to $14.2 billion in 2017. The dip in 2018 was primarily due to Textron's selling the Industrial segment's tools and test equipment division in mid-2018. Textron Systems' marine and land systems product line saw slower volumes in 2018 as did Bell's commercial helicopter line.

Net income increased nearly 300% to $1.2 billion 2018 compared to 2017 primarily due to reduced operating costs and higher operating profit in the company?s Textron Aviation Bell and Textron Systems segments.

Cash at the end of 2018 was $1.1 billion a decrease of $155 million from the prior year. Cash from operations contributed $1.1 billion to the coffers while investing activities brought in $620 million mainly from the sale of the tools and test equipment business. Financing activities used $1.9 billion primarily for repurchases of common stock.

Strategy

Textron is focused on innovation and developing new products to expand its customer base. The first Citation Longitude jets a new large-cabin business aircraft were delivered to customers in late 2019. Other projects in Textron Aviation's pipeline include a cargo version of the Cessna SkyCourier (a twin-engine large-utility turboprop aircraft) and the Cessna Denali a new single-engine turboprop.

Bell's new V-280 Valor which the company is developing for the US military contains a new vertical lift technology that it expects to define the future of tiltrotor vertical lift aircraft. Bell has also made strides in the development of the V-247 an unmanned aerial tiltrotor aircraft.

Textron is revamping its Industrial division. In 2018 it sold its tools and test equipment businesses to Emerson for $810 million. The company used the proceeds to fund additional share repurchases. The following year Textron announced it was exploring strategic alternatives for its Kautex business unit. Germany-based Kautex is a maker of blow-molded plastic fuel systems sold to automotive OEMs. Other products include automotive catalytic reduction systems and engine components.

Mergers and Acquisitions

The company occasionally beefs up its segments through acquisitions. In early 2019 Textron completed the acquisition of Howe & Howe Technologies Inc. of Waterboro Maine. Howe & Howe makes robotic land vehicles built for the most extreme conditions in the world. This includes the small and mobile Ripsaw Super Tank chosen by the U.S. Army as its first platoon load-carrying robot and the world's first and only purpose-built robotic firefighting solution its Thermite firefighting robot.

HISTORY

Pioneer conglomerate builder Royal Little founded Special Yarns Corporation a Boston textile business in 1923 and merged it with the Franklin Rayon Dyeing Company in 1928. The result Franklin Rayon Corporation moved its headquarters to Providence Rhode Island in 1930 and changed its name to Atlantic Rayon in 1938.

The company expanded during WWII to make parachutes and in 1944 adopted the name Textron to reflect the use of synthetics in its textiles. Between 1953 and 1960 Textron bought more than 40 businesses including Bell Helicopter before banker Rupe Thompson took over in 1960.

Thompson sold weak businesses such as Amerotron Textron's last textile business (1963) but also bought 20 companies between 1960 and 1965. By 1968 when former Wall Street attorney William Miller replaced Thompson as CEO Textron made products ranging from chain saws to watchbands. Miller sold several companies and bought Jacobsen Manufacturers (lawn care equipment 1978) before leaving Textron in 1978 to head the Federal Reserve and become treasury secretary under President Jimmy Carter.

EXECUTIVES

Vp And Cio, Diane K. Schwarz

Chairman President And Ceo, Scott C. Donnelly, age 57, $1,146,500 total compensation

Evp General Counsel Secretary And Chief Compliance Officer, E. Robert Lupone, age 59, $695,192 total compensation

President And Ceo Textron Aviation, Scott A. Ernest

Evp Human Resources, Cheryl H. Johnson, age 58, $445,192 total compensation

President And Ceo Textron Specialized Vehicles, Kevin P. Holleran

President And Ceo Textron Systems, Ellen Lord

Evp And Cfo, Frank T. Connor, age 59, $940,385 total compensation

President And Ceo Tru Simulation + Training, Ian K. Walsh

President And Ceo Textron Airborne Solutions, Russ Bartlett

President And Ceo Textron Financial, R. Danny Maldonado

President And Ceo Bell Helicopter, Mitch Snyder

President And Ceo Greenlee Textron Inc. Sherman + Reilly Inc. And Hd Electric Company, Jason Butchko

President And Ceo Kautex, J ¶rg Rautenstrauch

Vice President, James Runstadler

Vice President Audit Services, Thomas Nichipor

Vp Mergers And Acquisitions, Scott Hegstrom

Board Member, Kerry Clark

Auditors: Ernst & Young LLP

LOCATIONS

HQ: Textron Inc
  40 Westminster Street, Providence, RI 02903
Phone: 401 421-2800
Web: www.textron.com

2017 Sales

	$ mil.	% of total
United States	8,786	62
Europe	1,962	14
Asia and Australia	1,206	9
Canada	913	6
Latin and South America	883	6
Middle East and Africa	448	3
Total	**14,198**	**100**

PRODUCTS/OPERATIONS

2017 Sales

	$ mil.	% of total
Textron Aviation	4,686	33
Bell	3,317	23
Textron Systems	1,840	13
Industrial	4,286	30
Finance	69	1
Total	**14,198**	**100**

Selected Products

Textron Aviation
  Beechcraft
  Cessna
  Hawker
  Citation
  Business jets
  Turboprop aircraft
  Piston engine aircraft
  Military trainer and defense aircraft
Bell
  Commercial helicopters
  Military helicopters
  Tiltrotor aircraft
Industrial
  Fuel Systems and Functional Components (Kautex)
  Blow-molded plastic fuel systems
  Clear vision systems
  Catalytic reduction systems
  Plastic bottles and containers
  Specialized Vehicles
  E-Z-GO golf cars
  Textron Off Road
  Arctic Cat
  UG Technologies
  Douglas Equipment
  Jacobsen turf maintenance equipment
  Tools and Test Equipment
  Greenlee
  Greenlee Communications
  Greenlee Utility
  HD Electric
  Klauke
  Sherman+Reilly
  Endura
Textron Systems
  Unmanned systems and support solutions
  Marine and land systems
  Simulation and training systems
  TRU Simulation + Training
  Textron Airborne Solutions
  Electronic systems
  Lycoming
  Weapons and sensors
Finance (primarily for new and used aircraft and helicopters)

HISTORICAL FINANCIALS

Company Type: Public

Income Statement				FYE: December 29
	REVENUE ($ mil.)	NET INCOME ($ mil.)	NET PROFIT MARGIN	EMPLOYEES
12/18	13,972	1,222	8.7%	35,000
12/17	14,198	307	2.2%	37,000
12/16*	13,788	962	7.0%	36,000
01/16	13,423	697	5.2%	35,000
01/15	13,878	600	4.3%	34,000
Annual Growth	0.2%	19.5%	—	0.7%

*Fiscal year change

2018 Year-End Financials

Debt ratio: 27.00%	No. of shares (mil.): 236
Return on equity: 23.00%	Dividends
Cash ($ mil.): 987	Yield: 0.0%
Current ratio: 2.00	Payout: 2.0%
Long-term debt ($ mil.): 3,526	Market value ($ mil.): 10,756

	STOCK PRICE ($) FY Close	P/E High/Low		PER SHARE ($) Earnings	Dividends	Book Value
12/18	46.00	15	9	5.00	0.00	22.00
12/17	57.00	50	39	1.00	0.00	22.00
12/16*	49.00	14	9	4.00	0.00	21.00
01/16	42.00	19	15	3.00	0.00	18.00
01/15	42.00	21	15	2.00	0.00	15.00
Annual Growth	2.0%	—	—	22.7%	(0.0%)	9.3%

*Fiscal year change

TFS Financial Corp

TFS Financial is the holding company for Third Federal Savings and Loan a thrift with some 45 branches and loan production offices in Ohio and southern Florida. The bank offers such deposit products as checking savings and retirement accounts and CDs. It uses funds from deposits to originate a variety of consumer loans primarily residential mortgages. Third Federal also offers IRAs annuities and mutual funds as well as retirement and college savings plans. TFS subsidiary Third Capital owns stakes in commercial real estate private equity funds and other investments. Mutual holding company Third Federal Savings and Loan Association of Cleveland owns nearly three-quarters of TFS Financial.

EXECUTIVES

Board Member, William C Mulligan
Board Member, MARTIN COHEN
Auditors: DELOITTE & TOUCHE LLP

LOCATIONS

HQ: TFS Financial Corp
7007 Broadway Avenue, Cleveland, OH 44105
Phone: 216 441-6000
Web: www.thirdfederal.com

COMPETITORS

Bank of America	KeyCorp
Citigroup	PNC Financial
Fifth Third	U.S. Bancorp
Huntington Bancshares	Wells Fargo
JPMorgan Chase	

HISTORICAL FINANCIALS

Company Type: Public

Income Statement				FYE: September 30
	ASSETS ($ mil.)	NET INCOME ($ mil.)	INCOME AS % OF ASSETS	EMPLOYEES
09/19	14,542	80	0.6%	—
09/18	14,137	85	0.6%	—
09/17	13,693	89	0.6%	—
09/16	12,906	81	0.6%	—
09/15	12,369	73	0.6%	—
Annual Growth	4.1%	2.5%		

2019 Year-End Financials

Debt ratio: —	No. of shares (mil.): 280
Return on equity: 5.00%	Dividends
Cash ($ mil.): 275	Yield: 6.0%
Current ratio: —	Payout: 378.0%
Long-term debt ($ mil.): —	Market value ($ mil.): 5,045

	STOCK PRICE ($) FY Close	P/E High/Low		PER SHARE ($) Earnings	Dividends	Book Value
09/19	18.00	64	49	0.00	1.00	6.00
09/18	15.00	53	46	0.00	1.00	6.00
09/17	16.00	62	46	0.00	1.00	6.00
09/16	18.00	69	56	0.00	0.00	6.00
09/15	17.00	71	55	0.00	0.00	6.00
Annual Growth	1.1%	—	—	2.9%	34.7%	0.5%

The Bancorp Inc

The Bancorp is — what else? — the holding company for The Bancorp Bank which provides financial services in the virtual world. Targeting non-bank financial service companies across the US and Europe from start-ups to small and midsized businesses underserved by larger banks in the market The Bancorp Bank provides private-label online banking to 200 affinity groups; offers specialty lending; issues prepaid debit cards; and processes ACH and merchant credit card transactions. Its specialty lending products include securities backed lines of credit (SBLOC) auto fleet and equipment leasing SBA loans and commercial mortgage loans for sale in capital markets.

Operations

The Bancorp and The Bancorp Bank operate three business segments: Payments which made up 45% of the bank's total revenue in 2015 and provides prepaid cards card payments and ACH

processing services; Specialty Finance (31% of revenue) which consists of commercial mortgage loan sales small business administration (SBA) loans leasing and security backed lines of credit and related deposit business; and Corporate (24% of revenue) which includes the company's investment portfolio.

Unlike other banks which rely on interest income The Bancorp makes more than 60% of its revenue from fee-based income. About 38% of its total revenue came from loan interest (including fees) during 2015 while another 14% came from interest income on investment securities. The rest of its revenue came from prepaid card fees (22% of revenue) service fees on deposit accounts (3%) card payment and ACH processing fees (3%) leasing income (1%) debit card income (1%) affinity fees (2%) and non-recurring gains from the sale of its loans investment securities and health savings portfolio (27%).

Geographic Reach

Wilmington Delaware-based The Bancorp serves customers in the US and Europe from 16 offices in the two regions and Southeast Asia.

Sales and Marketing

The company targets non-bank financial services companies including start-ups small and medium businesses underserved by large banks and Fortune 500 companies. It spent $387000 on advertising during 2015 down from $621000 and $706000 in 2014 and 2013 respectively.

Financial Performance

The Bancorp's annual revenues and profits have nearly doubled since 2011 mostly as its Payments business income has nearly quadrupled over the period. Its loan assets have also nearly tripled spurring additional interest income growth.

The company's revenue jumped 39% to $216.5 million during 2015 thanks largely to a $33.5 million gain on the sale of the majority of its health savings business and a $14.4 million gain on the sale of its tax-exempt municipal bonds portfolio. The Bancorp's loan interest revenue was also up 37% as its specialty lending balances continued to grow with new SBLOC SBA leasing and loans-for-sale business.

Despite strong revenue growth in 2015 The Bancorp's net income plunged more than 75% to $13.43 million mostly as its discontinued operations (its discontinued Philadelphia commercial loan business) generated $27 million less in revenue than the year before and because in 2014 it had collected a $14.5 million income tax benefit from a reversal of valuation allowances. The company's operations used $234.8 million or more than four times more cash than in 2014 mainly on a steep decline cash-based earnings especially after accounting for net proceeds from sales of its loans-originated-for-resale.

Strategy

The Bancorp and The Bancorp Bank has been winding down its non-core operations in recent years to concentrate more in its national specialty lending business. In October 2015 the bank sold its $400 million-HSA portfolio to HealthEquity for $34..4 million after selling its regional Commercial Lending business in 2014. As a result the bank noted that its discontinued operations were reduced by 50% at the end of 2015 and expected its discontinued loan portfolio to shrink from there through loan repayments and opportunistic loan sales.

On the growth side The Bancorp continues to buy specialty financing assets from other financial companies to bolster its loan assets and extend its geographic reach. In December 2015 it expanded its commercial fleet leasing presence in the West Coast with a new California office after buying the commercial leasing assets of Ellis Brooks Leasing Inc.

EXECUTIVES

Evp Strategy Cfo And Secretary, Paul Frenkiel, age 67, $312,200 total compensation
President And Ceo, Damian Kozlowski, age 52
Evp And Chief Credit Officer The Bancorp Inc. And The Bancorp Bank, Donald F. (Don) McGraw, age 62, $317,500 total compensation
Evp Commercial Fleet Leasing And Chief Lending Officer, Scott R. Megargee, age 67, $202,541 total compensation
Evp And Cio, Peter (Pete) Chiccino
Svp; Managing Director Payment Solutions, Jeremy L. Kuiper, $458,060 total compensation
Svp And General Counsel, Thomas G. Pareigat, $347,500 total compensation
Evp And Coo, Gail S. Ball
Evp And Chief Risk Officer, Steven Turowski
Evp Commercial Mortgage Securitization, Ron Wechsler
First Vp Loan Committee, Genevieve Johnson
Senior Vice President Chief Information Security Officer, Anthony Meholic
Vice President Information Security Officer, Darin Wipf
First Vice President And Bro, Michael Terroni
Vice President Credit Risk, Dennis Day
First Vice President, Elizabeth Roy
Vice President, Carole Turansky
Vice President Sba Portfolio Manager, John Morgenthaler
Vp And Sba Business Development Officer, Jeffrey Fulcher
Vp Vendor Manager Ii, Michael Meiskey
Assistant Vice President Senior Risk Analyst, Craig Tabun
Vice President Threat And Vulnerability Management Officer, Peter Iancic
Chairman The Bancorp Inc. And The Bancorp Bank, Daniel G. Cohen, age 49
Board Member, John Chrystal
Auditors: Grant Thornton LLP

LOCATIONS

HQ: The Bancorp Inc
409 Silverside Road, Wilmington, DE 19809
Phone: 302 385-5000
Web: www.thebancorp.com

PRODUCTS/OPERATIONS

2015 sales

	$ mil.	% of total
Payments	98	45
Specialty finance	68	31
Corporate	51	24
Total	**217**	**100**

2015 Sales

	$ mil.	% of total
Interest income		
Loans including fees	50	23
Interest on investment securities:	31	14
Federal funds sold/securities purchased under agreements to resell	1	:
Interest earning deposits	2	1
Non-interest income		
Prepaid card fees	48	22
Gain on sale of health savings portfolio	34	15
Gain on sale of investment securities	14	7
Gain on sale of loans	10	5
Service fees on deposit accounts	8	3
Card payment and ACH processing fees	6	3
Affinity fees	3	2
Other	5	2
Change in value of investment in unconsolidated entity	2	1
Leasing income	2	1
Debit card income	2	1
Total	**217**	**100**

COMPETITORS

Citizens Financial Group
E*TRADE Bank
M&T Bank
PNC Financial
Republic First Bank
Royal Bancshares
Sovereign Bank
Sun Bancorp (NJ)
TD Bank USA
WSFS Financial

HISTORICAL FINANCIALS

Company Type: Public

Income Statement

FYE: December 31

	ASSETS ($ mil.)	NET INCOME ($ mil.)	INCOME AS % OF ASSETS	EMPLOYEES
12/18	4,438	89	2.0%	589
12/17	4,708	22	0.5%	538
12/16	4,858	(96)	—	589
12/15	4,766	13	0.3%	762
12/14	4,986	57	1.1%	684
Annual Growth	(2.9%)	11.6%	—	(3.7%)

2018 Year-End Financials

Debt ratio: 1.00%
Return on equity: 24.00%
Cash ($ mil.): 554
Current ratio: —
Long-term debt ($ mil.): —
No. of shares (mil.): 56
Dividends
Yield: —
Payout: —
Market value ($ mil.): 449

	STOCK PRICE ($) FY Close	P/E High/Low		PER SHARE ($) Earnings	Dividends	Book Value
12/18	8.00	7	5	2.00	0.00	7.00
12/17	10.00	26	12	0.00	0.00	6.00
12/16	8.00	—	—	(2.00)	0.00	5.00
12/15	6.00	31	18	0.00	0.00	8.00
12/14	11.00	13	5	1.00	0.00	8.00
Annual Growth	(7.5%)	—	—	1.0%	—	(3.9%)

THE CHARLOTTE-MECKLENBURG HOSPITAL AUTHORITY

TheÂ medical facilities under the watchful eye of theÂ Charlotte-Mecklenburg Hospital AuthorityÂ care for the injured and infirmed.Â As the largest health care system in the Carolinas the organizationÂ operating asÂ Carolinas HealthCare System (CHS)Â ownsÂ or managesÂ more thanÂ 30Â affiliated hospitals.Â It also operates long-term care facilities research centers rehabilitation facilitiesÂ surgery centersÂ home health agencies radiation therapy facilities and other health care operations.Â Collectively CHSÂ facilities have more than 6400 beds and affiliated physician practices employ more than 1700 doctors. The network's flagship facility is the 875-bedÂ Carolinas Medical Center in Charlotte North Carolina.

EXECUTIVES

Operating Room Dir, Ashley Sterchi
Director Of Pharmacy, Chris Barringer
Assistant Vice President Of Human Resources, Nehemie Owen
Auditors: KPMG LLP CHARLOTTE NORTH CAR

LOCATIONS

HQ: THE CHARLOTTE-MECKLENBURG HOSPITAL AUTHORITY
1000 BLYTHE BLVD, CHARLOTTE, NC 282035812
Phone: 704 355-2000
Web: WWW.ATRIUMHEALTH.ORG

PRODUCTS/OPERATIONS

2010 Revenue

	% of total
Tertiary & acute care services	72
Physicians' services	16
Post-acute care services	3
Specialty services	2
Other services & non-operating activities	7
Total	**100**

Selected Hospitals and Health Care Pavilions

AnMed Health Medical Center
AnMed Health Rehabilitation Hospital
AnMed Health Women's and Children's Hospital
Anson Community Hospital
Bon Secours/St. Francis Hospital
Cannon Memorial Hospital
Carolinas Medical Center
Carolinas Medical Center - Kannapolis (health care pavilion)
Carolinas Medical Center - Lincoln
Carolinas Medical Center - Mercy
Carolinas Medical Center - NorthEast
Carolinas Medical Center - Pineville
Carolinas Medical Center - Steele Creek (health care pavilion)
Carolinas Medical Center - Union
Carolinas Medical Center - University
Carolinas Medical Center - Waxhaw (health care pavilion)
Carolinas Rehabilitation
Carolinas Rehabilitation - Mount Holly
Cleveland Regional Medical Center
CMC - Randolph
Columbus Regional Healthcare System
Crawley Memorial Hospital
Grace Hospital
Kings Mountain Hospital
Levine Children's Hospital
MedWest - Harris
MedWest - Haywood
MedWest - Swain
Roper Hospital
Roper St. Francis - Mount Pleasant Hospital
Scotland Memorial Hospital
Stanly Regional Medical Center
St. Luke's Hospital
Valdese Hospital
Wallace Thomson Hospital
Wilkes Regional Medical Center

COMPETITORS

Alamance Regional Medical Center
CaroMont
Community Health Systems
Cone Health
Conway Medical Center
Cumberland County Hospital System
Davis Regional Medical Center
Duke University Health System
FirstHealth of the Carolinas
Georgetown Hospital System
Grand Strand Regional Medical Center
HCA
Haywood Regional High Point Regional Health System
McLeod Health
Mission Hospitals
Morehead Memorial Hospital
New Hanover Regional Medical Center
Novant Health
Palmetto Health
Presbyterian Healthcare
Rex Healthcare
Soliant Health
Tenet Healthcare
UNC Hospitals
Upstate Affiliate
Vidant Health
WakeMed

Income Statement				FYE: December 31
	REVENUE ($ mil.)	NET INCOME ($ mil.)	NET PROFIT MARGIN	EMPLOYEES
12/18	6,228	(70)	—	62,000
12/17	5,991	830	13.9%	—
12/16	5,676	493	8.7%	—
12/15	5,479	(248)	—	—
Annual Growth	4.4%	—	—	—

THE CLEVELAND CLINIC FOUNDATION

The not-for-profit Cleveland Clinic Foundation operates about 20 hospitals in Ohio Florida Abu Dhabi Toronto and soon in London. Combined the foundation's hospitals have nearly 6000 beds. Its flagship location is its namesake Cleveland Clinic an academic medical center in Cleveland Ohio. The campus specializes in cardiac care digestive disease treatment and urological and kidney care along with education and research opportunities. It has an international care center children's hospital and an outpatient center; it also contains research and educational institutes covering clinical drug research ophthalmic studies and cancer research as well as physician and scientist training programs.

Operations
The Cleveland Clinic Foundation operates more than 180 outpatient facilities in northern Ohio. These include outpatient family health centers ambulatory surgery centers physician offices specialized cancer centers and wellness centers. The system has more than 100 medical specialties and subspecialties.

The foundation operates the Lerner College of Medicine and the Lerner Research Institute through a partnership with Case Western Reserve University and it has continuing education nursing and residency programs. It also operates Cleveland Clinic Innovations a unit that oversees collaborative research and technology commercialization programs with partners including MedStar Health and the University of Notre Dame. Cleveland Clinic educates some 2000 residents and fellows and receives some $300 million in research funding (from grants contracts and federal support) each year.

Altogether the medical centers known as the Cleveland Clinic Health System include some 5400 beds and employ about 4000 full-time physicians. The group handles almost 240000 hospital admissions and around 8 million outpatient visits each year. In 2018 it had more than 220000 surgical cases.

Geographic Reach
In addition to its primary campus Cleveland Clinic Foundation operates regional hospitals and numerous family and specialty health centers in northeastern Ohio. It operates a handful of facilities in Florida and several brain clinics in Nevada.

Internationally Cleveland Clinic Foundation operates a health and wellness center in Canada and manages health centers in the United Arab Emirates.

Sales and Marketing
Cleveland Clinic Foundation receives about 55% of its net patient service revenue from managed care and commercial insurance reimbursements. Medicare reimbursements account for around 35% of net patient revenue with the remainder coming from self-pay and Medicaid customers.

Financial Performance
In 2018 Cleveland Clinic Foundation's total unrestricted revenue rose 6% to $8.9 billion. Net patient service revenue increased 3% to $8.0 billion while other revenue declined 1% to $895.8 million.

A 19% decline in operating income due to higher costs for providing care and falling reimbursement rates plus nearly $200 million in investment losses led to a sharp drop in excess revenue over expenses that year. That figure fell from $1.2 billion to $103.9 million.

The foundation ended 2018 with $444.8 million in net cash some $200000 more than it had at the end of 2017. Operating activities provided $745.5 million and financing activities provided another $134.2 million while investing activities used $671.2 million.

Strategy
Cleveland Clinic Foundation has been hailed by many as a model for delivering high-quality care at lower costs. Cleveland Clinic's cost-cutting innovations include paying doctors a salary rather than by procedure (the group practice model) and interactive supply closets that perform their own inventory and summon robotic refill carts from the warehouse. However care costs continue to rise and the company's operating income took a hit in 2018. To combat those expenses the system is focused on maximizing efficiency at its newer facilities. It is establishing a Center for the Study of Healthcare Delivery to help look for ways to ensure care is coordinated yet not redundant further cutting costs.

The foundation also improves its service offerings through facility and program expansion efforts as well as partnerships with other regional providers. In 2017 it expanded its sports medicine and rehabilitation operations by joining forces with Toronto-based Sports Medicine Specialists.

National and global expansion efforts are a big part of the organization's growth strategy. It hopes to double the number of patients it serves by 2024; telehealth and population health will be primary drivers of that growth.

Finally the system is investing in security measures to protect employees and patients.

Mergers and Acquisitions
In early 2019 Cleveland Clinic expanded its operations in the Sunshine State when it acquired Martin Health System and its three hospitals (with more than 520 beds) in Southeast Florida. It also acquired Indian River Medical Center which has more than 330 beds and is located on Florida's Treasure Coast. The system plans to invest millions in the newly added operations over the next few years.

Company Background
Cleveland Clinic Foundation traces its roots to 1921 when a group of Cleveland doctors teamed up to improve medical care and education. Its main campus has conducted breakthrough medical innovations through its history such as the first face transplant in 2008 and it is regularly named to the US News & World Report's list of America's Best Hospitals.

EXECUTIVES
Cio, C. Martin Harris
Chairman And Ceo, Delos M. (Toby) Cosgrove
Chairman Division Of Regional Medical Practice, David L. Bronson
Cfo And Treasurer, Steven C. Glass
Ceo Cleveland Clinic Abu Dhabi, A. Marc Harrison
Chief Medical Operations Officer, Robert Wyllie
Chief Of Operations, William (Bill) Peacock
Interim Ceo Sheikh Khalifa Medical City, Ben Frank
Interim Executive Chief Nursing Officer, K. Kelly Hancock
Chair Department Of Palm Ccm, Herbert Wiedemann
Vice President, Sanford Timen
Medical Director, Kevin Hopkins
Medical Director, Vladimir Burdjalov
Director Of Health Information, Bryan Holtz
Vice President Of Medical Operations, William Riebel
Vice President Of Operations, Kris Bennett
Medical Director, Annmarie Kozlowski
Vice President, Toribio Flores
Medical Director, Damon Kralovic
Medical Director, Michael Machuzak
Assistant Vice President Operations, Janet Gulley
Medical Director, John Donohue
Associate Medical Director, Faith Factora
Medical Director, Purva Grover
Vice President Oncology Services West, Susan Dunson
Pharmacy Manager Transitions Of Care, Erick Sokn
Vice President Market Leader, Grace Jen
Medical Director, Akhil Bindra
Medical Director Of Cardiac Rehabilitation, Rocco Michael
Chairman, Robert E. (Bob) Rich
Vice Chairman, Joseph M. (Joe) Scaminace
Secretary, Lynn Meyers
Medical Secretary, Judith Burdett
Secretary, Danielle Riedel
Secretary, Jennifer Gaizutis
Secretary, Marcie Chonko
Board Member, Donna Munic-Miller
Secretary, Christine Hughes
Unit Secretary, Karen Ginley
Medical Secretary, Heather Karn
Secretary, Caroline Walters
Secretary, Nancy Toll
Secretary, Joye Grebb
Department Secretary, Chris Morchak
Secretary, Marianne Simon
Medical Secretary, Barbara Szlamas
Medical Secretary, Lucy Bufkin
Medical Secretary, Linda Rosa
Auditors: ERNST & YOUNG LLP CLEVELAND

LOCATIONS
HQ: THE CLEVELAND CLINIC FOUNDATION
9500 EUCLID AVE, CLEVELAND, OH 441950002
Phone: 216 636-8335
Web: WWW.MY.CLEVELANDCLINIC.ORG

Selected Facilities
Ashtabula County Medical Center (Ashtabula Ohio; management contract)
The Cleveland Clinic (Cleveland Ohio)
Cleveland Clinic Children's Hospital
Cleveland Clinic International Center
Cleveland Clinic Canada (Toronto)
Cleveland Clinic Children's Hospital for Rehabilitation (Shaker Campus in Cleveland Ohio)
Cleveland Clinic Family Health Centers (multiple locations in northeast Ohio)
Cleveland Clinic Florida (Weston Florida)
Cleveland Clinic Florida (West Palm Beach Florida)
Cleveland Clinic Lou Ruvo Center for Brain Health (Elko Nevada)

Cleveland Clinic Lou Ruvo Center for Brain Health (Las Vegas Nevada)
Cleveland Clinic Lou Ruvo Center for Brain Health (Reno Nevada)
Euclid Hospital (Euclid Ohio)
Fairview Hospital (Cleveland Ohio)
Hillcrest Hospital (Mayfield Heights Ohio)
Lakewood Hospital (Lakewood Ohio)
Lutheran Hospital (Cleveland Ohio)
Marymount Hospital (Garfield Heights Ohio)
Medina Hospital (Medina Ohio)
Richard E. Jacobs Health Center (Avon Ohio)
South Pointe Hospital (Warrensville Heights Ohio)

Selected Institutes

Cleveland Clinic Institutes
  Anesthesiology and Pain Management
  Bariatric and Metabolic
  Cancer Center/Taussig Cancer Institute
  Cleveland Clinic Children's and Pediatric
  Dermatology and Plastic Surgery
  Digestive Disease and Surgery
  Emergency Services
  Endocrinology and Metabolism
  Genomics
  Head and Neck
  Heart and Vascular
  Imaging
  Medicine
  Neurological
  Nursing
  Orthopaedic and Rheumatologic
  Pathology and Laboratory Medicine
  Respiratory
  Urology and Kidney
  Wellness
Special Expertise Institutes
  Arts and Medicine
  Body Donation
  Patient Experience
  Philanthropy
  Professional Staff Affairs
  Quality and Patient Safety
  Research

PRODUCTS/OPERATIONS

2018 Sales

	$ mil.	% of total
Net patient service revenue		
Self-pay	4,466	50
Managed care & commercial	2,872	32
Medicare	649	7
Medicaid	45	1
Other	896	10
Total	**8,928**	**100**

COMPETITORS

Akron Children's Hospital
Catholic Health Initiatives
Deaconess Associations
Kettering Health Network
Lake Health
Mayo Clinic
Memorial Sloan-Kettering
MetroHealth System

OhioHealth
Parma Community General Hospital
Premier Health Partners
Robinson Memorial Hospital
Shriners Hospitals For Children
Summa Health System
University Hospitals Health System

HISTORICAL FINANCIALS

Company Type: Private

Income Statement   FYE: December 31

	REVENUE ($ mil.)	NET INCOME ($ mil.)	NET PROFIT MARGIN	EMPLOYEES
12/18	8,928	176	2.0%	44,000
12/17	8,407	1,150	13.7%	—
12/16	8,037	514	6.4%	—
12/14	4,291	405	9.4%	—
Annual Growth	20.1%	(18.8%)	—	—

THE FORD FOUNDATION

As one of the nation's largest philanthropic organizations the Ford Foundation can afford to be generous. The foundation offers grants to individuals and institutions worldwide that work to meet its goals of strengthening democratic values reducing poverty and injustice promoting international cooperation and advancing human achievement. The Ford Foundation's charitable giving has run the gamut from A (Association for Asian Studies) to Z (Zanzibar International Film Festival). The foundation has an endowment of about $10 billion. Established in 1936 by Edsel Ford whose father founded the Ford Motor Company the foundation no longer owns stock in the automaker or has ties to the founding family.

Operations

The foundation which is governed by an international board of trustees makes grants in all 50 US states and supports programs in more than 50 countries.

It boasts about 10 regional offices in Latin America Africa the Middle East and Asia.

Geographic Reach

Based in New York the Ford Foundation is a grantmaking foundation that primarily serves the US but also global programs.

Strategy

The Ford Foundation's programs address several social justice issues including democratic and accountable government freedom of expression access to education economic fairness and opportunity sexuality and reproductive rights sustainable development social justice metropolitan opportunity and human rights.

A small portion of its endowment is set aside for social investing. The foundation's funds typically finance critical projects set new business models and develop sustainable organizations. By investing $1 million or more in initiatives the Ford Foundation's investment strategy aims to make a noteworthy impact and encourage other investors to also fund projects.

EXECUTIVES

Secretary, Karen Mcburnie

LOCATIONS

HQ: THE FORD FOUNDATION
  320 E 43RD ST FL 4, NEW YORK, NY 100174890
Phone: 212 573-5370
Web: WWW.FORDFOUND.ORG

PRODUCTS/OPERATIONS

Selected Core Issues

Democratic and accountable government
Economic fairness
Education opportunity and scholarship
Freedom of expression
Human rights
Metropolitan opportunity
Sexuality and reproductive health rights
Social justice philanthropy
Sustainable development

HISTORICAL FINANCIALS

Company Type: Private

Income Statement   FYE: December 31

	ASSETS ($ mil.)	NET INCOME ($ mil.)	INCOME AS % OF ASSETS	EMPLOYEES
12/15	12,114	(270)	—	556
12/14*	12,400	(8)	—	—
09/11	10,345	(5)	—	—
09/09	10,235	0	—	—
Annual Growth	2.8%			

*Fiscal year change

The Gap Inc

The ubiquitous clothing retailer Gap has been filling closets with jeans and khakis T-shirts button-downs and poplin for some 50 years. The company which operates about 3700 owned and franchised stores worldwide built its iconic casual brand on basics for men women and children. Over the years it has extended its namesake brand to include GapBody GapKids and babyGap (among others) and has added brands such as the urban chic Banana Republic family budgeteer Old Navy women's activewear chain Athleta designer-focused Intermix and men's clothier Hill City. The company which has announced plans to split into two generates about 80% of its revenue from the US.

HISTORY

Donald Fisher and his wife Doris opened a small store in 1969 near what is now San Francisco State University. The couple named their store The Gap (after "the generation gap") and concentrated on selling Levi's jeans. The couple opened a second store in San Jose California eight months later and by the end of 1970 there were six Gap stores. The Gap went public six years later.

In the beginning the Fishers catered almost exclusively to teenagers but in the 1970s they expanded into activewear that would appeal to a larger spectrum of customers. Nevertheless by the early 1980s The Gap — which had grown to about 500 stores — was still dependent upon its largely teenage customer base. However it was less dependent on Levi's (about 35% of sales) thanks to its growing stable of private labels.

In a 1983 effort to revamp the company's image Donald hired Mickey Drexler a former president of AnnTaylor with a spotless apparel industry track record as The Gap's new president. Drexler immediately overhauled the motley clothing lines to concentrate on sturdy brightly colored cotton clothing. He also consolidated the stores' many private clothing labels into the Gap brand. As a final touch Drexler replaced circular clothing racks with white shelving so clothes could be neatly stacked and displayed.

Also in 1983 The Gap bought Banana Republic a unique chain of jungle-themed stores that sold safari clothing. The company expanded the chain which enjoyed tremendous success in the mid-1980s but slumped after the novelty of the stores wore off late in the decade. In response Drexler introduced a broader range of clothes (including higher-priced leather items) and dumped the safari lines in 1988. By 1990 Banana Republic was again profitable.

The first GapKids opened in 1985 after Drexler couldn't find clothing that he liked for his son. During the late 1980s and early 1990s the company grew rapidly opening its first stores in Canada and the UK. In 1990 it introduced babyGap in 25 GapKids stores featuring miniature versions of its GapKids line. The Gap announced in 1991 it would no longer sell Levi's (which had fallen to less than 2% of total sales) and would sell nothing but private-label items.

Earnings fell in fiscal 1993 because of Gap division losses brought on by low margins and high rents. The company shuffled management positions and titles as part of a streamlining effort. It rebounded in 1994 by concentrating on improving profit margins rather than sales and by launching Old Navy Clothing Co. named after a bar Drexler saw in Paris. Banana Republic opened its first two stores outside the US both in Canada in 1995.

Robert Fisher (the founders' son) became the new president of the Gap division (including baby-Gap and GapKids) in 1997 and was charged with reversing the segment's sales decline. The company refocused its Gap chain on basics (jeans T-shirts and khakis) and helped boost its performance with a high-profile advertising campaign focusing on those wares. Later in 1997 the Gap opened an online Gap store. In 1998 it began opening Torpedo Joe submarine-themed shops in select Old Navy flagships.

Also in 1998 the retailer opened its first Gap-Body stores and introduced its only catalog (for Banana Republic). In late 1999 amid sluggish Gap division sales Robert Fisher resigned and Drexler took over his duties. Gap misjudged fashion trends in 2000 which resulted in two years of disappointing earnings. After a 10% reduction in its workforce the company returned to a more conservative fashion approach.

The company split Gap and Gap International into two separate units in early 2002 to improve performance in the flagship brand. In September Drexler retired and was replaced by Paul Pressler a veteran of The Walt Disney Company.

Gap sold its 10 stores in Germany to Swedish retailer H&M in 2004 taking a $14 million writedown related to the sale.

The next year the retailer launched Forth & Towne its first new chain in a decade with the new stores catering to women over the age of 35. Also Gap dipped its toes into personal care products by signing an agreement with Inter Parfums in mid-2005. As part of the deal Inter Parfums develops formulates manufactures and packages the products which are branded under the Gap and Banana Republic names. The Gap markets and sells them in its GapBody stores.

In January 2006 Gap entered into a 10-year non-exclusive services agreement with International Business Machines valued at $1.1 billion. As a result IBM took over certain information technology functions from the retailer; up to 400 Gap employees joined IBM as a result of the deal. Gap Direct launched an online footwear business called Piperlime in November.

CEO Pressler left the company and the board in January 2007 after four years in the top job. He was succeeded as CEO on an interim basis by Robert Fisher previously the non-executive chairman of the retailer. In June the company shut down its Forth & Towne retail format after less than two years in business. In July Gap named a new chairman and CEO Glenn Murphy. Murphy joined the company from Canadian drugstore chain Shoppers Drug Mart where he had retired as chairman and CEO in March. Stung by allegations in the British press of forced child labor in India being used in the manufacture of apparel for its Gap Kids chain Gap in November announced a package of measures intended to strengthen its

commitment to eradicating the exploitation of children in the garment industry. Actions include a $200000 grant to improve working conditions and an upcoming conference dedicated to finding solutions to issues related to child labor.

In October 2008 Gap acquired Athleta a direct-marketer of women's active wear for about $150 million. Gap purchased Athleta as part of its strategy to diversify its brand offerings. The company also opened its first Banana Republic and Gap brand factory stores in Canada in late October extending its outlet busuiness launched in 1994 to Canada. The retailer opened 101 new stores and shuttered 119 locations in 2008.

Don Fisher Gap co-founder died in September 2009 at the age of 81. Also in 2009 Gap began opening stores inside Mexico's leading department store chain Distribuidora Liverpool via a franchise agreement.

In November 2010 Gap entered Italy with a store in Milan.

EXECUTIVES

President And General Manager Athleta, Nancy Green, age 57
President Growth Innovation And Digital, Arthur (Art) Peck, age 63, $1,330,288 total compensation
President And General Manager Intermix, Jyothi Rao
Global President Old Navy, Sonia Syngal, age 49, $850,000 total compensation
Head Of Gap China, Jeff Kirwan, age 53, $893,269 total compensation
Evp And Cfo, Teri L. List-Stoll, $30,288 total compensation
Evp; General Manager Greater China, Abinta Malik
Evp Global General Counsel Corporate Secretary And Chief Compliance Officer, Julie Gruber
Evp Strategy And Chief Customer Officer, Sebastian DiGrande, $505,385 total compensation
Evp And Cio, Paul Chapman
Evp Global Supply Chain Sourcing And Production, Michael Yee
Evp Global Supply Chain Logistics And Product Operations, Shawn Curran
Vice President Brand Creative, Stephanie Nahrgang
Vice President Ocm, Rita Martell
Senior Vice President And General Manager, Jodi Bricker
Vice President Of Stores, Steve Peters
Senior Vice President Human Resources And Communications, Brent Hyder
Executive Vice President Global Sourcing, Christophe Roussel
Vice President Of Women's Design, Sarah Holme
Vice President Visual Merchandising Design, Kristi Argo
Chairman, Robert J. (Bob) Fisher, age 64
Auditors: DELOITTE & TOUCHE LLP

LOCATIONS

HQ: The Gap Inc
   Two Folsom Street, San Francisco, CA 94105
Phone: 415 427-0100
Web: www.gapinc.com

2018 Sales

	$ mil.	% of total
US	13,340	81
Asia	1,233	7
Canada	1,193	7
Europe	603	4
Other regions	211	1
Total	**16,580**	**100**

PRODUCTS/OPERATIONS

2018 Sales

	$ mil.	% of total
Old Navy Global	7,840	47
Gap	5,160	31
Banana Republic Global	2,456	15
Other	1,124	7
Total	**16,580**	**100**

2018 Stores

	No.
Company-operated	
Gap	1,242
Old Navy	1,154
Banana Republic	601
Athleta	161
Intermix	36
Franchise	472
Total	**3,666**

Selected Stores and Brands

Athleta (women's activewear)
babyGap (clothing for infants and toddlers)
Banana Republic (upscale clothing and accessories)
Gap (casual and active clothing and body care products)
GapBody (intimate apparel)
GapKids (clothing for children)
Intermix (designer clothing for women)
Old Navy (lower-priced family clothing)

COMPETITORS

Abercrombie & Fitch	Kohl's
American Eagle	L Brands
Outfitters	Lululemon
Dillard's	Macy's
Express	Nordstrom
H&M	Ralph Lauren
Inditex	TJX Companies
J. Crew	Urban Outfitters

HISTORICAL FINANCIALS

Company Type: Public

Income Statement				FYE: February 2
	REVENUE ($ mil.)	NET INCOME ($ mil.)	NET PROFIT MARGIN	EMPLOYEES
02/19	16,580	1,003	6.0%	135,000
02/18*	15,855	848	5.3%	135,000
01/17	15,516	676	4.4%	135,000
01/16	15,797	920	5.8%	141,000
01/15	16,435	1,262	7.7%	141,000
Annual Growth	0.2%	(5.6%)	—	(1.1%)

*Fiscal year change

2019 Year-End Financials

Debt ratio: 16.00%
Return on equity: 30.00%
Cash ($ mil.): 1,081
Current ratio: 2.00
Long-term debt ($ mil.): 1,249

No. of shares (mil.): 378
Dividends
   Yield: 0.0%
   Payout: 37.0%
Market value ($ mil.): 9,450

	STOCK PRICE ($) FY Close	P/E High/Low		PER SHARE ($) Earnings	Dividends	Book Value
02/19	25.00	13	9	3.00	1.00	9.00
02/18*	32.00	16	10	2.00	1.00	8.00
01/17	23.00	18	10	2.00	1.00	7.00
01/16	25.00	19	10	2.00	1.00	6.00
01/15	41.00	16	12	3.00	1.00	7.00
Annual Growth	(11.7%)	—	—	(2.5%)	2.5%	7.3%

*Fiscal year change

THE HERTZ CORPORATION

EXECUTIVES

Pres-Ceo, Kathryn V Marinello
Non Exec Chb*, Henry R Keizer
Exec V Pres-Cfo, Jamere Jackson
Exec V Pres-Cmo, Jodi J Allen
Exec V Pres-Gen Counsel-Sec, M David Galainena
Sr V Pres-Cao, Richard E Esper
Evp Retail Oprs Officer, Paul E Stone
Evp-CIO, Opal G Perry
Evp-Chief Hr Officer, Murali Kuppuswamy
Director, Barry Beracha
Independent Lead Director, Linda Levinson
Auditors: PRICEWATERHOUSECOOPERS LLP FO

LOCATIONS

HQ: THE HERTZ CORPORATION
8501 WILLIAMS RD, ESTERO, FL 339283325
Phone: 239 301-7000
Web: WWW.HERTZ.COM

HISTORICAL FINANCIALS

Company Type: Private

Income Statement				FYE: December 31
	REVENUE ($ mil.)	NET INCOME ($ mil.)	NET PROFIT MARGIN	EMPLOYEES
12/17	8,803	332	3.8%	37,000
12/16	8,803	(488)	—	—
12/15	10,535	276	2.6%	—
Annual Growth	(8.6%)	9.7%	—	—

THE IRVINE JAMES FOUNDATION

EXECUTIVES

Pres-Ceo, Donald Howard
Director of Finance, Casey Budesilich
Director of Impact Assessment, Kim Howard
Senior Communications Officer, Leslie Payne
Senior Accountant, Michael Quach
Communications Officer, Mike Smith
Program Officer, April Yee
Senior Program Officer, Christina Garcia
Director of Finance, Eric Broque
Senior Program Officer, Jeanne Sakamoto
Leadership Awards Officer, Jessica Kaczmarek

LOCATIONS

HQ: THE IRVINE JAMES FOUNDATION
1 BUSH ST STE 800, SAN FRANCISCO, CA 941044494
Phone: 415 777-2244
Web: WWW.222SECOND.COM

HISTORICAL FINANCIALS

Company Type: Private

Income Statement				FYE: December 31
	ASSETS ($ mil.)	NET INCOME ($ mil.)	INCOME AS % OF ASSETS	EMPLOYEES
12/15	2,186	39	1.8%	36
12/14	1,611	44	2.7%	—
12/09	1,507	(58)	—	—
12/08	1,380	0	—	—
Annual Growth	6.8%	—	—	—

THE NEW YORK AND PRESBYTERIAN HOSPITAL

The New York and Presbyterian Hospital is a learned institution: The not-for-profit hospital is affiliated with both the Columbia University College of Physicians & Surgeons and the Weill Cornell Medical College of Cornell University. Known as NewYork-Presbyterian Hospital the organization includes two major medical centers Columbia University Medical Center and Weill Cornell Medical Center which conduct educational and research programs in partnership with the universities. The two facilities combined have about 2600 beds and offer specialized programs for burns digestive diseases pediatrics women's health and other conditions. NewYork-Presbyterian Hospital is part of the NewYork-Presbyterian Healthcare System.

Operations

Altogether the NewYork-Presbyterian Hospital campuses handle some 2 million patient visits each year (both on an inpatient and outpatient basis) including inpatient admissions and more than 310000 emergency room visits and about 15000 births. The facilities employ a total of more than 6500 physicians including residents and fellows. NewYork-Presbyterian Hospital provides more than $108 million in charity and community care services each year.

Geographic Reach

In addition to its flagship campuses NewYork-Presbyterian/Columbia and NewYork-Presbyterian/Weill Cornell NewYork-Presbyterian Hospital operates two small community hospitals in Manhattan — the Allen Hospital and the Lower Manhattan Hospital — and an inpatient mental health facility (the Westchester Division). The broader NewYork-Presbyterian Healthcare System operates facilities in other areas of New York as well as in New Jersey and Connecticut. The NewYork-Presbyterian Hospital/Columbia campus houses the Morgan Stanley Children's Hospital as well as other specialist units.

Sales and Marketing

Medicare and Medicaid recipients account for more than 60% of NewYork-Presbyterian Hospital's patients. Commercial managed care organizations and insurance firms as well as self-pay customers account for the rest.

Financial Performance

NewYork-Presbyterian Hospital's revenue in fiscal 2015 totaled $4.8 billion.

Strategy

As the health care landscape has become increasingly complex and competitive especially with changing regulations and the push to provide more integrated patient care NewYork-Presbyterian Hospital has made some major organizational changes. Chief among its goals is to provide a patient-centered model of care creating a system that can easily be accessed by its patient consumers. It recently established its Community and Population Health division which includes community programs and initiatives ambulatory care network sites and the management of its new Accountable Care Organization.

It has also expanded beyond its former base of Manhattan in order to provide a regional system of care. For example the system took ownership of former affiliate Brooklyn Methodist in early 2017 with the intention of investing in the hospital's development; the move falls in line with its strategy of providing integrated care for communities particularly in light of a number of recent hospital failures in the borough.

Mergers and Acquisitions

New York Methodist Hospital (now NewYork-Presbyterian Brooklyn Methodist Hospital) was added to the organization in early 2017. Brooklyn Methodist will gain funds for a new $400 million ambulatory care building as part of the new relationship.

Company Background

NewYork-Presbyterian Hospital was formed through the 1998 merger of the New York Hospital (founded in 1771) and the Presbyterian Hospital (founded in 1868). New York Hospital was known for advancing care in areas including women's health and surgery while the Presbyterian Hospital was known for its pediatric division and its cancer center.

EXECUTIVES

Vice President, Valerie Punnett
Svp Cfo And Treasurer, Phyllis R. Lantos
President And Ceo, Steven J. (Steve) Corwin
Svp And Chief Nursing Officer, Wilhelmina Manzano
Evp And Coo, Laura L. Forese
Svp And Chief Medical Officer, Richard S. Liebowitz
Cio, William Lee
Evp Chief Legal Officer And General Counsel, Maxine Frank
Finance Vice President, Ana Arroyo
Vice President Facilities Management, Joseph Lorino
Information Security Vice President, Howard Goldman
Vice President Compensation Benefits And Hris, Mary Falkowitz
Senior Vice President And Chief, Karen S Westervelt
Operations Vice President, Elizabeth Vega
Vice President Human Resources, Lorraine Orlando
Vice President Finance, William Farrell
Finance Vice President, Salvatore Logiudice
Senior Vice President And Chief Quality, Henry Ting
Vice President Of Human Resources, April Rodgers
Vice President Public Affairs, Karen Sodomick
Clinical Director, Gina A Rivera
Vice President Finance, Lugeion Y Carter
Vice President, Tanya Clark
Vice President Branding And Stakeholder Relations, Catherine Ryan
Vice President And Chief Administrative Officer, Kim Roldan-sanchez
Vp Operations And Engagement, Keren Rozenfeld
Vice Chairman, Frank A. Bennack, age 86
President Ceo And Trustee, Herbert Pardes, age 85
Medical Secretary, Matthew Swader

Treasurer, Karen Turi
Assistant Treasurer, Sedare Coradine
Surgical Secretary, Eileen Chavez

LOCATIONS

HQ: THE NEW YORK AND PRESBYTERIAN HOSPITAL
525 E 68TH ST, NEW YORK, NY 100654870
Phone: 212 746-5454

PRODUCTS/OPERATIONS

2016 Patient Mix

	% of total
Medicare Managed	9
Medicare FFS	22
Medicaid Managed	23
Medicaid FFS	7
Managed Care and Other	37
Self-Pay	1
Workers Comp	1
Total	**100**

Selected Services

Cancer
Children's Health
Digestive
Geriatrics
Heart
Mens Health
Neuroscience
Orthopedic
Psychiatry
Rehabilitation Medicine
Transplant
Vascular
Womens Health

COMPETITORS

Ascension Health
Beth Israel Medical
  Center
Bronx-Lebanon Hospital
Catholic Healthcare
  System
Continuum Health
  Partners
Lenox Hill Hospital
Lutheran HealthCare
Maimonides Medical
  Center

MediSys Health Network
Memorial
  Sloan-Kettering
Montefiore Medical
New York City Health
  and Hospitals
Northwell Health
Winthrop-University
  Hospital
Yale New Haven Health
  System

HISTORICAL FINANCIALS
Company Type: Private

Income Statement   FYE: December 31

	REVENUE ($ mil.)	NET INCOME ($ mil.)	NET PROFIT MARGIN	EMPLOYEES
12/18	8,484	527	6.2%	23,709
12/17	5,616	763	13.6%	—
12/16	4,935	496	10.1%	—
12/14	4,206	198	4.7%	—
Annual Growth	19.2%	27.8%	—	—

THE PENNSYLVANIA STATE UNIVERSITY

The Pennsylvania State University system is one of the largest state university systems in the US. Penn State has an enrollment of 100000 students; 15000 of them are graduate students. It offers 275 undergraduate and 200 graduate programs at about 25 campuses. The school's oldest and largest campus with about half of the system's undergraduate students is at University Park in central Pennsylvania. Other sites include the Penn State College of Medicine in Hershey Pennsylvania and the Dickinson School of Law in Carlisle Pennsylvania. Penn State contributes about $11.6 billion to the state's economy.

Financial Performance
Penn State had an annual operating budget in 2019-20 of $6.8 billion and an annual endowment of more than $2.5 billion. Its annual research funding is roughly $927 million of which $562 million comes from federal sources.

Strategy
Penn State is focused on fundraising and driving economic growth in the state through new programs tied to the university.

In 2019 the university's fundraising campaign A Greater Penn State for 21st Century Excellence surpassed its goal raising about $372 million in private donations. It marked the third consecutive year that the school raised more than $300 million in new commitments. Overall the campaign has raised about $1 billion toward its goal of $1.6 billion in 2021.

Through its Invent Penn State program the university has opened 21 innovation hubs across Pennsylvania that are designed to foster entrepreneurial and small business development.

Company Background
Chartered in 1855 to apply scientific principles to farming Penn State has conferred almost 800000 degrees since its founding.

The university's storied football program was hit in 2012 with a four year postseason ban the significant reduction of scholarships the vacating of 112 wins and a $60 million fine all stemming from the school's handling of the child molestation scandal involving former coach Jerry Sandusky. However in 2015 the NCAA reversed its decision on the vacating of wins restoring the late head coach Joe Paterno as the winningest coach in major college football history.

EXECUTIVES

Vice President For Student Affairs, Damon Sims
Svp Finance And Business And Treasurer, David J. Gray
Dean University Libraries And Scholarly Communications, Barbara I. Dewey
Dean Undergraduate Education, Robert N. Pangborn
Dean College Of Medicine, A. Craig Hillemeier
Dean College Of Arts And Architecture, Barbara O. Korner
Dean College Of Earth And Mineral Sciences, William E. Easterling
Dean College Of Education, David H. Monk
Dean College Of Health And Human Development, Ann C. (Nan) Crouter
Dean College Of The Liberal Arts, Susan Welch
Dean College Of Nursing, Paula Milone-Nuzzo
Dean Schreyer Honors College, Christian M. M. Brady
President, Eric J. Barron, age 68
Dean Smeal College Of Business, Charles H. Whiteman
Evp And Provost, Nicholas P. Jones
Chief Investment Officer, John Pomeroy
Dean Graduate School, Regina Vasilatos-Younken
Dean College Of Agricultural Sciences, Richard Roush
Dean College Of Communications, Marie Hardin
Dean College Of Engineering, Amr S. Elnashai
Vice President For Commonwealth Campuses, Madlyn Hanes
Department Head Learning And Performance Systems, Roy Clariana
Student Affairs Vice President Financial Officer, Rachael Diamond
Department Head, Mark Morrisson
Senior Vice President For Development And Alumni Relations, Tresa Ciprich
Vice President, Victor Sparrow
Vice President, Sandy Rothrock
Department Head Recreation Park And Tourism Management, Peter Newman
Assistant Vice President For Research And Industrial Partnerships, James Delattre
Vice President Development And Alumni Relations, Orrin Bundy
Department Head And Professor, Karen Thole
Chair Department Of Ophthlmlgy, David Quillen
Department Head, David Stensrud
Associate Vice President, Rachel Pell
Vice President, Katie Bridgens
Vice Chairman, Ira M. Lubert, age 69
Chairman, Keith E. Masser
Board Member, Jim Kustenbauter
Secretary, Hakan Can
Club Secretary, Jessica Baker
Board Member, Wilden Nuss
Board Member, Christine Igoe
Secretary, Bob Corman
Secretary Bookkeeper, Missie Estep
Board Member, Robert Martin
Board Member, Vickie Cunningham
Board Member, Ken Fohringer
Advisory Board Member, Tara Iona
Secretary [printing Services, Pamela Bechtel
Secretary [pulmonary Medicine, Joann Tucker
Auditors: DELOITTE & TOUCHE LLP PHILADE

LOCATIONS

HQ: THE PENNSYLVANIA STATE UNIVERSITY
201 OLD MAIN, UNIVERSITY PARK, PA 168021503
Phone: 814 865-4700

PRODUCTS/OPERATIONS

Selected Colleges
College of Agricultural Sciences
College of Arts and Architecture
Smeal College of Business
College of Communications
College of Earth and Mineral Sciences
College of Education
College of Engineering
College of Health and Human Development
College of Information Sciences and Technology
School of International Affairs
School of Law
College of the Liberal Arts
College of Medicine
School of Nursing
Eberly College of Science
Graduate School
Schreyer Honors College

Selected Campuses
Penn State Abington Penn State Altoona
Penn State Beaver
Penn State Berks
Penn State Brandywine
Penn State DuBois
Penn State Erie The Behrend College
Penn State Fayette The Eberly Campus
Penn State Greater Allegheny
Penn State Harrisburg
Penn State Hazleton
Penn State Lehigh Valley
Penn State Mont Alto
Penn State New Kensington
Penn State Schuylkill
Penn State Shenango
Penn State Wilkes-Barre
Penn State Worthington Scranton
Penn State York

HISTORICAL FINANCIALS

Company Type: Private

Income Statement   FYE: June 30

	REVENUE ($ mil.)	NET INCOME ($ mil.)	NET PROFIT MARGIN	EMPLOYEES
06/18	6,364	1,082	17.0%	44,000
06/17	6,059	636	10.5%	—
06/16	5,765	233	4.0%	—
06/15	5,293	290	5.5%	—
Annual Growth	6.3%	55.1%	—	—

THE PRIDDY FOUNDATION

EXECUTIVES

President, David Wolverton
Director, Debbie White

LOCATIONS

HQ: THE PRIDDY FOUNDATION
807 8TH ST STE 1010, WICHITA FALLS, TX
763013310
Phone: 940 723-8720
Web: WWW.PRIDDYFDN.ORG

HISTORICAL FINANCIALS

Company Type: Private

Income Statement   FYE: December 31

	REVENUE ($ mil.)	NET INCOME ($ mil.)	NET PROFIT MARGIN	EMPLOYEES
12/13	8,792	3	0.0%	4
12/12	3	(4)	—	—
12/10	32	28	86.7%	—
12/09	0	0	—	—
Annual Growth	—	—	—	—

THE SIMONS FOUNDATION INC

EXECUTIVES

Pres, Marilyn Simons
V Pres*, Mark Silver
Chb*, James H Simons
Cfo*, Marlow Kee
Coo*, Euan Robertson
Information Technology Manager, Chris Fleisch
Vice-President Administration, Marion Greenup
Director, Apoorva Mandavilli
Accounting Manager, Lawrence Bianco
Program Manager, Elizabeth Roy
Accountant, Jan Fernandez

LOCATIONS

HQ: THE SIMONS FOUNDATION INC
160 5TH AVE FL 7, NEW YORK, NY 100107037
Phone: 646 654-0066
Web: WWW.SIMONSFOUNDATION.ORG

HISTORICAL FINANCIALS

Company Type: Private

Income Statement   FYE: December 31

	ASSETS ($ mil.)	NET INCOME ($ mil.)	INCOME AS % OF ASSETS	EMPLOYEES
12/17	3,297	237	7.2%	350
12/16	3,027	(40)	—	—
12/15	2,632	(211)	—	—
12/14	2,359	(92)	—	—
Annual Growth	11.8%	—	—	—

THE TURNER CORPORATION

The Turner Corporation a subsidiary of German construction giant HOCHTIEF is the leading general building and construction management firm in the US (as ranked by Engineering News-Record) ahead of rivals Bechtel and Fluor. The firm operates primarily through subsidiary Turner Construction and has worked on notable projects such as Madison Square Garden the UN headquarters Yankee Stadium the Taipei 101 Tower and the 68000-seat open-air stadium for the San Francisco 49ers. Known for its large projects also offers services for midsized and smaller projects and provides interior construction and renovation services.

Operations

Turner works on more than 1500 projects in a year totaling $8 billion in volume. The group has divisions dedicated to serving the aviation health care biotechnology public assembly sports education justice and industrial sectors. Its homeland security group was established in order handle a growing demand for security systems and protection. The unit installed detection equipment in some 450 airports throughout the US. Turner Corporation also has an arm specializing in green building with a focus on Leadership in Energy and Environmental Design (LEED) -certified projects. Turner Green Building has more than 400 LEED projects and green projects either completed or in progress.

Turner Corporation has subsidiaries providing auxiliary operations. Turner's risk management department offers contract review project safety and claims handling. Turner Logistics handles procurement and supply chain management for projects and Turner Facilities Management Solutions offers ongoing operations services. Also the Turner School of Construction Management provides training for local subcontractors.

Geographic Reach

Dallas-based Turner Corporation boasts a network of offices across the US (with most in California and Ohio) and Canada (Vancouver and Toronto) with an global presence in 20 countries in Europe Africa East Asia India Latin America and the Caribbean.

Sales and Marketing

Turner works on variety of projects from several sectors. It's known for its work in the categories of healthcare education offices commercial properties cultural facilities sports facilities and hotels. The company is also a leader in the green building category.

Strategy

With the construction market rebounding from the economic downturn Turner is looking to high-growth markets in the US and overseas. As of early 2015 it was working on more than 1900 projects 80% of which were Education Commercial or Interior project-related. Some of these projects included the 17000 sq. ft- interior remodel for Salesforce's Vancouver office; the 325000 sq. ft-construction of the LEED-Certified RAND Corporation Headquarters in Santa Monica California; and the 25000-seat Charlotte Coliseum event arena for the City of Charlotte North Carolina.

The company has also been making moves to expand its business abroad in recent years. In 2012 for example Turner partnered with one of India's largest real estate developers Sahara Prime City Ltd. to form Sahara Turner which would lead the development and construction of multiple townships across the country with an approximate value of $2.5 billion by 2017. It also purchased a majority stake in Clark Builders Canada to capitalize on the country's growing construction market.

Turner often partners with fellow US-based HOCHTIEF subsidiary Flatiron which specializes in civil engineering. Examples of the teamwork are the expansions of airports in San Diego and Sacramento.

HISTORY

At the turn of the century an engineer and devout Quaker named Henry Chandlee Turner was convinced that a new type of steel-reinforced concrete (called the Ransome system) would change the construction industry. With this conviction and with the help of his partner D. H. Dixon Turner bought the rights to the technology for $25000 and in 1902 founded Turner Construction Company.

One of the company's early projects was building the stairways for New York's first subway stations. As the Ransome method proved to be successful Turner's reputation grew. Defense contracts during WWI raised Turner's take to $35 million in 1918.

Before the Depression Turner was building high-rises hotels and stadiums. During the economic crash that started in 1929 the company survived by building retail stores churches and public buildings a strategy it would employ successfully in later recessions.

Henry Turner retired in 1941. His brother Archer Turner managed the company during most of the war effort. As WWII raged more than 80% of the company's work was defense-related. Projects included building and managing a submarine base in Oak Ridge Tennessee during the development of the atomic bomb.

In 1947 Henry C. Turner Jr. the founder's son became president and within four years he had led the company to more than $100 million in sales. By the time he stepped down as chairman in 1970 the firm had built skyscrapers futuristic airports and such landmarks as Madison Square Garden and the United Nations Secretariat and Plaza in New York City. Turner went public in 1969.

Howard S. Turner (the final family member to head the business) led the company during the 1970s. The company extended its global presence opening offices in more countries including Iran Pakistan and the United Arab Emirates. Turner also developed construction management services.

In 1984 The Turner Corporation was formed as a holding company for the construction company and the subsidiaries created or acquired as a result of diversification. Property development was one of these activities but by 1987 Turner had begun to dispose of its real estate holdings. It did not move quickly enough however and when the real estate market crashed Turner was caught with a large portfolio.

As commercial projects slowed Turner sought work in more sectors including public works and amusement projects (aquariums arenas hospitals and universities). By 1994 these areas accounted for 70% of business. In 1993 as the building slump continued Turner began a cost-cutting plan which included laying off workers and closing offices. That year the company set up an $8.5 million restructuring reserve and as the real estate market eased into recovery Turner sold more of its real estate holdings.

In 1996 Turner won a contract to build a 10000-seat arena in Salt Lake City to be used for the 2002 Winter Olympics. In 1997 Turner contracted to renovate 811 schools and build two campuses in California's San Fernando Valley and in 1998 it was chosen to manage the construction of the Kansas City Motor Speedway.

Profits were recovering quickly. Nonetheless in 1999 the company agreed to be acquired by German construction giant HOCHTIEF in a $370 million deal that ended Turner's joint venture with Switzerland's Karl Steiner. The company also relocated its corporate headquarters to Dallas that year to take advantage of the construction boom in the US Southwest.

In 2000 Turner created three new business groups to serve the aviation pharmaceutical and sports sectors. By the next year Turner's sports group was working on 17 projects. In 2001 the company was a member of the construction team that responded to the September 11 devastation at Ground Zero in New York City.

The next year the company celebrated its 100th anniversary with an exhibit at the National Building Museum in Washington DC; the exhibit featured drawings and photos of some of Turner's notable projects during the past century. In 2003 Turner Construction acquired the assets of Tompkins Builders the third-largest construction company in the Washington DC area from former rival J.A. Jones Construction Co.

Turner Construction which celebrated its 100th anniversary in 2002 has ranked among the leading general builders in the US since WWI. For 80 of the 100 years the group had a Turner among its senior executives. Howard S. Turner was the last member of the family to serve in the company's senior ranks. The company's appointment of Peter Davoren in 2003 as president of Turner Construction reflected the rise of a new generation of leaders for the unit. Davoren was additionally appointed chairman and CEO in 2007.

Turner Construction announced in 2008 that it had signed the contract on its 15000th major project.

EXECUTIVES

Pres-Chb-Ceo, Peter J Davoren
Sr V Pres-Cfo & Treas, Karen Gould
V Pres-Finance & Asst Treas, Don Oshiro
Attrny, Richard L Smith Jr
Svp, Turner, Thomas B Gerlach Jr
Project Engineer, Bernardo Lomeli
Project Engineer, Blake Redmond
Office Manager, Lori Jackson
Senior Project Manager, Michael Weatherwax
Procurement Agent, Paul Dempsey
Information Manager, Shawn Daly
Auditors: DELOITTE & TOUCHE LLP DALLAS

LOCATIONS

HQ: THE TURNER CORPORATION
375 HUDSON ST RM 700, NEW YORK, NY 100143667
Phone: 212 229-6000
Web: WWW.TURNERCONSTRUCTION.COM

PRODUCTS/OPERATIONS

Selected Related Companies
E. E. Cruz (infrastructure)
Flatiron Construction Corp. (transportation construction civil engineering)
Clark Builders (51% Canada)

Selected Markets Served
Aviation
Commercial
Cultural and entertainment
Data center
Education
Government
Green building
Health care
Infrastructure
Industrial
Interiors
Pharmaceutical
Public Assembly
Religious
Research and development
Residential/hotel
Sports

Selected Services
Building information modeling
Building maintenance
Construction management
Design-build
Design-build/finance
Facilities management
General construction
Lean construction
Logistics
Medical planning and procurement
Preconstruction consulting
Program management
Project management

COMPETITORS

Balfour Beatty Construction	Hunt Construction
Bechtel	Imperial Construction Group
Clark Construction Group	Jacobs Engineering
Fluor	Parsons Corporation
Gilbane Building Company	Peter Kiewit Sons'
	Skanska
	Structure Tone

HISTORICAL FINANCIALS
Company Type: Private

Income Statement
FYE: December 31

	REVENUE ($ mil.)	NET INCOME ($ mil.)	NET PROFIT MARGIN	EMPLOYEES
12/15	10,524	108	1.0%	5,000
12/14	10,560	96	0.9%	—
12/13	9,522	80	0.8%	—
12/12	8,576	75	0.9%	—
Annual Growth	7.1%	12.9%	—	—

THE WHITING-TURNER CONTRACTING COMPANY

Whiting-Turner Contracting provides construction management general contracting and design/build services primarily for large commercial institutional and infrastructure projects conducted across the US. A key player in retail construction the employee-owned company also undertakes such projects as biotech cleanrooms theme parks historical restorations senior living residences educational facilities stadiums and corporate headquarters. Clients past and present include the US military AT&T General Motors and Texas A&M University. Whiting-Turner Contracting operates from more than 30 offices across the US.

Geographic Reach
The Baltimore-based company has offices in Arizona California Colorado Connecticut Delaware Florida Georgia Maryland Massachusetts Missouri Nevada New Jersey New York North Carolina Ohio Pennsylvania Texas Virginia and Washington DC.

Sales and Marketing
The contractor works on projects across a wide range of industries related to arts and entertainment education federal and military healthcare industrial office retail multi-family residential sports and fitness transportation and utilities among other fields.

Strategy
Whiting-Turner prefers to grow organically instead of making acquisitions. It has been steadily expanding by opening new offices in places such as California Texas and Virginia. The company in 2016 continued to rank among the Engineering News Record (ENR) top domestic general building contractors in the nation.

Some of the firm's recently awarded projects (as of mid-2016) include the Tropicana Pedestrian Bridge the Jacksonville Lung Bio Facility the Westowne Elementary School the Lexington Market the Costco Meat Production Plant the Sentara Norfolk General Hospital and the CoolSprings Galleria among others.

Whiting-Turner Contracting's past projects include the Joseph B. Whitehead Building at Emory University Vanderbilt Hall at Yale University projects at Universal Studios theme park and a vaccine facility at Chesapeake Biological Laboratories. Projects in the firm's hometown of Baltimore have included the city's convention center and the football stadium for the Baltimore Ravens. More recent projects include the Horseshoe Casino Cleveland University of Maryland Baltimore County (UMBC) Performing Arts & Humanities Naval Facilities Engineering Command (NAVFAC) Jacksonville Sentara Princess Anne Hospital Norwalk Community College Texas A&M University at Galveston Mary Moody Northen Student Center renovation Opry Mills the College of Business & Economics Vinson Hall Parking Garage a Coastal Studies Institute facility a Blue Diamond Growers building and a USPS Call Center.

Company Background
G.W.C. Whiting and LeBaron Turner classmates at MIT founded the company in 1909 to build sewer lines.

EXECUTIVES

Vp Richmond, Dani Niccolucci
Svp Allentown, Jack DaSilva

Division Vp Fort Lauderdale, Robert (Rob) Mitchell
Division Vp Delaware And Maryland, James (Jim) Martini
Svp District Of Columbia, Richard L. Vogel
Division Vp Pleasanton, Troy Caldwell
Svp Irvine, Len Cannatelli
Svp Baltimore, Gino J. Gemignani
Division Vp Dallas, Espen S. Brooks
Vp Bridgewater, Chris Martinson
Svp Atlanta, Keith Douglas
Vp, Daniel (Dan) Bauer
Vp Boston, Kevin Shields
Regional Manager Las Vegas, Paul Schmitt
Division Vp Chantilly, Kempton C. Haile
Vp Tampa, Brent A. Voyles
Vp Denver, Mark Faul
Vp San Diego, Steven Likins
Vp Orlando, Robert Minutoli
Division Vp Raleigh, Chris Carlson
Vp White Plains, David Brickley
Vp San Antonio, Daryl Steinbeck
Vp Norfolk, John Berotti
Senior Project Manager Sacramento, Jack Stackalis
Vp Cleveland, Jeff Maeder
Regional Manager Kansas City, Adam Eshelbrenner
Regional Manager Charlotte, Chris Woods
Regional Manager Houston, Michael Browning
President And Ceo, Timothy J. Regan, age 63
Vice President Worldwide Operations, Robert Ryan
Executive Vice President, Frank Palmer
Vice President, Vince Masciantonio
Vice President Mechanical Electrical Services, David Reitmeyer
Vice President Mission Critical Mechanical Electrical Services, Greg Botteon
Vice President Ashe Chc, Bob Moore
Vice President Finance And Operations, Nick Weiss
Leed Ap Banking Division C Vice President, Patricia Carper
Vice President, Karen Evans
Vice President, Irene Knott
Vice President, David McGinnis
Vice President, Damon Ellis
Vice President, Bruce Delawder
Vice President, Sam Abutaleb
Division Vice President, David Mallik
Vice President San Diego, Miguel Huerta
Vice President San Diego, Steve Likins
Vice President Information Technology, Joseph Dittmer
Division Vice President, Brian Ott
Vice President, Bill Wahl
Vice President, Jeffrey Baxter
Vice President, Craig Rayner
Vice President, Charles Konkolics
Vice President, Andrew Linden
Vice President, Maynard Grizzard
Vice President, Terry Powell
Senior Vice President, Stephen Lambertson
Senior Vice President, Ron Eisenberg
Vice President, Bill Whiting
Vice President, Thomas Monticup
Vice President, Pete Valianatos
Vice Chairman, Nick Bloch

LOCATIONS

HQ: THE WHITING-TURNER CONTRACTING COMPANY
300 E JOPPA RD STE 800, BALTIMORE, MD 212863047
Phone: 410 821-1100
Web: WWW.WHITING-TURNER.COM

Selected Locations
Maryland - Baltimore (Headquarters)
  California
California - Los Angeles
  California
  California
California - San Diego

Colorado -
Connecticut - New Haven
  Delaware -
District of Columbia
Florida - Ft. Lauderdale
  Florida -
  Florida -
  Georgia -
  Maryland -
  Massachuse
Missouri - Kansas City
Nevada - Las Vegas
  New Jersey
New York - White Plains
  North Caro
  North Caro
  Ohio - Cle
  Pennsylvan
  Texas - Da
  Texas - Ho
Texas - San Antonio
  Virginia -
  Virginia -
  Virginia -

PRODUCTS/OPERATIONS

Selected Services
Construction management
  Agency
  At-risk
Design/build
General contracting
Preconstruction

Selected Markets
Biotechnology and pharmaceutical
Cleanroom and high-technology
Education
Entertainment
Federal/military
Food/beverage distribution
Health care
Historical restoration
Industrial and manufacturing
Interiors
Life sciences
Lodging and hospitality
Mission critical facilities
Mixed use
Offices and headquarters
Parking garages
Restaurants
Retail
Senior living
Sports
Sustainable
Technology
  Microelectronics
  Nano
Theme parks
Utilities
Warehouse and distribution

COMPETITORS

Barton Malow	J.E. Dunn Construction
Bechtel	Group
Choate Construction	Jacobs Engineering
Clark Construction	Kitchell
Group	McCarthy Building
DPR Construction	Peter Kiewit Sons'
Fisher Development	Skanska
Fluor	Suffolk Construction
Gilbane	Swinerton
Hensel Phelps	Turner Corporation
Construction	Tutor Perini
Hoffman Corporation	Weitz

HISTORICAL FINANCIALS
Company Type: Private

Income Statement   FYE: December 31

	REVENUE ($ mil.)	NET INCOME ($ mil.)	NET PROFIT MARGIN	EMPLOYEES
12/16	5,522	91	1.6%	4,043
12/15	5,730	80	1.4%	—
12/14	6,347	75	1.2%	—
Annual Growth	(6.7%)	9.8%	—	—

THE WILLIAM PENN FOUNDATION

EXECUTIVES

President, Helen Davis Picher
Controller, Louise Foster
Member, David Haas
Director, Ronnie Bloom
Information Technology Manager, Edward Wagner
Director, Eugene Stone
Auditors: KPMG LLP

LOCATIONS

HQ: THE WILLIAM PENN FOUNDATION
2 LOGAN SQ FL 11, PHILADELPHIA, PA 191032763
Phone: 215 988-1830
Web: WWW.WILLIAMPENNFOUNDATION.ORG

HISTORICAL FINANCIALS
Company Type: Private

Income Statement   FYE: December 31

	ASSETS ($ mil.)	NET INCOME ($ mil.)	INCOME AS % OF ASSETS	EMPLOYEES
12/13	2,283	40	1.8%	27
12/00	1,170	(21)	—	—
12/99	1,203	129	10.7%	—
12/98	904	78	8.6%	—
Annual Growth	6.4%	(4.3%)	—	—

Thermo Fisher Scientific Inc

Thermo Fisher Scientific preps the laboratory for research analysis discovery or diagnostics. The company makes and distributes analytical instruments scientific equipment consumables and other laboratory supplies. Products range from chromatographs and spectrometers to Erlenmeyer flasks and fume hoods to gene-sequencers. Moving into other areas it offers testing and manufacturing of drugs including biologicals. Thermo Fisher also provides specialty diagnostic testing products as well as clinical analytical tools. The company tallies more than 400000 customers worldwide. Its key markets are pharmaceutical and biotech diagnostics and health care academic and government and industrial and applied research.

Operations

Thermo Fisher Scientific operates in four segments.

The Laboratory Product and Services unit which generates more than 40% of revenue provides basics for the lab. It sells equipment (refrigerators ovens filtration systems) consumables (slides dishes flasks) and chemicals (solvents and reagents). It also includes the Research and Safety Market Channel (catalogs and access to more than 1.5 million products) and Pharma Services (clinical trials).

Life Sciences Solutions about 25% of revenue provides reagents instruments and consumables used in biological and medical research drug discovery and drug production. The unit's businesses are Biosciences Genetic Sciences Clinical Next-Generation Sequencing and BioProduction.

Analytical Instruments more than 20% of revenue supplies instruments consumables software and services. Its businesses are Chromatography and Mass Spectrometry Chemical Analysis and Materials and Structural Analysis.

Specialty Diagnostics about 15% of revenue offers diagnostic test kits reagents culture media and instruments. Its businesses are Clinical Diagnostics ImmunoDiagnostics Anatomical Pathology Microbiology Transplant Diagnostics and the Healthcare Market Channel.

Products from those operational units are sold under Thermo Fisher's five main brands: Thermo Scientific Applied Biosystems Invitrogen Fisher Scientific and Unity Lab Services.

Thermo Fisher makes many of its products and it also works with third-party contractors for manufacturing.

Geographic Reach

About half of Massachusetts-based Thermo Fisher?s revenue comes from its US customers. China is the second biggest single-country market accounting for about 10% of revenue. Other key countries for Thermo Fisher are Japan the UK and Germany.

The country has office engineering laboratory and productions facilities in about 25 countries including Germany Japan UK and the US.

Sales and Marketing

Thermo Fisher?s sales channels include direct sales e-commerce distributors and catalogs. Its sales staff numbers about 12000. The company also offers supply chain management services.

Financial Performance

Thermo Fisher?s revenue has risen at a 9% annual rate from 2014-2018 lifted by the company?s penchant for acquisitions.

Sales in 2018 were $24.3 billion an increase of $3.4 billion from 2017 driven by stronger sales in each segment and geographic area as well as contributions from acquisitions. The Laboratory Products and Services had the strongest year-to-year growth at 25% from the research and safety and clinical trials businesses.

Thermo Fisher posted a profit of $2.9 billion in 2018 $700 million above the 2017 profit. The company?s operating margin improved a percentage point in 2018 compared to 15% in 2017.

Cash and equivalents in Thermo Fisher?s coffers totaled $2.1 billion in 2018 compared to $1.3 billion in 2017. In 2018 operations generated $4.5 billion while investing and financing activities used $1.2 billion and $2.2 billion respectively.

Thermo Fisher has about $19 billion in debt which could limit its ability to allocate capital to respond to changing economic and industry conditions. Interest expense rose to $667 million in 2018 from $592 million in 2017. The company can borrow up to $2.5 billion under a revolving credit facility.

Strategy

Thermo Fisher has been a deal-making machine spending more than $12 billion on acquisitions in the past three years. The company has expanded beyond supplying research labs with standard items like graduated cylinders and Bunsen burners to sophisticated equipment such as gene-sequencing and gene-editing tools. It also has added drug testing services including running clinical trials and drug manufacturing to its portfolio.

In 2018 Thermo Fisher beefed up its bioproduction and electron microscope offerings through acquisitions.

Thermo Fisher hasn't let its M&A carry the entire load for stocking the product pipeline. Its investment in R&D rose to more than $1 billion in 2018 from $888 million in 2017 and $750 million in 2016.

The company in 2018 offered new versions of products like the Orbitrap ID-X Tribrid and the Q Exactive UHMR mass spectrometry system for drug discovery and disease research. New in 2018 to the Torrent line of next-gen sequencers were the GeneStudio S5 Series benchtop instruments and the Invitrogen EVOS M5000 digital microscope for cell imaging.

Thermo Fisher has its sights set on expanding international sales particularly in China. Sales in China grew more than 20% in 2018 to account for 10% of the company's revenue. Overall about 20% of the company's revenue comes from emerging markets.

As Thermo Fisher tries to punch up sales and operations in China trade issues have become a hot topic. A trade war between the US and China could put a brake on the company's efforts to expand in China.

Mergers and Acquisitions

Thermo Fisher bought HighChem Ltd. a developer of mass spectrometry software based in Bratislava Slovakia in 2019. HighChem's software products are used to analyze complex data and identify small molecules in pharmaceutical and metabolomics research. The acquisition becomes part of Thermo Fisher's chromatography and mass spectrometry business in its Analytical Instruments segment.

In 2019 Thermo Fisher acquired Brammer Bio a viral vector manufacturer for gene and cell therapies for $1.7 billion. Brammer's technologies help Thermo Fisher?s biopharma customers deliver medicines based on gene therapies and gene-modified cell therapies.

Thermo Fisher bought Becton Dickinson's Advanced Bioprocessing business in 2018. The unit which has annual sales of $100 million provides peptones and services for biopharmaceutical applications. It will become part of Thermo Fisher's Life Sciences division.

In 2018 Thermo Fisher agreed to buy Gatan Inc. from Roper Technologies for $925 million in cash. However the companies canceled the deal in 2019 when they ran into trouble getting regulatory approval from UK authorities. Gatan makes instrumentation and software that improves the performance of electron microscopes.

In 2017 Thermo Fisher acquired Patheon NV which offers services from regulatory consulting to making drug ingredients and finished medicines including biological therapies for $7.2 billion. Patheon had about $1.9 billion in revenue in 2016.

Other 2017 deals included Finesse Solutions Inc. a developer of scalable control automation systems and software for bioproduction and Core Informatics a provider of a cloud-based platform for scientific data management.

Company Background

Predating the acquiring company Thermo Electron Fisher Scientific dates back to 1902 when 20-year-old Chester Fisher bought the stockroom of Pittsburgh Testing Laboratories (established 1884) and formed Scientific Materials Co. The company's earliest products supplied from Europe included simple tools such as microscopes balances and calorimeters. It published its first catalog in 1904.

When the outbreak of WWI disrupted supplies from Europe Scientific Materials established its own R&D and manufacturing facilities. It acquired Montreal-based Scientific Supplies in 1925 and the following year changed its name to Fisher Scientific Company. By 1935 Fisher had doubled its size adding glass-blowing operations and an instrument shop.

During the German occupation of Greece in WWII George Hatsopoulos part of a well-to-do family packed with politicians and engineering professors made radios for the Greek resistance. After the war he came to the US and became a professor of mechanical engineering at MIT. With a $50000 loan Hatsopoulos founded Thermo Electron in 1956 to identify emerging technology needs and create solutions for them.

In 2006 Thermo Electron merged with Fisher Scientific International in a stock-swap transaction valued at nearly $11 billion.

HISTORY

Predating the acquiring company Thermo Electron Fisher Scientific dates back to 1902 when 20-year-old Chester Fisher bought the stockroom of Pittsburgh Testing Laboratories (established 1884) and formed Scientific Materials Co. The company's earliest products supplied from Europe included simple tools such as microscopes balances and calorimeters. It published its first catalog in 1904.

When the outbreak of WWI disrupted supplies from Europe Scientific Materials established its own R&D and manufacturing facilities. It acquired Montreal-based Scientific Supplies in 1925 and the following year changed its name to Fisher Scientific Company. By 1935 Fisher had doubled its size adding glass-blowing operations and an instrument shop.

During the German occupation of Greece in WWII George Hatsopoulos part of a well-to-do family packed with politicians and engineering professors made radios for the Greek resistance. After the war he came to the US and became a professor of mechanical engineering at MIT. With a $50000 loan Hatsopoulos founded Thermo Electron in 1956 to identify emerging technology needs and create solutions for them.

In 2006 Thermo Electron merged with Fisher Scientific International in a stock-swap transaction valued at nearly $11 billion.

EXECUTIVES

Vice President Corporate Communications, Karen Kirkwood

Vp; President Life And Laboratory Sciences, Marc N. Casper, age 51, $1,407,471 total compensation

Evp And President Life Sciences Solutions, Mark P. Stevenson, age 56, $850,301 total compensation

Svp And Cfo, Stephen Williamson, age 53, $597,031 total compensation

Svp And Chief Commercial Officer, Thomas W. (Tom) Loewald, age 55, $610,115 total compensation

Svp And President Europe The Middle East And Africa (emea), Andrew J. (Andy) Thomson, age 54

Svp And President Asia-pacific And Emerging Markets, Syed A. Jafry

Svp And President Customer Channels, Gregory J. (Greg) Herrema

Svp; President Laboratory Products, Frederick M. (Fred) Lowery

Svp And Cio, Joseph C. (Joe) Beery

Svp And President Specialty Diagnostics, Patrick M. Durbin, age 53

Svp; President Analytical Instruments, Daniel P. (Dan) Shine, age 51

Vice President Marketing And Business Development, Mark Zacur

Vice President Sales And Marketing, Keith Whittlinger

Vice President Of Operations, Scot Hill

Senior Vice President And President Analytical Instruments, Dan Shine

Vice President Sales, Carlo Bertorelli

Vice President Global Operations, Bret Johnson

Vice President, Charles Lincoln

Vp Human Resources, Mark White

Executive Assistant; Office Of Steve Sheehan Vice President H, Shelly Goulet

Vice President Corporate Sales, Mark Covington

Vice President, Elizabeth Woo

National Sales Manager, Michael Bartlett

Vice President Information Technology, Krish Kumar

Vice President And Gm Growth Protection And Separation Products, Sung-Dae Hong

Vice President Of Engineering, Jerry Welch

Vice President Commercial And Corporate Finance, Marni Kirousis

Vice President Finance, Scott Spragale

Vice President Corporate Accounts, Susan Riley

Vice President World Wide Finance, Andy Long

Vice President Inside Sales, Kimberly Brown

Vice President Regional Sales, Greg Lauritzen

Vice President Tax Planning, Scott Egan

Vice President Of Sales, Samantha Wexler

Vice President Sales, Tami Janus

Vice President Information Technology, Liberino Martino

Rvp, Rick Curschman

National Sales Manager, Todd Baker

Global Vice President, Bill Hirschman

Vice President Human Resources Biosciences, Fiona Walker

Vice President Investor Relations And Treasurer, Ken Apicerno

Senior Vice President, Greg Herrema

Vp Tax And Treasurer, Anthony H Smith

Senior Vice President Sales, Peter Sandberg

Vice President Human Resources Laboratory Products Group, Joseph Baiunco

Vice President Sales, Michael Fuchs

Vice President Global Operations, Joseph Webb

Vice President Human Resources, Derek Mikuriya

Svp And President Life Sciences Solutions, Peter Silvester

Senior Vice President Corporate Strategy And Development, Shiraz Ladiwala

Vice President Information Technology, Manoj Prasad

Vice President E Business And Vertical Markets, Matthew Yoshikawa

Vice President Human Resources Chemical Analysis Division, Katie Ventura

Vice President Communications, Tyler Gronbach

Vice President Human Resources Cmd, Ivette Helal

Vice President Clinical Diagnostics Division, Christina Turner

Vice President And General Manager Latin America, Roberto Mendes

Vice President Operations, Mike Goloubef

Svp And President Pharma Services, Michel Lagarde

Vice President Corporate Global Security Please Note Our Office Address Has Changed, Lisa Quinn

Vice President And General Manager Cell Biology, Amy Butler

Vice President Engineering, Richard Duffy

Vice President, Steve Fox

Executive Vice President Global Marketing, Christopher Tama

Executive Assistant To Helge Bastian Vp And Gm Synthetic Biology And Ole Dahlberg Vp And Gm Sample Prep, Gabriela Ramirez

Vice President Information Technology Human Resources Services, Sean Murphy

Vice President Human Resources Nunc Gro, Anne Schwarz

Treasurer, Tony Smith

Auditors: PricewaterhouseCoopers LLP

LOCATIONS

HQ: Thermo Fisher Scientific Inc
168 Third Avenue, Waltham, MA 02451
Phone: 781 622-1000   **Fax:** 781 933-4476
Web: www.thermofisher.com

2017 Sales

	$ mil.	% of total
US	10,177	49
China	2,058	10
Other countries	8,683	41
Total	**20,918**	**100**

PRODUCTS/OPERATIONS

2018 Sales

	$ mil.	% of total
Laboratory Products & Services	10,035	39
Life Sciences Solutions	6,269	25
Analytical Instruments	5,469	21
Specialty Diagnostics	3,724	15
Adjustments	(1139)	-
Total	**24,358**	**100**

2018 Sales

	$ mil.	% of total
Products	18,868	77
Services	5,490	23
Total	**24,358**	**100**

Selected Services

Custom Services
Instrument & Qualification Services
Out-Licensing and OEM Sales
Most Popular Products
TaqMan Real-Time PCR Assays
Oligos Primers Probes & Nucleotides
Lipofectamine Reagents
TRIzol Reagents
SuperScript Reverse Transcriptase
eSolutions
eProcurement
Supply Center
Instrument Management

Selected Products

Analytical Instruments
Life Science Research consumables
Chemicals
Consumables
Custom Products
Diagnostics
Equipment
Software

Selected Brands

Thermo Scientific
Applied Biosystems
Invitrogen
Fisher Scientific
Unity Lab Services

COMPETITORS

Abbott Labs	IDEXX Labs
Agilent Technologies	Johnson & Johnson
Beckman Coulter	Life Technologies
Becton Dickinson	Corporation
Bio-Rad Labs	Mettler-Toledo
Danaher	PerkinElmer
Emerson Electric	Shimadzu
Harvard Bioscience	Waters Corp.
Hitachi	
Honeywell	
International	

HISTORICAL FINANCIALS

Company Type: Public

Income Statement

FYE: December 31

	REVENUE ($ mil.)	NET INCOME ($ mil.)	NET PROFIT MARGIN	EMPLOYEES
12/18	24,358	2,938	12.1%	70,000
12/17	20,918	2,225	10.6%	70,000
12/16	18,274	2,022	11.1%	55,000
12/15	16,965	1,975	11.6%	52,000
12/14	16,890	1,894	11.2%	51,000
Annual Growth	**9.6%**	**11.6%**	**—**	**8.2%**

2018 Year-End Financials

Debt ratio: 34.00%
Return on equity: 11.00%
Cash ($ mil.): 2,103
Current ratio: 2.00
Long-term debt ($ mil.): 17,719

No. of shares (mil.): 402
Dividends
  Yield: 0.0%
  Payout: 9.0%
Market value ($ mil.): 89,991

	STOCK PRICE ($) FY Close	P/E High/Low	PER SHARE ($) Earnings	Dividends	Book Value
12/18	224.00	34 26	7.00	1.00	69.00
12/17	190.00	36 25	6.00	1.00	63.00
12/16	141.00	31 24	5.00	1.00	55.00
12/15	142.00	29 24	5.00	1.00	53.00
12/14	125.00	27 23	5.00	1.00	51.00
Annual Growth	**15.6%**	**—**	**11.3%**	**3.2%**	**7.5%**

Thor Industries, Inc.

Thor Industries is a recreation vehicle builder that makes and sells a range of RVs from motor homes to travel trailers as well as related parts. Brands include Airstream and Dutchmen. RV manufacturing plants generally produce vehicles to dealer order; Thor's independent dealers dot the US and Canada catering to private purchasers and municipalities. The company has domestic facilities in Idaho Indiana Michigan Ohio and Oregon. The US is its largest market accounting for roughly 90% of total sales. Thor rolled out in 1980 when Wade Thompson and Peter Orthwein purchased Airstream's business.

Operations

Thor has two reportable segments: towable recreation vehicles (about three-quarters of revenue; travel trailers fifth wheels and motor homes) and motorized recreation vehicles (almost 30%).

Geographic Reach

Thor has facilities in the US (Idaho Indiana Michigan Ohio and Oregon) and Canada; the US accounts for nearly 90% of sales.

Sales and Marketing

Thor sells its products through a limited amount of consumer-oriented advertising for its recreation vehicles primarily in industry magazines product brochures direct mail advertising campaigns and on the Internet. The company markets its products through some 2200 independent dealerships carrying its products in the US and Canada. The company's dealer FreedomRoads accounts for 20% of its revenue.

Financial Performance

Thor has achieved unprecedented growth over the last few years. Revenues surged by 58% from $4.58 billion in 2016 to a record-smashing $7.2 billion in 2017. The historic growth was largely fueled by more than $1.8 billion in additional revenues from its Jayco acquisition. This acquisition helped spark sizable growth within its towable segments product lines including travel trailers and other (64%) and fifth wheels (40%).

The historic revenues for 2017 also caused Thor's profits to jump 46% from $257 million to $374 million and its operating cash flow to climb from $341 million to $419 million from 2016 to 2017.

Strategy

Thor's strategy is governed by strategic acquisitions and product introductions. RVs continue to be its mainstay line in terms of revenue as the RV industry enters its six year of recovery after the US recession according to the RV Industry Association.

In late 2016 Thor launched its Airstream Basecamp a sleek silver RV of aluminum that can be towed behind a truck. It contains one massive panoramic window solar power Italian cabinetry and a Bose Bluetooth speaker system.

Mergers and Acquisitions

Thor has achieved record-setting revenue growth over the years mainly through the use of acquisitions.

In 2019 Thor completed the acquisition of Germany-based RV manufacturer Erwin Hymer Group (EHG) for $2.45 billion making the combined company the world's largest RV manufacturer in the world with projected revenue of $11 billion.

HISTORY

Mergers and acquisitions specialist Wade Thompson and investment banker Peter Orthwein saw the potential of the RV market after buying Hi-Lo Trailer in 1977. Thor Industries was formed when they bought the troubled Airstream Trailers unit (founded in 1931) from Beatrice Foods in 1980. Named after the mythical Norse god of thunder and containing the first two letters of the founders' last names Thor Industries went public in 1984.

EXECUTIVES

President Four Winds, Jeffery L. (Jeff) Kime
Cfo, Colleen A. Zuhl, age 52, $500,000 total compensation
President Airstream, Robert H. Wheeler
President Keystone, Robert W. Martin, age 49, $750,000 total compensation
Vp Administration And Human Resources, Kenneth D. Julian, age 51, $500,000 total compensation
Director Information Technology, John Stukenborg
President Heartland, Christopher J. Hermon
President Keystone, Matthew T. Zimmerman
Svp General Counsel And Corporate Secretary, W. Todd Woelfer, age 51, $600,000 total compensation
Coo Kz, Aram Koltookian
President Crossroads Rv, Ryan Juday
Vice President Purchasing Thor Motor Coach, Sara Jessup
Vp Of Investor Relations, Mark Trinske
National Sales Manager, Darin Elswick
Executive Chairman, Peter B. Orthwein, age 73
Auditors: DELOITTE & TOUCHE LLP

LOCATIONS

HQ: Thor Industries, Inc.
  601 East Beardsley Ave., Elkhart, IN 46514-3305
Phone: 574 970-7460
Web: www.thorindustries.com

PRODUCTS/OPERATIONS

2017 Sales

	% of total
Recreation vehicles	
Towables	71
Motorized	27
Other	2
Intercompany elimination	-
Total	**100**

COMPETITORS

All American Group	Prevost Car
Collins Industries	Rexhall Industries
Featherlite	Skyline
Forest River	Supreme Industries
Motor Coach Industries	Winnebago

HISTORICAL FINANCIALS

Company Type: Public

Income Statement

FYE: July 31

	REVENUE ($ mil.)	NET INCOME ($ mil.)	NET PROFIT MARGIN	EMPLOYEES
07/19	7,865	133	1.7%	21,750
07/18	8,329	430	5.2%	17,500
07/17	7,247	374	5.2%	17,800
07/16	4,582	257	5.6%	14,900
07/15	4,007	199	5.0%	10,450
Annual Growth	18.4%	(9.6%)	—	20.1%

2019 Year-End Financials

Debt ratio: 34.00%	No. of shares (mil.): 55
Return on equity: 7.00%	Dividends
Cash ($ mil.): 426	Yield: 3.0%
Current ratio: 1.00	Payout: 64.0%
Long-term debt ($ mil.): 1,885	Market value ($ mil.): 3,282

	STOCK PRICE ($) FY Close	P/E High/Low	PER SHARE ($) Earnings	PER SHARE ($) Dividends	PER SHARE ($) Book Value
07/19	60.00	43 20	2.00	2.00	38.00
07/18	95.00	19 11	8.00	1.00	37.00
07/17	105.00	16 10	7.00	1.00	30.00
07/16	77.00	16 10	5.00	1.00	24.00
07/15	56.00	17 13	4.00	1.00	20.00
Annual Growth	1.6%	— —	(9.9%)	9.6%	16.8%

TJX Companies, Inc.

The TJX Companies operates more than 4300 stores worldwide under half a dozen retail brand names including the two largest off-price clothing retailers in the US: T.J. Maxx and Marshalls which operate 2300-plus stores nationwide. T.J. Maxx sells brand-name family apparel accessories shoes domestics giftware and jewelry at discount prices while Marshalls offers similar items plus a broader selection of shoes and menswear through more than 1100 stores. Its HomeGoods chain of 750-plus US stores focuses exclusively on home furnishings. It trades as T.K. Maxx in Europe with 600-plus stores in the UK Ireland Austria Germany Poland and the Netherlands. TJX keeps prices low by scooping up excess stock from manufacturers and department stores.

HISTORY

Cousins Stanley and Sumner Feldberg opened the first Zayre (Yiddish for "very good") store in Hyannis Massachusetts in 1956. During the next 15 years the number of stores grew to nearly 200.

Zayre purchased the Hit or Miss chain which sold upscale women's clothing at discounted prices in 1969. When the recession of the early 1970s hit superb results at Hit or Miss prompted Zayre to look for further opportunities in the off-price apparel marketplace. Zayre hired Ben Cammarata to create a new store concept and in March 1977 he opened the first T.J. Maxx in Auburn Massachusetts to market discounted upscale family clothing. Six years later Zayre formed the catalog retailer Chadwick's of Boston to sell Hit or Miss apparel by mail.

The company came to rely increasingly on its specialty operations to provide consistent sales and income as its flagship general merchandise stores often struggled. By 1983 the specialty chains were producing almost half of Zayre's sales.

In the second half of the 1980s Zayre's upscale (yet still off-priced) retailers' sales rose while its general merchandise stores (targeting lower-income customers) dropped. To keep its specialty stores unhindered by its flagging Zayre stores it established The TJX Companies as a public company in 1987. Zayre sold about 17% of its new subsidiary to the public with Cammarata as CEO.

Zayre sold its 400 general merchandise stores in 1988 to Ames for about $430 million in cash $140 million in Ames stock and a receivable note. The next year the company spun off its warehouse club operations as Waban (the warehouse component eventually became BJ's Wholesale) and merged with its subsidiary The TJX Companies taking that name.

TJX acquired Winners Apparel a Toronto-based five-store apparel chain in 1990. That year in the same month that Ames declared bankruptcy TJX established a $185 million reserve against losses it might suffer through its ownership of Ames' stock. Ames emerged from bankruptcy two years later and TJX was left with 4% of Ames' voting shares and over 100 empty Ames stores. TJX sold or leased most of them.

Also in 1992 TJX opened HomeGoods gift and houseware outlets in three of its remaining Ames stores and closed about 70 Hit or Miss stores. That year the company paid off about $128 million of its long-term debt. Encouraged by the success of its off-price operations in Canada in 1994 TJX opened five T.K. Maxx stores (similar to T.J. Maxx and Winners Apparel) in the UK.

A year later TJX paid $550 million for Melville's ailing chain of 450 Marshalls clothing stores. In addition the company sold its Hit or Miss apparel chain.

To help pay for Marshalls TJX sold the Chadwick's of Boston catalog in 1996 to retailer Brylane for about $325 million. Two years later the company opened two T.K. Maxx stores in the Netherlands and said it planned to have 75 stores in Europe in three years. It also debuted the A.J. Wright discount chain in New England in 1998.

In 1999 TJX elected Cammarata to the additional post of chairman and elevated Ted English to president and COO. In 2000 Cammarata relinquished his CEO post to English but remained chairman. Citing the successes of its new stores the company announced in early 2001 it expected to increase its total number of stores 12% annually for the next several years. Also that year the company shuttered its T.K. Maxx stores in the Netherlands. Seven TJX employees perished on September 11 2001 when their flight bound for Los Angeles crashed into the World Trade Center during the worst terrorist attack in US history.

In 2002 the company opened HomeSense a new Canadian home furnishings chain fashioned after its US counterpart HomeGoods. In December 2003 TJX finalized its acquisition of Bob's Stores a Connecticut-based discount retail chain with 31 stores in the Northeast.

In September 2005 English resigned abruptly after five years as the company's CEO. In October the company closed down its tjmaxx.com and homegoods.com Web sites citing poor sales.

In March 2006 TJX cut about 250 jobs in its corporate and divisional offices and reduced the salaries of a dozen senior executives including its chairman and acting CEO and its president by 10% in an effort to increase profits.

A year after the abrupt resignation of CEO Edmond English in September 2005 TJX named company president Carol Meyrowitz to the post effective January 2007. (Cammarata had been acting CEO of the company in the interim.) Also in January 34 A.J. Wright stores were closed.

In November 2007 TJX reached a settlement with Visa and Fifth Third Bancorp stemming from a breach of its computer systems in which customer data was stolen. Under the terms of the agreement TJX will fund up to $40.9 million for recovery payments for US Visa issuers. Also in the fall of 2007 the retailer's European arm T.K. Maxx entered the German market with five stores there.

In 2008 TJX sold money-losing Bob's Stores which has about 35 locations in the Northeast to the private equity firms Versa Capital Management and Crystal Capital for an undisclosed amount.

EXECUTIVES

President Ceo And Director, Ernie Herrman, age 58, $1,525,001 total compensation
Sevp And Group President, Richard Sherr, age 61, $921,232 total compensation
Sevp Finance And Cfo, Scott Goldenberg, age 65, $813,462 total compensation
Svp Corporate Controller, Ken Canestrari, age 58
President The Marmaxx Group, Michael MacMillan, age 62, $1,052,309 total compensation
Executive Vice President Merchandise Coaching And Development, Louis Luciano
Executive Vice President Secretary And General Counsel, Alicia Kelly
Vice President Merchandising, Joseph Domenick
Assistant Vice President Corporate Internal Audit, John Caban
Avp Total Rewards, Cindy Hillman
Assistant Vice President E Marketing, Melanie Campbell
Vice President Tax Audits Director, Joan Korzec-Brown
Senior Vice President And General Counsel, Beverly Kennedy
Divisional Vp, Mark Azar
Senior Vice President And Chief Technology Officer, John Reichelt
Vice President Merchandising, Paula Bingham
Assistant Vice President Loss Prevention, Steve Forgette
Assistant Vice President Merchandise Planning, Doreen Keville
Senior Vice President Store Operations A J Wright, Mike McGrath
Assistant Vice President, Brett Amosson
Assistant Vice President Director Store Operations, Kim Smith
Assistant Vice President Loss Prevention, Mike Marquis
Assistant Vice President Merchandise Planning, Debra Duprez
Vice President Gmm Ecommerce Merchandising And Planning, Mark Deoliveira
Vice President, Timothy Lippold
Assistant Vice President Merchandise Planning, Rose Riggieri
Vice President General Merchandise Manager, Shade Jennifer
Regional Vice President, David Wiese

Assistant Vice President Merchandise Manager Sheets Deco, Corina Roth
Vice President Human Resources, Kelli McNary
Assistant Vice President Global Talent Development, Sharon Hazard
Vice President Merchandising, Brian Francione
Dvp Merchandise Manager, Jeff Nesbit
Assistant Vice President Store Planning Design And Fixture Director, Cindy Buffi
Dvp Merchandise Manager, Paul Bibbo
Vice President Finance, Peter Daniels
Assistant Vice President Corporate Benefits Director, Lauren Mullin
Vice President Data Centers, George Stephatos
Vp Ecommerce Labs, Enzo Micali
Vice President End User Services, Sandra Rossetsky
Divisional Vice President Merchandise Manager, Kyle Garry
Vice President Gmm Mens, Ken Shuler
Assistant Vice President Loss Prevention, Kate Hughes
Assistant Vice President Merchandise Planning, Nancy Atchue
Assistant Vice President Loss Prevention, Kevin Taparausky
Assistant Vice President Store Planning, Jon Nelson
Assistant Vice President, Ken Downey
Vice President, Anand Devendran
Senior Vice President Total Rewards, Julio Mantilla
Assistant Vice President Workplace Services Director, Kathleen LaShoto
Divisional Vice President Market Manager, Narges Castillo
Avp Stores Business Solutions, Christina Oster
Assistant Vice President Director Loss Prevention, Frederick L Mullen
Vice President Of Merchandising, Tim Miner
Senior Vice President Gmm And Director Ladies Sportswear, Nancy Carpenter
Regional Vice President, Guy Reda
Assistant Vice President, Joanne Wolfe
Svp And Chief Logistics Officer, John Bauer
Vice President Office Services Director, Mike Brogan
Assistant Vice President, Jeff Botte
Divisional Vice President Merchandise Manager Ecommerce, Roland Webber
Assistant Vice President Talent Acquisition, Doug Corcoran
Assistant Vice President, Pam Richards
Dvp Dmm E Commerce, Inna Leipzig
Vp Chief Financial Officer Of Tjx Digital U.s., Mark Lussier
Divisional Vice President Merchandise Manager Ecommerce, Lisa Pena
Vice President, David Federico
Vice President Store Systems Director, Martin Whitmore
Assistant Vice President, Tom Sgammato
Assistant Vice President Corporate Communications, Colleen Beauregard
Vice President, Todd Landis
Assistant Vice President Human Resources Marshalls, Steve Dellazoppa
Sr Vice President, Peter Benjamin
Assistant Vice President Construction, John Cox
Senior Vice President, Richard Peck
Assistant Vice President, Matthew Garvey
Vice President, Cheryl Oldfield
Senior Vice President, Marc Boesch
Assistant Vice President Human Resources, Michelle Okimoto
Vice President, Charlotte Arnold
Vice President The Marmaxx Group, Celine Lewis
Vice President Of Planning And Allocation, Nancy Mendis
Vice President The Marmaxx Group, Manuela Millington

Vice President Human Resources Business Partner, Sharon Simons
Assistant Vice President Store Operations Home Goods, Mike Farrell
Vice President Marketing Director, Katherine Beede
Assistant Vice President Loss Prevention, Kevin Kurtz
Executive Vice President And Chro, Amy Fardella
Avp, Kevin Tubridy
Vice President Of Global Talent Development, Carolyn Fischer
Avp Supply Chain Business Services, Richard Oppenheimer
Senior Vice President Corporate Human Resources Business Partner, Nancy Maher
Assistant Vice President, Genevieve Barrett
Associate Vice President, Keith Schantz
Avp Merchandise Operations, Susan Arapoff
Vp Of It Finance, Scott Tomsik
Vice President Director Of Real Estate, Denise Downing
Vice President End User Services, Sandy Rossetsky
Vice President, Beverly Edgehill
Vice President, Scott Garozzo
Assistant Vice President Retirement Benefits Director, Colin Hamilton
Vice President, Tom Hayes
Vice President Human Resources Operations, Daniel Finacchio
Assistant Vice President Property Tax Director, Bradford Dunn
National Vice President Of Financial Affairs, Gautam Madineedi
Dvp Merchandise Manager, Jill Rodgers
Senior Vice President Merchandise Planning Allocation And Analysis, Mark Heitin
Regional Vice President Administrative Assistant, Steven Lipasek
Assistant Vice President And Director Store Operations Engineering, Antoinette Wallace
Senior Vice President Transportation And Logistics, Jeff Tawney
Assistant Vice President And Director Corporate Communications, Erika Tower
Rvp, Sheri Gaal
Avp Director Of Human Resources, Michael Doto
Assistant Vice President Marketing Services, Stephanie Games
Avp Organizational Development, Cindy Cercone
Associate Vice President Product Development, Carla Bossone
Vice President Financial Accounting, Mike Russo
Senior Vice President Infrasturcutre And Operations, Larry Foster
Assistant Vice President, Glen Brenner
Avp Ctc Data Center, Jeremy Anderson
Avp Network Operations, Tim Kearney
Divisional Vice President Merchandise Manager, Jennifer Shade
Vice President Transportation Network Operations, Carol Beaumont
Divisional Vice President Market Manager, Lindsay Snell
Senior Regional Vice President, Chris Jones
Avp Supply Chain It Solution Delivery, Adam Kaufman
Vice President Fulfillment Operations, Craig O'connor
Regional Vice President, Terrell Davis
Vice President Human Resources, Laura Johnson
Vice President Product Development, Chris Bourget
Vice President Global Sourcing Procurement Us, Brian Richard
Assistant Vice President Director, Patrick Flavin
Vice President, Lisa A Schwartz
Area Vice President Merchandising Tk Maxx, Alicia Garfield
Vice President Field Human Resources, Deborah Felix

Vice President, Sue Flynn
Avp Of Business Development, Julie Henly
Chairman, Carol M. Meyrowitz, age 65
Assistant Treasurer, Nancy Hendrickson
Auditors: PricewaterhouseCoopers LLP

LOCATIONS

HQ: TJX Companies, Inc.
  770 Cochituate Road, Framingham, MA 01701
Phone: 508 390-1000   **Fax:** 508 390-2091
Web: www.tjx.com

2019 Stores

	No.
US	
T.J. Maxx	1,252
Marshalls	1,091
HomeGoods	749
Sierra Trading Post	35
HomeSense	16
Canada	
Winners	271
HomeSense	125
Marshalls	88
Europe	
T.K. Maxx	567
HomeSense	68
Australia	
T.K. Maxx	44
Total	**4,306**

2019 Sales

	$ mil.	% of total
US		
Marmaxx	24,058	62
HomeGoods	5,787	15
TJX Canada	3,870	10
TJX International	5,258	13
Total	**38,972**	**100**

PRODUCTS/OPERATIONS

Selected Stores

HomeGoods (off-price home fashion chain)
HomeSense (off-price home fashion chain Canada and UK)
Marshalls (off-price retailer of apparel shoes home fashions)
Marshalls Mega-Stores (combination Marshalls and HomeGoods stores)
Sierra Trading Post (off-price online retailer of outdoor gear and apparel)
T.J. Maxx (off-price retailer of apparel shoes home fashions)
T.J. Maxx 'N More (combination T.J. Maxx and HomeGoods stores)
T.K. Maxx (off-price retailer of apparel shoes home fashions Europe)
Winners Apparel (off-price family apparel chain Canada)

2019 Sales

	% of total
Clothing & footwear	52
Home fashions	33
Jewelry & accessories	15
Total	**100**

COMPETITORS

ASDA	Kmart
Amazon.com	Kohl's
Bed Bath & Beyond	Liberty Interactive
Belk	Macy's
Big Lots	Primark
Burlington Coat Factory	Ross Stores
	Sears
Caleres	Sports Authority
Cato	Stage Stores
Charming Shoppes	Stein Mart
Children's Place	Tailored Brands
Claire's Stores	Target Corporation
Dillard's	Tesco
Dollar General	The Gap
Eddie Bauer LLC	Tuesday Morning
Foot Locker	Corporation
Inditex	Wal-Mart

HISTORICAL FINANCIALS

Company Type: Public

Income Statement
FYE: February 2

	REVENUE ($ mil.)	NET INCOME ($ mil.)	NET PROFIT MARGIN	EMPLOYEES
02/19	38,973	3,060	7.9%	270,000
02/18*	35,865	2,608	7.3%	249,000
01/17	33,184	2,298	6.9%	235,000
01/16	30,945	2,278	7.4%	216,000
01/15	29,078	2,215	7.6%	198,000
Annual Growth	7.6%	8.4%	—	8.1%

*Fiscal year change

2019 Year-End Financials

Debt ratio: 17.00%
Return on equity: 60.00%
Cash ($ mil.): 3,030
Current ratio: 2.00
Long-term debt ($ mil.): 2,477

No. of shares (mil.): 1,217
Dividends
Yield: 0.0%
Payout: 31.0%
Market value ($ mil.): 59,520

	STOCK PRICE ($) FY Close	P/E High/Low	PER SHARE ($) Earnings	Dividends	Book Value
02/19	49.00	45 17	2.00	1.00	4.00
02/18*	78.00	39 33	2.00	1.00	4.00
01/17	74.00	47 39	2.00	0.00	3.00
01/16	71.00	45 38	2.00	0.00	3.00
01/15	66.00	43 33	2.00	0.00	3.00
Annual Growth	(7.2%)	— —	11.5%	22.0%	7.4%

*Fiscal year change

Toll Brothers Inc.

Toll Brothers builds luxury homes in the US targeted at move-up empty nester and second-home buyers. Its single-family detached houses and condominium apartments sell for an average base price of over $850000. The company also develops communities for active adults and operates country club communities. Subsidiaries offer related services and products including architectural and engineering services title and mortgage services and landscaping. Toll Brothers has operations in about 50 markets in some 20 states. Traditionally a suburban developer Toll Brothers has branched out to mid- and high-rise condominiums in urban markets and luxury rentals.

Operations

Toll Brothers' two segments are Traditional Home Building and City Living. The former accounts for almost all company revenue at around 95% of sales.

The company's traditional homes sell at prices ranging from around $225000 to about $3 million and at an average of around $850000. Its City Living homes sold in more expensive urban areas are priced between $220000 and about $6.3 million and sell for an average of $1.9 million.

The firm operates a slew of subsidiaries that handle architecture engineering mortgage title land development and land sale golf course development and management home security and landscaping. It also has its own lumber distribution house component assembly and manufacturing operations.

The company also develops rental apartments?mainly via joint ventures. The company and its partners have controlling interests in more than 40 land parcels for rental projects totaling about 15400 units that it runs or will run under the

brand names Toll Brothers Apartment Living and Toll Brothers Campus Living.

Furthermore Toll Brothers' Gibraltar Capital and Asset Management subsidiary offers builders and developers land banking and venture capital and owns foreclosed real estate through joint ventures.

Geographic Reach

Horsham Pennsylvania-based Toll Brother's largest market California generates around 30% of sales; it also builds houses in the West (Arizona Colorado Idaho Nevada Washington; about 20% of sales) Mid-Atlantic (Delaware Maryland Pennsylvania Virginia; around 15%) South (Florida North Carolina Texas; about 15%) and North (Connecticut Illinois Massachusetts Michigan New Jersey New York; about 15%) regions of the US. It has development operations in the Salt Lake City Utah and Portland Oregon.

Toll Brothers' City Living builds in urban markets including Los Angeles California; Bethesda Maryland; Hoboken and Jersey City New Jersey; Manhattan and Brooklyn New York; Philadelphia Pennsylvania; and Seattle Washington. Its for-rent apartments are in the Boston-Washington DC corridor; Los Angeles San Francisco San Diego and Fremont California; Atlanta Georgia; Dallas Texas; and Phoenix Arizona.

Sales and Marketing

The homebuilder's sales and marketing strategy is centered on cultivating its reputation as a builder of high-quality luxury living spaces by focusing on promotion of its "Estate" and "Executive" home lines which it believes drives demand for all its product lines. It includes attractive décor in its less expensive homes to enhance its marketing and sales efforts.

Toll Brothers advertises its homes online through www.TollBrothers.com and via its own sales office and personnel. It also markets through newspapers local publications and billboards.

Advertising costs were $28.5 million $26.1 million and $23.1 million for fiscal years 2018 2017 and 2016 respectively.

Financial Performance

Toll Brothers has undergone solid growth of more than 80% over the last five years driven particularly by its performance in fiscal 2016 and 2018 when sales of higher-priced homes and prices increased?especially in California (its largest market). The company's net income and cash followed a similar trend?each has more than doubled since 2014; Toll Brothers also managed to control its long-term debt which expanded only about 10% in that time.

The homebuilder's revenue added 23% to $7.1 billion in 2018 while its net income jumped 40% to $748.2 million.

Toll Brothers added $469.4 million to its cash in 2018 to end the year with $1.2 billion. Operations contributed $602.4 million and investments provided $81.3 million?mostly from return of investments in its land development and banking home building rental property and venture capital joint ventures. The company used $214.3 million in its financing activities primarily for principle loan payments and treasury stock purchases.

Strategy

A major component of Toll Brothers' strategy is to reduce its risk exposure by maintaining low leverage high liquidity lengthy debt maturities. To that end the company is reducing the proportion of land it controls directly in favor of control though options. In 2016 30% of its home sites were optioned; in 2018 that percentage increased to 40%. It also forms joint equity ventures to develop its larger urban condominium properties some of its multi-year thousand-plus planned communities and its rentals. For example in early 2019 the company formed partnerships to develop apartment communities with Daiwa House Group in Frisco Texas; The Davis Companies in Atlanta Georgia; and J.P. Morgan Asset Management in Harrison New York.

Geographic diversification is another key to Toll Brothers' strategy. In addition to land acquisitions the company acquired other homebuilders in Seattle Washington in 2017; California in 2014; and Boise Idaho in 2016. From 2011 to 2018 the company increased the share of revenue it generated in western states (Arizona California Colorado Idaho Nevada Texas and Washington) from 29% to 58%.

The company has developed an internal value analysis system to compare its homes with other builders' homes in its regional markets and determine prices based features including house and community amenities location and reputation.

Company Background

Bob and Bruce Toll founded Toll Brothers in 1967 in southeastern Pennsylvania. In 1982 the company built its first home in the neighboring state of New Jersey. The company went public in 1986 with a listing on the New York Stock Exchange.

HISTORY

Homebuilder Albert Toll's two sons Robert and Bruce Toll founded their own business in 1967. The duo began by building starter homes in the Philadelphia suburbs of Elkins Park and Yardley. As Philadelphia's population began to sprawl beyond these older suburban areas the company grew and in 1982 it moved beyond Pennsylvania to build houses in New Jersey. The young firm also began to distinguish itself by catering to up-market customers.

Toll Brothers Inc. went public in 1986 and later expanded around New York City north to the Boston area and south to the suburbs of Washington DC. The firm survived the late 1980s real estate recession in the Northeast because unlike many builders it did not overextend itself.

Until the 1990s Toll Brothers operated primarily in the northeastern US but it expanded as the housing market began an upward cycle. It entered California and North Carolina in 1994 and Arizona Florida and Texas in 1995. Toll Brothers began work in Nashville Tennessee and Las Vegas in 1997. The next year the company entered the active adult market building its first two age-qualified communities in New Jersey. Also in 1998 the company joined other investors including the Pennsylvania State Employees Retirement System and formed the Toll Brothers Realty Trust to acquire and develop commercial property.

In 1999 Toll Brothers acquired Silverman Companies a leading homebuilder and developer of luxury apartments with more than 80 years of experience in Detroit. The company also began building homes in the Chicago San Diego and San Francisco markets that year and it teamed with Marriott International to begin developing an assisted-living community in Reston Virginia.

It also set up its cable and broadband subsidiary Advanced Broadband that year to provide its communities with Internet connectivity. Toll Brothers sold those operations to Comcast in 2007.

The company began operating in Rhode Island and New Hampshire in 2000 and the next year entered Colorado. In 2002 the company entered South Carolina in the Hilton Head area to develop Hampton Hall a luxury country club community with a master-planned golf course.

In 2003 Toll Brothers acquired Jacksonville Florida-based homebuilder Richard R. Dostie Inc. for an undisclosed cash amount. The company also expanded its luxury urban in-fill market operations by acquiring The Manhattan Building Company a developer of luxury mid- and high-rise con-

dos on northern New Jersey's waterfront. The next year Toll Brothers and Pinnacle Ltd. jointly began development of an 832-home luxury condominium community (Maxwell Place on the Hudson) on the waterfront of Hoboken New Jersey overlooking Manhattan.

For its 12th consecutive year Toll Brothers produced record fiscal-year-end results for earnings revenues contracts and backlog in 2004. The company's net income grew 57% over the previous year's earnings and it operated in more communities and offered more product lines than it had in previous years. Another record was set in 2005; revenue from home sales increased 50% and net income increased 97%. That year Toll Brothers began operations in West Virginia but stopped selling homes in Ohio.

Toll correctly predicted an industry slowdown in 2006 and for both 2006 and 2007 the number of homes it built dropped from 8600 to around 6700. As numbers continued to sink it sold land holdings reduced its backlog and divested its cable Internet and home security businesses.

CEO and co-founder Robert Toll stepped down as CEO in 2010. He was succeeded by Douglas Yearley.

EXECUTIVES

Svp Operations, Richard T. (Rick) Hartman, age 61, $1,000,000 total compensation
Svp Operations, Douglas C. (Doug) Yearley, age 58, $1,000,000 total compensation
Assistant Cfo, Martin P. (Marty) Connor, age 54, $970,833 total compensation
Svp And Chief Marketing Officer, Kira Sterling
Vice President Land Acquisition Land D, Edward Oliu
Vice President, Donald Barnes
Vice President Commercial Development, Richard Keyser
Central Florida Division Vice President, Andre Vidrine
Vice President Central Florida Division, Brock Fanning
Vice President Finance, Andy Lawhorn
Executive Vice President Ld, Joe Palka
Division Vice President, Kevin Rosinski
Division Vice President, Joshua M Rubinich
Assistant Vice President Benefits, Barbara Colaizzi
Vice President Of Land Acquistions, David Hutcheson
Svp And Chief Information Officer, John Critikos
Vice President And Regional Controller, Richard Hoelzle
Vice President, Kathy Gaffney
Senior Vice President, Brian Thierrin
Vp, Mike Klein
Vice President, Brad Hare
Divison Assistant Vice President, Matt Markovich
Senior Vice President, Gregory Lagreca
Assistant Vice President Land Development, Greg Leygraaf
Regional Ld Vice President, Terry Hodge
Senior Vice President Finance International Development And Ir, Frederick Cooper
Division Vice President, Brian Wulfestieg
Division Vice President, Daniel Wright
Division Vice President, Craig Cherry
Division Vice President, John Peck
Assistant Vice President, Reggie Carveth
Division Assistant Vice President, Ch Brittingham
Assistant Vice President And Counsel, Marsha Martin
Vice President Of Process Improvement Hr, Jay Lehman
Assistant Vice President Purchasing, Ron Zega
Division Assistant Vice President, Dan Walton
Assistant Vice President, Steve Savage

Senior Vice President And Controller, Kevin Mcmaster
Assistant Vice President, Glenn Phillips
Division Assistant Vice President, Christopher Kopitsky
Division President Home Building Operations, David Bauer
Vice President Marketing, Christine Sciarrolta
Vice President Land Entitlement, Aaron Hollingbery
Vice President, David Shea
Chro And Senior Vice President Hr, Joy Roman
Division Assistant Vice President, Scott Boegner
Division Vice President, Scott Tressler
Chairman, Robert I. Toll, age 77
Board Member, Richard Braemer
Board Member, Paul Shapiro
Board Member, John Mclean
Auditors: Ernst & Young LLP

LOCATIONS

HQ: Toll Brothers Inc.
250 Gibraltar Road, Horsham, PA 19044
Phone: 215 938-8000   **Fax:** 215 938-8023
Web: www.tollbrothers.com

2018 Number of Delivered Homes by Region

	No.
Mid-Atlantic	1,800
West	2,130
North	1,453
South	1,391
California	1,322
City Living	169
Total	**8,265**

2018 Sales

	$ mil.	% of total
Traditional Home Building		
California	2,209	31
West	1,451	20
Mid-Atlantic	1,141	16
South	1,045	15
North	976	14
City Living	321	4
Total	**7,143**	**100**

PRODUCTS/OPERATIONS

Selected Operations
Architectural design services
Golf course development and operation
Engineering services
House component assembly
Land development
Landscape services
Lumber distribution
Mortgage lending
Title insurance

COMPETITORS

D.R. Horton	Lennar
David Weekley Homes	PulteGroup
Hovnanian Enterprises	William Lyon Homes
KB Home	

HISTORICAL FINANCIALS

Company Type: Public

Income Statement				FYE: October 31
	REVENUE ($ mil.)	NET INCOME ($ mil.)	NET PROFIT MARGIN	EMPLOYEES
10/19	7,224	590	8.2%	5,100
10/18	7,143	748	10.5%	4,900
10/17	5,815	535	9.2%	4,500
10/16	5,170	382	7.4%	4,200
10/15	4,171	363	8.7%	3,900
Annual Growth	14.7%	12.9%	—	6.9%

Debt ratio: 36.00% No. of shares (mil.): 141
Return on equity: 12.00% Dividends
Cash ($ mil.): 1,286 Yield: 1.0%
Current ratio: 5.00 Payout: 9.0%
Long-term debt ($ mil.): 3,921 Market value ($ mil.): 5,605

	STOCK PRICE ($) FY Close	P/E High/Low		PER SHARE ($) Earnings	Dividends	Book Value
10/19	40.00	10	7	4.00	0.00	36.00
10/18	34.00	11	6	5.00	0.00	33.00
10/17	46.00	14	8	3.00	0.00	29.00
10/16	27.00	17	11	2.00	0.00	26.00
10/15	36.00	20	15	2.00	0.00	24.00
Annual Growth	2.5%	—	—	19.6%	—	10.5%

Tompkins Financial Corp

Tompkins Financial is the holding company for Tompkins Trust Company The Bank of Castile and Mahopac Bank which offer traditional banking services through some 45 offices in upstate New York. It also owns the 20-branch Pennsylvania-based VIST Bank. Funds from deposit products such as checking savings and money market accounts are mainly used to originate real estate loans and mortgages as well as commercial and consumer loans. Tompkins also offers trust and estate financial and tax planning and investment management services through Tompkins Financial Advisors. Tompkins Insurance Agencies sells property/casualty coverage in central and western New York and Pennsylvania.

Operations

Tompkins Financial operates in three segments: banking insurance and wealth management. Banking represents most of its revenue — more than 80%. About 70% of the banks' loan portfolios is made up of commercial and commercial real estate loans.

Tompkins' Insurance and Wealth Management divisions operate through subsidiaries and make up roughly 10% and 5% of sales respectively. Its subsidiary Tompkins Insurance Agencies Inc. offers property and casualty insurance services and employee benefit consulting services. The firm's trust company Tompkins Financial Advisors offers trust financial planning and wealth management services.

Geographic Reach

Between its four bank subsidiaries the Tompkins operates 66 branches in the US with more than two thirds of the branches in New York and around 20 branches in Pennsylvania.

Sales and Marketing

The company's banks target individual and small business customers for its financial services. Tompkins spent $4.94 million on its marketing expenses in 2014 or slightly less than the $4.96 million spent in 2013 but 22% more than what it spent in 2012.

Financial Performance

Tompkin's revenue rose for a second straight year growing by less than 1% to $255.26 million in 2014 most thanks to growth in the company's non-interest fee income from an increase in deposit account service charges card services income and growth in personal health and benefit insurance sales.

The company's net income ended higher for a second year as well thanks to higher revenue lower interest expense on deposits and lower provisions for loan losses as its loan portfolio's credit improved. Operations provided $77.36 million or 8% less cash than in 2013 mostly because in 2013 the company was able to use more funds from its prepaid accounts to pay for FDIC insurance.

Strategy

The company's strategy for growth includes making inroads into new markets and new business areas through acquisitions. It entered the southeastern Pennsylvania market with its 2012 acquisition of VIST Financial parent of VIST Bank (which continues to operate under a separate charter under existing management) VIST Insurance and VIST Capital Management. The deal added about 20 branches to Tompkins' network along with $889 million in new loan business and $1.2 billion in new deposits.

Mergers and Acquisitions

In August 2012 Tompkins Financial purchased VIST Financial Corp in an all stock transaction valued at $86 million. The deal added all 20 VIST Bank branches (and VIST Bank's assets) in Pennsylvania the VIST Capital Management business and the VIST Insurance business which doubled Tompkin's annual insurance revenue; all of which were folded into Tompkins' banking operations Tompkins Financial Advisors and Tompkins Insurance Agencies operations respectively.

EXECUTIVES

Evp President And Ceo Vist Bank, Robert D. (Bob) Davis, age 71
Director; Vice Chairman Tompkins Insurance Agencies, James R. Hardie, age 75
Executive Vice President Chief Operations Officer Chief Financial Officer & Treasurer, Francis M. Fetsko, age 54, $281,877 total compensation
Evp And Cfo Mahopac National Bank, Stephen S. Romaine, age 55, $474,898 total compensation
Executive Vice President, David S. Boyce, age 52, $185,000 total compensation
Executive Vice-president, Gregory J. Hartz, age 58, $237,107 total compensation
Executive Vice-president, Gerald J. Klein, age 60, $238,369 total compensation
Executive Vice President; President & Coo Of Vist Bank, Scott L. Gruber, age 63
Evp Corporate Marketing, Susan M. Valenti
Svp - Chief Technology Officer, Bradley G. James
Avp Corporate Compliance, Terri Brace
Vice President, Bill Steinmetz
Vice President Controller, David Kershaw
Senior Vice President Director Of Human Resources, Bonita Lindberg
Senior Vice President Banking Operations, Kimberly Dove
Vice President Commercial Lending Relationship Manager, Scott Pittinaro
Senior Vice President, Brian Bisaccio
Senior Vice President, Joseph Butto
Senior Vice President Regional, James Whitton
Vice President Agricultural Banking Relationship Manager, Travis Werley
Senior Vice President Chief Risk Officer, Steven Cribbs
Sr. Vice President, Kara Pass
Chairman Tompkins Financial Corporation And Tompkins Trust Company, James J. Byrnes, age 76
Vice Chairman, James W. (Jim) Fulmer, age 67
Board Member, Michael Spain
Board Member, John Alexander
Auditors: KPMG LLP

LOCATIONS

HQ: Tompkins Financial Corp
118 E. Seneca Street, P.O. Box 460, Ithaca, NY 14851
Phone: 888 503-5753
Web: www.tompkinsfinancial.com

PRODUCTS/OPERATIONS

2016 Sales

	$ mil.	% of total
Interest		
Loans	170	63
Available-for-sale securities	28	10
Held-to-maturity securities	4	1
Federal Home Loan Bank stock and Federal Reserve Bank stock	1	1
Trading securities	0	
Due from banks		
Non-interest		
Insurance commissions & fees	30	11
Investment services	15	6
Service charges on deposit accounts	9	3
Card services income	8	3
Mark-to-market gain on liabilities held at fair value	0	
Net gain on securities transactions	1	
Other	6	2
Mark-to-market loss on trading securities	(0.2)	
Total	272	100

2016 Sales

	$ mil.	% of total
Banking	227	84
Insurance	30	11
Wealth Management	16	5
Others	(1.2)	-
Total	272	100

COMPETITORS

Bank of America	Community Bank System
Chemung Financial	Elmira Savings Bank
Citigroup	HSBC USA
Citizens Financial Group	JPMorgan Chase
	M&T Bank

HISTORICAL FINANCIALS

Company Type: Public

Income Statement
FYE: December 31

	ASSETS ($ mil.)	NET INCOME ($ mil.)	INCOME AS % OF ASSETS	EMPLOYEES
12/18	6,758	82	1.2%	1,035
12/17	6,648	52	0.8%	1,041
12/16	6,237	59	1.0%	1,046
12/15	5,690	58	1.0%	1,038
12/14	5,270	52	1.0%	1,037
Annual Growth	6.4%	12.1%	—	(0.0%)

2018 Year-End Financials

Debt ratio: 0.00% No. of shares (mil.): 15
Return on equity: 14.00% Dividends
Cash ($ mil.): 80 Yield: 3.0%
Current ratio: — Payout: 36.0%
Long-term debt ($ mil.): — Market value ($ mil.): 1,142

	STOCK PRICE ($) FY Close	P/E High/Low		PER SHARE ($) Earnings	Dividends	Book Value
12/18	75.00	17	13	5.00	2.00	41.00
12/17	81.00	28	21	3.00	2.00	38.00
12/16	95.00	24	13	4.00	2.00	36.00
12/15	56.00	16	13	4.00	2.00	35.00
12/14	55.00	16	13	3.00	2.00	33.00
Annual Growth	7.9%	—	—	11.4%	4.6%	5.4%

TOMPKINS TRUST COMPANY

EXECUTIVES

Chb, James Byrnes
Prin, Steven Garner
Vice President, Bill Steinmetz
Wealth Management Associate, Dimitrios Alissandratos
Vice President Information TEC, James Frey
Assistant Vice President of Co, Jason Moore
Vice President, Scott Pronti
Vp Com Banking Rel Manager, John Bauda
Small Business Lending Manager, Brad Totman
Vice President, Karen Parks
Wealth Management Assistant, Colleen Jeffers

LOCATIONS

HQ: TOMPKINS TRUST COMPANY
110 N TIOGA ST, ITHACA, NY 148504320
Phone: 607 273-3210
Web: WWW.TOMPKINSTRUST.COM

HISTORICAL FINANCIALS

Company Type: Private

Income Statement FYE: December 31

	ASSETS ($ mil.)	NET INCOME ($ mil.)	INCOME AS % OF ASSETS	EMPLOYEES
12/17	2,118	22	1.0%	1
12/16	1,962	24	1.2%	—
12/15	1,805	24	1.3%	—
12/14	1,682	22	1.3%	—
Annual Growth	**8.0%**	**(0.7%)**	**—**	**—**

TowneBank

EXECUTIVES

BR Mgr, Becky Zambas
Executive Officer, Anne Conner
Morgans Admin, Bonnie Campbell
Assistant Vice President Loan, Cori Chapp
Senior Vice President, Duncan Owen
Senior Executive Vice Presiden, John Baiocco
Senior Vice President, Joseph Johann
Senior Vice President, Judy Carr
Market President, Susan Harris
Administrative Officer, Teresa Plummer
Auditors: Dixon Hughes Goodman LLP

LOCATIONS

HQ: TowneBank
5716 High Street, Portsmouth, VA 23703
Phone: 757 638-7500
Web: www.townebank.com

HISTORICAL FINANCIALS

Company Type: Public

Income Statement FYE: December 31

	ASSETS ($ mil.)	NET INCOME ($ mil.)	INCOME AS % OF ASSETS	EMPLOYEES
12/18	11,163	134	1.2%	2,897
12/17	8,522	88	1.0%	2,727
12/16	7,974	67	0.8%	2,529
12/15	6,297	62	1.0%	1,903
12/14	4,982	42	0.8%	1,737
Annual Growth	**22.3%**	**33.5%**	**—**	**13.6%**

2018 Year-End Financials

Debt ratio: 3.00%
Return on equity: 10.00%
Cash ($ mil.): 687
Current ratio: —
Long-term debt ($ mil.): —
No. of shares (mil.): 72
Dividends
Yield: 3.0%
Payout: 39.0%
Market value ($ mil.): 1,736

	STOCK PRICE ($) FY Close	P/E High/Low	PER SHARE ($) Earnings	Dividends	Book Value
12/18	24.00	18 12	2.00	1.00	21.00
12/17	31.00	25 21	1.00	1.00	18.00
12/16	33.00	29 14	1.00	1.00	17.00
12/15	21.00	18 12	1.00	0.00	16.00
12/14	15.00	14 11	1.00	0.00	17.00
Annual Growth	**12.2%**	**—**	**12.3%**	**9.6%**	**5.5%**

Toyota Motor Credit Corp.

Toyota Motor Credit (TMCC) is the US financing arm of Toyota Financial Services which is a subsidiary of Toyota Motor Corporation the world's largest carmaker. TMCC provides retail leasing retail and wholesale sales financing and other financial services to Toyota and Lexus dealers and their customers for the purchase of new and used cars and trucks. It offers similar services to Toyota industrial equipment dealers. TMCC which underwrites and services the finance contracts operates three regional customer service centers and some 30 dealer sales and service branches across the US and Puerto Rico.

Operations

TMCC organizes its business around two product categories: Finance and Insurance.

Its Finance segment which generates more than 90% of the company's total sales acquires a variety of retail finance products such as consumer and commercial installment sales contracts in the US and Puerto Rico as well as leasing contracts — either direct finance leases or operating leases from US vehicle or industrial equipment dealers. The segment also provides dealer financing (including wholesale financing revolving credit lines and working capital loans) and real estate financing for vehicle and industrial equipment dealers in the US and Puerto Rico.

The Insurance division operates through subsidiary Toyota Motor Insurance Services which underwrites and sells insurance products such as extended service coverage total loss protection and prepaid maintenance protection. It also provides marketing and claims administration services related to covering select risks of vehicle dealers and their customers in the US.

Broken down TMCC generated 67% of its total revenue from operating leases in fiscal 2015 (ended March) and another 20% from retail financing income. Its Insurance premium and contract revenue brought in 7% of total revenue while dealer financing revenue (4%) and investment income (2%) brought in the rest.

Geographic Reach

The California-based company serves dealers and their customers across the US. About 21% of TMCC's vehicle retail and lease contracts were based in California in fiscal 2015 while 10% were from Texas 8% were from New York and 6% came from New Jersey.

Financial Performance

TMCC has seen its revenues and profits trend downward for most of the past several years. However the company's revenue has been recovering since 2014.

TMCC's revenue inched up by more than 1% to $8.10 billion in fiscal 2015 (ended March) mostly as its Operating Lease business grew by 21% thanks to higher average outstanding earning asset balances as Toyota Motor Sales USA (the primary US distributor of Toyota Lexus and Scion vehicles) focused more on pushing lease subvention during the year. The company's Insurance business also grew thanks to higher premiums and contract revenues resulting from an increase in the average number of agreements in force during the year.

Higher revenue in fiscal 2015 allowed TMCC's profit to rebound sharply with net income jumping by 40% to $1.20 billion. Cash from operations declined by 23% to $3.77 billion as the company collected less in cash earnings after foreign exchange currency adjustments.

EXECUTIVES

President And Ceo; Cfo, Michael R. (Mike) Groff, age 64
Auditors: PricewaterhouseCoopers LLP

LOCATIONS

HQ: Toyota Motor Credit Corp.
6565 Headquarters Drive, Plano, TX 75024
Phone: 469 486-9300
Web: www.toyotafinancial.com

PRODUCTS/OPERATIONS

2016 Sales

	$ mil.	% of total
Financing		
Operating leases	7,141	68
Retail	1,859	18
Dealer	403	4
Insurance premiums earned & contract revenues	719	7
Investment & other	164	1
Gain on sale of commercial finance business	197	2
Total	**10,483**	**100**

2016 Sales

	$ mil.	% of total
Financing revenues	9,403	90
Insurance earned premiums and contract revenues	719	7
Investment and other income net	164	1
Gain on sale of commercial finance business	197	2
Total	**10,483**	**100**

COMPETITORS

Ally Financial	Ford Motor Credit
American Honda Finance	GM Financial
AutoNation	Mercedes-Benz Credit
Capital One Auto Finance	Volkswagen Financial Services
Daimler Financial Services	

HISTORICAL FINANCIALS

Company Type: Public

Income Statement

FYE: March 31

	REVENUE ($ mil.)	NET INCOME ($ mil.)	NET PROFIT MARGIN	EMPLOYEES
03/19	12,836	795	6.2%	3,200
03/18	11,856	3,410	28.8%	3,300
03/17	11,246	267	2.4%	3,185
03/16	10,483	932	8.9%	3,140
03/15	9,142	1,197	13.1%	3,251
Annual Growth	8.9%	(9.7%)	—	(0.4%)

2019 Year-End Financials

Debt ratio: 80.00%	No. of shares (mil.): 0
Return on equity: 6.00%	Dividends
Cash ($ mil.): 2,198	Yield: —
Current ratio: —	Payout: —
Long-term debt ($ mil.): 92,922	Market value ($ mil.): —

Tractor Supply Co.

Tractor Supply Company (TSC) does a whole lot more than its name might suggest. Besides providing agricultural machine parts TSC offers animal feed fencing power tools riding mowers work clothing and pet supplies as well as tools for gardening irrigation welding and towing. TSC offers both name-brand merchandise and its own crop of private-label goods. The company has nationwide scope operating more than 1850 stores in some 49 US states under the Tractor Supply Company Del's Farm Supply and Petsense banners. Stores are concentrated in rural areas and near large cities to cater to full- and part-time farmers ranchers and contractors. TSC also sells online.

Operations

TSC operates Tractor Supply Del's Feed & Farm Supply and Petsense stores. It breaks its operations into product categories.

Livestock and pet products which account for more than 45% of sales are sold under the Countyline Dumor Equistages and Producer's Pride brand names.

Hardware tools and truck products generating more than 20% of revenue are sold under the Jobsmart Traveller and TSC Tractor Supply Co. brand names.

Seasonal gift and toy products account for about 20% of sales with Groundwork Huskee Red Shed and Redstone brand products.

The clothing and footwear category 10% of sales offers items for men women and children under the Bit & Bridle Blue Mountain and C.E. Schmidt brand names.

The agriculture category accounts for about 5% of sales.

Of its nearly 1850 stores some 1700 are Tractor Supply or Del's stores and about 170 are Petsense stores.

Geographic Reach

TSC based in Brentwood Tennessee operates stores in 49 US states (Alaska is the state without a TSC store). Its largest market is Texas home to about 210 stores followed by Pennsylvania and North Carolina (about 95 each) Ohio and Tennessee (more than 90 each) Michigan and Georgia (about 85 each) and New York (more than 75). The company has distribution facilities in Arizona Georgia Indiana Kentucky Maryland Nebraska Texas and Washington.

Sales and Marketing

TSC's products are sourced through both US and international vendors. It purchases its products from a group of roughly 900 vendors 350 of which supply 90% of TSC's products.

TSC's customers are home and landowners and pet and livestock owners in rural areas and the outskirts of major metropolitan areas. While its customers are often recreational farmers i.e. those that enjoy the outdoor lifestyle but are non-professionals it also serves tradesmen and small businesses.

The company's advertising strategy is based on merchandise its website newspaper circulars direct mail and email and digital and social media.

Financial Performance

Tractor Supply Co.'s revenue has grown steadily for the past decade. Sales rose 7% to $7.3 billion in 2017 from $6.8 billion in 2016. Comparable store sales which make up about 94% of total sales increased about 3% in 2017 from higher traffic counts and the year-round strength of consumable usable and edible products primarily animal- and pet-related merchandise. Sales from stores opened less than a year including Petsense locations added $405 million to TSC's top line in 2017.

Net income slipped to about $423 million in 2017 from $437 million in 2016. The company recognized an expense of about $4.9 million in relation to the US Tax Cuts and Jobs Act of 2017.

TSC counted about $109 million in cash at the end of 2017 compared to about $54 million in 2016. Operating activities generated about $631 million in 2017 while investing and financing activities used $238 million and $338 million respectively. The company paid out more than $503 million to shareholders through stock buy backs and quarterly dividends.

Strategy

Although TSC's strategy is dubbed ONETractor part of the strategy involves opening scores of stores a year. The company planned to open 80 TSC stores and 20 Petsense stores in 2018 with more on the way in 2019 and 2020. The company believes there's room for about 2500 TSC stores in the US about 600 more than its 2018 total and 1000 Petsense stores.

In addition to adding stores the strategy intends to deliver better customer service with the help of data and its employees. The company collects customer data through its Neighbor's Club loyalty program which started in 2017. Those who sign up (about 7 million) receive communications tailored to their preferences while the company gets a comprehensive view into its customers' buying behaviors. TSC relies on employees to make suggestions about improvements as well as to share their expertise with customers.

The company has taken steps to improve its omni-channel capabilities relating to fulfillment options product information and site research. TSC has improved the site response time and added additional product offerings for vendor direct-to-customer drop shipments and configured its site to be viewed on mobile devices and tablets.

TSC maintains that its focus on customers living the rural lifestyle sets it apart. Many retailers offer similar products even if they sell to city dwellers as well as rural residents. The wide variety of merchandise available from Amazon.com makes it a competitor and Walmart is a competitor in brick-and-mortar and online sales.

Mergers and Acquisitions

In 2016 TSC acquired Petsense and its 136 retail outlets for $116 million. Petsense is a small-box specialty pet supply retailer. TSC's two Home-Town Pet stores serving a similar market were rebranded as Petsense.

Company Background

TSC was founded in 1938.

LOCATIONS

HQ: Tractor Supply Co.
5401 Virginia Way, Brentwood, TN 37027
Phone: 615 440-4000
Web: www.tractorsupply.com

2017 Stores

	No.
Texas	210
North Carolina	94
Pennsylvania	93
Tennessee	91
Ohio	90
Michigan	83
Georgia	83
New York	77
Kentucky	69
Florida	63
California	59
Indiana	57
Alabama	56
Virginia	55
Oklahoma	53
Louisiana	44
South Carolina	44
Mississippi	39
Arkansas	35
Arizona	34
Missouri	30
New Mexico	28
West Virginia	28
Colorado	22
Kansas	22
Maryland	22
New Hampshire	21
Maine	20
Massachusetts	20
Wisconsin	20
Connecticut	19
Washington	19
Nebraska	18
Illinois	17
New Jersey	17
Utah	15
North Dakota	14
Minnesota	12
Iowa	9
South Dakota	9
Wyoming	8

Vermont	8
Montana	6
Delaware	5
Idaho	4
Rhode Island	4
Oregon	3
Nevada	3
Hawaii	2
Total	**1,853**

PRODUCTS/OPERATIONS

2017 Sales

	% of total
Livestock and Pet	47
Hardware Tools Truck and Towing	22
Seasonal Gift and Toy Products	19
Clothing and Footwear	8
Agriculture	4
Total	**100**

PRODUCT CATEGORY

PRODUCT CATEGORY
Farm & Ranch
Poultry
Pets & Livestock
Lawn & Garden
Truck & Trailer
Hardware & Tools
Heating & Cooling
Outdoors
Home & Decor
Footware
Clothing
Big & Tall
Plus Sizes
Gift Cards
BRANDS
4health (pet foods and supplies)
Bit & Bridle (apparel and footwear)
Blue Mountain (apparel)
C.E. Schmidt (apparel and footwear)
Countyline (livestock farm and ranch equipment)
Dumor (livestock and horse feed and supplies)
Equistages (horse feed)
Groundwork (lawn and garden supplies)
Huskee (outdoor power equipment)
JobSmart (tools)
Paws & Claws (pet foods and supplies)
Producer's Pride (livestock and horse feed and supplies)
Red Shed (gifts collectibles and outdoor furniture)
Redstone (heating products)
Retriever (pet foods and supplies)
Royal Wing (bird feed and supplies)
Traveller (truck and automotive products)
TSC Tractor Supply Co (trailers truck tool boxes and animal bedding)

COMPETITORS

Ace Hardware	Northern Tool
Amazon.com	Southern States
Farm King	Tennessee Farmers
Home Depot	Co-op
Lowe's	True Value
Menard	Wal-Mart
Miles Enterprises	Wilbur-Ellis

HISTORICAL FINANCIALS

Company Type: Public

Income Statement				FYE: December 29
	REVENUE ($ mil.)	NET INCOME ($ mil.)	NET PROFIT MARGIN	EMPLOYEES
12/18	7,911	532	6.7%	29,000
12/17	7,256	423	5.8%	28,000
12/16	6,780	437	6.4%	26,000
12/15	6,227	410	6.6%	23,000
12/14	5,712	371	6.5%	21,100
Annual Growth	**8.5%**	**9.5%**	**—**	**8.3%**

2018 Year-End Financials

Debt ratio: 14.00%	No. of shares (mil.): 122
Return on equity: 36.00%	Dividends
Cash ($ mil.): 86	Yield: 0.0%
Current ratio: 2.00	Payout: 28.0%
Long-term debt ($ mil.): 410	Market value ($ mil.): 10,137

	STOCK PRICE ($) FY Close	P/E High/Low	PER SHARE ($) Earnings	Dividends	Book Value
12/18	83.00	22 13	4.00	1.00	13.00
12/17	75.00	23 15	3.00	1.00	11.00
12/16	76.00	29 19	3.00	1.00	11.00
12/15	86.00	32 25	3.00	1.00	10.00
12/14	78.00	29 21	3.00	1.00	9.00
Annual Growth	**1.7%**	**— —**	**12.8%**	**18.4%**	**7.8%**

Transamerica Advisors Life Insurance Co

EXECUTIVES

Pres, Marilyn Carp
Auditors: PricewaterhouseCoopers LLP

LOCATIONS

HQ: Transamerica Advisors Life Insurance Co
4333 Edgewood Road, NE, Cedar Rapids, IA 52499-0001
Phone: 800 346-3677
Web: www.transamerica.com

HISTORICAL FINANCIALS

Company Type: Public

Income Statement				FYE: December 31
	ASSETS ($ mil.)	NET INCOME ($ mil.)	INCOME AS % OF ASSETS	EMPLOYEES
12/17	8,622	99	1.2%	—
12/16	8,670	(21)		—
12/15	9,166	14	0.1%	—
12/14	10,108	34	0.3%	—
12/13	10,556	(254)		—
Annual Growth	**(4.9%)**	**—**		**—**

2017 Year-End Financials

Debt ratio: 0.00%	No. of shares (mil.): 0
Return on equity: 9.00%	Dividends
Cash ($ mil.): 270	Yield: —
Current ratio: —	Payout: 141.0%
Long-term debt ($ mil.): —	Market value ($ mil.): —

TransDigm Group Inc

TransDigm Group supplies a variety of behind-the-scenes componentry for aircraft manufacturing including audio systems pumps and valves and power conditioning devices. Operating through a plethora of subsidiaries TransDigm makes and distributes systems and components for commercial and military aircraft. Its products are found in several Boeing and Airbus airplanes Bombardier and Embraer regional jets and a number of military planes and helicopters. TransDigm is a frequent acquirer of companies recently averaging about four per year. The majority of the company's products are sold to customers in the US.

Operations

TransDigm operates in three segments: Power and Control (contributing more than 55% of revenue) Airframe (about 40%) and Non-aviation (less than 5%).

The Power and Control segment makes and sells systems and components that provide or control power for aircraft. Its products operate through electronics fluid (hydraulic) and mechanical motion control. The segment offers mechanical/electro-mechanical actuators and controls ignition systems pumps and valves power conditioning devices AC/DC electric motors and generators and cargo loading systems.

The Airframe division produces non-powered systems and products that are used in the airframe for example latching and locking devices connectors and elastomers cockpit security components and aircraft audio systems.

The Non-aviation segment includes products such as seat belts and safety restraints for ground transportation applications.

Geographic Reach

Cleveland Ohio-headquartered TransDigm operates about 130 subsidiaries throughout the US Europe and Asia.

Sales and Marketing

The company sells its products primarily through its own sales organization with a business unit manager assigned to specific products and supported by account managers and sales engineers. TransDigm also uses several distributors that provide logistical support and serve as the primary customer contact for certain smaller accounts. Its major distributors are Aviall (a subsidiary of Boeing) and Satair (a subsidiary of Airbus). The company's top ten customers account for more than 40% of sales.

TransDigm's business serving customers in the commercial regional business jet and general aviation aftermarket accounts for more than 35% of total sales. The commercial aerospace OEM market comprised of large commercial transport manufacturers and regional and business jet manufacturers accounts for roughly 25% of total sales. The defense market represents approximately 35% and non-aerospace sales make up about 5%.

Financial Performance

In recent years TransDigm steadily increased revenue lifting such results from just under $2 billion in FY2013 (ended September 30) to FY2018 results exceeding $3.8 billion. In FY2018 the company's $3.8 billion sales figure represents a 9% increase over 2017. Organic sales—those from subsidiaries already within its family—saw a 5% increase in sales primarily driven by commercial aftermarket and defense sales. Revenue from companies acquired within the previous twelve months was a little more than 3% of total sales.

Although faced with increased cost of sales increased SG&A expenses and higher interest expense TransDigm's net income still sailed 60% higher in 2017 to $957.0 million primarily due to higher net sales.

Cash on hand at the end of the year was $2.1 billion an increase of $1.4 billion from FY2017. The company generated $1.0 billion in cash from operating activities. Investing activities used $683.6 million with most of it going to acquisitions costs. Financing activities provided $1.0 billion primarily from net proceeds from term loans and issuance of notes.

Strategy

Strategically TransDigm focuses on specialized products rather than commodities. Most of the company's sales come from proprietary products for which TransDigm owns the design and/or is the sole-source provider for a particular aircraft. In 2017 TransDigm's subsidiaries innovated new components including the Aerocontrolex Potable Water Ozone Disinfection Cart the Airborne Systems Ram Air parachute system Amsafe's upgraded passenger seat belts and Whippany actuation systems.

TransDigm approaches operations and managerial oversight like a private equity firm. It owns about 130 subsidiaries and allows them all a certain amount of autonomy to serve the needs of their respective markets. The company continues to look to acquisitions to fuel its growth.

Another revenue producing endeavor arises from the proliferation of its componentry across manufacturers and industries. It has a large install base estimated to be some 95000 aircraft for which it is typically the sole source of replacement and aftermarket products.

Mergers and Acquisitions

TransDigm acquires companies that offer niche products that fit well with other subsidiary operations or have significant aftermarket sales.

The company went beyond that pattern in 2019 when it spent $4 billion to buy Esterline Technologies Corp an aerospace and defense parts supplier with a large aftermarket portfolio including knobs sensors and materials. (TransDigm had purchased the Kirkhill elastomers business from Esterline in 2018 for $49.3 million). Esterline which had $2 billion in annual revenue brings its platform of proprietary and sole-source products for the aerospace and defense industries including significant aftermarket offerings.

In 2018 TransDigm acquired Skandia Inc. from Graycliff Partners LP for a total purchase price of approximately $84 million. Skandia headquartered in Davis Junction IL offers seating foam foam fabrication flammability testing and acoustic products for the business jet market. It will operate within TransDigm's Airframe segment. The company also acquired Extant Components in 2018 for $533 million. Extant provides proprietary aftermarket products and repair and overhaul services to the aerospace and defense end markets.

In 2017 the company purchased three separate aerospace product lines for a total price of approximately for $106 million.

EXECUTIVES

President Elektro-metall, Uwe Basler
President Telair International, Axel Hauner
Chairman And Ceo, W. Nicholas (Nick) Howley, age 67, $1,085,000 total compensation
Evp, John F. Leary, age 72, $172,125 total compensation
Sevp, Gregory Rufus, age 63, $522,500 total compensation
President Telair Us, Tim Dumbauld
President And Coo, Kevin M. Stein, age 53, $558,750 total compensation
Evp, Roger V. Jones, age 60
Evp, Jorge Valladares
Evp, Peter Palmer
Evp And Interim Cfo, James Skulina, age 60
Evp Business Development And Mergers And Acquisitions, Bernt G. Iversen, age 62, $403,750 total compensation
President Adelwiggins Group, Jeff Zielinski
President Aero Fluid Products, Paula Wheeler
President Airborne Systems, Chris Rowe
President Airborne Systems North America, Bryce Wiedeman
President Amsafe Passenger Restraints, Willard Hagan
President Amsafe Restraints And Specialty Devices, Ian Kentfield

President Arkwin Industries, Frank Robilotto
President Pexco Aerospace, Herbert Mardany
President Aerosonic And Cda Intercorp, Joe Grote
President Champion Aerospace, Jason Marlin
President Electromech Technologies, Chad Ohl
Evp, Joel Reiss
President Marathonnorco Aerospace, Sergio Rodriguez
President Schneller, Alex Feil
President Skurka Aerospace, Michael Barnaba
President Technical Airborne Components Industries, Dirk Dhooge
President Harco Labaratories, Patrick Murphy
President Dukes Aerospace, Scott Cummings
President Avionic Instruments, Vince Ciolli
President Shield Restraint Systems, Brian Babin
President Aerocontrolex Group, Todd Loschelder
President Avtechtyee, Harry Ray
President Hartwell Corp., Michael Couitt
President Nordisk Aviation Products, Neal McKeever
President Pneudraulics, Dane Miller
President Whippany Actuation Systems, Rodrigo Rubiano
Executive Vice President, Bob Henderson
Vice Chairman, Robert S. Henderson, age 63
Board Member, Douglas Peacock
Board Member, Rob Small
Board Member, William Dries
Member Board Of Directors, Gary Mccullough
Auditors: Ernst & Young LLP

LOCATIONS

HQ: TransDigm Group Inc
1301 East 9th Street, Suite 3000, Cleveland, OH 44114
Phone: 216 706-2960
Web: www.transdigm.com

2016 Sales

	$ mil.	% of total
US	2,002	63
Other countries	1,170	37
Total	**3,171**	**100**

PRODUCTS/OPERATIONS

FY2018 Sales

	$ mil.	% of total
Power & Control	2,139	56
Airframe	1,531	40
Non-aviation	141	4
Total	**3,811**	**100**

FY2018 Sales

	$ mil.	% of total
Organic Sales	3,696	97
Acquisition Sales	115	3
Total	**3,811**	**100**

Selected Subsidiaries

Adams Rite Aerospace
AeroControlex Group
Aerosonic LLC
Airborne Systems LTD
Airborne Systems North America
Avionic Instruments Inc.
Breeze Eastern
Champion Aerospace
Data Device Corporation
Dukes Aerospace Inc.
Electromech Technologies
Elektro-Metall
HARCO
Hartwell Corporation
Marathon Norco Aerospace Inc.
Nordisk Aviation
Pexco Aerospace Inc.
Pneudraulics Inc.
Schneller LLC
Shield Restraint Systems Inc.
Tactair Fluid Controls Inc.
Technical Airborne Components
Telair International Gmbh
Telair US LLC
Whippany Actuation Systems

COMPETITORS

Air France
BAE Systems Inc.
Boeing
GE Aviation

Honeywell
International
Lockheed Martin
United Technologies

HISTORICAL FINANCIALS

Company Type: Public

Income Statement   FYE: September 30

	REVENUE ($ mil.)	NET INCOME ($ mil.)	NET PROFIT MARGIN	EMPLOYEES
09/19	5,223	890	17.0%	18,300
09/18	3,811	957	25.1%	10,100
09/17	3,504	597	17.0%	9,200
09/16	3,171	586	18.5%	9,300
09/15	2,707	447	16.5%	8,200
Annual Growth	**17.9%**	**18.8%**	—	**22.2%**

2019 Year-End Financials

Debt ratio: 104.00%
Return on equity: ***.***.**%
Cash ($ mil.): 1,467
Current ratio: 3.00
Long-term debt ($ mil.): 16,469

No. of shares (mil.): 53
Dividends
  Yield: 6.0%
  Payout: 225.0%
Market value ($ mil.): 27,836

	STOCK PRICE ($) FY Close	P/E High/Low		PER SHARE ($) Earnings	Dividends	Book Value
09/19	521.00	40	23	14.00	30.00	(54.00)
09/18	372.00	23	16	16.00	0.00	(34.00)
09/17	256.00	37	27	8.00	46.00	(57.00)
09/16	289.00	28	18	10.00	0.00	(12.00)
09/15	212.00	31	22	8.00	0.00	(19.00)
Annual Growth	**25.1%**	—	—	**15.3%**	—	—

TravelCenters of America Inc

TravelCenters of America (TCA) is in it for the long haul. The company operates or franchises some 540 travel centers standalone convenience stores and standalone restaurants primarily targeting truckers and highway motorists across the US. Its brands include TravelCenters of America/TA Petro Stopping Centers/Petro Minit Mart and Quaker Steak & Lube. TCA's travel centers which account for most of sales offer diesel fuel and gas truck repair and maintenance services full- or quick-service restaurants and showers and other customer amenities. The company leases about 200 of its locations from Hospitality Properties Trust (HPT) its largest shareholder.

Operations

TCA operates through two primary segments travel centers and convenience stores. Its travel center business which accounts for some 85% of revenue includes about 180 TravelCenters of Americas/TA locations and about 80 Petro Stopping Centers/Petro locations. The company operates nearly 230 of the centers and franchises the rest. The convenience stores business 10%-plus of revenue includes more than 230 Minit Mart locations that offer gasoline coffee groceries and other traditional convenience store fare. (The company announced plans in mid-2018 to sell its convenience store operations.) The remaining revenue comes from corporate and other and includes some 50 Quaker Steak & Lube restaurants.

Fuel generates about two-thirds of TCA's revenue; the rest comes from truck services and food and other items sold in it stores.

Geographic Reach

TCA operates or franchises about 540 travel centers convenience stores and restaurants across the US (as well as a single location in Ontario Canada). Its largest market is the Midwest with Kentucky Illinois Missouri Ohio and Wisconsin together accounting for nearly half of all locations.

Sales and Marketing

TCA caters to professional truck drivers and travelers who rely on gas stations and convenience stores while on the road. Customers include trucking fleets and their drivers independent truck drivers and motorists.

Financial Performance

Although TCA's revenue was up in 2017 it has fallen significantly over the past five years amid falling gas prices. It is down nearly 25% since 2013. Net income has suffered a more severe drop falling some 70% during that time.

In 2017 the company reported revenue of $6.1 billion an increase of more than 10% from the prior year. The growth was driven by a 16% jump in fuel revenue because of rising gasoline prices in the second half of the year. Boosted by the revenue growth net income was $9 million in 2017 compared to a loss of $2 million in 2016. An income tax benefit related to the resolution of previous uncertain tax positions also positively impacted the results.

Cash at the end of 2017 was $36 million a decrease of $25 million from the prior year. Cash from operations contributed $36 million to the coffers while investing activities used $62 million mainly for capital expenditures. Financing activities added just under $1 million primarily because of sale leaseback transactions with Hospitality Properties Trust.

Strategy

TCA is building its cross-country network of travel centers through acquisitions (by opportunistically buying up smaller competitors) and by opening new locations. Since 2011 the company has acquired and developed some 325 travel centers convenience stores and standalone restaurants (mostly convenience stores). It has invested roughly $910 million to develop purchase and improve locations.

In an effort to kickstart its travel center expansion in 2018 TCA launched a new brand called TA Express. The smaller travel center concept will offer a quicker customer experience and provide more site flexibility to the company. Large tracts of land along or near interstates are becoming scarcer. TCA hopes the new format will also spur interest in travel center franchising.

In addition to expansion efforts the company's growth plans include investments in its existing properties and services. Recent improvements have included parking lot expansions restaurant renovations and installation of car washes. TCA is also focused on enhancing its TA Truck Service offerings which include some 1100 repair bays more than 2600 service trucks RoadSquad and OnSite emergency maintenance vehicles and a commercial tire network.

In mid-2018 TCA announced plans to sell its stand-alone convenience store operations (about 225 stores) to UK-based EG Group for some $330 million. The deal will free up focus and funds for the company's travel center business.

EXECUTIVES

Marketing Vice President Director, Tom Liutkus
Svp Truck Service Marketing And Operations,
  Skip McGary

Svp Food Marketing And Operations, John Ponczoch
Evp Sales, Michael J. Lombardi, age 68, $339,000 total compensation
Ceo, Andrew J. Rebholz, age 55, $300,000 total compensation
Evp And General Counsel, Mark R. Young, age 56, $300,000 total compensation
President And Coo, Barry A. Richards, age 66, $300,000 total compensation
Svp Construction Maintenance And Environmental, Peter P. Ward
Svp Retail Marketing And Operations, Rodney Bresnahan
Evp Cfo And Treasurer, William E. Myers
Vice President Of Marketing, Rick Pavia
Vice President Retail Marketing, Tom Newbould
Vice President Director, John Mcgary
Vp Fleet Sales East, Sandra Sanford
Vice President Finance And Treasury, Gary Townsend
Vp Fuel Supply, Tom Komos
Vice President Compliance, John Adamich
Vice President Human Resources, Karen Kaminski
Managing Director Board Of Directors, Barry M. Portnoy, age 74
Board Member, Joseph Morea
Board Member, Lisa Jones
Auditors: RSM US LLP

LOCATIONS

HQ: TravelCenters of America Inc
  24601 Center Ridge Road, Suite 200, Westlake, OH 44145-5639
Phone: 440 808-9100
Web: www.tatravelcenters.com

PRODUCTS/OPERATIONS

2017 Location

	No.
Travel centers	
TravelCenters of America/TA	178
Petro Stopping Centers/Petro	78
Convenience stores	
Mini Mart	233
Restaurants	
Quaker Steak & Lube	49
Total	**538**

2017 Sales

	$ mil.	% of total
Fuel	4,091	68
Non-fuel	1,944	32
Rent & royalties from franchisees	17	-
Total	**6,052**	**100**

2017 Sales

	$ mil.	% of total
Travel Centers	5,181	86
Convenience Stores	751	12
Corporate and Other	119	2
Total	**6,052**	**100**

COMPETITORS

Bowlin Travel Centers	Pilot Flying J
Chevron	Royal Dutch Shell
Couche-Tard	Sapp Bros Travel Centers
Exxon Mobil	
Love's Country Stores	Stuckey's
Martin & Bayley	

HISTORICAL FINANCIALS

Company Type: Public

Income Statement

FYE: December 31

	REVENUE ($ mil.)	NET INCOME ($ mil.)	NET PROFIT MARGIN	EMPLOYEES
12/18	6,231	(121)	—	21,719
12/17	6,052	9	0.2%	23,877
12/16	5,511	(2)	—	25,204
12/15	5,851	28	0.5%	24,250
12/14	7,779	61	0.8%	22,330
Annual Growth	(5.4%)	—		(0.7%)

2018 Year-End Financials

Debt ratio: 47.00%
Return on equity: (-24.00%)
Cash ($ mil.): 314
Current ratio: 2.00
Long-term debt ($ mil.): 674

No. of shares (mil.): 8
Dividends
  Yield: —
  Payout: —
Market value ($ mil.): 30

	STOCK PRICE ($) FY Close	P/E High/Low		PER SHARE ($) Earnings	Dividends	Book Value
12/18	4.00	—	—	(15.00)	0.00	56.00
12/17	4.00	7	3	1.00	0.00	71.00
12/16	7.00	—	—	(0.00)	0.00	70.00
12/15	9.00	5	3	4.00	0.00	71.00
12/14	13.00	2	1	8.00	0.00	68.00
Annual Growth	(26.1%)	—	—	—	—	(4.8%)

Travelers Companies Inc (The)

Running a business is a risk The Travelers Companies will insure. While it does offer personal auto and homeowners insurance the company's largest segment is commercial property/casualty insurance to businesses big and small. It is one of the largest business insurers in the US providing commercial auto property workers' compensation marine and general and financial liability coverage to companies in North America (the largest percentage of business) and the UK. The company also offers surety and fidelity bonds as well as professional and management liability coverage for commercial operations.

Operations

Travelers operates in three segments — Business Insurance Personal Insurance and Bond & Specialty Insurance.

The Business Insurance segment (which accounts for about 50% of net earned premiums) offers property/casualty insurance and related services to clients — primarily in the US as well as in Canada the UK Ireland and throughout other parts of the world as a corporate member of Lloyd's.

The Personal Insurance segment offers homeowners auto flood and umbrella policies. That segment which is growing by geographic expansion accounts for more than 30% of the group's premiums.

The Bond & Specialty Insurance segment writes fidelity and surety general liability and property workers' compensation commercial automobile and commercial multi-peril lines. It accounts for about 10% of net earned premiums.

Travelers also offers reinsurance.

Geographic Reach

The vast majority (about 95%) of Travelers' business is in the US. It also operates in the UK through two arms: Travelers Insurance Company and Travelers Syndicate Management within Lloyd's of London. Those businesses offer commercial property/casualty and risk management services. Additionally Travelers has modest operations in Canada Brazil India China and Ireland. It's looking to expand in Latin America.

The company employs field claim management teams in 20 centers and 53 satellite and specialty-only offices in some 45 states.

Sales and Marketing

Travelers' customers include commercial businesses government agencies associations and individuals.

The company's offerings are distributed through independent agents and brokers across the US. In the Business Insurance segment some 11000 agents are supported by three customer service centers and about 115 field offices. The unit also writes business abroad where its products are distributed through Lloyd's wholesale and retail brokers.

Personal products are distributed through some 10300 independent agents employee and affinity groups and direct marketing. Meanwhile the Bond & Specialty Insurance segment distributes products through some 5600 independent agents and brokers.

Financial Performance

Travelers' revenues have maintained a slow-but-steady growth rate in recent years — a sign that the company has spread itself smoothly across industries and has taken no significant hits to its premiums. In 2017 revenue rose 3% to $28.9 billion as premiums and net realized investment gains grew. The Personal Insurance segment saw the highest relative gains with a 10% increase in earned premiums.

Net income has fallen for the past three years and in 2017 it declined 32% to $2.1 billion. This was largely due to an increase in claims and claim adjustment expenses. The company had catastrophe losses of $2 billion from the impact of hurricanes Harvey and Irma California wildfires and severe wind and hail storms.

The lower net income led to a decline in operating cash flow which fell 10% to $3.8 billion.

Strategy

Travelers targets growth in operating return on equity over time in the mid-teens with the notion that economic cycles weather patterns and other factors can impact its business from year to year. The company follows disciplined underwriting and investment strategies to help it stay immune to market fluctuations and lingering depressed interest rates.

The firm also follows a disciplined acquisition strategy seeking opportunities that will help it expand into new geographic markets or build on its existing product portfolio. Although Travelers is first and foremost a US-based insurer it has recently made acquisitions that have expanded its operations in Canada the UK and Brazil as well as providing it with entry into Colombia's market.

Another key strategy for Travelers is to innovate to improve the way it conducts business. It has its eye on technology from data and analytics to digital sales (as evidenced by its 2017 acquisition of UK-based Simply Business).

Travelers also innovates to create new types of coverage. In 2018 the company launched the Traverse personal insurance product marketed to consumers who don't need traditional auto or home coverage; it includes personal liability identity theft and property theft coverage. It also introduced Quantum Home 2.0 a homeowners product offering policy customization and simpler customer

communications. Also that year its Canadian division began offering human resources and legal assistance services (at no charge) to its small business customers.

Like all property/casualty insurers the company is vulnerable to severe weather and natural disasters. For example it had catastrophe losses of $2 billion in 2017 due to the impact of hurricanes wildfires and severe storms. To mitigate these types of losses Travelers prefers to raise prices in manageable gradual increments.

The company's three educational initiatives for 2018 are centered on reducing distracted driving increasing cybersecurity and tackling small business challenges. It has presented numerous forums free to the public around these issues.

Mergers and Acquisitions

Travelers Companies acquired Simply Business a UK-based online business insurance broker for $490 million in 2017. Simply Business offers small business coverage; the acquisition helped Travelers expand its digital channels in the UK and beyond.

HISTORY

St. Paul Minnesota was a boomtown in 1852 thanks to traffic on the Mississippi. Settlers knew fire insurance was a must in their wooden town but there were no local insurers. Buying policies from eastern companies and getting claims processed was difficult — especially in the winter when river traffic stopped.

In 1853 a group of local investors led by George and John Farrington and Alexander Wilkin formed St. Paul Mutual Insurance a mixed stock and mutual company (mutual members shared in the firm's profits and losses while stockholders could benefit by selling if the company's value rose). St. Paul Mutual sold its first policy the following year.

The company changed its name in 1865 to St. Paul Fire and Marine Insurance stopped offering mutual policies and expanded throughout the Midwest. Claims from the Chicago Fire in 1871 nearly sank the company which assessed its shareholders $15 for each share of stock but prompt and full payment of claims resulted in more business. By the turn of the century St. Paul Fire and Marine was operating nationwide.

Although the company was hard hit by shipping losses in WWI it continued expanding joining other US insurers in the American Foreign Insurance Association to market insurance in Europe.

In 1926 St. Paul Fire and Marine organized its first subsidiary St. Paul Mercury Indemnity to write liability insurance policies. Other additions included coverage for automobiles aircraft burglary and robbery and in 1940 turkey farming.

During WWII St. Paul Fire and Marine joined the War Damage Corp. a government-financed consortium that paid claims for war damage. The St. Paul Companies was formed in 1968 as the umbrella organization for the various subsidiaries and the firm grew through purchases.

Lines of business blossomed during the 1970s including life and title insurance leasing a mail-order consumer finance company oil and gas and real estate. Many of these were sold during the 1980s but one The John Nuveen Co. (1974) became the nucleus of St. Paul's financial services operations.

EXECUTIVES

Evp And Chief Administrative Officer, Andy F. Bessette, age 66

President And Coo, Brian W. MacLean, age 66, $962,548 total compensation

Vice Chairman And Cfo, Jay S. Benet, age 67, $1,000,000 total compensation

Evp And Chief Human Resources Officer, John P. Clifford, age 63

Evp Strategic Development And Corporate Treasurer, Maria Olivo, age 54

Evp And General Counsel, Kenneth F. (Ken) Spence, age 64

Evp Marketing And Communications, Lisa M. Caputo, age 55

Evp Enterprise Risk Management, Fred R. Donner, age 62

Vice Chairman Chief Legal Officer And Evp Financial Professional And International Insurance, Alan D. Schnitzer, age 54, $1,000,000 total compensation

President Field Management, Patrick J. Kinney

Evp; President Personal Insurance, Michael F. Klein

Evp Public Policy; President The Travelers Institute, Joan Kois Woodward

Evp; President Bond And Specialty Insurance, Thomas M. (Tom) Kunkel

Evp; President Business Insurance, Greg C Toczydlowski

Evp; President International, Kevin C. Smith

Evp And Cio, Madelyn Lankton

Evp Claim Services And Specialty Liability, Robert C. (Bob) Brody

Evp And Chief Underwriting Officer, Marlyss J. Gage

Evp And Chief Risk Officer, Bruce R. Jones

Evp President National Accounts And First Party, William C Malugen

Evp And President Small Commercial, Behram M. Dinshaw

Evp And President Middle Market, Scott F. Higgins

Evp Management Liability, Jeffrey P. (Jeff) Klenk

Vp Finance And Workforce Analytic, Todd Clements

Claim Center Vice President, Claude Howard

Senior Vice President Human Resources, Jason Angilan

Vice President Product Strategy, Patty Koziol

Vp And Cio Bond And Fp Information Systems, Dave Condren

Regional Vice President Construction, Carol Matthys

Second Vice President Corporate Audit, Debra Barlow

Regional Vice President, Greg Michels

Regional Vice President, Carl Miller

2vp Complex Claim Specialist, Milena Ivanis

Regional Vice President Select Group, Sean Ramalho

Vice President, John Komidar

Second Vice President Finance And Governance, Jeffrey Longo

Vice President, Ken Chapman

Assistant Vice President, Lisa Schultze

Legal Secretary, Tonya Church

Division President, Maureen Bass

Second Vice President Credit Risk Management, Charles Chamberlain

2 Vice President, John Caranfa

Corporate Vice President, Jim Stevenson

Regional Vice President Select Accounts Kansas City, Bryan Whipple

Regional Vice President, Mark Lear

Second Vice President Subro Major Case Unit, Jean Drufner

Vice President Finance And Investment, Robert Nelson

Second Vice President General Liability, Donald Nichols

Senior Vice President, Scott Belden

Field Product Line Manager 2vp Auto Claims, Trevor Engels

2vp, Carla Schirm

2vp And Actuary, Dan Carr

Vp Hr Compensation Benefits And Operations, Greg Landmark

Second Vp Information Systems, Vincent Bryan
Evp And President Business Insurance, Gregory
  Toczydlowski
Second Vp Bond And Financial Products;
  Enterprise Lead Cyber Insurance, Timothy Francis
Svp Auto Property And Catastrophe Claim, Patrick
  Gee
2vp And Senior Counsel, Lori Dube
Regional Vice President, Tad Cluff
Regional Vice President, Jim Jarvis
Vice President Human Resources, Janette Suffern
Vp Government Affairs, John Miletti
Vice President Finance, Carl Cavaliere
Vp Business Development, Peter Crichton
Svp And Group General Counsel Corporate
  Litigation, Peter Schwartz
Second Vice President Wc Product Group, Julie
  Morgan
Vice President, Alan Wirkman
Vice President, John Coyne
Vice President Southeast Region Select Accounts,
  James Albert
2nd Vice President, David Roy
Svp Chief Human Resource Officer, Axel
  Freudmann
Senior Vice President, James Scannell
National Accounts Vice President, Peter Heard
Second Vice President Benefits, Linda Scalzo
Second Vice President, Cynthia Mims
Regional Vice President Commercial Accounts
  Midwest Region, Genus Dalton
Regional Vice President Personal Insurance
  South Central Region, Doug Purcell
Second Vice President And Actuary, David Lesieur
Second Vice President Business Project Center,
  Michael Figulski
Second Vice President Pi Platform And
  Experience, Bill Zielinski
2vp Regional Risk Control Director, Harvey Berns
Zone Vice President, John Liptak
Assistant Vice President, Jose Flores
Claim Vice President, Keith Andersen
Regional Vice President Inland Marine, John
  Custer
Second Vice President Of Business Intelligence,
  Pranay Mittal
Senior Vice President Of Business Insurance
  Claims, Vincent J Armentano
Vice President Product Management Personal
  Insurance, Sigurd Peterson
Evp And Chief Investment Officer, William H. (Bill)
  Heyman, age 71
Vice Chairman And Chief Legal Officer, Avrohom J.
  Kess
Secretary, Nerissa Soufi
Auditors: KPMG LLP

LOCATIONS

HQ: Travelers Companies Inc (The)
485 Lexington Avenue, New York, NY 10017
Phone: 917 778-6000
Web: www.travelers.com

2017 Sales

	$ mil.	% of total
US	27,253	94
Canada	1,232	4
Other	417	2
Total	**28,902**	**100**

PRODUCTS/OPERATIONS

2017 Sales

	$ mil.	% of total
Premiums	25,683	89
Net investment income	2,397	8
Fees	447	1
Investment gains	216	1
Other	159	1
Total	**28,902**	**100**

Selected Products

Business
Commercial Automobile
Commercial Multi-Peril
Commercial Property
General Liability
Workers' Compensation
Individual
Affinity Auto and Home Program
Auto Insurance
Boat and Yacht Insurance
Condo Insurance
Flood Insurance
Homeowners Insurance
Identity Fraud Protection
Renters Insurance
Umbrella Insurance
Valuable Items Coverage
Wedding and Private Events Insurance

Selected Subsidiaries and Divisions

J. Malucelli Participacoes em Seguros e Resseguros S.A.
  (49.5% Brazil)
St. Paul Fire and Marine Insurance Company
Travelers Property Casualty Corp.
  The Standard Fire Insurance Company
  Travelers Casualty and Surety Company
  Travelers Casualty and Surety Company of America
  The Travelers Indemnity Company
  First Floridian Auto and Home Insurance Company
  The Premier Insurance Co. of Massachusetts
Travelers Insurance Company Limited (UK)
Travelers Syndicate Management Limited (UK)

COMPETITORS

AIG	Chubb Limited
AXA	Liberty Mutual Agency
Allianz	Markel
Allstate	Nationwide
American Financial	The Hartford
Group	W. R. Berkley
CNA Financial	Zurich Insurance Group

HISTORICAL FINANCIALS

Company Type: Public

Income Statement

FYE: December 31

	ASSETS ($ mil.)	NET INCOME ($ mil.)	INCOME AS % OF ASSETS	EMPLOYEES
12/18	104,233	2,523	2.4%	30,400
12/17	103,483	2,056	2.0%	30,800
12/16	100,245	3,014	3.0%	30,900
12/15	100,184	3,439	3.4%	30,900
12/14	103,078	3,692	3.6%	30,200
Annual Growth	0.3%	(9.1%)	—	0.2%

2018 Year-End Financials

Debt ratio: 6.00%
Return on equity: 11.00%
Cash ($ mil.): 373
Current ratio: —
Long-term debt ($ mil.): —

No. of shares (mil.): 264
Dividends
  Yield: 3.0%
  Payout: 33.0%
Market value ($ mil.): 31,566

	STOCK PRICE ($) FY Close	P/E High/Low		PER SHARE ($) Earnings	Dividends	Book Value
12/18	120.00	16	12	9.00	3.00	87.00
12/17	136.00	18	16	7.00	3.00	87.00
12/16	122.00	12	10	10.00	3.00	83.00
12/15	113.00	11	9	11.00	2.00	80.00
12/14	106.00	10	7	11.00	2.00	77.00
Annual Growth	3.1%	—	—	(3.5%)	9.0%	3.0%

TreeHouse Foods Inc

TreeHouse Foods Inc. is a leading manufacturer and distributor of private label and branded packaged foods and beverages in North America. The company makes shelf stable refrigerated frozen and fresh products including baked goods (refrigerated and frozen dough cereal pretzels and snack bars); beverages (broth single serve hot beverages creamers and powdered drinks); and meal solutions (dressings hot cereal macaroni and cheese and pasta). TreeHouse makes private-label products for foodservice distributors and restaurant chains as well as for supermarkets and mass merchandisers. The company also works with co-pack business and industrial customers. With most of its revenue generated in the US the company operates more than 40 manufacturing facilities across the US Canada and Italy.

Operations

TreeHouse's product categories include beverages salad dressings beverage enhancers pickles sauces cereals dry dinners jams and other products. It also offers natural organic and preservative-free ingredients in many categories. Before it sold its snacks business to Atlas Holdings in 2019 the company had five product segments. Baked goods is the largest segment accounting for about a quarter of total sales. Its condiments snacks and meals segments each accounted for about 20% each while the rest comes from beverages.

Geographic Reach

Headquartered in Oak Brook Illinois TreeHouse has offices in Green Bay Wisconsin; Omaha Nebraska; St. Louis Missouri; and Winona and Ontario Canada. It also operates over 40 manufacturing facilities across the US Canada and Italy. TreeHouse rings up more than 90% of its sales in the US while over 5% comes from Canada.

Sales and Marketing

TreeHouse markets its products to retailers such as supermarkets mass merchandisers and specialty retailers. It also markets to the foodservice industry including foodservice distributors and national restaurant operators. Retail giant Wal-Mart Stores is TreeHouse's largest customer accounting for more than 20% of its sales each year. Treehouse's ten largest customers account for nearly 60% of sales.

Financial Performance

Treehouse Foods has seen uneven revenue growth in recent years as consolidation of the retail grocery and foodservice industry has increased competition. Since 2014 sales have grown by 97% driven primarily by acquisitions.

Revenue fell to $5.8 billion in 2018 an approximately 8% decrease from the year prior. The decrease was driven by an SKU rationalization plan the divestiture of the McCann's oatmeal business and the sale of its canned soup and infant feeding business.

Net loss was $61.4 million in fiscal year 2018 smaller than the $286.2 million loss in fiscal year 2017. Operating expenses decreased by 40% in fiscal 2018 to $887.5 million.

Cash provided by operating activities was $505.8 million in fiscal 2018 while investing activities used $160.9 million. Financing activities used $311 million.

Strategy

To begin accelerating growth amid a challenging market Treehouse Foods has been streamlining and simplifying its operations and product offerings.

The company is facing an increased competitive environment in the retail and foodservice channels which have undergone significant consolidation in recent years. Treehouse Foods is competing for the business of fewer and larger customers while weighing the market impact of nimble e-commerce grocers.

In 2019 Treehouse Foods decided to sell its Snacks Division to Atlas Holdings in 2019. The company says the sale came after a strategic review of the snack business. Treehouse Foods sold its McCann oatmeal business to B&G Foods in 2018 as part of its strategy to concentrate on private label manufacturing.

The company sees growth potential in "premium" and "better-for-you" products and is investing in these areas.

Company Background

Treehouse Foods was incorporated in January 2005 by Dean Foods Company to accomplish a spin-off of certain specialty businesses to its shareholders which was completed on June 27 2005.

HISTORY

Dean Foods combined the businesses of its specialty foods group and its foodservice salad-dressing business in 2005 in order to create publicly traded TreeHouse Foods.

In 2006 the company it purchased pickle-maker Oxford Foods. It paid $275 million for the private-label soup and baby food (Nature's Goodness) businesses of Del Monte Foods. The following year it acquired San Antonio Farms a private-label Mexican sauce maker for about $89 million in cash. That year it also purchased DeGraffenreid a processor and distributor of pickles and related products for the foodservice industry from Bell-Carter Foods for $10.8 million. Strengthening its Canadian footprint in 2007 the company acquired Ontario-based E.D. Smith & Sons a manufacturer of branded sauces jellies jams and pie fillings for $220 million in cash plus the assumption of $100 million in debt.

TreeHouse also bought Sturm Foods a maker of private-label hot cereal and powdered soft drink mixes from HM Capital Partners for $660 million in 2010. The move strengthened TreeHouse's private-label operations as well as its packaging mixing and flavoring capabilities. Extending its reach in shelf-stable foods TreeHouse bought out S.T. Specialty Foods from Windjammer Capital Investors in an all-cash deal valued at about $180 million. S.T. Specialty Foods primarily makes private-label macaroni and cheese and skillet dinners mainstream staples of the dine-at-home

The company bought Naturally Fresh a privately-owned maker of refrigerated dressings sauces dips and marinades in 2012 for $25 million. The deal took TreeHouse from the shelf-stable grocery aisle to the refrigerated produce section providing a premium presence. In 2012 TreeHouse acquired the assets of the Aseptic Cheese and Pudding business from Associated Milk Producers Inc. The business sells products to foodservice and retail customers and strengthened the TreeHouse's existing Bay Valley Foods aseptic operation.

EXECUTIVES

Chairman President And Ceo, Sam K. Reed, age 73, $1,056,250 total compensation

Evp General Counsel And Chief Administrative Officer, Thomas E. O'Neill, age 64, $533,167 total compensation

Evp And Cfo, Matthew J. Foulston, age 55, $45,672 total compensation

Svp And Chief Strategy Officer, Rachel R. Bishop, age 45, $439,333 total compensation

Vp And Assistant General Counsel, Jo Osborn

Vice President, Eric Lockington

Vp Legal And Chief Compliance Officer, Courtney Esko

Senior Vice President Marketing, Tammy Gianfortune

Senior Vice President Human Resources, Lori Roberts

Svp And Chief Strategy Officer, Maurice Alkemade

Vice President And Treasurer, Lee Wise

National Account Manager, Alex Pesce

Vice President Of Sales, Dave Olson

Vice President Compensation Benefits And Human Resources Systems, Laurie Augustyn-Fierg

Vice President Regulatory And Food Safety, Sara Reddington

Vice President Of Marketing Snacks, Sarah Testa

Vice President Sales, Dean Erlandson

Vp Quality Systems, Stacey Popham

Evp Controller And Chief Accounting, John Waldron

Vice President Internal Audit, Allen Cooper

Senior Vice President Sales, Judy Clark

Vice President, Curt Balara

Vice President Continuous Improvement, David Hart

Vice President Of Supply Chain Services And Strategy, Ernest Chacon

Senior Vice President Sales, George Miketa

Senior Vice President Marketing, Harry Overly

Svp And Chief Commercial Officer, Dean General

Vice President Sales, Derek Glenzinski

Svp, Chris C Wilkins

Auditors: DELOITTE & TOUCHE LLP

LOCATIONS

HQ: TreeHouse Foods Inc
2021 Spring Road, Suite 600, Oak Brook, IL 60523
Phone: 708 483-1300
Web: www.treehousefoods.com

2016 Sales

	% of total
North America	91
Outside North America	9
Total	**100**

PRODUCTS/OPERATIONS

2016 Sales

	$ mil.	% of total
North American Retail Grocery	5,093	76
Food Away From Home	547	12
Industrial & Export	545	12
Unallocated	(9.9)	-
Total	**6,175**	**100**

2016 Sales

	$ mil.	% of total
Snacks	1,334	22
Retail bakery	663	11
Cookies and crackers	608	10
Cereals	552	9
Pasta and dry dinners	544	9
Beverages	492	8
Salad dressings	376	6
Soup and infant feeding	373	6
Sauces	336	5
Pickles	318	5
Beverage enhancers	314	5
Jams	108	2
Aseptic products	101	1
Other products	57	1
Total	**6,175**	**100**

Selected Products & Brands

Food Away From Home (foodservice)
  Saucemaker
  Schwartz
Jams & jellies
  E.D. Smith
  Habitant
Liquid egg substitute
  Second Nature
Non-dairy creamer
  Cremora
Pickles

  Farman's
  Nalley's
  Peter Piper
  Steinfeld
Refrigerated
  Mocha Mix
Salad dressings sauces & marinades
  Private label
Sauces & syrups
  Bennett's
  Hoffman House
  Roddenberry's Northwoods
  San Antonio Farms
Soups broths & gravies
  Private label

COMPETITORS

B&G Foods	Kellogg
Campbell Soup	Lancaster Colony
ConAgra	Marzetti
Cott	McCormick & Company
Dean Foods	Mondelez International
Farmer Bros.	Newman's Own
Flowers Foods	Pinnacle Foods Inc
General Mills	Post Holdings
Goya	Reser's Fine Foods
Hain Celestial	Smucker
Heinz	Snyder's-Lance
J & J Snack Foods	

HISTORICAL FINANCIALS

Company Type: Public

Income Statement

FYE: December 31

	REVENUE ($ mil.)	NET INCOME ($ mil.)	NET PROFIT MARGIN	EMPLOYEES
12/18	5,812	(61)	—	12,700
12/17	6,307	(286)	—	13,489
12/16	6,175	(229)	—	16,027
12/15	3,206	115	3.6%	5,880
12/14	2,946	90	3.1%	6,181
Annual Growth	**18.5%**	**—**		**19.7%**

2018 Year-End Financials

Debt ratio: 41.00%	No. of shares (mil.): 56
Return on equity: (-3.00%)	Dividends
Cash ($ mil.): 164	Yield: —
Current ratio: 2.00	Payout: —
Long-term debt ($ mil.): 2,297	Market value ($ mil.): 2,840

	STOCK PRICE ($) FY Close	P/E High/Low		PER SHARE ($)		
				Earnings	Dividends	Book Value
12/18	51.00	—	—	(1.00)	0.00	38.00
12/17	49.00	—	—	(5.00)	0.00	40.00
12/16	72.00	—	—	(4.00)	0.00	44.00
12/15	78.00	35	26	3.00	0.00	43.00
12/14	86.00	39	28	2.00	0.00	41.00
Annual Growth	**(12.3%)**	—	—	—	—	**(1.9%)**

TriCo Bancshares (Chico, CA)

People looking for a community bank in California's Sacramento Valley can try TriCo. TriCo Bancshares is the holding company for Tri Counties Bank which serves customers through some 65 traditional and in-store branches in 23 counties in Northern and Central California. Founded in 1974 Tri Counties Bank provides a variety of deposit services including checking and savings accounts money market accounts and CDs. Most patrons are retail customers and small to midsized businesses. The bank primarily originates real estate mortgages which account for about 65% of its loan portfolio; consumer loans contribute about 25%. TriCo has agreed to acquire rival North Valley Bancorp.

Operations

In addition to its retail banking products and services the company provides wholesale banking and investment services; TriCo offers brokerage services through an arrangement with Raymond James Financial. The company does not provide trust or international banking services.

Geographic Reach

Based in Chico California Tri Counties Bank operates 66 branches (41 traditional branches and 25 in-store branches) in 23 counties in Northern and central California including Fresno Kern Mendocino Napa Sacramento and Yuba counties.

Financial Performance

In 2013 net interest income the company's primary source of revenue rose 0.6% compared with 2012 to $102.2 million. The slight increase in net interest income was mainly due to a decrease in average balance of other borrowings a shift in deposit balances from relatively high interest rate earning time deposits to noninterest-earning demand and savings deposits an increase in the average balance of investments securities and an increase in the average balance of loans; all of which were substantially offset by a decrease in the average yield on loans.

Strategy

The bank's growth has been fueled by acquisitions and the opening of new branches; it frequently opens branches within grocery stores or other retailers including Wal-Mart. TriCo in 2010 acquired the three branches of Granite Community Bank which had been seized by regulators. The transaction which also included most of the failed bank's assets and deposits was facilitated by the FDIC and includes a loss-sharing agreement with the agency. The following year TriCo acquired Citizens Bank of Northern California. The FDIC-assisted deal included seven branches. The acquisitions are part of TriCo's strategy of adding new customers.

Mergers and Acquisitions

TriCo in January 2014 announced plans to buy its rival in Northern California North Valley Bancorp (NVB) for about $178.4 million. NVB is the parent company of North Valley Bank which had about $918 million in assets and 22 commercial banking offices across eight Northern California counties at the end of 2013. At closing which is expected in the second or third quarter of 2014 NVB will be merged into Tri Counties Bank. The combined bank would have about $3.6 billion in assets.

EXECUTIVES

Evp And Cfo Trico Bancshares And Tri Counties Bank, Thomas J. (Tom) Reddish, age 59, $309,601 total compensation

Evp And Chief Credit Officer, Craig B. Carney, age 60, $274,932 total compensation

Evp Wholesale Banking, Richard B. O'Sullivan, age 62, $260,890 total compensation

President And Ceo, Richard P. Smith, age 61, $549,846 total compensation

Evp And Coo, John S. Fleshood, age 57

Evp And Chief Retail Banking Officer, Daniel K. (Dan) Bailey, age 50, $268,335 total compensation

Svp And Cio, Bruce Barnett

Vice President Facilities Expansion Ma, Chimene Sonsteng

Vice President Marketing, Dan Herbert

Senior Vice President Special Assets Manager, Steve Macrae

Senior Vice President, Mark Davis

Senior Vice President, Brent Mcclure

Chairman, William J. Casey, age 74

Vice Chairman, Michael W. Koehnen, age 58

Board Member, Virginia Walker

Auditors: Moss Adams LLP

LOCATIONS

HQ: TriCo Bancshares (Chico, CA)
63 Constitution Drive, Chico, CA 95973
Phone: 530 898-0300
Web: www.tcbk.com

PRODUCTS/OPERATIONS

2015 Sales

	$ mil.	% of total
Interest		
Loans including fees	132	64
Debt securities	27	13
Dividends	2	1
Other	1	.
Noninterest		
Service charges & fees	32	16
Commissions	3	2
Gain on sale of loans	3	1
Other	7	3
Total	207	100

Selected Services

Business debit cards
Business online banking
Business workshops
Cash management
Education savings and CDs
Loans and credits
Merchant services
Order checks
Overdraft services
Pension and retirement
Personal certificates of deposit
Personal checking
Personal savings and money market
Retirement savings and CDs

COMPETITORS

Bank of America	MUFG Americas Holdings
Bank of the West	PremierWest
Central Valley	Wells Fargo
Community Bancorp	Westamerica

HISTORICAL FINANCIALS

Company Type: Public

Income Statement · FYE: December 31

	ASSETS ($ mil.)	NET INCOME ($ mil.)	INCOME AS % OF ASSETS	EMPLOYEES
12/18	6,352	68	1.1%	1,174
12/17	4,761	41	0.9%	1,023
12/16	4,518	45	1.0%	1,063
12/15	4,221	44	1.0%	1,011
12/14	3,916	26	0.7%	1,009
Annual Growth	12.9%	27.2%	—	3.9%

2018 Year-End Financials

Debt ratio: 1.00%
Return on equity: 10.00%
Cash ($ mil.): 228
Current ratio: —
Long-term debt ($ mil.): —

No. of shares (mil.): 30
Dividends
 Yield: 2.0%
 Payout: 37.0%
Market value ($ mil.): 1,028

	STOCK PRICE ($) FY Close	P/E High/Low	PER SHARE ($) Earnings	Dividends	Book Value
12/18	34.00	16 12	3.00	1.00	27.00
12/17	38.00	25 19	2.00	1.00	22.00
12/16	34.00	18 12	2.00	1.00	21.00
12/15	27.00	15 12	2.00	1.00	20.00
12/14	25.00	19 15	1.00	0.00	18.00
Annual Growth	8.1%	— —	14.8%	12.3%	10.3%

TRINITY HEALTH CORPORATION

EXECUTIVES

Pres-Ceo, Michael Slubowski

Sr V Pres-Cmo, Donald Bignotti

Sr V Pres-Chief Investment Off, James Bosscher

Sr V Pres, Paul F Conlon

Sr V Pres, Louis J Fierens II

Sr V Pres, Rebecca Havlisch

Sr V Pres-Chief Nursing Care, G Landstrom

Sr V Pres-Chief Info Officer, Marcus B Shipley

SEC, Paul G Neumann

Coo, Benjamin Carter

Chief Expi Officer, Cassandra Willis-Abner

Auditors: DELOITTE & TOUCHE LLP DETROIT

LOCATIONS

HQ: TRINITY HEALTH CORPORATION
20555 VICTOR PKWY, LIVONIA, MI 481527031
Phone: 734 343-1000
Web: WWW.TRINITY-HEALTH.ORG

COMPETITORS

Advocate Health Care	Odyssey HealthCare
Amedisys	OhioHealth
Ascension Health	Resurrection Health
Beaumont Health System	Care
Community Health	St. Luke's Health
Systems	System
HCA	Tenet Healthcare
Health Management	Universal Health
Associates	Services
HealthSouth	University of Chicago
Henry Ford Health	Medical Center
System	VITAS Healthcare
Hospice of Michigan	Vanguard Health
Johns Hopkins Medicine	Systems
Kindred Healthcare	Wheaton Franciscan
Mayo Clinic	Services
MedStar Health	
Memorial Hospital	
& Health System	

HISTORICAL FINANCIALS

Company Type: Private

Income Statement · FYE: June 30

	REVENUE ($ mil.)	NET INCOME ($ mil.)	NET PROFIT MARGIN	EMPLOYEES
06/18	18,345	1,359	7.4%	51,100
06/15	1,376	19	1.4%	
Annual Growth	137.1%	314.2%	—	—

TriState Capital Holdings Inc

TriState Capital Holdings has found its niche right in the middle of the banking industry. The holding company owns TriState Capital Bank a regional business bank that caters to midsized businesses or those annually earning between $5 million and $300 million. TriState Capital also offers private banking services nationally to high-net-worth individuals. Its loan portfolio consists of about 50% commercial loans 30% commercial real estate loans and 20% private banking-personal loans. The bank serves clients from branches in Cleveland; New Jersey; New York City Philadelphia and Pittsburgh. Altogether it has some $2 billion in assets. TriState Capital went public in mid-2013.

IPO
The company does not have any specific plans outlined for its proceeds but will likely use it for general corporate purposes which might include maintaining liquidity at the holding company providing equity capital to the bank to fund balance sheet growth and possibly investing in or acquiring wealth management businesses.

Strategy
The company's founders saw an opportunity in serving what they perceived was an underserved market — midsized businesses. Consolidation had left major national banks catering to individuals and large businesses while community banks served individuals and small businesses.

Company Background
TriState Capital was founded in 2007 by two banking industry executives — chairman and CEO James Getz who spent 20 years at Federated Investors and vice chairman William Schenck the former secretary of banking for Pennsylvania.

EXECUTIVES

Chairman President And Ceo, James F. (Jim) Getz, $1,500,000 total compensation
President Commercial Banking, David A. Molnar
Vice Chairman And Cfo, Mark L. Sullivan, $425,000 total compensation
Regional President New Jersey, Kenneth R. Orchard
Regional President New York, Thomas N. Gilmartin
Regional President Ohio, John D. Barrett
Regional President Eastern Pennsylvania, Joseph M. Finley
Regional President Western Pennsylvania, Vince Locher
President Private Bank Team, Charles C. Fawcett
President And Ceo Tristate Capital Bank, Brian S. Fetterolf
Senior Vice President Relationship Manager, Michael Blasko
Senior Vice President, Sheila Roberts
Senior Vice President, John Buglione
Senior Vice President Commercial Real Estate Finance, David Segal
Senior Vice President, Tim Moriarity
Senior Vice President, Paul Steiger
Vice Chairman, A. William (Bill) Schenck
Auditors: KPMG LLP

LOCATIONS
HQ: TriState Capital Holdings Inc
One Oxford Centre, 301 Grant Street, Suite 2700, Pittsburgh, PA 15219
Phone: 412 304-0304   **Fax:** 412 304-0391
Web: www.tristatecapitalbank.com

PRODUCTS/OPERATIONS

2015 Sales

	$ mil.	% of total
Interest income		
Loans	79	67
Investments	4	3
Interest-earning deposits	0	
Noninterest income		
Investment management fees	30	25
Commitment and other fees	2	2
Other income	4	3
Total	119	100

COMPETITORS

Bank of America	HSBC Private Bank
Bank of New York Mellon	Herald National Bank
	JPMorgan Private Bank
Boston Private	Julius Baer
Brown Brothers Harriman	Lakeland Bancorp
	M&T Bank
Citigroup	Safra Bank
Citigroup Private Bank	U.S. Trust
First Republic (CA)	

HISTORICAL FINANCIALS
Company Type: Public

Income Statement
FYE: December 31

	ASSETS ($ mil.)	NET INCOME ($ mil.)	INCOME AS % OF ASSETS	EMPLOYEES
12/18	6,036	54	0.9%	257
12/17	4,778	38	0.8%	230
12/16	3,930	29	0.7%	224
12/15	3,303	22	0.7%	192
12/14	2,847	16	0.6%	182
Annual Growth	20.7%	36.0%	—	9.0%

2018 Year-End Financials
Debt ratio: 7.00%
Return on equity: 13.00%
Cash ($ mil.): 184
Current ratio: —
Long-term debt ($ mil.): —
No. of shares (mil.): 29
Dividends
Yield: —
Payout: —
Market value ($ mil.): 562

	STOCK PRICE ($) FY Close	P/E High/Low		PER SHARE ($) Earnings	Dividends	Book Value
12/18	19.00	16	10	2.00	0.00	17.00
12/17	23.00	18	15	1.00	0.00	14.00
12/16	22.00	22	11	1.00	0.00	12.00
12/15	14.00	18	12	1.00	0.00	12.00
12/14	10.00	26	16	1.00	0.00	11.00
Annual Growth	17.4%	—	—	34.7%	—	11.1%

Triumph Bancorp Inc

Auditors: Crowe LLP

LOCATIONS
HQ: Triumph Bancorp Inc
12700 Park Central Drive, Suite 1700, Dallas, TX 75251
Phone: 214 365-6900
Web: www.triumphbancorp.com

HISTORICAL FINANCIALS
Company Type: Public

Income Statement
FYE: December 31

	ASSETS ($ mil.)	NET INCOME ($ mil.)	INCOME AS % OF ASSETS	EMPLOYEES
12/18	4,560	52	1.1%	1,122
12/17	3,499	36	1.0%	821
12/16	2,641	21	0.8%	705
12/15	1,691	29	1.7%	500
12/14	1,448	18	1.2%	466
Annual Growth	33.2%	30.7%	—	24.6%

2018 Year-End Financials
Debt ratio: 2.00%
Return on equity: 10.00%
Cash ($ mil.): 235
Current ratio: —
Long-term debt ($ mil.): —
No. of shares (mil.): 27
Dividends
Yield: —
Payout: —
Market value ($ mil.): 800

	STOCK PRICE ($) FY Close	P/E High/Low		PER SHARE ($) Earnings	Dividends	Book Value
12/18	30.00	22	13	2.00	0.00	24.00
12/17	32.00	19	11	2.00	0.00	19.00
12/16	26.00	24	12	1.00	0.00	16.00
12/15	17.00	11	8	2.00	0.00	15.00
12/14	14.00	10	8	2.00	0.00	13.00
Annual Growth	21.7%	—	—	7.5%	—	15.6%

Truist Financial Corp

BB&T provides traditional banking insurance investment banking and wealth management services through almost 1900 bank branches mostly in the south and southeastern US. The holding company's flagship subsidiary Branch Banking and Trust (BB&T) is the oldest North Carolina-headquartered bank and a leading originator of residential mortgages in the Southeast. Boasting assets of around $225 billion BB&T is one of the largest financial services holding companies in the US. In February 2019 BB&T agreed to merge with retail and commercial banking services company SunTrust Banks and rebrand as Truist in a $66 billion deal.

Operations
BB&T operates through four segments: Community Banking Retail and Consumer Finance (CB-Retail); Community Banking Commercial (CB-Commercial); Financial Services and Commercial Finance (FS&CF); and Insurance Holdings (IH).

CB-Retail provides standard banking products including loans deposit accounts cards and other financial services. The unit services owner-occupied residential mortgages originated by BB&T and other banks and offers short-term financing for first-lien residential mortgage loans held for sale by independent companies. It also conducts prime and non-prime automobile lending specialty finance and middle market equipment leasing. The CB-Retail segment generates about 45% of the holding company's revenue.

CB-Commercial targets small to large companies and markets business banking products including loans deposit accounts commercial real estate loans dealer inventory financing cash management and treasury. It accounts for roughly 25% of BB&T's revenue.

FS&CF and IH each represent around 15% of the company's total revenue. FS&CF's service offerings encompass personal trust estate planning wealth and asset management corporate retirement and capital markets. It houses BB&T's brokerage and investment bank BB&T Securities. The company's IH segment is the fifth largest insurance agency and brokerage network in the world. It sells property casualty and life insurance and employee benefits to businesses and individuals.

Approximately 60% of the bank's total revenue comes from interest and fees on loans and leases. Some 15% comes from insurance income and 10% comes from interest and dividends on securities.

Geographic Reach

Winston-Salem North Carolina-based BB&T has offices in Florida Pennsylvania Georgia Maryland the Carolinas the Virginias Kentucky Alabama Tennessee Texas Pennsylvania New Jersey and Washington DC. Its largest markets are North Carolina where it has about 300 bank branches; Virginia with around 290 branches; and Florida with some 270 branches.

Sales and Marketing

BB&T serves customers including small and middle-market companies corporations public and government entities and retail clients.

Financial Performance

BB&T has consistently grown its revenue each year since 2014 to yield an overall expansion of about 20%; net income added some 50% in that time.

The holding company's revenue ticked up 2% to $11.6 billion in 2018 spurred by larger loan and lease portfolios and interest rates in its Community Banking Retail and Consumer Finance (CB-Retail) and Community Banking Commercial (CB-Commercial) segments.

BB&T's net income jumped 35% to $3.2 billion that year on improved deposit funding spreads and loan mix.

The company added $904 million to its cash in 2018 to end the year at $4 billion. Operations provided $4.3 billion and financing activities?mainly net change in deposits?contributed $1.5 billion. Loan and lease originations and purchases drove investment spend of $4.9 billion.

Strategy

BB&T has in recent years been following a long-term strategy of diversifying its revenue streams through strategic bank acquisitions and a merger while cutting costs through physical branch closures and ramping up its suite of mobile and online banking offerings.

In 2019 the holding company announced it would merge with retail and commercial banking services company SunTrust Banks in a $66 billion deal that will create the sixth largest bank holding company in the US. The combined company which will rebrand as Truist will have $442 billion in assets $301 billion in loans and $324 billion in deposits.

The company has been carrying out branch closures and layoffs as it consolidates its acquired businesses. The call center for the former Susquehanna Bank (which BB&T acquired in 2015) was shut down in 2017. It has made other branch closures too as the viability of branches is eroded by the rise of internet banking which is also the cheaper option for bank. BB&T had 2136 branches at the end of 2015. By the end of 2018 it had 1874.

BB&T is working to beef up its U digital online banking platform by enhancing its features quarterly. In 2018 it added credit card controls and a personal financial management tool for wealth clients. It improved its digital security that year through its investment in Enigmóan anti-money laundering data-as-a-service company.

Mergers and Acquisitions

In February 2019 BB&T agreed to merge with SunTrust Banks a retail and commercial banking services company with some 1300 offices primarily in Florida Georgia Virginia North Carolina Tennessee Maryland South Carolina and Washington DC. The all-stock deal is valued at $66 billion. SunTrust's middle-market corporate and investment banking business and digital consumer lending platform will complement BB&T's community banking and insurance operations. With about $301 billion in loans the combined company will be the sixth largest US bank based on assets of around $442 billion and deposits of roughly $324 billion. BB&T shareholders will have a 57% stake in the combined company (which will rebrand as Truist) while SunTrust investors will receive 43%.

In 2018 BB&T acquired insurance broker Regions Insurance Group from Regions Financial. Regions has more than 60000 clients in the Southeast Texas and Indiana. The deal improves BB&T's insurance business's property and casualty and employee benefits products.

HISTORY

In 1872 Alpheus Branch son of a wealthy planter founded Branch and Company a mercantile business in Wilson North Carolina. He and Thomas Jefferson Hadley who was organizing a public school system created the Branch and Hadley bank later that same year. The private bank helped rebuild farms and small businesses after the Civil War.

In 1887 Branch bought out Hadley and changed the bank's name to Branch and Company Bankers. Two years later Branch secured a state trust charter for the Wilson Banking and Trust Company. He never got the business running however and died in 1893. The trust charter was amended to change the name to Branch Banking and Company and Branch and Company Bankers was folded into it in 1900.

In 1907 the bank finally got its trust operations running and began calling itself Branch Banking and Trust Company. In 1922 it opened its first insurance department; the next year it started its mortgage loan activities.

BB&T survived the 1929 stock market crash with the help of the Post Office. Nervous customers withdrew their funds from BB&T and other banks and deposited them in postal savings accounts unaware that BB&T was the local Post Office's bank and the withdrawn funds went right back to the bank. BB&T opened six more branches between 1929 and 1933.

After WWII consumerism skyrocketed resulting in more car loans and mortgages. During the 1960s and 1970s the bank embarked on a series of mergers and acquisitions forming the thin end of a buying wedge that would widen significantly in the coming decades.

By 1994 BB&T was the fourth-largest bank in North Carolina. In 1995 it merged with North Carolina's fifth-largest bank Southern National Corp. founded in 1897.

With banking regulations loosening to allow different types of operations BB&T in 1997 made several acquisitions including banks thrifts and securities brokerage Craigie.

BB&T's 1998 activities included three bank acquisitions that pushed it into metro Washington DC. The company also increased holdings in fields such as insurance sales venture capital for Southern businesses and investment banking (through its acquisition of Scott & Stringfellow Financial the South's oldest NYSE member).

In 1999 Craigie was melded into Scott & Stringfellow. That year BB&T bought several insurance companies and small banks. The company

continued its march through the South the following year buying several Georgia banks and Tennessee's BankFirst. In 2001 BB&T purchased South Carolina's FirstSpartan Financial multibank holding company Century South Banks Maryland-based FCNB Corporation and western Georgia's Community First Banking Company. To bolster its presence in the Washington DC market it bought Virginia Capital Bancshares and F&M National.

BB&T purchased Alabama-based Cooney Rikard & Curtin a wholesale insurance broker active in 45 states in 2002. Also that year it added about 100 branches in Kentucky after buying MidAmerica Bancorp and AREA Bancshares and entered the coveted Florida market following its purchase of Regional Financial the privately held parent of First South Bank.

Acquisitions continued the following three years as the bank swallowed First Virginia Banks among other targets. It took a break in 2005 to assimilate its holdings before joining the acquisition hunt in 2006 with deals for banks in Georgia (Main Street Banks) and Tennessee (First Citizens Bancorp) and in South Carolina (Coastal Financial) in 2007.

EXECUTIVES

Chairman And Ceo, Kelly S. King, age 70, $1,075,000 total compensation

President And Coo Bb&t Corporation And Branch Banking & Trust Company, Christopher L. (Chris) Henson, age 57, $700,000 total compensation

Sevp And Cio, Barbara F. Duck, age 52, $507,083 total compensation

Sevp And Deposit Services Manager, Donna C. Goodrich, age 56, $507,083 total compensation

Sevp And Chief Risk Officer, Clarke R. Starnes, age 60, $582,500 total compensation

Sevp And Cfo, Daryl N. Bible, age 57, $590,000 total compensation

Sevp And President Community Banking, David H. Weaver, age 53

Sevp General Counsel Secretary And Chief Corporate Governance Officer, Robert J. Johnson, age 46

Sevp President And Ceo Bb&t Securities Llc And Capital Markets Manager, W. Rufus Yates, age 61

President West Florida Region, Jim Daly, age 58

Sevp And Chief Digital Officer, W. Bennett Bradley, age 57

Sevp And Lending Group Manager, Brant J. Standridge, age 43

Sevp And Chief Client Experience Officer, Dont¯ L. Wilson, age 42

Sevp And Deputy Chief Risk Officer, Jim D. Godwin, age 50

Vice President, Cindy Powell

Vp It Service Management Program Manager, Christian Robinson

Senior Vice President, Ann Hardison

Senior Vice President Strategic Planning Manager Bbandt Corporation, James Anthos

Vice President, Debrah More

Vice President, Sharon Silvermintz

Assistant Vice President Cf Operations Manager, Karen Cruise

Vice President Production Control Manager, Gasford Brown

Vice President Change Management Analysis, Rainer Weppler

Wealth Advisor Assistant Vice President, Tommy Rhyne

Vice President Technology Manager Bank Of America, Stuart Jones

Vice President Benefits Administration Manager, Andrea Branscome

Assistant Vice President Area Operations Team Leader, Tim Frydrych

Senior Vice President, Chip Falk

Msr Valuation Manager Vice President Funds Management, Shiv Bansal
Senior Vice President, Greg Tawes
Vice President Bbandt Insurance, Ben Manning
Assistant Vice President Comme, Deborah Masley
Vice President, Rosie Blackburn
Vice President Infrastructure Technology, Jeffrey Trammell
Assistant Vice President And Team Lead Ediscovery, James Guziak
Senior Vice President, Craig Pascal
Vice President, Vicky Hamblin
Senior Vice President Consulting Actuary, Steven Bull
Assistant Vice President, Ken Zeller
Vice President, Jo Lynn Burgess
Vice President, Gregg Yanok
Vice President, Brett Walser
Assistant Vice President Financial Center Leader Hablo Espaiiol, Gil Rolon
Executive Vice President Chief Market And Liquidity Risk Officer, Steve Buisson
Assistant Vice President, Bonnie Edwards
Vice President Portfolio Risk Officer, Matt Wagner
Vice President, Michael Walter
Assistant Vice President, Jason Matthews
Assistant Vice President, Scott Parks
Vice President, Jane Phillips
Vice President, Karen Starnes
Vice President Personal Trust Specialist, Kim Lamm
Assistant Vice President Business Lendin, David Paske
Assistant Vice President And Underwriting Section Manager, Ana Restrepo
Svp Enterprise Information Management Strategy And Architecture, Michael Vaughan
Senior Vice President Corporate Bankin, Troy Weaver
Senior Vice President Credit Risk Review Team Leader, Nancy Ortkiese
Assistant Vice President Operations Division Production Manager, Rick Marino
Assistant Vice President Large, Cathy Lyons
Vice President, Michael Clevenger
Vice President, Scott Fisher
Senior Vice President Comm'l Fin Loan Admin Manager, John Davis
Vice President, Mark Grunder
Vice President Business Services Officer, Linda Shirley
Senior Vice President, Beth Sterner
Client Information Analyst Vice President, Terri-beth Heffernan
Senior Vice President, Barry Maness
Senior Vice President, Tom Butsch
Senior Vice President, Kelly Sain
Senior Vice President Commerci, Gus Phillips
Vice President, Rick Canipe
Assistant Vice President, Steve Eng
Vice President, Angela Britt
Vice President Network Support Manager, Cherie Otten
Svp And Market President Greensboro Winston Salem North Carolina Area, Jack Lynch
Vice President Business Services Officer Portfolio Manager, Anthony G Steele
Vice President Of Real Estate Acquisition, Brenda Shamloo
Vice President, Shelley Travis
Senior Vice President Senior Credit Officer, Scott Carpenter
Svp Energy Group Denver, Ryan Michael
Vice President Strategic Planning Analyst, Donna Garcia
Supply Chain Management Fulfillment And Governance Vice President, Diane Orzechowski
Vice President, Carol Steinmetz
Assistant Vice President, Terry Donahue
Vice President Commercial Cards, Melanie Epp

Vice President Comm Development, Marlo Scruggs
Vice President, Brian Westcott
Vice President, Lorie Garland
Vice President, David Wesley
Vice President, Jamie Humphrey
Regional Manager Vice President, Julie Simpson
Senior Vice President, Masoud Shahri
Senior Vice President, Bo Wayne
Vice President, Scott Snow
Assistant Vice President, Kevin Barrett
N L Eevp Of Marketing, Carol Bond
Vice President, Al James
Vice President Of Deposit Access, Catherine Kauffman
Senior Vice President It Services Manager Project Office, Gail Fuller
Vice President, Russell Seymour
Assistant Vice President, Paul McManus
Senior Vice President, Eric Lowman
Avp It Vendor Management, Patrick Cleary
Vice President, Abdul Labi
Residential Real Estate Lending Vice President, Keri Jackson
Financial Center Leader Assistant Vice President, Matthew Brown
Wealth Management Vice President, Cole Benoit
Senior Vice President, Len Lewan
Vice President Customer Credit Manager, Michael Catapano
Executive Vice President, Tol Broome
Vice President Employee Benefits Agent, Will Stewart
Senior Executive Vice President, Leon Wilson
Senior Vice President, Robert Searson
Vice President, Steve Paulk
Vice President, Christopher Pearce
Vice President Financial Center Leader, Michelle Haines
Senior Vice President, Mildred Henry
Vice President, John Kincaid
Vice President, Theresa Arrighi
Vice President, Mark Caspero
Vice President, Kelly Fallen
Vice President, Jennifer Weaver
Vice President Corporate Banker, Lamar Barnes
Vice President, Steve Jordan
Information Technology Infrastructure Engineer Client Server Engineer Cs Iv Assistant Vice President, Rufus Bynum
Vice President Surety, Peter Holley
Senior Vice President Corporate Banker Capital Markets, Eric Searls
Senior Vice President Bb And T Information Technology Risk Management, Charlie Hinnant
Vice President, Vanessa Hampton
Senior Vice President, James Holmes
Vice President, Mike Chou
Assistant Vice President It Problem Management Team Lead, Bobby Davenport
Vice President, Ken Powell
Vice President, Lynn Williams
Electronic Delivery Channel Strategist Vice President, Ken Nixon
Senior Vice President, Bradley Orr
Vice President Mortgage Loan Officer, Vincent Spadea
Assistant Vice President Information Technology Resource, Jill Deanhardt
Assistant Vice President Project Manager, Sharon McMichael
Team Lead Vice President, Monte Wheeler
Senior Vice President Operations, Robert Davis
Vice President Operations, Kelly Ferguson
Vice President, Barbara McAllister
Vice President Enterprise Data Governance Bbandt Corporation, Jan England
Vice President, David Samuel
Senior Vice President, Stan Crawford
Vice President, Doug Moore
Vice President, Allen Phinney

Vice President, Becky Barefoot
Vice President Major Accounts Division, William Glass
Vice President Fraud Technology Manager, Mark Steeber
Auditors: PricewaterhouseCoopers LLP

LOCATIONS

HQ: Truist Financial Corp
  200 West Second Street, Winston-Salem, NC 27101
Phone: 336 733-2000   Fax: 336 671-2399
Web: www.bbt.com

2018 sales

	No.
North Carolina	304
Virginia	291
Florida	272
Pennsylvania	221
Maryland	144
Georgia	137
Texas	110
South Carolina	97
Kentucky	86
Alabama	73
West Virginia	59
Tennessee	40
New Jersey	28
Washington D.C.	12
Ohio	3
Indiana	2
Total	**1,879**

PRODUCTS/OPERATIONS

2018 Sales

	$ mil.	% of total
Interest Income:		
Interest & fees on loans & leases	6,894	53
Interest & dividends on securities	1,160	9
Interest on other earning assets	66	1
Non-interest income:		
Insurance income	1,852	14
Service charges on deposits	712	5
Mortgage banking income	477	4
Investment banking & brokerage fees & commissions	358	3
Trust & investment advisory	285	2
Bankcard fees & merchant discounts	287	2
Checkcard fees	221	2
Operating lease income	145	1
Income from bank-owned life insurance	116	1
Other income	420	3
Securities gains (losses) net	3	-
Total	**11,558**	**100**

2018 Sales

	% of total
Community Banking Retail and Consumer Finance	42
Community Banking Commercial	34
Financial Services and Commercial Finance	17
Insurance Holdings	7
Total	**100**

Selected Services
Commercial
  Asset management
  Association services
  Capital markets services
  Commercial deposit and treasury services
  Commercial finance
  Commercial middle market lending
  Commercial mortgage lending
  Institutional trust services
  Insurance
  Insurance premium finance
  International banking services
  Leasing
  Merchant services
  Payment solutions
  Private equity investments
  Real estate lending
  Supply chain management
Retail
  Asset management
  Automobile lending
  Bankcard lending
  Consumer finance

Home equity lending
Insurance
Investment brokerage services
Mobile/online banking
Payment solutions
Retail deposit services
Sales finance
Small business lending
Wealth management/private banking

Selected Subsidiaries & Affiliates

American Coastal Insurance Company
BB&T Equipment Finance Corporation
BB&T Financial FSB
  Sheffield Financial
BB&T Insurance Services Inc.
BB&T Investment Services Inc.
BB&T Securities LLC
Branch Banking and Trust Company
Clearview Correspondent Services
CRC Insurance Services
Grandbridge Real Estate Capital LLC
Lendmark Financial Services Inc.
McGriff Seibels & Williams Inc.
MidAmerica Gift Certificate Company
Prime Rate Premium Finance Corporation Inc.
  AFCO Credit Corporation
Regional Acceptance Corporation
Stanley Hunt DuPree & Rhine Inc.
Sterling Capital Management LLC

COMPETITORS

Bank of America	PNC Financial
Capital One	Regions Financial
Fifth Third	SunTrust
First Citizens	Synovus
BancShares	United Bankshares
First Horizon	Wells Fargo
JPMorgan Chase	

HISTORICAL FINANCIALS

Company Type: Public

Income Statement

FYE: December 31

	ASSETS ($ mil.)	NET INCOME ($ mil.)	INCOME AS % OF ASSETS	EMPLOYEES
12/18	225,697	3,237	1.4%	35,852
12/17	221,642	2,394	1.1%	36,484
12/16	219,276	2,426	1.1%	37,500
12/15	209,947	2,084	1.0%	37,200
12/14	186,814	2,151	1.2%	33,400
Annual Growth	4.8%	10.8%	—	1.8%

2018 Year-End Financials

Debt ratio: 10.00%
Return on equity: 11.00%
Cash ($ mil.): 3,987
Current ratio: —
Long-term debt ($ mil.): —

No. of shares (mil.): 763
Dividends
  Yield: 4.0%
  Payout: 40.0%
Market value ($ mil.): 33,067

	STOCK PRICE ($) FY Close	P/E High/Low	PER SHARE ($) Earnings	Dividends	Book Value
12/18	43.00	14 10	4.00	2.00	39.00
12/17	50.00	18 15	3.00	1.00	38.00
12/16	47.00	17 11	3.00	1.00	37.00
12/15	38.00	16 13	3.00	1.00	35.00
12/14	39.00	15 13	3.00	1.00	34.00
Annual Growth	2.7%	— —	9.2%	13.2%	4.0%

Trustco Bank Corp. (N.Y.)

In Banking They Trust. TrustCo Bank Corp is the holding company for Trustco Bank which boasts more than 140 branches across eastern New York central and western Florida and parts of Vermont Massachusetts and New Jersey. The bank offers personal and business customers a variety of deposit products loans and mortgages and trust and investment services. It primarily originates residential and commercial mortgages which account for more than three-quarters of its loan portfolio. It also writes business construction and installment loans and home equity lines of credit.

Operations

TrustCo Bank Corp generated 77% of its total revenue from interest and fees on loans in 2014 while interest on its securities available for sale (which were mostly residential mortgage-backed securities and collateralized mortgage obligations but also its GSE SBA-backed securities) made up another 16% of the bank's revenue. Customer service fees and Trustco Financial Services income made up 6% and 3% of total revenue in 2014 respectively.

Sales and Marketing

Trustco provides personal and business banking services to individuals partnerships and corporations among other kinds of business and organizations. It spent $2.49 million on advertising in 2014 compared to $2.83 million and $3.84 million in 2013 and 2012 respectively.

Financial Performance

Trustco has struggled to grow its revenue in recent years though its profits have been rising at a healthy clip mostly because its loan loss provisions have dissipated with an improving credit portfolio amidst the strengthening economy.

TrustCo's revenue rose by nearly 4% to $176.85 million in 2014 mostly as new branch openings during the year added nearly double-digit loan business growth. The bank also collected more interest income from its securities as it invested more and made a gain on the sale of its Florida regional headquarters property.

Higher revenue and a decline in interest expense on deposits in the low-interest environment also drove the bank's net income up by 11% to $4.38 million. A continuing decline in loan loss provisions buoyed by improving economic conditions (especially in Florida) also helped boost the bank's bottom line.

Despite higher earnings in 2014 TrustCo's operating cash fell by 21% to $49.54 million during the year as it spent more toward acquiring additional assets.

Strategy

TrustCo has focused on building its loan business through new branch additions as well as through growth from its existing offices in recent years. Using this strategy in 2014 the bank added five new branches and successfully boosted its deposit business by 2.7% to $4.03 billion while loan balances swelled by 8.6% to $3.16 billion as the bank aggressively pushed its loan business during the year.

The bank underwent a major branch expansion from 2002 through 2009 and more than doubled its branch network in New York and Florida by opening new locations (more than 75 of them). It continues to open new branches albeit not as rapidly.

EXECUTIVES

President And Ceo, Robert J. McCormick, age 56, $880,000 total compensation
Administrative Vp Branch Administration/marketing Trustco Bank, Scot R. Salvador, age 53, $510,000 total compensation
Vp Branch Administration/marketing Trustco Bank, Robert M. Leonard, age 57, $260,000 total compensation
Treasurer Trustco And Svp Trustco Bank, Eric W. Schreck, age 52, $255,000 total compensation
Svp And Cfo Trustco Bank Corp Ny And Trustco Bank, Michael M. Ozimek, $142,500 total compensation
Senior Vice President, Kevin Curley
Vice President Commercial Lending, Pat Canavan
Vice President Mortgage Loans Trustco, Michael Lofrumento
Chairman, Thomas O. Maggs, age 75
Auditors: Crowe LLP

LOCATIONS

HQ: Trustco Bank Corp. (N.Y.)
  5 Sarnowski Drive, Glenville, NY 12302
Phone: 518 377-3311   Fax: 518 381-3668
Web: www.trustcobank.com

PRODUCTS/OPERATIONS

2011 Sales

	$ mil.	% of total
Interest		
Loans including fees	129	73
Securities	30	17
Other	1	1
Noninterest		
Fees for services to customers	9	5
Trustco Financial Services	5	3
Other	2	1
Total	177	100

COMPETITORS

Arrow Financial	HSBC USA
Ballston Spa Bancorp	Hudson Valley FCU
Bank of America	KeyCorp
Citizens Financial	M&T Bank
Group	NBT Bancorp

HISTORICAL FINANCIALS

Company Type: Public

Income Statement

FYE: December 31

	ASSETS ($ mil.)	NET INCOME ($ mil.)	INCOME AS % OF ASSETS	EMPLOYEES
12/18	4,959	61	1.2%	854
12/17	4,908	43	0.9%	846
12/16	4,869	43	0.9%	808
12/15	4,735	42	0.9%	787
12/14	4,644	44	1.0%	737
Annual Growth	1.7%	8.6%	—	3.8%

2018 Year-End Financials

Debt ratio: —
Return on equity: 13.00%
Cash ($ mil.): 504
Current ratio: —
Long-term debt ($ mil.): —

No. of shares (mil.): 97
Dividends
  Yield: 4.0%
  Payout: 49.0%
Market value ($ mil.): 663

	STOCK PRICE ($) FY Close	P/E High/Low	PER SHARE ($) Earnings	Dividends	Book Value
12/18	7.00	15 10	1.00	0.00	5.00
12/17	9.00	22 16	0.00	0.00	5.00
12/16	9.00	20 12	0.00	0.00	5.00
12/15	6.00	16 13	0.00	0.00	4.00
12/14	7.00	16 13	0.00	0.00	4.00
Annual Growth	(1.4%)	— —	8.1%	0.5%	5.1%

Trustmark Corp

Trustmark Corporation is the holding company for Trustmark National Bank which has 208 locations mainly in Mississippi but also in East Texas the Florida panhandle and Tennessee where it also operates its Somerville Bank & Trust subsidiary in the Memphis area. Focusing on individuals and small businesses Trustmark offers a range of financial products and services such as checking and savings accounts certificates of deposit credit cards insurance investments and trust services. The diversified financial services firm has about $11.7 billion in assets.

Operations

Trustmark operates through three operating segments: General Banking Insurance and Wealth Management.

The General Banking Division is responsible for all traditional banking products and services including a full range of commercial and consumer banking services such as checking accounts savings programs overdraft facilities commercial installment and real estate loans home equity loans and lines of credit drive-in and night deposit services and safe deposit facilities offered through 208 offices in Alabama Florida Mississippi Tennessee and Texas.

The Wealth Management Division serve Trustmark's customers as a financial partner providing reliable guidance and sound practical advice for accumulating preserving and transferring wealth.

Trustmark's Insurance Division provides a full range of retail insurance products including commercial risk management products bonding group benefits and personal lines coverage through Trustmark National Bank subsidiary FBBI a Mississippi corporation.

Subsidiary Fisher Brown Bottrell sells insurance while Trustmark Investment Advisors provides wealth management products and services including the proprietary Performance Fund family of mutual funds. The latter unit has approximately $9 billion of assets under management.

Geographic Reach

Mississippi by far is Trustmark's largest market accounting for 63% of 2013 revenues. Tennessee Texas and Florida contributed about 9% 7% and 10% respectively.

Financial Performance

After experiencing a revenue dip in 2012 due to decrease in interest income in 2013 Trustmark's revenues increased by 8% thanks to an increase in the net interest income due to a significant increase in interest and fees on acquired loans related to the BancTrust acquisition as well as modest declines in the cost of interest-bearing deposits. These gains were partially offset by downward repricing of loans and securities. After experiencing sizable growth over the last few years in 2013 Trustmark's net income decreased to $117.1 million (from $117.2 million in 2012) due to an increase in the noninterest expenses as a result of BancTrust non-routine merger expenses and increases in salaries and employee benefits services and fees and ORE/foreclosure expenses.

In 2013 the company's operating cash inflow increased to $155.4 million (compared to $92.1 million in 2012) was due to a major increase in net assets and liabilities and a decline in purchases and originations of loans held for sale.

Strategy

Trustmark is growing its branch network by opening or acquiring new offices with a focus on the Houston and Memphis markets.

In 2013 Trustmark opened a new 12000-sq.-ft. office location on the first and second floors of the Nexen Building in Bunker Hill. Trustmark operates 15 locations in the Houston market with loans outstanding of approximately $835 million and deposits of approximately $425 million.

Mergers and Acquisitions

In 2013 the company purchased two branches in Oxford Mississippi from SOUTHBank F.S.B. That year it also bought Mobile Alabama-based BancTrust Financial Group for $55 million providing Trustmark entry into more than 15 markets in Alabama and enhancing the Trustmark franchise in the Florida Panhandle.

Company Background

Trustmark grew in 2011 with the FDIC-assisted acquisition of Heritage Banking Group. It took over the failed bank's assets and deposits after the institution was closed by regulators. The transaction added four bank branches in Mississippi (four other locations were consolidated due to their proximity to existing Trustmark branches).

BlackRock Inc. owns more than 11% of Trustmark Corp's shares.

Trustmark National Bank traces its roots to 1889 when it was first chartered in Mississippi.

EXECUTIVES

President Ceo And Director Trustmark Corporation And Trustmark National Bank, Gerard R. (Jerry) Host, age 64, $730,000 total compensation
President Corporate Banking Trustmark National Bank, Duane A. Dewey, age 60, $348,840 total compensation
Treasurer And Principal Financial Officertrustmark Corporation And Evp And Cfo Trustmark National Bank, Louis E. Greer, age 64, $360,000 total compensation
President Mortgage Services Trustmark National Bank, Breck W. Tyler, age 61, $306,000 total compensation
President Wealth Management Trustmark National Bank, W. Arthur Stevens, age 54, $333,540 total compensation
Vice President Recovery Department, Terry Collins
First Vice President Corporate Planning, Joseph Rein
Vice President Human Resources, David Kenney
First Vice President, Ronnie Bethay
Vice President And Trust Officer In The Trust Department, Agnes Tribble
Assistant Vice President, Marian Alderman
Senior Vice President Trustmark National Bank, Murray Fincher
Senior Vice President And Sco, Tommy Lyle
Vice President Investments, Andy Leslie
Senior Vice President And Assistant Controller, Donnie Tynes
First Vice President, John Yow
Vice President Advertising, Kristine Jacobs
Vice President, Vincent Powell
Senior Vice President And Employee Services Manager And Of Human Resources, Janice Brown
Vice President Payroll And Compensatio, Mike Oconnell
Vice President And Portfolio Manager, Ben Edwards
Vice President Sales, Kristi Bradley
Executive Vice President, Kirk Whitehouse
Vice President Commercial Banking, Colby Calcote
Assistant Vice President, Sue Hancock
Senior Vice President And Corporate Private Banking Manager, Mark Lewis
Executive Vice President Commercial Banking Manager, Mark Hope
Assistant Vice President, Laura Ryan
Senior Vice President, Mitchell Campbell
First Vice President, Bethany L Smith
Assistant Vice President And Strategic Sourcing, Matt Noland
Vice President Corporate Treasury Services, Tiffany Hancock
Vice President Sugar Land Commercial Banking, John Martinez
Vice President Mortgage Loan Originator, Jason Hebert
Senior Vice President Commercial Banking, Scott Killman
Svp, Allen Hart
First Vice President, Bethany Smith
Vice President, Gloria Craig
Vice President, Bard Shirley
Vice President, Audrey Sylvester
First Vice President, Sherry Lawrence
Vice President, Randy Taylor
Mortgage Loan Originator And Assistant Vice President, Bobbie Mccowan
Chairman, R. Michael Summerford, age 70
Board Member, Calvin Brown
Auditors: Crowe LLP

LOCATIONS

HQ: Trustmark Corp
248 East Capitol Street, Jackson, MS 39201
Phone: 601 208-5111   **Fax:** 601 354-5053
Web: www.trustmark.com

2016 Sales

	% of total
Mississippi	65
Alabama	12
Florida	8
Texas	8
Tennessee	7
Total	**100**

PRODUCTS/OPERATIONS

2016 Sales

	% of total
General Banking	91
Insurance	5
Wealth Management	4
Total	**100**

2016 Sales

	$ mil.	% of total
Interest Income:		
Interest and fees on LHFS & LHFI	300	51
Interest on securities	81	14
Interest and fees on acquired loans	30	5
Other interest income	1	-
Noninterest Income:		
Service charges on deposit accounts	45	8
Insurance commissions	37	6
Bank card and other fees	28	5
Mortgage banking net	28	5
Wealth management	31	5
Other net	6	1
Securities (losses) gains net	(0.3)	-
Total	**586**	**100**

COMPETITORS

BancorpSouth	Hancock Holding
Capital One	Regions Financial
Citizens Holding	Renasant
First Horizon	Wells Fargo
Great Southern Bancorp	

HISTORICAL FINANCIALS

Company Type: Public

Income Statement   FYE: December 31

	ASSETS ($ mil.)	NET INCOME ($ mil.)	INCOME AS % OF ASSETS	EMPLOYEES
12/18	13,286	150	1.1%	2,856
12/17	13,798	106	0.8%	2,893
12/16	13,352	108	0.8%	2,788
12/15	12,679	116	0.9%	2,941
12/14	12,251	124	1.0%	3,060
Annual Growth	2.0%	4.9%	—	(1.7%)

2018 Year-End Financials

Debt ratio: 0.00%	No. of shares (mil.): 66
Return on equity: 9.00%	Dividends
Cash ($ mil.): 350	Yield: 3.0%
Current ratio: —	Payout: 48.0%
Long-term debt ($ mil.): —	Market value ($ mil.): 1,872

	STOCK PRICE ($) FY Close	P/E High/Low	PER SHARE ($) Earnings	Dividends	Book Value
12/18	28.00	16 12	2.00	1.00	24.00
12/17	32.00	23 18	2.00	1.00	23.00
12/16	36.00	23 12	2.00	1.00	22.00
12/15	23.00	15 12	2.00	1.00	22.00
12/14	25.00	15 12	2.00	1.00	21.00
Annual Growth	3.7%	—	4.8%	(0.0%)	3.5%

TURNER CONSTRUCTION COMPANY INC

Turner Construction has been the mastermind for scores of head-turning projects for more than a century. The company that built Madison Square Garden has ranked among the leading general builders in the US since the early 1900s. Turner provides construction and project management services for commercial and multifamily buildings airports and stadiums as well as correctional educational entertainment and manufacturing facilities. The company is also a leader in sustainable or green building practices. Founded in 1902 by Henry Turner the company is the main operating unit of The Turner Corporation which is a subsidiary of German construction group HOCHTIEF.

Operations

Turner Construction works on some 1500 projects each year. For decades Turner has kept tabs on construction prices with its quarterly Building Cost Index which forecasts construction costs by considering labor rates productivity and material prices.

The index is used by federal and state governments to track building costs and pricing trends.

As part of HOCHTIEF's Americas division Turner works alongside other contractors in the US and Canada such as Flatiron its subsidiary E.E. Cruz and Clark Builders. The Americas division generates about 55% of HOCHTIEF's total revenue.

Geographic Reach

Headquartered in New York Turner Construction has offices across North America and has worked in more than 60 countries. It has operations in Latin America and the Caribbean India Europe and Central Asia Southeast Asia and the Middle East.

Sales and Marketing

Turner Construction works on projects in industries including aviation transportation commercial entertainment government green building manufacturing pharmaceutical research & development retail and sports.

Strategy

Turner Construction's ties to HOCHTIEF have helped strengthen the company's services and extend its international reach. Turner often teams with sister company Flatiron to complete projects. By collaborating and marketing their services jointly the two companies combine strengths in refurbishment and construction services.

Some of Turner's more recent projects include The Spiral?a tapered tower with an exterior ribbon of grass and trees which ascends its entire height; the Leadership in Energy and Environmental Design (LEED)-certified Audi Field soccer stadium in Washington DC; and a 12-story hospital tower for MetroHealth in Cleveland Ohio.

Turner has also worked to meet growing demand for green and sustainable construction. More than 630 of HOCHTIEF's American projects have received LEED or other green building certifications. A few of its green projects include the Seattle office of Perkins+Will the Yale University Health Services Center and RAND corporate headquarters.

As the residential markets slowed in past years Turner pivoted toward securing commercial projects in the public healthcare and science and technology sectors. Sports projects also provided the company with a solid pipeline; the company's dedicated sports division had completed more than $5 billion in work since 2000.

Company Background

Notable projects in Turner Construction's history include the World War II Memorial in Washington DC the John F. Kennedy Memorial Library in Boston and the Rock and Roll Hall of Fame. Turner also built the new Yankee Stadium in New York. The company reached a milestone in 2008 by inking its 15000th major contract.

EXECUTIVES

President, Peter J. Davoren
Vp, Stephen W. Fort
Evp (new York New Jersey Maryland Pennsylvania Connecticut And New England), Pasquale A. (Pat) Di Filippo
Svp, Michael J. (Mike) Kuntz
Svp, Mark A. Boyle
Evp (ohio Nashville Huntsville Atlanta Florida And The Carolinas), Richard P. Homan
Svp Turner Industrial Group And Chairman The Lathrop Company, Thomas J. (Tom) Manahan
Svp; President And Ceo Turner International, Abrar Sheriff
Svp And Cfo, Karen O. Gould
Svp (mid-atlantic And Southeast), Tom Reilly
President The Lathrop Company, Steve Johnson
Vice President, Neil D Jensen
Vice President, Phillip Parker
Senior Vice President, Christa Andresky
Vice President, Christoph Verbeek
Vp And Operations Manager Of Central Texas, Jeremiah Hudson
Vice President And General Manager, Tom Stachowiak
Vice President And Financial Manager, Sarah Garner
Vice President And Construction Executive, Bob Grace
Vp And Operations Manager Of Connecticut, Tom Dutchyshyn
Vice President, Dave Welber
Executive Vice President Operational Services, David Benton

Vice President, Stephen J Spaulding
Vice President, Carlo A Disilvestro
Vice President And Construction Executive Middle Atlantic, Derek Brown
Vice President, Peter S Ramstedt
Vice President, Davey Mass
Vp Of Special Projects Division Of Dallas, Nick Barker
Vice President, Douglas W Cooper
Vice President, Charles Egbert
Vice President, Maureen Kirkpatrick
Vice President, Filippo Restivo
Auditors: DELOITTE & TOUCHE LLP DALLAS

LOCATIONS

HQ: TURNER CONSTRUCTION COMPANY INC
375 HUDSON ST FL 6, NEW YORK, NY 100143667
Phone: 212 229-6000
Web: WWW.TURNERCONSTRUCTION.COM

PRODUCTS/OPERATIONS

Selected Services
Turner Engineering Group
Design+Build
Turner Logistics: Procurement Services
Medical Planning and Procurement
Building Information Modeling (BIM)
Lean Construction

COMPETITORS

Bechtel	Hunt Construction
C. G. Schmidt	Jacobs Engineering
Catamount Constructors	PCL Employees Holdings
Dimeo Construction	Parsons Corporation
DooleyMack	Peter Kiewit Sons'
English Construction Company	Shook National
F.A. Wilhelm	Skanska USA Building
Fluor	Structure Tone
Gilbane Building Company	Tully Construction
Hensel Phelps Construction	Tutor Perini
	Winter Construction

HISTORICAL FINANCIALS

Company Type: Private

Income Statement   FYE: December 31

	REVENUE ($ mil.)	NET INCOME ($ mil.)	NET PROFIT MARGIN	EMPLOYEES
12/14	10,516	97	0.9%	5,000
12/13	9,489	77	0.8%	—
12/12	8,552	70	0.8%	—
Annual Growth	10.9%	17.2%	—	—

Two Harbors Investment Corp

Two Harbors Investment Corp. is ready to double its money. The real estate investment trust (REIT) is managed and advised by (and was founded by) PRCM Advisers a subsidiary of Pine River Capital Management. The trust primarily invests in agency residential mortgage-backed securities (RMBS) with fixed or adjustable interest rates that are backed by government-supported enterprises Fannie Mae Freddie Mac or Ginnie Mae.

About a quarter of its mortgage portfolio is made up of non-agency RMBS such as subprime mortgages which carry more risk than federally-backed securities but offer higher yields.

EXECUTIVES

Vice President Data Management, Sree Kunduru
Assistant Vice President Data Analytics, Billy Raleigh
Assistant Vice President Human Resources, Beth Petersen
Vice President, David Barberot
Vice President Loan Boarding Manager, Jesse Steinberg
Board Member, Hope Woodhouse
Assistant Treasurer, Sheila Lichty
Auditors: Ernst & Young LLP

LOCATIONS

HQ: Two Harbors Investment Corp
575 Lexington Avenue, Suite 2930, New York, NY 10022
Phone: 612 629-2500
Web: www.twoharborsinvestment.com

COMPETITORS

American Capital Agency Corp.	Invesco Mortgage Capital
Annaly Capital Management	MFA Financial New York Mortgage Trust
Capstead Mortgage	
Chimera	Putnam Mortgage
Drive Shack	Redwood Trust
Gramercy	iStar Financial Inc

HISTORICAL FINANCIALS

Company Type: Public

Income Statement   FYE: December 31

	ASSETS ($ mil.)	NET INCOME ($ mil.)	INCOME AS % OF ASSETS	EMPLOYEES
12/18	30,132	(44)	—	—
12/17	24,789	349	1.4%	—
12/16	20,112	353	1.8%	—
12/15	14,576	492	3.4%	—
12/14	21,084	167	0.8%	—
Annual Growth	9.3%	—	—	—

2018 Year-End Financials

Debt ratio: 2.00%
Return on equity: (-1.00%)
Cash ($ mil.): 1,098
Current ratio: —
Long-term debt ($ mil.): —

No. of shares (mil.): 248
Dividends
Yield: 15.0%
Payout: —
Market value ($ mil.): 3,185

	STOCK PRICE ($) FY Close	P/E High/Low		PER SHARE ($) Earnings	Dividends	Book Value
12/18	13.00	—	—	(1.00)	2.00	17.00
12/17	16.00	9	5	2.00	0.00	20.00
12/16	9.00	5	4	2.00	2.00	20.00
12/15	8.00	4	3	3.00	2.00	20.00
12/14	10.00	12	10	1.00	2.00	22.00
Annual Growth	6.4%	—	—	—	(2.5%)	(6.3%)

Tyson Foods Inc

Tyson Foods spreads its wings beyond the chicken coop. While it is one of the largest US chicken producers (with processing capacity of some 42 million a week) Tyson's Fresh Meats division makes it a giant in the beef and pork sectors as well. The company also offers value-added processed and pre-cooked meats and refrigerated and frozen prepared foods. Its chicken operations are vertically integrated — the company hatches the eggs supplies contract growers with the chicks and feed and brings them back for processing when ready. Tyson's brands include Tyson Jimmy Dean Hillshire Farm Ball Park Wright ibp Aidells and State Fair. Its customers include retail wholesale and food service companies worldwide although the US accounts for most sales.

HISTORY

During the Great Depression Arkansas poultry farmer John Tyson supported his family by selling vegetables and poultry. In 1935 after developing a method for transporting live poultry (he installed a food-and-water trough and nailed small feed cups on a trailer) he bought 500 chickens in Arkansas and sold them in Chicago.

For the next decade Tyson bought sold and transported chickens. By 1947 the year he incorporated the company as Tyson Feed & Hatchery he was raising the chickens himself. He emphasized chicken production opening his first processing plant in 1958 in Springdale where he implemented an ice-packing system that allowed the company to send its products greater distances.

John's son Don took over as manager in 1960 and in 1963 it went public as Tyson Foods. Tyson Country Fresh Chicken (packaged chicken that would become the company's mainstay) was introduced in 1967.

Rapid expansion included a new egg-processing building (1970) a new plant and computerized feed mill (1971) and the acquisitions of Prospect Farms (1969 precooked chicken) and the Ocoma Foods Division (1972 poultry) as well as hog operations.

Health-conscious consumers increasingly turned from red meats to poultry during the 1980s. Tyson became the industry leader with several key acquisitions of poultry operations including the Tastybird division of Valmac (1985) Lane Processing (1986) and Heritage Valley (1986). Its 1989 purchase of Holly Farms added beef and pork processing.

Don Tyson relinquished the CEO position to Leland Tollett in 1991. The company increased its presence in Mexico the next year through a joint venture with poultry producer Trasgo. Also in 1992 the firm plunged into seafood with the purchase of Arctic Alaska Fisheries and Louis Kemp Seafood.

Tyson bought Culinary Foods (frozen foods) and Trasgo in 1994 and the seafood division of International Multifoods in 1995. High feed costs and an oversupply of chickens brought down company earnings the next year. In 1997 the company pleaded guilty to charges that it illegally gave former Agriculture Secretary Mike Espy thousands of dollars' worth of gifts; the settlement included $6 million in fines and fees.

Tyson bought embattled Hudson Foods' poultry operations in 1998. The company said it would take a charge that year of $196 million to restructure. It also sold turkey processor Willow Brook Foods (now part of Cargill Meat Solutions) to Willow Brook management in 1998. That year John H. Tyson grandson of the founder was elected chairman.

In 1999 Tyson sold its seafood business for about $180 million in a two-part transaction to International Home Foods and Trident Seafoods. John Tyson became CEO in 2000.

As the winner in a bidding war with Smithfield Foods in 2001 Tyson agreed to buy IBP Inc. the #1 beef processor and #2 pork processor in the US for nearly $3.2 billion. Tyson tried to back away from the table after accounting irregularities were discovered at an IBP subsidiary but a Delaware judge ordered Tyson to sit down and finish dinner. The deal was made final in September and Tyson changed the beef processor's name to IBP Fresh Meats.

In late 2001 Tyson Foods and six managers were indicted for conspiring to smuggle illegal immigrants from Mexico and Central America to work for lower than legal wages in 15 of its US poultry processing plants. Two managers made plea bargains and testified for the government; another manager committed suicide. Tyson and the remaining three managers were acquitted of the conspiracy charges in 2003.

Suffering from mild indigestion after the merger in 2002 Tyson announced a restructuring to trim some fat from its fresh pork operations and agreed to sell its Specialty Brands (frozen foods) subsidiary. In early 2003 sold off its frozen appetizer business DFG Foods.

Following the discovery of bird flu on a Texas chicken farm in 2004 and the subsequent banning of the importation of US chicken products by other countries Tyson consolidated and automated its poultry operations resulting in hundreds of layoffs at the company.

Tyson announced in 2004 it was being formally investigated by the SEC regarding perquisites given to executives including retired senior chairman Don Tyson and then-current chairman and CEO John Tyson. By August the SEC recommended civil action against the company for its failure to disclose $1.7 million in corporate perks given to Don Tyson without authorization from Tyson's compensation committee. Although Don Tyson had already reimbursed the company $1.53 million for then-unspecified benefits the SEC also announced plans to recommend civil action be taken against him. With neither the company nor Tyson admitting any guilt the case was settled in 2005 with Tyson paying the SEC $700000 in fines and the company $1.5 million. Many of the perks were not disclosed because Don Tyson did not fill out SEC-required questionnaires; however disclosed perks included having the company pay for his housekeeping and lawn maintenance and routine non-business use of the corporate jet by his family and friends.

In 2005 the company opened its largest case-ready meat plant in Sherman Texas. However that January and February it suspended operations at four of its other beef plants and cut back at a fifth due to a shortage of cattle and the loss of beef exports due to the US's 2003 case of BSE (Bovine spongiform encephalopathy or "mad cow" disease).

Growing concern over the role of trans-fatty acids (from hydrogenated vegetable oils) in diet and health led Tyson to begin removing them from its processed foods such as breaded chicken nuggets and chicken tenders. The company announced the removal of trans-fats from all its retail poultry and school foodservice products in 2005.

Recognizing the growing market for alternative and renewable fuels and recognizing its unending supply of meat by-products (in this case such lovelies as fat tallow lard and grease) Tyson decided to get into the alternative fuel market in 2007 with the formation of a 50-50 joint venture with fuel refiner Syntroleum called Dynamic Fuels. The joint venture was set up to explore the possibility of producing synthetic fuel from Tyson's waste products for the diesel- jet- and military-fuel markets. In conjunction with this joint venture Tyson created a new business unit Tyson Renewable Products.

EXECUTIVES

Svp Legal Services And Assistant Secretary, David L. Van Bebber, age 63

Evp And Chief Human Resources Officer, Mary A. Oleksiuk, age 57

Coo, Noel White, age 61, $777,716 total compensation

Cfo, Stewart F. Glendinning, age 53

President North American Foodservice And International, Andrew P. (Andy) Callahan, age 52

President North American Retail, Sally Grimes, age 47

Evp Operations Services, Howell P. (Hal) Carper, age 64

President Ceo And Director, Thomas P. (Tom) Hayes, age 53, $712,954 total compensation

Chief Growth Officer, Monica McGurk, age 48

President Poultry Operations, Doug Ramsey

Cto, Scott Spradley

Executive Vice President Business Process And Continuous Improvement, Russell Tooley

Vice President Of Food Safety And Quality Assurance, Dean Danilson

Vice President Engineering, Jeff Sandorf

Vice President Foodservice Sales, Joel Sappenfield

Vp Is Manufacturing, Lyle Nicholson

Senior Vice President Chief Accounting O, Jerry Hartfield

Svp Sustainability And Chief Environmental Officer, Kevin Igli

Vice President Of Direct Materials, Lindsay Piepho

National Account Manager, Sally Kumasaki

Senior Vice President Operations, Steve Taylor

Vice President Of Marketing, Wendy Bruce

Vice President, Brandy Bilderack

National Accounts Manager, Lewis Mcclendon

Vice President Marketing, Bill Welsh

National Accounts Manager, Peter Chesna

Senior Vice President Operations, Roy Slaughter

Senior Vice President Raw Value Added, Ray McGaugh

Svp Foodservice Sales, Johnny Hughes

Vice President Marketing Services, Susan Quillin

Vice President Finance Growth And Sales, Kirk Wardlow

Vice President Marketing, Kim Cupelli

Vice President Operations, Richard Irvin

Evp And Chief Customer Officer, Scott Rouse

Vice President Marketing, James Miller

Senior Vice President Grocery Sales, David Bray

Vice President Government Relations, Chuck Penry

Vice President Food Safety And Quality Assurance, Scott Stillwell

Sls Deli Vice President, Brent Schmiegelow

Vice President Food Service Sales East, Mike Curtin

Senior Vice President Tax, Mark Elser

Senior Vice President And Marketing Manager, Jeff Sandore

National Account Manager, Rich Markich

Senior Vice President, Craig Hart

Svp Fresh Meats Pork Division, Shane Miller

National Account Manager, Steve Maher

National Accounts Manager, Jared Mitchell

Vice President Associate General Counsel And Asst. Secretary, Nate Hodne

Executive Vice President, Steven Hankins

Senior Vice President Wal Mart Operations, Jason Nichol

Senior Vice President Foodservice, Kristin Bird

Vice President National Accounts, Brian Roberts

Senior Vice President And General Manager Beef Enterprise, Dan Brooks

Executive Vice President And General Counsel, Amy Tu

Vice President Of Live Operations, Chip Miller

Vice President Of Network Strategy, Michael Ahmed

Vice President, Lee Slezak

Vp Fresh Meats Marketing And Premium Programs, Kent Harrison

Vp Fresh Meat Sales And Fresh Meats Division, Kevin Culver

Senior Vice President Chief Accounting Officer Controller, Steve Gibbs

Chairman, John H. Tyson, age 66

Board Member, Brad Sauer

Board Member, Samuel Banks

Board Member, Gaurdie E Banister

Secretary, Vicky Harp

Secretary, Ericka Patrick

Secretary Iv, Bobbie Meredith

Auditors: PricewaterhouseCoopers LLP

LOCATIONS

HQ: Tyson Foods Inc
2200 West Don Tyson Parkway, Springdale, AR 72762-6999
Phone: 479 290-4000   **Fax:** 479 290-7984
Web: www.tyson.com

PRODUCTS/OPERATIONS

2018 Sales

	$ mil.	% of total
Beef	15,473	38
Chicken	12,044	29
Prepared foods	8,668	21
Pork	4,879	12
Other	305	-
Inter segment Sales	(1317)	-
Total	**40,052**	**100**

COMPETITORS

Cargill	Pilgrim's Pride
ConAgra	Rosen's Diversified
Foster Farms	Sanderson Farms
Hormel	Smithfield Foods
JBS	U.S. Premium Beef
Koch Foods	WH Group
Kraft Heinz	Wayne Farms
Perdue Incorporated	

HISTORICAL FINANCIALS

Company Type: Public

Income Statement

FYE: September 28

	REVENUE ($ mil.)	NET INCOME ($ mil.)	NET PROFIT MARGIN	EMPLOYEES
09/19	42,405	2,022	4.8%	141,000
09/18	40,052	3,024	7.6%	121,000
09/17*	38,260	1,774	4.6%	122,000
10/16	36,881	1,768	4.8%	114,000
10/15	41,373	1,220	2.9%	113,000
Annual Growth	0.6%	13.5%	—	5.7%

*Fiscal year change

2019 Year-End Financials

Debt ratio: 36.00%
Return on equity: 15.00%
Cash ($ mil.): 484
Current ratio: 1.00
Long-term debt ($ mil.): 9,830

No. of shares (mil.): 366
Dividends
  Yield: 0.0%
  Payout: 27.0%
Market value ($ mil.): 31,183

	STOCK PRICE ($) FY Close	P/E High/Low		PER SHARE ($) Earnings	Dividends	Book Value
09/19	85.00	16	9	6.00	2.00	38.00
09/18	60.00	5	4	8.00	1.00	35.00
09/17*	70.00	15	11	5.00	1.00	29.00
10/16	75.00	16	9	5.00	1.00	27.00
10/15	44.00	15	12	3.00	0.00	26.00
Annual Growth	17.7%	—	—	17.0%	39.2%	10.0%

*Fiscal year change

U.S. VENTURE, INC.

Privately held U.S. Venture Inc. is a North American leader in the distribution of fuel and transportation products. U.S. Oil its largest division transports more than 2 billion gallons of fuel annually via pipelines rail light oil-barges and trucks. The division maintains around 7 million BOE in storage capacity and has access to 330 terminals. Through U.S. AutoForce the company is also a top distributor of tires and car parts to independent tire retailers auto repair shops and dealerships. The company's Lubricants division maintains a competitive business as well set up to blend and market chemical products to automotive industrial and metalworking industries. Through the GAIN Clean Fuel brand U.S. Venture also sells clean biofuels.

Operations

U.S. Venture has four business divisions.

U.S. Oil its largest business is a leading distributor of branded and unbranded refined products in the US and Canada. It transports some 2 billion gallons of energy products annually. U.S. Oil also engages in energy trading.

Tires car parts and lubricants are distributed through the U.S. AutoForce division another industry leader. Its portfolio includes 30 tire brands 15 lubricant brands and many branded car parts (mostly brakes chassis repair equipment and exhausts).

U.S. Lubricants blends and distributes lubricants under its THRIVE brand for automotive industrial and metalworking needs. It also provides support services like mobile filtration systems oil analysis lab services and fluids storage and handling systems.

U.S. Venture is also developing and building alternative fuel transportation networks and filling stations in the US. Headed by the U.S. GAIN division the company supplies compressed natural gas (CNG) and renewable natural gas (RNG) to more than 50 fueling stations.

Geographic Reach

Headquartered in Appleton Wisconsin U.S. Venture operates throughout North America. U.S. Oil handles fuel supply in the Midwest with about 20 terminals a barge and some 330 third-party terminal partners. The company has a concentration of fuel tires car parts and convenience store services in the Midwest.

Sales and Marketing

U.S. Ventures is a leading distributor of fuels car parts and lubricants in North America.

The U.S. Oil division distributes products from nine major oil brands including BP Shell Exxon and Phillips 66. It offers flexible pricing fixed-fuel contracts and commodity trading. Traded products include gasoline ethanol biodiesel jet and marine fuels propane and butane. In the Midwest the company also owns the Express chain of convenience stores. U.S. Oil serves nearly 40 million Americans daily.

U.S. AutoForce offers 30 tire brands including Michelin Bridgestone Dunlop and Firestone. It has an equally extensive inventory of car parts and lubricants. It. The service centers strategically placed across North America serve the agricultural construction forestry and mining industries.

Strategy

U.S. Venture wants to become the dominant petroleum products marketer and wholesale distributor of automotive parts and tires in North America. Its operating model focuses on expanding the brand portfolio beyond oil distribution to incorporate automotive services and clean energy distribution within its model.

U.S. Venture has expanded its product lines and market reach through joint ventures (2017 partnership with Harrigan Industrial Technologies Inc.) and acquisitions (2018 purchase of Tire's Warehouse Inc). These efforts have expanded its revenue stream and cushioned it from fluctuations in its oil business.

However U.S. Venture's expansion of services may come at a cost. For instance in September 2017 a federal court in Chicago found that the U.S. Oil division of U.S. Venture infringed upon patents held by Sunoco Partners related to a system for blending butane into gasoline at the point of distribution. Legal proceedings are a drain on resources and negatively impact a company's brand image.

Competition is also heating up in the tire distribution industry. In 2018 Michelin North America Inc. and Sumitomo Corporation of Americas formed a new joint venture to strengthen their distribution system. This was followed by TireHub a joint distribution system of Goodyear Tire & Rubber Co. and Bridgestone Americas Inc. U.S. Venture may find it difficult to expand beyond its home turf of the Midwest in such a crowded field.

Mergers and Acquisitions

In June 2018 U.S. AutoForce acquired California based Tire's Warehouse Inc for an undisclosed price. U.S. Autoforce retained the Tire's Warehouse name company structure employees and ways of business but expects the acquisition to gain market share in California and Arizona. Tire's Warehouse was established in 1969 by the Helmle family and remained family-owned before the acquisition.

Company Background

U.S. Oil was established in 1951 as Schmidt Oil by the sons of local fuel distributor Albert Schmidt. The company changed its name to U.S. Venture in 2010 to reflect the company's increasingly diverse portfolio of entrepreneurial businesses. It has remained family-owned since its inception and today it is one of the largest privately held companies in Wisconsin.

EXECUTIVES

President And Ceo, John Schmidt
Vp Marketing And Strategy, Jeff Van Brunt
Vp Business Development U.s. Oil, Mike Koel
Vice President Treasurer Assistant Secretary, Lori Karls
Vp Of Sales And Operations, Kevin Olson
Senior Vice President Merchandise Planning And Allocation, Mark Duenig
Treasurer, Martin Tomczyk
Secretary And Treasurer, Ray Schmidt
Treasurer, Judy Engen-pazdera
Auditors: DELOITTE & TOUCHE LLP MILWAU

LOCATIONS

HQ: U.S. VENTURE, INC.
425 BETTER WAY, APPLETON, WI 549156192
Phone: 920 739-6101
Web: WWW.USOIL.COM

PRODUCTS/OPERATIONS

Selected Operations
U.S. AutoForce (exhaust pipe manufacturing and autoparts distribution)
U.S. Lubricants (motor oil and related products)
U.S. Oil (gasoline fuel oil and natural gas)
U.S Gain (compressed natural gas)

COMPETITORS

American Tire Distributors
Guttman Oil
Petroleum Traders Corporation

HISTORICAL FINANCIALS

Company Type: Private

Income Statement   FYE: July 31

	REVENUE ($ mil.)	NET INCOME ($ mil.)	NET PROFIT MARGIN	EMPLOYEES
07/15	8,076	174	2.1%	1,182
07/14	9,089	49	0.5%	—
07/13	7,346	47	0.6%	—
Annual Growth	4.9%	91.7%	—	—

UAW RETIREE MEDICAL BENEFITS TRUST

EXECUTIVES

Head of Trustees, Robert Naftaly
Prin*, Rober Naftaly
Senior Manager Human Resources, Karen Blair
Director Communications, Matthew Wood
Carrier Coordinator, Lisa Mosner
Manager, Evelyn White-Bruton
Strategy Consultant, Vince Ferri
Senior Accountant, Amy Hawkins
Senior Managing Director, Benjamin Cotton
Controller, Garon Meikle
Tax Compliance Manager, Laura Howard
Auditors: DELOITTE TAX LLP DETROIT MI

LOCATIONS

HQ: UAW RETIREE MEDICAL BENEFITS TRUST
200 WALKER ST STE 400, DETROIT, MI 482074229
Phone: 313 324-5900

HISTORICAL FINANCIALS

Company Type: Private

Income Statement   FYE: December 31

	ASSETS ($ mil.)	NET INCOME ($ mil.)	INCOME AS % OF ASSETS	EMPLOYEES
12/17	63,226	89	0.1%	94
12/16	58,966	(1,840)	—	—
Annual Growth	7.2%	—	—	—

Uber Technologies Inc

Auditors: PricewaterhouseCooopers LLP

LOCATIONS

HQ: Uber Technologies Inc
1455 Market Street, 4th Floor, San Francisco, CA 94103
Phone: 415 612-8582
Web: www.uber.com

HISTORICAL FINANCIALS

Company Type: Public

Income Statement   FYE: December 31

	REVENUE ($ mil.)	NET INCOME ($ mil.)	NET PROFIT MARGIN	EMPLOYEES
12/18	11,270	997	8.8%	22,263
12/17	7,932	(4,033)	—	—
12/16	3,845	(370)	—	—
Annual Growth	71.2%	—	—	—

2018 Year-End Financials

Debt ratio: 29.00%
Return on equity: 19.00%
Cash ($ mil.): 6,473
Current ratio: 2.00
Long-term debt ($ mil.): 6,869

No. of shares (mil.): 457
Dividends
Yield: —
Payout: —
Market value ($ mil.): —

	STOCK PRICE ($) FY Close	P/E High/Low	PER SHARE ($) Earnings	Dividends	Book Value
12/18	0.00	— —	(0.00)	0.00	15.00
12/17	0.00	— —	(9.00)	0.00	8.00
Annual Growth	—	— —	—	—	34.3%

UGI Corp.

UGI Corporation is a leading energy products supplier to residential commercial agricultural and wholesale customers across the US and Europe. The company stores transports and markets propane liquefied petroleum gases (LPG) and natural gas; it also generates some electricity. In the US UGI serves some 2.2 million customers thanks to its partnership with AmeriGas Partners and several subsidiaries. In addition product installation and maintenance services are available to Pennsylvania Delaware and Maryland customers of UGI. Its trade names include AmeriGas America's Propane Company and Heritage Propane.

Operations

UGI operates through four segments: AmeriGas Propane UGI International Midstream and Marketing and UGI Utilities.

AmeriGas Propane (about 40% of revenue) primarily distributes propane across the US. It also sells installs and services related appliances in Pennsylvania Delaware and Maryland.

UGI International (some 30% revenue) distributes propane across some 20 countries in Europe through subsidiaries like UGI France SAS Flaga GmbH and AvantiGas. It also markets energy products in France Belgium Denmark the Netherlands and the UK.

Midstream and Marketing (15% revenue) markets energy products in the US mid-Atlantic region manages midstream assets produces some electricity and provides project management services in Pennsylvania.

UGI Utilities conducts the regulated natural gas and electric distribution business in Pennsylvania and one Maryland county and brings in another 15% of company revenue.

Geographic Reach

UGI has propane and LPG distribution and marketing customers across the US (with significant concentration in Pennsylvania) and nearly 20 countries in Europe primarily France Belgium Denmark the Netherlands and the UK.

The US accounts for about 70% of total revenue.

Sales and Marketing

UGI sells natural gas electricity and liquid fuels to some 12500 residential commercial and industrial customers across 35000 US locations while its Utilities segment serves about 642000 natural gas customers in Pennsylvania and some 500 customers in Maryland.

In Europe UGI sells some 950 million gallons of LPG to about 550000 customers in almost 20 countries.

Financial Performance

In the past ten years UGI revenue has vacillated between a low of $5.6 billion (2010) and a high of $8.3 billion (2014) with an average revenue fluctuation of $1 billion year-over-year. During the same period the company's net income has averaged around $250 million but has seen improvement in the last couple of years.

Revenue (ended September 30) increased 25% to $7.6 billion in 2018 thanks to higher gas usage due to colder than usual winter in the US.

Net income rose from $436 million in 2017 to $718 million in 2018 mostly due to a YOY $145 million reduction in income taxes.

Cash holdings at UGI stood at $452 million. Operations provided $1 billion in cash inflows offset by $747 million going towards investments and a further $438 million going towards financing activities.

Strategy

Facing a gradual decline in its propane sales UGI is betting its growth strategy on three fronts? capacity building in Midstream acquisition in the International segment and upgrades in Utilities.

Keen to expand inorganically UGI is busy acquiring companies on one hand and reducing operational costs on the other. Instances of acquisition include Texas Creek and the Endless Mountain gas gathering systems in UGI's Midstream & Marketing segment and the retail natural gas business of South Jersey Industries by UGI Energy Services. The larger US utility companies are following an M&A trend (for instance SCANA merged with Dominion) which is essential for vital infrastructure upgrades.

To raise money UGI is cutting costs through efficiency programs of legacy businesses as well as gaining synergy costs from integrating newer acquisitions. For instance within AmeriGas propane UGI reduced distribution costs while registering higher online customer accounts. Meanwhile higher than-expected synergies were reported by the integration of previously acquired companies (2015-18 period) including Finagaz and LPG businesses in Sweden Netherlands and Italy.

The company is equally focused on customer base expansion. A 2018 regulatory merger approval of its three utility companies and some $340 million in distribution system upgrades should help UGI Utilities to further expand. It added over 14000 new residential and commercial heating customers during the year.

Mergers and Acquisitions

In 2019 UGI bought midstream assets from Columbia Midstream Group a unit of TC Energy for $1.28 billion in 2019. The assets include four natural gas gathering systems and an interest in a company with gathering processing and liquids assets. They connect production to markets throughout western Pennsylvania eastern Ohio and northern West Virginia.

UGI Energy Services a subsidiary of UGI Corp. acquired the retail natural gas business of South Jersey Industries Inc. in December 2018. Through the agreement UGI gained 2500 commercial and industrial customer contracts of South Jersey Energy including supply service to nearly 6000 locations. The strategic acquisition will allow UGI to further grow its retail natural gas business strengthening its reach in the mid-Atlantic region.

Also in fiscal 2018 the company completed the purchase of Hunlock Energy LLC a 44-megawatt natural gas-fired peaking turbine in Luzerne County PA.

In 2017 UGI International through European subsidiaries Flaga and AvantiGas spent a total of $120 million to acquire Kosan Gas (LPG marketing and distribution) in Sweden DVEP Investeringen (natural gas and electric marketing) in the Netherlands and UniverGas (LPG distribution) in Italy.

UGI International also acquired several LPG distribution businesses with operations in Austria Norway and the UK for $24 million.

HISTORY

United Gas Improvement was set up in 1882 by Philadelphia industrialist Thomas Dolan and other investors to acquire a gasworks and a new coal-gas manufacturing process. The firm also bought electric utilities and street railways across the US and moved into construction. The 1935 Public Utility Holding Company Act led to United Gas Improvement's restructuring when the SEC ordered the divestiture of many of its operations in 1941. The company converted to natural gas in the 1950s and entered the liquefied petroleum gas (LPG) business in 1959. It became UGI Corporation in 1968.

UGI shifted its emphasis to propane in the late 1980s buying Petrolane in 1995 and combining it with AmeriGas Propane to create AmeriGas Partners which then went public. Overseas UGI launched a joint venture in 1996 to build an LPG import project in Romania. The next year it signed a deal to distribute propane in China.

EXECUTIVES

Vp New Business Development; President Ugi Enterprises And Ugi Energy Services, Bradley C. Hall, age 66, $390,723 total compensation
President And Ceo, John L. Walsh, age 64, $1,078,342 total compensation
Cfo, Kirk R. Oliver, age 61, $532,902 total compensation
Vp General Counsel And Secretary, Monica M. Gaudiosi, age 57, $434,611 total compensation
President And Ceo Ugi Utilities, Robert F. (Bob) Beard, age 53
Ceo Antargaz, Eric Naddeo
President And Ceo Amerigas, Jerry E. Sheridan, age 53, $526,474 total compensation
Managing Director Avantigas, Neil Murphy
President Ugi International, Roger Perreault
Vp It And Administration Energy Services, Amy Hunt
Vp Human Resources, Erika Spott
Regional Vice President, Steve Quagliana
Vice President Ugi Hvac Enterprises, Robert Pistor
Vice President Growth Amerigas, Warren Patterson
Vp Supply Chain Amerigas, Kevin Rumbelow
Vice President Operations And Engineering Ugi Energy Services, Mike Mara
Vice President Human Resources Amerigas, Troy Fee
Vp Chief Accounting Officer And Corporate Controller, Ann P Kelly
Vice Presidenr And General Counsel, Bob Knauss
Vp Hr Compensation And Leadership Development, Erika A Spott
Vice President Chief Accounting Officer And Corporate Controller, Laurie A Bergman
Vice President Information Technology, David Vance
Vice President Applications And Techno, Tom Slak
Vice President Information Technology, Tom Niccum
Chairman, Marvin O. Schlanger, age 71

LOCATIONS

HQ: UGI Corp.
460 North Gulph Road, King of Prussia, PA 19406
Phone: 610 337-1000
Web: www.ugicorp.com

PRODUCTS/OPERATIONS

2018 Sales

	$ mil.	% of total
AmeriGas propane	2,823	35
UGI International	2,684	33
Midstream & Marketing	1,422	18
UGI Utilities	1,092	14
Corporate	1	-
Adjustments	(370.8)	-
Total	**7,651**	**100**

Selected Subsidiaries and Affiliates

AmeriGas Inc.
AmeriGas Propane Inc.
  AmeriGas Partners L.P. (26%)
  AmeriGas Propane L.P.
  AmeriGas Technology Group Inc.
  Petrolane Incorporated
  Four Flags Drilling Company Inc.
Ashtola Production Company
  UGI Ethanol Development Corporation
Newbury Holding Company
UGI Enterprises Inc. (energy marketing and services)
  CFN Enterprises Inc.
  Eastfield International Holdings Inc.
  FLAGA GmbH (propane distribution; Austria the Czech Republic and Slovakia)
  Eurogas Holdings Inc.
  McHugh Service Company
  UGI Energy Services Inc.
  GASMARK (gas marketing)
  POWERMARK (electricity marketing)
  UGI International Enterprises Inc.
  UGI Europe Inc.
  Antargaz (propane distribution France)
  FLAGA GmbH (propane distribution Austria)
UGI Properties Inc.
UGI Utilities Inc. (natural gas and electric utility)
United Valley Insurance Company

COMPETITORS

Chesapeake Utilities	Ferrellgas Partners
Dominion Energy	National Fuel Gas
Duquesne Light	NorthWestern
Holdings	PPL Corporation
Energy Transfer	Suburban Propane
Exelon	

HISTORICAL FINANCIALS

Company Type: Public

Income Statement				FYE: September 30
	REVENUE ($ mil.)	NET INCOME ($ mil.)	NET PROFIT MARGIN	EMPLOYEES
09/19	7,320	256	3.5%	12,800
09/18	7,651	719	9.4%	13,000
09/17	6,121	437	7.1%	13,000
09/16	5,686	365	6.4%	13,320
09/15	6,691	281	4.2%	13,570
Annual Growth	2.3%	(2.3%)	—	(1.4%)

2019 Year-End Financials

Debt ratio: 49.00%	No. of shares (mil.): 209
Return on equity: 7.00%	Dividends
Cash ($ mil.): 447	Yield: 3.0%
Current ratio: 1.00	Payout: 76.0%
Long-term debt ($ mil.): 5,780	Market value ($ mil.): 10,507

Ulta Beauty Inc

EXECUTIVES

Ceo, Mary N Dillon
Non-Exec Chb*, Charles J Philippin
Cfo-Treas-Asst SEC, Scott M Settersten
Chief Hr Officer, Jeffrey J Childs
Chief Merchandising & Mkt Offi, David C Kimbell
General Counsel-Corp SEC, Jodi J Caro
Buyer, Cathy Bokar
Director, Dominick Archer
Senior Buyer, Jennifer Moran
CIO, Diane Randolph
Chief Store Operations Officer, Kecia Steelman
Auditors: Ernst & Young LLP

LOCATIONS

HQ: Ulta Beauty Inc
1000 Remington Blvd., Suite 120, Bolingbrook, IL 60440
Phone: 630 410-4800
Web: www.ulta.com

COMPETITORS

Bath & Body Works	Nordstrom
Bed Bath & Beyond	Premier Salons
Body Shop	Regis Corporation
CVS Caremark	Sally Beauty
Dillard's	Sephora USA
J. C. Penney	Supercuts
L'Oreal USA	Target Corporation
Lush Ltd.	Wal-Mart
Macy's	Walgreen
Merle Norman	

HISTORICAL FINANCIALS

Company Type: Public

Income Statement — FYE: February 2

	REVENUE ($ mil.)	NET INCOME ($ mil.)	NET PROFIT MARGIN	EMPLOYEES
02/19	6,717	659	9.8%	44,000
02/18*	5,885	555	9.4%	34,700
01/17	4,855	410	8.4%	31,800
01/16	3,924	320	8.2%	26,500
01/15	3,241	257	7.9%	22,400
Annual Growth	20.0%	26.5%	—	18.4%

*Fiscal year change

2019 Year-End Financials

Debt ratio: —
Return on equity: 37.00%
Cash ($ mil.): 409
Current ratio: 2.00
Long-term debt ($ mil.): —
No. of shares (mil.): 59
Dividends
Yield: —
Payout: —
Market value ($ mil.): 17,069

UMB Financial Corp

UMB Financial is the holding company for four UMB-branded commercial banks serving Arizona Colorado Illinois Kansas Nebraska Oklahoma and Missouri. Through some 110 branches the banks offer standard services such as checking and savings accounts credit and debit cards and trust and investment services. Commercial loans account for more than 50% of UMB's loan portfolio. Beyond its banking business it offers insurance brokerage services leasing treasury management health savings accounts and proprietary mutual funds through its more than 20 subsidiaries. Founded in 1913 the bank ranks first in the Kansas City market (based on deposits).

Operations

It operates through four business segments: Bank Payment Solutions Institutional Investment Management and Asset Servicing.

Its Bank segment focuses on traditional commercial and consumer banking treasury management leasing foreign exchange merchant bankcards wealth management brokerage insurance capital markets investment banking corporate trust and correspondent banking.

The Payment Solutions segment offers consumer and commercial credit and debit cards prepaid debit card solutions healthcare services and institutional cash management.

UMB Financial's Institutional Investment Management segment serves the intermediary and institutional markets through mutual funds traditional separate accounts and sub-advisory relationships using private equity and fixed income investment strategies.

The Asset Servicing segment caters to the asset management industry and supports investment products such as mutual funds alternative investments and managed accounts.

Geographic Reach

UMB Financial's four commercial banks are located in Arizona Colorado Kansas and Missouri. Its principal subsidiary bank Missouri-based UMB Bank n.a. also has branches in Illinois Kansas Nebraska and Oklahoma. In Texas the firm operates a loan production office.

Sales and Marketing

UMB Financial serves commercial retail government and correspondent bank customers through its branch locations call center Internet banking and network of ATMs.

The company spent $24.15 million toward marketing and business development expenses in 2014; up from $22.7 million in 2013 but down from the $24.6 million it spent in 2012.

Financial Performance

UMB Financial has enjoyed rising revenue and profit in recent years thanks to loan asset growth and . Revenue in 2014 grew by more than 2% to $862.56 million thanks to 8% growth in trust and securities processing fee income and thanks to higher loan interest income from another year of double-digit growth in average loan balances.

Following several years of profit growth net income in 2014 fell by 10% to $120.66 million mostly because the bank spent more toward salary raises and incurred higher benefit costs but also because it spent more on equipment and a contingency reserve it established in 2014 related to a settlement agreement involving the sellers and employees of PCM.

Cash from operations fell by 21% to $243.78 million partially from lower cash earnings but also because it adjusted for fewer non-cash items such as accrued expenses and taxes than it did in 2013.

The company's loan assets grew by 14% to $7.47 billion in 2014 while its total deposits increased slightly to $13.62 billion.

Strategy

UMB Financial is focused on four main strategies for growth. The first is to grow its fee-based business through acquisitions or organically as fee-based services are typically non-credit related and are not generally affected by fluctuations in interest rates. Accordingly the bank has boosted its non-interest income by 20% over the past three years from $414 million in 2011 to $498.7 million in 2014. In mid-2014 to add fuel to this growth UMB Bank purchased the Oklahoma Corporate Trust Business from RCB Bank to be incorporated into its own business in the region expanding the company's reach into the Oklahoma Corporate Trust Market.

The second strategy is to focus on net interest income through loan and deposit growth. In 2014 for example the bank grew its loan assets by a whopping 14% adding $16.8 million in net interest income (5% more than in 2013) to the bank's top line.

Thirdly UMB Financial aims to improve operating efficiencies by offering more services through its existing branch network which helped it grow its loan and deposit business greatly in 2014.

Fourth the firm is focused on managing its capital to promote investor confidence and acquisition opportunities.

Mergers and Acquisitions

In late 2014 UMB agreed to buy commercial finance firm Marquette Financial from longtime owners the Pohlad family for $182 million. The acquisition would increase UMB's presence in key growth markets Arizona and Texas – where Marquette operated Meridian Bank. As part of the deal the Pohlad family gained a 7% stake in UMB (the second-largest stake behind chairman Mariner Kemper who holds 12%).

Company Background

To grow its fee-based business and diversify its business model UMB has made several acquisitions in its past. The company built up its investment advisory and corporate trust business through several 2009 purchases. In 2010 UMB made 10 acquisitions including Prairie Capital Management and Indiana-based Reams Asset Management. The deals more than doubled UMB's Scout Investment Advisors' assets under management to more than $27 billion.

EXECUTIVES

Senior Vice President And Corporate Controller, Bryan Walker
Chairman President And Ceo, J. Mariner Kemper, age 46, $862,110 total compensation
Vice Chairman Umb Financial Corporation And President And Ceo Umb Bank, Michael D. (Mike) Hagedorn, age 53, $444,986 total compensation
Ceo Scout Investments, Andrew J. (Andy) Iseman, age 55, $6,048 total compensation

President Umb Fund Services Inc., Anthony J. (Tony) Fischer, age 60, $281,154 total compensation
Evp And Chief Credit Officer, Christian R. (Chris) Swett, age 63
Evp And Chief Lending Officer, Thomas S. (Tom) Terry, age 55
Cfo, Ram Shankar, age 46
Evp And Chief Human Resources Officer, Shannon A. Johnson, age 39
Evp And Director Of Operations Bank, Kevin M. Macke, age 46
Evp And Chief Risk Officer, Jennifer M. Payne, age 42
Vice President Of Commercial Underwriting, Rebecca A Lang
Vice President Marketing, Kelli Christman
Senior Vice President Investment Division, Raleigh Trovillion
Vice President Quality Assurance And Risk Management, Mark Kitchin
Vp Loan Review Team Lead, Christopher Nelson
Senior Vice President, Dan Dennis
Assistant Vice President And Financial Center Manager Ii, Jenna Harris
Assistant Vice President And Information Technology Manager And Data Architecture, Bob Eber
Vice President Banking Services Compliance Directo, Stephanie Boryla
Assistant Vice President Financial Center Manager, Chad Treacy
Vice President Of Commercial Banking, Mark Winker
Vice President Talent Development, Jillian Ciucci
Vice President Senior Loan Review, James Engelhart
Vice President Private Banking Client Manager, Chad Roberts
Assistant Vice President And Banking Center Manager, Erika Whitman
Senior Vice President, Phil Richter
Vice President Legal Counsel, James Ferraro
Executive Vice President And Managing Director, Andre Trudell
Vice President Commercial Banking, Jess Adams
Vp Retail Operations Officer, Michele Mcreynolds
Senior Vice President Loan Operations, Linda Gallagher
Vice President, Douglas Hare
Vp Fraud Strategy Manager, Clayton Wariner
Vice President, Jack Misiewicz
Executive Vice President, Christine Pierson
Avp Financial Center Manager Ii, Dustin Smith
Executive Vice President Director Bank Strategy And Administration, Rekha Patnaik
Senior Vice President Commercial Banking, Drue Thomas
Vice President Healthcare Services, Brenda Beachey
Avp And Senior Benefits Administrator, Rebecca Moodie
Senior Vice President, Gordon Gendler
Vice President Debit Product Manager, Hugh Meadows
Vice President, Sandy Battas
Vice President Financial Center Manager, Casey Kudrna
Senior Vice President, Gavin Wilkinson
Vice President Trust Custody Operations Manager, Melvin Porter
Vice President Enterprise Data Operations, Sara Rock
Executive Vice President Regional Credit Officer, Kurt Kastendick
Commercial Development Officer Vice President, Edin Salkic
Assistant Vice President Commercial Underwriting Officer, Brad Boeshaar
Vice President, Mark Volkmer
Assistant Vice President, Lori Kohler

Vice President Corporate Trust, Laura Roberson
Vice President Corporate Trust, Brian Krippner
Senior Vice President, Ann Porter
Senior Vice President Retail Banking, Eric Craine
Vice President And Program Operations Management Lssbb, Renee Taylor
Vice President Product Development And Marketing, Bruce Parker
Vice President Senior Loan Review Officer, Chris Landry
Vice President Of Commercial Underwriting, Rebecca Lang
Senior Vice President, Mark Hannah
Vice President Investment And Wealth Management, Kelley Lauer
Vice President Finance, Debbie Johnson
Assistant Vice President, Steve Collins
Executive Vice President Chief Lending Officer, Tom Terry
Executive Vice President, Thomas Hof
Vice President Commercial Banking, William Thomasjr
Assistant Vice President Trust Advisor, Karin Behnk
Senior Vice President, Randall Tharp
Senior Vice President, Rick Bennett
Senior Vice President Treasury Management, David Pucci
Vice President And Director Healthcare Services Risk And Compliance, Stacy King
Vice President, Beth Ewert
Vice President Private Banking Client Manager, Chris Herwig
Financial Center Manager Assistant Vice President, Nicholas Foreman
Vice President Business Banking, Randall Rodgers
Vice President Treasury Solutions Officer, Shannon Toney
Senior Vice President Commerci, Cydney Gurgens
Vp Financial Center Manager Ii, Benjamin Marx
Vice President, Laurie Box
Vice President, Rick Beaver
Senior Vice President, Robert Elbert
Assistant Vice President Financial Center Manager, Douglas Empson
Vice President, Jack Curtis
Senior Vice President, Janet Clements
Avp Commercial Technical Support, Elaine Wadehra
Healthcare Services Vp Product Management, Scott Joling
Assistant Vice President Marketing Activation, Jeff Bowers
Svp Customer Experience Strategy, Amy Mendenhall
Senior Vice President Corporate Communication, Barry Brakeville
Vp Third Party Risk Management, Jeff Hovious
Vice President Commercial Relationship Manager, Shawn Harbour
Vice President Treasury Management, Lanie Sedlacek
Vice President Assistant Manager, Sarah Read
Vice President Implementation Manager, Lori Lamanno
Vice President Private Banker, Shelly Parker
Senior Vice President Commercial Lending, Aaron Emel
Vice President Capital Markets, Nick Arthachinda
Vice President, Michael Scholten
Vice President Commercial Banking, Nate Farley
Vice President Commercial Lending, Josh Heinrich
Vice President Portfolio Manager, Jason Harrison
Vice President Trust Administration, Brian Thurston
Assistant Vice President Treasury Analyst, Mike Groff
Senior Vice President Chief Information Security Officer, Sara Flores

Vice President And Corporate Legal Counsel, Megan Mercer
Senior Vice President, John Misiewicz
Vice President Commercial Banking, Evan Weishar
Vice President And Private Banking Client Manager, Ellen Burris
Senior Vice President Public Finance, Chip Schultz
Vice President, Nancy Mogelnicki
Vice President And Senior Financial Planner, Dan Weeks
Vice President Regional Mortgage Sales Manager, Miguale Green
Vice President, Lloyd Thompson
Vice President Commercial Banking, Bryson Bowden
Vice President, Robert Gladu
Vice President, Clay Phillips
Senior Vice President Commercial Team Lead, Dennis Wright
Vice President, Marcia Matthews
Vice President Legal Counsel, Terri Munsell
Senior Vice President, Clinton Patterson
Vice President Organizational Effecitveness Business Partner, Diane Epley
Senior Vice President, Marion De Barros
Vice President Commercial Real Estate, Charles Gonzalez
Senior Vice President Compliance, Jeff Maxwell
Vice President, Julius Zamora
Vp Business Aviation Finance, Morgan Littell
Vprelationship Manager, Madelyn Wallace
Vice President Business Development, Richard Tailey
Fund Accounting Manager Assistant Vice President, Brian Schmidt
Vice President, Karen Kohl
Vice President Business Banking, Randy Rodgers
Assistant Vice President Information Technology Help Desk And Olbs Manager, Michael Meredith
Vice President Investment Banking, Sheri Catlett
Vice President Global Relationship Manager, Bart Woodson
Assistant Vice President, Pam Sudduth
Senior Vice President, Chris Orlowski
Vice President Commercial Card Sales Manager Payment Solutions, Cherie Figge
Vice President Credit Analysis Manager, Lisa Smith
Vice President And Aml Investigations Supervisor, Venus Griswold
Vice President And Tax Senior Manager, Megan Kimzey
Assistant Vice President Instutional Asset Management Iam Support Division Manager, Sarah Johnson
Vice President Construction Loan Manager, Sheila Mossey
Assistant Vice President Control Group Manager, John Effenheim
Executive Vice President, Frank Gorman
Assistant Vice President, Liz Angotti
Vice President Commercial Relationship Specialist, Christy Thomas
Vice President Construction Loan Manager, Sheila Larkey
Avp And Senior Benefits Plan Administrator, Chris Li-owens
Senior Vice President, Eric Crane
Auditors: KPMG LLP

LOCATIONS

HQ: UMB Financial Corp
 1010 Grand Boulevard, Kansas City, MO 64106
Phone: 816 860-7000   **Fax:** 816 860-7143
Web: www.umb.com

PRODUCTS/OPERATIONS

2016 Sales

	$ mil.	% of total
Interest income		
Loans	386	29
Securities	131	13
Federal funds and resell agreements	3	-
Interest-bearing due from banks	2.4	
Trading securities	0.6	
Non-interest income		
Trust and securities processing	240	24
Trading and investment banking	22	2
Service charges on deposit accounts	87	9
Insurance fees and commissions	4	-
Brokerage fees	18	2
Bankcard fees	69	7
Gains on sales of securities available for sale net	9	1
Equity earnings (losses) on alternative investments	3	-
Other	26	3
Total	**999**	**100**

Selected Subsidiaries & Affiliates

Grand Distribution Services LLC
J.D. Clark & Company
Kansas City Financial Corporation
Kansas City Realty Company
Prairie Capital Management LLC
Scout Distributors LLC
Scout Investment Advisors Inc.
UMB Banc Leasing Corp.
UMB Bank and Trust n.a.
UMB Bank Arizona n.a.
UMB Bank Colorado n.a.
UMB Capital Corporation
UMB Community Development Corporation
UMB Distribution Services LLC
UMB Financial Services Inc.
UMB Fund Services Inc.
UMB Insurance Inc.
UMB National Bank of America
UMB Realty Company LLC
UMB Redevelopment Corporation
UMB Trust Company of South Dakota
United Missouri Insurance Company

COMPETITORS

BOK Financial	Great Southern Bancorp
Bank of America	Guaranty Bancorp
Capitol Federal	TCF Financial
Financial	U.S. Bancorp
Commerce Bancshares	Zions Bancorporation
Dickinson Financial	
First National of	
Nebraska	

HISTORICAL FINANCIALS

Company Type: Public

Income Statement

FYE: December 31

	ASSETS ($ mil.)	NET INCOME ($ mil.)	INCOME AS % OF ASSETS	EMPLOYEES
12/18	23,351	196	0.8%	3,573
12/17	21,772	247	1.1%	3,570
12/16	20,683	159	0.8%	3,688
12/15	19,094	116	0.6%	3,830
12/14	17,501	121	0.7%	3,592
Annual Growth	**7.5%**	**12.8%**	**—**	**(0.1%)**

2018 Year-End Financials

Debt ratio: 0.00%	No. of shares (mil.): 49
Return on equity: 9.00%	Dividends
Cash ($ mil.): 1,754	Yield: 2.0%
Current ratio: —	Payout: 21.0%
Long-term debt ($ mil.): —	Market value ($ mil.): 2,995

	STOCK PRICE ($) FY Close	P/E High/Low		PER SHARE ($) Earnings	Dividends	Book Value
12/18	61.00	20	15	4.00	1.00	45.00
12/17	72.00	16	13	5.00	1.00	44.00
12/16	77.00	25	13	3.00	1.00	40.00
12/15	47.00	24	19	2.00	1.00	38.00
12/14	57.00	25	20	3.00	1.00	36.00
Annual Growth	**1.7%**	**—**	**—**	**10.4%**	**6.5%**	**5.9%**

Umpqua Holdings Corp

Umpqua Holdings thinks of itself not so much as a bank but rather a retailer that sells financial products. Consequently many of the company's 380-plus Umpqua Bank "stores" in northern California northern Nevada Idaho Oregon and Washington feature coffee bars and computer cafes. While customers sip Umpqua-branded coffee pay bills online attend a financial seminar catch a poetry reading or check out wares from local merchants staff members pitch deposit accounts mortgages loans life insurance investments and more. Subsidiary Umpqua Investments (formerly Strand Atkinson Williams & York) provides retail brokerage services through more than a dozen locations mostly inside Umpqua Bank branches.

Operations

Umpqua operates two business segments: Community Banking which made up 79% of the company's total revenue during 2015 and provides traditional banking services as well as wealth management and private banking services for wealthier individuals; and Home Lending (21% of revenue) which originates and sells residential mortgage loans.

The company makes more than 75% of its revenue from interest income. About 72% of its revenue came from loan interest (including fees) during 2015 with another 5% coming from interest on investment securities. The rest of its revenue came from residential mortgage banking revenue (9% of revenue) deposit account service charges (5%) brokerage revenue (2%) and other miscellaneous income streams.

Geographic Reach

Oregon-based Umpqua Bank has branches in Idaho Washington Oregon California and Northern Nevada. Umpqua Investments has offices in Portland Lake Oswego and Medford Oregon as well as Santa Rosa California.

Sales and Marketing

Umpqua Holdings promotes its brand through customer-facing channels public relations social media and community-based events. It spent $11.4 million on marketing to promote its brand during 2015 up from $9.5 million and $6.1 million in 2014 and 2013 respectively.

Financial Performance

The bank's annual revenues have doubled since 2011 as its loan and lease assets have tripled to $16.85 billion which has resulted in strong interest income growth. Exceptional revenue growth and effective cost controls have helped the bank's net income triple over the same period.

Umpqua Holdings' revenue jumped 20% to $1.21 billion during 2015 mostly as its earning assets (including loans investments and loans held for sale) swelled by 20% which led to higher interest income. The bank's non-interest income also rose 52% for the year mostly thanks to the 2014 acquisition of Sterling Financial with residential mortgage banking revenue brokerage commis-

sions and deposit service charges all growing during the year.

Strong revenue growth in 2015 drove the bank's net income up 51% to $222.54 million for the year. Umpqua's operating cash levels climbed 5% to $376.74 million as earnings rose.

Strategy

Umpqua Bank's primary mission is to become the top community-oriented financial services firm in the Western US by strategically acquiring banks in new markets and building its brand by offering unique personal experience for customers entering its "store" branches. Its mid-2014 acquisition of Sterling Financial — the largest ever acquisition in Umpqua's history — successfully extended the bank's presence in Southern California Eastern Washington Eastern Oregon and Idaho.

The bank differentiates itself by encouraging clients to come into its stores instead of using impersonal interfaces like ATMs and electronic banking more cost-effective methods preferred by many of its competitors. The bank's "Next Generation" stores feature interactive touch-screen walls fresh fruit and cold drinks. It hopes the comfortable environment will inspire customers to use more of the bank's financial services.

Hoping to build upon its one-of-a-kind branch experiences Umpqua Bank in 2015 launched its Silicon Valley-based Pivotus Ventures Inc subsidiary to explore disruptive new bank technologies.

In 2016 Umpqua launched its corporate banking division which is dedicated to providing companies with access to such offerings as treasury management international banking debt capital markets and others.

Mergers and Acquisitions

In April 2014 Umpqua Bank acquired $10-billion-in-assets Sterling Financial Corp. headquartered in Spokane Washington. The largest merger in Umpqua's history created the West Coast's largest community bank with some $22 billion in assets and 394 stores across five states. The Sterling branches were rebranded as part of the $1.9 billion deal.

Company Background

Traditionally consumer focused Umpqua Bank established a business banking division in 2011 to court small and mid-sized business clients. That year it pursued deposit growth assembled new lending teams and added new stores in key metropolitan areas like Portland Oregon; Seattle; San Francisco; and California's Silicon Valley.

Umpqua Holdings established a wealth management division in 2009 and launched a trust services group the following year. It provided asset management services through an agreement with independent firm Ferguson Wellman Capital Management.

EXECUTIVES

Evp Wealth Management Umpqua Holdings And Umpqua Bank, Kelly Johnson

Evp Creative Strategies Group Umpqua Bank, Lani Hayward, age 52

Evp And Chief Lending Officer Umpqua Holdings Corp And Umpqua Bank, David F. (Dave) Shotwell, age 60

Evp Cfo And Principal Financial Officer Umpqua Holdings And Umpqua Bank, Ronald L. (Ron) Farnsworth, age 49, $425,000 total compensation

Evp Treasurer And Principal Accounting Officer Umpqua Holdings And Umpqua Bank, Neal T. McLaughlin, age 51

Evp Corporate Communications Umpqua Bank, Eve Callahan, age 45

President Ceo And Director, Cort O'Haver, age 56, $565,000 total compensation

Evp And Chief Auditor Umpqua Bank, Joel Brandenburg, age 56

Evp Enterprise Risk Management Umpqua Holdings Corp And Umpqua Bank, Gary F. Neal, age 64

Evp Associate Relations Umpqua Holdings Corp And Umpqua Bank, Sheri T. Burns, age 51

Evp Cultural Enhancement And Government Relations Umpqua Bank, Marty J. Dickinson, age 49

Evp General Counsel And Corporate Secretary Umpqua Holdings Corp And Umpqua Bank, Andrew H. Ognall, age 47, $300,000 total compensation

Vice President Of Benefits, Jennifer Hollenbeck

Senior Vice President Data Processing, Bo Harrison

Vice President Rewards And Recognition, Sandy Hunt

Vice President Enterprise Risk Manager, Aretina Trepczyk

Senior Vice President Credit Review Manager Commercial Banking, Jim Storvick

Senior Vice President Network Security Operations, Ryan McGrory

Vice President Systems Administrator, Sherri Kittilstved

Assistant Vice President Technical Business Systems Analyst Supervisor, Erika Martin

Assistant Vice President Technical Business Systems Analyst, Nicole Jett

Vice President Commercial Banking Center Manager, Jamie Hudson

Vice President And Relationship Manager, Maria Talavera

Vice President Investments, Tinh Nguyen

Senior Vice President Investments, Keith Morgan

Vp Cyber Security Operations Center, Joshua Lewis

Chairman, Raymond P. (Ray) Davis, age 70

Vice Chairman, Bryan L. Timm, age 55

Auditors: DELOITTE & TOUCHE LLP

LOCATIONS

HQ: Umpqua Holdings Corp
One S.W. Columbia Street, Suite 1200, Portland, OR 97258
Phone: 503 727-4100
Web: www.umpquaholdingscorp.com

PRODUCTS/OPERATIONS

2015 Sales

	$ mil.	% of total
Interest		
Interest and fees on loans and leases	869	72
TaxableInterest and dividends investment securities	58	5
Other	2	-
Non-interest		
Mortgage banking	125	9
Service charges on deposit accounts	60	5
Brokerage	19	2
Gain on loan sales net	22	2
BOLI income	8	1
Gain on investment securities net	3	-
Other	46	4
Adjustments	(7.2)	
Total	**1,206**	**100**

2015 Sales

	$ mil.	% of total
Community Banking	955	79
Home Lending	251	21
Total	**1,206**	**100**

COMPETITORS

Bank of America	KeyCorp
Bank of the West	U.S. Bancorp
Banner Corp	Washington Federal
Cascade Bancorp	Wells Fargo
Columbia Banking	

HISTORICAL FINANCIALS

Company Type: Public

Income Statement

FYE: December 31

	ASSETS ($ mil.)	NET INCOME ($ mil.)	INCOME AS % OF ASSETS	EMPLOYEES
12/18	26,940	316	1.2%	3,928
12/17	25,741	246	1.0%	4,380
12/16	24,813	233	0.9%	4,295
12/15	23,387	223	1.0%	4,491
12/14	22,613	148	0.7%	4,569
Annual Growth	4.5%	21.0%	—	(3.7%)

2018 Year-End Financials

Debt ratio: 4.00%
Return on equity: 8.00%
Cash ($ mil.): 623
Current ratio: —
Long-term debt ($ mil.): —

No. of shares (mil.): 220
Dividends
  Yield: 5.0%
  Payout: 57.0%
Market value ($ mil.): 3,502

	STOCK PRICE ($) FY Close	P/E High/Low	Earnings	Dividends	Book Value
12/18	16.00	17 11	1.00	1.00	18.00
12/17	21.00	20 15	1.00	1.00	18.00
12/16	19.00	18 13	1.00	1.00	18.00
12/15	16.00	19 15	1.00	1.00	17.00
12/14	17.00	24 20	1.00	1.00	17.00
Annual Growth	(1.7%)	— —	16.4%	8.1%	1.8%

Under Armour Inc

Under Armour makes performance clothes for doing battle on the sports field and in the gym. The company is the official footwear supplier of the National Football League (NFL) and Major League Baseball (MLB) and partners with the National Basketball Association (NBA); it outfits everyday athletes as well. Under Armour claims its products made from moisture-wicking and heat-dispersing fabrics keep athletes dry and comfortable during workouts. The company also makes technology that helps customers track their fitness. It sells online by catalog and through retail and outlet stores worldwide. Its locker room of athlete endorsers include top performers in football basketball soccer and baseball. Under Armour operates worldwide but generates most of its revenue in the US.

Operations

Apparel designed for winter (COLDGEAR) summer (HEATGEAR) and year-round (ALLSEASONGEAR) wear accounts for more than 65% of sales. Footwear brings in about 20% of sales with accessories such as hats bags and gloves contributing just under 10%.

Under Armour also has a small but growing Connected Fitness business which includes fitness-related apps such as MapMyFitness MyFitnessPal Endonondo and UA Record. The free-to-use apps generate revenue from advertising and account for the remaining revenue (along with licensing fees).

Almost all of Under Armour's products are made by third-party manufacturers in some 15 countries. About 60% of the company's products are made in China Jordan Vietnam and Malaysia.

Geographic Reach

Under Armour operates globally. Beyond North America where it generates about 70% of sales the company's products are sold primarily in Germany and the UK. It also sells in Japan Hong Kong and South Korea through a third-party licensee.

In addition to its main headquarters in Baltimore Maryland Under Armour has headquarters locations in the Netherlands (for Europe) Panama (for Latin America) and Hong Kong and China (for the Asia-Pacific region and Greater China).

The company's distribution facilities are in Sparrows Point and Glen Burnie Maryland; Mount Juliet Tennessee; and Rialto California. It also operates some 320 brand and factory house stores located primarily in the US Canada China Chile and Mexico.

Sales and Marketing

Under Armour generates more than 60% of its sales through its wholesale business although its direct-to-consumer business is growing rapidly.

Sports marketing — on the high school collegiate and professional levels — is key for the company in building its brand and expanding its customer base. Under Armour uses outfitting agreements; professional club and collegiate sponsorships; and individual athlete and influencer agreements to attract attention. It also sponsors and hosts consumer sporting events such as youth camps and clinics.

The company's advertising expense was $543.8 million $565.1 million and $477.5 million in 2018 2017 and 2016 respectively.

Financial Performance

Under Armour's revenue has jumped nearly 70% in the past five years as more consumers clad themselves in Under Armour branded athletic wear. Net income had been following a similar upward trajectory until 2017 when it plummeted amid restructuring charges.

In 2018 the company reported revenue of $5.2 billion up 4% from the prior year. Growth in apparel driven primarily by training clothing led the charge. Increases in footwear and connected fitness also added to the results. Accessories sales however fell about 5% year-over-year. Geographically huge gains in the EMEA and Asia-Pacific regions were more than enough to offset a small decline in North American revenue.

Net loss that year improved just slightly from $48.2 million to $46.3 million but Under Armour still had a second consecutive year of significant restructuring and impairment charges related to a company plan to optimize operations.

Cash at the end of 2018 was $566.1 million an increase of $247.9 million from the prior year. Cash from operations contributed $628.2 million to the coffers while investing activities used $202.9 million mainly for capital expenditures. Financing activities used another $189.9 million for payments on long-term debt.

Strategy

After unbridled growth for most of the past decade Under Armour's sales slowed in 2017 and 2018 because of its struggling North American business which accounts for some 70% of total revenue. The company has responded with a broad restructuring that has reduced headcount consolidated facilities closed stores and refocused resources. As part of a five-year growth plan it is focused on creating innovative products — including digital integration — and investing in high-growth-opportunity areas such as international operations.

In 2017 and 2018 the company introduced several product advancements including Reactor temperature-regulating fabric and Threadborne sports performance fabric as well as the HOVR connected footwear platform. It is also building an ecosystem of products around its connected footwear and fitness apps such as MapMyFitness/MapMyRun. In early 2019 it announced integrations with Samsung's Galaxy smartwatch and JBL wireless headphones

Under Armour also plans to build on its growing international sales which account for about quarter of its revenue (compared to about half of that in 2015). In 2018 the company revamped its regional structure appointing new managing directors for Latin America and the Asia-Pacific and EMEA regions. It also announced plans to expand its Hong Kong headquarters. In early 2019 it opened a new regional headquarters in Amsterdam. Building a global brand would help Under Armour compete with larger rivals Nike and Adidas who generate much more revenue outside the US and have logos known around the world.

Company Background

Under Armour was founded in Washington DC in 1996 and moved to Baltimore Maryland two years later. It promoted apparel specifically for athletes fabric designed to keep them cool when it is hot and keep them warm when it is cold.

The company considers its inclusion in the 1999 film Any Given Sunday as its big break claiming that "athletes everywhere took notice."

It continued focusing on the sports world inking supplier or licensing deals with the NHL MLB and USA Baseball in the early 2000s. Under Armour went public in 2005.

The following year the company moved into footwear with a line of football cleats; it eventually became the official footwear supplier to the NFL.

EXECUTIVES

Vice President, Raphael Peck
Chairman And Ceo, Kevin A. Plank, age 46, $26,000 total compensation
President And Coo, Patrik Frisk, age 56
Cto, Paul Fipps
Chief Supply Chain Officer, Colin Browne, $169,231 total compensation
Chief Digital Officer, Michael Lee, $434,423 total compensation
President North America, Jason LaRose
Acting Cfo, David E. Bergman, age 46
National Sales Manager, Jeff Schwaninger
Vice President Of Technical Design, Lisa Struble
Senior Vice President Global Communications And Entertainment, Diane Pelkey
Senior Vice President Talent, Melissa Wallace
Vice President Materials, Randy Harward
Executive Vice President Operations, Ryan Shute
Vice President Operations, Brittany Mattheu
Vp Footwear Development And Engineering, Cameron Shayegi
Vice President Global Public Policy, Matthew Stanton
Vice President Global Total Rewards, Sarah Prost
Vp Gm Global Basketball, Ryan Drew
Vice President Commercialization Lab And Open Innovation, Sam Mccleery
Vice President Running, Fritz Taylor
Vice President Footwear Outdoor Training, Chris Lindgren
Vice President Global Brand And Sports Marketing, Peter Murray
Vice President Consumer Comms, Dean Stoyer
Svp Of Corporate Communications, Kelley Mccormick
Vice President Global Brand Marketing Womens And Youth, Attica Jaques
Vice President, Moore Roston
Secretary, Adam Householder
Board Member, Jerri Devard
Auditors: PricewaterhouseCoopers LLP

LOCATIONS

HQ: Under Armour Inc
1020 Hull Street, Baltimore, MD 21230
Phone: 410 454-6428
Web: www.underarmour.com

2018 Sales

	$ mil.	% of total
North America	3,735	72
EMEA	589	11
Asia-Pacific	558	11
Latin America	191	4
Connected Fitness	120	2
Total	**5,193**	**100**

PRODUCTS/OPERATIONS

2018 Sales

	$ mil.	% of total
Apparel	3,462	67
Footwear	1,063	20
Accessories	423	8
Licensing	125	3
Connected Fitness	120	2
Total	**5,193**	**100**

COMPETITORS

ASICS America	Lululemon
Apple Inc.	NIKE
Columbia Sportswear	New Balance
Fitbit	North Face
Fruit of the Loom	Patagonia Inc.
Hanesbrands	Skechers U.S.A.
Jockey International	adidas
L.L. Bean	

HISTORICAL FINANCIALS

Company Type: Public

Income Statement				FYE: December 31
	REVENUE ($ mil.)	NET INCOME ($ mil.)	NET PROFIT MARGIN	EMPLOYEES
12/18	5,193	(46)	—	15,000
12/17	4,977	(48)	—	15,800
12/16	4,825	257	5.3%	9,400
12/15	3,963	233	5.9%	13,400
12/14	3,084	208	6.7%	10,700
Annual Growth	**13.9%**		—	**8.8%**

2018 Year-End Financials

Debt ratio: 17.00%
Return on equity: (-2.00%)
Cash ($ mil.): 557
Current ratio: 2.00
Long-term debt ($ mil.): 704

No. of shares (mil.): 449
Dividends
　Yield: —
　Payout: —
Market value ($ mil.): 7,926

	STOCK PRICE ($) FY Close	P/E High/Low		PER SHARE ($)	
			Earnings	Dividends	Book Value
12/18	18.00	— —	(0.00)	0.00	4.00
12/17	14.00	— —	(0.00)	0.00	5.00
12/16	29.00	191 65	0.00	0.00	5.00
12/15	81.00	193 119	1.00	0.00	4.00
12/14	68.00	254 94	0.00	0.00	3.00
Annual Growth	**(28.6%)**	— —	—	—	**9.2%**

UNION BANK AND TRUST COMPANY

Union Bank & Trust a subsidiary of financial services holding company Farmers & Merchants Investment operates more than 35 branches throughout Nebraska and in Kansas. As Nebraska's third-largest privately-owned bank it offers traditional deposit and trust services as well

as insurance equipment finance and investment management services. Consumer loans account for the largest portion of the bank's portfolio followed by commercial real estate and farmland loans. Union Bank also originates business loans and residential mortgages. Affiliate company Union Investment Advisors manages the Stratus family of mutual funds. Another Farmers & Merchants unit Nelnet Capital offers brokerage services.

Operations

Union Bank has grown to become one of Nebraska's largest privately-owned banks. As of mid-2013 it boasted bank assets of $2.6 billion and trust assets of $11.8 billion.

Aside from its branches in Nebraska and Kansas Union Bank offers banking products and services through its online mobile and electronic banking services.

Geographic Reach

Union Bank operates mostly in Nebraska but also in Kansas.

Sales and Marketing

The bank primarily serves customers in Lincoln and Omaha as well as the Kansas City metropolitan area.

Strategy

Union Bank continues to expand its footprint in existing markets. The financial institution will have added three new Nebraska branches to its portfolio by 2014.

Company Background

The bank was originally founded in 1917 as Farmer's State Bank. It took on the Union Bank name in 1935 and became Union Bank & Trust in 1959.

EXECUTIVES

Vice President, Tom Marchael
Vice President Small Business Banking, Stephanie Dinger
Vice President And Business Development Officer, Michael G Kulas
Vice President Financial Reporting And Controller, Kimberly Keller
Executive Vice President And Commercial Banking Group Executive, David V Ring
Vice President, Raymond Grace
Vice President And Trust Services Advisor, Douglas J Koenig
Assistant Vice President, Nick Nash

LOCATIONS

HQ: UNION BANK AND TRUST COMPANY
3643 S 48TH ST, LINCOLN, NE 685064390
Phone: 402 323-1235
Web: WWW.UBT.COM

PRODUCTS/OPERATIONS

Selected Services
Business banking
Investment & retirement
Personal banking
Wealth management

Selected Affiliates
InfoVisa
Nelnet Capital LLC
Nelnet Inc.
Union Agency Inc.
Union Equipment Finance LLC
Union Investment Advisors
Union Title Company LLC
Zelle

Bank of America
Bank of the West
Citigroup
First National of
  Nebraska
Great Western Bancorp
JPMorgan Chase
Pinnacle Bancorp
U.S. Bancorp
Wells Fargo

HISTORICAL FINANCIALS

Company Type: Private

Income Statement   FYE: December 31

	ASSETS ($ mil.)	NET INCOME ($ mil.)	INCOME AS % OF ASSETS	EMPLOYEES
12/17	3,837	46	1.2%	800
12/16	3,596	41	1.1%	—
12/15	3,352	32	1.0%	—
12/14	3,040	30	1.0%	—
Annual Growth	8.1%	15.8%	—	—

Union Pacific Corp

Venerable Union Pacific Railroad (UP) has been chugging down the track since the 19th century. Owned by Union Pacific Corporation (UPC) UP is one of the nation's leading rail carriers operating about 64000 freight cars and nearly 8600 locomotives. UP transports automobiles chemicals energy and industrial agricultural and other bulk freight over a system of some 32000 rail miles in 23 states in the western two-thirds of the US. UPC owns more than 26000 route miles of its rail network; leases and trackage rights which allow it to use other railroads' tracks account for the rest. UP's customers have included such big names as automakers General Motors and Toyota.

HISTORY

In 1862 the US Congress chartered the Union Pacific Railroad (UP) to build part of the first transcontinental railway. The driving of the Golden Spike at Promontory Utah in 1869 marked the linking of the East and West coasts as UP's rails met those of Central Pacific Railroad (predecessor of Southern Pacific or SP) which had been built east from Sacramento California.

In 1872 the New York Sun revealed the Credit Mobilier scandal: UP officials had pocketed excess profits during the railroad's construction. Debt and lingering effects of the scandal forced UP into bankruptcy in 1893.

A syndicate headed by E. H. Harriman bought UP in 1897. After reacquiring the Oregon branches it lost in the bankruptcy UP gained control of SP (1901) and Chicago & Alton (1904). The Supreme Court ordered UP to sell its SP holdings in 1913 on antitrust grounds. In the 1930s UP diversified into trucking and in the 1970s and 1980s it moved into oil and gas production.

UP bought trucking firm Overnite Transportation in 1986. During the 1980s UP also built up its rail operations acquiring the Missouri Pacific and Western Pacific railroads in 1982 and the Missouri-Kansas-Texas Railroad in 1988. It joined Chicago and North Western (CNW) Railway managers in an investment group led by Blackstone Capital Partners that bought CNW in 1989.

CNW traced its roots to the Galena & Chicago Union Railroad which was founded by Chicago's first mayor W. B. Ogden in 1836 and merged with CNW in 1864. By 1925 the North Western (as it was then known) had tracks throughout the Midwest. In 1995 UP completed its purchase of CNW and made a bid for SP.

SP was founded in 1865 but its history dates to 1861 when four Sacramento merchants founded Central Pacific. By building new track and buying other railroads (including SP in 1868) Central Pacific had expanded throughout California Texas and Oregon by 1887. The two railroads merged in 1885 under the SP name. In 1983 SP was sold to a holding company controlled by Philip Anschutz which in 1995 agreed to sell the company to UP.

UP completed its SP acquisition in 1996 but assimilation of the purchase led to widespread rail traffic jams. UP also sold its remaining interest in Union Pacific Resources an oil company it had spun off the year before. In 1997 UP moved from Bethlehem Pennsylvania to Dallas and joined a consortium led by mining company Grupo México that won a bid to run two major Mexican rail lines. In the US however fatal collisions led to a federal review of UP which found a breakdown in rail safety such as overworked employees and widespread train defects. Meanwhile regulators seeking to resolve UP's massive freight backlog ordered the railroad to open its Houston lines to competitors.

The company decentralized its management into three regions (north south and west) in 1998 to improve traffic flow. It also hired more workers added new trains and realigned routes while selling Skyway Freight Systems its logistics services unit.

In 1999 UP moved its headquarters from Dallas to Omaha Nebraska where Union Pacific Railroad offices already were located. In 2000 it formed Fenix a holding company charged with developing and expanding the company's telecommunications and technology assets. (By 2003 however UP had reabsorbed Fenix and scaled back its support for its remaining technology subsidiaries.)

The company expanded its less-than-truckload operations into the western US in 2001 by buying Motor Cargo Industries. Also that year it completed the integration of Southern Pacific's operations.

UP sold its trucking unit Overnite Corporation (a holding company for Overnite Transportation and Motor Cargo Industries) in an IPO in 2003. (Overnite Corporation was acquired by United Parcel Service in 2005 and renamed UPS Freight the next year.) UP sold its Timera subsidiary (workforce management software) in 2004.

Traffic congestion in the UP system brought on by a shortage of train crews caused some freight from UPS and other customers to be rerouted onto trucks in 2004. The crew shortage was attributed in part to a greater-than-expected number of retirements in 2003. UP accelerated its hiring and training efforts but the company still had to restrict freight volume in an effort to minimize bottlenecks.

In 2006 Union Pacific Railroad reorganized its operating structure going from four regions to three: northern southern and western. Service units of the company's central region were reassigned to the northern and southern regions. The company added 45 miles of double track to its Sunset Corridor in 2008.

In the midst of the Great Recession UPC's 2009 freight volumes decreased 16% from 2008's numbers. The company was forced to raise its rates by about 6%; it also parked approximately 26% of its locomotives 18% of its freight car stock and furloughed about 3000 employees.

As the nation slowly recovered economically UPC realized a 13% increase in volume in 2010 over 2009 with automotive intermodal and industrial product shipments showing the strongest growth. Even with 2010 fuel prices more than 30% higher than 2009 the company's freight revenues increased 20% in 2010. UPC cited economic improvement across the majority of its market sectors as the reason for the recovery.

In mid-2012 UPC subsidiary PS Technology (PST) acquired the Yard Control Systems division of Ansaldo STS USA. The acquisition boosted PST's enterprise management capabilities by adding rail yard process control and automation technology.

EXECUTIVES

Evp And Cfo, Robert M. Knight, age 62, $575,000 total compensation
Svp And Cio, Lynden L. Tennison
Chairman President And Ceo, Lance M. Fritz, age 56, $1,000,000 total compensation
Evp And Chief Administration Officer, Eric L. Butler, age 58, $485,000 total compensation
Evp And Chief Legal Officer, Rhonda S. Ferguson, age 50, $200,000 total compensation
Evp And Chief Marketing Officer, Elizabeth F. (Beth) Whited, age 54
Evp And Coo, Cameron A. Scott, age 56, $457,500 total compensation
President Shipcarsnow Inc., Peter Decher
Vp; General Manager Chemicals, Kari Kirchhoefer
Vice President Energy, Linda Brandl
Assistant Vice President Information Technology, Ashok Fichadia
Avp Risk Management, Lee Myers
National Account Manager, Rachael Molinelli
Assistant Vice President Strategic Planning, Grant Janke
Senior Assistant Vice President Chemicals, Robert G Worrell
Vice President Engineering, Greg Workman
Assistant Vice President Health And Medical Services, Chandra Henley
Secretary Ii, Patty Cuppernull
Board Member, Annie Mccarthy
Auditors: DELOITTE & TOUCHE LLP

LOCATIONS

HQ: Union Pacific Corp
  1400 Douglas Street, Omaha, NE 68179
Phone: 402 544-5000
Web: www.up.com

PRODUCTS/OPERATIONS

2017 Sales

	$ mil.	% of total
Freight	19,837	93
Other	1,403	7
Total	**21,240**	**100**

2017 Sales

	$ mil.	% of total
Freight revenues		
Intermodal	3,835	18
Agricultural Products	3,685	17
Chemicals	3,596	17
Industrial Products	4,078	19
Coal	2,645	13
Automotive	1,998	9
Other revenues	1,403	7
Total	**21,240**	**100**

COMPETITORS

American Commercial
  Lines
Burlington Northern
  Santa Fe
CSX
Canadian National
  Railway
Canadian Pacific
  Railway
Ingram Industries
J.B. Hunt
Kansas City Southern
Kirby Corporation
Landstar System
Norfolk Southern
Schneider National
Werner Enterprises

Company Type: Public

Income Statement				FYE: December 31
	REVENUE ($ mil.)	NET INCOME ($ mil.)	NET PROFIT MARGIN	EMPLOYEES
12/19	21,708	5,919	27.3%	37,483
12/18	22,832	5,966	26.1%	41,967
12/17	21,240	10,712	50.4%	41,992
12/16	19,941	4,233	21.2%	42,919
12/15	21,813	4,772	21.9%	47,457
Annual Growth	(0.1%)	5.5%	—	(5.7%)

2019 Year-End Financials

Debt ratio: 41.00%	No. of shares (mil.): 692
Return on equity: 31.00%	Dividends
Cash ($ mil.): 831	Yield: 2.0%
Current ratio: 1.00	Payout: 44.0%
Long-term debt ($ mil.): 23,943	Market value ($ mil.): 125,125

	STOCK PRICE ($) FY Close	P/E High/Low		PER SHARE ($) Earnings	Dividends	Book Value
12/19	181.00	22	16	8.00	4.00	26.00
12/18	138.00	21	16	8.00	3.00	28.00
12/17	134.00	10	8	13.00	2.00	32.00
12/16	104.00	21	14	5.00	2.00	24.00
12/15	78.00	22	14	5.00	2.00	24.00
Annual Growth	23.3%	—	—	11.2%	13.9%	1.8%

United Airlines Holdings Inc

United Airlines Holdings (formerly United Continental Holdings) operates through its primary United Air Lines subsidiary. United Airlines is a leading passenger and cargo airline operating more than 4800 flights a day to more than 350 airports. It serves destinations across five continents from US hubs in Newark Chicago Denver Houston Los Angeles San Francisco Washington DC and the US island of Guam. The airline which also offers regional services via subsidiary United Express operates a fleet of more than 1300 aircraft. In addition United is a member of the Star Alliance a marketing and code-sharing group (the largest in the world) that includes several international airlines. In 2019 the company dropped "Continental" from its name eliminating the reference to the 2010 merger of United Airlines and Continental Airlines.

Operations

United Airlines reports its earnings in three segments: passenger revenue cargo revenue and other operating revenue. Passenger revenue generates more than 90% of sales and other operating revenue (includes loyalty program MileagePlus miles sales) about 5%. Cargo revenue accounts for less than 5% of total sales.

United's mainline operations are managed through a hub and spoke system which allows for the addition of new destinations from numerous cities using a limited number of aircraft. Its regional operations connect the hubs and allow for flights to smaller cities. This service is conducted through regional carriers branded as United Express some of which include Republic Commuter Air Express-Jet GoJet and Sky West.

United is a member of the Star Alliance airline network which provides reciprocal earnings sharing of frequent flyer miles access to airport lounges and code sharing of flight operations (flights marketed under another carrier's brand name). It also has joint business arrangements with Air Canada Lufthansa Air New Zealand and Avianca and Copa Airlines which provide United the ability to integrate schedules and fares with those airlines.

The company runs a loyalty program Mileage-Plus which offers awards benefits and services to program members. MileagePlus members can earn travel rewards on United United Express and Star Alliance member airlines. It also offers a Mileage-Plus credit card through Chase Bank.

Geographic Reach

The company serves destinations across North America as well as in Asia Europe the Middle East and Latin America. United leases airport facilities gates hangar sites terminal buildings and other facilities at destination airports. It has major terminal facility leases at its hubs at Newark Liberty International Airport Chicago O'Hare Denver International Houston Bush LAX (Los Angeles) SFO (San Francisco) Washington Dulles and A.B. Won Pat International Airport in Guam.

Domestic flights (the US and Canada) generate more than 60% of United Airline's global revenue Atlantic and Pacific routes each account for about 15% and Latin America less than 10%.

Sales and Marketing

United Airlines fares are sold through its direct sales website?www.united.com the company's mobile applications and through traditional and online travel agencies.

Its advertising expenses are more than $200 million annually.

Financial Performance

United's operating revenue has seen an upward climb in recent years. Sales in 2018 reached $41.3 billion up 9% from $37.8 billion the previous year. Passenger revenue was up by $3.2 billion primarily due to an increase in traffic. The company also saw an increase in cargo revenue resulting from higher freight volume and a higher yield in the Atlantic and Pacific markets. Other operating revenue increased with higher MileagePlus miles sales.

Net income remained relatively flat at $2.1 billion in 2018 decreasing slightly by $15 million compared with 2017. Higher fuel costs were the main factor for the decrease.

Cash at the end of fiscal 2018 was $1.8 billion an increase of $208 million from the prior year. Cash from operations contributed $6.2 billion to the coffers while investing activities used $4.6 billion mainly for purchases of aircraft and aircraft improvements facility and fleet-related costs and purchases of information technology assets. Financing activities used another $1.2 billion for the company's stock repurchase program.

Strategy

United Airlines set out a multi-year growth strategy in 2018 that focuses on key initiatives such as building out its three mid-continent hubs?Chicago Denver and Houston?as well as its coastal hubs and adding more flights to smaller cities where fares tend to be higher. It is also adding more than 30 regional aircraft to its operations.

In 2019 United will continue to improve its customers' experience with a series of new routes enhancements to its United mobile app and a new segmentation strategy?the addition of a new Premium Plus category of seating between coach and business class on international flights.

Growth at United Airlines is also benefiting from a cultural shift to a more agile and action-oriented approach to improving the customer and employee experience. Employees are encouraged to submit ideas for process and product innovations. Some ideas have been incorporated into the company's

new reservation system called Gemini that provides more accurate forecasting of customer demand allowing for the sale of higher-margin fares closer to departure dates.

Company Background

In 1929 aircraft designer Bill Boeing and engine designer Fred Rentschler of Pratt & Whitney joined forces to form United Aircraft and Transport. Renamed United Air Lines in 1931 the New York-based company offered one of the first coast-to-coast airline services. In 1934 United's manufacturing and transportation divisions split. Former banker Bill Patterson became president of the latter United Air Lines and moved it to the Chicago area. In 1969 UAL Corp. was formed as a holding company.

A subsidiary of UAL Corporation merged with and into Continental in October 2010 with Continental surviving as a wholly-owned subsidiary of UAL. Upon closing of the merger UAL became the parent company of both Continental and United Air Lines and UAL Corporation's name was changed to United Continental Holdings. The transaction created the world's largest airline. In 2013 United Air Lines Inc. was merged into Continental to form one legal entity and Continental's name and brand were changed to United Airlines Inc. In 2019 the company changed its name to United Airlines Holdings dropping all reference to Continental Airlines.

HISTORY

United Airlines traces its roots back to 1931 after the United Aircraft and Transport Corporation a partnership between Boeing Airplane Company and Pratt & Whitney established an operating division known as United Air Lines then one of the world's largest airlines flying coast-to-coast from New York to San Francisco and Los Angeles.

The company began its cargo service in 1940 flying freight between New York and Chicago and during World War II began service to Alaska and across the Pacific Ocean transporting men and materials over 21 million miles.

By the 1960s United had the highest number of passenger miles of any US airline ahead of American Eastern and TWA. It remained the largest domestic airline in the US for much of the 1970s until the Deregulation Act of 1978 forced the airline to cut back on its operations where it was no longer profitable. The recession in the 1990s followed and the company sold off some of its travel subsidiaries and canceled orders for new aircraft but United survived as one of the "Big Three" airlines along with Delta and American that still dominate US market.In 1997 United expanded into international markets by partnering with other carriers forming the Star Alliance network of airlines.

EXECUTIVES

Svp Finance And Procurement And Treasurer, Gerald (Gerry) Laderman, age 61, $500,000 total compensation

President, J. Scott Kirby, age 51, $301,763 total compensation

Evp And Chief Revenue Officer, Andrew P. Nocella

Ceo, Oscar Munoz, age 61, $1,193,909 total compensation

Evp And Cio, Linda P. Jojo, age 53

Svp Technical Operations, Kris B. Bauer, age 55

Evp And Cfo, Andrew C. Levy, age 49, $243,750 total compensation

Evp And General Counsel, Brett J. Hart, age 49, $715,000 total compensation

Evp And Coo, Gregory L. (Greg) Hart, age 53, $850,000 total compensation

Evp Human Resources And Labor Relations, Michael P. (Mike) Bonds, age 57, $650,000 total compensation

Svp And Chief Customer Officer, Toby J Enqvist

Vp And Corporate Secretary, Jennifer Kraft

Vp Global Operations Logistics And Postal Affairs United Cargo, Angel Ramirez

Senior Vice President Airport And Catering Operations, Jonathan Roitman

Evp Hr And Labor Relations, Kate Gebo

Senior Vice President United Express, Brad Rich

Vice President United Cargo Sales Asia Pacific, Mirco Renfer

Vice President United Cargo Sales Emeia, Jacques Leijssenaar

Vp And Cfo Of Operations, Tom Doxey

Senior Vice President Flight Operations, Howard W Attarian

Vice President Marketing, Mark Krolick

Vice President Loyalty And Business Development, Praveen Sharma

Senior Vice President Government Affairs, Teri Fariello

Senior Vice President Government Affairs, Terri Fariello

Svp Of Labor Relations, P Douglas Mckeen

Svp Of United Express, Tracy Lee

Vice President Operations Technology, Jason Birnbaum

Svp And Chief Communications Officer, Josh Earnest

Chairman, Robert A. Milton, age 59

Board Member, William Nuti

Auditors: Ernst & Young LLP

LOCATIONS

HQ: United Airlines Holdings Inc
233 South Wacker Drive, Chicago, IL 60606
Phone: 872 825-4000
Web: www.united.com

2018 Sales

	$ mil.	% of total
Domestic (US & Canada)	25,552	62
Atlantic	7,103	17
Pacific	5,188	13
Latin America	3,460	8
Total	**41,303**	**100**

PRODUCTS/OPERATIONS

2018 Sales

	$ mil.	% of total
Passenger Revenue	37,706	91
Cargo Revenue	1,237	3
Other Operating Revenue	2,360	6
Total	**41,303**	**100**

COMPETITORS

Air France-KLM	Japan Airlines
AirTran Airways	JetBlue
Alaska Air	Qantas
Alitalia	SkyWest
American Airlines Group	Southwest Airlines
Delta Air Lines	UPS
FedEx	Virgin Atlantic Airways
Frontier Airlines	

HISTORICAL FINANCIALS

Company Type: Public

Income Statement   FYE: December 31

	REVENUE ($ mil.)	NET INCOME ($ mil.)	NET PROFIT MARGIN	EMPLOYEES
12/18	41,303	2,129	5.2%	92,000
12/17	37,736	2,131	5.6%	89,800
12/16	36,556	2,263	6.2%	88,000
12/15	37,864	7,340	19.4%	84,000
12/14	38,901	1,132	2.9%	84,000
Annual Growth	**1.5%**	**17.1%**	**—**	**2.3%**

2018 Year-End Financials

Debt ratio: 33.00%
Return on equity: 23.00%
Cash ($ mil.): 3,950
Current ratio: 1.00
Long-term debt ($ mil.): 13,349

No. of shares (mil.): 270
Dividends
 Yield: —
 Payout: —
Market value ($ mil.): 22,600

	STOCK PRICE ($) FY Close	P/E High/Low		PER SHARE ($) Earnings	Dividends	Book Value
12/18	84.00	13	8	8.00	0.00	37.00
12/17	67.00	12	8	7.00	0.00	31.00
12/16	73.00	11	6	7.00	0.00	28.00
12/15	57.00	4	3	19.00	0.00	25.00
12/14	67.00	22	12	3.00	0.00	6.00
Annual Growth	**5.8%**	**—**	**—**	**27.3%**	**—**	**55.1%**

United Bankshares Inc

United Bankshares (no relation to Ohio's United Bancshares) keeps it together as the holding company for two subsidiaries doing business as United Bank (WV) and United Bank (VA). Combined the banks boast some $12 billion in assets and operate roughly 130 branches that serve West Virginia Virginia and Washington DC as well as nearby portions of Maryland Pennsylvania and Ohio. The branches offer traditional deposit trust and lending services with a focus on residential mortgages and commercial loans. United Bankshares also owns United Brokerage Services which provides investments asset management and financial planning in addition to brokerage services.

Operations

The company's loan portfolio is made up of commercial and construction commercial and residential real estate and consumer loans (including credit card and home equity loans).

United Bankshares generated 75% of its total revenue from interest and fees on loans in 2014 plus an additional 7% from interest and dividends on its investment securities. The company generated about 9% of its total revenue from deposit services fees and another 4% from trust and brokerage services fees.

Geographic Reach

United Bankshares boasts some 130 full-service branches including more than 55 across the state of West Virginia nearly 70 in the Shenendoah Valley region of Virginia and the Northern Virginia Maryland and Washington DC metro area and a handful of branches split between southwestern Pennsylvania and southeastern Ohio.

Sales and Marketing

The company spent $4.76 million on advertising in 2014 up from $3.78 million and $4.27 million spent in 2013 and 2012 respectively.

Financial Performance

United Bankshares' revenues and profits have trended higher over the past few years thanks to growth in its loan business from acquisitions increased trust and brokerage services fee income and declining interest expense on deposits amidst the low-interest environment.

The company's revenue jumped by nearly 34% to a record $499.50 million in 2014 mostly as its interest income spiked by 37% after its Virginia Commerce acquisition added new interest-earning assets and increased the average yields on its loans investments and security assets. United Bankshare's non-interest income also swelled by 22% thanks to higher income from fees from trust and brokerage services bankcard fees and merchant discounts and net gains on investment securities.

Higher revenue in 2014 boosted the company's profits by 52% to a record $129.89 million while the company's operating cash grew by 2% thanks to higher cash earnings.

Strategy

United Bankshares has historically expanded through small bank and branch acquisitions closing nearly 30 bank purchases in the past quarter-century. Its growth strategy has mainly been focused in on the Washington DC/suburban Maryland/northern Virginia market though its also expanded into Pennsylvania in recent years as well. In 2014 for example the company extended its reach into Washington DC while boosting its loan business by $2 billion after completing its largest-ever acquisition of Virginia Commerce Bancorp.

In 2016 the company agreed to buy Cardinal Financial which has some $4.2 billion in assets and operates 30 branches in Virginia Maryland and Washington DC.

Mergers and Acquisitions

In January 2014 United Bankshares acquired Arlington-based Virginia Commerce Bancorp for a total cost of $585.53 million. The deal expanded United's reach into the Washington DC metropolitan area and added $2.07 billion in new loan business and $2.02 billion in deposits.

Company Background

The 2011 acquisition of West Virginia-based Centra Financial Holdings gave United Bankshares its first branches in Pennsylvania and entry into the Pittsburgh market.

EXECUTIVES

Evp The Company And United Bank And Wv, James B. Hayhurst, age 73, $225,000 total compensation

President, Richard M. Adams, age 51, $328,846 total compensation

Coo, James J. Consagra, age 59, $334,462 total compensation

Evp And Coo United Bank (va), Craige L. Smith, age 67, $243,750 total compensation

Evp And Cfo, W. Mark Tatterson, age 44

Evp, Darren K. Williams

Vice President Risk Management, Connie Stone

Assistant Vice President Information Technology Audit Manager, Jason Moore

Senior Vice President, Dale Homan

Vice President Internal Audit Manager, Steve Hizak

Assistant Vice President Corporate Security Officer, Rachel Wilson

Assistant Vice President And C, Erica Fowler

Vp Financial Advisor, Cameron Stewart

Board Member, Peter Converse

Auditors: Ernst & Young LLP

LOCATIONS

HQ: United Bankshares Inc
300 United Center, 500 Virginia Street, East,
Charleston, WV 25301
Phone: 304 424-8716
Web: www.ubsi-inc.com

PRODUCTS/OPERATIONS

2014 Sales

	$ mil.	% of total
Interest		
Loans including fees	384	75
Interest and dividends on securities	34	7
Other	1	-
Noninterest		
Fees from deposit services	42	9
Fees from trust & brokerage services	18	4
Other	29	5
Adjustment (losses)	(8.4)	
Total	**500**	**100**

COMPETITORS

BB&T	JPMorgan Chase
Bank of America	M&T Bank
Burke & Herbert Bank	PNC Financial
Cardinal Financial	SunTrust
City Holding	United Bancorp
Fifth Third	Virginia Commerce
Fulton Financial	Bancorp
Huntington Bancshares	WesBanco

HISTORICAL FINANCIALS

Company Type: Public

Income Statement

FYE: December 31

	ASSETS ($ mil.)	NET INCOME ($ mil.)	INCOME AS % OF ASSETS	EMPLOYEES
12/18	19,250	256	1.3%	2,230
12/17	19,059	151	0.8%	2,381
12/16	14,509	147	1.0%	1,701
12/15	12,578	138	1.1%	1,701
12/14	12,329	130	1.1%	1,703
Annual Growth	**11.8%**	**18.5%**	**—**	**7.0%**

2018 Year-End Financials

Debt ratio: 1.00%
Return on equity: 8.00%
Cash ($ mil.): 1,020
Current ratio: —
Long-term debt ($ mil.): —

No. of shares (mil.): 102
Dividends
 Yield: 4.0%
 Payout: 68.0%
Market value ($ mil.): 3,183

	STOCK PRICE ($) FY Close	P/E High/Low		PER SHARE ($) Earnings	Dividends	Book Value
12/18	31.00	16	12	2.00	1.00	32.00
12/17	35.00	30	21	2.00	1.00	31.00
12/16	46.00	25	16	2.00	1.00	28.00
12/15	37.00	22	17	2.00	1.00	25.00
12/14	37.00	20	15	2.00	1.00	24.00
Annual Growth	**(4.5%)**	**—**	**—**	**6.3%**	**1.5%**	**7.4%**

United Community Banks Inc (Blairsville, GA)

United Community Banks is the holding company for United Community Bank (UCB). UCB provides consumer and business banking products and services through nearly 150 branches across Georgia North Carolina Tennessee and South Carolina. Commercial loans including construction loans and mortgages account for the largest portion of UCB's loan portfolio (more than 50%); residential mortgages make up 30%. The company which boasts roughly $10 billion in assets also has a mortgage lending division and provides insurance through its United Community Insurance Services subsidiary (aka United Community Advisory Services).

Operations

The bank's retail mortgage lending division United Community Mortgage Services (UCMS) sells and services mortgages for Fannie Mae and Freddie Mac and provides fixed and adjustable-rate home mortgages. It also offers retail brokerage services through an affiliation with a third-party broker/dealer.

About 65% of UCB's total revenue came from loan interest (including fees) in 2014 while another 16% came from taxable investments. The rest of its revenue came from service charges and fees (10%) mortgage loan fees (2%) and brokerage fees (2%) among other sources.

Geographic Reach

UCB's nearly 105 branches are located in Georgia (in the north the Atlanta-Sandy Springs-Roswell metro area Gainsville metro area and coastal areas); western North Carolina; eastern and central Tennessee; and South Carolina (in the Greenville-Anderson-Mauldin metro area).

Sales and Marketing

The bank provides community banking services for individuals small businesses and corporations.

Financial Performance

UCB has struggled to consistently grow its revenues in recent years due to shrinking interest margins on loans amidst the low-interest environment. Its profits however have been rising thanks to declining loan loss provisions as its loan portfolio's credit quality has improved with higher property valuations in the strengthened economy.

The bank's revenue inched higher by 1% to $304 million in 2014 thanks to an increase in interest income stemming from strategic business growth initiatives designed to add new business lines and expand into new markets as well as balance sheet management and restructuring actions taken in the second quarter of the year.

Despite higher revenue in 2014 UCB's net income dove 75% to $67.6 million mostly because in 2013 it had received a non-recurring income tax benefit of $238 million stemming from reversal of a deferred tax valuation allowance. Not counting this item however the bank's profit before taxes nearly tripled during the year. UCB's operating cash levels dropped by 47% to $101.9 million in 2014 due to lower cash earnings.

Strategy

UCB has been concentrating on growing its small business lending business in recent years. In 2014 it made "significant investments" in its SBA business after acquiring Business Carolina which specialized in SBA and USDA lending.

It also continues to pursue bank acquisitions to expand its reach in its existing core markets and boost its loan and deposit business. Its acquisitions in 2015 and 2014 alone have added over $1 billion in new loan business and $1.3 billion in new deposits.

Mergers and Acquisitions

In 2016 United Community Banks expanded into key markets in coastal South Carolina after buying Mt. Pleasant-based Tidelands and its seven Tidelands Bank branches in the Charleston Myrtle Beach and Hilton Head areas.

In 2015 UCB bought Tennessee-based MoneyTree Corporation and its 10 First National Bank branches in east Tennessee. The deal added $425 million in assets $354 million in deposits and $253 million in new loan business to UCB's books.

In 2014 the company purchased Palmetto Bancshares and its Palmetto Bank branches expanding its footprint into "major" southeastern metro markets in Greenville and the Upstate South Carolina area. The deal also added $1.2 billion in assets $832 million in loans and $967 million in deposits.

Also in 2014 UCB purchased Columbia-based Business Carolina a commercial lender that specialized in SBA and USDA loans for $31.3 million in cash. The deal included $25 million in loans $6 million in other assets and substantially all of the company's employees.

EXECUTIVES

President Of Specialized Lending, Richard W. Bradshaw, age 57

Chairman And Ceo, Jimmy C. Tallent, age 66, $750,000 total compensation

President Community Banking, William M. (Bill) Gilbert, age 66, $308,334 total compensation

President And Director United Community Banks Inc. And President Ceo And Director United Community Bank, H. Lynn Harton, age 57, $575,000 total compensation

Evp General Counsel And Chief Risk Officer, Bradley J. (Brad) Miller, age 48

Evp And Chief Credit Officer, Robert A. (Rob) Edwards, age 54, $305,000 total compensation

Evp And Cfo United Community Banks Inc. And United Community Bank, Jefferson L. Harralson

Senior Vice President, Robert Head

Vice President Mortgage Origination, Lisa Mericle

Vice President, Casey Brogdon

Vice President, Ronney Dixon

Avp Mortgage Loan Officer, Tabitha Helms

Senior Vice President, David Shelnutt

Assistant Vice President Incentive Marketing Manager, Diana White

Senior Vice President, Ron Altman

Assistant Vice President, Wendy Cawthon

Vice President Mortgage Banker, Angie Abston

Vice President Of Business Development And Marketing, Elaine Bell

Senior Vice President Commercial Lending, Sam Churchill

Vice President Commercial Lending, Brian Hill

Senior Vice President, Donald Harris

Senior Vice President Corporate Services Support, Jeanette Garrett

Vp Marketing, Greg Stephens

Senior Vice President Senior Risk Officer, Shep Calhoun

Vice President, Jane Callihan

Assistant Vice President Business Banking Underwriting, Eric Rivenbark

Vice President, Nick Harty

Senior Vice President Commercial Banking, Ben Walker

Senior Vice President, Phil Beaudette

Assistant Vice President, Rob Andrews

Executive Vice President Commercial Lender, Bud Turner

Executive Vice President, Wayne Lowrey
Vice President Commercial Banking, Michael Emigh
Senior Vice President, Alan Kumler
Senior Vice President Builder Finance, Scott Ernest
Vice President, Darryl Meadows
Vice President, Tyler White
Vice President, Anne Wade
Vice President And Private Banker, Terra Winter
Senior Vice President Commercial Lending, Fred Faulkner
Senior Vice President, Jessie Marolis
Vice President Branch Manager, Wendy Martin
Vice President Commercial Lender, Donna Clark
Vice President, David Brindley
Vice President Craft Beverage Lending, Ken Jernigan
Vice President, Shad Hill
Vice President Franchise Lending, Mike Stone
Senior Vice President United Community Bank, Dennis McBride
Senior Vice President, Sheila Stolorena
Vice President, Jeff Wilson
Vice President, David Ball
Senior Vice President And Corporate Controller, Alan H Kumler
Vice President Branch Manager, Liz Bowen
Senior Vice President, Will Ferguson
Vice President Commercial Relationship Manager, William Marcus
Vice President, Sandra Brown
Vice President Commercial Relationship Manager, Laura Hodge
Vice President Underwriting, Linda Durden
Assistant Vice President Branch Manager, Michelle Galarza
Assistant Vice President And Mortgage Processing Manager, Nalann Moss
Vice President, Frank Scott
Vice President Corporate Banking, James Boccardo
Vice President Customer Contact Center Team Manager Sc, Jeanie Roberts
Vice President, Kirby Butler
Vice President And Mortgage Origination Support Manager, Darin Scheidly
Vice President Relationship Management, Nate Rohler
Vice President Sba Business Development Officer, Lisa Morgan
Assistant Treasurer, Mitchell Bleske
Board Member, Kenneth Daniels
Board Member, David Wilkins
Board Member, David Shaver
Auditors: PricewaterhouseCoopers LLP

LOCATIONS

HQ: United Community Banks Inc (Blairsville, GA)
125 Highway 515 East, Blairsville, GA 30512
Phone: 706 781-2265
Web: www.ucbi.com

PRODUCTS/OPERATIONS

2011 Sales

	$ mil.	% of total
Interest		
Loans including fees	239	69
Taxable investment securities	55	16
Other	3	1
Noninterest		
Service charges & fees	29	8
Mortgage loans & related fees	5	2
Brokerage fees	3	1
Net securities gains	1	-
Other	12	3
Adjustment	(0.7)	-
Total	**348**	**100**

COMPETITORS

Atlantic Coast Financial
BB&T
Bank of America
Bank of Oak Ridge
First Citizens BancShares
Georgia Bancshares
Georgia-Carolina Bancshares

Peoples Bancorp (NC)
Regions Financial
Southeastern Bank Financial
Southeastern Banking
SunTrust
Synovus
WGNB

HISTORICAL FINANCIALS

Company Type: Public

Income Statement				FYE: December 31
	ASSETS ($ mil.)	NET INCOME ($ mil.)	INCOME AS % OF ASSETS	EMPLOYEES
12/18	12,573	166	1.3%	2,312
12/17	11,915	68	0.6%	2,137
12/16	10,709	101	0.9%	1,916
12/15	9,626	72	0.7%	1,883
12/14	7,567	68	0.9%	1,506
Annual Growth	13.5%	25.2%	—	11.3%

2018 Year-End Financials

Debt ratio: 2.00%
Return on equity: 12.00%
Cash ($ mil.): 327
Current ratio: —
Long-term debt ($ mil.): —

No. of shares (mil.): 79
Dividends
  Yield: 3.0%
  Payout: 28.0%
Market value ($ mil.): 1,700

	STOCK PRICE ($) FY Close	P/E High/Low	PER SHARE ($) Earnings	Dividends	Book Value
12/18	21.00	16 10	2.00	1.00	18.00
12/17	28.00	33 27	1.00	0.00	17.00
12/16	30.00	21 11	1.00	0.00	15.00
12/15	19.00	20 15	1.00	0.00	14.00
12/14	19.00	18 14	1.00	0.00	12.00
Annual Growth	3.2%	—	16.9%	51.5%	10.6%

United Fire Group, Inc.

The United Fire Group (UFG) companies join together to offer a range of property/casualty products. The group operates through its United Fire & Casualty subsidiary which in turn holds entities that carry a variety of property/casualty offerings including fidelity and surety bonds and fire auto employee liability homeowners and workers' compensation lines. Some 1600 independent agencies in around 45 states sell its property/casualty products to businesses and individuals. In 2018 UFG sold its life insurance unit United Life Insurance Company to Kuvare US Holdings for $280 million.

Operations
Prior to the 2018 sale of its life insurance business UFG's property/casualty offerings accounted for more than 90% of its annual insurance premiums with a majority of those policies being written to commercial group customers. The company also offers certain personal policies to individual customers.

Geographic Reach
UFG markets its products from its headquarters in Iowa and from five regional offices in California Colorado New Jersey and Texas. It primarily operates in adjacent areas of the midwestern southern and western US.

Sales and Marketing
To increase policy placement in its existing markets UFG offers profit-sharing and commission programs to its independent agents. It also seeks to provide modern technological tools to best serve both its agents and its policyholders.

The company is represented by some 1200 independent property/casualty agencies.

Financial Performance
With the exception of 2015 UFG's revenue has been growing year-over-year. Net income has been more volatile rising and falling from year to year.

In 2017 revenue increased 6% to $1.1 billion. Direct premiums written rose that year due to organic growth related to new business and geographical expansion.

Net income rose a modest 2% to $51 million in 2017. That increase was largely due to a tax benefit of $21.9 million as a result of the Tax Act passed that year. However a rise in losses and loss settlement expenses hurt UFG's bottom line. For example the company's commercial automobile business had a higher number of large losses (losses greater than $500000). Additionally 2017 was a record year for catastrophe losses in the insurance sector with major hurricanes and wildfires. UFG's catastrophe losses totaled $74 million versus $61.2 million in 2016.

UFG ended 2017 with $95.6 million in net cash some $6.4 million more than it had at the end of 2016. Operating activities provided $170.1 million while financing activities used $107.5 million and investing activities used $62 million.

Strategy
UFG looks to expand into new markets to reduce the risk potential in its concentrated areas of operation. Like the rest of the property/casualty sector the company suffered increased losses during 2017 the worst year for catastrophes on record. With much of its business located in the Midwest South and West UFG is vulnerable to future bad years that could result from climate change.

The United Life division of United Fire & Casualty sold life annuity and credit life products in more than 30 states but UFG sold that division in early 2018.

EXECUTIVES

Vp General Counsel And Secretary, Neal R. Scharmer, age 63, $250,000 total compensation
Coo, Michael T. Wilkins, age 56, $388,600 total compensation
Vp And Chief Investment Officer, Barrie W. Ernst, age 65, $305,000 total compensation
President And Ceo, Randy A. Ramlo, age 58, $595,000 total compensation
Vp And Chief Claims Officer, David E. Conner, age 61
Cfo, Dawn M. Jaffray, age 54
Vp Information Services, Scott A. Minkel, age 58
Vp Corporate Marketing, Colleen R. Sova, age 66
Assistant Vice President Midwest Regional Office, Corey J. Ruehle
Vp And Coo United Life Insurance Company, Michael J. Sheeley
Cto, Brian Frese
Assistant Vice President Personal Lines, Victoria Hefel
Vice President Of Accounting, Sue Haupert
Asst. Vice Presdient And Senior Portfolio Manager, Bob Cataldo
Vice President, Douglas Penn
Assistant Vice President And Great Lakes Reg. Marketing Manager, Patrick P Kane
Vice President, Kathy Booher
Assistant Vice President And Marketing Manager, Miguel Diaz
Vice President, Joseph Johnson

Vice President Surety, Dennis Richmann
Assistant Vice President Regional Underwriting
  Manager, Rob Diab
Vice Chairman, John A. Rife, age 77
Chairman, Jack B. Evans, age 71
Board Member, Sarah Gardial
Auditors: Ernst & Young LLP

LOCATIONS

HQ: United Fire Group, Inc.
  118 Second Avenue SE, Cedar Rapids, IA 52401
Phone: 319 399-5700
Web: www.ufginsurance.com

PRODUCTS/OPERATIONS

2017 Sales

	$ mil.	% of total
Net premiums earned	998	95
Net investment income	51	5
Net realized investment gains	4	-
Total	**1,053**	**100**

Selected Subsidiaries

United Fire & Casualty Company
  Addison Insurance Company
  American Indemnity Financial Corporation
  Texas General Indemnity Company
  Lafayette Insurance Company
  Mercer Insurance Group Inc.
  Financial Pacific Insurance Company
  Mercer Insurance Company
  Franklin Insurance Company
  Mercer Insurance Company of New Jersey Inc.
  United Fire & Indemnity Company
  United Fire Lloyds

COMPETITORS

AIG	John Hancock Financial
Allstate	Services
American Family	Liberty Mutual
Insurance	Progressive
American Financial	Corporation
Group	Prudential
CNA Surety	State Farm
Farmers Group	The Hartford
GEICO	Travelers Companies
Hanover Insurance	

HISTORICAL FINANCIALS

Company Type: Public

Income Statement   FYE: December 31

	ASSETS ($ mil.)	NET INCOME ($ mil.)	INCOME AS % OF ASSETS	EMPLOYEES
12/18	2,817	28	1.0%	1,183
12/17	4,183	51	1.2%	1,180
12/16	4,055	50	1.2%	1,112
12/15	3,890	89	2.3%	1,070
12/14	3,857	59	1.5%	981
Annual Growth	**(7.6%)**	**(17.3%)**	**—**	**4.8%**

2018 Year-End Financials

Debt ratio: —	No. of shares (mil.): 25
Return on equity: 3.00%	Dividends
Cash ($ mil.): 64	Yield: 8.0%
Current ratio: —	Payout: 104.0%
Long-term debt ($ mil.): —	Market value ($ mil.): 1,392

	STOCK PRICE ($) FY Close	P/E High/Low		PER SHARE ($) Earnings	Dividends	Book Value
12/18	55.00	55	37	1.00	4.00	35.00
12/17	46.00	24	19	2.00	1.00	39.00
12/16	49.00	26	18	2.00	1.00	37.00
12/15	38.00	11	8	4.00	1.00	35.00
12/14	30.00	14	10	2.00	1.00	33.00
Annual Growth	**16.9%**	**—**	**—**	**(17.4%)**	**52.4%**	**2.0%**

United Insurance Holdings Corp

United Insurance Holdings insures homeowners in the Sunshine State throughout the seasons even hurricane season. The company underwrites flood fire and homeowners insurance policies in Florida and provides property insurance for automotive service companies. It distributes its products through independent agents. United Insurance was founded in 1999 then underwent a reverse merger in 2008 when it bought the OTC-listed FMG Acquisition Corp. for $95 million ($25 million in cash and 8.75 million shares of stock.) The newly merged company has listed on the NASDAQ exchange.

EXECUTIVES

Chief Underwriting Officer, Paul DiFrancesco
Ceo, John L. Forney, $800,000 total compensation
Cfo, B. Bradford Martz, $300,000 total compensation
Cio, Andrew D. (Andy) Swenson, $210,000 total
  compensation
General Counsel And Chief Legal Officer, Kimberly
  Salmon
Board Member, Kern Davis
Chairman, Gregory C. Branch
Board Member, Patrick Maroney
Auditors: DELOITTE & TOUCHE LLP

LOCATIONS

HQ: United Insurance Holdings Corp
  800 2nd Avenue S, St. Petersburg, FL 33701
Phone: 727 895-7737
Web: www.upcinsurance.com

PRODUCTS/OPERATIONS

2015 Sales

	$ mil.	% of total
Net premiums earned	336	94
Investment income	9	3
Net realized gains	1	-
Other revenue	12	3
Total	**358**	**100**

COMPETITORS

AAA Auto Club South	Federated National
Allstate	Holding
American National	HCI Group
Insurance	Liberty Mutual
Bankers Financial	State Farm
Citizens Property	Universal Insurance
Insurance	Holdings

HISTORICAL FINANCIALS

Company Type: Public

Income Statement   FYE: December 31

	ASSETS ($ mil.)	NET INCOME ($ mil.)	INCOME AS % OF ASSETS	EMPLOYEES
12/18	2,321	0	0.0%	293
12/17	2,060	10	0.5%	210
12/16	1,000	6	0.6%	167
12/15	740	27	3.7%	120
12/14	584	41	7.0%	120
Annual Growth	**41.2%**	**(71.0%)**	**—**	**25.0%**

2018 Year-End Financials

Debt ratio: 7.00%	No. of shares (mil.): 43
Return on equity: 0.00%	Dividends
Cash ($ mil.): 113	Yield: 1.0%
Current ratio: —	Payout: 24.0%
Long-term debt ($ mil.): —	Market value ($ mil.): 714

	STOCK PRICE ($) FY Close	P/E High/Low	PER SHARE ($) Earnings	Dividends	Book Value
12/18	17.00	22381580	0.00	0.00	12.00
12/17	17.00	65 49	0.00	0.00	13.00
12/16	15.00	73 40	0.00	0.00	11.00
12/15	17.00	22 10	1.00	0.00	11.00
12/14	22.00	11 6	2.00	0.00	10.00
Annual Growth	**(6.7%)**	**—**	**(73.6%)**	**10.7%**	**5.6%**

United Natural Foods Inc.

United Natural Foods Inc. (UNFI) is one of the top wholesale distributors of natural organic and specialty foods in the US and Canada. It owns around 65 distribution centers that supply more than 250000 items to 30000 unique customer locations including independently-owned retailers supernatural chain Whole Foods (its #1 customer) and conventional supermarkets. The company offers groceries supplements produce frozen foods and ethnic and kosher food as well as foodservice products and personal care items. UNFI also produces roasted nuts dried fruits and other snack items through subsidiary Woodstock Farms. It acquired rival SUPERVALU in 2018 which more than doubled its size.

Operations

UNFI's operations are comprised of two principal divisions: Wholesale and Manufacturing and Branded Products.

The company's wholesale division generates virtually all of its sales and consists of the US and Canadian natural organic and specialty distribution business. Its operations cover major subsidiaries such as Tony's and Albert's as well as newly acquired businesses like the SUPERVALU. The division also distributes vitamins minerals and supplements through Select Nutrition and ethnic food items and related products through other subsidiaries. It distributes brand-name products as well as private-label products under names such as Culinary Circle Stockman and Dakota Wild Harvest Arctic Shores Seafoods Baby Basics and Shopper's Value.

The Manufacturing and Branded Products division consists of Woodstock Farms Manufacturing which specializes in importing roasting packaging and distributing nuts dried fruit seeds trail mixes granola natural and organic snack items and confections. The company has also built up its own food brands through subsidiary Blue Marble Brands which offers more than 700 products marketed under some 15 brand names directly to retailers as well as third party distributors.

Geographic Reach

Rhode Island-based United Natural Foods maintains about 65 distribution centers in US and Canada. It also has smaller administrative offices across the US including an executive office in Eden Prairie Minnesota.

The company serves customers in the US Canada and other countries but the US accounts for nearly 100% of revenue.

Sales and Marketing

UNFI is heavily reliant on Amazon subsidiary Whole Foods Market its largest wholesale customer representing about 20% of net sales. Conventional supermarkets — including Kroger Publix and Wegman's — and mass market chains account for about 60% of sales and independent stores and chains generate about 15%.

Foodservice e-commerce and international customers outside of Canada as well as sales to Amazon.com represent the rest.

Financial Performance

Powered by acquisitions UNFI has seen skyrocketing revenue growth over the past decade. Net income has not been as explosive but has grown steadily until impacted by one-time charges in fiscal 2019. Long-term debt has of course jumped along with the acquisitions jumping to $2.8 billion in fiscal 2019 from $309 million the prior year.

In fiscal 2019 (ended July) the company reported revenue of $21.4 billion more than double the prior year because of the 2018 purchase of rival SUPERVALU. The acquisition was most impactful in the traditional supermarket channel which grew 343% and jumped from 28% of UNFI's sales to 58%.

Net income fell into the red that year sinking to a -$285 million compared to $165.7 million in fiscal 2018. The results were hurt by goodwill and impairment charges and acquisition and integrated expenses that totaled $446.3 million.

Cash at the end of fiscal 2019 was $45.3 million an increase of $22 million from the prior year. Cash from operations contributed $284.5 million to the coffers while investing activities used $2.3 billion mainly for the SUPERVALU acquisition. Financing activities added another $2 billion primarily from proceeds from borrowings of long-term debt and revolving credit.

Strategy

UNFI has grown through the years both organically and through acquisitions. With the late 2018 purchase of rival SUPERVALU the company's primary focus going forward will be the successful integration of the acquisition — realizing costs savings leveraging technology and systems and taking advantage of cross-selling opportunities.

With customers in all 50 US states UNFI plans to exploit its substantial product portfolio to sell natural products to traditional customers and traditional products to natural customers while at the same time reducing the number of weekly deliveries customers receive. As part of the overall integration the company is consolidating distribution centers including moving from five to two in the Pacific Northwest and divesting the retail operations (about 95 grocery stores) that came as part of the SUPERVALU deal.

A primary component of the synergy aspect of the integration is workstream simplification. Dubbed Thrive2 the initiative is focused on an efficient standardized operating model that provides better experiences for customers suppliers and employees.

Mergers and Acquisitions

In late 2018 UNFI completed the acquisition of rival SUPERVALU for some $2.3 billion. The huge deal accelerated UNFI's growth diversified its customer base expanded market reach and scale and enhanced technology capacity and systems.

Company Background

Rhode Island retailer Norman Cloutier founded Cornucopia Natural Foods in 1978 and soon focused on distribution. During the 1980s Cornucopia grew by acquiring other natural foods distributors. It bought suppliers Natural Food Systems (seafood) and BGS Distributing (vitamins)

in 1987 and 1990 respectively. Cornucopia expanded into the Southeast in 1991 when it opened a distribution center in Georgia.

In 1996 Cornucopia merged with the leading natural foods distributor in the western US Sacramento-based Mountain People's and became United Natural Foods; it went public later that year.

The company continued to grow organically and through acquisitions over the decades. In 2018 it made the $2.3 billion purchase of rival SUPERVALU which more than doubled its size.

HISTORY

Rhode Island retailer Norman Cloutier founded Cornucopia Natural Foods in 1978 and soon focused on distribution. During the 1980s Cornucopia grew by acquiring other natural foods distributors. It bought suppliers Natural Food Systems (seafood) and BGS Distributing (vitamins) in 1987 and 1990 respectively. Cornucopia expanded into the Southeast in 1991 when it opened a distribution center in Georgia.

Reviving its interest in retailing Cornucopia formed Natural Retail Group in 1993 to buy and run natural foods stores. During the next two years it acquired several retailers. The company expanded its distribution operations in the West in 1995 adding Denver-based Rainbow Distributors.

In 1996 Cornucopia merged with the leading natural foods distributor in the western US Sacramento-based Mountain People's which Michael Funk had founded 20 years earlier. The combined company became United Natural Foods with Cloutier as chairman and CEO and Funk as president and vice chairman; it went public later that year.

United Natural Foods became the largest natural foods distributor when it bought New Hampshire-based Stow Mills in 1997. The next year it added Hershey Imports an importer and processor of nuts seeds and snacks and Albert's a distributor of organic produce. With the purchase of Mother Earth Markets in 1998 the company's retailing operations had grown to 16 stores but by mid-1999 it had sold four stores. That year United Natural Foods' East Coast consolidation problems became so profound that top customer Whole Foods announced it was finding backup distribution sources.

Funk replaced Cloutier as CEO and the company handed the chairman's post to board member Thomas Simone in 1999. In 2000 after the resignation of Cloutier from the board of directors United Natural Foods adopted a poison-pill plan to block potential takeovers. The company leased a distribution center in the Los Angeles area in 2001 to increase market share in the Southwest. It also acquired Florida's Palm Harbor Natural Foods.

In mid-2002 United Natural Foods lost one of its two largest customers — Wild Oats Markets— when that company defected to rival specialty foods distributor Tree of Life. However United Natural Foods soon won that business back. In October the company completed the acquisition of privately held Blooming Prairie Cooperative for approximately $31 million. In late 2002 the company merged with Northeast Cooperatives a natural foods distributor in the Midwest and Northeast.

That year United Natural Foods discontinued the management sales and support operations at its Hershey Imports subsidiary but continued to manufacture and distribute products from the Edison New Jersey plant.

In 2004 the company renewed its distribution agreement with Wild Oats with a five-year pact. United Natural Foods later announced a new three-year distribution agreement with Whole Foods which it renewed in 2006. Whole Foods later ac-

quired Wild Oats in 2007. That year United Natural Foods acquired ethnic and specialty food distributor Millbrook Distribution Services for about $85 million.

EXECUTIVES

Chairman President And Ceo, Steven L. (Steve) Spinner, age 60, $872,300 total compensation
Coo, Sean F. Griffin, age 59, $440,300 total compensation
Svp General Counsel Chief Compliance Officer And Corporate Secretary, Joseph J. (Joe) Traficanti, age 68, $367,150 total compensation
Svp Chief Administrative And Information Officer, Eric A. Dorne, age 57
President Atlantic Region, Christopher P. Testa, age 48
Svp Cfo And Treasurer, Michael P. Zechmeister
President Pacific Region, Paul S. Green
President Central Region, John M. Hummel
Vice President Of Sales And Marketing, Matt Mellet
Vice President Corporate Tax, Michael Markarian
Vice President Of Field Sales, Jack Murphy
Vice President National Supply Chain, Mike Seekins
Board Member, Denise Clark
Board Member, Peter Roy
Board Member, Eric Artz
Auditors: KPMG LLP

LOCATIONS

HQ: United Natural Foods Inc.
313 Iron Horse Way, Providence, RI 02908
Phone: 401 528-8634
Web: www.unfi.com

PRODUCTS/OPERATIONS

2019 Sales

	$ mil.	% of total
Supermarkets	12,505	58
Supernatural	4,393	21
Independents	3,179	15
Other	1,310	6
Total	**21,387**	**100**

2019 Sales

	$ mil.	% of total
Wholesale	21,325	99
Other	228	1
Adjustments	(166)	-
Total	**21,387**	**100**

COMPETITORS

Associated Wholesale Grocers	McLane
C&S Wholesale	Performance Food Group
DPI Specialty Foods	SpartanNash
KeHE Distributors	Sysco
	US Foods

HISTORICAL FINANCIALS

Company Type: Public

Income Statement				FYE: August 3
	REVENUE ($ mil.)	NET INCOME ($ mil.)	NET PROFIT MARGIN	EMPLOYEES
08/19*	21,387	(285)	—	19,000
07/18	10,227	166	1.6%	10,000
07/17	9,274	130	1.4%	9,700
07/16	8,470	126	1.5%	9,554
08/15	8,185	139	1.7%	8,700
Annual Growth	27.1%	—	—	21.6%
*Fiscal year change				

2019 Year-End Financials

Debt ratio: 42.00%
Return on equity: (-17.00%)
Cash ($ mil.): 42
Current ratio: 2.00
Long-term debt ($ mil.): 2,927

No. of shares (mil.): 53
Dividends
Yield: —
Payout: —
Market value ($ mil.): 445

	STOCK PRICE ($)	P/E		PER SHARE ($)		
	FY Close	High/Low	Earnings	Dividends	Book Value
08/19*	8.00	— —	(6.00)	0.00	29.00
07/18	33.00	16 10	3.00	0.00	37.00
07/17	38.00	19 13	3.00	0.00	33.00
07/16	50.00	22 12	3.00	0.00	30.00
08/15	46.00	30 16	3.00	0.00	28.00
Annual Growth (34.4%)		— —	—	—	0.9%

*Fiscal year change

United Parcel Service Inc

UPS is the world's largest package deliverer transporting nearly 21 million packages and documents per business day (more than 5 billion a year) throughout the US and in over 220 countries and territories. It deploys a fleet of approximately 123000 cars vans tractors and motorcycles and roughly 600 aircraft for pickups and deliveries. In addition to package delivery the company offers logistics and freight forwarding through UPS Supply Chain Solutions and less-than-truckload (LTL) and truckload (TL) freight transportation through UPS Freight. Nearly 80% of its revenue comes from the US.

Operations

UPS has three business segments: US Domestic Package International Package and Supply Chain & Freight.

US Domestic Package is the company's largest business segment accounting for more than 60% of sales. This division includes UPS SurePost an economy residential ground service for customers with non-urgent lightweight residential shipments. It acts as a contractual residential ground service that partners its UPS Ground network with final delivery often provided by the US Postal Service.

International Package delivers more than 20% of UPS' sales. It offers guaranteed time-definite express options through its Express Plus Express and Express Saver services. The company's Supply Chain & Freight segment which generates close to 20% of sales includes forwarding logistics truckload brokerage UPS Freight and financial services through UPS Capital.

Geographic Reach

UPS is headquartered in Atlanta GA (Its UPS Supply Chain Solutions group is based in Alpharetta.) and has about 2500 operating facilities. Its US transportation hub called Worldport is in Louisville KY. It also has US regional air hubs located in Texas California Philadelphia Pennsylvania and Illinois. Its European air hub is in Cologne Germany and it maintains Asia-Pacific air hubs in Shanghai and Shenzhen China and in Hong Kong. A facility in Ontario is the regional air hub in Canada and UPS' Miami FL hub covers Latin America and the Caribbean.

Almost 80% of the company's revenue is generated in the US.

Sales and Marketing

In addition to package delivery to consumers UPS targets B2B customers for its logistics services in industries such as health care life sciences government retail automotive industrial manufacturing and aerospace.

Financial Performance

UPS has enjoyed several years of steady revenue growth and solid profits. Its sales have increased 23% since 2014.

Revenue in 2018 reached a record $71.9 billion an 8% increase compared with $66.6 billion in 2017. The year's growth was fueled by increased volume in all segments and increased sales particularly in the retail healthcare and manufacturing industries. E-commerce sales continue to generate a larger percentage of the company's total growth.

Profit was $4.9 billion in 2018 down 2% from the previous year as a result of higher operating expenses including higher pension expenses and the cost of transformation initiatives in the US (new facility and technology projects).

Cash at the end of fiscal 2018 was $4.4 billion an increase of $598 million from the prior year. Cash from operations contributed $12.7 billion to the coffers while investing activities used $6.3 billion mainly for capital expenditures related to facility automation and capacity expansion projects and information technology. Financing activities used another $5.7 billion for loan payments dividends to stockholders and the company's stock repurchase program.

Strategy

UPS is in the midst of a transformation initiative aimed at generating higher-quality revenue and lowering operating costs through 2022. The company is expanding its logistics services business investing in technology to improve efficiency and expanding geographically.

UPS' extensive global reach is a selling point for its logistics offerings. The company sees a growing trend in businesses outsourcing supply chain management viewing it as a strategic advantage. The company is focusing on expanding its logistics services and solutions targeting small- and medium-sized businesses specifically in the healthcare and life sciences markets.

To increase its Global Business to Consumer (B2C) and Business to Business (B2B) e-commerce businesses it expanded its network by adding more than 1.6 million square feet of distribution capacity and nearly 400000 pieces per hour of automated sort capacity globally.

Investments in technology for improved operational efficiency include a new cloud-based transportation and warehouse management software platform resulting in better visibility and faster onboarding of customers. Investments in high-growth international markets include acquiring full ownership of its express services unit in India creating new opportunities in this region.

For now business is booming and so is competition. UPS faces carriers such as Fedex and XPO Logistics which also are investing to expand and improve their operations. Amazon.com is leading retailers in exploring how to handle delivery on their own. What's more smaller companies are popping up to make final-mile deliveries.

Company Background

Seattle teens Jim Casey and Claude Ryan started American Messenger Company a delivery and errand service in 1907. They were soon making small-parcel deliveries for local department stores and in 1913 changed the company's name to Merchants Parcel Delivery. Casey who led the company for 50 years established a policy of manager ownership best service and lowest rates. In 1916 new employee Charlie Soderstrom chose the brown paint still used on the company's vehicles. Service expanded outside Seattle in 1919 when Merchants Parcel bought Oakland California-based Motor Parcel Delivery later changing its name to United Parcel Service (UPS).

In 1930 the year after the stock market crash UPS moved its corporate headquarters to New York City where it remained for 45 years until a move to Greenwich Connecticut in 1975. By the 1990s the high-cost Connecticut housing market was making it difficult for the company to attract and retain employees so in 1991 it moved again to Atlanta to leverage its large airport and available labor market.

HISTORY

Seattle teens Jim Casey and Claude Ryan started American Messenger Company a delivery and errand service in 1907. They were soon making small-parcel deliveries for local department stores and in 1913 changed the company's name to Merchants Parcel Delivery. Casey who led the company for 50 years established a policy of manager ownership best service and lowest rates. In 1916 new employee Charlie Soderstrom chose the brown paint still used on the company's vehicles. Service expanded outside Seattle in 1919 when Merchants Parcel bought Oakland California-based Motor Parcel Delivery later changing its name to United Parcel Service (UPS).

EXECUTIVES

Coo, James J. (Jim) Barber, age 58, $500,706 total compensation
Chief Sales Marketing And Strategy Officer, Alan Gershenhorn, age 61, $565,956 total compensation
Chairman And Ceo, David P. Abney, age 64, $1,082,421 total compensation
President Us Operations, Myron A. Gray, age 62, $514,509 total compensation
Svp Cfo And Treasurer, Richard N. Peretz, age 57, $485,070 total compensation
Svp Global Engineering And Sustainability, Mark R. Wallace, age 56
Svp Chief Marketing And Business Services Officer, Teresa M. Finley, age 58
Svp And Cio, Juan R. Perez
President Operations Ups Latin America, Jose Maria (Chema) Odriozola
President Ups China, Harld Peters
Vice President Of Human Resources, Dan Shea
Vice President Marketing Healthcare Logistics, John Menna
Vice President Customer Communications, Betsy Wilson
Vp Corporate Plant Engineering, Rhonda Clark
Vice President Global Crm Technology, Tina Latuga
Vice President Customer Technology Group, Ken Finnerty
Vice President Administration, Charlie Covert
Vice President Of Sales And Marketing, Norm Brothers
Vice President Finance, John Colino
Vice President Of Marketing, Jerome Roberts
Vice President Enterprise Accounts Sales, Michael Tannian
Director Business Development Vice President Global Accounts Sales, Kathy Fantauzzi
Vice President, Rick Rufolo
Vice President, Beth Breihan
Vice President, Angela Jack
Vice President Administration, Lou Rivieccio
Vice President Enterprise Accounts Retail, Nola Wood
Vice President Of Engineering, Gregory Loppatto
Vice President; Sales And Marketing, Joe Racanelli
Vice President Administration, Michael Francesconi
Vice President Retail Sales, Michael Arias

Vice President Global Customs Policy And Public Affairs, Norm Schenk
Senior Vice President Marketing And Sales, James Thome
Vice President Global Retail And E Commerce Strategy At Ups, Nick Basford
Vp Global Talent And Leadership Development, Anne Schwartz
Vice President, Steven Gaut
Vice President, Carlos Cubias
Vp Business Development, Annie Outlaw
Vice President Strategic Sales, Frank Cole
Vice President Chicago Area Consolidation Hub Cach, Robert Latchford
Vice President, Ken Torok
Vp Investor Relations, Mike Jones
Vice President Operations Europe, Dominic Porporino
Vice President Of Enterprise Sales, Nakeya Shelton
Vice President Of Operations, George Willis
Vice President, Kathleen Parrish
Vice President, Bill Kruger
Vice President, Scott Heck
Vice President East Central Region, Joseph Zito
National Account Manager, Robert Musca
Vp Human Resources, Regina Hartley
Vice President Sales Global Accounts, Jerry Felton
Vice President Of Human Resources, Tom Upton
Vice President Corporate Public Affairs, Nicole Clifton
Vice President, Susan Ward
Vice Prespident Of Sales Americas, Pedro Anaya
Vice President Corporate Transportation Services, Kenneth Buenker
Vice President Enterprise Sales, Sheila Dunn
Regional Vice President, Keith Hall
Vice President Global Solutions Implemen, Brian Carrier
Vice President, Allen Hill
Senior Vice President Labor And Chief Human Resource Officer, Teri Mcclure
Vice President Human Resources Benefits Director, Deborah Hyman
Vice President Of Human Resources, David Cole
Vice President Enterprise Accounts, David Canning
Vice President State Government Affairs, Raymond Drake
Assistant Vice President And Sales Wes, Dave Mace
Vice President Of Human Resources, Juliana Atieno
Vice President Us Engineering, Mark Susor
Vice President Strategy And Innovation Europe, Yannick Mooijman
National Account Manager, Mike Buffon
Vice President Of Human Resources, Debra Harding
Vice President State Government Affairs, Mark Giuffre
Vice President Customs And Trade Compliance, John Vanwallaghen
Vice President Finance Services, Todd St John
Vice President Chief Operating Officer Eastern Operations, Joe Picone
Vice President Strategy, Anthony Poselenzny
Senior Vice President, Deryl Hill
Vice President Plant Engineering, Steven Carter
National Account Manager, Rick Higginson
Vice President, Keith Kellison
Vice President, David Lee
Vice President, David Birkmeyer
Vice President Europe Ups Capital Uk, Jorge Navarro
Senior Vice President And Chief Transformation Officer, Scott Price
Senior Vice President Global Trade Finance, Mike Bryant
Vice President, Arnold Wellman
Vice President Of Human Resources, Yvonne Mchenry

Vice President Finance, Joseph Tillman
Vice President Of Human Resources, Gary Carraway
Vp Of Hr, Dave Lovely
Senior Vice President, Jim Bruce
Senior Vice President General Counsel Secretary, Norman Brothers
Senior Vice President Chief Sales And Solutions Officer, Kathleen Gutmann
Vice Chairman Of The Board, John Alden
Assistant Treasurer, Ned Winsor
Security Manager Secretary, William Thibodeaux
Board Member, Wayne Powell
Board Member, Kevin Warsh
Board Member, Rodney Adkins
Board Member, Franck Moison
Board Member, John Stankey
Treasurer, Rony Pierre
Board Member, Willie Johnson
Board Member, Carol Tome
Board Member, Clark Randt
Board Member, Anna Burns
Auditors: Deloitte & Touche LLP

LOCATIONS

HQ: United Parcel Service Inc
55 Glenlake Parkway N.E., Atlanta, GA 30328
Phone: 404 828-6000
Web: www.ups.com

PRODUCTS/OPERATIONS

2018 Sales

	$ mil.	% of total
US Domestic Package	43,593	61
International Package	14,442	20
Supply Chain & Freight	13,826	19
Total	**71,861**	**100**

2018 Sales

	$ mil.	% of total
US Domestic Package		
Ground	31,223	43
Next day air	7,618	11
Deferred	4,752	7
International Package		
Export	10,973	15
Domestic	2,874	4
Cargo and other	595	1
Supply Chain & Freight		
Forwarding	6,580	9
Logistic	3,234	5
Freight	3,218	4
Other	794	1
Total	**71,861**	**100**

COMPETITORS

American Airlines Group	Panalpina
Canada Post	Royal Mail
Deutsche Post	Ryder System
FedEx	TNT Express
Japan Post	US Postal Service
Lufthansa	United Continental
Nippon Express	XPO logistics
	YRC Worldwide

HISTORICAL FINANCIALS

Company Type: Public

Income Statement   FYE: December 31

	REVENUE ($ mil.)	NET INCOME ($ mil.)	NET PROFIT MARGIN	EMPLOYEES
12/18	71,861	4,791	6.7%	481,000
12/17	65,872	4,910	7.5%	280,000
12/16	60,906	3,431	5.6%	434,000
12/15	58,363	4,844	8.3%	444,000
12/14	58,232	3,032	5.2%	435,000
Annual Growth	**5.4%**	**12.1%**	**—**	**2.5%**

2018 Year-End Financials

Debt ratio: 45.00%
Return on equity: 238.00%
Cash ($ mil.): 4,225
Current ratio: 1.00
Long-term debt ($ mil.): 19,931
No. of shares (mil.): 858
Dividends
 Yield: 4.0%
 Payout: 66.0%
Market value ($ mil.): 83,681

	STOCK PRICE ($) FY Close	P/E High/Low	PER SHARE ($) Earnings	Dividends	Book Value
12/18	98.00	24 16	6.00	4.00	4.00
12/17	119.00	22 18	6.00	3.00	1.00
12/16	115.00	31 23	4.00	3.00	0.00
12/15	96.00	21 18	5.00	3.00	3.00
12/14	111.00	34 28	3.00	3.00	2.00
Annual Growth	**(3.2%)**	**— —**	**13.8%**	**8.0%**	**10.5%**

United Rentals Inc

No cash to buy a bulldozer? Just lease one from United Rentals. The company considers itself the #1 commercial and construction equipment renter in the world serving customers in the commercial infrastructure industrial and residential sectors. It operates through a network of nearly 1000 locations in the US and Canada and provides about 3400 equipment items — everything from general to heavy construction and industrial equipment to hand tools special-event items (such as aerial towers) power (diesel generators) and HVAC equipment and trench-safety equipment. It also sells new and used equipment as well as contractor supplies and parts. United Rentals' original equipment cost (the initial purchase value of all rental equipment) is $11.5 billion. The US accounts for more than 90% of total sales.

Operations

United Rentals operates two business segments: General Rental and the Trench Power and Pump segment.

General Rental generates around 85% of sales and rents out construction aerial and industrial equipment general tools and light equipment and related services and activities.

The Trench Power and Pump segment rents out specialty construction products and related services. It offers trench safety equipment such as trench shields aluminum hydraulic shoring systems and construction lasers; Power and HVAC equipment such as portable generators and electric distribution equipment; and pumping equipment for use in the energy and petrochemical industries. The segment accounts for the remaining 15% of revenue.

Across both segments the company sells its used rental equipment to invest in new gear. Used rental sales account for 10% of total sales. It also sells construction consumables tools small equipment and safety supplies.

Geographic Reach

Of United Rentals' nearly 1000 rental locations more than 850 are in the US and the rest are in Canada.

United Rentals' General Rentals division comprises eleven geographic regions: Carolinas Gulf South Industrial (which serves the geographic Gulf region and has a strong industrial presence) Mid-Atlantic Mid Central Midwest Northeast Pacific West South Southeast and Western Canada

Sales and Marketing

United Rentals' customers include construction and industrial companies manufacturers utilities municipalities and homeowners. The Trench

Power and Pump segments serves primarily construction companies active in infrastructure projects municipalities and industrial companies.

United Rentals markets its products and services through sales staff at the company's branches and customer care centers; account managers dedicated to large customer accounts; its E-Rentals portal (online e-commerce site); and advertising (trade publications yellow pages the internet radio and direct mail).

Financial Performance

After a slight dip in 2016 United Rental's revenue in 2017 returned to the upward trajectory seen in recent years.

Sales increased 15% to $6.6 billion — a new record for the company — thanks to contributions from the acquired NES and Neff businesses. Underlying revenue increased 8% thanks to a 7% increase in rental equipment in use and a less-than-1% increase in rental prices.

Net income jumped 138% to $1.3 billion thanks partly to higher revenue but mostly due to a tax benefit from the 2017 US Tax Cuts and Jobs Act.

Cash from operations grew 14% to $2.2 billion due to higher net income partially offset by decrease in deferred taxes.

Strategy

Because of its size United Rentals rallies more resources over smaller businesses. Competitive advantages include more purchasing leverage a wider range of equipment and services and the more convenient movement of assets between locations. United Rentals enhances its operating efficiencies by ramping up through consolidation of functions including payroll and accounts payable. It primarily grows through acquisitions.

In order to manage the age composition and size of its fleet the company routinely sells used rental equipment and invests in new equipment. United Rentals acts as a dealer of new equipment for many leading equipment makers such as Genie Industries Skyjack (aerial lifts) Sullair (compressors) and Terex (telehandlers). At most branches United Rentals sells various supplies and merchandise and offers repair and maintenance services.

Mergers and Acquisitions

In 2018 United Rentals acquired BakerCorp International Holding for about $715 million. BakerCorp is a provider of tank pump filtration and trench shoring rental solutions. The deal will enhance United Rentals' fluid storage and transfer and treatment solutions. It also adds 46 branches in North America and 11 in Europe and about 950 employees. By the end of 2018 the company is scheduled close on a $2.1 billion deal to acquire BlueLine Rental a North American equipment rental company with operations in 25 US states Canada and Puerto Rico.

Late in 2017 the company acquired Neff Corporation a US provider of earthmoving and material handling equipment for $1.3 billion. Neff brings with it $867 million-worth of rental equipment and some 70 branch locations. It serves the infrastructure non-residential energy municipal and residential construction sectors. The deal boosts United's earthmoving capabilities and adds to efficiencies of scale in key markets particularly the fast-growing southern geographies.

In mid-2017 United Rentals acquired NES Rentals a provider of aerial rental equipment (from scissor and boom lifts to rough terrain and truck-mounted cranes) for $965 million. NES serves about 18000 customers across the industrial and non-residential construction sectors. The deal will enhance the company's density in strategically important markets including the East Coast Gulf States and the Midwest.

HISTORY

Bradley Jacobs had made a fortune in the garbage business having used United Waste Systems as a roll-up company to buy small trash-hauling firms in that fragmented industry. Flush with cash after he sold United Waste Systems in 1997 to USA Waste Services (now Waste Management) Jacobs launched the same roll-up strategy to consolidate the equipment-rental industry. He and his management team bought six leasing companies and started United Rentals. The company which went public in 1997 had acquired 38 rental companies in 20 states by mid-1998.

EXECUTIVES

Vice President Business Development, Ned Graham
Svp Performance Analytics, Kenneth Mettel
Vice President, Jonathan M Gottsegen
Vice President, Mark Tapia
Evp And Cfo, William B. Plummer, age 60, $595,504 total compensation
President And Ceo, Michael J. Kneeland, age 65, $950,000 total compensation
Evp And Coo, Matthew J. Flannery, age 54, $595,504 total compensation
Svp Business Services And Cio, Dale A. Asplund, age 51, $519,807 total compensation
Evp Chief Administrative And Legal Officer, Craig A. Pintoff, age 49, $473,046 total compensation
Vp Midwest Region, Chris Burlog
Vp Mid-central Region, Kevin M. OBrien
Svp And Chief Marketing Officer, Chris Hummel
Vp Pacific West Region, Robert C. Bower
Vp Southeast Region, Michael G. Cloer
Vp Western Canada Region, John (Scott) Fisher
Region Vp Tools And Industrial Solutions, Joshuah P. Flores
Vp Trench Safety Region, Todd M. Hayes
Vp Mid-atlantic Region, John J. Humphrey
Vp Pump Solutions, William A. (Bill) Kiker
Vp Industrial Region, Donald (Chad) Matter
Vp South Region, Jeffrey S. (Jeff) McGinnis
Vp Northeast Region, Craig Schmidt
Vp Power And Hvac Region, David C. Scott
Vp Gulf South Region, Larry (Don) Irwin
Vp Environmental Health And Safety, Jim Dorris
National Account Manager, John Bebout
Vice President Finance Operations, Joseph Pledger
National Account Manager, Jackie Volk
National Account Manager, Reggie Hall
National Account Manager, Frank Branca
National Account Manager, Robert Zupo
Vice President Investor Relations, Fred Bratman
Executive Vice President Corporate Services, Kurtis Barker
National Account Manager, Bill Kenyon
National Account Manager, Shelley Miles
National Account Manager, SHAWNA ERMOLD
Vice President Customer Service Operations, Kenneth Perkins
National Account Manager, Jeremy Epps
National Account Manager Oil And Gas, Brian Nagel
Vp Investor Relations, Ted Grace
National Accounts Manager, Stephen Hedrick
Svp Operations West, Michael Durand
National Account Manager, Ray Cruz
National Account Manager, Rick Clinaz
Region Vice President, Bill Kiker
Vp Mid Central Region, Kevin M O'brien
National Account Manager, Valerie Wheatstine
National Account Manager, Christopher Shoemaker
Senior Vice President And Chief Marketing Officer, Christopher K Hummel
Board Member, Filippo Passerini
Chairman, Jenne K. Britell, age 76
Auditors: Ernst & Young LLP

LOCATIONS

HQ: United Rentals Inc
100 First Stamford Place, Suite 700, Stamford, CT 06902
Phone: 203 622-3131
Web: www.unitedrentals.com

2017 Sales

	$ mil.	% of total
Domestic	6,076	91
Foreign	565	9
Total	**6,641**	**100**

PRODUCTS/OPERATIONS

2017 Sales

	$ mil.	% of total
General Rental	5,565	84
Trench power and pump	1,076	16
Total	**6,641**	**100**

2017 Sales

	$ mil.	% of total
Equipment rentals	5,715	86
Sales of rental equipment	550	8
Sales of new equipment	178	3
Contractor supplies sales	80	1
Service & other revenues	118	2
Total	**6,641**	**100**

Selected Products

Aerial lifts
Backhoes
Barricades
Compressors
Concrete & Masonry
Cones
Contractor supplies
Ditching equipment
Earth-moving equipment
Forklifts
Generators
Hand tools
Heaters
HVAC
Lawn & Landscape
Light towers
Material-handling equipment
Message boards
Pavement-marking systems
Portable power units
Power washers
Pumps
Skid-steer loaders
Trench shields
Trucks & Trailers
Warning lights
Water pumps
Welders & Accessories

COMPETITORS

AMECO
Atlas Lift Truck Rentals
Case Power & Equipment
Herc Holdings
Maxim Crane Works
RDO Equipment
Sunbelt Rentals
Ziegler inc

HISTORICAL FINANCIALS

Company Type: Public

Income Statement				FYE: December 31
	REVENUE ($ mil.)	NET INCOME ($ mil.)	NET PROFIT MARGIN	EMPLOYEES
12/19	9,351	1,174	12.6%	19,100
12/18	8,047	1,096	13.6%	18,500
12/17	6,641	1,346	20.3%	14,800
12/16	5,762	566	9.8%	12,500
12/15	5,817	585	10.1%	12,700
Annual Growth	12.6%	19.0%	—	10.7%

2019 Year-End Financials

Debt ratio: 60.00% No. of shares (mil.): 74
Return on equity: 32.00% Dividends
Cash ($ mil.): 52 Yield: —
Current ratio: 1.00 Payout: —
Long-term debt ($ mil.): 10,431 Market value ($ mil.): 12,401

	STOCK PRICE ($) FY Close	P/E High/Low		PER SHARE ($) Earnings	Dividends	Book Value
12/19	167.00	11	7	15.00	0.00	52.00
12/18	103.00	14	7	13.00	0.00	43.00
12/17	172.00	11	6	16.00	0.00	37.00
12/16	106.00	17	7	6.00	0.00	20.00
12/15	73.00	17	10	6.00	0.00	16.00
Annual Growth	23.1%	—	—	25.6%	—	33.8%

United States Steel Corp.

Steel crazy after all these years United States Steel (U.S. Steel) is North America's largest integrated steelmaker. The company operates mills throughout the US Midwest and in Slovakia. U.S. Steel makes a wide range of flat-rolled and tubular steel products and its annual production capacity is 22 million net tons of raw steel. Its customers are primarily in the automotive appliance construction oil and gas and petrochemical industries. In addition U.S. Steel mines iron ore and procures coke which provide the primary raw materials used in steel making. It is also engaged in railroad and barge operations and real estate. The US accounts for three-fifths of its revenue.

Operations

U.S. Steel has three reportable operating segments: Flat-Rolled Products about 65% of revenue US Steel Europe (USSE) about 20% of revenue and Tubular Products which accounts for the rest of revenue.

The company's North American integrated steel mills' flat rolled products include slabs rounds strip mill plates sheets and tin mill products. It also has ore and coke production facilities in the US.

U.S. Steel has annual raw steel production capability of 22 million net tons (17 million tons in the United States and 5 million tons in Europe) reflecting a reduction of 2.4 million tons due to the permanent shutdown some operations.

Its European operations produce and sell slabs sheet strip mill plate tin mill products and spiral welded pipe as well as heating radiators and refractory ceramic materials. U.S. Steel Kosice in Slovakia produces sheet steel. Its plant in Kosice has an annual capacity of 5 million tons.

U.S. Steel's tubular steel operation (about 1.5 million tons per year) serves the energy industry primarily providing both seamless and electric resistance welded products commonly called oil country tubular goods.

The company also participates in joint ventures with a number of its industry competitors. They include the world's #1 steelmaker ArcelorMittal Japanese producer Kobe Steel South Korean giant POSCO Russian metals company Severstal and US steel service center Worthington Industries.

The company's other businesses include railroad services and real estate operations.

Geographic Reach

In the US the company holds integrated steel plants including Gary Works East Chicago Tin and Midwest Plant all in Indiana. It also holds the Great Lakes Works in Michigan Mon Valley Works and Fairless Plant in Pennslvania and Granite City Works in Illinois. US Steel also has a steel mill and related facilities in Slovakia. North America accounts some 75% of the company's total sales.

The company has a research centers in Pittsburgh Pennsylvania and Kosice Slovakia. It also has an automotive center in Troy Michigan and Research and Development Laboratory and Test Facility for Tubular Products in Houston Texas.

Sales and Marketing

The majority of U.S. Steel's customers are located in North America and Europe.

U.S. Steel's integrated steel business serves North American customers in the service center conversion transportation construction container and appliance and electrical markets and European customers in the construction service center conversion container transportation appliance and electrical and oil gas and petrochemical markets.

Financial Performance

US Steel revenue has declined by half in the last decade from $24 billion in 2008 to just over $12 billion in 2017 mostly from divestments. In the same period it has had only three years of modest profit (2009 2014 2017). In comparison the company lost $2 billion during the financial years 2015-16 and some $3.7 billion during 2009-13 period.

Revenue increased 20% in 2017 to $12.3 billion mostly from $60 per ton increase in prices of flat-rolled products and its contracts but also from increased shipments and lower imports in the European sector along with higher prices and to a smaller extent increases in shipments of Tubular Products.

Net income made a strong comeback in 2017 posting $387 million in profit compared to $440 million loss the previous year mostly from $91 million reduction in restructing costs from the year prior a $86 million gain in income tax benefits as well as $72 million gain from spinning off US Steel Canada.

Cash holdings increased slightly from $1.51 billion to $1.55 billion. Operations contributed $800 million while investments utilized $390 million. A further $390 was utilized by financing activities mostly in long-term debt reduction.

Strategy

U.S. Steel has begun a $2 billion four-year upgrade of its steel-making processes to improve its competitiveness. The project comes as steel prices have risen with higher tariffs were placed on foreign steel in 2016. The upgrade emphasizes 13 of the company's critical assets: in iron and steel making and hot rolling and finishing. U.S. Steel expects the project to deliver an additional million tons of hot rolled band production capacity over the current 10 million tons and a boost of $275 million-$325 million in earnings before interest taxes depreciation and amortization by 2020.

The company also has taken steps to reduce its debt by refinancing issuing some $750 million of senior notes in 2017 due in 2025 to replace higher-interest notes that were due in 2021 and 2022.

In 2017 U.S. Steel and partner Kobe Steel said they would build a new continuous galvanizing line (CGL) at their subsidiaries' joint venture PRO-TEC Coating Co. in Leipsic Ohio to meet higher demand for advanced high-strength steels (AHSS) from the auto industry. The $400 million plant is to begin production in 2019.

But the previous decade has not been easy for the company. Revenue reduced by half between 2009 and 2017 and cheap imports made competition hard. It disposed of U.S. Steel Canada interests for $72 million in 2017. In the same year the company permanently shut down the Lorain #6 Quench & Temper Mill Lorain #4 and Lone Star #1 pipe mills as well as tubular operations. In 2015 it idled Tubular Processing and Granite City Works. Depreciation and amortization has cost the company more than $1.5 billion in the 2015-17 period.

However the performance of its flat-rolled segment of late offers hope as does an improving market and taxes on foreign steel introduced in 2018. CAPEX for 2017 was $505 million.

Mergers and Acquisitions

In 2019 US Steel took a 49.9% stake in Big River Steel for about $700 million in cash. The deal includes a call option for US Steel to buy the remaining 50.1% of Big River steel within the next four years. The investment in Big River increases US Steel's presence in the mini mill industry (smaller mills that make steel from steel scrap) and complements its existing integrated steel making capabilities (making new steel from iron ore in blast furnaces).

HISTORY

U.S. Steel was conceived through a 1901 merger of 10 steel companies that combined their furnaces ore deposits railroad companies and shipping lines. The deal involved industrial pioneers Andrew Carnegie Charles Schwab Elbert Gary and J. P. Morgan. Morgan had helped organize the Federal Steel Company in 1898 and he then wanted to create a centralized trust to dominate the soaring steel market. Carnegie owned the largest US steel company at the time Carnegie Steel but wanted to retire.

In 1900 Schwab Carnegie Steel's president outlined the idea of the steel trust based on a merger of the Carnegie and Federal steel companies. Morgan asked Schwab to persuade Carnegie to sell his steel mills and name his price. Morgan didn't haggle when Carnegie responded that he would sell for almost half a billion dollars.

The Carnegie-Morgan combination created the world's first billion-dollar company.

EXECUTIVES

President Ceo And Director, David B. (Dave) Burritt, age 63, $800,000 total compensation
Svp Consumer Solutions, Sara A. Greenstein, age 44
Svp Industrial Service Center And Mining Solutions, Douglas R. Matthews, age 54, $541,000 total compensation
Vp European Solutions And President Us Steel Koâšice, Scott D. Buckiso, age 52
Vp And Cio, Charles G. Balawajder, age 63
Svp Government Affairs General Counsel And Chief Compliance Officer, Suzanne R. Folsom, age 57, $700,000 total compensation
Svp Automotive Solutions, James E. Bruno, age 53, $403,500 total compensation
Vp And Chief Supply Chain Officer, Christine S. Breves
Evp And Cfo, Kevin P. Bradley
Executive Vice President And Chief Financial Officer, Joseph Stinnett
Vice President Commercial Tubular, Craig Horan
Vice President Human Resources, Martin Pitorak
Vice President Finance, Pipasu Soni
Vice President, Pat Mullarkey
Senior Vice President And Treasurer, Albert Ferrara
Vice President Strategic Planning And Corporate Development, Richard Fruehauf
Vice President, Leonard Chuderewicz
Svp General Counsel Chief Compliance Officer And Corporate Secretary, Duane D Holloway
Vice President Workplace Campaign, Linda Jones
Chairman, David S. (Dave) Sutherland, age 69

LOCATIONS

HQ: United States Steel Corp.
  600 Grant Street, Pittsburgh, PA 15219-2800
Phone: 412 433-1121   **Fax:** 412 433-4818
Web: www.ussteel.com

2016 Sales

	$ mil.	% of total
North America	8,018	78
Europe	2,243	22
Total	**10,261**	**100**

PRODUCTS/OPERATIONS

2016 Sales

	$ mil.	% of total
Flat-rolled	7,507	73
US Steel Europe	2,243	22
Tubular products	449	4
Other	62	1
Total	**10,261**	**100**

Selected Products

Steel
Tin
Tubular

Selected Subsidiaries

Acero Prime S. R. L de CV (44% steel processing and
  warehousing)
Delray Connecting Railroad Company (transportation)
Double Eagle Steel Coating Company (50% with
  Severstal; steel processing)
PRO-TEC Coating Co. (50% with Kobe Steel; steel
  processing)
Transtar Inc. (transportation)
U. S. Steel Kosice sro (steelmaking Slovakia)
USS-POSCO Industries (50% with Pohang Iron & Steel;
  steel processing)
Worthington Specialty Processing (50% with
  Worthington Industries; steel processing)

COMPETITORS

AK Steel Holding Corporation
Allegheny Technologies
ArcelorMittal
Baosteel
BlueScope Steel
B –HLER-UDDEHOLM
Carpenter Technology
Gerdau Ameristeel
JFE Holdings
Kobe Steel
Nippon Steel & Sumitomo Metal Corporation
Nucor
POSCO
SSAB North America
SSAB Svenskt
Salzgitter
Simec
Steel Dynamics
Tata Steel
Ternium
ThyssenKrupp Steel
Wuhan Iron & Steel

HISTORICAL FINANCIALS

Company Type: Public

Income Statement

FYE: December 31

	REVENUE ($ mil.)	NET INCOME ($ mil.)	NET PROFIT MARGIN	EMPLOYEES
12/18	14,178	1,115	7.9%	29,000
12/17	12,250	387	3.2%	29,200
12/16	10,261	(440)	—	29,800
12/15	11,574	(1,642)	—	33,200
12/14	17,507	102	0.6%	23,000
Annual Growth	**(5.1%)**	**81.8%**	**—**	**6.0%**

2018 Year-End Financials

Debt ratio: 22.00%
Return on equity: 30.00%
Cash ($ mil.): 1,000
Current ratio: 2.00
Long-term debt ($ mil.): 2,316

No. of shares (mil.): 175
Dividends
  Yield: 1.0%
  Payout: 3.0%
Market value ($ mil.): 3,183

	STOCK PRICE ($) FY Close	P/E High/Low		PER SHARE ($) Earnings	Dividends	Book Value
12/18	18.00	7	3	6.00	0.00	24.00
12/17	35.00	19	9	2.00	0.00	19.00
12/16	33.00	—	—	(3.00)	0.00	13.00
12/15	8.00	—	—	(11.00)	0.00	17.00
12/14	27.00	65	32	1.00	0.00	26.00
Annual Growth	**(9.1%)**	—	—	**73.5%**	**(0.0%)**	**(2.0%)**

United Technologies Corp

United Technologies (UTC) provides high-tech products and services for the aerospace commercial building and automated controls and security industries. It operates through engine aircraft manufacturer Pratt & Whitney; Carrier its former climate controls and security business; Collins Aerospace Systems maker of engine controls and flight systems for military and commercial aircraft; and Otis the world's largest elevator and escalator manufacturer. UTC announced in 2018 that it would split into three separate companies based on its business segments. Carrier and Otis will operate as standalone companies. In 2019 UTC said it would merge the Collins and Pratt & Whitney units with Raytheon in an all-stock deal.

Change in Company Type

UTC and Raytheon agreed in 2019 to merge in a deal valued at $121 billion creating a company with strong aerospace and defense offerings. The combined company would have annual revenue of about $74 billion making it the second biggest aerospace company behind Boeing. Called Raytheon Technologies the company would pair United's Collins Aerospace and Pratt & Whitney units with Raytheon's defense products which include the Patriot and Sidewinder missile systems. In the all-stock deal United shareholders would own 57% of the company and Raytheon shareholders would own the rest. The deal requires regulatory approval but the companies expect it to close in the first half of 2020.

UTC completed the acquisition of Rockwell Collins in a $30 billion deal in 2018. The company is spinning off its other units into independent companies to provide better focus and flexibility to each business. The Climate Controls and Secu-

rity business will be renamed Carrier and focus on heating and cooling products. Otis will continue to provide elevators escalators and moving walkways as the third independent company. The company expects the separation to be completed in 2020.

Operations

UTC operates through four segments: Pratt & Whitney Carrier Collins Aerospace Systems and Otis.

Pratt & Whitney (about 30% of total sales) makes and sells aircraft engines for the commercial military business jet and general aviation markets. It also provides fleet management and aftermarket maintenance services. Its Pratt & Whitney Canada is among the world's leading suppliers of engines for the general and business aviation markets and also supplies products for regional airlines utility airplanes and helicopters.

The Carrier segment (nearly 30%) makes HVAC refrigeration fire security and building automation products for the commercial government and residential sectors. It also provides refrigeration and monitoring products and solutions for the transportation industry. Many of Carrier's security and fire safety products are marketed under the Chubb and Kidde brand names.

Collins Aerospace Systems (roughly 25%) provides aerospace products and aftermarket services for aircraft manufacturers airlines the military and space and undersea operations. Products include power generation and management aircraft sensing and engine control systems and surveillance and reconnaissance systems among several others. It also provides information management services through voice and data communication networks worldwide.

The company's Otis segment (generating about 20% of revenue) is the world's largest elevator and escalator manufacturer. It designs installs and services a wide range of passenger and freight elevators as well as escalators and moving walkways. Otis also makes modernization products that improve the safety reliability and aesthetics of existing installations. Its CompassPlus product features a touch screen for destination management that gets people to their destinations 50% faster than traditional elevator systems.

Geographic Reach

Headquartered in Farmington CT UTC does business in more than 120 countries. It operates more than 650 major properties comprising approximately 96 million square feet of manufacturing space.

The US generates roughly 60% of the company's total sales followed by Europe (20%) and the Asia Pacific region (15%).

Sales and Marketing

Customers in the commercial and industrial sectors contribute more than 45% of UTC's total revenue. The commercial aerospace market generates almost 40% and the military aerospace and space sectors about 15%. The US government generates about 25% of Pratt & Whitney's sales and almost 20% of Collins Aerospace Systems' sales.

Carrier sells its products directly to customers and through manufacturers' reps distributors dealers and through retail channels. Otis sells directly to customers and through sales reps and distributors.

Financial Performance

UTC has seen a general upward trend in revenue for the last several years leading to record sales and earnings in 2018.

Revenue in 2018 spiked up by 11% to $66.5 billion compared with $59.8 billion the previous year. The increase in revenue was driven by higher sales in all its divisions. Pratt & Whitney grew by 14% with higher commercial aftermarket and military sales and higher commercial OEM sales. Growth in HVAC revenue at Carrier and higher service and equipment sales at Otis also contributed to the increase.

Net income reached $5.3 billion up 16% over $4.6 billion in 2017 mainly from increased sales.

Cash at the end of fiscal 2018 was $6.2 billion an increase of $2.8 billion from the prior year. Cash from operations contributed $6.3 billion to the coffers while investing activities used $17.0 billion mainly for the acquisition of Rockwell Collins. Financing activities provided $7.9 billion primarily from loans. This total includes $2.2 billion paid to stockholders.

Strategy

UTC is capitalizing on the growth in commercial aviation and an expanding middle class which is providing more sales opportunities in all its businesses. The company continues to introduce new and innovative products and is investing in digital technologies?such as data analytics autonomy and electricification?that it believes will drive future growth.

In 2018 the company's decision to spin off its Carrier and Otis operations as standalone companies aims to increase the value of both entities and focus on the commercial aerospace business under the UTC name.

Carrier has increased its business through more than 200 new product launches in the past two years. It opened a technology and customer experience center in Palm Beach Gardens FL where customers can see its products and services working to improve building efficiency. The business also streamlined its portfolio by divesting its Taylor Company (equipment manufacturer) and acquiring S2 Security a maker of video management solutions.

Otis introduced its Otis Signature Services and Otis ONE platform that uses digital technologies for remote diagnostics data analytics and machine learning to prevent shutdowns.

Mergers and Acquisitions

In the biggest aerospace deal in history UTC acquired aircraft parts manufacturer Rockwell Collins for $23 billion in 2018. Rockwell is now a new UTC division named Collins Aerospace Systems. UTC projects the new division will generate more than $23 billion in revenue per year and will make aviation electronics and communication equipment for commercial and military aircraft. UTC is making the deal to boost its aerospace business and position it as a springboard for future growth.

UTC intends to separate its other commercial businesses Otis and Carrier (formerly its Climate Controls & Security business) into independent companies. Expected to be completed in 2020 spinoff activities are underway and posing several challenges including separating tax filings and IT systems.

Company Background

United Technologies dates back to 1929 when William Boeing of Boeing Firms and Frederick Rentschler of Pratt & Whitney formed the United Aircraft and Transport Corporation. United Aircraft soon bought aviation companies Hamilton Aero Standard Steel Propeller and Sikorsky.

United Aircraft split in 1934 into three independent entities: United Airlines Boeing Airplane Company and United Aircraft. United Aircraft retained Pratt & Whitney and several other manufacturing interests. In 1975 the company changed its name to United Technologies Corporation representing the intent to diversify into other fields in addition to the aerospace industry.

HISTORY

In 1925 Frederick Rentschler and George Mead founded Pratt & Whitney Aircraft (P&W) to develop aircraft engines. P&W merged with Seattle-based Boeing Airplane Company and Chance Vought Corporation in 1929 to form United Aircraft & Transport. United Aircraft soon bought aviation companies Hamilton Aero Standard Steel Propeller and Sikorsky.

After congressional investigations led to new antitrust laws United Aircraft split in 1934 into three independent entities: United Airlines Boeing Airplane Company and United Aircraft. United Aircraft retained P&W and several other manufacturing interests.

A design flaw in engines produced for Boeing 747s sent P&W on an expensive trip back to the drawing board in the late 1960s. A concerned board of directors appointed Harry Gray a 17-year veteran of Litton Industries as president in 1971. Gray transformed the company into a conglomerate; it adopted its present name in 1975.

The company entered into a new stage of development with the milestone 2012 acquisitions of Goodrich and Rolls-Royce's share in the International Aero Engines (IAE) joint venture. The $16.5 billion acquisition of Goodrich an aircraft components manufacturer was one of UTC's largest. Through the transaction UTC absorbed $1.9 billion in assumed debt but it also sizably boosted its services to the commercial aerospace/defense industry and increased its revenues. Goodrich was combined with the former Hamilton Sundstrand operations and now form its UTC Aerospace Systems segment.

UTC in early 2013 sold its UTC Power unit to Oregon-based ClearEdge Power. In late 2015 it also sold its former Sikorsky helicopter subsidiary to Lockheed Martin for $9 billion.

EXECUTIVES

President Pratt & Whitney, Robert F. Leduc, age 63, $665,057 total compensation

Coo Americas Utc Building And Industrial Systems, Robert J. (Bob) McDonough, age 59, $806,250 total compensation

Chairman President And Ceo, Gregory J. Hayes, age 58, $1,450,000 total compensation

President Otis Elevator, Judy F. Marks

Evp And General Counsel, Charles D. Gill, age 55, $715,000 total compensation

Evp Operations And Strategy, Michael R. (Mike) Dumais, age 52

President Utc Aerospace Systems, David L. Gitlin, age 49

Evp And Chief Human Resources Officer, Elizabeth B. Amato, age 62

Evp And Cfo, Akhil Johri, age 58, $766,667 total compensation

Svp Digital And Cio, Vince Campisi

Svp And Cto, Paul Eremenko

Vice President Engineering And Technology Hamilton Sundstrand, Dave Carter

Vice President Actuation Systems, Rishi Grover

Vice President Finance, Rory Richardson

Vice President International Tax, Greg Marshall

Senior Vice President And Chief Communications Officer, Kelli Parsons

Vp Government Business Development Pratt And Whitney, David Manke

Vp Engineering Pratt And Whitney, Thomas Prete

Vice President Engineering And Technology, Stephane Dion

Vice President Interiors, Cheryl Gorman

Auditors: PricewaterhouseCoopers LLP

LOCATIONS

HQ: United Technologies Corp
10 Farm Springs Road, Farmington, CT 06032
Phone: 860 728-7000   **Fax:** 860 728-7028
Web: www.utc.com

2018 Sales

	$ mil.	% of total
US	39,481	58
Europe	12,857	19
Asia/Pacific	8,847	13
Other	6,672	10
Eliminations and other	(1356)	-
Total	**66,501**	**100**

PRODUCTS/OPERATIONS

2018 Sales

	$ mil.	% of total
Carrier	18,922	28
Pratt & Whitney	19,397	29
Collins Aerospace Systems	16,634	24
Otis	12,904	19
Eliminations	(1356)	-
Total	**66,501**	**100**

2018 Sales by Market

	$ mil.	% of total
Commercial & industrial	31,941	47
Commercial aerospace	26,591	39
Military aerospace & space	9,325	14
Eliminations and other	(1356)	-
Total	**66,501**	**100**

2018 Sales

	$ mil.	% of total
Product sales	46,643	69
Service sales	21,214	31
Eliminations	(1356)	
Total	**66,501**	**100**

Products & Brands Selected
Actuation & Propeller Systems
Air Management Systems
Carrier
Carrier Transicold
Chubb
Chubb eConnect Monitoring Solution
Delta Security Solutions

Selected Operations
Otis (elevators escalators moving walkways and service)
Pratt & Whitney (commercial military business jet and general aviation aircraft engines auxiliary power units and parts and services)
Collins Aerospace Systems (aerospace products and aftermarket services)
Carrier (heating ventilating air conditioning and refrigeration systems and security systems)

COMPETITORS

CFM International SA	Lockheed Martin
GE Aviation	Parker-Hannifin
General Dynamics	Raytheon
Hitachi	SAFRAN
Honeywell	Siemens AG
International	ThyssenKrupp
Kaman	Trane Inc.
L3 Technologies	

HISTORICAL FINANCIALS

Company Type: Public

Income Statement

	REVENUE ($ mil.)	NET INCOME ($ mil.)	NET PROFIT MARGIN	EMPLOYEES
12/19	77,046	5,537	7.2%	243,200
12/18	66,501	5,269	7.9%	240,200
12/17	59,837	4,552	7.6%	205,000
12/16	57,244	5,055	8.8%	201,600
12/15	56,098	7,608	13.6%	197,200
Annual Growth	**8.3%**	**(7.6%)**	**—**	**5.4%**

FYE: December 31

2019 Year-End Financials

Debt ratio: 31.00%	No. of shares (mil.): 864
Return on equity: 14.00%	Dividends
Cash ($ mil.): 7,378	Yield: 2.0%
Current ratio: 1.00	Payout: 50.0%
Long-term debt ($ mil.): 37,788	Market value ($ mil.): 129,447

	STOCK PRICE ($) FY Close	P/E High/Low	PER SHARE ($) Earnings	Dividends	Book Value
12/19	150.00	23 16	6.00	3.00	48.00
12/18	106.00	22 16	7.00	3.00	45.00
12/17	128.00	22 19	6.00	3.00	37.00
12/16	110.00	18 14	6.00	3.00	34.00
12/15	96.00	14 10	9.00	3.00	33.00
Annual Growth	11.7%	— —	(7.1%)	3.5%	10.3%

UnitedHealth Group Inc

UnitedHealth Group is a leading US health insurer offering a variety of plans and services to group and individual customers nationwide. Its UnitedHealthcare health benefits segment manages health maintenance organization (HMO) preferred provider organization (PPO) and point-of-service (POS) plans as well as Medicare Medicaid state-funded and supplemental vision and dental options. In addition UnitedHealth's Optum health services units ? OptumHealth OptumInsight and OptumRx ? provide wellness and care management programs financial services information technology solutions and pharmacy benefit management (PBM) services to individuals and the health care industry.

HISTORY

Dr. Paul Ellwood became known as the "Father of the HMO" for his role as an early champion of the health care concept. As a neurology student in the 1950s Ellwood recognized that applying business principles to medicine could minimize costs and make health care more affordable. Although the HMO was considered a radical approach to health care reform Ellwood got Congress and the Nixon administration to approve its HMO model in 1970; the next year he hired Richard Burke to put the model into action. Burke established United HealthCare (UHC) in 1974 to manage the not-for-profit Physicians Health Plan of Minnesota (PHP). UHC incorporated in 1977.

The company bought HMOs and began managing others operating 11 HMOs in 10 states by 1984 the year it went public. Its expansion continued with the purchases of HMOs Share Development (1985) and Peak Health Care (1986). Unfortunately acquisitions and startups began to eat away at UHC's financial health. Meanwhile Burke CEO of both UHC and PHP was accused by PHP doctors of having a conflict of interest after a change in the HMO's Medicare policy threatened to cut off patients from some member hospitals. Burke resigned in 1987 and was replaced by Kennett Simmons formerly president of Peak.

That year investment firm Warburg Pincus bought nearly 40% of UHC providing it with much-needed cash. UHC lost nearly $16 million in 1987 largely from a restructuring that axed the company's Phoenix HMO as well as startups in six other markets. The next year UHC sold its share of Peak Health Care.

In the late 1980s UHC adopted a new strategy of acquiring specialty companies that provided fee income. It also continued building its HMO network through acquisitions hoping to gain critical mass in such varied markets as the Midwest and New England.

Physician William (Bill) McGuire another former Peak president was named UHC's chairman and CEO in 1991. That year PHP and Share merged into Medica. Warburg Pincus distributed its UHC shares to several pension funds and financial institutions.

The company's expansion accelerated in the 1990s with a string of purchases in the Midwest but there were also divestitures. In 1994 UHC sold subsidiary Diversified Pharmaceutical Services providing cash for still more purchases including GenCare (St. Louis) Group Sales and Service of Puerto Rico and MetraHealth a former joint venture of Travelers Group and Metropolitan Life. UHC's interest in fee-based businesses continued with the 1997 purchase of Medicode a major provider of health care information products.

In 1998 the firm planned to buy rival Humana. However bloated UHC decided it should slim down to prepare to consummate the agreement; when UHC announced that it would charge $900 million in costs against earnings its plummeting stock price devalued the primary currency of the deal which quickly collapsed. That year it began offering MediGap and other supplements to AARP members.

The company changed its name to UnitedHealth Group in 2000. It also added UK-based contract research organization ClinPharm International to Ingenix that year and it announced it would let doctors — not administrators — choose what treatment patients would get partially because it was spending more on care scrutiny than the practice saved. Nevertheless many doctors claimed the process was still restrictive.

In 2000 the American Medical Association (AMA) and other parties sued the company claiming it used faulty Ingenix data to reduce payments to member doctors. (UnitedHealth settled the AMA lawsuit in 2009 for $350 million without admitting any wrongdoing as well as some state lawsuits related to the database.)

UnitedHealth's strategy for expansion in the early 21st century concentrated on acquisitions and joint ventures. To expand its Medicaid services business the firm bought AmeriChoice in 2002. The company also bought Mid Atlantic Medical Services because its HMOs and specialty health care operations complemented UnitedHealth's core operations. Golden Rule was acquired in late 2003 so UnitedHealth could enter the individual health insurance market by providing medical savings accounts. UnitedHealth also bought individual health care reimbursement account provider Definity Health in late 2004 for the same purpose. To increase its market share in the northeastern US the company bought Oxford Health Plans that year.

UnitedHealth spent $8.8 billion to acquire and integrate PacifiCare in 2005. Adding 3 million customers the acquisition gave UnitedHealth a leading position in the California and West Coast markets but it also prompted a landslide of complaints from customers alleging mishandled claims. The California Insurance Commissioner and other state agencies sought fines of more than $1 billion. While PacifiCare continued to exist as a health plan brand of UnitedHealth the PacifiCare administrative operations were integrated into other UnitedHealth units including UnitedHealthcare. The PacifiCare Prescription Benefits unit became separate operating division of UnitedHealth.

Chairman and CEO McGuire became the focus of inquiry in 2006 over a scandal involving the back-dating of stock options awarded to him and other company executives. Following a board inquiry McGuire was shown the door and was replaced by Stephen Hemsley formerly the company's president and COO. The back-dating brouhaha continued to be a distraction for UnitedHealth and in 2008 it opted to settle several related shareholder lawsuits by agreeing to pay more than $900 million.

Continuing the acquisitive strategy it laid out after the turn of the millennium the company in 2006 bought Deere & Company's employee health plan as well as Student Resources the student insurance division of HealthMarkets' MEGA Life subsidiary.

The company changed the name of its supplemental health division from Specialized Care Service to OptumHealth in 2007. As part of the restructuring a number of other UnitedHealth businesses were merged into OptumHealth including ACN Group United Resources Networks United Behavioral Health PacifiCare Behavioral Health Exante Bank and Exante Financial Services.

UnitedHealth completed several large acquisitions in 2008 spending $730 million to purchase Fiserv's health-related businesses including Fiserv Health (benefits administration for 2 million members) Avidyn Health (care facilitation) Fiserv Health Specialty Solutions (administration) and Innoviant Pharmacy Benefits Management. UnitedHealth also paid $980 million to acquire Unison Health Plans and used it to expand its AmeriChoice unit.

UnitedHealth completed its controversial purchase of Nevada insurance provider Sierra Health Services for approximately $2.6 billion in 2008 gaining some 600000 health plan members in the state and boosting its position in the growing Southwest market. The acquisition took nearly a year to receive approval from the Department of Justice due to competition concerns. Approval was finally gained on the contingency that UnitedHealth sell its Las Vegas Medicare Advantage program representing some 27000 customers to Humana for $185 million. Sierra Health's operating units including Health Plan of Nevada and Sierra Health and Life became part the UnitedHealthcare Nevada division following the acquisition.

EXECUTIVES

Executive Vice President, Simon Stevens
Evp, Jeannine M. Rivet, $465,000 total compensation
Vice Chairman And Ceo Optum, Larry C. Renfro, age 65, $1,100,000 total compensation
Evp Medical Affairs And Chief Medical Officer, Richard Migliori
Ceo, David S. Wichmann, age 57, $1,100,000 total compensation
Ceo Community Plan Of Kansas, Kevin P. Sparks
Evp Human Capital, D. Ellen Wilson, age 61, $701,923 total compensation
Evp And Chief Legal Officer, Marianne D. Short, age 67, $800,000 total compensation
Evp External Affairs, Cory B. Alexander
Ceo Employer And Individual Iowa-kansas-nebraska, Robert Broomfield
Evp And Cfo, John Rex, $721,923 total compensation
Svp And Chief Marketing Officer, Terry M. Clark
Vice President Goverment Programs West Region, Jeanine Donahue
Vice President Finance, Adam Koering
Vice President E Solutions, John O'Neil
Vice President Of Finance, Matthew Pioske
Vice President Technology, Mouli Venkatesan
Vice President Marketing Ovations, Ellen Sexton
Vice President Provider Experience And Nps Programs, Deborah Cooledge
Senior Director Vice President, Tom Brandt
Senior Vice President, Anne Gavel
Vp And Chief Information Security Officer, Robert Booker
Vice President, Gayle Adams
Vice President Sales, Philip Brun
Senior Vice President Human Capital, Chris Coleman
Vice President Relationship Office Solutions Group, Brent Muilenburg
Vice President Consumer Strategy, Nancy Brock

Senior Vice President Center For Nursing Advancement, Dawn Bazarko

Senior Vice President Business Platforms And Operations Optuminsight, Steven Mueller

Vp Pdl And Pharmacy Strategy Development, Tim Schwartz

Senior Vice President Strategic Solutions, Deborah Sundal

Vice President, Steven Burdick

Vice President Innovation And Randd, Robert Plourde

Vice President, Brennan Mcnally

Vice President Computer Services, Thomas Busse

Vice President Clinical Solutions, Kelley Nolan-maccione

Vice President Digital Product, Cara Sjodin

Vp Software Engineering Services, Srinivas Gazula

Vice President, Laurie Paidosh

Sr. Vice President Strategic Initiatives, Alison Richards

Vice President Community And Strategic Engagement Unitedhealthcare Community Plan, Ipyana Spencer

Vice President Product Management, Todd Spaulding

Vice President, Jeff Todd

Vice President Of Sales, Thomas Gormley

Executive Vice President, Chris Ritchie

Vp Medical Management, Stephen Griffiths

Vice President, Michele Duncan

Medical Director, Daniel Clute

Medical Director, Helene Goldsman

Medical Director, Edward Koza

Vice President Shared Services, Kim Farner

National Account Manager Specialty Benefits, Lori Pewitt

Vice President Sales And Service, Tammy Ohare

Vp Network Strategy And Innovation (unitedhealthcare), Karen Silgen

Medical Director, Ralph Naftaly

Vice President Global Health, David Powell

Vice President Network Programs Se Region, Patricio Cobos

Regional Vice President Account Manager, Kelli Lowery

Avp Network Integration Services, Rossana Salvadori

Vice President Market Development Optum Local Care Delivery, Kathy Winans

Vice President Marketing, Heidi Svendsen

Vice President Public Sector Business Development, Kenneth Anderson

Medical Director, Denise Callari

Vice President Operations, Wayne White

Market Vice President Underwriting, Karl Hermonat

Vp Client Services, Kimberly Burkhart

Vice President Employee Communication, Carla Nuzzo

Vice President Solutions Sales Payer Channel Optum, Laura Cahill

Vice President General Management, Susan Tonkin

Vice President Moment Health Unitedhealth Group Ventures, Erik Hokenson

Vice President Client Relations, Kelly Mcdevitt

Vice President Information Technology, Kevin Kantola

Vice President Executive Assistant Finance, Dan Cummings

Vice President Finance, Kevin Carlson

Vice President Sales, Danielle Peacock

Medical Director, Tony Sun

Vice President Information Technology, Oren Hermel

Vice President Investment Mgmt, Thomas Mcglinch

Vice President Application Development, Guy Grindberg

Vice President Risk Management, Randy Jacob

Vice President Small Business, Doug Metzger

Vice President Market Strategy And Marketing, Christi Kruse

Vice President Business Development, Neal Heyman

Vice President Regulatory Affairs (federal), Deborah Schreiber

Director Of Pharmacy Management, Susan Maddux

National Vice President Consulting Relations, Michael Finn

Vice President Clinical Strategy, Karen Keown

Vice President Sales, Kim Lewis

Vice President Sales, Geoff Buro

Vice President National Alliances, Randy Spicer

Vice President Business Development, Matthew Aaefedt

Vice President Quality Solutions, Peter Naumann

Vp Public Relations, Tyler Mason

Vice President Tax, John Kelly

Vice President Marketing Operations, Jordana Costello

Medical Director, Todd Johnson

Vice President Client Development, Denise Lindeen

Vice President Information Technology Customer Integration Behavioral Solutions Optumhealth, Adrian Sale

Senior Medical Director, Bethany Reeves

Vice President Strategic Insight And Innovation, Meredith Baratz

Vice President Of State Affairs, Michelle Marto

Vice President Of Financial Planning And Analysis, Robert Schweitzer

Vice President Finance, Darren C Moquist

Vice President Of Contracting, Rebecca Bausch

Vice President Client Management, David Twardy

Senior Vice President, Gayle Coyle-ikemoto

Vp Strategic Provider Solutions, Audra Kerkow

Vice President Government Relations, Leah Rummel

Vice President And Actuary, Drew Girton

Vice President, Bridgette Roberson

Vice President Enterprise Customer Experience And Strategy, Paul Long

Vice President Finance, Scott Taylor

National Vice President Appeals And Grievances, Mark Friedman

National Vice President Risk Adjustment Operations, Ovais Jalil

Senior Vice President Sales, Craig Lafiandra

Vice President Healthcare Economics, Tyner Wilson

Medical Director, Barry Stone

Vice President Product Optum Consumer Solutions Group, Glen Kvadus

Vice President Of Government Programs Central Region, Keely Gladieux

Regional Vice President Clinical Quality, Michelle Francisco

Senior Vice President And Chief Accounting Officer, Tom Roos

Vp Enterprise Operations, Tom Boudewyns

Vice President Client Relations National Accounts, Scott Roberge

Account Vice President, Christopher Chadbourne

Vice President Total Rewards (optum Compensation), Brad Fagerstrom

Associate Vice President Of Outpatient Behavioral Programs, Michael Brendzal

Vice President External Communications, Lisa Hawks

Vice President National Accounts At Optumrx, Kristin Rubino

Vice President Internal Audit And Advisory Services, Kendall Bishop

Vice President National Ancillary Contracting And Strategy, Dosedel Greg

Vice President Customer Service, Stephen Shipley

Medical Director, Olabisi Kuye

Medical Director, Ola Medhat

Medical Director Community And State, Sara Rinck

Senior Medical Director, Michael Haberman

Senior Medical Director Retiree Solutions, Joseph Agostini

Vice President Of Financial Planning And Analysis, Shingai Mavengere

Vice President Of Marketing Strategy, Kelley Ries

Vice President Compliance Exam Management, Joseph Keen

Vice President Government Program Administration, Anthony Dapp

Vp And Deputy General Counsel Unitedhealthcare, Jill Mitchell

Evp Operations Unitedhealthcare, Brian Brueckman

Vice President Regional Tpa Sales, Gregory Pavlic

Vice President Of Business Development, Warner Roberts

Vice President Network Contracting, Brian Ward

Vice President Innovation And Strategy, Matt Grimes

Vice President Enterprise Solutions Optum, Mary Joiner

Medical Director, Danesh Alam

Vice President Government Program Administration, Dapp Anthony

Account Vice President, Marc Savasta

Senior Vice President National Network Strategy And Innovation, Lisa Mcdonnel

Auditors: Deloitte & Touche LLP

LOCATIONS

HQ: UnitedHealth Group Inc
UnitedHealth Group Center, 9900 Bren Road East, Minnetonka, MN 55343
Phone: 952 936-1300
Web: www.unitedhealthgroup.com

PRODUCTS/OPERATIONS

2018 Sales

	$ mil.	% of total
UnitedHealthcare	184,476	65
Optum		
OptumRx	69,536	24
OptumHealth	24,145	8
OptumInsight	9,008	3
Adjustments	(59918)	-
Total	**226,247**	**100**

2018 Sales

	$ mil.	% of total
Premiums	178,087	79
Products	29,601	13
Services	17,183	8
Investment & other income	1,376	-
Total	**266,247**	**100**

Selected Operations

Optum (Health Services division)
  OptumHealth (specialty benefits)
  OptumInsight (formerly Ingenix information technology and consulting services)
  OptumRx (formerly Prescription Solutions pharmacy benefit management)
UnitedHealthcare (Health Plans division)
  UnitedHealthcare Community & State (former operations of AmeriChoice public-sector programs)
  UnitedHealthcare Employer & Individual (health plans for individuals businesses employers)
  UnitedHealthcare International (expatriate coverage for global accounts)
  UnitedHealthcare Medicare & Retirement (former operations of Ovations benefits for people age 50 and older)
  UnitedHealthcare Military & Veterans (TRICARE West Region contract)

COMPETITORS

Aetna	Humana
Anthem	Kaiser Foundation
Blue Cross	Health Plan
CIGNA	Molina Healthcare
Centene	Prime Therapeutics
Express Scripts	WellCare Health Plans

HISTORICAL FINANCIALS

Company Type: Public

Income Statement

FYE: December 31

	REVENUE ($ mil.)	NET INCOME ($ mil.)	NET PROFIT MARGIN	EMPLOYEES
12/18	226,247	11,986	5.3%	300,000
12/17	201,159	10,558	5.2%	260,800
12/16	184,840	7,017	3.8%	230,000
12/15	157,107	5,813	3.7%	200,000
12/14	130,474	5,619	4.3%	170,000
Annual Growth	14.8%	20.9%	—	15.3%

2018 Year-End Financials

Debt ratio: 24.00%
Return on equity: 24.00%
Cash ($ mil.): 10,866
Current ratio: 1.00
Long-term debt ($ mil.): 34,581

No. of shares (mil.): 960
Dividends
  Yield: 1.0%
  Payout: 28.0%
Market value ($ mil.): 239,155

	STOCK PRICE ($) FY Close	P/E High/Low	PER SHARE ($) Earnings	Dividends	Book Value
12/18	249.00	23 17	12.00	3.00	54.00
12/17	220.00	21 14	11.00	3.00	49.00
12/16	160.00	22 15	7.00	2.00	40.00
12/15	118.00	21 16	6.00	2.00	35.00
12/14	101.00	18 12	6.00	1.00	34.00
Annual Growth	25.3%	— —	20.9%	25.2%	12.2%

Univar Solutions Inc

Auditors: Ernst & Young LLP

LOCATIONS

HQ: Univar Solutions Inc
3075 Highland Parkway, Suite 200, Downers Grove, IL 60515
Phone: 331 777-6000
Web: www.univar.com

HISTORICAL FINANCIALS

Company Type: Public

Income Statement

FYE: December 31

	REVENUE ($ mil.)	NET INCOME ($ mil.)	NET PROFIT MARGIN	EMPLOYEES
12/18	8,633	172	2.0%	8,500
12/17	8,254	120	1.5%	8,600
12/16	8,074	(68)		8,700
12/15	8,982	17	0.2%	9,200
12/14	10,374	(20)	—	8,900
Annual Growth	(4.5%)	—		(1.1%)

2018 Year-End Financials

Debt ratio: 45.00%
Return on equity: 15.00%
Cash ($ mil.): 122
Current ratio: 2.00
Long-term debt ($ mil.): 2,350

No. of shares (mil.): 142
Dividends
  Yield: —
  Payout: —
Market value ($ mil.): 2,514

	STOCK PRICE ($) FY Close	P/E High/Low	PER SHARE ($) Earnings	Dividends	Book Value
12/18	18.00	26 13	1.00	0.00	8.00
12/17	31.00	39 32	1.00	0.00	8.00
12/16	28.00	— —	(1.00)	0.00	6.00
12/15	17.00	195116	0.00	0.00	6.00
Annual Growth	1.1%	— —	71.5%	—	9.2%

Universal Health Services, Inc.

With dozens of health care facilities in nearly every state Universal Health Services (UHS) isn't quite ubiquitous but it's working on it. One of the nation's largest for-profit hospital operators UHS owns or leases about 25 acute care hospitals with a total of more than 6000 beds primarily in rural and suburban communities. The system also operates outpatient surgery centers and radiation treatment facilities most located near its acute care hospitals. In addition UHS' behavioral health division operates some 500 psychiatric and substance abuse hospitals with a combined capacity of more than 23000 beds; its UK-based Cygnet unit operates about 40 more facilities. UHS is controlled by founder and CEO Alan Miller.

Operations

UHS receives slightly more than half of its annual revenues from its acute care segment which includes medical hospitals surgical outpatient facilities and radiation oncology centers. The remainder of the company's revenue comes from its portfolio of behavioral health hospitals which include residential facilities for teens adult psychiatric hospitals substance abuse facilities and special education schools for students with emotional problems.

UHS provides central resources to its network of facilities including purchasing information services finance facilities planning administrative personnel marketing public relations and physician recruitment.

Geographic Reach

UHS' acute care facilities are located in more than half a dozen states and are situated mostly in smaller towns and cities with limited competition though the division does have facilities in a few larger markets (such as Las Vegas and Washington DC). UHS' behavioral health hospitals are scattered across about 40 US states as well as Puerto Rico the US Virgin Islands and the UK. The company's biggest markets for both segments are Nevada Texas and California.

Headquartered in King of Prussia Pennsylvania UHS also has offices in Wayne Pennsylvania; Brentwood Tennessee; Denton Texas; and Reno Nevada.

Sales and Marketing

Both of UHS' operating segments (Acute Care Hospital Services and Behavioral Health Services) earn more than half of revenues from managed care providers (HMOs PPOs) with the remainder of revenues coming from traditional Medicare and Medicaid plans and other sources.

Financial Performance

UHS' growth strategies have helped it to steadily increase sales over the past several years. The company maintains a strong balance sheet which allows it to build new facilities and more frequently to buy existing facilities from other hospital operators. In general the system has seen increased patient admissions over the years bringing its revenue higher.

In 2017 net revenue increased 7% to $10.4 billion. This was driven by growth in both the Acute Care Hospital Services and Behavioral Health Services segments. Existing acute care hospital adjusted admissions increased 6% while adjusted patient days increased 3% which led to a 5% increase in that segment's net revenue. Existing behavioral health care facility adjusted admissions rose 2% while adjusted patient days increased less than 1% that year. Newly acquired or built facilities further boosted total revenue.

With the higher net revenue plus a decrease in the provision for income taxes net income also rose 7% to $752.3 million in 2017.

The system ended 2017 with $74.4 million in cash up some $40 million from 2016. Operating activities contributed $1.2 billion but investing activities used $624 million (primarily for property and equipment additions) and financing activities (largely share repurchases) used another $519 million.

Strategy

UHS has a focused strategy for growth: Add more facilities to its network improve the services and operations at its facilities and increase the efficiency of its services (including shifting to outpatient care when preferable).

By focusing its operations on high-growth regions UHS also works towards its goal of increasing hospital utilization rates (which is often a key indicator of the financial health of a hospital). To further draw more patients and high-quality physicians to its existing facilities the company invests in new technology makes capital improvements and increases the breadth of services it offers. Initiatives include upgrades to surgical equipment and billing systems as well as the installation of operating room light fixtures that continuously disinfect the environment. UHS is especially expanding its outpatient service capabilities as payers put pressure on hospitals to control inpatient care costs.

While the company's growth strategy is to build or purchase new facilities in rapidly growing areas — it has grown both of its units through selective acquisitions and construction efforts over the years — UHS also has no qualms about ridding itself of operations that just don't quite fit anymore.

UHS gets about 15% of its net revenues from facilities located in Nevada Texas and California. With that much exposure the system is somewhat vulnerable to potential changes in legislation regulations the economy and the competitive landscape that could occur in those states.

Furthermore there is growing scrutiny in many states with regards to for-profit systems (like UHS) buying not-for-profit care facilities and converting them to for-profit facilities. This trend could impact UHS's ability to grow its operations through acquisitions.

Mergers and Acquisitions

UHS is focused on acquiring hospitals and other facilities to expand operations. In mid-2018 UK unit Cygnet acquired The Danshell Group which owns 25 facilities serving adults with learning disabilities.

In 2017 the company acquired Mississippi-based Memorial Behavioral Health which operates a 109-bed facility for adults adolescents and children. It also operates two outpatient clinics. The three facilities are now known as Gulfport Behavioral Health System.

In late 2016 UHS acquired the adult services division of Cambian Group a UK operation for some $464 million; that purchase added 81 behavioral facilities housing some 1200 beds bringing UHS' UK holdings to more than 100 facilities. Also that year UHS acquired Desert View Hospital a 25-bed acute care facility in Nevada.

EXECUTIVES

Evp And Cfo, Steve G. Filton, age 61, $584,606 total compensation

Chairman And Ceo, Alan B. Miller, age 81, $1,600,061 total compensation

Evp; President Behavioral Health, Debra K. Osteen, age 63, $638,025 total compensation

Evp; President Acute Care, Marvin G. Pember, age 65, $618,502 total compensation

President, Marc D. Miller, age 48, $720,861 total compensation
Svp Information Services And Business Solutions, Michael S. Nelson
Vp Corporate Insurance, Bob Engelhard
Vice President And Director, Gayle Bowman
Vice President Center Applications, Lorraine Castro
Executive Vice President Of Finance, Debbie Onofrey
Assistant Vice President Clinical Trg An, Bill Lightfoot
Director Of Health, Emily Macko
Vice President And Director, Stephen Carlson
Executive Vice President Of Finance, Eileen Vido
Vice President E Health Financial Advisor, Andrew Ganti
Vice President Of Hawaii Division, Donna Murray
Vp Behavioral Health Services, John Hollinsworth
Vice President And Director, Jerilin Cummings
Director Of Radiology Services, Jeff Otto
Vice President And Director, Frank Pizzuto
Regional Vice President, Frank Lopez
Executive Vice President Of Finance, Andy Belen
Director Of Pharmacy, Kristen Palasthy
Vp Behavioral Health Services, Roz Hudson
Executive Vice President Of Finance, Stephanie Hill
Senior Vice President And Treasurer, Cheryl Ramagano
Vice President Financial Operations, Chris Recon
Vice President, Pj Moraci
Director Of Clinical Services, Kate McBride
Director Of Pharmacy, John Luther
Director Of Clinical Services, Becky Mcdonough
Vice President Of Operations, Cori Cole
Vice President Behavioral Health Services, Philip J Moraci
Director Of Clinical Services, Maegan Kemery
Vice President Acute Finance, Thomas Machozzi
Medical Director, Michael Vines
Vice President Supply Chain Operations, Raymond Davis
Director Of Radiology, Mark Lerner
Vice President Hospital Finance Bh, Lawrence Harrod
Staff Vice President Reimbursement, Bob Halinski
Radiology Director, Beth Louton
Director Of Nursing, Catherine Wright
Director Of Pharmacy, George Morton
Vice President Cno Acute, Jacalyn Liebowitz
Svp Finance Behavioral Health, Laurence Harrod
Director Of Him And Risk Management, Gayle Leonard
Medical Director Of Emergency Services, James Rhee
Director Of Nursing, Zachary Love
Director Of Admissions, Ivory Witherspoon
Director Of Clinical Services, Jeremy Wagoner
Svp Hr, Geraldine Johnson Geckle
Director Of Admissions, Fred Knox
Director Of Nursing, Bridgette Bishop
Secretary, Terry Shaw
Auditors: PricewaterhouseCoopers LLP

LOCATIONS

HQ: Universal Health Services, Inc.
Universal Corporate Center, 367 South Gulph Road, King of Prussia, PA 19406
Phone: 610 768-3300
Web: www.uhsinc.com

Selected Facilities

California
Corona Regional Medical Center (Corona)
Palmdale Regional Medical Center (Palmdale)
Southwest Healthcare System — Inland Valley Campus (Wildomar)
Southwest Healthcare System — Rancho Springs Campus (Murrieta)

Temecula Valley Day Surgery and Pain Therapy Center (Murrieta)
Florida
Lakewood Ranch Medical Center (Bradenton)
Manatee Memorial Hospital (Bradenton)
Palms Westside Clinic ASC (50% Royal Palm Beach)
Wellington Regional Medical Center (West Palm Beach)
Nevada
Centennial Hills Hospital Medical Center (Las Vegas)
Desert Springs Hospital (72% Las Vegas)
Northern Nevada Medical Center (Sparks)
Spring Valley Hospital Medical Center (72% Las Vegas)
Summerlin Hospital Medical Center (72% Las Vegas)
Valley Hospital Medical Center (72% Las Vegas)
South Carolina
Aiken Regional Medical Centers (Aiken)
Aurora Pavilion (Aiken)
Cancer Care Institute of Carolina (Aiken)
Oklahoma
St. Mary's Regional Medical Center (Enid)
Puerto Rico
First Hospital Panamericano (Cidra)
First Hospital Panamericano (Ponce)
First Hospital Panamericano (San Juan)
Texas
Cornerstone Regional Hospital (50% Edinburg)
Doctors' Hospital of Laredo (Laredo)
Fort Duncan Regional Medical Center (Eagle Pass)
Northwest Texas Healthcare System (Amarillo)
Northwest Texas Surgery Center (majority owned Amarillo)
The Pavilion at Northwest Texas Healthcare System (Amarillo)
South Texas Health System (Edinburg)
Edinburg Regional Medical Center (Edinburg)
Edinburg Children's Hospital (Edinburg)
McAllen Medical Center (McAllen)
McAllen Heart Hospital (McAllen)
South Texas Behavioral Health System (Edinburg)
Texoma Medical Center (Denison)
TMC Behavioral Health Center (Denison)
Washington D.C.
The George Washington University Hospital (80%)

PRODUCTS/OPERATIONS

2017 Sales by Segment

	$ mil.	% of total
Acute Care Hospital Services	5	53
Behavioral Health Services	4,907	47
Other	19	-
Total	**10,410**	**100**

COMPETITORS

Adventist Health System Sunbelt Healthcare
Adventist Health System West
Ascension Health
Banner Health
CHRISTUS Health
CRC Health
Community Health Systems
Devereux Foundation
HCA
Hazelden Betty Ford
LifePoint Health
Mercy Health
Northwestern Human Services
Sutter Health
Tenet Healthcare
Texas Health Resources
UBH
United Surgical Partners

HISTORICAL FINANCIALS

Company Type: Public

Income Statement   FYE: December 31

	REVENUE ($ mil.)	NET INCOME ($ mil.)	NET PROFIT MARGIN	EMPLOYEES
12/18	10,772	780	7.2%	87,100
12/17	10,410	752	7.2%	76,600
12/16	9,766	702	7.2%	75,325
12/15	9,043	681	7.5%	74,600
12/14	8,065	545	6.8%	68,700
Annual Growth	**7.5%**	**9.3%**	**—**	**6.1%**

2018 Year-End Financials

Debt ratio: 35.00%
Return on equity: 15.00%
Cash ($ mil.): 105
Current ratio: 1.00
Long-term debt ($ mil.): 3,935
No. of shares (mil.): 91
Dividends
　Yield: 0.0%
　Payout: 5.0%
Market value ($ mil.): 10,648

	STOCK PRICE ($) FY Close	P/E High/Low	PER SHARE ($) Earnings	Dividends	Book Value
12/18	117.00	17 13	8.00	0.00	59.00
12/17	113.00	16 12	8.00	0.00	53.00
12/16	106.00	19 14	7.00	0.00	47.00
12/15	119.00	21 15	7.00	0.00	43.00
12/14	111.00	21 13	5.00	0.00	38.00
Annual Growth	**1.2%**	**— —**	**11.3%**	**7.5%**	**11.7%**

UNIVERSITY OF PENNSYLVANIA

EXECUTIVES

Pres, Amy Gutmann
Market Researcher, Market Rese, Jane Anderson
Coordinator, Karen Stevenson
College and Career Programs Co, Laurie Engleman
Lsoca Coordinator, Mark Bardsley
University Recruiting Coordina, Marlene Williams
Administrative Coordinator, Patricia Kozak
Computer Analyst, Dan Bachovin Sr
Director Vpul Technology Servi, Mary Spada
Information Specialist, Caroline Elizabeth
Financial Support Spec, Janice Brown
Auditors: PRICEWATERHOUSECOOPERS LLP PH

LOCATIONS

HQ: UNIVERSITY OF PENNSYLVANIA
3451 WALNUT ST RM 100, PHILADELPHIA, PA 191046243
Phone: 215 898-5000
Web: WWW.UPENN.EDU

HISTORICAL FINANCIALS

Company Type: Private

Income Statement   FYE: June 30

	REVENUE ($ mil.)	NET INCOME ($ mil.)	NET PROFIT MARGIN	EMPLOYEES
06/18	10,094	2,327	23.0%	70
06/16	8,576	1,022	11.9%	—
06/15	0	0		—
Annual Growth	**—**	**—**	**—**	**—**

UNIVERSITY OF WASHINGTON INC

The University of Washington (UW) is Husky indeed with an annual enrollment of more than 54000 students. Founded in 1861 as the Territorial University of Washington UW (pronounced "U-dub" by those on campus) has smaller branches in Tacoma and Bothell in addition to its main campus in downtown Seattle. The university whose mascot is a Husky offers more than 600 undergraduate graduate and professional degree programs through 16 colleges and schools. It also operates four hospitals: University of Washington Medical Center Harborview Medical Center Northwest Hospital and Valley Medical Center.

Operations

With more than 300 programs University of Washington confers some 12000 bachelor's master's doctoral and professional degrees each year. Its graduates include about 135 Fulbright and 35 Rhodes scholars. The school's top five bachelor degree fields include biology psychology political science economics and communications.

Research is a cornerstone of the university which has nearly 300 specialized research centers. The school's annual sponsored grant and contract research funding exceeds $1.6 billion. Some 300 new companies have emerged based on UW research advances.

Financial Performance

In fiscal 2017 (ended June) operating revenue for University of Washington totaled $5.8 billion. Patient service revenues account for the largest amount of funds received (38%) followed by federal grants and contracts (about 21%).

Operating expenses totaled $5.7 billion that year. Salaries accounted for nearly half of those expenses.

EXECUTIVES

Dean School Of Medicine, Paul G. Ramsey
Svp Finance And Facilities, V'Ella Warren
Chancellor Bothell Campus, Bjong Wolf Yeigh
Dean School Of Law, Kellye Testy
Dean Libraries, Lizabeth A. (Betsy) Wilson
Interim Chancellor Tacoma Campus, Kenyon S. Chan
Dean School Of Public Health, Howard Frumkin
President, Ana Mari Cauce
Dean Undergraduate Academic Affairs, Ed Taylor
Vp Information Technology And Cio, Kelli Trosvig
Dean College Of Arts And Sciences, Robert Stacey
Interim Dean College Of Built Environments, John Schaufelberger
Dean School Of Dentistry, Joel H. Berg
Dean College Of Education, Tom Stritikus
Dean College Of Engineering, Michael B. Bragg
Dean College Of The Environment, Lisa Graumlich
Dean Evans School Of Public Affairs, Sandra Archibald
Dean Foster School Of Business, James Jiambalvo
Dean Graduate School, Dave Eaton
Dean Information School, Harry Bruce
Dean School Of Nursing, Azita Emami
Dean School Of Pharmacy, Thomas Baillie
Dean School Of Social Work, Edwina (Eddie) Uehara
Associate Vice President, Lee Heck
Associate Vice President Financial Management, Susan Camber
Medical Director, Jean Haulman
Senior Vice President Ecommerce Mobile D, Brian Jones

Vp Of Marketing, Jennifer Wong
Extension Lecturer Vice President For Continuing Ed, Barbara Bell
Vice President For Student Life, Denzil Suite
Assistant Vice President For Student Life And, Pam Schreiber
Director Of Government Relations, Ian Goodhew
Medical Director, Rob Sweet
Associate Vice President For Information Management, Aaron Powell
Associate Vice President College Access, Patricia Loera
Executive Vice President, Jeffrey Scott
Assistant Vice President, Joanna Glicker
Director Of Admissions, Erin Town
Vice President, Lou Cariello
Medical Director, Matthew Grierson
Vice President External Affairs, Brian Taubeneck
Vice President, Ross Heath
Associate Vice President, Barbara Wingerson
Medical Director Uw Center For Pain Relief, Brett Stacey
Executive Vice President Provost, Gerald Balsasty
Vice President, Sean Campbell
Vice Chairman, William S. (Bill) Ayer
Chairman, Orin C. Smith
Secretary Senior, Gregory Daigle
Board Member, Melissa Cunningham
Msim Advisory Board Member, Cheryl Scott
Secretary Senior, Victoria Parker
Secretary, Brianna Watts
Board Of Directors, Craig Mauer
Board Member, Dan Brettler
Assistant Secretary, Louise Hine
Auditors: KPMG LLP SEATTLE WASHINGTON

LOCATIONS

HQ: UNIVERSITY OF WASHINGTON INC
4311 11TH AVE NE STE 600, SEATTLE, WA
981056369
Phone: 206 543-2100

PRODUCTS/OPERATIONS

Selected Colleges and Schools
College of Arts and Sciences
College of Built Environments
College of Education
College of Engineering
College of the Environment
Evans School of Public Affairs
The Graduate School
Information School
Michael G. Foster School of Business
School of Dentistry
School of Law
School of Medicine
School of Nursing
School of Pharmacy
School of Public Health
School of Social Work

HISTORICAL FINANCIALS

Company Type: Private

Income Statement — FYE: June 30

	REVENUE ($ mil.)	NET INCOME ($ mil.)	NET PROFIT MARGIN	EMPLOYEES
06/18	5,172	490	9.5%	27,228
06/17	4,893	363	7.4%	—
Annual Growth	5.7%	35.1%	—	—

Univest Financial Corp

Univest Corporation of Pennsylvania will keep your money close to its vest. The holding company owns $3 billion-asset Univest Bank and Trust which serves the southeastern part of the Keystone State and the broader Mid-Atlantic region online and though 30 branches and provides standard retail and commercial banking services such as checking and savings accounts CDs IRAs and credit cards. Subsidiary Univest Capital provides small-ticket commercial financing while Univest Insurance offers personal and commercial coverage. Univest Investments which boasts some $3 billion in assets under management offers brokerage and investment advisory services.

Operations

Univest operates three main business segments: Banking which accounted for 79% of the company's total revenue during 2015 and provides traditional banking services to consumers businesses and government entities through Univest Bank and Trust; Wealth Management (12% of revenue) which offers investment advisory retirement plan trust municipal pension and broker/dealer services through Univest Investments; and Insurance (9% of revenue) which offers commercial and personal insurance lines as well as benefits and human resources consulting through Univest Insurance.

Broadly speaking Univest Corporation gets more than 60% of its revenue from interest income. About 61% of its total revenue came from loan interest (including fees on loans and leases) during 2015 while another 5% came from interest on its investment securities. The rest of its revenue came from insurance commissions and fees (8% of revenue) investment advisory commission and fee income (7%) trust fee income (5%) deposit account service charges (3%) mortgage banking sales (3%) and other miscellaneous income sources.

More than 40% of the company's loan portfolio was made up of commercial real estate loans at the end of 2015 while another 23% of loan assets were made up of commercial loans that were financial or agricultural-related. The remainder of the portfolio was made up of loans tied to residential properties secured for business purposes (10% of loan assets) residential properties for personal purposes (8%) lease financings (7%) construction real estate loans (4%) and loans to individuals (less than 2%).

Geographic Reach

Souderton Pennsylvania-based Univest Corporation and its subsidiaries serve clients across the Mid-Atlantic region. The company has around 30 bank branches and nearly 20 offices in the Montgomery Bucks Philadelphia Chester Berks Lehigh and Delaware counties of Pennsylvania as well as in Calvert County in Maryland Camden County in New Jersey and Lee County in Florida.

Sales and Marketing

Univest Corporation serves individuals businesses municipalities and non-profit organizations. It spent $2.25 million on marketing and advertising during 2015 to reach these clients up from $1.88 million and $1.95 million in 2014 and 2013 respectively.

Financial Performance

The bank's revenues and profits have been trending higher over the past several years thanks to 50% loan asset growth and 50% non-interest revenue growth since 2011 along with a continued reduction in loan loss provisions as its loan portfolio's credit quality has improved with higher property valuations in the strengthened economy.

Univest Corporation's revenue jumped 24% to a record $154.41 million during 2015 mostly as

35% loan asset growth (loan balances swelled to $2.16 billion) stemming from its Valley Green Bank acquisition helped boost interest income. The company's non-interest income also rose 9% as its mortgage banking gains doubled during the year on higher volumes and as its insurance commissions and fee income rose 20% after acquiring Sterner Insurance in mid-2014.

Strong revenue growth in 2015 drove the company's net income up 23% to $27.27 million for the year. Univest Corporation's operating cash levels climbed 12% to $35.63 thanks to the rise in earnings.

Strategy

Univest Corporation has been expanding its service lines and building its loan and deposit businesses by strategically acquiring other banks and investment or insurance-related financial firms.

Mergers and Acquisitions

In December 2015 Univest Corporation agreed to buy Fox Chase Bancorp along with its $1.1 billion in assets $768 million in loans $765 million in deposits and several Fox Chase Bank branches in Pennsylvania and New Jersey for a price exceeding $240 million. The deal would also expand Univest's presence in Bucks Chester Philadelphia and Montgomery counties in Pennsylvania as well as into Atlantic and Cape May counties in New Jersey.

In January 2015 the company purchased Valley Green Bank as well as its three branches and two loan production offices in the greater Philadelphia market for $77 million.

In July 2014 Univest bolstered its Univest Insurance subsidiary after acquiring Sterner Insurance Associates a full-service insurance and consultative risk management firm that served individuals and businesses across the Lehigh Valley Berks Bucks and Montgomery counties.

In January 2014 flagship subsidiary Univest Bank and Trust Co. bought registered investment advisory firm Girard Partners Ltd. as well as its $500 million in assets under management. The deal boosted Univest's assets under management by 20% to a total of $3 billion after the acquisition.

EXECUTIVES

President Corporate Banking, Philip C. (Phil) Jackson, $250,000 total compensation
Sevp And Chief Risk Officer, Duane J. Brobst, $200,000 total compensation
President And Ceo, Jeffrey M Schweitzer, $450,000 total compensation
Sevp And Cfo, Michael S Keim, $270,000 total compensation
Executive Vice President, John Duerksen
Vice President, Barry Keck
Senior Vice President In Credit Administration, Tami Garber
Senior Vice President, Karen Tejkl
Vice President Account Executive, Chip Schofield
Executive Vice President Chief Experience Officer And Director Corporate Planning, Annette Szygiel
Senior Vice President, Leanne Hayes
Senior Vice President, Richard Pearce
Vice President Relationship Manager Corporate Banking, Randall Beaman
Vice President, Brett Chesmar
Vice President Area Manager, Gregory Taber
Senior Vice President Employee Benefits Practice Leader, Dennis Boyle
Vice President, Barton Skurbe
Vice President And Operations Manager, Roxanne Tornetta
Senior Vice President Director Of Commercial Lending, Bryan Moyer
Vice President Business Banking, Patrick Mullen
National Accounts Manager, Kyle Hirsch
Svp Director Bank Systems, Jeffrey Groff

Vice President And Senior Benefits Consultant, Rick Mack
Vice President, Joe Panepresso
Vice President Relationship Manager, Nicholas Yelicanin
Vice President Commercial Lending, Andrew Leaman
Vice President Business Banking, Nan Kelly
Executive Vice President General Counsel And Chief Risk Officer Of The Corporation And The Bank, Megan Santana
Assistant Vice President Finance Business Unit Analytics, Mary Beth Osbeck
Senior Vice President Relationship Manager, John Thomas
Vice President, David Henrich
Senior Vice President Finance, Denise Joyce
Vice President Relationship Manager, Samantha Arland
Vice President Asset Recovery, Kevin Boyer
Vice President Commercial Lending, Ramzi Dagher
Vice President Commercial Lending, John P Hogan
Senior Vice President Commerical Lending, Joseph Gennett
Executive Vice President Chief Information Officer Of The Corporation And Of The Bank, Eric Deacon
Chairman, William S. Aichele, age 68
Board Member, Mark Schlosser
Treasurer, Bill Shelley
Board Member, Glenn Moyer
Auditors: KPMG LLP

LOCATIONS

HQ: Univest Financial Corp
14 North Main Street, Souderton, PA 18964
Phone: 215 721-2400
Web: www.univest.net

PRODUCTS/OPERATIONS

2015 sales

	$ mil.	% of total
Banking	121	79
Wealth Management	19	12
Insurance	14	9
Other	0	-
Total	**155**	**100**

COMPETITORS

Citizens Financial Group	PNC Financial
Fulton Financial	QNB Corp.
Harleysville Savings	Royal Bancshares
M&T Bank	Sovereign Bank

HISTORICAL FINANCIALS

Company Type: Public

Income Statement

FYE: December 31

	ASSETS ($ mil.)	NET INCOME ($ mil.)	INCOME AS % OF ASSETS	EMPLOYEES
12/18	4,984	51	1.0%	841
12/17	4,555	44	1.0%	855
12/16	4,231	20	0.5%	840
12/15	2,879	27	0.9%	717
12/14	2,235	22	1.0%	638
Annual Growth	**22.2%**	**22.8%**	**—**	**7.2%**

2018 Year-End Financials

Debt ratio: 5.00%	No. of shares (mil.): 29
Return on equity: 8.00%	Dividends
Cash ($ mil.): 109	Yield: 0.0%
Current ratio: —	Payout: 47.0%
Long-term debt ($ mil.): —	Market value ($ mil.): 631

	STOCK PRICE ($) FY Close	P/E High/Low		PER SHARE ($) Earnings	Dividends	Book Value
12/18	22.00	17	12	2.00	1.00	21.00
12/17	28.00	20	16	2.00	1.00	21.00
12/16	31.00	37	22	1.00	1.00	19.00
12/15	21.00	15	13	1.00	1.00	19.00
12/14	20.00	16	13	1.00	1.00	18.00
Annual Growth	**1.6%**	**—**	**—**	**6.0%**	**(0.0%)**	**5.0%**

Unum Group

Through injury or illness Unum works to keep employees employed. A top disability insurer in the US and the UK it offers short-term and long-term disability insurance supplemental health coverage and life and accidental death and dismemberment insurance to individuals and groups. Its Colonial Life unit offers expanded cancer critical illness vision products and dental insurance. Additional subsidiaries include Unum Life Insurance Company of America Provident Life and Accident First Unum Life Colonial Life & Accident and Paul Revere Life Insurance. The company operates as Unum Limited in the UK. Unum's products are sold through field sales agents and independent brokers.

Operations

About 65% of Unum's annual premiums come from the Unum US segment which offers group disability life and accident policies as well as supplemental and voluntary policies under the Unum America and Provident Brands.

The group's Colonial Life segment — which offers accident sickness and disability products — accounts for nearly 20% of sales while the Unum UK segment represents more than 5% of sales.

Unum also generates revenue from its Closed Block segment (more than 10% of sales) which services policies in the long-term care and non-workplace individual disability segments areas the company has exited.

The company covers roughly 36 million people worldwide and counts 193 businesses in the US and UK among its customers (including a third of the Fortune 500).

Geographic Reach

The US market contributes more than 60% of Unum's annual revenue. The company runs four primary operating centers (in Tennessee Maine Louisiana South Carolina) and more than 35 sales offices scattered across the US. Its Unum Limited office in Dorking is the headquarters for the smaller Unum UK operations which include Ireland. The company entered the Polish market in 2018 through its purchase of Pramerica Zycie.

Sales and Marketing

Unum uses its own sales force as well as independent agents consultants and brokers to market its products to employers.

Financial Performance

Unum's revenue has inched steadily upward for the past five years thanks to increases in net premiums written. Net income was also on the rise but took a steep dive in 2018.

Revenue rose 3% to $11.6 billion in 2018. Premiums in both the US and the UK rose as usual but those gains were partially offset by a decrease in net investment income. (Results for the brand-new Polish operations were not material to the year's results.)

Net income fell 47% to $523.4 million in 2018. The decline was primarily due to a reserve increase related to the company's long-term care block of business.

The company ended 2018 with $94 million in net cash about $17 million more than it had at the end of 2017. Operating activities provided $1.5 billion in cash while investing activities used $930 million and financing activities used another $589.8 million.

Strategy

Unum seeks to achieve a competitive edge by providing group individual and voluntary workplace products that can be combined with other coverage to better integrate benefits for customers. The insurer has stayed ahead of the game in the disability market by sticking to conservative investment and growth strategies primarily seeking to expand its group product offerings and its geographic presence through organic measures.

Specific goals include securing new customers investing in growth that meets new demands of the market and expanding into new geographic areas and distribution channels. Acquisitions play a part in reaching these goals. For example Unum expanded its presence in Europe by acquiring Polish insurer Pramerica ?ycie in 2018.

The company has especially seen growth in its voluntary benefits products which allow employees to purchase individual coverage products on a supplemental basis. Such options are increasingly important as economic difficulties put pressure on low and middle-income workers. Unum has also expanded its offering of services to help employers and government agencies manage costs such as its leave management program flexible corporate contribution programs and wellness initiatives.

While expanding in areas where the greatest market needs are seen the firm also occasionally exits (or places into run-off) certain businesses where demand has slowed.

Like most insurers Unum's profit margins have been negatively impacted by ongoing low interest rates. To minimize those effects the company is gradually increasing its investment activities around alternative assets.

Mergers and Acquisitions

In 2018 Unum acquired Pramerica ?ycie a Polish life insurer from Prudential Financial for an undisclosed amount. That deal allowed Unum to expand its European operations beyond the UK.

Also in 2018 the company acquired dental health maintenance organization Jaimini Health broadening its dental offerings especially in California.

Earlier that year Unum purchased Leavelogic which provides leave management technology. That deal enhanced the firm's existing family leave management offerings for employers.

Company Background

Unum traces its roots back to the 1870s when Provident Life & Accident Insurance was established to provide medical insurance to coal miners.

HISTORY

Coal was discovered in eastern Tennessee in the 1870s; in 1887 several Chattanooga professional men formed the Provident Life & Accident Insurance Co. to provide medical insurance to miners. But it was a case of the inexperienced serving the uninsurable and by 1892 the company was on the brink of ruin. The founders sold half the company for $1000 to Thomas Maclellan and John McMaster two Scotsmen who had failed at banking in Canada.

The partners bought the rest of the company in 1895. After a period of strained relations Maclellan bought out McMaster in 1900. Provident which by then operated nationally entered Canada in 1948.

The company began a major move into disability insurance in 1997. It sold its annuity business to American General (now a subsidiary of AIG) the following year.

In 1998 with both Provident and Unum Corporation looking for ways to enhance business the companies commenced merger negotiations and completed the transaction the next year. But the merger was more expensive than anticipated and problems in integrating the companies' sales forces slowed policy sales.

Company operations began melding more smoothly and UnumProvident began addressing the problems with its sales force as well as adding customer service staff in 2000. It pulled money out of reserves by reinsuring several blocks of acquisition-related businesses and sold an inactive shell subsidiary licensed to sell annuities in most states to Allstate.

EXECUTIVES

Evp And General Counsel, Lisa G. Iglesias, age 53, $492,692 total compensation

Vice President The Benefits Center, Rob Hecker

Svp Corporate Marketing And Public Relations, Joseph R. (Joe) Foley

President Ceo And Director, Richard P. (Rick) McKenney, age 51, $994,231 total compensation

President And Ceo Unum Us, Michael Q. Simonds, age 45, $594,231 total compensation

Evp And Cfo, John F. (Jack) McGarry, age 61, $588,461 total compensation

Evp Global Services, Christopher J. (Chris) Jerome, age 57

Evp And Chief Investment Officer, Breege A. Farrell, age 59, $451,500 total compensation

President And Ceo Colonial Life, Timothy G. (Tim) Arnold, age 56

President And Ceo Unum Uk, Peter G. O'Donnell, age 52

Svp And Global Cio, Katherine M. (Kate) Miller

Assistant Vice President And Special Counsel At Unum, Michael Parker

Vice President And Chief Information Security Officer, Lynda Fleury

Assistant Vice President Benefit Operations Finl Svcs, John Howard

Vice President Acquisitions, Steven Cudd

National Account Manager, Melana C Kipp

Assistant Vice President And Senior Counsel, Elle Donovan Mccann

Vice President Internal Controls, Rick Patton

Vice President Accounting Center Of Excellence, Roger Vancleave

Assistant Vice President, Jeff Smith

National Account Manager, Andrew Sapiente

Assistant Vice President, Ken Barber

Vice President Business Analysis, Marylou Murphy

Assistant Vice President Actuary, Paul Lavallee

Assistant Vice President, Jay Barriss

Vice President, Greg Breter

Assistant Vice President, Chris Castleberry

Assistant Vice President Digital Marketing, Bethany Branon

Assistant Vice President Ltd Benefit Operations, Bob Berry

Avp And Managing Counsel, Pamela Castrucci

Assistant Vice President Learning And Performance Development, Debra Chaloux

Assistant Vice President Consumerism, Jocelyn Grega

National Account Manager, Douglas Burnip

Vice President Distribution Partner Strategy, Benjamin Kahn

Assistant Vice President, Denise Houser

Vp Hr Business Support Colonial Life And Unum Us, Laura Coleman

Assistant Vice President, Anna Stein

Vice President Information Technology Customer Solutions, Randy Robinson

Assistant Vice President Contact Center, Cj Jackson

Assistant Vice President Idi Benefits, Laura Chillo

Assistant Vice President Hris, Tina West

Assistant Vice President Growth Operations Field Shared Services, Pierre Meahl

National Account Manager, Ellen Bronson

Vice President Individual Disability Insurance Operations And Market Development, Leston Welsh

Assistant Vice President Financial Reporting, Jonathan Sanford

National Account Manager, Donna Hewes

Vice President, William Stutts

Vice President Client Service And Support, Michelle Boucher

Avp And Sr. Counsel, Betsy Stivers

Assistant Vice President And Senior Counsel, Sandra Livingston

Vice President And Chief Litigation Counsel, Doug Baker

Assistant Vice President Senior Human Resources Business Partner, Kristen Prophater

Assistant Vice President Retirement Programs, Carl Gagnon

Assistant Vice President Ltd Benefits, Ahmad Sadaqatmal

Assistant Vice President Ltd Benefits, Joseph Pratico

Vice President And Managing Director Midwest Region, John Stibal

Vp, Laura Beckmann

Svp And Chief Supply Officer, William Bagley

Vice President Contact Centers, Eric Tracy

Legal Secretary, Alexa Grassi

Assistant Vice President, Matthew Purington

Vice President, Najla Frayha

Avp And Senior Counsel, Elizabeth Lacombe

Vice President And Director Of External Affairs, Mark Pare

Assistant Vice President Customer Experience, Susan Hoffman

Assistant Vice President And Senior Counsel, Brent Williams

Vp Employment Law, Glenn Felton

Vp Chief Regulatory Counsel, Michelle Lafond

Vice President Market Development, John King

Vice President Communications, Jim Sabourin

National Account Manager, Brooks Geiger

Vp Benefit Operations, Lori Whynot

Vp Operations Support Services It, David Mcmahon

Senior Vice President Corporate Commercial And Business Banking Manager, Jennifer Jacobs

Avp Sr. Hr Business Partner, Jennifer Watkins

Avp Shared Technology, Joanne McInnis

Senior Vice President Investor Relations, Tom White

Vp Diversity And Inclusion, Wade Hinton

Assistant Vice President Senior Human Resources Business Partner, Kathryn L Murray

Vice President Global Delivery Center, Goslant Tammy

Assistant Vice President Government Affairs, Warren Wells

Assistant Vice President Core Market Services (colonial Life), Stephen Bygott

Assistant Vice President Of Quality Assurance Policy A, Rasero Linda

Assistant Vice President Global Human Resources Systems And Solutions, Denise Ferguson

Vice President Distribution Channel Expan, Chris Quinn

Vice President, James Cofield

Chairman, Kevin T. Kabat, age 62

Secretary, Priscilla Fairbrother

Auditors: Ernst & Young LLP

LOCATIONS

HQ: Unum Group
1 Fountain Square, Chattanooga, TN 37402
Phone: 423 294-1011
Web: www.unum.com

PRODUCTS/OPERATIONS

2018 Sales

	$ mil.	% of total
Premiums	8,986	77
Net investment income	2,454	21
Other	198	2
Adjustments	(39.5)	-
Total	**11,599**	**500**

2018 Sales by Segment

	$ mil.	% of total
Unum US	5,736	64
Colonial Life	1,604	18
Closed Block	1,077	12
Unum UK	569	6
Total	**11,599**	**100**

Selected Products and Services

Accidental death and dismemberment
Dental insurance
Disability (long-term and short-term)
Life insurance
Supplemental health
Vision products
Voluntary benefits

Selected Subsidiaries and Brands

Colonial Life & Accident Insurance
First Unum Life Insurance
Provident Life and Accident Insurance
Provident Life and Casualty Insurance
Starmount Life Insurance Company
The Paul Revere Life Insurance
Unum Life Insurance Company of America
Unum Limited (UK)

COMPETITORS

AEGON	MetLife
Aflac	Mutual of Omaha
American General	Northwestern Mutual
CIGNA	Principal Financial
Guardian Life	Prudential
Liberty Mutual	Torchmark
Lincoln Financial Group	

HISTORICAL FINANCIALS

Company Type: Public

Income Statement   FYE: December 31

	ASSETS ($ mil.)	NET INCOME ($ mil.)	INCOME AS % OF ASSETS	EMPLOYEES
12/18	61,876	523	0.8%	9,600
12/17	64,013	994	1.6%	9,400
12/16	61,942	931	1.5%	9,400
12/15	60,590	867	1.4%	9,400
12/14	62,497	413	0.7%	9,500
Annual Growth	**(0.2%)**	**6.1%**	**—**	**0.3%**

2018 Year-End Financials

Debt ratio: 5.00%	No. of shares (mil.): 215
Return on equity: 6.00%	Dividends
Cash ($ mil.): 94	Yield: 3.0%
Current ratio: —	Payout: 41.0%
Long-term debt ($ mil.): —	Market value ($ mil.): 6,304

	STOCK PRICE ($) FY Close	P/E High/Low	PER SHARE ($) Earnings	Dividends	Book Value
12/18	29.00	25 11	2.00	1.00	40.00
12/17	55.00	13 10	4.00	1.00	43.00
12/16	44.00	11 6	4.00	1.00	39.00
12/15	33.00	11 9	4.00	1.00	36.00
12/14	35.00	23 19	2.00	1.00	34.00
Annual Growth	**(4.2%)**	**— —**	**10.3%**	**12.1%**	**4.3%**

UPMC PRESBYTERIAN SHADYSIDE

EXECUTIVES

Pres, John Innocenti
Cfo, Eileen Simmons
Nurse Practitioner, Kristen Baileys
Nurse Practitioner, Kristin Ermine-Baer
Director of Operations, Melanie Houston
Nurse Practitioner, Patti Gigliotti
Nurse Practitioner, Timothy Coleman
Manager, Vicki Bedel
Member, William S Dietrich II
Managing Partner, William Pietragallo II
Member, John Pelusi Jr
Auditors: ERNST & YOUNG LLP PITTSBURGH

LOCATIONS

HQ: UPMC PRESBYTERIAN SHADYSIDE
200 LOTHROP ST MH-N739, PITTSBURGH, PA
152132536
Phone: 412 647-2345
Web: WWW.UPMC.COM

HISTORICAL FINANCIALS

Company Type: Private

Income Statement   FYE: June 30

	REVENUE ($ mil.)	NET INCOME ($ mil.)	NET PROFIT MARGIN	EMPLOYEES
06/10	8,046	277	3.4%	8,200
06/09	1,724	84	4.8%	—
06/06	1,628	0	—	—
Annual Growth	**49.1%**	**—**	**—**	**—**

US Bancorp (DE)

Boasting more than $475 billion in assets U.S. Bancorp is the holding company for U.S. Bank (the US's fifth largest commercial bank). Through that and other subsidiaries the company provides consumer and commercial loans deposits and credit cards as well as merchant processing mortgage banking trust and investment management brokerage insurance and corporate payments. The bank has about 3000 branches and some 4700 ATMs in more than 30 states (primarily in the Midwest and West). Commercial loans account for about 35% of the holding company's loan portfo-

lio; residential mortgages represent more than 20% of the total.

Operations

U.S. Bancorp's major lines of business are: Consumer and Business Banking Payment Services Corporate and Commercial Banking Wealth Management and Securities Services and Treasury and Corporate Support. It also generates fee income through its Elavon subsidiary?a leading processor of merchant credit card transactions in the US Canada Mexico and Europe.

Consumer and Business Banking is the holding company's largest earner raking in more than 35% of revenue. Through that segment U.S. Bancorp markets standard banking products and services in community and metropolitan settings through physical locations telephone online ATMs and mobile devices.

Payment Services covers the company's business activities in cards (including consumer and business credit debit corporate and government cards) and merchant processing. It is responsible for about 25% of revenue.

The Corporate and Commercial Banking segment and Wealth Management and Investment Services segment each bring in about 15% of U.S. Bancorp's revenue from clients including middle-market large corporate real estate financial and public-sector entities and high-net worth individuals. The units' offerings encompass equipment finance small-ticket leasing and investment management. Treasury and Corporate Support accounts for about 5% of revenue and houses U.S. Bancorp's investment portfolios and capital and interest rate risk management.

Geographic Reach

Minneapolis Minnesota-based U.S. Bancorp runs a network of about 3000 branches and around 4700 ATMs in more than 30 states mainly in the West and Midwest. It is also active in Canada Mexico Brazil and Europe. The company has operations centers in about 10 US states.

Sales and Marketing

U.S. Bancorp provides an array of commercial and retail banking products and services to businesses governmental clients other financial institutions and individual customers. The company spends more than $400 million on marketing and business development annually.

Financial Performance

U.S. Bancorp's revenue has expanded reliably each year since 2014 to yield overall growth of more than 10% as increased interest rates and loan volume bolstered the company's performance. Despite stagnancy in 2015 and 2016 the company's net income has seen solid growth of about 20% over that period thanks to gains the last two years especially 2018 when U.S. Bancorp sold its ATM servicing business and most of its FDIC-covered loans.

The holding company's revenue added 3% to $22.6 billion in 2018; its Consumer and Business Banking Wealth Management and Investment Services and Payment Services segments each increased income while Corporate and Commercial Banking dipped slightly. Treasury and Corporate Support only marginally improved. Rising interest rates and greater earning assets and securities yields drove the gains.

U.S. Bancorp's net income increased by 14% to end the year at $7.1 billion. Its returns on average assets and common equity both increased compared with 2017. Severance charges asset impairments and legal fees partially offset gains from its business and loan sales and favorable outcomes related to tax reform.

The company grew its cash by $1.9 billion to $21.5 billion in 2018. About $10.6 billion and $361 million were garnered from operations and financing activities respectively. Investments used $8.9

billion primarily for purchases of held-to-maturity and available-for-sale investment securities and increased loans outstanding.

Strategy

U.S. Bancorp is strategically divesting its less lucrative assets while investing in cost-saving technologies that increase customer engagement. However it is still expanding physical operations in growing markets.

The next year the holding company completely rebuilt its mobile app based on customer feedback to include face ID enhanced mobile banking and easier account opening. That year it also launched its U.S. Bank Expense Wizard in partnership with Chrome River. The mobile app uses AI-driven chatbots to help employees make payments and report expenses associated with company-arranged travel.

Despite generally seeking to limit its physical location openings as customer banking preferences move increasingly toward online channels U.S. Bancorp does still open new branches in regions where demand exists. The company plans to open its first retail branch in North Carolina in 2019; it expects to have opened about 10 branches in the state by the end of 2020. Through a broader reinvestment initiative U.S. Bancorp expects also to develop between 60 and 80 new relocated or redesigned branches by that target date with an eye toward regional markets in Florida Georgia and Texas.

In 2018 the company sold its non-core third-party ATM and debit servicing business housed by the company's Elan Financial Services subsidiary to Fiserv. The transaction provided U.S. Bancorp a net gain of $340 million.

Company Background

U.S. Bancorp predecessor bank First National Bank of Cincinnati opened in 1863. U.S. Bank the holding company's bank subsidiary is now the US's fifth largest bank.

HISTORY

When Farmers and Millers Bank was founded in 1853 it operated out of a strongbox in a rented storefront. After surviving a panic in the 1850s the bank became part of the national banking system in 1863 as First National Bank of Milwaukee. The bank grew and in 1894 it merged with Merchants Exchange Bank (founded 1870).

In 1919 the bank merged again with Wisconsin National Bank (founded 1892) to form First Wisconsin National Bank of Milwaukee a leading financial institution in the area from the 1920s on.

First Wisconsin grew through purchases over the next decade though the number of banks fell after the 1929 stock market crash; by the end of WWII it had 11 banks. State and federal legislation particularly the 1956 Bank Holding Company Act (which proscribed acquisitions and branching) constrained postwar growth. In the 1970s Wisconsin eased restrictions on intrastate branching and the bank began to grow again.

Growth accelerated in the late 1980s after Wisconsin and surrounding states legalized interstate banking in adjoining states in 1987. That year First Wisconsin bought seven Minnesota banks and then moved into Illinois. The company focused on strong well-run institutions. Also that year it sold its headquarters and used the proceeds to fund more buys. In 1988 in its first foray outside the Midwest the company bought Metro Bancorp in Phoenix targeting midwestern retirees moving to Arizona.

In 1989 First Wisconsin changed its name to Firstar. The early 1990s saw the company move into Iowa (Banks of Iowa 1990) buy in-state rivals (Federated Bank Geneva Capital Corporation 1992) and roll into Illinois (DSB Corporation 1993). The next year it bought First Southeast

Banking Corp. (of Wisconsin) and merged it along with Firstar Bank Racine and Firstar Bank Milwaukee into one bank.

To strengthen its position against larger competitors Firstar continued its buying spree in 1995 (Chicago bank First Colonial Bankshares and Investors Bank Corp. of Minneapolis/St. Paul) and 1996 (Jacob Schmidt Company). The acquisitions left the company bloated: In 1996 Firstar began a restructuring designed to cut costs and increase margins. The restructuring project ended in 1997 but by then its performance lagged behind other midwestern banks considerably. In an effort to diversify it allied with EVEREN Securities to offer debt underwriting and sales fixed income products and public finance advisory services. But it was too little too late; under pressure from major stockholders to seek a partner Firstar began looking for a buyer.

It found Star Banc. Established in 1863 as The First National Bank of Cincinnati under a bank charter signed by Abraham Lincoln Star Banc over the years added branches and bought other banks. The company renamed all of its subsidiary banks Star Bank in 1988 and took the name Star Banc in 1989.

In 1998 Star Banc chairman Jerry Grundhofer approached Firstar about a combination. Negotiations proceeded quickly and a new Firstar was born.

The next year Firstar bought Mercantile Bancorporation. The purchase enabled the bank to expand its international banking services into such markets as Kansas Nebraska and Missouri. In 2000 the company made arrangements to buy U.S. Bancorp a Minneapolis-based bank with roots dating back to 1929. Under the terms of the acquisition Firstar would shed its own name in favor of the more appropriate U.S. Bancorp moniker. U.S. Bancorp completed the conversion of Firstar Bank branches to the U.S. Bank moniker during 2002.

EXECUTIVES

Vice Chairman Wholesale Banking, Leslie V. Godridge, age 63

Vice Chairman And Cfo, Terrance R. (Terry) Dolan, age 57, $545,833 total compensation

Senior Vice President National Sales Manager Small Business Specialty Finance, Erik Daniels

Vice President, Teri Charest

Evp Human Resources, Jennie P. Carlson, age 58

Regional President, Ward Wilson

President Ceo And Director, Andrew Cecere, age 58, $800,000 total compensation

Evp And General Counsel, James L. Chosy, age 55

Vice Chairman Wealth Management And Securities Services, Gunjan Kedia, age 48

Evp, John R. Elmore, age 63

Vice Chairman And Chief Risk Officer, P. William (Bill) Parker, age 62, $625,000 total compensation

Vice Chairman Technology And Operations Services, Jeffry H. (Jeff) von Gillern, age 53, $575,000 total compensation

Vice Chairman Consumer Banking Sales And Support, Kent V. Stone, age 61

Evp And Chief Credit Officer, Mark G. Runkel, age 43

Vice Chairman Payment Services, Shailesh M. Kotwal, age 54

Evp And Chief Strategy And Reputation Officer, Katherine B. Quinn, age 54

Vice Chairman Wholesale Banking, James B. Kelligrew, age 53

Executive Vice President Chief Innovation Officer, Dominic Venturo

Senior Vice President, Patricia Gnetz

Vice President Of Information Technology Security, Coni Pasch

Senior Vice President Dealer Services Regional Manager North Central Region, Dave Donarski

Senior Vice President Risk Infrastructure, Jim Putman

Assistant Vice President Application Consultant Commercial Leasing, Krishna Devarajulu

Vice President Procurement Operations Manager, Michael Lori

Senior Vice President Customer Solutions, Mary Ellen Carney

Senior Vice President Prepaid Card Services, Johnnie Carroll

Vice President, Carol Rossman

Vice President, Scott Miller

Vice President Director Of Marketing And Communications Wealth Management, Mark Iverson

Assistant Vice President Marketing Analytics, Scott May

Senior Vice President Risk Analytics, Jacob Seljan

Vice President And Area Sales Manager, Frank Annello

Senior Vice President Rmbs Risk Management, Edward Frere

Vp Credit Risk Assessment, Jennifer Briglia

Vice President, Chris Rodewald

Vice President Treasury Management Consultant, Paul Kozar Paul Kozar

Senior Vice President, Scott Farrell

Vice President Corporate Credit Risk Manager, Brian Richter

Vice President, Karmel Mizrahi

Svp Portfolio Marketing, Tim Stanton

Asst. Vice President, Trevor Brown

Vice President, Mark Sowinski

Vice President Information Technology Service Managment, Jim Berghs

Executive Vice President, Lisa Glover

Assistant Vice President Marketing Research, Molly McMahon

Vice President Global Treasury Management Pricing And Analytics, Jake Wilson

Vice President In Commercial Banking, Alphonso Hawkins

Senior Vice President, Mehrasa Raygani

Vice President Technology Finance Group, Gregory Giannone

Vice President Senior Property Manager, Andrew McGlenon

Vp And Sr. Manager Marketing, Jeff Pick

Vice President, Zenaida Maniates

Vice President Commercial Operations Manager, Victor Kapusinski

Vp And Project Manager, Cory Patrick

Vice President, Steve Kramer

Senior Vice President National Community Outreach Manager, Melissa Borino Melissa Borino

Senior Vice President, Marcia Palmer

Vice President, Spencer Goldsmith

Senior Vice President, Terry Neher

Senior Vice President Utilities Division, Felicia LaForgia

Vice President Corporate Banking Portfolio Manager, Daniel Yu

Assistant Vice President Call Center Analytics, Maureen Splettstaszer

Assistant Vice President Associate Client Manager, Nick Kapki Nick Kapki

Vice President, Alice Warren

Senior Vice President Regional Manager, Chris Venhoff

Vice President Of Operation, Sean Skaggs

Vice President, Jeff Sutherland

Senlor Vice President National Corporate Banklng, Barry Litwin

Senior Vice President, Donna Fletcher

Vice President Portfolio Manager, Magnus Mcdowell Magnus Mcdowell

Vice President Corporate Trust, Linda Mcconkey

Assistant Vice President Senior Recruiter, Corey Hoen
Vice President, Marty Barnett
Vice President, Kamal Nahhas
Vice President, Roger Gross
Assistant Vice President, Adam Henderson
Senior Vice President, Christopher Schaaf
Senior Vice President And Deputy General Counsel, Chris Lenhart
Vice President Technology Services, Paul Ylonen
Vice President District Manager, Sara Le
Vice President Commercial Real Estate Lender, Howard Goldberg
Senior Vice President Enterprise Risk Services, Bob Kellner
Vice President Information Services, Brian Mckeown
Senior Vice President And Market Credit Manager, Rick Shamberger
Vice President Of Marketing, Becky Hill
Assistant Vice President Finance Manager, Wendy Brock
Vice President And Site Manager, Elizabeth Thuning
Vice President Relationship Manager Commercial Lending, Dana Jergenson
Vice President Community Banking Sales Support Manager, Tiffany Muscala
Senior Vice President Treasury Management Product Management, Mary Burchette
Assistant Vice President Data Center Design And Planning, David Fortuna
Vice President, Suzanne Bedros
Executive Vice President Kansas City, Tim Petty
Vice President Information Technology Development, Thomas Kindler
Senior Of Vice President, David Albanesi
Assistant Vice President Commercial Relationship Manager, Scott Gruenke
Vice President Of Information Technology, Erik Lindell
Vice President Corporate Credit Risk Management, Gregory Gay
Vice President Loan Administration, Cheryl Dingess
Vice President, Rudy Fors
Vice President, Courtney Dowling
Vp And Associate General Counsel, Kyle Bakken
Vice President Ecrm Business Capabilities Team, Diane Morse
Vice President, John Pearson
Vice President Consumer Lending Project Management Office, John Gemrich
Senior Vice President, Andrew Hyde
Vice President Quality Management, Richard McCarthy
Senior Vice President, Douglas Boe
Vice President, Karen Bolton
Assistant Vice President Real Estate Asset Manager, Karen Thomas
Vice President, Dorothy Smaglick
Vice President And Senior Corporate Counsel, Benjamin Carpenter
Vice President Regional Sales Manager International Banking Group, Brian Cobb
Vice President Operations, Mark Sutherland
Vice President Personal Trust Relationship Manager, Patrick Grewe
Senior Vice President, David Draxler
Senior Vice President Risk Management Strategy Execution, Michael Leary
Assistant Vice President Voice Implementation Projects, Joy Abts
Vice President, Brian Miner
Vice President Information Technology, Alfonso Gonzalez
Vice President Business Systems Consultant, Sherri Marx
Senior Vice President Quality Assurance, AnnMarie Janke
Senior Vice President, Jeff Pape

Vice President And Assistant General Counsel, Ilyse Goldsmith
Vice President Credit Manager, Jared Baysinger
Vice President, Ken Case
Senior Vice President, Bill Mulvihill
Vice President National Sales Manager, Richard Struck
Assistant Vice President Application Architect, David Brus
Vice President And Director, Suzanne Galvin
Vice President, Jack Ellerin
Vice President Loan Capital Markets, Dipti Goel
Vice President Regional Manager, Chad Laipple
Senior Vice President, Brian Reisenauer
Senior Vice President, Frederick Body
Senior Vice President Regional Credit Officer, Randall Borchardt
Vice President, Regan Leon
Senior Vice President Relationship Manager, Karen Weathers
Vice President, Rod Swenson
Senior Financial Advisor Vice President Private Client Reserve, Joel Schwartz
Svp And Head Loan Capital Markets, Jeanne Rudelius
Vice President Director Capital Markets, Michael Luker
Vice President Comercial Team Lead, Corey Hansen
Vice President Business Banking, Brent Blume
Senior Vice President, Curt Steiner
Vice President, Kent Inman
Vice President Corporate Banking Relationship Manager Transportation, Daniel Washam
Senior Vice President California Region Manager, Stephen Johnson
Assistant Vice President, Becky Burton
Vice President Technology Group Manager, Genie Strachan-smith
Assistant Vice President, Lorra Donnelly
Auditors: Ernst & Young LLP

LOCATIONS

HQ: US Bancorp (DE)
  800 Nicollet Mall, Minneapolis, MN 55402
Phone: 651 466-3000
Web: www.usbank.com

Selected Locations

Arizona
Arkansas
California
Colorado
Florida
Idaho
Illinois
Indiana
Iowa
Kansas
Kentucky
Minnesota
Missouri
Michigan
Montana
Nebraska
Nevada
New Mexico
New York
North Dakota
Ohio
Oregon
South Dakota
Tennessee
Utah
Washington
Wisconsin
Wyoming

PRODUCTS/OPERATIONS

2018 Sales

	$ mil.	% of total
Interest		
Loans	13,120	51
Investment securities	2,616	10
Loans held for sale	165	1
Other	272	1
Taxable-equivalent adjustment	116	.
Interest Expense	(3254)	.
Non-interest Income	- -	
Merchant processing services	1,531	6
Trust & investment management fees	1,619	6
Credit & debit card revenue	1,401	5
Mortgage banking	720	3
Commercial products	895	3
Corporate payment products	644	3
Deposit service charges	762	3
Treasury management fees	594	2
ATM processing services	308	1
Investment products fees	188	1
Securities gains (losses) net	30	.
Other	910	4
Total	**22,637**	**100**

2018 sales

	$ mil.	% of total
Consumer and Business Banking	8,466	34
Payment Services	6,046	27
Corporate and Commercial Banking	3,782	15
Treasury and Corporate Support	1,473	14
Wealth Management and Securities Services	2,870	10
Total	**22,637**	**100**

2018 Loan Portfolio

	% of total
Commercial	36
Commercial Real Estate	14
Residential Mortgages	22
Credit Card	8
Other Retail	20
Covered Loans	.
Total	**100**

Selected Subsidiaries

111 Tower Investors Inc. (Minnesota)
Access Mortgage Solutions LLC (Delaware)
AIS Europe Limited (UK)
AIS Fund Administration Ltd. (Cayman Islands)
CF Title Co. (Delaware)
Daimler Title Co. (Delaware)
DSL Service Company (California)
Eclipse Funding LLC (Delaware)
Elan Life Insurance Company Inc. (Arizona)

COMPETITORS

Bank of America	Huntington Bancshares
Capital One	JPMorgan Chase
Citigroup	KeyCorp
Fifth Third	MUFG Americas Holdings
First National of	TCF Financial
Nebraska	Wells Fargo
Great Western Bancorp	Zions Bancorporation

HISTORICAL FINANCIALS

Company Type: Public

Income Statement   FYE: December 31

	ASSETS ($ mil.)	NET INCOME ($ mil.)	INCOME AS % OF ASSETS	EMPLOYEES
12/18	467,374	7,096	1.5%	73,333
12/17	462,040	6,218	1.3%	72,402
12/16	445,964	5,888	1.3%	71,191
12/15	421,853	5,879	1.4%	65,433
12/14	402,529	5,851	1.5%	66,750
Annual Growth	3.8%	4.9%	—	2.4%

2018 Year-End Financials

Debt ratio: 8.00%
Return on equity: 14.00%
Cash ($ mil.): 21,453
Current ratio: —
Long-term debt ($ mil.): —

No. of shares (mil.): 1,608
Dividends
  Yield: 3.0%
  Payout: 32.0%
Market value ($ mil.): 73,501

	STOCK PRICE ($) FY Close	P/E High/Low	PER SHARE ($) Earnings	Dividends	Book Value
12/18	46.00	14 11	4.00	1.00	32.00
12/17	54.00	16 14	4.00	1.00	30.00
12/16	51.00	16 12	3.00	1.00	28.00
12/15	43.00	14 13	3.00	1.00	26.00
12/14	45.00	15 13	3.00	1.00	24.00
Annual Growth	0.4%	— —	7.7%	8.6%	6.8%

US Foods Holding Corp

Auditors: DELOITTE & TOUCHE LLP

LOCATIONS

HQ: US Foods Holding Corp
  9399 W. Higgins Road, Suite 100, Rosemont, IL 60018
Phone: 847 720-8000
Web: www.usfoods.com

HISTORICAL FINANCIALS

Company Type: Public

Income Statement   FYE: December 29

	REVENUE ($ mil.)	NET INCOME ($ mil.)	NET PROFIT MARGIN	EMPLOYEES
12/18	24,175	407	1.7%	25,000
12/17	24,147	444	1.8%	25,053
12/16*	22,919	210	0.9%	25,000
01/16	23,128	168	0.7%	25,000
12/14	23,020	(73)	—	—
Annual Growth	1.2%	—	—	—

*Fiscal year change

2018 Year-End Financials

Debt ratio: 39.00%
Return on equity: 14.00%
Cash ($ mil.): 104
Current ratio: 1.00
Long-term debt ($ mil.): 3,351

No. of shares (mil.): 217
Dividends
  Yield: —
  Payout: —
Market value ($ mil.): 6,766

	STOCK PRICE ($) FY Close	P/E High/Low	PER SHARE ($) Earnings	Dividends	Book Value
12/18	31.00	22 15	2.00	0.00	15.00
12/17	32.00	16 13	2.00	0.00	13.00
12/16*	27.00	26 21	1.00	0.00	11.00
Annual Growth	3.2%	— —	16.1%	—	6.7%

*Fiscal year change

Valero Energy Corp

Valero Energy was not only named after a mission (the Mission San Antonio de Valero) it is on a mission to be the largest independent refiner in the US. Valero churns out about 3 million barrels per day refining low-cost residual oil and heavy crude into cleaner-burning higher-margin products including low-sulfur diesels. It operates 15 refineries in the US Canada and the UK. It also has 11 ethanol plants with a combined production capacity of about 1.4 billion gallons per year. Once a more diversified company Valero has exited the retail business in order to focus on its oil refining and ethanol operations.

HISTORY

Valero Energy was created as a result of the sins of its father Houston-based Coastal States Gas Corporation. Led by flamboyant entrepreneur Oscar Wyatt energy giant Coastal had established Lo-Vaca Gathering Company as a gas marketing subsidiary. Bound by long-term contracts to several Texas cities Coastal was not able to meet its contractual obligations when gas prices rose in the early 1970s and major litigation against the company resulted. The Texas Railroad Commission (the energy-regulating authority) ordered Coastal to refund customers $1.6 billion.

To meet the requirements 55% of Lo-Vaca was spun off to disgruntled former customers as Valero Energy at the end of 1979. The new company was born fully grown — as the largest intrastate pipeline in Texas — with accountant-cum-CEO Bill Greehey the court-appointed chief of Lo-Vaca at its head. Greehey relocated the company to San Antonio where it took its Valero name (from the Alamo or Mission San Antonio de Valero) and put some distance between itself and its discredited former parent. Under Greehey's direction Valero developed a squeaky-clean image by giving to charities stressing a dress code and keeping facilities clean.

Greehey diversified the company into refining unleaded gasoline. Valero bought residual fuel oil from Saudi Arabian refiners and in 1981 built a refinery in Corpus Christi Texas which went on line two years later. But in 1984 a glut of unleaded gasoline on the US market from European refiners undercut Valero's profits. To stay afloat Valero sold pipeline assets including 50% of its West Texas Pipeline in 1985 and 51% of its major pipeline operations in 1987. Refining margins finally began to improve in 1988. With one of the most modern refineries in the US Valero did not have to spend a bundle to upgrade its refining processes to meet the tougher EPA requirements of the 1990s.

In 1992 Valero expanded its refinery's production capacity and acquired two gas processing plants and several hundred miles of gas pipelines from struggling oil firm Oryx Energy (acquired by Kerr-McGee in 1999). That year Valero became the first non-Mexican business engaged in Mexican gasoline production when it signed a deal with state oil company Petr leos Mexicanos S.A. to build a gasoline additive plant there.

To expand its natural gas business substantially in 1994 Valero bought back the 51% of Valero Natural Gas Partners it didn't own. Valero also teamed up with regional oil company Swift Energy in a transportation marketing and processing agreement. As part of that arrangement Valero agreed to build a pipeline linking Swift's Texas gas field with a Valero plant.

In 1997 the company sold Valero Natural Gas to California electric utility PG&E gaining $1.5 billion for expansion. It then purchased Salomon's oil refining unit Basis Petroleum (two refineries in Texas and one in Louisiana) and the next year picked up Mobil's refinery in Paulsboro New Jersey.

With low crude oil prices hurting its bottom line in 1999 Valero explored partnerships with other refiners as a way to cut operating costs. In 2000 the company bought Exxon Mobil's 130000-barrel-per-day Benicia California refinery along with 340 retail outlets for about $1 billion.

In 2001 Valero gained two small refineries when it bought Huntway Refining a leading supplier of asphalt in California. Dwarfing that deal Valero also bought Ultramar Diamond Shamrock for $4 billion in cash and stock (it assumed about $2.1 billion of debt in the deal). As part of the deal and to comply with the demands of regulators in 2002 Valero sold the Golden Eagle (San Francisco-area) refinery and 70 retail service stations in Northern California to Tesoro for $945 million.

In 2003 the company acquired Orion Refining's Louisiana refinery for about $530 million and the next year it acquired an Aruba refinery from asset-shedding El Paso Corp. for $640 million. Suncor Energy bought a Colorado-based refinery from Valero for a reported $30 million in 2005.

The 2005 acquisition of Premcor made Valero the largest independent refiner on the Gulf Coast a major national player.

Greehey turned over the leadership reins to another company veteran Bill Klesse in early 2006. The following year the company sold its Lima Ohio refinery to Husky Energy.

In 2008 the company sold its Krotz Springs Louisiana refinery to Alon USA Energy for $333 million.

In 2009 Valero had an opportunity for international refinery expansion and a foothold in Europe when it agreed to acquire Dow Chemical's 45% interest in Dutch refinery Total Raffinaderij Nederland N.V. However the deal fell through and the stake was sold to LUKOIL.

That year it bought seven ethanol production facilities from VeraSun Energy for $475 million.

To cut costs in 2010 it sold its Delaware City refinery. It also sold its Paulsboro New Jersey refinery that year to PBF Holding for $340 million. It also sold its 50% stake in a pipeline that brings deepwater crude oil from the Gulf of Mexico to the US to Genesis Energy for $330 million.

Expanding its global footprint in 2011 Valero bought Chevron's Pembroke refinery and marketing and logistics assets across the UK for $1.7 billion. It also boosted its US assets that year buying Murphy Oil's refinery outside New Orleans for $585 million to complement its St. Charles facility. Valero also bought Chevron USA Inc.'s Louisville and Lexington Kentucky product terminals expanding its wholesale marketing presence in eastern Kentucky with product supplied primarily from the Valero Memphis Refinery.

It made its first foray into ethanol production in 2009 buying seven ethanol production facilities from VeraSun Energy which was operating under Chapter 11 bankruptcy protection. Valero paid about $475 million for the facilities.

In 2013 the new hydrocracker unit at the Valero St. Charles Refinery began operations.

To better control costs in 2014 the company abandoned our Aruba Refinery except for the associated crude oil and refined products terminal assets that it continues to operate. It also sold its Texas Crude Systems Business to VLP for $154 million.

To get better shareholder returns in 2013 the company spun off its retail business as an independent public company CST Brands. This unit held Valero's company-operated convenience stores in the US and Canada; and filling stations cardlock facilities and heating oil operations in Canada. Valero continues to supply fuel to CST Brands' retail sites through long-term supply agreements. (Valero subsequently sold its remaining 20% stake in the company.)

In 2013 the company's Valero Terminaling and Distribution unit formed a joint venture with TGS Development to start construction on a new marine terminal on the lower Sabine-Neches Waterway near Port Arthur Texas to support the expansion of oil receipts and the marine movements of other commodities at that strategic port.

Growing its foothold in the petrochemical segment that year Valero also announced plans to build a major methanol plant at its 270000 barrel per day St. Charles refinery near New Orleans. Scheduled to commence operating in 2016 the $700 million plant will yield 1.6 million tons of methanol per year.

EXECUTIVES

Vice President Internal Audit, Lee Bailey
Evp And General Counsel, Jay D. Browning, age 60, $595,000 total compensation
Senior Vice President, Anthony Jones
Vp And Cio, Cheryl Thomas
Evp And Cfo, Michael S. (Mike) Ciskowski, age 61, $890,000 total compensation
Vp Wholesale Marketing And International Commercial Operations, Eric Fisher
Chairman President And Ceo, Joseph W. (Joe) Gorder, age 61, $1,450,000 total compensation
Evp Refining Operations And Engineering, Lane Riggs, age 53, $640,000 total compensation
Svp Supply International Operations And Systems Optimization, Gary Simmons, $565,000 total compensation
Vice President Of Strategic, Craig Schnupp
Vice President Cost Analysis Transportation, Mark Swensen
Vice President Austin Technology Center, Mike Long
Vice President Of Sales And Marketing, Richard Garrett
Vice President Enterprise Architecture, Benjamin Salter
Vice President Of Marketing, Curt Lundquist
Vice President Refinery Accounting, Jeffrey L Jones
Board Of Director And Vice President, Michael Mazzei
Vice President Of Public Relations, Robbie Schaefer
Vice President Supply Chain Optimization, Greg Bram
Vice President Products Trading, Scott Lively
Board Of Director And Vice President, Srinivasa Papineni
Senior Vice President, John Roach
Vice President Event Marketing, John Hill
Svp Alternative Fuels, Martin Parrish
Vice President And General Manager, Don Wilson
Board Of Director And Vice President, Brad Mulsow
Vice President Product Supply, Daniel Collier
Vice President Of Human Resour, Nancy Stone
Vice President And General Manager, Lauren Bird
Vice President Risk Management, Joe Van Horn
Regional Vice President, Mark Skobel
Vice President Market Analysis, Anthony Rouse
Vice President Retail Marketing, Steve Motz
Vice President Sales, Mike Whyte
Vice President Project Execution, Tony Jones
Vice President Finance, Kenneth Sparks
Senior Vice President Wholesale Marketing, Gary Arthur
Legal Secretary, Bertha Vasquez
Executive Vice President Marketing, Dyfan Williams
Vp And Gm, Jack Merrill
Vice President Federal Affairs And Counsel, Salo Zelermyer
Svp And Chief Accounting Officer, Mark Schmeltekopf
Vice President And Deputy General Counsel, Rich Walsh
Vp And Treasurer, Christopher Quinn
Vp Accounting Process Optimization And Information Support, Seymour Battle
Vice President Tax, Stephanie A Davis

Treasurer, Dan Stanush
Board Member, Patrick Porter
Board Member, Kirstin Silberschlag
Board Member, Grace Batres
Treasurer, Richard Johnston
Assistant Secretary Disclosure And Compliance Offi, Steve Gilbert
Auditors: KPMG LLP

LOCATIONS

HQ: Valero Energy Corp
One Valero Way, San Antonio, TX 78249
Phone: 210 345-2000   **Fax:** 210 246-2646
Web: www.valero.com

2015 Sales

	$ mil.	% of total
US	60,319	68
UK and Ireland	11,232	13
Canada	6,841	8
Other countries	9,412	11
Total	**87,804**	**100**

PRODUCTS/OPERATIONS

2015 Sales

	$ mil.	% of total
Refining	84,521	96
Ethanol	3	4
Elimination	(151)	-
Total	**87,804**	**100**

Selected Products

Asphalt
Bunker oils
CARB Phase II gasoline
Clean-burning oxygenates
Conventional gasoline
Crude mineral spirits
Customized clean-burning gasoline blends for export markets
Ethanol
Gasoline blendstocks
Home heating oil
Jet fuel
Kerosene
Low-sulfur diesel
Lube oils
Petrochemical feedstocks
Petroleum coke
Premium reformulated and conventional gasolines
Reformulated gasoline
Sulfur

COMPETITORS

ADM	Motiva Enterprises
BP	National Cooperative
CITGO	Refinery Association
CVR	Phillips 66
Chevron	Sinclair Oil
Exxon Mobil	Sunoco
Green Brick Partners	TOTAL
HollyFrontier	TPC Group
Marathon Petroleum	Tesoro

HISTORICAL FINANCIALS

Company Type: Public

Income Statement   FYE: December 31

	REVENUE ($ mil.)	NET INCOME ($ mil.)	NET PROFIT MARGIN	EMPLOYEES
12/18	117,033	3,122	2.7%	10,261
12/17	93,980	4,065	4.3%	10,015
12/16	75,659	2,289	3.0%	9,996
12/15	87,804	3,990	4.5%	10,103
12/14	130,844	3,630	2.8%	10,065
Annual Growth	**(2.8%)**	**(3.7%)**	**—**	**0.5%**

2018 Year-End Financials

Debt ratio: 18.00%	No. of shares (mil.): 418
Return on equity: 14.00%	Dividends
Cash ($ mil.): 2,982	Yield: 4.0%
Current ratio: 2.00	Payout: 44.0%
Long-term debt ($ mil.): 8,871	Market value ($ mil.): 31,307

	STOCK PRICE ($) FY Close	P/E High/Low		PER SHARE ($) Earnings	Dividends	Book Value
12/18	75.00	17	9	7.00	3.00	52.00
12/17	92.00	10	7	9.00	3.00	51.00
12/16	68.00	15	10	5.00	2.00	44.00
12/15	71.00	9	6	8.00	2.00	43.00
12/14	50.00	9	6	7.00	1.00	40.00
Annual Growth	**10.9%**	—	—	**1.6%**	**32.1%**	**6.6%**

Valley National Bancorp (NJ)

Valley National Bancorp is high on New Jersey and New York. The holding company owns Valley National Bank which serves commercial and retail clients through more than 200 branches in northern and central New Jersey and in the New York City boroughs of Manhattan Brooklyn and Queens as well as on Long Island. The bank provides standard services like checking and savings accounts loans and mortgages credit cards and trust services. Subsidiaries offer asset management mortgage and auto loan servicing title insurance asset-based lending and property/casualty life and health insurance. Founded as The Passaic Park Trust Company in 1927 Valley National is looking to expand in Florida.

Operations

In addition to its commercial and retail banking operations Valley National Bancorp through its subsidiaries operates: an all-line insurance agency that offers property and casualty life and health insurance; a wealth management advisory business; title insurance agencies in New York and New Jersey. It also specializes in general aviation financing commercial equipment leasing and custom financing for health care professionals and law firms.

Financial Performance

Valley National reported revenue of $744.7 million in 2013 a decline of 6% versus 2012 on lower interest income caused by lower yields on average interest earning assets as a result of low long-term market interest rates. Net income fell 8% over the same period to about $132 million on lower revenue and an increase in non-interest expenses.

Strategy

One of the leading commercial banks in the New York and New Jersey metro areas Valley National has set its sights on Florida with its proposed acquisition of Boca Raton-based 1st United Bankcorp the largest commercial bank in Palm Beach County. The deal which is valued at $312 million would add a 21 branch network covering urban banking markets in Florida and approximately $1.7 billion in assets. Combined the two companies will have about $18.1 billion in assets nearly $13 billion in loans and $12.7 billion in deposits. The deal is expected to close in late 2014.

Commercial real estate and construction loans account for the largest portion of Valley's loan portfolio (47%). However the bank has ramped up its residential lending and has been actively marketing its home loan refinancing products amid continued low interest rates.

Mergers and Acquisitions

Valley National completed its approximately $222 million acquisition of New York-based bank holding company State Bancorp at the beginning of 2012. The deal which brought in 17 branches is part of Valley's overall strategy to expand its presence throughout New York City metropolitan area. It marked the company's first foray in Long Island and added locations in Manhattan and Queens as well. It also provides an opportunity to build retail relationships in new markets as State Bancorp focused more on commercial clients. Valley typically targets consumers disillusioned with larger banks.

In 2010 the company acquired the branches and most of the assets and deposits of failed Manhattan-based financial institutions LibertyPointe Bank and Park Avenue Bank in FDIC-assisted transactions. It also opened a loan production office in Bethlehem Pennsylvania to offer residential mortgages and title insurance. Valley continues to look for additional expansion opportunities.

EXECUTIVES

President And Chief Banking Officer Valley National Bank, Rudy E. Schupp, age 68, $425,000 total compensation

Sevp And Cfo, Alan D. Eskow, age 71, $545,750 total compensation

Chairman President And Ceo, Gerald H. Lipkin, age 79, $1,123,500 total compensation

Evp And Chief Retail Lending Officer, Albert L. Engel, age 71, $440,000 total compensation

Svp Shareholder And Public Relations, Dianne M. Grenz

Evp And Senior Community Reinvestment Act Officer, Bernadette M. Mueller, age 60

Sevp And Treasurer, Ira Robbins, age 44, $425,000 total compensation

Evp And Chief Administrative Officer, Andrea Onorato

Evp And Cio, Robert J. Bardusch

Evp And Chief Risk Officer, Melissa Scofield

Senior Vice President Human Resources Benefits, Terry Gehrke

Assistant Vice President Commercial Loans, John Kenny

Vice President, Peter Alvarez

Assistant Vice President, Tony Dibenedetto

Vice President, Dave Denoya

Vice President, Timothy Tierney

Assistant Vice President Branch Sales Manager, Marie Castro

Vice President, Claudia Orourke

Assistant Vice President Business Development Commercial Loans, Kristen Upadek

Vice President Sales Manager, Veronica Valentine

Vice President Community Lending, Angela Brauer

Vice President Territory Sales Manager, Melvin Madera

Senior Vice President Commercial Lending, John Murphy

Vice President Retail Training, Mary Black

Senior Vice President, Chip Woodbury

Vice President, Mark Stanek

Vice President, Karen Conway

Assistant Vice President, Paul Cronen

Vice President, Barbara Santos

First Vice President And Chief Compliance Officer, Manfred Brockmann

Vice President, Janet Knipfing

Vice President And Senior Counsel, Gary Michael

Vice President, Jennifer Yager

Vice President, Ruth A Finn

Senior Corporate Management Vice President Gm, Ralph Passafiume

Vice President, John Cina

Vice President And Branch Sales Manager, Tina Brand

First Senior Vice President, Wayne Fritsch

Senior Vice President, Eileen Sackman

Vice President, Tony Zeleszko

Senior Vice President; Regional Manager, Steven Vitale

Vice President, Geriann Smith

Vice President, Luba Gelman

Vice President Senior Marketing Manager, Jeffery Doberman

Vice President Of Sales, John Siberio

Vice President Commercial Lender, Janice Brunson

Vice President, Mark Sabow

Assistant Vice President Operations, Frank Reyes

Vice President Commercial Lending, Catherine Keller

Executive Vice President Chief Financial Officer And Chief Operating Officer, Stan Pinkham

Avp Branch Sales Manager, Robert Grasso

Vice President And Credit Officer, Peter Tomasi

Vice President Commercial Lender, Maggie Gonzalez

Vice President Commercial Middle Market Banking, Dan Smith

Vice President Territory Sales Manager, Mary Beltz

Senior Executive Vice President; Chief Lending Officer Of Valley National Bank, Thomas Iadanza

Regional Vice President, Drita Kukic

Senior Vice President Director Of Association Banking And Treasury Management, Marc Nuzzolo

First Vice President District Sales Manager, Nestor Roldan

Executive Vice President And Chief Credit Officer, Mark Saeger

Vice President, Joe Gargiulo

Senior Vice President Market Executive, Ivete Pinheiro

Vice President Commercial Relationship Manager, Cindy Dunlop

Vice President, Thomas Russo

Vice President, Mikel Sharpe

Vice President Commercial Lending, Art Shelley

Vice President, Oscar Hernandez

Senior Vice President, Valerie Pickert

Assistant Vice President Assistant Banking Office Manager One North Federal Highway Boca Raton, Ann Longworth

Vice President Branch Manager Residential Mortgage, Robert Nardone

Vice President Commercial Lending Valley National Bank Florida Division, Gus Treichel

Vice President Territory Sales Manager, Eddie Beylin

First Vice President, Martha Soper

Vice President Territory Sales Manager, Matthew Coppola

Vice President, Linda Diaz

Vp Aml Bsa Compliance, Rahsan Mumcuoglu

Vice President, Alan Gilman

Vice President, Daniel Maes

Vice President Director Of Sales, Amanda Miller

Vice President New Business Underwriting, Joseph Klapkowski

Vice President, David Beil

Vp And Residential Mortgage Project Manager, Scott Honey

Assistant Vice President Training, Jim Hatcher

Vice President Network Operations, Kenneth Aul

Vp Territory Sales Manager, Ijaz Mughal

Cfsa And Senior Auditor And Assistant Vice President, Colleen Moriarty

Vp And Territory Manager, Lee Stevenson

First Vice President Commercial Loan Team Leader, Dan Sorrell

First Vice President, Ron Fraser

First Senior Vice President, Dorothy Kahlau

First Senior Vice President, Russ Murawski

Board Member, Peter Baum

Auditors: KPMG LLP

LOCATIONS

HQ: Valley National Bancorp (NJ)
One Penn Plaza, New York, NY 10119
Phone: 973 305-8800
Web: www.valleynationalbank.com

PRODUCTS/OPERATIONS

2016 Sales

	$ mil.	% of total
Interest Income		
Interest and fees on loans	686	79
Interest and dividends on investment securities	80	9
Interest on federal funds sold and other short-term investments	1	0
Non-Interest Income		
Gains on sales of loans net	22	3
Service charges on deposit accounts	21	2
Insurance commissions	19	2
Trust and investment services	10	1
Bank owned life insurance	7	1
Fees from loan servicing	6	1
Gains on sales of assets net	1	0
Gains on securities transactions net	1	0
Change in FDIC loss-share receivable	(1.3)	0
Other	17	2
Total	**870**	**100**

COMPETITORS

Bank of America	JPMorgan Chase
Capital One	New York Community
Citigroup	Bancorp
Dime Community	PNC Financial
Bancshares	TD Bank USA
Hudson City Bancorp	Wells Fargo

HISTORICAL FINANCIALS

Company Type: Public

Income Statement

FYE: December 31

	ASSETS ($ mil.)	NET INCOME ($ mil.)	INCOME AS % OF ASSETS	EMPLOYEES
12/18	31,863	261	0.8%	3,192
12/17	24,002	162	0.7%	2,842
12/16	22,864	168	0.7%	2,828
12/15	21,613	103	0.5%	2,929
12/14	18,794	116	0.6%	2,907
Annual Growth	14.1%	22.5%	—	2.4%

2018 Year-End Financials

Debt ratio: 1.00%	No. of shares (mil.): 331
Return on equity: 9.00%	Dividends
Cash ($ mil.): 429	Yield: 5.0%
Current ratio: —	Payout: 59.0%
Long-term debt ($ mil.): —	Market value ($ mil.): 2,943

	STOCK PRICE ($) FY Close	P/E High/Low		PER SHARE ($) Earnings	Dividends	Book Value
12/18	9.00	18	11	1.00	0.00	10.00
12/17	11.00	22	18	1.00	0.00	10.00
12/16	12.00	19	13	1.00	0.00	9.00
12/15	10.00	27	22	0.00	0.00	9.00
12/14	10.00	19	16	1.00	0.00	8.00
Annual Growth	(2.2%)	—	—	7.6%	(0.0%)	5.9%

Veritex Holdings Inc

Auditors: Grant Thornton LLP

LOCATIONS

HQ: Veritex Holdings Inc
8214 Westchester Drive, Suite 800, Dallas, TX 75225
Phone: 972 349-6200
Web: www.veritexbank.com

HISTORICAL FINANCIALS

Company Type: Public

Income Statement
FYE: December 31

	ASSETS ($ mil.)	NET INCOME ($ mil.)	INCOME AS % OF ASSETS	EMPLOYEES
12/18	3,209	39	1.2%	330
12/17	2,946	15	0.5%	324
12/16	1,409	13	0.9%	171
12/15	1,040	9	0.8%	149
12/14	802	5	0.6%	125
Annual Growth	41.4%	65.8%	—	27.5%

2018 Year-End Financials

Debt ratio: 1.00%
Return on equity: 8.00%
Cash ($ mil.): 84
Current ratio: —
Long-term debt ($ mil.): —

No. of shares (mil.): 24
Dividends
 Yield: —
 Payout: —
Market value ($ mil.): 519

	STOCK PRICE ($) FY Close	P/E High/Low		PER SHARE ($) Earnings	Dividends	Book Value
12/18	21.00	20	13	2.00	0.00	22.00
12/17	28.00	36	30	1.00	0.00	20.00
12/16	27.00	23	11	1.00	0.00	16.00
12/15	16.00	20	15	1.00	0.00	12.00
12/14	14.00	23	18	1.00	0.00	12.00
Annual Growth	10.8%			22.1%	—	16.3%

Veritiv Corp

Auditors: DELOITTE & TOUCHE LLP

LOCATIONS

HQ: Veritiv Corp
1000 Abernathy Road N.E., Building 400, Suite 1700, Atlanta, GA 30328
Phone: 770 391-8200
Web: www.veritivcorp.com

HISTORICAL FINANCIALS

Company Type: Public

Income Statement
FYE: December 31

	REVENUE ($ mil.)	NET INCOME ($ mil.)	NET PROFIT MARGIN	EMPLOYEES
12/18	8,696	(16)	—	8,700
12/17	8,365	(13)	—	8,900
12/16	8,327	21	0.3%	8,700
12/15	8,718	27	0.3%	8,800
12/14	7,407	(20)	—	8,900
Annual Growth	4.1%	—	—	(0.6%)

2018 Year-End Financials

Debt ratio: 39.00%
Return on equity: (-3.00%)
Cash ($ mil.): 64
Current ratio: 2.00
Long-term debt ($ mil.): 987

No. of shares (mil.): 16
Dividends
 Yield: —
 Payout: —
Market value ($ mil.): 397

	STOCK PRICE ($) FY Close	P/E High/Low		PER SHARE ($) Earnings	Dividends	Book Value
12/18	25.00	—	—	(1.00)	0.00	34.00
12/17	29.00	—	—	(1.00)	0.00	35.00
12/16	54.00	43	21	1.00	0.00	35.00
12/15	36.00	32	20	2.00	0.00	33.00
12/14	52.00	—	—	(2.00)	0.00	32.00
Annual Growth	(16.7%)			—	—	1.6%

Verizon Communications Inc

Verizon Communications is the #1 wireless phone service in the US (ahead of rival AT&T) serving more than 118 million connections. Verizon's wireline unit provides local telephone long-distance internet access corporate networking and digital TV services to consumers carriers business and government customers. In addition Verizon offers a wide range of telecom managed network security and IT services to commercial and government clients in more than 150 countries. The company also sells device such as phones tablets and wearables. Verizon has expanded its video and advertising capabilities with the acquisitions of AOL and Yahoo assets.

Operations
Verizon Communications' Wireless segment accounts for about 70% of revenue. Verizon operates one of the most extensive wireless networks in the US and the largest 4G LTE network (available to more than 98% of the US population).

The wireline segment which accounts for about a quarter of revenue provides voice data and video communications products as well as broadband video and data corporate networking services data center and cloud services security and managed network services and local and long-distance voice services. The segment also includes Verizon's Fios service which offers high-speed internet and TV. The company reports more than 6 million Fios internet and about 5 million Fios video subscribers.

The corporate and other segment which includes Oath media businesses telematics and other businesses supplies about 5% of revenue.

Geographic Reach
Verizon based in New York City has operations throughout the US. It also has representation in countries around the world.

Sales and Marketing
Verizon sells its prepaid and postpaid wireless phone services through its website its own stores and national retailers. It also has a dedicated tele-marketing sales force. The average retail customer account pays about $134 a month.

The company is a major advertiser with a coordinated program of TV print radio outdoor signage internet and point-of-sale media promotions. Those Verizon ads commercials and other promotional vehicles cost the company about $2.6 billion a year.

Financial Performance
Verizon's revenue has risen in the past years after the company hit a sales peak of about $131 billion in 2015 before dropping in 2016.

Sales were just under $131 billion in 2018 about a 4% increase from 2017 driven by higher wireless revenue from higher value accounts and overall account growth. Equipment revenue also rose due to sales of higher priced handset and greater sales of wearables. Higher wireless and equipment sales offset a drop in wireline revenue.

Verizon's net income fell by about half dropping to $15.5 billion in 2018 compared to $30.1 billion in 2017 (when the company had a $16 billion tax benefit).

In 2018 Verizon had about $1 billion more in cash and equivalents $3.9 billion compared to the previous year. Operations generated $34.3 billion in cash while investing and financing activities used $17.9 billion and $15 billion respectively.

Verizon carries significant debt about $103 billion at the end of 2018 which could reduce the amount of money available for working capital expenditures and acquisitions and hinder the ability to obtain financing.

Strategy
When its rivals slash prices on wireless service Verizon Communications touts the coverage speed and reliability of its network. Maybe it costs a bit more Verizon tells customers but the network is worth it. Verizon is investing to expand and strengthen the network to develop new streams of revenue. The company now offers unlimited voice data and video plans which has reduced average revenue per user to about $134 a month.

Verizon has large capital expenditures about $17 billion that go to improve its network adding more fiber optic cable to improve 4G service and get ready for higher-speed 5G service.

The company had made strides in rolling out the early wave of 5G service including becoming the first company to complete a 5G data session on a smartphone as well at the first to commercially deploy 5G with its 5G Home product.

Verizon has put cost-cutting measures in place including a voluntary separation program for some US-based management employees. The program was to reduce headcount by some 10400. Verizon reorganized its segment reporting structure into consumer business and Verizon Media Group. The realignment which went into effect in the 2019 second quarter was to help the company better focus on customers.

Mergers and Acquisitions
In early 2019 Verizon closed its acquisition of ProtectWise a provider of cloud-delivered Network Detection and Response. This acquisition expands Verizon's security offerings.

In 2018 Verizon acquired Moment a New York-based design and strategy firm to develop customer experience materials for in-store online mobile and live customer service by phone or chat.

Also in 2018 Verizon closed the acquired Movildata Internacional a Spanish provider of commercial fleet management technologies.

In 2017 Verizon acquired the operating business of Yahoo! Inc. Verizon has combined these assets with its existing AOL business to create a new subsidiary Oath a diverse house of more than 50 media and technology brands that engages more than a billion people around the world.

Verizon in 2017 bought Straight Path Communications for more than $3 billion gaining a trove of 28 GHz and 39 GHz millimeter wave spectrum used in mobile communications. The spectrum could give Verizon a boost in developing 5G technology.

EXECUTIVES

Evp And Chief Strategy Officer, Roy H. Chestnutt, age 60
Chairman And Ceo, Lowell C. McAdam, age 65, $1,600,000 total compensation
Evp Wireless Network Operations, David Small
Evp And Chief Information And Technology Architect, Roger Gurnani, age 58
Evp And Chief Administrative Officer, Marc C. Reed, age 60, $792,307 total compensation
Evp And President Network And Technology, Hans Vestberg, age 54
Evp And President Customer And Product Operations, John G. Stratton, age 58, $896,154 total compensation
Evp And President Product Innovation And New Businesses, Marni M. Walden, age 51, $896,154 total compensation
Svp And Group President Verizon Enterprise Solutions, George J. Fischer, age 56
Svp And Group President Consumer Sales And Service, Kenneth (Ken) Dixon
Evp And Group President Verizon Wireless, Ronan Dunne

Evp Public Policy And General Counsel, Craig L. Silliman, age 51

Svp And Group President Verizon Business Markets (vbm), Martin Burvill

Evp Wireless Operations, Tami Erwin

Evp And Cfo, Matthew D. (Matt) Ellis, age 47, $488,462 total compensation

President Verizon Partner Solutions, Eric Cevis

Evp Solutions And Sales Channels, Joe Chuisano

Senior Vice President And Deputy General Counsel Public Policy And Government Affairs, Kathleen Grillo

Senior Vice President Business Development, Gregory Seiler

Vice President, Christopher Kimm

National Account Manager, Fran Morris

Senior Vice President Public Sector Verizon Enterprise Solutions, Michael Maiorana

Vice President Associate General Counsel, David Wheeler

Vice President Telematics, Shane Scoville

Regional Vice President Public Policy, Karen Campbell

Executive Director Network Operations Vps, Sam Luxton

Vice President, Roland Hicks

Vice President Of Marketing And Sales For Middle Atlantic Region, Mary Yarbrough

Vice President Of Marketing, Bob Gilbride

National Account Manager, Rob Parker

Vice President Federal Government Relations, Marcela Zamora

Vice President Of Sales, Philip Burroughs

Vice President, Cesar Gamarra

Vp And Associate General Counsel, Gregory Romano

Senior Vice President Global Real Estate, John Vazquez

National Account Manager, Shirley Bily

Manager Vps Marketing And Sales, Janice Crandall

Vice President, James Franke

National Account Manager, Lauren Williams

Vice President, Lizette Lizardi

Senior Vice President Supply Chain Services, Viju Menon

Vice President Customer Service Verizon Wireless, Joan Bowyer

Senior Vice President Financial Planning And Analysis, Shane Sanders

Vice President, Tara Mooar

Vp Corporate Communications, Mariana Agathoklis

Senior Vice President Investor Relations, Mike Stefanski

Svp It, Vivek Gurumurthy

Vice President Technology Planning, Adam Koeppe

Board Member, Beryl Thompson

Auditors: Ernst & Young LLP

LOCATIONS

HQ: Verizon Communications Inc
1095 Avenue of the Americas, New York, NY 10036
Phone: 212 395-1000
Web: www.verizon.com

PRODUCTS/OPERATIONS

2018 Sales

	$ mil.	% of total
Wireless	91,734	69
Wireline	29,760	23
Corporate and Other	10,942	8
Eliminations	(1573)	0
Total	**130,863**	**100**

2018 Sales

	$ mil.	% of total
Service revenues and other	108,605	83
Wireless equipment revenues	22,258	17
Total	**130,863**	**100**

COMPETITORS

AT&T	Frontier
Altice USA	Communications
CenturyLink	Netflix
Charter Communications	Sprint Communications
Comcast	T-Mobile USA
Cox Communications	Time Warner Cable
Cricket	U.S. Cellular
DIRECTV	Windstream

HISTORICAL FINANCIALS

Company Type: Public

Income Statement   FYE: December 31

	REVENUE ($ mil.)	NET INCOME ($ mil.)	NET PROFIT MARGIN	EMPLOYEES
12/18	130,863	15,528	11.9%	144,500
12/17	126,034	30,101	23.9%	155,400
12/16	125,980	13,127	10.4%	160,900
12/15	131,620	17,879	13.6%	177,700
12/14	127,079	9,625	7.6%	177,300
Annual Growth	**0.7%**	**12.7%**	**—**	**(5.0%)**

2018 Year-End Financials

Debt ratio: 43.00%—
Return on equity: 32.00%
Cash ($ mil.): 2,745
Current ratio: 1.00
Long-term debt ($ mil.): 105,873

Dividends
Yield: 4.0%
Payout: 63.0%
Market value ($ mil.): —

	STOCK PRICE ($) FY Close	P/E High/Low		PER SHARE ($) Earnings	Dividends	Book Value
12/18	56.00	16	12	4.00	2.00	13.00
12/17	53.00	7	6	7.00	2.00	11.00
12/16	53.00	18	14	3.00	2.00	6.00
12/15	46.00	12	10	4.00	2.00	4.00
12/14	47.00	21	19	2.00	2.00	3.00
Annual Growth	**4.7%**	**—**	**—**	**11.6%**	**2.6%**	**44.4%**

VF Corp.

VF Corp. has stitched together a lineup of apparel brands that range from denim to Northface. The company is a leading manufacturer and retailer in the outdoor and action sports apparel industry owning brands in specialist product categories: Timberland and The North Face (outdoor-oriented brands) and Vans (skateboard-inspired footwear). VF also makes the jeans scene owning the Lee Wrangler and Rock & Republic brands. The company sells directly to consumers online and through more than 1500 VF-operated retail stores worldwide. It also sells wholesale to department and specialty stores and mass merchants. In 2018 VF announced it would spin off the jeans business into a separate public company to concentrate on the outdoor and footwear brands.

Change in Company Type
VF Corp. in 2018 said it would split the company into two companies. One would focus on footwear such as the Vans brand outdoor wear brands such as the Northface and Timberland as well as the work category that include Dickie and Red Kap which have accounted for most of the company's growth. It would retain the VF Corp. name and set up its headquarters in Denver. The other company would sell denim brands Wrangler Lee Rustler and Rock & Republic which have struggled as retailers have promoted store brands.

Its headquarters would be in VF Corp.'s hometown Greensboro North Carolina.

The company expected the split to be completed in the first half of 2019.

Operations
VF operates three main business segments: Outdoor & Action Sports is the largest at more than 70% of total sales followed by Jeanswear (more than 20%) and Imagewear (more than 5%).

V.F.'s Outdoor & Action Sports segment has a closet of 10 popular outdoor brands across the apparel footwear equipment backpacks luggage and accessories categories. Vans a youth counter-culture brand is the segment's biggest earner and sells shoes and clothing through 650 VF-owned retail units online and through distributors. The North Face the next biggest brand sells tents sleeping bags backpacks and other such outdoor accessories alongside its rugged apparel and footwear lines. The segment also sells handbags luggage backpacks women's activewear and surf-inspired footwear across its various other brands.

The Jeanswear segment sells jeans and related clothing and accessories through a handful of brands. In the US the Lee brand is sold through mid-tier department stores and the Rustler and Rider by Lee brands are sold through regional discount stores. Outside the US Wrangler and Lee are sold as high-end brands.

The Imagewear segment provides uniforms and career occupational apparel for workers in North America and internationally under the Dickies and Red Kap brands (work apparel and footwear) Bulwark and Workrite brands (flame resistant and protective apparel primarily for the petrochemical utility and mining industries) the Walls Brand (outdoor workwear) the Kodiak brand (work and lifestyle footwear) the Terra brand (work footwear) and the Horace Small brand (apparel for law enforcement and public safety personnel). It includes a wide range of workwear pants coveralls shirts medical scrubs outerwear footwear and accessories

Geographic Reach
VF Corp. rings up about 55% of its sales in the US while the remainder mostly comes from Europe. It also sells in Asia Canada Mexico and Latin America. The apparel maker has about 20 manufacturing plants in the US Mexico Central and South America the Caribbean Europe and the Middle East.

The company operates more than 35 distribution centers primarily in the U.S. Argentina Belgium Canada Chile China Mexico the Netherlands and the UK.

Sales and Marketing
VF makes sales through specialty stores department stores national chains mass merchants and its direct-to-consumer (DTC) operations. The company makes direct-to-customer sales about 30% of revenue through owned-operated stores concession retail stores and online. It generates a significant chunk of its sales through third-party retail chains. V.F.'s 10 largest customers account for about 20% of sales.

The apparel maker advertises in trade publications and on radio and television. Its digital initiatives include social media mobile platforms and the internet.

Financial Performance
VF Corp.'s revenue has fluctuated in recent years but has surpassed $11.8 billion in two of the past four years. Net income consistently topped $1 billion since 2012 before dropping below the mark in 2017.

In 2017 VF's revenue rose 7% to $11.8 billion compared to 2016. Sales of the Outdoor & Action Sports segment increased 8% in 2017 while Jeanswear revenue slipped 3%. In terms of channels direct-to-consumer revenue rose 17% accounting for about a third of total revenue in 2017 and ecommerce revenue jumped 34% in 2017. International sales increased 12% and accounted for more than 40% of VF's revenue in 2017.

VF's net income fell to about $615 million in 2018 from about $1 billion in 2016. The company paid about $490 million more in US income tax in 2017 than 2016 because of the US Tax Cuts and Jobs Act. Income before tax was about $1.4 billion in 2017 compared to about $1.3 billion in 2016.

Cash generated by operations was flat at about $1.5 billion in 2016 and 2017. VF repurchased $1.2 billion of stock and paid about $685 million in dividends in 2017.

Strategy

The breakup of VF into a company for footwear and outdoor apparel and a company that sells jeans allows each to focus on its specific markets. VF had already sold the Nautica brand when it announced the split in August 2018. Without denim VF said it would have flexibility to make acquisitions and explore new businesses. Besides the active and outdoor brands VF would retain the work-oriented brands such as Dickies Red Kap and Kodiak. It expects revenue of about $11 billion a year.

The denim company's revenue would be around $2.5 billion from the Lee Wrangler Rock & Republic and Rustler brands. The company will look to increase sales in Asia particularly China. It intends to cut costs and streamline operations and scout for opportunities to add to its product line.

Mergers and Acquisitions

In early 2018 VF bought New Zealand-based Icebreaker to a complement VF's Smartwool brand. The two brands position VF as a leader in the Merino wool and natural fiber categories.

Company Background

The gear-and-apparel maker has invested heavily in acquisitions to further build its outdoor and action sports business which has grown to account for more than 50% of sales. V.F. in September 2011 acquired global footwear maker Timberland for $2 billion. Marking the biggest acquisition in the company's history V.F. was enticed by Timberland's overseas presence and its strong growth during the past decade.

In 2010 on the wholesaling side V.F. took control of its Vans-branded products marketing venture in Mexico. The roughly $30 million purchase also put V.F. in charge of Vans retail stores.

V.F. founded in 1899 is controlled in part by trusts established by its late founder John Barbey.

HISTORY

In 1899 six partners including banker John Barbey started the Reading Glove and Mitten Manufacturing Company. Barbey bought out his five partners in 1911 and changed the name of the Reading Pennsylvania company to Schuylkill Silk Mills in 1913. Barbey expanded the mills' production to include underwear and changed the mills' name to Vanity Fair Silk Mills (after a contest with a $25 prize in 1919).

Barbey (who banned the word "underwear") and his son J. E. led their lingerie company to national prominence. The mills made only silk garments until the 1920s when synthetics were developed. In response to the US embargo on silk in 1941 Vanity Fair changed to rayon finally converting to the new wonder fabric nylon tricot in 1948. Vanity Fair was then manufacturing all stages of its nylon products from filament to finished garment. It won awards for its innovative advertising with photographs of live models in Vanity Fair lingerie.

J. E. owned all of Vanity Fair's stock until 1951 when he sold one-third of his holdings to the public. In 1966 the stock previously traded over the counter was listed on the NYSE.V.F. Corp. is not afraid to cut brands that aren't profitable to free up resources. In 2012 for example it sold its majority stake in upscale men's designer brand John Varvatos to private equity Lion Capital.

In 2013 V.F. Corp. was hoping to boost its outdoor business and its bottom line further through its 2013 bid to take over Australia's boardwear maker Billabong but the Aussie company wanted more than the 526.8 million Australian dollars (US $556 million) V.F. was willing to pay.

EXECUTIVES

Assistant Vice President, Joseph Dzialo
Vice President Supply Chain, Tom Glaser
Vp And Group President International, Karl Heinz Salzburger, age 61, $798,324 total compensation
President Asia/pacific Region, Kevin D. Bailey
Vp; Group President Outdoor And Action Sports Americas, Scott H. Baxter, age 54, $659,200 total compensation
President Workwear Jeans And Sportswear Brands, Curt Holtz
Vp And Cfo, Scott A. Roe, age 54, $675,000 total compensation
Vp Global Business Technology, Sandra Harris
Vp; Group President Vf International, Aidan O'Meara, age 70
Vp And Cio, Martin Schneider
President Europe Middle East And Africa, Martino Scabbia Guerrini, age 55
Brand President Smartwool, Travis Campbell
Vp; President Supply Chain, Thomas A. Glaser
Chairman President And Ceo, Steven E. (Steve) Rendle, age 59, $945,000 total compensation
President Sportswear, Brendan Sullivan
Vice President Ebus, Joe Plaster
Vice President Global Compensation, Allan Polischak
Human Resources Vice President, Ronald Lawrence
Vice President Retail Marketing, Bill Clodfelter
Vice President Investor Relations And Financial Planning And Analysis, Joseph Alkire
Senior Vice President, Terri Miller
Vice President Sourcing Lee Jeans, Steve Miller
Vice President Customer Service, Amanda Ballard
Vice President Of Retail, Kurt Kleespies
Vice President Us Sales, Brett Barthel
Vice President General Manager, Doug Mathison
Vice President Global Strategy And Brand Management, Iain Douglas
Vice President Sales, Steve Morton
Vice President General Manager, Richard Blaya
Vice President Operations Kipling North America, Chris Young
Vice President Sales, Ken Wood
Vice President Human Resources Supply Chain, Rod Hewitt
Vice President General Manager Vans North America, Mitchell Whitaker
Vice President, Ellen Blake
Vice President Gmm, Bill Lynch
Vice President Design Research And Development, Paul Herron
Vice President Operations Supply Chain Sportswear Coalition, Karen Smith
Vice President Operation, Martin Duff
Vice President Retail Marketing, Jeff Sharp
Vice President Internal Audit, Scott Moree
Vice President And Human Resources Business Partner Jeanswear North America, Fran Mellette
Vice President, Jon E Anthony
Vice President Finance, Chastity Black
Vice President Of Merchandising, Dave Theiss
Vice President, Christopher Fuentes
Vice President Finance, Mark Thoma
Vp Global Consumer And Shopper Insights, Karyn Peterson
Vice President, Nina Flood
Management Vice President, Rick Wood

Vice President Gm, Hector Torres
Chief Accounting Officer Vice President Controller, Bryan Mcneill
Vice President And Managing Director Timberland And Sportswear Vf Asia Pacific, John Gearing
National Accounts Manager, Sam Leslie
Vice President Global Corporate Sustainability, Letitia Webster
Vp Marketing (imagewear), David Crace
Vice President Human Resources Vf International, Monica Valsechini
Vice President, Scott Moore
Vice President Sales, Scott Bowers
Vp And General Manager Kodiak Group, Katherine Cousins
Vp Global Product Creative Director Timberland, Chris Pawlus
Vice President Mass Operations, Julie Morgan
Vice President Human Resources, Scott Shoener
Vice President Customer Experience, Terence Fong
Board Member, Garrett Chapman
Board Member, Sandy Mcmullen
Board Member, Richard Carucci
Board Member, W Alan Mccollough
Auditors: PricewaterhouseCoopers LLP

LOCATIONS

HQ: VF Corp.
 8505 E. Orchard Road, Greenwood Village, CO 80111
Phone: 720 778-4000
Web: www.vfc.com

2017 Sales

	$ mil.	% of total
US	6,785	57
Foreign primarily Europe	5,026	43
Total	**11,811**	**100**

PRODUCTS/OPERATIONS

2017 Sales

	$ mil.	% of total
Net sales	11,736	99
Royalty income	76	1
Total	**11,811**	**100**

2017 Sales

	$ mil.	% of total
Outdoor & action sports	8,213	70
Jeanswear	2,655	23
Imagewear	830	7
Other	113	-
Total	**11,811**	**100**

Selected Brands

Imagewear
  Bulwark
  Horace Small
  Majestic
  Red Kap
  MLB (licensed)
  NFL (licensed)
  Harley-Davidson (licensed)
Jeanswear
  Lee
  Riders
  Rock & Republic
  Rustler
  Timber Creek by Wrangler
  Wrangler
Sportswear
  Kipling
  Nautica
Outdoor and action sports
  Eagle Creek
  Eastpak
  JanSport
  Kipling
  lucy
  Napapijri
  Reef
  SmartWool
  The North Face
  Timberland
  Vans

Harley-Davidson Motor Company
Major League Baseball
MLB Players Association
National Basketball Association
National Football League
National Hockey League

Selected major colleges and universities

COMPETITORS

Abercrombie & Fitch	Lululemon
American Eagle	NIKE
Outfitters	OshKosh B'Gosh
Calvin Klein	Patagonia Inc.
Columbia Sportswear	REI
Diesel SpA	Reebok
Gildan Activewear	Rocky Brands
Guess?	Russell Brands
Joe's Jeans	Sears Holdings
Johnson Outdoors	The Gap
Kate Spade	Tommy Hilfiger
Kellwood	True Religion Apparel
Koos Manufacturing	Under Armour
L Brands	Williamson-Dickie
L.L. Bean	Manufacturing
Levi Strauss	adidas

HISTORICAL FINANCIALS

Company Type: Public

Income Statement

FYE: March 30

	REVENUE ($ mil.)	NET INCOME ($ mil.)	NET PROFIT MARGIN	EMPLOYEES
03/19	13,849	1,260	9.1%	75,000
03/18*	3,045	253	8.3%	—
12/17	11,811	615	5.2%	69,000
12/16	12,019	1,074	8.9%	69,000
01/16	12,377	1,232	10.0%	64,000
Annual Growth	3.8%	0.8%	—	5.4%

*Fiscal year change

2019 Year-End Financials

Debt ratio: 27.00%
Return on equity: 32.00%
Cash ($ mil.): 543
Current ratio: 2.00
Long-term debt ($ mil.): 2,116

No. of shares (mil.): 397
Dividends
Yield: 0.0%
Payout: 62.0%
Market value ($ mil.): 34,488

	STOCK PRICE ($) FY Close	P/E High/Low	PER SHARE ($) Earnings	Dividends	Book Value
03/19	87.00	30 21	3.00	2.00	11.00
03/18*	74.00	131 113	1.00	0.00	9.00
12/17	74.00	48 31	2.00	2.00	9.00
12/16	53.00	26 21	3.00	2.00	12.00
01/16	62.00	27 21	3.00	1.00	13.00
Annual Growth	11.8%	— —	3.4%	13.4%	(5.0%)

*Fiscal year change

ViacomCBS Inc

You might say this company has a real eye for broadcasting. CBS Corporation known by some as the "Eye Network" due to its eye logo is a leading mass media conglomerate with television radio online content and publishing operations. Its portfolio is anchored by CBS Broadcasting which operates the #1 rated CBS television network along with a group of local TV stations. CBS also owns cable network Showtime and produces and distributes TV programming through CBS Television Studios and CBS Television Distribution. Other operations include CBS Interactive and book publisher Simon & Schuster. Chairman Emeritus Sumner Redstone controls CBS Corporation through National Amusements. CBS agreed to merge with Viacom its National Amusements sibling in 2019.

HISTORY

The company that would eventually become CBS Corporation began as Viacom in 1970. It was the result of numerous mergers and acquisitions dating back nearly 90 years combining everything from a movie studio to a company that made car bumpers. CBS launched Viacom after the FCC ruled that TV networks could not own cable systems and TV stations in the same market. Viacom took over CBS's program syndication division and bought TV and radio stations in the late 1970s and early 1980s. In 1978 it co-founded pay-TV network Showtime. Viacom became full owner in 1982 and combined Showtime with The Movie Channel the following year to form Showtime Networks. Viacom also began producing TV series and bought MTV Networks in 1986.

After a bidding war with renowned financier Carl Icahn and a Viacom management group Sumner Redstone's National Amusements bought 83% of Viacom in 1987. Viacom bought King's Entertainment (theme parks) shortly thereafter and followed that with two mega-deals in 1994: it bought Paramount Communications for about $10 billion (which included Simon & Schuster) and Blockbuster for $8.4 billion (which included Spelling Entertainment). The next year along with Chris-Craft Viacom launched UPN (United Paramount Network) the fifth commercial-broadcast TV network in the US.

Chiseling away at a mountain of debt Viacom dumped its radio stations and sold its share in USA Networks (now named IAC/InterActiveCorp) to Universal for $1.7 billion in 1997. In 1998 it sold the reference and education publishing divisions of Simon & Schuster to Pearson for $4.6 billion and unloaded the unprofitable Blockbuster Music chain to Wherehouse Entertainment for $115 million.

Viacom created an Internet division (MTV Networks Online) in 1999 to house its MTV VH1 and Nickelodeon Web sites (later decentralized into The MTVi Group and Nickelodeon Online). Later that year it sold 18% of Blockbuster in an IPO and sold 10% of MTVi to TCI Music (later Liberty Digital) in exchange for the SonicNet websites.

Viacom bought Chris-Craft's 50%-stake in the struggling UPN Network for a paltry $5 million in 2000 by exercising a buy-sell clause in the contract. BHC Communications (Chris-Craft's 80%-owned subsidiary that actually owned the stake in UPN) filed suit to block Viacom's merger with CBS claiming that it violated a non-compete clause in the contract but the New York Supreme Court ruled in Viacom's favor. Its $45 billion merger with CBS went through (reuniting two companies split apart by the government 30 years ago) and Viacom was given one year to sell UPN. However a federal law prohibiting ownership of more than one TV network was overturned in 2001 allowing Viacom to keep the network.

Later that year Viacom's victory over Chris-Craft turned to sour grapes when News Corp. agreed to buy Chris-Craft. The deal could have forced UPN to fold if News Corp. had turned Chris-Craft's large-market UPN stations into FOX affiliates (a new pact later signed with Chris-Craft keeps UPN as the stations' network).

In 2001 Viacom bought the rest of Infinity Broadcasting that it didn't already own as well as Black Entertainment Television (the media company targeting African-Americans) for $3 billion. It also folded MTVi back into parent MTV Networks. Other cost cutting measures in 2002 included combining the business operations of UPN and CBS and placing Simon & Schuster under the same division as its film and TV production holdings.

Two years later Viacom finally sold its majority stake in Blockbuster which never really fit in with Viacom's other media properties. The media firm also didn't want to deal with the new challenges facing Blockbuster such as stiff competition from video on demand services the cheap DVD market and mail order video rental company Netflix.

In a move designed to simplify the firm's operations and re-focus the company on its core assets in late 2005 Viacom split into two separately traded firms — one called CBS Corporation consisting of traditional television and radio broadcasting operations and headed by former co-COO Les Moonves; and the other called the "new" Viacom made up of cable television and film operations and headed by former co-COO Tom Freston. (Freston resigned in 2006.) Redstone retained his title as chairman of both firms as well as his majority control.

Shortly after the split CBS Corp. sold Paramount Parks to Cedar Fair for $1.2 billion. A newly formed network called The CW a combination of UPN and The WB debuted in 2006. The following TV season the CBS network fell from first place in the ratings for the first time in six years. CBS Corp. expanded its online publishing operations in 2008 with the $1.8 billion acquisition of CNET Networks.

In 2011 production on the eighth season of its hit comedy Two and a Half Men ceased as a result of the erratic behavior of actor Charlie Sheen. CBS fired Sheen and has put the show on hiatus for an undetermined period of time.

In 2014 the company spun off its CBS Outdoor Americas advertising business.

EXECUTIVES

Chairman President And Ceo, Leslie (Les) Moonves, age 69, $3,500,000 total compensation

Sevp And Chief Communications Officer, Gil Schwartz, age 68, $896,923 total compensation

Sevp Chief Administrative Officer And Chief Human Resources Officer, Anthony G. Ambrosio, age 59, $964,423 total compensation

Sevp And Chief Legal Officer, Lawrence P. (Larry) Tu, age 64, $1,200,000 total compensation

Evp Government Affairs, John Orlando

Evp Investor Relations, Adam Townsend

Evp Deputy General Counsel And Secretary, Jonathan H. Anschell

Coo, Joseph R. Ianniello, age 52, $2,500,000 total compensation

Evp General Tax Counsel And Chief Veteran Officer, Richard M. Jones, age 54

Evp Controller And Chief Accounting Officer, Lawrence (Larry) Liding, age 50

Executive Vice President Cbs Marketing Group, Anne O'grady

Evp And Chief Communications Officer, Dana Mcclintock

Vice President Government Relations, Bryce Harlow

Vice President Production, Al Kennedy

Vice President Advertising And Promotion, Michael Pollack

Vice President Of Sales, Betty E Berlamino

Vice President Sales, Alan Clack

Vice President, Robert Noethiger

Senior Vice President Current Programs, Jeanne Mau

Vice President, David Strouse

Vice President Counsel, Michael Arseneault

Senior Vice President, Jonathan Sarrow

Executive Vice President General Manager, Darin Bassin

Vice President Programming, Greg Trager

Vice President Human Resources Specialty Services, Michelle Martin

Evp Corporate Development, Bryon Rubin

Senior Vice President Western Regional Manager, Greg Guenther

Vice President And General Manager, Tom Herschel

Senior Vice President Information Systems Director, Brelinda Snoddy

Executive Vice President Sales, Dean Kaplan

Svp Deputy General Tax Counsel, Kenneth Koen

Vice President Creative Director, Chris Cranner

Vice President Of Web Development, Allan Bressler

Vice President Programming, Emilie Deutsch

Vice President Human Resources, Robin Bona

Vice President National Sports Sales, Bob Malmgren

Senior Vice President Workforce Development, Jennifer Suarez

Vice President Assistant General Co, Andrew Siegel

Vice President Of Detroit Sales, Joe Butkovich

Vice President Finance, Steve Grosso

Vice President Research, Patti Cohen

Vp Workforce Development, Bryn Berglund

Vp It Finance, Jeffrey Tsai

Senior Vice President And Director Of Sales Analysis Operations, Bob Kaplan

Vice President And Assistant General Counsel, Mary Tischler

Vice President Of Sales, Kevin Barth

Vice President And News Director, Jeff Kiernan

Vice President, George Lewis

Vice President Distribution, Ken Hinshaw

Senior Vice President Sales, Marty Daly

Vice President Drama Development, Bryan Seabury

Vice President Executive Creative Director, James Shefcik

Vice President Of Business Affairs, Alison Choi

Vice President On Air Promotion, Paul Friedman

Vice President Business Development At Cbs Interactive, Adam London

Senior Vice President And Associate General Counsel, Mark Engstrom

Senior Vice President Associate General Counsel, Rebecca Borden

Executive Vice President Controller And Chief Accounting Officer, Larry Liding

Senior Vice President And Chief Procurement Officer, Tom Hogan

Vice President Primary Research, Marc Scheer

Vice President Salt Tax Operations, Mike Koczko

Vice President Of Sales, Matt Flewelling

Vice President Corporate Finance, Chad Diacont

Vice President Client Services, Christoph Hesterbrink

Svp And Associate General Counsel Litigation, Anthony Bongiorno

Vice President Corporate Communications, Judy Dehaven

Vice President Group Sales, Brian Murphy

Senior Vice President For Standards And Special Projects, Linda Mason

Assistant Vice President, Per Wingerup

Vice President West Coast, Josh Comay

Vp Internal Audit Operations, Jeffrey Meyer

Vice President Payroll Services, Bill Condon

Vice President Finance, Susan Varo

Vice President, Susanna Lowy

Vice President, Jay Barnett

National Sales Manager, Vince Mccarthy

Senior Vice President Human Resources Cbs Radio, Mark Zulli

Vice President Ad Operations, Susan Meehan

Vice President Executive Search, Conway Shui

Vice President Associate General Counsel, Gigi Davis

Vice President Advanced Services, Mike Pannacciulli

Svp Cbs Sports Sales And Marketing And Director, Chris Simko

Senior Vice President Communications, Phil Gonzales

Evp Communications, Kelli Raftery

Executive Vice President Affiliate Relations, Kurt Davis

Vice President, Randall Lewis

Svp Tax Reporting And Operations, Richard Ciraulo

Senior Vice President Communications Cbs Interactive, Chris Castro

Executive Vice President Communications Cbs Television Distribution, SScott Grogin

Vice President Accounting, Janice Kruk

Svp Associate General Counsel Corporate And Securities, Kim Pittman

Executive Vice President Of Operations, Scott Herman

Vice President And Associate General Counsel, Ethan Tyer

Evp Business Affairs Cbs Television Studios, Dan Kupetz

Vice President Marketing, Jack Schuster

Senior Vice President Investor Relations, David Bank

Vice President Captioning And Video Description, Mark Turits

Vice President Creative Services, Betsy Siciliano

Vice President And General Manager, Scott Schuman

Vice President, Sharon Vuong

Vice President Business Affairs And Legal, Charles Gardner

Evp And General Counsel Tv Stations Sports And Broadcast Operations, David Hillman

Senior Vice President, Chris Leanza

Vice President Labor Relations, David Silberman

Executive Vice President Consumer Products, Liz Kalonder

Vice President Product, John Pacino

Senior Vice President Sports Sales, Tony Taranto

Vice President Comedy Development, Alex Botnick

Vice President Finance, Steven Haft

Vice President, Carter Skeath

Senior Vice President Information Technology, Elizabeth Gilmore

Executive Vice President, Nathan Mecham

Senior Vice President And Deputy General Counsel, Andrea Simon

Vice President Human Resources, Jessica Hurst

Vice President And Counsel, Mark Maher

Senior Vice President Corporate Communications (showtime Networks), Erin Calhoun

Senior Vice President Digital Sales, Andi Poch

Vice President Casting, Lucy Cavallo

Vice President And General Manager, Adam Levy

Senior Vice President Business Affairs And Legal, Peter Kane

Senior Vice President Communications, Laurie Metrose

Senior Vice President, Roni Mueller

Vice President Compensation, Julia Ambrose

Senior Vice President Business Development, Jeff Shultz

Vice President Associate General Counsel, Laura Burton

Vice President Search Strategies, Cameron Olthuis

Senior Vice President, Kim Metcalf

Senior Vice President Current Programming, Amy Reisenbach

Vice President Current Programs, Marci Cooperstein

Senior Vice President Specials, Courtney Conroy

Senior Vice President And Associate General Counsel, Naomi Waltman

Senior Vice President Supplier Category Management, Mike Smyklo

Executive Vice President Digital, JD Crowley

Vice President, Gene Mellevold

Vice President Post Production, Jeff Henry

Vice President Strategic Partnerships, Michael Gulbin

Vice President Production And Operations, Courtney James

Vice President Business Affairs, Allison Brightman

Executive Vice President Development, Elaine Brooks

Executive Vice President Theatrical Distribution, Steven Friedlander

Evp Entertainment Diversity Inclusion And Communications Cbs Entertainment, Tiffany Smith-anoa'i

Senior Vice President Television, Tiffany Grant

Senior Vice President, Paul Gilbert

Vice President Communications Cbs Television Distribution East Coast, Lauren Nowell

Executive Vice President Digital Sales And Sales Strategy, David Lawenda

Vice President Digital Sales, Trevor Frederickson

Vice President, Ross Molloy

Executive Vice President Operations And Engineering, Glenn Oakley

Vice President Latenight Programs East Coast, Vincent Favale

Vice President Short Term Capital Markets, Ken Woltersdorf

Senior Vice President Business And Legal Affairs, Christine Hagan

Auditors: PricewaterhouseCoopers LLP

LOCATIONS

HQ: ViacomCBS Inc
51 W. 52nd Street, New York, NY 10019
Phone: 212 975-4321
Web: www.cbscorporation.com

2017 Sales

	$ mil.	% of total
United States	11,676	85
International	2,017	15
Total	**13,692**	**100**

PRODUCTS/OPERATIONS

2017 Sales

	$ mil.	% of total
Entertainment	9,165	66
Cable Networks	2,501	18
Local Media	1,668	12
Publishing	831	4
Corporate/Eliminations	(471)	-
Total	**13,692**	**100**

2017 Sales

	$ mil.	% of total
Advertising	5,753	42
Content licensing & distribution	3,952	29
Affiliate & subscription fees	3,758	27
Other	229	2
Total	**13,692**	**100**

Selected Operations

CBS Television Network
CBS Entertainment
CBS News
CBS Sports
CBS Television Stations
CBS Television Studios
CBS Studios International
CBS Television Distribution
CBS Home Entertainment
CBS Consumer Products
CBS Films
The CW
Showtime
Smithsonian Channel
CBS Sports Network
CBS Interactive
Simon & Schuster
CBS Scene
Watch! Magazine
EcoMedia
Pop
CBS VISION

HISTORICAL FINANCIALS

Company Type: Public

Income Statement   FYE: December 31

	REVENUE ($ mil.)	NET INCOME ($ mil.)	NET PROFIT MARGIN	EMPLOYEES
12/18	14,514	1,960	13.5%	16,730
12/17	13,692	357	2.6%	16,730
12/16	13,166	1,261	9.6%	21,270
12/15	13,886	1,413	10.2%	16,260
12/14	13,806	2,959	21.4%	17,310
Annual Growth	1.3%	(9.8%)		(0.8%)

2018 Year-End Financials

Debt ratio: 46.00%	No. of shares (mil.): 373
Return on equity: 82.00%	Dividends
Cash ($ mil.): 322	Yield: 2.0%
Current ratio: 1.00	Payout: 14.0%
Long-term debt ($ mil.): 9,465	Market value ($ mil.): 16,308

	STOCK PRICE ($) FY Close	P/E High/Low		PER SHARE ($) Earnings	Dividends	Book Value
12/18	44.00	12	8	5.00	1.00	8.00
12/17	59.00	78	61	1.00	1.00	5.00
12/16	64.00	23	15	3.00	1.00	9.00
12/15	47.00	22	13	3.00	1.00	12.00
12/14	55.00	13	9	5.00	1.00	14.00
Annual Growth	(5.7%)	—	—	(0.6%)	7.5%	(14.0%)

VIRGINIA COLLEGE BUILDING AUTHORITY

EXECUTIVES

Prin, Robert F McDonnell

LOCATIONS

HQ: VIRGINIA COLLEGE BUILDING AUTHORITY
101 N 14TH ST FL 3, RICHMOND, VA 232193665
Phone: 804 225-2142
Web: WWW.VIRGINIA.GOV

HISTORICAL FINANCIALS

Company Type: Private

Income Statement   FYE: June 30

	ASSETS ($ mil.)	NET INCOME ($ mil.)	INCOME AS % OF ASSETS	EMPLOYEES
06/18	2,141	(146)	—	2
06/17	1,754	(99)	—	—
06/16	2,199	(328)	—	—
Annual Growth	(1.3%)	—	—	—

Virginia Electric & Power Co.

Virginia Electric and Power Company (Virginia Power) operates under the Dominion Virginia Power and Dominion North Carolina Power brands and provides regulated electric delivery services to about 2.4 million homes and businesses. Power generation is derived by means of coal gas oil hydro and nuclear plants. The utility's power plants (with 24300 MW of generating capacity) are managed by the Dominion Generation unit of parent Dominion Energy. Control of Virginia Power's transmission facilities is maintained by PJM Interconnection. Dominion Virginia Power also sells wholesale power to other users.

Geographic Reach

Virginia Power generates transmits and distributes electricity for sale in Virginia and North Carolina.

Sales and Marketing

Virginia Power primarily serves retail customers. It sells electricity at wholesale prices to rural electric cooperatives municipalities and wholesale electricity markets.

Strategy

Virginia Power is trying to beef up its green energy profile. In addition to exploring wind farm options to help produce alternative energy the company is pushing energy conservation programs with the aim of cutting peak demand by electric consumers in Virginia by 650 MW.

In 2016 the company announced plans to invest nearly $2 billion per year through 2020 to add cleaner generation to its infrastructure including solar energy. It also plans to expand secure and upgrade its electric grid in Virginia and northeastern North Carolina.

EXECUTIVES

President Dominion Virginia Power, Robert M. Blue
Auditors: DELOITTE & TOUCHE LLP

LOCATIONS

HQ: Virginia Electric & Power Co.
120 Tredegar Street, Richmond, VA 23219
Phone: 804 819-2000

HISTORICAL FINANCIALS

Company Type: Public

Income Statement   FYE: December 31

	REVENUE ($ mil.)	NET INCOME ($ mil.)	NET PROFIT MARGIN	EMPLOYEES
12/18	7,619	1,282	16.8%	6,800
12/17	7,556	1,540	20.4%	6,900
12/16	7,588	1,218	16.1%	6,800
12/15	7,622	1,087	14.3%	6,800
12/14	7,579	858	11.3%	6,800
Annual Growth	0.1%	10.6%	—	0.0%

2018 Year-End Financials

Debt ratio: 32.00%	No. of shares (mil.): 0
Return on equity: 10.00%	Dividends
Cash ($ mil.): 29	Yield: —
Current ratio: 1.00	Payout: —
Long-term debt ($ mil.): 11,321	Market value ($ mil.): —

VIRGINIA HOUSING DEVELOPMENT AUTHORITY

Though Virginia is famous for its Civil War-era plantations these historic estates represent a lifestyle out of reach for most. For Virginians seeking a more modest homestead there's the Virginia Housing Development Authority (VHDA). The not-for-profit quasi-government agency founded by the Virginia General Assembly in 1972 provides developers of rentalÂ propertiesÂ and low- to moderate-income borrowers with low interest rate loans to renovate or purchase houses and apartments across the state. Its loan products are offered by more than 140 authorized lenders throughout Virginia. The VHDA is self-supporting issuing bonds to raise capital.

EXECUTIVES

Executive Director, Susan F. Dewey
Managing Director Rental Housing, Arthur N. (Art) Bowen
Managing Director Community Outreach, J. Michael Hawkins
Managing Director Executive Services, Llewellyn C. Anderson
Managing Director Homeownership, Janet Wiglesworth
Managing Director Internal Audit And Risk Management, Julie Camus
Managing Director Finance, Pat Carey
Acting Managing Director Information Technology Services, J. Kyle Howard
Vice President Of Operation, Jackie Gibbs
Vice President Of Operation, Sherry Estridge
Executive Vice President Claims And Customer Service Operations, Dyson Darrell
Chairman, Timothy M. Chapman
Vice Chairman, Sarah B. Stedfast
Treasurer, Gary Murray
Auditors: KPMG LLP RICHMOND VIRGINIA

LOCATIONS

HQ: VIRGINIA HOUSING DEVELOPMENT AUTHORITY
601 S BELVIDERE ST, RICHMOND, VA 232206504
Phone: 804 780-0789
Web: WWW.VHDA.COM

HISTORICAL FINANCIALS

Company Type: Private

Income Statement				FYE: June 30
	ASSETS ($ mil.)	NET INCOME ($ mil.)	INCOME AS % OF ASSETS	EMPLOYEES
06/18	7,293	132	1.8%	300
06/16	8,025	172	2.1%	—
06/15	8,071	177	2.2%	—
06/14	8,015	133	1.7%	—
Annual Growth	(2.3%)	(0.1%)	—	—

VIRTU FINANCIAL LLC

Auditors: DELOITTE & TOUCHE LLP NEW YOR

LOCATIONS

HQ: VIRTU FINANCIAL LLC
1 LIBERTY PLZ, NEW YORK, NY 100061404
Phone: 212 418-0100
Web: WWW.VIRTU.COM

HISTORICAL FINANCIALS

Company Type: Private

Income Statement				FYE: December 31
	ASSETS ($ mil.)	NET INCOME ($ mil.)	INCOME AS % OF ASSETS	EMPLOYEES
12/14	3,325	190	5.7%	18
12/13	3,964	182	4.6%	—
Annual Growth	(16.1%)	4.3%	—	—

Visa Inc

Paper or plastic? Visa hopes you choose the latter. Visa operates the world's largest global consumer payment system (ahead of rivals MasterCard and American Express) and boasts more than 3.3 billion credit and other payment cards in circulation across more than 200 countries. As part of its business the company licenses the Visa name to member institutions which issue and market their own Visa products and participate in the VisaNet payment system that provides authorization processing and settlement services. The company also offers debit cards internet payment systems value-storing smart cards and traveler's checks. Visa's network connects thousands of financial institutions worldwide.

HISTORY

Although the first charge card was issued by Western Union in 1914 it wasn't until 1958 that Bank of America (BofA) issued its BankAmericard which combined the convenience of a charge account with credit privileges. When BofA extended its customer base outside California the interchange system controlling payments began to falter because of design problems and fraud.

In 1968 Dee Hock manager of the BankAmericard operations of the National Bank of Commerce in Seattle convinced member banks that a more reliable system was needed. Two years later National BankAmericard Inc. (NBI) was created as an independent corporation (owned by 243 banks) to buy the BankAmericard system from BofA.

With its initial ad slogan "Think of it as Money" the Hock-led NBI developed BankAmericard into a widely used form of payment in the US. A multinational corporation IBANCO was formed in 1974 to carry the operations into other countries. People outside the US resisted BankAmericard's nominal association with BofA and in 1977 Hock changed the card's name to Visa. NBI became Visa USA and IBANCO became Visa International.

By 1980 Visa had debuted debit cards begun issuing traveler's checks and created an electromagnetic point-of-sale authorization system. Visa developed a global network of ATMs in 1983; it was expanded in 1987 by the purchase of a 33% stake in the Plus System of ATMs then the US's second-largest system. Hock retired in 1984 with the company well on its way to realizing his vision of a universal payment system.

The company built the Visa brand image with aggressive advertising such as sponsorship of the 1988 and 1992 Olympics and by co-branding (issuing cards through other organizations with strong brand names such as Blockbuster and Ford).

In 1994 Visa teamed up with Microsoft and others to develop home banking services and software. Visa Cash was introduced during the 1996 Olympics. Visa pushed its debit cards in 1996 and 1997 with humorous ads featuring presidential also-ran Bob Dole and showbiz success story Daffy Duck.

Visa expanded its smart card infrastructure in 1997. It published with MasterCard encryption and security software for online transactions. The gloves came off the next year as the companies vied to convince the world to rally around their respective e-purse technology standards.

During the 1990s Visa fought American Express' attempts to introduce a bank credit card of its own by forbidding Visa members in the US from issuing the product; the Justice Department responded with an antitrust suit against Visa and MasterCard. The case went to trial in 2000 with the government claiming that Visa and MasterCard stifle competition and enjoy an exclusive cross-ownership structure. Visa eventually agreed to pay American Express $2.25 billion to settle the case.

Also in 2000 the company made a deal with Gemplus the French smart card company to enable payments over wireless networks. Visa then inked e-commerce agreements with telecommunications companies Nokia and Ericsson. The company continued its technology push with a deal with Financial Services Technology Consortium to test biometrics — the use of fingerprints irises and voice recognition to identify cardholders. The company also launched a prepaid card Visa Buxx targeted at teenagers.

The European Union in 2000 launched an investigation into the firm's transaction fees alleging that the fees could restrict competition. The following year Visa International agreed to drop its fee to 0.7% of the transaction value over five years.

Led by retail giant Wal-Mart some 4 million merchants claimed Visa and MasterCard violated antitrust laws and attempted to monopolize a legally defined market for debit cards. The plaintiffs sought up to $200 billion in damages in their class-action suit. Just as the 1996 lawsuit was to go to trial in early 2003 Visa settled agreeing to pay $2 billion (twice that of co-defendant MasterCard) over the next decade. Both agreed to pay $25 mil-

lion immediately as well as reduce the fee merchants pay for signature-based debit cards.

Visa settled a similar case with Discover Financial in 2008. Visa's net share of the deal totaled some $1.8 billion; MasterCard which was also named agreed to pay $862.5 million.

The group restructured in 2007 in order to offer a more seamless international payments processing platform and to take itself public. Visa International Visa Canada Visa U.S.A. and several other regional organizations merged to create Visa Inc. which became the new parent of the group. It raised about $17 billion in a 2008 IPO.

Visa dedicated some of the funds raised to exploring new payment-related technologies and expanding into more regions. It established joint ventures with payment processors and banks to strengthen its global payment network. Other funds were set aside to cover costs resulting from legal settlements with American Express and Discover Financial totaling more than $4 billion.

EXECUTIVES

Director, Alfred F. (Al) Kelly, age 61
Vice Chairman Risk And Public Policy, Ellen Richey, age 70, $600,023 total compensation
Evp And Cfo, Vasant M. Prabhu, age 58, $547,616 total compensation
Evp And Ceo European Operations, Charlotte M. Hogg, age 48
Evp Strategy Mergers And Acquisitions And Government Relations, William M. (Bill) Sheedy, age 52, $525,020 total compensation
Evp And General Counsel, Kelly M. Tullier, age 53
Evp Technology, Rajat Taneja, age 54, $750,029 total compensation
President, Ryan McInerney, age 44, $750,029 total compensation
Vice President, Brian Wood
Senior Vice President, Elizabeth Hurvitz
Vice President Head Of Payment Services Marketing Visa Europe, Neil Horseman
Vice President Processing Solutions, Manny Fernandez
Vice President Of Management, James Williams
Vice President Healthcare, Stacy Pourfallah
Vice President, Michael Lemberger
Vice President, Seth Friedman
Vice President, Jeff Allison
Vice President, Andrew Carpenter
Vice President Product Technology, Mark Rigby
Vice President, Julie Miller
Senior Vice President, Mark Nelsen
Vice President Corporate Initiatives, Sarah Suarez
Senior Vice President Innovation And Strategic Partnerships, Matt Dill
Vice President Marketing Planning, Stacey Taylor
Senior Vice President Global Government Affairs, Demetrios Marantis
Vice President, Joanna Gill
Vice President Of Product, Alan Johnson
Vice President Pricing And Costing, Philip Joseph
Vice President Client Readiness, Lori Degliantoni
Vice President, Biju Abraham
Vice President Digital Marketing, David Purcell
Vice President Global Product, Gourab Basu
Vice President Financial Institution Sales, Brent Vaughan
Vice President Digital Solutions, Todd Wade
Vice President, Kyle Mandry
Vice President Corporate Strategy, Saurabh Chopra
Senior Vice President Chief Corporate Counsel, Tracey Heaton
Senior Vice President Chief Audit Executive, Adrian Kilcoyne
Vice President Intellectual Property Strategy, Tim Bedard
Vice President Infrastructure Project Management Office, Amy Gradnik

Vice President Enterprise Workforce
Transformation And Planning, Manish Asnani
Svp Developer Platform India, Nitin Chandel
Senior Vice President Visa Research Labs, Min
Wang
Vice President. Consumer, Daniel Sanford
Vice President, Sang Lee
Vice President Strategic Initiatives, Jeff Kim
Vice President Business Development And
Strategy, Robert Steinmetz
Vice President Procurement, Brian Hall
Senior Vice President Investor Relations, Michael
Milotich
Vice President Head Of Global Infrastructure
Network Services, Justin Dustzadeh
Senior Vice President Data Platform, Sam
Hamilton
Vice President Head Of Product Strategy And
New Product Development North America,
Matthew Friend
Vice President Europe Information Security
Integration And Global Identity And Access
Management, Shirish Puranik
Vice President Marketing, Kevin Skirde
Vice President Information Security Architecture,
Subra Kumaraswamy
Vice President Data Architecture, Dirk Reinshagen
Senior Vice President Global Operations, Elizabeth
Rector
Vice President Innovation And Strategic
Partnerships (visa Innovation Center), Kellie
Goodwin
Vice President Marketing Strategy And Operations
(north America), Sheila Parmar
Senior Vice President Product Digital Solutions,
Ansar Ansari
Vice President Specialized Product Sales Prepaid,
Patrick Williams
Vice President Of Technology, Deepak Bapna
Vice President Global Tax, Carl Andersen
Vice President Risk And Authentication Product
Development, Zijian Zheng
Vp Global Merchant Support, Noel Pedroza
Senior Vice President Innovation Strategic
Partnerships, Jason Blackhurst
Vice President Of Risk, Rosetta Jones
Senior Vice President, Kirk Stuart
Evp General Counsel And Corporate Secretary,
Kelly Mahon Tullier
Chairman, Robert W. Matschullat, age 72
Auditors: KPMG LLP

LOCATIONS

HQ: Visa Inc
P.O. Box 8999, San Francisco, CA 94128-8999
Phone: 650 432-3200
Web: www.corporate.visa.com

2018 Sales

	$ mil.	% of total
United States	9,332	45
International	11,277	55
Total	**20,609**	**100**

PRODUCTS/OPERATIONS

2018 Sales

	$ mil.	% of total
Service Revenues	8,918	34
Data Processing Revenues	9,027	34
International Transaction Revenues	7,211	28
Other Revenues	944	4
Client Incentives	(5491)	-
Total	**20,609**	**100**

Selected Products and Services

Commercial and government
Visa Business Credit Card (small business)
Visa Business Debit Card (small business)
Visa Business Electron (international)
Visa Business Line of Credit
Visa Commercial One Card
Visa Corporate Card (travel and entertainment)
Visa Gift Card
Visa Incentive Card
Visa Purchasing Card
Visa Signature Business Card
Consumer credit
Visa Classic
Visa Gold
Visa Infinite
Visa Platinum
Consumer deposit
Interlink Debit (POS debit network)
Prepaid
Visa Debit
Visa Classic
Visa Gold
Visa Infinite
Visa Platinum
Visa Electron Debit

COMPETITORS

American Express	MasterCard
Apple Inc.	NYCE Payments Network
China UnionPay	PULSE Network
Citigroup	PayPal
Discover	Rewards Network
JCB International	

HISTORICAL FINANCIALS

Company Type: Public

Income Statement   FYE: September 30

	REVENUE ($ mil.)	NET INCOME ($ mil.)	NET PROFIT MARGIN	EMPLOYEES
09/19	22,977	12,080	52.6%	19,500
09/18	20,609	10,301	50.0%	17,000
09/17	18,358	6,699	36.5%	15,000
09/16	15,082	5,991	39.7%	—
09/15	13,880	6,328	45.6%	11,300
Annual Growth	**13.4%**	**17.5%**	**—**	**14.6%**

2019 Year-End Financials

Debt ratio: 23.00%
Return on equity: 35.00%
Cash ($ mil.): 7,838
Current ratio: 2.00
Long-term debt ($ mil.): 16,729
No. of shares (mil.): 1,974
Dividends
  Yield: 1.0%
  Payout: 19.0%
Market value ($ mil.): 339,548

	STOCK PRICE ($) FY Close	P/E High/Low	PER SHARE ($) Earnings	Dividends	Book Value
09/19	172.00	35 23	5.00	1.00	18.00
09/18	150.00	34 24	4.00	1.00	17.00
09/17	105.00	38 27	3.00	1.00	16.00
09/16	83.00	33 27	2.00	1.00	15.00
09/15	70.00	108 25	3.00	0.00	13.00
Annual Growth	**25.4%**	**— —**	**19.8%**	**20.1%**	**6.9%**

Vistra Energy Corp

Auditors: DELOITTE & TOUCHE
LLP

LOCATIONS

HQ: Vistra Energy Corp
6555 Sierra Drive, Irving, TX 75039
Phone: 214 812-4600
Web: www.vistraenergy.com

HISTORICAL FINANCIALS

Company Type: Public

Income Statement   FYE: December 31

	REVENUE ($ mil.)	NET INCOME ($ mil.)	NET PROFIT MARGIN	EMPLOYEES
12/18	9,144	(54)	—	5,275
12/17	5,430	(254)	—	4,150
12/16*	1,191	(163)	—	4,435
10/16	4,255	22,851	537.0%	—
12/15	5,704	(4,677)	—	—
Annual Growth	**17.0%**	**—**	**—**	**—**

*Fiscal year change

2018 Year-End Financials

Debt ratio: 43.00%
Return on equity: (-1.00%)
Cash ($ mil.): 636
Current ratio: 1.00
Long-term debt ($ mil.): 10,874
No. of shares (mil.): 493
Dividends
  Yield: —
  Payout: —
Market value ($ mil.): 11,290

	STOCK PRICE ($) FY Close	P/E High/Low	PER SHARE ($) Earnings	Dividends	Book Value
12/18	23.00	— —	(0.00)	0.00	16.00
12/17	18.00	— —	(1.00)	0.00	15.00
12/16*	16.00	— —	(0.00)	2.00	15.00
Annual Growth	**13.9%**	**— —**	**—**	**—**	**1.1%**

*Fiscal year change

VMware Inc

VMware develops software used to create and
manage virtual machines — computer functions
spread across multiple systems. Companies use its
cloud-based and on-premise applications to more
efficiently integrate and manage server storage and
networking functions which reduces their IT costs.
VMware also offers software maintenance and support training consulting services and hosted services. The company has marketing relationships
with top computer hardware vendors including
Hewlett Packard Enterprise IBM and Cisco Systems. VMware has strong geographic distribution
with international customers accounting for more
than half of its sales. Dell Technologies holds a
controlling stake in VMware through its acquisition
of EMC.

Financial Performance

VMware's virtualization products produce real
money driving revenue some $2.4 billion higher
from 2015 to 2019 (ended February). The company's net income fluctuated over the same time
but leaped in 2019 from 2018.

In 2019 VMware posted a 14% revenue increase
to reach $8.9 billion up about $1.1 billion from
2018. License revenue (40% of overall sales) rose
18% year over year with help from the company's
Hybrid Cloud Computing and SaaS offerings. Service revenue was 11% higher in 2019 from 2018
due to existing contracts and contracts added
though license sales during the year.

VMware recorded net income of $2.2 billion in
2019 compared to $659 million in 2018. The 2019
profit was lifted by higher revenue income from
the company's interest in Pivotal Software (which
had an IPO in fiscal 2019) and lower income taxes.

Cash in VMware's coffers totaled $2.9 billion in
2019 compared to $6 billion the year before. Op-
erations generated $3.6 billion in 2018 investing
activities provided $4.4 billion and financing activ-

ities used $11.1 billion (due to payment of a special dividend).

VMware has about $4 billion in debt which could require the company to devote cash flow to debt service instead of investments related to growth. A lack of cash could limit VMware's flexibility in responding to opportunities and crises. The company has a $1 billion unsecured revolving credit facility that it has yet to use.

Strategy

Although VMware is part of Dell Technologies that hasn't stopped the company from doing deals with Dell competitors. The company has agreements with IBM and Amazon Web Services (AWS) that help customers manage their private clouds and public clouds (running on IBM or AWS) using VMware software. The arrangements provide customers more flexibility with their cloud environments.

For products to run on those systems VMware has assembled a group of software-as-a-service and cloud technologies through in-house R&D and acquisitions including Heptio CloudHealth Technologies Inc. and VeloCloud Networks Inc.

Sales of VMware's network virtualization product NSX have continued to grow since it was introduced in 2013. Sold as part of other VMware products NSX allows networking hardware like routers and switches to be reconfigured and managed by software. NSX has been a hit for the company producing about $1.3 billion in revenue in 2019 (it's used by about 10000 customers).

Part of VMware's strategy is to pack its customers with as many of its products as it can. An increasing number of customers have gone with the company's full VMware Cloud Foundation or its full VMware Cloud on AWS offering generating bigger deals.

VMware relies on sales to distributors Arrow Electronics and Tech Data Corp. for more than 25% of sales. Sales to parent Dell Technologies accounts for another 25% of revenue.

Mergers and Acquisitions

In 2019 VMware agreed to spend about $4.8 billion to buy companies that broaden its cloud offerings and strengthen its security capabilities. The company said it would buy Pivotal Software for about $2.7 billion to build out its software for cloud computing environments and buy CarbonBlack for about $2.1 billion to beef up security throughout its products. The deals are to close by the end of VMware's 2020 fiscal year in January 2020. Like VMware Pivotal is partly owned by Dell Technologies.

VMware in 2019 acquired Intrinsic a cybersecurity company as part of its focus on the public cloud. Intrinsic's products allow software developers to securely access serverless computing by setting policies on how the systems work when certain conditions are met. The deal contributes to the expansion of VMware's AppDefense platform into the public cloud.

In 2019 VMware agreed to acquire Uhana which develops technology to help telecom carriers automate and improve network operations amid carriers' transition from 4G to 5G networks and the increasing need for reduced latency. Uhana's real-time deep learning engine operates in the operator private cloud or public cloud infrastructure. VMware intends to add Uhana's to its Telco Cloud and Edge Cloud portfolio and provide intelligence and analytics for VMware Smart Assurance and VMware Smart Experience products.

VMware agreed to buy Bitfusion which develops technology to make cloud computing workloads more efficient using artificial intelligence in 2019. VMware intends to integrate Bitfusion's tools into its vSphere platform. Bitfusion's technology allows cloud software to access computing power on individual CPUs no matter what server they're sitting on.

In another 2019 deal VMware agreed to buy Avi Networks a developer of multi-cloud application delivery services. Avi's technology is to help VMware to bring benefits of a public cloud experience to the entire data center making the process automated scalable and more secure for its customers. The deal was expected to close bu August 2020.

Also in 2019 VMware agreed to acquire Bitnami a developer of application packaging for cloud and Kubernetes environments. With Bitnami's technologies VMware customers would be able to deploy application packages on any cloud in the appropriate format. The deal is expected to close by the end of the 2019 second quarter.

Company Background

Founded in 1998 VMware was acquired by EMC for about $625 million in cash in 2004. Looking to unlock some of the value in its subsidiary EMC sold some of its stake in VMware in a 2007 IPO. In 2016 Dell bought EMC including VMware for more than $60 billion.

EXECUTIVES

Corporate Senior Vice President And Chief People Officer, Betsy Sutter

Ceo And Director, Patrick P. (Pat) Gelsinger, age 58, $1,000,000 total compensation

Coo Customer Operations, Sanjay Poonen, age 49, $605,000 total compensation

Evp Worldwide Sales, Maurizio Carli

Evp And Cfo, Zane C. Rowe, age 48

Co-coo Products And Cloud Services, Rajiv Ramaswami, age 53

Svp And Cio, Bask Iyer

Evp And General Manager Hybrid Cloud Services Business Unit, Bill Fathers

Co-coo Products And Cloud Services, Rangarajan (Raghu) Raghuram, age 56, $605,000 total compensation

Svp Strategy And Corporate Development And General Manager Telco Nfv Group, Shekar Ayyar

Corporate Svp Software-defined Data Center Division, Ray O'Farrell

Svp General Counsel Chief Compliance Officer And Secretary, S. Dawn Smith, age 55

Senior Vice President Finance And Chief Accounting Officer, Kevan Krysler

Vice President Americas End User Computmg, Robert Ruelas

Vice President U.s. Enterprise Sales, Corey Hutchison

Svp Worldwide Commercial And Channel Sales, Brandon Sweeney

Vice President And Deputy General Counsel, Laurie Hane

Vice President Ww Federation Sales And Gtm, John Sellers

Vice President Cloud Services Development And Operations, Velchamy Sankarlingam

Vice President Chief Information Security Officer, Alex Tosheff

Vice President Global Strategic Alliances, Tom Herrmann

Vice President Worldwide Sales Operations, Pradeep Vancheeswaran

Vice President Global Technical Support, John Dolan

Vice President, Nicola Acutt

Senior Product Manager Mvp, Debapriya Ray

Vice President Field Automation Services And Global Marketing Operations, Mia Leondakis

Quality Engineer For Mvp, Bryan Bozzi

Vice President Latin America Sales, Fernando Mollon

Vice President Products, Mark Lohmeyer

Vice President And Deputy General Counsel Corporate Securities And Mergers And Acquisitions, Craig Norris

Vice President And Treasurer, Len Rosenduft

Vice President Product Management, Paul Fazzone

Vice President Customer Operations Finance, Stephanie Joe

Vice President Research And Development Networking And Security Bu, Umesh Mahajan

Vice President Products, Lee Caswell

Vice President And Chief Open Source Officer, Dirk Hohndel

Vice President Partners And General Business Asia Pacific And Japan, Sharat Sinha

Senior Vice President And General Manager Americas, Brett Shirk

Vice President Cloud Management Business Unit, Jon Herlocker

Vice President Channel And Alliances And General Business In Emea, Jean-Phillipe Barleaza

Svp And Gm Cloud Management Business Unit, Ajay Singh

Vice President Americas Systems Engineering, Dave Gregory

Vice President Airwatch Siso Sales, Jeff Baum

Svp Product Development Cloud Services, Ajay Patel

Vice President Of Solutions Partners North America, Rich Figer

Vice President Cloud Management Product Marketing, Rob Smoot

Chairman, Michael S. Dell

Board Member, Karen Dykstra

Auditors: PricewaterhouseCoopers LLP

LOCATIONS

HQ: VMware Inc
3401 Hillview Avenue, Palo Alto, CA 94304
Phone: 650 427-5000
Web: www.vmware.com

2019 Sales

	$ mil.	% of total
US	4,205	47
Other countries	4,769	53
Total	**6,571**	**100**

PRODUCTS/OPERATIONS

2019 Sales

	$ mil.	% of total
Services	5,186	58
License	3,788	42
Total	**8,974**	**100**

COMPETITORS

AWS	IBM
CA Inc.	Microsoft
Cisco Systems	Nutanix
Google	Oracle
Hewlett Packard Enterprise	

HISTORICAL FINANCIALS

Company Type: Public

Income Statement				FYE: February 1
	REVENUE ($ mil.)	NET INCOME ($ mil.)	NET PROFIT MARGIN	EMPLOYEES
02/19	8,974	2,422	27.0%	24,200
02/18	7,922	570	7.2%	21,700
02/17*	496	(8)	—	—
12/16	7,093	1,186	16.7%	19,900
12/15	6,571	997	15.2%	19,000
Annual Growth	10.9%	34.4%	—	8.4%

*Fiscal year change

2019 Year-End Financials

Debt ratio: 29.00%
Return on equity: 58.00%
Cash ($ mil.): 2,830
Current ratio: 1.00
Long-term debt ($ mil.): 4,242

No. of shares (mil.): 411
Dividends
Yield: 18.0%
Payout: 458.0%
Market value ($ mil.): 61,817

	STOCK PRICE ($) FY Close	P/E High/Low		PER SHARE ($) Earnings	Dividends	Book Value
02/19	151.00	28	18	6.00	27.00	1.00
02/18	123.00	107	61	1.00	0.00	19.00
02/17*	89.00	—	—	(0.00)	0.00	20.00
12/16	79.00	29	16	3.00	0.00	20.00
12/15	57.00	39	24	2.00	0.00	19.00
Annual Growth	38.6%	—	—	35.7%	—	(58.5%)

*Fiscal year change

Voya Financial Inc

Auditors: Ernst & Young LLP

LOCATIONS

HQ: Voya Financial Inc
230 Park Avenue, New York, NY 10169
Phone: 212 309-8200
Web: www.ing.us

HISTORICAL FINANCIALS

Company Type: Public

Income Statement   FYE: December 31

	ASSETS ($ mil.)	NET INCOME ($ mil.)	INCOME AS % OF ASSETS	EMPLOYEES
12/18	154,682	875	0.6%	6,000
12/17	222,532	(2,992)	—	6,300
12/16	214,235	(428)	—	6,700
12/15	218,250	408	0.2%	7,000
12/14	226,951	2,300	1.0%	6,500
Annual Growth	(9.1%)	(21.5%)	—	(2.0%)

2018 Year-End Financials

Debt ratio: 2.00%
Return on equity: 10.00%
Cash ($ mil.): 1,538
Current ratio: —
Long-term debt ($ mil.): —

No. of shares (mil.): 151
Dividends
Yield: 0.0%
Payout: 1.0%
Market value ($ mil.): 6,060

	STOCK PRICE ($) FY Close	P/E High/Low		PER SHARE ($) Earnings	Dividends	Book Value
12/18	40.00	10	7	5.00	0.00	54.00
12/17	49.00	—	—	(16.00)	0.00	58.00
12/16	39.00	—	—	(2.00)	0.00	67.00
12/15	37.00	27	20	2.00	0.00	64.00
12/14	42.00	5	4	9.00	0.00	67.00
Annual Growth	(1.3%)	—	—	(12.9%)	(0.0%)	(4.9%)

WAKEFERN FOOD CORP.

Grocery stores getting supplies from this co-op may be on the "Rite" track. Wakefern Food is the largest member-owned wholesale distribution co-operative in the US supplying groceries and other merchandise to more than 250 supermarkets under the ShopRite and The Fresh Grocer banners in New Jersey New York Connecticut Delaware Maryland Pennsylvania and Virginia. It also operates more than 50 PriceRite stores in these states plus Rhode Island and Massachusetts. Beyond supplying its member-owned stores Wakerfern distributes products to other supermarkets across the northeastern US and Bermuda. Founded by seven grocers in 1946 the coop now boasts 50 members 70000-plus employees and over $15 billion in annual sales.

Operations

Wakefern Food supplies retail and wholesale members mostly in the Northeast US. PriceRite a subsidiary of Wakefern Food and its nearly 50 supermarkets offer over 500 grocery items at discounted prices such as fresh fruits and vegetables breads prepackaged meat and seafood kosher products and national brands. Stores average about 35000 square feet in size which are smaller than traditional supermarkets. While the vast majority of ShopRite brand stores are member owned subsidiary ShopRite Supermarkets Inc operates nearly 35 company-owned stores.

Sales and Marketing

The coop added its 50th member The Fresh Grocer in July 2013. Outside of its members the company also supplies grocery stores like Saker ShopRite (New Jersey) Village Super Market (New Jersey and Pennsylvania) and Inserra Supermarkets (New York and New Jersey).

Financial Performance

Wakern Food's revenues have been rising over the past several years thanks to new member additions and their store openings.

The company's retail sales rose 4% to a record $14.7 billion in fiscal 2014 (ended September 27) thanks to the addition of six new ShopRite stores five new PriceRite discount supermarkets and six new The Fresh Grocer stores over the course of the year. The company also continued to expand its ShopRite from Home services store reach which would be provided from a total of 214 of its stores.

Strategy

Like other grocery wholesalers Wakefern Food's success depends on its ability to distribute goods at the lowest possible cost to its customers meaning the company focuses on keeping expenses low and improving efficiencies throughout its supply operation. But as a member-owned cooperative the company differs from other wholesalers such as Nash-Finch in that its primary focus is on its member stores. Wakefern Food also has the added responsibility of promoting its ShopRite retail chain and helping its member retailers expand the chain's footprint.

The ShopRite chain boasts a loyal following in its core markets but the supermarkets have been feeling the pinch from rivals in the price-competitive grocery business. The company is especially feeling pressure from non-supermarket chains such as Wal-Mart CVS Health and Wawa. To help boost customer loyalty Wakefern has turned to new technology in the form of mobile applications (developed in partnership with technology firm MyWebGrocer) for the Apple iPhone that allow users to get alerts about weekly store specials in their area. The company also rolled out an online pharmacy where customers can place orders through the Internet.

Company Background

Wakefern Food announced in 2012 it was supplying New York-based Food Bazaar stores which had supermarkets in New York New Jersey and Connecticut. Wakefern will supply ShopRite private label brands along with non-private labels such as dairy frozen food grocery nonfoods and specialty products.

HISTORY

Wakefern Food was founded in 1946 by seven New York- and New Jersey-based grocers: Louis Weiss Sam and Al Aidekman Abe Kesselman Dave Fern Sam Garb and Albert Goldberg. The company got its name by taking the first letters of the last names of five of the original founders (Weiss Sam and Al Aidekman Kesselman and Fern). Like many cooperatives the association sought to lower costs by increasing its buying power as a group.

They each put in $1000 and began operating a 5000-sq.-ft. warehouse often putting in double time to keep both their stores and the warehouse running. The shopkeepers' collective buying power proved valuable enabling the grocers to stock many items at the same prices as their larger competitors.

In 1951 Wakefern members began pooling their resources to buy advertising space. A common store name — ShopRite — was chosen and each week co-op members met to decide which items would be sale priced. Within a year membership had grown to over 50. Expansion became a priority and in the mid-1950s co-op members united in small groups to take over failed supermarkets. One such group called the Supermarkets Operating Co. (SOC) was formed in 1956. Within 10 years it had acquired a number of failed stores remodeled them and given them the ShopRite name.

During the late 1950s sales at ShopRite stores slumped after Wakefern decided to buck the supermarket trend of offering trading stamps (which could then be exchanged for gifts) figuring that offering the stamps would ultimately lead to higher food prices. The move initially drove away customers but Wakefern cut grocery prices across the board and sales returned. The company did embrace another supermarket trend: stocking stores with nonfood items.

The co-op was severely shaken in 1966 when SOC merged with General Supermarkets a similar small group within Wakefern becoming Supermarkets General Corp. (SGC). SGC was a powerful entity with 71 supermarkets 10 drugstores six gas stations a wholesale bakery and a discount department store. Many Wakefern members opposed the merger and attempted to block the action with a court order. By 1968 SGC had beefed up its operations to include department store chains as well as its grocery stores. In a move that threatened to break Wakefern SGC broke away from the co-op and its stores were renamed Pathmark.

Wakefern not only weathered the storm it grew under the direction of chairman and CEO Thomas Infusino elected shortly after the split. The co-op focused on asserting its position as a seller of low-priced products. Wakefern developed private-label brands including the ShopRite brand. In the 1980s members began operating larger stores and adding more nonfood items to the ShopRite product mix. With its number of superstores on the rise and facing increased competition from club stores in 1992 Wakefern opened a centralized nonfood distribution center in New Jersey.

In 1995 30-year Wakefern veteran Dean Janeway was elected president of the co-op. The company debuted its ShopRite MasterCard co-branded with New Jersey's Valley National Bank in 1996. The following year the co-op purchased two of its customers' stores in Pennsylvania then threatened to close them when contract talks with the local union deteriorated. In 1998 Wakefern settled the dispute then sold the stores.

The company partnered with Internet bidding site Priceline in 1999 offering customers an opportunity to bid on groceries and then pick them up at ShopRite stores. Big V Wakefern's biggest customer filed for Chapter 11 bankruptcy protection in 2000 and said it was ending its distribution agreement with the co-op. In July 2002 however Wakefern's ShopRite Supermarkets subsidiary acquired all of Big V's assets for approximately $185 million in cash and assumed liabilities.

Infusino retired in May 2005 after 35 years with Wakefern Food. He was succeeded by former vice chairman Joseph Colalillo. The cooperative added to its footprint in 2007 when it acquired about 10 underperforming retail locations from Stop & Shop. The stores located mostly in South Jersey were rebranded under the ShopRite banner.

EXECUTIVES

Vice President Pharmacy, Jeffrey Mondelli
Vice President Quality Assurance Food Safety,
 Michael Ambrosio
Vice President Of Administration, Shawn Ravitz
Assistant Vice President Of Marketing, Maria Fiore
Vice President, Michael Rosenberg
Auditors: KPMG LLP SHORT HILLS NJ

LOCATIONS

HQ: WAKEFERN FOOD CORP.
 5000 RIVERSIDE DR, KEASBEY, NJ 088321209
Phone: 908 527-3300
Web: WWW.WAKEFERN.SHOPRITE.COM

PRODUCTS/OPERATIONS

2012 Corporate Stores

	No.
PriceRite	48
ShopRite	40
Total	**88**

COMPETITORS

A&P	IGA
Acme Markets	Krasdale Foods
Bozzuto's	SUPERVALU
C&S Wholesale	Stop & Shop
CVS	Wal-Mart
Hannaford Bros.	Wawa Inc.

HISTORICAL FINANCIALS

Company Type: Private

Income Statement				FYE: September 27
	REVENUE ($ mil.)	NET INCOME ($ mil.)	NET PROFIT MARGIN	EMPLOYEES
09/14	11,871	5	0.0%	3,500
09/13	11,456	0	0.0%	—
09/12	11,010	5	0.0%	—
Annual Growth	3.8%	(0.0%)	—	—

Walgreens Boots Alliance Inc

Whether you get your drugs from the pharmacist or the chemist Walgreens Boots Alliance has you covered. The company formed when US-based Walgreen Co. bought its European counterpart Alliance Boots includes more than 13200 retail pharmacies (or chemists in some parts of the world) in 11 countries mostly the US and its territories and the UK selling prescription and OTC drugs along with health and beauty products and general merchandise. The Alliance Boots part of the company also includes wholesale operations serving more than 230000 pharmacies hospitals and clinics in upwards of 20 countries. Walgreens Alliance Boots was formed in 2014.

Operations

Walgreens Boots Alliance operates three core segments: Retail Pharmacy USA Retail Pharmacy International and Pharmaceutical Wholesale.

The Retail Pharmacy USA segment generates around 75% of revenue and sells pharmacy and beauty and other items through 8100 retail stores under the Walgreens and Duane Reade banners. It sells third party and own-brand products in store and online. It also has a prescription management app for customers. The pharmacy arm accounts for around 70% of sales and its retail arm (beauty products toiletries and general merchandise) the remainder.

Retail Pharmacy International generates more than 10% of revenue and consists mainly of the Boots pharmacy network across the UK Norway Ireland the Netherlands and Thailand. The segment operates more than 4700 stores across the Boots brand as well as Benavides in Mexico and Ahumada in Chile. Boots stocks over 35000 products and offers around 640 in-store and standalone optician services alongside its retail and pharmacy operations.

The Pharmaceutical Wholesale segment (more than 10% of revenue) flies the Alliance Healthcare banner and delivers drugs and other healthcare products and services from around 290 distribution centers to about 110000 customers primarily in Europe; its the continents largest pharmaceutical distributor. It delivers to pharmacies hospitals clinics and doctor's offices and helps pharmacists develop their businesses. Its Alphega Pharmacy is a membership group for independent pharmacies.

Geographic Reach

Walgreens Boots Alliance is headquartered in the US and has stores in all fifty US states the District of Columbia Puerto Rico the US Virgin Islands Mexico Chile the UK Thailand Norway Ireland the Netherlands and Lithuania. The Walgreen part of the business is headquartered in the US while the Alliance Boots retail and wholesale operations are headquartered in Switzerland.

Altogether the company generates around 75% of its sales in the US while 15% comes from Europe (excluding the UK) and 10% of revenues were tied to business in the UK.

Sales and Marketing

Walgreens Boots Alliance sells in physical stores and online. It offers various loyalty programs such as Balance Rewards and the Boots Advantage Card.

Financial Performance

After posting explosive acquisition-driven growth between 2014 and 2016 in fiscal 2017 Walgreens Boots Alliance's sales grew by a relatively minor $1 billion or less than 1%. The company's USA segment grew 4% on the back of higher Medicare Part D prescriptions and the contribution from the newly formed AllianceRx Walgreens Prime specialty and mail services business. The balance of sales shifted further towards pharmacy sales which grew 7% and away from retail sales which fell 2%. Meanwhile the company recorded a 10% fall to $11.8 billion with the drop concentrated in comparable store sales mostly down to the weakness of the British pound against the dollar. The Wholesale business was likewise impacted by currency effects.

Net income fell 1% to $4.2 billion due to fluctuations in fair value adjustments of the company's AmerisourceBergen warrants and a gain in the previous year on equity interest in Alliance Boots.

Cash from operations fell 8% to $7.3 billion due to lower cash from changes in accrued expenses offset by higher cash inflows from changes in inventories.

Strategy

After years of using acquisitions to fuel growth at both Walgreen and Alliance Boots Walgreens Boots Alliance is looking to leverage its massive size as the world's largest purchaser of prescription drugs to lower costs. The company's presence in growing and untapped markets in South America and Asia give it great potential to continue expanding its footprint while its sheer size give it bargaining power with wholesalers of everything from prescription drugs to toothpaste to potato chips.

While it continues its store expansion the company's Retail Pharmacy USA division has been slowing its net new store openings in recent years and has been concentrating on emphasizing its exclusive private brand offerings to grow comparable store sales through technological innovations. It shed around 200 stores in 2016 while driving usage of its digital channels. The company believes customers that engage in-store and online are 3.5 times more valuable than in-store only and those that engage in in-store and mobile are 6 times more valuable. In 2016 Walgreens launched an app that allows users to refill or transfer prescriptions live chat with a pharmacy technician and create a shopping list. It also flips to "in-store mode" when a user enters a store pointing them to relevant needs.

Mergers and Acquisitions

In a long-running saga Walgreens' attempt to acquire Rite Aid ended after two years of back-and-forth in September 2017 with the retailer acquiring 1932 of Rite Aid's around 5500 stores. Regulators objected strongly to the move as it would have left the US with just two major pharmacist chains: Walgreens and CVS. The deal closed for around $4.4 billion; Rite Aid's stores will slowly be rebranded as Walgreens.

Company Background

Walgreen the largest drugstore company in the US bought 45% of Alliance Boots Europe's largest pharmacy retailer and wholesaler in 2012. The two got along well enough that in 2014 Walgreen exercised its option to purchase the rest of Alliance Boots. It formed Walgreens Boots Alliance and became a subsidiary of the parent along with Alliance Boots.

EXECUTIVES

Co-coo, Ornella Barra, age 65, $946,897 total compensation
Executive Vice Chairman And Ceo, Stefano Pessina, age 78
Evp And Global Cfo, George R. Fairweather, age 62, $977,118 total compensation
Co-coo, Alexander W. (Alex) Gourlay, age 58, $937,076 total compensation
Evp Global Chief Administrative Officer And General Counsel, Marco Pagni, age 56
Evp And Global Chief Human Resources Officer, Kathleen Wilson-Thompson, age 61, $627,000 total compensation
Evp And Chief Commercial Officer And President Global Brands, Ken Murphy, age 53
President Operations, Richard M. Ashworth
Cio, Steve Turner
Vice President And Director Global Accounts, Ruth Spencer
Vice President Global Enterprise Architecture, Brian DeMay
Pharmacy Manager, Jason Wood
Pharmacy Manager, Nisha Soung
Pharmacy Manager, Franklyn Osakwe
Pharmacy Manager, Denise Rhone
Pharmacy Manager, Anthony Silva
Pharmacy Manager, Pratik Shah

Pharmacy Manager, Pramod Allani
Vice President Global Executive Compensation And Stock Programs, Martha Peterson
Pharmacy Manager, Merykokeb Beyene
Pharmacy Manager, Hugh Zuengler
Pharmacy Manager, Jerry Huff
Pharmacy Manager, Joseph Rancour
Pharmacy Manager, Adel Shamseddine
Pharmacy Manager, Candice Reed
Pharmacy Manager, Ken Emelonye
Pharmacy Manager, Phuong Luc
Pharmacy Manager, Tamara Cisneros
Pharmacy Manager, Heather Rosenblum
Pharmacy Manager, Parnaz Najimi
Pharmacy Manager, Shenjin Orr
Pharmacy Manager, Dustin Hutmacher
Senior Vice President And Managing Director Boots, Elizabeth Fagan
Vp Hr Mergers And Acquisitions, Mark Wattley
Vp Corporate Operations, Lisa Badgley
Senior Vice President And Global Chief Public Affairs Officer, Charles Greener
Vp West Region, Bruce Bryant
Vice President Store Operations, Charles W Bernard
Division Vp Marketing Insights And Loyalty, Todd Vang
Vp Hr Walgreens Boots Alliance, Luca Loredan
Divisional Vice President And General Merchandise Manager Beauty And Personal Care, Shannon Petree
Divisional Vp Executive Communications And Events, Liz Roch
Group Vice President Global Sourcing, Moe Alkemade
Senior Vice President Supply Chain Retail And Pharmacy Renewal, Reuben Slone
Senior Vice President Director Global Consumer Brands, Andy Gibson
Market Vice President, Mike Arnoult
Group Vp Supply Chain Global, Dov Shenkman
Pharmacy Manager, Joel Neal
Pharmacy Manager, Eleni Mastromihalis
Pharmacy Manager, Brooke Bailey
Pharmacy Manager, Hugh Tobias
Vice President Global Financial Controls, Bill Zaman
Pharmacy Manager, Mike Corvino
Pharmacy Manager, Jennifer Iwegbue
National Account Manager, Christina Gabriel
Pharmacy Manager, Veronica Zavala
Director Of Pharmacy And Retail Operations, Vince Wilkinson
Pharmacy Manager, Gopal Pillai
Pharmacy Manager, Sofia Betancourt
Pharmacy Manager, Alejandra Russo
Group Vice President Walgreens Retail Brands, Helayna Minsk
Senior Vice President Global Controller And Chief Accounting Officer, Heather Dixon
Chairman, James A. (Jim) Skinner, age 74
Board Member, Leonard Schaeffer
Board Member, David Brailer
Board Member, Ginger Graham
Board Member, Jose Almeida
Board Member, John Lederer
Board Member, Nancy Schlichting
Board Member, Janice Babiak
Board Member, Dominic Murphy
Auditors: DELOITTE & TOUCHE LLP

LOCATIONS

HQ: Walgreens Boots Alliance Inc
108 Wilmot Road, Deerfield, IL 60015
Phone: 847 315-2500
Web: www.walgreensbootsalliance.com

PRODUCTS/OPERATIONS

2016 Sales

	$ mil.	% of total
Retail Pharmacy USA	83,802	72
Pharmaceutical Wholesale	20,293	17
Retail Pharmacy International	13,256	11
Total	**117,351**	**100**

2016 Sales

	$ mil.	% of total
United States	83,802	72
Europe (excluding the United Kingdom)	16,793	14
United Kingdom	14,081	12
Other	2,675	2
Total	**117,351**	**100**

COMPETITORS

BioScrip	OptumRx
Body Shop	Rite Aid
CVS	Sigma Pharmaceuticals
Costco Wholesale	Superdrug
H-E-B	Target Corporation
Kroger	UDG Healthcare
McKesson	Wal-Mart
Medicine Shoppe	

HISTORICAL FINANCIALS

Company Type: Public

Income Statement

FYE: August 31

	REVENUE ($ mil.)	NET INCOME ($ mil.)	NET PROFIT MARGIN	EMPLOYEES
08/19	136,866	3,982	2.9%	342,000
08/18	131,537	5,024	3.8%	354,000
08/17	118,214	4,078	3.4%	345,000
08/16	117,351	4,173	3.6%	360,000
08/15	103,444	4,220	4.1%	360,000
Annual Growth	**7.3%**	**(1.4%)**	**—**	**(1.3%)**

2019 Year-End Financials

Debt ratio: 25.00%
Return on equity: 16.00%
Cash ($ mil.): 1,023
Current ratio: 1.00
Long-term debt ($ mil.): 11,098

No. of shares (mil.): 895
Dividends
  Yield: 0.0%
  Payout: 41.0%
Market value ($ mil.): 45,835

	STOCK PRICE ($) FY Close	P/E High/Low	PER SHARE ($) Earnings	Dividends	Book Value
08/19	51.00	20 11	4.00	2.00	26.00
08/18	69.00	16 12	5.00	2.00	27.00
08/17	82.00	23 20	4.00	2.00	27.00
08/16	81.00	25 19	4.00	1.00	28.00
08/15	87.00	24 15	4.00	1.00	28.00
Annual Growth	**(12.3%)**	**— —**	**1.9%**	**14.5%**	**(1.9%)**

Walmart Inc

Walmart is an unstoppable retail force that has yet to meet any immovable object. It is the world's #1 retailer as well as the world's largest company by revenue and largest employer with 2.2 million associates. Walmart sells groceries and general merchandise operating some 5400 stores in the US including about 4800 Walmart stores and 600 Sam's Club membership-only warehouse clubs. Walmart's international division numbers about 6000 locations; operating through regional subsidiaries it's the #1 retailer in Canada and Mexico and has operations in Asia Africa Europe and Latin America. Some 275 million customers visit Walmart's stores and websites each week.

HISTORY

Sam Walton began his retail career as a J. C. Penney management trainee and later leased a Ben Franklin-franchised dime store in Newport Arkansas in 1945. In 1950 he relocated to Bentonville Arkansas and opened a Walton 5 & 10. By 1962 Walton owned 15 Ben Franklin stores under the Walton 5 & 10 name.

After Ben Franklin management rejected his suggestion to open discount stores in small towns Walton with his brother James "Bud" Walton opened the first Wal-Mart Discount City in Rogers Arkansas in 1962. Wal-Mart Stores went public in 1970 with 18 stores and sales of $44 million.

Avoiding regional retailers Walton opened stores in small and midsized towns in the 1970s. The company sold its Ben Franklin stores in 1976. By 1980 Wal-Mart's 276 stores had sales of $1.2 billion.

In 1983 Wal-Mart opened SAM'S Wholesale Club a concept based on the successful cash-and-carry membership-only warehouse format pioneered by the Price Company of California (now Costco Wholesale Corp.).

The company started Hypermart*USA in 1987 as a joint venture with Dallas-based supermarket chain Cullum Companies (now Randall's Food Markets). The 200000-sq.-ft. discount store/supermarket hybrid was later retooled as Wal-Mart Supercenters. Sam stepped down as CEO in 1988 and president David Glass was appointed CEO. Wal-Mart bought out Cullum the next year.

Wal-Mart acquired wholesale distributor McLane Company in 1990. In 1992 the year Sam died the company expanded into Mexico into a joint venture to open SAM'S CLUBS with Mexico's largest retailer Cifra (renamed Wal-Mart de México in 2000). Wal-Mart acquired 122 former Woolco stores in Canada in 1994. Co-founder Bud died a year later.

More international expansion included entering China in 1996; the acquisition of German hypermarket chain Wertkauf in 1997; the purchase of Brazilian retailer Lojas Americanas' 40% interest in a joint venture (1998); and the addition of four stores and other sites in South Korea. Also in 1998 the company began testing the Neighborhood Market format a 40000-sq.-ft. grocery and drug combination store. In 1999 Wal-Mart bought 74 German-based Interspar hypermarkets and acquired ASDA Group the UK's third-largest supermarket chain.

COO Lee Scott succeeded Glass as CEO in 2000; Glass stayed on as chairman of the executive committee. Wal-Mart later began testing its customers' demand for appliances by selling household appliances in selected stores.

Following the bankruptcy and closure of the Montgomery Ward department store chain in 2001 Wal-Mart offered to replace Ward's customers' credit cards with Wal-Mart branded cards. Wal-Mart also formed an alliance with America Online to offer Internet access and later launched its No Boundaries private-label cosmetics for preteens and teenagers. In June 2001 a group of six current and former female Wal-Mart employees filed a sex-discrimination lawsuit (seeking to represent up to 500000 current and former Wal-Mart workers) against the company. The next month Wal-Mart said it would acquire all the minority interests in Walmart.com and integrate its online operations with its store operations. It also laid off 100 employees at its corporate headquarters and eliminated 300 unfilled positions. In August it said it was testing the sale of Sealy and private-label mattresses in some of its superstores and it began offering college textbooks discounted up to 30% at its online College Bookstore.

2002 was a huge year for Wal-Mart both at home and abroad. In April the company was crowned America's largest corporation by FORTUNE magazine. In March Wal-Mart gained a foothold in Japan taking a 6% stake in one of Japan's top retailers SEIYU. That December it increased its SEIYU stake to 36% and retains the option to up that to nearly 67% by 2007. In a rare defeat Wal-Mart in July closed its first store in Germany and 2000 workers there went on a two-day strike over wages. (In 2001 Wal-Mart scrapped plans to open 50 more Supercenters there by 2003.) Also in 2002 Wal-Mart Puerto Rico acquired Supermercados Amigo the #1 supermarket chain on the island. (Wal-Mart opened its first Supercenter there in April 2001.)

Overall in 2002 Wal-Mart opened 178 supercenters 33 discount stores and 25 SAM'S CLUB stores. It opened 107 international units with two in Brazil 22 in Canada eight in China two in Germany three in South Korea 59 in Mexico two in Puerto Rico and nine in the UK. The company's attempt to open a state industrial bank in California in 2002 failed however after legislators barred retailers.

In May 2003 Wal-Mart sold its McLane grocery distribution business to Berkshire Hathaway; a rare divestment for the world's largest retailer. In July it opened its first store in Beijing.

In February 2004 a federal judge ruled that Wal-Mart should pay workers for overtime hours. The complaint which was brought by plaintiffs who said they were forced to work unpaid overtime between 1994 and 1999 came at a time when working conditions at the company were being scrutinized. Also that month Wal-Mart acquired the 118-store Bompre o chain of Brazilian supermarkets and hypermarkets from troubled Dutch retailer Royal Ahold for $300 million advancing the world's largest retailer from fifth to third place in the Brazilian market. In March Wal-Mart opened its online music store which sells digital downloads for 11 cents less than major competitors (including Apple's iTunes and Napster). In April voters in Inglewood California overwhelmingly rejected Wal-Mart's proposal to build a supercenter there over the objections of local officials. Wal-Mart had sought to bypass local development and environmental regulations by spending more than $1 million to take its case directly to the voters. Also in April Wal-Mart's Japanese partner Seiyu opened its first Wal-Mart-style supercenter in Numazu.

In May 2004 Wal-Mart agreed to pay $3.1 million in fines for violating the Clean Water Act at 24 sites in nine states. (The retailer was fined $1 million in 2001 for similar violations involving its failure to manage storm-water runoff.)

Vice chairman Tom Coughlin retired in January 2005 after 25 years with Wal-Mart. Coughlin remained on the company's board until March 25 2005 when he resigned prematurely following an internal investigation related to "the alleged unauthorized use of corporate-owned gift cards and personal reimbursements." He was due to retire from the board on June 3 2005. In June the company rescinded Coughlin's retirement agreement including stock awards and incentive payments which may total as much as $12 million.

Also in January Wal-Mart agreed to pay $135540 to settle federal charges that it violated child labor laws. The 24 violations which the retailer denied involved teenage workers in three states using hazardous equipment such as chain saws paper balers and fork lifts. Soon after Wal-Mart was ordered to pay $7.5 million in damages to a disabled former employee who claimed the retailer unfairly reassigned him. In March the retailer settled a high-profile lawsuit by agreeing to pay $11 million to the US government to close an investigation into the use of illegal immigrants by

Wal-Mart contractors to clean its stores. In May Wal-Mart increased its stake in SEIYU to 42% (up from 37%).

In August 2005 Wal-Mart signed Garth Brooks to a multiyear exclusive contract under which the country star's music will only be sold in Wal-Mart-owned stores. The deal marks the first time an artist has contracted himself and his entire catalog of music with a single chain. In October the company launched its Metro 7 line of urban women's apparel in 500 stores in and around urban areas. In December Wal-Mart opened its third superstore in the downtown Xuanwu District of Beijing. Also in December Wal-Mart acquired some 140 stores in Brazil from Portuguese retailer Sonae for about $757 million increasing the number of outlets it operates in Brazil to nearly 300.

In January 2006 Wal-Mart opened a supercenter in Santa Clarita California its second in Los Angeles County. In February the company acquired an additional 17.7% interest in CARHCO from Royal Ahold increasing its stake in the Central America supermarket operator to 51%. Wal-Mart's former vice chairman Thomas Coughlin who was accused of misusing more than $500000 in company funds pleaded guilty to fraud and tax charges in January 2006. In August he was sentenced to 27 months of house arrest and ordered to pay $400000 in restitution to his former employer. Wal-Mart itself was ordered by a Pennsylvania jury to pay more than $78 million in damages in a class-action suit brought by employees alleging that they were forced to work during breaks and off the clock. In October Wal-Mart disposed of its retail operations in Germany and South Korea. It sold the last of its 85 stores in Germany to rival METRO AG and sold 16 stores in South Korea to Shinsegae Co. for about $882 million.

In early 2007 Wal-Mart agreed to pay $33.5 million in back wages and interest to settle a federal lawsuit that accused the company of violating overtime laws involving more than 86000 employees. In February the company announced an agreement with all six major Hollywood studios to sell digital movies and TV shows on walmart.com becoming the first traditional retail chain to do so. In April Helen Robson Walton wife of Wal-Mart founder Sam Walton died at the age of 87. Wal-Mart and Bharti Enterprises formed a 50:50 joint venture in August to jointly build wholesale outlets that will buy goods from farmers and small manufacturers and sell to retailers through a nationwide supply chain. True to form Wal-Mart again cut prices of toys and some 15000 more items such as apparel home and food products for the 2007 holiday selling season.

In May 2008 the retailer revised its $4 prescription program launched in 2006 to cover 90-day prescriptions for $10. In November Mike Duke was named to Wal-Mart's board of directors in preparation for his elevation to president and CEO of the company in February 2009. Also in November Eduardo Castro-Wright president and CEO of Walmart US was promoted to vice chairman of Wal-Mart Stores. He assumed responsibility for the firm's global procurement operation.

The management shuffle continued in 2009 with Lee Scott retiring as CEO in February. Scott was succeeded by Duke who had headed the international arm of the company. In January Wal-Mart acquired a majority stake in Chile's largest food retailer Distribuci "n y Servicio through a tender offer. In May of that year it opened its first location in India via a joint venture with Bharti Enterprises.

In February 2010 the company opened its new Latin America regional headquarters in Miami Florida.

In June 2011 Walmart International acquired a 51% stake in South African retailer Massmart

which operates 288 stores in 13 countries in sub-Saharan Africa in a deal valued at about $2.4 billion. Massmart operates stores under the Makro Game Dion Wired Builders Warehouse Builders Express Builders Trade Depot CBW Jumbo Cash and Carry and the Shield buying group. On the day of the Massmart closing the company scored a huge win when the US Supreme Court threw out a massive employment discrimination class-action lawsuit (Dukes vs. Wal-Mart) brought filed back in 2001. While the court did not rule on whether or not Wal-Mart discriminated against women it said they could not proceed as a class.

EXECUTIVES

Vp Risk Management, David Stills
President And Ceo Walmart U.s., Gregory S. (Greg) Foran, age 57, $1,006,424 total compensation
President And Ceo, C. Douglas (Doug) McMillon, age 53, $1,278,989 total compensation
Chief Merchandising Officer Walmart U.s., Steve Bratspies
Evp And President And Ceo International, David Cheesewright, age 56, $1,071,743 total compensation
Evp And Cfo Walmart U.s., Michael P. Dastugue, age 55
Evp And Chief Administrative Officer Walmart International, Scott Price, age 58
Evp And President And Ceo Walmart Ecommerce U.s., Marc Lore, age 47, $346,154 total compensation
Evp Softlines And General Merchandise Walmart U.s., James A. (Andy) Barron
Evp Supply Chain Walmart U.s., Gregory L. (Greg) Smith, age 56
Evp Food Walmart U.s., Charles Redfield
Evp And Cfo Walmart International, Richard Mayfield
Evp Global Governance And Corporate Secretary, Jeffrey J. (Jeff) Gearhart, age 54
Evp Corporate Affairs, Daniel J. (Dan) Bartlett, age 47
Evp Consumables And Health And Wellness, Scott Huff
Evp And President Supercenters Walmart U.s., Michael S. (Mike) Moore
Evp And Cfo, M. Brett Biggs, age 50, $854,670 total compensation
Evp Membership And Technology And Ceo Samsclub.com, Jamie Iannone, age 46
Evp Operations Sam's Club, Gisel Ruiz, age 48
Evp And General Counsel, Karen Roberts
Evp And President And Ceo Walmart Latin America India And Africa And Chairman Walmart Mexico And Central America, Enrique Ostalé
Evp And Coo Walmart U.s., Judith McKenna
Svp And President Jet.com, Liza K. Landsman
Svp New England Division Walmart U.s., Julie Murphy
Evp And Global Chief Ethics And Compliance Officer, Jay T. Jorgensen
Svp And Chief Marketing Officer Walmart U.s., Tony Rogers
Evp Global People Division, Jacqueline P. (Jacqui) Canney, age 51
Evp And President And Ceo Sam's Club, John Furner, age 45
Evp Central Operations Walmart U.s., Mark Ibbotson
Evp And Cto, Jeremy King
Evp And Enterprise Chief Information Officer, Clay Johnson
Evp And Chief Merchandising Officer Sam's Club, Ashley Buchanan
Svp Chief Sustainability Officer And President Walmart Foundation, Kathleen McLaughlin
Evp Walmart Realty, JP Suarez
Vice President And Assistant Treasurer, Mike Cook

Safety Director Senior Vice President Of Sales And Business Development, Mike Trusty
Senior Vice President Operations, Don Frieson
Senior Vice President Pharmacy Merchandising And Support, Paul Beahm
Vice President Dmm Home Furnishings, Shawnda Schnurbusch
Senior Vice President And General Merchandise Manager, Robert DiPiazza
Vice President Corporate Affairs, Lee Culpepper
Vice President Product Development, Daria Beckom
Vice President Of Large Systems, Rita D Carney
Vice President Intl Merchandise Development, Ronald F Virta
Pharmacy Manager, Sharon Lynch
Senior Vice President Global Ecommerce Strategy, Gibu Thomas
Pharmacy Manager, Lydia Orr
Pharmacy Manager, Joby Young
Vice President Samsclubcom Merchandising, Fred Quandt
Vice President Operations, Todd Libbra
Vice President Planning Gm And Softlines, Mark Larsen
Senior Vice President For The Optical Division, Jeff McAllister
Vice President Creative Services, Patsy Hauer
Senior Vice President And Chief Data Officer, Suja Chandrasekaran
Vice President Information Systems, Susan Chambers
Exec Vp-sams Club Operations, Greg Johnston
Vice President Investor Relations, Carol Schumacher
Vice President Manager Director, Judith Sunderland
Senior Vice President Us Government Relations, Raymond Bracy
Vice President, Mehrdad Akbar
Pharmacy Manager, Terry Bennett
Vice President Facilities Management, Cassie Clark
Vice President Global Sourcing, Ashish Bharara
Vice President Regional General Manager, Michael Collischan
Divisional Human Resources Vice President, Marty Autrey
Pharmacy Manager, Tara Green
Senior Vice President Associate Experience, Drew Holler
Vice President, Sam Dunn
Regional Vice President, Gonzalez Varela
Senior Vice President Assistant Health And Wellness Operations, Michelle Hunsaker
Vice President Global Sourcing, John Mcdowell
Senior Vice President Global M, Michael Lewis
Vice President Multi Channel And Merchant Innovations, Shannon Letts
Executive Vice President, Celia Swanson
Senior Vice President Of Brand Merchandising, Andrea Thomas
Vice President Of Food Safety, Frank Yiannas
Vice President Marketing, Catherine Corely
Vice President Marketing, Marty Esarte
Vice President Operations, David Norman
Vice President Human Resources, Edward Mckissic
Vice President Of Human Resources, Anne Thomas
Vice President Dmm, Kristen Stevens
Vice President Strategic Planning, Anne Marie Kehoe
Vice President Finance And Strategy Services, Jonathan Hall
Vice President U.s. Benefits, Chris McSwain
Vice President Assistant Adult Beverage, Lorraine Spencer
Vice President Of Global Branded Imports, Fernando Serpa
Vice President Pharmaceutical Merchandising Walmart U.s., Jinali Desai
Vice President Corporate Affairs, Greg Hitt

Vice President Assistant To Manolo Reyes Produce And Floral, Philip Bentley
Vice President New Market Entry, Shawn Sederholm
Senior Vice President Global Compensation, Jackie Telfair
Vp Merchandising And Us Manufacturing, Cindi Marsiglio
Executive Vice President, Ed Kolodzieski
Assistant To Kerry Kilker Vice President Information Systems, Eileen Smith
Vice President Assistant, Sheila Musteen
Pharmacy Manager, Teresa Compton
Rph, Susan Long
Pharmacy Manager, Victor Hernandez
Pharmacy Manager, Dan Rafferty
Vice President Gmm Men's Kid's Baby, Thomas Dougherty
Executive Vice President And Treasurer, Pedro Farah
Vice President Of Finance, Alex Aguila
Vice President, Daniel Williams
Human Resources Director And Vice President, Erica Henson
Vp Cross Border Ecommerce, Robert Posey
Vice President Risk Management, William Newberg
Senior Vice President Assistant, Regina Mize
Vice President Regional General Manager, Ben Hassing
Vice President Of Financial, Tom Heffron
Vice President Real Estate, Volker Heimeshoff
Rvp 16, Ken Reese
Vice President Stragetic Real Estate Finance, Scott Carroll
Vice President Jewelry, Chris Callahan
Vice President Brand Merchandising Active Classics And Shoes, Jimmy Olsson
Evp Logistics, Chris Sultemeier
Divisional Vice President Logisitics, Joel Marpe
Vice President Corporate People Development, Kai Togami
P.e. Vice President Construction, Patrick Hamilton
National Accounts Manager, Matt Cockrell
Vice President Of Isd Infrastructure Engineering, James Martin
Vice President, Robert Fusillo
Vice President Merchandising, Rick Mangrum
Senior Vice President And Cont, James Walker
Vice President Of Finance, Par Stanfield
Vice President Head Of Global Ecommerce, Soren Mills
Pharmacy Manager, Ziad Labban
Pharmacy Manager, Will Hart
Executive Vice President Supply Chain, Catherine Smith
Vice President Of Engineering, Manu Thapar
Vice President International Strategy, Christine Allen
Senior Vice President Next Generation Supply Chain, Ami Spivey
Vice President Regional General Manager, Steve Schrobilgen
Svp International People, Jane Ewing
Pharmacy Manager, Lisa Morris
Vice President Corporate Strategy, Matthew Kistler
Vice President Finance And Global Treasury, Matt Allen
Vice President, Sherry Adams
Pharmacy Manager, Genie Crouch
Vp Apparel Product Development, Paul Burke
Senior Vice President Of Supply Chain, Bryan Boudreaux
Pharmacy Manager, Joe Bradac
Senior Vice President International Finance, Ken Plunk
Vice President And Gc Information Syst, Tim Cheatham
Vice President Technology And Product Global Ecommerce, Sriram Samu
Auditors: Ernst & Young LLP

LOCATIONS

HQ: Walmart Inc
702 S.W. 8th Street, Bentonville, AR 72716
Phone: 479 273-4000
Web: www.stock.walmart.com

2019 Sales

	$ mil.	% of total
US	392,265	76
Non-US	122,140	24
Total	514,405	100

PRODUCTS/OPERATIONS

2019 Sales

	$ mil.	% of total
Net sales	510,329	99
Membership and other income	4,076	1
Total	514,405	100

2019 Sales

	% of total
Wal-Mart US	65
International	24
SAM'S CLUB	11
Total	100

Selected Private Labels and Licensed Brands

Athletic Works
Better Homes & Gardens (licensed)
Black & Decker (licensed)
Canopy
Danskin Now (licensed)
Disney (licensed)
Equate (health and beauty aids)
Everstart
Faded Glory (jeans licensed)
General Electric (licensed)
George
Great Value (dairy dry grocery meat and produce)
Home Trends
Just My Size (licensed)
Mainstays
Marketside
No Boundaries
Oak Leaf
Ol' Roy (dog food)
OP (licensed)
Ozark Trail
Parent's Choice
Prima Della
Puritan
Rival (licensed)
Sam's Choice (grocery items)
Secret Treasures
Spring Valley
Starter
White Stag

COMPETITORS

Amazon.com	Home Depot
BJ's Wholesale Club	Kohl's
Best Buy	Kroger
Big Lots	Lowe's
CVS	Office Depot
Carrefour	Staples
Costco Wholesale	Target Corporation
Dollar General	

HISTORICAL FINANCIALS

Company Type: Public

Income Statement — FYE: January 31

	REVENUE ($ mil.)	NET INCOME ($ mil.)	NET PROFIT MARGIN	EMPLOYEES
01/19	514,405	6,670	1.3%	2,200,000
01/18	500,343	9,862	2.0%	2,300,000
01/17	485,873	13,643	2.8%	2,300,000
01/16	482,130	14,694	3.0%	2,200,000
01/15	485,651	16,363	3.4%	2,200,000
Annual Growth	1.4%	(20.1%)	—	0.0%

2019 Year-End Financials

Debt ratio: 26.00%—
Return on equity: 9.00%
Cash ($ mil.): 7,722
Current ratio: 1.00
Long-term debt ($ mil.): 50,203

Dividends
Yield: 2.0%
Payout: 92.0%
Market value ($ mil.): —

	STOCK PRICE ($) FY Close	P/E High/Low	PER SHARE ($) Earnings	Dividends	Book Value
01/19	96.00	46 36	2.00	2.00	25.00
01/18	107.00	33 20	3.00	2.00	26.00
01/17	67.00	17 14	4.00	2.00	26.00
01/16	66.00	19 12	5.00	2.00	25.00
01/15	85.00	18 14	5.00	2.00	25.00
Annual Growth	**3.0%**	**— —**	**(18.2%)**	**2.0%**	**(0.0%)**

Washington Federal Inc

Washington Federal is the holding company for Washington Federal Savings which operates about 190 branches in eight western states. The thrift which was founded in 1917 collects deposits from consumers and business by offering standard products such as CDs IRAs and checking savings and money market accounts. With these funds the bank mainly originates single-family residential mortgages which account for nearly three-quarters of its loan portfolio. The bank also writes business consumer construction land and multifamily residential loans. Washington Federal sells life home and auto coverage to individuals and businesses through its First Insurance Agency subsidiary.

Operations

In addition to its consumer and commercial banking operations Washington Federal has four wholly-owned subsidiaries: First Insurance Agency which offers a full line of individual and business insurance products to its customers and others; Statewide Mortgage Services Co. which holds about $18.6 million of real estate held for investment (REHI); Washington Services which also holds and markets REHI; and First Mutual Sales Finance a servicer of consumer loans.

Geographic Reach

As its name suggests Washington State is Washington Federal's largest market. Oregon and Arizona are other major markets for the bank.

Financial Performance

Washington Federal's fiscal 2012 (ends September) revenue fell by about 9.5% vs. the previous year due to a decrease both interest and non-interest income. Total interest income which accounts for about 97% of WF's total revenue declined 8% on fewer loans mortgage-backed securities and investment securities and cash equivalents. Other income fell 36%. With the exception of fiscal 2010 which saw a slight gain in revenue WF's revenue has been declining for several years. Net income increased 24% in fiscal 2012 vs. the prior year due to overall lower credit costs.

Strategy

Small relative to its national bank competitors Washington Federal has been building its business through acquisitions adding new markets and growing in established ones. Acquisitions have included both healthy smaller rivals and failed banks seized by regulators. In a bid to unify its brand and increase its name recognition WF rebrands acquired banks under its own moniker.

The bank is also working through its portfolio of nonperforming loans which peaked during the height of the recession in 2009 but now are on the decline.

Mergers and Acquisitions

In 2017 Washington Federal agreed to acquire Anchor Bancorp for $63.9 million. The combined company will have 248 offices in eight states in the Western US and total assets of $15.3 billion.

EXECUTIVES

Chairman President And Ceo, Roy M. Whitehead, age 66, $765,179 total compensation
President And Ceo, Brent J. Beardall, age 47, $390,925 total compensation
Svp And Cfo, Vincent L. Beatty, age 60
Evp And Chief Credit Officer, Mark A. Schoonover, age 60, $335,259 total compensation
Utah And Nevada Regional President, Marlise G. Fisher
Southern Oregon Regional President, Peggy L. Hobin
Evp And Cio, Angela D. Veksler, age 57
Northern Washington Regional President, Tom Kenney
Western Idaho Regional President, Tom Van Hemelryck
Northern Oregon Regional President, Gary Haines
Arizona Regional President, Mike Brown
New Mexico Regional President, Bill Synnamon
Southern Washington Regional President, Greg Toso
Texas Regional President, Tony Barnard
Executive Vice President, Jack Jacobson
Vice President, Patrick Wilson
Vice President, John Iasonides
Vice President, Jeff Birkelo
Vice President Division Manager N Wa Commericial Real Estate, Grace Peschek
Vp Commercial Relationship Manager, Eric Seidenberger
Executive Vice President And Commercial Banking Group Manager, Robert Peters
Vice President Mortgage Loan Production, Mark Hatate
Vice President And Manager, Mary Fling
Senior Vice President And Manager Seattle Commercial Real Estate, Thomas Pozarycki
Vice President Commercial Real Estate, Steve West
Auditors: DELOITTE & TOUCHE LLP

LOCATIONS

HQ: Washington Federal Inc
425 Pike Street, Seattle, WA 98101
Phone: 206 624-7930
Web: www.wafdbank.com

Selected Markets
Arizona
Idaho
Nevada
New Mexico
Oregon
Texas
Utah
Washington

PRODUCTS/OPERATIONS

2013 Sales

	$ mil.	% of total
Interest		
Loans	431	73
Mortgage-backed securities	80	14
Investment securities	23	4
Other income		
Deposit fee income	14	3
Loan fee income	8	1
Others	9	2
Total	**564**	**100**

COMPETITORS

Bank of America
Banner Corp
KeyCorp
U.S. Bancorp
Washington Banking
Wells Fargo
Zions Bancorporation

HISTORICAL FINANCIALS

Company Type: Public

Income Statement				FYE: September 30
	ASSETS ($ mil.)	NET INCOME ($ mil.)	INCOME AS % OF ASSETS	EMPLOYEES
09/19	16,475	210	1.3%	1,971
09/18	15,866	204	1.3%	1,877
09/17	15,254	174	1.1%	1,818
09/16	14,888	164	1.1%	1,806
09/15	14,568	160	1.1%	1,838
Annual Growth	**3.1%**	**7.0%**	**—**	**1.8%**

2019 Year-End Financials

Debt ratio: —
Return on equity: 10.00%
Cash ($ mil.): 419
Current ratio: —
Long-term debt ($ mil.): —

No. of shares (mil.): 79
Dividends
Yield: 2.0%
Payout: 31.0%
Market value ($ mil.): 2,916

	STOCK PRICE ($) FY Close	P/E High/Low	PER SHARE ($) Earnings	Dividends	Book Value
09/19	37.00	15 10	3.00	1.00	26.00
09/18	32.00	16 13	2.00	1.00	24.00
09/17	34.00	18 14	2.00	1.00	23.00
09/16	27.00	15 11	2.00	1.00	22.00
09/15	23.00	14 12	2.00	1.00	21.00
Annual Growth	**12.9%**	**— —**	**11.8%**	**10.1%**	**5.2%**

Washington Trust Bancorp, Inc.

Without seeming naive Washington Trust Bancorp can utter Washington and trust in the same breath. The holding company owns The Washington Trust Company one of the oldest and largest banks in Rhode Island and one of the oldest banks in the entire US. Chartered in 1800 the bank boasts over $3.5 billion in assets and operates nearly 20 branches in the state and one in southeastern Connecticut. Washington Trust offers standard services such as deposit accounts CDs and credit cards. The company's commercial mortgages and loans account for more than half of its loan portfolio while residential mortgages and consumer loans make up most of the rest. The bank also offers wealth management services.

Operations

Around one-third of the bank's loan portfolio was made up of commercial real estate loans in 2014 while business loans made up another 21%.

About 60% of Washington Trust's total revenue came from loan interest (including fees) in 2014 while another 7% came from interest on its taxable and tax-exempt investment securities. The rest of its revenue came from wealth management income (18%) deposit account charges (2%) card interchange fees (2%) merchant processing fees (1%) and other miscellaneous income sources. The bank had a staff of 590 employees at the end of 2014.

Washington Trust's wealth management division includes Washington Trust Investors Weston

Financial and 1800 Asset Management. The division offers financial planning investment management and trust services and has more than $4 billion of assets under administration.

Geographic Reach

Of its nearly 20 branches 10 of its branches are located in Southern Rhode Island (Washington County) nearly 10 branches are in the greater Providence area and one branch is in southeastern Connecticut. The company's commercial lending office in Providence and six residential mortgage lending offices in eastern Massachusetts (Sharon Burlington and Braintree); Glastonbury and Darien Connecticut; and Warwick Rhode Island.

Financial Performance

Washington Trust has struggled to consistently grow its revenues in recent years due to shrinking interest margins on loans amidst the low-interest environment. Its profits however have been rising thanks to declining interest expenses and falling loan loss provisions as its loan portfolio's credit quality has improved with higher property valuations in the strengthened economy.

The bank's revenue inched higher by 1% to $180 million in 2014 mostly as its interest income grew with higher average loan balances.

Higher revenue in 2014 combined with lower interest expenses on deposits lower loan loss provisions and lower non-interest expenses boosted Washington Trust's net income higher by 13% to $40.8 million for the year. The company's operating cash levels fell to half the levels of the prior year to $2.7 million after adjusting its earnings for non-cash items mostly related to its mortgage banking net loan proceeds.

Strategy

Washington Trust Bank has been growing its loan and deposit business organically by opening new branches and loan production offices in its target markets. In early 2015 it opened a new branch in Rumford making it the bank's second location in East Providence. In 2014 it opened a branch in Johnston Rhode Island and furthered its expansion into Connecticut with the opening of a new mortgage office in Glastonbury Connecticut.

The company also pursues acquisitions to expand its service offerings extend its reach into new geographic markets and bolster its existing business lines.

Mergers and Acquisitions

In 2015 Washington Trust purchased SEC-registered investment advisory firm Halsey Associates which added more than $850 million in assets under management to its Wealth Management business' books. Acquiring the New Haven Connecticut-based firm also expanded its reach in the Connecticut and metropolitan New York region.

EXECUTIVES

Vice President And Retail Lending Officer The Washington Trust Company, Linda S Smith

Vice Chair Secretary And Cfo, David V. Devault, age 65, $299,731 total compensation

Chairman And Ceo, Joseph J. (Joe) MarcAurele, $514,596 total compensation

Evp And Chief Lending Officer Of The Bank, James Hagerty

President And Coo, Edward O. (Ned) Handy, $385,000 total compensation

Evp Wealth Management And Treasurer, Mark K. W. Gim, $239,462 total compensation

Senior Vice President, Scott Ostrowski

Executive Vice President Chief Compliance Officer, Dennis L Algiere

Executive Vice President Of Retail Lending Of The Bank, Stephen Bessette

Executive Vice President, Maria N Janes

Senior Vice President Chief Marketing, Elizabeth B Eckel

Board Member, John J Bowen
Board Member, Kathleen E McKeough
Board Member, Edwin Santos
Board Member, Robert Dimuccio
Board Member, Katherine Hoxsie
Auditors: KPMG LLP

LOCATIONS

HQ: Washington Trust Bancorp, Inc.
23 Broad Street, Westerly, RI 02891
Phone: 401 348-1200
Web: www.washtrust.com

PRODUCTS/OPERATIONS

2014 Sales

	$ mil.	% of total
Interest		
Loans including fees	108	60
Securities	13	7
Other	1	-
Non-interest		
Wealth management services	33	18
Loan sales & commissions		**6.8**
4		
Gain on sale of business line	6	3
Service charges on deposit accounts	3	2
Other	9	6
Total	**180**	**100**

COMPETITORS

Bank of America	People's United
Citizens Financial	Financial
Group	Sovereign Bank
Liberty Bank	Webster Financial

HISTORICAL FINANCIALS

Company Type: Public

Income Statement   FYE: December 31

	ASSETS ($ mil.)	NET INCOME ($ mil.)	INCOME AS % OF ASSETS	EMPLOYEES
12/18	5,011	68	1.4%	623
12/17	4,530	46	1.0%	600
12/16	4,381	46	1.1%	596
12/15	3,772	43	1.2%	582
12/14	3,587	41	1.1%	590
Annual Growth	8.7%	13.8%	—	1.4%

2018 Year-End Financials

Debt ratio: 0.00%
Return on equity: 16.00%
Cash ($ mil.): 90
Current ratio: —
Long-term debt ($ mil.): —

No. of shares (mil.): 17
Dividends
Yield: 4.0%
Payout: 52.0%
Market value ($ mil.): 822

	STOCK PRICE ($) FY Close	P/E High/Low		PER SHARE ($) Earnings	Dividends	Book Value
12/18	48.00	16	12	4.00	2.00	26.00
12/17	53.00	22	18	3.00	2.00	24.00
12/16	56.00	21	13	3.00	1.00	23.00
12/15	40.00	16	14	3.00	1.00	22.00
12/14	40.00	17	13	2.00	1.00	21.00
Annual Growth	4.3%	—	—	13.0%	9.6%	5.8%

Waste Management, Inc. (DE)

Holding company Waste Management tops the heap in the US solid-waste industry. Through subsidiaries the company serves millions of residential industrial municipal and commercial customers in the US and Canada. Waste Management provides waste collection transfer recycling and resource recovery and disposal services. Its sites include more than 250 owned or operated landfills (the industry's largest network) more than 300 transfer stations and around 100 material recovery facilities. Collection services account for more than 50% of sales.

HISTORY

In 1956 Dean Buntrock joined his in-laws' business Ace Scavenger Service an Illinois company that Buntrock expanded into Wisconsin.

Waste Management Inc. was formed in 1971 when Buntrock joined forces with his cousin Wayne Huizenga who had purchased two waste routes in Florida in 1962. In the 1970s Waste Management bought companies in Michigan New York Ohio Pennsylvania and Canada. By 1975 it had an international subsidiary.

The company divided into specialty areas by forming Chemical Waste Management (1975) and offering site-cleanup services (ENRAC 1980) and low-level nuclear-waste disposal (Chem-Nuclear Systems 1982).

USA Waste was founded in 1987 to run disposal and collection operations in Oklahoma. It went public in 1988 and in 1990 Don Moorehead a founder and former CEO of Mid-American Waste Systems bought a controlling interest (most of which he later sold). Moorehead moved the business to Dallas and began buying companies in the fragmented industry. John Drury a former president of Browning-Ferris joined USA Waste in 1994 as CEO.

As USA Waste gathered steam Waste Management got off track. It diversified and Buntrock renamed the company WMX Technologies in 1993 to de-emphasize its waste operations. In 1997 however the company reverted to the Waste Management name and pressured by disappointed investor George Soros CEO Phillip Rooney resigned. After more management changes turnaround specialist Steve Miller became CEO the fourth one in eight months and Buntrock retired.

USA Waste picked up market share with large acquisitions including Envirofill (1994) Chambers Development Corporation (1995) and Western Waste Industries and Sanifill (1996). In 1996 the company moved to Houston. During the next two years it bought United Waste Systems Mid-American Waste the Canadian operations of Allied Waste and Waste Management and TransAmerican Waste Industries .

1998 saw the $20 billion merger between USA Waste and Waste Management. The new company bearing the Waste Management name and led by Drury and other former USA Waste executives controlled nearly a quarter of North America's waste business. The company finished the year by agreeing to pay shareholders $220 million in a suit over overstated earnings.

The new Waste Management bought Eastern Environmental Services for $1.3 billion in 1999. (A legal battle over negotiations between Eastern and Waste Management executives was settled out of court in 2000.) Drury took leave in 1999 because of an illness that would claim his life and director Ralph Whitworth known as a shareholder activist stepped in as acting chairman.

The company faced shareholder lawsuits after it was reported that executives had sold shares before a second-quarter earnings shortfall was announced. Waste Management said it would investigate the sales; later so did the SEC. (By 2001 the company had settled with both the SEC and shareholders.) In the fallout president and COO Rodney Proto who had sold shares before the earnings announcement was fired. Later that year the company tapped Maury Myers CEO of trucking company Yellow Corp. to take over as chairman and CEO.

In 2000 to concentrate on its core business in North America Waste Management sold operations in Europe Asia and South America in a series of transactions that raised about $2.5 billion. The next year the company established a pulp and paper trading group.

Waste Management announced plans in early 2002 to restructure the company by reorganizing its operating areas and cutting its workforce of 57000 by about 3.5%. Also that year the SEC sued six former Waste Management executives charging that they had enriched themselves through accounting fraud between 1992 and 1997.

The company formed a new recycling unit Recycle America Alliance in 2003 after acquiring Milwaukee-based The Peltz Group the largest privately held recycler in the US. The company also acquired 75 complementary collection businesses for about $337 million and divested some operations for about $18 million. That year two former executives of Waste Management Proto and CFO Earl DeFrates agreed to a settlement with the SEC on allegations that they had profited from insider trading in 1999.

In a bid to consolidate its leadership position in the US waste market in 2008 the company made a bid to acquire Republic Services but was rebuffed.

In 2009 the company acquired PharmEcology Associates a national pharmaceutical waste management consulting services firm and Mountain High Medical Disposal Services. In 2010 it added some medical waste assets from MedServe following that company's acquisition by Stericycle. It also acquired a medical waste processing facility and other assets from Milum Textile Services in Phoenix.

In 2010 it invested in Canadian waste-to-biofuels company Enerkem. Further expanding its "green" businesses the company acquired control of Garick LLC a leading maker and distributor of organic lawn and garden products. The deal helped grow Waste Management's organics recycling services business.

In 2011 it bought Access Computer Products a leading provider of cell phone ink and toner cartridge and consumer electronics reverse logistics remarketing and recycling services and acquired three recycling facilities in Maryland and Virginia in a separate deal.

Also that year Waste Management picked up Connecticut-based Oakleaf Global Holdings and its operations for $425 million. The unit manages a North American network of some 2500 operators who provide hauling disposal waste diversion and recycling services.

In 2012 the company removed a management layer in its four geographic groups consolidated and reduced its geographic areas from 22 to 17 and eliminated some 700 positions.

Expanding its recycling portfolio and supporting its efforts to manage 20 million tons of recyclable material in 2013 Waste Management acquired Greenstar LLC from NTR plc for $170 million.

Greenstar manages some 1.5 million tons of material through a dozen material recovery facilities.

That year the company acquired Summit Energy Services and Liquid Logistics two Williston North Dakota-based energy services companies. The acquisitions enhance Waste Management's environmental service offerings to oil and gas industry customers working in the Bakken Shale.

EXECUTIVES

Evp And Coo, James E. Trevathan, age 66, $676,885 total compensation

Svp Field Operations, Jeff M. Harris, age 65, $608,846 total compensation

Evp Corporate Operations; President Recycling, Puneet Bhasin, age 56

President And Ceo, James C. (Jim) Fish, age 57, $705,996 total compensation

Svp Field Operations, John J. Morris, age 49, $593,462 total compensation

Svp Cfo And Treasurer, Devina A. Rankin

Vice President Information Technology, Mark Madsen

Vice President Business Development And Sports Marketing, Steve Ness

Vice President Strategic Business Solutions, Paul Foody

Vice President Information Technology, Gail Trafton

Vice President Business Development, Joe Cassin

Vp Finance, Gregg Hassler

Vice President Commercial Lines Underwriting, Mary Fisher

Vice President Of Business Development, Brian Bauman

Vice President Customer Service, Katy Lydon

Vice President Shared Services And Fleet, David Logsdon

Vice President, Everett Bass

Vice President Market Area, Pittman Alec

Svp Corporate Affairs And Chief People Officer, Barry Caldwell

Area Vice President, Chris DeSantis

Vice President Legal Corporate And Securities, John Tsai

Vice President Area, Tim Wells

National Account Manager, Timothy Fraumann

Vp Renewable Energy, Paul Pabor

Svp Operations Safety And Environmental Compliance, Tara Hemmer

Government Relations Director, Henry Sori

Vice President, Frank Labarba

Director Of Government Relations, John Wohlrab

Area Vice President, Steve Batchelor

Vice President Commodity Sales, Don Majka

Vice President Public Affairs, Chuck Dees

Vice President Business Partner Operations, Buddy West

Svp, Jim Trevathan

Chairman, Bradbury H. (Brad) Anderson, age 68

Board Of Directors, Christine Chisholm-krosnicki

Board Member, Michael Parrent

Board Member, Melinda Holt

Auditors: Ernst & Young LLP

LOCATIONS

HQ: Waste Management, Inc. (DE)
 1001 Fannin Street, Houston, TX 77002
Phone: 713 512-6200
Web: www.wm.com

2018 Sales

	$ mil.	% of total
US & Puerto Rico	14,167	95
Canada	747	5
Total	**14,914**	**100**

PRODUCTS/OPERATIONS

2018 sales

	$ mil.	% of total
Collection	9,724	54
Landfill	3,560	20
Transfer	1,711	9
Recycling	1,293	7
Other	1,736	10
Adjustments	(3110)	-
Total	**14,914**	**100**

Selected Services

Collection
Disposal
Hazardous waste management
Landfill management
Portable sanitation services
Recycling
Transfer stations
Treatment

COMPETITORS

Casella Waste Systems	WCA Waste
Republic Services	Waste Connections
Rumpke	Waste Connections US
Safety-Kleen	

HISTORICAL FINANCIALS

Company Type: Public

Income Statement

FYE: December 31

	REVENUE ($ mil.)	NET INCOME ($ mil.)	NET PROFIT MARGIN	EMPLOYEES
12/18	14,914	1,925	12.9%	43,700
12/17	14,485	1,949	13.5%	42,300
12/16	13,609	1,182	8.7%	41,200
12/15	12,961	753	5.8%	40,600
12/14	13,996	1,298	9.3%	39,800
Annual Growth	1.6%	10.4%	—	2.4%

2018 Year-End Financials

Debt ratio: 44.00%
Return on equity: 31.00%
Cash ($ mil.): 61
Current ratio: 1.00
Long-term debt ($ mil.): 9,594

No. of shares (mil.): 424
Dividends
 Yield: 2.0%
 Payout: 42.0%
Market value ($ mil.): 37,730

	STOCK PRICE ($) FY Close	P/E High/Low		PER SHARE ($)		
				Earnings	Dividends	Book Value
12/18	89.00	21	18	4.00	2.00	15.00
12/17	86.00	19	16	4.00	2.00	14.00
12/16	71.00	27	19	3.00	2.00	12.00
12/15	53.00	33	28	2.00	2.00	12.00
12/14	51.00	18	14	3.00	2.00	13.00
Annual Growth	14.8%	—		12.4%	5.5%	3.7%

Wayfair Inc

Auditors: Ernst & Young LLP

LOCATIONS

HQ: Wayfair Inc
 4 Copley Place, Boston, MA 02116
Phone: 617 532-6100
Web: www.wayfair.com

HISTORICAL FINANCIALS

Company Type: Public

Income Statement
FYE: December 31

	REVENUE ($ mil.)	NET INCOME ($ mil.)	NET PROFIT MARGIN	EMPLOYEES
12/18	6,779	(504)	—	12,124
12/17	4,721	(245)	—	7,751
12/16	3,380	(194)	—	5,637
12/15	2,250	(77)	—	3,809
12/14	1,319	(148)	—	2,353
Annual Growth	50.6%	—	—	50.7%

2018 Year-End Financials

Debt ratio: 49.00%
Return on equity: ***.***.**%
Cash ($ mil.): 849
Current ratio: 1.00
Long-term debt ($ mil.): 922

No. of shares (mil.): 91
Dividends
Yield: —
Payout: —
Market value ($ mil.): 8,175

	STOCK PRICE ($) FY Close	P/E High/Low	PER SHARE ($) Earnings	Dividends	Book Value
12/18	90.00	— —	(6.00)	0.00	(4.00)
12/17	80.00	— —	(3.00)	0.00	(1.00)
12/16	35.00	— —	(2.00)	0.00	1.00
12/15	48.00	— —	(1.00)	0.00	3.00
12/14	20.00	— —	(3.00)	0.00	4.00
Annual Growth	46.0%				

Webster Financial Corp (Waterbury, Conn)

Webster Financial is the holding company for Webster Bank which operates about 170 branches in southern New England primarily in Connecticut but also in Massachusetts New York and Rhode Island. The bank provides commercial and retail services such as deposit accounts loans and mortgages and consumer finance as well as government and institutional banking services. It performs asset-based lending through its Webster Business Credit subsidiary and equipment financing through Webster Capital Finance. The company's HSA Bank division offers health savings accounts nationwide. Webster Bank provides brokerage and investment services through an agreement with UVEST a division of LPL Financial.

Operations

Webster Financial operates in three segments: Commercial Banking HSA Bank and Community Banking.

Commercial Banking provides lending deposit and treasury and payment services.

Community Banking services consist of personal and business banking. It operates about 170 banking centers more than 330 ATMs a customer care center and web and mobile banking services.

HSA Bank is focused on health savings accounts as well as providing health reimbursement arrangements flexible spending and commuter benefit account administration services to employers and individuals in all 50 states.

Geographic Reach

Webster's largest market is Connecticut with about 115 branches. Massachusetts has about 35 branches; Rhode Island about 10; and New York fewer than 10. Customers can conduct transactions at some 330 ATMs across throughout New England.

Financial Performance

Webster Financial's revenue and net income have appreciated in recent years. In 2017 the bank's revenue rose to $1.05 billion from $983 million in 2016 while net income rose to $255 million from $207 million.

Webster credited strong loan growth funded with growth in low-cost long-duration HSA deposits for achieving higher net interest margin in 2017. Net interest income increased about $78 million while provision for loan and lease losses dropped about $15 million. The bank reported that non-interest expense rose about $38 million and that it had one-time gain of about $7 million on the sale of an asset in 2016.

Strategy

Webster focuses on building its community banking and health savings account businesses. Tthe community banking unit is expansion in several metro areas led by Boston where the bank is on pace to meet its goal of $1 billion in new deposits and $500 million in loans over five years. While it faces fierce pricing competition in the Boston market it sees steady deposit growth in the core franchise there.

In the HSA Bank business Webster has invested in sales staff which helped drive compensation costs about $27 million higher in 2017 from 2016 and relationship management to gather new clients. The investment seems to be paying off with growth in clients and deposits and some $6 billion under administration. Webster uses deposits made in the HSA Bank to fund lending in its other businesses.

EXECUTIVES

Vice President Association Financial Services, Jordan Arovas
Chairman And Ceo Webster Financial Corporation And Webster Bank N.a., James C. (Jim) Smith, age 69, $882,435 total compensation
Evp General Counsel And Corporate Secretary Webster Financial Corporation And Webster Bank N.a., Harriet M. Wolfe, age 65
President And Coo Webster Business Credit Corporation (wbcc), Warren K. Mino
Regional President Boston Webster Bank N.a., Paul F. Mollica
Evp And Chief Human Resources Officer Webster Financial Corporation And Webster Bank N.a., Bernard M. Garrigues, age 60
Evp And Chief Marketing Officer Webster Financial Corporation And Webster Bank N.a., Dawn C. Morris, age 51
Regional President New Haven Conn. Webster Bank N.a., Jeffrey A. (Jeff) Klaus
Evp Commercial Banking; Chairman Of Regional Presidents' Council, John R. Ciulla, age 53, $363,479 total compensation
Evp And Head Of Community Banking, Nitin J. Mhatre, age 48, $358,521 total compensation
Evp And Cfo Webster Financial Corporation And Webster Bank N.a., Glenn I. MacInnes, age 57, $453,310 total compensation
Evp And Cio Webster Financial Corporation And Webster Bank N.a., Colin D. Eccles, age 60
Evp Consumer Deposits Investments And Network Management Webster Bank N.a., David D. Miree
Evp And Chief Risk Officer Webster Financial Corporation And Webster Bank N.a., Daniel H. Bley, age 50
Evp And Head Of Private Banking Webster Financial Corporation And Webster Bank N.a., Daniel M. (Dan) FitzPatrick, age 60, $300,000 total compensation
Evp Commercial Real Estate, William E. Wrang

Evp Webster Financial Corporation And Webster Bank N.a. And Head Of Hsa Bank, Charles L. (Chad) Wilkins, age 57
Regional President Metro New York, Abby Parsonnet
Regional President Southern Massachusetts And Rhode Island Webster Bank N.a., Douglas E. (Doug) Scala
Regional President Waterbury Conn. Webster Bank N.a., Michael L. (Mike) O'Connor
Regional President For Pennsylvania Webster Bank N.a., Scott C. Meves
Regional President Hartford Conn. Webster Bank N.a., Timothy D. Bergstrom
Evp Middle Market Banking Webster Bank N.a., Christopher J. (Chris) Motl
Vice President Information Technology, Tom Clark
Vice President Human Resources Technology, Chris Muller
Vice President Information Technology Applications, Jay Clark
Vice President Corporate Facilities Operations, Mark Nisbett
Senior Vice President Director Of Corporate Security, Michael Wolf
Vice President Loan Operations, Terri O'sullivan
Vice President Marketing, Joanne Renna
Vice President Ebanking, Chris Barlow
Vice President External Communications, Sarah Barr
Vice President Database, Jennifer Zbell
Vice President Finance, Shelly Abdella
Senior Vice President Middle Market Commercial Banking Webster Bank, Stephen Corcoran
Vice President Commercial Banking, Joe Pelliccia
Vice President Human Resources, Laura Chandler
Senior Vice President, Kevin Collins
Senior Vice President And Director Business And Professional Banking, John Guy
Senior Vice President Compensation Benefits And Hris, Carole Hynes
Senior Vice President, Torres Gilbert
Vice Chairman Webster Financial Corporation And Webster Bank N.a., Joseph J. (Joe) Savage, age 66
Board Member, Mark Pettie
Board Member, William Atwell
Auditors: KPMG LLP

LOCATIONS

HQ: Webster Financial Corp (Waterbury, Conn)
145 Bank Street, Waterbury, CT 06702
Phone: 203 578-2202
Web: www.websterbank.com

2017 Bank Branches

	No.
Connecticut	115
Massachusetts	35
Rhode Island	10
New York	7
Total	**167**

PRODUCTS/OPERATIONS

2017 Sales

	$ mil.	% of total
Interest		
Interest and fees on loans and leases	709	57
Taxable interest and dividends on securities	181	17
Non-taxable interest on securities	23	2
Loans held for sale	1	-
Non-interest		
Deposit service fees	151	13
Loan and lease related fees	26	3
Wealth and investment services	31	3
Mortgage banking activities	10	1
Increase in cash surrender value of life insurance policies	15	1
Gain on sale of investment securities net	— -	
Impairment loss on securities recognized in earnings	(0.13)	-
Other income	26	3
Total	**1,056**	**100**

COMPETITORS

Bank of America	New England Bancshares
Citibank	Patriot National
Citizens Financial	Bancorp
Group	People's United
Fairfield County Bank	Financial
First Connecticut	SBT Bancorp Inc.
Bancorp	SI Financial
JPMorgan Chase	TD Bank USA
KeyCorp	Washington Trust
Liberty Bank	Bancorp

HISTORICAL FINANCIALS

Company Type: Public

Income Statement

FYE: December 31

	ASSETS ($ mil.)	NET INCOME ($ mil.)	INCOME AS % OF ASSETS	EMPLOYEES
12/18	27,610	360	1.3%	3,265
12/17	26,488	255	1.0%	3,302
12/16	26,073	207	0.8%	3,168
12/15	24,678	206	0.8%	2,946
12/14	22,533	200	0.9%	2,764
Annual Growth	5.2%	15.9%	—	4.3%

2018 Year-End Financials

Debt ratio: 1.00%
Return on equity: 13.00%
Cash ($ mil.): 329
Current ratio: —
Long-term debt ($ mil.): —

No. of shares (mil.): 92
Dividends
  Yield: 3.0%
  Payout: 33.0%
Market value ($ mil.): 4,543

	STOCK PRICE ($) FY Close	P/E High/Low	PER SHARE ($) Earnings	Dividends	Book Value
12/18	49.00	18 12	4.00	1.00	31.00
12/17	56.00	22 17	3.00	1.00	29.00
12/16	54.00	25 14	2.00	1.00	28.00
12/15	37.00	19 13	2.00	1.00	26.00
12/14	33.00	16 13	2.00	1.00	26.00
Annual Growth	10.9%	— —	16.3%	13.6%	5.1%

WEC Energy Group Inc

WEC Energy Group keeps the lights illuminated and the gas fires burning for 4.4 million customers in four upper Midwest states. The utility holding company serves energy through its seven regulated utilities. It is one of the largest natural gas distributors in the US and even provides steam (for heating) to a few hundred customers in Milwaukee WI. It owns 8600 MW of electric generation capacity and thousands of miles of natural gas distribution and electrical transmission lines. The former Wisconsin Energy acquired for $9 billion Integrys Energy in mid-2015 and renamed the combined entity WEC Energy Group.

Operations

WEC Energy Group operates four reportable segments: Wisconsin Illinois Other States and Electric Transmission. Embedded within the segments WEC records the operations and results of its regulated utility companies.

The Wisconsin segment accounts for about 80% of total revenue and includes the electric and natural gas utility operations of Wisconsin Electric (WE) Wisconsin Gas and Wisconsin Public Service Corporation (WPS). The segment also included WE's and WPS's electric and natural gas operations in Michigan until it spun them into the separate Upper Michigan Energy Resources utility in

early 2017. The segment generates and transmits electric energy and distributes natural gas to some 3 million customers.

The Illinois segment produces about 15% of WEC revenue and includes the natural gas utility and non-utility operations of The Peoples Gas Light and Coke Company (PGL) and North Shore Gas Company (NSG). PGL and NSG provide energy to Chicago and its northern suburbs. PGL also owns and operates a 38 Bcf natural gas storage facility in central Illinois.

The Other States segment includes the natural gas utility and non-utility operations of Minnesota Energy Resources Corporation (MERC) and Michigan Gas Utilities Corporation (MGU).

WEC holds approximately 60% of the in American Transmission Company LLC which owns maintains monitors and operates electric transmission systems throughout WEC's service territory. These operations are recorded in WEC's Electric Transmission segment and contribute between $60 million and $140 million in annual equity earnings.

WEC serves Wisconsin Illinois Michigan and Minnesota with roughly 69000 miles of electric distribution lines and more than 45000 miles of natural gas distribution and transmission lines. The company generates two thirds of its energy needs and purchases the rest through power purchase agreements. Of its owned plants about 50% of energy is sourced from coal 20% from natural gas and 4% from renewables. Most of the purchased power is nuclear sourced.

Geographic Reach

WEC Energy Group has customers throughout Wisconsin though most are in the eastern portion of the state. It serves customers in southern Michigan and in that state's Upper Peninsula. It also provides energy in and around Chicago and in various portions of Minnesota.

Its power generation plants are located throughout Wisconsin.

Sales and Marketing

The company serves retail customers through its regulated utility operations. It also serves wholesale customers through unregulated sales of electricity. Most of its sales are to retail customers which include residential farming commercial business and industrial clients.

Financial Performance

WEC Energy produced steady financial results in recent years with revenue ranging between $4.1 billion and $5.0 billion and net income gradually climbing. The acquisition of Integrys in 2015 spiked both revenue and net income for that year and the next.

In 2016 revenue reached $7.5 billion up 26% from the prior year. The increase was largely due to the inclusion of Integrys revenue though warmer summer weather triggered additional cooling needs by retail customers.

The 2016 the company achieved $940 million in net income a 47% jump from 2015. The increase was the result of higher revenue (from Integrys) a favorable comparison against 2015's acquisition costs (about $100 million) and a $50 million boost from WEC's equity interest in American Transmission Company. Lower fuel costs helped as well but was almost completely offset by a rise in operating expenses.

Cash at the end of 2016 was $37 million $12 million lower than the prior year's amount. Operating activities provided $2.1 billion mainly from net income and deferred taxes. Investing activities used $1.2 billion mostly for capital improvement projects. Financing activities used $845 million to retire debt repurchase company stock shares and payout shareholder dividends.

Strategy

WEC is trying to modernizing its electric grid extending gas operations and addressing the push towards renewable energy sources. It is focusing on opportunities to deploy capital in renewable energy assets.

The company is on schedule to retire 1800 MW of coal-sourced generation by 2020 including its Pulliam Power Plant Edgewater 4 facility and Presque Isle Power Plant. It will replace some of that lost power with natural gas-fueled plants in Michigan and Wisconsin and with solar facilities. In 2019 the company acquired an 80% ownership interest in Coyote Ridge Wind Farm in South Dakota for $145 million. The site will be operated by Avangrid and has a long-term offtake agreement with Google Energy.

In early 2016 WEC divested components that were either acquired via Integrys or no longer fit into the company's business mix. It sold the ITF business a provider of compressed natural gas (CNG) fueling services as well as a provider of CNG facility design construction operation and maintenance. It also sold its Milwaukee County (steam) Power Plant and its chilled water generation and distribution assets in early 2016. In 2017 it acquired a natural gas storage facility in Michigan and formed the Upper Michigan Energy Resources utility into which WEC placed its utility operations serving the state's Upper Peninsula.

WEC's more typical strategic endeavors stem from its capital expenditure plan. Between 2018 and 2022 the firm plans to invest $11.8 billion across its operations. $2.7 billion is earmarked for its generation assets including buildout of new gas and renewable power plants. A similar amount is targeted for electric distribution operations to expand its transmissions reach and to modernize its grid. Gas delivery will get the largest investment at $5.5 billion including funding to replace 2000 miles of aging natural gas pipeline in and around Chicago.

Mergers and Acquisitions

In a major move in 2015 Wisconsin Energy acquired rival Integrys Energy in a transaction valued at $9.1 billion. The deal established WEC Energy Group as the energy leader serving the Midwestern US.

EXECUTIVES

Chairman Wec Energy Group Inc. And Wisconsin Electric Power Company, Gale E. Klappa, age 69, $589,043 total compensation

President Ceo And Director, Allen L. Leverett, age 53, $941,667 total compensation

Evp General Counsel And Corporate Secretary Wisconsin Energy Corp And We Energies, Susan H. Martin, age 66, $515,000 total compensation

Evp External Affairs, Robert M. (Bert) Garvin, age 52, $416,120 total compensation

Evp And President Michigan Gas Utilities Minnesota Energy Resources Corp. Wec Business Services Llc, J. Patrick Keyes, age 53, $546,400 total compensation

Evp And Cfo, Scott J. Lauber, age 53, $351,784 total compensation

President Â– We Energies And Wisconsin Public Service, J. Kevin Fletcher, age 60, $411,345 total compensation

President And Ceo Peoples Gas And North Shore Gas, Charles R. Matthews, age 62

President Wispark Llc, Jerold P. Franke

Evp Human Resources And Organizational Effectiveness And Compliance Officer, Joan M. Shafer, age 65

Vp And Cio, Molly Mulroy

Evp We Energies And Wisconsin Public Service, Tom Metcalfe, age 51

Vice President Chief Administrative Officer,
Kristine Rappe
Vp Wispark, Erica-Nicole Harris
Senior Vice President Corporate Communications And Investor Relations, Mary Straka
Board Member, Mary Stanek
Auditors: DELOITTE & TOUCHE LLP

LOCATIONS

HQ: WEC Energy Group Inc
231 West Michigan Street, P.O. Box 1331, Milwaukee, WI 53201
Phone: 414 221-2345   **Fax:** 414 221-2172
Web: www.wecenergygroup.com

PRODUCTS/OPERATIONS

2016 sales

	$ mil.	% of total
Wisconsin	5,805	78
Illinois	1,242	17
other States	377	5
We Power	25	-
Corporate and others	23	.
Total	**7,472**	**100**

Selected Subsidiaries

American Transmission Company LLC (partial ownership)
Michigan Gas utilities Corporation
Minnesota Energy Resources Corporation
North Shore Gas Company
The Peoples Gas Light and Coke Company
Upper Michigan Energy Resources
W.E. Power LLC (We Power regulated power plant construction)
Wisconsin Electric Power Company (operates as We Energies electric gas and steam utility)
Wisconsin Gas LLC (operates as We Energies gas and water utility)
Wisconsin Public Service Corporation
Wispark LLC (real estate development)

COMPETITORS

AEP	MGE Energy
ALLETE	Minnesota Power
Alliant Energy	SEMCO ENERGY
CMS Energy	Wisconsin Power & Light
Commonwealth Edison	
DTE	Xcel Energy
Dairyland Power	

HISTORICAL FINANCIALS

Company Type: Public

Income Statement
FYE: December 31

	REVENUE ($ mil.)	NET INCOME ($ mil.)	NET PROFIT MARGIN	EMPLOYEES
12/18	7,680	1,061	13.8%	7,878
12/17	7,649	1,205	15.8%	8,129
12/16	7,472	940	12.6%	8,164
12/15	5,926	640	10.8%	8,443
12/14	4,997	588	11.8%	4,248
Annual Growth	**11.3%**	**15.9%**	**—**	**16.7%**

2018 Year-End Financials

Debt ratio: 35.00%
Return on equity: 11.00%
Cash ($ mil.): 85
Current ratio: 1.00
Long-term debt ($ mil.): 9,994

No. of shares (mil.): 316
Dividends
 Yield: 3.0%
 Payout: 66.0%
Market value ($ mil.): 21,853

	STOCK PRICE ($) FY Close	P/E High/Low	PER SHARE ($) Earnings	Dividends	Book Value
12/18	69.00	22 17	3.00	2.00	31.00
12/17	66.00	18 15	4.00	2.00	30.00
12/16	59.00	22 17	3.00	2.00	28.00
12/15	51.00	24 19	2.00	2.00	28.00
12/14	53.00	21 15	3.00	2.00	20.00
Annual Growth	**7.0%**	**— —**	**6.6%**	**9.1%**	**12.1%**

Wells Fargo & Co (New)

Auditors: KPMG LLP

LOCATIONS

HQ: Wells Fargo & Co (New)
420 Montgomery Street, San Francisco, CA 94163
Phone: 866 249-3302
Web: www.wellsfargo.com

HISTORICAL FINANCIALS

Company Type: Public

Income Statement
FYE: December 31

	ASSETS ($ mil.)	NET INCOME ($ mil.)	INCOME AS % OF ASSETS	EMPLOYEES
12/18	1,895,883	22,393	1.2%	259,000
12/17	1,951,757	22,183	1.1%	262,700
12/16	1,930,115	21,938	1.1%	269,100
12/15	1,787,632	22,894	1.3%	264,700
12/14	1,687,155	23,057	1.4%	264,500
Annual Growth	**3.0%**	**(0.7%)**	**—**	**(0.5%)**

2018 Year-End Financials

Debt ratio: 12.00%
Return on equity: 11.00%
Cash ($ mil.): 173,287
Current ratio: —
Long-term debt ($ mil.): —

Dividends
 Yield: 4.0%
 Payout: 38.0%
Market value ($ mil.): —

	STOCK PRICE ($) FY Close	P/E High/Low	PER SHARE ($) Earnings	Dividends	Book Value
12/18	46.00	15 10	4.00	2.00	43.00
12/17	61.00	15 12	4.00	2.00	42.00
12/16	55.00	14 11	4.00	2.00	40.00
12/15	54.00	14 12	4.00	1.00	38.00
12/14	55.00	13 11	4.00	1.00	36.00
Annual Growth	**(4.2%)**	**— —**	**1.1%**	**5.0%**	**4.7%**

WesBanco Inc

WesBanco wants to be the "BesBanco" for its customers. The holding company owns WesBanco Bank which has about 210 branches in Indiana Kentucky Ohio Pennsylvania and West Virginia. In addition to providing traditional services such as deposits and loans the bank operates a wealth management department with offices in West Virginia and Ohio and some $4.7 billion of assets under management and custody including the company's proprietary WesMark mutual funds. Other units include brokerage firm WesBanco Se-
curities and multi-line insurance provider WesBanco Insurance Services.

Operations

Commercial loans including real estate and operating loans account for more than half of of WesBanco's loan portfolio. Its retail portfolio mainly consists of home equity loans and deposit overdraft limits. The bank usually sells new residential mortgages that it originates into the secondary market. It plans to continue to grow its portfolio of commercial and industrial loans.

Strategy

WesBanco likes to purchase smaller banks to expand its reach into new geographic markets while bolstering its loan and deposit business. It's acquired more than 50 banks and financial services firms in the past 25 years.

Mergers and Acquisitions

The company agreed in 2019 to acquire Old Line Bancshares for $500 million. The combined company will have about $15.6 billion in total assets and about 235 branches in more than five states. The deal give WesBanco more than 35 new offices primarily in Baltimore and Washington DC.

In 2018 WesBanco acquired Kentucky-based Farmers Capital Bank Corporation for $429.8 million and West Virginia-based First Sentry Bancshares for $107.5 million.

EXECUTIVES

Evp Treasury And Strategic Planning, Brent E. Richmond, age 56
Evp And Chief Credit Officer, Peter W. Jaworski, age 64, $212,101 total compensation
Evp And Cfo, Robert H. Young, age 63, $269,363 total compensation
President And Ceo, Todd F. Clossin, age 57, $466,923 total compensation
Evp And Chief Risk & Administrative Officer, Michael L. Perkins
Evp Retail Delivery, Lynn D. Asensio
Evp And Senior Operations Officer, Gregory A. Dugan
Evp Wealth Management, Jonathan D. Dargusch, age 61, $230,270 total compensation
Evp Human Resources Management, Anthony F. Pietranton
Evp And Chief Lending Officer, Jayson M. Zatta
Market President Kanawha Region, David L. Sayre
Vice President District Sales Manager, Nick Taylor
Senior Vice President Human Resources, Lee Blundon
Vice President Finance, Luanne Bush
Vice President And Manager Human Resources, Sheri Clarke
Vice President Risk Management Security Officer, James Thompson
Senior Vice President, Howard Bertram
Vice President Commercial Real Estate, Traci Boeing
Assistant Vice President, Bruce Bandi
Vice President, Allen Retton
Vice President, Tom Medovic
Senior Vice President Credit Risk Management, Edward Polli
Vice President Electronic Banking Manager, Jason Plotner
Assistant Vice President Business Development Manager, Lycia Maurits
Assistant Vice President Information Technology Services, W Terrance Naughton
Vice President Of Information Technology, Mike Robbins
Vice President Investments, Steve Kellas
Senior Vice President, Robert Booth
Executive Vice President Commercial Banking, Jay Zatta
Vice President Retail Operations, Lisa Copley
Senior Vice President Senior Lender, Bob Friend

Vice President And Loan Review Officer, Diane Todd
Vice President Business Development Officer, Neal Jackson
Senior Vice President Investments, Michael Klick
Assistant Vice President Commercial Banking Officer, Randall Trickett
Senior Vice President And Senior Credit Officer, David Knuth
Assistant Vice President Private Banker, Kerrie Smith
Vice President Of Commercial Banking, Michael Mistovich
Vice President And Business Banking Officer, Nathan Mcvicker
Assistant Vice President Branch Manager, Tom Wiggershaus
Banking Center Manager Assistant Vice President, Nicholas Beresh
Vice President Residential Lending, David Bendis
Vice President Secondary Marketing Manager, Ryan Freimark
Senior Vice President Corporate Banking, Charles Wharton
Vice President, Sabra Thomas Kershaw
Senior Vice President Enterprise Services, Jan Pattishall
Vice President Business Banking, John Mcdonough
Assistant Vice President Financial Advisor, Josh Schmalz
Vice President Commercial Lending, Kurt Bevan
Vice President Credit Risk Management, Ryan Potts
Vice President, James Bish
Assistant Vice President, Anthony Habbit
Senior Vice President, Jeff Ferry
Assistant Vice President Information Technology, John Busack
Assistant Vice President Bcm Business Development, Jason Lucarelli
Vice President Corporate Banking, Harry J Silvis
Vice President And Manger, Mary Bryson
Senior Vice President, Thomas Ziacik
Assistant Vice President Senior Underwriter, Tim Robinson
Assistant Vice President, Dan Baxter
Vice President, Brent Dapper
Assistant Vice President Banking Center Manager, Linda Yon
Vice President, Michael Puzausky
Vice President, Nathan Schoetz
Vice President Business Banking, Maher-dickerson Stephanie
Vice President Quality Assurance Manager, Pamela Jones
Vice President Corporate Banking, Jack Green
Vice President Private Banker, Leslie D Witzel
Vice President And Commercial Banker, Michael Epperley
Senior Vice President And Senior Commercial Banker, Michael T Misich
Vice President Commercial Lender, Robert E Krzeminski
Vice President Treasury Management Sales, Stacy Graf
Vice President Senior Trust Officer, Thomas D Barsody
Vice President Commercial Lending, Kurt C Bevan
Vice President Commercial Banker, Camde Skidmore
Senior Vice President, Ed Hensley
Vice President And Technology Services Coordinator, Stephanie Skivington
Vice President Commercial Banking, Daniel Hindman
Vice President Senior Trust Officer, Thomas Barsody
Vice President Private Banker, Leslie Witzel
Senior Vice President And Senior Commercial Banker, Michael Misich

Assistant Vice President And Appraisal Review Officer, Ann Scranton
Svp Financial Advisor Crc, Sherri Libersat
Vice President, Jeff Davis
Evp, David Ellwood Cfa
Evp Senior Operations Officer, Greg Dugan
Senior Vice President Private Client Services, Andy Mayer
Chairman, James C. (Jim) Gardill, age 73
Secretary, Cindy Dailer
Board Member, Ronald Owen
Board Member, Denise Knouse-snyder
Auditors: Ernst & Young LLP

LOCATIONS

HQ: WesBanco Inc
1 Bank Plaza, Wheeling, WV 26003
Phone: 304 234-9000
Web: www.wesbanco.com

PRODUCTS/OPERATIONS

2016 Sales

	$ mil.	% of total
Interest and Dividend Income		
Loans including fees	227	61
Interest and dividends on securities	57	15
Other interest income	2	1
Non-Interest Income		
Trust fees	22	6
Service charges on deposits	18	5
Electronic banking fees	16	4
Net securities brokerage	6	2
Bank-owned life insurance	4	1
Net gains on sales of mortgage loans	3	1
Net securities gains	2	1
Net gain / (loss) on other real estate owned and other assets	1	-
others	10	3
Total	**368**	**100**

Selected Products and Services
Personal Banking
Internet Banking
Checking
Savings
Time Deposits
Debit Cards
Credit Cards
Loans
Mortgage Lending
Other Services
Business
Internet Banking
Checking
Savings
Time Deposits
Credit Cards
Loans
Treasury Management
Insurance Services
Wealth Management

COMPETITORS

1st West Virginia Bancorp	Huntington Bancshares
BB&T	Ohio Valley Banc
Bank of America	PNC Financial
Cheviot Financial	United Bancorp
City Holding	United Bankshares
First Community Bancshares	

HISTORICAL FINANCIALS

Company Type: Public

Income Statement   FYE: December 31

	ASSETS ($ mil.)	NET INCOME ($ mil.)	INCOME AS % OF ASSETS	EMPLOYEES
12/18	12,459	143	1.1%	2,383
12/17	9,816	94	1.0%	1,940
12/16	9,791	87	0.9%	1,928
12/15	8,470	81	1.0%	1,633
12/14	6,297	70	1.1%	1,448
Annual Growth	18.6%	19.6%	—	13.3%

2018 Year-End Financials

Debt ratio: 2.00%
Return on equity: 8.00%
Cash ($ mil.): 169
Current ratio: —
Long-term debt ($ mil.): —

No. of shares (mil.): 55
Dividends
Yield: 3.0%
Payout: 47.0%
Market value ($ mil.): 2,003

	STOCK PRICE ($) FY Close	P/E High/Low	PER SHARE ($) Earnings	Dividends	Book Value
12/18	37.00	17 12	3.00	1.00	36.00
12/17	41.00	20 16	2.00	1.00	32.00
12/16	43.00	20 13	2.00	1.00	31.00
12/15	30.00	17 14	2.00	1.00	29.00
12/14	35.00	15 11	2.00	1.00	27.00
Annual Growth	1.3%	— —	5.1%	7.2%	7.7%

Wesco International, Inc.

When contractors and manufacturers need parts it's WESCO to the rescue. The company distributes general and electrical supplies (fuses terminals connectors enclosures circuit breakers transformers switchboards tools abrasives filters safety equipment) lighting (lamps fixtures ballasts) wire and conduit materials (wire cable raceway metallic and non-metallic conduit) and automation controls and motors (relays timers and interconnects). WESCO offers more than a million products from some 30000 suppliers with about 70000 customers worldwide. The company generates 75% of its sales in the US.

Operations

WESCO products offering include general supplies (about 40% of sales); communications and security (about 15%); wire cable and conduit (nearly 15%); electrical distribution and controls (about 10%); lighting and sustainability (about 10%); and automation controls and motions (nearly 10%). Company?s largest supplier Eaton Corporation accounts for about 10% of purchase while ten largest supplier accounted for about a third of its purchase

Geographic Reach

Headquartered in Pittsburgh Pennsylvania WESCO operates more than 500 branches of which some 340 are located in the US. Outside of the US about 130 are located in Canada seven are located in Mexico and the remainder are in other countries located in Africa Asia Europe and South America. International markets serviced by its 10 distribution centers located in the US Canada and Mexico. It boasts offices in about 15 additional countries. The US accounts for more than 75% of sales and the remaining sales comes from International primarily in Canada.

Sales and Marketing

WESCO caters to 70000 customers. Sales to industrial customers (more than 35%) range from major industrial commercial and data communication projects to small residential contractors. Construction customers (about one-third of sales) include contractors and engineering procurement and constructional firms for commercial and data and broadband communications projects. Utilities and specialty utility contractors (some 15%) include large and rural electric cooperatives and municipal power authorities which maintain transmission distribution lines and power plants.

Commercial institutional and governmental customers (accounting for about 15% of sales) include schools hospitals property management firms retailers and government agencies of all types.

Financial Performance

WESCO has seen limited revenue growth in recent years. Its annual revenues have risen about 3% since 2014.

Revenue increased to $8.1 billion in 2018 an approximately 6% increase from the year prior. The increase was driven by record sales with growth in all end markets and geographies.

Net income was $227 million in fiscal year 2018 an increase from $164 million in fiscal year 2017. Selling general and administrative expenses fell slightly in fiscal 2018 to $14.1 million.

Cash provided by operating activities was $296.7 million in fiscal 2018 while investing activities used $34.1 million. Financing activities used another $275.1 million.

Strategy

WESCO has been building its business through acquisitions and organic growth. As part of this effort the company's working to develop new end markets broaden its product and service offerings expand its geographic footprint and enhance its sales and customer service.

The company is focused on its global account and integrated supply programs to boost its customer base and extend its use of supply services to customers. It targets customers in the fields of construction contracting; education; engineering procurement and construction firms; government; healthcare; and utilities. Among product growth areas WESCO looks to data communications and security systems and to clean tech lighting systems.WESCO is boosting its lighting division through acquisitions. In 2019 its Wesco Services division acquired Sylvania Lighting Solutions (SLS) the lighting business of OSRAM Sylvania. The acquisition adds SLS's customer base an expanded geographic footprint and project management capabilities to WESCO's offerings.

Mergers and Acquisitions

In recent years WESCO has been buying up distributors and other firms to extend its reach and capabilities. In 2019 its Wesco Services division acquired Sylvania Lighting Solutions (SLS) the lighting business of OSRAM Sylvania. The acquisition adds SLS's customer base expanded geographic footprint and project management capabilities to WESCO's offerings.

Company Background

In 1922 Westinghouse Electric formed Westinghouse Electric Supply company to help sell and distribute their products. In 1994 Westinghouse divested their electrical manufacturing division. This opened the door for WESCO management along with a private investment company ? Clayton Dubilier & Rice (CD&R) ? to purchase Westinghouse Electric Supply Company and create WESCO Distribution Inc. WESCO traded on New York Stock Exchange in 1999

HISTORY

WESCO International got its start as a subsidiary of electrical power pioneer Westinghouse Electric Company. George Westinghouse founded the company bearing his name in Pittsburgh in 1886. The company installed the nation's first alternating current power system in Telluride Colorado in 1891. Two years later Westinghouse built the generating system that powered the Chicago World's Fair. The company also was chosen to provide generators for the hydroelectric power station at Niagara Falls.

George Westinghouse was ousted in 1910 after the company was unable to meet its debt obligations. He died four years later at the age of 67. During the next decade the company added the burgeoning radio and appliance markets to its portfolio of electrical distribution and production operations.

In 1922 the firm established Westinghouse Electric Supply Company (WESCO) to distribute power products and appliances. Westinghouse had its share of troubles over the years many of which were caused by ill-advised diversification attempts. These included forays into uranium supply financial services and real estate.

By the 1990s Westinghouse was buried under nearly $10 billion in debt and too busy putting out fires to tend to day-to-day operations properly. Not surprisingly WESCO was caught up in Westinghouse's problems: Sales declined four years in a row and employee turnover was around 25% a year.

Westinghouse embarked on a divestiture program and sold WESCO to investment firm Clayton Dubilier & Rice (CD&R) in 1994 for about $340 million. At the time WESCO had about 250 branch locations. The new owners brought in Roy Haley a veteran insurance and finance executive to turn the ailing business around. Haley tied pay and bonuses to performance and emphasized multisite customers such as contractors and companies with multiple retail industrial or administrative locations. WESCO grew through acquisitions and in 1995 sales reached $2 billion.

By 1996 the company had added 1000 employees; it operated about 300 distribution branches throughout the world. Sales reached $2.6 billion in 1997 as WESCO continued acquiring complementary companies and formed an alliance with Australian mining and steel company BHP (now BHP Billiton). Managers led a $1.1 billion buyout of the company in 1998 increasing their stake in WESCO from 15% to 33%. Costs related to acquisitions and the buyout caused WESCO to post a loss even though 1998 sales passed the $3 billion mark. The company opened sales offices in the UK Singapore and Mexico.

As it geared up for its IPO in 1999 WESCO bought distributors Industrial Electric Supply Company and Statewide Electrical Supply. The company continued to shop during 2000 adding electrical distributors Orton Utility Supply (Tennessee) Control Corporation of America (Virginia) and KVA Supply Company (Colorado and California).

In 2001 WESCO acquired two distributors (Herning Underground Supply and Alliance Utility Products) that supplied contractors who install gas lighting and communication utility infrastructure in Arizona California Utah and Washington.

The Cypress Group the private-equity firm that helped lead the $1.1 billion management buyout in 1998 sold most of its shares in WESCO in 2004 and 2005. Cypress owned nearly half of WESCO prior to those sales.

WESCO acquired fastener distributor Fastec Industrial and electronics distributor Carlton-Bates in 2005. The following year it bought Communications Supply Corporation (CSC) a distributor of

low-voltage network infrastructure and industrial wire and cable products for about $525 million in cash.

In 2007 WESCO acquired J-Mark a supplier of building products which strengthened the company's position in the manufactured housing industry. It also acquired the assets of Monti Electric Supply which provides electricity and furnishes lighting. The purchase gave WESCO a broader market position in the reconstruction of the Gulf Coast region. The company sold a 60% stake in LADD which is a distributor of industrial electrical connectors and accessories to Deutsch Engineered Connecting Devices for approximately $75 million. Proceeds were earmarked to purchase shares of WESCO's common stock.

In 2008 WESCO offered to purchase Industrial Distribution Group (IDG) for about $130 million in cash topping a bid for IDG by Platinum Equity.

Roy Haley stepped aside as CEO in 2009 becoming WESCO's executive chairman. SVP/COO John Engel was promoted to president and CEO as a result.

WESCO acquired TVC Communications for about $246 million in late 2010. The deal expanded WESCO's broadband and telecom distribution network in the Americas and its ties to manufacturers.

EXECUTIVES

LOCATIONS

HQ: Wesco International, Inc.
225 West Station Square Drive, Suite 700, Pittsburgh, PA 15219
Phone: 412 454-2200
Web: www.wesco.com

2016 Sales

	$ mil.	% of total
US	5,636	77
Canada	1,395	19
Mexico	62	1
Other countries	243	3
Total	**7,336**	**100**

PRODUCTS/OPERATIONS

2016 Sales

	% of total
Industrial customers	36
Construction	34
Utility	16
Commercial institutional & governmental customers	14
Total	**100**

Selected Services

Collaborative cross-functional cost savings teams;
Consultation on energy-efficient product upgrades
Dedicated on-site support personnel;
Inventory optimization programs including just-in-time delivery and vendor managed inventory;
Safety and product training for customer employee
Technical support for operational and transactional process improvements;

Selected Products

Automation equipment
Ballasts
Boxes
Busways
Cable
Circuit breakers
Connectors
Data communications products
Drives
Electrical products
Fittings
Fixtures
Fuses
Industrial supplies
Light bulbs
Lighting
Lugs
Metallic and nonmetallic conduits
Motor control devices
MRO supplies
Operator interfaces
Panelboards
Patch panels
Premise wiring
Programmable logic controllers
Pushbuttons
Switchboards
Tape
Terminals
Tools
Transformers
Wire
Wire and conduit products

COMPETITORS

Anixter International	HWC
Bearing Distributors	McNaughton-McKay
Border States Electric	Premier Farnell
Consolidated Electrical	Rexel Inc.
Electro-Wire	Richardson Electronics
Electrocomponents	SUMMIT Electric Supply
Graybar Electric	Sonepar USA
	W.W. Grainger

HISTORICAL FINANCIALS

Company Type: Public

Income Statement
FYE: December 31

	REVENUE ($ mil.)	NET INCOME ($ mil.)	NET PROFIT MARGIN	EMPLOYEES
12/18	8,177	227	2.8%	9,100
12/17	7,679	163	2.1%	9,100
12/16	7,336	102	1.4%	9,000
12/15	7,518	211	2.8%	9,300
12/14	7,890	276	3.5%	9,400
Annual Growth	0.9%	(4.7%)	—	(0.8%)

2018 Year-End Financials

Debt ratio: 27.00%
Return on equity: 11.00%
Cash ($ mil.): 96
Current ratio: 2.00
Long-term debt ($ mil.): 1,167
No. of shares (mil.): 45
Dividends
  Yield: —
  Payout: —
Market value ($ mil.): 2,165

	STOCK PRICE ($) FY Close	P/E High/Low	Earnings	Dividends	Book Value
12/18	48.00	14 9	5.00	0.00	47.00
12/17	68.00	22 15	3.00	0.00	45.00
12/16	67.00	31 16	2.00	0.00	41.00
12/15	44.00	16 8	4.00	0.00	42.00
12/14	76.00	15 11	5.00	0.00	43.00
Annual Growth	(10.9%)	— —	(1.8%)	—	2.2%

West Bancorporation, Inc.

West Bancorporation is the holding company for West Bank which serves individuals and small to midsized businesses through about a dozen branches mainly in the Des Moines and Iowa City Iowa areas. Founded in 1893 the bank offers checking savings and money market accounts CDs Visa credit cards and trust services. The bank's lending activities primarily consist of commercial mortgages; construction land and land development loans; and business loans such as revolving lines of credit inventory and accounts receivable financing equipment financing and capital expenditure loans to borrowers in Iowa.

Sales and Marketing

West Bank focuses on small to medium-sized businesses in its local markets. The thinking is that smaller local firms want to develop an exclusive relationship with a single bank.

Financial Performance

The company's revenue has been remarkably consistent year-over-year. It reported $61.2 million in annual revenue for fiscal 2013 after claiming $61.7 million in fiscal 2012 and $64.1 million in fiscal 2011.

Net income has also remained very consistent in recent years. The bank reported net income of $16.8 million for fiscal 2013 after clearing $16 million in fiscal 2012 and $15.27 million in fiscal 2011.

The company's net cash on hand has decreased dramatically in recent fiscal years however mostly as a result of property investments.

Strategy

West Bank has slowly but surely been expanding its territory. The company is working on building a new headquarters building and expanding into Minnesota.

EXECUTIVES

Evp; President West Bank, Brad L. Winterbottom, age 63, $275,000 total compensation
Evp Cfo And Treasurer, Douglas R. (Doug) Gulling, age 66, $275,000 total compensation
President And Ceo, David D. (Dave) Nelson, age 59, $400,000 total compensation
Evp And Chief Risk Officer, Harlee N. Olafson, age 62, $275,000 total compensation
Vice President, Donavon Paulson
Vice President, Nancy Behmer
Senior Vice President, Keith Kurth
Chairman, David R. Milligan
Board Member, Steven Gaer
Board Member, Kaye Lozier
Board Member, Lou Ann Sandburg
Member Board Of Directors, Sean McMurray
Auditors: RSM US LLP

LOCATIONS

HQ: West Bancorporation, Inc.
  1601 22nd Street, West Des Moines, IA 50266
Phone: 515 222-2300
Web: www.westbankstrong.com

PRODUCTS/OPERATIONS

2015 Sales

	$ mil.	% of total
Interest		
Loans including fees	53	77
Taxable investment Securities	4	6
Tax-exempt investment Securities	3	5
Federal funds sold	0	-
Noninterest		
Service charges on deposit accounts	3	4
Debit card usage fees	2	3
Trust services	1	2
Revenue from residential mortgage banking	0	-
Increase in cash value of bank-owned life insurance	1	1
Realized investment securities gains net	0	-
Other income	2	2
Total	**68**	**100**

COMPETITORS

BTC Financial	Regions Financial
Bank of America	U.S. Bancorp
Bank of the West	Wells Fargo
MidWestOne	

HISTORICAL FINANCIALS

Company Type: Public

Income Statement
FYE: December 31

	ASSETS ($ mil.)	NET INCOME ($ mil.)	INCOME AS % OF ASSETS	EMPLOYEES
12/18	2,297	29	1.2%	163
12/17	2,114	23	1.1%	162
12/16	1,854	23	1.2%	165
12/15	1,749	22	1.2%	174
12/14	1,616	20	1.2%	178
Annual Growth	9.2%	9.2%	—	(2.2%)

2018 Year-End Financials

Debt ratio: 2.00%
Return on equity: 15.00%
Cash ($ mil.): 46
Current ratio: —
Long-term debt ($ mil.): —
No. of shares (mil.): 16
Dividends
  Yield: 4.0%
  Payout: 51.0%
Market value ($ mil.): 311

	STOCK PRICE ($) FY Close	P/E High/Low	Earnings	Dividends	Book Value
12/18	19.00	15 10	2.00	1.00	12.00
12/17	25.00	20 15	1.00	1.00	11.00
12/16	25.00	17 11	1.00	1.00	10.00
12/15	20.00	15 12	1.00	1.00	9.00
12/14	17.00	14 11	1.00	0.00	9.00
Annual Growth	2.9%	—	8.6%	12.3%	7.6%

WestAmerica Bancorporation

Annie get your checkbook? Maybe not as wild as Buffalo Bill's West but Westamerica Bancorporation still shoots high with its subsidiary Westamerica Bank. The bank operates almost 100 branches in Northern and Central California. It offers individuals and businesses such standard fare as checking and savings accounts as well as electronic banking trust services and credit cards. It focuses on the banking needs of small businesses; business loans and commercial mortgages together account for more than half of the company's loan portfolio. Westamerica Bank chartered in 1884 also originates construction residential mortgage and consumer loans.

Operations

Westamerica Bancorporation provides a full range of banking services to individual and corporate customers through its subsidiary bank Westamerica Bank.

Westamerica Bank subsidiary Community Banker Services Corporation provides the company and its other subsidiaries with data processing and various support services.

Geographic Reach

The bank has 95 branches and 2 trust offices in 21 Northern and Central California counties. Westamerica owns 33 branch office locations and one administrative facility and leases 70 facilities.

Financial Performance

In 2012 the company had assets of $5 billion deposits of $4.2 billion and shareholders' equity of $560.1 million

Revenues declined by 10% in 2012 due to a drop in loan revenues a decrease in ATM processing fees (due to lower transaction volumes) and loss on sale of securities.

Net income dropped by 8% in 2012 due to lower revenues partially offset by a decline in expenses.

Strategy

Westamerica's conservative lending practices (it avoided the clamor around subprime lending) and operating principles helped it weather the economic recession better than some of its banking peers.

Company Background

However the company's revenues and profits have fallen since 2009 when Westamerica netted a record $125 million. In 2011 net income fell 7% to $88 million (versus the $95 million it made in 2010) partly due to higher expenses as the company absorbed the operations of the recently acquired Sonoma Valley Bank. Revenues also fell 5% to $268 million. The declines were attributed to interest and fee earnings which fell as the company's lending activities slowed down and regulatory changes limited the amount of service charges banks can charge. (However both merchant processing fees and trust fees increased as those businesses grew.)

Over the years Westamerica had grown through acquisitions of other banks. In 2010 it added three branches in northern California when it acquired most of the assets and deposits of the failed Sonoma Valley Bank; the deal included loss-sharing agreements with the FDIC. That deal followed a similar transaction when the bank acquired County Bank after it was seized by regulators. That deal added nearly 40 branches to Westamerica Bank's network most of them in California's Central Valley.

EXECUTIVES

Svp Operations And Systems, Dennis R. Hansen, $130,008 total compensation
Chairman President And Ceo, David L. Payne, $371,000 total compensation
Svp And Cfo, Robert A. Thorson, $149,000 total compensation
Svp Banking Division, David L. Robinson, $150,000 total compensation
Svp Credit Administrator, Russell Rizzardi, $120,960 total compensation
Vice President Accounting Manager, Glen Yasaki

Assistant Vice President And Commercial Loan Adjustment Officer, Christie Marriott
Senior Vice President, Joseph Dietzen
Executive Vice President Strategy And Development, Jennifer Finger
Vice President Of Sales, Scott Tucker
Vice President And Manager Community Relations, Debbie Friesen
Vice President Training And Development Manager, Gary Lepiane
Board Member, Catherine Macmillan
Board Of Directors, Patrick Lynch
Board Member, Etta Allen
Board Member, Joseph Bowler
Auditors: Crowe LLP

LOCATIONS

HQ: WestAmerica Bancorporation
1108 Fifth Avenue, San Rafael, CA 94901
Phone: 707 863-6000
Web: www.westamerica.com

PRODUCTS/OPERATIONS

2016 Sales

	$ mil.	% of total
Interest and Fee Income:		
Loans	69	38
Investment securities available for sale	34	19
Investment securities held to maturity	31	17
Noninterest Income:		
Service charges on deposit accounts	21	12
Merchant processing services	6	4
Debit card fees	6	4
Other service fees	3	1
Trust fees	3	1
ATM processing fees	2	1
Financial services commissions	1	-
Other	5	3
Total	**181**	**100**

COMPETITORS

Bank of America	MUFG Americas Holdings
Citigroup	Mechanics Bank
Comerica	U.S. Bancorp
First Republic (CA)	Wells Fargo
JPMorgan Chase	Western Alliance

HISTORICAL FINANCIALS

Company Type: Public

Income Statement — FYE: December 31

	ASSETS ($ mil.)	NET INCOME ($ mil.)	INCOME AS % OF ASSETS	EMPLOYEES
12/18	5,569	72	1.3%	762
12/17	5,513	50	0.9%	785
12/16	5,366	59	1.1%	783
12/15	5,169	59	1.1%	813
12/14	5,036	61	1.2%	858
Annual Growth	2.5%	4.2%	—	(2.9%)

2018 Year-End Financials

Debt ratio: —	No. of shares (mil.): 27
Return on equity: 12.00%	Dividends
Cash ($ mil.): 420	Yield: 3.0%
Current ratio: —	Payout: 76.0%
Long-term debt ($ mil.): —	Market value ($ mil.): 1,488

	STOCK PRICE ($) FY Close	P/E High/Low		Earnings	PER SHARE ($) Dividends	Book Value
12/18	56.00	24	20	3.00	2.00	23.00
12/17	60.00	34	26	2.00	2.00	22.00
12/16	63.00	28	18	2.00	2.00	22.00
12/15	47.00	23	18	2.00	2.00	21.00
12/14	49.00	24	19	2.00	2.00	20.00
Annual Growth	3.2%	—	—	3.6%	1.3%	3.0%

Western Alliance Bancorporation

Western Alliance Bancorporation and its flagship Western Alliance Bank (WAB) have an alliance with several bank brands in the West operating as the Alliance Bank of Arizona; Bank of Nevada; First Independent Bank (Nevada); as well as Bridge Bank and Torrey Pines Bank which are both located across California. Combined the banks operate nearly 50 branches that provide standard consumer and business deposit and loan products. About half of the Western Alliance's loan portfolio is made up of commercial and industrial loans while another 40% is made up of commercial real estate loans. It also makes land development loans and consumer residential mortgages and other lines of credit.

Operations

Western Alliance focuses on commercial lending. About 46% of the bank's loan portfolio consisted of commercial and industrial loans at the end of 2015 while another 39% was made up of commercial real estate loans. The bank also had construction and land development loans (10% of loan assets) residential mortgages (3%) commercial leases (1%) and consumer loans (less than 1%).

More than 90% of the bank's revenue comes from interest income. About 86% of its total revenue came from loan interest during 2015 while another 9% came from interest or dividends on investment securities. The remainder of its revenue came from service charges and fees (2% of revenue) card income (1%) and other miscellaneous sources.

Geographic Reach

Western Alliance's 40 branches and seven loan offices are spread across Arizona Nevada and California as well as Boston Dallas and Reston Virginia. At the end of 2015 its loan business was concentrated in the Los Angeles San Francisco San Jose Phoenix Tuscon Reno and Las Vegas metropolitan areas.

Sales and Marketing

The bank serves local businesses real estate developers and investors not-for-profit organizations and consumers. It specializes in lending to such customers operating in the healthcare professional services manufacturing and distribution resorts and timeshares technology and startups municipalities and local governments non-profit and renewable energy markets. Some of its clients (as of early 2016) include Cutter Aviation FNF Construction Hollenbeck Palms New American Funding and Signature Healthcare Services.

Western Alliance spent $2.89 million on marketing in 2015 up from $2.30 million and $2.58 million in 2014 and 2013 respectively.

Financial Performance

Western Alliance's annual revenues have risen nearly 70% since 2011 as its loan business has swelled. Meanwhile the bank's annual profits have ballooned more than five-fold as its credit portfolio's credit quality has improved with higher property valuations in the strengthened economy.

The group's revenue jumped 26% to $555 million during 2015 mostly thanks to new loan business more than half of which was obtained from the Bridge Bank acquisition which spurred more interest income for the year. Non-interest income especially service charges and lending-related fees grew by double digits during the year also thanks to the acquisition as well as from more organic deposit business growth.

Strong revenue growth and a continued decline in credit loss provisions in 2015 drove Western Alliance's net income up by 31% to $194 million for the year. The company's operating cash levels climbed 30% to $213 million mostly thanks to the rise in cash earnings.

Strategy

Western Alliance Bancorporation looks to expand its branch network and selectively acquire other banks to boost its loan and deposit business and extend its geographic reach. The bank may also buy other financial services businesses to bolster its line of service offerings.

Mergers and Acquisitions

In June 2015 Western Alliance bought $13 billion-asset Bridge Capital Holdings along with its 48 Bridge Bank branches in California Arizona and Nevada in a deal worth about $425 million. The purchase brought expertise in technology and international banking among other areas and expands Western Alliance's market into Northern California.

EXECUTIVES

Evp And Chief Credit Officer, Robert R. (Bob) McAuslan, age 66

Chairman And Ceo, Robert G. Sarver, age 58, $830,000 total compensation

Evp And Cfo, Dale M. Gibbons, age 58, $400,000 total compensation

Evp Northern California Administration And President And Ceo Bridge Bank Division, Daniel P. (Dan) Myers, age 58, $212,885 total compensation

Evp Southern Nevada Administration And Ceo Bank Of Nevada Division, John Guedry

Evp And Cio, John P. Peckham

Evp California Administration And President Torrey Pines Bank, Gerald A. (Gary) Cady, age 64, $360,000 total compensation

Evp And Chief Risk Officer, Patricia A. Taylor

Evp And General Counsel, Randall S. Theisen

Evp And Coo, Jim Haught

Evp Arizona Administration And Ceo Alliance Bank Of Arizona, Don Garner

Senior Vice President, Seth Davis

Vice President, Jennifer Holyoak

Senior Credit Analyst Vice President Warehouse Lending, Bryan Brooks

Chief Human Resource Officer Executive Vice President, Barbara Kennedy

Vp Of Relationship Manager Of Bank Of Nevada, Melanie Maviglia

Evp Bank Of Nevada, Bill Oakley

Board Member, Cary Mack

Board Member, William Boyd

Auditors: RSM US LLP

LOCATIONS

HQ: Western Alliance Bancorporation
One E. Washington Street, Suite 1400, Phoenix, AZ 85004
Phone: 602 389-3500
Web: www.westernalliancebancorporation.com

PRODUCTS/OPERATIONS

2015 Sales

	$ mil.	% of total
Interest income		
Loans including fees	476	86
Investment securities	38	7
Dividends	10	2
Other	1	-
Non-interest income		
Service charges and fees	15	2
Income from bank owned life insurance	4	1
Card income	4	1
Other	8	1
Total	555	100

Selected Services

Business Checking & Savings
Business Loans & Credit
Card Services
International Banking
Personal Banking
Treasury Management

COMPETITORS

Bank of America	PacWest Bancorp
Bank of the West	U.S. Bancorp
Desert Schools FCU	Wells Fargo
First Banks	Westamerica
MUFG Americas Holdings	Zions Bancorporation

HISTORICAL FINANCIALS

Company Type: Public

Income Statement

FYE: December 31

	ASSETS ($ mil.)	NET INCOME ($ mil.)	INCOME AS % OF ASSETS	EMPLOYEES
12/18	23,109	436	1.9%	1,787
12/17	20,329	325	1.6%	1,725
12/16	17,201	260	1.5%	1,557
12/15	14,275	194	1.4%	1,446
12/14	10,600	148	1.4%	1,131
Annual Growth	21.5%	31.0%	—	12.1%

2018 Year-End Financials

Debt ratio: 2.00%
Return on equity: 18.00%
Cash ($ mil.): 499
Current ratio: —
Long-term debt ($ mil.): —

No. of shares (mil.): 105
Dividends
  Yield: —
  Payout: —
Market value ($ mil.): 4,144

	STOCK PRICE ($) FY Close	P/E High/Low	Earnings	PER SHARE ($) Dividends	Book Value
12/18	39.00	15 9	4.00	0.00	25.00
12/17	57.00	19 14	3.00	0.00	21.00
12/16	49.00	20 11	3.00	0.00	18.00
12/15	36.00	19 12	2.00	0.00	15.00
12/14	28.00	17 12	2.00	0.00	11.00
Annual Growth	9.2%		25.5%	—	21.9%

Western Asset Mortgage Capital Corp

Auditors: PricewaterhouseCoopers LLP

LOCATIONS

HQ: Western Asset Mortgage Capital Corp
385 East Colorado Boulevard, Pasadena, CA 91101
Phone: 626 844-9400
Web: www.westernassetmcc.com

HISTORICAL FINANCIALS

Company Type: Public

Income Statement

FYE: December 31

	ASSETS ($ mil.)	NET INCOME ($ mil.)	INCOME AS % OF ASSETS	EMPLOYEES
12/18	4,497	26	0.6%	—
12/17	3,887	85	2.2%	—
12/16	3,156	(25)	—	—
12/15	3,415	(9)	—	—
12/14	4,909	101	2.1%	1
Annual Growth	(2.2%)	(28.4%)	—	—

2018 Year-End Financials

Debt ratio: 24.00%
Return on equity: 5.00%
Cash ($ mil.): 22
Current ratio: —
Long-term debt ($ mil.): —

No. of shares (mil.): 48
Dividends
  Yield: 15.0%
  Payout: 203.0%
Market value ($ mil.): 401

	STOCK PRICE ($) FY Close	P/E High/Low	Earnings	PER SHARE ($) Dividends	Book Value
12/18	8.00	19 14	1.00	1.00	10.00
12/17	10.00	5 5	2.00	1.00	11.00
12/16	10.00	— —	(1.00)	1.00	10.00
12/15	10.00	— —	(0.00)	2.00	12.00
12/14	15.00	6 5	3.00	3.00	15.00
Annual Growth	(13.2%)		(30.9%)	(18.0%)	(8.5%)

Western Digital Corp

When it comes to data storage Western Digital has drive and more than a splash of flash. The company is one of the largest independent makers of hard-disk drives (HDDs) which record store and recall volumes of data. It is also active in the fast-growing area of solid-state drives (SSDs). Drives for PCs account for a major portion of Western Digital's sales although the company also makes devices used in servers cloud computing data centers and home entertainment products such as set-top boxes and video game consoles. The company sells to manufacturers and through retailers and distributors. It generates more than half its sales from the Asia/Pacific region.

Operations

Western Digital reports its sales in terms of end markets. The company's biggest market nearly 50% of sales is client devices such as PCs smartphones gaming gadgets and security equipment. Data center devices high-capacity enterprise HDDs and high-performance enterprise SSDs data center software and systems account for about 30% of sales and client solutions which are external memory such as USB flash drives and wireless drives generate about 20% of sales.

Geographic Reach

Western Digital's largest market is Asia (which represents more than half of sales including more than 20% in China and about 20% in Hong Kong). The US is Western Digital's second biggest market accounting for about 20% of revenue. The EMEA region accounts for less 20%.

Western Digital has manufacturing facilities in the US as well as in China Japan Malaysia the Philippines Singapore and Thailand; it has sales offices worldwide. Its research and development facilities are in the US Malaysia Thailand India and Israel.

Sales and Marketing

Western Digital sells to OEMs as well as through distributors and retailers. The company's 10 biggest customers account for more than 40% of revenue. Two customers Apple Inc. and Dell Technologies each account for more than 10% of Western Digital's accounts receivable.

Financial Performance

Western Digital added a second year of revenue growth in 2018 (ended June) after ending a three-year revenue decline in 2017 with a 47% increase. Revenue rose 8% to $20.6 billion in 2018 a $1.5 billion increase from the previous year. Net income grew a robust 70% in 2018 from 2017 outpacing the 64% profit increase in 2017 from 2016.

Sales increased across Western Digital's segments in 2018 from 2017 led by a 6% increase in Client Devices (half of the company's revenue) from growth in embedded flash products. Sales rose 10% in Data Center Devices and Solutions and Client Solutions.

Profit jumped $675 million in 2018 from $497 million in 2017 on higher revenue and reduced research and development expenses while absorbing about a $1 billion increase in income taxes due to the US Tax Cuts and Jobs Act of 2017.

Western Digital's cash and equivalents dropped to $5 billion 2018 about $1.3 billion less than it had in 2017. Cash from operation was $4.2 billion in 2018 while the company used about $1.6 billion in investing activities and $3.9 billion in investing activities. In 2018 the company reduced the aggregate principal of its debt by $1.98 billion and reduced its interest cost.

Strategy

Western Digital took steps to reduce costs and consolidate hard disk drive operation closing a manufacturing facility in Malaysia and putting its HDD operations into Thailand. The process should be completed by the end of its 2019 fiscal year (June) and cost about $160 million.

With extensive operations in Asia Western Digital is susceptible to tariffs set in the course of trade disputes between the US and China. Tariffs could prompt customers may delay or reduce purchases and they could lead to a deterioration in economic conditions.

Mergers and Acquisitions

Western Digital has long used acquisitions to add new product lines and extend its geographic reach.

In 2019 Western Digital acquired Kazan Networks a provider of technology for data centers to expand its data infrastructure offerings. Kazan's technologies expand Western Digital's products for disaggregated data infrastructure and help speed its use of non-volatile memory express (NVMe) platforms.

In 2017 Western Digital made two deals acquiring UpThere a developer of cloud storage systems and Tegile Systems a maker of flash storage announcing the deals of the same day. UpThere makes apps for storing and accessing date in the cloud and making it available from multiple devices and operating systems. With Tegile Western Digital extends its reach into enterprise data storage. Tegile's IntelliFlash products offer quick access to match Western Digital's dig data programs. Western Digital also gains 1700 new customers from the deal.

EXECUTIVES

Evp Memory Technology, Siva Sivaram
Cto, Martin Fink, age 54
President And Ceo, Stephen D. (Steve) Milligan, age 56, $1,050,000 total compensation
Evp Silicon Operations, Manish Bhatia
President And Coo, Michael D. Cordano, age 55, $725,000 total compensation
Evp And Cfo, Mark P. Long, age 52, $500,000 total compensation
Evp And Chief Human Resources Officer, Jacqueline M. DeMaria, age 57
Evp Chief Legal Officer And Secretary, Michael C. Ray, age 52, $500,000 total compensation
Vice President Facilities Asia, Shahzad Mahmud
Vice President Gm Of Manufacturing Head Operations, Norm Armour
Executive Vice President Andchief Technology Officer, Steven Campbell
Vp Worldwide It, Cp Sin
Senior Vice President And General Manager Data Center Systems, Phil Bullinger

Vice President Engineering Director Engineering, Gerardo Bertero
Vice President Information Technology, Terry Dembitz
Vice President Marketing, Joan Wrabetz
Vice President Platform Engineering, Kurt Chan
Svp And Cto (fio) Vp And Senior Fellow (sndk)(wdc), Pankaj Mehra
Chairman, Matthew E. (Matt) Massengill, age 58
Board Member, Paula Price
Board Member, Kathleen Cote
Auditors: KPMG LLP

LOCATIONS

HQ: Western Digital Corp
  5601 Great Oaks Parkway, San Jose, CA 95119
Phone: 408 717-6000
Web: www.westerndigital.com

2018 Sales

	$ mil.	% of total
Asia		
China	4,393	22
Hong Kong	4,022	20
Rest of Asia	2,752	13
US	4,640	22
Europe Middle East & Africa	3,858	19
Other	982	5
Total	**20,647**	**100**

PRODUCTS/OPERATIONS

2018 Sales by Market

	$ mil.	% of total
Client Devices	10,108	49
Data Center Devices and Solutions	6,075	29
Client Solutions	4,464	22
Total	**20,647**	**100**

Selected Products

Portable Storage
Personal Cloud Storage
External Storage
Internal Hard Drive Storage
Internal SSD Storage
Network Attached Storage
Internal Hard Drives for Business
Surveillance Storage

COMPETITORS

Apple Inc.	SMART Modular
Dell	Technologies
Fujitsu	Samsung Electronics
Intel	Sanmina
LaCie	Seagate Technology
Micron Technology	TEAC
Roku	Toshiba
SK Hynix	

HISTORICAL FINANCIALS

Company Type: Public

Income Statement

FYE: June 28

	REVENUE ($ mil.)	NET INCOME ($ mil.)	NET PROFIT MARGIN	EMPLOYEES
06/19	16,569	(754)	—	61,800
06/18	20,647	675	3.3%	71,600
06/17*	19,093	397	2.1%	68,000
07/16	12,994	242	1.9%	72,878
07/15	14,572	1,465	10.1%	76,449
Annual Growth	**3.3%**	**—**	**—**	**(5.2%)**

*Fiscal year change

2019 Year-End Financials

Debt ratio: 40.00%	No. of shares (mil.): 295
Return on equity: (-7.00%)	Dividends
Cash ($ mil.): 3,455	Yield: 4.0%
Current ratio: 2.00	Payout: 392.0%
Long-term debt ($ mil.): 10,246	Market value ($ mil.): 14,027

	STOCK PRICE ($) FY Close	P/E High/Low		PER SHARE ($) Earnings	Dividends	Book Value
06/19	48.00	—	—	(3.00)	2.00	34.00
06/18	77.00	47	34	2.00	2.00	39.00
06/17*	89.00	68	31	1.00	2.00	39.00
07/16	46.00	86	35	1.00	2.00	39.00
07/15	81.00	18	12	6.00	2.00	40.00
Annual Growth	**(12.4%)**		**—**	**—**	**2.7%**	**(4.2%)**

*Fiscal year change

Western New England Bancorp Inc

Westfield Financial is the holding company for Westfield Bank which serves western Massachusetts' Hampden County and surrounding areas from more than 20 branch locations. Founded in 1853 the bank has traditionally been a community-oriented provider of retail deposit accounts and loans but it is placing more emphasis on serving commercial and industrial clients. Commercial real estate loans account for approximately 45% of the company's loan portfolio and business loans are more than 25%. The bank also makes a smaller number of consumer and home equity loans. In 2016 Westfield Financial merged with Chicopee Bancorp the holding company of Chicopee Savings Bank (another bank serving Hampden County).

EXECUTIVES

Vice President Retail Banking, Kevin O'Connor
Avp Residential Lending, Michael Laga
Assistant Vice President Financial Services, Libiszewski Darlene
Senior Vice President Of Retail Banking, Cidalia Inacio
Vice President Commercial Lender, Richard Hanchett
Vice President, Matthew Manganelli
Auditors: Wolf & Company, P.C.

LOCATIONS

HQ: Western New England Bancorp Inc
  141 Elm Street, Westfield, MA 01086
Phone: 413 568-1911
Web: www.westfieldbank.com

COMPETITORS

Bank of America	Sovereign Bank
Citizens Financial	TD Bank USA
Group	

HISTORICAL FINANCIALS

Company Type: Public

Income Statement

FYE: December 31

	ASSETS ($ mil.)	NET INCOME ($ mil.)	INCOME AS % OF ASSETS	EMPLOYEES
12/18	2,119	16	0.8%	320
12/17	2,083	12	0.6%	317
12/16	2,076	5	0.2%	310
12/15	1,340	6	0.4%	195
12/14	1,320	6	0.5%	200
Annual Growth	**12.6%**	**27.7%**	**—**	**12.5%**

2018 Year-End Financials

Debt ratio: 10.00%
Return on equity: 7.00%
Cash ($ mil.): 26
Current ratio: —
Long-term debt ($ mil.): —

No. of shares (mil.): 28
Dividends
Yield: 2.0%
Payout: 37.0%
Market value ($ mil.): 285

	STOCK PRICE ($) FY Close	P/E High/Low		PER SHARE ($) Earnings	Dividends	Book Value
12/18	10.00	20	16	1.00	0.00	8.00
12/17	11.00	27	22	0.00	0.00	8.00
12/16	9.00	38	30	0.00	0.00	8.00
12/15	8.00	25	22	0.00	0.00	8.00
12/14	7.00	23	20	0.00	0.00	8.00
Annual Growth	8.1%	—	—	13.8%	(6.6%)	2.3%

Western Union Co

Though the joy of receiving a singing telegram is mired in the dusty past of yesteryear you may still jump for joy at the receipt of a Western Union money transfer. The company provides in-person and electronic means to swiftly send remittances within and across country borders managing currency exchanges as needed. It achieves this with a global network of some 550000 agent locations in more than 200 countries and territories. Western Union agents work out of kiosks located in a variety of businesses including post offices banks and grocery stores. About 40% of its total sales comes from US.

Operations

Western Union operates two main segments: Consumer-to-Consumer (C2C) and Business Solutions. The C2C provides money transfer services around the world through a network of third-party agents who fulfill transactions in nearly 130 currencies. Roughly 90% of agent locations are outside the US. C2C?s top 40 agents generated some 60% of the segment?s revenue. The segment is experiencing growth in its online money transfers offered through mobile applications and the westernunion.com website. It accounts for about 80% of total sales. The Business Solutions (more than 5% of sales) segment facilitates payment and foreign exchange solutions typically across borders and between currencies mainly for small and medium businesses. The majority of this segment?s revenue is generated outside the US.

Geographic Reach

Colorado-based Western Union has offices in approximately 50 countries with four company-owned and over 400 international leased. Its international headquarters are located in Dublin Ireland. The company's reach is amplified by hundreds of thousands of worldwide agent locations. Western Union's customers primarily consumers use the company?s services around the globe. Western Union?s biggest single market is the US which generates nearly 40% of revenue.

Sales and Marketing

Western Union market its services to consumers directly or indirectly through its agents and sub-agents direct-to-consumer communications and digital advertising. Its marketing strategy includes loyalty programs such as My WU and Gold Card which are available in certain countries and territories. Business solutions services are offered primarily over the phone through third-party channels and online. Internet services are marketed through its own websites as well as co-branding arrangements with third-party websites. The com-

pany?s advertising costs were $180.9 million $168.3 million and $151.1 million for 2018 2017 and 2016 respectively.

Financial Performance

The Western Union Company has run into roadblocks to growth in recent years. Its annual revenues have remained relatively flat since 2014. Revenue increased slightly to $5.5 billion in 2018 a 1% increase from the year prior. The increase was driven by transaction growth in the Consumer-to-Consumer segment. Net income was $852 million in fiscal year 2018 compared to a loss of $557 million in fiscal year 2017. Selling general and administrative expenses fell by 5% in 2018 to $1.1 billion as a result of lower consulting service fees severance and related employee benefits and other expenses related to the WU Way and decreased employee incentive compensation expenses. Total cash at the end of 2018 was $973.4 million. Cash provided by operating activities was $821.3 million in 2018 while investing activities used $328.8 million. Financing activities used another $357.2 million.

Strategy

Western Union's corporate strategy is focused on protecting existing business growing through advancements in digital payment markets and technologies and improving regulatory compliance.To stay relevant the company continues to invest in a digital channels strategy by forming alliances with third parties and offering services via social and mobile networks. Western Union is working with Amazon on its Amazon PayCode service which allows shoppers to make a purchase online and pay for it with cash via Western Union. The company has also expanded its global payments offerings to include real-time account-to-account transfers to an account or mobile wallet for select banks or digital wallet providers in nearly 20 countries with plans to add another 100 countries. Given the recent hefty settlements with US government agencies over aiding and abetting wire fraud and failing to implement an effective anti-money laundering program Western Union is upping its regulatory compliance vigilance. The company's funding for compliance has increased 200% since 2012 and it spends approximately $200 million per year on compliance. Its settlement agreement includes a government mandate for continued oversight of the company's compliance in coming years.

EXECUTIVES

Chief Strategy And Product Officer, Elizabeth G. (Libby) Chambers, $535,000 total compensation
Evp Global Operations And Technology And Cio, John D. (David) Thompson, age 52, $540,000 total compensation
President And Ceo, Hikmet Ersek, age 58, $1,000,000 total compensation
Svp; President Business Solutions, Kerry Agiasotis
Evp General Counsel And Secretary, John R. Dye, age 59, $500,000 total compensation
Evp And Cfo, Rajesh K. (Raj) Agrawal, age 54, $566,500 total compensation
President Global Money Transfer, Odilon Almeida, age 57, $612,000 total compensation
Evp; President Middle East Africa Asia/pacific Eastern Europe And Cis, Jean Claude Farah, age 48
Svp; General Manager Digital, Khalid Fellahi
Evp And Chief Human Resources Officer, Richard L. Williams, age 53
Svp; General Manager Digital, Molly Shea
Svp And Chief Compliance Officer, Jacqueline Molnar
Chief Transformation Officer, Scott Coad
Vice President Of Marketing, Paul Jost

Vice President Operations Service Delivery At Western Union, Paul Blair
Vice President Aml Compliance, Fabrice Borsello
Vice President Global Public Affairs, Barbara Span
Vice President, Michael Hafer
Vice President Records And Information Management, Jim Keyes
Vice President Global Talent Acquisition, Chris Brabec
Vice President Sales, Jeff Zallaps
Vice President Global Compensation, Terry Lodes
Vice President Consumer Segments Usmt, Daniel Canning
Vice President Strategic Planning, Carrie Damon
Vice President Risk And Asset Management, Doug Groetken
Vice President Controller, Mary-Margaret Henke
Vice President Finance, Steve Cornell
Vice President Of Operations, Edgardo Torres
Vice President, Kelli Byers
Vice President Finance, Kimberly Patmore
Vice President Electronic Payment Products, Alexis Blackstead
Vice President, Karen Wolf
Regional Vice President, Rocco Pilla
Senior Vice President Total Rewards, Jeff Wilson
Vice President Global Customer Experience, Jennifer Ramirez
Vice President Corporate Communications Americas And European Union, Pia deLima
Vp Engineering, Nitika Chaganti
Vice President Legal Sales, Andrew Detavernier
Vice President, MIKE BROWN
Vice President Global Head Of Aml Operations, Jonathon Dyer
National Account Manager, Matthew Kurlapski
Vice President Aml Compliance, Antonio Alvarez Lorenzo
Executive Vice President General Counsel, Caroline Tsai
Vice President Policies Procedures And Vice President Engineering, Murali Rathnam
Chairman, Jeffrey A. Joerres, age 59
Treasurer, Robert Harrell
Auditors: Ernst & Young LLP

LOCATIONS

HQ: Western Union Co
7001 East Belleview Avenue, Denver, CO 80237
Phone: 866 405-5012
Web: www.westernunion.com

2016 Sales

	$ mil.	% of total
US	1,673	31
International	3,750	69
Total	**5,423**	**100**

PRODUCTS/OPERATIONS

2016 Sales

	$ mil.	% of total
Transaction fees	3,795	70
Foreign exchange revenue	1,490	27
Commissions & other	138	3
Total	**5,423**	**100**

2016 Sales by Segment

	$ mil.	% of total
Consumer-to-consumer		
Transaction fees	3,124	57
Foreign exchange	1,116	21
Other	65	1
Consumer-to-business		
Transaction fees	597	11
Foreign exchange & other	25	1
Business solutions		
Foreign exchange	353	7
Transaction fees & other	43	0
Other	101	2
Total	**5,423**	**100**

HISTORICAL FINANCIALS

Company Type: Public

Income Statement — FYE: December 31

	REVENUE ($ mil.)	NET INCOME ($ mil.)	NET PROFIT MARGIN	EMPLOYEES
12/18	5,590	852	15.2%	12,000
12/17	5,524	(557)	—	11,500
12/16	5,423	253	4.7%	10,700
12/15	5,484	838	15.3%	10,000
12/14	5,607	852	15.2%	10,000
Annual Growth	(0.1%)	(0.0%)	—	4.7%

2018 Year-End Financials

Debt ratio: 38.00%
Return on equity: ***,***.**%
Cash ($ mil.): 973
Current ratio: 1.00
Long-term debt ($ mil.): 3,309

No. of shares (mil.): 441
Dividends
Yield: 4.0%
Payout: 41.0%
Market value ($ mil.): 7,527

	STOCK PRICE ($) FY Close	P/E High/Low		PER SHARE ($) Earnings	Dividends	Book Value
12/18	17.00	11	9	2.00	1.00	(1.00)
12/17	19.00	—	—	(1.00)	1.00	(1.00)
12/16	22.00	43	32	1.00	1.00	2.00
12/15	18.00	14	10	2.00	1.00	3.00
12/14	18.00	12	9	2.00	1.00	2.00
Annual Growth	(1.2%)	—	—	4.1%	11.0%	—

Westlake Chemical Corp

Westlake Chemical produces petrochemicals and plastics. Its plastics offerings include polyvinyl chloride (PVC) and polyethylene both of which are common in packaging products and grocery bags. Its PVC pipe products are sold under the North American Pipe and Royal Building Products brands. Westlake also produces the chlorine used in PVC as well as caustic soda. Its petrochemicals include ethylene ethyl benzene and styrene?which are building blocks in plastics. Westlake produces about 40 billion pounds of product each year and is the third largest producer of both PVC and chlor-alkali in the world. TTWF which is controlled by the Chao family (Westlake's founders) owns more than 70% of Westlake. The US accounts for about 70% of company's total sales.

Operations

Westlake Chemical operates in two business segments: Vinyls and Olefins.

Westlake's Vinyls segment produces polyvinyl chloride (PVC) vinyl chloride monomer (VCM) ethylene dichloride (EDC) chlor-alkali (chlorine and caustic soda) and ethylene. The company is the third largest chlor-alkali producer in the world and can produce 2.3 billion pounds of chlorinated derivative products and 7.5 billion pounds of VCM each year. Its PVC products are fabricated into au-

tomotive sealants cable sheathing pipe house components and film and sheet products. Caustic soda is used in pulp and paper manufacturing chemicals and neutralization. The company's Vinyls segment accounts for around 75% of sales.

The Olefins segment makes polyethylene styrene monomer and ethylene co-products used in the company's polyethylene styrene and VCM operations. The company's primary ethylene co-products are chemical grade propylene crude butadiene pyrolysis gasoline and hydrogen. Olefins generate around 25% of Westlake's revenue.

Geographic Reach

Houston Texas-based Westlake Chemical has more than 50 manufacturing facilities: roughly 30 are in the US; six in each of Canada and Germany; two each in China and France; and one each in Japan Mexico Spain Taiwan the UK and Vietnam. The US accounts for around 70% of revenue while Canada and Germany each provide more than 5%. The remainder is garnered from China Italy and Taiwan.

Westlake's olefin production activity is clustered around Lake Charles Louisiana. Westlake's sites in Lake Charles include two Westlake Chemical OpCo-owned ethylene plants two polyethylene plants and a styrene monomer plant. Lake Charles also has a port terminal for worldwide shipping and is located near rail transport links. Westlake has a 22.8% limited partner interest in ethylene production and pipeline company OpCo which spun off from Westlake following the latter's IPO.

Sales and Marketing

Westlake Chemical's products are sold directly to polyethylene customers (some of the largest producers of film and flexible packaging in the US). It also sells ethylene and ethylene co-products to external customers.

The company has the capacity to use all its chlorine internally to produce vinyl chloride monomer (VCM) and ethylene dichloride (EDC) most of which is used in turn to produce polyvinyl chloride (PVC). It sells substantially all its caustic soda production to external customers. Most of its North American and Asian-produced PVC is used internally in the production of building products. The remainder of Westlake's PVC including the PVC produced at its European facilities is sold to downstream fabricators and the international markets. No single customer accounts for more than 10% of the company's sales.

Financial Performance

Westlake Chemical has nearly doubled its revenue since 2014 thanks largely to its 2016 acquisition of North American chemical and building products manufacturer Axiall which greatly bolstered sales volume in 2017 and made Westlake the world's third largest chlor-alkali and PVC producer. The company's net earnings have seen five-year growth of about 50% owing to the Axiall acquisition and a hefty income tax benefit in 2017 caused by US tax reform. Net income declined every other year since 2014.

Westlake's revenue added 7% in 2018 to end the year at $8.6 billion. Increased prices and sales volume of caustic soda and sales volume of polyvinyl chloride (PVC) resin and polyethylene drove the gains. Despite adding to its revenue net income fell 24% to $996 million as performance was dragged down by a high income tax provision.

The company's cash fell $779 million to $775 million in 2018. Operations provided $1.4 billion. Financing activities used $1.4 billion?primarily for redemption and repayment of notes payable. Investments in property plant and equipment mainly accounted for investment spend of $754 million.

Strategy

Westlake Chemical has adopted a two-pronged growth strategy involving both organic and ac-

quisitive expansion. Since 2013 the company has invested more than $7.4 billion in capital projects and acquisitions.

In furtherance of its organic growth efforts in 2018 the company expanded two plants in Germany and Louisiana which added 750 million pounds of polyvinyl chloride (PVC) and 200 million pounds of vinyl chloride monomer (VCM) to its production. The expansions also increased its chlorine and membrane caustic soda production capacity by 55 million and 60 million pounds respectively.

In 2019 the company acquired NAKAN for $265 million; the compounding company's offerings are used in the automotive building and medical industries. The deal expanded Westlake's compounding capabilities through NAKAN's eight production facilities in China France Germany Italy Japan Mexico Spain Vietnam and France.

Mergers and Acquisitions

In 2018 Westlake Chemical announced the acquisition of global compounder Nakan from Open-Gate Capital in a $265 million deal. The acquisition continues a recent trend of resin makers diversifying with compounding (both LyndondellBassel and Celanese Corp pursued similar deals). The addition of Reims-based Nakan is attractive to Westlake Chemical because of its suite of specialty products within the compounding business. With $300 million in annual sales Nakan already has eight production facilities in Europe Asia and Mexico. The transaction will close in early 2019.

In 2016 Westlake acquired Atlanta-based Axiall Corporation a major manufacturer of caustic soda chlorine VCM EDC and PVC resins for $3.8 billion. The acquisition made Westlake the world's third-largest chlor-alkali producer in the world and the second largest PVC producer in the US.

HISTORY

Westlake came into being in 1986 when T.T. Chao bought a polyethylene plant near Lake Charles Louisiana from Occidental Petroleum. Over the years the company has acquired or constructed about 20 more. The founding Chao family took Westlake Chemical public in 2004 with the hope of paying down some of the debt accumulated from those acquisitions

In 2008 a joint venture between Westlake and Chinese chemical company INEOS began producing some 33 million pounds of PVC film each year. Westlake owns 59% of the Suzhou Huasu Plastics.

Westlake made several changes to its PVC production in 2009. Early in the year the company acquired a PVC pipe plant in Janesville Wisconsin and opened its new PVC plant in Yucca Arizona to expand its operations. However to reduce costs Westlake closed its facilities in Bristol Indiana later that year and moved that production to its other PVC operations.

In 2010 Westlake purchased a 50% stake in Cypress Interstate Pipeline LLC from Kinder Morgan Energy Partners. The 104-mile pipeline supplies natural gas liquid feedstocks to Westlake's Lake Charles Louisiana petrochemical complex. The pipeline will continue to be operated by Kinder Morgan under a contract.

Westlake also made a move in 2012 to strengthen its presence in Asia by opening a Singapore office. Its operations there will focus on serving its existing customers and seeking new opportunities for growth in the region.

In early 2012 the company made an all cash offer for Atlanta-based Georgia Gulf one of North America's largest manufacturers of vinyl construction products. However Georgia Gulf rejected the $1.03 billion takeover bid as being financially inadequate and adopted a stockholder rights plan also called a poison pill that allows existing share-holders to buy stock at a discount when a suitor acquires more than 10% of outstanding shares. Westlake wanted to combine its resin and pipe production with Georgia Gulf's chemicals and vinyl products but later that year withdrew its proposal to buy the company.

The company has expanded capacity to meet growing demand. In 2013 it opened a new chlor-alkali plant in Greismar Louisiana that doubles Westlake's chlor-alkali production capacity. It also beefed up the ethylene capacity at its Lake Charles facility in 2013 (increasing the ethane-based ethylene capacity of the unit and its conversion to 100% ethane feedstock capability). It is also up-grading ethylene production facilities at Calvert City Kentucky.

In 2013 Westlake bought CertainTeed's Pipe and Foundation Group a leading producer of PVC pipe and fittings for municipal water well mining agriculture and irrigation applications for $175 million. It also acquired technologies and intellectual property for the production of a number of specialized products including Certa-Lok re-strained joint pipe and Yelomine branded products.

EXECUTIVES

President And Ceo, Albert Chao, age 69, $979,667 total compensation
Svp Cfo And Treasurer, M. Steven (Steve) Bender, age 62, $520,833 total compensation
Vp Manufacturing, Andrew Kenner, age 54, $377,167 total compensation
Svp Vinyls, Robert F. Buesinger, age 62, $406,333 total compensation
Vp Olefins, Lawrence E. (Skip) Teel, age 61
Vice President Olefins, Skip Teel
Vice President Logistics Information Technology And Business Process Improvement, Tom Janssens
Vice President Human Resources, M Joel Gray
Vice President Matrix Offshore Services, Subhakar Reddy
Chairman, James Y. Chao, age 71
Treasurer, Jeff Holy
Auditors: PricewaterhouseCoopers LLP

LOCATIONS

HQ: Westlake Chemical Corp
2801 Post Oak Boulevard, Suite 600, Houston, TX 77056
Phone: 713 960-9111
Web: www.westlake.com

2018 Sales

	$ mil.	% of total
US	6,114	71
Germany	500	6
Canada	649	7
China	155	2
Italy	105	1
Taiwan	102	1
Other countries	1,010	12
Total	**8,635**	**100**

PRODUCTS/OPERATIONS

2018 Sales

	$ mil.	% of total
Olefins		
Polyethylene	1,519	18
Feedstock styrene & other	500	6
Vinyls		
PVC caustic soda & other	5,359	62
Building products	1,257	14
Total	**8,635**	**100**

Selected Products

Olefins
  Ethylene
  Polyethylene
  Styrene
Vinyls
  Caustic soda
  Chlorine
  PVC
  VCM

COMPETITORS

BASF SE
Chevron Phillips Chemical
Diamond Plastics
Dow Chemical
ExxonMobil Chemical
Formosa Plastics
Formosa Plastics USA
J-M Manufacturing
LyondellBasell
Mexichem
NOVA Chemicals
Occidental Chemical
Oxy Vinyls
Shell Chemicals
Shintech

HISTORICAL FINANCIALS

Company Type: Public

Income Statement

FYE: December 31

	REVENUE ($ mil.)	NET INCOME ($ mil.)	NET PROFIT MARGIN	EMPLOYEES
12/18	8,635	996	11.5%	8,870
12/17	8,041	1,304	16.2%	8,800
12/16	5,075	399	7.9%	8,870
12/15	4,463	646	14.5%	4,225
12/14	4,415	679	15.4%	3,550
Annual Growth	**18.3%**	**10.1%**	—	**25.7%**

2018 Year-End Financials

Debt ratio: 23.00%
Return on equity: 19.00%
Cash ($ mil.): 753
Current ratio: 2.00
Long-term debt ($ mil.): 2,668
No. of shares (mil.): 128
Dividends
  Yield: 1.0%
  Payout: 12.0%
Market value ($ mil.): 8,501

	STOCK PRICE ($) FY Close	P/E High/Low		Earnings	PER SHARE ($) Dividends	Book Value
12/18	66.00	16	8	8.00	1.00	44.00
12/17	107.00	11	6	10.00	1.00	38.00
12/16	56.00	19	13	3.00	1.00	27.00
12/15	54.00	16	10	5.00	1.00	25.00
12/14	61.00	27	11	5.00	1.00	22.00
Annual Growth	**2.0%**		—	**10.7%**	**12.1%**	**18.7%**

WestRock Co

Auditors: Ernst & Young LLP

LOCATIONS

HQ: WestRock Co
1000 Abernathy Road N.E., Atlanta, GA 30328
Phone: 770 448-2193
Web: www.westrock.com

HISTORICAL FINANCIALS

Company Type: Public

Income Statement

FYE: September 30

	REVENUE ($ mil.)	NET INCOME ($ mil.)	NET PROFIT MARGIN	EMPLOYEES
09/19	18,289	863	4.7%	51,100
09/18	16,285	1,906	11.7%	45,100
09/17	14,860	708	4.8%	44,800
09/16	14,172	(396)	—	39,000
09/15	11,381	507	4.5%	41,400
Annual Growth	**12.6%**	**14.2%**	—	**5.4%**

2019 Year-End Financials

Debt ratio: 33.00%
Return on equity: 7.00%
Cash ($ mil.): 152
Current ratio: 1.00
Long-term debt ($ mil.): 9,502
No. of shares (mil.): 258
Dividends
  Yield: 5.0%
  Payout: 56.0%
Market value ($ mil.): 9,397

	STOCK PRICE ($) FY Close	P/E High/Low		Earnings	PER SHARE ($) Dividends	Book Value
09/19	36.00	16	10	3.00	2.00	45.00
09/18	53.00	9	7	7.00	2.00	45.00
09/17	57.00	21	16	3.00	2.00	41.00
09/16	48.00	—	—	(2.00)	2.00	39.00
09/15	51.00	22	17	3.00	0.00	45.00
Annual Growth	**(8.3%)**		—	—	**3.3%** **48.4%**	**(0.0%)**

Weyerhaeuser Co

Forest products company Weyerhaeuser pro-duces a variety of softwood lumber and other building materials in North America. One of the world's largest private owners of timberland the company harvests trees for its products from 12 million acres of forest that it owns in the US and 14 million acres that it manages in Canada. Ex-ports account for about 15% of the company's sales. Incorporated in 1900 as Weyerhaeuser Tim-ber Co. the company operates as a real estate in-vestment trust (REIT) because of its vast land hold-ings. The company merged with rival Plum Creek in a deal worth $10 billion bringing together the two biggest owners of timberland in the US; shortly after that deal Weyerhaeuser spun off its cellulose fibers business for $2.5 billion.

HISTORY

Frederick Weyerhaeuser a 24-year-old German immigrant bought his first lumberyard in 1858 in Illinois. He also participated in joint logging ven-tures in Illinois Minnesota and Wisconsin. In 1900 he and 15 partners bought 900000 timbered acres from the Northern Pacific Railway. The venture was named Weyerhaeuser Timber Company.

During the Depression the business recouped losses in the deflated lumber market by selling wood pulp. Frederick's grandson J. P. "Phil" Wey-erhaeuser Jr. took over as CEO in 1933.

Diversification into the production of container-board (1949) particleboard (1955) paper (1956) and other products led the company to drop "Tim-ber" from its name in 1959. In 1963 Weyerhaeuser went public and opened its first overseas office in Tokyo.

In the 1970s George Weyerhaeuser (Phil's son) diversified further to insulate the company from the forest-product industry's cyclical nature and ended up with a mishmash of businesses and prod-ucts from private-label disposable diapers to pet supplies.

The eruption of Mount St. Helens in 1980 de-stroyed 68000 acres of Weyerhaeuser timber. That disaster and the soft US lumber market depressed the company's earnings through 1982. Weyer-haeuser reduced its workforce by 25% during this period.

Under John Creighton (president in 1988 and CEO from 1991 until 1998) Weyerhaeuser refo-cused on forest products and organized along product lines rather than by geographic region. Less-successful ventures were put up for sale in-cluding milk carton hardwood and gypsum board plants. The company took a $497 million pretax charge in 1989 related to the decision to close unprofitable operations. Earnings improved in 1990 but dropped again in 1991 reflecting the recession in the US and plant closures.

In 1992 the company outbid Georgia-Pacific paying $600 million for two pulp mills three sawmills and more than 200000 acres of forest land to boost its market-pulp capacity by 40%. The following year the company sold its disposable-diaper business through a public offering in a new company Paragon Trade Brands. It also sold GNA Corporation to General Electric subsidiary GE Capital.

The federal government in 1995 allowed the company to harvest trees in an area inhabited by the endangered northern spotted owl. The move angered environmental groups. In 1997 Weyerhaeuser began to reorganize its recycling business by selling or closing noncore units. It also purchased a stake in 193000 acres on New Zealand's South Island the company's first overseas investment in more than a decade. In 1998 the company restructured its joint venture with Nippon Paper with Weyerhaeuser decreasing its stake in North Pacific Paper Company from 80% to 50% and closed a lumber mill in Canada. Also that year Steve Rogel a veteran from competitor Willamette succeeded Creighton as CEO and became the first outsider to head Weyerhaeuser.

In 1999 Weyerhaeuser paid $2.5 billion for Canada's MacMillan Bloedel and early in 2000 it acquired TJ International 51% owner of leading engineered lumber products company Trus Joist MacMillan (Weyerhaeuser already owned the other 49%). Also in 2000 Weyerhaeuser purchased two sawmills and a 70% stake in lumber distributor Pine Solutions from Australia-based CSR Limited. Weyerhaeuser sold its Marshfield Door architectural wood door business and closed some of its manufacturing operations to consolidate its business.

After a protracted courtship in March 2002 Weyerhaeuser acquired Oregon-based Willamette Industries in a $6.1 billion cash deal. The company closed three North American plants (in Colorado Louisiana and Oregon) later that year. In October the company closed a Canadian containerboard mill cutting 140 jobs in the process. At the close of the year Weyerhaeuser sold approximately 115000 acres of timberlands in western Washington to Boston-based Hancock Timber Resource Group (international timber investment and management) for about $211 million to aid in paying down its debt associated with the Willamette acquisition.

On the heels of the deals for MacMillan Bloedel Trus Joist MacMillan and Willamette Weyerhaeuser moved to pay down debt. It sold more than 320000 acres of the timberland (in the Carolinas and Tennessee) that it acquired with the Willamette purchase. Before the end of 2003 Fountain Investments had acquired about 168000 acres of the west-central Tennessee acreage and Forest Investment Associates purchased about 160000 acres of western North Carolina and South Carolina timberlands. Weyerhaeuser gained about $140 million in after-tax proceeds from the latter sale.

Also in 2003 Weyerhaeuser sold its Nipigon Multiply hardwood plywood underlayment operation in Ontario Canada to Columbia Forest Products. Late in the year the company closed its fine-paper operations in Longview Washington (eliminating 119 jobs there). Altogether Weyerhaeuser closed 12 facilities and sold about 444000 acres of non-strategic timberlands in 2003 in keeping with its plan to reduce company debt and increase productivity.

The company closed its Grande Cache Alberta sawmill in 2004 (affecting more than 150 jobs there) and sold its oriented strand board (OSB) mill in Slave Lake Alberta to Tolko Industries for about $43 million. Also in 2004 Weyerhaeuser sold roughly 270000 acres of timberlands in central Georgia for about $400 million to investment and property firms in Georgia and South Carolina.

Also in 2004 subsidiary Weyerhaeuser Brasil Participa •es acquired two-thirds ownership in Brazil-based Aracruz Produtos de Madeira (APM) a subsidiary of Aracruz Cellulose to produce lumber made from a eucalyptus hybrid for use in furniture flooring cabinetry and other applications. Aracruz Cellulose holds the remaining third ownership in the joint venture. Also that year Weyerhaeuser changed the name of its pulp business to Weyerhaeuser Cellulose Fibers to reinforce its focus on developing unique or specialized applications for cellulose fibers.

Weyerhaeuser agreed early in 2005 to sell five Canadian sawmills two finishing plants 635000 acres of timber and some government land-cutting rights to Brascan for $970 million. It had acquired the timber and sawmill assets when it bought MacMillan Bloedel in 1999.

The company's debt reduction strategy continued in 2004. Weyerhaeuser sold roughly 270000 acres of its timberlands in Georgia and several mills in the US and Canada. The sale of the assets helped the company more than quadruple net earnings for 2004: $1.3 billion its best result of the decade. It used the proceeds to reduce debt by some $730 million. In the meantime Weyerhaeuser reported that it wrung out the $300 million in expected Willamette-related synergies in half the time predicted.

Weyerhaeuser continued to streamline and focus on its softwood lumber business in 2005 selling $970 million in assets (five sawmills two finishing plants 635000 acres and timber rights) to Brascan. Weyerhaeuser also closed a Saskatchewan pulp and paper mill in 2006 cutting 690 jobs; not long afterward amid weak profits it announced multiple plant closures and sales including another pulp mill another sawmill several corrugated plants and a paper bag plant.

In 2007 Weyerhaeuser merged its fine paper business with Domtar. According to the terms of the $3.3 billion deal Weyerhaeuser shareholders got a 55% stake in the renamed company Domtar Corporation. Weyerhaeuser controls the board and several Weyerhaeuser executives manage the company.

The company sold its Trus Joist commercial business including four manufacturing plants to Atlas Holdings in 2009. Also that year Weyerhaeuser announced it was closing its noncore trucking division. Other divestitures in 2009 included non-strategic timberland in Oregon (representing about 10% of its holdings in the Pacific Northwest) in an effort to focus on Douglas fir production in that region.

Weyerhaeuser converted to a real estate investment trust (REIT) in 2010. The status allows the company to pay less in taxes and pay its shareholders larger dividends. Weyerhaeuser folded its timberland operations into the REIT while its real estate wood products and cellulose fibers units operate under a taxable REIT subsidiary.

EXECUTIVES

President Ceo And Director, Doyle R. Simons, age 55, $1,000,000 total compensation
Svp Real Estate Energy And Natural Resources, James A. (Jim) Kilberg, age 62, $428,778 total compensation
Svp Timberlands, Rhonda C. Hunter, age 56, $560,000 total compensation
Svp Wood Products, Adrian M. Blocker, age 62, $560,000 total compensation
Svp And Cfo, Russell S. Hagen, age 53, $434,201 total compensation
Svp Human Resources And Information Technology, Denise M. Merle, age 55
Senior Vice President General Counsel Corporate Secretary, Kristy Harlan
Vice President National Distribution, Kevin Toale
Vice President Operations, Satrick Anthony
Vice President Environmental Affairs, Traylor Champion
Chairman, Rick R. Holley, age 67
Auditors: KPMG LLP

LOCATIONS

HQ: Weyerhaeuser Co
  220 Occidental Avenue South, Seattle, WA 98104-7800
Phone: 206 539-3000
Web: www.weyerhaeuser.com

2017 Sales

	$ mil.	% of total
US	6,168	86
Japan	352	7
Canada	472	5
China	107	1
Other foreign countries	97	1
Total	**7,196**	**100**

PRODUCTS/OPERATIONS

2017 Sales

	$ mil.	% of total
Wood Products	4,974	69
Timberlands	1,942	27
Real Estate & ENR	280	4
Total	**7,196**	**100**

Selected Products and Services

Wood and Building Products
  Engineered lumber products
  Flooring
  Lumber (softwood)
  Oriented Strand Board
  Plywood
  Structural panels
  Veneer
Real Estate and Related Assets
  Master-planned communities
  Multifamily homes
  Residential lots
  Single-family homes
Timberlands
  Chips
  Logs
  Mineral resources
  Seedlings
  Weyerhaeser Select Douglas Fir seed
Other
  Recycling
  Transportation

COMPETITORS

Canfor
Cascades Boxboard
ENCE Energia y
  Celulosa SA
Georgia-Pacific
Indiana Veneers
Louisiana-Pacific
McFarland Cascade
Mendocino Redwood
  Company
Norbord
Packaging Corp. of
  America

Potlatch
Pratt Industries USA
Rayonier
Resolute Forest
  Products
Sierra Pacific
  Industries
Smurfit Kappa
Stora Enso
Tembec
Tenon
UPM-Kymmene
West Fraser Timber

HISTORICAL FINANCIALS

Company Type: Public

Income Statement

FYE: December 31

	REVENUE ($ mil.)	NET INCOME ($ mil.)	NET PROFIT MARGIN	EMPLOYEES
12/18	7,476	748	10.0%	9,300
12/17	7,196	582	8.1%	9,300
12/16	6,365	1,027	16.1%	10,400
12/15	7,082	506	7.1%	12,600
12/14	7,403	1,826	24.7%	12,800
Annual Growth	0.2%	(20.0%)	—	(7.7%)

2018 Year-End Financials

Debt ratio: 39.00%
Return on equity: 8.00%
Cash ($ mil.): 334
Current ratio: 1.00
Long-term debt ($ mil.): 5,419

No. of shares (mil.): 746
Dividends
Yield: 6.0%
Payout: 133.0%
Market value ($ mil.): 16,316

	STOCK PRICE ($) FY Close	P/E High/Low	PER SHARE ($) Earnings	Dividends	Book Value
12/18	22.00	39 21	1.00	1.00	12.00
12/17	35.00	47 39	1.00	1.00	12.00
12/16	30.00	24 16	1.00	1.00	12.00
12/15	30.00	41 30	1.00	1.00	10.00
12/14	36.00	11 9	3.00	1.00	10.00
Annual Growth	(11.7%)	—	(25.3%)	6.7%	4.6%

Whirlpool Corp

With brand names recognized by just about anyone who has ever separated dark colors from light Whirlpool is the world's top home appliance maker. It sells around 70 million laundry appliances refrigerators and freezers cooking appliances dishwashers and compressors each year under a bevy of brand names including Whirlpool Amana KitchenAid Maytag Jenn-Air and Roper. The company markets and distributes these major home appliances in North America Latin America EMEA (Europe the Middle East and Africa) and Asia. It has manufacturing operations in more than a dozen countries. Major customers include retailers Lowe's Home Depot and Best Buy.

HISTORY

Brothers Fred and Lou Upton and their uncle Emory Upton founded the Upton Machine Company manufacturer of electric motor-driven washing machines in 1911 in St. Joseph Michigan. Sears Roebuck and Co. began buying their products five years later and by 1925 the company was supplying all of Sears' washers. The Uptons combined their company with the Nineteen Hundred Washer Company in 1929 to form the Nineteen Hundred Corporation the world's largest washing machine company.

Sears and Nineteen Hundred prospered during the Great Depression and during WWII Nineteen Hundred's factories produced war materials. In 1948 it began selling its first automatic washing machine (introduced a year earlier) under the Whirlpool brand. In 1950 the company changed its name to Whirlpool following the success of the product and introduced its first automatic dryer.

During the 1950s and 1960s Whirlpool became a full-line appliance manufacturer while continuing as Sears' principal Kenmore appliance supplier. In 1955 the company bought Seeger Refrigerator

Company and the stove and air-conditioning interests of RCA. Three years later it made its first investment in Multibras Eletrodom sticos an appliance maker in Brazil. (It has increased that investment over the years.) Other purchases included the gas refrigeration and ice-maker manufacturing facilities of Servel (1958); a majority interest in Heil-Quaker makers of central heaters and space heaters (1964); Sears' major television set supplier Warwick Electronics (1966); and 33% of Canadian appliance maker John Inglis Company (1969). It made a deal with Sony in 1973 for the distribution of Whirlpool-brand products in Japan. Whirlpool sold its TV manufacturing business to SANYO of Japan three years later.

Between 1981 and 1991 despite a static US market Whirlpool's sales tripled to almost $6.6 billion. In 1986 the firm bought top-end appliance manufacturer KitchenAid (from Dart and Kraft) and 65% of Italian cooling compressor manufacturer Aspera. Also that year it sold its Heil-Quaker central heating business. David Whitwam was appointed CEO in 1987. Whirlpool took over total ownership of Inglis in 1990.

The company formed Whirlpool Europe a joint venture with Philips Electronics in 1989; in 1991 it bought out Philips. Two years later Whirlpool took control of appliance marketer SAGAD of Argentina and entered a joint venture with Slovakia's Tatramat (which it bought out in 1994).

Whirlpool acquired control of Kelvinator of India in 1994 and formed a joint venture in China with Shenzhen Petrochemical Holdings in 1995 to produce air conditioners. The following year Whirlpool merged its Whirlpool Washing Machines and Kelvinator of India companies to form Whirlpool of India. The company's European division plunged into the red when competition and a recession kept consumers away from its higher-priced appliances.

In 1997 Whirlpool initiated a restructuring (due to losses from its foreign operations) that included plant closures and substantial layoffs (as much as 10% of its workforce). The next year Whirlpool sold its appliance financing subsidiary to Transamerica. The company also began using a new more efficient product development model in 1998 similar to one used in the auto industry. In 2000 Whirlpool launched the Cielo Bath line of jetted tubs and in 2001 it introduced the Calypso dishwasher and the Duet washer and dryer.

Another global restructuring plan swept through the company in 2000 resulting in significant pretax charges ($373 million incurred in 2001 and 2002) and the elimination of about 6000 employees by October 2003.

In February 2002 Whirlpool bought the remaining 51% of Vitromatic it didn't already own. (Vitromatic — the second-largest appliance manufacturer in Mexico — is now called Whirlpool Mexico.) In March the company purchased 95% of Polar Poland's second-largest appliance maker.

Whirlpool introduced Gladiator GarageWorks (modular storage systems for the garage) and Polara (the first electric range with cooking and refrigeration capabilities) in 2002.

Whirlpool acquired Maytag in early 2006 for about $1.9 billion. The deal added several top brands to its already bulging portfolio including Admiral Amana Jenn-Air Magic Chef and of course the eponymous Maytag. Once the dust settled Whirlpool sold several businesses including Dixie-Narco the Amana commercial business its Hoover unit to Techtronic Industries and its Jade unit to Middleby Corporation. Buying Maytag also spurred Whirlpool to streamline operations and purge staff. In 2006 it laid off some 4500 employees consolidated duplicate functions related to administration and manufacturing and shuttered some offices including a Maytag research and development center

based in Newton Illinois. Whirlpool shuttered Maytag's Iowa-based administrative offices and moved them to Michigan and other locations. The company cut 700 jobs at several Tennessee plants the following year.

In 2007 Whirlpool acquired a minority stake in Elica Group in its effort to extend its reach into the global air ventilation market.

The company formed a 50-50 joint venture in 2008 with China's Hisense-Kelon Electrical Holdings to make and sell home appliances there.

In June 2010 Whirlpool closed its refrigerator factory in Evansville Indiana; some 1100 US jobs were lost as a result of the move.

EXECUTIVES

Executive Vice President And Chief Finan, Roy Templin
Vice President, Chris Hubbuch
Executive Vice President And President Of Whirlpool Europe Middle East And Africa, Esther Galindo
Ceo And Director, Marc R. Bitzer, age 54, $1,000,000 total compensation
Evp Global Product Organization, David T. (Dave) Szczupak, age 63, $746,667 total compensation
Evp And President Of Whirlpool Europe Middle East And Africa (emea), Esther Berrozpe Galindo, age 49, $659,041 total compensation
Evp And President Latin America, Jo o Carlos Brega, age 55, $498,901 total compensation
President Whirlpool North America, Joseph T. Liotine, age 46
Evp And Cfo, James W. (Jim) Peters, age 49, $456,667 total compensation
President Whirlpool Asia, Shengpo (Samuel) Wu
Vice President Operations, Tom Egan
Vice President Marketing, Andrew Batson
National Account Manager, Paula Saul
Vice President Sales Whirlpool Canada, Mark Williams
Vice President And General Manager Integrated Business Units, Brett Dibkey
Vp Human Resources, Kimberly Thompson
Vice President Information Technology, Michael Berendsen
Vice President Sales And Marketing, Daniel Clifford
National Sales Manager, Jason Wade
Vice President And Of General Manager Of Emerging Categories, Timothy Kee
Vice President Information Services, Nancy Berendsen
National Sales Manager Specialty Markets, Mark Wilson
Vice President, James Oh
Vice President, Daniel O'brien
Vice President Product Development And Innovation, Julio Moreira
Vice President Corporate Innovation And Information Systems, Jay Michael Berendsen
Vice President Of Information Technology, Derek Kovalcik
National Sales Manager, Erin Brown
Vice President Manufacturing Laundry And Dishwashers, Dale Laws
Vice President Product Development, David Klein
National Account Manager, Lee Collett
Corporate Vice President Strategic Com, Nancy Tennant
Executive Vice President Global Product Organizati, Dave Szczupak
Information Technology Management: Executive Vice President Senior Vice President, Mrutyunjaya Rao
Vice President Manager Director, Sandra Coons
National Account Manager, Jody Turner
National Sales Manager, Tom Kibler
Vice President Global Human Resources, David Binkleysenior

Vice President Global Quality, Ken Kleinhample
Vice President Human Resources Business, Cintia Bincoletto
Vice President Human Resources, Carey Martin
Division Vice President, Kenny D Thompson
Vice President For Human Resources Solutions, Abby Luersman
Vice President Quality, J D Rapp
Vice President, Alice Bomar
Vice President Market Operations Whirlpool Europe Europe Middle East And Africa, Juan Puente
Vice President Sales, Tamal Saha
National Sales Manager, Carlos Gomez
National Sales Manager, Nic Miller
Vice President Human Resources And Ehs, Levern Kelley
Senior Vice President Sales, Paul Bognar
Vice President And General Manager Integ, Brett Dibky
Global Vice President Internal Audit, Sidnei Sanches
National Sales Manager, Allen Prough
National Sales Manager, Randy Karn
Vp And Cfo North American Region, Christopher Bealer
Vp Consumer And Appliance Care Nar, Ken Kleinhemple
National Sales Manager National Contract, Dave Hoffman
Vice President Information Technology, Dave Langendonk
Vp And Chief Design Officer, J Mays
Senior Vice President Global Product Organization, Pamela Klyn
Board Member, William D Perez
Chairman, Jeff M. Fettig, age 62
Board Member, Harish Manwani
Treasurer Emea, Peter Davidsson
Board Member, Larry Spencer
Board Member, Greg Creed
Board Member, James Loree
Auditors: Ernst & Young LLP

LOCATIONS

HQ: Whirlpool Corp
2000 North M-63, Benton Harbor, MI 49022-2692
Phone: 269 923-5000
Web: www.whirlpoolcorp.com

2018 Sales

	$ mil.	% of total
North America	11,374	54
Europe the Middle East & Africa	4,536	21
Latin America	3,618	17
Asia	1,587	8
Other/eliminations	(78)	—
Total	21,037	100

PRODUCTS/OPERATIONS

2018 Sales

	$ mil.	% of total
Laundry	6,200	29
Refrigeration	6,051	29
Cooking	4,821	23
Dishwashing	1,645	8
Compressors	1,135	5
Spare parts and warranties	1,030	5
Other	155	1
Total	21,037	100

COMPETITORS

BSH Bosch und Siemens Hausger ote	Haier Group
Candy Group	Hitachi
Daewoo Electronics	LG Electronics
Electrolux	Panasonic Corp
Electrolux Home Appliances China	SANYO
	Samsung Electronics America

Fisher & Paykel Appliances Holdings
Gree Electrical Appliances
GuangDong Midea
Sears Holdings
Sharp Corp.
Sub-Zero
Viking Range

HISTORICAL FINANCIALS

Company Type: Public

Income Statement

FYE: December 31

	REVENUE ($ mil.)	NET INCOME ($ mil.)	NET PROFIT MARGIN	EMPLOYEES
12/18	21,037	(183)	—	92,000
12/17	21,253	350	1.6%	92,000
12/16	20,718	888	4.3%	93,000
12/15	20,891	783	3.7%	97,000
12/14	19,872	650	3.3%	100,000
Annual Growth	1.4%	—	—	(2.1%)

2018 Year-End Financials

Debt ratio: 33.00%
Return on equity: (-6.00%)
Cash ($ mil.): 1,498
Current ratio: 1.00
Long-term debt ($ mil.): 4,046
No. of shares (mil.): 64
Dividends
Yield: 4.0%
Payout: —
Market value ($ mil.): 6,840

	STOCK PRICE ($) FY Close	P/E High/Low		PER SHARE ($) Earnings	Dividends	Book Value
12/18	107.00	—	—	(3.00)	5.00	36.00
12/17	169.00	41	34	5.00	4.00	59.00
12/16	182.00	16	11	12.00	4.00	64.00
12/15	147.00	22	14	10.00	3.00	61.00
12/14	194.00	23	15	8.00	3.00	63.00
Annual Growth	(13.8%)	—	—	—	12.2%	(13.1%)

WHOLE FOODS MARKET, INC.

Whole Foods Market is the world's largest natural foods grocery chain. Founded in 1980 it pioneered the supermarket concept in natural and organic foods retailing. The company operates some 500 stores throughout the US Canada and the UK and focuses on organic perishable and prepared products. It sells private-label items through its 365 Organic Everyday Value and Allegro Coffee lines among others and offers a variety of non-GMO vegan and gluten-free foods. Whole Foods was acquired by Amazon.com for $13.7 billion in 2017.

HISTORY

With a $10000 loan from his father John Mackey started SaferWay Natural Foods in Austin Texas in 1978. Despite struggling Mackey dreamed of opening a larger supermarket-sized natural foods store. Two years later SaferWay merged with Clarksville Natural Grocery and Whole Foods Market was born. Led by Mackey that year it opened an 11000-sq.-ft. supermarket in the counterculture hotbed of Austin. The store was an instant success and a second store was added 18 months later in suburban Austin.

The company slowly expanded in Texas opening or buying stores in Houston in 1984 and Dallas in 1986. Whole Foods expanded into Louisiana in 1988 with the purchase of like-named Whole Food Co. a single New Orleans store owned by Peter Roy (who served as the company's president from

1993 to 1998). Sticking to university towns Whole Foods added another store in California the next year and acquired Wellspring Grocery (two stores North Carolina) in 1991. In 1992 it debuted its first private-label products under the Whole Foods name. Seeking capital to expand even more the company raised $23 million by going public in early 1992 with 12 stores.

Every competitor in the fragmented health foods industry became a potential acquisition and the chain began growing rapidly. In 1992 Whole Foods bought the six-store Bread & Circus chain in New England. The next year it added Mrs. Gooch's Natural Foods Markets (seven stores in the Los Angeles area). Its biggest acquisition came in 1996 when it bought Fresh Fields the second-largest US natural foods chain (22 stores on the East Coast and in Chicago). Although the purchase hurt profits in 1996 sales surpassed $1 billion for the first time in fiscal 1997 as Whole Foods neared 70 stores. In 1997 it introduced the less-expensive 365 private label and acquired the Granary Market (Monterey California) and Bread of Life (two stores South Florida) natural foods supermarkets.

Capitalizing on the growing popularity of nutraceuticals (natural supplements with benefits similar to pharmaceuticals) the company paid $146 million in 1997 for Amrion a maker of nutraceuticals and other nutritional supplements (merged with subsidiary WholePeople.com in 2000). It capped the year by buying coffee roaster Allegro Coffee. (Both companies are based in Boulder Colorado home of its former main rival the smaller Wild Oats.) Also in 1997 Whole Foods acquired the six-store Merchant of Vino natural foods and wine shop chain to foster the development of its wine departments.

In 1998 Whole Foods opened its first store in Boulder — a 39000-sq.-ft. superstore with amenities such as a juice bar and a prepared foods section. At year's end Roy resigned as president and was replaced by Chris Hitt. In 1999 Whole Foods bought four-store Boston-area chain Nature's Heartland.

In 2000 Whole Foods merged its online operations (wholefoods.com) with its direct marketing and nutritional supplement unit (Amrion) to form Wholepeople.com. Later that year the company merged Wholepeople.com with lifestyle marketing firm Gaiam; Whole Foods received a minority stake in Gaiam and started selling food online through Gaiam.com.

Hitt resigned in mid-2001 and Mackey took over his duties. Later that year Whole Foods acquired the three upscale Harry's Farmers Market stores in Atlanta; the sale did not include the Harry's In A Hurry stores which later shut down.

In 2002 Whole Foods crossed the border into Canada. Its first foreign store opened in downtown Toronto that May.

Mackey was named Entrepreneur of the Year in 2003 by consulting firm Ernst & Young. That year Whole Foods acquired Select Fish a Seattle-based seafood processor and distributor and opened a seafood distribution facility in Atlanta.

In 2004 Whole Foods opened a 59000-sq.-ft. store in the new Time Warner Center in Manhattan. The new store which includes a 248-seat cafe sushi bar wine shop and gourmet bakery is the largest supermarket in New York City. That year the company acquired the UK organic-food retailer Fresh & Wild for $38 million.

To support its rapid growth in 2004 Whole Foods Market expanded its number of operating regions from eight to 10 by separating the Southwest region into the Southwest and Rocky Mountain regions and the Northern Pacific region into the Northern California and Pacific Northwest region. The company announced the opening of its first Gluten-Free Bakehouse a dedicated gluten-free baking facility located outside Raleigh North Carolina. Overall the company opened 12 new stores in 2004.

In January 2005 Whole Foods launched the Animal Compassion Foundation an independent non-profit organization dedicated to the compassionate treatment of livestock. The company moved that month to its new corporate headquarters across the street from its old location in downtown Austin. Its new flagship store opened its doors in March at the same location. In October Whole Foods increased its number of operating regions from 10 to 11 by separating the North Atlantic region into the North Atlantic and Tri-State regions. Overall in fiscal 2005 the company opened a dozen new stores including its first in Nebraska and Ohio. In 2006 the company acquired a store in Portland Maine and converted it to the Whole Foods Market banner.

In August 2007 Whole Foods acquired its main competitor — Boulder Colorado-based Wild Oats Markets — in a deal valued at about $565 million (plus $106 million in debt). In early October the company sold 35 Henry's Farmers Market and Sun Harvest stores to a subsidiary of Los Angeles-based Smart & Final for about $166 million. The stores in California and Texas were acquired with Wild Oats.

The company launched a bi-monthly magazine called Whole Foods Market Magazine at its midwestern stores in 2008. On the heels of its disappointing third-quarter results in August 2008 shares of the company's stock fell to a six-year low and Whole Foods suspended its dividend. Blaming the poor economy the company announced the layoffs of some 50 employees at its Austin headquarters in August 2008. Overall in fiscal 2008 the company introduced about 300 new private-label items.

For the first time in its 29-year history Whole Foods reported negative same-store sales in the quarter ended December 2008 as traffic in its stores fell.

In March 2009 the company reached a settlement in its long-running dispute with the FTC over its acquisition of Wild Oats in 2007. Whole Foods agreed to sell 32 stores including 19 Wild Oats locations that had already been closed. In exchange the FTC dropped its crusade to undo the merger. In December 2009 John Elstrott was named chairman of Whole Foods Market after Mackey voluntarily relinquished the chairmanship which he had held since 1980. In May 2010 Walter Robb formerly co-president of the company was promoted to co-CEO of Whole Foods a title he now shares with Mackey.

EXECUTIVES

Ceo, John P. Mackey, $1 total compensation
President Northeast Region, A. C. Gallo, $501,110 total compensation
President Florida Region, Juan Nuñez
Chairman Whole Kids Foundation And Whole Cities Foundation, Walter E. Robb, $501,110 total compensation
Evp Operations U.s. And Whole Foods 365, David Lannon, $501,110 total compensation
Vp Purchasing Midwest Division, Jeff Turnas
Evp Operations, Christina Minardi
President Southern Pacific Region, Patrick Bradley
President Mid-atlantic Region, Scott Allshouse
President Rocky Mountain Region, Bill Jordan
President Midwest Region, Michael Bashaw
President North Atlantic Region, Laura Derba
Evp And Cio, Jason Buechel, $501,110 total compensation
President South Region, Omar Gaye
President Northern California Region, Rob Twyman

Evp Operations U.s. And The U.k., Kenneth (Ken) Meyer, $486,510 total compensation
Evp Growth And Business Development, James (Jim) Sud, $486,510 total compensation
Evp And Cfo, Keith Manbeck
President Pacific Northwest Region, Angela Lorenzen
Global Vp Marketing, Sonya Gafsi Oblisk
President Northeast Region, Nicole Wescoe
Global Vice President, Lee Matecko
Executive Vice President Operations, Kenny Meyer
Vice President And Marketing Manager, Desa Abbamondi
Vice President Vendor Manager, Ray Hudson
Vice President Administration, John Agnew
Senior Vice President Technology Manager, Pedro Adame
Global Vice President Commmunications, Brooke Buchanan
Vice President And Loan Officer And Branch Manager, Francisco Ibarra
Assistant Vice President And Mortgage Market Manager, Craig Moore
Assistant Vice President Product Manager Marketing, Merijoy Rucker
Regional Vice President, Scott Saulsberry
Regional Vice President, Tim Gates
Regional Vice President, Steve Epidendio
Vice President Digital Marketing Crm Loyalty And Ecommerce, Ryan Linders
Chairman, John B. Elstrott
Auditors: ERNST & YOUNG LLP AUSTIN TEX

LOCATIONS

HQ: WHOLE FOODS MARKET, INC.
550 BOWIE ST, AUSTIN, TX 787034644
Phone: 512 477-4455
Web: WWW.WHOLEFOODSMARKET.COM

PRODUCTS/OPERATIONS

Selected Product Categories

Bakery
Body care
Educational products
Floral
Grocery
Household products
Meat and poultry
Nutritional supplements
Pet products
Prepared foods
Produce
Seafood
Specialty (beer wine cheese)
Textiles

COMPETITORS

ALDI	Natural Grocers by
Albertsons	Vitamin Cottage
Costco Wholesale	Publix
Fiesta Mart	Safeway
GNC	Sprouts
H-E-B	Tesco
Kroger	Trader Joe's
Loblaw	Wal-Mart

HISTORICAL FINANCIALS

Company Type: Private

Income Statement				FYE: September 24
	REVENUE ($ mil.)	NET INCOME ($ mil.)	NET PROFIT MARGIN	EMPLOYEES
09/17	16,030	245	1.5%	89,000
09/16	15,724	507	3.2%	—
09/15	15,389	536	3.5%	—
09/14	14,194	579	4.1%	—
Annual Growth	4.1%	(24.9%)	—	—

Williams Cos Inc (The)

EXECUTIVES

MBR-Ceo, Steven J Malcolm
MBR, Joseph Williams
Vice President, Kevin Flanagan
Analyst, Olivia Cummisky
Auditors: Ernst & Young LLP

LOCATIONS

HQ: Williams Cos Inc (The)
One Williams Center, Tulsa, OK 74172-0172
Phone: 918 573-2000
Web: www.williams.com

HISTORICAL FINANCIALS

Company Type: Public

Income Statement				FYE: December 31
	REVENUE ($ mil.)	NET INCOME ($ mil.)	NET PROFIT MARGIN	EMPLOYEES
12/18	8,686	(155)	—	5,322
12/17	8,031	2,174	27.1%	5,425
12/16	7,499	(424)	—	5,604
12/15	7,360	(571)	—	6,578
12/14	7,637	2,114	27.7%	6,742
Annual Growth	3.3%			(5.7%)

2018 Year-End Financials

Debt ratio: 49.00%	No. of shares (mil.): 1,210
Return on equity: (-1.00%)	Dividends
Cash ($ mil.): 168	Yield: 6.0%
Current ratio: 1.00	Payout: —
Long-term debt ($ mil.): 22,367	Market value ($ mil.): 26,681

	STOCK PRICE ($) FY Close	P/E High/Low	PER SHARE ($) Earnings	Dividends	Book Value
12/18	22.00	— —	(0.00)	1.00	12.00
12/17	30.00	12 10	3.00	1.00	12.00
12/16	31.00	— —	(1.00)	2.00	6.00
12/15	26.00	— —	(1.00)	2.00	8.00
12/14	45.00	20 13	3.00	2.00	12.00
Annual Growth	(16.3%)	— —	—	(8.7%)	0.8%

Williams Sonoma Inc

EXECUTIVES

Pres-Ceo, Laura Alber
Chb*, Adrian Bellamy
Exec V Pres-Cfo, Julie Whalen
Exec V Pres-Gen Counsel-Sec, David King
Pres West Elm Brand, Alex Bellos
Pres Pottery Barn Brand, Marta Benson
Pres Williams Sonoma Brand, Janet Hayes
Manager, Adam Clark
Staff Consultant, Adrian Aguirre
Benefits Coordinator, Aimee Faustino
Document Administrator, Allen Simonitsch
Auditors: Deloitte & Touche LLP

LOCATIONS

HQ: Williams Sonoma Inc
3250 Van Ness Avenue, San Francisco, CA 94109
Phone: 415 421-7900   **Fax:** 415 434-0881
Web: www.williams-sonomainc.com

COMPETITORS

Ashley Furniture	King Arthur Flour
Bed Bath & Beyond	Lands' End
Brookstone	Levenger
Container Store	Longaberger
Cornerstone Brands	Macy's
Cost Plus	Neiman Marcus
Dean & DeLuca	Pampered Chef
Decorize	Pier 1 Imports
Eddie Bauer LLC	Restoration Hardware
Ethan Allen	Room & Board
Euromarket Designs	Target Corporation
Garden Ridge	Tuesday Morning
Hanover Direct	Corporation
IKEA	Z Gallerie

HISTORICAL FINANCIALS

Company Type: Public

Income Statement
FYE: February 3

	REVENUE ($ mil.)	NET INCOME ($ mil.)	NET PROFIT MARGIN	EMPLOYEES
02/19*	5,672	334	5.9%	28,200
01/18	5,292	260	4.9%	27,800
01/17	5,084	305	6.0%	28,300
01/16	4,976	310	6.2%	28,100
02/15	4,699	309	6.6%	26,800
Annual Growth	4.8%	2.0%	—	1.3%

*Fiscal year change

2019 Year-End Financials

Debt ratio: 11.00%
Return on equity: 28.00%
Cash ($ mil.): 339
Current ratio: 2.00
Long-term debt ($ mil.): 300

No. of shares (mil.): 79
Dividends
Yield: 0.0%
Payout: 42.0%
Market value ($ mil.): 4,256

	STOCK PRICE ($) FY Close	P/E High/Low	PER SHARE ($) Earnings	Dividends	Book Value
02/19*	54.00	18 11	4.00	2.00	15.00
01/18	53.00	18 14	3.00	2.00	14.00
01/17	48.00	18 13	3.00	1.00	14.00
01/16	52.00	26 14	3.00	1.00	13.00
02/15	78.00	25 16	3.00	1.00	13.00
Annual Growth	(8.9%)	— —	5.7%	6.8%	2.4%

*Fiscal year change

WILMINGTON TRUST COMPANY

EXECUTIVES

Executive Vice President, Mark A Graham
Chief Executive Officer, Robert Harra
Group Vice President, Richard Marsh
Vice President, Charles Gummey
Vice President, Peter Finkel
Assistant Vice President, Donald Haverstick
Vice President, Steven Cimalore
Vice President Global Capital Markets, Vito Iacovazzi
Vice President Private Banking, Heather Ford
Vice President Business Application Support Manager, Gary Powers
Vice President, Jared Grunig
Vice President Global Capital Markets, Nicholas Adams
Vice President, Mary Avery
Vice President, Margaret Pulgini

Vice President, Sergio Godinho
Vice President, Jennifer Matz
Training Manager Vice President, Lynn Dibonaventura
Vice President, Charles Hicks
Assistant Vice President, Steve Barone
Vice President, Lisa Fricke
Vice President Wilmington Trust Fsb, Josh Stump
Vice President, Wendy White
Vice President, Janice Cirillo
Vice President, George Chen
Vice President Of Marketing And Communications, Jim Klabe
Vice President Risk Management, Myfanwy Bonilla
Vice President Of Data Center, Ed Olkowski
Vice President Marketing, Sherry Costanzo
Senior Vice President Administration, John N Beeson
Vice President Corporate Client Services, Christie Longo
Vice President Client Development, Rob Barnett
Vice President, Jeanette Madaya
Vice President, Kevin Bruggeman
Vice President, Nadine Black
Vice President Risk Manager, Holly Stiefel
Assistant Vice President, Laura Barone
Senior Vice President Secretary, Michael Digregorio
Assistant Vice President, Deanne M Welsh
Vice President, Arlene Moyer
Vice President, Karen Touchstone
Assistant Vice President, Liz Hudgens
Vice President, Virginia Machamer
Vice President Network And Desktop Computing, Rob Averbach
Vice President, Robert Quinn
Vice President, Jane Snyder
Assistant Vice President, Greg Cherewko
Vice President And Portfolio Manager, Luke Betterly
Vice President, Joe Fahey
Senior Vice President, James Riley
Vice President Wealth Advisory Senior Private Client Fiduciary Advisor, Latonya Hubbard
Vice President, Steven Kochie
Vice President, Thomas Herring
Vice President And Senior Private Client Fiduciary Advisor, Cindy White
Vice President Esop Services, Kristy Britsch
Assistant Vice President, Ryan Thompson
Vice President, Jason Johnson
Executive Vice President, Bill Farrell
Vice President And Senior Client Development Officer For Wtris, Robert Barnett
Vice President, Chris Slaybaugh
Assistant Vice President, Thomas Kalafut
Vice President Wealth Advisory Services, Blair Talty
Assistant Vice President Of Lending, Mary Fisher
Group Vice President, Tom Pierce
Vice President, Clay Weisenberg
Assistant Vice President Loan Agency Group, Jennifer Anderson
Vice President Software Development Investment Management, John Driban
Vice President Equity Management, Mark Horst
Vice President And Portfolio Manager, Dan Rambert
Vice President Corporate Capital Markets, Aaron Soper
Assistant Vice President, Michael Moorehead
Assistant Vice President, Barry Butina
Vice President, Robert Reynolds
Assistant Vice President, Bonnie Metcalfe
Vice President, Joe Garniewski
Vice President, Robert Collins
Assistant Vice President Global Capital Markets, Clarice Wright
Vice President Institutional Relationship Manager, Jeffrey Petroske
Assistant Vice President, Melissa Jalace-vasold

Vice President Senior Private Client Advisor, Sandra Besso Plowinske
Vice President, Ann Harris-johnson
Vice President, Christopher Guardino
Vice President, Josh James
Assistant Vice President, Joann Petry
Avp, Lisa Lewis
Assistant Vice President, Carleen Terranova
Vice President Wealth Advisory Services, Paul Bartkowski
Assistant Vice President Commercial Real Estate, Rachel Skrabak
Vice President Channel Management, John J Hurley
Assistant Vice President, Greg Golden
Assistant Vice President, Melissa Marion
Vice President, Karen Bonn
Vp Senior Private Client Investment Advisor, Jim Mcdonald
Vice President And Senior Private Client Investment Advisor, Sue Schnaars
Vice President Private Banking, Julia Odonnell
Assistant Vice President, Brenda Parker
Vice President, Al Miller
Vice President, Barbara Obrien
Vice President, Charlie Buehler
Vice President And Senior Investment Advisor, Andrew Cloud
Assistant Vice President, Andrea Rybczynski
Vice President, Joseph Odonnell
Vice President, Renee Buchner
Assistant Vice President, Nancy Hagner
Assistant Vice President, Catherine Chandler
Vice President, Kyle Barry
Assistant Vice President, Maureen Auld
Vice President, Denise Sbraccia
Assistant Vice President, Sophie Pendolino
Assistant Vice President, Christopher Hickok
Assistant Vice President, Ruth Ann Mcmillen
Assistant Vice President, Jose Paredes
Vice President, Howard Gordon
Vice President, David Bagley
Vice President Private Client Advisor, Ed Barone
Vice President, Jeffrey Ritchie
Vice President, Kaye Crouch
Assistant Vice President, Kevin Ebert
Vice President, Nickole Garrison
Vice President Senior Private Banker, Nicholas Macechko
Assistant Vice President, Russell Whitley
Assistant Vice President, Matthew Lyndaker
Vice President And Investment Advisor, Darren Jordan
Vice President, Erin Miller
Vice President, William Gering
Vice President, Joseph Baker
Vice President, Stephen Seivold
Vice President, Theresa Drew
Assistant Vice President, Tammy Krawczyk
Vice President, Todd Bemiller
Vice President, Brooks Von Arx Jr
Vice President And Team Leader, Donald Hargadon
Vice President, Mindy Jones
Vice President, Patrick Wood
Vice President, Donna Oleary
Assistant Vice President, James Wisniewski
Vice President, Michael Edgington
Assistant Vice President, Susan Laratonda
Group Vice President Family Wealth, Anna Smith
Vice President Mortgage Backed Securities Trader And Analyst, Eric Smookler
Vice President, Glenn Klinger
Assistant Vice President, David Mcguire
Assistant Vice President, Stevie C Blackston
Vice President Administrative, Meghan Ashue
Vice President, Debra Berry
Vice President, Anne Stclair
Vice President, James Maloney
Vice President, Chris Sponenberg
Secretary Iii, Susan Alban
Board Member, Belinda Cunningham

LOCATIONS

HQ: WILMINGTON TRUST COMPANY
  1100 N MARKET ST, WILMINGTON, DE 198900001
Phone: 302 651-1000

HISTORICAL FINANCIALS

Company Type: Private

Income Statement · FYE: December 31

	ASSETS ($ mil.)	NET INCOME ($ mil.)	INCOME AS % OF ASSETS	EMPLOYEES
12/17	4,961	30	0.6%	518
12/16	3,685	18	0.5%	—
12/15	1,929	37	1.9%	—
Annual Growth	60.4%	(9.0%)	—	—

Wilson Bank Holding Co.

EXECUTIVES

Chairman; Chairman Of The Board, John Freeman
Vice President And Loan Officer Carthage, Lisa Gregory
Vice President And Marketing Director Main Office, Rebecca Jennings
Vice President And Loan Officer Smithville, Chad Colwell
Auditors: Maggart & Associates, P.C.

LOCATIONS

HQ: Wilson Bank Holding Co.
  623 West Main Street, Lebanon, TN 37087
Phone: 615 444-2265
Web: www.wilsonbank.com

HISTORICAL FINANCIALS

Company Type: Public

Income Statement · FYE: December 31

	ASSETS ($ mil.)	NET INCOME ($ mil.)	INCOME AS % OF ASSETS	EMPLOYEES
12/18	2,544	33	1.3%	487
12/17	2,317	24	1.0%	471
12/16	2,198	26	1.2%	444
12/15	2,022	24	1.2%	446
12/14	1,873	21	1.1%	406
Annual Growth	7.9%	11.9%	—	4.7%

2018 Year-End Financials

Debt ratio: —	No. of shares (mil.): 11
Return on equity: 12.00%	Dividends
Cash ($ mil.): 90	Yield: —
Current ratio: —	Payout: 29.0%
Long-term debt ($ mil.): —	Market value ($ mil.): —

Windstream Holdings Inc

Windstream Holdings offers a range of telecommunications services to consumers carriers and businesses over a fiber optic network measures nearly 150000 route miles. The company's business services include multi-site networking internet access cloud computing colocation online backup and other managed services. For residential customers Windstream offers high-speed internet (including gigabit speed in several markets) and voice services as well as video and bundles of services. The company provides infrastructure services such as call connection and backhaul connections to wireless carriers. In 2019 Windstream Holdings filed for Chapter 11 bankruptcy after a court ruling against it.

Bankruptcy

In February 2019 Windstream Holdings filed for Chapter 11 bankruptcy after the US District Court for the Southern District of New York ruled against the company in a suit initiated by hedge fund Aurelius Capital Management. Aurelius argued that a 2015 spinoff of Windstream's fiber-optic cable network assets violated a bond covenant that prohibited sale-leaseback transactions. The court awarded Aurelius a $310 million judgment and Windstream will receive $1 billion in debtor-in-possession financing from Citigroup Global Markets.

Operations

Windstream Holdings' operating segments are Consumer & Small Business Enterprise and Wholesale.

The Enterprise business which generates about half of revenue provides integrated voice and data services multi-site networking services cloud computing and colocation and managed services.

The Consumer & Small Business segment about a third of revenue is the company's incumbent local exchange carrier (ILEC) operation. It offers traditional local and long-distance voice services and high-speed internet services as well as consumer video services through DirecTV and Dish Network. It also and owns and operates cable TV franchises in some of service areas. Windstream's Kinetic video streaming service is part of the segments.

The Wholesale segment nearly 15% of revenue sells Windstream's infrastructure and related services to other telecom companies and network operators. It offers wave transport services dark fiber and colocation services data carrier Ethernet services fiber-to-the-tower connections to support backhaul services to wireless carriers and high-speed internet access.

The company sold its consumer CLEC operations in 2018. Prior to the sale the Consumer CLEC segment accounted for less than 5% of revenue and was composed of the company's competitive local exchange carriers.

Geographic Reach

Windstream Holdings is headquartered in Little Rock Arkansas. While its network runs 150000 route miles Windstream's operations are concentrated in rural areas in about 20 states in the Southeast Midwest and Southwest.

The company has rooms to grow with operating authority in 48 states and the District of Columbia. The company maintains more than 60 offices throughout the US.

Sales and Marketing

Windstream Holdings sells its products and services through several channels. It has a direct sales force; a dedicated customer advocate team; an indirect sales channel in which the company partners with third-party dealers who sell directly to customers; and third-party agents who refer sales leads to the company.

Financial Performance

Windstream's revenue has decreased in four of the last five years and it has posted net losses in five of the past six years.

Sales dropped 2% to $5.7 billion in 2018 compared to $5.8 billion in 2017 on lower revenue throughout its operations. A decrease in the Consumer & Small Business segment reflected lower priced plans aimed at reducing customer churn. The Enterprise segment's sales were lower on higher customer churn while Wholesale sales fell due to lower use of voice-only services and higher disconnect activity as carriers moved to fiber-based networks.

Expenses ate up Windstream's revenue resulting in a net loss of $273 million in 2018 compared to a 2017 loss of $2.1 billion (which included a $1.8 goodwill impairment charge).

The company held $361 million in cash and equivalents in 2018 compared to $43 million the year before. In 2018 operations generated $1 billion while investing activities used $554 million and investing activities used $141 million.

Strategy

Despite being in Chapter 11 bankruptcy Windstream Holdings is steaming ahead with its transition from a legacy telecommunications company to a provider of cloud streaming and other up-to-date services for businesses and consumers.

The company beefed up its business offerings through acquisitions of EarthLink and Broadview. EarthLink enabled Windstream to launch SD-WAN Concierge a managed network service for cloud computing offerings. The company claims to be the largest SD-WAN provider in the US with more than 1800 customers. With Broadview Windstream introduced OfficeSuite a Unified Communications-as-a-Service product across the company's footprint. Combined SD-WAN and Office-Suite offer comprehensive service to a wide range of Windstream customers.

In 2018 Windstream unloaded the EarthLink consumer internet business selling it to Trive Capital for $330 million. Windstream used the proceeds to shored up its balance sheet.

Trying to slow the flow of consumer households from its customer rolls Windstream began offering AT&T's DIRECTV satellite service and DIRECTV NOW streaming service to residential customers in 2018. The company sees the satellite service as a complement to it Kinetic high-speed internet service which offers speeds up to 1 Gigabit in some areas.

Windstream is one of the smaller telecommunications providers with a nationwide network. Its resources are dwarfed by the likes of AT&T Verizon and Comcast.

Mergers and Acquisitions

In 2018 Windstream Holdings acquired MASS Communications a privately held New York-based telecommunications network management company for about $37 million. MASS Communications' customers are small to mid-sized companies in the financial legal healthcare technology education and government sectors.

Windstream Holdings acquired Broadview Networks Holdings for nearly $230 million in 2017. Broadview provides cloud-based unified communications services for small and medium-sized businesses. Windstream plans to aggressively push Broadview's cloud operations and deploy its salesforce to compete across the country with companies like Vonage and RingCentral as well as cable companies. The deal was expected to close in the third quarter of 2017.

In 2017 Windstream completed its acquisition of EarthLink Holdings for $1.1 billion. The deal added EarthLink's networks around the country to Windstream's operations and filled in gaps of Windstream's map of service areas across the country.

EXECUTIVES

President Enterprise, Layne L. Levine

Evp Chief Human Resources And Legal Officer, John P. Fletcher, age 53, $515,000 total compensation

President And Ceo, Anthony W. (Tony) Thomas, age 47, $1,000,000 total compensation

Cfo And Treasurer, Robert E. (Bob) Gunderman, age 46, $450,000 total compensation

President Carrier, Mike Shippey

Evp Engineering, Jeff Small

Evp And Cio, Lewis Langston

Evp And Enterprise Chief Marketing Officer, Joe Harding

President Consumer Small And Medium Sized Businesses, Sarah Day, $298,615 total compensation

Clec Consumer Small And Medium-sized Business, Drew Smith

Evp Access, John Dobbins

Vice President Of Delivery, Rick Hausman

Svp Wholesale Sales, Joe Scattareggia

Svp Process Development And Project Management, Kevin Halpin

Svp Cloud Technology And Platform Development, Stephen Farkouh

Executive Vice President Senior Vice President Vice President, Rodney Hawkins

Vice President Of Sales, Chuck Flaherty

National Account Manager, Kristin Warren

Vice President Carrier Services, Mike Crimmins

Vice President Sales Operations, Brandon Prince

Vice President Channel Sales, Ron Beer

Division Vice President, Phillip McAbee

Division Vice President Of Operations, Stacy Hale

Area Vice President, Scott Spaulding

Vice President Network Operations, Gary Cooke

National Account Manager, Wendy Nevala

Vice President Benefits, Robert Boyd

Region Vice President Of Operations, Barry Bishop

Vice President Of Architecture And Technology, Art Nichols

Vice President Customer Support, Anne Brames

Vice President Finance, Daniel King

Vice President Wholesale Business Development, John Nishimoto

Vice President, Aaron Hepburn

Vice President Transport Engineering, Buddy Bayer

Vice President Enterprise Finance, David Schirack

First Vice President Origination Services, Hermand Lo

Vice President Enterprise Marketing Operations, Geoff Levy

Vice President Product Management, Mike Kozlowski

Vice President Channel Sales, David Dickson

Senior Vice President Application Development, Mark Wyman

Vice President Customer Account Management, Matthew Hepburn

Senior Vice President Consumer Services, Hope Streeter

Vice President Marketing, Ryan Turner

Vice President Service Delivery, Trish Dow

Chairman, Jeffrey T. Hinson, age 62

Auditors: PricewaterhouseCoopers LLP

LOCATIONS

HQ: Windstream Holdings Inc
4001 Rodney Parham Road, Little Rock, AR 72212
Phone: 501 748-7000
Web: www.windstream.com

PRODUCTS/OPERATIONS

2018 Sales

	$ mil.	% of total
Enterprise	2,932	51
Consumer and Small Business - ILEC	1,877	33
Wholesale	723	13
CLEC Consumer	181	3
Total	**5,713**	**100**

2018 Sales

	$ mil.	% of total
Service revenues	5,637	99
Product sales	76	1
Total	**5,713**	**100**

COMPETITORS

AT&T	FullNet Communications
CenturyLink	Momentum Telecom
Comcast	Sprint Communications
Cox Communications	Suddenlink
Crown Castle	Communications
International	Time Warner Cable
Equinix	Verizon

HISTORICAL FINANCIALS

Company Type: Public

Income Statement				FYE: December 31
	REVENUE ($ mil.)	**NET INCOME** ($ mil.)	**NET PROFIT MARGIN**	**EMPLOYEES**
12/18	5,713	(723)	—	11,945
12/17	5,853	(2,117)	—	1,223
12/16	5,387	(384)	—	11,870
12/15	5,765	27	0.5%	12,326
12/14	5,830	(40)	—	12,626
Annual Growth	(0.5%)	—		(1.4%)

2018 Year-End Financials

Debt ratio: 101.00%
Return on equity: ***.***.**%
Cash ($ mil.): 356
Current ratio: 0.00
Long-term debt ($ mil.): 73

No. of shares (mil.): 43
Dividends
　Yield: —
　Payout: —
Market value ($ mil.): 90

	STOCK PRICE ($) FY Close	**P/E** High/Low		**PER SHARE ($)** Earnings	Dividends	Book Value
12/18	2.00	— —		(18.00)	0.00	(45.00)
12/17	2.00	— —		(63.00)	2.00	(36.00)
12/16	7.00	— —		(21.00)	3.00	9.00
12/15	6.00	10 4		1.00	12.00	16.00
12/14	8.00	— —		(2.00)	30.00	11.00
Annual Growth	(29.0%)	—	—	—	—	—

Wintrust Financial Corp (IL)

Wintrust Financial is a holding company for 15 subsidiary banks (mostly named after the individual communities they serve) with more than 150 branches primarily in the metropolitan Chicago and southern Wisconsin (including Milwaukee)

markets. Boasting assets of more than $23 billion the banks offer personal and commercial banking wealth management and specialty lending services with business and commercial real estate loans making up 60% of the company's loan portfolio. Wintrust's banks target small business customers though some of Wintrust's banks also provide niche lending for homeowners associations medical practices franchisees and municipalities.

Operations

Wintrust operates three business segments: Community Banking which accounted for 77% of total revenue in 2015 and serves individuals and small businesses; Specialty Finance (13% of revenue) operating through First Insurance Funding and First Insurance Funding of Canada which provide financing for commercial insurance and life insurance premiums in the US and Canada respectively; and Wealth Management (10% of revenue) which offers financial planning and brokerage services through The Chicago Trust Company N.A. Wayne Hummer Investments LLC and Great Lakes Advisors LLC.

Wintrust makes more than 70% of its revenue from interest income. About 66% of its total revenue came from loan interest (including fees) during 2015 while another 6% came from interest on investment securities. The rest of its revenue came from mortgage banking (12%) wealth management services (7%) deposit account service charges (3%) and other miscellaneous income sources.

Geographic Reach

Wintrust's banks operate more than 150 branches and 220-plus automatic teller machines mostly located in communities throughout the Chicago metropolitan area and southern Wisconsin. Its wealth management offices are in Chicago; Appleton Wisconsin; and Safety Harbor Florida. Its Wintrust Mortgage subsidiary has 55 locations in a dozen states while its insurance subsidiaries have locations in Northbrook Illinois; Jersey City; Long Island New York; Toronto; Mississauga Ontario; and Vancouver.

Sales and Marketing

The bank's customers include individuals small to mid-sized businesses local governmental units and institutional clients residing primarily in the banks' local service areas.

Wintrust has been ramping up its advertising spend in recent years. It spent $21.9 million on advertising during 2015 up from $13.6 million and $11.1 million in 2014 and 2013 respectively.

Financial Performance

Wintrust Financial's annual revenues have risen more than 40% since 2011 as its loan assets have swelled by nearly 70% with rapid branch expansion. Its annual profits have doubled over the same period.

The banking group's revenue jumped 12% to $990.1 million during 2015 mostly as its average loan balances grew by 15% for the year. Mortgage banking revenue increased 26% for the year thanks to higher origination volumes and purchases on a more favorable mortgage banking environment also helping buoy the company's top-line growth.

Strong revenue growth in 2015 drove Wintrust's net income up 4% to $156.75 million despite a rise in acquisition-related professional and legal fees. The group's operating cash levels fell 82% to $37.95 million due to unfavorable working capital changes mainly tied to an increase in accrued interest receivable and other assets.

Strategy

Wintrust has developed its community-based banking franchise through rapid branch expansion stemming from either through new openings or small bank acquisitions. Indeed the bank's branch count has flourished by more than 50% since 2011 from 99 back then to 152 branches at the end of 2015.

Beyond branch expansion the company remains focused on making new loans especially of the commercial and commercial real estate type where opportunities that meet its underwriting standards exist.

Mergers and Acquisitions

In January 2016 Wintrust Financial expanded into Pewaukee Wisconsin after agreeing to buy Generations Bancorp and its Foundations Bank subsidiary. Later that year the company finalized the $33.5 million purchase of First Community Financial Corporation the holding company of First Community Bank (which operates two branches in Elgin Illinois).

In July 2015 the company purchased Community Financial Shares Inc. and its four Community Bank of Wheaton/Glen Ellyn bank branches in the respective communities they serve in Illinois for a total of $42.4 million.

Also in July 2015 the company bought $118 million-asset North Bank and its two branches in Chicago.

In April 2015 Wintrust acquired Suburban Illinois Bancorp and its 10 Suburban Bank & Trust Company (SBT) branches in Chicago and surrounding suburbs for $12.5 million. The SBT locations would operate under Wintrust's Hinsdale Bank & Trust Company subsidiary.

In January 2015 the bank group purchased $224 million-asset Delavan Bancshares Inc. and its Community Bank CBD subsidiary.

Company Background

In 2012 Wintrust expanded its premium funding business into Canada with the acquisition of Macquarie Premium Funding Inc which was a subsidiary of Macquarie Group. The deal marked Wintrust's first international venture.

EXECUTIVES

Evp Technology; President Wintrust Information Technology Services, Lloyd M. Bowden, age 66, $167,333 total compensation

Evp Cfo Secretary And Treasurer, David A. Dykstra, age 59, $759,167 total compensation

President Ceo And Director, Edward J. Wehmer, age 64, $1,100,000 total compensation

Evp And Regional Market Head, Frank J. Burke

Evp And Chief Credit Officer, Richard B. Murphy, age 60, $509,167 total compensation

Evp And Chief Administration Officer, Leona A. Gleason

Svp Finance, David L. Stoehr, age 60, $419,167 total compensation

Evp And Regional Market Head, Timothy S. (Tim) Crane, age 57

Evp Wealth Management, Thomas P. (Tom) Zidar

Evp General Counsel And Secretary, Lisa J. Pattis, $446,167 total compensation

Evp And Regional Market Head, David L. Larson

Evp And Coo Wintrust Commercial Finance (wcf), Joseph F. Thompson

Vice President Compliance, Kellie Oostendorp

Group Vp; Treasury Management Sales, Sarah Grooms

Executive Vice President, Ursula Moncau

Vice President Bsa Officer, Kathleen Franklin

Senior Vice President Middle Market, Dave Killpack

Vice President Managed Assets Division, Sandy Durek

Vice President Loan Operations, Sharon Hiller

Vice President Managed Assets Division, Irene Calzadilla

Vice President, Philip Sheridan

Senior Vice President Finance Credit Reporting, Mario Nudo

Senior Vice President Commercial Lender, Gregory Pinter

Avp Treasury Management, Judy Majon

Assistant Vice President Financial System Management, Marty Lavin

Avp Middle Market Treasury Management Sales, Lauren Hess

Vice President, Mary Koehler

Senior Vice President, Rhonda Pokoj

Vice President Marketing, Todd Younger

Vice President Wealth Services, Anna Fedus

Vice President Commercial Banking, Roy Gibson

Vice President Compliance, Christine Wujek

Assistant Vice President, Robert Murphy

Vice President, Sarah Withrow

Vice President Real Estate Services, Trey Meers

Vice President Commercial Banking, Jason Girardin

Senior Vice President, Darragh Griffin

Senior Vice President Planning, Scott Ernsteen

Senior Vice President Commercial Real Estate, Nick Cannon

Senior Vice President, George Reimnitz

Vice President Operations, Colleen Toft

Vice President, Joseph Ach

Senior Vice President Commercial Banking, Sean Dunn

Vice President, Sara Staniszewski

Vice President Commercial Banking, Michael Roman

Senior Vice President, Ryan Witte

Senior Vice President, William Robin

Vice President, Jon Swanson

Assistant Vice President Investments, Scott Weichle

Vice President Regulatory Reporting, Anita Chakravarthy

Assistant Vice President Commercial Real Estate, Kim Curschman

Senior Vice President Investments, David Galvan

Vice President Fair Lending Officer, Teresa Handley

Assistant Vice President Branch Management, Rick Butterly

Vice President, Caroline Gonos

Vice President Commercial Real Estate, Zornitsa Titova

Assistant Vice President, Todd Shifrin

Vice President Managed Assets Division, Hany Morsy

Vice President Human Resources, Janet Huffman

Vice President Marketing, Wendy Schenker

Assistant Vice President, Jeffrey Eversden

Vice President Assistant Counsel Litigation, Cindy Stuyvesant

Vice President Finance Regulatory Reporting, James Oranga

Executive Vice President And Chief Credit Officer, Paul Hallauer

Vice President Operations Manager Private Banker, Nicole Cox

Executive Vice President, Matthew Doucet

Vice President, Paul Varga

Executive Vice President, Christine Smith

Assistant Vice President, Darren Jamriska

Senior Vice President, Anish Saran

Senior Vice President Commercial Loan Review Manager, Cindy Bauer

Vice President, Nick Koricanac

Vice President Operations, Susan Puraleski

Vice President Loan Operations, Racquel Clemente

Vice President Assistant Controller, Dana French

Senior Vice President Sales, Steve Cusick

Vice President Executive, Sharon Moeller

Assistant Vice President Commercial Product Manager, Karon Gater

Assistant Vice President Retail Digital Product Manager, Natalie Fedus

Vice President, Jeffery Wolinski

Vice President Operations, Lisa Johnson

Vice President Credit, Juan Cabrera

Senior Vice President Information Services, Mike Nathan

Vice President Finance, Derek Ramsden

Assistant Vice President, Katie Cagney

Assistant Vice President Branch Manager, Anthony Scott

Senior Vice President, Joe Gensor

Senior Vice President Sales, Tom Forbes

Vice President, Kim Endsley

Vice President, Sharon Sagert

Vice President Risk, Tim Doran

Senior Vice President Treasury Management, Chris Lantman

Senior Vice President, Brian de la Houssaye

Assistant Vice President, Edward Semik

Vice President Of Operations Wintrust Commercial Finance, Lisa McNeme

Vice President Business Banking, Chris Dana

Senior Vice President Commercial Real Estate, Daniel Lawlor

Assistant Vice President, Richard Eber

Vice President Construction And Engineering Division, Chris Vantassel

Senior Vice President Commercial Real Estate, Joe Nitti

Senior Vice President Risk, Evan Bossard

Vice President Government Nonprofit Healthcare Lender, Erinn Siegel

Vp Eft Services, Crystal Tabar

Vice President Commercial Banking, Christopher Sobey

Assistant Vice President, Dhaval Gandhi

Vice President, Tara Fedorko

Vice President, Rafiq Harris

Senior Vice President, Dawn Mase

Vice President Business Lending, Katie Moore

Assistant Vice President Commercial Real Estate, Lauren Barnard

Senior Vice President, Tom Carlson

Vice President Senior Commercial Underwriter, Sean Little

Vice President Of Marketing, Jennifer Bohnen

Senior Vice President Of Operations, Anna Jimenez

Senior Vice President Operations, Stephen Milota

Assistant Vice President Bsa Compliance, Amber Schoenauer

Senior Vice President Of Commercial Banking, Lena Dawson

Vice President, Timmer John

Vice President Capital Markets, Clark Brian

Avp Eeo Compliance, Mary Rivers

Svp, Joseph Gregoire

Vp Senior Manager, Joseph White

Vice President, Rob Lewis

Vp New Business Development Wintrust Commercial Finance Irvine, Robert Harris

Assistant Vice President Learning And Development, Douglas Campbell

Assistant Vice President Marketing Commercial Banking, Kim Nagy

Vp Reconciliation Manager, Catherine Costanza

Vice President, Laura Sepulveda

Vice President Risk, Thomas Benkoske

Senior Vice President Commercial Banking, Vishal Patel

Vice President, Patrice Louis

Vice President Risk Management, Shipra Sethi

Vice President And Audit Manager, Paul Beierwaltes

Assistant Vice President Consumer Loan Documentation Manager, Christy Niemietz

Vice President And Assistant General Counsel, Erik Hsu

Assistant Vice President Default Servicing, Paul Hennessy

Senior Vice President, Ronald Calandra

Senior Vice President Of Finance, Daniel Tuerk

Senior Vice President Wealth Services, Kendra L Castelloni

Vice President Human Resources, Norah Larke Mba

Avp Fair Lending, Matt Sabatino

Senior Vice President, Brad Schotanus
Group Senior Vice President, Glenn Margraff
Vice President Vice Retail Branch Manager, Agnes Lyko
Vice President Cashier Controller, Lynn Dohnalik
Senior Vice President, Nicholas Begley
Vice President Business Banking, Sean Daly
Vice President, Tom Groth
Assistant Vice President Commercial Banking, Benjamin Johnson
Vice President Commercial Real Estate, John Koranda
Senior Vice President Managing Director, Richard Howard
Auditors: Ernst & Young LLP

LOCATIONS

HQ: Wintrust Financial Corp (IL)
9700 W. Higgins Road, Suite 800, Rosemont, IL 60018
Phone: 847 939-9000   **Fax:** 847 615-4091
Web: www.wintrust.com

PRODUCTS/OPERATIONS

2015 Sales

	$ mil.	% of total
Interest		
Loans including fees	652	66
Securities	61	6
Other	6	-
Non-interest		
Mortgage banking	115	12
Wealth management	74	7
Service charges on deposit accounts	27	3
Fees from covered call options	15	2
Other	41	4
Trading (losses) gains net	(0.2)	-
Total	**990**	**100**

Selected Subsidiaries and Affiliates
Banking
  Barrington Bank & Trust Company N.A.
  Beverly Bank & Trust Company N.A.
  Crystal Lake Bank & Trust Company N.A.
  Hinsdale Bank & Trust Company
  Lake Forest Bank & Trust Company
  Libertyville Bank & Trust Company
  North Shore Community Bank & Trust Company
  Northbrook Bank & Trust Company
  Old Plank Trail Community Bank N.A.
  Schaumburg Bank & Trust Company N.A.
  St. Charles Bank & Trust
  State Bank of The Lakes
  Town Bank
  Village Bank & Trust
  Wheaton Bank and Trust Company
Non-banking
  Chicago Trust Company N.A.
  First Insurance Funding Corporation
  Great Lakes Advisors LLC
  Tricom Inc. of Milwaukee
  Wayne Hummer Asset Management Company
  Wayne Hummer Investments LLC
  Wayne Hummer Trust Company N.A.
  Wintrust Information Technology Services Company
  Wintrust Mortgage Corporation (formerly WestAmerica Mortgage Company)

COMPETITORS

Associated Banc-Corp	Harris
Bank of America	JPMorgan Chase
Citigroup	MB Financial
Citizens Financial Group	Northern Trust
	PrivateBank
Fifth Third	U.S. Bancorp
First Midwest Bancorp	

HISTORICAL FINANCIALS
Company Type: Public

Income Statement   FYE: December 31

	ASSETS ($ mil.)	NET INCOME ($ mil.)	INCOME AS % OF ASSETS	EMPLOYEES
12/18	31,245	343	1.1%	4,727
12/17	27,916	258	0.9%	4,075
12/16	25,669	207	0.8%	3,878
12/15	22,917	157	0.7%	3,770
12/14	20,011	151	0.8%	3,491
Annual Growth	11.8%	22.7%	—	7.9%

2018 Year-End Financials

Debt ratio: 2.00%	No. of shares (mil.): 56
Return on equity: 11.00%	Dividends
Cash ($ mil.): 1,492	Yield: 1.0%
Current ratio: —	Payout: 13.0%
Long-term debt ($ mil.): —	Market value ($ mil.): 3,751

	STOCK PRICE ($) FY Close	P/E High/Low	PER SHARE ($) Earnings	Dividends	Book Value
12/18	66.00	16 11	6.00	1.00	58.00
12/17	82.00	19 14	4.00	1.00	53.00
12/16	73.00	19 10	4.00	0.00	52.00
12/15	49.00	18 14	3.00	0.00	49.00
12/14	47.00	16 14	3.00	0.00	44.00
Annual Growth	9.2%	— —	18.4%	17.4%	7.0%

WISCONSIN HOUSING AND ECONOMIC DEVELOPMENT AUTHORITY

EXECUTIVES

Exec Dir, Wyman B Winston
Chairman*, Ivan Gamboa
Exec Dir*, Joaquin Altoro
Coo*, Kim Plache
Chairman of The Board*, Brad Guse
Director, Wyman Winston
Real Estate Conultant, David Sheperd
Creative Coordinator, Dawn Gibbs

LOCATIONS

HQ: WISCONSIN HOUSING AND ECONOMIC DEVELOPMENT AUTHORITY
201 W WASHINGTON AVE # 700, MADISON, WI 537032760
Phone: 608 266-7884
Web: WWW.WHEDA.COM

HISTORICAL FINANCIALS
Company Type: Private

Income Statement   FYE: June 30

	ASSETS ($ mil.)	NET INCOME ($ mil.)	INCOME AS % OF ASSETS	EMPLOYEES
06/18	2,475	34	1.4%	171
06/17	2,201	23	1.1%	—
06/16	2,082	39	1.9%	—
Annual Growth	9.0%	(6.2%)	—	—

World Fuel Services Corp.

World Fuel Services can't yet affect the earth's spin but it plays a part in moving mostly everything else across its surface. The company sells fuel and fuel handling services to small-to-midsized air carriers cargo and charter carriers and private aircraft. as well as support activities such as flight planning weather reports and card payment services. It is also a marine fuel reseller on hand to deliver marine fuel to the shipping industry and commercial vessels and supplies land transport markets via hundreds of terminals in the US and Watson Fuels in the UK. It has almost 50 offices around the world and does business or virtually every country. The company was founded in 1985 as a marine fuel brokerage firm.

Operations

World Fuel Services operates three distinct fueling segments: Aviation Land and Marine. It also offers a range of support services (such as fuel market analysis flight planning ground-handling services and weather reports) to its aviation and marine customers.

The Aviation segment generates about 40% of sales and markets fuel and related products and services to major commercial airlines second and third tier airlines cargo carriers regional and low cost carriers airports fixed based operators corporate fleets fractional operators private aircraft military fleets and to the US and foreign governments.It purchases fuel from suppliers worldwide and can deliver directly into aircraft or to a storage facility.

The Marine fueling services business brings in more than 25% of sales and markets fuel lubricants and related products and services. It arranges fueling for ships on a brokered basis and extends credit to a global customer base which includes container lines cruise ships dry bulk carriers fishing fleets refrigerated vessels and tankers.

The Land transportation segment accounts for nearly 35% of sales and offers fuel and related services to petroleum distributors retail petroleum operators and other fuels users. It also engages in crude oil marketing activities.

Geographic Reach

Florida-based World Fuel Services has operations in Argentina Australia Brazil Canada Chile Colombia Costa Rica Denmark Germany Gibraltar Greece Hong Kong India Japan Mexico the Netherlands Norway Puerto Rico Russia Singapore Switzerland South Africa South Korea Sweden Taiwan the UAE the UK and the US.

The Americas account for more than 60% of World Fuel Services' revenue; EMEA (Europe Middle East and Africa) generates more than 20%; and the Asia-Pacific region more than 15%.

Sales and Marketing

World Fuel Services (WFS) purchases inventory at airport locations or has it shipped via pipelines and held at multiple locations. The company sells fuel via supply contracts wheree customers commit to purchasing fuel over the contract term. It also conducts spot sales (or non-contract) sales. WFS' fuel prices are tied to market‑based formulas or are government controlled. The majority of its marine segment activity consists of spot sales. WFS also contracts with third parties to provide various services for our customers including fueling of vessels in ports and at sea and transportation and delivery of fuel and fuel-related products.

None of its customers account for more than 10% of total consolidated revenue.

Financial Performance

World Fuel Services' revenue has taken a battering from the low oil price. In fiscal 2016 sales fell a further 11% to $27.0 billion due to lower average prices across the board although the Marine segment was particularly badly affected accounting for two-thirds of the revenue shortfall. The Aviation segment was able to increase volumes sold by 12% as was Land which increased volume sales by 9%.

Net income fell 28% to $126.5 million due to lower revenue particularly in the Marine segment which remains beset by overall industry weakness. The lower price environment led to reduced demand for its price risk management offerings and lower overall margins. It laso made fewer sales to its largest customers.

Cash from operations fell 54% to $205.2 million due to unfavorable changes in assets and liabilities; $130.9 million in cash was used to finance the increase in inventory levels needed to support higher volume sales.

Strategy

World Fuel Services (WFS) is focused on long-term growth by developing organic initiatives and investing in strategic opportunities to build a comprehensive service-oriented business that takes it beyond its core fuel procurement activities.The company ultimately sees its future beyond just fuel and will evolve into a software financial tech and energy management company as reliance on hydrocarbons is gradually balanced by LNG renewables and special fuel blends. WFS is expanding its energy types under management through acquisitions and strategic investment: it acquired two European companies that combined tech and physical fulfillment in 2015 and 2016 while in the US its subsidiary KTM is expanding its energy management and regulatory offerings and Xisot is building cloud-based predictive analytics to manage the multitude of electricity sources.

World Fuel Services has increased its geographic coverage and the depth of its portfolio through acquisitions. It plans to continue to explore acquisition opportunities of fuel resellers logistics and transaction management and payment processing companies including other services and technology. For instance in 2016 it acquired the aviation fueling operations of 83 airports in Canada France the UK Germany Italy Australia and New Zealand. And in Asia WFS expanded its international trip support services to meet growing demand of operators traveling within and into the region. The company has also entered into joint venture arrangements to complement its core businesses and divests non-core operations as needed.

Mergers and Acquisitions

In 2017 World Fuel Services acquired British energy management consultancy Orchard Energy from Lakehouse for Å 12.4 million.

In 2016 the company bought Exxon Mobil's aviation fueling operations at 83 airports in Canada the UK Germany Italy Australia and New Zealand for $260 million. It also bought PAPCO Inc. and Associated Petroleum Products Inc. (both in the US) for $230 million.

HISTORY

Neighbors Ralph Weiser and Jerrold Blair founded International Oil Recovery an oil recycling company in Florida in 1984. The company moved into aviation fueling by acquiring Advance Petroleum in 1986. Two years later International Oil Recovery diversified further entering the hazardous waste market by buying Resource Recovery of America a soil remediation company. In 1989 the firm acquired JCo Energy Partners an aviation fuel company and subsequently renamed its aviation fueling division World Fuel Services. The company set up International Petroleum in 1993 to operate a Delaware used-oil and water-recycling plant.

The company changed its name to World Fuel Services Corporation in 1995 to reflect its expanded range of operations. Also that year it nearly doubled its revenue base with the purchase of Trans-Tec the world's #1 independent marine fuel services company. World Fuel also exited the environmental services business in 1995 to focus on its fuel services and oil recycling businesses.

The following year the company formed World Fuel International a subsidiary based in Costa Rica that serves World Fuel's aviation customers in South and Central America Canada and the Caribbean. In 1998 it acquired corporate jet fuel provider Baseops International which has offices in the UK and Texas.

In 1999 the company expanded its share of the marine fuel market with the acquisition of the Bunkerfuels group of companies one of the world's top marine fuel brokerages.

To focus on its marine and aviation fueling businesses World Fuel exited the oil recycling segment in 2000 when it sold its International Petroleum unit to waste services company EarthCare for about $33 million.

The company expanded into the United Arab Emirates with its 2001 acquisition of fuel services provider Marine Energy of Dubai. World Fuel acquired Rotterdam-based marine fuel reseller Oil Shipping Group in 2002.

In 2004 World Fuel Services acquired UK-based marine fuel reseller Tramp Holdings for $83 million.

The company diversified further in 2007 acquiring AVCARD a leading provider of contract fuel sales and charge card services to the aviation industry for $55 million.

In 2009 it bought wholesale motor fuel distributor TGS Petroleum. The company combined TGS with Texor to expand World Fuel Services' presence as the largest independent wholesale motor fuel distributor in Illinois.

Expanding its UK market share in 2009 the company acquired the Henty Oil Group of Companies a leading independent provider of marine and land fuels in the UK.

In 2010 it beefed up its position in the branded onshore wholesale market to 1 billion gallons a year by acquiring Lakeside Oil Company based in Milwaukee. It also boosted its market position through the acquisition of leading independent petroleum marketing company Western Petroleum for $95 million.

Boosting its aviation fuel segment in 2011 (for an undisclosed amount) World Fuel Services acquired The Hiller Group an aviation fuel supplier to more than 600 fixed base operators. It also bought Ascent Aviation a national branded reseller of aviation fuel for ConocoPhillips and deicing fluid for Dow Chemical and which supplies more than 450 airports and fixed base operators and NATO aviation fuel and logistics supplier Nordic Camp Supply (for $68.5 million.)

In 2012 the company acquired CarterEnergy's wholesale motor fuel distribution business. Kansas-based CarterEnergy with an annual volume of more than of 500 million gallons distributes branded fuel to more than 700 retail operators and is a supplier to industrial commercial and government customers in more than a dozen states. The deal boosted World Fuel Services' land fuel volume to more than 3.5 billion gallons.

In 2013 to improve its payment processing operations it also bought certain assets from Multi Service Corporation (which specializes in fleet government and commercial payment programs) for $137 million. The Multi Service acquisition expands World Fuel Services' presence in the payment processing industry.

EXECUTIVES

President Coo And Director; Chairman And Ceo Marine Fueling Services, Michael J. Kasbar, age 63, $875,100 total compensation

Evp And Cfo, Ira M. Birns, age 57, $583,400 total compensation

Evp; Regional Managing Director Asia, Francis L Boon Meng

Evp And Coo, Jeff S. Smith

Evp; Regional Managing Director Emea, Wade N. DeClaris

Svp And Cio, Massoud Sedigh, age 64

Evp Global Aviation And Marine, John P. Rau, $475,100 total compensation

Evp Global Land, Michael J. Crosby, $487,550 total compensation

Vice President People And Performance Development, Marcia Morales-jaffe

Senior Vice President, Carlos Cuervo

Vice President Supply And Trading, Peggy Meyer

Vice President Application Development, Russ Sabbag

Vice President Application Development, Scott DeLoach

Vice President Human Resources, Sue Rider

Vice President Information Security, Timothy Ramsay

Vice President Supply And Trading, Steven Fiedler

Executive Vice President And Chief Financial Officer, Guru Acharya

Auditors: PricewaterhouseCoopers LLP

LOCATIONS

HQ: World Fuel Services Corp.
9800 Northwest 41st Street, Miami, FL 33178
Phone: 305 428-8000   **Fax:** 305 392-5621
Web: www.wfscorp.com

2016 sales

	$ mil.	% of total
Americas	16,726	62
Asia/Pacific	6,019	22
Europe & Middle East & Africa	4,271	16
Total	**27,016**	**100**

PRODUCTS/OPERATIONS

2016 sales

	$ mil.	% of total
Aviation	10,914	40
Marine Land	8918.8	33
Marine	7,183	27
Total	**27,016**	**100**

Selected Subsidiaries

Ascent Aviation Group Inc.
Baseops Europe Ltd. (UK)
Baseops International Inc.
Casa Petro S.R.L. (Costa Rica)
Henty Oil Limited (UK)
Marine Energy Arabia Co. (L.L.C.) (United Arab Emirates)
Nordic Camp Supply ApS (Denmark)
PetroServicios de Costa Rica S.R.L.
TGS Petroleum
The Hiller Group Incorporated
Tramp Holdings Limited (UK)
Trans-Tec International S.R.L. (Costa Rica)
Western Petroleum Company
World Fuel International S.R.L. (Costa Rica)
World Fuel Services Inc.
World Fuel Services Ltd. (UK)
World Fuel Services (Singapore) Pte. Ltd.

Selected Products and Services

Aviation
Business and General Aviation
Request an Authorization
Validate a Card
Report a Lost Card
Commercial Aviation
Deicing Services

Export Supply
Fuel Management
Risk Management
Tax Information
Marine
Marine Fuels
Lubricants
Operations
Consulting
Yacht Services
Quality Assurance
Physical Supply
Risk Management

COMPETITORS

BBA Aviation
BP Marine
Exxon Mobil
Fuchs Lubricants

Mercury Air Group
Shell Aviation
Sun Coast Resources

HISTORICAL FINANCIALS
Company Type: Public

Income Statement
FYE: December 31

	REVENUE ($ mil.)	NET INCOME ($ mil.)	NET PROFIT MARGIN	EMPLOYEES
12/18	39,750	128	0.3%	5,000
12/17	33,696	(170)	—	5,000
12/16	27,016	127	0.5%	5,000
12/15	30,380	187	0.6%	4,700
12/14	43,386	222	0.5%	4,041
Annual Growth	(2.2%)	(12.9%)	—	5.5%

2018 Year-End Financials

Debt ratio: 12.00%
Return on equity: 7.00%
Cash ($ mil.): 212
Current ratio: 1.00
Long-term debt ($ mil.): 660

No. of shares (mil.): 67
Dividends
Yield: 1.0%
Payout: 13.0%
Market value ($ mil.): 1,434

	STOCK PRICE ($) FY Close	P/E High/Low		PER SHARE ($) Earnings	Dividends	Book Value
12/18	21.00	17	11	2.00	0.00	27.00
12/17	28.00	—	—	(3.00)	0.00	25.00
12/16	46.00	28	20	2.00	0.00	28.00
12/15	38.00	22	13	3.00	0.00	27.00
12/14	47.00	16	12	3.00	0.00	26.00
Annual Growth	(17.8%)	—	—	(11.7%)	12.5%	1.3%

WORLD WIDE TECHNOLOGY HOLDING CO., LLC

EXECUTIVES

Ceo, James P Kavanaugh
Chb*, David Steward
Cfo*, Tom Strunk
Director, Holly Kriegesmann
Project Coordinator, Jennifer Barrett
Business Manager, Nicole Reichert
Project Manager, Vidhya Borade
Specialist, Jennifer Geisler
Client Director, Scott Wilson
Human Resources Manager, Paul Koetting
Project Manager, Mike Brown
Auditors: ERNST & YOUNG LLP ST LOUIS

LOCATIONS

HQ: WORLD WIDE TECHNOLOGY HOLDING CO., LLC
    1 WORLD WIDE WAY, SAINT LOUIS, MO 631463002
Phone: 314 919-1400
Web: WWW.2.WWT.COM

HISTORICAL FINANCIALS
Company Type: Private

Income Statement
FYE: December 31

	REVENUE ($ mil.)	NET INCOME ($ mil.)	NET PROFIT MARGIN	EMPLOYEES
12/14	6,702	89	1.3%	1,052
12/13	6,393	77	1.2%	—
12/12	5,041	68	1.3%	—
Annual Growth	15.3%	14.2%	—	—

WORLD WIDE TECHNOLOGY, LLC

World Wide Technology (WWT) has a broad view of its business. The company primarily provides such IT services as network design and installation systems and application integration and procurement. It also offers a range of Web-based products and services including e-commerce systems development order tracking and catalog management. WWT serves businesses in the automotive retail and telecommunications industries as well as government agencies. Top clients have included Dell the State of Missouri and the State of Alaska. WWT was founded in 1990.

Geographic Reach

WWT has more than 25 facilities throughout the world and about 2 million-sq.-ft of warehouse and distribution space in the US. It also has three distribution outlets in Brazil Mexico and Singapore as well as facilities in London; Amsterdam; Hong Kong; and Chengdu China.

Mergers and Acquisitions

In 2015 WWT purchased St. Louis-based software development firm Asynchrony. The strategic acquisition will allow WWT to deliver complete custom user-facing software and the systems and infrastructure that support it.

EXECUTIVES

Ceo, James P. (Jim) Kavanaugh
President Commercial Sales, Mark J. Catalano
Cfo, Thomas W. (Tom) Strunk
Vp Corporate Properties, Dan B. Svoboda
President, Joseph G. (Joe) Koenig
Vp Professional Services, Matt Horner
Vp Supply Chain Operations, Kurt Grimminger
Vp Global Supply Chain, Mark Franke
Vice President Of Information Technology, Mike P. Taylor
Vice President Sales Operations, Tim Loughman
Vice President Engineering And Innovation, Christopher Black
Vice President Professional Services, Tom Gain
Vice President Of Sales, John Lynch
Vice President Of Federal Sales, Bill Mckeon
Vice President Global Accounts, Leo Makhlin
Vice President Head Of Asia Pacific, Nilesh Mistry
Senior Vice President, Kraig Ecker
Vice President, Jeree Hanavec
Chairman, David L. Steward

LOCATIONS

HQ: WORLD WIDE TECHNOLOGY, LLC
    1 WORLD WIDE WAY, SAINT LOUIS, MO 631463002
Phone: 314 569-7000

PRODUCTS/OPERATIONS

Selected Services
IT Products and Solutions
  Facilities Infrastructure
  Integration and Staging
  Leasing
  Managed Services
  Order Management and Reporting

                                    Pre-Sales Support

  Value Added Reseller
Professional Services
  Configuration
  Implementation
  Planning and Design
  Training
Supply Chain Services
  Business Process Outsourcing
  Logistics/Warehousing
  Material Planning and Scheduling
  Outsourced Procurement
  Supplier Management

COMPETITORS

Accenture
Black Box
Computer Sciences
  Corp.
DataSpan
Dynamics Research
En Pointe

HP Enterprise Services
IBM Global Services
PC Mall
Rose International
Unisys
WebLinc

HISTORICAL FINANCIALS
Company Type: Private

Income Statement
FYE: December 31

	REVENUE ($ mil.)	NET INCOME ($ mil.)	NET PROFIT MARGIN	EMPLOYEES
12/15	5,928	95	1.6%	1,052
12/14	5,057	95	1.9%	—
12/13	4,546	78	1.7%	—
12/12	3,396	57	1.7%	—
Annual Growth	20.4%	18.3%	—	—

WSFS Financial Corp

WSFS isn't a radio station but it is tuned to the banking needs of Delaware. WSFS Financial is the holding company for Wilmington Savings Fund Society (WSFS Bank) a thrift with nearly $5 billion in assets and more than 75 branches mostly in Delaware and Pennsylvania. Founded in 1832 WSFS Bank attracts deposits from individuals and local businesses by offering standard products like checking and savings accounts CDs and IRAs. The bank uses funds primarily to lend to businesses: Commercial loans and mortgages account for about 85% of its loan portfolio. Bank subsidiaries Christiana Trust Cypress Capital Management and WSFS Wealth Investment provide trust and investment advisory services to wealthy clients and institutional investors.

Operations

Its Christiana Trust division boasts nearly $9 billion in assets under administration and provides investment fiduciary agency bankruptcy and commercial domicile services from offices in Delaware and Nevada.

The company's Cash Connect division operates more than 450 ATMs for WSFS Bank which boasts the largest branded ATM network in Delaware. The division also manages some $490 million of vault cash in approximately 15000 ATMs nationwide and provides online reporting and ATM cash management predictive cash ordering armored carrier management and ATM processing and equipment sales.

Overall the bank generated roughly 57% of its total revenue from interest and fees on loans in 2014 plus an additional 10% from interest on its mortgage-back and other investment securities. About 7% of its total revenue came from wealth management income while mortgage banking income contributed another 2%. The majority of the remaining revenue came from credit/debit card and ATM income and deposit service charges.

Geographic Reach

WSFS Bank has 45 branches throughout Delaware nearly 10 branches in Pennsylvania one branch in Nevada and one in Virginia.

Financial Performance

WSFS Financial's revenues and profits have been trending higher in recent years thanks to sustained growth in its lending business organically and through acquisitions and thanks to declining loan loss provisions as its loan portfolio's credit quality has improved with the strengthened economy.

The company's revenue rose by 5% to $238.62 million in 2014 thanks to interest income growth mostly driven by increased loan business and higher securities interest; which stemmed from a combination of the bank's First Wyoming Financial Corporation acquisition improvements in its balance sheet mix and additional income from its reverse mortgage-related assets.

Higher revenue and a continued decline in loan loss provisions in 2014 pushed WSFS Financial's net income up by 15% to $53.73 million during the year while the company's operating cash levels jumped by 17% to $67.06 million thanks to higher cash earnings.

Strategy

WSFS Financial reiterated its long-term growth strategy in 2015 which included growing the bank's lending business boosting its Trust and Wealth Management group's assets under administration and expanding Cash Connect's ATM customer base and customer cross-sell.

Beyond utilizing its community-oriented and local commercial lending teams the company has been growing its loan business and its branch reach through strategic acquisitions of banks and bank branches in target markets with preference toward markets in southeastern Pennsylvania. Its 2014 acquisition of First Wyoming Financial Corp for example bolstered WSFS' presence in Kent county while strengthening its position as the one of Delaware's top independent community banks.

Mergers and Acquisitions

In mid-2018 WSFS Financial agreed to purchase Philadelphia-based Beneficial Bancorp in a deal worth $1.5 billion. The transaction will create the largest locally headquartered community bank in the Greater Delaware Valley region with about $13 billion in assets.

EXECUTIVES

Chairman President And Ceo, Mark A. Turner, age 56, $639,336 total compensation
Evp And Chief Risk Officer, Thomas W. Kearney
Evp And Chief Retail Banking Officer, Richard M. (Rick) Wright, age 66, $337,173 total compensation

Evp And Coo, Rodger Levenson, age 57, $348,721 total compensation
Evp And Chief Human Capital Officer, Peggy H. Eddens, age 63
Evp And Chief Wealth Officer, Paul D. Geraghty, $310,671 total compensation
Evp And Cto, S. James (Jim) Mazarakis, $337,173 total compensation
President Cash Connect, Tom Stevenson
Cfo, Dominic Canuso
Vice President Retail Banking, Adrienne Hawes
Senior Vice President And General Counsel, John Olsen
Senior Vice President Middle Market Team Leader, James Gise
Senior Vice President, Dennis Matarangas
Executive Vice President Human Resources, Robert Silwa
Vp Division Controller, Ruth Mcdevitt
Assistant Vice President Network Services Director, Jason Berkowitz
Vice President Audit Manager, Rene Lopez
Vice President Retail Office Manager, Patricia Frechette
Executive Vice President, Cynthia Cole
Executive Vice President Chief Commercial Banking Officer, Steve Clark
Assistant Vice President Small Business Lender Retail Office Manager, Carol Brindle
Senior Vice President Commercial R E Lending, Joseph C Walker
Executive Vice President And Chief Commercial Banking Officer, Stephen Null Clark
Vice President Financial Advisor, Nick Frake
Assistant Vice President, Paul Roughton
Avp Facilities Manager, Bill Hornung
Senior Vice President And Director, Steven G Kochie
Assistant Vice President Digital Banking And Payments Solutions Manager, Chris Zupko
Assistant Vice President T, Nicole Monroe-cole
Assistant Vice President Senior Training Specialist, Marcedes Carter
Avp Asset Recovery Relationship Manager, William Madgey
Vice President Credit Card Product Management, Paul Brutsche
Vp Directorgovernment Guaranteed Lending, Candice Caruso
Vice President Small Business Relationship Manager, Amy Flynn
Vice President Sba Lending, Tom Dowling
Avp Retail Office Manager, Chris Graham
Vice President Regional Manager, Jeremy Shackleford
Board Member, Marvin Schoenhals
Vice Chairman, Charles G. Cheleden, age 75
Board Member, Jennifer Davis
Board Member, Eleuthere Du Pont
Board Member, Christopher Ghysens
Auditors: KPMG LLP

LOCATIONS

HQ: WSFS Financial Corp
500 Delaware Avenue, Wilmington, DE 19801
Phone: 302 792-6000
Web: www.wsfsbank.com

2012 Branches

	No.
Delaware	42
Pennsylvania	7
Nevada	1
Virginia	1
Total	**51**

PRODUCTS/OPERATIONS

2014 Sales

	$ mil.	% of total
Interest		
Loans including fees	137	57
Mortgage-backed securities	14	6
Investment securities	10	4
Noninterest		
Credit/debit card & ATM income	24	11
Deposit service charges	17	7
Wealth management income	17	7
Mortgage baning activities	4	2
Other	16	6
Total	**239**	**100**

COMPETITORS

Bank of America	M&T Bank
Citizens Financial Group	PNC Financial
	Sovereign Bank
Fulton Financial	TD Bank USA
JPMorgan Chase	The Bancorp

HISTORICAL FINANCIALS

Company Type: Public

Income Statement
FYE: December 31

	ASSETS ($ mil.)	NET INCOME ($ mil.)	INCOME AS % OF ASSETS	EMPLOYEES
12/18	7,249	135	1.9%	1,177
12/17	7,000	50	0.7%	1,159
12/16	6,765	64	0.9%	1,116
12/15	5,586	54	1.0%	947
12/14	4,853	54	1.1%	841
Annual Growth	10.5%	25.8%	—	8.8%

2018 Year-End Financials

Debt ratio: 2.00%	No. of shares (mil.): 31
Return on equity: 17.00%	Dividends
Cash ($ mil.): 621	Yield: 1.0%
Current ratio: —	Payout: 10.0%
Long-term debt ($ mil.): —	Market value ($ mil.): 1,189

	STOCK PRICE ($) FY Close	P/E High/Low		PER SHARE ($) Earnings	Dividends	Book Value
12/18	38.00	13	9	4.00	0.00	26.00
12/17	48.00	33	27	2.00	0.00	23.00
12/16	46.00	22	13	2.00	0.00	22.00
12/15	32.00	42	13	2.00	0.00	20.00
12/14	77.00	40	33	2.00	0.00	17.00
Annual Growth	(16.2%)	—		21.4%	25.4%	10.8%

Wynn Resorts Ltd

Wynn Resorts operates a handful of luxury casino resorts including the Wynn Las Vegas in Las Vegas and the Wynn Macau and the Wynn Palace in Macau China the only place in China where gambling is legal. It opened its first US resort and casino outside Vegas the $2.6 billion Encore Boston Harbor in June 2019. The company's properties integrate luxury hotel rooms high-end retail an array of dining and entertainment options meeting and convention space and gaming. Most revenue comes from China. The firm works to attract international customers through marketing offices in Hong Kong Singapore Japan Taiwan and Canada. The Wynn brand is the brainchild of gaming mogul and former Mirage Resorts chairman Steve Wynn.

Operations

Wynn Resorts gets about 70% of its revenue from its casino segment; more than 10% from food and drink; and more than 10% from hotel rooms fees. The remainder comes from entertainment retail and other operations.

In Macau China its Wynn Palace features a luxury hotel tower with more than 1700 guest rooms approximately 425000 square feet of casino space some 37000 square feet of meeting and convention space and more than 105000 square feet of retail space. Its smaller Chinese property Wynn Macau features two hotel towers with more than 1000 rooms along with casino and retail space and meeting and convention rooms.

Wynn Las Vegas boasts two hotel towers with more than 4700 rooms and space for casino gaming meetings and conventions and retail.

The company's newest property Encore Boston Harbor is a resort in Everett Massachusetts near Boston along the Mystic River. The resort contains a hotel a waterfront boardwalk meeting and convention space casino space a spa retail offerings and food and beverage outlets.

Geographic Reach

Wynn Resorts owns approximately 72% of its operations in China (Wynn Macau Limited) and 100% of its operations in the US (Wynn Las Vegas). Highly dependent on consumer spending in China the company generates some 75% of total revenues from Macau while Las Vegas accounts for the remaining 25%.

Sales and Marketing

Wynn Resorts offers loyalty programs at its properties. Customers who earn points redeem them for free play gifts and complimentary dining and retail shopping. It seeks to attract high-networth international tourists to its properties.

The company spent $41 million on advertising and promotional expenses in fiscal 2018 up from about $38 million in fiscal 2017.

Financial Performance

Wynn Resorts has reported year-over-year revenue growth since 2015 thanks in part to the strength of the gambling industry in the US and a rebound in Macau casinos. Any sudden downturn in Macau will hinder earnings despite costly upgrades and new hotels. The company has also demonstrated commitment to growth through development and expansion of its properties. The company has reported positive net income over the last five years with profits reaching a low of $295 million in 2015 and a high of $747 million in 2017.

Wynn reported more than $6.7 billion in revenue for fiscal 2018 versus $6.1 billion in fiscal 2017. The increase was largely the result of increases in VIP turnover and table drop at Wynn Palace in Macau.

In 2018 net income dropped 23% from the prior year to reach $572.4 million. The company attributes the decrease to a litigation settlement expense related to founder and former Chairman and CEO Steve Wynn and his separation from the company over sexual harassment allegations.

Cash at the end of 2018 was $2.2 billion. Cash from operations was $961.5 million while investing activities used $1.2 billion. Financing activities used $324.3 million.

Strategy

Wynn Resorts regularly seeks opportunities to expand or enhance its existing properties as well as develop new ones. It is currently investing big in development renovation and remodeling projects at its Las Vegas and Macau properties and in 2019 opened a new resort outside Boston.

In Las Vegas it is constructing some 430000 square feet of additional meeting and convention space and has begun plans to reconfigure its golf course. Wynn is also exploring various development opportunities on about 38 acres of land on the Las Vegas Strip directly across from Wynn Las Vegas.

In China it is remodeling its Wynn Club gaming area at Wynn Macau adding table games a refurbished high-limit slot area two new restaurants and retail space and will provide for improved pedestrian access. In 2019 Wynn Resorts announced plans to spend $2 billion on expanding Wynn Palace. Construction will start in 2021 and is expected to take 36-plus months.

Amid these growth efforts the company was embroiled in controversy when its founder Steve Wynn was hit with sexual assault charges from Wynn Resorts' employees in 2018. He resigned less than a month after The Wall Street Journal reported on the allegations and in February 2019 regulators in Nevada fined the company $20 million for ignoring complaints about Wynn's behavior. The fine was the largest ever imposed against a gambling licensee in Nevada. Wynn Resorts responded with statements that it is committed to maintaining a safe and respectful culture requires annual anti-harassment training for all and offers an anonymous hotline.

Company Background

Steve Wynn founded Wynn Resorts in after buying the Desert Inn hotel and casino in Las Vegas for $270 million from Starwood Hotels & Resorts as a birthday gift for his new wife in 2000. The deal followed his sale of Mirage Resorts to MGM Grand. Wynn reportedly received nearly $500 million from the Mirage sale.

Wynn resigned as chairman and CEO in 2018 in response to sexual misconduct allegations spanning decades.

EXECUTIVES

President, Matt Maddox, age 43, $1,500,000 total compensation

Evp General Counsel And Secretary, Kim Sinatra, age 58, $873,654 total compensation

Chairman And Ceo, Stephen A. Wynn, age 77, $2,500,000 total compensation

President Wynn International Marketing, Linda Chen, age 52, $1,500,000 total compensation

President Wynn Resorts (macau), Ian M. Coughlan, age 60

Coo Wynn Las Vegas, Maurice Wooden

President And Coo Wynn Design & Development, John Littell

Cfo, Craig S. Billings

Vice President Of Uniforms, Jacque Phillips

Svp Entertainment Production, Joe Leone

Executive Vice President, Brian Gullbrants

Vice President Human Resources, Troy Mitchum

National Sales Manager, Laurae Clifford

Vice President Benefits, Elaine Lo

Executive Vice President Of Casino Operations, Debra Nutton

Vice President Player Development, Maryann Pascal

Vice President Player Development, Stephen Battaglini

Vice President Sales And Marketing, Karolyn Graves

Vice President Of International Marketing, Pete Lexis

Vice President Of Facilities, Marty Brown

Vice President Of Purchasing, Laura Herzog

Vice President Of Korean Marketing, Charlie Kim

Svp Hr North America, Rose Huddleston

Executive Vice President Of Hotel Sales And Marketing, Chrisann Flatt

Auditors: Ernst & Young LLP

LOCATIONS

HQ: Wynn Resorts Ltd
3131 Las Vegas Boulevard South, Las Vegas, NV 89109
Phone: 702 770-7555
Web: www.wynnresorts.com

PRODUCTS/OPERATIONS

2016 Sales

	$ mil.	% of total
Casino	3,268	68
Food and Beverages	603	12
Rooms	602	12
Entertainment Retail and Others	363	8
Promotional Allowances	(370.1)	-
Total	**4,466**	**100**

2016 Sales

	$ mil.	% of total
Macau Operations	2,847	64
Las Vegas Operations	1,619	36
Total	**4,466**	**100**

Properties

Properties
Las Vegas
  Wynn Las Vegas
  Encore at Wynn Las Vegas
Macau China
  Wynn Macau
  Encore at Wynn Macau

COMPETITORS

Boyd Gaming	Marriott
Caesars Entertainment	Melco Crown
Carnival plc	Entertainment
Emperor Entertainment	Priceline
Hotel	Riviera Holdings
Golden Resorts	SJM
Hard Rock Hotel	Starwood Hotels &
Hyatt	Resorts
Las Vegas Sands	Station Casinos
MGM Resorts	

HISTORICAL FINANCIALS

Company Type: Public

Income Statement

FYE: December 31

	REVENUE ($ mil.)	NET INCOME ($ mil.)	NET PROFIT MARGIN	EMPLOYEES
12/18	6,718	572	8.5%	26,000
12/17	6,306	747	11.8%	25,200
12/16	4,466	242	5.4%	24,600
12/15	4,076	195	4.8%	20,800
12/14	5,434	732	13.5%	16,800
Annual Growth	5.4%	(5.9%)	—	11.5%

2018 Year-End Financials

Debt ratio: 71.00%	No. of shares (mil.): 107
Return on equity: 38.00%	Dividends
Cash ($ mil.): 2,215	Yield: 3.0%
Current ratio: 1.00	Payout: 48.0%
Long-term debt ($ mil.): 9,411	Market value ($ mil.): 10,606

	STOCK PRICE ($) FY Close	P/E High/Low	PER SHARE ($) Earnings	Dividends	Book Value
12/18	99.00	38 17	5.00	3.00	19.00
12/17	169.00	23 12	7.00	2.00	9.00
12/16	87.00	45 22	2.00	2.00	2.00
12/15	69.00	83 27	2.00	3.00	(1.00)
12/14	149.00	34 19	7.00	6.00	(0.00)
Annual Growth	(9.7%)	— —	(7.1%)	(18.6%)	—

Xcel Energy Inc

Xcel Energy is a utility holding company distributing electricity to 3.6 million customers and natural gas to 2 million in eight states through its four regulated utilities: Northern States Power Minnesota Northern States Power Wisconsin the Public Service Company of Colorado and Southwestern Public Service. Colorado and Minnesota account for most of the company's customers. Xcel owns power plants that have combined capacity of more than 18200 MW of electricity. It also owns transmission and distribution lines as well as natural gas assets. It is investing in wind power and operates wind farms in Colorado Minnesota and a half-a-dozen other states. The company traces its roots back to 1881.

Operations

Xcel Energy's reportable segments are Regulated Electric Utility Regulated Gas Utility and Other. Regulated Electric is the largest segment producing about 85% of total revenue through the generation purchase transmission and distribution of electricity. Regulated Natural Gas transports stores and distributes natural gas to generate most of the remaining revenue.

The two power segments achieve their objectives through several subsidiaries: Northern States Power Minnesota (NSP-M) Northern States Power Wisconsin (NSP-W) the Public Service Company of Colorado (PSCo) and Southwestern Public Service (SPS).

Xcel owns and operates roughly 18200 MW of electric generating capacity and purchases additional power from third parties through long-term power purchase agreements. Generally Xcel's power plants produce about two-thirds of its needs and the company purchases the other third. Of its generated electricity a third comes from coal another third comes from natural gas 15% comes from nuclear and the rest is generated from wind hydroelectric and other sources.

The Regulated Natural Gas segment purchases the natural gas from producers and contracts with transmission pipeline companies to move it to Xcel's distributions facilities. From there the company sends natural gas to customers.

Xcel's Other segment generates about 1% of the company?s revenue and includes steam revenue appliance repair services and non-utility real estate activities.

Geographic Reach

Minneapolis Minnesota-based Xcel Energy serves a number of US states. It's Northern States Power Minnesota serves 2 million customers in North and South Dakota and in Minnesota. Northern States Power Wisconsin delivers energy to about 400000 customers in Wisconsin and Michigan. Public Service Company of Colorado provides energy to 2.9 million customers throughout the state while Southwestern Public Service Company serves nearly 400000 in New Mexico and Texas.

Xcel's supply of natural gas comes from basins in Colorado Montana Wyoming Texas Kansas New Mexico and Canada.

Sales and Marketing

Xcel Energy's major commercial and industrial electric sales are to customers in the petroleum coal and food products industries. The company also serves small commercial and industrial customers. Commercial and industrial customers account for nearly half of the company's total revenue.

Residential customers account for a third of Xcel's revenue.

Financial Performance

As is true with electric service companies Xcel Energy's revenue has remained essentially unchanged over the past five years.

In 2018 revenue rose 1% to $11.5 billion with both electricity and natural gas revenue increasing slightly from the previous year. The amount of delivered electricity (kilowatt hours) was up primarily due to favorable weather conditions.

Net income in 2018 rose to $1.2 billion up $113 million from the previous year. While operating expenses were higher in 2018 the company paid less in income taxes than it did in the previous period which resulted in the modest bottom line increase.

Cash at the end of the year was $147 million up $64 million from the previous period. Operating activities provided $3.1 billion investing activities (mostly capital expenditures) used $3.9 billion and financing activities provided $928 million largely through issuance of additional debt.

Xcel carries a hefty long-term debt load. In 2018 the company held $15.8 billion in debt and has become more leveraged over the past five years. Just a few years prior in 2014 Xcel's long-term debt sat at $11.5 billion.

Strategy

Like many electricity companies Xcel Energy is pursuing a long-term shift towards carbon-neutral and renewable energy sources. It also invests in its infrastructure modernizing its grid for safety security and reliability. In the coming five years it anticipates spending $20.1 billion on such projects.

Infrastructure will receive the lion's share of the $20.1 billion in capital expenditures planned for the 2019-2023 period. Electric transmission & gas distribution systems are targeted to receive about $10 billion electric generation (such as maintenance of power facilities and refueling nuclear plants) is earmarked for $2.9 billion. Input fuel ? mainly natural gas ? is allotted $2.3 billion while the build-outs of its renewable wind and solar energy resources are expected to receive $3.6 billion.

Company Background

The Minnesota Electric Light & Electric Motive Power Company was founded in 1881 and changed its name to Minnesota Brush Electric the next year. In the 1890s it provided street lighting and power for trolleys and became Minneapolis General Electric.

In 1909 Henry Byllesby formed rival firm Washington County Light and Power Co. (soon renamed Consumers Power Company) then created holding company Northern States Power Company of Delaware (NSPD). In 1910 he founded Standard Gas and Electric a holding company overseeing NSPD and many other US utilities.

The company took on its most recent incarnation as Xcel Energy in August 2000 following the merger of Northern States Power Company and New Century Energies Inc.

HISTORY

The Minnesota Electric Light & Electric Motive Power Company was founded in 1881 and changed its name to Minnesota Brush Electric the next year. In the 1890s it provided street lighting and power for trolleys and became Minneapolis General Electric.

In 1909 Henry Byllesby formed rival firm Washington County Light and Power Co. (soon renamed Consumers Power Company) then created holding company Northern States Power Company of Delaware (NSPD). In 1910 he founded Standard Gas and Electric a holding company overseeing NSPD and many other US utilities.

NSPD bought Minneapolis General Electric in 1912 and Consumers Power was renamed the Northern States Power Company (NSP) in 1916. During the 1920s NSPD connected its subsidiaries via transmission lines. Byllesby died in 1924.

In 1931 NSP was placed under NSPD but the Public Utility Holding Company Act of 1935 dissolved Standard and NSPD. NSP became independent in the 1940s and spent $335 million on new facilities after WWII.

During the 1960s NSP moved into Michigan South Dakota and Wisconsin and brought its first nuclear power plant on line in 1964 (converted to natural gas in 1968). It began operating the Monticello and Prairie Island nukes in the early 1970s.

Company sales nearly doubled in the 1980s. In 1989 NSP created NRG Energy (incorporated 1992) to invest in independent power projects. The Federal Energy Policy Act allowed wholesale power competition in 1992 and NSP lost nine of its 19 municipal customers.

NSP acquired Viking Gas Transmission which owned an interstate pipeline in 1993. It also began developing affordable housing. In 1995 NSP and Wisconsin Electric planned to merge but dropped the deal amid antitrust concerns. NSP continued to diversify forming telecommunications provider Seren Innovations in 1996 and starting its cable-testing business in 1997. The next year NSP formed a power marketing unit.

NRG Energy began a shopping spree abroad in 1994 buying interests in plants in Germany and Australia. In 1996 it bought a 48% stake in Bolivia's COBEE (increased to 99% in 2001). Also that year it acquired PacifiCorp's Pacific Generating unit which owned stakes in a dozen geographically scattered plants.

In 1999 NRG Energy gained nearly 7600 MW of capacity through power plant acquisitions in California Connecticut Massachusetts and New York. The next year NRG Energy picked up another 1700 MW in Louisiana and it agreed to buy fossil-fueled plants (1875 MW) from Delaware's Conectiv for $800 million (half of the deal was completed in 2001 the other half was canceled the following year). NSP spun off part of NRG in 2000 in an IPO.

Meanwhile as the utility-merger trend gathered steam in 1999 NSP agreed to acquire Denver-based New Century Engines in a $4.9 billion deal. The acquisition was completed in 2000 and the expanded company changed its name to Xcel Energy.

The next year Xcel sold nearly all of its stake in UK-based Yorkshire Power Group which had been held by New Century Energies to Innogy (now RWE npower). It sold its remaining 5% stake in Yorkshire Power in 2002. NRG purchased several Latin American projects from Swedish utility Vattenfall in 2001. NRG also agreed to purchase four coal-fired plants (2500 MW) in Ohio from FirstEnergy for $1.5 billion; however the deal was later canceled.

In 2002 Xcel repurchased the 26% stake in NRG that it sold to the public in 2000-01.

EXECUTIVES

Evp And Group President Operations, Kent T. Larson, age 59, $550,000 total compensation

Chairman President And Ceo, Benjamin G. S. (Ben) Fowke, age 61, $1,200,000 total compensation

President Xcel Energy - Colorado, David L. Eves, age 61

Svp And Cio, David C. Harkness

Evp And Group President Utilities And Chief Administrative Officer, Marvin E. McDaniel, age 59, $550,000 total compensation

President Xcel Energy Michigan Wisconsin, Mark E. Stoering, age 58

Svp And Chief Nuclear Officer, Timothy (Tim) O'Connor, age 59

President Xcel Energy New Mexico Texas, David T. Hudson, age 58

President Xcel Energy Minnesota South Dakota North Dakota, Christopher B. (Chris) Clark, age 52

Evp And General Counsel, Scott M. Willensky, age 62, $505,000 total compensation

Evp And Cfo, Robert C. (Bob) Frenzel, age 48, $397,500 total compensation

Chief Sales Officer, Candace Morse

Evp And General Counsel, Scott Wilensky

Vice President Gas Operations, Luke Litteken

Vice President Construction Operations And Maintenance, Tim Brossart

Vice President, Sarah Soong

Auditors: DELOITTE & TOUCHE LLP

LOCATIONS

HQ: Xcel Energy Inc
 414 Nicollet Mall, Minneapolis, MN 55401
Phone: 612 330-5500
Web: www.xcelenergy.com

PRODUCTS/OPERATIONS

2018 Sales

	$ mil.	% of total
Electric	9,719	84
Natural Gas	1,739	15
Other	79	1
Total	**11,537**	**100**

COMPETITORS

AEP	CenterPoint Energy
ALLETE	DTE
Alliant Energy	FirstEnergy
Ameren	NextEra Energy
Atmos Energy	OGE Energy
Basin Electric Power	PPL Corporation
Black Hills Power	WEC Energy
CMS Energy	

HISTORICAL FINANCIALS

Company Type: Public

Income Statement   FYE: December 31

	REVENUE ($ mil.)	NET INCOME ($ mil.)	NET PROFIT MARGIN	EMPLOYEES
12/18	11,537	1,261	10.9%	11,092
12/17	11,404	1,148	10.1%	11,134
12/16	11,107	1,123	10.1%	11,512
12/15	11,024	984	8.9%	11,687
12/14	11,686	1,021	8.7%	11,691
Annual Growth	(0.3%)	5.4%	—	(1.3%)

2018 Year-End Financials

Debt ratio: 38.00%	No. of shares (mil.): 514
Return on equity: 11.00%	Dividends
Cash ($ mil.): 147	Yield: 3.0%
Current ratio: 1.00	Payout: 63.0%
Long-term debt ($ mil.): 15,803	Market value ($ mil.): 25,327

	STOCK PRICE ($) FY Close	P/E High/Low		PER SHARE ($) Earnings	Dividends	Book Value
12/18	49.00	22	17	2.00	2.00	24.00
12/17	48.00	23	18	2.00	1.00	23.00
12/16	41.00	21	16	2.00	1.00	22.00
12/15	36.00	20	16	2.00	1.00	21.00
12/14	36.00	18	13	2.00	1.00	20.00
Annual Growth	8.2%	—	—	5.0%	6.1%	4.2%

Xerox Holdings Corp

Xerox Corp. is not a copy of its former self. The company whose name has been a synonym for "to copy" remains a leading seller of copiers and printers from basic black-and-white output to high-end color systems. These days Xerox makes most of its revenue from its post-sale services such as document management maintenance supplies and paper and financing. Xerox also sells software for automating and integrating print jobs from start to finish. Its products are used in offices of large and small- and medium-sized businesses and in production plants of commercial printing companies. US customers account for about 60% of revenue.

Operations

Xerox makes machines that make copies print send faxes scan documents and more as well as the ink paper and support that keeps the equipment running. The company charges from a few hundred to thousands of dollars for its equipment but it makes 80% of its revenue from those post-sale products and services.

Xerox manages its offerings in three segments: Intelligent Workplace Services Workplace Solutions and Product Solutions.

Intelligent Workplace Services helps customers get the most out of their printing and related document workflow and business processes

Workplace Solutions consists of Xerox's Entry and Mid-Range equipment products which share common technology manufacturing and product platforms.

Services offered by the Production Solutions business are for customers in the graphic communications in-plant and production print environments with high-volume printing requirements.

Geographic Reach

Although Xerox Corp. operates in more than 160 countries about 60% of sales are from customers in the US. About 30% of sales are from Europe with the rest of the world accounting for the rest.

The company has primary facilities in Canada France India Ireland Jamaica Guatemala Mexico the Netherlands the Philippines Romania the UK and the US.

Xerox outsources a significant amount of its manufacturing to third parties while maintaining its own production facilities in the US Ireland France and the Netherlands.

Sales and Marketing

Xerox complements its global sales team and sales website with a network of third-party sales channels such as independent agents dealers value-added resellers and systems integrators.

The Xerox brand is well-known (the company has been around for about 115 years) and its customers are in a wide range of businesses that include banking education government healthcare manufacturing and graphic arts.

Financial Performance

Xerox's revenue remained on a years-long slide in 2018 falling to $9.8 billion down 4% from 2017 as the company's equipment business continued to lose ground. The company has shed about $2.8 billion of revenue since 2014.

In 2018 equipment sales were 7% lower than in 2017 although sales of entry and mid-level machines increased. Sales of higher-end higher margin equipment however dropped 9% for color systems and 18% for black-and-white systems. Revenue from the post-sale segment slipped 4% in 2018 from 2017 because of fewer signings and installations.

Xerox's profit popped 85% higher to $361 million in 2018 up $166 million from 2017 boosted by cost reductions that offset revenue declines.

The company's cash and equivalents stood at $1.1 billion in 2018 compared to $1.3 billion in 2017. Operations generated $1.1 billion in 2018 while investing activities used $29 million and financing activities used $1.3 billion (including $700 million in stock buybacks).

Xerox has substantial debt ($4.2 billion in long-term debt) and other obligations that could increase its vulnerability to economic downturns and limit its ability to obtain financing for working capital capital expenditures acquisitions and other general corporate uses.

Strategy

Xerox is a well-known name in corporate America but it might not carry the gleam of innovation that the company would like. Its sales have declined over the past five years as its copiers and printers have elicited little excitement in the market. The company is moving to change that with new technologies and increased efficiency.

Xerox prioritizes technology development in four areas: Digital packaging and print 3D printing and digital manufacturing artificial intelligence capabilities and sensors and services for the Internet of Things. One of the company's recent offerings was its ConnectKey software that allows Xerox devices to integrate into digital workflows.

The company is also taking steps to make its operations more efficient by increasing use of shared service centers consolidating its IT infrastructure and real estate footprint and speeding up its supply chain. It plans to get $640 million of cost savings in 2019 as part of $1.5 billion in savings between 2019 and 2021. In a related matter Xerox plans to merge into a holding company which it said would eliminate duplicate administrative requirements and costs. The move was approved by shareholders but needs regulatory approval.

To improve its overall sales structure Xerox reorganized its geographic units into two the Americas and Europe the Middle East and Africa (EMEA). The Americas region combines the US Canada Mexico Central and South America while India becomes part of the EMEA region.

Mergers and Acquisitions

Xerox made no acquisitions in 2018. In 2017 it bought: Global Imaging Systems a multiple-brand dealer in Iowa and MT Business Technologies a multi-brand dealer in Ohio; Intellinex a Seattle-based provider of outsourced learning services; RSA Medical a provider of health assessment and risk management for members interacting with health and life insurance companies; Healthy Communities Institute a California-based company with a cloud platform for health analytics; and inVentiv Patient Access Solutions a patient access and reimbursement services hub.

Company Background

The Haloid Co. was incorporated in 1906 to make and sell photographic paper. In 1935 it bought photocopier company Rectigraph which led Haloid to buy a license for a process called electrophotography (renamed xerography from the ancient Greek words for "dry" and "writing") from the Battelle Memorial Institute in 1947.

Haloid commercialized xerography with the Model A copier in 1949 and the Xerox Copyflo in 1955 and by 1956 xerographic products represented 40% of sales. The company changed its name to Haloid Xerox in 1958 (Haloid was dropped from the name in 1961) and in 1959 it introduced the first simplified office copier. That machine took the world by storm beating out such competing technologies as mimeograph (A.B.Dick) thermal paper (3M) and damp copy (Kodak). Sales soared to nearly $270 million in 1965.

EXECUTIVES

Evp And Chief Commercial Officer, Kevin M. Warren, age 56

Ceo, Jeffrey (Jeff) Jacobson, age 59, $812,500 total compensation

President Xerox Canada, John Corley

Evp; President International Operations, Hervé Tessler, age 55

Svp And Chief Strategy And Marketing Officer, Farooq Muzaffar, age 44

Evp; President North America Operations, Michael (Mike) Feldman, age 52

Evp And Chief Human Resources Officer, Darrell L. Ford, age 54

Svp And Chief Delivery Officer, Yehia Maaty

Evp And Cfo, William F. (Bill) Osbourn, age 54

Svp And Cto, Stephen (Steve) Hoover, age 58

President Northern Southern And Central European Operations, Al Varney

Evp General Counsel And Corporate Secretary, Sarah Hlavinka McConnell, age 54

Assistant Vice President Information Technology Vendor Management, James Burnell

Vice President And Center Manager, Monica Beltrametti

Senior Vice President Of Technology, Stephen Garner

Senior Vice President And Managing Director Xerox Healthcare Provider Solutions, Justin Lanning

Vice President Of Sales, Michael Hartman

Vice President And Center Manager, Hadi Mahabadi

Svp Sales - It Outsourcing, George Love

Vice President Information Technology, Karin Gleissle

Vice President And General Manager, Jack Lafferty

Vice President, Ajay Dhingra

Vice President Sales, Peter Reynolds

Vice President, Ivy McKinney

Vice President Of Engineering And Product Development, Doug Jenkins

Corporate Vice President And Chief Financial Officer Xerox Technology Business, Grant Fitz

Vice President Of Strategy And Alliances, Tom Kavassalis

Vice President Global Advertising, Barbara Basney

Vice President Client Support Services, Linda Harrison

Vice President And General Manager, Steve Simpson

Vice President Technical Services Mountan Operations, Michael Styles

Vice President Client Services, Michael Sheridan

Vice President Industry Marketing, Dale Sedgwick

Vice President Information Technology Program Services, Tracy Johnson

Vice President, Michael Weldon

Vice President Operations North Dakota, Greg Bryant

Vp Media Entertainment Hospitality Travel Vertical, Scott Aiken

National Sales Manager, David Stahler

Vice President Strategy And Workplace Services, David Nappi

Vice President Global Delivery Im Group, Robert Lyubomirsky

Sbu Division Vice President, Jim Selwood

Vice President National Field Controller, Nate Loomis

Vice President, Shreve Bill

Vice President, Dick Jennings

Vice President Of Business Development, Matt Bologna

Xsbg Vice President Of Finance, Enos Steve

Vice President, Terence Oi

National Account Manager, Friedman Karen

Vice President Of Operations, Jeff Dalrymple

Vice President Service, Betty Mitchell

Vice President Finance Us Solutions Group, Dave Aquilla

Vpse, Jules Roche

Vice President Mps Business Operations, Robert Coward

National Account Manager, Amanda Carmichael

Vice President, Eric West

Vice President, Carl R Bothner

Senior Vice President, Joe Valenti

Division Vice President, Rebecca Taylor

Vice President Sales Operations, Brian Cannatelli

Senior Vice President, Nicola Posa

Vice President, Gavin Jordan-smith

Vice President Of Operations Travel And Retail, Patrick White

Vice President, Bob Tisone

Vice President Operations, Tom Hinds

Assistant Vice President Recruiting Operations, Craig Deaton

Vice President Human Resources And Administration, George Dourlias

Assistant Vice President Talent Acquisition And Staffing, Darrin Johnson

Vice President Sales, Dennis Antishin

Assistant Vice President Talent Leader Executive And Corporate Talent, James Munson

Vice President Business Development, Gloria D'Arezzo

Vice President Human Resources, Jamie Son

Vice President Of Sales Commercial Health Plans, Robert Levy

Vice President Of Sales, Tami Angelo

Vice President Applications And Project Management Office, Kim Ringold

Sbu Director And Vice President, Tom Boyle

Vice President And Senior Corporate Counsel Legal, Don Delorenz

Senior Vice President Southwest Operations, Mary Nelson

Vice President Midrange Hosting, Martin Webb

Senior Vice President Global Service Operations An, Jimmy Brown

Senior Vice President Managing Director Hro Services, Esther Laspisa

Assistant Vice President, Daneen Muto

Vice President Corporate Counsel, Priscilla K Park

Vice President Of Corporate Internet Marketing, Duane Schulz

Vice President Information Technology, Tim Lilly

Corporate Vice President And Chief Accounting Officer, Joseph Mancini

Vice President Contracts, Bruce Eddy

Vice President Atlantic Operations, Christianna Kellman

Vice President, Jeffrey Dalrymple

Vice President Sales And Operations, Douglas Chastain

Vice President Strategic Alliances, Scott Bartos

Vp And Gm Marketing Communications Channel Group Operations Uk And Director, Mark Duffelen

Vice President Epic Solutions, Bradford Grow

Vice President Production Inkjet Sales, Steve Welkley

Pa To Bertrand Cerisier Vice President Global Marketing Office Solutions Business Group, Tracy Styles

Vice President Corporate Communications, Kevin Lightfoot

Vice President Quality, John Lawerence

Svp Acquisitions Corporate Services And Marketing Global Imaging Systems, Michael Pietrunti

Vice President Sales And Marketing, Valerie Keating

Svp Chief Communications And Brand Officer, Anne Marie Squeo

Chairman, Robert J. (Bob) Keegan, age 72

Secretary, Jonathan Verna

Secretary, Habiba Soares

Auditors: PricewaterhouseCoopers LLP

LOCATIONS

HQ: Xerox Holdings Corp
P.O. Box 4505, 201 Merritt 7, Norwalk, CT 06851-1056
Phone: 203 968-3000
Web: www.xerox.com

2018 Sales

	$ mil.	% of total
US	5,778	58
Europe	2,625	27
Canada	569	6
Other	858	9
Total	**10,265**	**100**

PRODUCTS/OPERATIONS

2018 Sales

	$ mil.	% of total
Post-sales	2200	78
Equipment sales	7,630	22
Total	**9,830**	**100**

2018 Sales

	$ mil.	% of total
Sales	3,972	40
Services	5,590	57
Financing	268	3
Total	**9,830**	**100**

2018

	$ mil.	% of total
Equipment	2,200	22
Supplies paper and other	1,772	18
Maintenance agreements	2,469	25
Service arrangements	2,426	25
Rental and other	695	7
Financing	268	3
Total	**9,830**	**100**

Selected Services

Banking Industry Solutions
Communication & Marketing
Document Management Landing
Document Transaction Processing Services
Education Solutions
Enterprise Content Management
Government Solutions
Healthcare Industry Solutions
Managed Print Services
Manufacturing Industry Solutions
Retail Industry Solutions
Workflow Automation

Selected Products

Office (commercial government and education sectors)
  Copiers
  Displays
  Multifunction devices (copy fax print scan)
  Printers
  Projectors
  Scanners
Production (graphics communications industry and large corporations)
  Digital presses
  High-volume printers
  Software
Other
  Services
  Wide-format printers

COMPETITORS

Brother Industries	Lexmark
Canon	NEC
Epson	Océ
FUJIFILM	Oki Data
Fujitsu	Panasonic Corp
HP	Pitney Bowes
Heidelberger Druckmaschinen	Ricoh Company
Hitachi	Sharp Corp.
Konica Minolta	Toshiba
Kyocera Document Solutions	

Company Type: Public

Income Statement				FYE: December 31
	REVENUE ($ mil.)	NET INCOME ($ mil.)	NET PROFIT MARGIN	EMPLOYEES
12/18	9,830	361	3.7%	32,400
12/17	10,265	195	1.9%	35,300
12/16	10,771	(477)	—	37,600
12/15	18,045	474	2.6%	143,600
12/14	19,540	969	5.0%	147,500
Annual Growth	(15.8%)	(21.9%)	—	(31.5%)

2018 Year-End Financials

Debt ratio: 35.00%	No. of shares (mil.): 230
Return on equity: 7.00%	Dividends
Cash ($ mil.): 1,084	Yield: 0.0%
Current ratio: 1.00	Payout: 72.0%
Long-term debt ($ mil.): 4,269	Market value ($ mil.): 4,537

	STOCK PRICE ($) FY Close	P/E High/Low		PER SHARE ($) Earnings	Dividends	Book Value
12/18	20.00	24	14	1.00	1.00	23.00
12/17	29.00	48	10	1.00	1.00	21.00
12/16	9.00	—	—	(2.00)	1.00	20.00
12/15	11.00	8	6	2.00	1.00	37.00
12/14	14.00	4	3	3.00	1.00	39.00
Annual Growth (12.8%)	9.3%	—	—	(19.2%)	(0.0%)	

XPO Logistics, Inc.

XPO Logistics is a global provider of transportation and supply chain solutions. It is one of the top five providers of freight brokerage and managed transportation services in the world. It also provides less-than-truckload (LTL) services where carriers consolidate freight from multiple shippers into a single truckload. Through its Logistics segment XPO offers services such as warehousing and distribution e-commerce fulfillment and reverse logistics (moving goods backward from their final destination for the purpose of reuse or disposal). Its customers include companies in the retail and e-commerce food and beverage consumer packaged goods and industrial markets. XPO operates more than 1500 locations in over 30 countries primarily in North America and Europe. The US is its largest market generating almost 60% of revenue.

Operations

XPO Logistics operates through two business segments ? Transportation and Logistics.

Transportation generates about 65% of sales and provides services through five divisions. Freight brokerage operations match shippers' freight with trucking companies; last mile specializes in heavy goods such as appliances furniture and large electronics; and less-than-truckload (LTL) comprises regional and transcontinental freight services using company tractors and trailers and employee drivers. Global forwarding includes logistics services using a network of ground air and ocean carriers and managed transportation serves customers who want to outsource their transportation needs.

The Logistics segment (about 35%) provides services such as warehousing and distribution e-fulfillment cold chain solutions reverse logistics packaging and labeling and inventory management. In addition Logistics provides customized supply chain optimization services such as volume flow management predictive analytics and advanced automation.

Geographic Reach

XPO Logistics is based in Greenwich CT. It operates through over 1500 locations across North America Europe and Asia. The US is its largest market accounting for about 60% of its revenue with France and the UK each accounting for more than 10%.

Sales and Marketing

XPO Logistics has nearly 12000 independent carriers and owner-operators under contract to provide drayage expedite last mile and LTL services to customers. It also has more than 50000 independent brokered carriers representing more than 1 million trucks on the road.

The company has more than 50000 customers in a wide range of industries including retail e-commerce consumer packaged goods industrial and food and beverage.

Financial Performance

XPO Logistics has experienced monumental growth over the years due to a flurry of acquisitions. Revenue has increased more than sevenfold since 2014.

Sales in 2018 rose to $17.3 billion up 12% from $15.4 billion in 2017. Growth was driven by increased sales in the contract logistics business in Europe and North America and by the expansion of the LTL freight brokerage and last-mile transportation businesses.

XPO's profits have increased significantly topping out at $422 million in 2018 compared with $340 million the previous year ? a 24% spike. Contributing to the increase was higher pension income and a gain related to the sale of its investment in a private company.

Cash at the end of fiscal 2018 was $514 million an increase of $65 million from the prior year. Cash from operations contributed $1.1 billion to the coffers while investing activities used $400 million mainly for purchases of property and equipment. Financing activities used another $620 million for loan payments dividends to stockholders and the company's stock repurchase program.

Strategy

XPO Logistics is growing each of its divisions by expanding networks and increasing the use of technology to beef up sales and service. In 2019 XPO plans to invest $550 in technology up from $498 million in 2018. It is making investments in things like autonomous devices robotics virtual operations and intelligent warehouse management.

The company continues to develop its XPO Direct network which grew to more than 90 facilities in 2018. XPO Direct allows omnichannel and retail manufacturing customers to rent capacity for contract logistics last mile LTL labor technology and storage directly from XPO and not have to incur large fixed costs.

In the Transportation segment XPO is increasing automation with enhancements to its XPO Connect digital platform and XPO Smart labor productivity tools. It is adding analytics and algorithms to the application that improve margins and increase efficiency in its warehouses.

The LTL business is diversifying its customer base by expanding service to more local markets. It's developing a new optimized routing system for pickups and deliveries with improved visibility for its customers. The company plans to launch a new LTL technology platform for network optimization that uses artificial intelligence and machine learning to create flexible pricing models.

Mergers and Acquisitions

Although sales were up 2018 was a turbulent year for XPO Logistics with the loss of a major European customer to bankruptcy the economic slowdown in France and the UK and being hit by an illegal "short-and-distort" securities fraud scheme that sent its stocks tumbling. As a result the company has suspended M&A activity temporarily and opted instead for buying back its own stock.

EXECUTIVES

Chairman And Ceo, Bradley S. Jacobs, age 62, $607,000 total compensation

Managing Director Logisticsâ–europe, Malcolm Wilson

President Less-than-truckload (ltl), Tony Brooks

Cio, Mario A. Harik, age 38

President Of Transportation North America, Christopher R. Synek

President Intermodal, Paul V. Smith

Cfo, John J. Hardig, age 54, $498,385 total compensation

Chief Strategy Officer, Scott B. Malat, age 42, $472,308 total compensation

Coo And Ceo Europe, Troy A. Cooper, age 49, $511,539 total compensation

Chief Human Resources Officer, Meghan A. Henson

Managing Director Transportâ–europe, Luis-Angel Gomez Izaguirre

President Supply Chain Americas And Asia Pacific, Ashfaque Chowdhury

President Last Mile, Charles Hitt

Senior Vice President Strategic Accounts, Robert Almazan

Vice President Of Transportation, Don Ingersoll

Vice President Of Strategic Initiatives, Christopher Duffell

National Account Manager, David Hannegan

Vp Strategic Accounts, Tom Ford

National Account Manager, Ed Skarda

Vice President Strategic Accounts, Michael Doumas

Vice President Strategic Accounts, Keith Weaver

Vice President, Dennis McCaffrey

Regional Vice President, David Coker

Vice President Operations, Roger Lekberg

Senior Vice President Operation Last Mile, Fernando Rabel

Vice President Strategic Accounts, Greg DiPalma

Vp Strategic Accounts, Kevin Hollenbush

Vice President Transportation, Nick Caragher

Region Vice President Sales, Anthony Hoereth

Vp Strategic Accounts, Ben Grime

Region Vice President, Jeff Groat

Vice President Procurement, Mitch Plaat

National Account Manager, Craig Robertson

Senior Vice President Financial Planning And Analysis, Liam Harrington

Senior Vice President Development Supply Chain Europe, Jean-Luc Declas

Vp It Services, Joe Pardini

Vice President Client Solutions, Jennifer Williams

Vice President Strategic Accounts, Jay Lambert

Vice President Information Technology Client Support, Tim Merritt

Senior Vice President And Treasurer, Ravi Tulsyan

Senior Vice President Sales Supply Chain Europe, Mark Wilkinson

Svp Global It Infrastructure, Grant Richard

Senior Vice President Sales Transport Europe, Christophe Haviland

Senior Vice President Communications, Erin Kurtz

Senior Vice President Global Information Technology Infrastructure, Patrick Petersen

Vice President Information Technology Global Vendor Management, Ronald Durham

Senior Vice President Global Talent Acquisition, Bertrand Dussert

National Account Manager, Brad Rouse

Freight Brokerage Regional Vice President, Drew Wilkerson

Vice President Business Development, Dirk Christensen

Senior Vice President Client Services, Jared Baker
Vice President Internal Audit, Lon Staub
Vice President Strategic Accounts, Drew Paxton
Vice President Operations, Shawn Getchell
Vice President Business Development, Richard Reed
Vice President Strategic Accounts, Rick Mathews
Vice President Strategic Accounts, Terence McCarthy
Vice President Strategic Accounts, Eric Thompson
Vice President Strategic Accounts, Garrett Lutgen
Vice President Strategic Accounts, George Holland
Vice President Of Strategic Accounts, Randall Cason
Vice President And General Counsel, Richard Valitutto
Senior Vice President Corporate Real Estate, Russ Marzen
Vice President Business Development, Errol Keel
Vice President Business Development, Paul Palmieri
Senior Vice President Sales :ess Than Truckload (ltl) North America, Russell Hoch
Vice President Midwest Region, Anthony Graham
Less Than Truckload Vice President Human Resources, Matt Hladki
Vice President Market, Eddie Jones
Vice President Of Operations, Triccia Barrera
Senior Vice President Corporate Counsel, Karlis P Kirsis
Senior Vice President Strategic Sales Europe, Patrick Oestreich
Senior Vice President Global Sales Operations, Michele Chapman
Senior Vice President Transportation Sales, Katrina Liddell
Senior Vice President Human Resources, Jacopo Mazzolin
Board Member, Michael Jesselson
Treasurer And Assistant Controller, Tammy Chupa
Auditors: KPMG LLP

LOCATIONS

HQ: XPO Logistics, Inc.
Five American Lane, Greenwich, CT 06831
Phone: 855 976-6951
Web: www.xpologistics.com

2018 Sales

	$ mil.	% of total
United States	10,232	59
North America (excluding US)	341	2
France	2,165	12
United Kingdom	2,070	12
Europe (excluding France and UK)	2,359	14
Other	112	1
Total	**17,279**	**100**

PRODUCTS/OPERATIONS

2018 Sales

	$ mil.	% of total
Transportation	11,343	65
Logistics	6,065	35
Eliminations	(129)	-
Total	**17,279**	**100**

Service

Service
Full Truckload
Less-Than-Truckload (LTL)
Drayage
Last Mile
Intermodal
Global Forwarding
Managed Transportation
Expedite
Freight Brokerage

COMPETITORS

C.H. Robinson Worldwide	Forward Air
	J.B. Hunt
CSX	Norfolk Southern
DHL	Ryder System
Daylight Transport	Schneider National
Deutsche Post	UPS
Expeditors	Union Pacific
FedEx	YRC Worldwide

HISTORICAL FINANCIALS

Company Type: Public

Income Statement — FYE: December 31

	REVENUE ($ mil.)	NET INCOME ($ mil.)	NET PROFIT MARGIN	EMPLOYEES
12/18	17,279	422	2.4%	100,000
12/17	15,381	340	2.2%	95,000
12/16	14,619	69	0.5%	87,000
12/15	7,623	(191)	—	89,000
12/14	2,357	(64)	—	10,000
Annual Growth	**64.6%**	**—**		**77.8%**

2018 Year-End Financials

Debt ratio: 35.00%
Return on equity: 12.00%
Cash ($ mil.): 502
Current ratio: 1.00
Long-term debt ($ mil.): 3,902
No. of shares (mil.): 116
Dividends
 Yield: —
 Payout: —
Market value ($ mil.): 6,599

	STOCK PRICE ($) FY Close	P/E High/Low		Earnings	Dividends	Book Value
12/18	57.00	36	14	3.00	0.00	31.00
12/17	92.00	34	16	2.00	0.00	30.00
12/16	43.00	87	34	1.00	0.00	24.00
12/15	27.00	—	—	(3.00)	0.00	25.00
12/14	41.00	—	—	(2.00)	0.00	21.00
Annual Growth	**8.7%**	**—**	**—**	**—**	**—**	**9.7%**

Xylem Inc

Xylem makes fluid-handling and related products used across the entire water cycle from the delivery and measurement of drinking water to the testing and treatment of wastewater. The company serves customers in the water sector as well as the electric and gas industries. Its products include water and wastewater pumps filtration and disinfection equipment heat exchangers and sensors and meters to name a few. Xylem's products are sold under about 35 different brands including Flygt Goulds and Pure. About 45% of its sales comes from the US.

Operations

Xylem operates in three reportable segments: Water Infrastructure Applied Water and Measurement & Control Solutions.

Water Infrastructure (about 40% of net sales) serves the utility and industrial markets. It makes water and wastewater pumps filtration and disinfection equipment biological treatment products and dewatering equipment (for draining riverbeds or construction sites to allow for building and infrastructure repairs). Primary brands in this segment include Flygt Godwin Leopold Sanitare and Wedeco.

Applied Water (30%) offers products for the residential commercial and industrial sectors sold primarily through independent distributors with some sales going through direct sales channels. Products include pumps valves heat exchangers controls and dispensing equipment systems sold under names such as A-C Fire Pump Flojet Goulds Jabsco Lowara and Standard Exchange.

The Measurement & Control Solutions segment (30%) provides technology-based products enabling better conservation of critical water and energy supplies for its water electric and natural gas customers. It offers smart metering systems networked communication devices data analytics controls and sensors and software and managed services. These products are used to monitor and control resources for water electricity and natural gas. In addition the company offers smart lighting solutions that improve efficiency and safety. Brands in this division include Emnet Pure Sensus Smith Blair Visenti WTW and YSI.

Geographic Reach

Headquartered in Rye Brook NY Xylem sells its products to customers in approximately 150 countries around the world. It operates more than 385 facilities?plants warehouses and offices?in 50-plus countries. The company generates about 55% of its revenue outside the US.

Sales and Marketing

Xylem sells its products through global direct sales and indirect channels such as independent distributors and targets the residential commercial and industrial markets. Besides residential consumers Xylem's commercial customers are owners and managers of properties such as apartment buildings retail stores institutional buildings restaurants schools hospitals and hotels.

In the industrial market Xylem caters to OEMs exploration and production firms and developers and managers of industrial facilities including electrical power generators chemical manufacturers machine shops clothing manufacturers beverage dispensing and food processing firms and car washes.

Financial Performance

Xylem's revenue has been on a generally upward trend over the last several years with 2018 sales reaching record highs.

Revenue in 2018 was $5.2 billion an 11% increase over $4.7 billion the previous year. The company realized growth in all end markets and geographic regions as well as $111 million in acquisition revenue.

The company's profits spiked up to $549 million in 2018 compared with $331 million in 2017 a 66% increase. This was due to higher sales as well as a non-recurring tax benefit of $136 million in 2017.

Cash at the end of fiscal 2018 was $296 million a decrease of $118 million from the prior year. Cash from operations contributed $586 million to the coffers while investing activities used $643 million mainly for the acquisition of Pure Technologies ($433 million) and capital expenditures for software development and building up its dewatering rental fleet. Financing activities used another $40 million for dividends to stockholders and the company's stock repurchase program.

Strategy

Xylem is leveraging its extensive installed base and increased digital offerings to grow its business. Through its recent acquisitions of Sensus (smart meters) and Pure Technologies (leak detection) the company has developed new solutions that are increasing sales.

Its new FlexNet communications network allows customers to monitor their water network remotely to identify issues and deploy personnel to solve problems such as leaks that might affect a community's clean water supply. Xylem has also built a digital Advanced Infrastructure Analytics (AIA) platform which uses data analytics diagnostics and leak detection technology to assess the condition of a water system's infrastructure. With increasingly scarcer water supplies and increased costs the need for efficient monitoring of water systems is accelerating demand for Xylem's solutions. The company has already seen higher revenue from sales of its AIA platform to utilities in the US and is focused on increasing its presence in Europe and Asia.

Company Background

Xylem was spun off from ITT Corp. as a stand-alone company in October 2011.

EXECUTIVES

Svp And Cfo, E. Mark Rajkowski, age 60, $461,538 total compensation
Svp General Counsel And Corporate Secretary, Claudia S. Toussaint, age 55, $427,346 total compensation
Svp And President Americas Commerical Team And Applied Water Systems, Kenneth (Ken) Napolitano, age 57, $416,938 total compensation
Svp And President Dewatering, Colin R. Sabol, age 51, $420,408 total compensation
President And Ceo, Patrick K. Decker, age 54, $975,384 total compensation
Svp And Cio, Nicholas R. Colisto
Svp And President Transport And Treatment And President Xylem Europe Gmbh, Tomas Brannemo, age 47
Svp And Chief Marketing Officer, Joseph P. (Joe) Vesey
Svp And President Emerging Markets, Pak (Steven) Leung, age 62, $302,220 total compensation
Svp And Chief Innovation And Technology Officer, Jayanthi (Jay) Iyengar
Svp And President Dewatering, David Flinton, age 47
Svp And President Europe Commercial Team, Christian Blanc
Vp Corporate Development, Hyman Buchwald
Vp Americas Region Aws, Marc Blais
Vice President Growth Center Analytics Emea And Ap, Sean Donnelly
Vice President Global Real Estate And Facilities Management, Bill Alexander
Senior Vice President Continuous Improvement, Anthony Milando
Vice President And Chief Tax Officer, Justin Stalls
Vice President Of Sales, Alan Fey
Vice President Global Strategic Sourcing, Chris Mapes
Vice President Of Sales Nawater, Tim Harriger
Vice President Outsourced Operations And Supply Chain, Graupman Duane
Vice President Of Engineering And Development, Dean Berkebile
Chairman, Markos I. Tambakeras, age 68
Secretary, Hannah Skeete
Board Member, Jerome Peribere
Auditors: DELOITTE & TOUCHE LLP

LOCATIONS

HQ: Xylem Inc
1 International Drive, Rye Brook, NY 10573
Phone: 914 323-5700   **Fax:** 914 323-5800
Web: www.xyleminc.com

2018 Sales

	$ mil.	% of total
US	2,424	47
Europe	1,449	28
Asia/Pacific	660	13
Other	674	12
Total	**5,207**	**100**

PRODUCTS/OPERATIONS

2018 Sales

	$ mil.	% of total
Water Infrastructure	2,176	42
Applied Water	1,534	29
Measurement and Control Solutions	1,497	29
Total	**5,207**	**100**

2018 Sales

	$ mil.	% of total
Pumps Accessories Parts and Service	3,322	64
Others	1,885	36
Total	**5,207**	**100**

Selected Brands

AC Fire Pump
Bell & Gossett
Bellingham & Stanley
ebro
Essence of Life
FloJet
Flygt
Global Water
Godwin
Goulds
Jabsco
Leopold
Lowara
McDonnell & Miller
OI Analytical
Royce Technologies
Rule
Sanitaire
Sensus
SI Analytics
SonTek
Standard
Tideland
Visenti
Wachs Water Services
Wedeco
WTW
YSI

Selected Products and Services

Boiler controls
Flow switches
Heat exchangers
Liquid level controls
Mixers
Pumps
Reverse osmosis watermakers
Valves
Water treatment systems
  Biological wastewater - aeration
  Backwash water recover
  Ozone oxidation
  Sludge collection systems
  Ultraviolet disinfection

COMPETITORS

Badger Meter	KSB AG
Danaher	Mueller Water Products
Elster Group SE	Pentair
Evoqua	Roper Technologies
Franklin Electric	Sulzer
Grundfos	United Rentals
Itron	

HISTORICAL FINANCIALS

Company Type: Public

Income Statement				FYE: December 31
	REVENUE ($ mil.)	NET INCOME ($ mil.)	NET PROFIT MARGIN	EMPLOYEES
12/18	5,207	549	10.5%	17,000
12/17	4,707	331	7.0%	16,200
12/16	3,771	260	6.9%	16,000
12/15	3,653	340	9.3%	12,700
12/14	3,916	337	8.6%	12,500
Annual Growth	**7.4%**	**13.0%**	**—**	**8.0%**

2018 Year-End Financials

Debt ratio: 32.00%
Return on equity: 21.00%
Cash ($ mil.): 296
Current ratio: 2.00
Long-term debt ($ mil.): 2,051
No. of shares (mil.): 180
Dividends
  Yield: 1.0%
  Payout: 28.0%
Market value ($ mil.): 11,991

	STOCK PRICE ($) FY Close	P/E High/Low	PER SHARE ($) Earnings	Dividends	Book Value
12/18	67.00	27 20	3.00	1.00	15.00
12/17	68.00	38 26	2.00	1.00	14.00
12/16	50.00	38 23	1.00	1.00	12.00
12/15	37.00	20 16	2.00	1.00	12.00
12/14	38.00	22 17	2.00	1.00	12.00
Annual Growth	**15.1%**	**— —**	**13.4%**	**13.2%**	**7.2%**

YOSEMITE FARM CREDIT, ACA

EXECUTIVES

Pres, Leonard Van Eldern
Cfo*, Tracy Sparks
Vice President, Brian Lemons
Vice President Marketing, Melba Miyamoto
Manager, Ray Koopman
Vice President, Robert Fuller

LOCATIONS

HQ: YOSEMITE FARM CREDIT, ACA
  806 W MONTE VISTA AVE, TURLOCK, CA 953827242
Phone: 209 667-2366
Web: WWW.YOSEMITEFARMCREDIT.COM

HISTORICAL FINANCIALS

Company Type: Private

Income Statement				FYE: December 31
	ASSETS ($ mil.)	NET INCOME ($ mil.)	INCOME AS % OF ASSETS	EMPLOYEES
12/17	2,889	53	1.8%	100
12/16	2,661	43	1.6%	—
12/15	2,368	41	1.7%	—
12/14	2,154	39	1.8%	—
Annual Growth	**10.3%**	**11.2%**	**—**	**—**

Yum China Holdings Inc

Auditors: KPMG Huazhen LLP

LOCATIONS

HQ: Yum China Holdings Inc
  7100 Corporate Drive, Plano, TX 75024
Phone: 469 980-2898
Web: www.yumchina.com

Company Type: Public

Income Statement — FYE: December 31

	REVENUE ($ mil.)	NET INCOME ($ mil.)	NET PROFIT MARGIN	EMPLOYEES
12/18	8,415	708	8.4%	450,000
12/17	7,144	403	5.6%	450,000
12/16	6,752	502	7.4%	420,000
12/15	6,909	323	4.7%	400,000
12/14	6,934	(7)	—	—
Annual Growth	5.0%	—	—	—

2018 Year-End Financials

Debt ratio: 1.00%
Return on equity: 25.00%
Cash ($ mil.): 1,266
Current ratio: 2.00
Long-term debt ($ mil.): 25

No. of shares (mil.): 379
Dividends
 Yield: 1.0%
 Payout: 23.0%
Market value ($ mil.): 12,708

	STOCK PRICE ($) FY Close	P/E High/Low		PER SHARE ($) Earnings	Dividends	Book Value
12/18	34.00	26	17	2.00	0.00	8.00
12/17	40.00	41	25	1.00	0.00	7.00
12/16	26.00	22	19	1.00	0.00	6.00
Annual Growth	6.4%			7.1%	—	5.1%

Yum! Brands Inc

For those who find chicken pizza and tacos especially yummy there's only one place to turn. YUM Brands is the largest fast-food operator in the world in terms of number of locations with more than 48000 KFC Pizza Hut and Taco Bell outlets in some 140 countries. (It trails only hamburger giant McDonald's in sales.) The company's flagship chains are #1 chicken fryer KFC (with more than 22600 units) top pizza joint Pizza Hut (more than 18400) and quick-service Mexican leader Taco Bell (more than 7000). Franchisees affiliates and licensed operators run about 98% of the company's restaurants. More than 60% are located outside the US.

HISTORY

Yum Brands took its original name TRICON from the three brand icons — KFC Pizza Hut and Taco Bell— it inherited from former parent PepsiCo. The soft drink company entered the fast-food business with its acquisition of Pizza Hut in 1977. The pizza chain had begun in 1958 when brothers Dan and Frank Carney borrowed $600 from their mother and opened the first Pizza Hut in Wichita Kansas with partner John Bender. Their first franchise opened the next year in Topeka Kansas. By 1971 the company had become the world's largest pizza chain with more than 1000 restaurants. Pizza Hut went public the following year. The chain had grown to 3000 locations by the time it was acquired.

In 1978 PepsiCo acquired Taco Bell. After trying other fast-food formats Glen Bell settled on the Mexican-style market. He bought and sold several chains before beginning Taco Bell in Downey California in 1962. The first franchise was sold two years later and by 1967 — the year after it went public — Taco Bell had more than 335 restaurants most of them franchised.

KFC was acquired in 1986. It had been founded by Harland Sanders — that's Colonel Sanders to you — who developed his secret 11-herbs-and-spices recipe and method of pressure-frying chicken during the 1930s. The Colonel began franchising the secret in 1952 and founded Kentucky Fried Chicken in 1955. More than 600 outlets in the US and Canada were open by 1963. It went public in 1969 and was operating some 6600 units in 55 countries when it was acquired by PepsiCo.

Through these acquisitions PepsiCo hoped to diversify and build sales channels for its beverages but the company had also incurred a huge debt load and fast-food competition had intensified. As same-store sales faltered shareholders clamored for PepsiCo to spin off the restaurants. Restaurant officials grumbled that PepsiCo put more effort into marketing blitzes than into building restaurants (its 1991 renaming of Kentucky Fried Chicken as KFC didn't fool many health-conscious consumers).

In 1997 PepsiCo created a new restaurant subsidiary which it spun off in the fall as TRICON Global Restaurants. To improve cash flow it stepped up efforts to close or franchise underperforming Pizza Huts and KFCs. TRICON also began opening "three-in-one" restaurants featuring all its brands under one roof. In 1998 it launched a Taco Bell advertising campaign featuring a bilingual Chihuahua; the sassy pooch quickly became a cultural icon.

The KFC Taco Bell and Pizza Hut cooperatives joined in 1999 to form Unified FoodService Purchasing the largest purchasing cooperative for fast-food restaurants in the US. Also that year TRICON spent some $2 billion on a massive Star Wars: Episode I — The Phantom Menace promotion that failed to increase traffic at its restaurants. Vice chairman David Novak took over as CEO in 2000. Additionally in 1999 the company joined Burger King in lending $150 million to its distributor AmeriServe (now McLane Foodservice) which had filed for bankruptcy. The following year TRICON began experimenting with debit and credit cards at Pizza Huts and KFCs. It also opened more than 300 multi-branded sites.

In 2002 TRICON acquired Yorkshire Global Restaurants for $320 million which brought Long John Silver's and A&W All-American Food Restaurants into the fold. Now a five-pack of well-known brands rather than a trio TRICON changed its name to YUM Brands. Later that year it formed a joint venture with Favorite Restaurants Group (a leading franchisee of KFC and Pizza Hut in Indonesia and Hong Kong) to open a chain of Yan Can Asian restaurants based around popular international chef Martin Yan. (YUM Brands dissolved its partnership in Yan Can and liquidated the business in 2004.)

Being market leaders did not save YUM's chains from the overall downturn in the economy however nor from the effects of changing eating habits as Americans sought healthier meal alternatives. KFC was hit particularly hard prompting the company to appoint veteran Gregg Dedrick the chain's new president in 2003. Both KFC and Pizza Hut saw same-store sales and the number of transactions decline in the US during 2003.

In 2004 KFC opened its 1000th restaurant in China where the chain had been operating since 1987. As YUM Brands' China operations continued to grow it formed a separate division in 2005 to oversee its expansion. The company acquired the 50% stake it didn't already own in Pizza Hut (UK) from joint venture partner Whitbread in 2006 for almost $185 million plus the assumption of about $25 million in debt.

The following year YUM was stung by an E. coli outbreak at some of its Taco Bell outlets. The source of the outbreak was traced to a lettuce sup-

plier; the company announced new steps to test its food supply. YUM also sold its 31% stake in KFC Japan to Mitsubishi that same year.

YUM Brands sold its Long John Silver's chain and A&W All-American Food locations in 2011. The divestitures were made to allow the company to focus on growing its international business particularly in China.

In 2012 the company upped its stake in Chinese restaurant operator Little Sheep Group to 93%.

In 2015 YUM Brands announced plans to spin off its Chinese operations which it did in 2016.

EXECUTIVES

Ceo, Greg Creed, $1,188,942 total compensation
General Counsel Corporate Secretary And Chief Government Affairs Officer, Marc L. Kesselman, $530,769 total compensation
President And Cfo, David W. Gibbs, $792,115 total compensation
Ceo Taco Bell, Brian R. Niccol, $803,846 total compensation
Ceo Kfc Division, Roger G. Eaton, $812,500 total compensation
Svp Corporate Finance And Controller, David E. Russell, $476,867 total compensation
Chief Transformation And People Officer, Tracy Skeans
Vice President And Treasurer, Larry Gathof
Vice President Global Talent And Organization Development, Mark Lagestee
Vp Assistant Treasurer, Connie Hayes-badon
Vice President And Global Chief Information Security Officer, Marc Varner
Chairman, Robert D. (Bob) Walter
Board Member, Mirian Graddick-weir
Auditors: KPMG LLP

LOCATIONS

HQ: Yum! Brands Inc
 1441 Gardiner Lane, Louisville, KY 40213
Phone: 502 874-8300
Web: www.yum.com

PRODUCTS/OPERATIONS

2017 Sales

	$ mil.	% of total
Company sales	3,572	61
Franchising and License fees	2,306	39
Total	**5,878**	**100**

2017 sales

	$ mil.	% of total
KFC Division	3,110	53
Taco Bell Division	1,880	32
Pizza Hut Division	893	15
Unallocated	(5)	0
Total	**5,878**	**100**

COMPETITORS

A&W Restaurants
American Dairy Queen
Arby's
Biglari Holdings
Burger King
CKE Restaurants
Chick-fil-A
Chipotle
Church's Chicken
Dairy Queen
Del Taco
Domino's

Fiesta Restaurant Group
Jack in the Box
Little Caesar's
Long John Silver's
McDonald's
Papa John's
Popeyes
Quiznos
Sonic Corp.
Subway
Wendy's

HISTORICAL FINANCIALS

Company Type: Public

Income Statement
FYE: December 31

	REVENUE ($ mil.)	NET INCOME ($ mil.)	NET PROFIT MARGIN	EMPLOYEES
12/18	5,688	1,542	27.1%	34,000
12/17	5,878	1,340	22.8%	60,000
12/16	6,366	1,619	25.4%	90,000
12/15	13,105	1,293	9.9%	505,000
12/14	13,279	1,051	7.9%	537,000
Annual Growth	(19.1%)	10.1%	—	(49.8%)

2018 Year-End Financials

Debt ratio: 244.00%
Return on equity: ***,***.**%
Cash ($ mil.): 292
Current ratio: 1.00
Long-term debt ($ mil.): 9,751

No. of shares (mil.): 306
Dividends
Yield: 2.0%
Payout: 31.0%
Market value ($ mil.): 28,128

	STOCK PRICE ($) FY Close	P/E High/Low	PER SHARE ($) Earnings	Dividends	Book Value
12/18	92.00	19 16	5.00	1.00	(26.00)
12/17	82.00	22 16	4.00	1.00	(19.00)
12/16	63.00	22 15	4.00	2.00	(16.00)
12/15	74.00	32 23	3.00	2.00	2.00
12/14	73.00	35 28	2.00	2.00	4.00
Annual Growth	5.9%	— —	19.2%	(1.3%)	

ZEN-NOH GRAIN CORPORATION

EXECUTIVES

Ceo, John D Williams
Exec V Pres*, Shin Inoue
Sr. V Pres*, Charles E Colbert
Ctlr*, Robin Gerarve
Dir*, Hiroyuki Kawasaki
Dir*, Yoshihiro Sugiyama
Dir*, Yoshinori Ohara
Executive Vice-President, Osamu Yako
Executive Vice-President, Tomoaki Miyamoto
Purchasing Manager, David Falgout
Vice President Secretary and C, Frank Beguiristain

LOCATIONS

HQ: ZEN-NOH GRAIN CORPORATION
1127 HWY 190 E SERVICE RD, COVINGTON, LA
704334929
Phone: 985 867-3500
Web: WWW.CGB.COM

HISTORICAL FINANCIALS

Company Type: Private

Income Statement
FYE: May 31

	REVENUE ($ mil.)	NET INCOME ($ mil.)	NET PROFIT MARGIN	EMPLOYEES
05/18	6,971	102	1.5%	188
05/17	7,047	68	1.0%	—
05/16	5,722	37	0.7%	—
05/15	6,001	86	1.4%	—
Annual Growth	5.1%	5.7%	—	—

Zimmer Biomet Holdings Inc

Zimmer Biomet is the top global manufacturer of reconstructive implants used in knee or hip replacement surgery. It makes a variety of other orthopedic devices including shoulder implants bone and tissue grafting materials sports medicine products dental implant systems spinal implants and trauma products for broken bones (such as plates screws and pins). Additionally Zimmer Biomet makes medical equipment used in orthopedic surgeries including tourniquets and devices for wound cleansing. The firm's products are sold around the globe primarily in the Americas.

Operations

Zimmer Biomet makes most of its money from sales of knee and hip replacement products (around 35% and 25% of revenue respectively). Some of its lead offerings are the Persona and NexGen knee systems Zimmer M/L taper hip prosthesis and Taperloc hip system. In addition to knee and hip replacements the company makes partial replacement early intervention and joint preservation products.

The SET category of products accounting for more than 20% of sales includes the surgical extremities and trauma (SET) offerings and the sports medicine foot and ankle and biologics lines. These products support surgical procedures and treat soft tissue injuries fractures arthritic conditions and broken bones. Products include the JuggerKnot soft anchor system ATS tourniquets and the Zimmer trabecular metal reverse shoulder system.

The Spine and CMF product groups which together bring in 10% of the company's revenue include devices and instruments that treat back and neck injuries and craniomaxillofacial and thoracic (CMF) injuries. Offerings include the Polaris spinal system Timberline lateral fusion system and face skull and chest reconstruction items.

The dental products division (which bring in about 5% of sales) makes or distributes implants prosthetics and regenerative products including the Tapered Screw-Vent dental implant system and the 3i T3 implant.

Other products include Zimmer Biomet's office-based technology and bone cement offerings.

Geographic Reach

Zimmer Biomet's operations are managed through three major geographic segments: Americas; Asia/Pacific; and Europe Middle East and Africa (EMEA).

The Americas segment (largely consisting of US operations) accounts for more than 60% of annual revenue which makes the company vulnerable to declines in its core market though sales in international markets are rising. The Asia/Pacific region which includes such markets as Australia China India and Japan has grown to account for about 15% of sales. The EMEA segment including sales in France Germany Italy and Spain accounts for about 25% of revenue. Zimmer Biomet's products are sold in more than 100 countries worldwide and the company has direct operations in more than 40 countries.

The company's corporate headquarters are located in Warsaw Indiana and it has regional headquarters in Singapore and Switzerland. Zimmer Biomet's primary manufacturing facilities are located in the US (Indiana Colorado Ohio Texas Florida and New Jersey) the Netherlands Puerto Rico Ireland China France Germany Singapore Spain South Wales and Switzerland.

Sales and Marketing

Zimmer Biomet sells its orthopedic products directly to health care providers such as hospitals surgery centers and surgeons. It also sells to purchasing organizations distributors and health care dealers. Its dental products are sold directly to dental practices and laboratories. Zimmer Biomet markets biologic bone and tissue allografts for dental spinal and trauma procedures through a partnership with RTI Surgical.

The US sales force is made up of direct employees and contracted exclusive agents. European sales are handled by direct associates support employees commissioned agents and independent distributors while Asia/Pacific sales are handled through a network of dealers and associates. Direct channels account for about 80% of the company's net sales.

Financial Performance

Zimmer Biomet's revenue has seen steady upward growth in recent years including sharp increases in 2015 and 2016 due to its acquisition of Biomet. Sales growth was sluggish in 2017 and 2018 as the company worked to overcome manufacturing issues but overall revenue increased 70% between 2014 and 2018. Net income fluctuated but remained in the black until 2018 when the company reported a net loss.

The company reported a 2% sales increase to $7.9 billion in 2018 due to increased product sales in the Asia/Pacific region (7%) and the EMEA region (3%); sales in the Americas region were flat. Hip replacement and SET (surgical extremities and trauma) offerings showed the strongest growth both around 3%; knee replacement products increased nearly 2%. The knee and hip replacement categories recovered from production delay issues that year; knee sales also improved on new product launches. Overall company revenue growth was offset by continuing slight declines in the dental and other products categories.

The company reported a net loss of $379.2 million in 2018 the first loss reported by the firm in the past decade and a sharp drop from record earnings in 2017. The earnings decline was primarily attributed to $979.7 million in goodwill and asset impairments and $186 million in litigation charges (related to product liabilities). Net income had skyrocketed nearly 500% to $1.8 billion in 2017 thanks largely to a $1.3 billion income tax benefit (related to the 2017 Tax Act) and lower operating costs.

Zimmer Biomet ended 2018 with $542.8 million in cash up $18.4 million from 2017. Operating activities contributed $1.7 billion while investing activities used $416.6 million (mostly from spending on instrument property plant and equipment additions) and financing activities used $1.3 billion (largely on term loan payments and redemption of senior notes).

Strategy

Zimmer Biomet launched a two-year quality remediation project at the start of 2018 to improve its supply chain and manufacturing processes and return to strong revenue growth. The company successfully increased stock levels and reduced backorders on key knee hip and SET product lines during 2018 as it corrected production delays at the Warsaw North Campus manufacturing center. The company has been working to correct quality issues at the facility after receiving a warning letter from the FDA. It is also working to adopt automation technologies at many of its factories.

Zimmer Biomet works to boost sales through new product development efforts and by introducing next-generation versions of existing best-sellers. The company expects to see gains in its knee segment from new product launches including the ROSA knee system for robotically-assisted procedures. Other new products include the Zyston strut open titanium interbody spacer system (its first spinal implant using 3D printing) and the Persona trabecular metal tibia. The firm also launched my-mobility a digital health platform created in partnership with Apple to better connect patients with surgical teams. The company spent $391.7 million on R&D in 2018 up from $369.9 million in 2017.

Along with increasing its sales through product growth Zimmer Biomet expands through acquisitions partnerships and international expansion efforts. The company expects overall industry trends to help keep its sales in the black: The aging US population chronic obesity and advances in surgical techniques are all expected to contribute to increased demand for its products.

Like all medical equipment makers the company's performance is regularly impacted by product recall and liability issues. It can also be vulnerable to economic conditions (causing patients to decrease non-essential expenses) and government and hospital cost-control programs.

Company Background

Zimmer Biomet's history can be traced to the 1927 founding of orthopedic splint maker Zimmer Manufacturing in Warsaw Indiana. The company expanded its product offerings over time and was acquired by Bristol-Myers (now Bristol-Myers Squibb) in 1972. Zimmer Holdings was spun off into an independent operation in 2001.

In mid-2015 Zimmer acquired fellow implant maker Biomet for $14 billion. The deal made the combined company the #2 orthopedics seller worldwide behind Johnson & Johnson. It also doubled Zimmer's knee and dental lines and gave it entry into the lucrative sports medicine business. Upon completion of the transaction Zimmer took on the Zimmer Biomet name.

In 2016 Zimmer Biomet completed a number of acquisitions to expand its product portfolio including LDR Holding (spinal products $1 billion) Cayenne Medical (sports medicine) Clinical Graphics (hip preservation) and Ortho Transmission (skeletal implants for amputees).

EXECUTIVES

Executive Vice President Finance And Chief Financial Officer, James T Crines
Group President Joint Reconstruction, Daniel E. (Dan) Williamson, age 53, $224,329 total compensation
Group President Biologics Extremities Sports Medicine Surgical Trauma Foot Ankle And Bone Healing, David A. Nolan
Svp General Counsel And Secretary, Chad F. Phipps, age 48, $470,615 total compensation
Svp Cfo And Interim Ceo And Director, Daniel P. (Dan) Florin, age 55, $562,692 total compensation
President Europe Middle East And Africa, Katarzyna Mazur-Hofsaess, age 55, $612,644 total compensation
Group President Spine Dental Cmf And Thoracic, Adam R. Johnson, age 42
President Asia/pacific, Sang Yi, $459,156 total compensation
President Americas, Robert D. (Rob) Delp
Svp Global Operations And Logistics, Adrian Furey
Vice President, Russell Fleeger
Vp Global Integration, Derek Davis
Vice President Manager Director, Randy Verberkmoes
Vice President Associate Corporate Counsel And Assistant Secretary, Heather Kidwell
Vice President Business Development, Indraneel Kanaglekar
Senior Vice President Strategy, Rachel Ellingson
Chairman, Larry C. Glasscock, age 70
Auditors: PricewaterhouseCoopers LLP

LOCATIONS

HQ: Zimmer Biomet Holdings Inc
345 East Main Street, Warsaw, IN 46580
Phone: 574 267-6131
Web: www.zimmer.com

2017 Sales

	$ mil.	% of total
Americas	4,866	62
EMEA	1,745	22
Asia/Pacific	1,213	16
Total	**7,824**	**100**

PRODUCTS/OPERATIONS

2017 Sales

	$ mil.	% of total
Knees	2,737	35
Hips	1,879	24
SET	1,709	22
Spine & CMF	760	10
Dental	419	5
Other	321	4
Total	**7,824**	**100**

Selected Products

Reconstructive implants
  Alloclassic hip system
  Anatomical shoulder implants
  Bigliani/Flatow shoulder implants
  MIS 2-Incision Total Hip Replacement
  MIS Mini-Incision Total Knee Procedure
  NexGen knee replacement
  Trabecular Metal Primary Hip Prosthesis
  VerSys Hip System
  Zimmer Collagen Repair Patch (rotator cuff repair)
Trauma products
  I.T.S.T. Nail System (hip and proximal femur fractures)
  M/DN Intramedullary Fixation (for long bone fractures)
  NCB Locking Plate System (complex long bone fractures)
  Sirus Intramedullary Nail System (for long bone fractures)
Dental products
  AdVent dental implant system
  Tapered screw-vent implant system
Spine products
  CopiOs Bone Void Filler
  Dynesys Dynamic Stabilization System
  Optima ZD Spinal Fixation System
  Puros allografts
  ST360 Spinal Fixation System
Surgical products
  A.T.S. Tourniquet Systems
  Brasseler USA surgical power tools (for long bones)
  Pneumicro surgical power tools (for small bones)
  Pulsavac Plus (wound cleaning)
  Zimmer Ambulatory Pump (pain management)

COMPETITORS

Corin Group	Nobel Biocare
DJO Global	NuVasive
DePuy	Orthofix
Dentsply Sirona	ReGen Biologics
Exactech	Smith & Nephew
Genzyme Biosurgery	Straumann
Globus Medical	Stryker
JRI Orthopaedics	Synthes
MAKO Surgical	

HISTORICAL FINANCIALS

Company Type: Public

Income Statement
FYE: December 31

	REVENUE ($ mil.)	NET INCOME ($ mil.)	NET PROFIT MARGIN	EMPLOYEES
12/18	7,933	(379)	—	19,000
12/17	7,824	1,814	23.2%	18,200
12/16	7,684	306	4.0%	18,500
12/15	5,998	147	2.5%	17,500
12/14	4,673	720	15.4%	10,000
Annual Growth	**14.1%**	**—**	**—**	**17.4%**

2018 Year-End Financials

Debt ratio: 37.00%
Return on equity: (-3.00%)
Cash ($ mil.): 543
Current ratio: 2.00
Long-term debt ($ mil.): 8,414

No. of shares (mil.): 204
Dividends
  Yield: 1.0%
  Payout: —
Market value ($ mil.): 21,159

	STOCK PRICE ($) FY Close	P/E High/Low	PER SHARE ($) Earnings	Dividends	Book Value
12/18	104.00	— —	(2.00)	1.00	55.00
12/17	121.00	15 12	9.00	1.00	58.00
12/16	103.00	87 60	2.00	1.00	48.00
12/15	103.00	156 118	1.00	1.00	49.00
12/14	113.00	27 21	4.00	1.00	38.00
Annual Growth	**(2.2%)**	**— —**	**—**	**2.2%**	**9.5%**

Zions Bancorporation, N.A.

Originally formed at the behest of Brigham Young Zions Bancorporation outgrew its early roots to become one of the largest banks in the US. The corporation is a holding company for ZB National Association Nevada State Bank National Bank of Arizona Vectra Bank Colorado The Commerce Bank of Washington California Bank & Trust and Texas-based Amegy Bank. Combined they operate some 430 bank branches in 11 mostly Western US states. The Zion banks focus on commercial and retail banking as well as mortgage and construction lending deposit accounts home mortgages credit cards and trust and wealth management services.

Operations

Zions Bancorporation is comprised of seven regional business segments each of them operating as an affiliated bank. The banks focus on community banking geared towards small and medium-sized business and offer corporate banking commercial & residential development retail banking cash management and trust & wealth management. The banks are some of the nation's largest providers of small business administration (SBA) lending and together are a top originator of secondary market agricultural real estate loans.

The banks provide a range of personal banking services such as home mortgages home equity lines of credit checking & savings accounts safe deposit boxes internet and mobile banking.

Zion Bancorporation generates most of its revenue through interest payments on the loans it issues. Interest income generated by loans money marketing investments and other securities account for around 80% of Zions' revenue with the remainder coming from fees for deposit accounts and other service-related charges.

Geographic Reach

Based in Utah the holding company operates more than 430 bank branches throughout Utah Idaho California Texas Arizona Wyoming Nevada Colorado New Mexico Oregon and Washington.

Sales and Marketing

The banking subsidiaries of Zion Bancorporation markets its services locally through company websites digital advertising and word-of-mouth referrals. Each bank approaches its market with the mindset of a community bank working with small and medium business owners as well as retail consumers located within a geographic proximity of its branches.

Financial Performance

Only recently did Zions' revenue hit bottom following the 2008-2009 financial crisis. Since 2015 revenue has been on the upswing though its results are still some 20% below the 2009 result. The holding company however has learned how to turn a profit. Earning moved higher in all but one year since 2011 and have more than tripled between 2011 and 2017.

Revenue in 2017 rose 11% to $2.7 billion. Interest income accounted for $2.2 billion of the total and non-interest income (fees service charges etc.) made up the rest. Zions' loan portfolio grew 5% in the year with upswings occurring in residential mortgages commercial & industrial loans and municipal lendings. Oil & Gas and term commercial real estate lending slid shaving nearly $550 million from the portfolio. Rising interest rates which pushed Zions' net interest margin to 3.45% (from 3.37% in 2016) helped expand interest income. Customer-related fee income rose 8% due to improvements in credit card fees and trust & wealth management income.

Net income rose 34% to $550 million an excellent result following the prior year's 66% jump. Wages and salaries and general expenses rose a bit compared to 2016 but all other costs were in line with the prior year. Income taxes shaved off about $100 million more than 2016 but overall the increased revenue flowed down well to the bottom line.

Cash on hand at the end of 2017 was $548 million down nearly $190 million from the previous year. Financing activities added $2.8 billion to the cash coffers mainly from debt issuance and short-term borrowed funds. Investing activities used $3.9 billion for purchasing investment securities and accounting for changes in its loan & lease portfolio. Operating activities contributed $928 million primarily from the bank's annual net income.

Strategy

Looking forward Zions expects to maintain a mid-single digit growth rate in the size of its loan portfolio and in customer-related fee income. It anticipates strong growth from residential mortgage and municipal loans and moderate growth in C&I and commercial real estate loans. Although loans out to oil & gas (O&G) companies (mainly through Amegy Bank) have performed poorly in recent years the upswing in oil prices has lessened the pinch on many firms enabling Zions to take fewer loan loss provisions against that portion of its portfolio. To further reduce the risk it decreased the O&G commercial lending portfolio size by 9% in 2017.

With such distinct and localized bank subsidiaries Zions strives to maintain a local community and regional bank approach as opposed to a larger bank that doesn't have a local management team. It does centralize many non-customer facing operations such as risk and capital management technology and back-office operations making for a more cost-effective endeavor.

Company Background

Zions which built its business through acquisitions strategically managed to extend its reach during the economic downturn in part by helping the FDIC clean up failed banks and it continues to search for acquisition opportunities. It is also building its business by growing its wealth management and advisory services organically.

HISTORY

Zions' history is entwined with that of the Mormon Church. Founded by the church in 1873 to take over the savings department of the Bank of Deseret when it obtained a national charter the new bank was headed by Brigham Young and other church leaders. The church kept control of the bank until 1960 when it sold its interest to a group of investors led by Roy Simmons who moved it into the holding company that became Zions Bancorporation. It went public in 1966.

It has grown over the years by picking up struggling or failing banks during various financial crises. It almost bought fellow Utah bank First Security in 2000 and would have dropped the Zions name to further distance itself from the Mormon Church. But the deal fell through and the name remains.

EXECUTIVES

Executive Vice President Marketing And Communications, Rob Brough

Evp; President And Ceo Zions First National Bank, A. Scott (Scott) Anderson, age 72, $548,000 total compensation

Chairman And Ceo, Harris H. Simmons, age 64, $940,000 total compensation

Evp; President And Ceo Vectra Bank Colorado, Bruce K. Alexander, age 66

Evp; President And Ceo The Commerce Bank Of Washington, Stanley D. Savage, age 73, $312,000 total compensation

Evp; President And Ceo California Bank & Trust, David E. Blackford, age 70, $510,000 total compensation

President And Coo, Scott J. McLean, age 62, $644,000 total compensation

Evp And Chief Banking Officer, Keith D. Maio, age 61

Evp Retail Banking, LeeAnne B. Linderman, age 64

Evp And General Counsel, Thomas E. Laursen, age 68

Evp And Chief Risk Officer, Edward P. (Ed) Schreiber, age 61, $518,000 total compensation

Evp And Chief Human Resources Officer, Dianne R. James, age 66

Evp And Cio, Jennifer A. Smith, age 47

Evp; Ceo Amegy Bank Of Texas, Steven D. Stephens, age 60

Evp And Chief Technology Strategist, Joe Reilly, age 66

Evp And Chief Credit Officer, Michael J. Morris, age 61

Evp; President And Ceo National Bank Of Arizona, Mark R. Young, age 60

Cfo, Paul E. Burdiss, age 54, $550,000 total compensation

Evp And Director Wealth Management, Rebecca K. Robinson, age 45

Vice President, Matt Millis

Vice President And Relationship Manager, Adam Whitefield

Senior Vice President Compliance, Norman Merritt

Vice President And Relationship Manager, Cheryl Ginn

Vice President, Steve Earley

Senior Vice President And Chief Credit Administrator C And I Lending, Dennis Spencer

Assistant Vice President Capital Markets, Karen Keeley

Vice President Sales Manager, Howard Anderson

Vice President, Jennifer Jolley

Vice President Technology, Deva Annamalai

Vp And Business Analyst, Kazi Suzuki

Vice President Commercial Loans, David Kohler

Senior Vice President Corporate Procuremen And Vendor Management, Kelly Foreman

First Vice President, James Grether

Applications Developers Vice President Applications, Brent Briggs

Vice President Treasury Management Sales Manager, Jesse Ronnow Jesse Ronnow

Vice President, Zac Nelson

Vice President Business Development Officer, Mark Petrasso

Vice President Financial Analyst, Ian Spencer

Senior Vice President Information Technology Support Services, Lorilee Stoddard

Vice President, Ryan Theriault

Svp Credit Risk Management, Mark Medina

Senior Vice President, Tom Etzel

Auditors: Ernst & Young LLP

LOCATIONS

HQ: Zions Bancorporation, N.A.
  One South Main, Salt Lake City, UT 84133
Phone: 801 844-7637
Web: www.zionsbancorporation.com

PRODUCTS/OPERATIONS

Selected Subsidiaries
Amegy Corporation
California Bank & Trust
National Bank of Arizona
Nevada State Bank
The Commerce Bank of Washington
Vectra Bank Colorado
ZB National Association

2017 Sales

	$ mil.	% of total
Interest income		
Interest and fees on loans	1,847	68
Interest on securities	19	1
Interest on money market investment	326	12
Non-interest income		
Other service charges commission and fees	217	8
Service charges and fees on deposit accounts	171	6
Wealth management income	42	2
Loan sales and servicing income 1		**25**
Dividends and other investment income	40	1
Capital markets and foreign Exchange	30	1
Equity securities gains net	14	-
Others	5	-
Total	**2,736**	**100**

COMPETITORS

BOK Financial
Bank of America
Bank of the West
Capital One
Citigroup
Cullen/Frost Bankers
First National of Nebraska

Great Western Bancorp
JPMorgan Chase
MUFG Americas Holdings
Prosperity Bancshares
U.S. Bancorp
Washington Federal
Wells Fargo

Company Type: Public

	ASSETS ($ mil.)	NET INCOME ($ mil.)	INCOME AS % OF ASSETS	EMPLOYEES
12/18	68,746	884	1.3%	10,201
12/17	66,288	592	0.9%	10,083
12/16	63,239	469	0.7%	10,057
12/15	59,670	309	0.5%	10,200
12/14	57,209	398	0.7%	10,462
Annual Growth	4.7%	22.0%	—	(0.6%)

2018 Year-End Financials

Debt ratio: 1.00%	No. of shares (mil.): 188
Return on equity: 12.00%	Dividends
Cash ($ mil.): 1,233	Yield: 1.0%
Current ratio: —	Payout: 9.0%
Long-term debt ($ mil.): —	Market value ($ mil.): 7,641

	STOCK PRICE ($) FY Close	P/E High/Low		PER SHARE ($) Earnings	Dividends	Book Value
12/18	41.00	13	9	4.00	0.00	40.00
12/17	51.00	19	14	3.00	0.00	39.00
12/16	43.00	22	10	2.00	0.00	38.00
12/15	27.00	27	20	1.00	0.00	37.00
12/14	29.00	20	15	2.00	0.00	36.00
Annual Growth	9.3%	—		24.8%	17.0%	2.7%

Zoetis Inc

Whether you have cats or cattle Zoetis has medicines to keep them healthy. The company manufactures and sells veterinary products such as parasiticides (to protect against fleas ticks and worms) anti-infectives medicated feed additives vaccines and other pharmaceuticals for companion and farm animals. Zoetis boasts more than 300 product lines sold in more than 100 countries around the world making it one of the world's largest animal health businesses. In addition to medications and vaccines Zoetis offers diagnostics genetic tests devices and services such as dairy data management and consulting.

Operations

Zoetis makes about 55% of its sales from medicines and vaccines for livestock (including cattle swine poultry and fish) which assist in the global food supply chain. Products for companion animals such as dogs cats and horses bring in some 45% of sales.

The company's offerings are diverse — with 300 different lines no single product accounts for more than 10% of sales. This give Zoetis a lack of dependence on any specific product offerings and allows it to meet the needs of customers in various geographies and specialties. Its top sellers include canine dermatitis treatment Apoquel antibiotic Draxxin the ceftiofur antibiotic line (sold under the brands Excede Excenel Spectramast and Naxcel) and antiparasitics Revolution and Stronghold.

Vaccine sales provide more than a quarter of total revenues followed by anti-infectives (over 20%) parasiticides (about 15%) medicated feed additives (about 10%) and other pharmaceuticals including allergy dermatology oncology reproductive sedation and pain medicines (some 25%). The remaining earnings come from non-pharmaceuticals (nutritionals and agribusiness) diagnostics and contract manufacturing services provided to third parties.

Geographic Reach

The US is Parsippany New Jersey-based Zoetis' largest single market accounting for about half of all sales. Internationally the company operates in Europe the Middle East Africa the Asia/Pacific region Canada and Latin America. Emerging markets including Brazil China and Mexico contribute more than 20% of sales.

Zoetis has about 25 manufacturing plants in a dozen countries as well as 20 research centers in 10 countries. Of these properties 10 plants and five research facilities are located in the US. The company's largest research and development (1.5 million-sq.-ft.) and manufacturing (0.6 million-sq-ft.) facilities are located in Kalamazoo Michigan. It also relies on about 170 contract manufacturers (including former parent Pfizer).

Sales and Marketing

Zoetis has a direct sales presence in 45 countries (in the Americas Europe the Asia/Pacific region and Africa) where it sells directly to livestock producers and veterinarians. In the nearly 60 other countries where it does not have a direct sales presence the company uses distributors. The company's top two customers both distribution firms together account for 20% of sales.

Zoetis's products are available by prescription from veterinarians. The company also sells directly to retail outlets including farming supply outlets pet stores and pharmacies. Some livestock products are sold directly to ranchers.

Marketing efforts target veterinarians livestock producers and pet owners. Advertising and promotional expenses in 2018 totaled some $158 million compared to $154 million in 2017 and $119 million in 2016.

Financial Performance

New product sales and acquisitions have driven Zoetis' revenue steadily up over the past five years with the exception of flat sales in 2015. Net income also increased each year excluding a drop in 2015 due to restructuring and acquisition-related expenses. Overall revenue rose 22% over the period and net income nearly tripled.

Revenue increased 10% to $5.8 billion in 2018. Growth largely occurred in the companion animal segment which reported a 17% revenue increase on higher sales of key dermatology products sales of new products including Simparica and the acquisition of diagnostics firm Abaxis. Livestock revenue rose 4% on increased product sales and new product launches. Geographically US sales rose 10% and international sales increased 9%.

Net income rose 65% to $1.4 billion in 2018 in tandem with higher revenue. The company also benefited from lower provisions for income taxes related to the 2017 Tax Act.

Zoetis ended 2018 with $1.6 billion in cash up by about $38 million from 2017. Operating activities contributed $1.8 billion while investing activities used $2.2 billion (mostly on the Abaxis acquisition) and financing activities contributed $533 million via an expanded credit line.

Strategy

With a focus on animals Zoetis enjoys certain benefits over human pharmaceutical makers including less-rigorous regulatory processes shorter research and development times (about three years) and lower expenses. In addition pet owners and ranchers pay out-of-pocket for products so Zoetis doesn't have to wait for insurance reimbursement.

To broaden its portfolio the company develops new products and expands existing product lines to new species. New products launched in 2018 include the Core EQ Innovator vaccine and the Stronghold Plus/Revolution Plus antiparasitic. In 2018 Zoetis spent some $432 million on research and development compared to $382 million in 2017 and $376 million in 2016.

Zoetis' plan for sustained growth includes expanding in emerging markets where economic development is raising demand for both livestock and companion animals. The company is pursuing growth in Brazil China and India by introducing more expensive products.

The company also expands its product offerings and geographic reach through acquisitions as well as by expanding or building research and manufacturing facilities. Zoetis plans to build on its 2018 purchase of companion diagnostics firm Abaxis by branching into livestock diagnostics. It is building a vaccine R&D and manufacturing facility in Suzhou China and is expanding its plant in Kalamazoo Michigan.

Like human pharmaceutical makers Zoetis must keep its pipeline robust to minimize the impact of losing patents and the exclusivity of its products. The firm has a number of patents expiring over the next few years including active ingredients in its Draxxin antibiotic and Revolution antiparasitic products. Sales of its pain medicine Rimadyl are already declining due to generic competition.

Mergers and Acquisitions

Zoetis has made a number of key acquisitions recently but its largest deal was completed in 2018. That year the company purchased Abaxis which makes veterinary diagnostic equipment for some $2 billion. Among Abaxis' recent offerings is its test to detect heartworm and Lyme disease in dogs. The purchase boosts Zoetis' position in the growing animal diagnostics market.

The company also expanded into digital technologies and data analytics through the purchase of Smartbow which uses bovine electronic ear tags and machine learning to collect and analyze health and behavioral data; the two companies had formed a partnership the previous year.

Company Background

Formerly named Pfizer Animal Health Zoetis was separated from former parent Pfizer in 2013 in an initial public offering worth some $2.2 billion.

Acquisitions following the spinoff have included the 2016 purchase of Scandinavian company Micro Bio-devices a specialist in diagnostics for veterinary point-of-care services ($80 million) and the 2017 purchase of Nexvet Biopharma which is developing monoclonal antibody therapies to ease pain in pets ($85 million).

EXECUTIVES

Evp And Cio, Andrew Fenton

Ceo, Juan R. Alaix, age 68, $1,150,000 total compensation

Evp And Group President, Kristin C. Peck, age 48, $636,375 total compensation

Evp; President Us Operations, Clinton A. (Clint) Lewis, age 53, $630,054 total compensation

Evp; President Europe Africa And Middle East Region, Alejandro Bernal, age 47

Evp And General Counsel, Heidi C. Chen, age 53

Evp; President Research And Development, Catherine A. (Cathy) Knupp, age 59, $499,625 total compensation

Evp And Chief Human Resources Officer, Roxanne Lagano, age 55

Evp And Cfo, Glenn C. David, $483,030 total compensation

Evp; President Global Manufacturing And Supply, Roman Trawicki, age 56

Vice President Financial Shared Service, Dean Mullane

Vice President U.s. Pork Business Unit, Gloria Basse

Vice President Pharma And Aseptic Operations, Matt Everhart

Vice President External Innovation, Scott Brown
Av President, Fabiana Pires Carvalho
Chairman, Michael B. McCallister, age 67
Board Member, William Steere
Board Member, Frank D'amelio
Assistant Treasurer, Scott Hunter
Auditors: KPMG LLP

LOCATIONS

HQ: Zoetis Inc
  10 Sylvan Way, Parsippany, NJ 07054
Phone: 973 822-7000
Web: www.zoetis.com

2017 Sales

	$ mil.	% of total
International	2,643	50
US	2,620	49
Contract manufacturing	44	1
Total	**5,307**	**100**

PRODUCTS/OPERATIONS

2017 Sales

	$ mil.	% of total
Livestock	3,037	57
Companion animals	2,226	42
Contract manufacturing	44	1
Total	**5,307**	**100**

2017 Sales by Product

	$ mil.	% of total
Vaccines	1,373	26
Anti-infectives	1,253	24
Parasiticides	763	14
Medicated feed additives	475	9
Other pharmaceuticals	1,181	22
Other non-pharmaceuticals	218	4
Contract manufacturing	44	1
Total	**5,307**	**100**

Selected Species

Beef Cattle
Cats
Dairy Cattle
Dogs
Fish
Horses
Pigs
Poultry
Sheep
Product line / ProductAnti-infectivesCeftiofur injectable
  lineDraxxin®;Spectramast®;Terramycin®;
  lineVaccinesBovi-Shield lineRispoval lineSuvaxyn PCV
  / Fostera PCVParasiticidesCydectinDectomaxMedicated
  Feed AdditivesAureomycinBMDLasalocid lin

COMPETITORS

American Animal Health	IDEXX Labs
Bayer Animal Health	Kindred Biosciences
Boehringer Ingelheim	Merck Animal Health
Dechra Pharmaceuticals	Phibro Animal Health
ECO Animal Health	Skystar
Eli Lilly	Virbac
Heska	Vétoquinol

HISTORICAL FINANCIALS

Company Type: Public

Income Statement

FYE: December 31

	REVENUE ($ mil.)	NET INCOME ($ mil.)	NET PROFIT MARGIN	EMPLOYEES
12/18	5,825	1,428	24.5%	10,000
12/17	5,307	864	16.3%	9,200
12/16	4,888	821	16.8%	9,000
12/15	4,765	339	7.1%	9,000
12/14	4,785	583	12.2%	10,000
Annual Growth	5.0%	25.1%	—	0.0%

2018 Year-End Financials

Debt ratio: 60.00%
Return on equity: 72.00%
Cash ($ mil.): 1,602
Current ratio: 4.00
Long-term debt ($ mil.): 6,443

No. of shares (mil.): 480
Dividends
  Yield: 1.0%
  Payout: 21.0%
Market value ($ mil.): 41,022

	STOCK PRICE ($) FY Close	P/E High/Low		PER SHARE ($) Earnings	Dividends	Book Value
12/18	86.00	32	24	3.00	1.00	5.00
12/17	72.00	41	30	2.00	0.00	4.00
12/16	54.00	32	24	2.00	0.00	3.00
12/15	48.00	81	58	1.00	0.00	2.00
12/14	43.00	39	24	1.00	0.00	3.00
Annual Growth	18.7%	—	—	26.1%	15.0%	14.9%

Hoover's Handbook of

American Business

The Indexes

Index by Headquarters

AK

Anchorage
First National Bank Alaska 347

JUNEAU
ALASKA PERMANENT FUND
CORPORATION 29

AL

Birmingham
Regions Financial Corp (New) 711
Alabama Power Co 27
Protective Life Insurance Co 683
ProAssurance Corp 678
ServisFirst Bancshares Inc 754

AR

Bentonville
Walmart Inc 900

Conway
Home BancShares Inc 426

El Dorado
Murphy USA Inc 579

Little Rock
Dillard's Inc. 267
Windstream Holdings Inc 923
Bank OZK 113

Lowell
Hunt (J.B.) Transport Services, Inc.
441

Pine Bluff
Simmons First National Corp 759

Springdale
Tyson Foods Inc 854

AZ

Chandler
Microchip Technology Inc 563

PEORIA
R. DIRECTIONAL DRILLING &
UNDERGROUND TECHNOLOGY,
INC. 700

Phoenix
Avnet Inc 99
Freeport-McMoRan Inc 365
Republic Services Inc 720
Southern Copper Corp 771
ON Semiconductor Corp 627
Knight-Swift Transportation Holdings
Inc 495
Sprouts Farmers Market Inc 775

Western Alliance Bancorporation 912
BANNER HEALTH 116

Scottsdale
Magellan Health Inc. 531

Tempe
Insight Enterprises Inc. 457

CA

Beverly Hills
Live Nation Entertainment Inc 521
PacWest Bancorp 638

Burbank
Disney (Walt) Co. (The) 271

Chico
TriCo Bancshares (Chico, CA) 846

Cupertino
Apple Inc 72

Dublin
Ross Stores Inc 730

Foster City
Gilead Sciences Inc 385

Fremont
Synnex Corp 794
Lam Research Corp 505

Glendale
Avery Dennison Corp 96

Irvine
Pacific Premier Bancorp Inc 636
Opus Bank (Irvine, CA) 631
First Foundation Inc 342
PACIFIC PREMIER BANK 636

La Jolla
Silvergate Capital Corp 759

Lodi
Farmers & Merchants Bancorp (Lodi,
CA) 313

Long Beach
Molina Healthcare Inc 570
Farmers & Merchants Bank of Long
Beach (CA) 313

Los Angeles
CBRE Group Inc 174
AECOM 15
Reliance Steel & Aluminum Co. 716
Mercury General Corp. 555
Cathay General Bancorp 174
Hope Bancorp Inc 431
Hanmi Financial Corp. 403
Preferred Bank (Los Angeles, CA) 675
RBB Bancorp 707
American Business Bank (Los Angeles,
CA) 50

CAPITAL INCOME BUILDER, INC.
166
AMERICAN HIGH INCOME TRUST
56
AMCAP FUND INC 45

Los Gatos
Netflix Inc 586

Menlo Park
Facebook Inc 310
Robert Half International Inc. 725

Mill Valley
Redwood Trust Inc 709

Mountain View
Alphabet Inc 38
Intuit Inc 470

Newport Beach
Chipotle Mexican Grill Inc 192

Novato
Bank of Marin Bancorp 110

Oakland
Clorox Co (The) 207
KAISER FOUNDATION HOSPITALS
INC 484
CHEVRON FEDERAL CREDIT UNION
191

Ontario
CVB Financial Corp 249

Palo Alto
HP Inc 437
Tesla Inc 817
VMware Inc 896

Pasadena
East West Bancorp, Inc 284
Western Asset Mortgage Capital Corp
913

Porterville
Sierra Bancorp 757

Redwood City
Oracle Corp 632

ROCKLIN
FARM CREDIT WEST 313

Rosemead
Edison International 289
Southern California Edison Co. 769

SACRAMENTO
STATE OF CALIFORNIA 782
SUTTER HEALTH 791

San Diego
Qualcomm Inc 694
Sempra Energy 752
AXOS BANK 100
AMERICAN ASSETS TRUST, INC. 48

San Francisco
Wells Fargo & Co (New) 908
Visa Inc 895
PG&E Corp (Holding Co) 659
The Gap Inc 825
Federal Reserve Bank of San
Francisco, Dist. No. 12 321
Salesforce.Com Inc 738
Uber Technologies Inc 856
Schwab (Charles) Corp (The) 745
Levi Strauss & Co. 513
Williams Sonoma Inc 921
First Republic Bank (San Francisco,
CA) 349
Federal Home Loan Bank Of San
Francisco 318
LendingClub Corp 511
DIGNITY HEALTH 265
LEVI STRAUSS & CO. 513
AMERICAN BALANCED FUND, INC.
50
THE IRVINE JAMES FOUNDATION
827

San Jose
Cisco Systems Inc 197
Hewlett Packard Enterprise Co 419
PayPal Holdings Inc 643
Western Digital Corp 913
Adobe Inc 11
eBay Inc. 286
Sanmina Corp 741
Heritage Commerce Corp 414

San Mateo
Franklin Resources Inc 362

San Rafael
WestAmerica Bancorporation 911

San Ramon
Chevron Corporation 189

Santa Ana
First American Financial Corp 331
Banc Of California Inc 103

Santa Clara
Intel Corp 459
Applied Materials, Inc. 73
NVIDIA Corp 612
Advanced Micro Devices Inc 13
Agilent Technologies, Inc. 22
SVB Financial Group 792

Santa Monica
Activision Blizzard, Inc. 9
Anworth Mortgage Asset Corp. 70

Santa Rosa
Luther Burbank Corp 529
Exchange Bank (Santa Rosa, CA) 303
REDWOOD CREDIT UNION 709

Oak Ridge
Lakeland Bancorp, Inc. 503

Parsippany
PBF Energy Inc 643
Avis Budget Group Inc 97
Zoetis Inc 941

Princeton
NRG Energy Inc 610

Red Bank
OceanFirst Financial Corp 618

Roseland
Automatic Data Processing Inc. 93

Secaucus
Quest Diagnostics, Inc. 697

Short Hills
Investors Bancorp Inc (New) 472

SOMERSET
SHI INTERNATIONAL CORP. 757

Teaneck
Cognizant Technology Solutions Corp. 216

Union
Bed, Bath & Beyond, Inc. 124

Woodbridge
Northfield Bancorp Inc (DE) 607
DHPC TECHNOLOGIES, INC. 264

NV

Las Vegas
Las Vegas Sands Corp 506
MGM Resorts International 561
Caesars Entertainment Corp 159
Wynn Resorts Ltd 929
Axos Financial Inc 100

Reno
Employers Holdings Inc 293

NY

ALBANY
STATE UNIVERSITY OF NEW YORK 784
SEFCU SERVICES, LLC 751

Armonk
International Business Machines Corp 464

Bridgehampton
Bridge Bancorp, Inc. (Bridgehampton, NY) 149

Brooklyn
Dime Community Bancshares, Inc 268

Buffalo
M & T Bank Corp 529

Corning
Corning Inc 239

DeWitt
Community Bank System Inc 226

Glen Head
First of Long Island Corp 348

Glens Falls
Arrow Financial Corp. 82

Glenville
Trustco Bank Corp. (N.Y.) 851

Ithaca
Tompkins Financial Corp 838
TOMPKINS TRUST COMPANY 839

Long Island City
Altice USA Inc 39
JetBlue Airways Corp 477

Melville
Schein (Henry) Inc 743

Montebello
Sterling Bancorp (DE) 786

New York
JPMorgan Chase & Co 482
Verizon Communications Inc 889
Citigroup Inc 202
MetLife Inc 558
Federal Reserve Bank of New York, Dist. No. 2 319
Pfizer Inc 657
Goldman Sachs Group Inc 389
Morgan Stanley 573
American International Group Inc 57
American Express Co. 53
INTL FCStone Inc. 469
Travelers Companies Inc (The) 843
Philip Morris International Inc 660
Bristol-Myers Squibb Co. 151
Bank of New York Mellon Corp 111
Colgate-Palmolive Co. 217
Omnicom Group, Inc. 625
Marsh & McLennan Companies Inc. 539
Lauder (Estee) Cos., Inc. (The) 507
ViacomCBS Inc 892
BlackRock Inc 134
Loews Corp. 524
Consolidated Edison Inc 234
Equitable Holdings Inc 301
Icahn Enterprises LP 450
Fox Corp 362
Consolidated Edison Co. of New York, Inc. 234
News Corp (New) 595
Interpublic Group of Companies Inc. 468
PVH Corp 691
Coty, Inc. 242
Voya Financial Inc 898
Assurant Inc 87
Foot Locker, Inc. 358
Sirius XM Holdings Inc 762
Alleghany Corp. 31
Blackstone Group Inc (The) 136
S&P Global Inc 737
HSBC USA, Inc. 439
ABM Industries, Inc. 7
Hess Corp 418
Ralph Lauren Corp 701
Tapestry Inc 801
National General Holdings Corp 581
Federal Home Loan Bank New York 317
CIT Group Inc (New) 199
E*TRADE Financial Corp 282
Annaly Capital Management Inc 68
Signature Bank (New York, NY) 758
Valley National Bancorp (NJ) 887
Chimera Investment Corp 191
Two Harbors Investment Corp 853
Ladder Capital Corp 503
Ambac Financial Group, Inc. 43
Metropolitan Bank Holding Corp 560
AG Mortgage Investment Trust Inc 20
THE TURNER CORPORATION 829
TURNER CONSTRUCTION COMPANY INC 853
NEW YORK CITY HEALTH AND HOSPITALS CORPORATION 588
METROPOLITAN TRANSPORTATION AUTHORITY 560

NEW YORK UNIVERSITY 591
THE NEW YORK AND PRESBYTERIAN HOSPITAL 827
TATA AMERICA INTERNATIONAL CORPORATION 805
NIELSEN HOLDINGS PLC 599
SIGNATURE FINANCIAL LLC 759
RECKSON OPERATING PARTNERSHIP, L.P. 708
VIRTU FINANCIAL LLC 895
THE SIMONS FOUNDATION INC 829
THE FORD FOUNDATION 825
BRIXMOR LLC 152
NEW YORK COMMUNITY TRUST AND COMMUNITY FUNDS INC 590
STATE OF NEW YORK MORTGAGE AGENCY 782

Norwich
NBT Bancorp. Inc. 583

Purchase
PepsiCo Inc 653
Mastercard Inc 543
MBIA Inc. 546

REGO PARK
NEW YORK STATE CATHOLIC HEALTH PLAN, INC. 590

ROCHESTER
HOME PROPERTIES, LIMITED PARTNERSHIP 428

Rye Brook
Xylem Inc 935

Tarrytown
Regeneron Pharmaceuticals, Inc. 709

Uniondale
Flushing Financial Corp. 356

Victor
Constellation Brands Inc 236

Warsaw
Financial Institutions Inc. 330

Westbury
New York Community Bancorp Inc. 589

OH

Akron
Goodyear Tire & Rubber Co. 391
FirstEnergy Corp 350

Canfield
Farmers National Banc Corp. (Canfield,OH) 314

Cincinnati
Kroger Co (The) 497
Procter & Gamble Company (The) 679
Macy's Inc 531
Fifth Third Bancorp (Cincinnati, OH) 327
American Financial Group Inc 55
Cintas Corporation 196
Federal Home Loan Bank Of Cincinnati 318
First Financial Bancorp (OH) 339
GENERAL ELECTRIC INTERNATIONAL, INC. 375
PHILLIPS EDISON - ARC SHOPPING CENTER REIT INC. 663

Cleveland
Sherwin-Williams Co (The) 755
Parker Hannifin Corp 639
KeyCorp 490
TransDigm Group Inc 841

TFS Financial Corp 822
THE CLEVELAND CLINIC FOUNDATION 824
EATON CORPORATION 286

Columbus
American Electric Power Co Inc 50
L Brands, Inc 499
Alliance Data Systems Corp. 33
Huntington Bancshares Inc 443
Big Lots, Inc. 131
State Auto Financial Corp. 781

Defiance
First Defiance Financial Corp 339

Dublin
Cardinal Health, Inc. 169

Fairfield
Cincinnati Financial Corp. 194

Findlay
Marathon Petroleum Corp. 534
MPLX LP 578

Marietta
Peoples Bancorp Inc (Marietta, OH) 652

Maumee
Dana Inc 253

Mayfield Village
Progressive Corp. (OH) 680

Medina
RPM International Inc (DE) 732

Newark
Park National Corp (Newark, OH) 639

Orrville
Smucker (J.M.) Co. 764

Perrysburg
O-I Glass Inc 616

Sandusky
Civista Bancshares Inc 206

Toledo
Owens Corning 634

West Chester
AK Steel Holding Corp. 26

Westlake
TravelCenters of America Inc 842

OK

Oklahoma City
Devon Energy Corp. 263
Chesapeake Energy Corp. 188
BancFirst Corp. (Oklahoma City, Okla) 104
CANDID COLOR SYSTEMS, INC. 165
STATE OF OKLAHOMA 782

Tulsa
NGL Energy Partners LP 598
ONEOK Inc 629
Williams Cos Inc (The) 921
BOK Financial Corp 141
ONEOK PARTNERS, L.P. 631

OR

Beaverton
NIKE Inc 599

Medford
Lithia Motors Inc 520

Index of Executives

A

Aaefedt, Matthew 877
Aaholm, Sherry A 247
Aakre, Scott 434
Aaron, Thomas J. (Tom) 228
Aaron, Susan 433
Aase, Rune 301
Aass, Luke 25
Abad, Rafael Lopez 771
Abadir, Jeffrey 242
Abadir, Jeff 242
Abarca, Jose 654
Abate, Victor (Vic) 374
Abate, Christopher J. 709
Abba, Diego 10
Abbamondi, Desa 921
Abbasi, Azher 319
Abbate, Mark L. 556
Abbate, Sam 608
Abbene, David 540
Abbey, Jared 126
Abbey, Anna B 790
Abbey, Anna 790
Abbondante, Joseph 726
Abbott, Lynn 60
Abbott, Todd 533
Abbott, Sarah 562
Abbott, Beth 686
Abbott, Mark 704
Abbott, Dean 715
Abbott, Greg 782
Abboud, Andy 506
Abboud, Ali El 783
Abdella, Shelly 906
Abdoo, Elizabeth A. 436
Abdullah, Rao 401
Abe, Karrie 791
Abel, Greg 127
Abel, Donna 248
Abel, Brandi 437
Abel, Bryon 528
Abel, Melissa 818
Abel-Hodges, Cheryl 692
Abela, John 559
Abell, Elaine 450
Abellera, Philip 723
Abelli, Donna L. 455
Abello, Marc P 222
Abelman, David 722
Abercrombie, John 771
Abiteboul, Jean 187
Abji, Minaz B. 436
Abkin, Kimberly 325
Abler, Bill 296
Ables, Grady L. 71
Abney, David P. 870
Aboaf, Eric 783
Abood, Steven 715
Aboulafia, Joseph 111
Abraham, Jai 242
Abraham, JJ 512
Abraham, Frank 569
Abraham, Biju 895
Abrahamson, Laura 16
Abramowicz, Daniel A. 245
Abrams, Sarah 147
Abrams, Murray 166
Abrams, Ed 465
Abreu, Christopher 408
Abston, Chris L 599
Abston, Angie 866
Abts, Brad 85
Abts, Joy 885
Abutaleb, Sam 831
Accogli, Giuseppe 119
Acevedo, Alejandro 538
Ach, J. Wickliffe 340

Ach, J 340
Ach, Joseph 925
Achary, Michael M. 401
Acharya, Guru 927
Achenbach, Mark 509
Achkire, Debra 349
Acito, Paiul 3
Acito, Joe 329
Ackerman, Michelle 36
Ackerman, Joel 257
Ackerman, Brian 482
Ackerman, Dean M 508
Ackermann, Peter 107
Ackerson, Vince A. 818
Ackroyd, Jim 9
Acoca, Bernard 779
Acosta, Jennifer 483
Acosta, Navia 590
Acott, Sarah 137
Acquafredda, Rita 744
Acton, Michael 741
Acutt, Nicola 897
Adair, Charles 389
Adair, Bryan 465
Adair, Charles 809
Adam, Rolf 458
Adam, David 606
Adamczyk, Darius 431
Adame, Pedro 921
Adamich, John 843
Adamo, Terri 325
Adamo, John 686
Adamos, Tara 452
Adams, Dennis 36
Adams, John 85
Adams, Brian 91
Adams, Douglas 100
Adams, Michael 154
Adams, Robert 171
Adams, Kraig 215
Adams, Kevin D 235
Adams, Melissa 246
Adams, Bruce 249
Adams, Craig L. 304
Adams, Isaac 409
Adams, Lisan 413
Adams, Michael 444
Adams, Joseph 460
Adams, David 462
Adams, Gregory A. 485
Adams, Amy 525
Adams, Calvin 527
Adams, Romaneo 540
Adams, Jennifer 540
Adams, Fay 571
Adams, John 590
Adams, Erin 592
Adams, Ann 604
Adams, Annie 604
Adams, Matt 606
Adams, Scott 621
Adams, Cathryn 658
Adams, D. Scott 683
Adams, Jennifer 709
Adams, Wayne 714
Adams, Patricia (Trish) 804
Adams, Trish 804
Adams, Tim 811
Adams, Dian 811
Adams, Jess 859
Adams, Richard M. 865
Adams, Gayle 876
Adams, Sherry 902
Adams, Nicholas 922
Adamson, Nancy 117
Adamson, Adam 133
Adan, Paul 538
Adcock, Robert H. 426
Addiego, Gino 74

Addison, Linda 389
Addison, Ann M. 509
Addison, James 538
Addison, John 676
Addy, R Mark 663
Adelman, Marty 16
Adelson, Sarah 319
Adelson, Sheldon G. 506
Adesnik, Ryan 510
Adger, Ellis 354
Adham, Allen 10
Adiletta, Mark 530
Adkerson, Richard C. 365
Adkins, Dan 228
Adkins, Chuck 461
Adkins, Rodney 674
Adkins, Rodney 871
Adkison, Jeffrey 481
Adler, Dean S 125
Adler, Paul F. 197
Adornato, Theodore C. (Ted) 774
Adornetto, Charles 646
Adreani, Lou 784
Aertker, Gayle 158
Agarwal, Anil 54
Agarwal, Pankaj 203
Agarwal, Sahil 484
Agarwal, Achal 493
Agarwal, Manu 574
Agarwal, Parag 628
Agate, Chris 731
Agathoklis, Mariana 890
Aggarwal, Rohit 447
Aggarwal, Lokesh 784
Aghai-Yazdy, Dana 794
Aghili, Aziz S 253
Agiasotis, Kerry 915
Agnello, Alexis 530
Agnew, John 921
Agnos, Alexandra 751
Agostini, Joseph 877
Agostino, Rich 804
Agrawal, Nancy 554
Agrawal, Rajesh K. (Raj) 915
Agresta, Richard 751
Agricola, Michael 329
Agroskin, Daniel 156
Agudio, Sharon 704
Aguila, Alex 902
Aguilar, Alfredo 219
Aguilar, Douglas 318
Aguilar, Edgard Corrales 771
Aguilar, Corinna 780
Aguinaga, Liz 525
Aguirre, Pascal 216
Aguirre, Edward 489
Aguirre, Jean 540
Aguirre, Vanessa 623
Aguirre, Adrian 921
Agulnek, Barbara 409
Agusti, Sandra 107
Agyen, George 405
Ahearn, Tracey 527
Ahee, Joseph 444
Ahern, R 320
Ahern, Michael 390
Ahern, Patrick 796
Ahlmann, Kaj 723
Ahmad, Usman 613
Ahmad-Taylor, Ty 310
Ahmar, Wasim 14
Ahmed, Anwar 111
Ahmed, Riffat K 414
Ahmed, Sohail U. 460
Ahmed, Michael 855
Ahn, Sang 432
Ahn, Janice 793
Aho, Todd R 414

Ahrendts, Angela 72
Ahrens, Shelly 538
Ahrens, Steve 686
Ahrens, Blake 723
Ahuja, Deepak 818
Aichele, William S. 881
Aicher, Allison 713
Aidi, Ali 544
Aiken, Jim 19
Aiken, Jason W. 373
Aiken, Scott 933
Aing, Melissa 552
Ainsworth, Julie 750
Aiosa, Lisa 701
Aires, Dave 460
Aitken, Murray L. 474
Ajdaharian, Paul 761
Akalski, Frank J. 356
Akbar, Mehrdad 902
Akbarzadeh, Hosai 167
Akhtar, Muhammad 530
Akin, Virginia 367
Akin, Stacie 682
Akins, Nicholas K. (Nick) 51
Akins, D. Wayne 796
Akinwande, Wale 738
Akolawala, Joher 573
Akotia, Dennis 571
Akrout, Chekib 14
Aksdal, Roy 166
Al-joulani, Omar 522
Al-Khudhair, Mariam 251
Alabran, Jeffrey 211
Alaix, Juan R. 941
Alam, Mahmood 658
Alam, Danesh 877
Alama, Bernie 109
Alameddine, Rima 613
Alban, Carlos 6
Alban, Susan 922
Albanese, William 449
Albanese, Gerard 536
Albanesi, David 885
Albarado, Rose 296
Alber, Laura 921
Alberico, Robert 742
Albers, Lisa 142
Albert, Don 287
Albert, Scott 391
Albert, Justin 727
Albert, Gary 749
Albert, James 845
Albertson, Paul 588
Albi, Chris 498
Albinson, Brock 93
Albor, John 352
Albouy, Laurent 692
Albrecht, Vicki 63
Albrecht, Geoffrey 698
Albrecht, Julie 768
Albright, Steven 782
Alchin, John R 702
Alcorn, Lee 528
Alday, Truitt 481
Alden, John 871
Alderman, Keith 123
Alderman, Mark 540
Alderman, Marian 852
Alderoty, Stuart 200
Alderson, Christopher D. 799
Aldrete, Eddie 463
Aldridge, Tracey 717
Aleardi, Keith P 368
Alec, Pittman 905
Alekseeva, Marina B 461
Aleksic, Aleksandar 15
Aleman-Bermudez, Aurelio 333
Alemany, Ellen R. 200
Alena, Luz 164

Blake, Tim 630
Blake, Christopher D. 638
Blake, David M. 677
Blake, Lynn S. 783
Blake, Ellen 891
Blakemore, Jim 232
Blakemore, Anthony 770
Blakeney, John 224
Blakewood, Benjamin F. 22
Blalock, Pam 559
Blanc, Farron 715
Blanc, Christian 936
Blanchard, Dan 262
Blanchard, Brent 518
Blanco, Alex 289
Bland, Maryanne 153
Bland, Christine 343
Bland, Mickey 458
Blankenship, Charles P. (Chip) 79
Blankenship, Dave 538
Blankfein, Lloyd C. 390
Blankmeyer, Erik 807
Blanton, Hamilton 166
Blase, William A. (Bill) 89
Blaser, Brian J. 5
Blasini, David P 167
Blaske, Stephen 60
Blasko, Michael 848
Blatcher, Kevin 164
Blaug, Suzanne 64
Blaya, Richard 891
Blaylock, Isaac 756
Blazejewski, Steve 169
Blazer, Robert 536
Bledsoe, Vallerie M 324
Bledsoe, Steve 400
Bledsoe, Matthew 713
Bleisch, N. David 620
Blerman, Mike 811
Bleske, Mitchell 867
Bless, Michael 210
Blestowe, James 59
Blevins, Tony 72
Blevins, P. Rodney 275
Blevins, Meriem 329
Blew, Clinton J. (C.J.) 194
Bley, Daniel H. 906
Bleyl, Steven 462
Blihovde, Valerie 804
Blincoe, Donna 719
Blinder, Warren 800
Blissett, Julian 378
Blitzer, David S. 137
Blivice, Marni 137
Bloch, Jeremy 180
Bloch, Nick 831
Block, Robert 36
Block, Seth 296
Block, Keith G. 739
Blocker, Jeff 527
Blocker, Jeffrey 527
Blocker, Adrian M. 918
Blondia, Jeanne 789
Blood, Richard 544
Bloodgood, Debra 609
Bloom, Leah 7
Bloom, Brent 74
Bloom, Richard S 213
Bloom, William A. (Bill) 408
Bloom, Alfred H. 592
Bloom, Ronnie 831
Blose, James 786
Blough, Lynn E 460
Blount, Sally 5
Blount, Eddie 665
Bloxam, Richard 481
Bludau, Laurence 228
Bludworth, Jed 72
Blue, Robert M. (Bob) 275
Blue, Tamara 746
Blue, Robert M. 894
Blum, Jeffrey 271
Blum, Donald W. 684
Blum, Jason 746
Blume, Brent 885
Blumenfeld, Stephen 391
Blumensaadt, Karen 713

Blumer, David J. 135
Blumeyer, Greg 215
Blumhardt, James 910
Blundell, Alan 527
Blundon, Lee 908
Blunt, Chris 137
Blunt, Mary L. 754
Bluth, Tom 173
Blutman, Gary 505
Blye, Jeffrey C 320
Blyth, Lord 68
Blyth, Lesley 779
Blyze, Scott 264
Boada, Robert C 770
Boas, Nancy 702
Boatright, Michael 686
Bobb, Stevan B. 138
Bobb, Stevan B. 157
Bobbie, Frances D 727
Bober, Sharon 641
Bobitz, Ward E. 381
Bobrow, Michelle 786
Bobrowsky, Bill 711
Boccardo, James 867
Bochette, William C. 769
Bockhorst, Daniel E. 181
Bockhorst, Cheri 203
Bodakowski, Steven 651
Bodapati, Ramesh 199
Bodenhafer, Scott 520
Bodenheimer, George 762
Bodi, Attila 254
Bodine, Bruce 576
Bodisch, Laurie 368
Bodman, Ryan 544
Bodnar, Vincent 381
Body, Frederick 885
Boe, Ryan 571
Boe, Douglas 885
Boedeker, Kenneth W. 301
Boegner, Scott 837
Boehn, Michael 224
Boehnlein, Glenn 789
Boeing, Traci 908
Boeka, Amy 452
Boelstler, Doreen 222
Boening, Bj 533
Boersma, Brad 329
Boesch, Marc 835
Boeshaar, Brad 859
Bogan, Gary 444
Boggess, Michael 108
Boggetto, Brian 305
Boggs, Gregory 170
Boggs, Rod 559
Boggs, Darrell 613
Bogler, John A. 104
Bognar, Paul 920
Boguski, Michael L. 678
Bohaboy, Scott 119
Bohannon, Jason 442
Bohanon, Chris 317
Bohaty, Brian R. 35
Bohbrink, Marshall 399
Bohl, Chris 219
Bohl, Nicki 226
Bohling, Brian 418
Bohlinger, Thomas 175
Bohlke, Sherri 725
Bohm, David 321
Bohmler, April 540
Bohn, William M. 85
Bohn, Don 479
Bohnen, Jennifer 925
Bohnsack, Gary 494
Bohrer, Scott 428
Boigegrain, Barbara 347
Boike, Brian D.J. 353
Boim, Dave 571
Boisier, Pierre 123
Boisten, Bernd 724
Boisvert, Laura 281
Boitano, Robert 327
Bojanowski, Mark 686
Bojdak, Robert J. 530
Bok, Cathleen 204
Bokan, Mike 565

Bokar, Cathy 858
Bokerman, Grant 137
Bokina, Erin 686
Bolander, Larry Bolander Larry 355
Bolanos, Steve 640
Bold, William 694
Boldea, Lucian 285
Bolden, Tod 126
Bolduc, Ellyn 751
Boles, Tim 713
Bolgar, Paulo 120
Bolger, Andrea 36
Bolick, Patrick 481
Bolin, Amy 812
Boline, Chad 224
Boling, Keith 713
Bolisay, Eric 799
Bollin, Bonnie 413
Bollinger, Kathy 117
Bollinger, Lee C. 320
Bollinger, Paul 509
Bologna, Matt 933
Bols, Ivo 24
Bolt, Cynthia 739
Bolt, Gregg 813
Bolton, C. Anderson (Andy) 245
Bolton, Jon 727
Bolton, Karen 885
Bolts, George 550
Boltz, William P 527
Bolwerk, Dave 86
Bolze, Steve 374
Bomar, Alice 920
Bombara, Beth A. 408
Bomboy, David 334
Bommarito, Bruce 160
Bommentre, Frank 248
Bona, Robin 893
Bonadio, Bill 140
Bonalle, David 53
Bonanno, Kelly 369
Bonano, Charles 329
Bonanotte, Gino A. 577
Bonarti, Michael A 93
Bond, Simon 468
Bond, Richard E 583
Bond, Richard 600
Bond, Robert W. (Bob) 640
Bond, Martine 783
Bond, Carol 850
Bondada, Vijay 281
Bondel, Mary Lou 538
Bondeson, Rusty 258
Bonds, Michael P. (Mike) 865
Bondur, Thomas 505
Bone, Ronald 550
Bone, Doug 795
Bonfanti, Brian 298
Bonfield, Andrew R J 173
Bongiorno, Anthony 893
Bongiovi, Joseph 540
Bonham, Jeff 180
Bonick, Martin J. 228
Bonilla, Eduardo 704
Bonilla, Myfanwy 922
Bonn, Nicholas T. (Nick) 783
Bonn, Karen 922
Bonnett, John W 414
Bonney, Joseph 198
Bonnick, Peter 722
Bonomo, Stuart 284
Bontcheva, Milena 271
Bonza, Craig 417
Bonzani, Andrew 468
Boocock, Richard 24
Boogaards, Arjan 289
Booher, David 778
Booher, Kathy 867
Booker, Martin W. 66
Booker, Robert 876
Booles, Angela 36
Boomer, Stephen L. 339
Boone, Michael 179
Boone, Kevin 245
Boone, Elsie 246
Boone, Elwood B. (Bernie) 754
Boortz, Kevin 442

Boosin, Greg 544
Boote, John 175
Booth, William 167
Booth, Steven G. (Steve) 726
Booth, Mike 739
Booth, Robert 908
Boothe, Dorrett 114
Boothe, Steven 799
Bor, Chris 485
Borade, Vidhya 928
Boragine, Ellie 54
Boras, Stephen 329
Borba, George A. 249
Borchardt, Randall 885
Borcherding, Tricia 212
Borchers, Bradford D. 629
Borchers, Susan C. 716
Borcke, Wulff-Erik von 6
Bordelon, John W 426
Bordelon, Jennifer 449
Borden, Alexia 28
Borden, Rob 140
Borden, Ian 548
Borden, Rebecca 893
Borders, Carolynne 744
Bordes, Michael P. (Mike) 292
Bordo, Julie 371
Borer, Mark 258
Borges, Steven D. (Steve) 475
Borgman, Charles L 219
Borgmann, Kevin S. 166
Borgonovi, Barbara 706
Boring, Daniel 176
Borino, Melissa Borino Melissa 884
Boriskey, Karen 448
Borja, Paul D. 353
Borkowski, Tim 315
Borman, J Richard 380
Bormann, Scott 554
Bornhorst, Donald 262
Bornhurst, Don 262
Bornmann, David E. 688
Bornmann, David E. 689
Borns, Chad 86
Borowiecki, Jeff 179
Borowy, Don 220
Borrego, Susan E. 711
Borrelli, Jerry 32
Borsello, Fabrice 915
Borst, Walter G 583
Borton, Chad M. 329
Borucki, Bethany 804
Borum, Andrea 704
Borup, Steve 481
Boryla, Stephanie 859
Borzi, James 123
Borzileri, Darcey 219
Boschelli, John M. 489
Bosco, Paul 198
Bosco, Teresa 222
Bosco, Sara Y 292
Bosco, Michael 481
Bose, Robert 44
Bose, Supratim 149
Boshoff, Chris 658
Bosi, Benoit 686
Bosler, Chris 502
Bosma, Laura 484
Boss, Daniel 299
Boss, R Daniel 299
Bossard, Evan 925
Bosscher, James 847
Bosse, J 385
Bosshart, Andrea 228
Bossmann, Lori 9
Bosso, Leonard 590
Bossone, Carla 835
Bost, Philippe 10
Bostic, Raphael W. 319
Boston, Steve 27
Boston, Michelle 108
Bostrom, Robert 364
Bostrom, Brent 399
Bosway, William T. 277
Botbol, Michel 701
Botfield, Helen 800
Bothe, Albert 371

J

Myers, Cynthia M. 353
Myers, Curtis J. 367
Myers, Eric 409
Myers, Ben 478
Myers, Thomas D. 489
Myers, Bradley 530
Myers, Daniel 573
Myers, Fred 592
Myers, Landon 704
Myers, William E. 843
Myers, Lee 863
Myers, Daniel P. (Dan) 913
Myler, Jerold 492
Myrick, Bradan 773
Myron, Paul 79
Myron, Thomas R 132

N

Nabel, Elizabeth G. (Betsy) 641
Nacey, Sean 910
Nachmann, Marc 390
Nackley, Janey 452
Nadarajan, Gunalan 711
Naddeo, Eric 857
Nadeau, Renee 160
Nadeau, Gerard F. 455
Nadella, Satya 565
Nadkarni, Pranay 43
Naftaly, Robert 856
Naftaly, Rober 856
Naftaly, Ralph 877
Nagaishi, Robert 56
Nagar, Sumeet 135
Nagarajan, Rajesh 177
Nagarajan, Sundaram (Naga) 453
Nagarajan, Sundaram 768
Nagarkar, Niranjan 135
Nagata, Ron 410
Nageer, Tarique 540
Nagel, David 376
Nagel, Troy 409
Nagel, Brian 507
Nagel, Brian 872
Naggar, Lela 818
Nagji, Bansi 549
Nagle, Margaret 88
Nagy, Richard 248
Nagy, Kate 329
Nagy, Shayne 580
Nagy, Kim 925
Nahhas, Kamal 885
Nahrgang, Stephanie 826
Naik, Sangeeta 54
Naik, Piyush 135
Naik, Harshad 447
Naik, Sundip 804
Nair, Vas 79
Nair, Raj 360
Nair, Mahesh 502
Nair, Roopa 692
Nair, Suresh 713
Najbicz, Christopher 161
Najimi, Parnaz 900
Najjar, Fred 266
Najjar, Ted 390
Nakahara, Tina 109
Nakahara, Steven 109
Nakamura, Galen 109
Nakano, Damon 191
Nakano, Tom 609
Nakatsuka, Ralph Y. 817
Nalamasu, Omkaram (Om) 74
Nalbach, Doug 595
Naljayan, Mihran 257
Nalluri, Prathima 135
Nally, Thomas A (Tom) 807
Nama, Veeresh 414
Nambiar, Vinod 218
Nanavaty, Maulik 149
Nanda, Ann 686
Nandakumar, Anita 391
Nangia, Nikhil 108
Nannen, John 706
Naples, Richard J. 123
Napol, Marcello 3

Napoli, Frank 63
Napoli, Gus 436
Napoli, Joe 798
Napolitan, Raymond S. 612
Napolitano, Glen 329
Napolitano, Kenneth (Ken) 936
Nappi, David 933
Naquin, Robbie 167
Narang, Manu 54
Narang, Steve 117
Narasimhan, Laxman 654
Narayan, Sandeep 332
Narayanan, Lakshmi 216
Narayanan, Gowri 544
Narayen, Shantanu 11
Nardone, Mary Kaye 504
Nardone, Michael 559
Nardone, Robert 888
Narenda, Vish M. 395
Narisetti, Raju 596
Narmi, Charles 727
Narmouq, Samir 608
Narro, Oscar 571
Narula, Veru 201
Narvaez, Lorena 89
Narwani, Gaurav 776
Nash, Nata 85
Nash, William D. (Bill) 171
Nash, Alexis 441
Nash, Joseph 556
Nash, Nick 862
Nasir, Paul 798
Nassar, Daniel 14
Nassetta, Christopher J. (Chris) 423
Nassos, John 600
Nasta, David 332
Nastanski, Cynthia 654
Natale, J 123
Natale, Tom 343
Natale, Lisa 619
Natarajan, Sanjay 74
Natarajan, Krishna 575
Natarajan, Stephen 588
Natarajan, Venkata 686
Natarajan, Murali 723
Natarajan, Shekar 804
Natesan, Ganesh 107
Nath, Deepak 5
Nath, Munindra 200
Nathan, Scott 114
Nathan, Mike 925
Natoli, Jerry 471
Natsis, Elaine 170
Naughton, Marc G. 185
Naughton, Duncan C. Mac 273
Naughton, Mary 540
Naughton, W Terrance 908
Naughton-Gerdes, Joan 36
Naumann, Michael 19
Naumann, Peter 877
Nava, Carmen P 89
Nava, Mario 222
Navale, Sunil 608
Navarra, Eric 128
Navarro, Jen 373
Navarro, Mary W. 444
Navarro, Imelda 463
Navarro, Jorge 871
Navia, Frank 156
Nayak, Vinayak 17
Nayak, Harsh 461
Nayak, Ajit 680
Naylor, Katie 54
Naylor, Lisa 228
Nazak, Keith 358
Nazarian, Jeanette 478
Nazzaro, Stephen F. (Steve) 783
Ndemanga, Sekai 544
Neagle, Kelly 627
Neal, Michelle M. 111
Neal, Annmarie 199
Neal, Krista 200
Neal, Stephen C. 514
Neal, Stephen C. 516
Neal, Cheryl 809
Neal, Gary F. 861
Neal, Joel 900

Neale, Donna 527
Neale, George A. 751
Nealon, Thomas M 773
Nearhood, William 329
Nebreda, Julian 18
Necastro, Daniel Butch 36
Nedder, Michael 356
Nedl, Katie 135
Neeb, Greg Null 761
Need, Thomas 533
Needham, Wendy 380
Needles, Adam 25
Neely, Stephanie 36
Neely, Eric 489
Neff, Clay 190
Neff, Doug 224
Neff, Lorraine 246
Neff, Scott 444
Negr--n, Eduardo J. 670
Neher, Terry 884
Neidorff, Michael F. 179
Neifert, Kevin T. 706
Neikirk, Chris 604
Neil, Jesse 228
Neill, James R. (Jim) 379
Neill, Gregory 527
Neilsen, Troy 575
Neis, Eric 575
Neizman, Kai 219
Nell, Steven E. 141
Nelms, Cary T 798
Nelms, Cary 798
Nelsen, Keith J. 130
Nelsen, Kathy 325
Nelsen, Denise 779
Nelsen, Mark 895
Nelso, Nelson 425
Nelson, Amy 71
Nelson, David 80
Nelson, Ronald L. (Ron) 98
Nelson, Roy 103
Nelson, Shelby 117
Nelson, Christopher (Chris) 121
Nelson, Kevin 168
Nelson, Wade 177
Nelson, Joan 213
Nelson, Rosemary 218
Nelson, Faye A. 279
Nelson, Ann W. 293
Nelson, John P. 293
Nelson, Yvonne 325
Nelson, Christian 349
Nelson, Paul 369
Nelson, Kimberly A. (Kim) 376
Nelson, Rick 399
Nelson, William 451
Nelson, Mike 467
Nelson, Brad 522
Nelson, Steven 525
Nelson, Philip B 536
Nelson, Philip 536
Nelson, John 540
Nelson, Susan K. 551
Nelson, Linda 567
Nelson, Linda A 567
Nelson, Jeff 602
Nelson, Peggy 623
Nelson, Jonathan B. 626
Nelson, Rick 665
Nelson, Ryan 740
Nelson, Travis 747
Nelson, Brian 761
Nelson, Rick 764
Nelson, Scott 804
Nelson, Jon 835
Nelson, Robert 844
Nelson, Christopher 859
Nelson, Michael S. 879
Nelson, David D. (Dave) 911
Nelson, Mary 933
Nelson, Zac 940
Nemecek, Donna 111
Nemeth, Kathy 115
Nemeth, Matt 320
Nemeth, Jeffery 360
Nemeth, Julio 680
Nemeth, Rudolph 684

Nemphos, Ann 409
Nenadal, Cody 793
Nentwig, Robert J. 147
Nepveux, Kevin 657
Nerbonne, Daniel 668
Nerbonne, Dan 668
Nerenhausen, Frank R 632
Neri, Antonio 420
Neri, Marc 793
NESBIT, JONATHAN 784
Nesbit, Jeff 835
Nesbitt, Stephen R. 439
Nesbitt, Douglas 716
Nesci, James D. 684
Nesemeyer, Ron 224
Nesi, Victor J. 787
Ness, Steve 905
Nesta, Cheryl 405
Neth, Bryan 755
Netherton, Linda 327
Neto, Paulo 512
Nettesheim, Susan 479
Nettles, Kwicha 346
Nettles, Richard 479
Neugarten, Lisa 452
Neugent, Christopher J. 672
Neuman, Jennifer 592
Neumann, Spencer 10
Neumann, Karl-Thomas 378
Neumann, Dan 665
Neumann, Paul G 847
Neumeyer, Daniel J. 444
Nevala, Wendy 924
Nevens, T Michael 586
Neville, Brian 51
Neville, Robert M. 105
Neville, Bob 105
Nevins, Michael 761
Newallis, David 57
Newberg, William 902
Newbern, Thomas B. 95
Newberry, Stephen G. (Steve) 505
Newbery, Michelle M. 527
Newbould, Tom 843
Newcom, Jeff 347
Newcomb, Jorey 236
Newcomer, Mark 304
Newcomer, John 383
Newcomer, Patti 471
Newcomer, Nate 722
Newfield, Richard U. 581
Newhouse, Greg 491
Newkirk, Christopher T. 166
Newkirk, Jesse 347
Newkirk, Melanie 621
Newlands, William A. (Bill) 236
Newlin, Karl 281
Newman, Randy 31
Newman, Kenneth Kenneth Newman 111
Newman, Rebecca 112
Newman, Sallie 246
Newman, Jenifer 306
Newman, Tim 351
Newman, John 352
Newman, Margaret 412
Newman, Deon 419
Newman, Michael 452
Newman, Amy 452
Newman, Deon 465
Newman, Rainer 479
Newman, Mark 482
Newman, Margaret 489
Newman, Gerald 548
Newman, Brian 654
Newman, Robert 664
Newman, Peter 828
Newport, Roger K. 27
Newsom, Brittany 58
Newsom, Richard W. (Rick) 229
Newsom, Gavin 782
Newsome, Mark 8
Newton, Opal 23
Newton, Wayne 29
Newton, Vera 360
Newton, Carl 749
Newton, Heather 780

Tucker, Jeff 665
Tucker, Crystal 717
Tucker, Joann 828
Tucker, Scott 912
Tudor, Sorin 135
Tueckes, Amy 325
Tuerk, Daniel 925
Tuffaha, Sam 89
Tuffin, Mark 498
Tufo, Lou Del 355
Tuftee, Debbie 222
Tuggle, Charles T. 343
Tull, Andrea 179
Tullett, Lindsey 742
Tullier, Kelly M. 895
Tullier, Kelly Mahon 896
Tulsi, Japjit 287
Tulsyan, Ravi 934
Tumma, Madhu 483
Tummillo, Michael 527
Tumminello, Antonette 248
Tumulty, Timothy 540
Tung, Caroline 702
Tuori, Jeffery C 40
Turansky, Carole 823
Turchet, Tom 465
Turetsky, Larisa 112
Turi, Carol 112
Turi, Karen 828
Turiano, Vincent C 211
Turits, Michael 704
Turits, Mark 893
Turkienicz, Jose 164
Turnage, Greg 156
Turnage, Sue 246
Turnas, Jeff 921
Turnbull, Robert 246
Turner, John 3
Turner, George 25
Turner, Henry 41
Turner, Dustin J 126
Turner, Dustin 126
Turner, Jill 184
Turner, Aprile 191
Turner, Gregory 212
Turner, Greg 212
Turner, Jeffrey 224
Turner, Jim 245
Turner, Jim L. 259
Turner, Keene S. 298
Turner, Greg 315
Turner, Mark 323
Turner, Mark 360
Turner, Matthew 381
Turner, Joseph W. (Joe) 397
Turner, William V. 397
Turner, Michael R. (Mike) 418
Turner, Ladd 432
Turner, Simon 447
Turner, Ethan 452
Turner, Cynthia 496
Turner, John C. 569
Turner, Vince 580
Turner, Debra 584
Turner, Chris 654
Turner, M. Terry 664
Turner, John M. 712
Turner, David J. 712
Turner, Michele 723
Turner, Nicole 735
Turner, Christina 833
Turner, Bud 866
Turner, Steve 899
Turner, Jody 919
Turner, Ryan 924
Turner, Mark A. 929
Turney, John 606
Turowski, Arthur 482
Turowski, Steven 823
Turpan, Natalie 692
Turrentine, Don 713
Turton, Daniel 296
Tuten, Chris 583
Tuthill, Allen 88
Tutin, Ken 245
Tutkovics, Julie C. 444
Tutor, Jonathan 713

Tutson, Tracy 69
Tutt, James 621
Tutt, Jame 621
Tuttle, Mark 565
Tuttle, Russ 761
Tutunjian, Brad 180
Tuzun, Tayfun 329
Tverskoy, Kirill 658
Tveter, Brian 746
Twardy, David 877
Tweel, Benjamin 108
Twohig, Paul 779
Twomey, Mike 296
Twornay, Michael 296
Twyman, Rob 921
Ty, Fred 709
Tye, Chris 355
Tyer, Ethan 893
Tyle, Craig S. 363
Tyler, Michele 487
Tyler, Robyn 620
Tyler, Gail 704
Tyler, Chris 812
Tyler, Breck W. 852
Tylski, Scott 232
Tymchenko, Viktor 460
Tymms, Jason 544
Tyner, Benjamin 107
Tynes, Donnie 852
Tyra, Heidi 449
Tyree, Sarah 213
Tyren, Almeda 14
Tyrholm, Laura 135
Tyrrell, Joseph 161
Tyrrell, Linda 326
Tyrrell, Nathan S. 436
Tyser, Matthew C 379
Tyson, Vern 403
Tyson, Dylan 686
Tyson, Sharon 772
Tyson, John H. 855
Tywater, TY 748
Tzitzouris, Jim 799

U

Ubell, Elizabeth 394
Uchida, Kathryn 63
Udy, Brad 444
Uebelhor, Steve 664
Uehara, Edwina (Eddie) 880
Ugalde, Philip 713
Ugarte, Alfonso J 222
Uhl, Michael C 461
Uhl, Michael 465
Uhlir, Beth 346
Ulander, Peder 198
Ulbrich, Christian 481
Ulbricht, Will 575
Ulizzi, Holly 324
Ullmann, Michael H. 479
Ullrich, Michael 54
Ulm, Scott J. 80
Ulrey, Sharissa 345
Ulrich, Travis 497
Umanoff, Adam S. 290
Umberto, Anna M 251
Umfleet, Jason 774
Umlah, Jason 137
Ummersen, Gordon Van 790
Umpleby, D James 173
Unangst, Walter 651
Unberger, Dave 227
Underberg, Scott 713
Underhill, Kim 493
Underhill, Mike 500
Underwood, Michelle 278
Underwood, Jacqueline 414
Underwood, Neil L 523
Ung, Brenda 654
Unger, Keith 206
Unthank, Ryan 727
Upadek, Kristen 888
Upchurch, Wes 232
Upchurch, John 281
Upchurch, W. Howard 403

Uppal, Jinny 125
Uppala, Sathyadev 695
Upton, Ray 820
Upton, Tom 871
Urban, Lauren 246
Urban, Larry 398
Urban, Thomas 398
Urban, Kevin J. 692
Urdapilleta, Eduardo 101
Urech, Greg 512
Uribe, Elias 200
Urland, Taisha 538
Urovsky, Teri 538
Urrabazo, Ignacio 463
Urschel, Ned 778
Urso-Rio, Kristen 375
Urtin, Charles G. 737
Urtz, Deborah 530
Usmani, Farukh 462
Utermark, D. Chad 612
Utermark, D 612
Utermark, Chad 612
Utermark, Douglas 612
Utne, Jeff 654
Utrup, Brian 491
Utsude, Tomoya 19
Utsugi, Susan 182
Utz, John A. 85
Uyeda, Dean 109

V

Vaccaro, Frank 54
Vaccaro, Daniel 115
Vaccaro, Kenneth 651
Vadell, Tomeu 202
Vadlamannati, Ramaparasad (Ram) 673
Vaez-iravani, Mehdi 74
Vagelos, P. Roy 710
Vagner, Janice 796
Vagt, Robert 494
Vaidyanathan, Krishnamurthy 390
Vail, Bob 374
Vail, Angela 641
Vailes, Kathy 161
Vaillant, Frederic 146
Vaina, Alan 294
Vainisi, William 35
Vaio, Robert 418
Vaishnav, Mike 794
Vajda, Neil 329
Valavanis, Spero 433
Valdez, James 18
Valdez, James 246
Valdez, Ruth 642
Valdez, Hernan 657
Valdez, Arthur 804
Valdés, Luis 677
Vale, Michael G. 3
Vale, Mike 255
Vale, MaryAnn 692
Valenca, Alan 799
Valencia, Rick 695
Valencia, Veronica 731
Valente, Dan 528
Valente, Donna 743
Valenti, Natalia 115
Valenti, Franco 243
Valenti, Alessandro 701
Valenti, Susan M. 838
Valenti, Joe 933
Valentine, Melinda 112
Valentine, Ken 329
Valentine, Jerry 441
Valentine, Leanne 677
Valentine, Raymond 767
Valentine, Veronica 888
Valentino, James 559
Valentzas, Anne 544
Valenzano, Don 573
Valenzuela, Dan 30
Valenzuela, Elvira 285
Valera, Fernando 202
Valeva, Sanya 492
Valianatos, Pete 831

Valine, Yousef A. 343
Valitutto, Richard 935
Valiveti, Srihari 784
Valkenburg, Tina Van 552
Valladares, Jorge 842
Vallee, Roy A. 321
Vallejos, Vincent 793
Vallely, Art 649
Valletta, Robert 321
Valley, Richard 258
Vallone, James 153
Vallone, Paul 640
Valls, Juan 453
Valovcin, David 465
Valsechini, Monica 891
Vamvalis, Laura 82
Van, David 473
Van-praag, Mary 243
Vanags, Art 577
Vanamburgh, Suzanne 219
Vance, Tyler 113
Vance, Linda 222
Vance, Daniel 264
Vance, Brian L. 415
Vance, Quonta 428
Vance, David 857
Vance, Anna 910
Vancheeswaran, Pradeep 897
Vancleave, Roger 882
VanCleef, Alan 383
Vancourt, Donna 84
Vandecasteele, Jeff 260
Vandenbergh, Robert A. 504
Vanderhaar, Brett 774
Vanderhoof, Ashley 707
Vanderkooi, Joel 487
Vanderlind, Gary 392
Vandervinne, Jeri 693
Vanderzee, Steven 15
VanDeVelde, Doug 487
Vandewater, Christopher 309
Vaness, Craig 329
Vang, Todd 900
Vangilder, Grant 599
Vangrevenhof, Heather 36
Vanhoff, Kathleen 469
Vankirk, Trudy 90
VanKirk, James 690
VanLeuven, Megan 196
Vanneste, Jeffrey H. 508
Vanni, Rob 240
Vannorman, Steven 451
Vannorman, Raymond 717
VanNoy-Pineda, Kathleen 528
VANOPSTALL, EARL 806
Vantassel, Chris 925
Vantrieste, Martin 65
Vanvleet, Mike 789
Vanwallaghen, John 871
Vanwelzen, Jim 613
Vanzo, Kendra L. 621
Vara, Raymond 110
Varadarajan, Sesha 505
Varadhan, Ashok 390
Vardas, Michael 605
Vardeleon, Christian 137
Varela, Javier 484
Varela, Gonzalez 902
Varelas, Panayiotis 414
Varga, Paul 925
Vargas, Gilberto A 460
Vargas, Carlota 540
Vargas, Franklyn 670
Varghese, George 68
Varghese, Jasmine 115
Vargo, Alla 552
Vari, Jamie 482
Varilek, James A. 624
Varin, Valerie 207
Varley, Elizabeth 61
Varma, Ravi 54
Varma, Vivek 779
Varma, Prasad 818
Varner, Carol 54
Varner, Marc 937
Varney, Al 933
Varni, Sara 740

This Page left intentionally blank